NON LEAGUE CLUB DIRECTORY 2005

(27th Edition)

EDITORS
MIKE & TONY WILLIAMS

ISBN 1 869833 49/X

Published by Tony Williams Publications Ltd
Printed by Unwins Bros of Woking
All distributing queries to Pat Vaughan
Tel: 01823 490080 or 01458 241592

Front Cover caption:
Telford United's Richard Lavery closes down Canvey Island's ace marksman Lee Boylan. Photo: Roger Turner.

FOREWORD

This year sees the conclusion of the first phase in the restructuring of the National League System, the most significant and comprehensive review of the Non-League pyramid in 25 years and one which should bring great benefits.

In recent years, the profile and interest in Non-League football has achieved unprecedented levels. With the ever-improving quality of football, rising attendances, better quality of stadia and the excitement of the play-offs, one can say with confidence that football at this level is very much in the ascendancy.

Last season, Scarborough took Chelsea to the wire in an FA Cup tie which captured the imagination of public and media alike, and the two promoted clubs from the Conference, Doncaster Rovers and Yeovil Town, performed with huge distinction in Division Three.

In the other knock-out competitions, Hednesford Town and Winchester City took the honours in hugely entertaining FA Trophy and FA Vase Finals, while the England National Game XI entertained Belgian and Italian representative sides in front of gates of over 3,500 at Darlington and Shrewsbury Town. Paul Fairclough's team also played a ground-breaking match against the Iraq national team at Macclesfield Town, watched by over 4,000 enthusiastic spectators and acquitted themselves very well.

We also saw a successful conclusion to the newest addition to the domestic calendar, The FA National League System Cup, with the Mid-Cheshire League qualifying to represent England in the 2004/05 UEFA Regions Cup for amateur teams.

The summer months give clubs the chance to start dreaming again, and planning for the fresh demands and challenges ahead.

The Non-league Directory, now in its 27th edition, will once again provide a vital resource for everyone involved at this level of the game, and congratulations and thanks go to those who have put this comprehensive publication together.

I would like to wish you all the best of luck for the coming season, and look forward to following your fortunes as they unfold over the next 10 months.

Sir Trevor Brooking
FA Director of Football Development

ACKNOWLEDGEMENTS

It is staggering to think that this is our twenty seventh annual non-league book and it is even more impressive when one checks how many years our contributors have helped us with their specialised knowledge and expertise.

James Wright, who publishes his own Cherry Red Records Non-League Newsdesk Annual, has helped us with clubs' season match by match records in steps 1,2 and 3 plus many league tables, and another old friend **Steve Whitney** , whose own Players Book was a great success last season, has provided the clubs' playing squads for the same level.

Our team of photographers have obviously had less to do since the demise of Team Talk but we still have a terrific supply from **Gordon Whittington, Alan Coomes, Peter Barnes, Roger Turner, Eric Marsh, Keith Clayton, Francis Short, Bill Wheatcroft, Darren Thomas, Peter Lirettoc, Graham Cotterill, Graham Brown, John Vass, Alan Watson, Garry Letts, Neil Thaler, Colin Stevens, Dennis Nicholson, Mark Wood, Roger Thomas, Tim Lancaster** and **Paul Carter** backed up by **Andrew Chitty, Keith Gillard, Ken Gregory, Paul Dennis, Tim Edwards** and **Martin Wray.**

Our two stalwarts **John Anderson** and **Arthur Evans** have again supplied an invaluable service with competition stats from John and match reports plus photos from Arthur. They are also regulars at our functions and their support has been greatly appreciated.

Jen O'Neill, editor of 'FairGame' the excellent women's football magazine and television expert has helped with the women's section and **Mike Simmonds** has once again compiled the excellent section of schoolboy football. The Amateur Football Alliance has once again been well presented by **Wally Goss** and **Mike Brown** but sadly the Bureau of Non League Football was discontinued this year so **Mike Ford** was not in a position to supply all the county cup results in detail. We wish him all the best in his retirement.

As usual we have had much appreciated co-operation from the sports departments of the Guernsey, Jersey and Isle of Man newspapers and of course the support from secretaries of clubs, leagues and counties throughout the country has been magnificent

It has given me great satisfaction and pleasure to have had my eldest son Michael working alongside me with this year's Directory. He originally learnt the football side of the business with me, at a time when George Brown was leading the learning curve regarding I.T. and computer skills. Michael is now an expert in his own right having worked as Publications Manager for Coventry City when they were in the Premier Division. He also edited The Football League Club Directory while at Coventry and then moved to London where he worked in the City for a Sports News Agency. It is a pleasure to have him back with the family book and very reassuring for me to have his knowledge available for the cause.

CONTENTS

Educated at Malvern College, one of the country's best football schools in the late sixties, he represented England Under 18 against Scotland at Celtic Park before serving as an administrative officer in the Royal Air Force for five years.

He was on Reading's books from the age of 16 to 22, but also represented F.A. Amateur XI's and the R.A.F. while playing mainly in the old Isthmian League for Corinthian Casuals, Dulwich Hamlet and Kingstonian and joining Hereford United and Grantham during R.A.F. postings.

After taking an F.A. Coaching badge he coached at Harrow Borough, Epsom & Ewell and Hungerford Town and was asked to edit Jimmy Hill's Football Weekly after initial experience with the Amateur Footballer. Monthly Soccer and Sportsweek followed before he had the idea for a football Wisden and was helped by The Bagnall Harvey Agency to find a suitable generous sponsor in Rothmans.

After launching the Rothmans Football Yearbook in 1970 as its founder and co-compiler with Roy Peskett, he was asked to join Rothmans (although a non-smoker!) in the company's public relations department and was soon able to persuade the Marketing Director that Rothmans should become the first ever sponsor of a football league.

After a season's trial sponsoring the Hellenic and Isthmian Leagues, it was decided to go national with the Northern and Western Leagues and for four years he looked after the football department at Rothmans, with Jimmy Hill and Doug Insole presenting a brilliant sponsorship package which amongst many other innovations included three points for a win and goal difference.

So Non-League football led the way with league sponsorship and two, now well accepted, innovations.

Sportsmanship and goals were also rewarded in a sponsorship that proved a great success for football and for Rothmans. Indeed the sportsmanship incentives could be of great value to-day in the Football Association's bid to improve the game's image by ridding the game of dissent and cheating.

After the cigarette company pulled out of their sports sponsorship Tony produced the first Non-League Annual and later The Football League Club Directory, launching 'Non-League Football' magazine with "The Mail on Sunday" and then "Team Talk."

After his ten years with Hungerford Town, he moved West and served Yeovil Town as a Director for seven years but was thrilled when David Emery's plans for the exciting Non-League Media emerged and came into reality, thus giving the grass roots of the game the publicity and promotion that he and his team had been attempting to set up since the Annual (now Directory) was launched in 1978.

Sadly Non-League Media Plc is no more, although the excellent Non-League Newspaper has continued to flourish. Tony Williams Publications has been brought back into action, and for the last two seasons, greatly helped by Ladbrokes'support, has published the Directory, a Non-League Diary, and organised a national non-league quiz. A club for non-league enthusiasts was formed with the fortnightly "Fairplay" magazine published for members.

Unfortunately Ladbrokes'much appreciated involvement is over, but the Diary is available and with the welcome assistance of "Arena Seating" the very popular National Non-League Club Quiz will be contested for the third time.

What started out as a holiday job in 1988 helping put together (literally in those days) the Non-League Club Directory and League Club Directory, in the end forged a career which saw him work for Coventry City Football Club, e-comsport in London and finally return to Tony Williams Publications in 2003.

During his eight year spell with TW Publications he learned the ropes of all aspects of publishing culminating in the roll of production manager for the Non-League Directory, Team Talk Magazine, the League Club Directory and many more publications published by the company.

1995 saw the opportunity to take up the post of Publications Manager at Coventry City Football Club, and the transfer was made in the April of that year. Sky Blue Publications was formed and the League Club Directory became their leading title. Re-branded as the Ultimate Football Guide he was to deal with all aspects of the book, from design to sales and was also put on a steep learning curve into the world of Premiership programme production.

The three years spent at the Midland's club gave him a great incite into all departments of a Premiership club, having produced publications for them all, but by 1998 it was time to move on again and the world of freelance design and editing beckoned. That was until, at the final hour, Grant Bovey and his newly formed company Sportscheck diverted his route back to the West Country by luring him to London.

The challenge of creating an online data base of football players from europe and the rest of world, to aid professional clubs in their quest to better their squads was one which he relished and the company rapidly grew. Juggling the day job with the editing of the Ultimate Football Guide proved to be even more of a challenge, which ultimately was to no avail as Sky Blue Publications did not publish the 1999 edition.

This released him to work full time on the players data-base for the newly named ecomsport and in the January of 2000 he was promoted to Data Manager, looking after a multi-national team of football analysts. As with most 'dot com' companies of that time flotation was shortly followed by closure and in 2001 the move back to the West Country, which had been on hold since 1998, was finally made.

The desire to start up his own design/publishing company still remained and in the April of 2003 MCsolutions was officially formed and his return to the 'non-league' family was complete.

Having gone to a rugby school his football playing career was delayed. However, becoming the youngest player to have played for the First XV and representing Torbay Athletics club at 100 and 200m proved his sporting background. At the age of 20 he begun his football career which, at it's height, saw him playing for Chard Town in the Western League Premier Division. Now 34 he has the 'experience' but, unfortunately, not the legs! Nevertheless he enjoys turning out for Loddiswell Athletic Reserves in the South Devon League every Saturday, and will do so until he can't!

REVIEW OF THE 2003-04 SEASON

The whole season was contested to a background of negotiations, arguments, conjecture and meetings regarding the re structuring of the whole senior section of the country's pyramid of non-league football leagues.

Originally the Conference, possibly worried by the idea that The Football League might take the very reasonable move of developing two regional third divisions by inviting the Conference clubs to join them, had suggested a second division of their own. Neither of these moves came about but the clubs had been alerted.

Constant disagreements between the Isthmian and the Southern League over the sensible ideas that each should have their own set boundaries, encouraged renewed suggestions for North and South Conference Divisions One. This time it was taken seriously along with complete re-structuring.

So the idea took off and despite the aforementioned arguments, discussions and disagreements, patient work by the Football Association's Mike Appleby and the appropriate F.A.Committee plus the League officials eventually produced a new structure.

The majority seemed reasonably satisfied. The Isthmian League were the ones to suffer in reduced numbers and apart from the inevitable handful of clubs who seem to have been given a lot more travelling, the vast majority of non-league clubs are looking forward to the 2004-2005 season with an extra excitement.

I am sure the few unlucky clubs will find their way back to their most geographically suitable leagues as the dust settles on the readjustments in the next few seasons. Most clubs however, will be looking forward to visiting new grounds, welcoming new friends to the home games and taking their place in a new exciting structure which should lift players, coaches, supporters and administrators alike.

To take their places in this new pyramid, practically every club found themselves in their own little play off situation at the end of last season and this brought great joy to clubs like **Lewes** who moved up two levels, but despair to previously consistent performers such as **Tiverton Town** who managed to be virtually relegated without finishing in the bottom four.

UNLUCKY HEREFORD

Following the excitement at the top of most senior competitions at the end of the previous season, nearly all the Championships were decided well before the last weeks of the season. **Chester City's** consistency and excellent defence held off unlucky **Hereford United** by a point The Runners-Up scored 103 goals (18 more than Chester), won 28 matches (one more than Chester) and took four out of six points from the champions in their two meetings

A thrilling play off competition was a wonderful way to give the Conference a suitable climax to their season, although a very upsetting refereeing decision left Hereford playing the majority of their first game with ten men. They lost on penalties, and although we all know the rules were accepted at the beginning of the campaign, the sight of a club who had finished twenty one points ahead of the team beating them, must have sickened all fair minded football people. Many of the Bulls best players have now moved on and **Graham Turner**, who has dedicated so much time, love and money to his club, will do well to produce a side ever again that plays as well as his boys performed last season. Good luck to him!

THRILLING TROPHY FINAL

For the second consecutive year no Conference club reached the F.A.Trophy final but this certainly wasn't for the lack of trying. The tie where **Telford United** beat **Shrewsbury Town** in a local derby replay, the **Aldershot** success against **Exeter City** and their amazing defeat at home to **Hednesford Town** or even the tremendous semi-final second leg when **Canvey Island** won a magnificent cup tie against Telford, all saw terrific efforts by the clubs from the senior competition.

One of the most exciting acts of giant killing was achieved by **Arlesey Town** who drew a 3-3 thriller at **Dagenham & Redbridge** and then beat the famous cup fighters 4-2 at home.

The eventual finalists however, turned out to be very similar to the previous season, in so much as one club had been promoted as champions of their league and was Conference bound and their opponents had not only had a disappointing campaign, they had been relegated!

The result was the same, with the underdog emulating **Burscough**'s defeat of **Tamworth** when **Hednesford Town** won an absolute thriller against a very good **Canvey Island** side.Two outstanding goalscorers had inspired their respective clubs to the F.A.Trophy and F.A.Vase finals. **Lee Boylan** had a quiet first half at Villa Park but, with his club trailling by a single goal at half time he had given Canvey a 2-1 lead within four minutes of the restart. This should have been enough to put the favourites well and truly on top, but the West Midland locals, inspired by a brilliant performance by **Carl Palmer** in midfield, stormed back showing great character and won with two glorious goals - a fine free kick from **Les Hines** and a spectacular volley by centre half and manager for this season **Chris Brindley.**

WINCHESTER CITY"S TRIUMPH

The other quite outstanding goalscorer for the season was **Winchester City**'s **Andy Forbes.** Perhaps the squad his club had assembled were too good for their league but you can only be judged against the opposition in your particular competitions and a total of well over seventy goals during the season was very special indeed so it was no surprise when he opened the scoring at St Andrews with his ninth F.A.Vase goal of the campaign. Winchester City joined the small list of clubs who actually did themselves more than justice on their big occasion. Playing superb controlled passing football it was surprising that they were not leading by more at half time. **AFC Sudbury** certainly raised their game in the second half and until they were unluckily deprived of a defender, sent off after an off balance collision had convinced the referee that a red card penalty offence had occurred, the game was in the balance.

The F.A.Vase was once again enjoyed by everyone. The competition is contested by more and more clubs every season (483 this campaign) and although the two favourites reached the final last season, we always see some little clubs 'coming of age' as they experience a national cup run for the first time. This year the new **Colne Football Club** reminded us of the ill fated **Colne Dynamoes** by giving **AFC Sudbury** two tough semi-final ties after beating the much fancied **AFC Wimbledon** in London. They also beat Western League minnows **Bitton** in the Fifth Round and the west country club, along with **Studley, Stone Dinamoes** and **Keynsham Town** all enjoyed exciting Vase campaigns that their supporters could surely never have envisaged at the beginning of season.

Since the Trophy and Vase finals have been played away from **Wembley**, attendances have not been impressive. But apart from the difficulty in getting transport across the country on Sundays, the obvious 'magic' for non-league players and supporters going to Wembley with their clubs is missing. Reaching the respective finals is still special with facilities better than those at the 'old Wembley', but although the atmosphere and organisation at **Villa Park**, **Upton Park** and **St Andrews** have been enjoyed by those present, there is no doubt that more than double the numbers will emerge once the pilgrimage to Wembley becomes the climax of the season for non-league fans again in the future,

Earlier in the season we had enjoyed the excitement of our non-league successes against Football League opposition.Initially it looked as if Essex clubs had taken it upon themselves to represent us as **Grays Athletic, East Thurrock United, Thurrock, Hornchurch, Canvey Island** and **Ford United** all featured in the first Round draw and they were backed up by neighbours **Histon, Stevenage Borough** and **Bishop's Stortford** !

When the excitement settled down we were well represented by nine Conference clubs who reached the Second Round with **Hornchurch** (Isthmian) and **Weston Super Mare** (Southern) representing the feeder leagues. **Accrington Stanley** brought back fond memories by beating Huddersfield Town and Bournemouth, while Telford claimed the scalps of **Brentford** and **Crewe Alexandra** in what proved to be their last season as 'United". **Burton Albion** won brilliantly against a very good Torquay United side in Devon and one of the highlights of the season for **Stevenage Borough** was their 2-1 victory over Stockport County .

It was **Scarborough** however, whose home game against the glamourous **Chelsea** caught the public's imagination. They were extremely unlucky not to earn at least a replay and once again it seemed strange that a defenders' arm raised high to strike a ball above his head in the penalty area could possibly be missed by the referee and linesman. But full credit to the 'Seadogs' as a lively and enjoyable non-league F.A.Cup season came to an exciting closure.

FINANCIAL PROBLEMS

The mention of **Telford United**'s good F.A.Cup and F.A.Trophy results and the sight of the wonderful improvements at the New Bucks Head ground makes it even more tragic that the club's ever present membership of the Alliance/ Conference has been brought to a tragic end as their owner was made bankrupt and the club has had to disband. Good luck to the newly formed **AFC Telford.**

Ironically, the fact that all three relegated clubs have been re-instated into the Conference Premier division has given **Northwich Victoria** the chance to retain their own unbroken membership of the senior competition and of course they are now the only one of the original twenty two still competing at the top level.

The **Exeter City** story dragged on all season and while one has sympathy with the new team of executives and their loyal supporters who have worked so had to keep the club going, there is still a large amount of money to be paid back to football clubs and individuals which their predecessors in charge of the club failed to honour. Hopefully the club will be able to keep their playing standards up to Conference standards while making every effort to pay off the debts and allow the club to sign new players once again. It is certainly lucky that the club's youth scheme under the wonderful guidance of **MIke Radford** and **Tiv Lowe** could well supply a stream of young talent, but they will need some experienced players to ease them into senior football.

Hopefully the Football Association is making every effort to ensure their clubs do not get high jacked by unscrupulous egotistical executives who completely fail to the run the club with any moral or business ethics. How many times have you read about the new board of directors who have stormed into a club with a three, four or five year plan to take them up the pyramid and into the Football League. Silly money is paid, often to undeserving players, and very soon the expected success isn't coming, and the executives tire of their new plaything which isn't as much fun or ego massaging as expected. So they move out, and the real supporters are left with their beloved club in a terrible position, much worse than it would have been if they had sensibly worked their way up the pyramid as quickly as their steady fundraising allowed.

'OUR' ENGLAND TEAM

If the **Football Association** have responsibilities to keep an eye out for the 'con men' they also have the opportunity to lift the image of the England team representing the largest section of the national game in this country.

Before the abolition of the 'amateur,' **England Amateur Internationals** were well respected players in their own right. Then as 'shamateurism' became rife and we had the ridiculous situation where amateurs in the **Isthmian** and **Athenian** Leagues were earning more from football than the honest semi-professionals in the **Southern League**. This was rectified when the term 'amateur' was abolished in 1974 and everyone became just 'players'. The glamourous **F.A.Amateur Cup** disappeared but the **F.A.Vase** was introduced for the genuinely smaller clubs. **The F.A.Trophy** had already been introduced to give the honest semi-professionals their own national knock out tournament with a Wembley Final in 1971. There was a cup for everyone. But there was no International team to represent the 97 % of footballers that existed outside the fulltime professional ranks. This just wasn't right, as every player should have the chance to reach the top and represent their country at the sport of their choice?

Eventually after many meetings and the help of supportive sponsors a four nations tournament was played and hosted twice each by **England, Scotland, Holland** and **Italy**. Many very good players were spotted in the England team and went on to enjoy excellent careers throughout The Football League. To have been an **England Semi-Pro International** was a much admired and respected honour and clubs were proud of 'their' players with international caps. These honours added value to potential transfer fees and the tournaments were watched by rows and rows of club talent scouts.

There was a fifteen year gap in which the England team representing non-league football played occasional friendlies but a competitive tournament was definitely needed and it wasn't until 2002 that England hosted an end of season competition that included **Wales, Scotland** and **The Republic of Ireland.**

Sadly, by this time, the attitudes of many executives in charge of Conference clubs had changed. They had no experience of the pride enjoyed by clubs when their players had been picked to represent their country. Many of them had no background in Non-League Football in general, and the thrill of reaching the top of the pyramid and one's players being considered the very cream of the huge non-league world meant nothing to them.

Many had been relegated as failures as the very **worst clubs** from the top full time leagues. It had probably been the worst moment of their football lives, so you would have thought that the change in status, to suddenly being part of a club representing **the best** of a huge section of the game would have been a pleasant relief. And perhaps their players being considered for international honours could give their supporters a lift.

But no, many of the Conference club representatives have made it quite clear that despite knowing there would be certain weeks kept free for England International games they were not interested, as getting into the Football League and making more money was too important.

Brian Lee, a Conference Vice President is a lone patriotic voice who helps link the F.A.Committee with the senior club competition administrators. His background as a past **Wycombe Wanderers** manager and chairman and England's first ever Semi-Pro International manager gives him the pedigree and he has experienced the pride in representing his country at his specific level of the game.

Paul Fairclough the England manager, who is now also in charge of **Barnet**, had a horrific time last season as every one of his selections suffered when many players were pulled out. Despite the problems, he produced some spirited performances but playing for England should be special. The manager should have the very best with whom to work giving him a chance of achieving top class international performances for England.

I honestly believe that if the same attitudes are confirmed by the Conference Premier Division clubs again this year, then the England team should revert to being a purely Semi-Professional XI selected from Conference North and South and below. You would then have clubs proud of their players selection for their country and players thrilled to wear the three lions once again.

'NON-LEAGUE' A TERM OF ENDEARMENT

If the senior Conference clubs really prefer to be considered as the bottom rung of the full time game rather than the very best and the cream of talent representing the F.A.'s national game, then good luck to them. There seem to be very few clubs left at that level proud to be associated with the traditional non-league spirit and indeed they do not want to be considered 'non-league' clubs.

The term was adopted to cover all clubs outside 'The Football League' ie. 'Non-Football League'. It is used as one of endearment, especially around F.A.Cup time when everyone loves a brave 'non-league' club battling against the full time giants. There is nothing degrading about being 'non-league' with ambitions to become a proud member of The Football League. Or if you are not in a position to challenge for that elusive promotion, just enjoy the very special spirit that still exists around the country in the 'real non-league' competitions and their clubs.

THE NON-LEAGUE PAPER

One of the most encouraging aspects of last season was the way The Non-League Paper really established itself as the game's special newspaper with editions now published on Fridays and Sundays. With a combined circulation of up to a quarter a million a month it must surely have the best distribution of any football publication in the country. This is particularly rewarding to **Chris Ingram**, the **Woking** chairman, who has invested over one million pounds in the paper to ensure it recovered from its early upsets and to **David Emery** who has had to take severe personal risks to make sure the paper survived.

IS GOOD SPORTSMANSHIP APPRECIATED ?

There was a time last season when football collected a stream of very depressing headlines as our better known Premier League players misbehaved on and off the field. Obviously it was only a minority off the field but certainly on it there seemed to be no honour or standards left in the game at all.

I appreciate that money is important, but is it important enough to deliberately cheat? Should our youngsters be brought up thinking that if you cannot achieve your aims fairly then just break the rules as it's all right unless you get caught.

The mass brawls are degrading, the deliberate feigning of injury and simulating a foul is pathetic and deliberately attempting to get your opponent cautioned is despicable.

The television panels of experts were usually of the opinion that 'professionals,'if they couldn't stop an opponent fairly, their coaches and colleagues would be expected to cheat! You have to feel sorry for referees who can be completely conned as we saw very clearly in the Champions League semi-finals but they have brought it on themselves in one way as they now seem to show a card for any tackle that isn't exactly perfect and this encourages all sorts of very easy simulation.

At its worst last season, referees all over the country were complaining about grass roots and non-league players copying their heroes and indeed giving abuse, which we also see being ignored on television. Non-League football isn't generally in a bad state. But during the season I suggested to The Football Association that perhaps we could take the initiative at non-league level by really rewarding our clubs for behaving well and at the same time make life easier for the referees.

I was lucky enough to run the Rothmans sponsorship of the Isthmian, Northern, Western and Hellenic leagues in the seventies. Jimmy Hill and Doug Insole put together a brilliant package that rewarded sporting and successful football and generous prizes were available as rewards for successful clubs . But no money would be paid out to a club at the end of a season who had lost a set amount of cautions during the season and not even the bonuses for a three goal win would be paid out if the winners had received a caution during the game.

Only eight sportsmanship points were given to each club and one was lost for each caution and four for a dismissal. These days with referees modern attitudes it would have to be twenty points, but the principle would be the same and the system worked brilliantly. The clubs were more disciplined, the referees enjoyed their football more and became far better officials as they could concentrate on the game without abuse, and the clubs did better in the knock out competitions as well,as referees are human and if one team abused them and the other kept quiet who do think benefited?

Hopefully, this season will see the F.A.lead a campaign to improve attitudes and the pride in our national sport. Good luck to leagues who make an effort like the the GLS Hellenic competition whose new ideas are highlighted on page thirteen, and here's to a happy and successful season for us all. **Tony Williams**

INTRODUCTION TO THE BOOK

This year's Directory, like non-League football, has been subject to a change of structure.
The book kick's off as always with the Non-League awards but is followed by the 'Non-League Club Directory' which is broken down into Steps, as per the new structure published by Mike Appleby.
Where a league covers more than one Step, the clubs and tables from each division follow on. For example: Isthmian Premier (Step 3), Isthmian Division One (Step 4) and Isthmian Division Two (Step 5) are all contained within the same section.
As Steps 5 and 6 pool together to supply only eight teams to Step 4, their section is in alphabetical order. Step 7 is broken down into three sections, the Northern, Southern and Isthmian. Throughout the book there Pyramid pages which should hopefully make it all clear!
Following on from the 'Non-League Club Directory' is the Football Association's Competition section which contains all the results, statistics and photographs from all the F.A. competitions played last during the season.
Finally the end section of the book includes County Association Football, Amateur Football, Schools, Women's and Scottish football, plus much more.

Key to results

				Att.
Team A	v	Team B	0-3* 2-2r 4-3p	120

* - After Extra Time r - Reply p - Penalties
Where a cup tie was contested over two legs, the first named club played the 1st Leg at home.

RESOLUTIONS FOR SEASON 2004-2005

For Players

To cut out agressive dissent to referees.
It only brings the player, his club, his league and the game itself
into even more disrepute
and
have you ever seen a referee change his mind after listening to abusive complaints?

For Referees

To refrain from cautioning
players who honestly mistime a tackle or are just beaten by skill or pace
and obviously had no intent to foul. At lower levels this happns a great deal.
but to caution players who do deserve to be booked for deliberately holding and body
checking at corners.
Be braveand regularly give penalties and bookings
and this plague will be eliminated

For FIFA and The FA

Eliminate over night the embarrassing and degrading mass brawl
and pathetic mass pushing and shoving
by
Threatening all clubs with such strict penalties
(i.e. deduction of 10 points in a league or elimination from a cup competition)
that chairmen and managers would ensure their players controlled themselves
and behaved as disciplined professional sportsmen,
who after all, are role models for the young.

G.L.S.HELLENIC LEAGUE SET AN EXAMPLE.

GLS FOOTBALL
HELLENIC FOOTBALL LEAGUE

GLS
FOOTBALL

Mind YOUR Language

The GLS Football Hellenic Football League has implemented a policy to remove the use of 'INAPPROPRIATE LANGUAGE' from Hellenic League Grounds.
Players, Managers, Coaches etc are advised that the use of Inappropriate Language on and near the football pitch is likely to result in Disciplinary Action.

Spectators using Inappropriate Language may be asked to leave the Ground.
So for everyone's sake, please do your bit and mind your language!

Michael Broadley
Michael Broadley
Chairman
GLS Football Hellenic League

Derek Turner
Derek Turner
Chairman
Abingdon United FC

Brian King
Brian King
General Secretary
GLS Football Hellenic League

John Blackmore
John Blackmore
Secretary
Abingdon United FC

The 2003-2004 season was littered with examples of appaling sportsmanship which were regularly shown on television with numerous repeats. Youngsters all over the country copied their role models and referees' lives became increasingly unpleasant as foul and abusive language was also a regular occurrence, mainly because the senior players were often seen to show dissent without even the ten yard rule being used as a punishment.

With even more high profile and distressing headlines affecting our game and involving the Football Association throughout the season, perhaps it was understandable that leadership from our parent body wasn't forthcoming. We read about fewer and fewer youngsters taking up refereeing and many qualified officials retiring early. It wasn't difficult to understand reasons for this situation.

Having been responsible for running the day to day Rothmans football sponsorship of the Isthmian, Northern, Western and Hellenic Leagues in the seventies I knew how well the sponsorship package set up by Jimmy Hill and Doug Insole had worked. Very briefly, the financial incentives rewarded attacking and sporting play but the important factor was that no prize money could be claimed by any successful clubs if they had lost their allocation of just eight sportsmanship points.

This allocation could be lost by cautions (one point each) and dismissals (three points) and, believe it or not, only a third of the 80 clubs lost all eight points. Blyth Spartans actually won the very competitive and tough Northern League without losing a point!

Dissent and retaliation were cut out overnight as chairmen instructed managers and the latter passed on instructions to concentrate on disciplined football. Referees enjoyed their football more and tended to give players who were competing in the right spirit a little extra understanding with tackles. Another result of disciplined football brought better results in cup ties, especially against clubs from leagues without the sportsmanship incentives. If you were a referee and one side continually bombarded you with 'verbals' and one didn't, to whom would you give any benefit of doubt?

When we reached the depths last season with particularly regular examples of holding shirts, feigning fouls and injuries, getting opponents into trouble, violent dissent and mass brawls, I suggested to the Football Association that the old Rothmans brainchild of Messrs Insole and Hill would be perfect for at least the level of the new 'step five' leagues, to show the football world that sportsmanship can bring results and rewards. I thought this would be an ideal opportunity for the F.A. to reassure the non-league world that they would be protected from the bad examples at the senior levels.

So it was reassuring good news that one of the old Rothmans quartet, The Hellenic League, who have shown determination to lift the standards of sportsmanship within their divisions by accepting a new sponsorship from Gladwish Land Sales. The Northern League also has a strong disciplinary ethic and many other leagues have excellent Fair Play awards with Ladbrokes giving impressive support in the last two years.

The League and Victor Gladwish have put together an exciting package which is explained by General Secretary Brian King:-

The attached document is a sample of that sent to all member clubs for posting in changing rooms and club houses in respect of the League Policy on the use of 'inappropriate language' and the 'zero' tolerance that member clubs wish to invoke.

The GLS Football Hellenic League has a fund of £25.000 to be distributed to member clubs this season.

League and Cup winners will receive £10,000 which includes awards down to fourth place in first team competitions.

The other £15,000 (60%) is for distribution to clubs based on Sportsmanship, Fair Play and Club Administration.

Each member club starts the season with an account balance of £100 and can gain funds for :

1. goals scored
2. sportsmanship marks awarded at each league match by match officials
3. clean sheet awards - no on field misconduct and no breaches of competition rules for an associated match.

Clubs incur losses from their club account by:-

1. conceding goals

2. having players cautioned and/or sent off (these are broken into two groups by the offence coding)
   - **a)** cautions that are part of match play suffer a single penalty - such as: unsporting behaviour, persistently infringing the laws of the game, entering and re-entering the field of play without permission of the referee and deliberately leaving the field without permission of the referee.
   - **b)** cautions that are controllable by individual players suffer a double penalty - such as dissent by word or action, delaying the re-start of play, failure to respect the required distance for re-starts from corner kicks and free kicks.

3. players sent off are also broken into two groups by offence coding: -
   - **a)** dismissals that are part of match play suffer a single penalty - such as incidents of serious foul play, denying an obvious goal scoring opportunity by deliberately handling the ball or by committing an offence punishable by a free-kick or penalty kick.
   - **b)** sendings-off that are controlable by individual players suffer a double penalty - such as incidents of violent conduct, spitting at an opponent or other person, use of offensive, insulting or abusive language.

These initiatives are an excellent step forward and my only slight worry is that an unscrupulous club could 'kick' their way to a title and its prize money while ignoring the chance of rewards for sportsmanship. Hopefully, this will not happen but it might have been better if it **couldn't** happen.

FOOTBALL CREDITOR RULE OFF SIDE? NOT YET

Throughout the whole of last season news flashes regarding Exeter City's survival battle were to be found throughout the football media.. The club's legal team consisted of Steve Allinson a director, who had already been a great help to Yeovil Town in their succesfull progress from semi-professional non-league football to full time membership of the Football League. He received excellent support from a partner Trevor Watkins, his assistant Sue Bunning and appreciated the help from Stephen Davies QC and Hugh Sims as barristers.

Exeter City relied on their judgment completely and although it was often very heavy going, on completion, the whole of football must surely have been very grateful for the work put in on behalf of the game's traditions and Exeter City in particular. The Football Creditor 'rule' stayed in tact but for how long I wonder?

The man at the helm, Steven Allinson describes how Exeter City's year of turmoil could effect the game:-

For many years there has been much academic debate surrounding the "football creditor" rule and how it interacts with general insolvency law. It is fair to say that it is a rule that has not sat happily with a number of insolvency lawyers and it is also a rule that of course has caused considerable commercial interest as more and more football clubs have found themselves having to face insolvency situations.

In a nutshell, the rule can be summarised as the football authorities requiring insolvent football clubs to make provision to pay all their football creditors in full as a condition of retaining their membership of the relevant football league in which they operate.

It has been well known for a number of years that the Inland Revenue as an institutional creditor, has found this rule particularly difficult and unpalatable. A significant change however in the Inland Revenue's relationship with football clubs and the operation of this rule took place on 15 September 2003 when the Inland Revenue lost its preferential status in any insolvency, pursuant to the coming into force of the relevant provisions of the Enterprise Act 2002.

In effect therefore, since that date the Inland Revenue stands fairly and squarely with all other unsecured creditors and yet a special category of preferential creditors ("the football creditors") remains and these creditors must be paid in full in any football club insolvency, if the club is to maintain its membership of its league.

It is worth remembering that the definition of football creditors is quite widely drawn but most significantly it includes all full time employees of the club (most commonly of course the players) or indeed former full time employees who are owed arrears of remuneration. It also includes monies that are due to other football clubs (possibly in respect of player transfer or loan monies) and monies due to the various football authorities.

Exeter City AFC Limited was the first football club to enter into a corporate voluntary arrangement after 15 September 2003. It therefore became something of a "test case" for this particular rule in the light of the Inland Revenue's new status. It's Corporate Voluntary Arrangement was a relatively standard one in terms of football club insolvencies. It provided that football creditors would be paid in full over a number of years but that other creditors would receive only 10p in the pound. In October 2003 the creditors voted by the requisite majority to support this arrangement. Exeter City football fans breathed a huge sigh of relief as this gave the Club an opportunity to move forward – with the support of their creditors – and alleviate what was a crippling debt problem of around £4m. However, to the dismay of the Supporters Trust who (again through legal moves) had taken control of the Club, the Inland Revenue challenged this insolvency procedure (on the very last day that it was open to them so to challenge) on the grounds that it was "unfairly prejudicial" to their interest. The main ground of this challenge was that football creditors were paid in full and all other creditors received only 10p in the pound.

This particular legal challenge then promoted a series of litigation struggles which have only just been completed and took place against the backdrop of Exeter City's first season in the Nationwide Conference League – they having been relegated on the final day of the 2002/2003 season.

Through its lawyers, Exeter City mounted a strategic counter attack to the Revenue by initially issuing proceedings against the Nationwide Conference Board of Directors on the grounds that it was unfairly prejudicial to the Club to be threatened with a removal from that competition if they did not pay their football creditors in full. Linked with this legal action was a separate challenge that the "sporting sanctions" – namely the removal of points through going into a formal insolvency process – was also unfairly operated by the Conference and this challenge centred around a number of complex company law arguments.

The Inland Revenue stood on the side lines whilst Exeter and the Conference slugged out these actions. One interesting element of the action was the applicability of the arbitration clauses in the Football Association Rules (which has been the subject of a previous article in this journal). Eventually these proceedings were compromised with both parties agreeing that they should stand together to defend the football creditor rule against the Inland Revenue. This decision was a good one from the Club's point of view in that the Football Association worked with them in the following months and from the Exeter City's fans point of view, it was a particularly good result because the threat of points sanctions was dropped. Ultimately therefore the Football Club played out last season challenging throughout for a quick return to the Football League, only to find that opportunity was missed on the last day of the season when football results transpired against them. The season however ended with the Club knowing that it had protected its position throughout all the legal challenges but the spectre of the Inland Revenue remained. The outcome of that case would decide whether Exeter could maintain its Corporate Voluntary Arrangement or whether (if the Inland Revenue won) it would be revoked and the Club once again would be plunged into financial mire. By this time many other clubs and those involved in the business of football were closely watching this case, because if the Inland Revenue defeated Exeter, then it would in essence bring an end to the football creditor rule which had been one of the bedrocks of the way football had operated for many years.

With Exeter's case due to be heard in mid July, there was a significant development in that the Inland Revenue also challenged Wimbledon Football Club Limited's insolvency. This had in fact predated the Revenue loss of preferential status and the whole case was therefore based on a separate point of the Insolvency Act, section 4(4)(a), which provided that a meeting should not approve the proposed voluntary arrangement under which (without the concurrence of the preferential creditor concerned) "any preferential debt of the company is to be paid otherwise than in priority to such of its debts as are not preferential debts." This particular case was expedited because of the needs of the proposed new owner of the club and at both first instance (Mr Justice Lightman) and the Court of Appeal, (both sets of proceedings taking place in May 2004), the Inland Revenue's contentions were rejected. This was despite the fact that at first instance Mr Justice Lightman passed comment that "the power of the League to impose the obstacle and secure full payment for creditors of its choice, may be objectionable and indeed the Party Parliamentary Group in its first Inquiry Report has found it objectionable and recommended its abolition".

Exeter City's case did not concern the rights of competing classes of preferential creditors and indeed all new insolvency rescues in football clubs will not face matters in the same way as Wimbledon. Nevertheless faced with the Wimbledon judgment and a detailed expert's report secured by Exeter City setting out the rationale and basis for the football creditor rule in a closed environment, the Inland Revenue agreed to withdraw its case against Exeter prior to the trial.

So where does this leave the football creditor rule? Given that there was no definitive ruling in the Exeter City case no binding legal principle can be gained from it. There is no doubt that all football clubs who are forced to enter into any kind of formal insolvency, will have to give due recognition to the fact that the Inland Revenue remains unhappy about the football creditor rule and if it is a significant creditor in any such insolvencies, it may well flex its muscles. The football authorities remain however committed to the rule and will continue to justify its scope and applicability through the particular and special characteristics of the economic market which the football industry represents and within which clubs operate. Interest in the issue remains at Parliamentary level and the issue will no doubt continue to be debated both within the twin worlds of football and the law. Football insolvency has been a significant factor over recent years. Of course, the problems of the scope and operation of the football creditor rule would be avoided if all those involved with football clubs recognised the financial realities of running businesses with their means. There is optimism that that position is improving but it is unlikely to change overnight.

Lest we forget, amongst the detailed and intricate legal analysis that all this litigation has promoted, Exeter City's management, players and fans are looking forward to the 2004/2005 season in the knowledge that they can now concentrate on events on the field, rather than fighting legal battles off it. As the lawyer who has been intricately and deeply involved in their survival battle for the last twelve months, I wish them every success on the field.

Stephen Allinson, Partner, Licensed Insolvency Practitioner
Clarke Willmott, Solicitors for Exeter City AFC Limited.

The Non-League Club Directory

2003-2004 AWARDS

• ROLL OF HONOUR •

FOOTBALLER OF THE YEAR
Andrew Forbes (Winchester City)

MANAGER OF THE YEAR
Graham Turner (Hereford United)

ENGLAND PLAYER OF THE YEAR
David Perkins (Morecambe)

REGIONAL AWARDS
Dunston Federation Brewery ~ Droylsden
Loughborough Dynamo ~ A.F.C. Sudbury
Canvey Island ~ Lewes ~ Weston-Super-Mare ~ Rhyl

F.A. CUP
Scarborough

INDIVIDUAL MERIT AWARDS
Mike Appleby ~ Victor Gladwish ~ Chris Ingram
Les James ~ Stuart Norman ~ Carl Palmer

• REGIONAL CLUB AWARDS 2003-04 •

NORTH EAST

DUNSTON FEDERATION BREWERY F.C. produced a memorable campaign which will be treasured by the players and officials alike. The Northern League championship was won for the first time as they pulled well away from Durham City and they completed 'the double' with the League Cup. Add to that a best ever F.A.Cup run to the 4th Qualifying Round and a very satisfying season was well deserved and thoroughly enjoyed. Not surprisingly, Bobby Scaife their popular manager, won the League's special award.

NORTH WEST

DROYLSDEN enjoyed their best ever season and, although they were never really challenging Hucknall at the top of the N.P.L. championship, they finished proudly as runners up for the first time ever. They scored in their first 31 League games and finished with a top scoring 96 goals in the premier division. The two other prestigious N.P.L. competitions, The Challenge Cup and Challenge Shield, were both won to give The Bloods a tremendous season.

MIDLANDS 1

LOUGHBOROUGH DYNAMO have enjoyed an exciting development in recent seasons and the 2003-2004 campaign rewarded them with four trophies and promotion to the Midland Alliance. Dynamo won their Leicester Senior League and Cup 'double' plus Leicester Charity Cup and the Presidents Trophy. There are other Midland challengers emerging like Nuneaton Griff and Leamington F.C., but Loughborough Dynamo are the first to reach the Alliance. Congratulations.

MIDLANDS 2

A.F.C.SUDBURY have kept their standards remarkably well and last season retained their dominance in the Eastern Counties League by winning the Championship once again and they also continued their drive for that elusive F.A.Vase success. Having reached the semi-finals in 2002 they were beaten in the last minute of the final in 2003, but battled through in determined fashion to reach the final again last season. Unfortunately, they came up against a very special Winchester City side who were too good for them on the day. But who's to say the drive won't continue as they strive to achieve their ambition?

HOME COUNTIES EAST

CANVEY ISLAND were most people's favourites to win the Isthmian Championship and they didn't let anyone down. They did even better reaching the F.A.Trophy Final, although surprisingly beaten by Hednesford Town, and they also enjoyed another good F.A.Cup run which was brought to a halt by old friends Southend United. The rise of the club from obscurity to the Conference has brought great credit to those in charge and it will be a thrill for the 'Islanders' to see top quality football, possibly in a brand new stadium.

• REGIONAL CLUB AWARDS 2003-04 •

HOME COUNTIES SOUTH

LEWES achieved a feat that has never before been recorded and probably never will be again! They started the season in Division One South of the Isthmian League, having missed promotion by two points in the previous campaign. They then won an exciting championship from Worthing by two points, who were just one point ahead of Windsor & Eton. This brought them into a play off system which, if they proved successful, would see them vault the Isthmian Premier and arrive a little flushed and excited in the Conference South. And this is exactly what they have achieved!

WEST OF ENGLAND

WESTON-SUPER-MARE will find themselves in the exalted heights of the Conference South next season and that really is progress for a club, who may well have doubted their ability to stay in the Southern Premier Division earlier in the campaign. A fine F.A.Cup run ended at Northampton Town in the Second Round and, despite flirting with the F.A.Trophy until losing at Telford United in the Fourth Round, 'The Seagulls' finished strongly and became the second club for whom manager Frank Gregan had provided Conference Football.

WALES

RHYL enjoyed a truly remarkable season in Wales, winning the League of Wales Championship and Cup double in style.They also won the prestigious Welsh Cup and then, having beaten Swansea City in the semi-final, they were only denied a complete clean sweep by a full Wrexham side, who beat them in the final of the F.A.W.Premier Cup Final.

F.A.CUP

SCARBOROUGH finished their cup run with a wonderful home tie against glamourous Chelsea and could well have forced a replay at least if decisions had just been normally administered. But, before television cameras showed the country the quality of 'The Seadogs' and indeed the Conference, they had beaten three Football League Clubs in Doncaster Rovers (H) , Port Vale (A) and after a replay, Southend United (H). This was a superb cup run for which they deserved all the good publicity they received.

NON LEAGUE FOOTBALLER OF THE YEAR

ANDREW FORBES
(Winchester City)

Photo: Roger Turner

Goalscorers are always in the headlines, but Winchester City's leading marksman was truly outstanding. Andy Forbes scored an amazing 76 goals for his club last season and helped them win The Wessex League and Cup 'double' and of course the F.A.Vase in a stylish performance at St Andrews, Birmingham. Forbes has pace, uses both feet equally well and is lethal in the air. He enjoys his day job so much that it will take an exceptional offer to lure him into full time football - but he is an exceptional footballer. His critics suggest he should put himself about a bit more and work harder (memories of the great Jimmy Greaves!), but I am sure a good coach could improve those facets and after all, natural goalscoring flare cannot be taught. It is a wonderful gift which Andrew Forbes thoroughly enjoys.

PAST WINNERS

2002-03	Darren Way (Yeovil Town)	1992-93	Steve Guppy (Wycombe Wndrs)
2001-02	Daryl Clare (Boston United)	1991-92	Tommy Killick (Wimborne Town)
2000-01	Ray Warburton (Rushden & Dia)	1990-91	Mark West (Wycombe Wndrs)
1999-00	Gary Abbott (Aldershot Town)	1989-90	Phil Gridelet (Barnet)
1998-99	Neil Grayson (Cheltenham Town)	1988-89	Steve Butler (Maidstone Utd)
1997-98	Phil Everett (Tiverton Town)	1987-88	David Howell (Enfield)
1996-97	Howard Forinton (Yeovil Town)	1986-87	Mark Carter (Runcorn)
1995-96	Barry Hayles (Stevenage Boro)	1985-86	Jeff Johnson (Altrincham)
1994-95	Kevan Brown (Woking)	1984-85	Alan Cordice (Wealdstone)
1993-94	Chris Brindley (Kidderminster H.)	1983-84	Brian Thompson (Maidstone Utd)

NON LEAGUE MANAGER OF THE YEAR

GRAHAM TURNER

(Hereford United)

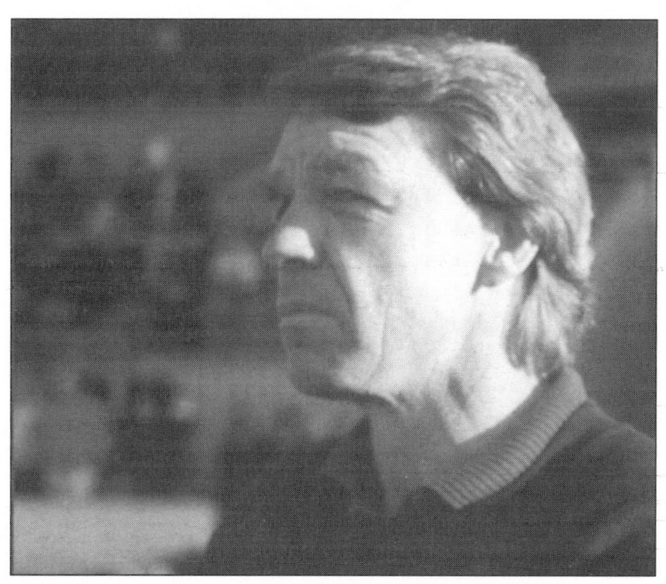

Having proved himself as a top quality manager in the old First Division, Graham Turner chose to dedicate himself to his beloved Hereford United. He took over as Chairman-Owner-Manager when the club suffered financial troubles after leaving the Football League and gradually he re-built the club to a point when last season his squad were obviously the best footballing side in the Conference. Injuries and a blip in mid-season form resulted in a close finish just one point behind the most consistent club, Chester City. But The Bulls scored more goals and won more games than any other Conference club and they claimed four of the six points against the champions. In the play-offs a very doubtful refereeing decision helped to see Hereford United eliminated by a club who had finished 21 points below them in the table. Graham Turner kept his dignity, and showed outstanding sportsmanship at all times. He was a real credit to the game.

PAST WINNERS

2002-03	Gary Johnson (Yeovil Town)
2001-02	Nigel Clough (Burton Albion)
2000-01	Jeff King (Canvey Island)
1999-00	Jan Molby (Kidderminster Harr.)
1998-99	Brendan Phillips (Nuneaton Boro)
1997-98	Steve Cotterill (Cheltenham Town)
1996-97	Paul Futcher (Southport)
1995-96	Paul Fairclough (Stevenage Boro)
1994-95	Sammy McIlroy (Macclesfield T)
1993-94	Bill Punton (Diss Town)
1992-93	Martin O'Neill (Wycombe Wndrs)

ENGLAND PLAYER OF THE YEAR
DAVID PERKINS
(Morecambe)

In a season when team selection proved difficult for the England manager, one player, who was always available and, when selected, wore the shirt with obvious pride, was David Perkins. He always gave the appearance of a 'winner' who loved the game. He constantly drove forward from his left back position, never hid when the going was tough and was particularly brilliant in the vital match against Scotland and on the American tour. The youngster also won his club's Player of the Year award so he has completed a wonderful season which augers well for his future career.

• INDIVIDUAL MERIT AWARDS 2003-04 •

MIKE APPLEBY

The 2003-2004 season must have seemed like five years in the life of Mike Appleby, the Football Association executive responsible for introducing the much discussed and very controversial re-structuring of the national pyramid system. Despite much press comment, criticism from some league and club officials, plus squabbles between negotiating leagues, Mike always kept cool and polite. He never outwardly panicked and he listened to all advice, ideas and complaints. He proved a fine example to many football dignitaries who would do well to take note.

VICTOR GLADWISH

After a lifetime as a football fanatic and avid follower of the lower levels of the game, Victor Gladwish had sampled all types of business success, so he decided he would like to put something back into the game he loved. Over 30 clubs have now benefited from G.L.S. sponsorship and the Hellenic League will also be carrying his name in their title next season. His support for publications such as the Non League Paper and the Fair Play magazine have also been appreciated, but sadly his busy season ended with the news that he needed a serious operation. We can only thank Victor for all his generosity and help given to Non-League Football and wish him a full and speedy recovery.

CHRIS INGRAM

The Non League Paper was one of the best football ideas to emerge for many years, but when the original chairman brought the organisation to a stuttering halt it was only the bravery and foresight of Woking Football Club chairman Chris Ingram that enabled editor David Emery and his team to develop the paper. They have now proved to would be advertisers that it is here to stay and has the biggest readership of any football publication. Chris is an extremely successful businessman and has now invested over one million pounds in ensuring the Non League Paper has an exciting future. The game can only benefit.

LES JAMES

In 1953, at the tender age of twenty-two, **Les James** became secretary of the Brierley Hill Youth League and created such a good impression that he was appointed as Secretary of the Midland Combination just four years later. He looked after the competition with much appreciated dedication until 1994 and since then has served just as enthusiastically as President. Les has seen the league grow dramatically from membership of eighteen as the Worcestershire Combination and has pleasure in seeing a much larger and stronger competion ready to take its place in the new national structure.

STUART NORMAN

Receives this award on behalf of players all over the country, who cannot give up the game. I have seen him playing over the last ten years and he is now 52. He represents his home town club, Watchet Town Blue Waves in Somerset Saturday and Sunday Football and has now completed 36 consecutive seasons. These competitions are not veteran leagues and Stuart still merits a place with sound performances every week.

CARL PALMER

With his club suffering from poor league form and his management being changed after a mixed season, it is fitting that this red haired midfielder should receive an award as the representative of **Hednesford Town,** the F.A.Trophy winners. His outstanding performances particularly impressed in the semi-finals and final, but he obviously enjoyed a consistent season as he also won his club's player of the year award.

PECKING ORDER 2003-2004

by A J Sarnecki

Position in Season 00-01	01-02	02-03	03-04	Lge Code	League	FA Cup ent	FA Cup xmt	FA Cup won	FA Trophy ent	FA Trophy xmt	FA Trophy won	FA Vase ent	FA Vase xmt	FA Vase won	C pts	T pts	V pts	Total pts
						1	4/8	1	4	4/6	1	1	4/6	1				
1	1	1	1	fc	FOOTBALL CONFERENCE	22	176	28	22	132	25	0	0	0	226	245	0	471
3	3	2	2	isa	ISTHMIAN Premier	24	96	29	24	40	34	0	0	0	149	170	0	319
2	2	3	3	npa	NORTHERN PREMIER Premier	23	92	28	23	46	26	0	0	0	143	164	0	307
4	4	4	4	soa	SOUTHERN Premier	22	88	24	22	40	26	0	0	0	134	154	0	288
(5	5)	6	5	isbn	ISTHMIAN First North	24	0	40	24	0	20	0	0	0	64	116	0	180
(8	9)	5	6	isbs	ISTHMIAN First South	24	0	27	24	0	22	0	0	0	51	118	0	169
7	7	7	7	sow	SOUTHERN Western	22	0	32	22	0	20	0	0	0	54	108	0	162
9	8	9	8	soe	SOUTHERN Eastern	22	0	34	22	0	16	0	0	0	56	104	0	160
6	6	8	9	npb	NORTHERN PREMIER First	22	0	30	22	0	15	0	0	0	52	103	0	155
11	11	14	10	nwca	NORTH WEST COUNTIES First	22	0	24	0	0	0	22	28	39	46	0	89	135
12	12=	11	11=	ecoa	EASTERN COUNTIES Premier	20	0	22	0	0	0	20	40	31	42	0	91	133
14	14	12	11=	wsx	WESSEX	21	0	24	0	0	0	21	26	41	45	0	88	133
10	10	10	13	nora	NORTHERN First	21	0	22	0	0	0	21	32	26	43	0	79	122
15	12=	13	14	ncea	NORTHERN COUNTIES EAST Premier	20	0	22	0	0	0	20	20	24	42	0	64	106
13	16	15	15	mda	MIDLAND ALLIANCE	20	0	9	0	0	0	23	26	23	29	0	72	101
18	17	16	16	ucoa	UNITED COUNTIES Premier	19	0	14	0	0	0	21	20	19	33	0	60	93
16	19	17	17	wesa	WESTERN Premier	18	0	17	0	0	0	18	16	23	35	0	57	92
17	15	18	18	isd	ISTHMIAN Second	16	0	9	0	0	0	16	22	23	25	0	61	86
22	22	19	19	coca	COMBINED COUNTIES Premier	18	0	12	0	0	0	21	10	17	30	0	48	78
21	21	22	20	ken	KENT	15	0	13	0	0	0	15	12	21	28	0	48	76
20	20	21	21	ssma	SPARTAN SOUTH MIDLANDS Premier	17	0	10	0	0	0	20	8	15	27	0	43	70
23	23	23	22	hela	HELLENIC Premier	12	0	11	0	0	0	19	8	19	23	0	46	69
19	18	20	23	ssxa	SUSSEX COUNTY First	17	0	6	0	0	0	19	18	8	23	0	45	68
24	24	24	24	nceb	NORTHERN COUNTIES EAST First	17	0	14	0	0	0	18	0	15	31	0	33	64
26	25	25	25	norb	NORTHERN Second	18	0	11	0	0	0	20	6	6	29	0	32	61
27	28	27	26	esxs	ESSEX SENIOR	11	0	4	0	0	0	13	12	14	15	0	39	54
28	27	26	27	wesb	WESTERN First	12	0	7	0	0	0	14	0	16	19	0	30	49
25	26	28	28	nwcb	NORTH WEST COUNTIES Second	14	0	7	0	0	0	15	0	12	21	0	27	48
29	32	30	29	ecob	EASTERN COUNTIES First	7	0	2	0	0	0	17	0	9	9	0	26	35
36	36	34	30	ssxb	SUSSEX COUNTY Second	6	0	2	0	0	0	11	0	7	8	0	18	26
33=	34	32=	31	mdca	MIDLAND COMBINATION Premier	0	0	0	0	0	0	13	0	12	0	0	25	25
30	33	35	32=	lesa	LEICESTERSHIRE SENIOR Premier	0	0	0	0	0	0	13	0	11	0	0	24	24
31=	29	29	32=	swe	SOUTH WESTERN	4	0	2	0	0	0	8	6	4	6	0	18	24
31=	30	31	34	wmda	WEST MIDLAND REGIONAL Premier	0	0	0	0	0	0	12	0	9	0	0	21	21
33=	31	32=	35	cmda	CENTRAL MIDLANDS Supreme	0	0	0	0	0	0	9	0	8	0	0	17	17
	37	39	36	ucob	UNITED COUNTIES First	0	0	0	0	0	0	6	0	2	0	0	8	8
33=	35	37	37=	ssmb	SPARTAN SOUTH MIDLANDS Senior	0	0	0	0	0	0	5	0	1	0	0	6	6
37=	41=	40	37=	nala	NORTHERN ALLIANCE Premier	0	0	0	0	0	0	2	0	4	0	0	6	6
40=	39=	38	37=	wcha	WEST CHESHIRE First	0	0	0	0	0	0	2	0	4	0	0	6	6
		45=	40=	cmdb	CENTRAL MIDLANDS Premier	0	0	0	0	0	0	3	0	2	0	0	5	5
39	43=	41=	40=	dvc	DEVON COUNTY LEAGUE	0	0	0	0	0	0	3	0	2	0	0	5	5
	43=	45=	42=	hebe	HELLENIC First East	0	0	0	0	0	0	2	0	2	0	0	4	4
		45=	42=	dspr	DORSET PREMIER	0	0	0	0	0	0	1	0	3	0	0	4	4
	38	36	44	hama	HAMPSHIRE Premier	0	0	0	0	0	0	3	0	0	0	0	3	3
		45=	45=	mana	MANCHESTER Premier	0	0	0	0	0	0	1	0	1	0	0	2	2
			45=	wrca	WEST RIDING COUNTY AMATEUR Premier	0	0	0	0	0	0	1	0	1	0	0	2	2
40=	43=	43=	47=	hebw	HELLENIC First West	0	0	0	0	0	0	1	0	0	0	0	1	1
	43=	45=	47=	wea	WEARSIDE	0	0	0	0	0	0	1	0	0	0	0	1	1
			47=	hrta	HERTS SENIOR COUNTY Premier	0	0	0	0	0	0	1	0	0	0	0	1	1
					others (accepted but did not play)	2	0	0	0	0	0	4	0	0	2	0	4	6

Points are given for status (acceptance into each of the three competitions), for prestige (exemption from early rounds) and performance (number of wins, however achieved, even by walkover). Entry to the Vase is valued at one point, that to the Trophy at 4. Cup entry gives a further bonus of one point. The number of entries from each league is shown in the appropriate column. Points for exemptions are valued at two for each round missed. The entry in the table is of the total points so gained by the given league, not the number of teams given exemptions. Finally, all wins are valued at one point, regardless of opposition: giving extra points for defeating 'stronger' opponents would be too arbitrary. After all, if they lost then they were not stronger on the day!

FOOTBALL LEAGUE

STEP 1

FOOTBALL CONFERENCE

STEP 2

CONFERENCE NORTH

CONFERENCE SOUTH

STEP 3

NORTHERN PREMIER

SOUTHERN PREMIER

ISTHMIAN PREMIER

STEP 4

NORTHERN PREMIER DIV.1

SOUTHERN LEAGUE EAST

SOUTHERN LEAGUE WEST

ISTHMIAN DIVISION 1

STEP 5/6

Combined Counties	p474	Hellenic	518	Midland Alliance	552	North West Counties	602	United Counties	658
Essex Senior	490	Isthmian Division 2	462	Northern League	564	Spartan South Midlands	620	Wessex	676
Eastern Counties	500	Kent	542	Northern Counties East	584	Sussex County	638	Western	694

STEP 7

Northern Section	p713	Southern Section	759	Isthmian Section	831

CONFERENCE NATIONAL

SPONSORED BY: NATIONWIDE
Founded 1979
President: J C Thompson MBIM, Minst.M
Chairman: W J King **Chief Executive:** J A Moules
Secretary: Kellie Discipline
51 Highfield Road, Dartford, Kent DA1 2JS
Tel: 01322 280837 Fax: 01322 294480 email: kellie@footballconference.co.uk

'Old Boys' Return

The Conference season started with a welcome to two relegated clubs from the Football League for the first time. Shrewsbury Town were considered one of the pre-season favourites along with Hereford United, Morecambe, Chester City and Stevenage Borough but Exeter City off field financial problems were so complicated no one knew how they would react.

From early in the season Hereford United established themselves as the club to watch. and two 7-1 victories and a quite shattering 9-0 victory at Dagenham, live on Sky TV were outstanding performances. However, like all colourful attacking sides, a lapse of form is more likely to occur for them than the dour clubs churning out good disciplined defensive performances. And as Chester City edged away from their rivals in this way they also had an attacking ace in goalscorer Daryl Clare who topped the competition's charts and won a championship medal for the second time.

It was obvious very early in the campaign that the ex Football League clubs, who were mostly full time outfits were dominating the top third of the table. Shrewsbury were there as expected but they were joined by the two promoted clubs with 'famous' names, Accrington Stanley and Aldershot Town, while Barnet had pulled themselves together impressively and of course Exeter City were hovering on the outskirts of the challenging group.

In the end, late challenges from Morecambe, Stevenage and Woking were held off and Hereford United, Barnet, Shrewsbury and Aldershot faced each other in the most evenly fought play offs imaginable. The Bulls had a player sent off early after an incredibly tough refereeing decision and then lost to Shots on penalties, while Shrewsbury also qualified from the spot. A lot has been said about Hereford's 21point advantage over Aldershot and the fact they scored more goals than any other club, but amidst their terrible ordeal all credit to Graham Turner for never once publically complaining. In the final another close encounter was eventually won by Shrewsbury Town who had proved to be a very popular club during their short stay in the Conference.

Relegation was expected by Farnborough Town, Leigh RMI and Northwich Victoria for some time before their apparent fate was decided. However, ever present Conference club Telford United were declared bankrupt, Margate couldn't move into their new ground in the allotted time and Hucknall Town didn't want promotion! So it was relief all round and welcome to Crawley Town and Canvey Island from the Home counties. The Vics are now the only club to compete in every Conference campaign.

Attendances were magnificent during the season with eight clubs averaging over 2,000 and in the F.A.Cup, Scarborough, Accrington Stanley, Telford United and Burton Albion enjoyed collecting more Football league scalps and the Chelsea visit to Scarborough was one of the season's classics. Perhaps the Conference clubs are waiting until 'New Wembley' is ready to welcome them, but just at the present time the F.A.Trophy is not their favourite competition!

In this season's line up, nine clubs have enjoyed Football League membership in recent seasons.They are operating on a full time basis, so the magic of working there way up the non-league pyramid and achieving that wonderful ambition of a place in the mystical promised land is not quite the same as it used to be. The thrill enjoyed by previously promoted champions such as Wycombe Wanderers, Kidderminster Harriers and Yeovil Town was different to the professional satisfaction achieved by Chester City and Shrewsbury Town.

This is just a sign of the times as the structure of the game changes and perhaps it will be the thrill of the clubs winning promotion to the Nationwide Conference from Conference North and South that will take on even more importance and will give clubs an exciting ambition at which those at the heart of non-league football can now concentrate their efforts.

Tony Williams

Aldershot fans celebrate as their club has qualified for the promotion play offs in their first season in the Conference. Photo: Eric Marsh.

FINAL LEAGUE TABLE 2003-04

			HOME					AWAY					TOTAL					
		P	**W**	**D**	**L**	**F**	**A**	**W**	**D**	**L**	**F**	**A**	**W**	**D**	**L**	**F**	**A**	**Pts**
1	Chester City	42	16	4	1	45	18	11	7	3	40	16	27	11	4	85	34	92
2	Hereford United	42	14	3	4	42	20	14	4	3	61	24	28	7	7	103	44	91
3	Shrewsbury Town *	42	13	6	2	38	14	7	8	6	29	28	20	14	8	67	42	74
4	Barnet	42	11	6	4	30	17	8	8	5	30	29	19	14	9	60	46	71
5	Aldershot Town	42	12	6	3	40	24	8	4	9	40	43	20	10	12	80	67	70
6	Exeter City	42	10	7	4	33	24	9	5	7	38	33	19	12	11	71	57	69
7	Morecambe	42	14	4	3	43	25	6	3	12	23	41	20	7	15	66	66	67
8	Stevenage Borough	42	10	5	6	29	22	8	4	9	29	30	18	9	15	58	52	63
9	Woking	42	10	9	2	40	23	5	7	9	25	29	15	16	11	65	52	61
10	Accrington Stanley	42	13	3	5	46	31	2	10	9	22	30	15	13	14	68	61	58
11	Gravesend & Northfleet	42	7	6	8	34	35	7	9	5	35	31	14	15	13	69	66	57
12	Telford United	42	10	3	8	28	28	5	7	9	21	23	15	10	17	49	51	55
13	Dagenham & Redbridge	42	8	3	10	30	34	7	6	8	29	30	15	9	18	59	64	54
14	Burton Albion (-1 pt)	42	7	4	10	30	29	8	3	10	27	30	15	7	20	57	59	51
15	Scarborough	42	8	9	4	32	25	4	6	11	19	29	12	15	15	51	54	51
16	Margate	42	8	2	11	30	32	6	7	8	26	32	14	9	19	56	64	51
17	Tamworth	42	9	6	6	32	30	4	4	13	17	38	13	10	19	49	68	49
18	Forest Green Rovers	42	6	8	7	32	36	6	4	11	26	44	12	12	18	58	80	48
19	Halifax Town	42	9	4	8	28	26	3	4	14	15	39	12	8	22	43	65	44
20	Farnborough Town	42	7	6	8	31	34	3	3	15	22	40	10	9	23	53	74	39
21	Leigh RMI	42	4	6	11	26	44	3	2	16	20	53	7	8	27	46	97	29
22	Northwich Victoria	42	2	8	11	15	38	2	3	16	15	42	4	11	27	30	80	23

* Promoted via the play-offs.

ATTENDANCES 2003-04

		Final Lge Pos.	Highest	verses	03-04 Average	02-03 Ave.	Diff
1	Shrewsbury Town	3	6738	Telford	4007	n/a	-
2	Hereford United	2	7240	Chester City	3704	2037	1667
3	Exeter City	6	8256	Accrington	3664	n/a	-
4	Aldershot Town	5	4637	Woking	3293	n/a	-
5	Chester City	1	5987	Scarborough	3064	2405	659
6	Woking	9	4158	Aldershot Town	2321	1986	335
7	Telford United	12	4337	Shrewsbury	2077	985	1092
8	Stevenage Borough	8	3019	Barnet	2002	1897	105
9	Barnet	4	2988	Leigh RMI	1830	1342	488
10	Accrington Stanley	10	3143	Shrewsbury	1796	n/a	-
11	Morecambe	7	3084	Accrington	1780	1462	318
12	Burton Albion	14	3203	Shrewsbury	1682	1746	-64
13	Halifax	19	2160	Morecambe	1505	1752	-247
14	Dagenham & Redbridge	13	1948	Stevenage	1442	1599	-157
15	Tamworth	17	2535	Burton Albion	1335	n/a	-
16	Scarborough	15	2503	Woking	1334	1381	-47
17	Gravesend & Northfleet	11	1725	Margate	1178	1228	-50
18	Farnborough Town	20	3233	Aldershot	945	881	64
19	Forest Green Rovers	18	1576	Hereford United	902	857	45
20	Northwich Victoria	22	3268	Shrewsbury	851	751	100
21	Margate	16	1030	Gravesend & N'fleet	566	684	-118
22	Leigh RMI	21	2002	Chester City	565	483	82

In order of average attendance.

		1	2	3	4	5	6	7	8	9	10	11	12	13	14	15	16	17	18	19	20	21	22
1	Accrington Stanley		4-2	2-0	3-1	0-2	2-3	1-2	3-1	4-1	3-3	2-1	2-0	4-1	3-2	1-0	2-2	1-0	0-1	2-1	3-0	1-5	3-3
2	Aldershot Town	2-1		1-1	3-1	1-1	2-1	2-1	2-0	3-0	2-2	3-1	1-2	2-0	0-2	2-2	4-3	1-2	1-1	2-0	1-1	3-1	2-1
3	Barnet	0-0	2-1		2-1	0-0	2-4	2-3	0-2	5-0	1-0	4-1	1-1	2-1	3-1	2-1	1-0	0-0	0-1	0-0	1-0	2-0	0-0
4	Burton Albion	1-1	1-4	2-3		1-1	0-1	3-4	1-0	2-3	3-0	2-2	4-1	3-2	0-1	0-1	0-1	2-0	0-1	1-1	0-1	2-1	2-0
5	Chester City	3-3	4-2	1-0	3-1		2-1	3-2	3-2	1-0	2-2	2-0	0-0	5-0	3-0	2-1	4-0	1-0	2-1	1-2	1-0	0-0	2-1
6	Dagenham & Redbridge	0-1	2-3	5-2	0-2	0-0		0-2	1-0	5-2	0-4	0-1	0-9	1-2	4-0	1-3	2-0	1-0	5-0	1-2	0-0	1-1	1-0
7	Exeter City	3-2	2-1	1-1	2-0	2-1	1-1		1-1	2-2	0-1	1-1	0-1	3-2	1-1	4-0	2-0	0-0	3-2	1-0	3-2	0-3	1-2
8	Farnborough Town	1-1	4-0	1-1	2-1	1-2	2-2	1-2		1-3	1-2	1-0	0-5	1-1	1-1	2-4	2-0	1-2	1-3	2-0	3-3	2-1	1-0
9	Forest Green Rovers	2-1	3-1	1-1	1-1	2-1	1-3	2-5	1-1		1-2	1-2	1-7	2-2	1-2	1-2	0-0	4-0	1-1	3-1	2-1	0-0	2-2
10	Gravesend & Northfleet	0-0	1-3	1-1	1-2	0-4	1-2	3-2	2-0	1-1		1-0	2-5	3-1	2-1	6-0	2-2	1-1	0-3	2-3	2-0	1-2	2-2
11	Halifax Town	1-1	1-2	1-2	1-4	0-3	3-0	2-0	2-0	0-1	1-0		1-2	2-1	0-1	1-0	5-3	1-0	0-0	2-1	1-2	1-1	2-2
12	Hereford United	1-0	4-3	2-0	1-2	2-1	1-1	1-1	2-0	5-1	3-3	7-1		0-1	2-1	3-0	1-0	2-1	2-1	1-0	0-1	2-1	0-1
13	Leigh RMI	1-2	2-2	1-4	0-1	2-6	2-1	1-1	0-2	1-2	1-2	1-1	0-5		4-2	3-1	1-0	1-4	2-2	1-3	1-1	1-1	0-1
14	Margate	3-1	1-2	0-1	1-2	1-2	3-3	0-1	3-0	2-0	1-3	2-0	1-3	2-0		1-1	3-1	0-2	0-2	1-4	3-2	1-0	1-2
15	Morecambe	1-0	2-0	1-3	2-1	0-1	3-2	0-3	3-2	4-0	2-2	2-0	2-2	1-0	3-3		3-0	2-1	3-3	2-1	4-0	1-0	2-1
16	Northwich Victoria	3-3	1-1	1-1	1-2	0-4	0-1	1-1	1-1	0-4	0-0	0-1	1-5	0-1	0-3	1-1		1-1	0-2	1-2	1-0	1-0	1-4
17	Scarborough	2-1	1-0	2-2	1-2	2-2	0-0	2-3	2-1	2-2	2-0	1-0	3-3	4-1	0-1	1-0	1-0		1-1	2-2	0-1	1-1	2-2
18	Shrewsbury Town	0-0	1-2	0-1	1-0	0-0	2-1	2-2	3-0	2-0	1-1	2-0	4-1	3-1	1-1	2-0	3-1	4-1		3-1	3-1	0-0	1-0
19	Stevenage Borough	2-1	0-1	1-2	1-0	0-0	0-2	2-2	3-2	2-1	2-2	1-0	0-2	4-0	2-1	0-1	1-0	2-2	2-0		3-1	0-1	1-1
20	Tamworth	1-1	3-3	2-0	1-1	1-5	2-0	2-1	2-1	1-0	1-3	2-0	1-3	4-3	1-1	2-3	2-1	0-0	1-1	1-2		0-1	2-0
21	Telford United	1-0	2-5	1-2	2-2	0-2	1-0	2-0	2-4	0-2	1-1	2-1	0-3	5-0	1-1	2-1	0-1	2-1	1-0	0-2	2-0		1-0
22	Woking	2-2	2-2	2-2	1-0	1-2	0-0	1-0	3-2	1-1	3-2	2-2	0-1	2-0	0-0	4-1	3-0	2-1	3-3	1-1	4-0	3-1	

TOP GOALSCORERS

PLAYER	CLUB	APPS	LGE	FA	LDV	TOTAL
Daryl Clare	Chester City	32	29	1	0	30
Steve Guinan	Hereford United	40	25	3	1	29
Giuliano Grazioli	Barnet	41	24	2	0	26
David McNiven	Leigh RMI	42	25	0	0	25
Paul Mullin	Accrington Stanley	47	20	3	0	23
Roscoe D'Sane	Aldershot Town	43	21	2	0	23
Sean Devine	Exeter City	36	20	2	0	22
Darryn Stamp	Chester City	40	20	0	0	20
Jody Banim	Shrewsbury Town (18 with Radcliffe Boro')	38	20	0	0	20
Anthony Elding	Stevenage Borough	40	17	2	0	19
Tim Sills	Aldershot Town	42	18	1	0	19
Lutel James	Accrington Stanley	47	17	1	0	18
Danny Carlton	Morecambe	39	17	0	0	17
David Brown	Hereford United	43	14	1	2	17
Roy Essandoh	Gravesend & Northfleet (6 for Bishop's S.)	32	16	0	0	16
Mark Quayle	Scarborough	44	14	1	0	15
Mark Cooper	Tamworth	39	15	0	0	15
Robert Talbot	Burton Albion	40	12	2	0	14
Ben Smith	Hereford United	31	13	1	0	14
Chris Moore	Dagenham & Redbridge (4 for Northwood)	28	14	0	0	14
Luke Rodgers	Shrewsbury Town	36	13	0	0	13
Duane Darby	Shrewsbury Town (2 for Rushden & Dia.)	38	12	0	0	12
Lee Mills	Telford United	32	9	2	1	12
Dino Maamria	Stevenage Borough	29	9	3	0	12
Ryan Lowe	Shrewsbury Town	40	9	2	1	12
Craig Midgley	Halifax Town	43	11	0	1	12
Colin Cramb	Shrewsbury Town	36	12	0	0	12
Wayne Curtis	Morecambe (4 for Barrow)	32	12	0	0	12
Jon Challinor	Aldershot Town	39	12	0	0	12
Steve Ferguson	Woking	42	9	2	0	11
Tony Naylor	Telford United	28	11	0	0	11
Chris Murphy	Telford United	31	7	3	0	10
Ian Selley	Woking	33	8	2	0	10
Dale Anderson	Burton Albion	40	7	3	0	10

Lee Charles scores the goal that gave Aldershot Town the final point needed for a promotion play off place.
Photo: Bill Wheatcroft

FOOTBALL CONFERENCE PLAY-OFF SEMI-FINAL FIRST LEG

ALDERSHOT TOWN	**1 (1)**	**1 (1)**	**HEREFORD UNITED**
D'Sane 45(p)			Brown 7

Att: 6,379

TEAM:	**TEAM**:
Bull	Mathew Baker
Sterling	James
Ray Warburton	Tretton
Giles	Smith
Charles	Green
Gosling	Pitman
Antwi (S75)	Purdey
Challinor	Travis
Downer (S68)	Rose
D'Sane	Carey-Bertram (S68)
Sills	Brown
Substitutes:	**Substitutes**:
Richard Barnard	Beesley (S68)
Chewins (S75)	Cozic
McLean (S68)	MacKenzie
Smith	Daniel Williams

FOOTBALL CONFERENCE PLAY-OFF SEMI-FINAL SECOND LEG

HEREFORD UNITED	**0 (0)**	**0 (0)**	**ALDERSHOT TOWN**
Penalties: 2	A.E.T.		Penalties 4

Att: 7,044

TEAM:	**TEAM**:
Mathew Baker	Bull
James	Sterling
Tretton (Sent-Off 21)	Ray Warburton
Smith	Giles
Green	Charles (S70)
Pitman	Gosling
Daniel Williams (S109)	Antwi
Rose	Challinor
Travis (S80)	Downer (S60)
Guinan (S73)	McLean (S84)
Brown	Sills
Substitutes:	**Substitutes**:
Betts (S80)	Richard Barnard
Beesley (S73)	Chewins (S60)
Carey-Bertram	D'Sane (S70)
Cozic (S109)	Nutter (S84)
MacKenzie	Johnson

Promotion Play offs

FOOTBALL CONFERENCE PLAY-OFF SEMI-FINAL FIRST LEG

BARNET	**2 (1)**	**1 (1)**	**SHREWSBURY TOWN**
Strevens 13 (p), Clist 90	Att: 4,171		Rodgers 43 (p)

TEAM:	**TEAM:**
Gore	Howie
Hendon	Moss
Plummer	Tinson (S45)
Maddix	Ridler
King	Challis (S78)
Yakubu	Lowe
Lopez (S67)	O'Connor
Gamble	Tolley
Strevens	Aiston
Grazioli	Darby
Hatch	Rodgers (S87)
Substitutes:	**Substitutes:**
Clist (S67)	Edwards
Millard	Hart
Pearson	Lawrence (S78)
Rooney	Quinn (S87)
Redmile	Sedgemore (S45)

FOOTBALL CONFERENCE PLAY-OFF SEMI-FINAL SECOND LEG

SHREWSBURY TOWN	**1 (1)**	**0 (0)**	**BARNET**
Ridgers 44 (p) Penalties: 5	A.E.T.		Penalties 3
	Att: 7,012		

TEAM:	**TEAM:**
Howie	Gore
Moss	Hendon
Ridler	Plummer
Tinson	Maddix (S59)
Challis	King
Lowe	Yakubu
Tolley	Gamble
O'Connor (S45)	Lopez (S55)
Aiston (S114)	Strevens
Rodgers	Grazioli
Darby (S105)	Hatch
Substitutes:	**Substitutes:**
Cramb (S105)	Clist (S55)
Edwards (S45)	Millard
Hart	Pearson
Quinn	Redmile (S59)
Sedgemore (S114)	Rooney

FOOTBALL CONFERENCE PLAY-OFF FINAL

ALDERSHOT TOWN **1 (1)** **1 (1)** **SHREWSBURY TOWN**

McLean 35 Penalties: 0 | Penalties 3 Darby 43

A.E.T.

Att: 19,216

TEAM:	**TEAM:**
Bull	Howie
Downer (S66)	Sedgemore
Sterling	Challis
Giles	Tolley
Ray Warburton	Tinson (S.b)
Gosling	Ridler
Miller	Lowe
Challinor	O'Connor (S.a)
Antwi	Darby (S.c)
D'Sane (S86)	Rodgers
McLean (S60)	Aiston
Substitutes:	**Substitutes:**
Richard Barnard	Cramb (S.c)
Charles (S86)	Edwards
Chewins	Hart
Hooper (S66)	Lawrence (S.b)
Sills (S60)	Street (S.a)

Photos by: Bill Wheatcroft

Aldershot Town and Shrewsbury Town enter the field of play before their play-off final.

Aldershot's Aaron McLean (No.11) puts his side 1-0 up after 35 minutes....

....eights minutes later Shrewsbury were on level terms thanks to this Duaen Darby goal....

...wth the scores level after extra time, this penalty clinched Shrewsbury's return to the Football League.

THE LDV TROPHY
CONFERENCE CLUB INVOLVEMENT ONLY

CHESTER CITY - (Northern Section)

Round	Opponents (Division)	Venue	Result	FT	HT	Goalscorer(s)	Att:
1st	Doncaster Rovers (3rd)	H	L	0-1	0-0		1,141

TEAMS

Chester: Brown ,McIntyre ,Guyett ,Collins ,Heard ,Carey (Dogun ,82(sent off 89)) ,Harris ,Brady ,Twiss (Buckley ,79) , Rapley ,Foster (Beesley ,68) Subs not used: McCaldon,Bolland

Doncaster: Richardson ,Price ,Morley (Maloney ,49) ,Albrighton ,Beech ,Tierney ,Ravenhill ,Doolan ,McIndoe ,Barnes ,Gill (Fortune-West ,87) Subs not used Warrington,Paterson,McGrath.

HALIFAX TOWN - (Northern Section)

Round	Opponents (Division)	Venue	Result	FT	HT	Goalscorer(s)	Att:
1st	York City (3rd)	H	W	2-1	1-0	Mallon 31, Quinn 79	1,148

TEAMS

Halifax: Cartwright ,Hockenhull ,Quinn ,Dudgeon (sent off 69),Sandwith ,Mallon ,Hudson ,Bushell ,Elam (Midgley ,83), Killeen (Senior ,83) ,Sagare (Tozer ,76). Subs not used: Heinemann,Toulson.

York: Ovendale ,Cooper ,Smith ,Wise ,Hope (Merris ,67) ,Downes ,Brackstone ,Dunning ,Wilford (Nogan ,84), Dove (George ,66) ,Parkin. Subs not used Porter,Wood.

Round	Opponents (Division)	Venue	Result	FT	HT	Goalscorer(s)	Att:
2nd	Scarborough (Conference)	A	W	1-0	0-0	Midgley 64 (pen)	899

TEAMS

Halifax: Cartwright ,Hockenhull ,Dudgeon ,Quinn ,Sandwith ,Mallon ,Bushell ,Hudson ,Midgley ,Lee ,Sagare (Killeen ,55) Subs not used Senior,Garnett,McAuley,Heinemann.

Scarborough: Walker ,Baker ,Redmile ,Cryan ,Capper ,Sestanovich (Senior ,65) ,Kelly ,Kerr ,Marcelle (Bachelor ,77) Quayle (Gill ,68) ,Rose. Subs not used: Lyth,Sollitt.

Round	Opponents (Division)	Venue	Result	FT	HT	Goalscorer(s)	Att:
QF	Lincoln City (3rd)	H	W	1-0	1-0	Sandwith 21	1,162

TEAMS

Halifax: Cartwright ,Sandwith ,Colley ,Dudgeon ,Yates ,Midgley (Hockenhull ,77) ,Bushell (Hudson ,45) ,Owen ,Mallon ,Sagare ,Farrell (Allan ,86). Subs not used: Lee,Killeen

Lincoln: Marriott ,Mayo ,Morgan ,Futcher ,Bailey (Bloomer ,87) ,Gain ,Butcher ,Liburd (Sedgemore ,65) ,Yeo , Cropper ,McNamara (Pearce ,61). Subs not used May,Wattley

Round	Opponents (Division)	Venue	Result	FT	HT	Goalscorer(s)	Att:
SF	Blackpool* (2nd)	A	L	2-3	2-2	Killeen 19, Owen 34	4,764

TEAMS

Halifax: Cartwright ,Hockenhull ,Colley ,Monington ,Sandwith ,Owen ,Bushell ,Midgley (Quinn ,81) ,Mallon (Lee ,62) , Killeen ,Sagare (Farrell ,61). Subs not used Hudson,McAuley

Blackpool: Jones ,Grayson ,Elliott ,Davis ,Hilton (Evans ,24) ,Bullock ,McMahon ,Wellens (Burns ,75) ,Coid ,Taylor , Sheron (Mike Flynn ,87). Subs not used: Barnes,Blinkhorn

*Competition winners.

MORECAMBE - (Northern Section)

Round	Opponents (Division)	Venue	Result	FT	HT	Goalscorer(s)	Att:
1st	Wrexham (2nd)	A	L	1-4	0-1	Morgan 72 (og)	1,078

TEAMS

Morecambe: Mawson ,Lane ,Murphy (sent off 63),Swan ,Perkins (McKearney ,45) ,Thompson (Rogan ,81) ,Walmsley , Collins ,Rigoglioso ,Howell ,Sugden (Carlton ,81). Subs not used Curtis,Osborne

Wrexham: Whitfield ,Roberts ,Morgan ,Lawrence ,Carlos Edwards (Thomas ,65) ,Whitley ,Ferguson (Crowell ,60) ,Llewellyn, Paul Edwards ,Lee Jones (Mark Jones ,77) ,Sam. Subs not used: Holmes,Pejic

SCARBOROUGH - (Northern Section)

Round	Opponents (Division)	Venue	Result	FT	HT	Goalscorer(s)	Att:
1st	Port Vale (2nd)	H	W	2-1	0-1	Senior 77, Kelly 89	1,003

TEAMS

Scarborough: Walker ,Lyth (McSweeney ,73) ,Baker ,Hotte ,Price ,Senior ,Kelly ,Kerr ,Gill ,Marcelle , Blackman (Graydon ,82). Subs not used: Henry,Gareth Downey,Bachelor.

Port Vale: Brain ,Brisco ,Pilkington ,Rowland ,Brightwell ,Armstrong (Boyd ,61) ,Bridge-Wilkinson ,Cummins , Littlejohn ,Paynter ,McPhee. Subs not used Delaney,Birchall,Eldershaw,Brown.

Round	Opponents (Division)	Venue	Result	FT	HT	Goalscorer(s)	Att:
2nd	Halifax Town (Conference)	H	L	0-1	0-0		899

TEAMS

Scarborough: Walker ,Baker ,Redmile ,Cryan ,Capper ,Sestanovich (Senior ,65) ,Kelly ,Kerr ,Marcelle (Bachelor ,77) Quayle (Gill ,68) ,Rose. Subs not used: Lyth,Sollitt.

Halifax: Cartwright ,Hockenhull ,Dudgeon ,Quinn ,Sandwith ,Mallon ,Bushell ,Hudson ,Midgley ,Lee ,Sagare (Killeen ,55) Subs not used Senior,Garnett,McAuley,Heinemann.

SHREWSBURY TOWN - (Northern Section)

Round	Opponents (Division)	Venue	Result	FT	HT	Goalscorer(s)	Att:
1st	Scunthorpe United (3rd)	A	L	1-2	1-0	Lowe 18	1,265

TEAMS

Shrewsbury: Sam Russell ,Stanton ,Butler ,Byrne (Jackson ,45) ,Sharp ,Sparrow ,Kell ,Calvo-Garcia (Barwick ,7) , Beagrie ,Hayes ,MacLean (Torpey ,45). Subs not used: Evans,Graves

Scunthorpe: Howie ,Moss ,Tinson ,Ridler ,Rioch ,Tolley ,Bell ,O'Connor ,Aiston (Fitzpatrick ,74) ,Watts (Cramb ,84) ,Lowe Subs not used Quinn,Sedgemore,Tolley.

TELFORD UNITED - (Northern Section)

Round	Opponents (Division)	Venue	Result	FT	HT	Goalscorer(s)	Att:
1st	Lincoln City (3rd)	A	L	1-3	0-1	Mills 54	1,503

TEAMS

Telford: MacKenzie ,Clarke (Grant ,62) ,Challis (Blackwood ,74) ,Green ,Whitehead ,Williams ,Simpson ,Murphy , Ricketts ,Mills ,Naylor (Rowe ,78). Subs not used Taylor, Daniels.

Lincoln: Marriott ,Weaver ,Bloomer ,Futcher ,Bailey ,Frecklington (Sedgemore ,86) ,Butcher (Willis ,86) ,Green , Mayo ,Richardson ,Taylor-Fletcher (Yeo ,65). Subs not used: Horrigan,Wattley.

BARNET - (Southern Section)

Round	Opponents (Division)	Venue	Result	FT	HT	Goalscorer(s)	Att:
1st	Brentford (2nd)	H	D	3-3	2-0	Lopez 6, Henry 34 (pen), Hatch 104	1,248
			(Brentford won 3-1 on penalties a.e.t)				

TEAMS

Barnet: Gore ,Rooney ,Cumberbatch (sent off 84),King ,Taggart ,Baimass ,Hogg ,Lopez ,Sylla (Hatch ,79) , Henry (Freeman ,90) ,Roache. Subs not used: Millard,Jamie Smith,Smith.

Brentford: Smith ,Dobson ,Roget ,Kitamirike ,Frampton (Smith ,103) ,Rougier (Hutchinson ,45) ,Evans ,Tabb ,Hunt , Olugbodi (O'Connor ,46) ,May (sent off 54). Subs not used Somner,Lennie.

DAGENHAM & REDBRIDGE - (Southern Section)

Round	Opponents (Division)	Venue	Result	FT	HT	Goalscorer(s)	Att:
1st	Leyton Orient (3rd)	H	W	4-1	0-0	Bentley 49,69, Scully 56, Braithwaite 66	1,852

TEAMS

Dagenham: Roberts ,Vickers ,Beckwith ,Janney (McGowen ,84) ,Scully ,Hill ,Braithwaite ,Bentley ,Mustafa , Meechan (Shipp ,58) ,Kimble. Subs not used: Pullen,Chris Piper,Lenny Piper

Orient: Harrison ,Hunt ,Lockwood ,McGhee ,Peters ,Purser ,Ebdon ,McCormack (Billy Jones ,61) ,Forbes (Thorpe ,68) ,Tate (Alexander ,61) ,Ibehre. Subs not used Morris,Saah

Round	Opponents (Division)	Venue	Result	FT	HT	Goalscorer(s)	Att:
2nd	Q.P.R. (2nd)	A	L	1-2	0-1	Scully 87	3,036

TEAMS

Dagenham: Roberts ,Mustafa ,Cole ,Matthews (Kimble ,47) ,Vickers ,Bentley ,Hill ,Scully ,Bruce (Meechan ,72) , Janney (Chris Piper ,62) ,Braithwaite. Subs not used Knight,Lenny Piper.

QPR: Culkin ,Barton (Edghill ,5) ,Forbes ,Carlisle ,Padula ,Ainsworth ,Palmer ,Bean (Gallen ,70) ,McLeod , Pacquette (Thorpe ,84) ,Sabin. Subs not used: Day,Oli.

EXETER CITY - (Southern Section)

Round	Opponents (Division)	Venue	Result	FT	HT	Goalscorer(s)	Att:
1st	Hereford Utd (Conference)	A	L	0-2	0-0		1,513

TEAMS

Exeter: Rice ,Duncan (Afful ,65) ,Jeannin ,Gaia (Reed ,89) ,Moxey ,McConnell ,Taylor ,Cronin ,Sheldon ,Canham ,Flack Subs not used Bittner,Todd,Lee.

Hereford: Mathew Baker ,Green ,Mkandawire ,Teesdale ,Rose ,Daniel Williams (Craven ,61) ,Pitman ,King ,Parry ,Guinan ,Brown (Carey-Bertram ,74). Subs not used: Scott,James,Moon.

FOREST GREEN ROVERS - (Southern Section)

Round	Opponents (Division)	Venue	Result	FT	HT	Goalscorer(s)	Att:
1st	Brighton & H.A. (2nd)	A	L	0-2	0-1		3,969

TEAMS

Forest Green: Perrin ,Phillips ,Ingram ,Richardson ,Searle ,Kennedy (Rogers ,68) ,Owers ,Stoker ,Foster , Moralee (Luke Jones ,81) ,Grayson. Subs not used Adams,Cant,Langan

Brighton: Kuipers ,Watson ,Pethick ,Butters ,Mayo ,Hart ,Rehman ,Carpenter ,Jones ,McPhee ,Knight (Robinson ,57) Subs not used: Piercy, Hinshelwood, Flitney.

HEREFORD UNITED - (Southern Section)

Round	Opponents (Division)	Venue	Result	FT	HT	Goalscorer(s)	Att:
1st	Exeter City (Conference)	H	W	2-0	0-0	Brown 46, Guinan 87	1,513

TEAMS

Hereford: Mathew Baker ,Green ,Mkandawire ,Teesdale ,Rose ,Daniel Williams (Craven ,61) ,Pitman ,King ,Parry , Guinan ,Brown (Carey-Bertram ,74). Subs not used: Scott,James,Moon.

Exeter: Rice ,Duncan (Afful ,65) ,Jeannin ,Gaia (Reed ,89) ,Moxey ,McConnell ,Taylor ,Cronin ,Sheldon ,Canham ,Flack Subs not used Bittner,Todd,Lee.

Round	Opponents (Division)	Venue	Result	FT	HT	Goalscorer(s)	Att:
2nd	Northampton Town (3rd)	H	D	1-1	0-0	Brown 87	1,517

(Northampton won 4-3 on penalties a.e.t)

TEAMS

Hereford: Mathew Baker ,Green ,Mkandawire ,James ,Rose ,Purdey (Harrhy ,103) ,Pitman ,Smith (King ,102), Craven (Teesdale ,88) ,Guinan ,Brown. Subs not used: Scott, Moon.

Northampton: Harper ,Lyttle ,Willmott ,Chambers ,Carruthers ,Asamoah (Smith ,71) ,Harsley (Trollope ,83),Reeves , Low ,Walker ,Richards (Dudfield ,64). Subs not used Thompson, Smith.

STEVENAGE BOROUGH - (Southern Section)

Round	Opponents (Division)	Venue	Result	FT	HT	Goalscorer(s)	Att:
1st	Luton Town (2nd)	H	L	0-1	0-0		1,754

TEAMS

Stevenage: Westhead ,Warner ,Gould (Flynn ,45) ,Laker ,Costello ,Travis ,Wormull ,Gary Holloway ,Richards (Cook ,49), Battersby ,Elding. Subs not used: Brennan,Perez

Luton: Brill ,Coyne ,Davis (Deeney ,88) ,Barnett ,Mansell ,Robinson ,Leary ,Okai (Judge ,68) ,Brkovic ,Showunmi ,Hillier Subs not used Beckwith,Forbes,O'Leary.

2003 -2004 CONFERENCE MANAGER & TEAM OF THE YEAR

Hereford United

Barnet

Hereford United

Chester City

Hereford United

Aldershot Town

Morecambe

Hereford United

Chester City

Hereford United

Aldershot Town

Chester City

NATIONWIDE PLAYER OF THE YEAR: Daryl Clare **FAIR PLAY AWARD:** Burton Albion

PROGRAMME OF THE YEAR: Woking

Chester City's Darren Stamp heads past Farnborough Town goalkeeper Mark Osborn but hits the crossbar.
Photo: Bill Wheatcroft

Dagenham's lively winger Mark Janney is faced by Arlesey's Steve Magona in the F.A.Trophy.Photo: Alan Coomes

...ACTION EXTRA...ACTION EXTRA...ACTION EXTRA...

Farnborough Town's James Donovan is challenged as he shoots and the action is watched by both skippers; Nick Burton (Farnborough) and Darren Stride (Burton Albion) Photo Eric Marsh

Hereford United's international goalkeeper Matt Baker gathers a first half effort by Aldershot Town in the play offs.
Photo: Eric Marsh

ACCRINGTON STANLEY

As one of the country's best known football clubs below the Football League, Accrington Stanley were welcomed into the Conference with a televised away game at old adversaries Aldershot. Although this game was lost, the level of publicity continued through an exciting season.

A strengthened squad had perhaps only consolidation in it's sights originally but excellent home form and tremendous F.A.Cup results lifted expectations and ensured the football world realised that another ex Football League club had recovered and was back in serious contention.

Although Stanley's away league form, with only two victories, was extremely disappointing their supporters were more than compensated by their cup exploits. After seeing off fellow Conference opposition in Leigh R.M.I., a home draw against Huddersfield Town,another famous name, brought the club a home 'live'appearance on television. A thrilling last minute winner fromAndy Gouck in front of 3,468 brought more headlines and an away tie at Bournemouth. This time an early goal from Paul Mullin gave the League club more time to equalise and this they did, forcing a replay which went goalless all the way to penalties and a thrilling 5-3 success for the 'underdogs'. A crowd of 4,368 watched another goalless ninety minutes, so it was off to Essex and a rather frustrating story of strange refereeing decisions and missed chances brought the memorable run to an end.

Another tie against Conference opposition produced a thrilling but disappointing 4-2 defeat in the F.A.Trophy at Burton Albion. But this was played just three days before the Colchester replay and proved one cup tie too much.

The club's home form throughout its Conference programme kept Stanley in touch with the play-off challengers for most of the campaign and one of the highlights was a 2-0 victory over the free flowing Hereford United side. But the club's away form didn't improve and a first season in the Conference produced a mid table tenth position. Surely the perfect consolidation!

T.W.

ACCRINGTON STANLEY

Match Facts 2003-04

The number shown directly below the player's name is his squad number.
Where a number is shown instead of an "X' in the columns this represents a substitute appearance and the number indicates the player replaced.

Comp.	Date	Opponents	Venue.	Result	Goalscorers	Att.
Conf 1	Aug 10	Aldershot T	A	L 1-2	Procter	3471
Conf 2	Aug 13	Leigh RMI	H	W 4-1	James(2) Mullin Prendergast	2003
Conf 3	Aug 16	Shrewsbury T	H	L 0-1		3143
Conf 4	Aug 23	Forest Green R	A	L 1-2	Jenkins(og)	711
Conf 5	Aug 25	Scarborough	H	W 1-0	Mullin	2017
Conf 6	Aug 30	Tamworth	A	D 1-1	Cavanagh	1215
Conf 7	Sep 06	Barnet	A	D 0-0		1621
Conf 8	Sep 13	Margate	H	W 3-2	James(2) Durnin	1718
Conf 9	Sep 20	Dagenham & R	A	W 1-0	Mullin	1542
Conf 10	Sep 23	Burton A	H	W 3-1	Mullin Hollis James(p)	1911
Conf 11	Sep 27	Woking	H	D 3-3	James(3,1p)	2115
Conf 12	Oct 04	Northwich V	A	D 3-3	Prendergast Mullin Gouck	865
Conf 13	Oct 07	Halifax T	A	D 1-1	Gouck	2116
Conf 14	Oct 11	Farnborough T	H	W 3-1	Mullin Cavanah James(p)	1806
Conf 15	Oct 18	Exeter C	H	L 1-2	Mullin	2342
FAC 4q	**Oct 25**	**Leigh RMI**	**H**	**W 2-0**	**James Mullin**	**1350**
Conf 16	Nov 01	Gravesend & N	A	D 0-0		1274
FAC 1	**Nov 09**	**Huddersfield Town**	**H**	**W 1-0**	**Gouck**	**3129**
Conf 17	Nov 11	Hereford U	H	W 2-0	James Mullin	1824
Conf 18	Nov 15	Stevenage B	A	L 1-2	Mullin	2121
Conf 19	Nov 22	Telford U	H	L 1-5	Mullin	1448
Conf 20	Nov 25	Chester C	A	D 3-3	Cook James Prendergast	2432
Conf 21	Nov 29	Barnet	H	W 2-0	Mullin(2)	1120
FAC 2	**Dec 06**	**Bournemouth**	**A**	**D 1-1**	**Mullin**	**7551**
Conf 22	Dec 13	Aldershot T	H	W 4-2	Mullin(2) Gouck Howarth	1407
FAC 2r	**Dec 15**	**Bournemouth**	**H**	**D 0-0***	**(won 5-3 on pens)**	**2585**
Conf 23	Dec 20	Leigh RMI	A	W 2-1	Gouck Howarth	612
Conf 24	Dec 26	Morecambe	H	W 1-0	James	2954
Conf 25	Jan 01	Morecambe	A	L 0-1		3084
FAC 3	**Jan 03**	**Colchester United**	**H**	**D 0-0**		**4368**
FAT 3	**Jan 10**	**Burton A**	**A**	**L 2-4**	**Howarth Mullin**	**1402**
FAC 3r	**Jan 13**	**Colchester United**	**A**	**L 1-2**	**Mullin**	**5611**
Conf 26	Jan 17	Shrewsbury T	A	D 0-0		3777
Conf 27	Jan 20	Tamworth	H	W 3-0	Mullin(2) James	1301
Conf 28	Jan 24	Burton A	A	D 1-1	McEvilly	1614
Conf 29	Feb 07	Dagenham & R	H	L 2-3	Prendergast James	1601
Conf 30	Feb 14	Woking	A	D 2-2	James Mullin	2312
Conf 31	Feb 21	Northwich V	H	D 2-2	James(p) Prendergast	1427
Conf 32	Feb 28	Farnborough T	A	D 1-1	McEvilly	571
Conf 33	Mar 06	Halifax T	H	W 2-1	Flitcroft Calcutt	1717
Conf 34	Mar 13	Hereford U	A	L 0-1		3230
Conf 35	Mar 16	Margate	A	L 1-3	Kempson	345
Conf 36	Mar 20	Stevenage B	H	W 2-1	James Mullin	1124
Conf 37	Apr 03	Chester C	H	L 0-2		2561
Conf 38	Apr 08	Telford U	A	L 0-1		2031
Conf 39	Apr 10	Forest Green R	H	W 4-1	Mullin(2) Brannan Durnin	1058
Conf 40	Apr 12	Scarborough	A	L 1-2	Gouck	1523
Conf 41	Apr 17	Gravesend & N	H	D 3-3	Durnin(2) Prendergast	1139
Conf 42	Apr 24	Exeter C	A	L 2-3	Proctor Flitcroft	5345

STEP 1
CONFERENCE

STEP 2 - P177
CONFERENCE Nth & Sth

STEP 3 - P269
NPL, Southern, Isthmian Premiers

STEP 4 - P269
NPL 1, Southern W&E, Isthmian 1

STEP 5/6 - P473

STEP 7 - P713
Current level 4 leagues

Jamie SPEARE	Peter CAVANAGH	Steve HOLLIS	Steve HALFORD	Jonathan SMITH	Andy PROCTOR	Dean CALCUTT	Paul COOK	Lutel JAMES	Paul MULLIN	Rory PRENDERGAST	Andy GOUCK	Jon KENNEDY	Robbie WILLIAMS	Jerome FITZGERALD	Steve FLITCROFT	Gordon ARMSTRONG	Paul HOWARTH	Brian WELCH	Ged BRANNAN	Andrew WAINE	John DURNIN	Lee MADIN	Justin JACKSON	Damien HINDLE	Lee McEVILLY	Darren KEMPSON
1	**2**	**3**	**4**	**5**	**6**	**7**	**8**	**9**	**10**	**11**	**12**	**13**	**14**	**15**	**16**	**18**	**19**	**20**	**20**	**21**	**22**	**23**	**24**	**26**	**29**	**30**
x	x	x	5	x	x	18	x	x	x	x		11	x			x										
	x	x		x	x	x	x	x	x	8	18	x	x			x					9					
	x	x		x	x	8	x	x	x	x	18	x	x			x					9					
	x	x	x	4	x	x	x	x	x	x	8	x	x													
	x	x		x	x	x	x	x	x	x	7	x	x							9						
	x	x		x	8	x	x	x	x	x	x	x	x													
	x	x		x	16		x	x	x	x	x	x	x		x	12										
	x	x		x	x			x	x	x	x	x	x			12		x			20					
	x	x	x		x	11		x	x	x	x	x	x		x	12					4					
	x	x	x	4	x			x	x	x	x	x	x		22	12					x					
	x	x	5	x	x		22	x	x	x	x	x	x			14					x					
	x	x		x			x	x	x	x	x	x	x		x											
	x	x	x	4	x		x	x	x	x	x	x	x			12										
	x	x	x		x		x	x	x	x	x	x	x					12				11				
	x	x	x		x		x	x	x	x	x	x	x										12			
	x	x	x		x		x	x	x	x	x	x	x		10	12						8				
		x	x	19	x	x	x	x		x		x	x		8	7	x				x					
	x	x	x	4	x	x	x	x	x	x	8	x	x										7			
	x	x		x	x		x	x	x	x	x	x	x			12										
	x	x		x	x	24	x	x	x	x	x	x	x								12		11			
	x	x		x	x	16	x	x	x		8	x	x		x						x	22				
	x		x	x	x	8	x	x	x	x		x	x						x							
x			x	x	x			x	x	x	x					x	x		x							
x	x		x	x	x		x	x	x	x	x		x		8	12	5									
x	x				x		x	x	x	x	x		x		8		x		x		11					
x	x		x		x		x	x	x	x	x	1	x		12	10	x									
x	x		x				x	x	x		x		x		x	12	x		x							
x	x		x		x		x	x	x	x			x		8		x		x							
x		x	x		x		12	x	x	x	x		x				x		x							
x		x	x		x	6	x	x	x	x	x		x		12	4	x									
x	8	x	x	14		3	x	x	x	x			x		x		x		x							
	x		x	19	x	16	x	x	x	x		x	x		x		x									
	x	20	x		x		x	x	x	x		x	x		8		x		x							
13	x	9	x		x			x	x	x		x	x		x		x								x	
	x			x	x	9		x	x	x		x	x		x		x		6		19				x	
		x			x			x	x	x		x	x		29		x		x						x	x
		x			x		x	x	x	x	x	x	x		8				x		12				20	x
		x	x			8	x	x	x	x	x	x			x		x								3	x
	x		x		x		x	x	x	x	x	x			8		x								12	x
	x		x		20	x	7	x	x	x		x		x	x				x							x
	x		x		x	16	20	x	x	x		x		x	x		11		x							x
	x		x		x	16	20	x	x	19		x		x	x		x		x							x
	x		x		x		x	x	x	x		x	x	x	8				x							
	x	x			x	3	x	x	x			x	x	x	8				x		15					x
x	x	x		x	x	19	x	20	x	x			x		8		x		x							
x	x	x	x		x	6	16	x	x	x			x		x				x		9					
x	19		x	x	x	5		x	x	x	x			x			x		x							12
x	x	x	x		x		x		x	x	6								x		26			x		x
	x		x	x	x		x	x	x			x		x	x		15		x		16					5

ACCRINGTON STANLEY

GROUND DETAILS

The Interlink Express Stadium, Livingstone Road, Accrington, Lancs. BB5 5BX

Tel: 01254 383235
Office: 01254 397869
Website: www.accrington stanley.co.uk
email Address: info@accringtonstanley.co.uk

Directions: Arriving on A680 from Clayton-le-Moors Livingstone Rd is on left 50 yds past Crown Hotel. From M62/M66, through town centre on A680 -Livingstone Rd 500 yds on right after Victoria Hospital.
1 1/2 miles from Accrington(BR).

Capacity: 5,000
Cover: 2,000
Seats: 1,200

Clubhouse: Open five nights and matchdays. Private functions. Well stocked tea-bar in ground.
Club Shop: Sells replica kits, sweaters,etc
Contact: Liz Rackstraw (01254 397869)

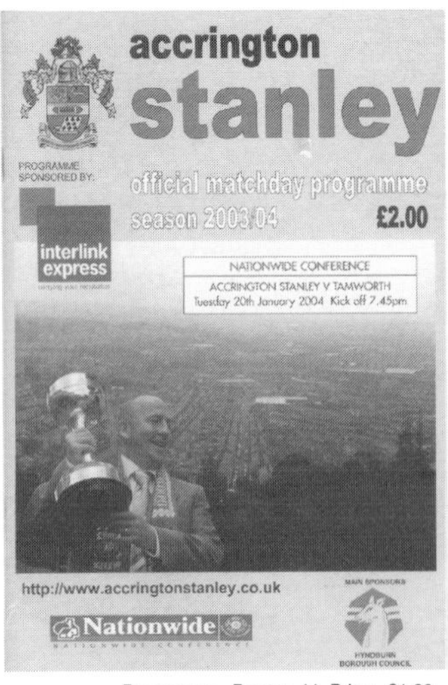

MATCHDAY PROGRAMME

Programme - Pages: 44 Price: £1.20
Editor: P Terry. (01282 866768)

Local Press:
Accrington Observer, Lancashire Evening Telegraph.
Local Radio:
Radio Lancashire, Red Rose Radio.

Formed: 1968
Nickname: Reds
Sponsors: Hyndburn Borough Council
Colours: Red/red/red
Change colours: All White
Midweek home matchday: Tuesday
Youth Confe: Lancs Youth Floodlit League.
Reserves: Lancashire League

CLUB OFFICIALS

Chairman: Eric Whalley

President: J C Prescott/J Hudson

Secretary: Philip Terry
8 Princess Street, Colne, Lancs BB8 9AN.
Tel: 01286 866768 (H), 01282 866768 (B).

e-mail: philipterry@tiscali.co.uk

Commercial Manager: Mick schultt

FOOTBALL MANAGEMENT TEAM

MANAGER:	**JOHN COLEMAN**
Date of Appointment	July 1999
Date of Birth:	12 Oct. 1962
Place of Birth:	Kirby
PREVIOUS CLUBS	
As manager	Ashton United
As player	Kirby, Burscough, Marine,Southport, Runcorn, Macclesfield, Rhyl, Morecambe, Lancaster C.
HONOURS	
As Manager:	N.P.L. Div. 1, NPL Cup

* * *

Asst Manager:	Jimmy Bell
Chief Scout:	Mike Carter
Osteopath:	Martin Dixon D.O.
Physio:	Ian Liversidge

Season	League	Div.	Pos.	Home P	W	D	L	F	A	Away W	D	L	F	A	Pts	Manager
03-04	Conference		10	42	13	3	5	46	31	2	10	9	22	30	58	John Coleman
02-03	NPL	Prem	1	44	18	4	0	53	20	12	6	4	44	24	100	John Coleman
01-02	NPL	Prem	6	44	10	7	5	47	27	11	2	9	42	37	72	John Coleman
00-01	NPL	Prem	9	44	12	4	6	44	34	6	6	10	28	33	63	John Coleman
99-00	NPL	Div 1	1	42	14	5	2	55	19	11	4	6	41	24	84	John Coleman
98-99	NPL	Prem	22	42	5	5	11	24	37	4	4	13	23	40	36	Bill Rodaway
97-98	NPL	Prem	20	42	5	9	7	28	30	3	5	13	21	38	38	Tony Greenwood
96-97	NPL	Prem.	11	44	11	4	7	45	36	7	8	7	32	34	66	Stan Allen
				P	W	D	L	F	A	Pts						
95-96	NPL	Prem.	7	42	17	14	11	62	54	*62						Stan Allen
94-95	NPL	Prem	15	42	12	13	17	55	77	49						Eric Whalley
93-94	NPL	Prem	16	42	14	7	21	63	85	49						Phil Staley

HONOURS

NPL Challenge Cup 01-02
NPL Challenge Shield 01-02
N West Counties Conf R-up 86-87
Cheshire County Conf Div 2 80-81 (R-up 79-80)
Lancs Comb 73-74 77-78 (R-up 71-72 75-76)
Conf Cup 71-72 72-73 73-74 76-77
George Watson Trophy 71-72 73-74
John Duckworth Trophy 85-86
Lancs Jun. Cup (now MarsdenTrophy) 01-02, R-up 83-84 96-97;03-04
Lancs U18 Cup 89-90
N.W.All Div Cup 94-95; Anglo-Barbados Cup 95
NW Alliance Cup Finalists 95-96
Lancs Floodlit Youth Confe 2001-02
Lancashire League Cup Finallists 2003-04

PREVIOUS

Leagues:
Lancs Combination 70-78
Cheshire County 78-82
North West Counties 82-87
Northen Premier League1988-2003

Names: None
Grounds: None

Past Players who progressed to the Football League

David Hargreaves (Blackburn R. 77),
Ian Blackstone (York C.),
Gus Wilson (Crewe),
Glen Johnstone (Preston),
DarrenLyons (Bury),
Martin Clark (Crewe 92-93),
Mark Wright (Wigan 93-94),
Paul Collings (Bury 93-94),
Brett Ormerod (Blackpool 96-97),
Harvey Cunningham (Doncaster R.),
Gareth Seddon (Bury)

CLUB RECORDS

Attendance: 2,465
v Farsley Celtic 06.05.01 Unibond Div. 1.
(10,081 v Crewe Alexandra, F.A. C. 2nd Rd 5/12/92 - played at Ewood Park,Blackburn).
Career Goalscorer: David Hargreaves 328.
Career Appearances: Chris Grimshaw 362.
Win: 10-0 v Lincoln United 99-00
Fee Paid : £15,000 Paul Mullin from Radcliffe Borough 00-01
Fee Received: £60,000 for Gary Williams from Doncaster R

BEST SEASON

FA Trophy: 3rd Rd .2003-2004

F.A.Cup: 3rd Rd replay 2003-2004
1-2 v Colchester United (H)
League clubs defeated: Huddersfield Town & Bournemouth
League: Northern Premier League Champions 2002-2003

LAST SEASON

F.A. Cup: 3rd Round
F.A. Trophy: 3rd Round
League: 10th
Top Goalscorer: Paul Mullin
Player of the Year: Paul Mullin
Captain: Peter Cavanagh

ACCRINGTON STANLEY PLAYING SQUAD

	Birthplace	D.O.B.	Previous Clubs
GOALKEEPERS			
DEFENDERS			
Peter Cavanagh	Liverpool	14.10.81	Liverpool
Steve Halford	Bury	21.09.80	Bury, Chester City
Steve Hollis	Liverpool	22.08.72	Ashton United, Fleetwood, Hyde United (L), Wigan Athletic, Liverpool.
Paul Howarth	Lancashire	06. 07.81	Rossendale Utd., Accrington Stanley, Shrewsbury T.
Stteve Howson	Chorley	30.09.81	Chesterfield, Northern Split (Australia), Blackburn R.
Steve Jagielka	Manchester	10.03.78	Sheffield U, Shrewsbury T, Stoke c
Jonathon Smith	Lancashire	11.02.76	Great Harwood, Darwen.
Robbie Williams	Liverpool	12.04.79	St DFominics, Southport
MIDFIELD			
Ged Brannan	Prescot	15.01.72	Wigan A, Motherwell, Man City,Tranmere R
Dean Calcutt	Yorkshire		Bradford P.A., Emley, Brackenhall United
Paul Carvill	Co Armagh	20.08.85	Preston,Glenavon,Potters F.C.
Paul Cook	Liverpool	22.02.67	Burnley, Wigan Ath. (L), Stockport Co., Tranmere Rov., Coventry C., Wolves, Norwich C, Wigan Ath., Marine.
Ian Craney	Liverpool	21.07.82	Altrincham, Runcorn
Steve Flitcroft			Blackburn Rovers, Hyde United (L)
Andy Gouck	BLackpool Pontefract	08.06.72 06.04.78	Morecambe, Rochdale, BlackpoolRory Prendergast Bradford P.A.,Frickley Athletic, Emley, Nuneaton Bor. (L), Northwich Vic. (L), York City, Barnsley
Andy Procter	Lancashire	13.03.83	Great Harwood T.
Andrew Waine	Manchester	24.02.83	Burnley
FORWARDS			
Lutel James	Manchester	02.06.72	Bury, Hyde United, Guiseley, Scarborough, Selby Town, Yorkshire Amateurs
Lee McEvilly	Liverpool	15.04.82	Rochdale, Burscough, Bootle.
N.Ireland U21 & Full International			
Paul Mullin	Lancashire		Radcliffe Borough, Clitheroe Town, Trafford, Darwen, Accrington Stanley (Juniors)

Bold print denotes England semi-professional international.

ALDERSHOT TOWN

The satisfaction and excitement of reaching the Conference after the club's tough battling journey up the non-league pyramid from Isthmian League Division Three in 1992 was a pure joy for all real supporters of 'The Shots'. Here they were, facing old friends in Accrington Stanley live on television and the glamour was back. Could Terry Brown, an experienced non-league player and manager, take the club to that longed for final step back to the Football League?

Well, he didn't manage it at the first time of asking, but no one will be disappointed in the club's fantastic season in which most expectations were exceeded.

The campaign opened with the club proudly including six Non-League Internationals on their books in Dean Hooper, Steve Perkins, Nick Roddis, Lee Charles, Roscoe D'Sane and Tim Sills plus a past Non-League National Player of the Year in the vastly experienced Ray Warburton at the heart of the defence. Their early much publicised victory over Accrington set the standard for the season and The Shots soon commanded an impressive reputation as an entertaining attacking outfit.

The F.A. Cup brought an away tie at Forest Green and an impressive 3-1 success. Another away trip to Grays Athletic in the Essex hotbed of vastly improved Isthmian clubs, produced a hard fought 2-1 victory and a return to the county to face Colchester United. Unfortunately the run finished at Layer Road but morale was high and the goalscoring team of Sills, D'Sane, Charles and Aaron McLean always produced the goals in the Conference and it was soon clear that Aldershot could actually be in with a chance of a second consecutive promotion.

As the Conference season edged to a climax, Aldershot supporters also found their club very much involved with a superb F.A. Trophy run. Away wins at Bishop's Stortford (4-2) and Blyth Spartans (3-1 were followed by two home ties. Firstly with fellow Conference newcomers Tamworth which was drawn, but the reply brought a 2-0 victory and an exciting home match against one of the favourites Exeter City.This gave the 3,814 fans a real thriller with a Sills goal making the score 2-1 just before the final whistle. Sadly the pressure of confirming a play off place and reaching the Trophy Final proved just too much. Hednesford Town played extremely well to deservedly win the two, legged Trophy semi-final 3-1 but the real excitement was still to come.

A play off semi-final against everyone's favourites Hereford United seemed a daunting prospect but sometimes it's good to be the 'underdog' and much to poor Hererford's dismay it proved to be Aldershot's day and they were now just one step from League Football.However, if penalties were to be celebrated at Hereford they proved to be fatal at Stoke, as Shrewsbury booked their quick return to the big time. A great season was over but Terry Brown's Aldershot Town were back as a force in the game, and they will be challenging again this season.

T.W.

L-R - Back Row: Chris Giles, Tim Sills, Steve Watson, Nikki Bull, Adam Miller, Tobi Jinadu, and Ray Warburton, Middle Row: William Antwi, Jon Challinor, Arron McClran, Roscoe D'Sane,Nick Crittenden, Hugh McCauley and Brett Johnson. Front row: Tyron Smith, Martin Kuhl (Coach), Terry Brown (Manager), Stuart Cash (Assistant Manager) and Phil Warner.

ALDERSHOT TOWN

Match Facts 2003-04

The number shown directly below the player's name is his squad number.
Where a number is shown instead of an "X' in the columns this represents a substitute appearance and the number indicates the player replaced.

Comp.	Date	Opponents	Venue.	Result	Goalscorers	Att.
Conf 1	Aug 10	Accrington S	H	W 2-1	Sills D'Sane	3471
Conf 2	Aug 12	Margate	A	W 2-1	Sills D'Sane	1005
Conf 3	Aug 16	Telford U	A	W 5-2	Mclean(2) Challinor Sills Manuella	2206
Conf 4	Aug 23	Woking	H	W 2-1	Challinor D'Sane	4637
Conf 5	Aug 25	Hereford U	A	L 3-4	Sills McLean James(og)	4985
Conf 6	Aug 30	Northwich V	H	W 4-3	Challinor(2) D'Sane Sills	2801
Conf 7	Sep 06	Morecambe	A	L 0-2		1948
Conf 8	Sep 13	Shrewsbury T	H	D 1-1	L Charles	3829
Conf 9	Sep 20	Barnet	A	L 1-2	Sills	2208
Conf 10	Sep 23	Farnborough T	H	W 2-0	McLean Challinor	4166
Conf 11	Sep 27	Burton A	H	W 3-1	Chewins L Charles McLean	2687
Conf 12	Oct 04	Leigh RMI	A	D 2-2	Challinor Sills	545
Conf 13	Oct 07	Gravesend & N	A	W 3-1	Sills(2) Warburton	1477
Conf 14	Oct 11	Halifax T	H	W 3-1	D'Sane(2p) L Charles	2882
Conf 15	Oct 18	Tamworth	A	D 3-3	D'Sane(p) Taylor Ayres(og)	1538
FAC 4q	**Oct 25**	**Forest Green R**	**A**	**W 3-1**	**Sills Warburton McLean**	**1137**
Conf 16	Nov 01	Forest Green R	H	W 3-0	Warburton Miller L Charles	2398
FAC 1	**Nov 08**	**Grays Athletic**	**A**	**W 2-1**	**D'Sane(2,1p)**	**1500**
Conf 17	Nov 11	Exeter C	H	W 2-1	Sills Flack(og)	4112
Conf 18	Nov 15	Scarborough	A	L 0-1		1624
Conf 19	Nov 22	Chester C	H	D 1-1	Challinor	3610
Conf 20	Nov 29	Morecambe	H	D 2-2	L Charles D'Sane	2584
FAC 2	**Dec 06**	**Colchester United**	**A**	**L 0-1**		**4255**
Conf 21	Dec 13	Accrington S	A	L 2-4	D'Sane(2,1p)	1407
Conf 22	Dec 16	Stevenage B	A	W 1-0	Thomas	1794
Conf 23	Dec 20	Margate	H	L 0-2		2529
Conf 24	Dec 26	Dagenham & R	A	W 3-2	Miller(2) Mumford	1624
Conf 25	Jan 01	Dagenham & R	H	W 2-1	Sills McLean	4168
Conf 26	Jan 03	Northwich V	A	D 1-1	Sills	752
FAT 3	**Jan 10**	**Bishops Stortford**	**A**	**W 4-2**	**D'Sane(2) Miller Nutter**	**957**
Conf 27	Jan 17	Telford U	H	W 3-1	D'Sane(2,1p) Sills	2831
Conf 28	Jan 24	Farnborough T	A	L 0-4		3233
FAT 4	**Feb 03**	**Blyth Spartans**	**A**	**W 3-1**	**McLean(2) Sills**	**829**
Conf 29	Feb 06	Barnet	H	D 1-1	Challinor	4217
FAT 5	**Feb 14**	**Tamworth**	**H**	**D 1-1**	**Warburton**	**2515**
FAT 5r	**Feb 17**	**Tamworth**	**A**	**W 2-0**	**Miller(2)**	**1067**
Conf 30	Feb 21	Leigh RMI	H	W 2-0	D'Sane(2)	2412
Conf 31	Feb 24	Halifax T	A	W 2-1	Sills(2)	843
FAT 6	**Feb 28**	**Exeter C**	**H**	**W 2-1**	**Sills Challinor**	**3800**
Conf 32	Mar 06	Gravesend & N	H	D 2-2	Challinor D'Sane(p)	2736
Conf 33	Mar 13	Exeter C	A	L 1-2	Sills	3982
Conf 34	Mar 16	Burton A	A	W 4-1	D'Sane(2) Challinor Sills	1295
Conf 35	Mar 20	Scarborough	H	L 1-2	D'Sane(p)	2442
Conf 36	Mar 23	Shrewsbury T	A	W 2-1	Challinor D'Sane	3371
FAT SF1	**Mar 27**	**Hednesford Town**	**H**	**L 0-2**		**3500**
Conf 37	Mar 30	Stevenage B	H	W 2-0	D'Sane Gosling	2540
FAT SF2	**Apr 03**	**Hednesford Town**	**A**	**D 1-1**	**D'Sane(p)**	**2094**
Conf 38	Apr 06	Chester C	A	L 2-4	Miller Charles	3432
Conf 39	Apr 10	Woking	A	D 2-2	Challinor Miller	4158
Conf 40	Apr 12	Hereford U	H	L 1-2	Sills	4400
Conf 41	Apr 17	Forest Green R	A	L 1-3	D'Sane(p)	1330
Conf 42	Apr 24	Tamworth	H	D 1-1	Charles	4212
PO SF1	**Apr 29**	**Hereford U**	**H**	**D 1-1**	**D'Sane(p)**	**6379**
PO SF2	**May 03**	**Hereford U**	**A**	**D 0-0***	**(won 4-2 on pens)**	**7044**
PO F	**May 16**	**Shrewsbiry T**	**N**	**D 1-1***	**McLean (lost 0-3 on pens)**	**19216**

STEP 1 CONFERENCE | STEP 2 - P177 CONFERENCE Nth & Sth | STEP 3 - P269 NPL, Southern, Isthmian Premiers | STEP 4 - P269 NPL 1, Southern W&E, Isthmian 1 | STEP 5/6 - P473 | STEP 7 - P713 Current level 4 leagues

Nikki BULL	Dean HOOPER	Jason CHEWINS	Brett JOHNSON	Ray WARBURTON	Dominic STERLING	Nick RODDIS	Jim RODWELL	Andrew MUMFORD	Chris GILES	Tom SILLS	Roscoe D'SANE	Aaron McLEAN	Jay LOVETT	John NUTTER	Tyrone SMITH	Jamie TAYLOR	Simon DOWNER	Michael HARPER	Luke GEDLING	Jamie GOSLING	John CHALLINOR	Fiston MANUELLA	Richard BARNARD	Lee CHARLES	Stuart TANFIELD	Adam MILLER	Dean HAMMOND	Tony SHIELDS	Matt REES	Bradley THOMAS	ROB WESTELL	Will ANTWI
1	2	3	4	5	6	7	8	8	8	9	10	11	12	14	15	16	16	17	18	18	19	21	22	23	24	26	27	29	30	34	35	37
x	x			x	x	x	x			x	x	x		24				11	9		x				x							
x	x			x	x	x	x			x	x	x		10				11			x	x										
x	x	8		x	x	x	x			x	x	x						9	10		x	x										
x	x	8		x	x	x	x			x	x	x						9	10		x	x										
x		x		x	x	x				x	x	x		23				11			x	x	1	x								
	x	x		x	x	x				x	x	x							7		x	x	x	11	10							
	x	6		x	x		x			x	x	x							x		x	x		18								
	x	x		x	8		x			x		x									x	x		x	23		x					
	x	x		x	x		6			x	x	x									x	x	1		21		x					
	x	x		x		x	x			x	x	x									x		x		10		x					
	x	x		x		x	x			x	x	x									x		x	10			x					
	x			x	19	x	x			x	x	x		x							x		x	7	10		x					
	x	x		x	x		x			x	x	x		x									x	9			x					
	x	x		x	x		23			x	x			x					14				x	x			x		x			
		x		x	x		x			x	x	x		8		11							x	x				x	x			
	x	x		x	19					x	x	x				10					x		x		11	x		x	x			
	x	7		x	x	11				x	x	x				10							x	x		x		x	x			
	x	x		x	x					x	x	x									11		x	3		x		x	x			
	x	x		x	19					x	x	9									x		x	x		x		x	x			
	x	x		x	23					x	x	10		19							x		x	x		x		x	x			
x	x	x		x						x	11	x									x			x		x		x	x			
x		x		x	x						x	x		x							x			x		x			x			
x		x		x	x					x	x					5					x			x		x		x	x			
x	x	x			x					x	x	23				10		34			x			x		x		x		x		
x	x	x		x	x					x	x	9									x			x		23		x		x		
x	x	x		x	x					x	x	34		3				23			x			x		x				x		
x	x	x		x	x			x			x	x		3				11			x					x				x	19	
x		x		x	x			x		x	x	x		10				11			x					x				x		
x		10		x	x			x		x	x	x		x										9		x		x				x
x	x	x		x				x		x	x	x		10										x		x					26	x
	x	x		x	x					x	x			37									x	x		x		x				x
	x	x		x	x					x	x	6		3				9			x		x	x		x		x				
				x	x			x		x	x	10		x							x		x	14		x		x				x
x	x	8	3	x	x			x		x		x									x		1	x		x						x
	x			x	x					x	9	x									x		x	x		x		x				x
	x			x	x					x	x	10		x	26						x		x	x		x						x
	x		11	x	x					x	x	x		x	6				26		x		x	x		x						
	x		x							x	x	29	x	x							x		x			x		x				x
	x	14		x	x					x		x		x	26						x		x	9		x		x				x
	x	x		x	x					x	x						x	9			x		x			x		6				x
	x	x		x	x					x	x			2			x	5			x		x	3				x				x
x		14		x	x					x	x	10		x			x	9			x			x		x						x
x		x		x	x				5	x	x	37					x			23	x			x		x						x
x				x	x				x		x	x					x			x	x			11		x						x
		5		x	x				x	x	x	x					x			x	x		x	11								x
x				x	26				x	x	x	10		x			x			x	x					x						x
x				x	5				x	18	x	37		x			x			x	x			x		x						x
x	x	16		x	x					x	x						x			x	x			19		x						x
x		x	23	x	x					x	x	10			x					x	x			x		x						
x		x	14	x	x					x	x	23		x						x	x			x		x						
		16		x	x				x	x	x	x					x			x	x		x									x
		x	3	x	x				x	x	x	9			x					x	x		x	15								x
x		37		x	x				x	x	x	16		10			x			x	x			x								x
x		16		x	x				x	x	23	x		11			x			x	x			x								x
x	16			x	x				x	11	x	x					x			x	x			10		x						x

ALDERSHOT TOWN

GROUND DETAILS

Recreation Ground,
High Street,
Aldershot,
Hants GU11 1TW
Tel: 01252 320211
Fax: 01252 324347
Club Newsline: 09066 55585
Website: www.shotsweb.co.uk

Directions: Ground situated on eastern end of High Street next to large multi-storey B.T. building. From M3 (jct 4) take A325 to Aldershot. After five miles at r'bout take 1st exit marked town centre (A323) into Wellington Ave. At Burger King r'bout take 2nd exit into High Street - ground on left, large carpark adjacent. 5 mins walk from Aldershot (BR)
Capacity: 7,500
Cover: 6,850
Seats: 1,800
Clubhouse:
Open on matchdays and for special functions
Steward: Wally Clarke 01252 320211 x212
Club Shop:
Range of souvenirs, programmes, replica kits.
Open matchdays or
contact Janet Guess (01252-528007) for mail order

Formed: 1992

Nickname: The Shots

Sponsors: Charters Peugeot

Colours: Red /Blue /Red

Change Colours: Sky Blue

Midweek matchday: Tuesday

Reserves League: Combination

CLUB OFFICIALS

Chairman: Karl Prentice

Vice Chairman: John McGinty

Club Secretary: Andy Morgan

all correspondence to Andy at the club please.

Press Officer: Nick Fryer Tel:01252 32011

MATCHDAY PROGRAMME

Pages: 44 Price: £2.00
Editors: Karl Prentice, Rachel Pearce
Tel: 01256 471630

Local Press: Aldershot News, Farnham Herald
Local Radio: County Sound (96.4, 1476 khz), BBC Southern Counties (104.6 fm)

FOOTBALL MANAGEMENT TEAM

MANAGER:	**TERRY BROWN**
Date of Appointment	
Date of Birth	5th August 1952
Place of Birth	Hillingdon
PREVIOUS CLUBS	
As manager	Hayes (93-02)
As coach	Wokingham Town
As player	Hayes, Slough Town, Hayes, Wokingham Town
HONOURS	
as manager	Isthmian League Championship 95-96, 02-03
As player	None

Asst Man.:	Stuart Cash
Coach:	Martin Kuhl
Physio:	Alan McCreanney

Season	League	Div.	Pos.	Home P	W	D	L	F	A	Away W	D	L	F	A	Pts	Manager
03-04	Conference		5	42	12	6	3	40	24	8	4	9	40	43	70	Terry Brown
02-03	Isthmian	P	1	44	17	3	3	41	19	16	3	4	40	20	105	Terry Brown
01-02	Isthmian	P	3	42	12	4	5	44	23	10	3	8	32	28	73	George Borg
00-01	Isthmian	P	4	41	15	4	1	41	11	6	7	8	32	28	74	George Borg
99-00	Isthmian	P	2	42	13	2	6	39	23	11	3	7	32	28	77	George Borg
98-99	Isthmian	P	7	42	11	4	6	53	21	5	10	6	30	27	62	George Borg
97-98	Isthmian	1	1	42	16	3	2	48	12	12	5	4	41	24	92	Steve Wigley
96-97	Isthmian	1	7	42	10	7	4	32	21	9	7	5	35	24	71	Steve Wigley

Season	League	Div.	Pos.	P	W	D	L	F	A	Pts	Manager
95-96	Isthmian	1	5	42	21	9	12	81	46	72	Steve Wigley
94-95	Isthmian	1	4	42	23	5	14	80	53	74	Steve Wignall

HONOURS

Isthmian — Premier Division 02 - 03, R-up: 99 - 00
Division 1 97 - 98
Division 3 92 - 93
Isthmian League Cup: 98 - 99
Isthmian Charity Shield: 99 - 00

Hampshire Senior Cup	98 - 99, 99 - 00, 01 - 02
Suburban West Division	94 - 95
Allied Counties (West)	93 - 94
Suburban Shield	95 - 96
Hampshire Floodlit Cup	97 - 98, 98 - 99, 01 - 02
Southern Youth League	99 - 00, 01 - 02
Southern Youth League Cup	98 - 99

PREVIOUS

Name None

Ground None

Leagues Isthmian
Div.3 92-3,
Div 2 93-94,
Div 1 94-98,
Prem.98-03

Past Players who progressed to the Football League

CLUB RECORDS

Attendance: 7,500
v Brighton & Hove Albion FA Cup 1st Rd 18.11.00
"Ground" record: 19,138
Aldershot FC v Carlisle Utd,
FA Cup 4th Rd replay 28/1/70

Win: 8-0
v Bishop's Stortford (a) League 5.9.98
9-1
v Andover (n) Hants Senior Cup Final 99-00

Defeat: 0-6
v Worthing (a) Puma Cup 2.3.99

Career Goalscorer: Mark Butler 155. (92-98)
Career Appearances: Jason Chewins 400
(93 – Present)

Transfer Fee Paid: £20,000
to Woking for Grant Payne (11.99)

Transfer Fee Received: £6,000
for Leon Gutzmore from Bedford Town (11.99)

BEST SEASON

FA Cup: Second Round
99-00 v Exeter City

FA Trophy: Semi-Final 2003-04

FA Vase: Quarter Final 93-94

LAST SEASON

F.A. Cup: 2nd Round
F.A. Trophy: Semi-Final
League: Conference Play Offs (5th)
Top Goalscorer: Roscoe D'Sane
Player of the Year: Ray Warburton
Captain: Ray Warburton

ALDERSHOT TOWN PLAYING SQUAD

	Birthplace	D.O.B.	Previous Clubs	Bold print denotes England semi-professional international.
GOALKEEPERS				
Richard Barnard	Frimley	27.12.80	Maidenhead United, Millwall	
Nikki Bull	Hastings	02.10.81	Q.P.R., Aston Villa (Trainee)	
DEFENDERS				
Will Antwi	London	19.10.82	Llungskile (Sweden) Crystal P (**Ghana Int)**	
Brett Cooper	Portsmouth	27.03.85	From Youth Team	
Chris Giles	Milborne Port	16.04.82	Yeovil Town, Sherborne	
NC FAT				
Tobi Jinadu	London	14.07.84	Sutton U, Welling U, Cambridge C, Wembley,	
			Harrow B, Clapton, Mullingar T, Bristol Rovers	
Brett Johnson	Hammersmith	15.08.85	Ashford Town	
John Nutter	Hants	13.06.82	Wycombe W, Blackburn R (Trainee)	
Ray Warburton NC	Rotherham	07.10.67	Boston United, Rushden & Diamonds, Northampton Town, York City, Rotherham U	
MIDFIELD				
Nick Crittenden	Ascot	11.11.78	Yeovil Town, Chelsea	
ESP, NC, FAT,				
Jeff Goulding	Surrey		Agham T, Clapton, Croydon, Molesey	
Hugh McAuley NC Bangor C, Liverpool	Plymouth	13.05.77	Forest Green,Vauxhall M, Northwich, Stalybridge, Burscough, Kiderminster, Cheltennham, Leek, Cobwy U, Northwich, Burscough,	
Adam Miller	Suffolk	19.02.82	Gravesend& N, Grays A, Canvey I, Ipswich T	
Tyrone Smith	Frimley	04.08.76	Fronm Youth Team	
Steve Watson (Jnrs)	Surrey ESP		Stevenage B, Farnborough T, Sutton U, Croydon, Whyteleafe, Crystal Palace	
FORWARDS				
Lee Charles ESP	Hillingdon	20.08.71	Nuneaton Borough, Hayes, Barnet, Q.P.R.,Chertsey T.	
Roscoe D'Sane ESP RP	London		Woking, Slough Town, Southend, Crystal Palace	
Michael Harper	Guildford	04.02.85	From Youth Team	
Aaron McLean	Hammersmith	25.05.83	Leyton Orient	
Tim Sills ESP	Surrey	10.09.79	Kingstonian, Basingstoke T., Camberley T., Millwall	
Stuart Tansfield	Berks		Wokingham Town	

BARNET

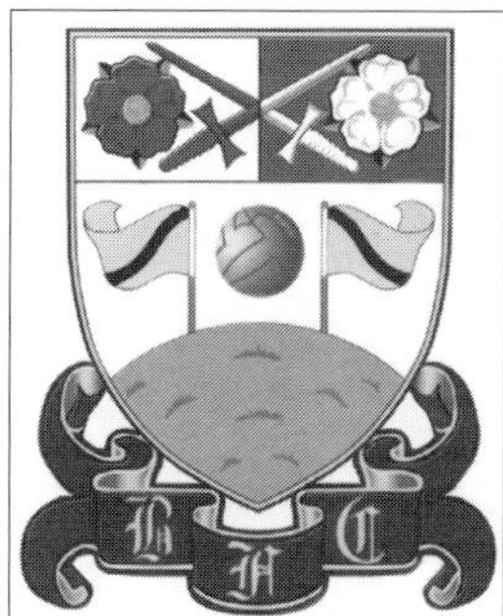

After many a disrupting headline suggesting the club might have to leave their Underhill ground a steady start to the 2003-2004 season under the enthusiastic managership of Martin Allen lifted supporters morale. Indeed, the early goalscoring form of Giuliana Grazioli and only one defeat in the first dozen conference matches combined to lift expectations to a dangerous high.

League form continued to be consistent while exits from the LDV Trophy (to Brentford) and F.A.Cup (at Yeovil) didn't affect their progress and another fine run in the New Year brought them towards the last third of the season with every chance of promotion.

Suddenly the bubble burst however, as, after an eleven match unbeaten run their young manager's outstanding achievements caught up with the club and he accepted the vacant Brentford manager's job.

With the future at Barnet still not at all clear and on the assumption that he might not ever have such a successful run to attract future offers, one can understand Martin Allen's decision to move up. It was a nasty shock for the Bees players, supporters and staff but the experienced Paul Fairclough took temporary charge and after a quiet period, including a vital home loss to rivals Shrewsbury, some sort of rythem returned.

An administrative error brought an irritating departure from the F.A.Trophy after a 3-2 victory over Dover Athletic. Barnet had included a player who was 'cup-tied' for the competition and Dover were given the tie after an appeal.

However, by the last day of the Conference season, there was all to play for at Burton and a famous victory took the Bees into the play-offs, and once again anything seemed possible.

A very late winner at home to Shrewsbury in the first leg of the play off created an near unbearable tension in the second game. The Shrews battled hard to grab an equalizer and took the game to extra time before eventually winning on penalties.

A campaign memorable for Barnet in many ways, had seen the club steady themselves in the Conference and with the very experienced and successful Fairclough at the helm, there is no reason why the coming season should not be just as exciting and possibly even more successful.

T.W.

BARNET

Match Facts 2003-04

The number shown directly below the player's name is his squad number.
Where a number is shown instead of an "X' in the columns this represents a substitute appearance and the number indicates the player replaced.

Comp.	Date	Opponents	Venue.	Result	Goalscorers	Att.
Lg 1	Aug 09	Telford U	H	W 2-0	Strevens Hendon	1319
Lg 2	Aug 12	Farnborough T	A	D 1-1	Grazioli	1063
Lg 3	Aug 16	Dagenham & R	A	L 2-5	Grazioli(2,1p)	1735
Lg 4	Aug 23	Hereford U	H	D 1-1	Hendon	1475
Lg 5	Aug 25	Burton A	A	W 3-2	Grazioli(2) Henshaw(og)	1675
Lg 6	Aug 30	Halifax T	H	W 4-1	Grazioli(3) Plummer	1341
Lg 7	Sep 06	Accrington S	H	D 0-0		1621
Lg 8	Sep 13	Stevenage B	A	W 2-1	Beadle Grazioli	3019
Lg 9	Sep 20	Aldershot T	H	W 2-1	Strevens Grazioli	2208
Lg 10	Sep 23	Margate	A	W 1-0	Grazioli	780
Lg 11	Sep 27	Shrewsbury T	A	W 1-0	Grazioli	4063
Lg 12	Oct 04	Morecambe	H	W 2-1	Strevens Hendon	1776
Lg 13	Oct 07	Exeter C	H	L 2-3	Plummer Grazioli(p)	2037
Lg 14	Oct 11	Tamworth	A	L 0-2		1304
LDVT 1	**Oct 14**	**Brentford**	**H**	**D 3-3**	**Lopez, Henry(p) Hatch**	**1248**
Lg 15	Oct 18	Leigh RMI	A	W 4-1	Grazioli(3) Hogg	348
FAC 4q	**Oct 25**	**Bracknell Town**	**A**	**W 3-0**	**Hatch Gamble Underwood(og)**	**990**
Lg 16	Nov 01	Northwich V	H	W 1-0	Grazioli	1852
FAC 1	**Nov 08**	**Stalybridge Celtic**	**H**	**D 2-2**	**Gamble Beadle**	**1736**
Lg 17	Nov 11	Gravesend & N	H	W 1-0	Plummer	1542
Lg 18	Nov 15	Chester C	A	L 0-1		2638
FAC 1r	**Nov 18**	**Stalybridge Celtic**	**A**	**W 2-0**	**Grazioli(2)**	**1549**
Lg 19	Nov 22	Forest Green R	H	W 5-0	Beadle(2) Taggart Strevens Hendon(p)	1378
Lg 20	Nov 25	Scarborough	A	D 2-2	Yakubu Hendon(p)	1208
Lg 21	Nov 29	Accrington S	A	L 0-2		1120
FAC 2	**Dec 06**	**Yeovil T**	**A**	**L 1-5**	**Beadle**	**5973**
Lg 22	Dec 13	Telford U	A	W 2-1	Pitcher Grazioli	1562
Lg 23	Dec 20	Farnborough T	H	L 0-2		1547
Lg 24	Dec 26	Woking	A	D 2-2	Strevens(2)	2856
Lg 25	Jan 01	Woking	H	D 0-0		2304
Lg 26	Jan 03	Halifax T	A	W 2-1	Grazioli Strevens	1517
FAT 3	**Jan 10**	**Dover Athletic**	**H**	**W 3-2***	**Pitcher(2) Roach (tie awarded to Dover)**	**1405**
Lg 27	Jan 17	Dagenham & R	H	L 2-4	Grazioli(2)	2006
Lg 28	Jan 24	Margate	H	W 3-1	Grazioli(2) Hendon(p)	1591
Lg 29	Feb 06	Aldershot T	A	D 1-1	Redmile	4217
Lg 30	Feb 21	Morecambe	A	W 3-1	Gamble Strevens Clist	2014
Lg 31	Feb 28	Tamworth	H	W 1-0	Hatch	1899
Lg 32	Mar 06	Exeter C	A	D 1-1	Hatch	3531
Lg 33	Mar 09	Stevenage B	H	D 0-0		2066
Lg 34	Mar 13	Gravesend & N	A	D 1-1	Pearson	1516
Lg 35	Mar 20	Chester C	H	D 0-0		2455
Lg 36	Mar 27	Forest Green R	A	D 1-1	Strevens	1013
Lg 37	Mar 30	Shrewsbury T	H	L 0-1		1966
Lg 38	Apr 03	Scarborough	H	D 0-0		1560
Lg 39	Apr 10	Hereford U	A	L 0-2		4447
Lg 40	Apr 12	Burton A	H	W 2-1	Hatch Hendon(p)	1505
Lg 41	Apr 17	Northwich V	A	D 1-1	Hatch	728
Lg 42	Apr 24	Leigh RMI	H	W 2-1	Yakubu Grazioli	2988
PO SF1	**Apr 29**	**Shrewsbury T**	**H**	**W 2-1**	**Strevens(p) Clist**	**4171**
PO SF2	**May 03**	**Shrewsbury T**	**A**	**L 0-1**		**7012**

STEP 1 CONFERENCE | STEP 2 - P177 CONFERENCE Nth & Sth | STEP 3 - P269 NPL, Southern, Isthmian Premiers | STEP 4 - P269 NPL 1, Southern W&E, Isthmian 1 | STEP 5/6 - P473 | STEP 7 - P713 Current level 4 leagues

Danny NAISBITT	Shane GORE	Mark ROONEY	Simon KING	Ian HENDON	Chris PLUMMER	Danny MADDIX	Mark WILLIAMS	Guy LOPEZ	Guiliano GRAZIOLI	Ben STREVENS	Tony TAGGART	Lee PLUCK	Peter BEADLE	Ademola BANKOLE	Ricky MILLARD	Ismael YAKUBU	Joe GAMBLE	Bai Mass LETTE JALLOW	Adam CAMPION	Simon CLIST	Mark CUMBERBATCH	Lee ROACH	Solomon HENRY	Liam HATCH	Lewis HOGG	Geoff PITCHER	Matt REDMILE	Neil SAUNDERS	Norman SYLLA	Gary SILK	Brett FREEMAN	David FORDE	Tony SCULLY	Greg PEARSON	Anthony McNAMEE
1	1	2	3	4	5	6	7	8	9	10	11	12	12	12	13	14	15	16	16	16	18	19	20	21	22	22	22	23	24	24	25	26	26	26	27
x		x	x	x	x	x	3	x	x	x	x	2					x								8										
x		x		x	x	x	x	x	x	x	x						x								8				7						
x		x	x	x	x	x	2	22	x	x	x					5	x								x										
x		x	x	x	x	x	10	x	x	x	x						x								8				11						
x		14	x	x	x	x	x		x	x						x	x								x			22							
x		6	x	x	x	x	x		x	x						x	x						14		x				9						
x			x	x	x	x	x	22	x	x	14					x	x								x										
		4		x	x	x	x		x	11	x		x			x	x								x							x			
		x			x	x	x		x	x	12		x			x	x								x							x			
		x			x	x	x	22	x	x			x			x	x								x							x			
		x	7	2	x	x	x	x	x	x			x			x	x															x			
			x	x	x	x	x	x		x	3		x			x	x												7			x			
			x	x	x	x	3	15	x	x	12		x			x	x								x							x			
			11	x	x	x	10	x	x	x	x		x			x	x								15							x			
	x	x	x					x			x							x			x	x	x	24	x				x		20				
		x	x	x	x	x			x		14		21		x	x	x						9	x	x										
	x	x	x	x	x		x	x		x	8		21			x	x							x											
	x	x	x	x	x	x	2	x	x	14			21			x	x							x											
	x	x	x	x	x	x	2	x	x				x			x	x					8		12											
	x		x	x	x	x	x		x	21			7			x	x							x	x										
	x		x	x	x	x	21		x	x			x			x	x					12		x											
	x	x	x	x	x	x	9	22	x	x						x	x								x										
	x	x	x	x	x	x	x			x	x		x			6	x						12		15										
	x	x	x	x	x	x	x		x	7			x			x	x							12											
	x	x	x	x	x		21	22	x	x	14					x	x							x	x										
	x	6	x	x	x	x	12	x	x	x			x			x	x							15											
	x	x	x	x	x	x			x	x	10					3	x							x		x									
	x	x			x		x				7					x	x		27				21	x		x				x			x		x
	x	x	x	x	x	x			x	x						x	x							14		x									3
	x	x		x	x		21	22	x	x						x	x							x		x									x
	x	9	x	x		x	x	x	x	x	x					x	x																		11
		x	x			x	16	22		x	x				x	x	x		x			11				x									x
	x		x	x	x	x	21	x	x	x						x								x		x									14
			x	x	x	x	6	10	x	x	9			x		x	x			x				x											
			x	x		x			x	x				x		x	x			x				x			x								
		x	x	x			x	x	x	x	9			x		x	x			x															
		x	x	x	x		3	7	x	x				x		x	x			x				14			x								
		x		x	x		2	10	x	x				x		x	x			x				x			x							9	
			x	x		x	21	x	x	x				x		8	x			x				x			x							16	
			x	x		x	x	7		x				x		x	x			x				x			x							14	
			x	x		x	14		x	x				x		x	x			x				x			x								
	x	x	x			x	x		x	x	15					7	x			x				26			x							x	
	x	7	x	x		x	x		x	x	21					x				x				26			x							x	
	x		x	x	x		x		x	x						x	x			x							x							14	
	x	x	x	x	x			x	x	x	10					2	x			x							x							8	
	x	x	x	x	x			x	x	x						10	x			x				16			x							9	
	x	x	x	x	x			x	x		14					x	x			11				x			x							9	
	x	14	x	x	x	x		x	x	x						x	x			10				x										9	
	x		x	x	x	x		x	x	x						x	x			8				x											
	x		x	x	x	x		x	x	x						x	x			8				x			6								

BARNET

GROUND DETAILS

Underhill Stadium,
Westcombe Drive,Herts.EN5 2DN

TEL: 020 8441 6932(office)
020 8449 6325 (ticket office)
Fax: 020 8447 0655
email: info@barnetfc.com
Club Call: 09068 121 544

Directions: Take junction 23 off the M25, follow signs for Barnet (A100), the ground is located at the foot of Barnet Hill. Tube :High Barnet (Northern Line), 400 yds
Train: New Barnet (1.5 miles)

Capacity: 4,800

Match Tickets:
From £9 - £16. (£11/£12 for away fans)

Club Shop:
Contact: Simon Hart 0208440 0725

Refreshments:
Bar for all post match and five tea-bars

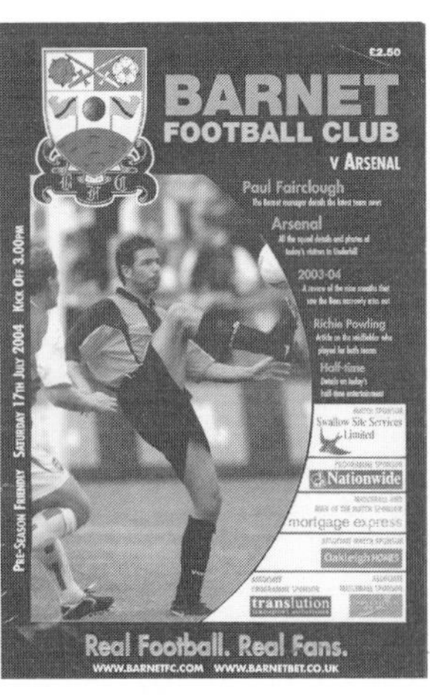

MATCHDAY PROGRAMME

Pages: 56 Price: £2.50
Editor: Kevin Mullen
Tel Nos: 020 84416932 (H) 07774132066 (M)
WEBSITE: www.barnetfc.com
Club call: 09068 121 544

Founded:	1888
Nickname:	The Bees
Sponsors:	T.B.A.
Colours:	Black & amber shirts, black shorts & socks
Change colours:	All Red
Midweek matchday:	Tuesday 7.45
Newsline:	09068 12 15 44 (calls charged at premium rate)
Reserve League:	None

CLUB OFFICIALS

Chairman:	Tony Kleanthous
Directors:	A.Adie,G. Slyper, C.Bean
Chief Executive / Secretary	Andrew Adie Tel Nos: 0208441 6932 X204 (W) 07719 287453 (M) 0208447 0655 Fax) Email: aadie@barnetfc.com
Company Secrrtary:	Christopher Bean
P.R.Consultant to the Board:	Dennis Signy OBE
Commercial Manager:	Kevin Mullen

FOOTBALL MANAGEMENT TEAM

HEAD COACH	**PAUL FAIRCLOUGH**
Date of Appointment	3rd May 2004
Date of Birth:	32 January 1950
Place of Birth:	Liverpool
PREVIOUS CLUBS	Stevenage Borough
First Team Coach:	N/A
Physiotherapist:	Andy Smith
Club Playing Status:	Full Time

Season	League	Div.	Pos.	Home P	W	D	L	F	A	Away W	D	L	F	A	Pts	Manager
03-04	Conference	-	4	42	11	6	4	30	17	8	8	5	30	29	71	Martin Allen/Paul Fairclough
02-03	Conference	-	11	42	9	4	8	32	28	4	10	7	33	40	53	Peter Shreeves
01-02	Conference	-	5	42	10	4	7	30	19	9	6	6	34	29	67	John Still / Peter Shreeves
00-01	Football Confe	3	24	46	9	8	6	44	29	3	1	19	23	52	45	John Still/Tony Cottee/John Still
99-00	Football Confe	3	6	46	12	6	5	36	24	9	6	8	23	29	75	John Still
98-99	Football Confe	3	16	46	10	5	8	30	31	4	8	11	24	40	55	John Still
97-98	Football Confe	3	7	46	10	8	5	35	22	9	5	9	26	29	70	John Still
96-97	Football Confe	3	15	46	9	9	5	32	23	5	7	11	14	28	58	Terry Bullivant
95-96	Football Confe	3	8	46	13	6	4	40	19	5	10	8	25	26	70	Ray Clemence
94-95	Football Confe	3	12	42	8	7	6	37	27	7	4	10	19	36	56	Ray Clemence

HONOURS

FA Amateur Cup 1945-46. Runners-up 1947-48, 1958-59.
FA Trophy runners-up 1971-72.
Athenian League x 5. Athenian Premier Div. x 2.
Southern League Div.1 1965-66. Div. 1 South 1976-77.
Southern League Cup 1976-77.
London League 1897, 1906, 1907.
London Senior Cup x 3. London Charity Cup x 2.
Middlesex Senior Cup x 2. Middlesex Charity Cup x 2.
Herts Senior Cup x 12. Herts Charity Cup x 25.
Wendy Fair Capital League 1988-89.
Clubcall Cup 1988-89.
Football Conference Winners 1990-91.
Football Conference runners-up 1986-87, 1987-88, 1989-90.

PREVIOUS

Leagues: Olympian League, London League, Athenian League, Southern League, Alliance Premier*, Gola League*, Vauxhall Conference*, Football League.

Names: Barnet Alston.

Grounds: Queens Road, Totteridge Lane.

* Same competetion different title.

Past Players who progressed to the Football League

Colin Powell (Charlton Ath), Gary Borthwick (AFC Bournemouth), Graham Pearce (Brighton & H.A), Russell Townsend (Northampton Tn), Colin Barnes (Torquay Utd), Gary Phillips (Brentford), Keith Alexander (Grimsby Town), Nicky Bissett (Brighton & H.A.), Robert Codner (Brighton & H.A.), Lee Payne (Newcastle Utd), Phil Gridelet (Barnsley), david Regis & Paul Harding (Notts County).

CLUB RECORDS

Attendance: 11,026
v Wycombe W., FA Amateur Cup 4th Rnd, 1951-52.

Career Goalscorer: Arthur Morris, 400, 1927-34.

Career Appearances: Les Eason, 648, 1965-74, 1977-78.

Transfer Fee Paid: £130,000
to Peterborough Utd for Greg Heald.

Transfer Fee Received: £800,000
from Crystal Palace for Dougie Freedman.

BEST SEASON

FA Cup: 3rd Round
1964-65, 1970-71, 1972-73, 1981-82, 1990-91, 1991-92, 1993-94.

League Clubs Defeated (as a non-league club) Newport County (1970-71, a Northampton Town1990-91

FA Trophy: Finalists 1971-72.

League: Conference Champions 1990-91.

LAST SEASON

F.A. Cup: 2nd Round
F.A. Trophy: 3rd Round
Conference: Conference Play Offs (4th)
Top Goalscorer: Giuliano Grazioli
Captain: **Ian Hendon**
Player(s) of the Year: Giuliano Grazioli

BARNET PLAYING SQUAD

Bold print denotes England semi-professional international.

	Birthplace	D.O.B.	Previous Clubs
GOALKEEPERS			
Shane Gore	Kent	28.10.81	Wimbledon
Ricky Millard	London	03.05.84	Youth Team
DEFENDERS			
Ian Hendon E.u21,Y	Ilford	05.12.71.	Sheffield Wednesday, Tottenham Hotspur (Trainee)
Simon King	Oxford	11.04.83	Oxford United
Danny Maddix	Ashford	11.10.67	Tottenham Hotspur (Trainee), Q.P.R., Sheffield Wed.
Adw Olyinka	London		From Youth Team
Chris Plummer E u21	Isleworth	12.10.76	Q.P.R.
Lee Pluck	London		From Trainee
Jamie Smith			From Trainee
Tony Taggart	London		Farnborough Town, Brentford (junior)
Ismail Yakubu	London		Barnet School of Excellence
MIDFIELD			
Simon Clist	Dorset	13.06.81	Bristol City
Wes Daly	Hammersmith	07.03.84	Q.P.R.
Richard Graham N.Ire Y & U21	Newry	05.08.79	Kettering , Billericay, Chesham, Barnet, Q.P.R.
Bai Mass Lette 'Max' Jallow	London		Youth Team
Guy Lopez	Calais		Local Football
Mark Williams	London	19.10.81	Brentford
FORWARDS			
Giuliano Grazioli	Marylebone	23.03.75	Wembley, Yeovil Town(L), Woking (L), Peterborough U. Stevenage B (L), Swindon Town, Bristol Rovers.
Liam Hatch E NG I, RP	Kent		Gravesend & Northfleet, Herne Bay £25,000
Lee Roach			Protec Youth Academy
Ben Strevens	Edgware	24.05.80	Wingate & Finchley

BURTON ALBION

Quite often the second season after promotion is a little bit of an anti-climax..The opposition are no longer new to the players or supporters, you are not considered underdogs any more and your supporters expect more from you now that the club has 'consolidated' in a higher division.

All these feelings were experienced by Albion last season as Manager Nigel Clough quietly strengthened his squad. As one of the ever diminishing band of part timers in the Conference, expectations were not very high and a mid table position was perhaps the aim for most followers of the Brewers.

As it turned out, an early burst of excitement in the F.A.Cup lifted the season, as six goals were scored against Buxton before a trip to high flying Division Three club Torquay United produced a brilliant performance to give the Conference another well deserved scalp. It was Robbie Talbot, one of Clough's close season signings who proved to be the matchwinner, accepting a superb pass from his player-manager and joyfully driving home a goal which eliminated the Torquay team who were later to gain promotion and brought a home tie against Hartlepool United. Unfortunately a single goal decided the Second Round tie in favour of the North Easterners, although the tie did give Nigel's father a chance of refreshing a few memories of his first managerial job.

The F.A.Trophy brought mixed fortunes. A 4-2 home victory over Accrington Stanley was followed by a replay victory at Kettering, but then an awkward visit to a confident Hornchurch side who had excelled in the F.A.Cup brought defeat by the only goal of the game.

It was a quiet season, finishing with a mid table place for the Brewers, but the manager will now know more about the strengths and weaknesses of the Conference and its members. The club is stable and I am sure sensible steady progress will be made without any unnecessary financial stress.

T.W.

Back Row (L-R): Ray Hudson, Matt Brown, Glenn Kirkwood, Darren Stride, Colin Hoyle, Aaron Webster, Dan Robinson, Matt Duke, Barry Williams, Ian Wright,Lee Colkin, Ryan Sugden, Steve Booth, Andy Garner
Front Row (L-R): Dale Anderson, Andy Sinton, Robbie Talbot, Andy Ducros, Nigel Clough, Gary Crosby, Christian Moore, Terry Henshaw, Darren Wassall, Jon Howard

BURTON ALBION

The number shown directly below the player's name is his squad number.
Where a number is shown instead of an "X' in the columns this represents a substitute appearance and the number indicates the player replaced.

Comp.	Date	Opponents	Venue.	Result	Goalscorers	Att.
Conf 1	Aug 09	Gravesend & N	A	W 2-1	Howard Wright	1137
Conf 2	Aug 12	Shrewsbury T	H	L 0-1		3203
Conf 3	Aug 16	Stevenage B	H	D 1-1	Anderson	1572
Conf 4	Aug 23	Scarborough	A	W 2-1	Stride Anderson	1445
Conf 5	Aug 25	Barnet	H	L 2-3	Talbot Chettle	1675
Conf 6	Aug 30	Morecambe	A	L 1-2	Williams	1789
Conf 7	Sep 06	Woking	H	W 2-0	Anderson Moore	1482
Conf 8	Sep 13	Telford U	A	D 2-2	Kirkwood(2)	2035
Conf 9	Sep 19	Hereford U	H	W 4-1	Talbot(3) Howard	2532
Conf 10	Sep 23	Accrington S	A	L 1-3	Talbot	1911
Conf 11	Sep 27	Aldershot T	A	L 1-3	Webster(p)	2687
Conf 12	Oct 03	Exeter C	H	L 3-4	Webster(2p) Moore	1985
Conf 13	Oct 08	Chester C	H	D 1-1	Webster(p)	1711
Conf 14	Oct 11	Forest Green R	A	D 1-1	Twigg	867
Conf 15	Oct 18	Dagenham & R	A	W 2-0	Sinton Williams	1483
FAC 4q	**Oct 25**	**Buxton**	**H**	**W 6-0**	**Anderson(3,1p) Webster(2,1p) Talbot**	**1980**
Conf 16	Nov 01	Farnborough T	H	W 1-0	Stride	1601
FAC 1	**Nov 08**	**Torquay United**	**A**	**W 2-1**	**Talbot Woods(og)**	**2790**
Conf 17	Nov 14	Halifax T	H	D 2-2	Ducros Webster(p)	1541
Conf 18	Nov 22	Margate	A	W 2-1	Anderson (2)	564
Conf 19	Nov 25	Leigh RMI	H	W 3-2	Anderson Howard Corbett	1327
Conf 20	Nov 29	Woking	A	L 0-1		1947
Conf 21	Dec 02	Northwich V	A	W 2-1	Talbot Williams	686
FAC 2	**Dec 07**	**Hartlepool United**	**H**	**L 0-1**		**3132**
Conf 21	Dec 13	Gravesend & N	H	W 3-0	Colkin Talbot Stride	1403
Conf 23	Dec 26	Tamworth	H	L 0-1		3164
Conf 24	Jan 01	Tamworth	A	D 1-1	Stride	2535
Conf 25	Jan 03	Morecambe	H	L 0-1		1478
FAT 3	**Jan 10**	**Accrington S**	**H**	**W 4-2**	**Webster(2) Anderson Howard**	**1402**
Conf 26	Jan 17	Stevenage B	A	L 0-1		2003
Conf 27	Jan 24	Accrington S	H	D 1-1	Webster	1614
FAT 4	**Jan 31**	**Kettering Town**	**H**	**D 1-1**	**Webster**	**1751**
FAT 4r	**Feb 03**	**Kettering Town**	**A**	**W 2-1**	**Howard Talbot**	**1215**
Conf 28	Feb 07	Hereford U	A	W 2-1	White Talbot	3417
FAT 5	**Feb 14**	**Hornchurch**	**A**	**L 1-2**	**Stride**	**1205**
Conf 29	Feb 21	Exeter C	A	L 0-2		2885
Conf 30	Feb 24	Shrewsbury T	A	L 0-1		3115
Conf 31	Feb 28	Forest Green R	H	L 2-3	Talbot Howard	1442
Conf 32	Mar 06	Chester C	A	L 1-3	Talbot	3318
Conf 33	Mar 09	Telford U	H	W 2-1	Wright Talbot	1244
Conf 34	Mar 13	Northwich V	H	L 0-1		1416
Conf 35	Mar 16	Aldershot T	H	L 1-4	Stride	1295
Conf 36	Mar 27	Margate	H	L 0-1		1240
Conf 37	Mar 30	Halifax T	A	W 4-1	Kirkwood Ducros Gill Anderson	1128
Conf 38	Apr 03	Leigh RMI	A	W 1-0	Anderson	339
Conf 39	Apr 10	Scarborough	H	W 2-0	Kirkwood McMahon	1370
Conf 40	Apr 12	Barnet	A	L 1-2	Talbot	1505
Conf 41	Apr 17	Farnborough T	A	L 1-2	Henshaw	812
Conf 42	Apr 24	Dagenham & R	H	L 0-1		1361

STEP 1
CONFERENCE

STEP 2 - P177
CONFERENCE Nth & Sth

STEP 3 - P269
NPL, Southern, Isthmian Premiers

STEP 4 - P269
NPL 1, Southern W&E, Isthmian 1

STEP 5/6 - P473

STEP 7 - P713
Current level 4 leagues

Matt DUKE	Terry HENSHAW	Lee COLKIN	Barry WILLIAMS	Ian WRIGHT	Darren WASSALL	Darren STRIDE	John HOWARD	Ryan SUGDEN	Christian MOORE	Sam SHILTON	Andy DUCROS	Glenn KIRKWOOD	Aaron WEBSTER	Coiln HOYLE	Dale ANDERSON	Andy SINTON	Robbie TALBOT	Sean GUMMER	Nigel CLOUGH	Steve CHETTLE	Craig DUDLEY	Gary CROSBY	Gart TWIGG	Adam WILLIS	Andy CORBETT	Adam MURRAY	Sam McMAHON	Andy WHITE	Alex JOHN-BAPTISTE	Robert GILL
1	**2**	**3**	**4**	**5**	**6**	**7**	**8**	**9**	**10**	**10**	**11**	**12**	**14**	**15**	**16**	**17**	**18**	**19**	**20**	**21**	**22**	**23**	**24**	**24**	**25**	**26**	**27**	**28**	**29**	**30**
x	x	x		x		x	x		x		x	x	3		x		16			x										
x	x	x	5	x		x	x	x	x		17				3	x	x			x										
x	x		x		x	x	x	18	8			x	x		x		x			x										
x	x		x		x	x	x	18	x			x	x		x		6		21	x										
x	x		x		x	x	7	x	x				x		8	x	x			x	17									
x	x	4	x	x		x	x		18				x		x	22	x			x	x									
x	x	14	x	x		x	x		x			7	x		x	16				x	x									
x	x	x		x	5		x				8	x			x		x		x	x	x									
x	x			x	x		x				18	x	x		x		x		x		x	6								
x	x		5	x			x				16	x	x		x		x		x	x	x									
x	x		x		x		x		x		x		x		22		10		8	x	x		x							
x	x		x		x		x		18		x		x		x		x		x	x			16							
x	x		x		x	x	x		x			18	x				x		8	x			x							
x	x		x		x	x	x		x		8	x	x					24	7	x			x							
x	x	x	x		x		20				x	x	x		x	4	16		x	x										
x	x	x			x	x					x	x	x		x	6	x		x											
x	x	x	18		x	x	3				x	6	x		x		x		x					x						
x		x				x	x				x	x	x		x		3		x	x		21		x						
x			x			x	x				x	x	x		x		x		x					x	18					
x	x	x	12		x	x						x	x	6	x							3		x	x	x				
x	x				x	22	x					20	x		x		x		x		x			x	16	x				
x	x	x			x	x	x					x	x	6	22		3				x			x	x					
x	x	x	x			x						27	x	x	18		x		15					x	x		x			
x	x	x			x	x	x				16	x	x		x		3			x	x									
x	x	x			21	x	x				8	x	x		18		x		8	x	x				x					
x	x	x			x	x	x				x				x		22		x	x	x				x					
x	x	x			x	x	x				x	x	8		x		6			x	x				22					
x	x	x	x		x	x					x	x	x		3		x		18		x				x					
x	x				x	x	x				x		x		x		x		27		25				x		x			
x	x		11		x	x	x						x		x		x		18		x				4		x			
x	x				x	x	x						x		x		x		x		x				18		x			
x	x	8			x		x				x		x		3		x		x	x	x				x		x			
x	x				x	x	x						x		x		16		x	11	x				22		x			
x				x	x	x				x			x		18		x		27		10				x		x	x	x	
x				x	x	x				x	x		x				x		7	5	25				x		x	x	x	
x					x		x			x	x		x		x		28			x	21				11		x	x	x	
x					x		x			x	x		x	x	28		x		x		x				18			x		
x				29	x		x			x	x		x	x	x		16				x				x		15		x	
x	11			x	x		x			x	x		x	5	x		x				x				16		x			
x				x	x		x			x	x		x	8	x		x				x				16		x			
x				x	x					x	x		x	x	18		x		27		x				22		x			x
x				x	x	14	x			x	x		x	x	x				x	5					16					x
x				x	x	x	x			x	x		8	x	30		x								5		x			x
x				12		x				x		x		x	x		x		x	x	x						20			18
x				12		x	x			x		x		x	x				8	x	x				16		x			x
x	18			21		x	x			x	x	x		x	x		x			x	x				16		x			
x	x			x	20	x	18			x	x	27		x			x		x						x		x			
x	x			x		x	11			x		x		x			x		12	15	x				x					
x	x					x	12			x		x	x	x			x		x	x	x				22		7			

BURTON ALBION

GROUND DETAILS

Eton Park,Princess Way,Burton-on-Trent
DE14 2RU
Tel: 01283 565938

Directions: No1. From M1 South: Take Jct 23 (A50 Derby).Join A38 south at Toyota factory(A38 B'ham & Lichfield) .Leave A38 at Burton North Clay Mills (A5121), over first roumdabout, past Pirelli factory and turn right at next r'bout . Ground on left past Metro supermarket.**No.2 From M! North:Jct 28** (A38 Derby) , Follow A38 through Derby until A5121(Burton North Clay Mills) then as No 1.**No.3 From South M5:** M40 join M42 North. Leave at Jct 9, A446 (Lichfield & Belfry Golf). Join A38 North sign posted Burton. Leave A38 at second turn for Burton (Clay Mills) A5121 then as No.1 **No.4 From M6 North:** Leave at Jct 15 (A500 to Stoke) join A50 (to Uttoxeter& Burton), follow A50 until junction with A38 at Toyota factory. Then as No.1

Parking: Large Car Park at the ground.

Capacity: 4,500
Cover: 2,500
Seats: 464

Clubhouse: `The Football Tavern' - open normal pub hours. Full hot & cold menu.
Steward: T.B.A

Club Shop: Yes
Match Tickets:

MATCHDAY PROGRAMME

Pages: 48 Price: £2
Editor: Fleur Robinson(01283 537272)
Clubcall:09066 555 883

Local Press: Burton Daily Mail (01283 43311)
Local Radio: Radio Derby,Centra F.M.,Ram F.M.

Founded: 1950

Nickname: Brewers

Sponsors: Bison Concrete Products Ltd

Shirt Sponsors Knott Ltd.

Colours: Yellow with black trim/black/black

Change colours: All Royal Blue

Midweek matchday: Tuesday

Club Websites www.burtonalbionfc.co.uk

CLUB OFFICIALS

Chairman: C B Robinson
01283 537272W)

Directors: C.B.Robinson,
Spiers (Co Sec), P.A.Brown, R.Bowering

P.Simpson,D.Amott,C.Brodie,C.Simpson,T.Whyman

R.Hinton, P.Keeton and J.Williams

Secretary & Commercial Manager: Fleur Robinson

c/o Club

Tel. Nos: 01283 537272 & 07774 102485 (M)

Press Officer: Rex Page Tel No: 01283 524845 (W)

FOOTBALL MANAGEMENT TEAM

MANAGER **NIGEL CLOUGH**
Date of Appointment: March1999
Date of Birth: 19th March 1966
Place of Birth: Sunderland

PREVIOUS CLUBS
As manager
As asst. manager/coach
As player Heanor Town, Nottm. Forest, Liverpool

HONOURS
As manager: N.P.L. Champions 2001-02
F.A. Trophy Semi-Finalists 01-02

As player England - Full & u21 caps
Assistant Manager: Gary Crosby
Physiotherapist:
Matthew Brown
Scout: Steve Booth
Club's Playing Status: Part-time.

Season	League	Div.	Pos.	Home P	W	D	L	F	A	Away W	D	L	F	A	Pts	Manager
03-04	Conference	-	14	42	7	4	10	30	29	8	3	10	27	30	51	Nigel Clough
02-03	Conference	-	16	42	6	6	9	25	31	7	4	10	25	47	49	Nigel Clough
01-02	N.P.L.	Prem	1	44	17	5	0	59	12	14	6	2	47	18	104	Nigel Clough
00-01	Southern	Prem.	2	42	14	6	1	36	13	11	7	3	40	23	88	Nigel Clough
99-00	Southern	Prem.	2	42	15	3	3	47	15	8	6	7	26	28	78	Nigel Clough
98-99	Southern	Prem.	13	42	7	2	12	29	27	10	5	6	29	25	58	John Barton
97-98	Southern	Prem.	3	42	12	4	5	39	19	9	4	8	25	24	71	John Barton
96-97	Southern	Prem.	6	42	10	7	4	37	32	8	5	8	33	31	66	John Barton

Season	League	Div.	Pos.	P	W	D	L	F	A	Pts	Manager
95-96	Southern	Prem.	16	42	13	12	17	55	56	51	John Barton
94-95	Southern	Prem.	3	42	20	15	7	55	39	75	John Barton

HONOURS

Southern League
Conf Cup 63-64 96-97, 99-00 (R-up 88-89),
Div 1 (Nth) R-up 71-72 73-74;

Northern Premier Champions 2001-02
Conf Chall Cup 82-83 (R-up 86-87),
Presidents Cup R-up 85-86 (SF 86-87);

FA Trophy R-up 86-87;

Birmingham Snr Cup 53-54 70-71 (R-up 86-87);
GMAC Cup SF 86-87;
Bass Charity Vase 81-82 85-86,
Challenge Cup 84-85;
West Mids Conf R-up 53-54;
Staffs Sen Cup 55-56

CLUB RECORDS

Attendance: **5,860**
v Weymouth, Southern Lgef Cup Final 2nd leg, 1964
(22,500 v Leicester City, F.A. Cup 3rd Rd 1984 - played at Derby County F.C.)

Goalscorer: Ritchie Barker, 157

Appearances: Phil Annable, 567

Win:

Fee Paid: **£21,000**
to Kidderminster H.for R Jones and J Pearson

Fee Received: **£60,000**
for Darren Carr to Crystal Palace 1989

PREVIOUS

Leagues: West Midlands 1950-58
Southern 58-79, 80-2001
Northern Premier 79-80, 01-02

Grounds: Wellington Street 50-57

Names: None

BEST SEASON

FA Trophy: R-up 86-87 (SF 74-75)

FA Cup: 3rd Rd Prop 55-56, 84-85. 1st Rd 9 times
League: Champions Northern Prem. 01-02

Past Players who progressed to the Football League

L Green & T Parry & S Aston (Hartlepool65/66),
G Hunter (Lincoln 65), D Jones (Newport 68),
R Barker & J Bourne & T Bailey (Derby 67/69/70),
M Pollock & S Buckley (Luton 74),
P Ward (Brighton75), Tony Moore (Sheffield Utd 79),
C Swan & G Clayton (Doncaster 80 & 86),
RJobson (Watford 82), P Haycock (Rotherham 86),
A Kamara (Scarborough 87),
P Groves (Leicester City 88),
S Cotterill & J Gayle (Wimbledon 89),
D Carr(Crystal Pal. 89),
D Smith & D Roberts (Wolves 90 & 92)

LAST SEASON

F.A. Cup: 2nd Round Proper
F.A. Trophy: 5th Round
Conference: 14th
Top Goalscorer: Dale Anderson
Captain: Darren Stride

BURTON ALBION PLAYING SQUAD

Bold print denotes England semi-professional international.

	Birthplace	D.O.B.	Previous Clubs
GOALKEEPERS			
Dan Robinson	Derby	01.09.82	Blackpool, Derby County (Junior)
Martin Taylor	Tamworth	09.12.66	Telford U, Wycombe W, Derby C, Mile Oak
DEFENDERS			
Terry Henshaw	Nottingham	29.02.80	Notts Co.
Colin Hoyle DMP, UP	Derby	15.01.72	Boston Utd, King's Lynn, Mansfield T, Notts Co., Bradford C, Barnsley, Arsenal
Michael Simpkins	Sheffield	28.11.78	Rochdale, Cardiff C, Chesterfield
Darren Wassall UP	Edgbaston	27.06.68	Birmingham C, Derby Co., Nottingham Forest
Ian Wright	Lichfield	10.03.72	Hereford United, Hull City, Bristol Rovers, Stoke City,
MIDFIELD			
Nigel Clough Eu-21, E 'B', E-Full Int., UP	Sunderland	19.03.66	Manchester C, Liverpool, Nottingham Forest, AC Hunters
Jon Howard	Sheffield	7.10.71	Chesterfield, Shefield United.
Sam Shilton	Nottingham	21.07.78	Kidderminster H, Hartlepool, Coventry C, Plymouth A.
Darren Stride ESP, UP	Burton-on-Trent	28.09.75	From Youth team
Aaron Webster ESP, UP	Burton-on-Trent	19.12.80	From Youth team
Barry Williams	Birmingham	19.12.80	Alvechurch,Ely City,Redditch United
ESP,DMP			
Laurie Wilson	Sheffield		Sheffield Wednesday
FORWARDS			
Dale Anderson ESP UP	Birmingham	10.11.79	Bromsgrove R, Hednesford T, WBA, Nottingham Forest
Andy Corbett	Worcester	20.02.80	Nuneaton B, Solihull T, Kidderminster H
Andy Ducros	Nuneaton	16.09.77	Nuneaton Boro , Kidderminster H(£100,000),Nuneaton B
Craig Dudley	Newark	12.09.79	Oldham Ath. Notts Co. (England Youth Int)
Chris Hall	Lincoln		Lincoln United
Glenn Kirkwood	Chesterfield	03.12.76	Ilkeston T, Doncaster R, Eastwood T
Robbie Talbot	Liverpool	31.10.79	Burscough (£10,000), Marine, Rochdale

CANVEY ISLAND

Canvey Island started the season as overwhelming favourites to win the Ryman Premier League after finishing runners up three years on the trot.

They didn't disappoint, losing just six league games, scoring over100 goals and collecting over100 points to finish a massive nineteen points clear of nearest rivals Sutton United. After an inconsistent start in which they lost to Bishop's Stortford and Hendon, Canvey really got into gear with a run of 27 league games unbeaten which was eventually ended by Sutton in mid March.

During this time, Canvey produced impressive performances in putting four past Aylesbury United, Bedford Town and Kettering Town, five past Bishop's Stortford and six past Kingstonian. In November title rivals Carshalton were beaten 2-0 and Canvey picked up a useful point at big spending Hornchurch who many had predicted would provide a stiff challenge to the Gulls in the New Yea.r. Canvey's excellent form continued into 2004 with victories over title rivals Hendon and Carshalton putting them firmly in control at the top of the table.

Despite a minor blip in March when they failed to win three games, Canvey had wrapped up the title by Easter and over1000 fans were there to see the championship decided with the 2-1victory at Thurrock

All this time Canvey were enjoying exciting runs in both the F.A.Cup and F.A.Trophy, they came back from 0-3 down to beat Dover Athletic in a qualifying round before gaining a dream draw with local rivals Southend United. They drew at Roots Hall to earn a home replay and in front of Sky cameras they produced a gutsy display but, despite leading twice, lost in an entertaining cup tie.

In the Trophy they reached the final beating Conference opposition twice. FarnborouGh Town 6-0 (H) and Telford United in a thrilling two legged semi-final.0-0 (A) and 3-2(H) after extra time.Although favourites to win the flnal it wasn't to be their day and Hednesford Town played well to finish 3-2 winners of another magnificent game.

Lee Boylan's goals were a wonderful contribution to the successful season but Jeff Minton and Jon Kennedy also had outstanding campaigns and the club is now looking forward to the challenge of Conference football.

David Powell

CANVEY ISLAND

Match Facts 2003-04

Date	Comp	Opponents	Att.	Result	Goalscorers
16/08/03	Isth. Prem	BASINGSTOKE TOWN	579	3 - 1	Gregory 13, Gooden 40, Boylan 86
19/08/03	Isth. Prem	Bishop's Stortford	512	0 - 2	
23/08/03	Isth. Prem	Maidenhead United	259	0 - 0	
25/08/03	Isth. Prem	THURROCK	591	4 - 3	Boylan 17 70, Kennedy 32, N Gregory 40
30/08/03	Isth. Prem	Harrow Borough	255	1 - 0	Boylan 70[p]
02/09/03	Isth. Prem	ST ALBANS CITY	589	4 - 0	N Gregory 17, Boylan 20 30, Parmenter 78
06/09/03	Isth. Prem	Hendon	318	0 - 1	
09/09/03	Isth. Prem	BRAINTREE TOWN	446	4 - 1	Midgley 11, Boylan 13, N Gregory 32 90
13/09/03	Isth. Prem	NORTHWOOD	583	1 - 1	Boylan 48
16/09/03	Isth. Prem	Hitchin Town	280	3 - 1	Boylan 6, Minton 22, Kennedy 90
20/09/03	Isth. Prem	Sutton United	600	1 - 0	Duffy 29
23/09/03	Isth. Prem	HEYBRIDGE SWIFTS	613	2 - 0	Boylan 50, N Gregory 79
27/09/03	**FA Cup Q2**	**UXBRIDGE**	**321**	**6 - 1**	**Midgeley 4, Boylan 16 88, Dobinson 19, N Gregory 32, Gooden 85**
04/10/03	Isth. Prem	AYLESBURY UNITED	535	4 - 0	Minton 12, N Gregory 74, Berquez 77 90
11/10/03	**FA Cup Q3**	**DOVER ATHLETIC**	**528**	**4 - 3**	**Minton 56 81 90, Boyland 84[p]**
18/10/03	Isth. Prem	KINGSTONIAN	509	6 - 1	Boylan 17 34, Gregory 64 68 70, McDougald 88
21/10/03	Isth. Prem	Bedford Town	460	4 - 2	N Gregory 20 32, Duffy 40, Minton 69
26/10/03	**FA Cup Q4**	**Mangotsfield United**	**1083**	**2 - 1**	**Gregory 64, Boylan 70**
01/11/03	Isth. Prem	Kettering Town	988	4 - 1	Minton 7, Midgley 50, N Gregory 64, Godden 71
03/11/03	**Essex SC 3**	**Harlow Town**	**123**	**1 - 4**	**Kirby 17[og]**
09/11/03	**FA Cup 1**	**Southend United**	**9234**	**1 - 1**	**Chenery 7**
15/11/03	Isth. Prem	Carshalton Athletic	719	2 - 0	Boylan 43[p], Cowan 83
19/11/03	**FA Cup 1r**	**SOUTHEND UNITED**	**2731**	**2 - 3**	**Boylan 10, Minton 45**
22/11/03	Isth. Prem	Hornchurch	1168	0 - 0	
29/11/03	**FAT 2**	**Windsor & Eton**	**302**	**3 - 1**	**McDougald 15, Minton 52 82**
06/12/03	Isth. Prem	FORD UNITED	509	3 - 1	Boylan 15 68, McDougald 86
13/12/03	Isth. Prem	Basingstoke Town	352	2 - 1	Boylan 15, N Gregory 90
16/12/03	Isth. Prem	BOGNOR REGIS TOWN	411	3 - 1	Boylan 56, Kennedy 62, N Gregory 79
19/12/03	Isth. Prem	BISHOP'S STORTFORD	441	5 - 1	Boylan 35[p] 40 53, Chenery 58, McDougald 82
23/12/03	**Lge Cup 2**	**HENDON**	**232**	**0 - 3**	
26/12/03	Isth. Prem	Billericay Town	1037	3 - 0	Boylan 28 32[p] 90
01/01/04	Isth. Prem	MAIDENHEAD UNITED	684	3 - 1	Theobald 17, Boylan 70 90
03/01/04	Isth. Prem	Braintree Town	485	3 - 0	Gooden 21, Boylan 57, Berquez 81
10/01/04	**FAT 3**	**FARNBOROUGH TOWN**	**685**	**6 - 0**	**Boylan 5 26 59[p], Berquez 55 65 87**
17/01/04	Isth. Prem	HENDON	626	1 - 0	Boylan 25
24/01/04	Isth. Prem	Northwood	421	5 - 1	
27/01/04	Isth. Prem	HITCHIN TOWN	589	4 - 0	N Gregory 3, Theobald 23, Midgeley 64, Parmenter 77
31/01/04	**FAT 4**	**Stafford Rangers**	**1163**	**2 - 0**	**Boylan 47, Duffy 90**
07/02/04	Isth. Prem	HAYES	698	2 - 1	Boylan 3 21
10/02/04	Isth. Prem	Grays Athletic	722	1 - 1	Youds 40[og]
14/02/04	**FA T 5**	**Stalybridge Celtic**	**832**	**0 - 0**	
17/02/04	**FAT 5r**	**STALYBRIDGE CELTIC**	**761**	**4 - 0**	**Boylan 4, Dootson 48[og], Gregory 56, Robinson 63**
21/02/04	Isth. Prem	CARSHALTON ATHLETIC	772	3 - 0	
23/02/04	**Essex TST2**	**Chelmsford City**	**n/k**	**1 - 2**	
24/02/04	Isth. Prem	BEDFORD TOWN	337	3 - 1	N Gregory 12[p], McDougald 43 75
28/02/04	**FAT QF**	**MAIDENHEAD UNITED**	**921**	**4 - 0**	**Boylan 6[p], Minton 16, Duffy 37, Cowan 90**
06/03/04	Isth. Prem	Heybridge Swifts	574	4 - 1	
09/03/04	Isth. Prem	GRAYS ATHLETIC	732	1 - 1	Boylan 44
13/03/04	Isth. Prem	SUTTON UNITED	727	1 - 3	Jinadu 47[og]
16/03/04	Isth. Prem	Hayes	298	1 - 2	Boylan 63[p]
20/03/04	Isth. Prem	Aylesbury United	320	2 - 0	Boylan 17, Minton 90
27/03/04	**FAT SF(1)**	**Telford United**	**3061**	**0 - 0**	
03/04/04	**FAT SF(2)**	**TELFORD UNITED**	**1433**	**2 - 2**	**Boylan 52 108 4 2 (all-ticket)**
06/04/04	Isth. Prem	Kingstonian	267	2 - 1	Berquez 36, Boylan 79[p]
09/04/04	Isth. Prem	Thurrock	1003	2 - 1	Berquez 3, Boylan 75
12/04/04	Isth. Prem	BILLERICAY TOWN	1046	0 - 2	
17/04/04	Isth. Prem	St Albans City	341	1 - 4	Minton 28[p]
20/04/04	Isth. Prem	Bognor Regis Town	325	0 - 0	
22/04/04	Isth. Prem	HARROW BOROUGH	284	1 - 1	Cowan 40
24/04/04	Isth. Prem	Ford United	336	3 - 0	
27/04/04	Isth. Prem	KETTERING TOWN	356	1 - 1	McDougald 80
01/05/04	Isth. Prem	HORNCHURCH	911	3 - 2	Boylan 78 79 89[p]
23/05/04	**FAT Final**	**HEDNESFORD TOWN**	**6635**	**2 - 3**	**(at Aston Villa)**

Home matches indicated by opponents being in capitals.

Canvey Island fans celebrating their clubs' success.....

CANVEY ISLAND

GROUND DETAILS

Park Lane, Canvey Island, Essex SS8 7PX

Tel: 01268 682991

Admin Office: Tel No: 01268 511888

FAX: 01268 511556

Web site:www.canveyislandfc.com

SIMPLE DIRECTIONS:

A130 from A13 or A127 at Sdalers Farm Roundabout
One mile through town centre, first right past old bus garage
Bus 3 or 151 from Benfleet (BR) to stop
after Adrmiral Jellicoe public house

MATCH TICKETS:

CAPACITY:	4,100
SEATED:	500
COVERED TERRACING:	827
Refreshments:	Always available on matchdays

Clubhouse: OpenTuesdays, Thursdays and Saturdays plus ant other matchdays & for private bookings

Contact:

CLUB SHOP: Open matchdays selling programmes, badges and shirts etc.

MATCHDAY PROGRAMME

Pages: 52 Price: £2.00

Editor: Keith Johnson

Tel No; 07773 959125

Local Press: Evening Echo

Local Radio: Essex F.M. BBC Essex

Founded:	1926
Nickname:	The Gulls
Club Sponsors:	Kings Park Homes
Club colours:	Yelow/white/white
Change colours:	Orange/Navy/Navy
Midweek home matchday:	Tuesday
Reserves' League:	Essex & Herts Border Comb
Clubcall	

CLUB OFFICIALS

President Dr.Bob Spink M.P..

Chairman Keith Johnson

Secretary Wayne Purser
C.I.F.C., Kings Park, Hindles Road,
Canvey Island,Essex SS88HE
Mobile : 07719598260
e-mail: wpurser.cifc@kings-leisure.co.uk

Press Officer Keith Johnson
c/o C.I.F.C. Mobile: 07773 959125

FOOTBALL MANAGEMENT TEAM

MANAGER:	JEFF KING
Date of Appointment	1992
Date of Birth:	23.05.1959
Place of Birth:	Hornchurch

PREVIOUS CLUBS

As manager N/A

HONOURS

As manager Isthmian Premier, Div.1 & Div.2 champions
F.A. Trophy winners & runners-up

As player

* *

Assistant Manager:	Glenn Pennyfather
Physiotherapist:	Ken Steggles
Youth development:	
Community Officer	
Club's Playing Status:	Part Time

HONOURS

Ryman Isthmian League Premier Division
Champions 2003-04, Runners -Up 00-01,01-02,02-03
Division One:Champions 1993-94
DivisonTwo: 95-96, 97-98 Runners-Up 1998-99
Division Three Runners-Up: 1994-95
Carlton Trophy: 1995-96
Essex Senioe Cup: Winners 98-99, 99-00,01-02
Essex Senior League: Champions: 1986-87, 1992-93
Essex Senior League Cup 1979-80 1992-93
Essex Thameside Trophy 1993-94
Harry Fisher Memorial Trophy 1993-94
Metropolitan League 1967-68 68-69
Metropolitan League Cup 1967-68 68-69
Thameside Cup 95-6 97-8 Parthenon Lg Cup 1958-59

CLUB RECORDS

Attendance: 3,553 v Aldershot Town Isthmian League 2002-2003

Record win: 10-1 v Enfield Isthmian League

Record defeat: 0-7 v Halstead, Essex Senior League

Career goalscorer: Andy Jones

Career appearances: Steve Price 407

Transfer fee paid: £5,000 to Northwich Victoria for Steve Duffy

Transfer fee received: £4,500 from Farnborough Town for Brian Horne

PREVIOUS

Leagues: The Combination 1890-1899, 1901-1910
Lancashire Combination 1910-1914
Cheshire County League 1919-1931
Football League 1931-2000

Grounds: Faulkner St. 1885-98; Old Showground 1898-99
Whipcord Lane 1901-06; Sealand Road. 1906-1990
Moss Rose, Macclesfield (ground share) 90-92

Names: Chester F.C. until 1983

BEST SEASON

FA Trophy: Winners 2000-01

FA Cup: 3rdh Round 1-4 v Burley (A) 2001-02

League Clubs Defeated Port Vale 2-1 (A) after 1-1 (H) 2001-02

Conference First Season

Past Players who progressed to the Football League

not yet applicable

LAST SEASON

F.A. Cup: 1st Round
FA Trophy: Finallists
Ryman (Isthmian): Champions
Top Goalscorer: Lee Boylan, 60
Player of the Year: Jon Kennedy
Captain: Neil Gregory

	Birthplace	D.O.B.	Previous Clubs

Bold print denotes England semi-professional international.

GOALKEEPERS			
Ashley Harrison FAT ,British Uni., IL	Southend		Dover Athletic., Canvey Island, Southend Manor
Danny Potter(IL)	Ipswich	18.03.79	Weymouth, Exeter C,Colchester U, Chelsea
DEFENDERS			
Ben Chenery FAT, IL	Ipswich	28.01.77	Kettering Town, Colchester United, Luton T
Gavin Cowan	Hanover	24.05.81	Braintree T, Exeter C
Matthew Joseph	Bethnal Green	30.09.72	Leyton O, Cambridge U,Gillingham,Arsenal
David McGhee	Worthing	19.06.76	Leyton O , Stevenage B, Brentford
Peter Smith FAT, IL	Cannock	12.07.69	Grays A, Canvey I, Woking, Brighton, Alma Swanley
Dominic Sterling E NG I	Isleworth	08.07.69	Aldershot T, Hayes, Wealdstone, Wimbledon
Tony Quinton	Surrey		Sutton U, Croydon A, Epsom & Ewell
Dave Theobald	Cambridge	15.12.78	Cambridge U,Swansea C, Brentford,
IL			Ipswich T, Cambridge U
Steve Ward (FAT)	Essex		Grays Athletic
MIDFIELD			
Dean Brennnan	Luton	17.06.80	Stevenage B, Hitchin T, Luton T,
Kevin Dobinson	Ipswich		Chelmsford C, Ipswich Town
Chris Duffy	Manchester	31.10.76	Northwich V, Wigan Athletic, Crewe Alex.
FAT, IL			
Ty Gooden Div 2 IL	Canvey Island	23.10.72	Gillingham, Swindon T,Wycombe W, Arsenal
John Kennedy	Newmarket	19.08.78	Ipswich Town
ENG I, FAT,IL			
Jon Keeling	Essex		Hornchurch, Thurrock, Tilbury, Concord R
Jeff Minton RI	Hackney	28.12.73	Grays A, LeytonO, Rotherham U, Port Vale, Brighton, Tottenham H
Steve Parmenter	Chelmsford	17.01.77	Dorchester T,Yeovil T, Bristol R, Q.P.R.
Wales U21			Southend U
FORWARDS			
Ollie Berquez IL	Essex		Braintree T, Dag & Red, Chelmsford C, St Albans C, Chelmsford, Heybridge, IpswichT
Lee Boylan iE NG I, IL	Chelmsford	02.09.78	Heybridge S, Stevenage B, Hayes, Kngstonian, Exeter C, Trelleborg (Sweden), West Ham U.
Junior McDougald ESP IL	Texas	12.01.75	Dag & red, Leyton O. Camb.Utd.,Mil;lwall, Camb C,Toulon, Rotherham,Brighton,Spurs
Neil Midgley	21.10.78	Cambridge	Barnet, Kidderminster H, Ipswich T

CARLISLE UNITED

In recent seasons Carlisle United seem to have been consistently battling away at the foot of the Football League and until the last campaign there was always a happy ending. Some more spectacular than others!

However, many will remember the Cumbrians in the seventies when they rose from Division three in1974, passed through Division Two in one season and were proudly featured at the top of Division One (the senior competition before premier days) at the beginning of the 1975-76 season.

Those were heady days ,which sadly didn't last long. The Blues supporters had two seasons at the top before sliding back to Division Three by1977 and ever since the club has bounced up and down in the lower regions of the Football League until last season, when they just could not recover from a terrible first half to the campaign.

On the positive side, Paul Simpson led a magnificent second half revival which produced form more suitable for a promotion rather relegation prospect.Having sunk to fifteen points from the pack at the bottom of the table it needed a miracle. However, at the end of the year in just three results they picked up more points than had been accrued since August.

So was it possible? York City had sunk dramatically and gradually Carlisle edged towards safety. With just three games to go, victories were needed so when a fantastic three points were won at high flying Mansfield and the Cumbrians moved off the bottom for the first time, the miracle seemed a possibility but they were still four points behind with two games to go.

It is now history that the great revival didn't have a happy ending. The club has shown how it can fight against adversity, now perhaps we could see how they can cope with life at the top as Carlisle United are certainly one of The Conference favourites this season. T.W.

Photo: CumbrianNewspaers Ltd.

CARLISLE UNITED

Match Facts 2003-04

Comp		Score		Result	Date
Football League Two	Carlisle United	1-2	York	L	09-08-2003
League Cup	**Walsall**	**2-1**	**Carlisle United**	**L**	**12-08-2003**
Football League Two	Yeovil	3-0	Carlisle United	L	16-08-2003
Football League Two	Carlisle United	0-2	Bristol Rovers	L	23-08-2003
Football League Two	Boston United	1-0	Carlisle United	L	25-08-2003
Football League Two	Carlisle United	0-0	Cambridge United	D	30-08-2003
Football League Two	Darlington	2-0	Carlisle United	L	06-09-2003
Football League Two	Carlisle United	3-2	Rochdale	W	13-09-2003
Football League Two	Northampton Town	2-0	Carlisle United	L	16-09-2003
Football League Two	Southend United	2-2	Carlisle United	D	20-09-2003
Football League Two	Carlisle United	1-2	Swansea City	L	27-09-2003
Football League Two	Carlisle United	0-1	Leyton Orient	L	30-09-2003
Football League Two	Kidderminster Harriers	2-1	Carlisle United	L	04-10-2003
Football League Two	Hull City	2-1	Carlisle United	L	12-10-2003
LDV Vans Trophy	**Carlisle United**	**2-0**	**Rochdale**	**W**	**14-10-2003**
Football League Two	Carlisle United	0-1	Macclesfield Town	L	18-10-2003
Football League Two	Carlisle United	1-4	Scunthorpe United	L	21-10-2003
Football League Two	Huddersfield Town	2-1	Carlisle United	L	25-10-2003
Football League Two	Lincoln City	2-0	Carlisle United	L	01-11-2003
LDV Vans Trophy	**Carlisle United**	**2-0**	**Huddersfield Town**	**W**	**04-11-2003**
FA Cup	**Oldham Athletic**	**3-0**	**Carlisle United**	**L**	**08-11-2003**
Football League Two	Carlisle United	0-2	Mansfield Town	L	15-11-2003
Football League Two	Cheltenham Town	2-1	Carlisle United	L	22-11-2003
Football League Two	Carlisle United	0-1	Doncaster Rovers	L	29-11-2003
LDV Vans Trophy	**Carlisle United**	**0-3**	**Sheffield Wednesday**	**L**	**09-12-2003**
Football League Two	Oxford United	2-1	Carlisle United	L	13-12-2003
Football League Two	Carlisle United	2-0	Torquay	W	20-12-2003
Football League Two	Bury	1-3	Carlisle United	W	26-12-2003
Football League Two	Carlisle United	1-1	Darlington	D	28-12-2003
Football League Two	Carlisle United	2-1	Boston Utd	W	03-01-2004
Football League Two	York City	2-0	Carlisle United	L	10-01-2004
Football League Two	Carlisle United	2-0	Yeovil	W	17-01-2004
Football League Two	Bristol Rovers	1-0	Carlisle United	L	24-01-2004
Football League Two	Carlisle United	2-1	Bury	W	07-02-2004
Football League Two	Carlisle United	1-1	Hull City	D	14-02-2004
Football League Two	Cambridge United	2-2	Carlisle United	D	17-02-2004
Football League Two	Macclesfield Town	1-1	Carlisle United	D	21-02-2004
Football League Two	Torquay United	4-1	Carlisle United	L	06-03-2004
Football League Two	Carlisle United	1-0	Huddersfield Town	W	09-03-2004
Football League Two	Carlisle United	2-0	Oxford United	W	13-03-2004
Football League Two	Carlisle United	1-1	Northampton Town	D	16-03-2004
Football League Two	Rochdale	2-0	Carlisle United	L	20-03-2004
Football League Two	Scunthorpe United	2-3	Carlisle United	W	23-03-2004
Football League Two	Carlisle United	1-2	Southend United	L	27-03-2004
Football League Two	Swansea	1-2	Carlisle United	W	03-04-2004
Football League Two	Carlisle United	1-0	Kidderminste Harriersr	W	10-04-2004
Football League Two	Leyton Orient	1-1	Carlisle United	D	12-04-2004
Football League Two	Carlisle United	0-2	Lincoln City	L	17-04-2004
Football League Two	Mansfield Town	2-3	Carlisle United	W	24-04-2004
Football League Two	Carlisle United	1-1	Cheltenham Town	D	01-05-2004
Football League Two	Doncaster Rovers	1-0	Carlisle United	L	08-05-2004

CARLISLE UNITED FOOTBALL CLUB
CARLISLE UNITED
ISSUE 1 ■ £2.20
OFFICIAL MATCHDAY PROGRAMME SEASON 2004/05
Nationwide
NATIONWIDE CONFERENCE
EDDIE STOBART LTD
STORY RAIL
EDDIE STOBART LTD
v Canvey Island
SATURDAY 14th August 2004 ■ K.O 3.00PM ■ NATIONWIDE CONFERENCE LEAGUE

CARLISLE UNITED

GROUND DETAILS

Brunton Park ,Carlisle CA1 1LL

Tel: 01228 526 237

Admin. Office Fax:01228 530138

emails:

Web site: http://wwwcarlisle united.co.uk

SIMPLE DIRECTIONS:

Exit M6 at jct 43.Take first right at roundabout to city cenre .Through two sets of lights and ground will be seen on right There is plenty of Parking.

Nearest B.P.- Carlisle Station - approx 1mile from ground

MATCH TICKETS:

CAPACITY: 20,000

SEATED: 8,000

COVERED TERRACING: 14,000

Refreshments: Several bars and food outlets in stands

CLUB SHOP: Yes Contact Jenny Anderson 01228 524014

Founded: 1904

Nickname: The Cumbrians orThe Blues

Club Sponsors: Eddie Stobart Ltd.

Club colours: Royal Blue/White/Royal Blue

Change colours: White/Blue/White

Midweek home matchday: Tuesday

Reserves' League: Pontins North West

Clubcall

CLUB OFFICIALS

President T.B.A.

Chairman John Courtenay

Directors Fred Story, Andrew Jenkins, Steven Pattison, Paul Bell, Dick Young, John Nixon and Lord Clark of Windermere

Commercial Director Dick Young

Chief Executive John Nixon

Club Secretary Sarah McKnight

Head of Media Phil Holmes

MATCHDAY PROGRAMME

Pages: 48 Price: £2.00

Editor: c/o C.U.F.C.

Tel No: 01228 526237

FOOTBALL MANAGEMENT TEAM

MANAGER: PAUL SIMPSON

Date of Appointment 29th August 2003
Date of Birth: 19th April 1966
Place of Birth: Carlisle
PREVIOUS CLUBS
As manager Rochdale
As player Man.City,Wolves,Derby Co.,Blackpool

HONOURS
As manager
As player * *
First Team Coach: Dennis Booth
Physiotherapist: Neil Dalton
Youth development:
Community Officer
Club's Playing Status: Full Time

Season

Season	League	Div.	Pos.	P	W	D	L	F	A	Pts	Manager
				Home							
03-04	Football Lge	3	23	46							Paul Simpson
02-03	Football Lge	3		46							RoddyCollins
01-02	Football Lge	3	22	46	11	15	20	42	65	22	Roddy Collins
00-01	Football Lge	3	22	46	11	15	20	42	65	22	Ian Atkins
99-00	Football Lge	3	23	46	9	12	25	42	75	3	Martin Wilkinson
98-99	Football Lge	3	23	46	11	16	19	43	53	23	David Wilkes & John Halpin
97-98	Football Lge	2	23	46	12	8	26	57	73	23	Mervyn day
96-97	Football Lge	3	3	46	24	12	10	67	44	84	Mervyn Day
95-96	Football Lge	2	21	46	12	13	21	57	72	49	Mick Wadsworth
94-95	Football Lge	3	1	42	27	10	5	67	31	91	Mick Wsdsworth

HONOURS

Promotion from Div 2 (3rd) 1973-74
Champions Div 3 1964-65 1994-95
Runners-Up Div 3 1981-92
Promotion from Div 3 1996-97
Division 4 Runners-Up 1963-64
Football League Cup Semi-Final 1970
Auto Windscreens Shield winners 1997
Finalists 1995

PREVIOUS

Leagues: Lancashire Combination Div 2 1905-06
Div 1 1906-1928
Elected to Football League1928 (Div 3 North)

Grounds: Devonshire Park

Names: Amalgamation o f Shaddongate United and Carlisle Red Rose

Past Players who progressed to the Football League

not yet applicable

CLUB RECORDS

Attendance: 27,500 v Birmingahm C 3rd F.A.Cup 05.01.57
v Middlesbrough 5th Rd 07.02.70

Record win: 8-0 v Hartlepool U Div 3 (North) 01.09.28
v Scunthorpe U Div 3(North) 25.12.52

Record defeat: 1-11 v Hull City Siv 3 (North) 14.01.39

Career goalscorer: Jimmy McConnell 126 1928-29

Career League appearances: Allan Ross 466 1963-79
Transfer fee paid: £121,000
to Notts County for David Reeves December 1993

Transfer fee received: £1,500,000
from Crystal Palace for Matt Jansen Feb. 1998

BEST SEASON

Football League: 22nd Division One 1974-75

FA Cup: 6th Rd 1975

Football League Cup S-Final 1970

FA Trophy: N/A

League Clubs Defeated N/A

LAST SEASON

F.A. Cup: First Round
FA Trophy: N/A
Football Lge Div 3: 23rd
Top Goalscorer: Craig Farrell & Brendan McGill 7
Player of the Year: Brendan McGill
Captain: Peter Murphy

CARLISLE UNITED PLAYING SQUAD

Bold print denotes England semi-professional international.

	Birthplace	D.O.B.	Previous Clubs
GOALKEEPERS			
Matt Glennon	Stockport	08.10.78	Hull City , Bolton Wanderers
Peter Keen	Middlesbrough	16.11.76	Newcastle United
DEFENDERS			
Lee Andrews	Carlisle	23.04.83	Club Trainee
Paul Armison	Hartlepool	18.09.77	Hartlepool U, Newcastle U
Tom Cowan	Bellshill	28.08.69	Dundee, York C, Camb.Utd.,Burnley, Huddersfield T, Sheff.Utd., Rangers, Clyde, Netherdale BC.
Kevin Gray	Sheffield	07.01.72	Tranmere R., Huddersfield T, Mansfield T
Will McDonough	Dublinn	14.03.83	Bohemians
Peter Murphy	Sublin	27.10.80	Blackburn Rovers
Brian Shelley	Dublin	15.11.81	Bohemians
MIDFIELD			
Chris Billy	Huddersfield	02.01.73	Bury, Notts Co.,Plymouth A, Huddersfield T.
Brendan McGill	Dublin	22.03.81	Sunderland
Andy Preece	Evesham	27.03.67	Bury, Blackpool,Crystal P,Stockport Co. Wresham, Worcester City, Northampton T, Evesham U.
Carlos Roca	Manchester	04.09.84	Oldham Athletic
Paul Simpson E. Y & U21	Carlisle	26.07.66	Rochdale, Blackpool, Wolves, Derby Co., Oxford Utd., Manchester City
FORWARDS			
Craig Farrell	Middlesboro'	05.12.82	Leeds
Karl Hawley	Walsall	06.12.81	Walsall
Lee Hamilton	Carlisle		Club Trainee
Kevin Henderson	Ashington	08.06.74	Hartlepool, Burnley, Morpeth
Adam Rundle	Durham	08.07.84	Darlington

CRAWLEY TOWN

The very smart and well appointed Broadhall Stadium has been crying out for senior football since it became a much admired addition on the Crawley ring road. You know you are at a proper club when you arrive at the stadium and now, thanks to a memorable Southern League campaign, Crawley Town line up alongside the other twenty one members of the Conference for a place in the Football League. The League Challenge Cup and the Championship Challenge Match trophies joined the one that mattered - the Southern League Premier Championship, in a season which manager Francis Vine .originally a convert from A.F.A.football, had proved himself to be a very shrewd manager.

Relatively disappointing cup campaigns really became of no consequence as Crawley emerged from the pack and pulled away from all challengers at the top of the division. After reaching the First Round of the F.A.Cup, a disappointing draw at Telford United produced a good game but a 3-2 defeat. The F.A.Trophy is a competition in which the club has never really shone and once again the Third Round brought defeat, this time at the hands of Dagenham & Redbridge.

These comparatively early exits may well have been a blessing in disguise however, as rivals Weymouth were beginning to falter at the top of the Division and after a vitally important 1-0 victory in Dorset, Crawley never looked back.Their defence was generally extremely difficult to breach and their attack inspired by the splendid form of Charlie McDonald , combined to produce consistent performances and results that must have broken the hearts and determination of their challengers.

Hopefully, the Sussex football fans will rally round to help the club face the challenge from many full time and high powered clubs in the Conference. A very good administrative structure is in place with good leadership and an excellent caring sponsor in the Gladwish Land Sales.. The club is entering the most exciting period of its life and it will be interesting to see how it faces the challenge.

T.W.

CRAWLEY TOWN

Match Facts 2003-04

Date	Comp	Opponents	Att.	Result	Goalscorers
12/07/03	**SL Shield**	**Tamworth**	**448**	**3 - 0**	**McDonald(2), Armstrong**
09/08/03	**Roy Hayden**	**BURGESS HILL TOWN**	**n/k**	**1 - 1**	
16/08/03	Sth. Prem	MERTHYR TYDFIL	831	1 - 2	C McDonald 45
19/08/03	Sth. Prem	Dover Athletic	1002	2 - 2	Payne 9, Dennis 41
23/08/03	Sth. Prem	Bath City	618	0 - 0	
25/08/03	Sth. Prem	HAVANT & WATERLOOVILLE	764	3 - 1	Marney 23 57, Hemsley 26
30/08/03	Sth. Prem	WORCESTER CITY	864	4 - 0	Marney 45, Wilson-Dennis 45 49 70[p]
02/09/03	Sth. Prem	Eastbourne Borough	1239	1 - 1	Hemsley 17
06/09/03	Sth. Prem	Tiverton Town	591	2 - 2	Brake 47, Harkin 65[p]
09/09/03	Sth. Prem	CAMBRIDGE CITY	748	2 - 0	Marney 3, Harkin 29[p]
13/09/03	Sth. Prem	Newport County	632	2 - 1	Harkin 68[p], Marney 74
16/09/03	Sth. Prem	CHELMSFORD CITY	748	0 - 0	
20/09/03	Sth. Prem	NUNEATON BOROUGH	1864	2 - 2	Hemsley 39, Richardson 52
27/09/03	**FA Cup Q2**	**Harlow Town**	**372**	**4 - 0**	**Gregory 8, Judge 36, Brake 57 62**
04/10/03	Sth. Prem	Hednesford Town	487	0 - 0	
11/10/03	**FA Cup Q3**	**CROYDON ATHLETIC**	**897**	**6 - 1**	**Pullan 17, Hemsley 54, Armstrong 76 77, Brake 83 89**
18/10/03	Sth. Prem	STAFFORD RANGERS	1023	2 - 0	Wilson-Dennis 50, Harkin 78
21/10/03	Sth. Prem	Cambridge City	307	5 - 2	Hemsley 5 33 75[p], Wilson-Dennis 62 67
25/10/03	**FA Cup Q4**	**Cirencester Town**	**715**	**4 - 2**	**Gregory 12, Vansittart 61 75, Harkin 90**
01/11/03	Sth. Prem	CHIPPENHAM TOWN	1142	3 - 2	Armstrong 34, Vansittart 65, Forde 80
08/11/03	**FA Cup 1**	**Telford United**	**1581**	**2 - 3**	**Armstrong 8, Gregory 28**
11/11/03	**Sussex SC2**	**HORSHAM YMCA**	**367**	**7 - 1**	**McDonald 4 7 33 44, Plummer 40, Harkin 60, Forde 81**
15/11/03	Sth. Prem	Hinckley United	452	0 - 4	
22/11/03	Sth. Prem	DORCHESTER TOWN	1023	2 - 3	McDonald 49, Armstrong 89
29/11/03	**FA Trophy 2**	**St Albans City**	**327**	**0 - 0**	
02/12/03	**FA Trophy 2r**	**ST ALBANS CITY**	**445**	**4 - 1**	**Campbell 18[og], Vansittart 91, Hemsley 101, Brake 120**
06/12/03	Sth. Prem	TIVERTON TOWN	848	2 - 1	Smith 57, McDonald 79
16/12/03	**Lge Cup 3**	**Havant & Waterlooville**	**176**	**3 - 2**	**Kirkwood 67, Brake 71, Seldon 98**
20/12/03	Sth. Prem	BATH CITY	805	2 - 0	McDonald 41[p], Hemsley 58
27/12/03	Sth. Prem	Havant & Waterlooville	583	3 - 1	McDonald 6, Holligan 46, Fear 57
01/01/04	Sth. Prem	WELLING UNITED	1640	0 - 0	
03/01/04	Sth. Prem	Weymouth	2016	1 - 0	Holligan 31
06/01/04	Sth. Prem	Grantham Town	325	0 - 1	
10/01/04	**FA Trophy 3**	**Dagenham & Redbridge**	**1157**	**0 - 0**	
13/01/04	**FA Trophy 3r**	**DAGENHAM & REDBRIDGE**	**917**	**1 - 2**	**Judge 20**
17/01/04	Sth. Prem	MOOR GREEN	993	2 - 2	Armstrong 69, McDonald 88
20/01/04	**Lge Cup 4**	**WELLING UNITED**	**450**	**1 - 0**	**McDonald 88**
24/01/04	Sth. Prem	GRANTHAM TOWN	1109	4 - 2	Holligan 15 70, McDonald 45[p], Armstrong 80
03/02/04	**Sussex SC3**	**BOGNOR REGIS TOWN**	**570**	**2 - 1**	**Vansittart 76 90**
07/02/04	Sth. Prem	WESTON-SUPER-MARE	1426	2 - 0	Traynor 22, McDonnell 44[p]
14/02/04	Sth. Prem	EASTBOURNE BOROUGH	1437	3 - 1	Vansittart 69, Armstrong 71, Harkin 90
17/02/04	**Sussex SC QF**	**Worthing**	**358**	**0 - 1**	
21/02/04	Sth. Prem	Dorchester Town	701	0 - 2	
24/02/04	**Lge Cup QF**	**DOVER ATHLETIC**	**381**	**1 - 0**	**Harkin 101**
28/02/04	Sth. Prem	Stafford Rangers	952	1 - 0	Marney 25
02/03/04	**Lge Cup SF**	**EASTLEIGH**	**581**	**2 - 0**	**Fear 32, Traynor 69**
06/03/04	Sth. Prem	WEYMOUTH	4522	2 - 1	Armstrong 51, Hemsley 53
08/03/04	Sth. Prem	Chelmsford City	519	4 - 0	Vansittart 14, McDonald 38 56 64
13/03/04	Sth. Prem	Chippenham Town	830	1 - 0	Marney 67
16/03/04	Sth. Prem	HEDNESFORD TOWN	1404	6 - 1	McDonnell 8, Armstrong 39, Fear 51 58, Hankin 59, Vansittart 86
23/03/04	Sth. Prem	Merthyr Tydfil	534	1 - 2	McDonnell 75[p]
27/03/04	Sth. Prem	Moor Green	322	2 - 1	McDonald 9, Hemsley 32
29/03/04	Sth. Prem	Worcester City	1856	1 - 0	McDonald 24
06/04/04	**Lge Cup F(1)**	**Moor Green**	**286**	**2 - 1**	**Marney 45, Tait 61**
10/04/04	Sth. Prem	DOVER ATHLETIC	2290	2 - 0	McDonald 1, Vansittart 53
12/04/04	Sth. Prem	Welling United	1138	3 - 0	
17/04/04	Sth. Prem	Nuneaton Borough	837	1 - 0	Traynor 56
20/04/04	**Lge Cup F(2)**	**MOOR GREEN**	**1642**	**2 - 0**	**Marney 53, McDonald 88**
24/04/04	Sth. Prem	HINCKLEY UNITED	1844	0 - 3	
26/04/04	Sth. Prem	NEWPORT COUNTY	1669	1 - 2	Tait 49
01/05/04	Sth. Prem	Weston-super-Mare	579	2 - 1	

Home matches indicated by opponents being in capitals.

CRAWLEY TOWN

MEMBERS OF

Dr. Martens SOUTHERN FOOTBALL LEAGUE

PREMIER DIVISION

CLUB SPONSORS

GLS

www.GLSFootball.com
email: sales@GLSFootball.com

TODAY'S MATCHBALL SPONSOR

JO GOMM

TEAM OF THE WEEK

ROFFEY ROBINS ROCKETS

football club

CRAWLEY TOWN v DOVER ATHLETC - Dr Martens League - Premier Division - Saturday 10th April 2004 - Kick off 3.00pm - OFFICIAL MATCH PROGRAMME No. 30 - PRICE £1.50

CRAWLEY TOWN

GROUND DETAILS

Broadfield Stadium, Brighton Road,Crawley
RH11 9RX

Tel: 01293 410000

emails:

Web site: www.crawley-town-fc.co.ukfc.co.uk

SIMPLE DIRECTIONS:
From M23 Exit 11 take second exit off roundabout which is A23 towards Crawley. Turn left at next roundabout to ground

MATCH TICKETS:

CAPACITY:	4,996
SEATED:	1,080
COVERED TERRACING:	4,200

Refreshments:
Clubhouse: Open matchdays & for private bookings
Mon-Fri Evenings 7-11p.m. Sat 12-11p.m. Sun 12-8p.m.
Contact:
CLUB SHOP: Yes.Progs,badges,hats,scarves,mugs,shirts etc

Founded:	1896
Nickname:	Red Devils
Club Sponsors:	Gladwish Land Sales
Club colours:	Royal Blue & White Royal Blue Shorts and Socks
Change colours:	White/black/white
Midweek home matchday:	Tuesday
Reserves' League:	Pontins League
Clubcall	N/A

CLUB OFFICIALS

President	Les Turnbull
Chairperson	N/A
Vice Chairman	N/A
Chief Executive:	John Duly
Managing Director:	Steve Duly
Secretary	Barry Munn
Commercial Manager	Steve Duly

MATCHDAY PROGRAMME

Pages: 32 Price: £1.50
Editor: Steve Duly
01293 410000
Local Press: Crawley Observer, Crawley News, The Argus
Local Radio: Radio Mercury,BBC Southern Counties

FOOTBALL MANAGEMENT TEAM

MANAGER: FRANCES VINES

Date of Appointment	January 2003
Date of Birth:	31.01.1962

PREVIOUS CLUBS

As manager	N/A
As player	Sutton United

HONOURS

As manager	Southern League & Cup double 03/04
Assistant Manager:	Dave Swindlehurst
Physiotherapist:	Richard Masimo
Youth development:	
Community Officer	
Club's Playing Status:	Part Time

HONOURS

Southern League Championship 2003-04
Southern League Cup Winners 2002-03.2003-04R-up 0-1
Sussex Senior Cup 88-89, 90-91, 02-03 R-up 58-9, 95-6
Sussex Intermediate Cup 1926-27,01-02
Sussex Professional Cup 1969-70
Sussex Fllodlit Cup (3)
Southern League Southern Div. Runners-Up 1983-84
Southern Lerague Merit Cup 1970-71
Sussex League Div 2 Runners-Up 1955-56
Gilbert Rice Floodlit Cup 79-80, 83-84
Southern Co Comb Floodllit Cup 1985-86
Metropolitan League Challenge Cup: 1958-59
Mid Sussex Snr 02-03 Montgomery Cup 25-26
Southern League Championship Match 2002-03 03-04

CLUB RECORDS

Attendance: 4,522
v Weymouth, Southern Premier 06.03,04

Record win: 10-0
v Chichester United Sussex Co.Lg. Div 2 17.12.55
v Crowborough A Sussex Floodlit Cup 25.0901

Record defeat: 0-10
v Arundel Sussex County league 09-02-52

Career goalscorer: Phil Basey 108 (1968-72)

Career appearances: John Maggs 652 (63-73 75-79)

Transfer fee paid: Undisclosed
to Wycombe W for Ian Simpemba (July 2004)

Transfer fee received: £75,000
for Jay Lovett from Brentford (2000)

PREVIOUS

Leagues: Sussex County 1951-56
Metropolitan1956-63
Southern League 1964-2003

Grounds: Malthouse Farm 1896-1914, 1938-40
Victory Hall & Rectory Field 1918-38
Yetmans Field 1945-49
Town Mead 1949-53, 1954-97
Ifield Recreation ground 1953-54

Names: None

BEST SEASON

FA Trophy: 3rd Rd 1998-99

FA Cup: 3rd Rd Proper
1991-92 0-5 v Brighton & H

League Clubs Defeated

Conference First Season

Past Players who progressed to the Football League

Ray Keeley and Graham Brown (Mansfield Town 1968)
Andy Ansah (Brentford 1987)
Craig Whittington (Scarborough 1983)
BenAbbey (Oxford United 1999)
John Mackie (Reading 1999)
Jay Lovett (Brentford 2000)
Ernie Cooksey (Oldham Athletic 2003)

LAST SEASON

F.A. Cup: 1st Round
FA Trophy: 3rd Round
Southern Premier: Champions
Top Goalscorer: Charlie McDonald
Player of the Year: Charlie McDonald
Captain: Kevin Hemsley

CRAWLEY TOWN PLAYING SQUAD

	Birthplace	D.O.B.	Previous Clubs
			Bold print denotes England semi-professional international.
GOALKEEPERS			
Andy Little	London		Banstead Athletic.,Sutton United,Croydon,
			Sheffield Wednesday
Paul Smith	Harrow	14.12.79	Margate, Dover Ath., Folkestone, Millwall
DEFENDERS			
Sean Hankin	Camberley	28.02.82	NorwichV.,Margate,Torquay U, Crystal P
Kevin Hemsley	Brighton	28.11.82	Brighton
Ben Judge	London		Croydon, Crystal Palace
Fiston Manuella E.NG I	London	13.08.81	Farnborough T, Aytlesbury U, Hampton , Chertsey, Brentford, Crystal Palace
Ian Simpemba	Dublin	28.03.83	Wycombe Wanderers
MIDFIELD			
Paul Armstrong	Dublin	05.10.78	Airdrie, Brighton
SL			
Maurice Harkin N.Ireland Y & U21	Derry	16.08.79	Nuneaton B, Aldershot T, Carlilse U, Wycombe W
Neil Jenkins	Carshalton	06.01.82	Southend United, Wimbledon
Rob Kember	Wimbledon	21.08.81	Basingstoke T, Woking, Crystal Palace.
SL			
Scott Kirkwood	Brighton		Brighton
SL			
Charlie Mapes	Middlesex	04.07.86	Wycombe W, Berkhamstead T, Wealdstone, Edgware, Hayes.
Nick Roddis ESP & Uni	Rotherham	18.02.73	Aldershot T, Margate, Woking, Hayes, Yeading, Boston Townm Nottingham Forest
Rob Traynor	London	01.11.83	Brentford
FORWARDS			
Danny Davidson	Derby	23.10.79	Stafford R, Hereford U, Leek T, Rocester, Burton Albion
Charlie MacDonald	Southwark	13.02.81	Stevenage B, Margate, Charlton Athletic
SL			
Daniel Marney	Sidcup	02.10.81	Brighton
SL			
Allan Tait	Derby	23.10,79	Folkestone Inv., Deal T, Crawley T, Spurs.

DAGENHAM & REDBRIDGE

Having enjoyed three fabulous campaigns in the Conference and the F.A.Cup it probably surprised everyone that the Daggers slumped so dramatically last season. On closer inspection perhaps a few of the squad were reaching the end of their careers together but there was still much quality within the club and maybe it was the dressing room upset, when manager Garry Hill was accused of racial remarks after an aggravating defeat, that destroyed their consistency. Whatever the rights or wrongs two very good and popular players left the club and some strange results took the Daggers away from the play off zone.

The knock-out competitions underlined the famous club's waning influence, as they went out 1-2 in the Fourth Qualifying Round of the F.A.Cup at local rivals Thurrock, and in the F.A.Trophy, after a replay victory at Crawley, two thrilling but unsatisfactory ties against Arlesey Town brought a 3-3 home draw and a 2-4 defeat in the replay.

League form varied from week to week but the real disaster was a Sky televised match at home to Hereford United when everything went well for the visitors and the quite unbelievable score of 0-9 gave the Bulls a famous victory which they could hardly believe themselves.

The reaction was good with four draws and a victory, but manager Hill who had achieved so much at Victoria Road , announced he would be leaving at the end of the season and as so often happens, once it is announced, the departure is often hurried through, so it was no surprise when the club had to search for a replacement.

Dagenham finished in thirteenth position and with John Still a popular 'old boy' available to return, a new squad has been brought together with some promising young attacking players form the lower leagues.. Garry Hill has given the club some wonderful memories but now with fresh faces and a good start to the season, perhaps the very stable administrative team and the loyal supporters will all be enjoying life at the top of the table again. T.W.

Back Row (left to right): Tony Perfect, Tom McGowen, Lee Goodwin, Shane B;ackett, Ashley Vickers, Jack Midson, Anwar Uddinamnd Chris Moore, **Middle Row:** Alan Dafforn (Chief Scout), Bill Edmans (Kit Manager), Tony Boot, Warren Ryan, Glen Southam, Abiodun Baruwa, Tim Cole, Tony Roberts, Jake Laberl, Lee Flynn, Danny Hill, John Gowens (Physio) and Mick Payne (Goalkeeping Coach) **Front row**: Charlie Bull, Scott Griffiths, Warren Barton, Terry Harris (Coach), JohnStill (Manager), JohnTaylor, Mark Janney and Craig Mackail-Smith.

DAGENHAM & REDBRIDGE

The number shown directly below the player's name is his squad number.
Where a number is shown instead of an "X' in the columns this represents a substitute appearance and the number indicates the player replaced.

Comp.	Date	Opponents	Venue.	Result	Goalscorers	Att.
Conf 1	Aug 09	Leigh RMI	A	L 1-2	Bruce	419
Conf 2	Aug 12	Stevenage B	H	L 1-2	Vickers	1948
Conf 3	Aug 16	Barnet	H	W 5-2	Stein(3) Bentley(2)	1235
Conf 4	Aug 23	Morecambe	A	L 2-3	Stein(2)	1477
Conf 5	Aug 25	Forest Green R	H	W 5-2	Bentley(2) Shipp(2) Meechan	1540
Conf 6	Aug 30	Shrewsbury T	A	L 1-2	Bentley	3468
Conf 7	Sep 06	Telford U	H	D 1-1	C Piper(p)	1503
Conf 8	Sep 13	Northwich V	A	W 1-0	Cole	575
Conf 9	Sep 20	Accrington S	H	L 0-1		1542
Conf 10	Sep 22	Exeter C	A	D 1-1	Cole	3344
Conf 11	Sep 27	Tamworth	A	L 0-2		1147
Conf 12	Oct 04	Chester C	H	D 0-0		1497
Conf 13	Oct 07	Margate	H	W 4-0	Bruce Shipp Meacham Braithwaite	1540
Conf 14	Oct 13	Hereford U	A	D 1-1	Beckwith	4325
LDVT 1	**Oct 15**	**Leyton O**	**H**	**W 4-1**	**Bentley(2) Scully Braithwaite**	**1857**
Conf 15	Oct 18	Burton A	H	L 0-2		1483
FAC 4q	**Oct 25**	**Thurrock**	**A**	**L 1-2**	**Shipp**	**957**
Conf 16	Nov 01	Halifax T	A	L 0-3		1379
LDVT 2	**Nov 04**	**Q P R**	**A**	**L 1-2**	**Scully**	**3036**
Conf 17	Nov 11	Farnborough T	H	W 1-0	Watts	1269
Conf 18	Nov 15	Woking	A	D 0-0		2256
Conf 19	Nov 22	Scarborough	H	W 1-0	Bentley	1107
Conf 20	Nov 25	Gravesend & N	A	W 2-1	C Piper Watts	1274
Conf 21	Nov 29	Telford U	A	L 0-1		1321
Conf 22	Dec 06	Northwich V	H	W 2-0	Mustafa Goodwin	1163
Conf 23	Dec 13	Leigh RMI	H	L 1-2	Cole	1037
Conf 24	Dec 20	Stevenage B	A	W 2-0	Moore Cole	1749
Conf 25	Dec 26	Aldershot T	H	L 2-3	Moore Watts	1624
Conf 26	Jan 01	Aldershot T	A	L 1-2	Moore	4168
Conf 27	Jan 03	Shrewsbury T	H	W 5-0	Moore(2) C Piper(p) Pacquette Goodwin	1571
FAT 3	**Jan 10**	**Crawley Town**	**H**	**D 0-0**		**1157**
FAT 3r	**Jan 13**	**Crawley Town**	**A**	**W 2-1**	**Pacquette Bentley**	**917**
Conf 28	Jan 17	Barnet	A	W 4-2	Cole Janney Hill Plummer(og)	2006
Conf 29	Jan 24	Exeter C	H	L 0-2		1909
FAT 4	**Jan 31**	**Arlesey Town**	**H**	**D 3-3**	**K Jackson(2) Braithwaite**	**1045**
FAT 4r	**Feb 03**	**Arlesey Town**	**A**	**L 2-4**	**Rees Shipp**	**766**
Conf 30	Feb 07	Accrington S	A	W 3-2	C Piper Moore K Jackson	1601
Conf 31	Feb 21	Chester C	A	L 1-2	Braithwaite	2990
Conf 32	Feb 27	Hereford U	H	L 0-9		1617
Conf 33	Mar 06	Margate	A	D 3-3	J Jackson Moore Shipp	508
Conf 34	Mar 09	Tamworth	H	D 0-0		984
Conf 35	Mar 13	Farnborough T	A	D 2-2	Braithwaite Moore	787
Conf 36	Mar 20	Woking	H	W 1-0	Shipp	1345
Conf 37	Mar 27	Scarborough	A	D 0-0		1302
Conf 38	Apr 03	Gravesend & N	H	L 0-4		1421
Conf 39	Apr 10	Morecambe	H	L 1-3	Moore	1122
Conf 40	Apr 12	Forest Green R	A	W 3-1	Janney Braithwaite Moore	762
Conf 41	Apr 17	Halifax T	H	L 0-1		1344
Conf 42	Apr 24	Burton A	A	W 1-0	Braithwaite	1361

STEP 1
CONFERENCE

STEP 2 - P177
CONFERENCE Nth & Sth

STEP 3 - P269
NPL, Southern, Isthmian Premiers

STEP 4 - P269
NPL 1, Southern W&E, Isthmian 1

STEP 5/6 - P473

STEP 7 - P713
Current level 4 leagues

Tony ROBERTS	Tim COLE	Ashley VICKERS	Lee GOODWIN	Mark SMITH	Dean BECKWITH	Robert GILL	Ben EATON	Chris PIPER	Mark JANNEY	Paul TERRY	Tony SCULLY	Richard PACQUETTE	Danny SHIPP	Mark STEIN	Tristram WHITMAN	Tony PERFECT	Paul BRUCE	Lenny PIPER	James PULLEN	Danny HILL	Leon BRAITHWAITE	Jimmy JACKSON	Lee MATTHEWS	Kirk JACKSON	Mark BENTLEY	Colin HOYLE	Matt REES	Tarkan MUSTAFA	Alex MEECHAN	Steve WATTS	Mark VENUS	Chris MOORE	Tom McGOWEN	Alan KIMBLE	Danny NAISBITT
1	2	3	4	5	5	5	5	6	7	8	8	8	9	10	10	10	11	12	13	14	15	16	17	17	18	18	18	19	20	22	22	23	24	26	73
	x	x							x	x			x	x			x		x		x	x	2		11			x	7						
		x		x					19	x			x	x			16		x		x	x	x		x			x	9						
x		x		x				x	x				6	x			x	7			x		x		x			x	15						
x		x	7	x					x				x	x			x	15			x		x		x			x	10						
x			x	x					12				x	x			x	x		15	x	x	x		x				10						
x		16	x	x					x								x	4		x	x	x	x		x			x	14						
x	x		x					x	8		x							14		x	x		x		x			4	x					x	
x	x							x	14		x			x			8			x	20		x		x			x	x					x	
	x							x			x		20				15	14	x	x	x		x		x			x	x					x	
	x							x	12		x		x				x	x	x	9	19		x		x			x						x	
	x	x						x	12		x		x				x	x	x	x			x		x				18						
		x			x			x	x				x				x	x	x						x				x					x	
		x			x			x			x		x				x	x	x	19	12				x			x	x				8		
		x			x			x			x		x				x	x	x	12	20				x			x	x					11	
x		x			x				x		x		20							x	x				x			x	x				7	x	
		x			x			x	x		x		x					7	x		x				x			x	9	8				x	
x		x			x						x		x					x			x				x			x		x				x	
x	x	x							22		x						x			x	x		x		x			x	8	x					
x	x	x						7	x		x						x			x	x		x		x			x	11					17	
x	x	x				x		x	6				14		x					x	10				x			x		x				x	
x	x	x	14			x			8		x		x		x					x	10				x			x						x	
x	x	x	x			x		8	x		x		x		x										x				5	10				x	
x	x		x			x		x	2				x				x						x		x			x		x		5			
x		x	x			x		x	4		x		x		8		x				5		x					x		x					
x		x	x					x	4		x		x				x				x		x		6			x		x				15	
	x	x	x					x	4				x				x			6			x		x			x		x					x
	x	x	x					x	4				x				x			23	x				x			x		15		x			x
	x	x						x					x				x			6	x	x			x			x		11		x			x
	x	x					11	x	8			x	x				x					9			x			x		x		x			x
	x	x	x					x				x				3	x			x		x						x		8		x	6		x
	x		x					x	x			x					x			x	22	x			6			x		x					x
	x		x					x	x			x					x			x	22	x			4			x		x				14	x
	x							x	x			x	6				x			x	8	x				x		x		7		x			x
	x							x	x				14				x			x	7	x		x			x	x		23		x			x
		x						x	x				x				x			6	x	x		x			x	x						11	x
x		x						x	18				x							x	x	x		x			x	x		6				x	
x	x	x						x	x								x			x	3	x		x				x				x			
x	x	x							x				x				x	14		x	16	x		x				x				x		23	
x	x	x						7	x				x				x	14		x		x		x				x				x			
x	x	x						19	x				x				16	14		x	x	x						x				x		x	
x	x	x						x	x				x				16				x	x						x				x		x	
x	x		7				23	x	x							11	x				x	x						x			x	x		x	
x	x		23					x	x				15				x			6	x	x						x			x	x		x	
x	x		7					x	x				x				x				23	x						x			x	x		x	
x		x	x					x	x				x			11	x				23	x									x	x		x	
x		x	x					14	x				x			11	x			x	22							x			x	x		x	
x	x	x	x					x	x				x								x							x				x		x	
x	x	x	x						x				x			x	15				x	23						x				x	19	x	
x	x	x	x					x	x				x				x				x											x	15	x	

DAGENHAM & REDBRIDGE

GROUND DETAILS

Victoria Road, Dagenham,RM10 7XL

Tel: 0208 592 1549 Fax: 0208 593 7227

Clubcall: 09066 555 840

email: info@daggers.co.uk

web site:www.daggers.co.uk

DIRECTIONS: On A112 between A12 & A13. Buses 103 & 174, Dagenham East tube station, turn left and after approximately 500 yards take 5th turning left into Victoria Road.

MATCH TICKETS: Adults £9-£13 concessions £6
No concessions in Carling Stand unless Season Ticket holders
Family(I adult with up to two children) £19 in the family stand

CAPACITY: 6,077
SEATS: 1,028
COVERED: 3,000

CLUBHOUSE: Open 7 days 11am-11pm.
Refreshnments: Hot & cold food available plus three tea bars
Two bars and sponsors bar
Available for Functions: Tony Manhood 0208 592 7194
Shop Contact: SteveThompson 0208 5927194

CLUB SHOP: Open on matchdays
for enquiries on other days contact Steve, above.

MATCHDAY PROGRAMME

Pages: 48 **Price:** £2.50
Editor: Dave Simpson Tel: 07860 119430 (M)

Local Press: Dagenham Post, Ilford Courier,Yellow Advertiser, Walthamstow Guardian, Barking & Dagenham Recorder

Local Radio: BBC Radio Essex, Capital Gold, GLR London Live

Formed: 1992
Nickname: Daggers
Colours: Red shirts, white shorts, red socks
Change strip: Blue shirts,blue shorts and black socks.
Midweek matchday: Tuesday
Reserves Lge: Capital League
Sponsors Main: Compass Plumbing Supplies
Kit: Vandanell
Programme: Recorder Group Newspapers
Match Reports: 0930 555840

CLUB OFFICERS

Chairman: Dave Andrews

Joint Presidents: John & Brian East

Vice Chairman: David Ward

Secretary: Derek Almond, 97 Clays Rd.,Walton-on-the-Naze, CO148SD
Tel: 01255 677086

Commercial Manager: Steve Thompson c/o Club

Press Officer: Dave Simpson
Tel: 07860 119430

FOOTBALL MANAGEMENT TEAM

MANAGER: JOHN STILL
Date of appointment: 20.04.04
Date of Birth:
Place of Birth:
PREVIOUS CLUBS
As manager:
As player:
HONOURS
As manager:
As player: N.A.

Asst Manager: Terry Harris
Chief Scout: Alan Dafforn
Safety Officer: Phil Milchard
Physio: John Gowans
Playing Status: Part-t ime

Season	League	Div.	Pos.	Home P	W	D	L	F	A	Away W	D	L	F	A	Pts	Manager
03-04	Conference	-	13	42	8	3	10	30	34	7	6	8	29	30	54	Garry Hill/John Still
02-03	Conference	-	5	42	12	5	4	38	23	9	4	8	33	36	72	Garry Hill
01-02	Conference	-	2	42	13	6	2	35	20	11	6	4	35	27	84	Garry Hill
00-01	Conference	-	3	42	13	4	4	39	19	10	4	7	32	35	77	Garry Hill
99-00	Isthmian	Prem.	1	42	20	1	0	58	13	12	4	5	39	22	101	Garry Hill
98-99	Isthmian	Prem.	3	42	10	8	3	40	15	10	5	6	31	29	73	Ted Hardy
97-98	Isthmian	Prem.	4	42	11	6	4	43	25	10	4	7	30	25	73	Ted Hardy
96-97	Isthmian	Prem.	4	42	11	3	7	32	21	7	8	6	25	22	65	Ted Hardy

Season	League	Div.	Pos.	P	W	D	L	F	A	Pts	Manager
95-96	Conference	-	21	42	7	12	23	43	73	33	Graham Carr
94-95	Conference	-	15	42	13	13	16	56	69	52	Dave Cusack

HONOURS

(Ryman) Isthmian League Prem. Div. 99-00

(Ryman) Isthmian one2one Charity Shield 2000-01

F.A. Trophy Runners-up 96-97

Essex Senior 97-98

PREVIOUS

Names:
Ilford FC (1881) & Leytonstone (1886) merged in 1979 to form Leytonstone-Ilford.
They & Walthamstow Avenue (1900) merged in 1988 to form Redbridge Forest
who in turn merged with Dagenham (1949) in 1992 to form Dagenham & Redbridge.

Grounds: None

Leagues: GMV Conference 92-96; Isthmian Lge 96-2000

Past Players who progressed to the Football League

Warren Barton (via Maidstone Utd '89 to Wimbledon '90)
Andy Hessenthaler (Watford '91)
Juan Mequel DeSouza (Birmingham C. '94)
Ian Richardson (Birmingham City '95)
Rerry Hurlock (Millwall)

CLUB RECORDS

Attendance: 5,500 v Leyton Orient - FA Cup 1st Rnd - 14.11.92
5,492 v Charlton A - F.A.Cup 3rd Rd Replay- 27.01.01
5,949 v Ipswich Town F.A.Cup 3rd Rd -03-01-02

Career goalscorer (all competitions): Paul Cobb 84 (97-01)
Danny Shipp 102 (95-04)

Career appearances (all competitions): Jason Broom - 338
(Steve Corner - 257. Paul Watts - 174)

Win: 8-1 v Woking (A)
GMV Conference 19/4/94
7-0 v Oxford (H) Isthmian Lge1/11/97

Defeat: 0-5
v Stalybridge Celtic (A) GMV Conference 31/4/94
v Northwich Victoria, GMV Conference 3/9/94
v Hyde Utd (H) FA Trophy 2nd Rd.
v Croydon ,Isthmian Lg.Cup(A) 99/00

Transfer fee paid as Dagenham & Redbridge F.C. £15,000
to Purfleet for Paul Cobb in August 1997

Transfer fee received as Dagenham & Redbridge F.C. £65.00
from Birmingham City for Ian Richardson in May 1995

BEST SEASON

FA Cup: Fourth Round v Norwich City (A) 0-12002-03
League clubs defeated Lincoln City 00-01,Exeter C01-02
Plymouth Argyle 02-03

FA Trophy: Runners-up 96-97

League: Conference Runners-up 01-02
Promotion Play Offs 2002-03

LAST SEASON

F.A. Cup: 4th Qual. Round

F.A. Trophy: 4th Round

Conference: 13th

Top Goalscorer: Chris Moore & Mark Bentley

Player of the Year: Tim Cole

Captain: Tim Cole

DAGENHAM & REDBRIDGE PLAYING SQUAD

Bold print denotes England semi-professional international.

	Birthplace	D.O.B.	Previous Clubs
GOALKEEPERS			
Tony Roberts	Holyhead	04.08.69	QPR, Millwall, St.Albans C
Wales: Full & SP.			
DEFENDERS			
Tim Cole	London		Walthamstow Pennant, Leyton Pennant
RP			
Lee Flynn	London	04.0973	Stevenage B, Barnet, Hayes, Hendon, Boreham W, Romford
Lee Goodwin	Stepney	05.09.78	West Ham
RP			
Jake Leberl;	Morden	02.04.77	Margate, Dover Athletic, Crewe Alexandra
Anwar Uddin	London	01.11.81	Bristol Rovers, Sheffield Wednesday, West Ham United
Ashley Vickers	Sheffield	14.06.72	Sheffield U, Worcester C, Malvern T, 61 Club, Heybridge S
RP			
MIDFIELD			
Shane Blackett	London		Arlesey Town, Dunstable Town
Danny Hill	Enfield	01.01.74	Cardiff, Oxford Utd, Tottenham
Eu-21			
Mark Janney	Romford	02.12.77	Spurs
RP			
Craig Mackail-Smith	Hertford	25.02.84	Arlesey Town, St Albans City
Glen Southam	London		Bishop's Stortford, Enfield, Fulham
E N-G Int			
FORWARDS			
Tony Boot	Essex	08.09.82	Slough Town, Welling U, Harlow T, Southend
Chris Moore	Middlesex	13.01.80	Northwood, Uxbridge, Hendon, Brentford.
Tony Perfect	Surrey		St Albans City, Wingate& Fibnchley, Leyton Pennant, Leatherhead, Hampton & Richmond B

EXETER CITY

It seemed there was more taking place off the field rather than on it, as Exeter City began their first season in the Nationwide Conference.

The fact that there was a professional team at St James1 Park at all was something of a miracle.

Riddled with debt, and no one knew just how large that was, the Club was in grave danger of going into oblivion.

Along came the Supporters Trust, and after weeks of negotiations they gained control and became the majority shareholders.Had it not been for the goodwill of the fans themselves and many local businesses, then Exeter City would not have played their opening day fixture, let alone complete the season.

But the problems didn't end there, as there were obstacles to overcome, such as a possible points deduction for fielding a player, supposedly signed after the transfer embargo was placed on the Club.

There were delicate negotiations with regards the C.V.A. arrangement, enabling the Club to agree a schedule of repayments with the creditors.

Yet whilst this was taking place, and the season began to take shape, manager Eamonn Dolan and Director of Football Steve Perryman were making the best of the resources available to them - which was virtually nothing.

City quickly adapted to life in the Conference, brought through younger players from the ranks of trainee, and managed to add a couple of free transfer signings in the summer.

They surprised a lot of people by eventually only just missing out on a play off place. This was a tremendous achievement in view of all the problems that had been experienced.The Grecians also enjoyed a good run in the FA Trophy, before losing at Aldershot Town.

Slowly but surely the finances were being sorted, the fans rallied round which was reflected in increased attendances, and there was a whole new air of optimism in and around St James Park. Volunteers could be seen beavering away at the ground itself, undertaking repairs and giving the place a spruce of paint, something that had been neglected for several years.

In complete contrast to the summer of 2003, twelve months later, there is a bright new world albeit, still a very difficult one, but at least progress, lots of it, has been made thanks to the Supporters Trust, the fans, local businesses, management and players.

Mike Blackstone

Back Row (L-R): Dixie Dean (Physio), Gareth Sheldon, Alex Stanley, Alex Jeannin, Barry McConnell, Olivier Brassart, Lewis Reed, Leslie Afful, Judith Ansell (Physio). Middle Row: John Wills (Fitness adviser) Reinier Moor, Sean Canham, Steve Flack, James Bittner, Chris Todd, Martin Rice, Santos Gaia, Kwame Ampadu, Martin Thomas, Dick Bedford (Matchday staff). Front Row: Tiv Lowe (Centre of excellence manager), Sean Devine, Julian Tagg (Director), Scott Hiley (player-coach), Eamonn Dolan (manager), Steve Perryman (Director of Football), Glenn Cronin, Ian Huxham (Director), James Coppinger, Mike Redford (Youth Development).

EXETER CITY

Match Facts 2003-04

The number shown directly below the player's name is his squad number.
Where a number is shown instead of an "X' in the columns this represents a substitute appearance and the number indicates the player replaced.

Comp.	Date	Opponents	Venue.	Result	Goalscorers	Att.
Conf 1	Aug 09	Halifax T	H	D 1-1	Flack	3723
Conf 2	Aug 12	Telford U	A	L 0-2		2830
Conf 3	Aug 16	Margate	A	W 1-0	McConnell(p)	890
Conf 4	Aug 23	Chester C	H	W 2-1	Thomas Moor	3030
Conf 5	Aug 25	Woking	A	L 0-1		2556
Conf 6	Aug 30	Farnborough T	H	D 1-1	Flack	2672
Conf 7	Sep 06	Stevenage B	H	W 1-0	Lee	3012
Conf 8	Sep 13	Forest Green R	A	W 5-2	Lee(2) Devine(2) Gaia	1342
Conf 9	Sep 20	Gravesend & N	A	L 2-3	Moor Gaia	1155
Conf 10	Sep 22	Dagenham & R	H	D 1-1	Devine(p)	3344
Conf 11	Sep 27	Scarborough	H	D 0-0		2776
Conf 12	Oct 03	Burton A	A	W 4-3	Devine(3) Coppinger	1985
Conf 13	Oct 07	Barnet	A	W 3-2	Gaia Todd Cronin	2037
Conf 14	Oct 11	Northwich V	H	W 2-0	Devine(2)	3090
Conf 15	Oct 18	Accrington S	A	W 2-1	Devine Sheldon	2342
LDVT 1	**Oct 21**	**Hereford U**	**A**	**L 0-2**		**1513**
FAC 4q	**Oct 25**	**Gravesend & N**	**H**	**D 0-0**		**2686**
FAC 4qr	**Oct 28**	**Gravesend & N**	**A**	**D 3-3***	**Devine(2) Lee (lost 5-6 on pens)**	**1227**
Conf 16	Nov 01	Tamworth	H	W 3-2	Sheldon(2) Cronin	2979
Conf 17	Nov 11	Aldershot T	A	L 1-2	Devine	4112
Conf 18	Nov 15	Morecambe	H	W 4-0	Devine(2) Jeannin Sheldon	2993
Conf 19	Nov 22	Leigh RMI	A	D 1-1	Coppinger	634
Conf 20	Nov 25	Shrewsbury T	H	W 3-2	Coppinger McConnell Devine(p)	3470
Conf 21	Nov 29	Stevenage B	A	D 2-2	Cronin Gaia	2007
Conf 22	Dec 06	Forest Green R	H	D 2-2	Cronin Sheldon	3637
Conf 23	Dec 13	Halifax T	A	L 0-2		1267
Conf 24	Dec 20	Telford U	H	L 0-3		3114
Conf 25	Dec 26	Hereford U	A	D 1-1	Flack	4010
Conf 26	Jan 01	Hereford U	H	L 0-1		4943
Conf 27	Jan 03	Farnborough T	A	W 2-1	Devine Cronin	1354
FAT 3	**Jan 10**	**Hereford U**	**H**	**W 3-2**	**Devine Coppinger Sheldon**	**2740**
Conf 28	Jan 17	Margate	H	D 1-1	Devine	3439
Conf 29	Jan 24	Dagenham & R	A	W 2-0	Canham Coppinger(p)	1909
FAT 4	**Feb 04**	**Kings Lynn**	**A**	**W 3-0**	**Sheldon Devine Flack**	**3127**
Conf 30	Feb 07	Gravesend & N	H	L 0-1		3303
FAT 5	**Feb 14**	**Arlesey Town**	**H**	**W 3-0**	**Flack(2) Sheldon**	**2541**
Conf 31	Feb 21	Burton A	H	W 2-0	Sheldon Flack	2885
FAT 6	**Feb 28**	**Aldershot T**	**A**	**L 1-2**	**Devine**	**3800**
Conf 32	Mar 06	Barnet	H	D 1-1	Devine	3531
Conf 33	Mar 13	Aldershot T	H	W 2-1	Devine Jeannin	3982
Conf 34	Mar 16	Northwich V	A	D 1-1	Foran(og)	547
Conf 35	Mar 20	Morecambe	A	W 3-0	Coppinger(p) Canham Afful	1877
Conf 36	Mar 23	Scarborough	A	W 3-2	Sheldon Coppinger Canham	1200
Conf 37	Mar 27	Leigh RMI	H	W 3-2	Devine(2) Moxey	3635
Conf 38	Apr 03	Shrewsbury T	A	D 2-2	Moxey Flack	4185
Conf 39	Apr 10	Chester C	A	L 2-3	Devine Canham	4046
Conf 40	Apr 12	Woking	H	L 1-2	Sheldon	5236
Conf 41	Apr 17	Tamworth	A	L 1-2	Afful	1803
Conf 42	Apr 24	Accrington S	H	W 3-2	Coppinger Canham Flack	5345

STEP 1
CONFERENCE

STEP 2 - P177
CONFERENCE Nth & Sth

STEP 3 - P269
NPL, Southern, Isthmian Premiers

STEP 4 - P269
NPL 1, Southern W&E, Isthmian 1

STEP 5/6 - P473

STEP 7 - P713
Current level 4 leagues

James BITTNER	Scott HILEY	Martin THOMAS	Santos GAIA	Chris TODD	James COPPINGER	Glen CRONIN	Reiner MOOR	Sean DEVINE	Gareth SHELDON	Steve FLACK	Barry McCONNELL	Lewis REED	Martin RICE	Sean CANHAM	Kwame AMPADU	Alex JEANNIN	Dean MOXEY	Leslie AFFUL	Graham CHEESEMAN	Dwayne LEE	Andy TAYLOR	Lyndon DUNCAN
1	**2**	**4**	**5**	**6**	**7**	**8**	**9**	**10**	**11**	**14**	**15**	**16**	**17**	**18**	**19**	**20**	**21**	**22**	**23**	**26**	**28**	**29**
x	x	11		x	x	x	x		x	x	x			9	x	x		19				
x	x	x	x	x	x	x	x		x	x				2	4	x		11				
x	x	x	x	x	x	x	x			x	2				x	x		9				
x	x	x	x	x	x	x	x			x				7	x	x		19	9			
x	x	x	x	x	x	x	x			x	2				x	x		9	4			
x	x	x	x	x	x	x	x			x				4	x	x		9				
x	x		x	x	x	x		14		x	22			x	x	x		x		19		
x	x		x	x		x		18	22	x	x	15		x	x			x		x		
x	x		x	x	x	x	7	18	19	x	x			x	x					x		
x	x		x	x	x	x	26	x		x				14	22	x		x		x		
x	x		x	x	x			x	5	x					x	x		x		x		
x	x		x	x	x	x		x		x				26	22	x		x		x		
	x		x	x	x	x		x		x			x	19	x	x				x		
	x		x	x	x	x		x	7	x	19		x	10	x	x				x		
x		x	x		x		x	x	x	x		x			x	6			x			
			x			x			x	x	x	5	x	x		x	x	29			x	x
	x		x	x		x			x	x	x		x	x	18	x				x		
	x		x	x		x		19	x	x	x		x		x	x				x	26	
	x		x	x	11	x		x	x	x	x		x		15	x				x		
	x		x	x	11	x	2	x	x	x	x		x		x	x					19	
x	x		x	x	x	x	15	x	x		x				11	x				x	7	
x	x		x	x	x	x		x	x	15	x				11	x				x		
x	x		x	x	x	x		x	x	10	x				11	x				x	15	
x	x		x	x	x	x		x	x	11	x				15	x				x		
x	x		x	x	x	x		x	x	2	x					x		15		x		
x	x		x	x	x			x	x	2	x				x	x		15		x	19	
x	x			x	x	x		x	x	15	x				6	x	x	21		x		
x	x		x		x	x	x		x	x			9		8	x	x			x		
x	x		x	x	x	x		x	x	x			7			x		5		x		
x	x		x	x	x	x		x	x	x					x	x				2	19	
	x		x	x	x	x		x	x	x			x	7	26		x			x	14	
x	x		x	x	x	x		x	x					10	x	x	22	x			7	
x	x		x		x	x	22		x					x	x	x	x	x				
x	x			x	x	x		22	x	18				x	x	x	x	x			19	
x	x	19	x	x	x	x		x	x	x					x	x	2	14				
x	x	19	x	x		x	22	x	x	x					x	x	10	x				
x	x	11	x	x	21	x		22	x	x					x	x	x	x				
x	x		x	x	21	x		x	x	x					x	x	14	x				
x	x		x	x	x	x		x	x						x	x	20	x		19		
x	x		x	x	x	x		x	x	22	6				x	x	10	x				
x	x		x	x	x	x		x	x	10	2				x	x		x				
x	x	22	x	x	x	x			x		5			x	x		x	x			19	
x	x	11		x	x	x		22	x	18				x	x	x	x	x				
x	x		x		x	x		22	x	18				x	x	x	x	x				
x	x		x	x	x	x		18	x	5				x	x	x	7	x				
x	x		x	x	x	x		x	x	x				14	x	x	5	19				
x	x		x	x	x	x		22	x	18				x	x	x	20	x				
x	x	20	x	x		x		x	x	x				14	x	x	x	21				
x	x		x	20	x	x		22	x	6				x	x	x	x	x				

EXETER CITY

GROUND DETAILS

St James' Park, Exeter EX4 6PX

Office Opening Hours:
Mon-Fri: 9.00am-5.00pm.
Sat Matchdays: 9.30am-until end of match

General Enquiries: 01392 411243
Fax: 01392 413959
Commercial Dept: 01392 413954
Centre of Excellence: 01395 233883

Official Web Sites:
www.exetercityfc.co.uk
www.ecfst.org.uk

Independent Web Sites:
www.exeterexiles.co.uk
www.ecfc.co.uk
Gnet@domeus.co.uk
http://thegrecian.homestead.com

SIMPLE DIRECTIONS:

By Road:
Take the M5 exiting at junction 30, follow signs for Exeter City Centre, along Sidmouth Road and onto Heavitree Road, at the roundabout take the 4th exit into Western Way and then the second exit onto Tiverton road, then take the next left into St. James Road. On-street car parking, otherwise city centre car parks and walk to ground.

By Rail:
Nearest station: St James' Park. served by Exmouth branch line trains. Half hourly throughout the day.
Nearest main line stations, Exeter Central or Exeter St Davids.

MATCH TICKETS:
Adults £10 upwards. Concessions available.
Ticket office: Tel: 01392 411243.

CAPACITY: 9,036

Refreshments:
Centre Spot Social Club in adjacent St James' Centre; Corporate Hospitality rooms; Kiosks around the ground.

Club Shop:
At ground in St James' Centre; In city centre at Bedford street, Exeter (manned voluntarily by members of Exeter City Supporters Trust).

Founded: 1904
Nickname: Grecians
Team Sponsors: Flybe
Club Colours: Red & White striped shirts/ black/black
Change Colours: All Sky Blue
Midweek Home Matchday: Tuesday
Reserves' League: None - Only friendlies played.

CLUB OFFICIALS

Honorary Life President: Clifford Hill

Honorary President: Ivor Doble

Board of Directors: Dr David Trehearne (Chairman) Ian Huxham (Managing.Director); Julian Tagg (Vice-Chairman), Geoff Styles, Barry Sansom, Roger Monksummers and RogerHamilton-Kendal

Associate Directors:
Dave Bennett, Paul Dobson, Keith Hartshorn, Dave Newbery, Steve Perryman MBE, Malcolm Shelbourne, Norman Warne

Football Administrator & Club Secretary: Sally Cooke

Tel Nos: o1392 413958 (W) 07703323769 (M)

Commercial Director: Andy Gillard 07876 451635(M)

Shop Manager: Kelly Ingleson **Club Chaplain:** Richard Chewter**Head Groundsman:** Martin Vaughan
Groundstaff: Dave Richards

St James' Centre Manager: Sally Anne Fenwick

Ground Safety Officer: Malcolm Thompson

FOOTBALL MANAGEMENT TEAM

Director of Football:	Steve Perryman MBE
Date of Appointment:	June 2003
Date of Birth:	21st December 1951
Place of Birth:	Ealing
Previous Clubs	
as manager:	Managed Clubs in Japan's J-League; Brentford
as a player:	Tottenham Hotspur; Oxford United; Brentford

Team Manager:	Eamonn Dolan
Date of Appointment:	June 2003
Date of Birth:	20th September 1967
Place of Birth:	Dagenham
Previous Clubs	
as manager:	None
as player:	West Ham U.; Bristol C.; Birmingham C.; Exeter City

Player-Assistant Manager:	Scott Hiley
Centre of Excellence Manager:	Tiv Lowe
Youth Development Officer:	Mike Radford
Football in the Community Officer:	Jamie Vittles
Club Doctor:	Dr. David Kernick
Consultant Orthopaedic Surgeon:	Peter Schranz FRCS

Season	League	Div.	Pos.	Home P	W	D	L	F	A	Away W	D	L	F	A	Pts	Manager
03-04	Conference	-	6	42	10	7	4	33	24	9	5	7	38	33	69	Eamonn Dolan
02-03	Football Lge	3	23rd	46	7	7	9	24	31	4	8	11	26	33	48	John Cornforth/Neil McNab/Gary Peters
01-02	Football Lge	3	16th	46	7	9	7	25	32	7	4	12	23	41	55	John Cornforth
00-01	Football Lge	3	19th	46	8	9	6	22	20	4	5	14	18	38	50	Noel Blake
99-00	Football Lge	3	21st	46	8	6	8	27	30	3	5	15	19	42	44	Peter Fox
98-99	Football Lge	3	12th	46	13	6	5	32	18	4	7	12	15	32	63	Peter Fox
97-98	Football Lge	3	15th	46	10	8	5	39	25	5	7	11	29	38	60	Peter Fox
96-97	Football Lge	3	22nd	46	6	9	8	25	30	6	3	14	23	43	48	Peter Fox
95-96	Football Lge	3	14th	46	9	9	5	25	22	4	9	10	21	31	57	Peter Fox
94-95	Football Lge	3	22nd	42	5	5	11	25	36	3	6	13	11	34	34	Terry Cooper

HONOURS

Fourth Division Champions 1990
Promoted Fourth to Third Division: 1964; 1977
Division Three South Runners-Up 1932-33
Third Division South Cup winners 1934

PREVIOUS

Leagues: East Devon Senior League 1904-05
Plymouth & District League 1905-08
Southern League 1908-20
Football League 1920-2003

Past Players who progressed to the Football League

Not applicable

MATCHDAY PROGRAMME

Pages: 48 Price: £2.00
Editor: Mike Blackstone
email: MJ.blackstone@virgin.net
01524 853605
Printers: Kingfisher Print & Design, Totnes
Tel: 01803 867087
Local Press: Express & Echo; Western Morning News
Local radio: BBC Radio Devon; Gemini Radio

CLUB RECORDS

Attendance: 21,018
v Sunderland, FA Cup quarter-final replay, 1931

Football League victory: 8-1
v Coventry City, Div 3 South 1926
v Aldershot, Div 3 South 1935

Cup victory: 14-0
v Weymouth, FA Cup, 1908

Football League Defeat: 0-9
v Notts County, Div 3 South 1948
v Northampton Town, Div 3 South 1958

Career league goalscorer: Tony Kellow
129, 1976-78, 1980-83, 1985-88.

Career league appearances: Arnold Mitchell
495, 1952-66

Transfer fee paid: £65,000
to Blackpool for Tony Kellow, March 1980

Transfer fee received: £500,000
from Manchester City for Martin Phillips, November 1995

BEST SEASON

Football League:
8th Division Three (now Div 2), 1979-80

Conference:

FA Cup: Quarter-Final 1931; 1981

FA Trophy: 6th Round 2003-04

LAST SEASON

FA Cup:	**4th Q**
F.A.Trophy:	6th Round
Confernece:	6th
Top Goalscorer:	Sean Devine
Player of year:	Glenn Cronin
Captain:	Glenn Cronin

EXETER CITY — PLAYING SQUAD

	Birthplace	D.O.B.	Previous Clubs
			Bold print denotes England semi-professional international.
GOALKEEPERS			
James Bittner		1978	Chippenham Town, Salisbury City, Chippenham Town, Fulham
DEFENDERS			
Chris Curran	**Birmingham**	**17.09.71**	**Plymouth Argyle, Torquay United**
Lyndon Duncan	**Ealing**	**12.01.83**	**Q.P.R.**
Santos Gaia Brazil u18	Brazil	1980	Corinthians of Brazil
Scott Hiley	Plymouth		Portsmouth, Southampton, Manchester City, Birmingham City (£1090,000), Exeter C
Alexandre Jeannin	France	30.12.80	Lens, Racing club Paris, Darlington, Troy
Wayne O'Sullivan	Akrotiri (Cyprus)r	25.02.74	Plymouth Argyle, Cardiff City, Swindion Town
Chris Todd	Swansea	22.08.81	Drogheda United, Swansea City
MIDFIELD			
Kwame Ampadu Eire u21	Bradford	20.12.70	Leyton O, Swansea C, W. B. A.(£50k), Plymouth Argyle (L), Arsenal
Glenn Cronin Eire u18	Dublin	14.09.81	Youth Team
Barry McConnell	Exeter	01.01.77	Weston-super-Mare (L), Youth Team
FORWARDS			
Les Afful	Liverpool	04.02.84	Youth Team
Sean Devine	Lewisham	06.09.72	Wycombe W, Barnet, Millwall (YTS), Bromley, Erith & Belvedere, Fisher Athletic
Jake Edwards	Manchester	11.05.76	Yeovil Town, Telford United, Wrexham
Steve Flack	Cambridge	29.05.71	Cardiff City, Cambridge City, Foxton £10,000
Reinier Moor Eire u20	Holland	12.06.83	Youth Team
Gareth Sheldon	Birmingham	31.0180	Scunthorpe United

FARNBOROUGH TOWN

The rollercoaster ride that is Farnborough Town started with a long trip to Scarborough for what was to be a turbulent trip. With a new Chairman, Manager and NINE players making their Boro debuts at The Theatre of Chips. A narrow defeat was to follow, although that was down to a disputed retaken penalty late on.

We reached October without a league victory, and Tamworth somehow left Hampshire with a point in a 3-3 draw. Boro led 3-1 at one point. Forest Green then took all the points three days later. Our first ever trip to Accrington Stanley followed, so did our tenth defeat of the season. This was to be the last straw for the manager Tommy Taylor who resigned after the game. Ian McDonald was relieved of his duties. Now the Chairman had become the manager as well. The first hurdle was not against Conference high fliers, but Horndean in the Hampshire Senior Cup. A win at last, albeit by a single goal. Telford were next to visit Cherrywood Road, would this become winless game number fifteen? No-one had read the script as Adie Hayes blasted home form 25 yards to give Boro their first three points of the season. The following week was our first game in the FA Cup since we tackled a team called Arsenal (not sure what happened to them!!). We had to make the short journey to Thame United, now managed by ex-Boro striker Mark West. A 2-1 win gave us a home tie with Weston-super-Mare.

Would our luck change? Not much, as our Trophy run ended at the first hurdle at Canvey Island, with the home side scoring six. Boro's most important game of the season followed as we went to Leigh RMI. Ken Charlery and Howard Forinton secured a 2-0 win. Then followed the strangest Rushmoor derby. Aldershot dominated the first half, but still went in behind and by the end it was 4-0 and our biggest win to date,

We remained unbeaten in March and a 6-3 aggregate scoreline against Lymington & New Milton sent us into our first County Cup Final for several years. But we had sunk into real trouble by the end of the season so with Halifax beating fellow strugglers Leigh RMI on Good Friday a defeat for Boro at Gravesend would seal our fate mathematically anyway. The final two games of the season gave us a 2-1 success over Nigel Clough's Burton Albion and a 4-2 triumph, in the last game to be played at Telford United. Thankfully they are now up and running once again.

Farnborough then won the Hampshire Senior Cup beating Fareham Town 2-1 at The Friends Provident St. Mary's Stadium in Southampton. Adie Hayes scoring both goals with almost 2,000 fans watching.

So there we were 5,500 miles, 42 league games, 53 players, 2 managers and we have remained in the Conference! Now we have an ownership battle, with Tony Theo, the Chairman & Owner as introduced by Victor Searle in April competing with two other businessmen who had bought Searte's shares.. How it will resolve itself, we don't know, but one thing that goes without saying is the everybody at Farnborough Town is 100% behind Tony Theo.

Mark Hardy, Programme Editor

Back row, left to right : Tony Taggart, Lee Miles, Craig Holloway, Mark Osbon, Anthony Charles,Gary Holloway and Danny Allen-Page **Middle row:** Ali Chaaban, Ben Townsend, Jermaine Hamilton, John Mulhern, Adam Theo, Mark Rooney, Lloyd Blackman and Robert Hughes. **Front row:** Issufo Jalo, Sasha Opinel, Tony Theo (Chairman), Nick Burton and Paul Harkness.**Photo: Eric Marsh**

FARNBOROUGH TOWN

Match Facts 2003-04

The number shown directly below the player's name is his squad number.
Where a number is shown instead of an "X' in the columns this represents a substitute appearance and the number indicates the player replaced.

Comp.	Date	Opponents	Venue.	Result	Goalscorers	Att.
Conf 1	Aug 09	Scarborough	A	L 1-2	Charlery	1415
Conf 2	Aug 12	Barnet	H	D 1-1	Weatherstone	1063
Conf 3	Aug 16	Leigh RMI	H	D 1-1	Weatherstone	594
Conf 4	Aug 23	Shrewsbury T	A	L 0-3		3403
Conf 5	Aug 25	Gravesend & N	H	L 1-2	Beconfrave	839
Conf 6	Aug 30	Exeter C	A	D 1-1	Griffiths(p)	2672
Conf 7	Sep 06	Hereford U	H	L 0-5		1334
Conf 8	Sep 13	Woking	A	L 2-3	Charlery Hodgson	2791
Conf 9	Sep 20	Chester C	H	L 1-2	Fashanu	748
Conf 10	Sep 23	Aldershot T	A	L 0-2		4166
Conf 11	Sep 27	Morecambe	A	L 2-3	Chabaan(2)	1636
Conf 12	Oct 04	Tamworth	H	D 3-3	Hodgson Fashanu(p) Beconfrave	770
Conf 13	Oct 07	Forest Green R	H	L 1-3	Fashanu	525
Conf 14	Oct 11	Accrington S	A	L 1-3	Beall	1806
Conf 15	Oct 18	Telford U	H	W 2-1	Hayes Hodgson	579
FAC 4Q	**Oct 25**	**Thame United**	**A**	**W 2-1**	**Clarke Hayes**	**909**
Conf 16	Nov 01	Burton A	A	L 0-1		1601
FAC 1	**Nov 08**	**Weston-S-M**	**H**	**L 0-1**		**936**
Conf 17	Nov 11	Dagenham & R	A	L 0-1		1269
Conf 18	Nov 15	Northwich V	H	W 2-0	Manuella Burton	626
Conf 19	Nov 22	Halifax T	A	L 0-2		1250
Conf 20	Nov 29	Hereford U	A	L 0-2		2630
Conf 21	Dec 06	Margate	H	D 1-1	Burton	595
Conf 22	Dec 09	Woking	H	W 1-0	Semple	1005
Conf 23	Dec 13	Scarborough	H	L 1-2	Chabaan	620
Conf 24	Dec 20	Barnet	A	W 2-0	Burton Semple	1547
Conf 25	Dec 26	Stevenage B	H	W 2-0	Hodgson Chabaan	1403
Conf 26	Jan 01	Stevenage B	A	L 2-3	Hodgson(p) Harkness	2285
Conf 27	Jan 03	Exeter C	H	L 1-2	Forinton	1354
FAT 3	**Jan 10**	**Canvey Island**	**A**	**L 0-6**		**685**
Conf 28	Jan 17	Leigh RMI	A	W 2-0	Charlery Forinton	295
Conf 29	Jan 24	Aldershot T	H	W 4-0	Charles Burton Doudou Sombili	3233
Conf 30	Feb 07	Chester C	A	L 2-3	Burton Hodgson	2665
Conf 31	Feb 14	Morecambe	H	L 2-4	Hodgson Perkins(og)	704
Conf 32	Feb 21	Tamworth	A	L 1-2	Hodgson	1084
Conf 33	Feb 28	Accrington S	H	D 1-1	Harkness	571
Conf 34	Mar 06	Forest Green R	A	D 1-1	Harkness	781
Conf 35	Mar 13	Dagenham & R	H	D 2-2	Fashanu Roberts(og)	787
Conf 36	Mar 20	Northwich V	A	D 1-1	Hodgson(p)	510
Conf 37	Mar 27	Halifax T	H	W 1-0	Burton	644
Conf 38	Apr 03	Margate	A	L 0-3		386
Conf 39	Apr 10	Shrewsbury T	H	L 1-3	Hayes	1041
Conf 40	Apr 12	Gravesend & N	A	L 0-2		1284
Conf 41	Apr 17	Burton A	H	W 2-1	Burton Mulhern	812
Conf 42	Apr 24	Telford U	A	W 4-2	Burton Fashanu Forinton(p) Harkness	3323

STEP 1 CONFERENCE | STEP 2 - P177 CONFERENCE Nth & Sth | STEP 3 - P269 NPL, Southern, Isthmian Premier | STEP 4 - P269 NPL 1, Southern W&E, Isthmian 1 | STEP 5/6 - P473 | STEP 7 - P713 Current level 4 leagues

Mark OSBORN	Jay LOVETT	Ben MARTIN	James DONOVAN	Adie HAYES	Nick BURTON	Ross WEATHERSTONE	Carl HUTCHINGS	Danny ALLEN-PAGE	Dean GREEN	Billy BEALL	Ken CHARLERY	Barrington BELGRAVE	Dominic REECE	Mark PETERS	Paul HARKNESS	Will PACKHAM	Jon ASHWOOD	Ali CHABAAN	Michael MOUSSALI	Fraser TOMS	Adam THEO	Richard HODGSON	Sasha OPINEL	Tom NEILL	James DEACONS	Matt PATTISON	Leroy GRIFFITHS	Mupepele IFURA	Geoff PITCHER	Anthony CHARLES	Mark THOMPSON	at SAPPLETON	Andre FASHANU	Alex STANLEY	Fiston MANUELLA	imieon HOWELL	Dwayne CLARKE	Jalo SOMBILI	Howard FORINTON	Ryan SEMPLE	Bruno MENDONCA	Dennis OLI	John MULHERN	Ebeli DOUDOU	Alex CHRISTOU
	2	2	2	3	4	5	6	6	7	8	9	10	11	11	12	13	13	14	15	15	15	16	17	18	18	19	20	20	20	21	22	23	24	25	25	25	26	26	27	28	29	29	29	30	32
	8			20	x	x	x			x	x	x			10							x	x	x																					
	9			x	x	x	x			3	x	x			x							x	x	x																					
	x				x	x	x			x		x	18		16							x	x	x			x				4														
	7			x		x	x		x			x	x		11							x	x	x			x				6														
	6				x	x	x					18			x			x				x	x	x		14	x				x														
	x			x		x	x			x		14			3			x				x	x				x				2	x													
					x	x	x			x		x			x							x	x				x					x	10	12			20								
	x			x	x	x	x			x	5				x							19	x			x							26				x								
					x	x	x			x	x	9				x		x				x	x					x			14		26				x								
	14				x	x	x			x		6				x		x				x	x									x	x				x								
				17	x	x	x			x					26			x				x	x					x				x	16				x								
	10			x			x				24	x			14			x				x	x			x		x				x	x												
				x		x	x					19			15			x	x				x			x		x				x	x				24								
				25		x			15	x	x	x						x	5			x	x					x				x			x										
				x	x	22				x	x	x						x				x	x					21		x	x						14								
				x	x					x		x			26			x	14			x	x							x	x						x								
				x	x		x			x	x	22			3							x	x							x	x						x								
				x	x	x	x			x	x				x			9				x	x							x					6		12								
				25			x			x	26				14			x				x	x							x	x				x		x		x						
				8	x					x	x				27			19				x	x			x				x	x				x				x						
				x	x		x			x	x	28			27							x	x								x								x	x					
				25	x					x	27	16			x							x	x							x	x				x				x	x					
				x	x	22				x	x	9			x			3												x	x				x					x					
				25	x	x				x		x						x				x	x								x				x			16	14	x					
				x	x	x				x		x						x					x			8					x				x			3	10	x					
				x	x	x	x					x						x				x	x							x	4				6				10	x					
				x		x	x					x			10			x				x				28				x	x				27				x	x					
				x		x	x			27	14				x			x				x	x			16				x	x								x						
				x		x	x			26					x							x	x			27				x	x							x	x		3				
				x	x		x			12	4				x			x					x							x	x				26			x	x						
				x						x	x							30		x		x	x							x					15			28	x	x				x	
				x	x					x	4							27		x		x	x							x								15	x	x				x	
		x		x	x													x		x		x	x								x				22			15	x					x	2
		21			x					x								15		x		x	x							x	x							27	x			x		x	
		x		x	x					x	30				27							x	x								x				22				x			x		x	
		27		x	x					x	16				x							x	x							x					x			12	x			x			
				x	x						29				x			x			x	x				25				x					x				x			x		27	
				x	x					x	27				x			x			x	x				x				x			12						x					14	
			x	x	x					x											4	x	x			20			x				x						x				x	24	
			x	x	x					x				x									x		x	29			x										x				x		11
			x	x	x			18		x				32											x	x			x							x		20	x						x
			x	x						x	x	12		x	x						x					x							27			11			x				x		
			x					x		x	x	27			x						29					x							x			19		x	x				x		
			x		x			x		x		26			x								x			8							x			x		x	24				x		
			x	x	x			x		x		24			x		x						x		29	27							x						x				x		

so PLayed: John MARTIN (20) Conf 1 - Dalvinder PARDESAI (15) Conf 2 - Rep 12. Gerard LEVIN (20) Conf 21.

FARNBOROUGH TOWN

GROUND DETAILS

Cherrywood Road,
Farnborough, Hampshire GU14 8UD

Telephone: 01252 541469
Fax: 01252 372640

Directions: From M3 exit 4, take A325 towards Farnborough, right into Prospect Ave. (club signposted), 2nd right into Cherrywood Rd, ground on right.
20-30 min walk from Farnborough Main, Farnborough North , Frimley BR stations and town centre.
Whippet mini-bus 19 No 12 Bus passes ground.
Parking: 200 spaces at club at £1.00 plus local streets
Match Tickets: Adults £9-10 concessions £6-7

Capacity: 4,163
Seated: 627
Covered Terracing: 1,350

Clubhouse: OpenThur/Fri/Sat/Sun. Bar
Refreshments: Two tea bars

Club Shop:
Boro' Leisurewear shop - all types of club leisurewear and matchballs (contact Gaye Hoyle 01252 691129)
Supporters Club shop:
Old programmes, scarves, badges etc (contact Paul Doe).

Founded:	1967
Nickname:	The "Boro" or "Town"
Club Sponsor:	World Wide Carpets.
Club Colours:	Red & white shirts,
Change colours:	Yellow & Blue
Midweek matchday:	Tuesday
Reserves' League:	Capital League
Club Website:	www.farnboroughtownfc.com

CLUB OFFICIALS

President:	**Charles Mortimer**
Chairman:	Tony Theo
Directors:	**T.B.A**
Football Secretary:	**Vince Williams** Tel: 01252 541469
Commercial Consultant:	**David Hughes** Tel No: 01252 541469
Press Officer:	**Vince Williams**

MATCHDAY PROGRAMME

Pages: 48 Price: £2.50
Editor: Mark Hardy
Clubcall: 09068 440 088
Local Press: Farnborough News
Local Radio: BBC Southern Counties
County Sound

FOOTBALL MANAGEMENT TEAM

MANAGER: **DEAN AUSTIN**
Date of Appointment: 10.06.04
Date of Birth: 26.04.70
Place of Birth: London

PREVIOUS CLUBS
As manager: None
As player: Spurs,C.Palace,Southend U, Watford, St Albans City

HONOURS
As manager
As player: F.A.Cup Semi-Final (2)

* * *

Asst. Manager/Coach: Gerry Murphy
Reserve Team Manager: Les Ryder
Physio: Steve Hockhamt
Club Playing Status: Part Time

Season	League	Div.	Pos.	Home P	W	D	L	F	A	Away W	D	L	F	A	Pts	Manager
03-04	Conference	-	20	42	7	6	8	31	34	3	3	15	22	40	39	Tommy Taylor/Ian McDonald/Vic Searle
02-03	Conference	-	13	42	8	6	7	37	29	5	6	10	20	27	51	Graham Westley/ Tommy Taylor
01-02	Conference	-	7	42	11	3	7	38	23	7	4	10	28	31	61	Graham Westley / Ian McDonald
00-01	Isthmian	P	1	42	14	5	2	43	13	17	1	3	43	14	99	Graham Westley
99-00	Isthmian	P	12	42	8	5	8	25	19	6	6	9	27	36	53	Graham Westley
98-99	Conference	-	22	42	6	5	10	29	48	1	6	14	12	41	32	Alan Taylor
97-98	Conference	-	18	42	10	3	8	37	27	2	5	14	19	43	44	Alan Taylor
96-97	Conference	-	7	42	9	6	6	35	29	7	7	7	23	24	61	Alan Taylor
95-96	Conference	-	10	42	8	6	7	29	23	7	8	6	34	35	59	Alan Taylor
94-95	Conference	-	14	42	8	5	8	23	31	7	5	9	22	33	55	Alan Taylor

HONOURS

Southern League — Prem. Div. 90-91 93-94,

Isthmian League — Prem. Div. 00-01, R-up 88-89, Div 1 84-85, Div 2 78-79, Lge Cup 99-00,

Athenian Lg — Div 2 78-79,

Spartan Lge — 72-73 73-74 74-75 (Lg Cup 74-75),

London Spartan Lge — 75-76 (Lg Cup 75-76),

Hants Senior Cup 74-75 81-82 83-84 85-86 90-91 03-04

PREVIOUS

Leagues: Surrey Senior 68-72; Spartan 72-76; Athenian 76-77; Isthmian 77-89 99-01; Alliance Premier (Conference) 89-90 91-93 94-99; Southern 90-91 93-94.

Grounds: Queens Road, Farnborough (1969-1976)

Past Players who progressed to the Football League

Dennis Bailey (Crystal Palace),
Paul Mortimer (Charlton Athletic),
Tommy Jones (Aberdeen),
Allan Cockram (Brentford),
Paul Holsgrove (Millwall),
Maik Taylor (Barnet),
Martin Rowlands (Brentford)

2001 FT FC

CLUB RECORDS

Attendance: 3,581 v Brentford 22/11/95 (FA Cup)

Win: 11-0 v Chertsey Town (H), Spartan League 72-73

Defeat: 2-10 v Worplesdon (H), Surrey Senior Lge Div. 1 68-69

Career Goalscorer: Simon Read 209, 1986-1994

Career Appearances: Brian Broome 529, 1980-1994

Season Goalscorer: Simon Read 53, 1988-89

Transfer Fee Paid: Undisclosed

Transfer Fee Received: £50,000 from Dover Athletic for David Leworthy, August1993

BEST SEASON

FA Cup: 4th Rd Proper 2002-2003 1-5 v Arsenal(H) but played at Highbury

League club defeated: Torquay Utd 91-92, Darlington 2002-03

FA Trophy: Quarter Final 92-93,02-03

FA Vase: Semi-Final 75-76 76-77

League: 5th Conference 91-92

LAST SEASON

F.A. Cup: 1st Round.

F.A. Trophy: 3rd Round

League: 20th Conference

Top Goalscorer: Richard Hodgson

Player of the Year: Mark Osborn

Captain: Nick Burton

FARNBOROUGH TOWN PLAYING SQUAD

Bold print denotes England semi-professional international.

	Birthplace	D.O.B.	Previous Clubs
GOALKEEPERS			
Craig Holloway	Blackheath	10.08.84	Arsenal(F.A.Youth Cup Winner)
Mark Osborne	Bletchley	19.06.81	Wycombe Wanderers
DEFENDERS			
Danny Allen-Page	London	30.10.83	Brentford
Nick Burton RP	Norfolk	02.10.75	Gravesend & Northfleet, Hampton & Richmond B., Aldershot T., Yeovil T., Torquay U., Portsmouth
Anthony Charles	Isleworth	11.03.81	Aldershot, Hayes, Crewe A, Broook House
E NG Int			
Sasha Opinel			Casteinau-le-Cres,France
Mark Rooney	London	19.05.78	Barnet, Dagenham & R, St Albans ,Aylesbury,Watford
Ben Townsend	Reading	08.10.81	Woking, Wycombe W
Adam Theo	Reading		Yeading, Reading
MIDFIELD			
Matthew Beall	Enfield	04.12.77	Dover A (L),.Leyton Orient, Cambridge United
Dean Green	London	-	Hampton & Richmond, Leyton Pennant, Dulwich Hamlet, Crawley T, Dulwich Hamlet, Waltham Abbey, Fulham
Adie Hayes	Norwich	22.05.78	Cambridge City, Kings Lynn, Boston Utd, Diss Town, Kettering T., Cambridge U.
Gary Holloway	Surrey		Stevenage B, Farnborough T,Hampton & R B,Walton &H
Matt Pattison			Camberley Town.
FORWARDS			
Ali Chaaban			Leratherhead, Dorking
Ebeli M'Bombo	Kinshasa	11.09.80	Q.P.R., AS Monaco (France)
Paul Harkness			Walton & Hersham, Leatherhead, Basingstoke Town, Camberley T. North Shore Utd. (N.Z.), Walton & Hersham
,			Camberley, Brighton (Juniors).
Dalvinder Pardesi			Bournemouth, Southampton
Mark Peters	Frimley	04.10.83	Brentford, Southampton

FOREST GREEN ROVERS

The club from a very small village on a hill above Nailsea, a few miles from Stroud , once again defied the experts who forcast that they couldn't possibly hold their own againts more and more full time clubs in the big and powerful Conference.

Rovers never really enjoyed a run to enable their supporters to relax, niether did they ever sink to the relegation zone and when a money saving move encouraged an amicable agreement with manager Colin Addison to stand down, his assistant Tim Harris took over and did well enough to be given the job until the end of the season.

The club has reached the F.A.Trophy Final twice in the last six seasons and a 4-0 home victory over Sutton United raised hopes once again. This was followed by more goals in a 3-3 draw with DoverAthletic but the away replay was lost 1-2 and hopes of a third final were over for another year. As the F.A.Cup had brought a home exit at the hands of a lively Barnet side at the first hurdle, there was little excitement from the knock out competitions and worse still, not too much of a cash injection.

A home defeat by local rivals Hereford United brought everyone down to earth as 'The Bulls' hit top form with a scintillating 7-1 victiory at The Lawn but an impressive defeat of high flying Chester City was a boost to Tim Harris and despite a poor finish to the league season he has worked hard to build a brand new squad for the coming campaign.

On a personal point of view, I will miss the wonderful enthusiasm and love for football always shown by John Dickinson on my visits to Forect Green. He epitomised all that is best in the dedication of a non-league football follower devoted to a club, its members and its players. John, even in his last difficult days, was wheeled in to say good bye to his 'special family' . He will be remembered with a smile. T.W.

Back Row: Jason Ford (masseur),Adie Adams, Simon Bryant, Scott Rogers, Michael Green, Matt Bown, Ben Cleverley, Ryan Trowbridge and Ray Brown (Kit Manager).**Middle Row:** Nick Cornwall (Chief Scout), Charlie Griffin, Jon Holloway, Matt Gadsby, Danny Greaves, Steve Perrin, Andy Thompson, Tom Gould, Matt Aubrey, Stuart Martin (Goalkeeper Coach). **Front row:** Luke Jones, Steve Cowe, Mark Beesley, Alan McLoughlin(Asst. Manager), Tim Harris (Manager), Steve Lock (Physio), Jon Richardson (Captain), Alex Sykes and Darren Davies.

FOREST GREEN ROVERS

Match Facts 2003-04

The number shown directly below the player's name is his squad number.
Where a number is shown instead of an "X" in the columns this represents a substitute appearance and the number indicates the player replaced.

Comp.	Date	Opponents	Venue.	Result	Goalscorers	Att.
Conf 1	Aug 09	Northwich V	H	D 0-0		628
Conf 2	Aug 12	Hereford U	A	L 1-5	Grayson	3195
Conf 3	Aug 16	Chester C	A	L 0-1		1881
Conf 4	Aug 23	Accrington S	H	W 2-1	Cowe Owers	711
Conf 5	Aug 25	Dagenham & R	A	L 2-5	Cowe(2)	1540
Conf 6	Aug 30	Margate	H	L 1-2	Cowe	569
Conf 7	Sep 06	Leigh RMI	A	W 2-1	Grayson(2)	415
Conf 8	Sep 13	Exeter C	H	L 2-5	Rogers(2)	1342
Conf 9	Sep 20	Scarborough	A	D 2-2	Grayson(2,1p)	1208
Conf 10	Sep 23	Woking	H	D 2-2	Rogers Brodie	712
Conf 11	Sep 27	Halifax T	H	L 1-2	Rogers	722
Conf 12	Oct 04	Gravesend & N	A	D 1-1	Brodie	1190
Conf 13	Oct 07	Farnborough T	A	W 3-1	Brodie Kennedy Hutchins(og)	525
Conf 14	Oct 11	Burton A	H	D 1-1	Grayson	867
LDVT 1	**Oct 13**	**Brighton & Hove A**	**A**	**L 0-2**		**3969**
Conf 15	Oct 18	Stevenage B	H	W 3-1	Moralee(2) Foster	676
FAC 4q	**Oct 25**	**Aldershot T**	**H**	**L 1-3**	**Cowe**	**1137**
Conf 16	Nov 01	Aldershot T	A	L 0-3		2398
Conf 17	Nov 11	Shrewsbury T	A	L 0-2		3263
Conf 18	Nov 15	Tamworth	H	W 2-1	Rogers Cant	782
Conf 19	Nov 22	Barnet	A	L 0-5		1378
Conf 20	Nov 25	Morecambe	H	L 1-2	Grayson	605
Conf 21	Nov 29	Leigh RMI	H	D 2-2	Meechan Sykes	554
Conf 22	Dec 06	Exeter C	A	D 2-2	Phillips(2)	3637
Conf 23	Dec 13	Northwich V	A	W 4-0	Bowen(3) Meechan	474
Conf 24	Dec 20	Hereford U	H	L 1-7	Searle	1576
Conf 25	Jan 01	Telford U	H	D 0-0		1071
Conf 26	Jan 04	Margate	A	L 0-2		255
FAT 3	**Jan 10**	**Sutton United**	**H**	**W 4-0**	**Rogers Grayson Foster Ingram(p)**	**701**
Conf 27	Jan 17	Chester C	H	W 2-1	Cowe Rogers	1164
Conf 28	Jan 24	Woking	A	D 1-1	Foster	1815
FAT 4	**Feb 03**	**Dover Athletic**	**H**	**D 3-3**	**Grayson(3)**	**427**
Conf 29	Feb 07	Scarborough	H	W 4-0	Rogers(2) Grayson(2)	848
FAT 4r	**Feb 10**	**Dover Athletic**	**A**	**L 1-2**	**Grayson**	**710**
Conf 30	Feb 21	Gravesend & N	H	L 1-2	Meechan	752
Conf 31	Feb 28	Burton A	A	W 3-2	Moore Foster Rogers	1442
Conf 32	Mar 06	Farnborough T	H	D 1-1	Ingram(p)	781
Conf 33	Mar 09	Halifax T	A	W 1-0	Meechan	883
Conf 34	Mar 13	Shrewsbury T	H	D 1-1	Ingram	1484
Conf 35	Mar 20	Tamworth	A	L 0-1		1112
Conf 36	Mar 23	Telford U	A	W 2-0	Meechan Sykes	1354
Conf 37	Mar 27	Barnet	H	D 1-1	Searle(p)	1013
Conf 38	Apr 03	Morecambe	A	L 0-4		1259
Conf 39	Apr 10	Accrington S	A	L 1-4	Searle(p)	1058
Conf 40	Apr 12	Dagenham & R	H	L 1-3	Meechan	762
Conf 41	Apr 17	Aldershot T	H	W 3-1	Langan Searle(p) Cowe	1330
Conf 42	Apr 24	Stevenage B	A	L 1-2	Sykes	1747

Steve PERRIN	Gareth STOKER	Steve JENKINS	Jon RICHARDSON	Denny INGRAM	Matthew RUSSELL	Tom JORDAN	Kevin LANGAN	Martyn FOSTER	Neil GRAYSON	Gary OWERS	Alex SYKES	Steve COWE	Steve JONES	Scott ROGERS	Luke JONES	Adi ADAMS	Chris GIANNANGELO	John CANT	Rob COOK	Dave GILROY	Scott MORGAN	Sam BOWEN	Jimmi Lee JONES	Matt AUBREY	Steve BRODIE	Jamie MORALEE	Richard KENNEDY	Michael GREEN	Damon SEARLE	Lee PHILLIPS	Darren JONES	Alex MEECHAN	Hugh McAULEY	Paul MOORE	Sekani SIMPSON	Ian FITZPATRICK
1	**2**	**3**	**4**	**5**	**6**	**6**	**7**	**8**	**9**	**10**	**11**	**12**	**14**	**15**	**16**	**18**	**19**	**20**	**21**	**22**	**23**	**23**	**24**	**24**	**25**	**26**	**27**	**27**	**28**	**29**	**30**	**31**	**32**	**33**	**34**	**35**
x	x	x	x	x				x	x	x	x	14	x	2					22	x																
x		x	x	x	x			x	x	x	x	11	x	10				22		x																
x		x	x	x	x			x	x	x			x	24							x		x													
x		x	x	x	12			x	x	x		x	x	8						24	x		x													
x		x	x	x	x			x	x	x		x	x	6						12	x		14													
x		x	x					x	x	x	3	x	x	x		8				24	x		x													
x		x	x	x			15	x	x	x		x	x	x											x											
x		x	x	x			8	x	x	x		x	x	x									10		x											
x		x	x	x			x	x	x				x	x							x				x	15										
x		x		x			x	x	x	x			x	x							x				x											
x	x	2		x			x	x	x	x			x	x							x				x	15										
x	x			x			x	x	x	x				x	27	7									x	18	x		x							
x	x		x	x				x	x	x				29											x	25	x		x	x						
x	x		x	x				x	x	x				10				29								x	x		x	x						
x	**x**		**x**	**x**				**x**	**x**	**x**				**27**	**26**			**8**								**x**	**x**		**x**	**x**						
x	x		x	x			5	x	x	x				9	29											x	x		x	x						
x	**x**			**x**			**x**	**x**			**29**	**x**		**x**			**1**									**x**	**x**		**x**	**x**						
x	x		x	x			x	x			12	x		x	15			7								x	x		x							
x	x		x	x			x	x	x			26		x				15								x	4		x	x						
x				x			x	x	x		7	x		x				26								x	x		x	x						
x	x			x				x	x		8	x		x	12			x									x		x	x						
x	x		x					x	x			2		x		29		x									4		x	x	x	x				
x				x				x	x		12	x		x	15												x		x	x	x	x				
x				x				x			x	15		x				11								x	x		x	x	x	x				
x				x			x	x				7			23			x				x					x		x	x	x	x				
x				x				x			27	x		20	12			x				x					x		x	x	x	x				
x	x		x	x				x	x			x		12															x	x	x	x				
x	x		x	x				x	x			x		12				28											x	x	x	x				
x	**x**		**x**	**x**				**x**	**x**		**9**	**x**		**x**		**15**											**29**		**x**	**x**	**x**					
x	x		x	x				x			29	x		x															x	x	x	x	12			
x	x		x	x			5	x				x		x															x	x	x	x	29			
x	**x**		**x**	**x**				**x**	**x**		**30**	**x**		**x**															**x**	**x**	**x**					
x			x	x			x	x	x		x	9		x															x	7	x	x	11			
x			**x**	**x**			**x**	**x**	**x**		**x**	**x**		**x**	**12**			**11**											**x**	**9**	**x**					
x	x		x	x				x			32	x		x	2														x	x		x	x	31		
x	x		x	x				x			x	33		x															x	x		x		x		
x	x		x	x				x	33		x	31		x															x	11		x		x	x	
x	x		x	x				x	x		x	11		x															x	x		x		31		
x	x		x	x				x			x	34		x										33					x			x	11	x	x	
x	x		x					x			x	x		x										33					x	x		x	29	x		
x	x		x			x		x			x	x		x										35					x			x	12			x
x	x		x			x		x			x	x		x		35								31					x			x	12			x
x	x		x			x		x			x	35												11				x	x			x	x		6	x
x			x			x	35	x			x	x												31				x	x			x	x			x
x			x			x		x			x	x		x	12													x	x			x	x			11
x			x				x	x			x	31		x										x				x	x			x	x			
x	x		x				x	x			x	x		2										x				x	x				x			

FOREST GREEN ROVERS

GROUND DETAILS

'The Lawn',
Nympsfield Road,
Forest Green,
Nailsworth,
Glos. GL6 0ET

TELEPHONE NUMBERS:

01453 834860
(Matchday & Club AdministrationCentre)
Fax: 01453 835291
Lawnside Fitness Suite: 01453 832268
Social Club: 01453 833295

SIMPLE DIRECTIONS:

About 4 miles south of Stroud on the A46 towards Bath. InNailsworth turn into Spring Hill from the mini roundabout and the ground is approx. half a mile up the hill on the left. The nearest BR station is Stroud

CAPACITY:	5,141
COVERED TERRACING:	2500
SEATED:	526

SOCIAL FACILITIES: Clubhouse open every evening. Bar and lounge. Open before and after Saturday matches.

CLUB SHOP: Open only on matchdays selling souvenirs and programmes. Contact Andy Whiting.

MATCHDAY PROGRAMME

Pages: 52 Price: £2.50
Editor: Clive White

Local Press: Stroud News & Journal
Gloucester Citizen

Local Radio: Star FM
BBC Radio Gloucestershire

Founded:	1890
Nickname:	Rovers
Sponsors:	Sheffield Insulations & Smiths (Gloucester) Ltd
Club Colours:	Black & white striped shirts, black shorts, red socks.
Change Colours:	Green & White
Midweek matchday:	Tuesday
Reserves' League:	College Academy
Youth League:	Glos. CountyYouth Lge
Club's Playing Status:	Part Time

CLUB OFFICIALS

President	Peter Vick
Vice President	John Duff
Chairman	Ken Boulton (acting)
Secretary	Colin Peake (acting)

c/o The Lawn, Nympsfield Road,
Forest Green, Nailsworth, Glos. GL6 0ET
Tel: 01453 834860 Fax: 01453 835291

Press Off. Heather Cook(daytime in club office)
Tel: 01453 823281 Mobile 07775 603287

Marketing: Robin Eaves

FOOTBALL MANAGEMENT TEAM

MANAGER: **TIM HARRIS**

Date of appointment
Date of Birth:
Place of Birth:

PREVIOUS CLUBS
As manager

As Asst. Man/Coach
As player

HONOURS
As manager
As player

Coach:	Alan McLoughlin
Physio:	Steve Lock
Youth Academy:	

Season	League	Div.	Pos.	Home P	Home W	Home D	Home L	Home F	Home A	Away W	Away D	Away L	Away F	Away A	Pts	Manager
03-04	Conference	-	18	42	6	8	7	32	36	6	4	11	26	44	48	Colin Addison
02-03	Conference	-	9	42	12	3	6	41	28	5	5	11	20	33	59	N Spink/ Colin Addison
01-02	Conference	-	18	42	7	7	7	28	32	5	8	8	26	44	51	Nigel Spink
00-01	Conference	-	16	42	6	9	6	28	28	5	6	10	15	26	48	F Gregan/ N. Spink & D. Norton
99-00	Conference	-	19	42	11	2	8	35	23	2	6	13	19	40	47	Frank Gregan
98-99	Conference	-	12	42	9	5	7	28	22	6	8	7	27	28	58	Frank Gregan
97-98	Southern	Prem	1	42	16	3	2	51	20	11	5	5	42	35	89	Frank Gregan

Season	League	Div.	Pos.	P	W	D	L	F	A	Pts	Manager
96-97	Southern	Southern	1	42	27	10	5	87	40	91	Frank Gregan
95-96	Southern	Southern	8	42	22	8	12	85	55	74	Frank Gregan
94-95	Southern	Midland	18	42	11	13	18	56	76	46	Frank Gregan

HONOURS

FA Trophy R-up 98-99,00-01
FA Vase 81-82,
Southern League - Premier Div . 97-98,
Southern Div . 96-97;
Hellenic Lg 81-82,
Gloucs Nthn Sen Lg 37-38 49-50 50-51,
Gloucs Sen Cup 84-85 85-86 86-87,
Gloucs Sen Amat Cup (N) 26-27 45-46 71-72 75-76 77-78,
Gloucs Sen Prof Cup 84-85 85-86 86-87.

PREVIOUS

Leagues: Stroud & Dist. 1890-1921, Glos Northern Snr 22-67, Glos Co. 67-73, Hellenic 73-82, Southern League 82-98, Conference 98-.

Name: Stroud FC, 1989-92

Ground: None

Past Players who progressed to the Football League

G Rogers (Newport Co. 85)
K Gill (Newport Co. 85),
M England (Bristol Rov 85).
Wayne Hatswell (Oxford Utd. 00)

CLUB RECORDS (since 1998)

Attendance: 3,002
v St. Albans City, FA Umbro Trophy 18.04.99

Win: 8-0
v Fareham Town Southern Lge. Southern Div. 96-97

Defeat: 0-7
v Moor Green, Southern Lge. Midland Div. 85-86.

Career Goalscorer: Karl Bayliss

Career Appearances: Alex Sykes

Transfer Fee paid: £20,000
for Adrian Randall from Salisbury City

Transfer Fee Received: £35,000
for Marc McGregor to Nuneaton Borough (July 2000)
for Wayne Hatswell to Oxford United (Dec. 2000)

BEST SEASON

FA Cup: 2nd Round 99-00
0-3 v Torquay Utd. (H)

FA Trophy: Runners-up 98-99, 00-01

FA Vase: Winners 81-82.

League: 12th Conference 98-99

LAST SEASON

F.A. Cup: 4th qualifying
F.A. Trophy: 4th round
Conference: 18th
Top Goalscorer: Neil Grayson
Player of the Year: Scott Rogers
Captain: **Jon Richardson**

FOREST GREEN ROVERS PLAYING SQUAD

	Birthplace	D.O.B.	Previous Clubs

Bold print denotes England semi-professional international.

GOALKEEPERS

Danny Greaves	**Bristol**	**07.12.83**	**Bristol Rovers**
Steve Perrin	Wiltshire	27.10.70	Melksham T, Trowbridge T

DEFENDER

Darren Davies	**Port Talbot**	**13.08.78**	**Dover A, Morton, Barry T, Tottenham`H**
Matt Gadsby	**Sutton Coldf'd**	**06.09.79**	**Kidderminster H, Mansfield T, Walsall**
Tom Gould	**Bristol**		**Chippenham T, Team Bath, Bath, Odd Down**
Kevin Langan British Univ.	Jersey	07.04.78	Team Bath, Bristol C
Jon Richardson	Nottingham	29.08.75	Oxford United, Exeter City

MIDFIELD

Daniel Allen	Swindon	09.09.83	From Youth team
Simon Bryant	Bristo	22.11.82	Bristol Rovers
Ben Cleverley	Bristol	12.09.81	Cheltenham T, Bristol City
Rob Cook DMP	Stroud	28.03.70	Basingstoke T, Forest Green R, Cinderford T, Forest Green R, Shortwood Utd
Jonn Holloway	Swindon	11.02.77	Worcester C, Bath C, Gloucester C, Swindon T
Scott Rogers	Bath	23.05.79	Tiverton Town
Matthew Russell	Dewsbury	17.01.78	Exeter City, Scarborough, Halifax Town, Doncaster Rovers Scarborough.
Alex Sykes British Univ., DMP	Newcastle-u-Lyme	02.04.74	Nuneaton B, Forest Green R, Endsleigh, Cheltenham T, Mansfield T., Westfields

FORWARDS

Adi Adams	Rinteln, Germany	12.06.84	Youth Team
Mark Beesley	Lancaster		Hererford United, Chester City, P.N.E.
Steve Cowe	Gloucester	29.09.74	Newport County, Hereford Utd., Swindon Town (£100,000), Aston Villa (YT)
Charlie Griffin	Bath	25.06.79	Chippenham T, Woking, Swindon T, Chippenham T,
			Melksham Town
Luke Jones			YouthTeam

GRAVESEND & NORTHFLEET

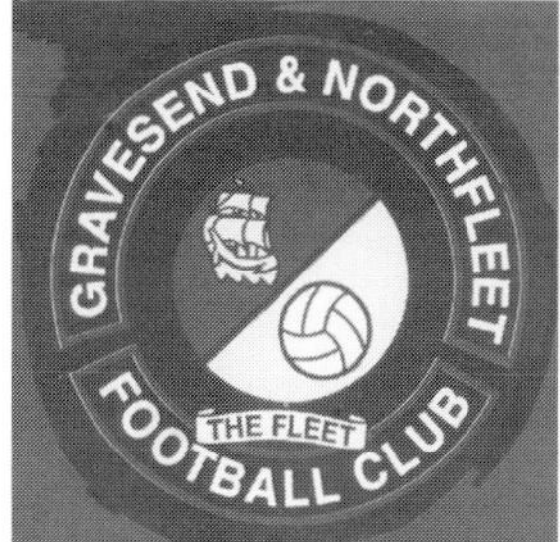

THE FLEET had an initially nerve wracking campaign, which would have been almost a disaster had the side not done so well in the FA Cup, in which the team reached the Second Round Proper after some difficult moments first involving two Fourth Qualifying matches against Exeter City, the first being without a goal and the replay going to extra-time and six shared goals followed by penalties and a six-five survival.

A First Round Proper trip to ultimate Conference Champions Chester City was settled by a Justin Skinner penalty and brave defence, but the Second Round visit of Notts County before a crowd of nearly 3,000 was almost a success with a single goal bringing departure from the competition.

The FA Trophy was not an occasion for headlines as Weston-super-Mare came to Stonebridge Road, left with an equal share of four goals and then scored the only one in the replay, but this seemed to galvanised the side and two inspired signings in February - Manny Omoyinmi from Oxford United on loan and Roy Essendoh (scorer of ten goals in fourteen outings) for £4,000 from Bishop's Stortford - led to a run of victories with no defeats in the season's last dozen games, which included a six clear goal thrashing of highly placed Morecambe.

The final league position was eleventh, it's an improvement on the previous campaign's sixteenth and this brought an added bonus of a place in the 2004-05 LDV Vans Trophy, so manager Andy Ford can look forward with optimism to the team's immediate future - as if anyone ever can in what Jimmy Greaves has described as a 'funny old game'!

W.M.

GRAVESEND & NORTHFLEET

Match Facts 2003-04

The number shown directly below the player's name is his squad number.
Where a number is shown instead of an "X' in the columns this represents a substitute appearance and the number indicates the player replaced.

Comp.	Date	Opponents	Venue.	Result	Goalscorers	Att.
Conf 1	Aug 09	Burton A	H	L 1-2	Strouts	1137
Conf 2	Aug 12	Woking	A	L 2-3	Pinnock Abbey	2096
Conf 3	Aug 16	Halifax T	A	L 0-1		1675
Conf 4	Aug 23	Telford U	H	L 1-2	Gradley	834
Conf 5	Aug 25	Farnborough T	A	W 2-1	McKimm Pinnock	839
Conf 6	Aug 30	Chester C	H	L 0-4		939
Conf 7	Sep 06	Scarborough	A	L 0-2		1249
Conf 8	Sep 13	Leigh RMI	H	W 3-1	Owen Howarth Moore	723
Conf 9	Sep 20	Exeter C	H	W 3-1	Pinnock(2) Haworth	1155
Conf 10	Sep 23	Stevenage B	A	D 2-2	Drury Lee	1732
Conf 11	Sep 27	Hereford U	A	D 3-3	Haworth(2) Miller	3731
Conf 12	Oct 04	Forest Green R	H	D 1-1	Drury	1190
Conf 13	Oct 07	Aldershot T	H	L 1-3	Haworth	1477
Conf 14	Oct 11	Morecambe	A	D 2-2	Abbey Gradley	1539
Conf 15	Oct 18	Northwich V	A	D 0-0		542
FAC 4q	**Oct 25**	**Exeter C**	**A**	**D 0-0**		**2686**
FAC 4qr	**Oct 28**	**Exeter C**	**H**	**D 3-3***	**Moore Abbey Howarth (won 6-5 on pens)**	**1227**
Conf 16	Nov 01	Accrington S	H	D 0-0		1274
FAC 1	**Nov 08**	**Chester C**	**A**	**W 1-0**	**Skinner(p)**	**2251**
Conf 17	Nov 11	Barnet	A	L 0-1		1542
Conf 18	Nov 15	Shrewsbury T	H	L 0-3		1397
Conf 19	Nov 22	Tamworth	A	W 3-1	Perkins(2) Drury	1178
Conf 20	Nov 25	Dagenham & R	H	L 1-2	Drury	1274
Conf 21	Nov 29	Scarborough	H	D 1-1	Perkins	747
FAC 2	**Dec 06**	**Notts County**	**H**	**L 1-2**	**Perkins**	**2998**
Conf 22	Dec 13	Burton A	A	L 0-3		1403
Conf 23	Dec 20	Woking	H	D 2-2	Abbey Drury(p)	975
Conf 24	Dec 27	Margate	A	W 3-1	Moore Haworth Abbey	1030
Conf 25	Jan 01	Margate	H	W 2-1	Moore Duku	1725
Conf 26	Jan 03	Chester C	A	D 2-2	Moore(2)	2670
FAT 3	**Jan 10**	**Weston Super Mare**	**H**	**D 2-2**	**Haworth Abbey**	**670**
Conf 27	Jan 17	Halifax T	H	W 1-0	Evans	985
FAT 3r	**Jan 20**	**Weston Super Mare**	**A**	**L 0-1**		**325**
Conf 28	Jan 24	Stevenage B	H	L 2-3	Drury(p) Moore	1230
Conf 29	Feb 07	Exeter C	A	W 1-0	Essandoh	3303
Conf 30	Feb 14	Hereford U	H	L 2-5	Abbey(2)	1230
Conf 31	Feb 21	Forest Green R	A	W 2-1	Essandoh(2)	752
Conf 32	Feb 28	Morecambe	H	W 6-0	Perkins(2) Pinnock(2) Owen Drury(p)	1061
Conf 33	Mar 06	Aldershot T	A	D 2-2	Essandoh Omoyinmi	2736
Conf 34	Mar 13	Barnet	H	D 1-1	Moore	1516
Conf 35	Mar 27	Tamworth	H	W 2-0	Omoyinmi Drury	1157
Conf 36	Mar 30	Leigh RMI	A	W 2-1	Pinnock Essandoh	304
Conf 37	Apr 03	Dagenham & R	A	W 4-0	Walshe(2) Essandoh Pinnock	1421
Conf 38	Apr 10	Telford U	A	D 1-1	Sidibe	1746
Conf 39	Apr 12	Farnborough T	H	W 2-0	Drury Essandoh	1284
Conf 40	Apr 17	Accrington S	A	D 3-3	Essandoh(2) Perkins	1139
Conf 41	Apr 20	Shrewsbury T	A	D 1-1	Shearer	2869
Conf 42	Apr 24	Northwich V	H	D 2-2	Essandoh Pinnock	1436

STEP 1
CONFERENCE

STEP 2 - P177
CONFERENCE Nth & Sth

STEP 3 - P269
NPL, Southern, Isthmian Premier

STEP 4 - P269
NPL 1, Southern N&S, Isthmian 1

STEP 5/6 - P473
Current level 3 leagues

STEP 7 - P713
Current level 4 leagues

Alex O'REILLY	Charlie MITTEN	Matt LEE	Justin SKINNER	Adrian PENNOCK	Robin TROTT	Paul GIBBS	Manny OMOYINMI	Francis DUKU	Steve McKIMM	Robert OWEN	Ben ABBEY	Louie EVANS	Dennis OLI	Ludovic QUISTIN	Roy ESSANDOH	Paul WILKERSON	Leroy HUGGINS	Rob HAWORTH	Jamie PINNOCK	Tostao KWASHI	Ben WALSHE	Jimmy STROUTS	Lee SHEARER	Scott GOODWIN	Chris MOORE	Eddie McCLEMENTS	Steve PERKINS	Pat GRADLEY	Andy DRURY	Adam MILLER	Moussa SIDIBE	Anthony FINN	Tony BATTERSBY	Lee PROTHEROE	Wes DALY	Lee GLEDHILL	Ben SUREY	Matthew ROUSE
1	**1**	**2**	**3**	**4**	**5**	**5**	**5**	**6**	**7**	**8**	**9**	**10**	**11**	**11**	**11**	**12**	**14**	**14**	**15**	**16**	**16**	**17**	**18**	**19**	**19**	**20**	**21**	**22**	**23**	**25**	**25**	**26**	**26**	**27**	**28**	**29**	**30**	**31**
x			x	x	x			x	x		x						x		4	14		x				x	x	9										
x		x		x				x	x	16	x						x		14	x		x	21			x	x											
x		x	x	x	6			x	x	x		8							x			x	x	21			x											
x		x	x	x					x	x		3						x	x			2	x	4			x	x										
x		x	x						x	x	15							x	x				x			x	x	x										
x		x	x						x	x	20							x	x				x			x	x	x										
x		x	x					x	x	x								x	x		x	6	x			15	14	x										
x		x	x						x	x	14					1		x	x		x		x		x		16	x										
		x								x						x		x	x		x	25	x		x	x		x	22	x								
		x								x						x		x	x		x		x		x	x		x	20	x								
								15		x						x		x	x		x	x	x		x	x	17	x	20	x								
			x						23	x						x		x	x			25	x		x		x	x	x	x								
			x						x		3					x		x	x		x		x		x		x	x	x			23						
		x						x	x	x	15					x		x	x		x	18	x				x	x	16									
		x						x	x	x	15					x		x	x		x				x		x	x	22									
		x	**x**					**x**	**x**	**x**	**x**					**x**		**x**	**9**		**x**		**x**					**x**	**22**									
		x	**x**					**x**	**x**	**x**	**x**					**x**		**x**	**16**		**x**				**x**		**x**		**21**									
		x	x					x	x	x	x	16				x		x			x				x		x		21						3			
		x	**x**					**x**	**x**	**x**						**x**		**x**	**x**		**x**				**x**		**x**		**16**									
		x	x					x	x	x	15					x		x	x			3			x		x		x									
		x				x		x	x	x	x					x		x	2		8		14		x		x		x									
		x						x	x	x			x			x					x				x	x	x		x									
		x						x	x	x			x			x					x	7			x	x	x		x									
		x							x	x			x			x		x	14		23		x		x	x	x		x									
12		**x**				**x**			**x**		**15**					**x**			**x**		**x**	**x**	**x**		**x**		**x**	**16**	**x**									
		x				x		19	x		23					x		x			x		x		x		x		x					x				
		x						x	x		x		x			x					x				x		x		x					x				
								x	x	x	x	16				x		x			x				x	x			x					x				
		27						x	x	x	x	16				x		x			x				x	x	23		x					x				
		x						x	x	x	14		x			x		x			21				x		x		x					x				
		x						**x**	**x**	**x**	**x**	**9**				**x**		**x**			**x**		**x**			**x**			**x**									
12			x					x	x	x		x				x		x			x		x				23		x					x		16		
x		**x**	**x**					**x**	**x**	**x**		**x**		**16**				**x**	**10**		**x**				**x**				**x**									
x			x					x	x	x	x	9			x								29		x		11		x					x		x		
x			x							x	x				x				9				x		x		x		x					x		x		
			x						21	x	x				x	x		29					x		x		x		x					x		x		
			x						x	x	x				x	x			9				x		x		x		x		8			x				
			x				15		x	x					x	x			x				x		x		x		x		23		11			x		
		9	x				x		x	x	29				x	x			x				x		x		x				8					x		
			x				x		x	x	15					x			x				x		x		x		x		23					x		
			x				x		x	x					x	x							x		x		x		x		8					x	19	
		18	x				x		x						x	x			5		11		x		x				x		x					x	x	
		x	x						x	21					x	x			x		15				x		x				x					x	x	3
	x	x	x						x						x				25						x		x		x		x					x	x	
	x	x	x				15		x						x				x		x				x		30		x		23					x	x	
	x	29	x				15		x						x				x				x		x		x				x					x	x	
	x	x	x						x						x				x				x		x		x		x		21						x	
	x	x							x	30	19				x				x		25		x		x				x		x						x	x

GRAVESEND & NORTHFLEET

GROUND DETAILS

Stonebridge Road,
Northfleet,
Kent
DA11 9GN
Tel: 01474 533796

Directions: From A2 take Northfleet/Southfleet exit (B262), follow toNorthfleet then B2175 (Springhead Rd) to junc A226, turn left (The Hill, Northfleet), road becomes Stonebridge Rd, grd on right at bottom of steep hill after 1 mile - car parking for 400-500. 2 mins from Northfleet BR station

Capacity:	4,184
Cover:	3,000
Seats:	500

Clubhouse: Fleet Social Centre. Hot and cold food available at tea bars on matchdays

Club Shop: Sells progs, hats, scarves, badges etc, & other memorabilia. Contact: Jessica McQueen

MATCHDAY PROGRAMME

Pages: 46 Price: £2.00
Editor: Paul Harrison
Clubcall: 09066 555844
Local Press: Gravesend Reporter, Kent Messenger. Gravesend Messenger
Local Radio: Invicta Radio, Radio Kent.

Formed:	1946
Nickname:	The Fleet
Sponsors:	Gravesend Reporter
Colours:	Red/white/red
Change colours:	Sky Blue/Green/Green
Midweek matchday:	Tuesday
Youth Team:	P.A.S.E. League
Website:	www.gnfc.co.uk
Clubcall line:	09066 555844

CLUB OFFICIALS

Chairman: Brian Kilcullen

Vice Chairman: Jason Botley

Directors: Bob Gunton, Adrian Felstead, MIck Ward and GlennAitken,Roly Edwards and Mark Lindop.

Company & Football Secretary: Roly Edwards c/o Football Club

Commercial Manager &Press Officer: Glen Aitken
Tel: 01474 533796 (W)
email: info@gnfc.co.uk

FOOTBALL MANAGEMENT TEAM

MANAGER	**ANDY FORD**
Date of Appointment	September 1997
Date of Birth:	4th May 1954
Place of Birth:	Minehead
PREVIOUS CLUBS	
As manager	
As asst. manager/coach	
As player	Minehead, AFC Bournemouth, Southend U., Swindon T., Gillingham
HONOURS	
As manager	Isthmian Lge Premier Div. 01-02, Full Members Cup 00-01, Kent Senr Cup 99-00, 00-01,01-2

Assistant Manager:	Phil Handford
Coach:	Ron Hillyard and Neil Withington
Physio:	Dave Lawson
Club's Playing Status:	Part -time

Season	League	Div.	Pos.	Home P	W	D	L	F	A	Away W	D	L	F	A	Pts	Manager
03-04	Conference	-	11	42	7	6	8	34	35	7	9	5	35	31	57	Andy Ford
02-03	Conference	-	17	42	8	5	8	37	35	4	7	10	25	38	48	Andy Ford
01-02	Isthmian	Prem.	1	42	14	4	3	43	18	17	2	2	47	15	99	Andy Ford
00-01	Isthmian	Prem.	6	42	12	3	6	32	21	10	2	9	31	25	71	Andy Ford
99-00	Isthmian	Prem.	11	42	9	6	6	36	25	6	4	11	30	42	55	Andy Ford
98-99	Isthmian	Prem.	10	42	11	2	8	31	23	7	4	10	23	30	60	Andy Ford
97-98	Isthmian	Prem.	13	42	10	5	6	41	25	5	3	13	24	42	53	Steve Lovell
96-97	Southern	Prem.	14	42	10	4	7	34	27	6	3	12	29	46	55	Chris Weller

Season	League	Div.	Pos.	P	W	D	L	F	A	Pts	Manager
95-96	Southern	Prem.	11	42	15	10	17	60	62	55	Gary Aldous
94-95	Southern	Prem.	14	42	13	13	16	38	55	52	Gary Aldous

HONOURS

Isthmian League (Rymans) Champions: 2001-2002
Isthmian Lague Full Members Cup 2001-02
Southern League Southern League 57
Southern Div 94-95,
Div 1 Sth 74-75 R-up 70-71 88-89,
Lg Cup 77-78 R-up 57-58,
Champ Cup 77-78;
Kent Sen Cup 48-49 52-53 80-81, 99-00,00-01,01-02
R-up 47-48 76-77 90-91 97-98;
Kent Floodlit Cup 69-70 R-up 72-73;
Kent Sen Shield R-up 47-48 51-52;
Kent Interm Cup R-up 87-88;
Kent Midweek Lg 95-96, R-up 92-93 93-94 94-95;
Kent Youth Lg 95-96 96-97;
Lg Cup 82-83 86-87 96-97

PREVIOUS

Leagues: Kent (Gravesend Utd), Southern 46-79, 80-96 Alliance Prem. 79-80 Isthmian 1997-2002

Names: Gravesend Utd.and Northfleet Utd (merged 1946)

Ground: Central Avenue (Gravesend Utd) (Northfleet always played at StonebridgeRd)

Past Players who progressed to the Football League

Several incl. most recently:
K Baron (Aldershot 60), R Dwight (Coventry 62), R Cameron (Southend 63), R McNichol (Carlisle 65), A Humphreys (Mansfield 64), B Thornley (Brentford 65), P Jeavons (Lincoln 66), B Fry (Orient 66), B Gordine (Sheffield Utd 68), T Baldwin (Brentford 77), L Smelt (Nottm Forest 80), T Warrilow (Torquay 87), J.Bullard (West Ham U.98)

CLUB RECORDS

Attendance: 12,036
v Sunderland, FA Cup 4th Rd 12.2.63.
26.081
v Aston Villa FA Cup 3rd Rd 95-96 at Villa Park
Goalscorer: Steve Portway 150+(92-94, 97-01)
Appearances: Ken Burrett 537
Win: 8-1
v Clacton Tn, Sth Lge 62-63, (7-0 Godalming 95-96 FAC).
Defeat: 0-9
v Trowbridge Tn, Southern Lge Prem Div 91-92
Fee Paid: £8,000
for Richard Newbery (Wokingham 96), & for Craig Williams(Tonbridge 97)
Fee Received: £35,000
for Jimmy Bullard (West Ham 1998)

BEST SEASON

FA Cup: 4th Round
Replay 1963, 2-5 v Sunderland (A), 1-1 (H)

FA Trophy: Fifth Round 01-02

League: 5th in The Alliance Premier 79-80

LAST SEASON

F.A. Cup: 1st Round Proper
F.A. Trophy: 3rd Round
League: 11th
Top Goalscorer: Roy Essandoh
Player of the Year: Chris Moore
Captain: Steve McKimm

GRAVESEND & NORTHFLEET PLAYING SQUAD

Bold print denotes England semi-professional international.

	Birthplace	D.O.B.	Previous Clubs
GOALKEEPERS			
John Slade			Youth Team
Paul Wilkerson	Hertford	11.12.74	Stevenage B, Welling Utd, Hayes, Slough T, Watford
DEFENDERS			
Francis Duku RP	London	-	Dulwich Hamlet, Grays Ath., Crawley T, Romford, Crawley T., Maidenhead U., Collier Row, Reading, West Ham
Adrian Pennock	Ipswich	27.03.71	Gillingham, Bournemouth, Molde (Nor.), Norwich (App)
Graham Porter	Kent	29.10.74	Margate, Ashford T, Erith & B, Horsham, Maidstone U
Matthew Rouse	London	12.11.83	FIsher Athletic, Bristol City, Arsenal
Jay Saunders	Kent	15.01.79	Margate, Gravesend & N, Gillingham
Lee Shearer	Rochford	23.10.77	Margate, Dover Athletic, Jaro FC (Finland), Leyton Orient
Justin Skinner RP	Dorking	17.09.72	Aylesbury Utd, Wimbledon
Robin Trott	Orpington	17.08.74	Grays Athletic, Stevenage Borough, Welling United, Mansion F.C. (Hong Kong), Gillingham (YTS)
MIDFIELD			
Andrew Drury	Kent	28.11.83	Sittingbourne (£1,700)
Lee Gledhill	Bury	01.11.80	St Albans City, Barnet
Jimmy Jackson	Kent		Dagenham & R, Gravesend, Charlton A
Steve McKimm RP	London	30.07.75	Kingstonian, Hayes, Farnborough T, Dulwich Hamlet, Molesey, Hendon
Robert Owen RP	Kent	-	Sittingbourne, Tonbridge, Sittingbourne, Gillingham
FORWARDS			
Ben Abbey	Reading		Macclesfield T., Woking, Stevenage Bor.Southend Utd, Oxford Utd, CrawleyT., Maidenhead Utd, Osterlerly
Roy Essandoh	Belfast	17.02.76	Bishop's St.,Grays, Billericay,Bishop's St,Camb.City
	Barnet, Wycombe W, Rushden& D, St Polten (Austria), VPS Vaasa (Finland), East Fife, Motherwell		
Francis Kumbu **Nigeria Full Int**	Nigeria		Scarborough, Aldershot,Molesey, Haywards Heath, Yeovil T, Gaylang (Singapore)
Dennis Oli	Newham	28.01.84	Q.P.R.
Manny Omoyinmi	Nigeria	28.12.77	Oxford United, West Ham United
Robert Owen	Kent	-	Sittingbourne, Tonbridge, Sittingbourne, Gillingham
James Pinnock	Dartford	01.08.78	Kingstonian, Chesham Utd (L), Dover Ath. (L), Gillingham (App)

HALIFAX TOWN

FOR The Shaymen this was a most frustrating season, but it could have been worse as a good start meant that hopes were entertained that they might qualify for the play-offs, but this was an illusion after an excellent start.

A poor period in September was later followed by a run of ten successive defeats from 8th February, which left the spectre of relegation, and this disaster was only averted by eight points being obtained from the final four games, so Conference fare in the new campaign is better than something worse, and there is still the chance of a step up to the Football League in the near future.

Cup competitions brought varied results with a visit to Northwich Victoria in the Fourth Qualifying Round producing a single goal for the hosts and departure, while in the FA Trophy Chester City finished on he wrong end of a three goal match on their own pitch, and this was followed by a tough tie against Staines Town, who shared two goals at The Shay and then lost in extra-time in the replay by the odd goal in five, so prospects of a big day in May looked very good until Maidenhead United arrived for the Fifth Round and scored the only two goals of the encounter.

There was another bright note to record in a difficult season, which was a fine performance in the LDV Vans Trophy and this saw victories at home to York City (2-1), at Scarborough by a single counter and by the same score at home to Lincoln City before Blackpool made home advantage count in the Northern Semi-finals by the odd goal in five - a thriller and the best effort so far in the short history of competition.

All was not doom and gloom, but that kind of form showed that the potential exists but it must be repeated on a regular basis before the promised land is reclaimed.

W.M.

Back Row (L-R): Adam Quinn, Simon Parke, Ryan Poole (GK), Shaun Garnett, Clint Davies (GK), Christian Lee, Mark Monington. Middle Row: Tommy Geldert (Fitness coach), Michael Senior, Kevin Sandwith, Jon Cullen, Darren Hockenhull, Andy Farrell, Ryan Hindley, Alan Jackson (Club physio). Front Row: Daniel Hudson, Craig Midgley, Lewis Killeen, Paul Stoneman (youth team manager), Chris Wilder (Manager), Sean McAuley (Asst. Manager), Steve Bushell, Lee Elam, Ryan Mallon.

HALIFAX TOWN

Match Facts 2003-04

The number shown directly below the player's name is his squad number.
Where a number is shown instead of an "X' in the columns this represents a substitute appearance and the number indicates the player replaced.

Comp.	Date	Opponents	Venue.	Result	Goalscorers	Att.
Conf 1	Aug 09	Exeter C	A	D 1-1	Killeen	3723
Conf 2	Aug 12	Morecambe	H	W 1-0	Cameron	2160
Conf 3	Aug 16	Gravesend & N	H	W 1-0	Mallon	1675
Conf 4	Aug 23	Leigh RMI	A	D 1-1	Midgley	849
Conf 5	Aug 25	Tamworth	H	L 1-2	Midgley	1849
Conf 6	Aug 30	Barnet	A	L 1-4	Midgley	1341
Conf 7	Sep 06	Northwich V	H	W 5-3	Killeen(2) Elam Lee Midgley(p)	1440
Conf 8	Sep 13	Chester C	A	L 0-2		2628
Conf 9	Sep 20	Margate	H	L 0-1		1452
Conf 10	Sep 23	Shrewsbury T	A	L 0-2		3807
Conf 11	Sep 27	Forest Green R	A	W 2-1	Elam Farrell	722
Conf 12	Oct 04	Stevenage B	H	W 2-1	Farrell Lee	1437
Conf 13	Oct 07	Accrington S	H	D 1-1	Lee	2116
Conf 14	Oct 11	Aldershot T	A	L 1-3	Monington	2882
LDVT 1	**Oct 14**	**York City**	**H**	**W 2-1**	**Mallon Quinn**	**1148**
Conf 15	Oct 18	Woking	A	D 2-2	Mallon Bushell	1917
FAC 4q	**Oct 26**	**Northwich V**	**A**	**L 0-1**		**1101**
Conf 16	Nov 01	Dagenham & R	H	W 3-0	Lee Sandwith McCombe	1379
LDVT 2	**Nov 04**	**Scarborough**	**A**	**W 1-0**	**Midgley(p)**	**889**
Conf 17	Nov 11	Telford U	H	D 1-1	Lee	1332
Conf 18	Nov 14	Burton A	A	D 2-2	Killeen Midgley(p)	1541
Conf 19	Nov 22	Farnborough T	H	W 2-0	Midgley(2p)	1250
Conf 20	Nov 25	Hereford U	A	L 1-7	Killeen	1875
Conf 21	Nov 29	Northwich V	A	W 1-0	Bushell	757
Conf 22	Dec 06	Chester C	H	L 0-3		1928
Conf 23	Dec 13	Exeter C	H	W 2-0	Sagare Midgley(p)	1267
LDVT 3	**Dec 16**	**Lincoln City**	**H**	**W 1-0**	**Sandwith**	**1162**
Conf 24	Dec 20	Morecambe	A	L 0-2		1603
Conf 25	Dec 26	Scarborough	H	W 1-0	Lee	2136
Conf 26	Jan 03	Barnet	H	L 1-2	Killeen	1517
FAT 3	**Jan 10**	**Chester C**	**A**	**W 2-1**	**Killeen Farrell**	**1561**
Conf 27	Jan 17	Gravesend & N	A	L 0-1		985
LDVT 4	**Jan 20**	**Blackpool**	**A**	**L 2-3**	**Killeen Owen**	**4764**
Conf 28	Jan 24	Shrewsbury T	A	D 0-0		1830
Conf 29	Feb 08	Margate	A	L 0-2		391
FAT 4	**Feb 10**	**Staines Town**	**H**	**D 1-1**	**Sills(og)**	**1020**
FAT 4r	**Feb 12**	**Staines Town**	**A**	**W 3-2**	**Farrell(2,1p) Quinn**	**728**
FAT 5	**Feb 14**	**Maidenhead Utd**	**H**	**L 0-2**		**1345**
Conf 30	Feb 21	Stevenage B	A	L 0-1		1715
Conf 31	Feb 24	Aldershot T	H	L 1-2	Mallon	843
Conf 32	Mar 06	Accrington S	A	L 1-2	Owen	1717
Conf 33	Mar 09	Forest Green R	H	L 0-1		883
Conf 34	Mar 13	Telford U	A	L 1-2	Killeen	1337
Conf 35	Mar 25	Scarborough	A	L 0-1		1220
Conf 36	Mar 27	Farnborough T	A	L 0-1		644
Conf 37	Mar 30	Burton A	H	L 1-4	Little	1128
Conf 38	Apr 03	Hereford U	H	L 1-2	Midgley(p)	1389
Conf 39	Apr 10	Leigh RMI	H	W 2-1	Allan Bushell	1415
Conf 40	Apr 12	Tamworth	A	L 0-2		1095
Conf 41	Apr 17	Dagenham & R	A	W 1-0	Midgley(p)	1344
Conf 42	Apr 24	Woking	H	D 2-2	Little(p) Midgley	1191

STEP 1
CONFERENCE

STEP 2 - P177
CONFERENCE Nth & Sth

STEP 3 - P269
NPL, Southern, Isthmian Premiers

STEP 4 - P269
NPL 1, Southern N&S, Isthmian 1

STEP 5/6 - P473
Current level 3 leagues

STEP 7 - P713
Current level 4 leagues

Clint DAVIES	Darren HOCKENHULL	Kevin SANDWITH	Steve BUSHELL	Mark MONINGTON	Shaun GARNETT	Denny INGRAM	Ryan MALLON	Craig MIDGLEY	Christian LEE	Lewis KILLEEN	Lee ELAM	Val OWEN	Adam QUINN	Mark CARTWRIGHT	Paul STONEMAN	Michael SENIOR	Simon PARKE	Lewis TOZER	Karl COLLEY	Colin LITTLE	Dave CAMERON	Clayton DONALDSON	Rory MAY	Jon CULLEN	Jamie McCOMBE	Ben THORNLEY	Danny HUDSON	Jake SAGARE	James DUDGEON	ndy FARRELL	Sean McCAULEY	Jamie PRICE	Adam YATES	Jon ALLAN	Peter NAYLOR	Ryan GOLDEN	Matthew HOYLE	Scott LOWE	David CARNEY	Craig Parry
1	2	3	4	5	6	6	7	8	9	10	11	11	12	13	14	15	16	16	16	16	17	17	17	18	18	18	19	20	21	22	23	24	24	25	26	27	28	29	30	31
x	x	x	x	x	x		x	2		x	x						11				x			x			7													
x		x	x	x	x		x	7		x	x						17				x			x			11					x								
x		x		x	x		x	19	17	x	x		5								x			x			x					x								
x		x	19		x		x	x	17	x	x		x				6				x						x					x								
x		x	x		x		x	18	x	x	x		x				9							x						7		x								
x		x	x		x		11	x	17	x	x		x								x						x			24		x								
x	x	x	x	x	x		x	x	x	x	x										9									7	11									
x	x	x	x	x	x		9	x	x	x	x		2				18							x																
	x	x	x		x		11	x	x	x	x		x	x							9			x				18												
	x	x	x	x	x			x	18	x	16			x				x			x			x				17												
	x	x	x	x	x		x	11	x		x			x				x									x	9		16										
	x	x	x	x			x	4	x		x			x				11									x	22	x	x										
	x	x	x	x			x		x	11	x			x							9						x		x	x										
	x	x	x	x			x	22		x	x			x													x	11	x	x										
	x	x	x				x	11		x	x		x	x		10		20									x	x	x											
	x	x	x	x			x	10	20	x	x		x	x													x	x	5											
	x	x	x	x			x	7	x	x	x		x	x													x	11	5											
	x	x	x				x	x	x				x	x		9									x		x	x							20	7				
	x	x	x				x	x	x	20			x	x													x	x	x											
	x	x	x				x	x	x	x			x	x											x		x	9												
	x	x				x	x		x			x	x											x		x	x			20		x								
	7	x	x				x	x	x	x				x											x		x		x	9	8		x							
		x	x	21			x	x	x	x				x											x		x	10	x	9			x							
	8	x	x	x			x	x		x				x											x		x	22		x			x							
			x	x			x	x	x	20		19		x											x		x	x			x		x	9						
		x	x				x	19	x			x		x					x								x	9	x	23	x		x							
	8	x	x				x	x				x		x					x								4	x	x	x			x	22						
		x					x	x	22	8		x		x					x								x	x	x	x			x	20						
	7	x	x				x	x	22			x		x					x								20	x	x	x			x							
				x			x	x	x	x		x		x													x	19	x	9	x		x							
	x	x		x			x	x		x						x											x	7		25	x			x						x
	x	x		x				x		x		x	19						x								x	23		8	x			x						x
	x	x	x	x			x	x	7	x		x	8	x					x									x		20										
	x	x	x	x			x	x	20	x		x		x					x								8	x												
	x	x	x	x			x	11	x			x	9	x					x			20					x	x												
	x	x	x	x			x	x	x	x		x	x	x													10			9										
	x	x	x	x			x	x	x			x	x	x													11	9		x			2							
	25	x	x	x			24	x		x			x	x													x	x		10			x	x						
	x	x	x	x			8	x				x	x	x					20			x					11	x						x						
	x	x	x	x			x	x				x	x	x								x					11	17			7			x						
	x	x	x	x			x	x				x	x	x		25						20						x						x						
	20	x	x	x			x	x				x	x										x			7		x					x	24						x
	x		x	x				x	8	x		x	x	x									x			x		17			x								11	
	x		x			x	x			x			x	x						x			2			30	x	7			x								x	
	x		x	x			11		x	x		x	x	x						x											x		x	10						
	x		x				x		x	x		x	x	x	7					x											x		x	9						
	x		x			x	11	x		x		x	x	x						x							25			2	x			x						
	x		x	25		x		x		x		30	x	x						x										16	x			x					x	
	x		x	x		x	23	x		x			x	x		25				x										10	x			x						
	x		x	x		x		x		x			x	x						x														x				x		
	x		x	x		x	10	x		x			x	x		6				x														x			8	x		

HALIFAX TOWN

GROUND DETAILS

The Shay Stadium
Halifax
West Yorks.
HX1 2YS
Tel: 01422 341222
Fax: 01422 349487
email: theshay@halifaxafc.co.uk
Website: halifaxafc.co.uk

Directions: M62, J24, head towards the city centre. The ground is on the right signposted "The Shay"
Nearest Railway station: Halifax, 1/2 mile from ground

Capacity:	**9,500**
Covered Seating:	**2,500**
Covered Standing:	**7,000**

Clubhouse: Yes, open during normal licensing hours.

Club Shop: Yes, contact club.

MATCHDAY PROGRAMME

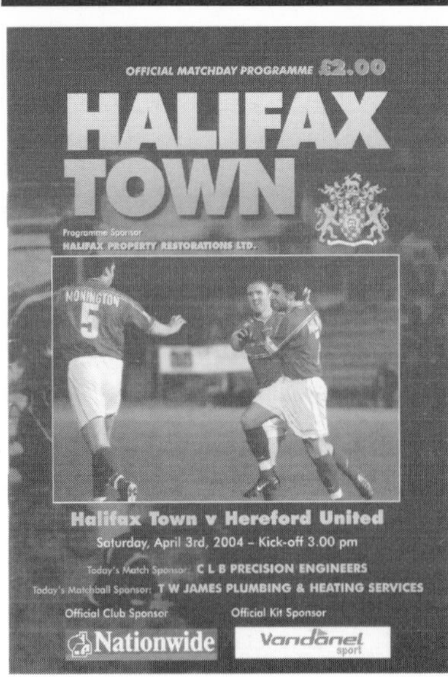

Price: £2 Pages: 32
Editor: Tony Charlton

Founded:	1911
Nickname:	The Shaymen
Sponsors:	Nationwide B.S.
Colours:	Blue shirts, white shorts, blue socks
Change colours:	White shirts, blue shorts, white socks
Midweek matchday:	Tuesday 7.45

CLUB OFFICIALS

President: Bob Holmes

Chairman: David Cairns

Vice-Chairman: Adrian Hall

Other Directors: Bob Bland, T Charlton, Martin Fox,Richard Harrison, Ray Moreland (HTST Representative), Phil Jewitt

Chief Executive: Tony Kniveton

Club Secretary: Richard Groves
c/o the club Tel: 0771 5254323 (M)

Commercial Manager: Gavin Butler
Tel:07966 167078
e-mail:commercial@halifaxafc.co.uk

FOOTBALL MANAGEMENT TEAM

MANAGER: CHRIS WILDER

Date of Appointment	June 2002
Date of Birth:	23rd September 1967
Place of Birth:	Wortley

PREVIOUS CLUBS

As player/manager	Alfreton Town 01-02
As player	Southampton (A), Sheffield Utd., Rotherham Utd., Notts Co., Bradford C., Sheffield Utd., Brighton & H.A., Halifax T., Alfreton T.

HONOURS

As manager	NCE 01-02 - League Championship, League Cup, President's Cup

* * *

Player Coach	Sean McCauley
Youth Team Coach:	Paul Stoneman
Physiotherapist:	Alan Jackson

Season	League	Div.	Pos.	Home (or total)						Away						
				P	W	D	L	F	A	W	D	L	F	A	Pts	Manager
03-04	Conference	-	19	42	9	4	8	28	26	3	4	14	15	39	44	Chris Wilder
02-03	Conference	-	8	42	11	5	5	34	28	7	5	9	16	23	64	Chris Wilder
01-02	League	Div.3	24	46	5	9	9	24	28	3	3	177	15	56	36	Paul Bracewell/Alan Little
00-01	League	Div.3	23	46	7	6	10	33	32	5	5	13	21	36	47	Paul Bracewell
99-00	League	Div.3	18	46	15	9	22	44	58						54	Mark Lillis
98-99	League	Div.3	10	46	10	8	5	33	25	7	7	9	25	31	66	Kieran O'Regan
97-98	Conference		1	42	17	4	0	51	15	8	8	5	23	28	87	G. Mulhall & K. O'Regan
96-97	Conference		19	42	9	5	7	39	37	3	7	11	16	37	48	J. Carroll/G. Mulhall&K. O'Regan
95-96	Conference		15	42	13	13	16	49	63						52	John Bird/John Carroll
94-95	Conference		8	42	17	12	13	68	54						63	John Bird

CLUB RECORDS

Attendance: 36,885
v Tottenham H., FA Cup 5th Rd, 14.02.53

Win: 12-0
v West Vale Ramblers, FA Cup 1st Q. Rd. 13-14

Defeat: 0-13
v Stockport C., Div. 3 North, 33-34

Career Goalscorer: Albert Valentine

Career Appearances: John Pickering

Transfer Fee Paid: £50,000
for Ian Juryeff to Hereford Utd.

Transfer Fee Received: £250,000
for Wayne Allison from Watford

PREVIOUS

Leagues: Yorkshire Comb. 1911-12
Midland League 1912-21
Football League - Division 3 North 1-21-58
- Division 3 1958-63, 69-76, 92
Division 4 1963-69

Grounds: Sandhall Lane 1911-15, Exley 1919-21

Names: None

Chris Wilder

HONOURS

Conference Champions 1997-98
Promotion to Division 3 1968-69

Past Players who progressed to the Football League between 93-98

Geoff Horsfield (Fulham)

BEST SEASON

FA Cup: Fifth Round 1913-14, 52-53

FA Trophy: 3rd Round 93-94

Football League: 3rd, Division 3 1969-70

Conference: Champions 1997-98

LAST SEASON

F.A. Cup: 4th Qualifying Round
F.A.Trophy: 5th Round Round
Conference: 19th
Leading Goalscorer: Ryan Mallon
Captain: Shawn Garnett
Player of the Year: Craig Midgley

Bold print denotes England semi-professional international.

	Birthplace	D.O.B.	Previous Clubs
GOALKEEPERS			
Mark Cartwright	Chester	13.01.73	Shrewsbury T, Brighton, Wrexham, Stockport C, York C.
Ian Dunbavin	Knowsley	27.05.80	Shrewsbury T, Liverpool
DEFENDERS			
Matthew Doughty	Warrington	02.11.81	Rochdale, Chester C.
Lee Duffy	Oldham	24.07.82	Rochdale
Darren Hockenhull			Rochdale, Blackburn Rovers
Dean Howell	Nottingham		Morecambe, Southport,Crewe Alex, Notts Co.
Denny Ingram	SunderlaND	27.06.76	Forest Green R, Northwich V, Scarborough, Hartlepool
Sean McAuley	Sheffield	23.06.72	Manchester U., St. Johnstone, Hartlepool U., Scunthorpe U., Rochdale, Portland Timbers (USA).
Mark Monington	Mansfield	21.10.70	Boston United, Rotherham United, Rochdale, Burnley
Adam Quinn	Sheffield	02.06.82	Sheffield Wednesday
Kevin Sandwith	Workington	30.04.78	Doncaster Rovers, Carlisle United, Telford United
Paul Stoneman	Whitley Bay	26.02.73	Blackpool, Colchester Utd.
MIDFIELD			
Steve Bushell	Manchester	28.12.72	York City, Blackpool, Stalybridge Celtic.
Dave Carney	Camden (Aussi)	16.08.83	OldhaM A , Everton
Martin Foster	Rotherham	29.10.77	Forest Green R, Doncaster R, Morton, Leeds U.
Ryan Mallon	Sheffield	22.03.83	Sheffield United
Craig Midgley	Bradford	24.06.76	Bradford C., Hartlepool U.
Val Owen	Manchester		Northwich, Southport,Hednesford, Northwich V, Hyde Un.
Jake Sagare	Wahington (US)	04.05.80	Portland Timbers (USA), Griumsby, Portland T(USA)
Mick Senior	Huddersfield	03.03.81	Huddersfield Town (App)
Scott Willis	Liverpool	20.02.82	Lincoln C, Carlisle U, Mansfield T, Wigan A
FORWARDS			
Jonny Allen	Penrith	24.05.83	Lancaster C, Northwich V, Carlisle U
Andy Farrell	Easington	21.12.83	from trainee
Lewis Killeen	Peterborough	13.04.82	Shefield United
Christian Lee	Aylesbury	08.10.76	Eastwood T, Rushden & Diamonds, Farnborough T Bristol R, Rochdale, Northampton, Gillingham, Doncaster R
Ryan Mallon	Sheffiled	22.03.83	Sheffield United
Craig Midgley	Bradford	24.06.76	Hartlepool , Bradford City
Ryan Sugden(E NG I)	Bradford	26.12.80	Morecambe,Burton A,Chester C,Scarborough, Oldham Ath.

HEREFORD UNITED

IF there is anything called 'justice' it can reasonably be said that it by-passed The Bulls, who finished the Conference campaign with a massive 91 points obtained and 103 goals scored (against 44 conceded), but could only manage second spot, because Chester City had also enjoyed an outstanding programme and ended up a single point clear.

However, all things being equal they should have gone through to a Football League place via the play-offs, particularly as they had done the double over their semi-final opponents, Aldershot Town, but fate was again to play a scurvy trick, as an over enthusiastic match official reduced them to ten men before half-time by dismissing Tretton, alleging that he was the 'last man', when subsequent evidence suggested otherwise.

Even so, the depleted side gallantly took the match to extra-time with a share of two goals before the dreaded penalties were decreed and Terry Brown's lads won that mini-competition (4-2).

Conference performances in any normal season would have brought direct promotion as only seven matches were lost (four at home) and a 9-0 drubbing of Dagenham & Redbridge in February was the start of an eleven game winning run, but Chester City just had that little bit extra in hand and could afford a final day defeat at Edgar Street and still advance.

Challenges in cup competitions for once were undistinguished with a Second Round exit from the LDV Vans Trophy at home to Northampton Town on penalties after a 1-1 draw, which followed a two clear goal home success against Exeter City.

In the FA Cup a resounding 6-1 triumph at the Fourth Qualifying stage away to Harrow Borough meant another away tie - at Peterborough United - with the side finishing on the wrong end of a two unanswered goals scoreline, while in the FA Trophy an unkind draw for Round Three lad to another journey - to Exeter City - and a five goal thriller, which went the way of the hosts.

Steve Guinan with 29 goals in all matches earned himself selection for the England Semi-Professional squad in the Aberdeen Area competition, where he was also appointed captain, but other potential England players were less keen on being honoured and Wales emerged as winners.

Having tasted Football League fare The Bulls want to be there again and the only thing lacking recently has been good fortune, which few would begrudge them and their admirable Director/Manager Graham Turner.

W.M.

Back Row (L-R): Adam Stansfield, Tom Smith, Craig Stanley, Ben Scott, Andrew Tretton, Tamika Mkandawire, Andrew Williams. **Centre Row:** Bernard Day (Goalkeeper Coach), Ryan Green, Simon Travis, David Brown, Danny Carey-Bertram, Tony Ford (Fitness Adviser). **Front Row:** Rob Purdie, Jamie Pitman, Graham Turner (Manager), Tony James (Capt.), John Trewick (Coach), Danny Williams, Graham Hyde.

HERFORD UNITED

Match Facts 2003-04

The number shown directly below the player's name is his squad number.
Where a number is shown instead of an "X' in the columns this represents a substitute appearance and the number indicates the player replaced.

Comp.	Date	Opponents	Venue.	Result	Goalscorers	Att.
Conf 1	Aug 09	Tamworth	A	W 3-1	Smith(2) Guinan	2250
Conf 2	Aug 12	Forest Green R	H	W 5-1	Guinan(2) Purdie(2) Carey-Bartram	3195
Conf 3	Aug 16	Morecambe	H	W 3-0	Smith(2) Guinan	2941
Conf 4	Aug 23	Barnet	A	D 1-1	James(p)	1475
Conf 5	Aug 25	Aldershot T	H	W 4-3	Williams Rose James(p) Brown	4985
Conf 6	Aug 30	Stevenage B	A	W 2-0	Smith Guinan	2705
Conf 7	Sep 06	Farnborough T	A	W 5-0	Parry Smith Guinan James(p) Brown	1334
Conf 8	Sep 13	Scarborough	H	W 2-1	Parry Rose	4850
Conf 9	Sep 19	Burton A	A	L 1-4	Parry	2532
Conf 10	Sep 23	Telford U	H	W 2-1	Guinan Green	4190
Conf 11	Sep 27	Gravesend & N	H	D 3-3	Guinan Brown Smith	3731
Conf 12	Oct 04	Woking	A	W 1-0	Guinan	2906
Conf 13	Oct 07	Northwich V	A	W 5-1	Guinan(2) Williams Brown Parry	1008
Conf 14	Oct 13	Dagenham & R	H	D 1-1	Smith	4325
Conf 15	Oct 18	Chester C	A	D 0-0		4481
LDVT 1	**Oct 21**	**Exeter C**	**H**	**W 2-0**	**Brown Guinan**	**1513**
FAC 4q	**Oct 25**	**Harrow Borough**	**A**	**W 6-1**	**Guinan(3) Brown Smith Carey-Bartram**	**655**
Conf 16	Nov 01	Leigh RMI	H	L 0-1		3231
LDVT 2	**Nov 04**	**Northampton T**	**H**	**D 1-1***	**Brown Guinan (lost 3-4 on pens)**	**1517**
FAC 1	**Nov 08**	**Peterborough U**	**A**	**L 0-2**		**4479**
Conf 17	Nov 11	Accrington S	A	L 0-2		1824
Conf 18	Nov 15	Margate	H	W 2-1	Parry Murphy(og)	2320
Conf 19	Nov 22	Shrewsbury T	A	L 1-4	Mkandawire	6585
Conf 20	Nov 25	Halifax T	H	W 7-1	Guinan(3) Smith(2) Purdie Brown	1875
Conf 21	Nov 29	Farnborough T	H	W 2-0	Smith Pitman	2630
Conf 22	Dec 13	Tamworth	H	L 0-1		2561
Conf 23	Dec 20	Forest Green R	A	W 7-1	Parry(3) Smith(2) Purdie Pitman	1576
Conf 24	Dec 26	Exeter C	H	D 1-1	Purdie	4010
Conf 25	Jan 01	Exeter C	A	W 1-0	Williams	4943
Conf 26	Jan 03	Stevenage B	H	W 1-0	Parry	2875
FAT 3	**Jan 10**	**Exeter C**	**A**	**L 2-3**	**Carey-Bartram Purdie**	**2740**
Conf 27	Jan 17	Morecambe	A	D 2-2	Uddin Teesdale	2003
Conf 28	Feb 03	Scarborough	A	D 3-3	Brown Uddin Guinan	1459
Conf 29	Feb 07	Burton A	H	L 1-2	James(p)	3417
Conf 30	Feb 14	Gravesend & N	A	W 5-2	Brown(2) Guinan(2) James(p)	1230
Conf 31	Feb 21	Woking	H	L 0-1		2817
Conf 32	Feb 27	Dagenham & R	A	W 9-0	Brown(3)Guinan(2)Williams(2)BeesleyJames(p)	1617
Conf 33	Mar 02	Telford U	A	W 3-0	Brown(2) Tretton	2554
Conf 34	Mar 06	Northwich V	H	W 1-0	Guinan	3064
Conf 35	Mar 13	Accrington S	H	W 1-0	James(p)	3230
Conf 36	Mar 20	Margate	A	W 3-1	Guinan Willis Purdie	604
Conf 37	Mar 27	Shrewsbury T	H	W 2-1	Purdie Guinan	5850
Conf 38	Apr 03	Halifax T	A	W 2-1	Guinan Tretton	1389
Conf 39	Apr 10	Barnet	H	W 2-0	Willis James(p)	4447
Conf 40	Apr 12	Aldershot T	A	W 2-1	Purdie Carey-Bertram	4400
Conf 41	Apr 17	Leigh RMI	A	W 5-0	Guinan(2) James(p) Travis Carey-Bertram	836
Conf 42	Apr 24	Chester C	H	W 2-1	Brown Beesley	7240
PO SF1	**Apr 29**	**Aldershot T**	**A**	**D 1-1**	**Brown**	**6379**
PO SF2	**May 03**	**Aldershot T**	**H**	**D 0-0***	**(lost 2-4 on pens)**	**7044**

STEP 1 **CONFERENCE** | STEP 2 - P177 CONFERENCE Nth & Sth | STEP 3 - P269 NPL, Southern, Isthmian Premiers | STEP 4 - P269 NPL 1, Southern N&S, Isthmian 1 | STEP 5/6 - P473 Current level 3 leagues | STEP 7 - P713 Current level 4 leagues

Matt BAKER	Ryan GREEN	Michael ROSE	Jamie PITMAN	Andy TRETTON	Tony JAMES	Danny WILLIAMS	Ben SMITH	Steve GUINAN	David BROWN	Paul PARRY	Simon TRAVIS	Robert PURDIE	Richard TEESDALE	Rob SAWYERS	Anwar UDDIN	Jordan KING	Danny CAREY-BERTRAM	Dean CRAVEN	Rob BETTS	Chris PALMER	Nick HARRHY	Scott WILLIS	Tom SMITH	Bertrand COZIC	Mark BEESLEY	Tamika MKANDAWIRE	Danny MOON
1	**2**	**3**	**4**	**5**	**6**	**7**	**8**	**9**	**10**	**11**	**11**	**12**	**15**	**16**	**16**	**17**	**18**	**19**	**20**	**20**	**21**	**22**	**23**	**24**	**25**	**26**	**.**
x	x	x	x	x	x	x	x	x		x		x		12			9										
x	x	x	x	x	x	x	x	x		x		x					9										
x	x	x	x	x	x	x	x	x	12	x		x					9										
x	x	x	x	x	x	x	x	x	18	x		x					12	9									
x	x	x	x	x	x	x	x	x	9	x		x															
x	x	x	x	x	x	x	x	x	12	x		x															
x	x	x	x	x	x	x	x	x	7	x		x															
x	x	x	x	x	x	x	x	x	12	x		x															
x	x	x	x	x	x	x	x	x	12	x		x	4				9										
x	x	x	x		x	x	x	x	x	x			x				10										
x	x	x	x		x	x	x	x	x	x			x				10										
x	x	x	x		x	x	x	x	x	x							10									x	
x	x	x	x		x	x	x	x	x	x							10									x	
x	x	x	x		x	x	x	x	x	x							10									x	
x	x	x	x		x	x	x	x	x	x							10									x	
x	**x**	**x**	**x**			**x**		**x**	**x**	**x**			**x**			**x**	**10**	**7**								**x**	
x		**x**	**x**		**x**	**x**	**x**	**x**	**x**	**x**			**x**			**x**	**10**	**11**									**7**
x	x	x	x		x	x	x	x	18			19					x	x								x	
x	**x**	**x**	**x**		**x**		**x**	**x**	**x**			**x**	**19**			**8**		**x**			**12**					**x**	
x	**x**	**x**	**x**		**x**	**x**	**x**	**x**	**x**	**x**		**8**	**10**													**x**	
x	x	x	x		x	x		x	17	x		x				x										x	
x	x	x			x	x	x	x		x		x						x								x	
x	x		x		x	x	x	x	8	x		x					12	x								x	
x	x	x	x		x	x	x	x	7	x		x	26					11								x	
x	x	x	x		x	x	x	x	12	x		x	x														
x	x	x	x		x	x	x		x	x		x			x		12										
x	x	x	x		x	x	x		x	x		x	6		x	8		7									
x	x	x	x		x	x	x		x	x		x			x										7		
x		x	x		x	x	x	7		x		x	x		x			11							x		
x	x	x			x	x	x		20	x		x	12		x			x							x		
x	**x**	**x**	**x**		**x**		**x**		**x**			**x**	**19**		**x**		**25**	**x**							**x**		
x	x	x	x		x	x			x			x	10		x		25	7	x						x		
x	x		x		x	x	x	25	x			20			x			x	x						x		
x	x	x	x		x	x	x	x	x			x	2		x										7		
x		x		x	x	x	x	x	x			x	8		x				x								
x		x	x	x	x	x		x	x		x	x	11				7								5	x	
x	x	x	x	x	x	22		x	x			x						4				x			9	x	
x		x	x	x	x			x	x		x	x										x				x	
x	x	x	x	x	x			x	x			x										x			22	x	
x	x	x	x	x	x			x	x			x					22					x	x				
x	x	x	x	x	x	22		x	x			x										x				x	
x	x	x	x	x	x	22		x	x			x										x	x				
x	x	x	x	x	x	23		x	x			x								22		x	x				
x	x		x	x	x	10		x	x		x	x								12		x	x				
x	x		x	x	x			x	x		x	x					4			x			x	12	10		
x	x	10	x	x	x			x	x		x	x					12			x			x		4		
x	x	x	x	x	x	20			x			x					x			x			x	18	10		
x	**x**	**x**	**x**	**x**	**x**				**x**		**x**	**x**					**x**			**12**			**x**		**18**		
x	**x**	**x**	**x**	**x**	**x**	**x**		**x**	**x**		**x**									**11**			**x**	**7**	**9**		

HEREFORD UNITED

GROUND DETAILS

Edgar Street,
Hereford.
HR4 9JU

Telephone Tel: 01432 276666
Fax 01432 341359
Club Call 09068 121645

E-mail HUFCbulls@hotmail.com
Website: http://www.herefordunited.co.uk

SIMPLE DIRECTIONS: From Hereford city centre follow signs to Leominster (A49) into Edgar Street. Car parking for 600 near the ground(60p Sats,free mid week). Nearest railway station Hereford

Match Tickets: Adults £12 concessions £9 plus family combinations.

CAPACITY: 8,843
SEATED: 2,761
COVERED TERRACING: 6,082

SOCIAL FACILITIES: Clubhouse open on matchdays
REFRESHMENTS: Three Tea Bars
CLUB SHOP: Yes

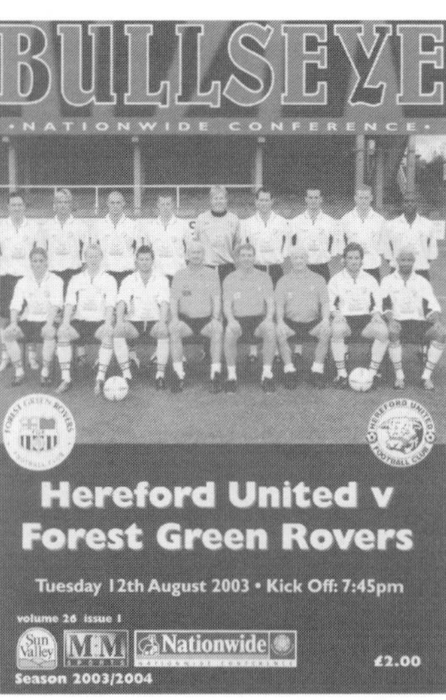

BULLSEYE
NATIONWIDE CONFERENCE
Hereford United v
Forest Green Rovers
Tuesday 12th August 2003 • Kick Off: 7:45pm
volume 26 issue 1
Sun Valley
Nationwide
£2.00
Season 2003/2004

MATCHDAY PROGRAMME

Pages: 32 Price: £2.00
Editor: Lee Symonds
Clubcall: 09068 121 645

Other club publications: None

Local Press: Hereford Journal; Hereford Times; Worcester Evening News
Local Radio: BBC Hereford & Worcester

Founded: 1924

Nickname: The Bulls

Sponsors: Sun Valley

Club Colours: All White

Change Colours: All Yellow

Midweek matchday: Tuesday

CLUB OFFICIALS

Chairman/Director of Football Graham Turner

Company Secretary Joan Fennessy

Directors
Grenville Smith, Hugh Brookes, Aidan McGivern.

Club Secretary Joan Fennessy c/o the club
Tel: 01432 276666 Fax: 01432 341359

FOOTBALL MANAGEMENT TEAM

MANAGER: **GRAHAM TURNER**

Date of Appointment August 1995
Date of Birth: 5th October 1947
Place of Birth: Ellesmere Port

PREVIOUS CLUBS
As manager Shrewsbury T., Aston Villa, Wolverhampton W.
As player Wrexham, Chester City, Shrewsbury T.
HONOURS
As manager League: Div.3 78-79 (Shrewsbury), Div.4 87-88, Div.3 88-89; S.V.T. 87-88 (Wolves)
As player England - Youth cap.

* * *

Coach John Trewick

Club Playing Status: Full Time

Season	League	Div.	Pos.	Home P	W	D	L	F	A	Away W	D	L	F	A	Pts	Manager
03-04	Conference	-	2	42	14	3	4	42	20	14	4	3	61	24	91	Graham Turner
02-03	Conference	-	6	42	9	5	7	36	22	10	2	9	28	29	64	Graham Turner
01-02	Conference	-	17	42	9	6	6	28	15	5	4	12	22	38	52	Graham Turner/Phil Robinson
00-01	Conference	-	11	42	6	12	3	27	19	8	3	10	33	27	57	Graham Turner
99-00	Conference	-	8	42	9	6	6	43	31	6	8	7	18	21	59	Graham Turner
98-99	Conference	-	13	42	9	5	7	25	17	6	5	10	24	29	55	Graham Turner
97-98	Conference	-	6	42	11	7	3	30	19	7	6	8	26	30	67	Graham Turner

Season	League	Div.	Pos.	P	W	D	L	F	A	Pts	Manager
96-97	F. League	3	24	46	11	14	21	50	65	47	Graham Turner
95-96	F. League	3	6	46	20	14	12	65	47	74	Graham Turner
94-95	F. League	3	16	42	12	13	17	45	62	49	Graham Turner

HONOURS

Football League Div. 3 75-76, Div. 4 R-up 72-73;

Southern League R-up 45-46 50-51 71-72
NW Championship 58-59
Div. 1 58-59,
Cup Winners 52 57 59

Welsh Cup Winners 89-90,
R-up 3 times;

PREVIOUS

Leagues: Birmingham League; Birmingham Combination; Southern League 39-72; Football League 72-97

Names: None

Ground: None

Past Players who progressed to the Football League

Since joining the Conference: Gavin Mahon (Brentford), Michael McIndoe, Gavin Williams, Michael Rose (Yeovil Town), Steve Guinan (Cheltenham Town) and Ben Smith (Shrewsbury Town) and Paul Parry (Cardiff City and Wales)

CLUB RECORDS

Attendance: 18,114
v Sheffield Wed., FA Cup 3rd Rd, 4.1.58

Career Goalscorer: Unknown
Career Appearances: unknown

Win: 6-0 v Burnley (A), Div. 4 24.1.87

Defeat: 0-6 v Rotherham Utd (A), Div. 4 29.4.89

Transfer Fee Paid: £75,000
to Walsall for Dean Smith, 7.94

Transfer Fee Received: £250,000
for Darren Peacock from Q.P.R., 3.91
+ a further £240,000
when he moved to Newcastle Utd. 3.91

BEST SEASON

FA Trophy: Semi-Finals 00-01

FA Cup: 4th Rd 71-72 (as Southern League side), 76-77, 81-82, 89-90, 91-92

League Clubs Defeated (as a non-league club): Exeter C 53-54,Aldershot 56-57,Q.P.R. 57-58,Millwall 65-66,North"ton T 70-71, Northampton T,Newcastle U71-72,Colchester United & Brighton & H 97-98,Hartlep'l U&YorkC 99-00 Wrexham01-2

League: 22nd Football League Div.ision 2 1976-77

LAST SEASON

F.A. Cup: First Round
F.A. Trophy: 3rd Round
Conference: 2nd
Top Goalscorer: Steve Guinan
Player of the Year: Tony James/Matt Baker
Captain: Tony Jamest

HEREFORD UNITED PLAYING SQUAD

Player	Birthplace	D.O.B.	Previous Clubs

Bold print denotes England semi-professional international.

GOALKEEPERS

DEFENDERS

Player	Birthplace	D.O.B.	Previous Clubs
Ryan Green Wales Full			Wolves,Torquay U, Millwall, Cardiff C. Sheffield W
Tony James Wales SP	Birmingham		W.B.A.
Tamika Mkandawire	Malawi	28.05.83	W.B.A.
Richard Teesdale	Birmingham	-	Walsall
Simon Travis ESP	Preston	22.03.77	Stevenage B, Forest Green R, Telford U, Stockport C, Holywell, Torquay U
Andy Tretton	Derby	09.10.76	Shrewsbury Town, Derby County

MIDFIELD

Player	Birthplace	D.O.B.	Previous Clubs
Jamie Pitman FA XI	Trowbridge	06.01.76	Woking, Yeovil T, Hereford Utd, Swindon Town
Robert Purdie	Leicester	-	Leicester
Rob Sawyers			Barnet, Wolverhampton Wanderers
Craig Stanley	Bedworth	03.03.83	Telford United, Walsall
Danny Williams	Sheffield	02.03.81	Chesterfield

FORWARDS

Player	Birthplace	D.O.B.	Previous Clubs
David Brown	Bolton	02.10.78	Telford United, Chester C, Torquay U, Hull C, Man.Utd
Robert Purdie			Leicester City
Adam Stansfield E NG I, FAT NC	Tiverton	10.09.78	Yeovil Town, Elmore, Cullompton Rangers, Tiverton T , Cullompton Rangers

LEIGH R.M.I.

GALLANT Leigh RMI remain in the Conference - probably much to their own surprise - thanks to the misfortunes of others, as they ended the 2003-04 campaign only one place above Northwich Victoria, who also had to rely on disasters elsewhere for the retention of their status.

Right from the start of the season it was clear that Leigh would struggle, but it can at least be said that they probably reserved their best form for the latter stages of the programme, which at least gave the final picture an aura of respectability.

One thing that can redeem a club's season can be a run in one of the national knock-out competitions, but luck was even absent in this respect, as the FA Cup stint ended abruptly with a visit to Accrington Stanley (0-2) in the Fourth Qualifying Round, while the Trophy challenge was also short lived thanks to a draw at home against Stalybridge Celtic being followed by a protest and ignominious disqualification (ineligible player), while even in the Lancashire FA Trophy there was little joy with a 3-1 success at Squires Gate being followed by a visit to Chorley and dismissal (1-4).

The most consistent player in Manager Phil Starbuck's outfit was striker David McNiven, who was picked for the England Semi-Pro squad and performed well, but he has moved on to try his luck in Dumfries with Queen of the South. Five goalkeepers were used during the campaign, but defenders Neil Durkin and Martyn Lancaster were models of consistency, even though on paper the defence was not a source of strength, as were Warren Peyton and Damien Whitehead, but with money in short supply big salaries for players are a virtual impossibility, so a lot of luck and bravery in the new programme will be needed. W.M.

Back Row (L-R): Asst. Kit Man, Kit Man, C Gaunt, M Moran, B Ashmole, N Smith, D Morton, I Martin, C Simm, C Lane, K Rose, B Miller, Physio, Asst. Physio.
Front Row: G Tench, G Holmes, S Smith, G Stoker, P Starbuck (Manager), G Kelly (Asst. Manager), A Meechan, W Peyton, C Mitchell, C Adams.

LEIGH R.M.I.

Match Facts 2003-04

The number shown directly below the player's name is his squad number.
Where a number is shown instead of an "X' in the columns this represents a substitute appearance and the number indicates the player replaced.

Comp.	Date	Opponents	Venue.	Result	Goalscorers	Att.
Conf 1	Aug 09	Dagenham & R	H	W 2-1	McNiven(2)	419
Conf 2	Aug 13	Accrington S	A	L 1-4	McNiven	2003
Conf 3	Aug 16	Farnborough T	A	D 1-1	McNiven	594
Conf 4	Aug 23	Halifax T	H	D 1-1	McNiven	849
Conf 5	Aug 25	Northwich V	A	W 1-0	Maden	582
Conf 6	Aug 30	Woking	H	L 0-1		435
Conf 7	Sep 06	Forest Green R	H	L 1-2	Robinson	415
Conf 8	Sep 13	Gravesend & N	A	L 1-3	McNiven	723
Conf 9	Sep 20	Tamworth	H	D 1-1	Redmond	427
Conf 10	Sep 23	Morecambe	A	L 0-1		1393
Conf 11	Sep 27	Stevenage B	A	L 0-4		1734
Conf 12	Oct 04	Aldershot T	H	D 2-2	McNiven(2)	545
Conf 13	Oct 11	Margate	A	L 0-2		429
Conf 14	Oct 18	Barnet	H	L 1-4	McNiven(p)	348
FAC 4q	**Oct 25**	**Accrington S**	**A**	**L 0-2**		**1350**
Conf 15	Nov 01	Hereford U	A	W 1-0	Barrowclough	3231
Conf 16	Nov 11	Scarborough	H	L 1-4	Maden	375
Conf 17	Nov 15	Telford U	A	L 0-5		1377
Conf 18	Nov 18	Shrewsbury T	H	D 2-2	McNiven(2)	1219
Conf 19	Nov 22	Exeter C	H	D 1-1	Maden	634
Conf 20	Nov 25	Burton A	A	L 2-3	McNiven Maden	1327
Conf 21	Nov 29	Forest Green R	A	D 2-2	McNiven Peyton	554
Conf 22	Dec 13	Dagenham & R	A	W 2-1	Shepherd McNiven	1037
Conf 23	Dec 20	Accrington S	H	L 1-2	McNiven	612
Conf 24	Dec 26	Chester C	A	L 0-5		3044
Conf 25	Jan 01	Chester C	H	L 2-6	Daniel Peyton	2002
Conf 26	Jan 03	Woking	A	L 0-2		2105
FAT 3	**Jan 10**	**Stalybridge Celtic**	**H**	**D 1-1 ***	**McNiven (expelled for inel.player(S Rowe)**	**402**
Conf 27	Jan 17	Farnborough T	H	L 0-2		295
Conf 28	Jan 24	Morecambe	H	W 3-1	McNiven(3,1p)	605
Conf 29	Feb 07	Tamworth	A	L 3-4	McNiven Barrowclough Roscoe	905
Conf 30	Feb 14	Stevenage B	H	L 1-3	McNiven	270
Conf 31	Feb 21	Aldershot T	A	L 0-2		2417
Conf 32	Feb 28	Margate	H	W 4-2	Brodie(2) McNiven(p) Daniel	302
Conf 33	Mar 08	Shrewsbury T	A	L 1-3	Brodie	3307
Conf 34	Mar 13	Scarborough	A	L 1-4	Brodie	1093
Conf 35	Mar 20	Telford U	H	D 1-1	Lancaster	315
Conf 36	Mar 27	Exeter C	A	L 2-3	McNiven Durkin	3635
Conf 37	Mar 30	Gravesend & N	H	L 1-2	McNiven	304
Conf 38	Apr 03	Burton A	H	L 0-1		339
Conf 39	Apr 10	Halifax T	A	L 1-2	Daniel	1415
Conf 40	Apr 12	Northwich V	H	W 1-0	McNiven	339
Conf 41	Apr 17	Hereford U	H	L 0-5		836
Conf 42	Apr 24	Barnet	A	L 1-2	McNiven(p)	2988

STEP 1
CONFERENCE

STEP 2 - P177
CONFERENCE Nth & Sth

STEP 3 - P269
NPL, Southern, Isthmian Premiers

STEP 4 - P269
NPL 1, Southern N&S, Isthmian 1

STEP 5/6 - P473
Current level 3 leagues

STEP 7 - P713
Current level 4 leagues

Stuart COBURN	James SALISBURY	Gerry HARRISON	Nicky HILL	Carl REZAI	Paul SHEPHERD	Martyn LANCASTER	Neil DURKIN	Ian MONK	Damien WHITEHEAD	Warren PEYTON	David McNIVEN	Marcus HALLOWS	arl BARROWCLOUGH	Tristram WHITMAN	Andy HEALD	Andy ROSCOE	Wayne MADEN	Phil STARBUCK	Paul RICKERS	Ged COURTNEY	Adie ORR	Carl ALFORD	Steve BRODIE	Chris McGRATH	Ged KIELTY	Michael PRICE	Martyn FORREST	Ian MARTIN	Ian FITZPATRICK	Chris LANE	Graham TENCH	Neil ROBINSON	Steve SMITH	Steve REDMOND	Chris DOWNEY	Mike HARRIS	Kris McHALE	Robbie WILLIAMS	Dave TICKLE	Steve GUNBY	Gary KELLY	Mario DANIEL	Liam COYNE	Gareth HOLMES	Gavin ELLISON
	1	**2**	**3**	**3**	**4**	**5**	**6**	**7**	**7**	**8**	**9**	**10**	**10**	**10**	**11**	**11**	**12**	**14**	**14**	**15**	**15**	**15**	**15**	**15**	**16**	**16**	**17**	**17**	**18**	**18**	**18**	**20**	**20**	**21**	**22**	**22**	**22**	**22**	**23**	**23**	**24**	**25**	**26**	**27**	**28**
x		x	x			x	x	x		x	x	9			x					20					x							x													
x		x	x		7	x	x	x		x	x				x		2			11					x							x													
x			x		x	x	x	11		x	x	9			x		x			20					x							x													
x			x		x	x	x	x		x	x	20								21					x							x		x											
x			x			x	x	x		x	x	20					x			9					x							x		x											
x			x		16	x	x	x		x	x	20					x								x							x		x											
x			22		x	x	x	x		x	x	9					23															x		x											
x					x	x	x	11		x	x	9				x	x										x					x		x	20										
					x	x	x	14		x	x					x	22	x									x					x		x	20						x				
x			x			x	x	x		x	x					x	x	x									x																		
x		11	x		x		x	x		x	x					x		x									x							x	14										
		x	x				x	x		x	x					x	x	x									x							2					11		x				
		x			x		x	14		x	x		x			8	x	x									x								9				x		x				
		x			x	x	x	x		5	x		x			23	x																	x					x		x				
		x			**x**	**x**	**x**	**10**		**x**	**x**		**x**			**x**	**x**	**12**																**x**							**x**				
		x				x	x	x		x	x		x			x	x	2																x							x				
		x			10	x	x	x		x	x		x			x	x				21													x							x				
		x		x	x	x	x	x		x	x					x		7			x																				x				
		x		x	x	x	x	x		x	x					x	x				7																		11		x				
		x		x	x	x	x	8		x	x		x			x	x				10																				x				
		x		x	x	x	x	8		x	x		x			x	x				11																				x				
		x		x	x	x	x	11		x	x		x			x	x								12									3							x				
		x			x	x	x			2	x		x			x	x				10								x					x							x				
		x		18	x	x	x			6	x		x			x	x								10				x					x							x				
				x	x	x				x	x		x				x				21				x									x		x					x				
		x		x	x	x			3	12	x					x	x		x									x						x		21						x			
		x			x	x			10	x	x		x			x			x						2			x						x		21						x			
		x		**x**	**x**	**x**			**x**	**x**	**x**					**x**			**x**																				**3**			**x**			
				x	x	x			5	x	x		15			x			x			x						x						x			x								
		x		x	x	x	x		22	2	x		3			x												x		x				x			x								
				x	x	x	x			x	x		x			x	x											x		x			10									4			
		4		x	x	x	x			x	x					x							x					x						x			x					22			
		x			x		x			x			11			x							x					x					8	x			x			x		x		23	
		x			x	4	x		9		x					x							x					x						x			25			x		x		x	
	x	x				x	x		25	x	x					x							x														11			x		x		x	
	x	x		25		x	x				x					x	23						x											5			x			x		x		x	
		x		27		x	x		12		x			x		x	x											x						x						x		10		x	
		x				x	x			2	x			x		16	x									x		x										x		x		23		x	
		x		x			x			21	x			x			x									x		x			10			x				x				16		x	
		x		18			x		25		x			x		x	x	4										x			x							x		12		x		x	
		x		x	23		x				x			2		x								x				x												x		15	x	x	x
				x	x		x		25		x			x		x								x				x												15		x		x	x
				x			x		9		x			x		x										x		x			23			28						x		x		x	x
				x		x			25		x			x		x								11		x		x					x									x	28	x	x

ALSO PLAYED: Ian PENDLEBURY (19) Conf 1 - rep 11. Ben ASHMOLE (19) Conf 24 - rep 8. Lee HARDY (22) Conf 7. Jamie MILLIGAN (23) Conf 7. Sebastian ROWE FAT 3.

LEIGH R.M.I.

GROUND DETAILS

Hilton Park,
Kirkhall Lane,
Leigh WN7 1RN
Tel: 01942 743743 (Office)
Fax: 01942 768856
Web site: http://www.leigh-rmi.co.uk

DIRECTIONS:
From M61 junction 5, follow the Westhoughton sign to r'about, then follow signs to Leigh. Keep on main road to the traffic lights, left into Leigh Road, carry on about 3 miles to the traffic lights. Turn left and first right to the next set of lights. Right onto Atherleigh Way, A579 at the first set of traffic lights, turn left (B & Q on right), at the next set of lights turn right into Kirkhall Lane (Leigh town centre), at the 2nd opening on right turn into Prescott St., carry on to top, turn right, ground on left.

CAPACITY:	8000
COVER:	4,000
SEATS:	2,000

CLUBHOUSE: Open matchdays with food available.
Pre-match meals can be arranged.
2 separate function facilities for 200 and 100.

CLUB SHOP: At the ground & open most days. Contact club.

MATCHDAY PROGRAMME

Pages: 32 Price: £2.00
Editor: Secretary

Local Press: Bolton Evening News

Local Radio: Radio Lancs, Red Rose Radio, G.M.R.

Formed:	1896
Nickname:	Railwaymen
Sponsors:	Kit - Widdows Mason
Colours:	Red & white striped shirts red shorts and red socks
Change colours:	All Yellow
Midweek home matchday:	Tuesday
Reserve Team	Lancs League

CLUB OFFICIALS

Chairman:	William Taylor.
Vice Chairman:	Alan Leach
Directors:	L Berry, K Freer, M.Peck, S Walker, A.Hogan, G Culshaw
President:	T.B.A.
Secretary:	Alan Robinson 55 Janice Drive, Fulwood, Preston, Lancs. PR2 9TY. Tel: 01772 719266 (H) 07974 651231 (M)
Press Officer:	Secretary

FOOTBALL MANAGEMENT TEAM

MANAGER:	**PHIL STARBUCK**
Asst Manager	G Kelly
Physiotherapist:	B Miller
Club's Playing Status:	Part - time

Season	League	Div.	Pos.	Home P	Home W	Home D	Home L	Home F	Home A	Away W	Away D	Away L	Away F	Away A	Pts	Manager
03-04	Conference	-	21	42	4	6	11	26	44	3	2	16	20	53	29	Steve Waywell
02-03	Conference	-	18	42	8	5	8	26	34	6	1	14	18	37	48	Steve Waywell / Mark Patterson
01-02	Conference	-	16	42	6	4	11	29	29	9	4	8	27	29	53	Steve Waywell
00-01	Conference	-	5	42	11	5	5	38	24	8	6	7	25	33	68	Steve Waywell
99-00	N.P.L.	Premier	1	44	15	3	4	42	17	13	5	4	49	28	92	Steve Waywell
98-99	N.P.L.	Premier	8	42	6	10	5	30	26	10	5	6	33	28	63	Steve Waywell
97-98	N.P.L.	Premier	3	42	12	6	3	32	15	9	7	5	31	26	76	Steve Waywell

Season	League	Div.	Pos.	P	W	D	L	F	A	Pts	Manager
96-97	N.P.L.	One	2	42	24	11	7	65	33	83	Steve Waywell
95-96	N.P.L.	One	14	40	14	7	19	53	59	49	Steve Waywell
94-95	N.P.L.	Premier	22	42	9	4	29	49	94	31	Mick Holgate

HONOURS

Northern Premier League Champions 1999-2000
NPL League Cup 99-00, Division 1 R-up 96-97;
Premier Inter League (GMAC) Cup 87-88;
Cheshire County Lg 78-79,
Challenge Shield 78-79;
Lancs Combination 57-58
R-up 29-30 55-56 66-67,
Lg Cup 28-29 53-54 56-57 65-66,
Div 2 R-up 48-49 50-51;
West Lancs League 10-11 11-12;
Lancs Junior Cup 24-25 29-30 (R-up x 4);
Lancs Floodlit Trophy 84-85 (R-up 83-84);
Lancs FA Cup 84-85
Lancs Trophy 2002-03

PREVIOUS

Leagues: Lancashire Alliance 1891-97;
Lancashire League 1897-1900;
Lancashire Combination 17-18, 19-39, 46-68;
Cheshire County League 68-82;
North West Counties League 82-83;
Northern Premier League 83-2000

Name: Horwich R.M.I. until 1995

Ground: Grundy Hill, Horwich until 1994

PastPlayers who progressed to the Football League

Harold Lea (Stockport 58),
David Holland (Stockport 59),
Jim Cunliffe (Stockport 60),
Frank Wignall (Everton 58),
Gary Cooper (Rochdale73),
Tony Caldwell (Bolton 83),
Raymond Redshaw (Wigan 84),
Tony Ellis (Oldham 86),
Paul Jones (Oldham , Nov. 99),
SteveJones (Crewe Alex 01).

CLUB RECORDS

Attendance:
(at Horwich) 8,500 v Wigan Ath Lancs Jnr Cup 54
(at Leigh) 7,125 v Fulham, FAC 98-99

Career Appearances: Neil McLachlan

Career Goalscorer: Neil McLachlan

Defeat: 2-9 v Brandon Utd (H)
FA Cup 1998-99

Transfer fee paid: £6,000
to Prescot Cables for Peter Cumiskey 99-00

Transfer fee received: £75,000
from Crewe A. for Steve Jones 2001

BEST SEASON

FA Trophy: Quarter Final 90-91

FA Cup: First Round
28-29, 1-2 v Scarborough (H),
82-83, 0-3 v Blackpool (A)
98-99 (replay), 0-2 v Fulham (H) after 1-1,
00-01, 0-3 v Millwall (H - played away)

FA Vase: N/A

League: 00-01 5th Conference

LAST SEASON

F.A. Cup: 4th Qual.Round
F.A. Trophy: 3rd Round
Conference: 21st
Top Goalscorer: David McNiven
Player of the Year: David McNiven
Captain: Gerry Harrison

LEIGH R.M.I. PLAYING SQUAD

Player	Birthplace	D.O.B.	Previous Clubs

Bold print denotes England semi-professional international.

GOALKEEPER

Gary Kelly	Preston	29,03.66	Sheffield United, Northwich Vics., Oldham Ath., Bury, Newcastle United

DEFENDERS

Craig Gaunt	Nottingham	31.03.73	Hucknall T, Moor Green, Chester C, Woodlands Wellington (Singapore), Grantham, W.W.(Singapore), Ilkeston T, Kettering T, Bromsgrove R Scarborough, Arsenal.
Gerry Harrison	Lambeth	15.04.72	Prestwich Heys, Halifax Town, Sunderland, Burnley, Huddersfield T (L), Hereford United (L), Cardiff City (L), Bristol City,Watford
Martyn Lancaster	Wigan	10.11.08	Chester City
Chris Lane	Liverpool	24.05.79	Chester City, Morecambe, Southport,Hereford, Everton
Wayne Maden	Preston	17,04.83	Blackpool
Barry Miller UPL	Ealing	29.03.76	Hucknall; T, Gainsborough T, Doncaster R, Gillingham, Farnborough T, Wokingham.
Paul Shepherd			Oldham Athletic, Luton Town, Ayr United, Leeds United

MIDFIELD

Carl Adams	Birmingham	13.03.74	Hucknall T, Hednesford T, Bedford T, Kettering T, Stevenage B, Weymouth, BirminghamC
Neil Durkin ENP	Blackburn	01.07.76	Darwen, Padiham, Feniscowles
Mike Harris	Liverpool		Runcorn, Trafford.
Gareth Holmes	Sutton-in-Ashfield		Gresley R, Hucknall T, Nuneaton B, Bradford P.A., Derby
Warren Peyton ESP, NC	Bury		Doncaster Rovers, Nuneaton Borough, Bury, Rochdale
Andy Roscoe	Liverpool Liverpool	04.06.73	Halifax T, Exeter C, Mansfield T, Rotherham U, BoltonW
Gareth Stoker	Bishop Auckland	22.02.73	Forest Green, Scarborough, Rochdale, Cardiff C, Hereford U, Hull C, Leeds U

FORWARD,

Mario Daniel Trinidad & Tobago U18	Manchester		Mossley,AthertonColls.,Trafford, Altrincham
Craig Mitchell	Mansfield		Mansfield Town, Hucknall Town.
Damien Whitehead	Whiston	24.04.79	Macclesfield Town, Drogheda (L), Warrington Town

MORECAMBE

Following the success of the previous season, hopes were high that the Shrimps would take that final step up to the Football League.But the club's miserable away form in the first two thirds of the season proved a major stumbling block to those ambitions. With the club forced to rely on other challenger's results it was remarkable that the Shrimps still found themselves in with a chance of the play offs as the season came to a close.Eventually draws at Margate and at home to Shrewsbury saw them finish in a very respectable seventh place.

Shrewsbury Town, eventually promoted through the play offs, turned out to be the club's nemesis in cup competitions.Firstly in the F.A.Cup 4th Qualifying Round, they came to Christie Park and won 4-2 in a game that saw Adriano Rigoglioso's final appearance for Morecambe (being sent off after three minutes) before being transferred to Doncaster Rovers for a fee of £30,000. So after two 3rd Round appearances in the previous three years, it was a bitter pill to swallow. The F.A.Trophy 3rd Round draw threw the two teams together again and the Shrews emerged two goal winners at Gay Meadow.

The LDV Vans Trophy has not been the Shrimps happiest hunting ground, three away ties, had brought defeats at the hands of Lincoln City, Shrewsbury Town (yet again) and last season, a 1-4 defeat at Second Division Wrexham. A home draw in this year's competition would not go a miss.

The Lancashire Marsden Trophy brought silverware to the Christie Park sideboard, with a 3-1 two legged victory over fellow Conference outfit Accrington Stanley with nearly 3,000 watching the two games.The Reserves however, under the guidance of Jeff Udal and Tony Gibbins, won the Lancashire League Championship for a fourth consecutive year, and to put the icing on the cake won the cup as well.

Neil Marsden

Back Row: Dean Howell, Jim Bentley, Stewart Drummond, Michael Stringfellow, Iain Swan, Adriano Rigoglioso, Wayne Curtis.
Middle Row: Nik Rogan, Chris Lane, Gary Thompson, Craig Mawson, Keiron Walmsley, Danny Carlton, Dale Gordon.
Front Row: Gary Hunter, Paul Osborne, Jim Harvey (manager) Andy Mutch (assistant manager) Lee Dodgson, David Perkins

MORECAMBE

Match Facts 2003-04

The number shown directly below the player's name is his squad number.
Where a number is shown instead of an "X' in the columns this represents a substitute appearance and the number indicates the player replaced.

Comp.	Date	Opponents	Venue.	Result	Goalscorers	Att.
Conf 1	Aug 09	Woking	H	W 2-1	Rigoglioso Bentley	1772
Conf 2	Aug 12	Halifax T	A	L 0-1		2160
Conf 3	Aug 16	Hereford U	A	L 0-3		2941
Conf 4	Aug 23	Dagenham & R	H	W 3-2	Carlton (2) Lane	1477
Conf 5	Aug 25	Telford U	A	L 1-2	Collins	1910
Conf 6	Aug 30	Burton A	H	W 2-1	Howell Drummond	1789
Conf 7	Sep 06	Aldershot T	H	W 2-0	Stringfellow Drummond(p)	1948
Conf 8	Sep 13	Tamworth	A	W 3-2	Drummond(2) Carlton	1247
Conf 9	Sep 20	Northwich V	A	D 1-1	Curtis	853
Conf 10	Sep 23	Leigh RMI	H	W 1-0	Rigoglioso(p)	1393
Conf 11	Sep 27	Farnborough T	H	W 3-2	Rigoglioso(p) Curtis Thompson	1636
Conf 12	Oct 04	Barnet	A	L 1-2	Thompson	1776
Conf 13	Oct 07	Scarborough	A	L 0-1		1219
Conf 14	Oct 11	Gravesend & N	H	D 2-2	Bentley Walmsley	1539
LDVT 1	**Oct 14**	**Wrexham**	**A**	**L 1-4**	**Morgan(og)**	**1078**
Conf 15	Oct 18	Shrewsbury T	A	L 0-2		3404
FAC 4q	**Oct 25**	**Shrewsbury T**	**H**	**L 2-4**	**Sugden Collins**	**1951**
Conf 16	Nov 01	Margate	H	D 3-3	Carlton(2) Rogan	1499
Conf 17	Nov 11	Chester C	H	L 0-1		1959
Conf 18	Nov 15	Exeter C	A	L 0-4		2993
Conf 19	Nov 22	Stevenage B	H	W 2-1	McFlynn Thompson	1354
Conf 20	Nov 25	Forest Grren R	A	W 2-1	Thompson Carlton	605
Conf 21	Nov 29	Aldershot T	A	D 2-2	Carlton Thompson	2584
Conf 22	Dec 06	Tamworth	H	W 4-0	Bentley Carlton Howell Sugden	1449
Conf 23	Dec 13	Woking	A	L 1-4	Rogan	1588
Conf 24	Dec 20	Halifax T	H	W 2-0	McFlynn Rogan	1603
Conf 25	Dec 26	Accrington S	A	L 0-1		2954
Conf 26	Jan 01	Accrington S	H	W 1-0	Halford(og)	3084
Conf 27	Jan 03	Burton A	A	W 1-0	Carlton	1478
FAT 3	**Jan 10**	**Shrewsbury T**	**A**	**L 0-2**		**2413**
Conf 28	Jan 17	Hereford U	H	D 2-2	Carlton Sugden	2003
Conf 29	Jan 24	Leigh RMI	A	L 1-3	Sugden	605
Conf 30	Feb 07	Northwich V	H	W 3-0	Carlton(2,1p) Thompson	1597
Conf 31	Feb 14	Farnborough T	A	W 4-2	McFlynn Carlton Howell Sugden	704
Conf 32	Feb 21	Barnet	H	L 1-3	Carlton	2014
Conf 33	Feb 28	Gravesend & N	A	L 0-6		1061
Conf 34	Mar 06	Scarborough	H	W 2-1	Carlton Murphy	1623
Conf 35	Mar 13	Chester C	A	L 1-2	Drummond	3512
Conf 36	Mar 20	Exeter C	H	L 0-3		1877
Conf 37	Mar 27	Stevenage B	A	W 1-0	Walmsley	1687
Conf 38	Apr 03	Forest Grren R	H	W 4-0	Curtis(3) Sugden	1259
Conf 39	Apr 10	Dagenham & R	A	W 3-1	Curtis(p) Carlton Sugden	1122
Conf 40	Apr 12	Telford U	H	W 1-0	Bentley	1642
Conf 41	Apr 18	Margate	A	D 1-1	Carlton	414
Conf 42	Apr 24	Shrewsbury T	H	D 3-3	Curtis(2,1p) Rogan	2876

STEP 1
CONFERENCE

STEP 2 - P177
CONFERENCE Nth & Sth

STEP 3 - P269
NPL, Southern, Isthmian Premier

STEP 4 - P269
NPL 1, Southern N&S, Isthmian 1

STEP 5/6 - P473
Current level 3 leagues

STEP 7 - P713
Current level 4 leagues

Craig MAWSON	Dave McKEARNEY	David PERKINS	Jamie MURPHY	Jim BENTLEY	Stewart DRUMMOND	Adriano RIGOGLIOSO	Michael STRINGFELLOW	Wayne CURTIS	Dean HOWELL	Gary THOMPSON	Chris LANE	Iain SWAN	Danny CARLTON	Lee COLLINS	Nick ROGAN	Terry McFLYNN	Ryan Zico BLACK	Lee DODGSON	Garry HUNTER	Paul OSBOURNE	Keiron WALMSLEY	Shaun GARNETT	Ryan SUGDEN	Chris BLACKBURN	Ian DUNBAVIN
1	**2**	**3**	**4**	**5**	**6**	**7**	**8**	**9**	**10**	**11**	**12**	**14**	**15**	**16**	**17**	**18**	**19**	**20**	**21**	**22**	**23**	**25**	**26**	**29**	**31**
x		x		x	x	x	x	x	x	x	x	x	9				11								
x	12	x		x	x	x	x	x	x	x	x	x	9				7								
x	14	x		x	x	x	x	16	x	x	x	x		x			11								
x	x	x			x	x	x	10	x	x	x	x	x						11						
x	10	x	16	x	x	x	11		x	x	x	x	x	x											
x	14	x		x	x	x	x		x	x	x	x	x	7			11								
x	x	x	14	x	x	x	x	8			x	x	x	x									15		
x	x	x	x	x	x		x	x	3	15	x		x	x									9		
x	x	x	x	x	x		x	x		15	x		x	x									9		
x	7	x	x	x	x	x	16	x		x	x		26	x									x		
x		x	x	x	x	x	x	x	26	x			8								x		x		
x	x	x	x	x	x	x		x	6	x	x		x		10								15		
x	x	x	x	x		x		x	x		x	x	26		14								x		
x	x	x		x		x		x	x	x	2	x	11	x	10						x				
x	**3**	**x**	**x**			**x**			**x**	**x**	**x**	**x**	**26**	**x**	**11**						**x**		**x**		
x	x			x		x	x		x	x	x	x	7	x				10					x		
x	**10**	**x**		**x**		**x**	**x**	**14**	**x**	**x**	**x**	**x**	**11**	**x**									**x**		
x		x		x			x	x		x	x	x	x	x	11				9				x		
x		x	15	x			x	x		x		x	x	x	4				9		x	x			
x	23	x		x			x	x	9	x	x	x							14		x	x	x		
x	x	x		x			x		x	x			x		18	x					x	x	15		
x	x	x		x			x		x	x		25	x		15	x					x	x	18		
x	x	x	x	x			x		x	x		4	x		15	x					x		2		
x	x	x	x	x			x		x	x			x	2	15	x					x		18		
x	x	x	x	x			x		x	x		5	x		15	x					x		18		
x	x	x	x		x		x		x	x			x		18	x		11			x		15		
x	x	x	x		x		x		x	x			x		15	x			10		x		18		
x	x	x	x		x		3		x	x			26		18	x					x	x	x		
x	x		x		x		x		x	x		25	x		x	15					x	x	17		
x	**x**		**x**	**11**	**x**		**x**		**x**	**x**			**x**		**x**	**10**		**15**			**x**	**x**			
x		x		x	x		x		x	x			x		18	x		10			x	x	15		
x	x	x	x	x	x		x		4						x	2					x	x	x		
x	x	x		x	x		x		x	x			x		18	x			10		x				
x	25	x	15	x	x		x		x	x			x			x					x	x	18		
x	x	x		x	x		x	18	x	x			x			x					x		10	2	
x	11	x		x	x				x	x		5	x			x					x	x	10	x	
	x	x	x	x	x				17				x		x				x	15	x		2	x	x
	x	x	x	x	x			26	x				x		15				10		x		x	x	x
31	x	x	x	x	x								x		25				x	3		x	x	x	x
x	x	x	25	x	x			x					26						x	x	x	x	x		
x	x	x	x		x			x		2		x	22			26			x	x	x		x		
x		x	x	x	x			x		18			x		21	x			x	x	x		15		
x		x	x	x	x			x		18			x		21	x			x	x	x		22		
x		x	x	x	x			x		18			x		21	x			x	x	x		15		
x	x		x	x	x			x		x					26				x	x	x		x		

MORECAMBE

GROUND DETAILS

Christie Park,
Lancaster Road,
Morecambe,
Lancashire LA4 5TJ

TELEPHONE 01524 411797
Fax: 01524 411797

email: neil@morecambefc.com
Web site: http://www.morecambefc.com

DIRECTIONS:
From south leave M6 motorway at junction 34. Follow signs for Morecambe through Lancaster, on A589, go straight across the first 2roundabouts, and at the third (with the Shrimp pub on your left), follow thesigns for Town Centre - Christie Park is approx. 600 metres on your left

CAPACITY:	6,300
SEATED:	1,200
COVERED TERRACING:	4,300

CLUB SHOP: On ground and open on matchdays. Also commercial office open Monday to Friday 9.00 - 5.00 selling the same goods

SOCIAL FACILITIES: J B's open normal licensing hours

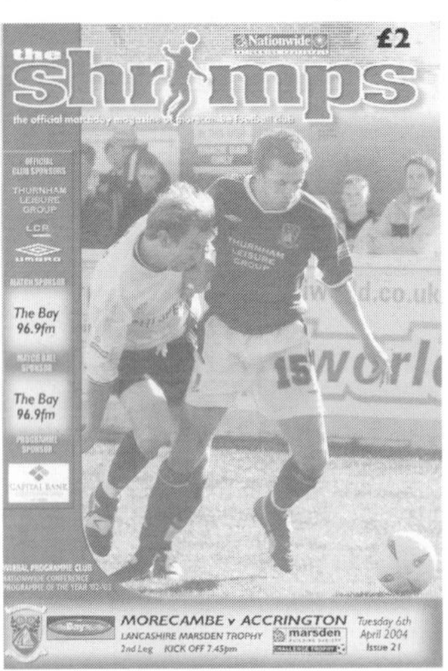

MATCHDAY PROGRAMME

Pages: 48 Price: £2,00
Editor: Sean O'Connor
Other club publications: "Gazetta de la Shrimpa"
Clubcall: 09066 555966

Local Press: Morecambe Visitor; Morecambe Guardian; Lancashire Evening Post; The Citizen
Local Radio: Radio Lancashire; Red Rose Radio; Bay Radio

Founded:	1920
Nickname:	The Shrimps
Club sponsor:	Wright & Lord (Solicitors) & UMBRO
Club colours:	Red shirts, white shorts, black socks
Change colours:	Yellow shirts, black shorts and yellow socks.
Midweek home matchday:	Tuesdays, 7.45pm kick-off
Reserve Team's League:	Lancashire Lge Div. 1 & North West All. Yth Div.

CLUB OFFICIALS

Chairman	Peter McGuigan
Vice Chairman	Graham Hodgson
Directors	Peter Cross, Stuart Forrest, Rod Taylor
Club Secretary	Neil Marsdin
Commercial Manager	Peter Howard

FOOTBALL MANAGEMENT TEAM

MANAGER **JIM HARVEY**

Date of Appointment June 1994
Date & Place of Birth: 2nd May 1958,Lurgan N.Ireland
PREVIOUS CLUBS
As manager None
As asst. manager Morecambe (Jan - June 1994)
As player Glenavon, Arsenal, Hereford Utd., Bristol C., Tranmere Rov., Crewe Alex.
HONOURS
As manager Spalding Cup 97-98; NPL R-up 94-95
Conference Runners-Up 2002-2003
As player N. Ireland - u23.,
Leyland Daf Cup, Mercantile Trophy
Promotion from Division 4 & Division 3

Assistant Manager	Andy Mutch
Second Team Manager	Jeff Udall
2nd Team Asst. Manager	Tony Gribbins
Football in the Community	Janet Preston**Sports**
Therapist	David Edge

Club's Playing Staus: Mainly full time players

Season	League	Div.	Pos.	Home P	Home W	Home D	Home L	Home F	Home A	Away W	Away D	Away L	Away F	Away A	Pts	Manager
03-04	Conference	-	7	42	14	4	3	43	25	6	3	12	23	41	67	Jim Harvey
02-03	Conference	-	2	42	17	3	1	52	13	6	6	9	34	29	78	Jim Harvey
01-02	Conference	-	6	42	12	5	4	30	27	5	6	10	33	40	62	Jim Harvey
00-01	Conference	-	19	42	8	5	8	35	29	3	7	11	29	37	45	Jim Harvey
99-00	Conference	-	3	42	10	7	4	46	29	8	9	4	24	19	70	Jim Harvey
98-99	Conference	-	14	42	9	5	7	31	29	6	3	12	29	47	53	Jim Harvey
97-98	Conference	-	5	42	11	4	6	35	30	10	6	5	42	34	73	Jim Harvey
96-97	Conference	-	4	42	10	5	6	34	23	9	4	8	35	33	66	Jim Harvey

Season	League	Div.	Pos.	P	W	D	L	F	A	Pts	Manager
95-96	Conferece	-	9	42	17	8	17	78	72	59	Jim Harvey
94-95	N.P.L.	Premier	2	42	28	10	4	99	34	94	Jim Harvey

HONOURS

F.A. Trophy 73-74,
Spalding Cup 97-98,
Conference Runners-up 2002-2003
Northern Premier Lge R-up 91-92 94-95,
Presidents Cup 91-92,
Lancs Combination 24-25 61-62 62-63 66-67 67-68
R-up 1923-24, 25-26,
Lg Cup 26-27 45-46 64-65 66-68;
Lancashire Junior Cup (now ATS Trophy) x8
25-27 61-63 68-69 85-87 92-93, 95-96;03-04
Lancashire Senior Cup 67-68,

PREVIOUS

Leagues: Lancs Combination 1920-68, Northern Premier 1968-1995

Grounds: Woodhill Lane 1920-25, shared with cricket club who still play there

Past Players who progressed to the Football League

Fred Blondel (Bury 1946),
Herbert Harrison (Accrington 1947),
Gordon Milne (Preston 1956),
Ray Charnley (Blackpool 1957),
Geoff Slack (Stockport 1958),
Ron Mitchell (Leeds 1958), Derek Armstrong (Carlisle 1961),
Alan Taylor(Rochdale 1973),
John Coates (Southport via Burscough & Skelmersdale 1975),
Keith Galley (Southport 1975),
Brian Thompson (West Ham 1977),
Malcolm Darling (Bury 1978)
David Eyres (Blackpool), Kenny Lowe (Barnet via Barrow),
Steve Gardner (Bradford City), Dave Lancaster (Chesterfield)

CLUB RECORDS

Attendance: 9,324 v Weymouth FA Cup 4.1.62

Win: 14-0 v Rossendale Utd, Lancs Combination Sept 1967 (Arnold Timmins scored 8)

Defeat: 0-14 v Chorley(A), 19th April 1946

Transfer fee paid: £25,000 to Northwich V. for Steve Walters, July 2000

Transfer fee received: £175,000 from Rushden & Diamonds for Justin Jackson, July 2000

Career Goalscorer: Keith Borrowdale 289 1956-68, 78-79 Lancashire Combination
John Coleman 130 1990-1995 (Northern Premier League)

Career Appearances: Steve Done 523 + 7 sub 1968-78

BEST SEASON

FA Cup: 3rd Round 1961-62 v Weymouth (H) 0-1
2000-01 v Ipswich T (H) 0-3

League clubs defeated: Chester City 1961-62, Cambridge Utd.(2000-01)

FA Trophy: Winners 73-74,
S-Final: 2001-02
Quarter Final: 72-73, 77-78, 93-94

League: 3rd Conference 1999-2000

LAST SEASON

F.A. Cup: 4th Qual.Td.

F.A. Trophy: 3rd Round

Conference: 7th

Top Goalscorer: Danny Carlton

Player of the Year: David Perkins

Club Captain: Jim Bentley

Semi-Professional Capped Players

John Coleman, Mike Bignall, Brian Healy, Stewart Drummond, Justin Jackson, Lee Elam, Adriano Rigoglioso and Gary Thompson (U23), David Perkins and Danny Carlton.

MORECAMBE PLAYING SQUAD

Player	Birthplace	D.O.B.	Previous Clubs
			Bold print denotes England semi-professional international.
GOALKEEPERS			
Adam Sollitt	Sheffield	22.06.77	Scarborough, Kettering Town, Northampton T.
DEFENDERS			
Jim Bentley	Liverpool	11.06.76	Telford Utd, Manchester C
MIchael Howard	Birkenhead	02.12.78	Swansea City , Tranmere Rovers
David Perkins	Blackpool	21.06.83	From YouthAcademy
Carl Ruffer	Chester	20,12.74	Chester City
Iain Swan	Glasgow	16.10.79	Leigh RMI, Partick Thistle, OldhamAthletic
Kieron Walmsley	Preston	11.12.83	From Youth Aacademy
MIDFIELD			
Chris Blackburn	Crewe	11,06.76	Northwich Victoria, Chester City
Lee Collins	Belshill	03.02.74	Blackpool, Swindon T, Albion Rovers, Possil U
Dean Howell	Burton on Trent	29.11.80	Southport,Stoke City, Notts Co., Crewe Alexandra
James Kelly	Liverpool	14.02.73	Scarborough, Doncaster R, Hednesford T, Wolves, Wrexham
Terry McFlynn	Co.Derry	27.03.81	Margate,Woking, Q.P.R. (**N. Ireland U21 & U23)**
Russell McKenna	Morecambe		From YouthTeam
Paul Osborne	Preston	08.06.83	From Youth Academy
Mike Stringfellow	Lancaster	09.10.81	From Youth Academy
FORWARDS			
Danny Carlton	Leeds	22.12.83	Youth Team
Wayne Curtis	Barrow	06.03.80	Holker OB
Gary Hunter	Morecambe	01.01.85	From Youth Academy
Sean O'Connor	Cannock	07.07.81	Queen of the South,Dundee United,Hednesford Town
Nick Rogan	Blackpool	15.1083	Kendal Town
Gary Thompson	Kendal	24.11.80	Youth team
Ryan Sugden	Bradford	26.12.80	Burton Albion,Chester City, Scarborough, Oldham Athletic
Michael Twiss	Salford	26.12.83	Chester City, Leigh R.M.I., Port Vale, Manchester United

NORTHWICH VICTORIA

The Vics' first home game last season was against Scarborough, and it was celebrated for being their 1000th game in the top echelon of non-league football. In 1979 Northwich and nineteen other clubs founded the Alliance Premier League. The only other club to have been at the same level for an unbroken stint of 25 years was Telford United and how strange a fact that was going to turn out to be ten months later.

Vics had a miserable season after losing their manager of the last two seasons,Jimmy Quinn to Shrewsbury, Steve Davis took five points from the opening three games but only one from the next eight and Davis was replaced by Alvin McDonald from Vauxhall Motors. He too had eleven games and after only one victory the Northwich board decided that more drastic action was needed and in December Shaun Teale was appointed as Vic's third manager.

Unfortunately for the Vics the rot had set in and they proceeded to occupy bottom position in the Conference for the rest of the season and relegation became a certainty.

Quite obviously the main problem was the lack of a proven goalscorer and whilst it was accepted that the previous season's leading scorer - Greg Blundell would do well at his new club Doncaster Rovers - it was hard for the faithfull Vics fans to see that Dave McNiven was also banging them in at Leigh RMI.

Vics season ended as it had started, with a win - that secured a double over Telford United - and two draws, but the club began to prepare itself for the new Conference North, when the unfortunate events at Telford gave Vics an unexpected lifeline and the chance to be the only club starting their 26th consecutive season in the Conference. Fresh hopes came with the appointment of Steve Burr as manager, but he will have his work cut out to improve the club's fortunes. **Brian Edge**

October 2003 - Back Row (L-R): Lee Woodyatt, Mark Foran, Andy Ralph, Andy Woods, Chris Ward, Kieran Charnock. **Middle:** Phil Lea (Physio), Mark Devlin, Val Owen (now left the club), Mark Barnard (now left the club), Richard Norris, Chris Thompson, Chris Blackburn, Chris Royle, Ray Walker (Coach – now left the club) **Front:** Johnny Allan (now left the club), Ryan Zico-Black (now left the club), Peter Carroll (Asst Manager – now left the club), Alvin McDonald (Manager – now left the club)), Phil Brazier (Capt), Steve Garvey.

NORTHWICH VICTORIA

Match Facts 2003-04

The number shown directly below the player's name is his squad number.
Where a number is shown instead of an "X' in the columns this represents a substitute appearance and the number indicates the player replaced.

Comp.	Date	Opponents	Venue.	Result	Goalscorers	Att.
Conf 1	Aug 09	Forest Green R	A	D 0-0		628
Conf 2	Aug 12	Scarborough	H	D 1-1	Ward	854
Conf 3	Aug 16	Tamworth	H	W 1-0	Devlin	712
Conf 4	Aug 23	Stevenage B	A	L 0-1		1869
Conf 5	Aug 25	Leigh RMI	H	L 0-1		582
Conf 6	Aug 30	Aldershot T	A	L 3-4	Ward Devlin Garvey	2801
Conf 7	Sep 06	Halifax T	A	L 3-5	Thompson Garvey Ward	1440
Conf 8	Sep 13	Dagenham & R	H	L 0-1		575
Conf 9	Sep 20	Morecambe	H	D 1-1	Ross	853
Conf 10	Sep 23	Chester C	A	L 0-4		2817
Conf 11	Sep 27	Margate	A	L 1-3	Garvey	478
Conf 12	Oct 04	Accrington S	H	D 3-3	Allan(2) Ward	865
Conf 13	Oct 07	Hereford U	H	L 1-5	Norris	1008
Conf 14	Oct 11	Exeter C	A	L 0-2		3090
Conf 15	Oct 18	Gravesend & N	H	D 0-0		542
FAC 4q	**Oct 26**	**Halifax T**	**H**	**W 1-0**	**Thompson**	**1101**
Conf 16	Nov 01	Barnet	A	L 0-1		1852
FAC 1	**Nov 08**	**Kidderminster H**	**A**	**L 1-2**	**Thompson**	**2052**
Conf 17	Nov 15	Farnborough T	A	L 0-2		626
Conf 18	Nov 22	Woking	H	L 1-4	Wright	627
Conf 19	Nov 25	Telford U	A	W 1-0	Foran	1560
Conf 20	Nov 29	Halifax T	H	L 0-1		757
Conf 21	Dec 02	Burton A	H	L 1-2	Potts	686
Conf 22	Dec 06	Dagenham & R	A	L 0-2		1163
Conf 23	Dec 13	Forest Green R	H	L 0-4		474
Conf 24	Dec 20	Scarborough	A	L 0-1		1265
Conf 25	Dec 26	Shrewsbury T	A	L 1-3	Wright	5059
Conf 26	Jan 01	Shrewsbury T	H	L 0-2		3268
Conf 27	Jan 03	Aldershot T	H	D 1-1	Thompson	752
FAT 3	**Jan 10**	**Marine**	**A**	**L 0-1**		**565**
Conf 28	Jan 17	Tamworth	A	L 1-2	Robinson(og)	1158
Conf 29	Jan 24	Chester C	H	L 0-4		2141
Conf 30	Feb 07	Morecambe	A	L 0-3		1597
Conf 31	Feb 14	Margate	H	L 0-3		428
Conf 32	Feb 21	Accrington S	A	D 2-2	Thompson Garvey	1422
Conf 33	Mar 06	Hereford U	A	L 0-1		3064
Conf 34	Mar 13	Burton A	A	W 1-0	Foran	1416
Conf 35	Mar 16	Exeter C	H	D 1-1	Nicholas	547
Conf 36	Mar 20	Farnborough T	H	D 1-1	Ward	510
Conf 37	Mar 27	Woking	A	L 0-3		1857
Conf 38	Apr 10	Stevenage B	H	L 1-2	Devlin	487
Conf 39	Apr 12	Leigh RMI	A	L 0-1		339
Conf 40	Apr 17	Barnet	H	D 1-1	Garvey(p)	728
Conf 41	Apr 21	Telford U	H	W 1-0	Wright	479
Conf 42	Apr 24	Gravesend & N	A	D 2-2	Wright Ward	1436

STEP 1 CONFERENCE | STEP 2 - P177 CONFERENCE Nth & Sth | STEP 3 - P269 NPL, Southern, Isthmian Premiers | STEP 4 - P269 NPL 1, Southern N&S, Isthmian 1 | STEP 5/6 - P473 Current level 3 leagues | STEP 7 - P713 Current level 4 leagues

Andy WOODS	Chris ROYLE	Lee WOODYATT	Phil BRAZIER	Mark FORAN	Shaun CAME	Steve GARVEY	Val OWEN	Shaun TEALE	Chris THOMPSON	Chris WARD	Mark DEVLIN	Richard NORRIS	Chris BLACKBURN	Kieran CHARNOCK	Lee BROUGH	Dean BUTTERWORTH	Colin POTTS	James McCOY	Ben CONNETT	Mark BARNARD	Greg RIOCH	Ryan Zico BLACK	Jon ALLAN	Karl BROWN	Neil ROSS	Chris BENNETT	Hugh McAULEY	Paul McGUIRE	Karl MURRAY	Peter WRIGHT	Andy RALPH	Nicky YOUNG	Ben BRISCOE	Jamie McGUIRE	Michael SAWTELL	Sean HANKIN	Craig MITCHELL	Steve NICHOLAS	Scott WILLIS	Glenn TOLLEY
1	**2**	**3**	**4**	**5**	**6**	**7**	**8**	**8**	**9**	**10**	**11**	**12**	**14**	**15**	**16**	**17**	**17**	**18**	**20**	**21**	**21**	**22**	**23**	**23**	**24**	**24**	**25**	**26**	**27**	**28**	**30**	**31**	**31**	**32**	**32**	**33**	**34**	**35**	**36**	**37**
x	x	x	x	x		x	x		x	23	x		x		3								x																	
x	x	x	x	x		x	x		x	3	x		x		8								x																	
x	x	x	x	x	7	x	x		x	x	x		x										10																	
x	x		x	x		x	x		x	7	x		x	16	x	8							x																	
x	x		x	x	4	x			x	16	x		x	x	x	9							x																	
x	x	x	x	x		x			14	17	x		x	16	x	x				x			x																	
x	x		x	x		x	14		x	22	x	7	x							x		x	x																	
x	x		x	x		12	x		x	x	x	x	23			10				x			x																	
x	x		x	x		x	x		x	9	x	8	23							x			x		x															
x	x		x			x	23		x	9	x	14	x	x						x			x		x															
x	x		x	x		x	23		24		x	x	12	x						x			x		x															
	x	2	x	x		x	x		10	x	x		x						x				x																	
x		x	x	x		x	x		10	x	x	8	x	x								11	x																	
x	x	x	x	x		9	12		x		x	x	x	x						x		5	x																	
	x	x	x			x	11		23	x	x		x	x						4		7	x								x									
x		**x**	**x**	**x**		**x**	**12**		**x**	**x**	**10**	**x**	**x**	**x**						**x**		**x**																		
		x		x					x		x	11	x	x								x	x				14	22	x		x									
x		**x**	**x**	**x**		**x**	**11**		**21**		**x**	**x**		**x**								**x**	**x**						**x**											
	x	x	x	x		x			x				x	x		3										7			x	x	x									
		33	x	x		x							x	x								7							x	x	x	x		x		x				
	x		x	x						31	x		x	x										x						x	x	x		x						
	x		x	x							x	14	x	x			32							x						x	x	x		x						
	x		x	x						23	x	14	x	x			x							x						x	x	x								
	x		x	x		23			31		x	32		x			x							x						x	x	x		x						
	x		x	x		x			2		x		x	x			x													x	x	x								
x		10	x	x		x				x	x	x	x	x			x													x		12								
x	3	x	x	x		x					x	x	x	x			x													x		17								
x	x	2	x	x		x			x		x	x		17			x	7						x						x										
x		x	x			x		x	x			x					x							x				x		x		23								
x		**x**	**x**			**x**		**x**	**x**		**31**	**x**	**x**				**3**											**x**		**x**		**x**								
x			x	4				x			x	11	x	x			x											x		17							x	x	x	
x				15		17		x			x	11	x	x			x											x		x							x	x	x	
x	x	26		2	x			x	34		x		x				x											x									x	x	x	
x		x		x	x			x	x		x	11	x																	32					x			x	x	
x		x		x	x	x			x	x		x						10												x					x			x		
x	x	35		x	x	x			x	x	x	10									x									x								x		
	x	9	6	x	x	x			x	x	x	10							x		x									x								x		
	x	x	12	x	x	x				x		x							x		x									x			3					x		
	x	x	x	x	x	x				x									x		x									x			35					x		
	x		x	x	x	x				x		37		35					x		x									x			2					x		x
	x	x	x	x	x	x			10	x	x	7		x					x														15					x		
	x	x	x	x	x	35		31			x	x		2					x														x					x		x
	x	x	x	x	x	x					x	31		x					x									x					37							x
	7	x	x	x	x	x				x	x			37					x		x							4		x										x
	37		x	x	x	x				x	x	4		x					x		x							21		x										x

NORTHWICH VICTORIA

GROUND DETAILS

Club Office (for correspondance) NVFC, Leftwich House, Queen St,Northwich CW9 5JN

Tel No: 01606 41450 and Fax 01606 330577

Ground: Wincham Park,Wincham, Northwich, Cheshire

Tl/Fax:01606 43008

Directions: At.Jct 19 M6 take A556 towards Northwich for 3 miles, then right at dual carriageway into A539 for half a mile to lights.. Turn right and after 3/4 mile, turn left opposite BlackGreyhound Inn. Ground is half a mile on left after canal bridge.

CAPACITY 4,000 **SEATED** 800
COVERED TERRACING 1,500

Large social club with members lounge and seperate function room-both available for hire. Bass Beer, Pool, Darts, TV etc. Witton Albion Social Club at Wincham Park welcomes all away supporters.

The club is hoping to move to The New Victoria Stadium by the end of November

The club shop is at Leftwich House during the week and at the ground on matchdays

MATCHDAY PROGRAMME

Editor: Brian Edge

Pages: 48 Price: £2.00

Other club publications: 'Distant Vics'
(a bi-monthly magazine for exiled Vics' fans)

Local Press: Northwich Guardian (Wed.); Northwich Chronicle (Wed.); Daily Post; Manchester Evening News Pink (Sat.)
Local Radio: GMR (BBC Manchester); Piccadilly Radio; Signal Radio

Founded:	1874
Nickname:	Vics,Greens or Trickies.
Club Sponsors:	Britannia Carpets
Club colours:	Green & white hooped shirts, white shorts and white socks
Change colours:	Sky Blue / navy /navy
Midweek home matchday:	Tuesday
Reserve Team's league:	Lancashire League

CLUB OFFICIALS

Chairman Dave Stone

Company Secretary Graham Cookson

Directors Derek Nuttall

Associate Directors

Graham Cookson (Co.Sec), Dave Edgeley, Ted Carthy, Peter Garret & Dave Thomas(Gen Man).

President &
Football Secretary Derek Nuttall c/o the club
Tel: 01606 41450 Fax: 01606 330577

Commercial Manager: Brian Edge Tel : 01606 41450 or 07711 505414

FOOTBALL MANAGEMENT TEAM

MANAGER: STEVE BURR

Assistant Manager:	Peter Wragg**First Team**
Player/Coach:	Gregor Rioch
Physio:	Phil Lea
Res& YouthTeam Manager:	Ted Carthy
Club's Playing Status:	Part-time

Season	League	Div.	Pos.	Home P	W	D	L	F	A	Away W	D	L	F	A	Pts	Manager
03-04	Conference	-	22	42	2	8	11	15	38	2	3	16	15	42	23	Steve Davis/Alvin McDonald/Shaun Teale
02-03	Conference	-	14	42	6	5	10	26	34	7	7	7	40	38	51	Jimmy Quinn
01-02	Conference	-	13	42	9	4	8	32	34	7	3	11	25	36	55	Jimmy Quinn
00-01	Conference	-	17	42	8	7	6	31	24	3	6	12	18	43	46	Mark Gardiner/Keith Alexander
99-00	Conference	-	18	42	10	8	3	33	25	3	4	14	20	53	51	Mark Gardiner
98-99	Conference	-	7	42	11	3	7	29	21	8	6	7	31	30	66	Phil Wilson/Mark Gardiner
97-98	Conference	-	9	42	8	9	4	34	24	7	6	8	29	35	60	Phil Wilson
96-97	Conference	-	6	42	11	5	5	31	20	6	7	8	30	34	63	Mark Hancock/ Phil Wilson

Season	League	Div.	Pos.	P	W	D	L	F	A	Pts	Manager
95-96	Conference	-	8	42	16	12	14	72	64	60	Brian Kettle
94-95	Conference	-	10	42	14	15	13	77	66	57	John Williams

HONOURS

Welsh Cup R-up 1881/82,1888-89;
FA Trophy 1983/84, R-up 1982/83 & 1995/96;
Bob Lord Trophy 1979/80, 92/93;
Northern Premier Lge R-up 1976/77;
Northern Premier Lge Cup 1972/73, R-up 1978/79;
Cheshire County Lge 1956/57, R-up 1924/25, 47/48;
Cheshire County Lge Cup 1925/35;
Manchester Lge 1902/03, R-up 1900/01, 03/04, 07/08, 08/09, 11/12; The Combination R-up 1890/91;
Cheshire Senior Cup 1880-81, 81/82, 82/83, 83/84, 84/85, 85/86,1928/29, 36/37, 49/50, 54/55, 71/72, 76/77, 78/79, 83/84, 93/94. R-up 1891/92,96/97, 1905/06, 08/09, 47/48, 50/51, 63/64, 65/66, 69/70, 70/71, 77/78, 85/86; 98/99
Staffordshire Senior Cup 1978/79, 79/80, 89/90, R-up 1986/87, 90/91;
CheshireAmateur Cup 1901/02, R-up 1898/99, 02/93,
Northwich Senior Cup 1948/49, 58/59,59/60, 63/64, 64/65, 65/66, 67/68, 68/69, 69/70, 71/72, 74/75, R-up x7;
Mid Chesh Sen Cup 1984/85, 85/86, 87/88, 89/90, 00-01 91/92, 93/94, 94/95, 96/97,98/99,01-02, R-up 1982/83, 83/84, 90/91, 92/93;02-03;
North-West Floodlit Lge 1966/67, 75/76;
Cheshire Lge Lancs. Comb. Inter-Lge Cup 1961/62;
Guardian Charity Shield 1985/86, 86/87, 87/88

PREVIOUS

Leagues: The Combination 1890-1892, Football League Div.2 1892-94, The Combination 1894-1898, The Cheshire League 1898-1900, Manchester League 1900-12, Lancashire 1912-19, Cheshire County League 1919-68, Northern Premier League 1968-79

Grounds: The Drill Field

Past Players who progressed to the Football League

Tony Hemmings (Wycombe W), Tony Bullock (Barnsley), Darren Tinson (Macclesfield T) Lee Steele (Shrewsbury) Paul Tait (Crewe Alex),Shaun Teale (Tranmere R & Aston Villa) , Mark Birch (Carlisle U),Mark Birch (Carlisle U) and Gary Fletcher (Leyton O,Mark Bailey &Adie Mike (LincolnC) Kevin Street (Bristol R) and Greg Blundell (Doncaster R)

CLUB RECORDS

Attendance: 11,290 v Witton Albion, Cheshire League, Good Friday 1949

Win: 17-0 v Marple Ass. 15.12.1883
Defeat: 3-10 v Port Vale 7.2.1931

Career Goalscorer: Peter Burns 160 - 1955-65
Career Appearances: 970 by Ken Jones 1969-85

Transfer Fee paid: £12,000
to Hyde United for Malcolm O'Connor - August 1988
Transfer Fee received: £50,000
from Leyton Orient for Gary Fletcher - June 2001
from Chester City for Neil Morton -October 1990

BEST SEASON

FA Cup: Quarter Finals 1883-84
League clubs defeated: Rochdale,Peterborough,Watford (all 76-7),Chester C (82-3).,Crewe A(84-5) & Bury (00-1)

FA Trophy: Winners 83-84
R-up 82-83 95-96

League: 4th Conference 80-81

LAST SEASON

F.A. Cup: 1st Round
F.A. Trophy: 3rd Rd Round
Conference: 22nd
Top Goalscorer: Chris Ward 6
Player of the Year: Mark Foran
Captain: Phil Beazier

Player	Birthplace	D.O.B.	Previous Clubs	Bold print denotes England semi-professional international.
GOALKEEPERS				
Ben Connett	Knutsford	01.09.83	Liverpool	
Andrew Ralph	Manchester		Vauxhall Motors, Kidsgrove A, Tranmere R	
DEFENDERS				
Phil Brazier	Liverpool	03.09.77	Vauxhall Motors, Liverpool	
Shaun Came	Crewe	15.06.83	Macclesfield Town	
Keiron Charnock	Preston	03.08.84	Wigan Athletic	
Mark Foran	Aldershot	30.10.73	Telford United, Bristol Rovers 75,000),Crewe Alexandra, Peterborough United, Sheffield United, Millwall.	
Paul McGuire	Manchester	17.11.79	Hyde United, Morecambe	
Gregor Rioch	Sutton Coldfield	24.06.75	Shrewsbury T, Northwich T, Shrewsbury T, Macclesfield T, Hull C, Peterborough U, Luton T	
Chris Royle	Manchester	30.01.81	Winsford Utd, Congleton T, Witton Alb., Northwich V, Reading	
MIDFIELD				
Mark Devlin	Irvine	08.01.73	Stoke, Exeter	
Steve Garvey	Stalybridge	22.11.73	Blackpool, Crewe Alexandra	
Richard Norris	Birkenhead	05.01.78	Marine, Crewe	
Paul Santus	Wigan	08.09.83	Wigan Athletic.	
Glenn Tolley	Knighton	24.09.83	Shrewsnbury Town	
FORWARDS				
Phil Hadland	Warrington	20.10.80	Leek T, Colchester U, Leek T, Chester C, Darlington, Leyton O, Rochdale, Reading	
Steve Nicholas	Stirling	08.07.81	East Fife, Stirling Alb.Motherwell, Stirling Alb.	
Mark Quayle	Liverpool	02.10.78	Scarborough, Nuneaton B, Telford U, Morecambe, Altrincham, Ilkeston T, Leigh Halifax T, Notts Co, Everton.	
Chris Thompson	Liverpool	07.02.82	Grimsby Town	

SCARBOROUGH

THE SEADOGS' season can be summarised by one thing - the FA Cup, in which the scalps of League clubs Doncaster Rovers (1-0 at home), Port Vale (1-0 away) and Southend United (1-1 at Roots Hall and 1-0 in the home replay) were captured after Hinckley United had been despatched in the Fourth Qualifying Round.

This meant a Fourth Round Proper visit from mighty rich men Chelsea and a superb effort was almost rewarded by a draw and a replay visit to Stamford Bridge, but a late goal and some controversial refereeing foiled all that. How often have we heard that story before? No answers, please!

However, it was a series of bright spots in an otherwise mediocre campaign, in which only fifteenth place was achieved in the Conference and, almost inevitably, there was an immediate exit from the FA Trophy at home to Stafford Rangers by the odd goal in three.

One beneficiary of the Cup run was manager Russell Slade, who was given the difficult job of reviving the fortunes of Grimsby Town, a task for which his record suggested that he was well qualified, as in the 2002-03 season he had managed to rescue Scarborough from the ignomy of relegation, and his successor Nick Henry will hope that the legacy of his time spent at McCain Stadium will bring sufficiently good returns so that Football League status can be regained.

W.M.

Back Row (L-R) Martin Barnes, James Beadle, Tony Hackworth, Glen Downey (Nowat Grimsby), Colin Cryan, Gareth Downey, Leigh Walker, Ricky Ossai, Steve Burton, Robert Gill, Steve Baker, Keith Gilroy, Nick Heinemann, Michael Coulson.
Front Row (L-R) John Blackburn, Chris Senior, Ashley Lyth, Scott Kerr (Captain), Martin Woodmansey (Physio), Neil Redfearn (Assistant Coach), Nick Henry (Head Coach), Mitch Cook (Assistant Coach), Brian Hodgson (Kit Man), Mark Hotte, David Pounder, Tyrone Thompson, Ryan Blott

SCARBOROUGH

The number shown directly below the player's name is his squad number.
Where a number is shown instead of an "X' in the columns this represents a substitute appearance and the number indicates the player replaced.

Comp.	Date	Opponents	Venue.	Result	Goalscorers	Att.
Conf 1	Aug 09	Farnborough T	H	W 2-1	Rose Gilroy(p)	1415
Conf 2	Aug 12	Northwich V	A	D 1-1	Gill	854
Conf 3	Aug 16	Woking	A	L 1-2	Henry	1901
Conf 4	Aug 23	Burton A	H	L 1-2	Quayle	1445
Conf 5	Aug 25	Accrington S	A	L 0-1		2017
Conf 6	Aug 30	Telford U	H	D 1-1	Quayle	1113
Conf 7	Sep 06	Gravesend & N	H	W 2-0	Quayle(p) Senior	1249
Conf 8	Sep 13	Hereford U	A	L 1-2	Quayle	4850
Conf 9	Sep 20	Forest Green R	H	D 2-2	Quayle(2,1p)	1208
Conf 10	Sep 23	Tamworth	A	D 0-0		1004
Conf 11	Sep 27	Exeter C	A	D 0-0		2776
Conf 12	Oct 04	Shrewsbury T	H	D 1-1	Quayle	1201
Conf 13	Oct 07	Morecambe	H	W 1-0	Price	1219
Conf 14	Oct 11	Stevenage B	A	D 2-2	Hotte Senior	1774
LDVT 1	**Oct 14**	**Port Vale**	**H**	**W 2-1**	**Senior Kelly**	**1003**
Conf 15	Oct 18	Margate	H	L 0-1		1263
FAC 4q	**Oct 25**	**Hinckley United**	**H**	**W 3-1**	**Kerr(2) Lyth**	**1206**
Conf 16	Nov 01	Chester C	H	D 2-2	Quayle(p) Marcelle	1441
LDVT 2	**Nov 04**	**Halifax T**	**H**	**L 0-1**		**899**
FAC 1	**Nov 08**	**Doncaster R**	**H**	**W 1-0**	**Rose**	**3497**
Conf 17	Nov 11	Leigh RMI	A	W 4-1	Quayle(2,1p) Rose Senior	375
Conf 18	Nov 15	Aldershot T	H	W 1-0	Redmile	1624
Conf 19	Nov 22	Dagenham & R	A	L 0-1		1107
Conf 20	Nov 25	Barnet	H	D 2-2	Redmile Kelly	1208
Conf 21	Nov 29	Gravesend & N	A	D 1-1	Cryan	747
FAC 2	**Dec 06**	**Port Vale**	**A**	**W 1-0**	**Sestanovich**	**4651**
Conf 22	Dec 13	Farnborough T	A	W 2-1	Sestanovich Quayle	620
Conf 23	Dec 20	Northwich V	H	W 1-0	Sestanovich	1265
Conf 24	Dec 26	Halifax T	A	L 0-1		2136
FAC 3	**Jan 03**	**Southend United**	**A**	**D 1-1**	**Kerr**	**6902**
FAT 3	**Jan 10**	**Stafford Rangers**	**H**	**L 1-2**	**Senior**	**1117**
FAC 3r	**Jan 14**	**Southend United**	**H**	**W 1-0**	**Quayle**	**4859**
Conf 25	Jan 17	Woking	H	D 2-2	Williams Quayle(p)	2503
FAC 4	**Jan 24**	**Chelsea**	**H**	**L 0-1**		**5379**
Conf 26	Feb 03	Hereford U	H	D 3-3	Marcelle Downey Redmile	1459
Conf 27	Feb 07	Forest Green R	A	L 0-4		848
Conf 28	Feb 21	Shrewsbury T	A	L 1-4	Senior	3333
Conf 29	Mar 06	Morecambe	A	L 1-2	Quayle	1623
Conf 30	Mar 13	Leigh RMI	H	W 4-1	Hackworth Nicholson Rose Harrison(og)	1093
Conf 31	Mar 16	Tamworth	H	L 0-1		1059
Conf 32	Mar 20	Aldershot T	A	W 2-1	Ketchanke Senior	2442
Conf 33	Mar 23	Exeter C	H	L 2-3	Kelly(p) Hackworth	1200
Conf 34	Mar 25	Halifax T	H	W 1-0	Senior	1220
Conf 35	Mar 27	Dagenham & R	H	D 0-0		1302
Conf 36	Apr 03	Barnet	A	D 0-0		1560
Conf 37	Apr 06	Stevenage B	H	D 2-2	Marcelle Rose	1018
Conf 38	Apr 10	Burton A	A	L 0-2		1370
Conf 39	Apr 12	Accrington S	H	W 2-1	Hackworth Gilroy	1523
Conf 40	Apr 14	Telford U	A	L 1-2	Marcelle	1654
Conf 41	Apr 17	Chester C	A	L 0-1		5987
Conf 42	Apr 24	Margate	A	W 2-0	Gilroy Quayle	404

Leigh WALKER	Mark HOTTE	Michael PRICE	Nick HENRY	James DUDGEON	Steve BAKER	Keith GILROY	Scott KERR	Mark QUAYLE	Karl ROSE	Jacques WILLIAMS	Jamie BURT	Tristram WHITMAN	Tom RAW	Glen DOWNEY	Wayne GILL	Jamie SHERLOCK	Alex NESOVIC	Chris BATCHELOR	Stephen CAPPER	Lloyd BLACKMAN	Stephen LEADBETTER	Paul O'NEILL	Matt REDMILE	Tony HACKWORTH	Chris SENIOR	Iain DAVIDSON	Clayton DONALDSON	Bertrand KETCHANKE	Adam SOLLITT	Leon McSWEENEY	Andy BROWNRIGG	Ashley LYTH	Jimmy KELLY	Clint MARCELLE	Colin CRYAN	Ashley SESTANOVICH	Keith GRAYDON	Kevin NICHOLSON	Mark ROBINSON
1	2	3	4	5	6	7	8	9	10	12	14	14	15	16	18	19	20	20	21	22	22	22	23	24	25	26	27	27	28	29	29	30	31	32	33	34	35	36	37
	x	x				x	x	x	x	x					x				x				x		12				x										
	x	x	x			x	x	x	x					x	9			x				x		10				x										
	x	x	x			x	x	x				25		x				x				x		x				x										
	x	x				x	x	x	7	x					x	27			x				x		12		x		x										
	x	x					x	x	x				x		x	10			x				x		x				x										
	x	x			x			x	x		x		x		x				x				x		14				x										
x	x		x		x			x	x				x	x	x	4	15						x		16								x					
x	x	x	x	16	x			x						x	x	4								x		32		x							x					
x	x	30	x		x		4	x						x				x	x			x		18							x	x					
x	x	21	x		x		x	x				4		x				x	x					22							x	x					
x	x	6	x		x		x	x				x		22					x			x		4							x	x					
x	x	x					x	x						x				x	x			x		22					18		x	x	3					
x	x	x			x		x	x				x		3									x		15							x	x	x					
x	x				x		x	x				x						x	9			x		30					15		x	x	x					
x	x	x			x		x							x					x					x					24		x	x	x			22		
x		x			x		x							6				x	x			x		x					21		x	x	x			22		
x		x					x	x	25						x				x				x		x				1			x	x	x			18		
x					x		x	x	x										x				x		32							x	x	x	x			
x					x		x	x	x						9			32	x				x		34							x	x	x	x			
x					x		x	x	x										x				x									6	x	x	x	x			
x					x		x	x	x	9					32				x				x		10							x	x	x	x			
x	21		x		x		x	x		4					x				x				x		34								x	x	x			
x	x				x		x		x	x					x			32						x		12							6	x	x	x				
x	x					10	x		x	x					x										x		12							x	x	x	x				
x	x	x				18	x	x	x	32					x											9							x	x	x	x				
x	x						x	x	9						x								x									x	x	x	x	x			
x	x	34			18		x	x		8					x								x									x	x	x	x	x			
x	x				x		x	x		18					x											32							x	x	x	x	x			
x	x						x	x		9		8			x								x		30							x	x	x	x	x			
x	x				x		x	x		20		18			x																			x	x	x	x	x			
		x								x		x	14	x				x	x		26				x				x				x		x		x		
x	x				x		x	x				x																					x	x	x	x	x			
x	x				x			x		x		x							6						32							x	x	x	x	x			
x	x				x		x	x				x							6						14							x	x	x	x	x			
x	x						x		23	x		x		x	x				x				x		18				1				x	x					
x							x	x	19			x		x		x			x			x			14								x	x	x					
x	x	x					x	x				x		x	x											x							3	x						x
x	x				x			x	x			37		x		26									x	x								x	x					x
x	x				x		x	x	x							31									x	9			x				x	x					x	
x	x				x		x	x	x							6									x	9			x				x	x	30				x	
x	x						x		x						x										x	27			x			x		x	x				x	
x	x						x	x	x						8										x	32			x			x	29	x	x				x	
x	x						x	x	x					24										x	30			x			27	x	x	x				x	
x	x						x	x	21					x	x				x						x							36	x	x				x	
x	x					25	x	x	x					x	x				32						x							x		x				x	
x	x						x	x	x				32	x	x										x	24							x		x				x	
x	x					30	x	x	x				32	x	x										x	9							x		x				x	
x	x					18	x	x	x					x	x				x					x	9									x				x	
	x					32	x	x	x				x	x										x	9	x			x		26		x				x	
x	x					x	x		x					x	x										x	18							x	x	10				x	
x	x					10	x	24	x					x	x										x					1			x	x	x				x	

SCARBOROUGH

GROUND DETAILS

McCain Stadium
Seamer Road
Scarborough
N. Yorkshire YO12 4HF

TELEPHONE Tel: 01723 375094
Fax: 01723 366211
Newsline: 0891 121650

SIMPLE DIRECTIONS The ground is situated on the main Scarborough to York road (A64), about half a mile beyond B&Q on the left as you go into Scarborough. Scarborough central (BR) about 2 miles.
Car Parking: Ample in streets around the ground.

CAPACITY	5,900
SEATING	3,500
COVERED TERRACING	1,000

CLUB SHOP: Open matchdays

SOCIAL FACILITIES: Clubhouse - open matchdays only

MATCHDAY PROGRAMME

Scarborough Football Club
Season 2002 / 2003
V Nationwide Conference
Nuneaton Borough
Monday 21st April 2003, k.o. 3 pm
The Boro Review
£2.00

Pages: 44 Price: £1.50
Editor: Dereck Meginson
Other club publications: None

Local Press:
Scarborough Evening News; The Mercury

Local Radio: Radio York; Y.C.R. Radio

Founded:	1879
Nickname:	The Seadogs
Club Sponsors:	OCM Ltd
Colours	All Red.
Change colours:	Black/blue/black
Midweek Matchday:	Tuesday

CLUB OFFICIALS

Chairman	Malcolm Reynolds
President	John R Birley
Company Secretary	Philip Webster

Directors : M.Reynolds, J Birley & I.Scobbie

Secretary,Press Off.& Commercial Manager

Stephen GrahamTel Nos: 01723 375094 (W)
07798 538318 (M) 01723 366211 (Fax)
Email:infoscarboroughfc@yahoo.co.uk.
Correspondance to club.

FOOTBALL MANAGEMENT TEAM

MANAGER: RUSSELL SLADE

Date of Appointment:	November 2001
Date of Birth:	10.10.60
Place of Birth:	Wokingham

PREVIOUS CLUBS

As manager:	Notts County, Jt Manager Sheff.Utd
As coach:	Northampton T, Notts C,Sheff U.
As player:	Notts County

Firts Team Coach	N.Henry
Physiotherapist	Kevin Farley
Centre of Excellence Director	Mitch Cook
Youth Team Manager	Ian Kerr
Kit Man:	Brian Hogson

Season	League	Div.	Pos.	Home P	Home W	Home D	Home L	Home F	Home A	Away W	Away D	Away L	Away F	Away A	Pts	Manager
03-04	Conference	-	15	42	8	9	4	32	25	4	6	11	19	29	51	Russ Slade
02-03	Conference	-	7	42	12	3	6	41	28	6	7	8	22	26	64	Russ Slade
01-02	Conference	-	12	42	9	6	6	27	22	5	8	8	28	41	*55	Neil Thompson
00-01	Conference	-	10	42	7	9	5	29	25	7	7	7	27	29	58	C. Addison/ Neil Thompson
99-00	Conference	-	4	42	10	6	5	36	14	9	6	6	24	21	69	Colin Addison
98-99	F. League	3	24	46	8	3	12	30	39	6	3	14	20	38	48	Mike Wadsworth

Season	League	Div.	Pos.	P	W	D	L	F	A	Pts	Manager
97-98	F. League	3	6	46	19	15	12	67	58	72	Mike Wadsworth
96-97	F. League	3	12	46	16	15	15	65	68	63	Mike Wadsworth
95-96	F. League	3	23	46	8	16	22	39	69	40	Ray McHale
94-95	F. League	3	21	42	8	10	24	49	70	34	Philip Chambers

HONOURS

FA Trophy 72-73 75-76 76-77
Vauxhall Conference 86-87
Bob Lord Trophy 83-84
NPL Lge Cup 76-77
North Eastern Cos Lge 62-63, Lge Cup 62-63
Midland Lge 29-30
Scarborough & Dist. Lge 45-46
E. Riding Cup x 8; N. Riding Sen. Cup x 17

PREVIOUS

Leagues: Northern 1898-1910 14-26
Yorkshire Combination 10-14; Yorkshire 26-27;
Midland 27-40 46-60 63-68
Scarborough & Dist. 45-46
Northern Counties 60-62; North Eastern 62-63;
Northern Premier 68-79
Alliance Premier 79-87 99-
Football League 87-99

Name: None

Past Players who progressed to the Football League

when Scarborough was a Non-League club.

CLUB RECORDS

Attendance: 11,162
v Luton Town, FAC 3rd Rd, 1938

Victory: 6-0 v Rhyl Athletic, FA Cup 29.11.30

Defeat: 0-8 v Mansfield Town (H), FA Cup 22.11.52

Career Goalscorer: Unknown

Career Appearances: 196 Steve Richards 87-91

Transfer Fee Paid: £100,000
for Martin Russell to Leicester C., Feb. 87

Transfer Fee Received: £350,000
for Craig Short from Notts Co. (£150K 7/89 + £250K9/92)

BEST SEASON

FA Cup: 3rd Round 30-31 37-38 75-76 77-78

League Clubs Defeated (as non-league club):LincolnC(30-1) York C (32-3), Darlington (37-8), Bradford C(64-5),Oldham A (72-3),Crewe A(73-4), P.N.E(75-6),Crewe A & Rochdale (77-8)

FA Trophy: Winners 72-73 75-76 76-77

Football League: 5th in Division 4, 88-89

League Cup: 4th Round 92-93

LAST SEASON

F.A. Cup: 4th Round
F.A. Trophy: 3rd Round
Conference: 15th
Top Goalscorer: Mark Quayle
Player of the Year: Mark Hotte
Captain: Scott Kerr
Highest League Attendance:

SCARBOROUGH PLAYING SQUAD

Player	Birthplace	D.O.B.	Previous Clubs

Bold print denotes England semi-professional international.

GOALKEEPERS

Player	Birthplace	D.O.B.	Previous Clubs
Gareth Downey	Sunderland	08.02.81	Hartlepool United
Leigh Walker	Sheffield	27.02.81	Stalbridge Celtic, Emley, South Normanton Ath., Barnsley, Sheffield Utd

DEFENDERS

Player	Birthplace	D.O.B.	Previous Clubs
Steve Baker Ire u21	Pontefract	08.09.78	Middlesbrough, Huddersfield Town (L), Darlington (L), Hartlepool (L)
Steve Capper	Ireland		Sunderland
Colin Cryan	Dublin	23.03.81	Sheffield United
Iain Davidson	Glasgow		Brechin City, Sunderland
Paul Foote	Hull	31.03.81	Sheffield United
Mark Hotte	Bradford	27.09.78	Oldham

MIDFIELD

Player	Birthplace	D.O.B.	Previous Clubs
Glen Downey	Newcastle	20.09.78	Bishop Auckland, Hartlepool United (YTS)
Scott Kerr	Leeds	11.12.81	Hull City,Bradford City
Ashley Lyth	Whitby		Leicester City, Scarborough
Nick Henry Div 2	Liverpool	21.02.69	Tranmere, Walsall, Sheffield Utd, Oldham
Neil Redfearn Div I Winner	Dewsbury	20.06.65	Rochdale, Boston U,Halifax T, Wigan A, Bradford C, Charlton A, Barnsley, Oldham A, Watford, Crystal P, Doncaster R, Lincoln C, Bolrton W, Nott'm F.
Tyrone Thompson	Sheffield	05.08 81	Huddersfield Town, Sheffield United
Jacques Williams	Liverpool	25.04.83	Birmingham City, Bordeaux (trainee)

FORWARDS

Player	Birthplace	D.O.B.	Previous Clubs
Keith Gilroy Eire u21	Sligo	08.07.83	Middlesbrough, Sligo Rovers
Toiny Hackworth	Durham	19.05.80	Notts Co., Leeds United
David Pounder	Newcastle	03.02.80	From Trainee
Karl Rose	Barnsley	12.10.78	Barnsley
Chris Senior	Huddersfield	03.03.81	Huddersfield Town

STEVENAGE BOROUGH

THE new broom from the 2002-03 campaign with its large influx of players from Farnborough Town accompanied by its manager Graham Westley did not have too many initial benefits as form in the Conference at the outset was inconsistent after a good start with five straight wins bringing the prospect of at least an ultimate play-off position, but in the end eighth place was the final outcome albeit an improvement on the previous season's twelfth spot, itself a minor miracle after earlier trauma; another six points on this occasion would have made all the difference..

The FA Cup was altogether a more encouraging story as the First Round Proper was reached after a tough Fourth Qualifying Cup tie against Eastbourne Borough (2-2 away and a lone home goal) and this brought a visit from Stockport County and a fine victory by the odd goal in three, which in itself leading to a trip to Swansea City and a brave if unavailing effort against a good side (1-2).

Hopes of big success now rested with the FA Trophy and there was a good start with a Third Round visit to Folkestone Invicta and advancement (3-1), but away games against lower rated opposition in knock-out competitions are all too often recipes for ambushes and so it proved in this case with Hornchurch scoring the only goal of their Fourth Round tie.

Football League status is the ambition of this enterprising club - nothing else will be enough - and fans will be demanding that very thing sooner rather than later. The potential is there as is the will, but there are many Conference teams with the same ideas, particularly those who have lost their own places, so it will be anything but easy.

W.M.

L-R - Back: Jamie Cook, Lee Flynn, Justin Richards, Sam McMahon, Simon Travis, Simon Wormull, Micky Warner.
Middle: Anthony Elding, Tony Battersby, Peter Costello, Mark Westhead, Lionel Perez, Barry Laker, Rocky Baptiste, Jamie Gould
Front: Graham Pearce (Asst. Manager), Danny Carroll, Jason Goodliffe, Graham Westley (Manager), Steve Watson, Gary Holloway, Graham Benstead.

STEVENAGE BOROUGH

The number shown directly below the player's name is his squad number. Where a number is shown instead of an "X' in the columns this represents a substitute appearance and the number indicates the player replaced.

Comp.	Date	Opponents	Venue.	Result	Goalscorers	Att.
Conf 1	Aug 09	Chester C	H	D 0-0		2503
Conf 2	Aug 12	Dagenham & R	A	W 2-1	Elding Costello	1948
Conf 3	Aug 16	Burton A	A	D 1-1	Elding	1572
Conf 4	Aug 23	Northwich V	H	W 1-0	Elding	1869
Conf 5	Aug 25	Margate	A	W 4-1	Holloway(2) Baptiste Elding	755
Conf 6	Aug 30	Hereford U	H	L 0-2		2705
Conf 7	Sep 06	Exeter C	A	L 0-1		3012
Conf 8	Sep 13	Barnet	H	L 1-2	Baptiste	3019
Conf 9	Sep 20	Telford U	A	W 2-0	Elding Goodliffe	1703
Conf 10	Sep 23	Gravesend & N	H	D 2-2	Baptiste Elding	1732
Conf 11	Sep 27	Leigh RMI	H	W 4-0	Elding(2) Battersby Richards	1734
Conf 12	Oct 04	Halifax T	A	L 1-2	Battersby	1437
Conf 13	Oct 07	Woking	A	D 1-1	Travis	2592
Conf 14	Oct 11	Scarborough	H	D 2-2	Battersby(p) Gould	1776
LDVT 1	**Oct 14**	**Luton Town**	**H**	**L 0-1**		**1754**
Conf 15	Oct 18	Forest Green R	A	L 1-3	Bunce	676
FAC 4q	**Oct 25**	**Eastbourne Borough**	**A**	**D 2-2**	**Maamria Elding**	**1305**
FAC 4qr	**Oct 28**	**Eastbourne Borough**	**H**	**W 1-0**	**Watson**	**1205**
Conf 16	Nov 01	Shrewsbury T	H	W 2-0	Maamria Wormull	2172
FAC 1	**Nov 08**	**Stockport County**	**H**	**W 2-1**	**Maamria(2)**	**2538**
Conf 17	Nov 11	Tamworth	A	W 2-1	Wormull Holloway	1006
Conf 18	Nov 15	Accrington S	H	W 2-1	Elding(2)	2121
Conf 19	Nov 22	Morecambe	A	L 1-2	Cook	1354
Conf 20	Nov 29	Exeter C	H	D 2-2	Elding(2)	2007
FAC 2	**Dec 06**	**Swansea City**	**A**	**L 1-2**	**Elding**	**6125**
Conf 21	Dec 13	Chester C	A	W 2-1	Elding Baptiste	2145
Conf 22	Dec 16	Aldershot T	H	L 0-1		1794
Conf 23	Dec 20	Dagenham & R	H	L 0-2		1749
Conf 24	Dec 26	Farnborough T	A	L 0-2		1403
Conf 25	Jan 01	Farnborough T	H	W 3-2	Carroll Maamria Charles(og)	2285
Conf 26	Jan 03	Hereford U	A	L 0-1		2875
FAT 3	**Jan 10**	**Folkestone Invicta**	**A**	**W 3-1**	**Brady Maamria Richards**	**912**
Conf 27	Jan 17	Burton A	H	W 1-0	Richards	2003
Conf 28	Jan 24	Gravesend & N	A	W 3-2	Maamria(2,2p) Rogers	1230
FAT 4	**Feb 03**	**Hornchurch**	**A**	**L 0-1**		**741**
Conf 29	Feb 07	Telford U	H	L 0-1		1744
Conf 30	Feb 14	Leigh RMI	A	W 3-1	Maamria Elding Richards	270
Conf 31	Feb 21	Halifax T	H	W 1-0	Maamria	1715
Conf 32	Mar 06	Woking	H	D 1-1	Elding	2489
Conf 33	Mar 09	Barnet	A	D 0-0		2066
Conf 34	Mar 13	Tamworth	H	W 3-1	Maamria(2,1p) Elding	1646
Conf 35	Mar 20	Accrington S	A	L 1-2	Brennan	1124
Conf 36	Mar 27	Morecambe	H	L 0-1		1687
Conf 37	Mar 30	Aldershot T	A	L 0-2		2540
Conf 38	Apr 06	Scarborough	A	D 2-2	Brough Brennan	1018
Conf 39	Apr 10	Northwich V	A	W 2-1	Elding Boyd	487
Conf 40	Apr 12	Margate	H	W 2-1	Maamria Laker	1548
Conf 41	Apr 17	Shrewsbury T	A	L 1-3	Barnard	3650
Conf 42	Apr 24	Forest Green R	H	W 2-1	Brough Flack	1747

STEP 1
CONFERENCE

STEP 2 - P177
CONFERENCE Nth & Sth

STEP 3 - P269
NPL, Southern, Isthmian Premiers

STEP 4 - P269
NPL 1, Southern N&S, Isthmian 1

STEP 5/6 - P473
Current level 3 leagues

STEP 7 - P713
Current level 4 leagues

Mark WESTHEAD	Simon TRAVIS	Ross WEATHERSTONE	Lee FLYNN	Nathan BUNCE	Jason GOODLIFFE	Barry LAKER	Simon WORMULL	Jon BRADY	Justin RICHARDS	Tony BATTERSBY	Michael BROUGH	Jamie COOK	Nathan ABBEY	Matt LANGSTON	Dean BRENNAN	Leonel PEREZ	Danny CARROLL	Peter COSTELLO	Dean CRACKNELL	Clint MARCELLE	Ben CAMARA	Jamie GOULD	Rocky BAPTISTE	Richard HODGSON	Gary HOLLOWAY	Mark ROGERS	Lee BARNARD	Geoff PITCHER	Mark SMITH	Jo FLACK	Dino MAAMRIA	Richard SCOTT	Micheal WARNER	George BOYD	Steve WATSON	Anthony ELDING	Darren WILLIAMS
1	**2**	**2**	**3**	**4**	**5**	**6**	**7**	**8**	**9**	**10**	**10**	**11**	**13**	**14**	**15**	**16**	**18**	**19**	**19**	**20**	**20**	**21**	**22**	**22**	**23**	**24**	**24**	**25**	**25**	**26**	**27**	**28**	**32**	**33**	**34**	**37**	**38**
	x		x		x	x				x		x				x	x	25					37					x							x	x	
	x		x		x	x				x		x	x	18			x	x					37		11										x	x	
	x		x		x	x				x		x	x				x	x					34		11			19							x	x	
	x		x	x		x				x		x	x				x	x		37			10		25			x								x	
	x		x	x		x				22		x	x					x		37			x		x			x					19			x	
	x		x	x		x			4			x	x				19	x		11			x		x			x								x	
	x		x		x	x						x	x	6			x	x					27								x		37		x	x	
	x		x		x	x			37			x				x	x	x					x		19								18		x	x	
	x		x	x	x	x	x					22				x	x					7	x		x								2			x	
	x		x	x	x	x	x		18			3				x	x	22					x		x											x	
	x		x	x	x	x	x		10	x		5			x	x									x								7			x	
	x		x	x		x	x		15	x		14		x	x	x							4		x											x	
	x		x	x		x	x		10	x		7				x		4				x			x								x			x	
	x		x	x		x	x		37	x		2				x						x			x								x			x	
x	x		21			x	x		x	x		9						x				x			x						19		x				
	x		x	x		x				x		x				x		x							x						x		x		27	10	
x			x	x		x	x					x				1	x					7	37								x		x		x	x	
			x		x	x	x					x				x	x	7				11	37								x		x		x	x	
	19		x		x	x	x									x	x	5				x	34								x		x		x	x	
	x		x	x		x	x								2	x						x	37		7						x		x		x	x	
	x		x	x		x	x			21					2	x						x	x		7						x		x		x		
	x		x	x		x				27		x				x						x			2						x		x		x	x	
	x		x	x		x						x				x	11					x	4		2						x		x		x	x	
			x	x		x	x		27			3				x	x					x	18		x						x		x			x	
				x		x	x					23				x	4	x				x	19		x						x		x		x	x	
				x		x	x					37				x						x	x		x				27		x		x		x	x	
				x		x	x	7				4				x	23					x	x		x						x		x		x	x	
			x	x		x	x	x				21				x						x	3		7						x		x		x	x	
			x			x	x	x				3				x	x						x		7				x		x		x		x	27	
							x	x	37			x				x	x					x							x		x		x		x	x	
							x	x	7			x				x						x	28		x				x		x	x	x		x		
							x	x	10	x		x				x						x			x				x		x	8	x		x		
	7						x	x	x			x				x						x			8	x			x		x	11	x		x		
	x						x	2	x	18		x				x	x					xs				x			x		x	21	x				
	x						x	x	x	21		x				x	x					x	18			x			x		x		8				
	x						x	25	x	x					28	x						x				x			x			x	x		x	21	
				x				x	21						x	x					25	x				x			x		x	37	x		x	x	
				x		x	x	x	7						x	x						x									x	34	x	37	x	x	
		10		x		x			x		x				x	x			9			x									x		x	27	x	x	
16				x		x		21	x		x				x	x						x									x		x	15	x	x	
x		21		x		x		9	x		x				x							x									x		x	15	x	x	
x		x		x		x		15	2		x				x		4														x		x	x	x	x	
x				x		x		4	x		x				x							x		34			9						x	x	x	x	
x		x				x	15	x	37		x				x		x							x			x		10				x			x	
x							x	x	x		x				18		x					x		x					x				x	7		x	22
x						x		x	34		x				x							x							x		x		x	21	x	x	
x						x		x	21		x				x							x		37					x		x		x	x		x	
x						x		x	x		x				x		25					x		15			27		x		x		x	x			
x						x		x			x				34							x		x			x		x	22	x		x	21	x		

STEVENAGE BOROUGH

GROUND DETAILS

Stevenage Stadium,
Broadhall Way,
Stevenage,
Herts SG2 8RH
Tel: 01438 223223
Fax: 01438 743666
email:roger@stevenageborofc.com
Web site: http://www.stevenageborofc.com

SIMPLE DIRECTIONS:
Stevenage South exit off A1(M) - ground on right at second roundabout.Spectators are however advised to go straight on at this roundabout and park inthe Showground opposite the stadium. The stadium is one mile from Stevenage BRstation. Buses SB4 and SB5

CAPACITY: 7,107

SEATED: 3,404
(included away stand all seater)

COVERED TERRACING: 3,703

Groundsman: Ken Watters

CLUB SHOP: Mon - Sat 9-5.30. Broadhall Way, Stevenage. 01438 218061. Sells a complete range of club merchandise including a customising service. Mail Order, credit cards accepted, contact Tracey Levy (01438 218061)

SOCIAL FACILITIES:
Tel.: 01438 218079. Clubhouse at ground open Monday to Friday 7 - 11pm,Saturday noon - 2.00 & 4.30 - 11pm, Sunday: All day from noon. Contact: Jenny Cairns

Clubcall: 09066 555982

FOOTBALL MANAGEMENT TEAM

MANAGER:	**GRAHAM WESTLEY**
Date of Appointment:	2003
Date of Birth:	4th March 1968
Place of Birth:	Isleworth

PREVIOUS CLUBS

As manager	Enfield, Kingstonian, Farnborough T.
As player	QPR, Gillingham, Walton & Hersham

HONOURS

As manager: Ryman Lge Champs. 2000-01
Ryman Lge Cup 99-00

* * *

Assistant Manager	Graham Pearce
1st Team Coach	Graham Benstead
Physiotherapist	Karl Ballard
Chief Scout	Alan Carrington
Scouts	Paul Tippins and Gary Isott

Nickname:	Boro'
Club Sponsors:	Sun Banking Corporation
Club colours:	Red/red/white
Change colours:	All Yellow
Midweek home matchday:	Tuesday
Reserve Team's League:	Capital League
Club's Playing Status:	Some Full time players

CLUB OFFICIALS

Chairman:	Phillip Wallace
Club Administrator:	Roger Austin 01438 218072
Director:	Michael Every
Commercial Manager:	Clive Abrey 01438 218073
Press Officer:	Steve Watkins

Tel Nos: 01438 218072 (W) 07771 523661 (M)

PROGRAMME
Pages: 36 Price: £2.00
Editor: Stuart Govier Tel: 01438 210895

Other club publications: The Borough Yearbook

Local Press: Stevenage Gazette; Comet; Stevenage Mercury; Herald
Local Radio: Chiltern Radio; BBC Three Counties Radio and Hertbeat

Season	League	Div.	Pos.	Home P	W	D	L	F	A	Away W	D	L	F	A	Pts	Manager
03-04	Conference	-	8	42	10	5	6	29	22	8	4	9	29	30	63	Graham Westley
02-03	Conference	-	12	42	7	6	8	31	25	7	4	10	30	30	52	W. Turner / Graham Westley
01-02	Conference	-	11	42	10	4	7	36	30	5	6	10	21	30	55	P. Fairclough / Wayne Turner
00-01	Conference	-	7	42	8	7	6	36	33	7	11	3	35	28	63	Paul Fairclough
99-00	Conference	-	10	42	8	5	8	26	20	8	4	9	34	34	57	R./ Steve Wignall /P Fairclough
98-99	Conference	-	6	42	9	9	3	37	23	8	8	5	25	22	68	Paul Fairclough / Richard Hill
97-98	Conference	-	15	42	8	8	5	35	27	5	4	12	24	36	51	Paul Fairclough
96-97	Conference	-	3	42	15	4	2	53	23	9	6	6	34	30	82	Paul Fairclough

Season	League	Div.	Pos.	P	W	D	L	F	A	Pts	Manager
95-96	Conference	-	1	42	27	10	5	101	44	91	Paul Fairclough
94-95	Conference	-	5	42	20	7	15	68	49	67	Paul Fairclough

HONOURS

GM Vauxhall Conference 95-96,
Isthmian Lge Prem 93-94,
Div 1 91-92, Div 2 (North) 85-86 90-91;
Utd Counties Lg Div 1 80-81 (Div 1 Cup 80-81),
Herts SnrCup R-up 85-86, 93/94;
Herts Charity Cup R-up 93-94,
Herts Charity Shield R-up83-84,
Televised Sports Snr Floodlit Cup 89-90,
Eastern Professional F'lit Cup Group winner
81-82 85-86 86-87 88-89 90-91 91-92,
South Co's Comb. Cup 91-92;
Essex & Herts Border Comb.(Reserves) 94/95
Essex & Herts (Western Div) 95-96

PREVIOUS

Leagues: Chiltern Youth 76-79; Wallspan South Combination 79-80; United Counties 80-84; Isthmian 84-94

Grounds: King George V Playing Field 1976-80

Past Players who progressed to the Football League

Richard Wilmot & NeilTrebble (Scunthorpe Utd) 1993,
Simon Clark (Peterborough United) 1994,
Leo Fortune West (Gillingham) 1995,
Phil Simpson (Barnet) 1995,
Barry Hayles (Bristol Rovers) 1997)

CLUB RECORDS

Attendance: 6,489 v Kidderminster H., GM Vauxhall Conference 25.1.97

Win: 11-1 v British Timken Athletic (H), United Counties League Div.1, 1980-81

Defeat: 0-7 v Southwick (H), Isthmian League Div. 1, 1987-88

Career goalscorer: Barry Hayles

Career appearances: Martin Gittings

Transfer fee paid: £20,000 for Richard Leadbetter to Hereford United 1999

Transfer fee received: £300,000 for Barry Hayles (Bristol R.) July 97

BEST SEASON

FA Cup: Fourth Round replay 97-98. 1-2 v Newcastle Utd. (A) after 1-1 also 3rd Round 1996-97. 0-2 v Birmingham City (A)

League clubs defeated: Leyton Orient 96-97; Cambridge Utd., Swindon Town 97-98

FA Trophy: Runners-up 01-02

League: Conference Champions 95-96

LAST SEASON

F.A. Cup: 2nd Round
F.A. Trophy: 4th Round
Conference: 8th
Top Goalscorer: Anthony Elding
Player of the Year:
Captain:

STEVENAGE BOROUGH PLAYING SQUAD

Player	Birthplace	D.O.B.	Previous Clubs	Bold print denotes England semi-professional international.

GOALKEEPERS

Player	Birthplace	D.O.B.	Previous Clubs
Lionel Perez	France	24.04.67	Cambridge United,Newcastle United,Sunderland
Andy Woodman	Camberwell	11.08.71	Oxford U, Colchester U,Brentford,Northampton T
			Exeter C, Crystal Palace

DEFENDERS

Player	Birthplace	D.O.B.	Previous Clubs
Stuart Fraser	Edinburgh	09.0180	Luton
S U21			
Jason Goodliffe ESP	Hillingdon	07.03.74	Hayes, Brentford
Matt Hocking	Boston	30.01.78	Boston United, York City, Hull City, Sheffield United
Barry Laker RL	London		Sutton Utd, Banstead Ath., Wimbledon (Junior)
Mark Rogers	Geulph(Canada)	03.11.75	Wycombe W, Burnaby, Canadians F.C. (Canada)
Martk Smith	Luton		Dagenham & R, Stevenage B, Hitchin T, Woking,
ESP, NC,IL			Hitchin T, Letchworth, Hitchin T.
Michael Warner RL	Harrogate	17.01.74	Northampton, Tamworth, Redditch Utd

MIDFIELD

Player	Birthplace	D.O.B.	Previous Clubs
Jon Brady NC	Newcastle (Aus)	14.01.75	Chester C, Woking, Rushden & D, Hayes, Mjolner (Norway), Hayes, Wycombe W, Brentford, Swansea C, Adamstown R(Aus)
Michael Brough	Nottingham	0.08.81	Notts County
Dannie Bulman	Ashford	24,0179	Wycombe W, Ashford Town
Jamie Gould	Northampton	15.01.82	Boston United, Northampton (YTS)
Richie Hanlon NC	Wembley	26.05.78	Rushden & D, Peterborough U, Welling U, Peterborough, Rushden & Diamonds, Welling U, Southend, Chelsea
Rob Quinn	Sidcup	08.11.76	Bristol R,Oxford U, Bremtford, Crystal P.
Sam McMahon	Newark	10.02.76	Leicester, Camb.U

FORWARDS

Player	Birthplace	D.O.B.	Previous Clubs
Ben Camasra	Tavistock		Torquay United, Tavistock
Anthony Elding	Boston	16.04.82	Boston United, Lincoln C (Jnrs), Grimsby T (Jnrs)
Richard Hodgson	Sunderland	01.10.79	Farnborough T, Darlington, Nottingham Forest
Craig McAllister	Hampshire	01.10.79	Basingstoke T, Eastleigh
Jon Nurse	London		Sutton United
Brian Quailey St Kitts & Nevis Int	Leicester	21.03.78	Tamworth,NuneatinB, Halifax T, Doncaster R, Scunthoirpe U, W.B.A.., Nuneaton B, Deeping Rovers.

TAMWORTH

EVEN though they had carried off the Dr Martens League Premier Division title with aplomb the previous campaign The Lambs had no illusions about the task ahead of them if they were to retain their Conference status and so it proved with consistency lacking in tougher company, which was not helped by the departure of Scott Rickards t Kidderminster Harriers.

Eventually survival was achieved thanks to wins against fellow strugglers Northwich Victoria, Farnborough, Forest Green Rovers and, ultimately, Leigh RMI (thanks to a last gasp winner from Paul Barnes in a seven goal thriller), and then it transpired that due to various bizarre events no-one was relegated from th competition in any case!

The cups can be a bonus or a distraction, but the FA Cup stint was short lived (albeit exciting) with six goals shared at Telford United and the home replay being lost in extra-time by the odd goal in five, which left the FA Trophy as a challenge and revenge of a sort in the Third Round at Burscough for the previous season's final defeat (a single goal success), and this meant a visit to Marlow and a four clear goal triumph. So far, so good!

The draw for the Fifth Round decreed a trip to Aldershot Town where an excellent effort brought a share of two goals, but in the replay at The Lamb Ground two counters were recorded - both to the visitors, alas for the big hopes.

Darron Gee, meanwhile, has stepped down as manager to spend more time with his family and skipper Mark Cooper has taken over the hot seat; all will wish him well in his herculean task.

W.M.

TAMWORTH

Match Facts 2003-04

The number shown directly below the player's name is his squad number.
Where a number is shown instead of an "X' in the columns this represents a substitute appearance and the number indicates the player replaced.

Comp.	Date	Opponents	Venue.	Result	Goalscorers	Att.
Conf 1	Aug 09	Hereford U	H	L 1-3	Cooper	2250
Conf 2	Aug 12	Chester C	A	L 0-1		2267
Conf 3	Aug 16	Northwich V	A	L 0-1		712
Conf 4	Aug 23	Margate	H	D 1-1	Setchell	1056
Conf 5	Aug 25	Halifax T	A	W 2-1	Rickards Robinson	1849
Conf 6	Aug 30	Accrington S	H	D 1-1	Setchell(p)	1215
Conf 7	Sep 07	Shrewsbury T	A	L 1-3	Rioch(og)	3882
Conf 8	Sep 13	Morecambe	H	D 2-2	Powell Cooper	1247
Conf 9	Sep 20	Leigh RMI	A	D 1-1	Rickards(p)	427
Conf 10	Sep 23	Scarborough	H	D 0-0		1004
Conf 11	Sep 27	Dagenham & R	H	W 2-0	Whitman(2)	1147
Conf 12	Oct 04	Farnborough T	A	D 3-3	Cooper(2) Follett	770
Conf 13	Oct 07	Telford U	A	L 0-2		1725
Conf 14	Oct 11	Barnet	H	W 2-0	Cooper(2)	1304
Conf 15	Oct 18	Aldershot T	H	D 3-3	Watson(2) Whitman	1538
FAC 4q	**Oct 25**	**Telford U**	**A**	**D 3-3**	**Jordan Robinson Darby**	**1471**
FAC 4qr	**Oct 28**	**Telford U**	**H**	**L 2-3**	**Fisher Setchell(p)**	**1221**
Conf 16	Nov 01	Exeter C	A	L 2-3	Follett Cooper	2979
Conf 17	Nov 11	Stevenage B	H	L 1-2	Cooper	1006
Conf 18	Nov 15	Forest Green R	A	L 1-2	Blunt	782
Conf 19	Nov 22	Gravesend & N	H	L 1-3	Rickards	1178
Conf 20	Nov 25	Woking	A	L 0-4		1565
Conf 21	Nov 29	Shrewsbury T	H	D 1-1	Cooper	1761
Conf 22	Dec 06	Morecambe	A	L 0-4		1449
Conf 23	Dec 13	Hereford U	A	W 1-0	Dryden	2561
Conf 24	Dec 20	Chester C	H	L 1-5	Sylla	1520
Conf 25	Dec 26	Burton A	A	W 1-0	Sylla	3164
Conf 26	Jan 01	Burton A	H	D 1-1	Sylla	2535
FAT 3	**Jan 10**	**Burscough**	**A**	**W 1-0**	**Warner**	**601**
Conf 27	Jan 17	Northwich V	H	W 2-1	Follett Robinson	1158
Conf 28	Jan 20	Accrington S	A	L 0-3		1301
FAT 4	**Jan 31**	**Marlow**	**A**	**W 4-0**	**Barnes(3) Blunt**	**744**
Conf 29	Feb 07	Leigh RMI	H	W 4-3	Brooks Scully Cooper(p) Barnes	905
FAT 5	**Feb 14**	**Aldershot T**	**A**	**D 1-1**	**Quailey**	**2515**
FAT 5r	**Feb 17**	**Aldershot T**	**H**	**L 0-2**		**1067**
Conf 30	Feb 21	Farnborough T	H	W 2-1	Cooper Dryden	1084
Conf 31	Feb 28	Barnet	A	L 0-1		1899
Conf 32	Mar 06	Telford U	H	L 0-1		1115
Conf 33	Mar 09	Dagenham & R	A	D 0-0		984
Conf 34	Mar 13	Stevenage B	A	L 1-3	Cooper	1646
Conf 35	Mar 16	Scarborough	A	W 1-0	Cooper	1059
Conf 36	Mar 20	Forest Green R	H	W 1-0	Barnes	1112
Conf 37	Mar 27	Gravesend & N	A	L 0-2		1157
Conf 38	Apr 03	Woking	H	W 2-0	N Smith Cooper(p)	1053
Conf 39	Apr 10	Margate	A	L 2-3	N Smith Robinson	448
Conf 40	Apr 12	Halifax T	H	W 2-0	Cooper(p) Sylla	1095
Conf 41	Apr 17	Exeter C	H	W 2-1	Barnes(2)	1803
Conf 42	Apr 24	Aldershot T	A	D 1-1	Ebdon	4212

Ryan PRICE	Richard FOLLETT	Gary SETCHELL	Jim RODWELL	Mark NOON	Dave ROBINSON	Joe TAYLOR	Richard DRYDEN	Mark COOPER	Rob WARNER	Matt FISHER	Marcus EBDON	Darren COLLINS	Armand ONE	Brian QUAILEY	Marc McGREGOR	Scott RICKARDS	Tony SCULLY	Lee COLKIN	Brett DARBY	Lee WILSON	Mark TURNER	Phil TRAINER	Joe HANNEY	Jamie BROOKS	Karl JOHNSON	Mark BARNARD	Edward STANFORD	Paul BARNES	Alex JOHN-BAPTISTE	Norman SYLLA	James LINDLEY	Keith SCOTT	Andy WATSON	James FOX	Tom JORDAN	Paul POWELL	Nick SMITH	Tristram WHITMAN	Lee AYRES	Jason BLUNT	Adie SMITH	Scott GOODWIN	Richard BRUSH	Wayne HENDERSON
1	2	3	3	3	4	5	5	6	7	8	8	9	9	9	10	11	11	11	12	13	14	15	16	16	17	18	18	18	19	20	21	22	22	22	23	24	24	25	26	27	28	29	30	30
	x	x			x	x		x	x	x		x			x	15			10			x				4																		
		x						x	x	x		x			x	x			11			x				x									x									
		x			x			x	x	x						x			7		15	x				x						x			x									
		x			x			x	x	x		x			9	15						x				24						x			x	x								
		x			x			x	x	x		22				x			x							24						x			x	x								
		x			x			x	x	x		12				x			x			6				x						x				x								
		x			x			x	x	x		x				x			25				24													x		x						
	x				x	x		x	x	x						24			x						12								x			x								
	x				x	x			x	x						15			x			x					x								9				x					
	x					x			x	x						x			x				18		5		x						x		x				x					
	x	x						12	x	x						x			x								x						x		x			22	x					
	x	x						18	x	x			x			x			x						26		x								x			12	x					
	x	x			x			x	4	x			x			9											27								x			x	x	x				
	x					26		x	x				x			x			25								x						9		x			x	x	x				
	x							x	x	25																	x			x			x		x			x	x	x				
	x				x			x	x	22			x						9								x			x			x		x					x				
	x	x			x	4			x	x			x						x								x			7	1				x					x				
	x	x				x		25		x			x			9														22	x		x		x			x		x		x		
	x	x					x	x			x				x	x			27											11	x		x		x					x		22		
	x	x					x		x		x				x	x			10	20										x	x				x					x				
	x	x					x	x	x		x			x		x									7					23	x				x					x				
	x	x					x	x	29		x			x					20						x					x					5					x		x	x	
	x	x						x	9		x			x					x						x					12					x				x	x			x	
	x	x						x	17		x			23		x									x			x							x				x	x		8	x	
	x		x				x	x	x					x					x						x				x										x				x	
	x		x				x	x	6					x					x						x				x	24							x			x			x	
	x		x		20		x	x	x					x					9										x	x									x	x			x	
	x		x		x		x	x						x					26									20	x	x									x	x			x	
	x		x		x		x	x	x					x					20									x		x	x									x				
	x		x		x		x	x	x					x	9													x		x							20			x			x	
	x		x		x		x	x	x					x					7									x		9				12			x			x			x	
	x				x		x	x	8		x						x											x		x				2	x		6			x			x	
	x				x		x	x	x								x							x				x		16							2			x	x		x	
	x				x			x			x			x	16									x				x		9									x	x	x		x	
	x				x		x	x	27		x			x							5							x		8									x	x	x			
	x				x		x	x	x		x			x							28							x		9	x									x	x			
	x				x		x	x	x		x			x	9						x							x		2	x						8			x				
x	x			5			x	x	x					x					x									x		9					x		27		x	x				
x	3			x	x		x	x	x					20				x										x		x									x	x				
	5			x	x		x	x	x					20				x			3							x		x									x	x				x
				x	x		x	x	x					x				x										x		9							3		x	x				x
				x	x		x	x	x					x				x			18							x		9									x	x				x
x				x	x		x	x	x		20							x	3		26							x		x									x	x				
x				6	x			x	x		x							x	x		x							x									x		x					
x	14				x		x	x	x		x								x		x							x		7							x		x					
x	17						x	x	x		x							x	11						x			x		x							x		x	8				
x					x		x	x	x		x							x										x		x									x	x	5			
x	7				x				x		x							x							28			x		x							x		x	x	x			

O PLAYED: Kelvin LANGMEAD (9) Conf 8,9.

TAMWORTH

GROUND DETAILS

The Lamb Ground, Kettlebrook,
Tamworth, Staffs B77 1AA

Tel: 01827 65798
Fax: 0182762236
website: www.thelambs.co.uk
email: russell@thelambs.co.uk

Directions: Follow the signs for Town Centre/Snowdome, then for Kettlebrook. The entrance to the ground &car parks is in Kettlebrook Road, 50yards from the traffic island by the railway viaduct (B5000)

Capacity: 4,100
Cover: 1,191
Seats: 518

Clubhouse: Club on ground - open matchdays, training nights and tote night only

Clubshop: Yes

Formed: 1933

Sponsors: Ocean Finance

Nickname: Lambs or Town

Colours: All Red

Change colours: White,black,black

Midweek home matchday: Tuesday

Reserves' League: Mid. Comb. Reserve Div.

CLUB OFFICIALS

Chairman: Bob Andrews

President: Len Gendle

Secretary & General Manager:

Russell Moore,
97 Honeybourne, Belgrave, Tamworth,
Staffs B77 2JG
Tel No: 07811 267304 (M)

Press Officer: Dave Clayton

07815 046899 (M)

Commercial Manager: Pete Cook

07974 867823 (M)

Safety Officer: Tony Reeves

FOOTBALL MANAGEMENT TEAM

MANAGER:	**MARK COOPER**
Date of Appointment	May 2004
Date of Birth:	
Place of Birth:	
PREVIOUS CLUBS	
As manager	None
As asst. man.	Tamworth
As player	
HONOURS	
As Manager:	None
As Player:	F.A.Trophy Finalist(twice) Southern League Premier

* * *

Asst Manager:	Richard Dryden
Chief Scout:	T.B.A.
Youth Development:	Ian Wilson
Physio:	Chris Leary

MATCHDAY PROGRAMME

Pages: 44 Price: £2.00
Editor: Pete Cook
email:peter@thelambs.co.uk

Press: Tamworth Herald,Tamworth Times
Radio: Centre FM,Captal Gold/Radio WM

Season	League	Div.	Pos.	Home P	W	D	L	F	A	Away W	D	L	F	A	Pts	Manager	
03-04	Conference	-	17	42	9	6	6	32	30	4	4	13	17	38	49	Darron Gee	
02-03	Southern	P	1	42	12	6	3			14	4	3			88	Darron Gee	(73-32)
01-02	Southern	P	2	42	16	5	0	46	14	8	8	5	28	36	75	Gary Mills	
00-01	Southern	P	12	42	11	4	6	38	24	6	4	11	20	31	59	Paul Hendrie	
99-00	Southern	P	6	42	12	4	5	50	26	8	6	7	30	41	70	Paul Hendrie	
98-99	Southern	P	9	42	10	5	6	37	30	9	0	12	25	37	62	Paul Hendrie	
97-98	Southern	P	15	42	10	4	7	43	30	4	7	10	25	35	53	Paul Hendrie	
				P	W	D	L	F	A						Pts		
96-97	Southern	M	1	40	30	7	3	90	28						97	Paul Hendrie	
95-96	Southern	M	6	42	22	3	17	97	64						69	Paul Hendrie	
94-95	Southern	M	3	42	24	8	10	98	70						80	Les Green	

HONOURS

F.A.Trophy Finalists 02-03, FA VaseWinners 88-89; West Mids Lge 63-64 65-66 71-72 87-88, R-upx2 67-69, Div 2 55-56, Lg Cupx5 64-66 71-72 85-86 87-88, R-up 70-71; Birmingham Senior Cup 60-61 65-66 68-69, R-up 36-37 63-64;00-01 Staffs Senior Cup 58-59 63-64 65-66 01-02, R-up 55-56 66-67 70-71; Midland F'lit Cup R-up 71-72 72-73; Camkin Cup 71-72 (R-up 70-71); Southern Lge.Prem. Div 2002-03 Midland Div 96-97 Premier Div. 02-03, R-up 01-02

PREVIOUS

Leagues:
Birmingham Combination 33-54,
West Midlands (initially Birmingham Lg) 54-72, 84-88
Southern 72-79 83-84 89-03
Northern Premier 79-83

Grounds: Jolly Sailor Ground 33-34

CLUB RECORDS

Attendance: 4,920
v Atherstone Tn, Birm Comb 48

Season Goalscorer: Percy Vials 64 (36-37)
Career Appearances: Dave Seedhouse 869
Career Goalscorer: Graham Jessop 195

Defeat: 0-11
v Solihull (A), Birmingham Comb. '40
Win: 14-4
v Holbrook Institute (H), Bass Vase '34

Transfer Fee paid: £7,500
for Tony Hemmings (Ilkeston Town) Dec 2001
Transfer Fee received: £7,500
for Martin Myers (Telford Utd, 90)

BEST SEASON

FA Cup: 2nd Rd 69-70
(0-6 at Gillingham)

FA Trophy: Runners-up 02-03

FA Vase: Winners 88-89

Past Players who progressed to the Football League

P Hilton (WBA 49),
A Godridge (Swansea 50),
W Ealing (Doncaster),
Higgins (Fulham),
P Weir (Cardiff),
S Fox (Wrexham),
S Cartwright (Colchester 88),
S Ryder (Walsall),
D Williams (Brentford)

LAST SEASON

F.A. Cup: 4th Qual.Rd.
F.A. Trophy: 5th Rd
League: 17th
Top Goalscorer: Mark Cooper 15
Player of the Year: Dave Robinson
Captain: Mark Cooper

TAMWORTH

	Birthplace	D.O.B.	Previous Clubs	Bold print denotes England semi-professional international.
GOALKEEPERS				
Ryan Price ESP,NC	Wolverh'ton	13.03.70	Stafford R, Telford U, Macclesfield, Birmingham C, Stafford R,Bolton W	
Philip Whitehead	Halifax	17.12.69	Reading, W.B.A., Oxford United, Halifax T (L) Scunthorpe (L) Halifax T (L), Barnsley, Halifax T.	
DEFENDERS				
Lee Ayres	Birmingham	28.08.82	Kidderminster H, Evesham U	
Lee Colkin	Nuneaton	15.07.74	Grantham, Burton,Morecambe, Hednesford Northampton T	
Paul Hatton	Kidderminster	02.11.78	Hednesford U , Birmingham City	
Matt Redmile	Nottingham	12.11.76	Barnet, Scarborough, Shrewsbury T, Notts Co.	
E NG I				
Dave Robinson	Nottingham	14.07.75	KIngs Lynn, Grantham T, Gresley R, IlkestonT., HeanorT	
Adie Smith ESP	Birmingham	11.08.73	Kidderminster H, Bromsgrove R, Birmingham C, Willenhall	
Kyle Storer	Nuneaton		Bedworth U, Leicester C.	
MIDFIELD				
Jason Blunt E Youth Int	Penzance	16.08.77	Doncaster R, Scarborough, Grottaglie (Italy) Blackpool, Leeds U	
Mark Cooper	Wakefield	18.12.69	Forest Green R,Hednesford T, Rushden &Diamonds Leyton O,Hartlep'l U,Exeter C,Wycombe W, Fulham, Birmingham C, Exeter C,BristolCity	
Marcus Ebdon	Pontypool	27.10.70	Leyton O, Chesterfield, Peterborough U, Everton	
E.Youth Int				
Peter Hynes	Dublin	28.11.83	Aston Villa	
Karl Johnson	Birmingham	12.09.81	Reserves	
Chad Sheppard	Birmingham	28.01.86	Birmingham City	
Phil Trainer	Wolv'hampton	03.07.81	Halesowen T,Kidsgrove A,Northwich V, Crewe A	
Mark Turner	Bebington	04.10.72	Kings Lynn, Telford United	
FORWARDS				
Brett Darby	Leicester	10.11.83	Southend United, Leicester City	
Rory May	Coventry		Halifax Town, Lincoln City, Coventry City	
Norman Sylla OxfordUtd..	France		Barnet, Havant & Waterlooville, Banbury Utd,	

WOKING

NINTH place in the Conference meant that the 2003-04 campaign for the Cardinals under the excellent management of Glenn Cockerill could be described as 'satisfactory; would like to do better', and this might have been the case as crucial injuries to the charismatic Chris Sharpling and Ian Selley deprived the team of their services for lengthy periods.

Even so, there was never any apparent danger of relegation and nine points adrift of fifth placed Aldershot Town, whose game at Kingfield Stadium produced a crowd of 4,000 and a thriller of four shared goals, would suggest that a play-off place was seldom a realistic prospect.

In the knock-out competitions there was modest prolonged interest, as in the FA Cup Fourth Qualifier there was a tough tie against East Thurrock United (1-1 away, 2-0 at home) and First Round Proper advancement thanks to a good home win over Histon (3-1), which meant a Second Round visit from Kidderminster Harriers, who scored all the match's three counters, while in the FA Trophy Third Round a scoreless draw at Kettering Town was followed by a five goal nail-biter in the home replay, which went the way of The Poppies, so the programme's moments of excitement ended right there.

The Cardinals neither under-performed nor over-performed, which probably meant that no-one needed sessions with 'shrinks', but supporters will probably prefer to have nervous breakdowns rather than possible boredom in the next few months.

W.M.

Left to right - Back Row: Nixon Ajoge, Raphael Nade, Jefferson Louis, Davis Haule
Middle Row: Ron Rawlings - Kit Manager, Joe McNab, Jamie Campbell, Chris Sharpling, Liam Cockerill, Ben Townsend, Ashley Bayes, Jon Boardman, Ryan Northmore, Dean Clark, Gary MacDonald, Phil Parsons, Steve Ferguson, Neil Sharp, Steve Snelling - Physio
Front Row: Amos Foyewa, Ian Proctor, Ian Selley, Matt Crossley - Assistant Manager, Glenn Cockerill, Peter Johnson - Reserve & Youth Team Manager, Neil Smith - Club Captain, Scott Canham, Narada Bernard.

WOKING

Match Facts 2003-04

The number shown directly below the player's name is his squad number.
Where a number is shown instead of an "X' in the columns this represents a substitute appearance and the number indicates the player replaced.

Comp.	Date	Opponents	Venue.	Result	Goalscorers	Att.
Conf 1	Aug 09	Morecambe	A	L 1-2	Louis	1772
Conf 2	Aug 12	Gravesend & N	H	W 3-2	Louis(2,1p) Foyewa	2096
Conf 3	Aug 16	Scarborough	H	W 2-1	Louis Foyewa	1901
Conf 4	Aug 23	Aldershot T	A	L 1-2	Canham	4637
Conf 5	Aug 25	Exeter C	H	W 1-0	Louis	2556
Conf 6	Aug 30	Leigh RMI	A	W 1-0	Ferguson	435
Conf 7	Sep 06	Burton A	A	L 0-2		1482
Conf 8	Sep 13	Farnborough T	H	W 3-2	Foyewa Canham Ferguson	2791
Conf 9	Sep 20	Shrewsbury T	H	D 3-3	Haule Foyewa Selley(p)	2539
Conf 10	Sep 23	Forest Green R	A	D 2-2	Selley(p) Boardman	712
Conf 11	Sep 27	Accrington S	A	D 3-3	Foyewa Ferguson Nade	2115
Conf 12	Oct 04	Hereford U	H	L 0-1		2906
Conf 13	Oct 07	Stevenage B	H	D 1-1	Selley	2592
Conf 14	Oct 11	Chester C	A	L 1-2	Nade	2085
Conf 15	Oct 18	Halifax T	H	D 2-2	Haule Ferguson	1917
FAC 4q	**Oct 25**	**East Thurrock**	**A**	**D 1-1**	**Haule**	**1250**
FAC 4qr	**Oct 28**	**East Thurrock**	**H**	**W 2-0**	**Ferguson(2)**	**1781**
Conf 16	Nov 01	Telford U	A	L 0-1		1334
FAC 1	**Nov 08**	**Histon**	**H**	**W 3-1**	**Selley(2,1p) Sharpling**	**2217**
Conf 17	Nov 11	Margate	A	W 2-1	Zoricich(og) Sodje(og)	550
Conf 18	Nov 15	Dagenham & R	H	D 0-0		2256
Conf 19	Nov 22	Northwich V	A	W 4-1	Sharpling(2) Nade(2)	627
Conf 20	Nov 25	Tamworth	H	W 4-0	Sharpling(2) Ferguson Selley	1565
Conf 21	Nov 29	Burton A	H	W 1-0	Haule	1947
FAC 2	**Dec 06**	**Kidderminster H**	**H**	**L 0-3**		**3484**
Conf 22	Dec 09	Farnborough T	A	L 0-1		1005
Conf 23	Dec 13	Morecambe	H	W 4-0	Sharp Sharpling Harris Nade	1588
Conf 24	Dec 20	Gravesend & N	A	D 2-2	Harris Ferguson	975
Conf 25	Dec 26	Barnet	H	D 2-2	Smith Nade	2856
Conf 26	Jan 01	Barnet	A	D 0-0		2304
Conf 27	Jan 03	Leigh RMI	H	W 2-0	Sharp Foyewa	2105
FAT 3	**Jan 10**	**Kettering Town**	**A**	**D 0-0**		**1259**
FAT 3r	**Jan 13**	**Kettering Town**	**H**	**L 2-3**	**Nade(2)**	**1126**
Conf 28	Jan 17	Scarborough	A	D 2-2	Smith(2,1p)	2503
Conf 29	Jan 24	Forest Green R	H	D 1-1	Haule	1815
Conf 30	Feb 14	Accrington S	H	D 2-2	Foyewa Nade	2312
Conf 31	Feb 21	Hereford U	A	W 1-0	Ferguson	2817
Conf 32	Feb 28	Chester C	H	L 1-2	Ferguson	2554
Conf 33	Mar 02	Shrewsbury T	A	L 0-1		3029
Conf 34	Mar 06	Stevenage B	A	D 1-1	Noble	2489
Conf 35	Mar 13	Margate	H	D 0-0		2109
Conf 36	Mar 20	Dagenham & R	A	L 0-1		1345
Conf 37	Mar 27	Northwich V	H	W 3-0	Cornwall Murray Ferguson	1857
Conf 38	Apr 03	Tamworth	A	L 0-2		1053
Conf 39	Apr 10	Aldershot T	H	D 2-2	Selley(p) Cornwall	4158
Conf 40	Apr 12	Exeter C	A	W 2-1	Cornwall Foyewa	5236
Conf 41	Apr 17	Telford U	H	W 3-1	Johnson Selley(p) Foyewa	2326
Conf 42	Apr 24	Halifax T	A	D 2-2	Foyewa Selley(p)	1191

STEP 1 CONFERENCE | STEP 2 - P177 CONFERENCE Ntn & Sth | STEP 3 - P269 NPL, Southern, Isthmian Premiers | STEP 4 - P269 NPL 1, Southern N&S, Isthmian 1 | STEP 5/6 - P473 Current level 3 leagues | STEP 7 - P713 Current level 4 leagues

Ashley BAYES	Ben TOWNSEND	Jamie CAMPBELL	Luke OLIVER	Neil SMITH	Jon BOARDMAN	Gary McDONALD	Chris SHARPLING	Scott CANHAM	Davis HAULE	Amos FOYEWA	Joe McNAB	Phil PARSONS	Izedin HARLISHA	Chris GILES	Raphael NADE	Liam COCKERILL	Nixon AJOGE	Stuart NOBLE	Jefferson LOUIS	Steve FERGUSON	Ian SELLEY	Narada BERNARD	Michael JOHNSON	Neil SHARP	Ian SIMPEMBA	Geoff PITCHER	Lee ALLUM	Richard HARRIS	Luke CORNWALL	Karl MURRAY	Scott BEVAN	Adriano BASSO
1	**2**	**3**	**3**	**4**	**5**	**6**	**7**	**8**	**9**	**10**	**14**	**15**	**16**	**17**	**18**	**19**	**20**	**20**	**21**	**22**	**23**	**24**	**24**	**25**	**26**	**27**	**27**	**28**	**28**	**29**	**33**	**33**
x	x			x	x		22	x		21					x		18		x	x	x	x		x								
x	x			7	x		x	x		x					x				x	10	x	x		x								
x	x			21	x		22	x	10	x					x				x	x	x	x		x								
x	x			x			22	x	10	x					x	2	x		x	x	x			x								
x				x	x		18	x		x					x		x		x	x	x	x										
x	x			x	x		22	x		21					x		x		x	x	x	x										
x	x			x	x		18	x	8	4					x		x		x	x	x	x										
x	22			x	x		10	x		x					x		x		x	x	x	x										
x	24			26	x		x	x	7	x					x		x			x	x	x			x							
x	x			x	x	x		x	6	22					x		x			x	x				x							
x	x			x	x	x	22	x	8	x					x					x	x				x							
x	x			x	x	x	4	10	18	x					x					x	x				x	x						
x	x			x	x	x	4	x	8						x					x	x				x	x						
x	x			x	x	x		x	x						4	8				x	x			x		x						
x	x				x	x	x	x	x						x	19				x	x			x								
x	**x**			**x**	**x**	**x**	**x**	**x**	**x**						**x**	**5**				**x**				**x**								
x	**x**			**x**	**x**		**x**	**x**	**x**	**x**					**10**	**9**				**x**	**x**			**x**								
x	x				x	x	9	x	x	x					x					x	x		22	x								
x	**x**			**x**	**x**	**x**	**x**	**2**	**x**	**x**					**x**						**x**			**x**								
x	x			x	x	x	x	x	4	x					x						x		7	x								
	x				x	x	x	x	7	x					x					24	x		x	x							x	
	x				x	x	x	x	19						x	x				x	x			x							x	
	x				x	x	x	x							x	x				x	x			x							x	
	x			5	x	x	x	x	18	22					x	x				x	x			x							x	
	x			**5**	**x**	**x**	**x**	**x**	**22**	**x**					**x**	**2**				**x**	**x**			**x**							**x**	
x	x	x		x		x	x	19	x	9					3	x				x	x			x								
x	x	x		x		x	x								x	x				28	x		19	x				x				
x	x	x		x		x	x			28					x	x				7	x			x				x				
x	x			x	x	x				28					x	x				x	x			x				x				
x	x	6		x	x	x		x	28	19					x	x				x				x				x				
x				x	x	x		x	28	x	8	29			x								x	x				x		x		
x	x				x	x		x	28	x											x		x	x				x		x		
x	x			x	x	x		23		x					x						x		x	x				2		x		
x	x			x	x	x			28	x					x								x	x				x		x		
x	x			x	x	x		24	x	22					x					x			x	x						x		
x	x			x	x			24		x				x	x	x				x			28					x		x		
x	x			x	x	x		x	19	22				x	x	x				x										x		
x	x			x	x	x		x	2	x				x		x				x										x		
x	x			x	x	x			17	x				x	x	x				x				19						x		
x	18			x	x	x		x		20				x	x	x		x		x			19							x		
x	x		20	x	x	x		x	8					x		x		x		x			19							x		
x				x	x	x		x								x		x		x			20	x					x	x		
	24			x	x	x		x		20						x		x		x			28	x					x	x		x
x	x			x	x	x		x		20								x		x	x		x						23	x		
x	4			x	x	x		x		x					25	x				x	x		x	x					22			
	x				x	x		x		x			28		x	x				10	x		x						x			x
	x				x	x		x		x		8			x	x				28	x		x				10		x			x
x			x			x		x		x		8			x	x				24	x		x						x	x		

WOKING

GROUND DETAILS

Kingfield Stadium,
Kingfield Road,
Woking,
Surrey. GU22 9AA.

Tel: 01483 772470
Fax: 01483 888423
Football Office Fax: 01483729230
Email: admin@wokingfc.co.uk
Web site: http://www.wokingfc.co.uk

Simple Directions:
M25 J10 or 11, signposted from outskirts of Town. Ground 1 mile. Woking B.R. Station & buses from Woking.

Capacity: 6,000
Seated: 2,500
Terracing - **Covered:** 1,400
Uncovered: 2,100

SOCIAL FACILITIES:
Clubhouse open on matchdays. Food available.

CLUB SHOP: Phone 01483 772470 for details.

Founded: 1889

Nickname: The Cards

Club colours: Red & white halved shirts, with black shorts and black socks.

Change colours: Sky blue shirts, with white shorts and socks

Midweek home matchday: Tuesday 7.45pm.

Club Sponsors: Colbornes.

Newsline 09066 555070

CLUB OFFICIALS

Chairman: Chris Ingram
Directors: Chris Ingram,Phil Ledger JP, Keith Owen, John Buchanan,Bob Brown and David Seward(Company Secretary)

Football Director Phil J Ledger J.P.
19 Ainsdale Way, Woking, Surrey. GU21 3PP.
Tel: 01483 725295 (H) 07831 271 369 (M)

Press Officers Phil Ledger & Brian Blower
Club Administrator Sue Day

MATCHDAY PROGRAMME

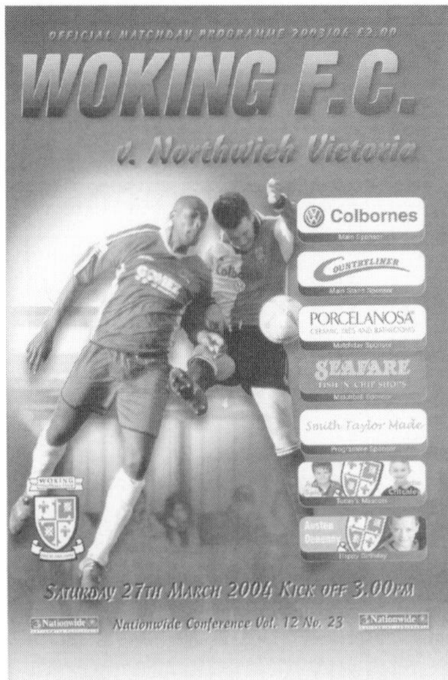

FOOTBALL MANAGEMENT TEAM

MANAGER: GLEN COCKERILL

Assistant Manager: Matt Crossley
Reserve & Youth Team Manager: Peter Johnson
Physio: Steve Snelling
Club's Playing Status: Full time

Pages: 48 **Price:** £2.50
Editor: Paul Beard 01344 482018
Clubcall: 09066 555 070

Other club publications:
"Winning isn't Everything" (fanzine)
Local Press: Woking News & Mail; Woking Herald; Surrey Advertiser
Local Radio: BBC Surrey Sussex; County Sound; BBC Southern Counties

Season	League	Div.	Pos.	P	Home W	D	L	F	A	Away W	D	L	F	A	Pts	Manager
03-04	Conference	-	9	42	10	9	2	40	23	5	7	9	25	29	61	Glenn Cockerill
02-03	Conference	-	19	42	8	7	6	30	35	3	7	11	22	46	47	Geoff Chapple / Glenn Cockerill
01-02	Conference	-	19	42	7	5	9	28	29	6	4	11	31	41	48	Colin Lippiatt/Geoff Chapple
00-01	Conference	-	14	42	5	10	6	30	30	8	5	8	22	27	54	Colin Lippiatt
99-00	Conference	-	14	42	5	6	10	17	27	8	7	6	28	26	52	Brian McDermott/Colin Lippiatt
98-99	Conference	-	9	42	9	5	7	27	20	9	4	8	24	25	63	John McGovern/Brian McDermott
97-98	Conference	-	3	42	14	3	4	47	22	8	5	8	25	24	74	John McGovern
96-97	Conference	-	5	42	10	5	6	41	29	8	5	8	30	34	64	Geoff Chapple

Season	League	Div.	Pos.	P	W	D	L	F	A	Pts	Manager
95-96	Conference	-	2	42	25	8	9	83	54	83	Geoff Chapple
94-95	Conference	-	2	42	21	12	9	76	54	75	Geoff Chapple

HONOURS

FA Trophy 93-94, 94-95, 96-97
FA Amateur Cup 57-58
GM VauxhallConference R-up 94-95, 95-96
Isthmian League: 91-92, R-up 56-57
Div.2 South 86-87
Isthmian Lge Cup: 90-91, R-up 89-90
Surrey Senior Cup: 12-13, 26-27, 55-56, 56-57, 71-72, 90-91, 93-94, 95-96, 99-00;
London Senior Cup R-up 82-83
Isthmian League Charity Shield 91-92, 92-93
Vauxhall Championship Shield 94-95, R-up 95-96.

PREVIOUS

Leagues: Isthmian 1911-92

Grounds: Wheatsheaf, Ivy Lane (pre 1923)

Past Players who progressed to the Football League

Ray Elliott (M'wall 46), Charlie Mortimore (A'shot 49), Robert Edwards (Chelsea 51), Ron Newman (Portsmouth 55), Mervyn Gill (Southampton 56),John Mortimore (Chelsea 51), Reg Stratton (Fulham 59), George Harris (Newport Co. 61), Norman Cashmore (A'shot 63), Alan Morton (C. Palace 67), William Holmes (Millwall 70), Richard Forbes (Exeter 79), Kevin Rattray (Gillingham 95), Steve Foster (Bristol Rov. 97), Justin Jackson (Notts Co. 98), Kevin Betsy (Fulham 98).

CLUB RECORDS

Attendance: 6,000 v Swansea, FA Cup - 1978/79; v Coventry C., FA Cup - 1996-97

Win: 17-4 v Farnham, 1912-13

Defeat: 0-16 v New Crusaders, 1905-06

Career Goalscorer: C Mortimore 331, 1953-65

Career Appearances: B Finn 564, 1962-74

Transfer Fees

Paid: £60,000 for Cris Sharpling (C.Palace) - 2001

Received: £150,000 for Steve Foster (Bristol Rovers) - May 1997; £150,000 for Kevin Betsy (Fulham)

BEST SEASON

FA Cup: 4th Round 90-91,0-1 v Everton (A) Att 34,724
League clubs defeated: West Bromwich Albion (90-91) Cambridge United & Millwall (96-97)

FA Trophy: Winners 93-94, 94-95, 96-97.

FA Amateur Cup: Winners 75-58

League Conference Runners-up 94-95, 95-96

LAST SEASON

F.A. Cup: 2nd Round
F.A. Trophy: 4th Round
Conference: 9th
Top Goalscorer:
Player of the Year: Neil Smith
Captain: Neil Smith
Highest League Attendance: 4,158 v Aldershot

WOKING PLAYING SQUAD

Player	Birthplace	D.O.B.	Previous Clubs

Bold print denotes England semi-professional international.

GOALKEEPERS

Shwan Jalal	Baghdad	14.08.83	Tottenham H

DEFENDERS

Jonathan Boardman	Reading	27.01.81	Crystal Palace
Gary McDonald			Stevenage Bor.,Peterborough United,Havant & Waterlooville, Portsmouth

MIDFIELD

Scottt Canham	Newham	05.11.74	Leyton Orient,Brentford,Torquay United(L),West Ham United
Liam Cockerill			Youth Team
Michael Johnson	Surrey	22.05.82	Carshalton Ath., Croydon, Sutton United, Fulham
Karl Murray	Highbury	24.11.82	Shrewsbury Town
Ian Selley	Chertsey	14.06.74	Wimbledon, Fulham, Arsenal
Neil Smith	Lambeth	30.09.71	Stevenage B, Reading, Fulham, Gillingham, Spurs(YTS)

FORWARDS

Nick Bailey	Surrey		Sutton United
Luke Cornwall	Lambeth	23.07.80	Bradford City, Fulham
Amos Foyewa			Bournemouth,West Ham United
Steve Ferguson	Scotland		Tottenham Hotspur, East Fife
Raphael Nade	Paris		Welling United, Hampton & Richmond B,Troyes (France), Le Havre (France)
Justin Richards	Sandwell	16.10.80	Stevenage B, Bristol R, W.B.,A.
Chris Sharpling	Bromley	21.04.81	Crystal Palace (£60,000

YORK CITY

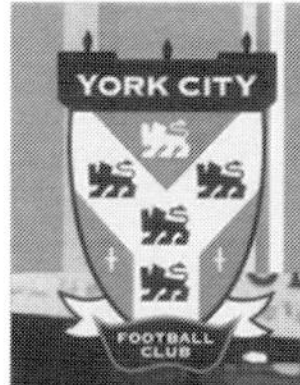

Seventy five years proud membership of the Football League ended for York in in May 2004.

Under the new managership of Chris Brass and his assistant Lee Nogan, City equalled a club record by winning their first four league games and at the end of August topped Division Three. They failed to maintain this great start, however, but early in the New Year still harboured hopes of a top seven play off position. Victory over Carlisle United on the 10th January maintained their place in 10th position and they were just three points from seventh placed Lincoln City and 18 points clear of second from bottom Darlington.Their record at that point read P26 W10 D9 L7 F.25 A28 Pts 39.

Then came a nightmare sequence in which the club failed to win any of their remaining twenty fixtures, drew five, lost fifteen and finished bottom of the table.

No joy in the cup competitions either with first round dismissals in the F.A.Cup, Carling Cup and LDV Vans Trophy when they lost to Conference club Halifax Town.

The last three years have been a traumatic time for the club with massive problems regarding the ground and crippling debts.

Magnificent work by fans and the Supporters Trust, which now runs the club, have put financial matters back on an even keel and after tremendous efforts behind the scenes, Bootham Crescent is now once again owned by York City F.C.

Relegation to the Conference is a bitter pill to swallow but the club is still very much alive and still at Bootham Crescent their headquarters and home since 19321

Chris Brass has assembled a strong squad of experience and youth for 2004--5 and every effort will be made to restore Football League status at the earliest opportunity.

Back Row (L-R): Brian Neaves, Jeff Miller, Bryan Stewart, Paul Robinson, Gary Pearson, Chris Clarke, Chris Porter, Andy Bishop, Paul Groves, Sean Davies, Levent Yalcin, Kane Ashcroft, Paul Stancliffe, Kevin Hornsby.
Front Row: Adam Arthur, Graeme Law, Darren Dunning, Chris Brass, Steve Davis, Lee Nogan, Kevin Donovan, Dave Merris, Shaun Smith, Matthew Coad.

YORK CITY

Match Facts 2003-04

Comp		Score		Result	Date
Football League Two	Carlisle United	1-2	York City	W	09-08-2003
League Cup	**Rotherham United**	**2-1**	**York City**	**L**	**12-08-2003**
Football League Two	York City	1-0	Northampton Town	W	16-08-2003
Football League Two	Huddersfield Town	0-1	York City	W	23-08-2003
Football League Two	York City	2-0	Southend United	W	26-08-2003
Football League Two	Lincoln City	3-0	York City	L	30-08-2003
Football League Two	York City	1-2	Rochdale	L	06-09-2003
Football League Two	Yeovil Town	3-0	York City	L	13-09-2003
Football League Two	York City	1-1	Darlington	D	16-09-2003
Football League Two	York City	2-1	Bristol Rovers	W	20-09-2003
Football League Two	Macclesfield Town	0-0	York City	D	27-09-2003
Football League Two	Bury	2-0	York City	L	30-09-2003
Football League Two	York City	2-0	Cambridge United	W	04-10-2003
Football League Two	Mansfield Town	2-0	York City	L	11-10-2003
LDV Vans Trophy	**Halifax Town**	**2-1**	**York City**	**L**	**14-10-2003**
Football League Two	York City	1-1	Boston United	D	18-10-2003
Football League Two	York City	2-2	Oxford United	D	21-10-2003
Football League Two	Scunthorpe United	0-0	York City	D	25-10-2003
Football League Two	Cheltenham Town	1-1	York City	D	01-11-2003
FA Cup	**York City**	**1-2**	**Barnsley**	**L**	**09-11-2003**
Football League Two	York City	1-0	Doncaster Rovers	W	15-11-2003
Football League Two	Leyton Orient	2-2	York City	D	22-11-2003
Football League Two	York City	0-0	Swansea City	D	29-11-2003
Football League Two	Darlington	3-0	York City	L	06-12-2003
Football League Two	Torquay United	1-1	York City	D	13-12-2003
Football League Two	York City	1-0	Kidderminster Harriers	W	21-12-2003
Football League Two	York City	0-2	Hull City	L	26-12-2003
Football League Two	Rochdale	1-2	York City	W	28-12-2003
Football League Two	York City	2-0	Carlisle United	W	10-01-2004
Football League Two	Northampton Town	2-1	York City	L	17-01-2004
Football League Two	York City	0-2	Huddersfield Town	L	25-01-2004
Football League Two	Southend United	0-0	York City	D	27-01-2004
Football League Two	Hull City	2-1	York City	L	07-02-2004
Football League Two	York City	1-2	Mansfield Town	L	14-02-2004
Football League Two	York City	1-4	Lincoln City	L	17-02-2004
Football League Two	Boston United	2-0	York City	L	21-02-2004
Football League Two	Oxford United	0-0	York City	D	03-03-2004
Football League Two	Kidderminster Harriers	4-1	York City	L	06-03-2004
Football League Two	York City	1-3	Scunthorpe United	L	09-03-2004
Football League Two	York City	0-0	Torquay United	D	13-03-2004
Football League Two	Bristol Rovers	3-0	York City	L	27-03-2004
Football League Two	York City	0-2	Macclesfield Town	L	04-04-2004
Football League Two	Cambridge United	2-0	York City	L	09-04-2004
Football League Two	York City	1-1	Bury	D	13-04-2004
Football League Two	York City	0-2	Cheltenham Town	L	17-04-2004
Football League Two	York City	1-2	Yeovil Town	L	20-04-2004
Football League Two	Doncaster Rovers	3-1	York City	L	24-04-2004
Football League Two	York City	1-2	Leyton Orient	L	01-05-2004
Football League Two	Swansea City	0-0	York City	D	08-05-2004

YORK CITY

GROUND DETAILS

Bootham Crescent,York YP30 7A

Office: 01904 624447

FAX: 01904 631457

Email: info@ycfc.net

WHO'S WHO?

Chairman

Steve Back

Managing Director

Jason McGill

Financial Director

Terry Doyle

Stadium Development Director

Ian McAndrew

Communications Director

Sophie McGill

Chief Executive /Secretary

Keith Usher

HONOURS

Division 4Champions
1983-84

Promoted from Division 4

1958-59, 1964-65, 1970-71, 1992-93(via PIAY OFFS)

Promoted from Division 3

1973-74

F.A.Cup Semi-Finalists

1954-55

F.A.Cup Quarter Finalists

1961-62

FOOTBALL MANAGEMENT TEAM

Head Coach: Chris Brass

Date of Appointment June 2003

Date of Birth: 24July 1975

Place of Birth Easington

Previous Clubs: as Manager: N/A

As Player: Burnley, Torquay(L),Halifax T (L) York C

First Team Coach: Lee Nogan

Physiotherapist: Jeff Miller

Club Playing Status Full Time

MATCHDAY PROGRAMME

Pages:44 Price:£2.50

Editor: Terry Doyle Tel No: 01904 624447

Club Website: www.ycfc.net

YORK CITY — PLAYING SQUAD

	Birthplace	D.O.B.	Previous Clubs

Bold print denotes England semi-professional international.

GOALKEEPERS			
Paul Crichton	Pontefract	03.10.68	Norwich C, Burnley, W.B.A., Grimsby T, Doncaster R, Peterborough U, NottinghamF
Chris Porter	Middlesbrough	17.07.79	Darlington, Southend U, Hartlepool, Darlington, Sunderland
DEFENDERS			
Chris Brass	Easington	24.07.75	Torquay U (L), Halifax T (L),Burnley
Chris Clarke	Leeds	09.04.71	Cambridge U, Blackpool, Halifax T, Wolverhampton W
Sean Davies	Niddlesbrough	27.02.85	From Youth Team
Steve Davis	Hexham	30.10.68	Blackpool, Burnley, LutonT, Burnley, Southampton
Graeme Law	Fife	06.10.84	Club Trainee (Scotland U19)
Shaun Smith	Leeds	09.04.71	Rochdale, Hull C, Crewe A, Emley, Halifax T
MIDFIELD			
Kane Ashcroft	Leeds	19.03.86	From Youth Team
Matthew Coad	Darlington	25.09.84	From Youth Team
Kevin Donovan	Halifax	17.12.71	Rochdale, Barnsley, Grimsby T, W.B.A., Huddersfield T
Darren Dunning	Scarborough	08.01.81	Blackburn Rovers
Paul Groves	Derby	28.02.66	Scunthorpe, Grimsby T, W.B.A., Grimsby T, Blackpool, Leicester C, Burton Albion, Belper Town
Dave Merris	Rotherham		Harrogate T, Guiseley, Rotherham United
Gary Pearson	Derby	28.02.66	Darlington, Durham City, Whitby Town, Stalybridge C, Gateshead, Sheffield United
Bryan Stewart	Stockton	133.09.85	Club Trainee
FORWARDS			
Adam Arthur	Nottingham	27.10.85	From Youth Team
Andy Bishop	Stone	19.10.82	Walsall
Lee Nogan	Cardiff	21.05.69	Luton T, Darlington, Grimsby T, Reading, Watford, Oxford United
Paul Robinson	Sunderland	20.11.78	Hartlepool, Blackpool, Wimbledon,
			Newastle U, Darlington
Levent Yalcin	Middlesbrough	25.03.85	Club Trainee

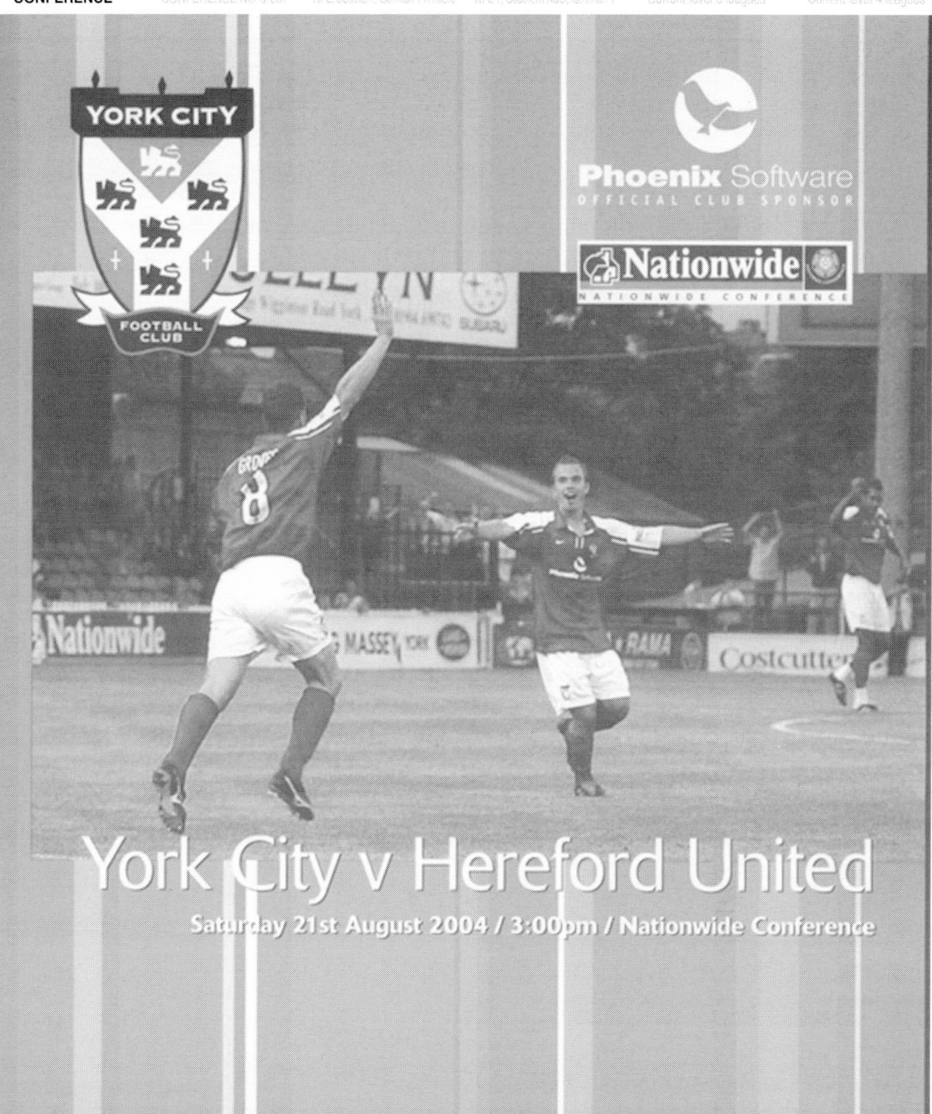

YCFC / OWNED BY THE SUPPORTERS £2.50

Arena Spectator Facilities

From Arena Seating the following spectator facilities are available for purchase to enhance all Sports Arenas and provide comfort for spectators

Arena Stadia Tip-Up Seats, floor or riser mounted on existing or new build terracing

Arena Sports Stand and Tiered Spectator Seating.
A classic design, with a cantilevered roof cover providing an unimpeded view for the spectator.

Can be supplied in 4, 7 and 13 rows covered seat options with or without end enclosures.

The roof cover is built in modules that can be added to as need and finance dictate.

Arena Sports Shelter
A smaller, lightweight 4 row version of the Arena Sports Stand where space is at a particular premium

Arena LT Grandstand and Arena LT Super Grandstand Prefabricated and delivered to location via lorry with crane.

Supplied complete with 50 or 74 tip up seats or as a tiered standing stand with capacity for 85 or 120 spectators.

Wheelchair spaces can be incorporated.

End enclosures available as an optional extra.

Can be linked together for greater capacity.

Arena Seating Limited, Arena House, Membury, Lambourn Woodlands, Hungerford, Berkshire RG17 7TQ
Tel: 01488 674800 Fax: 01488 674822 Email: info@arenaseating.com

Match Facts 2003-04

The number shown directly below the player's name is his squad number.
Where a number is shown instead of an "X' in the columns this represents a substitute appearance and the number indicates the player replaced.

Comp.	Date	Opponents	Venue.	Result	Goalscorers	Att.
Conf 1	Aug 09	Stevenage B	A	D 0-0		2502
Conf 2	Aug 12	Tamworth	H	W 1-0	Ruffer	2267
Conf 3	Aug 16	Forest Green R	H	W 1-0	Davies	1881
Conf 4	Aug 23	Exeter C	A	L 1-2	Foster(p)	3030
Conf 5	Aug 26	Shrewsbury T	H	W 2-1	Stamp Bolland	4665
Conf 6	Aug 30	Gravesend & N	A	W 4-0	Twiss(2) Bolland Stamp	939
Conf 7	Sep 06	Margate	A	W 2-1	Stamp Brady	634
Conf 8	Sep 13	Halifax T	H	W 2-0	Hatswell Stamp	2628
Conf 9	Sep 20	Farnborough T	A	W 2-1	Stamp(2)	748
Conf 10	Sep 23	Northwich V	H	W 4-0	Collins Carden Foster Rapley	2817
Conf 11	Sep 27	Telford U	H	D 0-0		2688
Conf 12	Oct 04	Dagenham & R	A	D 0-0		1497
Conf 13	Oct 08	Burton A	A	D 1-1	Stamp	1711
Conf 14	Oct 11	Woking	H	W 2-1	Davies Twiss	2085
LDVT 1	**Oct 14**	**Doncaster R**	**H**	**L 0-1**		**1141**
Conf 15	Oct 18	Hereford U	H	D 0-0		4481
FAC 4q	**Oct 25**	**Blyth Spartans**	**A**	**W 1-0**	**Clare**	**1105**
Conf 16	Nov 01	Scarborough	A	D 2-2	Stamp Clare(p)	1441
FAC 1	**Nov 08**	**Gravesend & N**	**H**	**L 0-1**		**2251**
Conf 17	Nov 11	Morecambe	A	W 1-0	Clare	1959
Conf 18	Nov 15	Barnet	H	W 1-0	Smith	2638
Conf 19	Nov 22	Aldershot T	A	D 1-1	Stamp	3610
Conf 20	Nov 25	Accrington S	H	D 3-3	Clare(2) Davies	2432
Conf 21	Nov 29	Margate	H	W 3-0	Davies Clare Stamp	1971
Conf 22	Dec 06	Halifax T	A	W 3-0	Davies Collins Clare	1928
Conf 23	Dec 13	Stevenage B	H	L 1-2	Twiss	2145
Conf 24	Dec 20	Tamworth	A	W 5-1	Clare(3) Ruffer Smith	1520
Conf 25	Dec 26	Leigh RMI	H	W 5-0	Stamp(3) Clare Rapley	3044
Conf 26	Jan 01	Leigh RMI	A	W 6-2	Clare(3) Stamp(2) Smith	2002
Conf 27	Jan 03	Gravesend & N	H	D 2-2	Clare(2,1p)	2670
FAT 3	**Jan 10**	**Halifax T**	**H**	**L 1-2**	**Bolland**	**1561**
Conf 28	Jan 17	Forest Green R	A	L 1-2	Clare	1164
Conf 29	Jan 24	Northwich V	A	W 4-0	Stamp(2) Clare McIntyre	2141
Conf 30	Feb 07	Farnborough T	H	W 3-2	Clare(2) Stamp	2665
Conf 31	Feb 21	Dagenham & R	H	W 2-1	Clare(p) Stamp	2990
Conf 32	Feb 28	Woking	A	W 2-1	Collins Twiss	2554
Conf 33	Mar 06	Burton A	H	W 3-1	Clare(2) Guyett	3318
Conf 34	Mar 13	Morecambe	H	W 2-1	Smith Clare	3512
Conf 35	Mar 20	Barnet	A	D 0-0		2455
Conf 36	Mar 31	Telford U	A	W 2-0	Clare(2,1p)	3503
Conf 37	Apr 03	Accrington S	A	W 2-0	Guyett Clare(p)	2561
Conf 38	Apr 06	Aldershot T	H	W 4-2	Bolland(2) Clare(2,1p)	3432
Conf 39	Apr 10	Exeter C	H	W 3-2	Twiss(2) Clare	4046
Conf 40	Apr 13	Shrewsbury T	A	D 0-0		5827
Conf 41	Apr 17	Scarborough	H	W 1-0	Stamp	5987
Conf 42	Apr 24	Hereford U	A	L 1-2	James(og)	7240

STEP 1
CONFERENCE

STEP 2 - P177
CONFERENCE Nth & Sth

STEP 3 - P269
NPL, Southern, Isthmian Premiers

STEP 4 - P269
NPL 1, Southern N&S, Isthmian 1

STEP 5/6 - P473
Current level 3 leagues

STEP 7 - P713
Current level 4 leagues

Wayne BROWN	Danny COLLINS	Kevin McINTYRE	Paul CARDEN	Phil BOLLAND	Wayne HATSWELL	Peter DOGUN	Alex SMITH	Andy HARRIS	Ben DAVIES	Kevin RAPLEY	Daryl CLARE	Jon BRADY	Carl REGAN	Ian FOSTER	Shaun CAREY	Mark BEESLEY	Michael TWISS	Carl RUFFER	Chris LANE	Danny WILLIAMS	Ian McCALDON	Steve BRODIE	Lee ELAM	Dean BUCKLEY	Robert GILL	Iain TURNER	Darryn STAMP	Scott GUYETT	Jamie HEARD	Andy WOODS
1	**2**	**3**	**4**	**5**	**6**	**6**	**6**	**7**	**8**	**9**	**10**	**11**	**11**	**12**	**14**	**15**	**16**	**17**	**18**	**19**	**20**	**21**	**21**	**22**	**23**	**23**	**24**	**25**	**26**	**30**
x	x	x	x		x			x	x	x				23		9		x							x				x	
x	x	x	x		x			x	x	x				7		9		x				23			x				x	
x	x	x	x		x				x	x				9	x		14	x				23			x				x	
	x	x	x	x	x				x			x		x		12	17	x			x						x			
x	x	x	x	x	x				x			x		x			11								12		x		x	
x	x	x	x	x	x			24	x			x		x			26	4									x		x	
x	x	x	x	x	x			x	x	12		x		x			7										x			
x	x	x	x	x	x			x	x	12		x		x													x			
x	x	x	x	x				x	x	12		x		x				x									x			
	x	x	x	x				x	x	11		x		x			12	x			x						x			
x	x	x	x	x				x	x	12	24	x		x			11	x									x			
x	x	x	x	x					x	12	16	x		x			x	x									x			
	x	x	x	x					x	x	12			x			9	x			x						x		x	
	x	x	x	x					x	10	x			24			x	x			x						x	17	x	
x	x	x				14		x		x		x		x	x	12	x							16				x	x	
	x	x	x	x					x	16	x			10			x	x			x						x		x	
	x			x					x	10	x	12		x	x		x	x			x						x	17	x	
	x	x	x	x					x		x	x			x		10	x			x						x	24		
	x	x	x	x					x	10	x	26		x			12	x			x						x		x	
20	x	x	x	x			x		x		x	x		10				x			x						x	6		
x	x	x					x	6	x		x	x			x		10	x									x	x		
x	x	x	6				x		x		x	x		11	x			x									x	x	17	
x	x	x					x	x	x	24	x	x		10	x												x	x		
x	x	x		25			x		x	x	x	x		11	x			x									9	x		
x	x	x	6	26			x		x	x	x				x			x										x	x	
x	x	x		x			x		x	x	x				x		9	x									25	x		
	x	x	x	3			x	6		10	x		x		x			x			x						x	x		
	x	x	x				x		6	24	x		x		x		10	x			x						x	x		
	x	x	x	25			x				x		x		x		3	x			x						x	x		
	x		x	6			x		14	24	x		x		x		x	x			x						x	x		
	x		x	x			x		14	24			x	x	x		x	x			x						x			
	x	x	x	x			x	x		6	x						24	x			x						x		x	
	x	x	x	x			x		14	10	x				x		24				x						x	x	x	
	x	x		x			x		x		x				x		6									x	x	x	x	
	x	x		x			x		14		x				x		6			x						x	x	x	x	
	x	x	x	x			x				x						6			x						x	x	x	x	
	x	x	x	x			x				x				19					x						x	x	x	x	
	x	x	x	x			x		19		x									x						x	x	x	x	
	x	x	x	x			x			10	x						6		26	x						x	x	x	x	
	x	x	x	x			x		24		x				x		6										x	x	x	x
	x	x	x	x							x				x		x		24							x	x	x	x	
	x	x	x	x					24		x				x		x		14				26			x	x	x	x	
	x	x	x	x					14	24	x				x		x						10			x	x	x	x	
	x	x	x	x					14	x					x		x									x	x	x	x	
	x	x	x	x				16	x	10	x						x						2			x	x	x	x	
				x				x	x	x				14	x		x		x				x			x	9	x	x	

SHREWSBURY TOWN

Match Facts 2003-04

The number shown directly below the player's name is his squad number.
Where a number is shown instead of an "X' in the columns this represents a substitute appearance and the number indicates the player replaced.

Comp.	Date	Opponents	Venue.	Result	Goalscorers	Att.
Conf 1	Aug 09	Margate	H	D 1-1	Watts	4015
Conf 2	Aug 12	Burton A	A	W 1-0	Rodgers	3203
Conf 3	Aug 16	Accrington S	A	W 1-0	Cramb	3143
Conf 4	Aug 23	Farnborough T	H	W 3-0	Cramb Jagielka Lowe	3403
Conf 5	Aug 26	Chester C	A	L 1-2	Tolley	4665
Conf 6	Aug 30	Dagenham & R	H	W 2-1	Tolley Cramb	3468
Conf 7	Sep 07	Tamworth	H	W 3-1	Rodgers(3)	3882
Conf 8	Sep 13	Aldershot T	A	D 1-1	Cramb	3329
Conf 9	Sep 20	Woking	A	D 3-3	Rodgers(3,1p)	2539
Conf 10	Sep 23	Halifax T	H	W 2-0	Cramb Lowe	3807
Conf 11	Sep 27	Barnet	H	L 0-1		4063
Conf 12	Oct 04	Scarborough	A	D 1-1	Quinn	1201
LDVT 1	**Oct 14**	**Scunthorpe Utd**	**A**	**L 1-2**	**Lowe**	**1265**
Conf 13	Oct 18	Morecambe	H	W 2-0	Rodgers Quinn	3404
FAC 4q	**Oct 25**	**Morecambe**	**A**	**W 4-2**	**Lowe(2) Aiston Quinn**	**1951**
Conf 14	Nov 01	Stevenage B	A	L 0-2		2172
FAC 1	**Nov 08**	**Scunthorpe Utd**	**A**	**L 1-2**	**Quinn**	**3232**
Conf 15	Nov 11	Forest Green R	H	W 2-0	Tolley Quinn	3263
Conf 16	Nov 15	Gravesend & N	A	W 3-0	Lowe(2) Cramb	1397
Conf 17	Nov 18	Leigh RMI	A	D 2-2	Cramb Street	1219
Conf 18	Nov 22	Hereford U	H	W 4-1	O'Connor Cramb Street Darby	6585
Conf 19	Nov 25	Exeter C	A	L 2-3	Rodgers Cramb	3470
Conf 20	Nov 29	Tamworth	A	D 1-1	Cramb(p)	1761
Conf 21	Dec 09	Telford U	H	D 0-0		6738
Conf 22	Dec 14	Margate	A	W 2-0	Lowe Banim	635
Conf 23	Dec 26	Northwich V	H	W 3-1	Cramb Lowe Tinson	5058
Conf 24	Jan 01	Northwich V	A	W 2-0	Ridler Cramb	3268
Conf 25	Jan 03	Dagenham & R	A	L 0-5		1571
FAT 3	**Jan 10**	**Morecambe**	**H**	**W 2-0**	**Aiston Cramb(p)**	**2413**
Conf 26	Jan 17	Accrington S	H	D 0-0		3777
Conf 27	Jan 24	Halifax T	A	D 0-0		1830
FAT 4	**Jan 31**	**Hucknall Town**	**H**	**W 2-1**	**Street Moss**	**2501**
FAT 5	**Feb 14**	**Altrincham**	**A**	**W 1-0**	**Lowe**	**1758**
Conf 28	Feb 21	Scarborough	H	W 4-1	Darby(2) Sedgemore O'Connor	3333
Conf 29	Feb 24	Burton A	H	W 1-0	Rodgers	3115
FAT 6	**Feb 28**	**Telford U**	**H**	**D 1-1**	**Cramb**	**6050**
Conf 30	Mar 02	Woking	H	W 1-0	Rodgers	3029
Conf 31	Mar 08	Leigh RMI	H	W 3-1	Darby Lowe Banim	3307
Conf 32	Mar 13	Forest Green R	A	D 1-1	Rogers(og)	1484
FAT 6r	**Mar 16**	**Telford U**	**A**	**L 1-2**	**Darby**	**4447**
Conf 33	Mar 23	Aldershot T	H	L 1-2	Darby	3371
Conf 34	Mar 27	Hereford U	A	L 1-2	Lawrence	5850
Conf 35	Mar 30	Barnet	A	W 1-0	Darby	1966
Conf 36	Apr 03	Exeter C	H	D 2-2	Lawrence Darby	4185
Conf 37	Apr 06	Telford U	A	L 0-1		4337
Conf 38	Apr 10	Farnborough T	A	W 3-1	Darby(2) Rodgers	1041
Conf 39	Apr 13	Chester C	H	D 0-0		5827
Conf 40	Apr 17	Stevenage B	H	W 3-1	Ridler Lowe Darby	3650
Conf 41	Apr 20	Gravesend & N	H	D 1-1	Rodgers	2869
Conf 42	Apr 24	Morecambe	A	D 3-3	Lowe Sedgemore(p) Quinn	2876
PO SF1	**Apr 29**	**Barnet**	**A**	**L 1-2**	**Rodgers(p)**	**4171**
PO SF2	**May 03**	**Barnet**	**H**	**W 1-0**	**Rodgers(p) (won 5-3 on pens)**	**7012**
PO F	**May 16**	**Aldershot T**	**N**	**D 1-1***	**Darby (won 3-0 on pens)**	**19216**

STEP 1
CONFERENCE

STEP 2 - P177
CONFERENCE Nth & Sth

STEP 3 - P269
NPL, Southern, Isthmian Premiers

STEP 4 - P269
NPL 1, Southern N&S, Isthmian 1

STEP 5/6 - P473
Current level 3 leagues

STEP 7 - P713
Current level 4 leagues

Ian DUNBAVIN	Darren MOSS	Greg RIOCH	Jamie TOLLEY	Darren TINSON	Dave RIDLER	Steve JAGIELKA	Jody BANIM	Jake SEDGEMORE	Luke RODGERS	Colin CRAMB	Sam AISTON	Martyn O'CONNOR	Leon DRYSDALE	Karl MURRAY	Trevor CHALLIS	Ian FITZPATRICK	Ryan LOWE	Steve WATTS	Duane DARBY	Neville THOMPSON	Glenn TOLLEY	David EDWARDS	Ross STEPHENS	Scott HOWIE	Jimmy QUINN	Lee BELL	Lee LAWRENCE	Graham POTTER	Kevin STREET	Joe HART
1	**2**	**3**	**4**	**5**	**6**	**7**	**7**	**8**	**9**	**10**	**11**	**12**	**14**	**15**	**15**	**16**	**17**	**18**	**18**	**19**	**20**	**21**	**23**	**25**	**26**	**27**	**27**	**28**	**29**	**30**
x	x	x	x	x	x	x			x		16	x				x		x												
x	x	x	x	x	x	x		16	x	18		x		12		x		x												
x	x	x	x	x	x	x		3	x	x		x				x	16							1						
	x		x	x	x	x		x	x	x	x	x		12			9							x						
			x	x	x	x		x	x	x	x	x	x			7	8	10						x						
	x	x	x	x	x	x		3	x	x	x	x					10	11						x						
	x	x	x	x	x	x			x	x	x	x				11	4	10						x						
		x		x	x	x		x	x	x	x	x		x				11				7		x						
	x	x		x	x	15		6	x	x	x	x		x				x						x	18					
	x	x		x				x	x	x	x	x		x		11	18	x						x						
	x	x		x		12		x	x	x	x	x		x		11	x							x	2					
	x	x	x	x	x	10				x	x						x							x	x	x				
	x	**x**	**x**	**x**	**x**					**18**	**x**	**x**				**11**	**x**	**x**						**x**		**x**				
	x	x	x		x			x	x		x	x					26							x	x	12			x	
		x	**x**	**x**	**x**			**x**	**x**		**x**	**x**				**11**	**12**			**26**				**x**	**x**				**x**	
	8	x	x	x	x			x	x		x	x					6							x	x	4			x	
	x	**x**	**x**	**x**	**x**				**x**	**6**	**x**	**x**					**29**							**x**	**x**				**x**	
	x	x	x		x			x	x	9	x	x					x						11	x	x				17	
	x	x	x	x	x				26	17	x	x					x		x					x	x				11	
	x	x	x	x	x			5	11	x	x	x					x		x					x					3	
	x		x	x	x				12	x		x					x		x					x				x	x	
	x		x	x	x			12	17	x		x					x		x					x	6			x	x	
	x	10		x	x			x		x		x					x		x			18		x	6			x	x	
	x		x	x	x		18		x	x	x	x					9		x					x				11	x	
	x	11	x	x	x		9	x	x		x						4							x	x			x	x	
	x	x		x	x		x	x		x	x	x					29					12		x					x	
	x	x		x	x		x	x		x	x	x					x		7					x	10				17	
	x	x		x	x		x	x		x	x	x					x		10					x	3				17	
		26		**x**	**x**			**x**		**x**	**x**								**x**	**10**	**23**	**x**	**x**	**x**	**x**				**x**	
	x			x	x		26	x		x	x	10							x			x		x	x				x	
	x			x	x			x	x	18	x	x							x		12	x		x					x	
	x			**x**	**x**			**x**	**x**	**18**	**x**	**x**							**x**			**x**		**x**					**x**	
	x			**x**	**x**			**x**	**x**	**9**	**x**	**x**					**29**		**x**			**x**	**6**	**x**					**x**	
	x		x	x	x			x	x	12	x	x					x		x			4		x					11	
	x			x	x		18	x	x	x	9	x					x		x			x		x					21	
	x		**18**	**x**	**x**			**x**	**x**	**x**	**21**	**x**					**x**		**x**			**x**		**x**					**12**	
	x		x	x	x		17	x	x	x	x	x					x		10			12		x						
	x		x	x	x		18	x		x	x	x					x		x			4		x					11	
	x		x	x	x		10	x	29	x		x					x		x			4		x					x	
	x		**x**	**x**	**x**				**x**	**x**		**x**				**29**	**21**		**x**			**x**		**x**					**x**	
	x			x	x		x	x	x	12		x							x			x		x	27		21		x	
	x			x	x		17	x	x						x		x		x					x	18		x		x	
	x			x			x	x	7	17		x			x		x		x					x			x		x	
				x	x		x	x	7	18		x			x		x		x					x			x		x	
			12	x	x		x	x	7		x	x			x		11		x					x			x		x	
	x		x	x	x			21	x	9	x				x		11		x			x		x					x	
	x		x	x	x				x		x				x				x			x		x					x	
	x		x	x	x			4	x	9	x				x		21		x			x		x					x	
	x		x	12	x			x	x	x	x	x					x		10			11					x			x
	x		x		x		12	x			x	x			27		x					4			x		x		x	x
	x		**x**	**x**	**x**			**5**	**x**		**x**	**x**			**x**		**x**		**x**					**x**	**9**		**15**			
x		**x**	**x**	**x**			**11**	**x**	**18**	**x**	**x**			**x**		**x**		**x**			**12**		**x**							
		x	**x**	**x**			**x**	**x**	**18**	**x**	**x**			**x**		**x**		**x**					**x**			**5**		**12**		

FOOTBALL LEAGUE

STEP 1

FOOTBALL CONFERENCE

STEP 2

CONFERENCE NORTH

CONFERENCE SOUTH

STEP 3

NORTHERN PREMIER

SOUTHERN PREMIER

ISTHMIAN PREMIER

STEP 4

NORTHERN PREMIER DIV.1

SOUTHERN LEAGUE EAST

SOUTHERN LEAGUE WEST

ISTHMIAN DIVISION 1

STEP 5/6

STEP 7

ALFRETON TOWN

CLUB OFFICIALS

Chairman: Wayne Bradley **V- C**: Sam Egan

Secretary: Tom Hill, 4 Westwood Drive,Swanpool,Lincoln LN6 0HJ

Tel Nos 01522 683630 (H) 07885020797(M)

Commercial Manager:

DonnaWheatley: 01159 390290 (W)

Press Officer: Kev Miles 07717 417669 (M)

Match Day Sec: Roger Taylor 9 Priory Rd, Alfreton, Derbys. DE55 7J T(01773 835121)

FACT FILE

Formed: 1959
Nickname: The Reds
Sponsors: Impact Marketing & Publicity Ltd
Colours: all red Change colours: all white
Midweek home matchday: Tuesday
Res League: Mid Regional Alliance + Under 19s,18s, 16s, 15s, 13s, & 12s

FOOTBALL MANAGEMENT TEAM

Manager:David Lloyd
Assistant Manager: Charlie Wiliamson
Physio: Mick Jenkins

PROGRAMME - Pages: 32 Price: £1.50
Editor: Chris Tacey (01302 722415)

Newsline: 01773 830277
Local Radio: Radio Derby
Local Press: Derbyshire Times; Derby Evening Telegraph; Chad, Ripley & Heanor News

GROUND: Town Ground, North St., Alfreton, Derbys Tel: 01773 521734 Admin.
Club Website: alfretontownfc.com

Directions: M1 junction 28 and follow A38 towards Derby for 1 mile,left onto B600, right at main road to town centre and left after1/2 mile down North St.- ground on right. Half mile from Alfreton (BR) station.Buses:91,92,93 from Derby and Mansfield.Rainbow 1 from Nott'ingham

Capacity: 5,000 Cover: 1,000 Seats:1,600

Clubhouse: H & C food & drinks on ground.Exclusive Bar open on ground matchdays Supporters Club bar outside ground open every day.

Club Shop: Programmes & club souvenirs. Contact Brian Thorpe Tel: 01773 836251

PREVIOUS **Leagues:** Central All.(pre-reformation 21-25) 59-61; Midland (Counties) 25-27 61-82; N.C.E. 82-87; Northern Premier 87-99

BEST SEASON **FA Trophy:** 1st Rd Proper 94-95. **FA Vase:** 5th Round 99-00
FA Cup: 1st Rd 3rd replay 69-70. Also 1st Rd 73-74. - League clubs defeated: Lincoln 24-25

RECORDS **Attendance:** 5,023 v Matlock Tn, Central All 60.
Scorer: J Harrison 303 **Win:** 15-0 v Loughborough, Midland Lge. 69-70
Appearances: J Harrison 560 **Defeat:** 1-9 v Solihull FAT 97, 0-8 v Bridlington 92.
Fees - Paid: £2,000 for Mick Goddard (Worksop Town)) **Received:** £7,000 for Paul Eshelby (Ilkeston Tn 96-97)

HONOURS: N.C.E. Lg 84-85,2001-02 (Lg Cup 84-85,01-02); Midland Co. Lg 69-70 73-74 76-77 (R-up 71-72 80-81 81-82), Lg Cup 71-72 72-73 73-74; Derbyshire Sen Cup (7) and Runners -up (8) Div Cup (N) 64-65; Evans Halshaw Floodlit Cup 87-88 95-96; Cent All Lg.R-Up 63-64; NPL Div 1 R-Up 95-96 NCE Presidents Cup Winners 2001-02 Unibond Div 1 Champions 2002-03

Players progressing: M Wright (68), A Kowalski (73), A Henson (81), Philip Greaves (86) (All Chesterfield), A Woodward (Grimsby T. 70), A Taylor (Chelsea72), R Greenhough (Chester C. 85), K Smith (Exeter C. 89) M Duke (Sheff.Utd 99)

Date	Comp.	Opponents	Att.	Score	Goalscorers
16/08	LP	ALTRINCHAM	511	0 - 0	
19/08	LP	Gainsborough Trinity	533	4 - 2	France 10 40, Goddard 70 73
23/08	LP	Whitby Town	337	4 - 0	**FRANCE 4 41 87,** Nwadike 63
25/08	LP	HUCKNALL TOWN	805	2 - 1	**Godber 47 90**
30/08	LP	LANCASTER CITY	489	3 - 0	Goddard 4, **Godber 16**, Nwadike 55
02/09	LP	Frickley Athletic	308	3 - 0	Grayson 17, Goddard 62, **Godber 87**
06/09	LP	Marine	302	1 - 0	Goddard 58
09/09	LP	STALYBRIDGE CELTIC	664	3 - 1	**Godber 32 45,** Bradshaw 85
13/09	LP	BRADFORD PARK AVENUE	517	1 - 1	Goddard 4
15/09	LP	Droylsden	271	1 - 2	Bettney 18
20/09	LP	Spennymoor United	276	0 - 1	
23/09	LP	ASHTON UNITED	424	**5 - 0**	Hemmings 16, Nwadike 53, Bettney 62 67, **Godber 86**
27/09	**FA Cup Q2**	**Gedling Town**	280	0 - 1	
30/09	LP	WAKEFIELD & EMLEY	440	2 - 1	**Godber 5**, Hemmings 65[p]
04/10	LP	Burscough	189	1 - 4	Goddard 19
07/10	LP	Stalybridge Celtic	441	**0 - 3**	
17/10	LP	WORKSOP TOWN	**903**	2 - 1	Grayston 6 21
25/10	LP	Radcliffe Borough	294	0 - 1	
28/10	LP	Wakefield & Emley	181	3 - 0	**Godber 75,** Bettney 82, Hemmings 88[p]
01/11	**FA Trophy 1**	**PRESCOT CABLES**	249	0 - 0	
04/11	**FA Trophy 1 rep**	**Prescot Cables**	201	4 - 1	**Godber 21,** Bettney 33, Brown 38, Tansley 71
08/11	LP	BARROW	430	1 - 1	Robinson 88
15/11	LP	VAUXHALL MOTORS	404	5 - 1	Robinson 9[og], Bettney 13, Sale 31, **Godber 57**, Robinson 67
22/11	LP	Ashton United	204	1 - 1	Sale 79
29/11	**FA Trophy 2**	**VAUXHALL MOTORS**	181	1 - 1	Sale 30
02/12	**FA Trophy 2 rep**	**Vauxhall Motors**	147	4 - 2	**Godber 7, 77**, Knapper 68, Goddard 90
06/12	LP	FRICKLEY ATHLETIC	340	1 - 2	Dolby 6
13/12	LP	BLYTH SPARTANS	311	2 - 1	**Godber 19**, Forster 90[og]
26/12	LP	Hucknall Town	1323	3 - 3	**Godber 1 17,** Goddard 36
03/01	LP	DROYLSDEN	404	4 - 2	Fisher 18, 70 Goddard 76 Knapper 90
13/01	**FA Trophy 3**	**Telford United**	2105	0 - 2	
24/01	LP	SOUTHPORT	397	0 - 2	
07/02	LP	RUNCORN HALTON	248	0 - 2	
14/02	LP	Southport	749	0 - 1	
17/02	LP	Harrogate Town	538	0 - 1	
02/03	LP	WHITBY TOWN	201	3 - 0	Bettney 5, Hume 35, Robinson 62
06/03	LP	Vauxhall Motors	232	0 - 2	
09/03	LP	HARROGATE TOWN	169	2 - 0	Knapper 45[p], **Godber 66**
13/03	LP	MARINE	235	4 - 0	**Godber 18,38,** Fisher 24, Nwadike 72
17/03	LP	Bradford Park Avenue	240	1 - 0	Knapper 4[p]
20/03	LP	Lancaster City	261	1 - 0	**Godber 60**
23/03	LP	BURSCOUGH	197	1 - 0	**Godber 80**
01/04	LP	Worksop Town	657	0 - 0	
03/04	LP	SPENNYMOOR UNITED	212	1 - 1	Holmes 88
06/04	LP	GAINSBOROUGH TRINITY	203	3 - 1	Sale 24 31, Nwadike 79
08 /04	LP	Runcorn Halton	187	2 - 2	Sale 15, Nwadike 19
10 /04	LP	RADCLIFFE BOROUGH	251	0 - 0	
12 /04	LP	Altrincham	570	1 - 0	Knapper 42[p]
20 /04	LP	Barrow	1451	2 - 1	Hume 7, Dolby 90
24 /04	LP	Blyth Spartans	411	0 - 1	

Average Home League Attendance: **402** 83-52 Top Goalscorer: **Mick Godber 21** (18+ 3FAT)

Bold Print indicates 1) F.A.Cup & F.A.Trophy ties 2) Biggest Victory 3) Biggest Defeat 4) Largest home attendance 5) Top Scorer's Goals. Opponent's name in CAPITALS denotes home fixtures and goalscorer's names in **BOLD CAPITALS** denotes hat tricks.

PLAYING SQUAD 2004-2005

Goalkeepers:

Lee Butler (Halifax), Gavin Saxby (Clipstone MW)

Defenders:

Carl Bradshaw (Scunthorpe), Grant Brown (Telford Utd), Mark Blount (Burton Alb), Mark Hume (Barrow), Ben Chapman (Boston Utd)

Midfield:

Mitch Ward (York), Ian Robinson (Ilkeston), Emeka Nwadike (Ilkeston), John Knapper (Ilkeston), Matt Fisher (Tamworth), Anthony Tansley (Borrowash V)

Forwards:

Mick Godber (Sheffield FC), Mick Goddard (Worksop), Mark Sale (Tamworth), Peter Duffield (Boston Utd), Chris Dolby (Bradford PA), Chris Bettney (Ilkeston), David Holmes (Worcester)

ALTRINCHAM

CLUB OFFICIALS
Chairman: Geoffrey Goodwin
President: Noel White
Directors
Grahame Rowley, Andrew Shaw,
Secretary: Graham Heathcote
c/o club
01619 739325(H) 07867 523286 (M)
Press Officer: John Pollit
Tel.No: 07739 925069 (M)
Commercial Manager: Barry Pond
07870 852042 (M)

FACT FILE
Formed: 1903
Nickname: The Robins
Sponsor: Go Goodwins Coaches
Colours: Red & white stripes/black/red&white
Change colours: All Yellow
Midweek matchday: Tuesday
Youth League: North West Youth Alliance
Website: www.altrinchamfc.com

FOOTBALL MANAGEMENT TEAM
Manager: Graham Heathcote
Assistant Manager: Dalton Steele
Physiotherapist: T.B.A.

GROUND: Moss Lane, Altrincham, Cheshire WA15 8AP. **e.mail** www.altyfc.u-net.com
Tel: 0161 928 1045(Office) 0161 9228 1045 (Club) Fax: 0161 926 9934
Directions: M6 junction 19; A556/M56 (Manchester Airport) to junction 7; signs Hale and Altrincham; through 1st traffic lights then 3rd right into Westminster Road and continue into Moss Lane. Ground on right.
CAPACITY: 6,085 **COVER:** Yes **SEATS:** 1,154
Clubhouse: Bar under the stand open on match days only. Two snack bars on ground for pies, crisps, soft drinks etc **Club Shop:** Yes (Contact: Jenny Heslop 0161 928 1045

Pages: 40 Price: £1.50
Editor: Graham/Terry Rowley 0161 928 1045
Local Radio: GMR (BBC);
Signal Radio; Piccadilly Radio
Local Press: Sale & Altrincham Messenger;
Manchester Evening News

PREVIOUS **Leagues:** Manchester 03-11, Lancashire Comb. 11-19, Cheshire County 19-68, Northern Premier 68-79, 97-99; Conference 79-97 99-00 **Grounds:** Pollitts Field -1903-1910 **Names:** None

RECORDS **Attendance:**10,275 Altrincham Boys v Sunderland Boys,English Schools Shield 3rd Round 28.02.25
Goalscorer: Jack Swindells 252 - 1965-71 **Appearances:** JohnDavison 677 - 1971-86
Win: 9-2 v Merthyr Tydfil,Vauxhall Conference, Feb 1991 **Defeat:** Unknown
Fee Paid: £15,000 to Blackpool for Keith Russell
Fee Received: From Scarborough for Kevin Ellison £45,000

BEST SEASON **FA Trophy:** Winners 77-78, 85-86 **League:** Conference Champions 1979-80, 80-81
FA Cup: 85-86 4th Round, 0-2 v York City (A) League clubs defeated:15

HONOURS FA Trophy 77-78, 85- 86; Alliance Premier League 79-80, 80-81; Bob Lord Trophy 80-81; Northern Prem. Lge: Champions 98-99; Lge.Cup 69-70 97-98; N.P.L. Shield 79-80; Cheshire County League: Champions 65-66, 66-67; Lge Cup 50-51, 52-53, 63-64; Cheshire Senior Cup 04-05, 33-34, 66-67,81-82; Manchester League 04-05; Cheshire Amateur Cup 03-04.

Players Progressing: Several, most recent being G Barrow (Wigan Ath. 81), J Rogers(Wigan Ath., 82), P Conning (Rochdale, 86), E Bishop (Tranmere R. 88), P Edwards (Crewe, 88), A Kilner (Stockport C. 90), P Showler (Barnet, 91), S Johnson & A Reid (Bury 92), C Freeman (Doncaster R. 93), T Carke (Shrewsbury T. 93),Nicky Daws (Bury), Kevin Ellison (Leicester City), Danny Adams (Macclesfield Town)

Back row, left to right: Neil Ryan, Peter Band, Jason Gallagher, Simon Woodford, Andy Mooore, StephenRose, Andy Macdonald Mark Maddox.
Front: Alex Frost, Shaun Smith, Geoff Goodwin(Chairman), Rod Thornley, Ian Craney, Andy Tinnicliffe and Gary Scott

Date	Comp.	Opponents	Att.	Score	Goalscorers
16/08	LP	Alfreton Town	511	0 - 0	
19/08	LP	MARINE	579	3 - 3	Aspinall 67[p], Craney 72, Gardner 77
23/08	LP	FRICKLEY ATHLETIC	469	1 - 1	Band 86
25/08	LP	Droylsden	502	4 - 1	Thornley 33, Craney 53[p], Matthews 57, Gardner 90
30/08	LP	Harrogate Town	475	0 - 1	
02/09	LP	BARROW	683	1 - 1	Aspinall 68[p]
06/09	LP	GAINSBOROUGH TRINITY	584	2 - 2	Hughes 46 58
09/09	LP	Vauxhall Motors	303	1 - 1	Craney 81
13/09	LP	Wakefield & Emley	254	0 - 2	
23/09	LP	Southport	702	2 - 2	Thornley 18 40
27/09	**FA Cup Q2**	**Lancaster City**	489	0 - 2	
30/09	LP	Radcliffe Borough	423	3 - 1	Thornley 35, Shuttleworth 45, Gardner 49
04/10	LP	BLYTH SPARTANS	614	1 - 2	Maddox 71
07/10	LP	SPENNYMOOR UNITED	434	1 - 1	Craney 38
18/10	LP	Hucknall Town	645	1 - 2	Hardy 17
25/10	LP	BURSCOUGH	491	3 - 0	Maddox 6, Hardy 55 75
28/10	LP	SOUTHPORT	679	1 - 0	Talbot 19
01/11	**FA Trophy 1**	**Gateshead**	222	2 - 1	Welton 88 90
08/11	LP	Worksop Town	635	0 - 0	
15/11	LP	HARROGATE TOWN	701	0 - 0	
22/11	LP	Bradford Park Avenue	320	1 - 1	Shuttleworth 62
29/11	**FA Trophy 2**	**SOUTHPORT**	711	1 - 0	Band 38
06/12	LP	Radcliffe Borough	669	4 -1	**Hallows 6,** Craney 39,90 Welton 89
13/12	LP	Barrow	1138	1 - 2	Salmon 39[og]
16/12	LP	LANCASTER CITY	503	0 - 0	
26/12	LP	STALYBRIDGE CELTIC	795	3 - 3	Aspinall 48 76, Holt 56
01/01	LP	Stalybridge Celtic	1022	0 - 1	
03/01	LP	WHITBY TOWN	501	**4 - 0**	Rose 34, 45Lunt 51 **Hallows 60**
10/01	**FA Trophy 3**	**RUNCORN HALTON**	**707**	**2 - 1**	Band 5, **Hallows 73**
17/01	LP	Marine	454	1 - 0	**Hallows 51**
31/01	**FA Trophy 4**	**Weymouth**	**1722**	**2 - 0**	Wright 8, Hardy 72
07/02	LP	Ashton United	409	2 - 0	Scott 29, Thornley 78
14/02	**FA Trophy 5**	**SHREWSBURY TOWN**	**1758**	**0 - 1**	
17/02	LP	VAUXHALL MOTORS	570	3 - 1	**Hallows 37**, Maddox 71, Aspinall 86
21/02	LP	Spennymoor United	220	1 - 2	Craney 51
24/02	LP	ASHTON UNITED	447	1 - 2	Craney 90
02/03	LP	WAKEFIELD & EMLEY	453	1 - 2	Rose 90
09/03	LP	Gainsborough Trinity	357	3 - 2	**Hallows 36 56**, Baguley 47
13/03	LP	BRADFORD PARK AVENUE	622	1 - 0	Baguley 39
16/03	LP	Runcorn Halton	383	3 - 0	Craney 23, Bailey 38, **Hallows 49**
20/03	LP	DROYLSDEN	588	1 - 0	Burke 76
27/03	LP	Frickley Athletic	294	1 - 1	**Hallows 54**
03 /04	LP	Lancaster City	340	0 - 1	
05 /04	LP	HUCKNALL TOWN	529	2 - 3	Bailey 37, Craney 87
10 /04	LP	Burscough	361	**1 - 3**	**Hallows 70**
12 /04	LP	ALFRETON TOWN	570	0 - 1	
14 /04	LP	Blyth Spartans	242	2 - 2	Bailey 70, Leeson 74[og]
17 /04	LP	Whitby Town	379	3 - 2	Aspinall 6[p], Band 13, **Hallows 59**
20 /04	LP	WORKSOP TOWN	484	2 - 1	Scott 2, Craney 60
24 /04	LP	RUNCORN HALTON	**874**	1 - 0	Shuttleworth 1

Average Home League Attendance:**583** 69-55 Top Goalscorers: Hallows 11 (10 + 1 FAT)
Craney 11

PLAYING SQUAD 2004-2005

Goalkeepers:

Stuart Coburn (Leigh RMI)

Defenders:

Chris Adams (Ashton Utd), Steve Aspinall (Vauxhall Motors), Mark Maddox (Barrow), Barry Shuttleworth (Accrington Stanley), Gary Talbot (Witton Alb)

Midfield:

Jamie Almond (Woodley Sports), Peter Band (Hyde), David Holt (Stockport), Eddie Hussin (Marine), Ged Kietly (Leigh RMI), Danny Murphy (Mossley), Colin Potts (Stalybridge), Joey Roberts (Accrington Stanley), Stephen Rose (Chester), Gary Scott (Leigh RMI), Sean Smith (Local football), Stuart Wright (Vauxhall Motors)

Forwards:

Marcus Hallows (Chorley), Niell Hardy (Radcliffe), Colin Little (Halifax), Kieran Lugsdon (New Mills), Stephen Lunt (Youth team), Rod Thornley (Congleton), Peter Wright (Northwich)

ASHTON UNITED

CLUB OFFICIALS

Chairman:Tony Ryan
President: Ronnie Thomasson
Vice Chairman: Terry Hollis
Directors: Jackie Tierney (financial), Mike Bennett,Tony Collins,Graham Connell, Mike Cummings, Dickie Daye, John North, Kevin O'Carroll, Jim Pinder and Eric Staffiord
Secretary: John North, 21 Portland House, Ashton-under-Lyne, Lancs. OL6 7BS
Tel Nos: 0161 3441831 (H)
07881 731904(M)
Press Officer: Tony Ryan 07950 865682
Com. Manager: Terry Hollis 07801 600602

FACT FILE

Formed: 1878 Nickname: Robins
Club Sponsors: Wheelbrook Services
Colours: Red & white halves/black/red
Change colours: Sky/naroon/maroon
Midweek matchday: Monday
Website: www.aufc4.freeserve.co.uk

FOOTBALL MANAGEMENT TEAM

Manager: Gerry Quinn
Assistant Manager: Andy Johnson
Physio: Martin Grose

PROGRAMME
Pages: 22 Price: £1
Editor:Ken Lee (0161 330 9800)
Local Press: Ashton Reporter, Ashton Advertiser Local Radio: GMR

GROUND Surrey Street, Hurst Cross, Ashton-u-Lyne OL6 8DY.
Tel: 0161339 4158. (office) 01613 301511 (Social Club). Fax 0161 339 4158
Directions: M62 jct 20, A627(M) to Oldham, keep in right hand 2 lanes, leave at Ashton sign after 2 miles passing Belgrade Hotel, take A627 at next island,keep in left lane and take slip road signed Ashton-under-Lyme, at island follow Stalybridge/Park Road sign, go straight ahead for 3 miles to ground at Hurst Cross. BR to Charles Street (Ashton), or Stalybridge. Buses 331, 332, 337, 408(Ashton-Stalybridge) all pass ground
Capacity: 4,500 Seats: 250 Cover: 750
Clubhouse: Open 11am-11pm. Refreshment bar open matchdays
Club Shop: Yes - contact Ken or Steve Lee (0161 330 9800)

PREVIOUS **Leagues:** Manchester; Lancs Comb 12-23, 48-64, 66-68; Midland 64-66; Cheshire Co. 23-48, 68-82; Nth West Count 82-92.
Name: Hurst 1878-1947. Ground: Rose Hill 1878-1912

CLUB RECORDS **Attendance:** 11,000 v Halifax Town, FA Cup First Round 1952.
Scorer: Mark Edwards, 37 **Appearances:** Micky Boyle, 462.
Win: 11-3 v Staylbridge Manchester Interm Cup 55 **Defeat:** 11-1 v Wellington Town Cheshire Lge 46-47.
Fee Paid: £9,000 for Andy Whittaker (Netherfield, 1994) **Fee Received:** £15,000 for Karl Marginson (Rotherham, Mar. 1993)

BEST SEASON **FA Trophy**: Qtr Final v Dagenham (0-1) (A0 96-97
FA Cup: 1st Rd replay 52-53, 1-2 v Halifax T (A), after 1-1. Also 1st Rd 55-56, 1-6 v Southport (A)

HONOURS Northern Prem Lge Div 1 Cup 94-95; Manchester Sen Cup 1884-85 13-14 75-76 77-78; Manchester Lge 11-12; Lancs Comb. Div 2 60-61 (Lge Cup 62-63); Manchester Prem. Cup 79-80 82-83 92-93 00-01 01-02; N.W.C. Lge 91-92;Challenge Cup 91-92, Div 2 87-88; F' lit League 90-91; Challenge Shield 92-93; Manchester Chall Shield 35-36 38-39 49-50 53-54 R-up 34-35 39-40, Manchester Interm Cup 58-59 62-63 65-66, R-up 60-61 64-65; Manchester Jnr Cup 1894-95 10-12 32-33; Unifilla Div 1 Cup 96-97,98-99

Players progressing: A Ball (Blackpool), J Mahoney (Stoke C.), B Daniels(Manchester C.), R Jones (Rotherham U.), A Arrowsmith (Liverpool), N Stiffle(Crystal Palace), K Marginson (Rotherham U), P Wilson (Plymouth Argyle)

Back row, left to right: A.Jones, A.Kirk, P.Garvey, L.Adams, D.Trueman, D.White, A.Connor, D.Johnson, J.Mitten, A.Johnston (Assistant Manager) and G.Quinn (Manager). **Front row:** M.Grose (Physio), S.Smith, A,Bailey, C.Fleury, A.Thackeray, P.Cooney, P.Carty, N.Clee and M.Allison.

Date	Comp.	Opponents	Att.	Score	Goalscorers
16/08	LP	Blyth Spartans	481	0 - 2	
19/08	LP	BRADFORD PARK AVENUE	210	0 - 2	
23/08	LP	LANCASTER CITY	172	2 - 1	Dormer 22, **Garvey 40**
25/08	LP	Stalybridge Celtic	673	1 - 1	Fleury 49
30/08	LP	MARINE	188	4 - 3	Adams 25, Fleury 53, Miller 58, Thackery 63
02/09	LP	Hucknall Town	512	0 - 2	
06/09	LP	Wakefield & Emley	201	2 - 1	Denney 14 23
09/09	LP	WHITBY TOWN	188	1 - 3	Smith 16
13/09	LP	Barrow	1013	0 - 3	
16/09	LP	BLYTH SPARTANS	147	2 - 0	Miller 26, **Garvey 69**
20/09	LP	SOUTHPORT	382	2 - 1	Denney 64, **Garvey 90**
23/09	LP	Alfreton Town	424	0 - 5	
27/09	**FA Cup Q2**	**HYDE UNITED**	446	1 - 1	Denney 50[p]
29/09	**FA Cup Q2 rep**	**Hyde United**	489	2 - 1	Denney 23, Fleury 69
04/10	LP	SPENNYMOOR UNITED	**614**	1 - 2	**Garvey 45**
07/10	LP	Gainsborough Trinity	403	0 - 3	
11/10	**FA Cup Q3**	**BARROW**	429	2 - 1	**Garvey 30,** Fleury 68[p]
18/10	LP	Frickley Athletic	163	2 - 1	Allison 44, Denney 79
25/10	**FA Cup Q4**	**GRANTHAM TOWN**	413	1 - 2	White 53
28/10	LP	Worksop Town	453	0 - 3	
01/11	**FA Trophy 1**	**LANCASTER CITY**	206	1 - 1	Carty 45
04/11	**FA Trophy 1 rep**	**Lancaster City**	201	2 - 3	**Garvey 47,** Cooney 85
15/11	LP	Runcorn Halton	239	2 - 1	Denney 56, Fleury 78
22/11	LP	ALFRETON TOWN	204	1 - 1	**Garvey 65**
29/11	LP	WAKEFIELD & EMLEY	166	2 - 3	**Garvey 7**, Smith 63
06/12	LP	Droylsden	515	2 - 1	Fleury 2, Denny 30
09/12	LP	STALYBRIDGE CELTIC	413	2 - 1	Carty 73, Miller 89
13/12	LP	Harrogate Town	438	1 - 2	Dormer 75
27/12	LP	RADCLIFFE BOROUGH	468	3 - 3	Miller 22, Allison 29, Johnson 82
03/01	LP	Vauxhall Motors	209	2 - 1	White 65 Denney 72
10/01	LP	DROYLSDEN	548	1 - 1	**Garvey 40**
17/01	LP	FRICKLEY ATHLETIC	192	3 - 2	Dormer 41, **Garvey 66**, Johnson 68
07/02	LP	ALTRINCHAM	409	0 - 2	
14/02	LP	HUCKNALL TOWN	162	**1 - 6**	Carty 86
21/02	LP	Burscough	227	2 - 1	Fleetwood 46, Fleury 67
24/02	LP	Altrincham	447	2 - 1	Johnson 15 21
06/03	LP	RUNCORN HALTON	204	**4 - 2**	Carty 9, White 45, **Garvey 62 90**
09/03	LP	Marine	219	2 - 0	**Garvey 33**, Cooney 39
13/03	LP	Lancaster City	298	1 - 1	Fleury 69
16/03	LP	BURSCOUGH	153	0 - 0	
23/03	LP	VAUXHALL MOTORS	202	0 - 1	
27/03	LP	Whitby Town	307	1 - 0	Fleury 45
31/03	LP	Bradford Park Avenue	314	1 - 2	White 63
03 /04	LP	GAINSBOROUGH TRINITY	152	1 - 1	Denney 5
06 /04	LP	Spennymoor United	84	2 - 3	Smith 40, Johnson 45
10 /04	LP	BARROW	277	1 - 2	Fleury 39[p]
12 /04	LP	Radcliffe Borough	241	2 - 1	Foster 32 (og) Johnson 87
14 /04	LP	WORKSOP TOWN	193	0 - 3	
17 /04	LP	Southport	702	0 - 0	
24 /04	LP	HARROGATE TOWN	274	3 - 4	Allison 36, **Garvey 61**, Adams 88
27 /04	**Play-Off QF**	**HYDE UNITED**	**578**	2 - 1	Smith 72, Adams 104
01/05	**Play-off SF**	**BRADFORD PARK AVENUE**	**354**	1 - 2	**Garvey 51**

Average Home League Attendance: **267** 71-91 Top Goalscorer: **Paul Garvey 15** (12 + 1FAC+1FAT+!PO)

PLAYING SQUAD 2004-2005

Goalkeepers:
Andy Johnston (Great Harwood), Danny Trueman (Huddersfield)

Defenders:
Andy Thackeray (Nuneaton), Brendan Aspinall (Ossett T), Danny White (Buxton), Darren Royle (Flixton), Jamie Brook (Storthes Hall), Lee Connor (Farsley Celtic), Lincoln Adams (Wakefield-Emley)

Midfield:
Marcus Mitchell (Brackenhall), Martyn Allison (Golcar Utd), Phil Cooney (Skelmersdale), Jason Dormer (Hyde Utd), Craig

Forwards:
Brighton Mugadza (Sikh Temple), Jamie Miller (Storthes Hall), Paul Garvey (Flixton)

BARROW

Pages: 44 Price: £1.50
Editor: Russell Dodd (01229 827286)

Local Press: North West Evening Mail, Barrow & West Cumberland Advertiser
Local Radio: BBC Radio Cumbria, Bay Radio

CLUB OFFICIALS

President: Alan Dunn
Chairman: Brian Keen
Football Secretary; Russell Dodd,
9 Keswick Avenue,Barrow in Furness, Cumbria.LA14 4LL
Tel: 01229 827286(H) 07778 700137 (M)
Press Officer: Phil Yelland
83 Camus Drive, Edinburgh EH10 6QY
Tel: 0131 445 1010 (H)
0131 476 8131 (W) 0776 1235538(M)
Barrow Soccer Hotline: 09066 555820
Manager: Lee Turnbull

FACT FILE

Founded: 1901
Nickname: Bluebirds
Sponsors: T.B.A.
Colours:Blue/white/blue
Change: Yellow/black/yellow
Midweek matchday: Tuesday
Website: www.barrowafc.com

2003-004

Top Scorer: Gavin Knight
Player of the Year: Mark Salmon
2004-2005 Captain: Mark Salmon

GROUND: Holker Street Stadium, Wilkie Road, Barrow-in-Furness, CumbriaLA14 5UW
Tel: 01229 820346 e-mail: enquiries@barrowafc.com
Directions: M6 to junction 36, A590 to Barrow, enter Barrow on Park Road and after about 2 miles turn left into Wilkie Rd - ground on right. B.R.1/4 mile
Capacity: 4,500 **Seated:** 1000 **Covered Terracing:** 1,200

Clubhouse: Barrow F.C. Cross Bar next to ground. Open matchdays and Functions only. Snack bars on ground **Club Shop:** Situated on the ground.

PREVIOUS **Leagues:** Lancs Comb 01-21; Football League 21-72; Northern Premier 72-79, 83-84, 86-89, 92-98; 99-04 GM Vauxhall Conference 79-83, 84-86, 89-92, 98-99 **Grounds:** The Strawberry & Little Park, Roose **Names:**None

RECORDS **Attendance:** 16,854 v Swansea Town, FA Cup 3rd Rd. 1954
Career Appearances: Colin Cowperthwaite 704 **Career Goalscorer:** Colin Cowperthwaite 282 (Dec '77-Dec '92).
Defeat: 1-10 v Hartlepool Utd, Football Lge Div 4, 1959 **Win:** 12-0 v Cleator, FA Cup 1920.
Transfer Fee Paid: £9,000 for Andy Whittaker (Ashton Utd, July 94).
Transfer Fee Received: £40,000 for Kenny Lowe (Barnet, Jan 91)

BEST SEASON **FA Trophy:** Winners 1989-90, Semi-Final 87-88
FA Cup: Third Round Proper 9 times including once as a non-League club 90-91, 0-1 v Bolton Wanderers (A)

HONOURS F.A. Trophy Winners 89-90, Northern Premier League 97-98, 88-89, 83-84; R-up 2002-03. Lge Cup R-up 87-88, Lge Shield 84-85 R-up 89-90 98-99; Bob Lord Trophy R-up 90-91, Cumbrian Cup 82-8383-84 (R-up 84-85), Lancs Floodlit Cup R-up 86-87, Lancs Sen Cup 54-55 (R-up 51-52 65-66 66-67 69-70), Lancs Challenge Trophy 80-81 (R-up 81-82 84-85 01-02), Lancs Comb 20-21, R-up 13-14, Div 2 R-up 04-05 10-11. Unibond Chairman's Cup (00-01)President's Cup 01-02 03-04

Players progressing: I McDonald, N McDonald, J Laisby, B Diamond, F Gamble, B Knowles, G Skivington, P Byron, L Edwards, K Lowe, M Dobie, T Rigby, N Doherty. and G.Holt

Match Facts 2003-04

Date	Comp.	Opponents	Att.	Score	Goalscorers
16/08	LP	Droylsden	423	1 - 1	Gaughan 20[p]
19/08	LP	BURSCOUGH	1285	3 - 3	Gaughan 37 61, Oliver 90
23/08	LP	STALYBRIDGE CELTIC	1140	0 - 2	
25/08	LP	Blyth Spartans	776	2 - 0	Oliver 31, Rankine 71
30/08	LP	FRICKLEY ATHLETIC	1004	3 - 1	Oliver 39, Knight 63, Rankine 76
02/09	LP	Altrincham	683	1 - 1	Kewley 76
06/09	LP	Bradford Park Avenue	315	2 - 2	Knight 19, Gaughan 22
09/09	LP	MARINE	1114	1 - 1	Oliver 11
13/09	LP	ASHTON UNITED	1013	3 - 0	Knight 8, Arnold 81 90
16/09	LP	Radcliffe Borough	396	3 - 2	Knight 42, Salmon 71, Rankine 80
20/09	LP	Gainsborough Trinity	555	0 - 0	
23/09	LP	RUNCORN HALTON	1095	1 - 0	Arnold 6[p]
27/09	**FA Cup Q2**	**HARROGATE TOWN**	1250	2 - 0	**Campbell 17**, Hume 71
30/09	LP	Southport	859	1 - 1	Rankine 89
04/10	LP	WAKEFIELD & EMLEY	1254	3 - 2	**Campbell 2, 81[p]**, Brough 57
11/10	**FA Cup Q3**	**Ashton United**	429	1 - 2	Rankine 55
14/10	LP	Spennymoor United	217	4 - 2	**Campbell 23 87,** Knight 76, Brough 90
18/10	LP	Vauxhall Motors	270	1 - 1	Rankine 83
25/10	LP	HARROGATE TOWN	1177	1 - 2	Gaughan 12
01/11	LP	Hucknall Town	626	1 - 3	**Campbell 25**
04/11	LP	SOUTHPORT	805	1 - 1	Hume 81
08/11	LP	Alfreton Town	430	1 - 1	Knight 66
15/11	LP	WORKSOP TOWN	1010	1 - 0	Salmon 45
22/11	LP	Burscough	292	1 - 1	Salmon 69
29/11	**FA Trophy 2**	**Harrogate Town**	**503**	2 - 2	Aspin 67[og], Curtis 73
02/12	**FA Trophy 2 rep**	**HARROGATE TOWN**	1095	4 - 2	**Campbell 44 61,** Curtis 66, Hume 85
06/12	LP	SPENNYMOOR UNITED	1038	2 - 0	Knight 29, Curtis 45
13/12	LP	ALTRINCHAM	1138	2 - 1	Hume 30, Knight 90
26/12	LP	Lancaster City	822	3 - 0	Hill 16, Hume 39, Curtis 73
01/01	LP	LANCASTER CITY	**1750**	4 - 3	Knight 42, Anthony 47, **Campbell 65,** Kilbane 74[og]
03/01	LP	Frickley Athletic	300	**2 - 4**	Hill 39 **Campbell 58**
10/01	**FA Trophy 3**	**Blyth Spartans**	**789**	**0 - 1**	
17/01	LP	GAINSBOROUGH TRINITY	1121	3 - 0	Curtis 15, Anthony 34, Maxfield 66
07/02	LP	BRADFORD PARK AVENUE	1043	**4 - 0**	**Campbell 13 55,** Anthony 66, Curtis 82
14/02	LP	Wakefield & Emley	198	5 - 2	Arnold 26, **Campbell 48**, Salmon 78, Knight 80, Rankine 89
21/02	LP	RADCLIFFE BOROUGH	1213	2 - 0	Arnold 29[p], **Campbell 77**
02/03	LP	Marine	251	2 - 1	Oliver 14, **Campbell 41**
09/03	LP	VAUXHALL MOTORS	1027	0 - 1	
13/03	LP	Harrogate Town	527	1 - 2	Gaughan 24[p]
16/03	LP	DROYLSDEN	1235	2 - 1	Gaughan 82[p] 85[p]
22/03	LP	Whitby Town	210	2 - 3	Mayers 18 56
27/03	LP	HUCKNALL TOWN	1416	1 - 0	Knight 14
30/03	LP	Runcorn Halton	259	0 - 0	
03 /04	LP	WHITBY TOWN	1022	0 - 0	
10 /04	LP	Ashton United	277	2 - 1	Rankine 76, Ridley 90
12 /04	LP	BLYTH SPARTANS	1145	3 - 0	
17 /04	LP	Worksop Town	538	4 - 2	**Campbell 8 15,** Knight 30, Hill 73
20 /04	LP	ALFRETON TOWN	1451	1 - 2	Gaughan 37[p]
24 /04	LP	Stalybridge Celtic	555	2 - 2	Kewley 70, Mayers 76

Average Home League Attendance: **1,145** 91-59 Top Goalscorer:**Neil Campbell 17** (14 + 1FAC + 2FAT)

PLAYING SQUAD 2004-2005

Goalkeepers:
Simon Bishop (Dunston Fed), Ross Liddicott (Local football)

Defenders:
James Cotterill (Scunthorpe), Guy Heffernan (Leigh RMI), Andy Hill (Vickers SC), Jon McDonald (Youth team), Paul Raven (Carlisle), Lee Rogers (Furness Cavaliers), Craig Rutherford (Local football), Mark Salmon (Bishop Auckland), Simon Shaw (Doncaster)

Midfield:
Lee Warren (Doncaster), Graham Anthony (Carlisle), Ian Kilford (Scunthorpe), Scott Maxfield (Doncaster), Jamie Paterson (Doncaster), Steve Ridley (Scunthorpe), Phil Rowland (Brigg), Michael Oliver (Rochdale)

Forwards:
Neil Campbell (Scarborough), Michael Rankine (Armthorpe Welfare), Michael Kewley (Preston), Gavin Knight (North Ferriby)

BRADFORD PARK AVENUE

CLUB OFFICIALS

Chairman: Frank Thornton

President: Charlie Atkinson

Secretary: Steven Burnett
21 Edward Turner Close, Low Moor,
Bradford BD12 0AS
Tel: 01274 608344(H) 07866 076220 (M)

Press Officer: Tim Clapham
email;timothy@clapham8436.freeserve.co.uk

Commercial Manager: Paul Grayson
Tel No: 07720419279

FOOTBALL MANAGEMENT TEAM

Manager: Carl Shutt

Physio: Ray Killick

FACT FILE

Formed: 1907
Reformed: 1988
Nickname: Avenue
Club Sponsor: Bakes & Lord
Colours: All white
Change colours All Sky Blue
Midweek Matches: Wednesday
Reserves' league: Lancashire League
Local Press: Telegraph & Argus
Local Radio: Radio Leeds

PROGRAMME

Pages: 36 Price: £1.20
Editor: Ian Smith
email: ian.smith@bpafc.com

GROUND Horsfall Stadium, Cemetery Rd., Bradford, West Yorks BD6 2NG (01274 604578)

Directions: M62 J 26. Along M606 to the end. At roundabout take A6036 (signed Halifax) and pass Odsal Stadium on left hand side. At next r'about take 3rd exit A6036 (Halifax), in approx. 1 mile turn left into Cemetery Rd (by Kings Head Pub). Ground 150 yards on left

Capacity: 5,000 Cover: 2,000 Seats: 1,247

Club Shop: Yes - contact Russell Foulds (c/o Ground) or 01924 440901 **Clubhouse:** Yes

PREVIOUS
Leagues: Southern 07-08; Football League 08-70; Northern Premier 70-74; West Riding County Amtr 88-89; Central Mids 89-90; N. W. Counties 90-95
Grounds: Park Avenue 07-73; Valley Parade 73-74; Manningham Mills 88-89; Bramley R.L.F.C., McLaren Field 89-93; Batley 93-96

CLUB RECORDS
Attendance: 1,007 v Bradford City 97 (Centenary Chall). 32,810 v Blackpool, War Cup 1944
Win: 11-0 v Denby Dale FAC 1908 **Defeat:** 0-7 v Barnsley 1911
Scorer: Len Shackleton 171 1940-46 **Appearances:** Tommy Farr 542 1934-50
Fee Received: £34,000 for K Hector (Derby County 1966)
Fee Paid: £24,500 for L Leuty (Derby County 1950)

BEST SEASON
FA Vase: 2nd Rd Prop 94-95 **FA Trophy:** 3rd Rd 98-99
FA Cup: Qtr finals 1912-13 v Aston Villa (0-5), 19-20 v Bristol City (A) 0-2, 45-46 v Birmingham City 2-2 (H) 0-6 (A) Agg 2-8

HONOURS
Football Lge Div 2 R-up 1914; 3rd Div N 28; Yorkshire Lge 21, 23; Midland Lge 32; West Riding Snr Cup 11,13, 25, 27, 32,36, 51, 53, 63; West Riding County Cup 28-29, 90-91; N.W.C. Lg 94-95, Challenge Trophy 94-95. N.P.L. (Unibond) Division One Champions 2000-01

L-R - Back Row: D Wilson (Kit Man), Simon Collins, Andy Hayward, Richard Tracey, Matthew Boswell, Jason Maxwell, Ryan Crossley, Nicky Wood Andy Wright. **Front Row:** Martin James, Andy Quinn, Wayne Benn (Captain), Danny Walsh, Craig Smith, Stephen Olekseywcz, Carl Serrant

Date	Comp.	Opponents	Att.	Score	Goalscorers
16/08	LP	HUCKNALL TOWN	297	1 - 2	Tracey 23
19/08	LP	Ashton United	210	2 - 0	Collins 16, Walsh 39
23/08	LP	Runcorn Halton	271	2 - 1	Collins 7 80
25/08	LP	RADCLIFFE BOROUGH	347	1 - 1	**Hayward 54**
30/08	LP	Vauxhall Motors	204	**2 - 6**	Walsh 33, **Hayward 39**
03/09	LP	WORKSOP TOWN	367	0 - 1	
06/09	LP	BARROW	315	2 - 2	**Hayward 10 67**
09/09	LP	Spennymoor United	268	4 - 2	**Oleksewycz 30 41**, **Hayward 31**, Collins 44
13/09	LP	Alfreton Town	517	1 - 1	Walsh 23
17/09	LP	WHITBY TOWN	295	2 - 3	C Smith 13, **Oleksewycz 78**
20/09	LP	STALYBRIDGE CELTIC	283	2 - 3	**Oleksewycz 15 23**
23/09	LP	Blyth Spartans	356	0 - 0	
27/09	**FA Cup Q2**	**Chester-le-Street Town**	201	2 - 0	Collins 10, **Oleksewycz 27**
04/10	LP	SOUTHPORT	393	0 - 1	
11/10	**FA Cup Q3**	**VAUXHALL MOTORS**	321	1 - 1	Stansfield 61
14/10	**FA Cup Q3 rep**	**Vauxhall Motors**	278	3 - 1	Maxwell 34, Smith 69, **Oleksewycz 90**
25/10	**FA Cup Q4**	**Runcorn Halton**	379	1 - 0	Hayward 28
28/10	LP	Burscough	154	1 - 1	Mitchell 67
01/11	LP	VAUXHALL MOTORS	360	**6 - 2**	**Oleksewycz 3**, **Hayward 45 85**, Collins 47, Crossley 84, Walsh 88
09/11	**FA Cup 1**	**BRISTOL CITY**	1945	2 - 5	**Hayward 5,** Coles 13
12/11	LP	RUNCORN HALTON	266	1 - 1	**Oleksewycz 47**
15/11	LP	Marine	328	0 - 2	
22/11	LP	ALTRINCHAM	320	1 - 1	Maxwell 37
29/11	**FA Trophy 2**	**Whitby Town**	251	1 - 1	**Hayward 88**
03/12	**FA Trophy 2 rep**	**WHITBY TOWN**	279	1 - 0	Collins 54
06/12	LP	Wakefield & Emley	319	1 - 0	**Hayward 54**
13/12	LP	Southport	746	1 - 0	Smith 90
26/12	LP	HARROGATE TOWN	**530**	2 - 3	**Oleksewycz 30,** Smith 67
03/01	LP	Radcliffe Borough	319	0 - 2	
10/01	**FA Trophy 3**	**Hucknall Town**	573	0 - 1	
24/01	LP	Stalybridge Celtic	439	0 - 2	
07/02	LP	Barrow	1043	0 - 4	
10/02	LP	Lancaster City	265	3 - 1	**Hayward 55 70**, Maxwell 78
14/02	LP	BURSCOUGH	281	0 - 2	
21/02	LP	FRICKLEY ATHLETIC	288	0 - 0	
23/02	LP	Droylsden	188	0 - 3	
28/02	LP	Gainsborough Trinity	495	3 - 3	Burley 24[og], Maxwell 49, **Hayward 54**
03/03	LP	DROYLSDEN	223	0 - 2	
06/03	LP	BLYTH SPARTANS	275	1 - 1	**Hayward 66[p]**
10/03	LP	Whitby Town	197	1 - 0	Serrant 71
13/03	LP	Altrincham	622	0 - 1	
17/03	LP	ALFRETON TOWN	240	0 - 1	
23/03	LP	Worksop Town	374	2 - 1	Smith 37, Maxwell 72
31/03	LP	ASHTON UNITED	314	2 - 1	**Oleksewycz 31,** Smith 82
03 /04	LP	WAKEFIELD & EMLEY	326	1 - 2	Smith 74
06 /04	LP	Frickley Athletic	287	1 - 0	**Oleksewycz 87**
10 /04	LP	SPENNYMOOR UNITED	256	0 - 0	
12 /04	LP	Harrogate Town	662	1 - 0	
17 /04	LP	Hucknall Town	510	0 - 0	
19 /04	LP	MARINE	226	1 - 1	**Oleksewycz 65[p]**
21 /04	LP	GAINSBOROUGH TRINITY	247	0 - 0	
24 /04	LP	LANCASTER CITY	306	0 - 2	
28 /04	**Play-off QF**	**SPENNYMOOR UNITED**	303	3 - 1	Painter 8, Heinemann 29 46
01/05	**Play-off SF**	**Ashton United**	354	2 - 1	Helliwell 19, Crossley 75
03/05	**Play-off F**	**BURSCOUGH**	670	2 - 0	**Oleksewycz 93**, Russell 113

Average Home League Attendance: **307** 66-73 Top Goalscorer: **Oleksewcz 14** (11 +2FAC = 1PO)
Andy Haywood 14 (10 +3FAC +1FAT)

PLAYING SQUAD 2004-2005

Goalkeepers: Andrew Britton (Sheffield Utd)

Defenders:

Karl Colley (Hucknall), Michael Naylor (Halifax), Ryan Crossley (Wakefield-Emley), Dean Jones (Belper), Adam Oldham (Barnsley), Gareth Clayton (Rotherham)

Midfield:

Paddy Mumbley (Youth team), Andy Quinn (Gainsborough), James Russell (Youth team), Craig Smith (Halifax), Marc Thompson (Farnborough), Danny Walsh (Kettering)

Forwards:

Dan Sheriffe (Frickley), Allan Pearce (Barnsley), Steve Oleksewycz (Ossett T), Ben Jones (Aberystwyth), Paul Helliwell (Youth team), Tom Greaves (Youth team)

DROYLSDEN

Pages: 24 Price: £1.00
Editor: Srteve Jarvis
Local Press:
Tameside Reporter, Tameside Advertiser
Local Radio: BBC Manchester

CLUB OFFICIALS

Chairman: **David Pace**

Secretary: **Alan Slater**
83 King Edward Rd.,Hyde,
Cheshire SK14 5JJ
Tel & Fax: 0161 368 3687

FOOTBALL MANAGEMENT TEAM

Manager: David Pace
Asst Manager: Aeon Lattie
Physio Alan Cross

FACT FILE
Formed: 1892
Nickname: The Bloods
Sponsors:AMICUS
Colours: Red /black/black
Change: Sky & navy/navy/Sky & Navy
Midweek matchday: Monday
Club Website: www.droylsdenfc.co.uk
2003-2004
Captain: Garry Burke
Top Scorer: Danny Byrne 27
Player of the Year: Danny Byrne

GROUND The Butchers Arms Ground, Market Street, Droylsden, Manchester M43 7AY
Tel: 0161 370 1426/8341 FAX: 0161 370 8341

Directions: Jct 23 M60 signed .A635 to Manchester fromOldham direction and A6140 Ashton under Lyme from Stockpoort direction. Join A635 towards Manchester (1.5 miles from ground).Rt at lights onto A662 to Droylsden.Turn right into Market Street after half a mile.Over lights ground on left.

Capacity: 3,500 Cover: 2,000 Seats:500

Clubhouse: Pub hours except matchdays. Pool and darts **Shop:** Yes Metal Badges

PREVIOUS **Leagues:** Manchester; Lancs Com 36-39, 50-68; Cheshire County 39-50, 68-82; NW Counties 82-87 N.P.L.1986-2004

CLUB RECORDS **Attendance:** 4,250 v Grimsby, **FA Cup** 1st rd 1976
Scorer: E Gillibrand 78 (1931-32) **Win:** 13-2 v Lucas Sports Club
Fee Received: £11,000 for Tony Naylor (Crewe)

BEST SEASON **FA Cup:** 2nd Rd 78-79 v Altrincham (H) 0-2. League clubs defeated: Rochdale 78-79
FA Vase: **FA Trophy:**

HONOURS Northern Prem Lge Premier R-Up 2003-04 NPL CHal;lenge Cup and Challenge Shield Winners 03-04 Div 1 98-99, R-up 89-90, Div 1 Cup 87-88, R-up 88-9, 98-9 NPL President's Cup 98-99 Chairmans Cup R-up: 01-0202-03; NW Counties Lge Div 2 86-87; Cheshire County Lge R-up 39-40 45-46, Lge Cup 77-78 (R-up 76-77); Lancs Comb Div 2 R-up 55-56 58-59 62-63; Manchester Lge 30-31 32-33 (Lge Cup 23-24 33-34); Manchester Prem Cup 80-81 99-00 03-04 (R-up 83-84 90-91 93-94 00-01 02-03); Man Sen Cup 72-73 75-76 78-79 (R-up 71-72 76-77); Manchester Interm Cup 59-60 64-65 69-70; Manchester Chall Shield 46-47

Players progressing: Albert Butterworth & F Letchford (Blackpool 1931), William Davies & Maurice Randall (Crewe 1947), William Mellor (Accrington 1950), Geoff Tonge (Bury 1960), David Campbell (WBA 1962), Kevin Randall (Bury 1965), Peter Litchfield (Preston 1979), Tony Naylor (Crewe 1990)

Date	Comp.	Opponents	Att.	Score	Goalscorers
16/08	LP	BARROW	423	1 - 1	Wright 30
19/08	LP	Runcorn Halton	264	2 - 2	Burke 61, Wright 66
23/08	LP	Gainsborough Trinity	291	2 - 1	Kilheeney 33,73
25/08	LP	ALTRINCHAM	502	**1 - 4**	Kilheeney 63
01/09	LP	VAUXHALL MOTORS	232	2 - 1	Hall 26[p], Furlong 77
06/09	LP	BURSCOUGH	203	2 - 0	Porter 9, Salmon 39
09/09	LP	Radcliffe Borough	268	2 - 4	Chambers 10, Wright 90
13/09	LP	Southport	759	1 - 4	Glendenning 3
15/09	LP	ALFRETON TOWN	271	2 - 1	Morris 21, Wright 65
20/09	LP	BLYTH SPARTANS	226	3 - 3	Kilheeney 10, **Byrne 53**, Hall 80[p]
23/09	LP	Wakefield & Emley	180	2 - 0	**Byrne 4,** Kilheeney 75
27/09	**FA Cup Q2**	**BURSCOUGH**	251	2 - 2	Hall 13[p], Burke 82
30/09	**FA Cup Q2 rep**	**Burscough**	166	2 - 1	Hall 20, Wright 94
04/10	LP	FRICKLEY ATHLETIC	216	4 - 0	Murphy 4, **Byrne 8,** Porter 86, Kevan 90
07/10	LP	Marine	236	2 - 1	O'Brien 36, **Byrne 42**
11/10	**FA Cup Q3**	**GAINSBOROUGH TRINITY**	345	0 - 2	
13/10	LP	STALYBRIDGE CELTIC	**612**	2 - 0	Morris 38, **Byrne 69**
18/10	LP	Harrogate Town	428	4 - 4	Chambers 35, Warner 54, Hall 59[p] 62[p]
25/10	LP	HUCKNALL TOWN	201	3 - 1	Porter 22, Cameron 27, Chambers 90
01/11	LP	WHITBY TOWN	287	2 - 1	**Byrne 76**, Murphy 90
04/11	LP	Vauxhall Motors	202	4 - 2	Murphy 58, Burke 65, **Byrne 74,** Chambers 78
08/11	LP	Spennymoor United	142	1 - 0	**Byrne 54**
15/11	LP	GAINSBOROUGH TRINITY	338	2 - 1	Morris 43, O'Brien 71
22/11	LP	Worksop Town	519	3 - 1	Chambers 36, Cameron 44, Whitehead 66[og]
24/11	LP	RADCLIFFE BOROUGH	401	5 - 4	**Byrne 7,** Morris 43, Cameron 48, Brodie 75, Hall 77
29/11	**FA Trophy 2**	**Worksop Town**	341	0 - 1	
06/12	LP	ASHTON UNITED	515	1 - 2	Morris 6
13/12	LP	Frickley Athletic	204	3 - 0	Robinson 3og, Furlong 37 75
26/12	LP	RUNCORN HALTON	327	1 - 2	Murphy 8
03/01	LP	Alfreton Town	404	2 - 4	Cameron 9, **Byrne 53**
10/01	LP	Ashton United	548	1 - 1	**Byrne 15**
17/01	LP	SPENNYMOOR UNITED	229	2 - 0	Morris 21, **Byrne 57**
07/02	LP	Burscough	238	3 - 1	Chambers 15, Morris 22, **Byrne 23**
14/02	LP	MARINE	268	4 - 2	Morris 6, Burke 10, **Byrne 15 60**
21/02	LP	Stalybridge Celtic	654	1 - 2	**Byrne 31**
23/02	LP	BRADFORD PARK AVENUE	188	3 - 0	Cameron 50 75[p], **Byrne 90**
28/02	LP	Lancaster City	358	1 - 2	Cameron 42
03/03	LP	Bradford Park Avenue	223	2 - 0	Challinor 20, Chambers 33
13/03	LP	WAKEFIELD & EMLEY	322	3 - 1	Morris 29, Cameron 80, **Byrne 88**
16/03	LP	Barrow	1235	1 - 2	Kilheeney 45
20/03	LP	Altrincham	588	0 - 1	
27/03	LP	HARROGATE TOWN	278	3 - 1	**Byrne 28,** Burke 59, Salmon 85
03 /04	LP	WORKSOP TOWN	389	2 - 2	O'Brien 12, **Byrne 90**
06 /04	LP	Blyth Spartans	246	**5 - 1**	Brodie 42 44, Chambers 52, Salmon 67 82
10 /04	LP	SOUTHPORT	423	3 - 2	Brodie 32 45, Morris 82
12 /04	LP	Hucknall Town	956	1 - 1	Salmon 47
19 /04	LP	LANCASTER CITY	301	0 - 0	
24 /04	LP	Whitby Town	292	2 - 1	Cameron 35 79

Average Home League attendance: **325** 100-70 Top Goalscorer: **Danny Byrne:20**

PLAYING SQUAD 2004-2005

Goalkeepers:

Paul Phillips (Curzon Ashton), Jon Worsnop (Aberysywyth)

Defenders:

Aeon Lattie (Flixton), Danny Warner (Curzon Ashton), Gary Burke (Northwich), Adam Farley (Altrincham), Carl Serrant (Bradford PA), Carl Regan (Hull), Carl Robinson (Vauxhall Motors), Phil Baker (Aberystwyth)

Midfield:

Neil Hall (Hyde Utd), Ged Murphy (Stalybridge), Gareth Morris (Ashton Utd), Chris O'Brien (Chester), Peter Dogun (Chester), Neil Grayston (Bradford PA), Danny Williams (East Manchester)

Forwards:

Carl Furlong (Colwyn Bay), Gavin Salmon (Hyde Utd), Danny Byrne (Chester), Ciran Kilheeney (Mossley), David Cameron (Chester), Andy Lee (Aberystwyth)

GAINSBOROUGH TRINITY

CLUB OFFICIALS

Chairman: Patrick Lobley
President : Ken Marsden
Secretary/Press Officer: Frank Nicholson
9 North Street, Morton,
Gainsborough, Lincs DN213AS.
Tel. 01427 615239, Fax 01427 615239

FOOTBALL MANAGEMENT TEAM

Manager: Paul Mitchell
Asst Manager & Capt: Neil Allison
Physio: T.B.A.

FACT FILE

Formed: 1873
Nickname: The Blues
Sponsors: T Bland Welding
Colours: Blue/white/blue.
Change colours: All yellowMidweek home matchday: Tuesday
Youth League: Northern Youth Alliance
2003-004
Top Scorer:Gareth Grant
Player of thge Year:Chris Hurst

GROUND The Northolme, Gainsborough, Lincs DN21 2QW
Tel: 01427 - 613295 (office) 679109 (club) 613295 (Fax)
Website: www.gainsboroughtrinity.co.uk email: nicholsons.northstreet@virgin.net
Directions: The Northolme is situated opposite the Total petrol station on the A159 Gainsborough to Scunthorpe road. Two miles from Lea Road (BR)
Capacity: 4,000 Cover: 2,500 Seats: 504
Clubhouse: Executive `Club on the Park' (01427 613688) open Saturday matchday lunchtimes. Half time and Match night evenings.
Club Shop: Souvenirs - Wendy Godley (01427 611612)
Programmes - Nigel Tasker (01522 542014)

PROGRAMME
Pages: 64 Price: £1.50
Editor: Mark Southern (01302 719614)

Local Press: Gainsborough News, Lincolnshire Echo.
Local Radio: BBC Radio Lincs, Lincs FM

PREVIOUS Leagues: Midland Counties 1889-96, 12-60, 61-68, Football Lge 1896-1912, Central Alliance 60-61.**Names :& Grounds** None

CLUB RECORDS **Attendance:** 9,760 v Scunthorpe Utd. Midland Lge. 1948.
Fee Paid: £3,000 for Stuart Lowe (Buxton 89-90). **Fee Received:** £30,000 for Tony James (Lincoln 1988).
Win: 7-0 v Fleetwood Town and Great Harwood Town. **Defeat:** 1-7 v Brentford F.A.Cup 1st Rd 03-04.
1-7 vStalybridge Celtic N.P.L. 00-01

BEST SEASON **FA Cup:** 3rd Rd 1886-87 v Lincoln C (A) 0-1 after 2-2, 1st Rd on 33 occasions. **FA Trophy:** 4th Rd, 2002-2003

HONOURS Northern Prem Lge Cup 81-82 96-97 (R-up 71-72 97-98); Midland Co's Lge 1890-91,1927-28, 48-49, 66-67 (R-up 1891-92, 1895-96, 13-14, 28-29); Lincs Senior Cup 1889-90, 92-93, 94-95, 97-98, 1903-05, 06-07, 10-11, 46-49, 50-51, 57-59, 63-64,2002-2003. Unibond Chairman's Cup: R-up: 2001-2002 Lincoln Senior Shield R-Up 03-04

Players Progressing: Since 1980 - Stewart Evans (Sheffield Utd 80), Tony James, Ian Bowling & John Schofield (Lincoln 88), Dave Redfern(Stockport 91), Richard Logan (Huddersfield 93), Glenn Humphries (Hull City).

Back row, left to right: Neil Allison, Stuart Reddington, Adam Burley, Jamie Hoilmshaw, Ben Purkiss, Gareth Grant, Lee Ellington Barry Miller and Carl Alford. **Front Row:** Chris Hurst, Krysrof Kotylo, Luke Staton, David Jervis and Carl Smith. **Photo**: Chris Etchells

Date	Comp.	Opponents	Att.	Score	Goalscorers
16/08	LP	Stalybridge Celtic	504	0 - 2	
19/08	LP	ALFRETON TOWN	533	2 - 4	Jervis 25, Miller 51
23/08	LP	DROYLSDEN	291	1 - 2	Alford 41
30/08	LP	BLYTH SPARTANS	310	2 - 0	Timons 7, **Grant 19**
03/09	LP	Whitby Town	255	1 - 2	**Grant 59**
06/09	LP	Altrincham	584	2 - 2	Ellington 36 Band 85[og]
09/09	LP	WAKEFIELD & EMLEY	387	3 - 0	Ellington 32 86, **Grant 52**
13/09	LP	Vauxhall Motors	201	2 - 0	Hurst 26, Ellington 90
16/09	LP	HARROGATE TOWN	389	2 - 0	Hurst 40, Timons 53
20/09	LP	BARROW	555	0 - 0	
23/09	LP	Frickley Athletic	234	0 - 0	
27/09	**FA Cup Q2**	**SKELMERSDALE UNITED**	**376**	**6 - 0**	Hurst 31, **GRANT 35 53 87**, Ellington 68, Kotylo 89
04/10	LP	LANCASTER CITY	358	3 - 2	Smith 44 63, Ellington 69
07/10	LP	ASHTON UNITED	403	3 - 0	Ellington 11, Hurst 21, Staton 44
11/10	**FA Cup Q3**	**Droylsden**	**345**	**2 - 0**	**Grant 26 86**
18/10	LP	Spennymoor United	146	**6 - 0**	**GRANT 20 30 53**, Hirst 50, Timons 72 73
25/10	**FA Cup Q4**	**Farsley Celtic**	**774**	**1 - 1**	Ellington 35
28/10	**FA Cup Q4 rep**	**FARSLEY CELTIC**	**845**	**3 - 0**	Smith 24, **Grant 45**, Ellington 90
01/11	**FA Trophy 1**	**Guiseley**	**361**	**0 - 2**	
08/11	**FA Cup 1**	**Brentford**	**5041**	**1 - 7**	Ellington 80
11/11	LP	FRICKLEY ATHLETIC	465	3 - 0	Reddington 14, Staton 20, Hurst 65
15/11	LP	Droylsden	338	1 - 2	Cropper 6
18/11	LP	Runcorn Halton	172	2 - 2	Hurst 55, Ellington 85
22/11	LP	MARINE	352	2 - 0	Hurst 43, **Grant 50**
29/11	LP	Burscough	171	0 - 0	
02/12	LP	HUCKNALL TOWN	513	2 - 1	Ellington 37, **Grant 63**
06/12	LP	Blyth Spartans	347	1 - 1	Allison 77
13/12	LP	BURSCOUGH	393	4 - 1	Timons 10, Byrne 22, Hurst 60, Ellington 84
26/12	LP	Worksop Town	1168	0 - 0	
03/01	LP	STALYBRIDGE CELTIC	500	0 - 0	
10/01	LP	RADCLIFFE BOROUGH	462	6 - 2	Ellington 5, **Grant 35,** O'Brien 47, Timons 50, Hurst 69, Byrne 84
17/01	LP	Barrow	1121	**0 - 3**	
31/01	LP	WHITBY TOWN	527	2 - 2	Byrne 59, Ellington 72[p]
03/02	LP	Hucknall Town	531	0 - 2	
07/02	LP	Marine	253	1 - 3	**Grant 56**
17/02	LP	SOUTHPORT	499	1 - 2	Ellington 79[p]
21/02	LP	Harrogate Town	490	2 - 0	**Grant 26**, Ellington 38
28/02	LP	BRADFORD PARK AVENUE	495	3 - 3	Allison 8, **Grant 43 82**
09/03	LP	ALTRINCHAM	357	2 - 3	Ellington 60, Allison 67
13/03	LP	Radcliffe Borough	242	1 - 2	Timons 40
20/03	LP	RUNCORN HALTON	248	0 - 1	
23/03	LP	Southport	601	0 - 2	
27/03	LP	VAUXHALL MOTORS	306	0 - 0	
03 /04	LP	Ashton United	152	1 - 1	Hurst 31
06 /04	LP	Alfreton Town	203	1 - 3	Reddington 85
10 /04	LP	Wakefield & Emley	118	2 - 0	Staton 67[p], **Grant 85**
12 /04	LP	WORKSOP TOWN	**708**	2 - 1	Haran 44 (og) **Grant 62**
17 /04	LP	Lancaster City	303	1 - 0	Smith 59
21 /04	LP	Bradford Park Avenue	247	0 - 0	
24 /04	LP	SPENNYMOOR UNITED	398	3 - 1	Jones 54, Hurst 78, Ellington 83
		Average home league attendance:	**429**	83-62	Top Goalscorer: **Gareth Grant 21**(15+6FAC)

PLAYING SQUAD 2004-2005

Goalkeepers:
Jamie Holmshaw (Bradford PA)

Defenders:
Ben Purkiss (Sheffield Utd), Adam Burley (Stocksbridge PS), Neil Allison (Geylang Utd), Ben Dixon (Whitby)

Midfield:
Carl Smith (Worksop), Chris Hurst (Frickley), Jamie Sherlock (Scarborough), Matty Caudwell (Worksop), Luke Staton (Merthyr), Rob O'Brien (Doncaster)

Forwards:
Lee Ellington (Exeter), Gareth Grant (Lincoln C), Jason Maxwell (Bradford PA), Simon Bird (Louisville Cardinals (USA))

HARROGATE TOWN

CLUB OFFICIALS

Chairman: Bill Fotherby

Vice Chairman: Howard Matthews

President: George Dunnington

Company Secretary:
Brian Russell 24 Hall Lane, Harrogate, HG13DK Tel/Fax: 01423 525341

Managing Director/Club Secretary:

Nigel Pleasants

FOOTBALL MANAGEMENT TEAM
Team Manager: John Reed
Player Coach: Shaun Garnett

FACT FILE

Formed: 1919

Nickname: Town

Colours: Yellow & Black stripes/black/black

Change colours:All whiteMidweek home matchday: Tuesday

Website:www.harrogatetownafc.co.uk

2003-004

P.o.Y. & Top Scorer: James Turley

2004-2005 Captain: Simon Sturdy

GROUND: Wetherby Road, Harrogate.
Tel: 01423 880675 Office & Fax Sec.& Admin.Tel. & Fax: 01423 525341
Directions: From Leeds turn right at traffic lights (Nidd Vale Motors) into Hookstone Road, continue to Woodlands Hotel (traffic lights) turn left into Wetherby Road, ground on the right. From Harrogate (BR), turn left and left again, cross road (Odeon Cinema), proceed for about 400yds to main road, crossover to The Stray (open land) using footpath which leads to Wetherby Rd, ground 200yds on left. From A61 turn right onto southern by pass then left on to A661.Ground 400 yds on right after Sainsburys, lights and Woodlands Hotel.
From the West on A59 straight on to Wetherby Rd from Empress roundabout. ground on left.
From North: A59 exit from M1 then southern bypass to Wetherby Rd
Capacity: 3,800 Cover: 1,300 Seats: 500 Shop: Yes.Contact: Alan Williams 0781 411937
Clubhouse: Oopen every match day, for functions & special events. Tel: 01423 883671

Pages: 40 Price: £1.50
Editor: Bob Head
01423 549153 - 07799 834918M

Local Press: Yorkshire Post Group
Harrogate Advertiser Series
Local Radio: Radio Leeds, Radio North Yorkshire ,Stray F.M.Stray FM.

PREVIOUS **Names:** Harrogate FC1919-32, Harrogate Hotspurs 35-48 **Ground:** Starbeck Lane 1919-20
Leagues: West Riding 1919-20 Yorkshire 20-21, 22-31, 57-82; Midland 21-22; Northern 31-32; Harrogate & District 35-37 7 40-46 WRCAL 37-40 West Yorkshire 46-57; Northern Counties East 82-87

CLUB RECORDS **Attendance:** 4,280 v Railway Athletic, Whitworth Cup final 1950.
Win: 13-0 v Mackelfield **Defeat:** 1-10 v Methley United 1956

BEST SEASON **FA Vase:** 4th Round 89-90 **FA Cup:** 1st Round Proper v Farnborough Town (a) 1-5 2002-2003
F.A.Trophy: 3rd Rd Replay v Spennymoor United 99-00 & 2001-02 v Doncaster Rovers (away) 0-2

HONOURS N.P.L. Div 1 Champions 2001-02, Div 1 Cup 89-90; N.C.E.L. Div 1(Nth) R-up 84-85 plus 3rd 85-86 & promoted.(Reserve Div 85-86, Reserve Div Cup 86-87); Yorkshire League Div 1 26-27 R-up 62-63 Div 2 81-82, Div 3 R-up 71-72 80-81; West Riding County Cup 62-63 72-73 85-86; 01-02, 02-03; West Riding Challenge Cup 24-25 26-27

Players progressing: Tony Ingham (Leeds 47), Stewart Ferebee (York C. 79),Tim Hotte (Halifax T. 85), Andy Watson (Halifax T. 88), Ian Blackstone (York C. 95) , Eric Stephenson (Leeds Utd 1932)

L-R - Back Row: Neil Aspin, Scott Bonsall, Simon Sturdy, Mark Atkins, Mick McNaughton, Liam Sutcliffe, Michael Ord, Ashley Connor, Marc Smith, James Riordan, Thomas Woollard. **Front:** Colin Hunter, James McDaid, Richard Dunning, Gary Bradshaw, Bill Fotherby, Robbie Whellans, John Reed, James Turley, Ben Sherwood, Glen Naylor. Mascot: Flynn McNaughton

Date	Comp.	Opponents	Att.	Score	Goalscorers
H16/08	LP	Burscough	216	0 - 1	
19/08	LP	WHITBY TOWN	478	1 - 0	**Turley 79**
23/08	LP	MARINE	353	4 - 1	**Turley 44**, Bradshaw 45 77, Whellans 50
25/08	LP	WORKSOP TOWN	521	0 - 2	
30/08	LP	ALTRINCHAM	475	1 - 0	Smith 31
02/09	LP	Wakefield & Emley	225	2 - 0	M Smith 42, Fowler 67[og]
06/09	LP	Lancaster City	266	4 - 1	Smith 58, Atkins 61, Bradshaw 68 83[p]
09/09	LP	BLYTH SPARTANS	505	2 - 1	Stuart 41, Ford 52
13/09	LP	RUNCORN HALTON	427	1 - 1	Hunter 83
16/09	LP	Gainsborough Trinity	389	0 - 2	
20/09	LP	Hucknall Town	456	0 - 1	
23/09	LP	SPENNYMOOR UNITED	430	3 - 1	Sturdy 38, Parke 45, Dunning 65
27/09	**FA Cup Q2**	**Barrow**	**1250**	**0 - 2**	
04/10	LP	Radcliffe Borough	271	1 - 3	Hunter 80
08/10	LP	Whitby Town	276	2 - 0	Sherwood 25, Naylor 31
11/10	LP	FRICKLEY ATHLETIC	387	2 - 1	Hunter 75, Naylor 89
18/10	LP	DROYLSDEN	428	4 - 4	**NAYLOR 2 31 52 75**
25/10	LP	Barrow	1177	2 - 1	Smith 20 72
01/11	LP	Stalybridge Celtic	489	2 - 1	**Turley 13,** Naylor 29
08/11	LP	BURSCOUGH	518	2 - 1	Naylor 61, McNaughton 88
11/11	LP	Worksop Town	603	0 - 1	
15/11	LP	Altrincham	701	0 - 0	
22/11	LP	SOUTHPORT	601	3 - 1	**Turley 13 74,** Smith 45
29/11	**FA Trophy 2**	**BARROW**	**503**	**2 - 2**	Sturdy 44, **Turley 75[p]**
02/12	**FA Trophy 2 rep**	**Barrow**	**1095**	**2 - 4**	Hunter 34, Naylor 45
06/12	LP	Marine	348	2 - 2	**Turley 30[p] 64**
13/12	LP	ASHTON UNITED	438	2 - 1	Naylor 27, Parton 53
26/12	LP	Bradford Park Avenue	530	3 - 2	Naylor 11, **Turley 24**, Parton 48
10/01	LP	Spennymoor United	192	5 - 1	**HUNTER 5 34 87, Turley 37[p]**, Naylor 60
17/01	LP	VAUXHALL MOTORS	602	3 - 2	**NAYLOR 20 38 89**
07/02	LP	LANCASTER CITY	579	0 - 1	
14/02	LP	Frickley Athletic	268	0 - 0	
17/02	LP	ALFRETON TOWN	538	1 - 0	Atkins 30
21/02	LP	GAINSBOROUGH TRINITY	490	0 - 2	
28/02	LP	HUCKNALL TOWN	**766**	1 - 2	Naylor 89
09/03	LP	Alfreton Town	169	0 - 2	
13/03	LP	BARROW	527	2 - 1	Smith 77, **Turley 88**
16/03	LP	Vauxhall Motors	173	0 - 3	
20/03	LP	Southport	838	2 - 3	Smith 15, Whellans 66
27/03	LP	Droylsden	278	1 - 3	Hunter 57
03 /04	LP	STALYBRIDGE CELTIC	389	4 - 3	Smith 7, **Turley 9,** Bowker 12[og], McNaughton 69
06 /04	LP	RADCLIFFE BOROUGH	246	3 - 0	Atkins 17, **Turley 70 71**
10 /04	LP	Blyth Spartans	342	4 - 3	Sturdy 27 53, Smith 38, **Turley 59**
12 /04	LP	BRADFORD PARK AVENUE	662	0 - 1	
17 /04	LP	WAKEFIELD & EMLEY	381	**5 - 0**	Smith 31 50, McNaughton 33, **Turley 67**, Atkins 81
20 /04	LP	Runcorn Halton	188	**1 - 4**	Ness 22[og]
24 /04	LP	Ashton United	274	4 - 3	**Turley 42 90**, Riordan 53, Hunter 85
		Average Home Lerague Attendance:	**488**	83-71	Top Goalscorer: **James Turley 18** (17+1FAT)

PLAYING SQUAD 2004-2005

Goalkeepers:
Paul Pettinger (Hucknall), Nick Buxton (Glapwell)

Defenders:
Mark Barnard (Belper), Lennie Curtis (Kettering), James McDaid (Harrogate Railway), Michael Ord (SorrentO (Aust)), Paul Shepherd (Leigh RMI), Simon Sturdy (Pickering), Leigh Wood (York)

Midfield:
Mark Atkins (Shrewsbury), Richard Dunning (Whitby), Christian Fox (York), Colin Hunter (Morecambe), Dominic Krief (Frickley), James Turley (Stalybridge), Andy Wright (Wakefield-Emley)

Forwards:
Andy Farrell (Halifax), Lee Morris (Frickley), Marc Smith (Eastwood T)

HINCKLEY UNITED

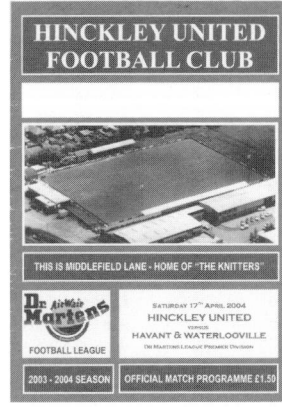

HINCKLEY UNITED FOOTBALL CLUB

THIS IS MIDDLEFIELD LANE - HOME OF "THE KNITTERS"

Dr. AirWair Martens FOOTBALL LEAGUE

SATURDAY 17TH APRIL 2004
HINCKLEY UNITED
VERSUS
HAVANT & WATERLOOVILLE
DR MARTENS LEAGUE PREMIER DIVISION

2003 - 2004 SEASON | OFFICIAL MATCH PROGRAMME £1.50

Pages: 60   Price: £1.50   Editor:Andy Gibbs
Local Radio: BBC Radio Leicester, Fosseway Radio
Local Press: Heartland Evening News, Hinckley Times, Leicester Mercury, Coventry Evening Telegraph

CLUB OFFICIALS

Chairman: **Kevin Downes**
Vice Chairman: **Rob Mayne**
Secretary: **Ray Baggott**
37 Laneside Drive, Hinckley, Leics.
LE10 1TG (01455 447278)
Press Officer: **Andy Gibbs** (01455 617828)

FOOTBALL MANAGEMENT TEAM

Manager: Dean Thomas
Coach:Charlie Palmer
Captain: Stuart Storer
Physio: Julie Hayton

FACT FILE

Formed: 1997
Sponsors: Triumph Motor Cycles
Colours: Red & blue stripes/blue/red
Change colours: Amber & black stripes/black/amber
Midweek matchday: Tuesday
Reserves' League: Mid Comb Res Div
Unofficial Website:
www.hinckleyunitedfc.co.uk
2003-2004
Leading Goalscorer: Justin Jenkins
Player of the Year:Stuart Storer

GROUND Middlefield Lane, Hinckley, Leics. LE10 0RB 01455 613553/615012
Directions: From M69 junction 1 take A5 north to Dodwells Island, then A47(sign Leicester). At 3rd r/about turn right (Stoke Road) then first left(Tudor Road), until crossroads. Turn left (Middlefield Lane), ground at end oflane on left
Capacity:2,700   Cover: 1,300 Seats: 301   Floodlights: Yes
Clubhouse: Social club with lounge, games room and concert hall
Club Shop: Sells programmes, books, vidoes, badges, mugs , replica shirts,scarves, hats,etc.
THE CLUB ARE HOPING TO MOVE INTO A NEW GROUND IN NOVEMBER 2004

PREVIOUS **Names:** Hinckley Athletic (1889) & Hinckley Town (prev. Westfield Rovers 58-66) merged in 1997
Grounds: Westfield Playing Field 58-60; Coventry Rd Rec Grd 60-68; Leicester Rd68-97m
Leagues: Town: S Leicester & Nuneaton Amat, Leics Snr 72-86, Central Mids 86-88, West Mids 88-90
Athletic: Leics. & Northants; Leics. Sen.; Birmingham Comb. 14-39 47-54; West Midlands (Regional) 54-59 64-94; Southern 63-64

CLUB RECORDS **Attendance: Town:** 2,000 v Real Sociedad 86. **Athletic:** 5,410 v Nuneaton Boro 49
United: 2,661 v Cheltenham Town (F.A.Cup 2nd Rd. (H) 2001-02
Win: 9-1 vRocester (Away) 28.8.2000   **Defeat:** 0-6 v Redditch United (a) 7.11.1988
Career Goalscorer: David Sadler 72 **Career Appearances:** Morton Titterton 213

BEST SEASON **FA Trophy:** United: 4th Rd 2-3 v Yeovil Town 98-99
FA Cup: 2nd Round Proper v Cheltenham Town (Home) 0-2. 2001-02

HONOURS Dr. Martens (Southern) Western Division Champions 2000-2001, Westerby Challenge Cup Winners 2000-2001,2001-02,2003-04
Players progressing: Athletic: John Allen (Port Vale), Keith Scott (Swindon via Wycombe W.), Gary Pick (Hereford), Mike Love (Wigan)

Date	Comp.	Opponents	Att.	Score	Goalscorers
16/08	LP	Dorchester Town	521	1 - 1	Jackson 9
19/08	LP	HEDNESFORD TOWN	394	**4 - 0**	**Jenkins 24**, Smith 66, Jackson 69, Piercewright 90
23/08	LP	TIVERTON TOWN	383	2 - 0	Penny 2, Dyer 90
25/08	LP	Nuneaton Borough	1901	0 - 2	
30/08	LP	WEYMOUTH	401	1 - 2	Lenton 85[p]
01/09	LP	Worcester City	1060	0 - 2	
06/09	LP	Eastbourne Borough	543	2 - 0	Lewis 18 89
09/09	LP	STAFFORD RANGERS	405	1 - 1	Jackson 16
13/09	LP	WELLING UNITED	327	2 - 1	Smith 44, Lewis 89
16/09	LP	Moor Green	272	1 - 0	Lewis 34
20/09	LP	NEWPORT COUNTY	480	**1 - 4**	**Jenkins 87**
27/09	**FA Cup Q2**	**Moor Green**	271	2 - 1	Smith 44, Peer 48[og]
04/10	LP	Bath City	549	2 - 0	**Jenkins 66,** Lewis 68
11/10	**FA Cup Q3**	**Wakefield & Emley**	248	2 - 0	**Jenkins 61,** Smith 82
18/10	LP	Weston-super-Mare	243	2 - 2	**Jenkins 21 52**
21/10	LP	WORCESTER CITY	281	0 - 0	
25/10	**FA Cup Q4**	**Scarborough**	1207	1 - 3	Lenton 87[p]
01/11	**FA Trophy 1**	**Rugby United**	**328**	0 - 0	
04/11	**FA Trophy 1 rep**	**RUGBY UNITED**	229	3 - 2	Dyer 23, Lenton 31 37[p]
08/11	LP	Cambridge City	520	2 - 1	Jackson 52, Smith 72
11/11	LP	DOVER ATHLETIC	345	3 - 1	Sadler 13, **Jenkins 16**, Penny 51
15/11	LP	CRAWLEY TOWN	452	**4 - 0**	**Jenkins 20**, Lenton 36[p], Murray 85, Voice 88
122/11	LP	Weymouth	1573	0 - 2	
29/11	**FA Trophy 2**	**Gresley Rovers**	330	2 - 3	**Jenkins 5**, Lenton 12
06/12	LP	Newport County	676	3 - 0	Jackson 28, Murray 38, Penny 64
20/12	LP	Tiverton Town	473	0 - 3	
26/12	LP	NUNEATON BOROUGH	**2013**	1 - 1	Smith 90
01/01	LP	Grantham Town	511	1 - 1	Jackson 87
03/01	LP	CHELMSFORD CITY	338	1 - 2	Stone 38
17/01	LP	Chelmsford City	317	3 - 0	Lewis 11 89, Smith 67
24/01	LP	Stafford Rangers	936	0 - 2	
07/02	LP	Havant & Waterlooville	418	0 - 2	
14/02	LP	MOOR GREEN	280	0 - 0	
17/02	LP	WESTON-SUPER-MARE	248	1 - 0	Smith 13
21/02	LP	MERTHYR TYDFIL	353	1 - 2	Jackson 11
24/02	LP	CAMBRIDGE CITY	218	0 - 0	
28/02	LP	Chippenham Town	487	1 - 2	Jackson 29
06/03	LP	BATH CITY	362	1 - 2	**Jenkins 74**
09/03	LP	DORCHESTER TOWN	201	1 - 0	Smith 30
13/03	LP	Dover Athletic	822	1 - 1	**Jenkins 53**
20/03	LP	Welling United	622	3 - 2	Lenton 45, Smith 48, Lewis 87
27/03	LP	EASTBOURNE BOROUGH	330	2 - 2	**Jenkins 26,** Lenton 83[p]
03 /04	LP	Merthyr Tydfil	402	1 - 1	Clarke 73[og]
10 /04	LP	Hednesford Town	511	1 - 1	Jackson 71
12 /04	LP	GRANTHAM TOWN	351	0 - 1	
17 /04	LP	HAVANT & WATERLOOVILLE	303	2 - 2	Sadler 85 88
24 /04	LP	Crawley Town	1844	3 - 0	Sadler 22 34, Lenton 63
01/05	LP	CHIPPENHAM TOWN	355	0 - 0	

Average Home League Attendance`:**409** 65-55 Top Goalscorer: **Jenkins 12** (10 +1FAC+1FAT)

PLAYERS SQUAD 2004-2005

Goalkeepers:
Chris Taylor (Nuneaton), Tom Whittle (Oldham)

Defenders:
Adam Willis (Kidderminster), Brad Piercewright (Kettering), Gavin Stone (Halesowen), Neil Cartwright (Youth team), Tommy Goodwin (Shepshed), Tyrone Mintus (Oadby)

Midfield:
Stuart Storer (Chesham), Richard Lavery (Telford Utd), Jamie Lenton (Rugby Utd), Sam McMahon (Burton Alb), Steve Marriner (Dartford), Wayne Dyer (Sutton Coldfield), Leon Jackson (Worcester), John Burns (Ilkeston)

Forwards:
Paul Barnes (Tamworth), Nathan Lamey (Halesowen), Chris Smith ((Solihull), Matt Lewis (Kidderminster)

HUCKNALL TOWN

CLUB OFFICIALS

Chair:Brian Holmes **V-Chair:** David Gamble
President: Glen Lathall
Hon.President: Andy Stewart
Secretary: Brian Scothern,93 Brookfield Avenue, Shortwood Estate, Hucknall, Notts.NG15 6FF
Commercial Manager: Daniel Lewis 01773 838340 (H) 07802 266268)M)
General Manager: David Green
Press Officer: Andy Donaldson

FOOTBALL MANAGEMENT TEAM

Manager:Ernie Moss
Asst.Manager: Sean O'Neil
Physio: Jason Truscott

FACT FILE

Founded: 1987
Nickname: The Town
Sponsors: T.B.A.
Colours: Yellow/black/yellow
Change colours: Allblue
Midweek matches: Tuesday
Club Website: www.hucknalltownfc.co.uk

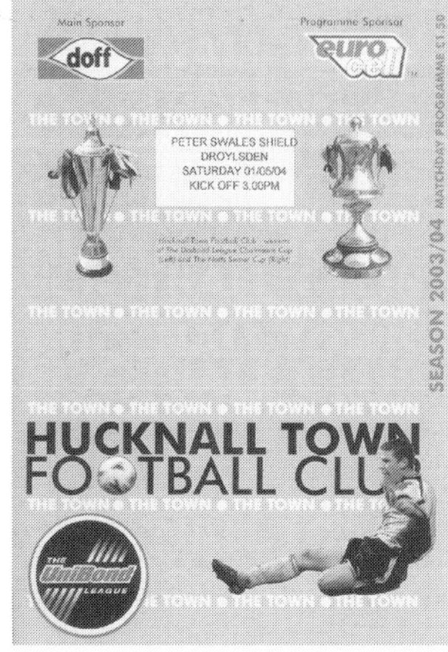

Pages: 92 Price: £1.30
Editor: Drew Baker(07811 117789)

Local Press: Hucknall & Bulwell Dispatch; Nottm Evening Post; Nottm Football Post

GROUND Watnall Road, Hucknall, Notts NG15 6EY Tel: 0115 956 1253
Directions: M1 jct 27, A608 to lights, right onto A611 to Hucknall, right at r'bout (new by-pass), over next r'bout, right at next r'bout into Watnall Rd -grd on right.(B6009) From M1 jct 26 follow Nottm signs to lights on island, left onto A610, right at Three Ponds Pub onto B600 towards Watnall, 200 yds past Queens Head turn right signed Hucknall, follow over m'way and past Rolls Royce -ground on left. Nearest station Hucknall
Capacity: 2,500 Seats: 500 Covered Terrace: 800
Clubhouse: Open mid day and evenings every day
Club Shop: Yes, Lynne Taylor - 0115 9630206

PREVIOUS
Leagues: Bulwell & Dist. 46-59 60-65; Central All. 59-60; Notts Spartan 65-70; Notts All. 70-89; Central Midlands 89-92 Northern Counties East 92-97, Unibond 97-
Ground: Wigwam Park 46-54 Name: Hucknall Colliery Welfare (until pit closure 1988)

CLUB RECORDS
Attendance: 1,436 v Ilkeston Town, FA Cup 4th Qual 28/10/00 **Appearances:** Dave McCarthy 282,Paul Tomlinson 240
Goals: Maurice Palethorpe approx 400 (80s & 90s)

BEST SEASON
FA Cup: 4th Q Rd v Ilkeston Town 00-01 lost 0-1 and 2001-02 v Cambridge City (A) 1-3 after 1-1
FA Vase: Quarter Final 85-86 **FA Trophy:** 4th Round 2004 v Shrewsbury Town (A)

HONOURS
Northern Counties (East) Lg Div 1 R-up 92-93 (Lg Cup 93-94 96-97 97-98) Presidents Cup 96-97; Central Mids Lg x2 89-91 R-up 91-92, Lg Cup x3 89-92; Notts All.Sen (4) 76-78 87-89, Div 1 Div 1 72-73 80-81 86-87 Div 2 70-71; Intermediate Cup 72-73 78-81 84-84; Lge Cup 78-79; Unibond Chairmans Cup Winners 2002-2003 Notts Snr Cup 84-85 90-91 97-98 99-00,02-03 R-up 83-84 85-86 87-88 89-90 98-99 00-01 Unibond Lg.: Div 1 R-Up 98-99

Date	Comp.	Opponents	Att.	Score	Goalscorers
16/08	LP	Bradford Park Avenue	297	2 - 1	Winder 40, Bacon 47
19/08	LP	FRICKLEY ATHLETIC	482	3 - 0	Bacon 17, Winder 19, Gaunt 76
23/08	LP	BURSCOUGH	433	1 - 0	Hunter 26
25/08	LP	Alfreton Town	805	1 - 2	Mayman 76
30/08	LP	Spennymoor United	203	3 - 1	McCarthy 10, Bacon 40, **Ricketts 69**
02/09	LP	ASHTON UNITED	512	2 - 0	Bacon 4, **Ricketts 89**
06/09	LP	SOUTHPORT	701	4 - 0	Adams 7[p], **Ricketts 12 33**, Gaunt 47
13/09	LP	Lancaster City	277	**1 - 3**	**Ricketts 5**
16/09	LP	WAKEFIELD & EMLEY	374	0 - 1	
20/09	LP	HARROGATE TOWN	456	1 - 0	Bacon 65
23/09	LP	Stalybridge Celtic	416	2 - 1	McCarthy 50, Hunter 67
27/09	**FA Cup Q2**	**CONGLETON TOWN**	447	1 - 1	Soar 45
30/09	**FA Cup Q2 rep**	**Congleton Town**	290	2 - 3	Mayman 44, Barrick 60
04/10	LP	Marine	270	1 - 1	Bacon 20
07/10	LP	Wakefield & Emley	233	3 - 0	**Ricketts 30 53**, Mayman 38
14/10	LP	WORKSOP TOWN	817	3 - 1	Asher 5, Bacon 7 62
18/10	LP	ALTRINCHAM	645	2 - 1	**Ricketts 36 49**
25/10	LP	Droylsden	201	**1 - 3**	**Ricketts 43**
01/11	LP	BARROW	626	3 - 1	McCarthy 47[p], Hunter 48, Gaunt 59
08/11	LP	Southport	775	1 - 1	Miller 47
15/11	LP	Blyth Spartans	420	2 - 1	McCarthy 16[p], Moore 37
22/11	LP	RUNCORN HALTON	416	1 - 0	Balon 84
29/11	**FA Trophy 2**	**NUNEATON BOROUGH**	625	2 - 1	**Ricketts 11 39**
02/12	LP	Gainsborough Trinity	513	1 - 2	Bacon 32
06/12	LP	Vauxhall Motors	207	3 - 1	Bacon 19, **Ricketts 30**, Mayman 50
13/12	LP	Radcliffe Borough	213	6 - 1	**MCCARTHY 21 77 90,** Hunter 25, **Ricketts 71**, McSweeney 90
26/12	LP	ALFRETON TOWN	**1323**	3 - 3	**Ricketts 25,** McCarthy 45, Mayman 53
03/01	LP	Runcorn Halton	272	2 - 1	Todd 7,76
10/01	**FA Trophy 3**	**BRADFORD PARK AVENUE**	573	1 - 0	McSweeney 41
17/01	LP	LANCASTER CITY	499	3 - 0	McSweeney 61, **Ricketts 75 80**
31/01	**FA Trophy 4**	**Shrewsbury Town**	2501	1 - 2	**Ricketts 20**
03/02	LP	GAINSBOROUGH TRINITY	531	2 - 0	**Ricketts 52**, Miller 76
14/02	LP	Ashton United	162	**6 - 1**	Todd 2, Gaunt 33, Bacon 41, **Ricketts 48 52,** White 85[og]
21/02	LP	BLYTH SPARTANS	617	1 - 0	**Ricketts 9**
28/02	LP	Harrogate Town	766	2 - 1	Bacon 54 62
02/03	LP	VAUXHALL MOTORS	557	2 - 0	Todd 4, Miller 57
13/03	LP	Burscough	247	1 - 0	Bacon 6
16/03	LP	WHITBY TOWN	605	1 - 0	Todd 57
20/03	LP	RADCLIFFE BOROUGH	366	1 - 1	**Ricketts 71[p]**
22/03	LP	SPENNYMOOR UNITED	425	2 - 1	Bacon 6, Mayan 77
24/03	LP	Whitby Town	224	0 - 0	
27/03	LP	Barrow	1416	0 - 1	
30/03	LP	Frickley Athletic	299	1 - 0	McSweeney 51
03 /04	LP	MARINE	458	1 - 1	**Ricketts 15**
05 /04	LP	Altrincham	529	3 - 2	Bacon 31, Shuttleworth 58[og], Todd 85
10 /04	LP	Worksop Town	841	3 - 0	Bacon 2, **Ricketts 7,** Todd 35
12 /04	LP	DROYLSDEN	956	1 - 1	Todd 5
17 /04	LP	BRADFORD PARK AVENUE	510	0 - 0	
20 /04	LP	STALYBRIDGE CELTIC	316	**1 - 3**	Bacon 42

Average Home League Attendance: **574** 90-45 Top Goalscorer: **Gary Ricketts 25** (22+3FAT)

PLAYING SQUAD 2004-05

Goalkeepers:
Matt Taylor (Matlock)

Defenders:
Alistair Asher (Halifax), Joe Taylor (Worksop), Chris Timons (Gainsborough), Dean Barrick (Nuneaton), Nathan Winder (Chesterfield), Russell Cooke (Ilkeston), Simon Brown (Notts Co)

Midfield:
Andy Todd (Worksop), Danny Bacon (Mansfield), Steve Palmer (Hednesford), Frazer McHugh (Bradford C), Danny Mayman (Clipstone Welfare)

Forwards:
Mark Ward (Belper), Danny Holland (Matlock), Gary Ricketts (Hinckley Utd), Mark Smith (Frickley)

KETTERING TOWN

CLUB OFFICIALS
President Sid Chapman
Chairman Peter Mallinger
Vice Chairman Michael Leech
Directors Les Manning, David Dunham, David Tailby
Club Secretary/Press Off.
Graham Starmer, c/o the club

FOOTBALL MANAGEMENT
Manager: Kevin Wilson
Physio: Chris Palmer
Youth & Comunity Dev.: Dominic Genovese

2003-04
P.o.Y. Richard Graham
Leading Scorer: Paul Fewings

FACT FILE
Founded: 1872
Nickname: Poppies
Club Sponsors: Weldon Plant Ltd.
Club colours: Red/black/red
Change colours: Blue/blue/white
Midweek home matchday: Tuesday
Local Press: Evening Telegraph; Chronicle & Echo; Herald & Post; Citizen
Local Radio:
Radio Northampton; Northants 96; Connect F.M.
Clubcall: 09068 101567

PROGRAMME
Pages: 32 Price: £2

GROUND Rockingham Road, Kettering, Northants, NN16 9AW Tel: 01536 83028/410815 (Office) Fax: 01536 412273
email: info@ketteringtownafc.co.uk web site: http://www.ketteringtownafc.co.uk

DIRECTIONS: From south - M1 junction 15, A43 to Kettering use A14 exit Junct. 7, follow A43 to Corby/Stamford to 1st roundabout, turn right A6003, ground half a mile. **From north** - M1 or M6 use junction 19 then A14 to Kettering. Exit Junct. 7 then as above.
British Rail - Inter-City Midland - 50 mins from London (St.Pancras), 20 mins from Leicester

Capacity: 6,170 **Covered - Seating:** 1,800 **Terracing:** 2,200

Club Shop: Open before & after matches, & on request on non-match days. Situated in front of main stand. Also Alex Elmores in town centre

Clubhouse: Social Club (Poppies) 01536 410962, Vice-Presidents Bar & Sponsor's Lounge

PREVIOUS **Leagues:** Southern League??-79, 01-02; Northants League, Midland League, Birmingham League; Central Alliance, United Counties League; Conference 79-01 02-03 **Grounds:** North Park; Green Lane

CLUB RECORDS **Attendance:** 11,536, Kettering v Peterborough (pre-Taylor report)
Win: 16-0 v Higham YMCI (FA Cup 1909) **Defeat:** 0-13 v Mardy (Southern League Div. 2, 1911/12)
Transfer fee paid: £25,000 to Macclesfield for Carl Alford, 1994
Transfer fee received: £150,000 from Newcastle United for Andy Hunt
Career goalscorer: Roy Clayton 171 (1972 - 1981) **Career appearances:** Roger Ashby

BEST SEASON **FA Trophy:** Runners-up 78-79 99-00 **League:** Conference Runners-up 1980-81; 88-89; 93-94; 98-99
FA Cup: 4th Round - 88-89, 1-2 v Charlton Ath.; 91-92, 1-4 v Blackburn R. League clubs defeated: Swindon T. 61-62, Millwall 63-64, Swansea C. 74-75, Halifax T. 88-89, Bristol R. 88-89, Maidstone U. 91-92, Hull C. 00-01

HONOURS Premier Inter League Cup; FA Trophy Runners-up 78-79; Alliance Premier League (Conference) R-up x 4; Southern League Champions x 4, County Cup Winners, Daventry Charity Cup Winners x 2; Northants Senior Cup x 28; Maunsell Cup Winners x 12

Players P rogressing: Billy Kellock(Peterborough), Gary Wood (Notts Co.), Dave Longhurst (Nott'm Forest), Scott Endersby (Ipswich), Steve Fallon (Cambridge U.), Andy Rogers (Plymouth), Martyn Foster (Northampton), Cohen Griffith (Cardiff C.), Andy Hunt (Newcastle), Richard Brown (Blackburn R.) ,Ben Wright (Bristol C.),Kofi Nyamah (Stoke C.) + Adam Sollitt(North'tonT)

Date	Comp.	Opponents	Att.	Score	Goalscorers
216/08	LP	NORTHWOOD	1072	2 - 1	Solkhon 2, **Fewings 70**
19/08	LP	Harrow Borough	403	2 - 1	Murphy 27 66[p]
23/08	LP	Hornchurch	564	1 - 1	King 44
25/08	LP	BRAINTREE TOWN	1123	1 - 2	King 46
30/08	LP	Thurrock	442	2 - 0	Turner 52, Norman 55[p]
02/09	LP	MAIDENHEAD UNITED	958	3 - 1	Paschalis 27, **Fewings 45,** Norman 90[p]
06/09	LP	Carshalton Athletic	571	2 - 3	Turner 1, Norman 33
09/09	LP	HITCHIN TOWN	996	1 - 1	Paschalis 85
13/09	LP	BOGNOR REGIS TOWN	1012	3 - 1	**Fewings 50,** Murphy 66, Paschalis 83
16/09	LP	Billericay Town	347	1 - 3	King 68
20/09	LP	HAYES	939	0 - 3	
23/09	LP	Grays Athletic	350	1 - 1	Remy 3
27/09	**FA Cup Q2**	**Stamford**	862	3 - 0	**Fewings 18,** Graham 47, Clarke 65
04/10	LP	Kingstonian	437	0 - 1	
11/10	**FA Cup Q3**	**ST MARGARETSBURY**	790	2 - 0	Norman 40[p] 69[p]
18/10	LP	Basingstoke Town	338	2 - 2	Ositola 55, Taschaus 69
21/10	LP	HEYBRIDGE SWIFTS	601	**4 - 1**	Norman 26[p], Solkhan 33, Butterworth 75, ing 90
25/10	**FA Cup Q4**	**Boreham Wood**	501	0 - 1	
01/11	LP	CANVEY ISLAND	988	**1 - 4**	Solkhon 77
08/11	LP	Hayes	278	1 - 0	Norman 66[p]
11/11	LP	St Albans City	334	1 - 0	King 84
15/11	LP	FORD UNITED	771	0 - 3	
22/11	LP	Hendon	214	2 - 1	Turner 64, Paschalis 85
25/11	LP	SUTTON UNITED	517	0 - 1	
29/11	**FA Trophy 2**	**Hendon**	225	1 - 1	Paschalis 54
02/12	**FA Trophy 2 rep**	**HENDON**	602	2 - 2	Lodge 6, **Fewings 90** Won 5 - 4 pens
06/12	LP	AYLESBURY UNITED	807	2 - 2	**Fewings 13, 54**
13/12	LP	Northwood	211	2 - 1	King 26, **Fewings 43**
26/12	LP	Bedford Town	1174	3 - 2	Butterworth 12, **Fewings 37**, Solkhon 70
01/01	LP	HORNCHURCH	1212	3 - 2	Turner 63 83, **Fewings 69**
03/01	LP	Bishop's Stortford	561	**1 - 4**	**Fewings 90**
10/01	**FA Trophy 3**	**WOKING**	1259	0 - 0	
13/01	**FA Trophy 3 rep**	**Woking**	1126	3 - 2	Paschalis 13, **Fewings 70**, Solkhon 86
17/01	LP	CARSHALTON ATHLETIC	984	0 - 3	
24/01	LP	Bognor Regis Town	405	0 - 1	
31/01	**FA Trophy 4**	**Burton Albion**	1751	1 - 1	Turner 72
03/02	**FA Trophy 4 rep**	**BURTON ALBION**	1215	1 - 2	Turner 14
07/02	LP	Sutton United	586	1 - 2	Difante 87
10/02	LP	ST ALBANS CITY	703	2 - 0	Turner 72, Butterworth 81
14/02	LP	BASINGSTOKE TOWN	785	0 - 3	
21/02	LP	Ford United	156	0 - 2	
28/02	LP	BISHOP'S STORTFORD	821	3 - 2	**DIFANTE73,76,89**
02/03	LP	Heybridge Swifts	237	0 - 1	
06/03	LP	GRAYS ATHLETIC	734	0 - 0	
13/03	LP	Hitchin Town	428	1 - 1	McKenzie 83
16/03	LP	HARROW BOROUGH	689	1 - 1	Norman 88
20/03	LP	KINGSTONIAN	715	1 - 1	Lynch 33
30/03	LP	BILLERICAY TOWN	726	1 - 0	Lynch 75
03 /04	LP	THURROCK	722	2 - 1	Lynch 42, Gould 89
10 /04	LP	Braintree Town	338	1 - 0	Lynch 41
12 /04	LP	BEDFORD TOWN	**1260**	0 - 0	
17 /04	LP	Maidenhead United	339	2 - 1	Solkhon 66, Lynch 79
24 /04	LP	Aylesbury United	742	2 - 0	Graham 48 Lynch 49(p)
27 /04	LP	Canvey Island	356	1 - 1	**Fewings54**
01/05	LP	HENDON	1066	**4 - 1**	McIlwain 59, Difante 62, Graham 69, Duke 89
		Average Home League Attendance:	**874**	76-72	Top Goalscorer:**Paul Fewings 13** (11+1FAC+1FAT)

PLAYING SQUAD 2004-2005

Goalkeepers:
Steve Corry (Oldham)

Defenders: Brett Solkhon (Rushden & Diamonds), Craig McIlwain (Rothwell), Martin Matthews (King's Lynn), Lee Howey (Bedford), Liam Folds (Bedford), Rob Gould (Grantham), Derek Brown (St Albans), Matt Harris (Youth team), Liam Carson (Youth team)

Midfield: Ollie Burgess (Basingstoke), Daniel French (Bedford), Neil Lazarus (Bedford), Danny Burke (Daventry T), Wayne Duik (Gedling), Jamie Kearns (Grantham), Scott McCafferty (Northampton)

Forwards:
Drew Roberts (Bedford), Darren Lynch (Aylesbury), Chris Difante (Youth team), Simon Underwood (Harrow)

LANCASTER CITY

CLUB OFFICIALS

Chairman:Ron Moore **Pres:** M Woodhouse

Vice Chairman: Andrew Pye

Secretary: Barry Newsham
104 Willow Lane, Forest Park, Lancaster,
Lancs LA1 5QF Tel No: 01524 32430
e-mail: barry.newsham@tiscali.co.uk

Match Sec: Mike Sparks (01524 64024)

Com. Man.: Les Taylor (01524 841710)

Email : lancasrtercity@tiscali.co.uk

FOOTBALL MANAGEMENT TEAM

Manager: Phil Wilson
Asst.Man.: Peter Ward
Physio: D Hughes and A.Pearson

FACT FILE

Formed: 1905
Nickname: Dolly Blues
Sponsors: Reebok
Colours:Sky Blue/white/sky blue
Change colours: White/navt /white
Midweek matchday: Tuesday
Reserve League: Lancashire League
Club Website: www.lancastercityfc.com

2003-004
James Hughes31
Player of the Year: Paul Sparrow
2004-2005 Captain: Gary Bauress

GROUND Giant Axe, West Road, Lancaster LA1 5PE Tel: 01524 382238 (Office).
e-mail: lancastercity@tiscali.co.uk
Capacity: 3064 Cover: 900 Seats: 513
Directions: M6 junc 33, follow into city, left at lights immediately after Waterstones bookshop, 2nd right, pass railway station on right, follow road down hill, ground 1st right. 5 mins walk from both bus & rail stations
Clubhouse: "The Dolly Blue Tavern" just outside the ground. Also Dollies Diner inside ground serving food and drinks. **Club Shop:** Inside ground, selling metal badges, pennants,

Pages:40 Price: £1.50
Editor:Les Taylor Local Press:
Lancaster Guardian, Morecambe Visitor, Lancashire Evening Post, Lancaster Citizen.
Local Radio:
Red Rose, Radio Lancashire, Bay Radio

PREVIOUS
Leagues: Lancs Combination 05-70; Northern Premier 70-82; North West Counties82-87.
Names: Lancaster Town and City of Lancaster **Ground:** Quay Meadow 05-06 (club's 1st 2 games only!)

CLUB RECORDS
Attendance: 7,500 v Carlisle, FA Cup 1936.
Goalscorer: David Barnes 130 League & cup. **Appearances:** Edgar J Parkinson, 591 league & cup.
Win: 8-0 v Leyland Motors (A), 83-84. **Defeat:** 0-10 v Matlock T, NPL Division One, 73-74

BEST SEASON
FA Vase: Second Rd 86-87 90-91. **FA Cup:** 2nd Rd 46-47 (1-4 (A) v Gateshead) 72-73 (1-2 (A) v Notts County)
FA Trophy: Third Rd 74-75 75-76. League Clubs defeated: Barrow, Stockport County 21-22

HONOURS
Northern Prem. Lg Cup R-up 79-80 (Div 1 Cup R-up 90-91), Lancs Combination 21-22 29-30 34-35 35-36 (R-up 19-20 22-23 27-28 51-52, Lg Cup 21-22, Div 2 R-up14-15), Lancs Jun. Cup (ATS Challenge Trophy) 27-28 28-29 30-31 33-34 51-52 74-75 (R-up 06-07 08-09 19-20 26-27,00-01), Lancs Yth (u18) Cup 87-88 88-89 (R-up 86-87 89-90), President's Cup 1994-95 Unibond Div 1 95-96, Div 1 Lge Cup 95-96., Lg.Challenge Cup 99-00 , 00-01

Players Progressing: J McNamee (Workington 75), B O'Callaghan (Stoke C.), I Stevens (Stockport Co. 86), G Johnstone (P.N.E. 93), M Clark & W Collins (Crewe Alex.), G Wilson (Crewe Alex.). P.Thomson (NAC Breda 99) Chris Ward (Birmingham City)

Back row, left to right: Hughie Sharky (Kit Manager), Farrell Kilbane, Jimmy Love, Steven Miller, Ricky Mercer, Richard Whiteside, Stephen Jones, Kevin Welsby, Tony Sullivam, Phil Clarkson, Paul Sparrow, John Robertson and Dave Hughes (Physio).
Front Row: Andy Scott, Ryan Elderton, Neil Prince, Peter Ward, Phil Wilson, Gary Bauress, MichaelYates and Neil Uberschar.

Date	Comp.	Opponents	Att.	Score	Goalscorers
16/08	LP	VAUXHALL MOTORS	343	0 - 0	
19/08	LP	Southport	1213	0 - 3	
23/08	LP	Ashton United	172	1 - 2	Yates 30
25/08	LP	RUNCORN HALTON	313	0 - 1	
30/08	LP	Alfreton Town	489	0 - 3	
06/09	LP	HARROGATE TOWN	266	**1 - 4**	**Hughes 45**
09/09	LP	Burscough	184	1 - 0	**Hughes 45**
13/09	LP	HUCKNALL TOWN	277	3 - 1	Kilbane 14, Uberschar 19, **Hughes 90**
20/09	LP	Worksop Town	624	0 - 0	
23/09	LP	RADCLIFFE BOROUGH	391	4 - 2	Clarkson 27, Kilbane 34, **Hughes 42 52**
27/09	**FA Cup Q2**	**ALTRINCHAM**	489	2 - 0	**Hughes 68,** Sullivan 85
04/10	LP	Gainsborough Trinity	358	2 - 3	**Hughes 19 66**
07/10	LP	SOUTHPORT	706	1 - 0	**Hughes 45**
11/10	**FA Cup Q3**	**Chorley**	616	1 - 1	Kilbane 5
14/10	**FA Cup Q3 rep**	**CHORLEY**	452	1 - 0	**Hughes 6**
18/10	LP	WHITBY TOWN	287	4 - 3	Jones 25, Prince 34, **Hughes 69 79**
25/10	**FA Cup Q4**	**Dunston Federation Brewery**	310	1 - 0	Jones 21
28/10	LP	Stalybridge Celtic	413	3 - 0	Sullivan 43, Elderton 50, Jones 77
01/11	**FA Trophy 1**	**Ashton United**	206	1 - 1	Clarkson 42
04/11	**FA Trophy 1 rep**	**ASHTON UNITED**	201	3 - 2	Jones 39, **Hughes 40 51**
08/11	**FA Cup 1**	**CAMBRIDGE UNITED**	1864	1 - 2	**Hughes 35[p]**
15/11	LP	Wakefield & Emley	166	0 - 1	
22/11	LP	BLYTH SPARTANS	245	1 - 1	Jones 83
29/11	**FA Trophy 2**	**HEDNESFORD TOWN**	294	1 - 1	Sullivan 54
02/12	**FA Trophy 2 rep**	**Hednesford Town**	276	0 - 1	
06/12	LP	Whitby Town	193	1 - 2	Jones 82
09/12	LP	MARINE	249	3 - 1	Sullivan 6, Kilbane 28, Elderton 79
13/12	LP	Runcorn Halton	212	1 - 0	Kilbane 44
16/12	LP	Altrincham	503	0 - 0	
26/12	LP	BARROW	**822**	0 - 3	
01/01	LP	Barrow	1750	3 - 4	Thomson 31 77[p], Hume 73[og]
03/01	LP	WAKEFIELD & EMLEY	271	3 - 0	**HUGHES 14,46,62.**
10/01	LP	FRICKLEY ATHLETIC	288	1 - 1	Kilbane 64
17/01	LP	Hucknall Town	499	0 - 3	
07/02	LP	Harrogate Town	579	1 - 0	Thomson 16
10/02	LP	BRADFORD PARK AVENUE	265	1 - 3	Prince 15
14/02	LP	SPENNYMOOR UNITED	279	**6 - 0**	**HUGHES 1, 6,10. Sullivan 41, 67, 74.**
21/02	LP	Vauxhall Motors	204	1 - 2	**Hughes 74**
24/02	LP	BURSCOUGH	249	4 - 0	Jones 32, **Hughes 48**, Elderton 65, Bauress 3
28/02	LP	DROYLSDEN	358	2 - 1	**Hughes 10**, Thomson 81
06/03	LP	Frickley Athletic	242	2 - 0	Kilbane 34, Jones 54
09/03	LP	STALYBRIDGE CELTIC	272	2 - 1	Kilbane 23, **Hughes 76**
13/03	LP	ASHTON UNITED	298	1 - 1	Thomson 90
20/03	LP	ALFRETON TOWN	261	0 - 1	
23/03	LP	Radcliffe Borough	180	2 - 0	Clark 52, Thomson 74
27/03	LP	Spennymoor United	130	1 - 0	**Hughes 78**
30/03	LP	WORKSOP TOWN	273	2 - 0	Thomson 71, Sullivan 90
03 /04	LP	ALTRINCHAM	340	1 - 0	Jones 74
08 /04	LP	Blyth Spartans	198	0 - 0	
10 /04	LP	Marine	341	1 - 1	Robertson 88
17 /04	LP	GAINSBOROUGH TRINITY	303	0 - 1	
19 /04	LP	Droylsden	301	0 - 0	
24 /04	LP	Bradford Park Avenue	306	2 - 0	Thomson 52, Jones 60
		Average Home League Attendance:	**334**	73-57	Top Goalscorer: **Jamie Hughes 25** (20+3FAC+2FAT)

PLAYING SQUAD 2004-2005

Goalkeepers:

Jamie Speare (Accrington Stanley)

Defenders:

Gary Bauress (Aberyystwyth), Jamie Udall (Leigh RMI), Jimmy Graham (Guiseley), Martin Clark (Burscough), Andy Scott (Southport), Paul Sparrow (Preston), Neil Uberschar (Morecambe), Joe McMahon (Colwyn Bay)

Midfield:

Neil Prince (Leigh RMI), Steve Jones (Southport), Ryan Elderton (Morecambe), Jamie Hughes (Vauxhall Motors)

Forwards:

Peter Thomson (Southport), Tony Sullivan (Altrincham)

MOOR GREEN

CLUB OFFICIALS

Chairman: Ian Childs
Vice-Chairman: John Bassford
Directors: Nigel Collins, Geof Hood,John Basssford and IanChilds
Secretary: Nigel Collins
7 The Morelands, West Heath, Birmingham B31 3HA
Tel: 0121476 4944 (H) 0121 777 8961 (W) 07801248211 (M)
Email: nigelcollins@lineone.net
Press Officer: Rob Hyde
email: robhyde@blueyonder.co.uk
Commercial Man.: Commercial Dept.0121 777 8961

FACT FILE

Formed: 1901
Nickname: The Moors
Sponsors:Alexander Forbes Insurance
Colours: Navy Blue with sky blue band
Change colours: Yellow & Green
Midweek matchday: Tuesday
Reserve League: No reserve team
Website:www.moorgreenfc.co.uk

FOOTBALL MANAGEMENT TEAM

Manager: Bob Faulkner
Coach: Mark Harrison
Physio: Steve Shipway

Programme: Pages: 40 Price: £1.50
Editor:Martin North(0121 603 7357)
Local Press: Solihull News, Solihull Times, Birmingham Post & Mail, Express &Star
Local Radio: Radio WM, BRMB

GROUND `The Moorlands', Sherwood Rd., Hall Green. B28 OEX
Tel: 0121 777 8961 or 0121 624 2727
Directions: Off Highfield Rd, which is off A34 (B'ham to Stratford)
Hall Green & Yardley (BR) half mile
Capacity: 3,250 Cover: 1,200 Seats: 250 Floodlights: Yes
Clubhouse: Two bars, dance floor. Open nightly & weekend lunch
Club Shop: Selling scarves, mugs, stickers, programmes etc

PREVIOUS **Leagues:** (friendlies only 1901-21) Birmingham & Dist. A.F.A. 1908-36; Central Amateur 36-39; Birmingham Comb 45-54; West Mids 54-65; Midland Comb 65-83
Grounds: Moor Green Lane 1901-02; numerous 02-22; Windermere Road 1910-30

CLUB RECORDS **Attendance:** 5,000 v Romford, FA Amtr Cup 51
Career Goalscorer: Phil Davies 221 **Career Appearances:** Michael Hawkins 800
Transfer fee paid: £1,000 for Adrian O'Dowd (Alvechurch)
Transfer fee received: £90,000 for Ian Taylor (Port Vale)

BEST SEASON **FA Cup:** 1st Rd Proper 79-80 (lost 2-3 Stafford Rgs),02-03 v Barrow 0-2
FA Trophy: 1st Rd Prop 90-91, 0-3 v Burton Albion; 96-97, 3-5 v AshtonUnited

HONOURS Southern Lg Mid Div R-up 87-88, Mids Comb 80-81 (R-up(4) 74-76 79-80 82-83, Div 185-86, Presidents Cup(2) 66-68 78-79), Mids Comb Chall Cup 80-81 (R-up 69-7082-83), Lord Mayor of B'ham Charity Cup 90-91, Mids F'lit Cup(2) 90-92, Tony Allden Tphy 81-82, B'ham Snr Cup 57-58, Worcs Snr Cup 2000-01 R-up 86-87, 01-02 B'ham Jnr Cup66-67, Worcs Jnr Cup 85-86, Solihull Charity Cup 85-86, Smedley Crook Mem.Cup 87-88, Cent Amat Lg 36-37 37-38 38-39, Verviers (Belg) Tphy 32-33 36-37,AFA Chall Cup 38-39, AFA Snr Cup 26-27 35-36, Mids F'lit Yth Lg Cup R-up 87-88,B'ham County Yth Lg Cup R-up 83-84. Birmingham Senior Cup: 2000-01

Players progressing: H Smith/R Jefferies (Aston Villa 47/50), F Pidcock(Walsall 53), P Woodward/B Mack (W B Abion 54), S Cooper (Birmingham City 83), K Barnes (Manchester City), P Brogan (Mansfield Town), I Taylor (Pt Vale 92), S Talbot (Pt Vale 94), D Busst (Coventry 92)

Back row, left to right: Guy Sanders, Dean Peer, Nathan Lamey, Jamie Petty, Rob Elmes, Adam Rachel, Joe Martin, and Josh Walker.
Front: Richard Robinson, Danny Scheppel (now Bromsgrove Rovers), Peter Foulds, Chris Gillard, Jai Stanley, Craig Woodley, Declan Chinedu

Date	Comp.	Opponents	Att.	Score	Goalscorers
16/08	LP	Tiverton Town	698	1 - 2	Doyle 22
19/08	LP	GRANTHAM TOWN	298	0 - 0	
23/08	LP	EASTBOURNE BOROUGH	239	0 - 1	
25/08	LP	Worcester City	1258	0 - 3	
30/08	LP	WESTON-SUPER-MARE	228	0 - 0	
02/09	LP	Stafford Rangers	751	2 - 1	Elmes 9 53
06/09	LP	Welling United	563	1 - 2	Martin 57
09/09	LP	NEWPORT COUNTY	296	1 - 1	Bailey 44
13/09	LP	Chelmsford City	614	0 - 1	
16/09	LP	HINCKLEY UNITED	272	0 - 1	
20/09	LP	Dover Athletic	710	0 - 2	
27/09	**FA Cup Q2**	**HINCKLEY UNITED**	**271**	**1 - 2**	**Doyle 55[p]**
04/10	LP	DORCHESTER TOWN	224	1 - 3	Martin 58
18/10	LP	Merthyr Tydfil	458	2 - 1	Bailey 6, Stanley 89
21/10	LP	NUNEATON BOROUGH	497	**2 - 0**	Sanders 44, Elmes 76
01/11	**FA Trophy 1**	**CINDERFORD TOWN**	**211**	**2 - 3**	**Frain 48 68**
15/11	LP	WELLING UNITED	257	0 - 2	
22/11	LP	Havant & Waterlooville	271	0 - 0	
25/11	LP	DOVER ATHLETIC	230	1 - 0	Elmes 85
29/11	LP	CAMBRIDGE CITY	204	1 - 1	Peer 30
06/12	LP	Grantham Town	340	1 - 0	Doyle 55
20/12	LP	Eastbourne Borough	400	1 - 0	Martin 90
26/12	LP	WORCESTER CITY	**643**	1 - 1	Faulds 50
01/01	LP	Hednesford Town	536	4 - 4	Elmes 26, Doyle 32 36, Davis 60
03/01	LP	TIVERTON TOWN	247	**2 - 0**	Trainer 47, Faulds 71
10/01	LP	CHELMSFORD CITY	277	1 - 0	Davis 47
17/01	LP	Crawley Town	993	2 - 2	Martin 15, Davis 44
24/01	LP	Bath City	622	1 - 0	Saunders 57
07/02	LP	CHIPPENHAM TOWN	320	3 - 2	Martin 9, Elmes 63, Faulds 70
14/02	LP	Hinckley United	280	0 - 0	
21/02	LP	BATH CITY	323	0 - 3	
28/02	LP	Weymouth	1402	0 - 3	
06/03	LP	Nuneaton Borough	764	0 - 1	
09/03	LP	WEYMOUTH	383	1 - 2	Faulds 76
13/03	LP	STAFFORD RANGERS	368	1 - 2	Faulds 66
16/03	LP	Weston-super-Mare	258	3 - 2	Martin 22, Teesdale 51, Dodell 55
20/03	LP	Dorchester Town	429	1 - 0	Martin 87
27/03	LP	CRAWLEY TOWN	322	1 - 2	J Petty 41
03 /04	LP	Cambridge City	355	1 - 1	Williams 43
10 /04	LP	Newport County	566	1 - 1	Davis 13
12 /04	LP	HEDNESFORD TOWN	285	2 - 1	Davies 2 Bailey 46
17 /04	LP	MERTHYR TYDFIL	296	1 - 1	Davis 84
24 /04	LP	Chippenham Town	447	**0 - 4**	
01/05	LP	HAVANT & WATERLOOVILLE	349	2 - 1	Faulds 34, 49
		Average Home League Attendance:	314	45-59	Top Goalscorer: Faulds 7

PLAYING SQUAD 2004-2005

Goalkeepers:
Adam Rachel (Blackpool), Matt Harris (Walsall)

Defenders:
Lee Collins (Halesowen), Guy Sanders (Bedworth), Richard Follett (Tamworth), Richard Robinson (GMP Sports), Chris Gillard (Port Vale), Barry Williams (Burton Alb), John Frain (Northampton)

Midfield:
Peter Faulds (Kidderminster), Ben Petty (Burton Alb), Phil Trainer (Halesowen), Daire Doyle (Nuneaton), Jae Martin (Woking), Matty Hall (Redditch), David Foy (Worcester)

Forwards:
Neil Davis (Newport Co), Darren Middleton (Worcester), Rob Elmes (Boldmere), Sean Dowdell (Birmingham)

NUNEATON BOROUGH

CLUB OFFICIALS

Chairman: Roger Stanford
Secretary: Paul Lewis
7 Garfitt Road, Kirby Muxloe, Leics.
Tel: 0116 239 4981 (H) 07711 410642 (M)
General Manager: Alan Prince c/o the club
Commercial Manager: Graham Wilson
Press Officers: Phil Clayton c/o the club

FOOTBALL MANAGEMENT TEAM

Manager: Roger Ashby
Physio: Paul Egan
Reserves Manager: Kevin Wilkin
Youth Team Manager: Terry Angus
Scout: Kenny Mist

FACT FILE

Formed: 1937
Nickname: The Boro
Club colours:
Blue & white stripes,white shorts
Change colours: All amber**Reserves' league:** Central Conference
Midweek matchday: Tuesday 7.45pm
Club Sponsors:
Website: www.nbafc.net

2003-04

Captain: Neil Moore
P.o.Y.: Gez Murphy
Leading Scorer: Gez Murphy

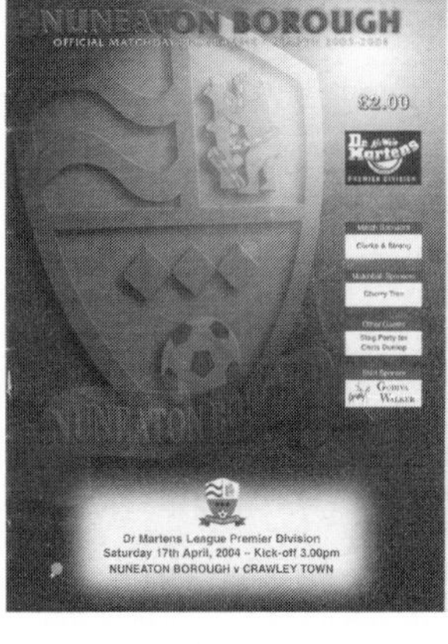

Pages: 56 **Price:** £2.00
Editor:Graham Wilson
Tel: 01400250332 (H), 07788 800505 (M)

Local Press:
Nuneaton Telegraph & Weekly Tribune
Local Radio: Mercia Sound, BBC CWR

GROUND Manor Park, Beaumont Road, Nuneaton, Warks. CV11 5HD
Tel.: 02476 385738 Fax: 02476 342690 Clubcall: 09066 555 848

Simple Directions: A444 to Nuneaton from M6 junction 3, 2nd exit at 1st roundabout, 2nd exit at 2nd r'about, left at 3rd r'bout, 2nd right into Greenmoor Rd, turn right at the end, grd on left. Ground 1 mile from Nuneaton Trent Valley (BR)

Capacity: 6,500 **Seated:** 520 **Terracing - Covered:** 3,000 **Uncovered:** 3,500

Clubhouse: Open every evening, weekend lunchtimes & matchdays.

Club Shop: Sells souvenirs, programmes & club kits. Contact Commercial department

PREVIOUS **Leagues:** Central Amateur 37-38; B'ham Comb 38-52; West Mids (B'ham) 52-58;Southern 58-79 81-82 88-99. GM Conference (Alliance Premier & Gola) 79-81 82-88 99-03 **Names:** None **Ground:** None

CLUB RECORDS **Attendance:** 22,114 v Rotherham, FA Cup 3rd Rd 1967
Defeat: 1-8 (55-56 & 68-69) **Win:** 11-1 (45-46 & 55-56)
Goalscorer: Paul Culpin 201 (Career), 55 (Season - 92/93)
Career Appearances: Alan Jones 545 (62-74)
Transfer Fee Paid: £35,000 to Forest Green R. 2000 for Marc McGregor
Transfer Fee Received: £80,000 from Kidderminster H. 2000 for Andy Ducros

BEST SEASON **FA Cup:** Third Round replay 66-67Rotherham U(H)1-1(A 0-1). 1st Rd 19 times
League Clubs defeated: Watford (53-4),Swansea C(66-67), Oxford U(77-78),Swansea C. (93-4) Stoke City (2001-02)
FA Trophy: Quarter final- 76-77(rep), 79-80, 86-87 **League:** Runners-up Conference 83-84, 84-85

HONOURS Alliance Prem Lge R-up (2) 83-85; Southern Lg Premier Div. 98-99, R-up 66-67 74-75, League Cup Win 95-96, Midland Div 81-82 92-93, Champ 95-96, Lg Cup R-up 62-63, Merit Cup 92-93 (jt); Birmingham Lg 55-56 (Nth Div 54-55); Birmingham Comb. R-up 3; Birmingham Snr Cup 7(inc 2001-02), R-up 3

Players P rogressing: A Morton (Fulham 70), R Edwards (Port Vale 72), K Stephens (Luton 78), T Peake (Lincoln C. 79), P Sugrue (Man City 80), M Shotton & T Smithers (Oxford U. 80), D Thomas (Wimbledon 81), P Richardson (Derby C. 84), P Culpin (Coventry 85), R Hill/T Morley/E McGoldrick/A Harris, (North'ton 85/86), D Bullock (Hudd'field 93), M Christie (Derby Co. 98), A Ducros (Kidd'minster H) 2000 S.Weaver (Lincoln C)

Date	Comp.	Opponents	Att.	Score	Goalscorers
16/08	LP	CHIPPENHAM TOWN	1114	1 - 1	**Murphy 51[p]**
19/08	LP	Stafford Rangers	1265	3 - 0	Quailey 19 75, Corbett 47
23/08	LP	Weymouth	1379	1 - 1	Quailey 36
25/08	LP	HINCKLEY UNITED	**1901**	2 - 0	Quailey 75, **Murphy 86**
30/08	LP	EASTBOURNE BOROUGH	1303	4 - 0	Moore 36, Quailey 57, Angus 79, Corbett 80
02/09	LP	Hednesford Town	972	0 - 0	
06/09	LP	NEWPORT COUNTY	1097	2 - 0	Fitzpatrick 14, Clifford 88
08/09	LP	Chelmsford City	455	2 - 1	Corbett 44 76
13/09	LP	Weston-super-Mare	478	1 - 1	**Murphy 36**
16/09	LP	GRANTHAM TOWN	1013	1 - 1	Whittaker 32
20/09	LP	Crawley Town	1864	2 - 2	**Murphy 16**, Clifford 20
27/09	**FA Cup Q2**	**WORCESTER CITY**	1352	1 - 0	Whittaker 62
04/10	LP	WORCESTER CITY	1091	2 - 1	Clifford 40, **Murphy 73**
11/10	**FA Cup Q3**	**RUNCORN HALTON**	1201	1 - 1	Quailey 59
14/10	**FA Cup Q3 rep**	**Runcorn Halton**	347	2 - 2	Moore 46, **Murphy 90**
18/10	LP	TIVERTON TOWN	902	0 - 1	
21/10	LP	Moor Green	497	0 - 2	
25/10	LP	MERTHYR TYDFIL	747	2 - 1	McGorry 55, Lake 70
01/11	LP	Dover Athletic	826	2 - 3	Moore 19, Corbett 90
08/11	LP	HAVANT & WATERLOOVILLE	869	1 - 2	**Murphy 90**
15/11	LP	Bath City	653	3 - 1	Collins 35 75, Whittaker 87
29/11	**FA Trophy 2**	**Hucknall Town**	**625**	**1 - 2**	**Murphy 5**
06/12	LP	HEDNESFORD TOWN	761	3 - 0	Collins 31 52, Brown 70
26/12	LP	Hinckley United	2013	1 - 1	**Murphy 42**
01/01	LP	CAMBRIDGE CITY	798	2 - 1	Moore 35, **Murphy 68**
03/01	LP	Chippenham Town	581	1 - 1	Collins 88
10/01	LP	Welling United	592	1 - 2	Williams 81
17/01	LP	STAFFORD RANGERS	1077	0 - 0	
24/01	LP	Worcester City	1073	0 - 4	
07/02	LP	Dorchester Town	522	0 - 0	
14/02	LP	WELLING UNITED	647	2 - 2	**Murphy 65[p]**, Moore 69
21/02	LP	DOVER ATHLETIC	641	1 - 1	Lamb 90
24/02	LP	BATH CITY	471	2 - 1	**Murphy 6, 83**
28/02	LP	Grantham Town	444	**5 - 0**	Fitzpatrick 3, 32, McGorry 28, Angus 59, **Murphy 73**
06/03	LP	MOOR GREEN	764	1 - 0	Wilkin 60
13/03	LP	Tiverton Town	547	0 - 0	
20/03	LP	WESTON-SUPER-MARE	656	1 - 1	Fitzpatrick 21
23/03	LP	WEYMOUTH	836	4 - 3	Whittaker 23, 56, **Murphy 40**, Fitzpatrick 81
27/03	LP	Newport County	644	2 - 1	**Murphy 23[p]**, Whittaker 31
03 /04	LP	Havant & Waterlooville	461	**1 - 5**	Brown 26
06 /04	LP	Merthyr Tydfil	371	3 - 4	**Murphy 9, 35**, Wilkin 38
10 /04	LP	CHELMSFORD CITY	621	1 - 2	Wilkin 6
12 /04	LP	Cambridge City	426	3 - 1	
17 /04	LP	CRAWLEY TOWN	837	0 - 1	
24 /04	LP	Eastbourne Borough	893	0 - 0	
01/05	LP	DORCHESTER TOWN	653	2 - 0	
		Average Home League Attendance	**890**	70-54	Top Goalsciorer: **Gez Murphy 18** (16+1FAC+1FAT)

PLAYING SQUAD 2004-2005

Goalkeepers:

Darren Acton (Tamworth)

Defenders:

Mark Clifford (Boston Utd), Chris Tullin (Youth team), Andy Crabtree (Youth team), Neil Moore (Mansfield), Steve Farmer (Sutton Coldfield), Mickey Love (Stevenage)

Midfield:

Gary Fitzpatrick (Telford), Matty Collins (WBA), Avun Jephcott (Coventry), Stuart Wilson (Grantham), Mark Noon (Coventry)

Forwards:

Kevin Wilkin (Grantham), Gez Murphy (Kettering), Stuart Whittaker (Leigh RMI), Michael Frew (Yaxley)

REDDITCH UNITED

CLUB OFFICIALS

Chairman: Pat Cremin

President: Major Jim Gillespie MBE

Secretary: Ken Rae c/o club

Tel Nos: 01217 091535(H)

01215 573837 (W)

07747 025417 (M)

Commercial Manager:Richard Shields

Tel No:07876 452375(M)

Press Officer: Pat Cremin

Tel No: 07762 559133 (M)

FACT FILE

Formed: 1891
Nickname: The Reds
Colours: Red with white trim
Change colours:All Blue
Midweek matchday: Tuesday
Reserves' League: Midland Comb. Res Div
Local Press: Redditch Advertiser, Birmingham Evening Mail, Redditch Standard
Local Radio: BBC Hereford & Worcester
The Bear Radio FM102

FOOTBALL MANAGEMENT TEAM

Manager: Rod Brown
Assistant Manager: Gary Whild
Coach: Kim Casey Captain Mark Taylor
Physio: Peter James

GROUND Valley Stadium, Bromsgrove Road, Redditch B97 4RN Tel: 01527 67450
Directions: Access 7 on town centre ring-road takes you into Bromsgrove Road (via Unicorn Hill) - ground entrance 400yds past traffic lights on right.Arriving from Bromsgrove take first exit off dual carriageway. Ground 400 ydsfrom Redditch BR station and town centre
Capacity: 5,000 Cover: 2,000 Seats: 400 Floodlights: Yes
Clubhouse: Large clubroom and lounge boardroom. Open matchdays and for private hire. Food available on matchdays; steaks hot dogs, burgers, chips, bovril etc Tel No: 01527 76450
Club Shop: Not at Present

PROGRAMME

Pages: 50 Price: £1.00
Editor: Gordon Wilkie
Tel Nos: 01527 534999 (H)
07799 686200 (M)
emailgordon.wilkie@ntlworld.com

PREVIOUS **Leagues:** B'ham Comb. 05-21 29-39 46-53, West Midlands 21-29 53-72, Southern 72-79, 81- Alliance Premier (Conf) 79-80
Name: Redditch Town **Ground:** HDA Spts Ground, Millsborough Rd

CLUB RECORDS **Attendance:** 5,500 v Bromsgrove, league match 54-55
Transfer fee paid: £3,000 for Paul Joinson from Halesowen Town
Transfer fee received: £42,000 for David Farrell (Aston Villa, 1991)

BEST SEASON **FA Cup:** 1st Rd replay 71-72, 0-4 v Peterborough U (A) after 1-1 draw. Also 1st Rd 71-72
FA Trophy: 4th Round 1998-99 0-2 v Boston Umited

HONOURS Southern Lg Div 1 Nth 75-76 (Midland Div R-up 85-86) S.Lg Cup R-up 97-98 West Mids (B'ham) Lg Southern Sect. 54-55, Birmingham Comb. 13-14 32-33 52-53 (R-up 06-07 14-15 51-52), Staffs Snr Cup 90-91, Birmingham Snr Cup 24-25 31-32 38-39 76-77, Worcs Snr Cup 894-95 1930-31 74-75 76-77 (R-up 1888-89 1929-30 52-53 73-74), Worcs Jnr Cup 90-91

Players progressing: Hugh Evans (Birmingham 1947), Trevor Lewes (Coventry1957), David Gilbert (Chesterfield 1960), Mike Tuohy (Southend Utd 1979), NeilSmith (Liverpool), David Farrell (Aston Villa 1992), Neil Davis (Aston Villa 1991)

Match Facts 2003-04

Date	Comp.	Opponents	Att.	Score	Goalscorers
16/08	LW	Ilkeston Town	379	**6 - 0**	**Leadbeater 30**, Ross 45, **MYERS 56 59 89**, Quiggan 62
19/08	LW	ATHERSTONE UNITED	260	5 - 0	**LEADBEATER 5,40,73**, Quiggan 7, Hall 20
23/08	LW	CLEVEDON TOWN	230	1 - 0	**Leadbeater 12**
25/08	LW	Bromsgrove Rovers	805	1 - 0	**Leadbetter 15**
30/08	**FA Cup P**	**Leek CSOB**	**105**	3 - 2	**Leadbeater 13,** Burgess 47, Hall 70
06/09	LW	Yate Town	189	5 - 1	Softly 25, Hall 37[p] 49, Myers 47, Hill 71
13/09	**FA Cup Q1**	**Solihull Borough**	416	3 - 0	Hall 43,50 Burgess 67
20/09	LW	HALESOWEN TOWN	526	0 - 2	
23/09	LW	RUGBY UNITED	270	1 - 0	Myers 86
27/09	**FA Cup Q2**	**SHIREBROOK TOWN**	337	1 - 1	Ross 76
01/10	**FA Cup Q2 rep**	**Shirebrook Town**	340	2 - 2	Myers 38, Arshad 90
04/10	LW	SWINDON SUPERMARINE	203	2 - 0	Ross 17, Burgess 70
14/10	LW	EVESHAM UNITED	288	3 - 1	**Leadbeater 12 75,** Ross 66
18/10	LW	SOLIHULL BOROUGH	294	1 - 2	Ross 21
21/10	LW	Shepshed Dynamo	106	0 - 0	
25/10	LW	TEAM BATH	180	2 - 1	Cowley 7, Ross 25
01/11	**FA Trophy 1**	**CIRENCESTER TOWN**	213	6 - 2	**BURGESS 13 22 52 64,** Sawyer 33**, Leadbeater 65**
08/11	LW	Gresley Rovers	396	3 - 2	Burgess 31, Softley 39, **Leadbeater 52**
15/11	LW	Taunton Town	324	2 - 0	Shepherd 68, Myers 89
18/11	LW	SUTTON COLDFIELD TOWN	289	1 - 1	Ross 84
22/11	LW	MANGOTSFIELD UNITED	201	3 - 0	Shepherd 16 65, Hall 64
29/11	**FA Trophy 2**	**STALYBRIDGE CELTIC**	288	0 - 3	
06/12	LW	Bedworth United	149	1 - 0	**Leadbeater 49**
13/12	LW	ILKESTON TOWN	252	1 - 1	Myers 42
16/12	LW	Mangotsfield United	146	3 - 2	Cowley 44 85, Hall 65[p]
20/12	LW	Clevedon Town	129	3 - 0	Hall 22, **Leadbeatter 45 85**
27/12	LW	BROMSGROVE ROVERS	**1384**	4 - 0	Voice 35, Hall 71 86, Cowley 76
01/01	LW	Stourport Swifts	269	4 - 0	Cowley 3, Burgess 9 52, Myers 88
03/01	LW	CINDERFORD TOWN	300	5 - 2	Burgess 12, Voice 51 66, Quiggan 64, Taylor 72
10/01	LW	BEDWORTH UNITED	414	1 - 1	Burgess 66
17/01	LW	Evesham United	393	**0 - 2**	
24/01	LW	TAUNTON TOWN	286	0 - 0	
31/01	LW	Solihull Borough	312	1 - 1	Burgess 85
07/02	LW	CIRENCESTER TOWN	326	2 - 1	Cowley 5, Myers 30
14/02	LW	Sutton Coldfield Town	202	0 - 1	
21/02	LW	Rugby United	437	3 - 2	Hall 61 90, **Leadbeater 71**
28/02	LW	GRESLEY ROVERS	346	2 - 0	Myers 3, Voice 58
06/03	LW	Gloucester City	459	1 - 1	Softley 39
20/03	LW	YATE TOWN	260	4 - 0	Flynn 51 62, Myers 58, Shepherd 77
22/03	LW	Team Bath	158	2 - 1	Knight 17, **Leadbetter 70**
27/03	LW	Halesowen Town	636	0 - 0	
03 /04	LW	SHEPSHED DYNAMO	318	1 - 0	Cowley 67
10 /04	LW	Cinderford Town	202	**0 - 2**	
12 /04	LW	STOURPORT SWIFTS	336	1 - 1	**Leadbetter 46**
17 /04	LW	Swindon Supermarine	131	2 - 1	**Leadbeater 44**, Myers 72
24 /04	LW	GLOUCESTER CITY	1088	0 - 1	
01/05	LW	Cirencester Town	510	3 - 0	Bird 56 (og), Cowley 60 Shepherd 72
03/05	**Play-off**	**King's Lynn**	2014	1 - 0	Burgess 55
08/05	**Play-off**	**Merthyr Tydfil**	907	3 - 0	**Leadbetter 10, 53** Shepherd 26

Average Home League Attendance:**336** 99-40 Top Goalscorer: **Leadbetter 20** (17+1FAC+1FAT+1PO)

PLAYING SQUAD 2004-2005

Goalkeepers Richard Anstiss (Moor Green)

Defenders:

Matt Clarke (Telford), Neil Manton (Sutton Coldfield), Matt Gardiner (Evesham), Gary Knight (Gresley R), Andy Penny (Hinckley Utd)

Midfield:

Jordan King (Hednesford), Mark Taylor (Halesowen), Sean Flynn (Evesham), Luke Prince (Team Bath), Craig Woodley (Worcester)

Forwards:

Simon Hollis (Halesowen), Danny Scheppel (Moor Green), Scott Voice (Hinckley Utd), Richard Leadbeater (Halesowen), Paul Moore (Telford), Rob Taylor (Stourport Swifts), Alex Cowley (Stourport Swifts)

RUNCORN F.C. HALTON

CLUB OFFICIALS

Chairman: Dr David Robertson

Vice Chairman: Ian Burgess

Directors: Headley Edwards&d Michael Hill

Secretary: Alan Jones,49 Beech Road, Runcorn, Cheshire WA7 5LN

Tel : 01928 563781(H) 07980 125067(M)

Commercial Manager: Secretary

Press Officer: Martin Fallon

Tel No: 07808 737773

FOOTBALL MANAGEMENT

Manager: Chris Lightfooot

Physio: Geoff Hughes

FACT FILE

Formed: 1918

Nickname: The Linnets

Midweek matchday: Tuesday

Colours: Yellow/&green/yellow

Change: Sky blue/dark blue/darkblue.

No Reserve team

Youth's league: Northwest Alliance

Website: www.runcornfchalton.co.uk

Local Press: Runcorn Weekly News, Liverpool Echo, Runcorn World, Manchester Evening News.

Local Radio:

Radio Merseyside, GMR.Wire F.M

GROUND HaltonStadium, Lowerhouse Lane, Widnes, Cheshire. WA8 7DZ
Tel No: Matchdays only 0151 5106000 Fax matchdays only 0151 510 6001

Directions: From M62 take junction 7 and follow signs to Widnes and Auto quest Stadium. Follow Widnes by -pass and then turn right onto Ashley Way. At roundabout take second exit and go straight onto the next roundabout where the Stadium ia on the right.

Capacity: 12,500 Covered Seats: 12,500

Clubhouse: Open on matchdays. Light snacks available.

Club Shop: Phone club.

PROGRAMME

Pages: 36 Price: £1.20

Editor: Derek Greenwood

email: kinnettdg@onetl.net.uk

Tel No: 01282 843819

PREVIOUS **Leagues:** Lancs Combination; Cheshire Co. Lg; Northern Prem. Lge. 68 -81; Alliance Premier (Conference) 81-96.
Names: Runcorn **Grounds:** Canal Street, Runcorn

CLUB RECORDS **Attendance:** 10,111 v Preston - FA Cup 1938-39.
Goalscorer: Alan Ryan (66 goals in 64 appearances 67-68).
Win: 11-1 v Congleton Town 64-65. **Defeat:** 0-9 v Wellington 46-47.
Fee Paid: £17,000 for Simon Rudge, Hyde Utd, 1989. **Fee Received:** £80,000 for Ian Woan, Nottm Forest, 1990.

BEST SEASON **FA Trophy:** Runners-up 85-86, 92-93, 93-94. **FA Cup:** Second Round Replay 85-86,0-4 v Wigan Ath. (A), after 1-1. Second Round also 47-48, 67-68, 77-78, 86-87,87-88, 88-89. League clubs defeated: Scunthorpe Utd. 1947-48, Notts. Co (1967-68), Chester City 1987-88, Wrexham 1988-89.

HONOURS Lancs Jnr Cup 1918-19; Cheshire Lg 1919-20, 36-37, 38-39, 39-40, 62-63;Cheshire Snr Cup 24-25, 35-36, 61-62, 64-65, 67-68, 73-74, 74-75, 84-89 (5times), R-up 93-94; Cheshire Co. Bowl 37-38; Northern Premier Lg 75-76, 80-81(R-up 74-75); NPL Chall Cup 74-75, 79-80, 80-81; NPL Challenge Shield 80-81,81-82; Alliance Premier Lg 81-82, Gola Lg Championship Shield 82-83, 85-86; Bob Lord Trophy 82-83, 84-85, R-up 91-92. FA Trophy R-up 85-86, 92-93, 93-94.NPL Pres.Cup 98-99

Players Progressing: Mark McCarrick, Eddie Bishop, Jim Cumbes, Graham Abel,Barry Knowles, Mark Jones, Don Page, David Pugh, Ian Woan, Gary Brabin, Paul Robertson, Mike Smith,Mark Carter

Left to right

Back row: Mal Liptrot (Kit Manager), John Ryder, David Robinson, Mark Winstanley, Mike Tomlinson, David Ness, David Gamble.

Middle row: Gary Lunt, Michael Short, Neil Whalley (Asst Man.), Liam Watson (Player/Man.), Steve Latham.

Front row: Steve Carragher, Alan Cowley, Tony Ward, John McAllister, Chris Price

Date	Comp.	Opponents	Att.	Score	Goalscorers
R16/08	LP	Frickley Athletic	221	2 - 1	Price 5 44
19/08	LP	DROYLSDEN	264	2 - 2	Lightfoot 31[p], Daly 63
23/08	LP	BRADFORD PARK AVENUE	271	1 - 2	Daly 35
25/08	LP	Lancaster City	313	1 - 0	Leadbetter 36
30/08	LP	Worksop Town	518	1 - 0	Daly 36
02/09	LP	RADCLIFFE BOROUGH	310	2 - 2	Ness 2, Daly 3
06/09	LP	SPENNYMOOR UNITED	331	1 - 2	**Courtney 60**
09/09	LP	Southport	828	3 - 0	McGinn 6, Leadbetter 57, Daly 75
13/09	LP	Harrogate Town	427	1 - 1	Daly 60
20/09	LP	WHITBY TOWN	242	1 - 1	Leadbetter 78
23/09	LP	Barrow	1095	0 - 1	
27/09	**FA Cup Q2**	**GUISELEY**	234	3 - 0	Leadbetter 41, Price 73, Carden 88
30/09	LP	MARINE	259	0 - 2	
07/10	LP	Vauxhall Motors	242	**0 - 6**	
11/10	**FA Cup Q3**	**Nuneaton Borough**	1201	1 - 1	Leadbetter 31
14/10	**FA Cup Q3 rep**	**NUNEATON BOROUGH**	347	2 - 2	Leadbetter 20, Daly 55 5 4
18/10	LP	Stalybridge Celtic	524	2 - 2	Leadbetter 44, Daly 76
25/10	**FA Cup Q4**	**BRADFORD PARK AVENUE**	379	0 - 1	
28/10	LP	Marine	284	3 - 1	Lightfoot 3 55, **Courtney 48**
01/11	**FA Trophy 1**	**BISHOP AUCKLAND**	184	7 - 0	**Courtney 10, 68**, Daly 27, 40, Carden 42, Spearritt 44, Hogan 56
04/11	LP	Burscough	173	3 - 1	Ness 5, **Courtney 51**, Leadbetter 87
08/11	LP	VAUXHALL MOTORS	229	1 - 1	Ness 73
12/11	LP	Bradford Park Avenue	266	1 - 1	Brierley 82
15/11	LP	ASHTON UNITED	239	1 - 2	Leadbetter 47[p]
18/11	LP	GAINSBOROUGH TRINITY	172	2 - 2	Nolan 49, Ness 53
22/11	LP	Hucknall Town	416	0 - 1	
29/11	**FA Trophy 2**	**FRICKLEY ATHLETIC**	152	3 - 2	McGinn 18, **Courtney 48**, Lightfoot 90
06/12	LP	WORKSOP TOWN	253	2 - 3	Carragher 37, Sykes 59[og]
13/12	LP	LANCASTER CITY	212	0 - 1	
26/12	LP	Droylsden	327	2 - 1	Leadbetter 70, **Courtney 72**
03/01	LP	HUCKNALL TOWN	272	1 - 2	Morley 45
10/01	**FA Trophy 3**	**Altrincham**	707	1 - 2	**Courtney 84**
24/01	LP	Spennymoor United	141	1 - 2	McGinn 27
07/02	LP	Alfreton Town	248	2 - 0	Lightfoot 20, Rendell 90
14/02	LP	Blyth Spartans	377	3 - 3	Rendell 29 55, McGinn 70
21/02	LP	SOUTHPORT	**733**	1 - 1	Kissock 19
24/02	LP	Radcliffe Borough	170	2 - 1	Kissock 51[p], Garrity 88
06/03	LP	Ashton United	204	2 - 4	Rendell 23, **Courtney 75[p]**
13/03	LP	FRICKLEY ATHLETIC	203	2 - 0	Rendell 49, Garrity 51
16/03	LP	ALTRINCHAM	383	0 - 3	
20/03	LP	Gainsborough Trinity	248	1 - 0	**Courtney 88**
27/03	LP	Wakefield & Emley	136	5 - 3	Rendell 26, **LIGHTFOOT 65 75 90**, Spearritt 77
30/03	LP	BARROW	259	0 - 0	
03 /04	LP	BLYTH SPARTANS	182	1 - 0	**Courtney 80**
06 /04	LP	Whitby Town	186	0 - 1	
08 /04	LP	ALFRETON TOWN	187	2 - 2	Kissock 37[p], Lightfoot 87
14 /04	LP	BURSCOUGH	243	0 - 0	
17 /04	LP	STALYBRIDGE CELTIC	274	3 - 0	Rendell 9, Lightfoot 25, Garrity 75
20 /04	LP	HARROGATE TOWN	188	**4 - 1**	Spearritt 2, Rendell 8 74, Platt 90
22 /04	LP	WAKEFIELD & EMLEY	251	5 - 3	Rendell 19 38, Morley 52, Lightfoot 60, **Courtney 61**
24 /04	**LP**	**Altrincham**	**874**	**0 - 1**	
		Average Home League Attendance:	**270**	84-71	Top Goalscorer: **Courtney 12** (8+4FAT)

PLAYING SQUAD 2004-2005

Goalkeepers:
Tony McMillan (Wigan), Mark Cartwright (Wrexham)

Defenders:
Chris Lightfoot (Morecambe), David Ness (Youth team), Ged Nolan (St Helens), John Robertson (Lancaster), Lee Prior (Newton), Peter Ellis (Knowsley), Robbie Moore (General Chemicals), Steve Carragher (Accrington Stanley), Tom Spearritt (Southport)

Midfield:
Anton Lally (Marine), Kieran Durkan (Swansea), Lee Parle (Local football), Matthew McGinn (Local football), Mike Garrity (Salford C)

Forwards:
Carl Rendell (Prescot Cables), Ged Courtney (Leigh RMI), Lee Kissock (Vauxhall Motors), Nicky Young (Marine)

SOUTHPORT

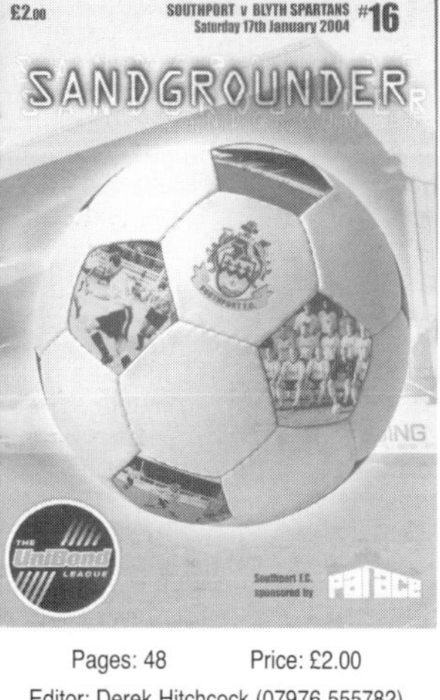

Pages: 48 Price: £2.00

Editor: Derek Hitchcock (07976 555782)

Clubcall: 09066 555 875

Local Press: Southport Visiter; The Champion

Local Radio: Dune F.M.; Radio Merseyside; Radio City; Radio Lancashire

CLUB OFFICIALS

Chairman: Charles Clapham

Directors

C Clapham,S Shrouder (Vice Chairman), B J Hedley, A Pope, P Abrams,T Medcroft, S Porter, G.Tait

Football Secretary: Ken Hilton
34 Mill Lane, Burscough, Ormskirk L40 5TS
Tel: 01704 894504 (H) 07802 661906 (M)

Sales & Marketing Manager:
Derek Hitchcock
Tel: 07976 555782
e-mail: derek@hitchcock98.freeserve.co.uk

Press Officer: Haydn Reece(07768 000818)

FOOTBALL MANAGEMENT TEAM

Manager: Liam Watson

Reserve Team Coach: Tony Rodwell

Physio: Brett Harris Captain: Chris Price

FACT FILE

Founded: 1881

Nickname: The Sandgrounders

Club Sponsors: V K Vodka Kick

Club colours: Old Gold / black /black

Change colours: All white

Midweek home matchday: Tuesday

Reserves' League: Lancashire League

Club's Playing Status: Part-time

2003-04

P.o.Y.:Neil Fitzhenry

Leading Scorer: Neil Robinson

GROUND Haig Avenue, Southport, Merseyside. PR8 6JZ
Ground: 01704 533422 Fax: 01704 533455 Ticket Office: 01704 533422

DIRECTIONS: From M6 - M58 through Ormskirk (A570) to Southport. Straight on at Tesco/McDonalds roundabout. Right at the mini r'about and the ground is on the right

Capacity: 6,008 **Seated:** 1,660 **Covered Terracing:** 1,100

Clubhouse: Open 6.00-11.00 every night and match days. Tel: 01704 530182

Club Shop: Scarves, replica kits and large range of souvenirs for sale.
Contact D Hitchcock, c/o Southport F.C or e-mail: derek@hitchcock98.freeserve.co.uk

PREVIOUS **Leagues:** Conference, Northern Premier League, Football League, Lancashire Combination
Grounds: Ash Lane **Names:** Southport Central; Southport Vulcan

CLUB RECORDS **Attendance:** 20,010 v Newcastle United, FA Cup - 1932
Record win: 8-1 v Nelson - 01.01.31 **Record defeat:** 0-11 v Oldham - 26.12.62
Career goalscorer: Alan Spence 98 **Career appearances:** Arthur Peat 401 - 1962-72
Transfer fee paid: £20,000, for Martin McDonald from Macclesfield Town - 1995
Transfer fee received: £25,000, from Rochdale for Steve Whitehall - 1991

BEST SEASON **FA Cup:** Quarter Final, 1930-31,.1-9 v Everton (A) (The first Division 3 North team to reach the Quarter Finals)
League club defeated: Mansfield Town (1998-9) (as a non-league club)
FA Trophy: Runners-up 97-98, 0-1 v Cheltenham Town **League:** Football League Div. 3 23rd 73-74

HONOURS FA Trophy R-up 97-98; Football League Division Four 1972/73 Runners-up 1966/67; Third Division North Section Cup 1937/38; Northern Premier League 1992/93, League Cup 1990/91, League Shield 1993/94; Liverpool Senior Cup 1930/31, 1931/32, 1943/44, 1957/58 (shared), 1963/64 (shared), 1974/75, 1990/91, 1992/93, 1998/99; Lancashire Senior Cup 1904/05; Lancashire Junior Cup 1919/20, 1992/93, 1996-97, 1997-98

Players P rogressing: Shaun Teale, Andy Mutch, Steve Whitehall, Tony Rodwell

Date	Comp.	Opponents	Att.	Score	Goalscorers
16/08	LP	Wakefield & Emley	321	1 - 0	Veart 90[p]
19/08	LP	LANCASTER CITY	**1213**	3 - 0	Ashcroft 73, Wright 77, Thomson 86
25/08	LP	Burscough	1249	3 - 0	Ashcroft 21[p] 53, Thompson 69
30/08	LP	WHITBY TOWN	1032	3 - 0	Ashcroft 44, Whittaker 71, Jones 77
02/09	LP	Stalybridge Celtic	801	1 - 2	Ashcroft 4
06/09	LP	Hucknall Town	701	**0 - 4**	
09/09	LP	RUNCORN HALTON	828	0 - 3	
13/09	LP	DROYLSDEN	759	4 - 1	Beesley 17, Mulvaney 21, Soley 26, Wright 56
16/09	LP	Worksop Town	601	0 - 1	
20/09	LP	Ashton United	382	1 - 2	Ashcroft 63[p]
23/09	LP	ALTRINCHAM	702	2 - 2	Hallam 45, Mulvaney 61
27/09	**FA Cup Q2**	Vauxhall Motors	492	1 - 3	Ashcroft 86[p]
30/09	LP	BARROW	859	1 - 1	Ashcroft 11
04/10	LP	Bradford Park Avenue	393	1 - 0	Ashcroft 80
07/10	LP	Lancaster City	706	0 - 1	
18/10	LP	RADCLIFFE BOROUGH	743	2 - 1	Thomson 36 40
25/10	LP	Frickley Athletic	215	2 - 1	Hallam 53, Mulvaney 72
28/10	LP	Altrincham	679	0 - 1	
01/11	LP	WORKSOP TOWN	801	2 - 3	Mulvaney 65, Thomson 83
04/11	LP	Barrow	805	1 - 1	Thomson 59
08/11	LP	HUCKNALL TOWN	775	1 - 1	Thomson 52
15/11	LP	SPENNYMOOR UNITED	713	2 - 3	Thomson 22, Daly 49
22/11	LP	Harrogate Town	601	1 - 3	Aspin 60[og]
29/11	**FA Trophy 2**	Altrincham	711	0 - 1	
13/12	LP	BRADFORD PARK AVENUE	746	0 - 1	
26/12	LP	Marine	953	1 - 1	Price 89
01/01	LP	BURSCOUGH	1122	2 - 1	Pickford 20 25
10/01	LP	WAKEFIELD & EMLEY	653	1 - 1	Pickford 2
17/01	LP	BLYTH SPARTANS	713	1 - 0	Daly 88
24/01	LP	Alfreton Town	397	2 - 0	Robinson 40[og], Daly 44
31/01	LP	Vauxhall Motors	385	2 - 3	Leadbetter 17, **Robinson 60**
07/02	LP	Whitby Town	282	**5 - 0**	**LEADBETTER 3 12 43**, Ashcroft 52, Pickford 80
14/02	LP	ALFRETON TOWN	749	1 - 0	Baker 56
17/02	LP	Gainsborough Trinity	499	2 - 1	Ashcroft 45, Baker 90[p]
21/02	LP	Runcorn Halton	733	1 - 1	Baker 27
28/02	LP	VAUXHALL MOTORS	822	1 - 1	**Robinson 66**
06/03	LP	Spennymoor United	217	2 - 0	**Robinson 29 74**
13/03	LP	Blyth Spartans	441	4 - 1	**ROBINSON 3 11 40**, Leadbetter 18
20/03	LP	HARROGATE TOWN	838	3 - 2	**Robinson 38**, Daly 50, Baker 61[p]
23/03	LP	GAINSBOROUGH TRINITY	601	2 - 0	**Robinson 78,90**
03 /04	LP	Radcliffe Borough	407	3 - 1	Leadbetter 63, Mulvany 74, **Robinson 90**
06 /04	LP	MARINE	860	0 - 0	
10 /04	LP	Droylsden	423	2 - 3	**Robinson 18, 81**
12 /04	LP	STALYBRIDGE CELTIC	923	2 - 3	Laedbetter 18 Baker 27 (p)
17 /04	LP	ASHTON UNITED	702	0 - 0	
24 /04	LP	FRICKLEY ATHLETIC	649	3 - 1	**Robinson 37**, Price 48, Leadbetter 56
		Average Home League Attendance:	**809**	72-56	Top Goalscorer: **Robinson 14**

PLAYING SQUAD 2004-2005

Goalkeepers:
Steve Dickinson (Guiseley), Ian Lowe (Vauxhall Motors)

Defenders:
Neil Fitzhenry (Workington), Earl Davis (Burnley), Alex Mortimer (Gainsborough), Jimmy Williams (Swindon), Farrell Kilbane (Lancaster), Jerome Fitzgerald (Accrington Stanley)

Midfield:
Kevin Lynch (Vauxhall Motors), Darren Brookfield (Liverpool), Dominic Morley (Droylsden), Chris Price (Runcorn), Carl Baker (Prescot Cables), Steve Pickford (Stalybridge), Daryl Allen (Blackburn)

Forwards:
Lee Mulvaney (Youth team), Neil Robinson (Macclesfield), Kevin Leadbetter (Runcorn), Steve Daly (Runcorn), Terry Fearns (Vauxhall Motors)

STAFFORD RANGERS

CLUB OFFICIALS

Chairman: C.Went
Vice-Chairman: M.Hughes
Secretary: Michael Hughes,1 Rambleford Way,Parkside,Staffoord St16 1TW
Tel: 01785 254879 (H) 07850 996386 (M)

FOOTBALL MANAGEMENT TEAM

Manager: Phil Robinson
Coach: T.B.A.
Physio: Eddie Silk

FACT FILE

Formed: 1876 Nickname: The Boro
Colours: Black & White stripes/black/black
Change: All Red
Midweek matchday: Tuesday
Local Press: Staffordshire Newsletter, Express & Star, Evening Sentinel
Local Radio:
Radio Stoke, Beacon Radio, Signal Radio
2003-2004
P.o.Y.: Wayne Daniel
Top Scorer" Daniel Davidson
2004-2005 Captain: Wayne Daniel

STAFFORD RANGERS
V
BATH CITY
SATURDAY 20TH MARCH 2004.
KICK OFF 3.00PM MATCH No. 18

MAIN SPONSOR
STAN ROBINSON (STAFFORD) LTD

PROGRAMME
Pages: 40 Price: £180
Editor: K.Hunt

GROUND Marston Road Stafford ST16 3BX Tel: 01785 602430 Fax : 01785 602431
Club Website: www.staffordrangers.co.uk

Directions: From M6 junction 14, A34 (Stone) to roundabout, straight over into Beaconside, take third right into Common Road, ground one mile ahead. From Town Centre, follow signs for B5066 (Sandon) turn left by new housing estate. Two miles from railway station

Capacity 3,000 Cover 1,500 Seats: 426 Floodlights: Yes

Clubhouse: Yes - Open every evening
Club Shop: Two shops, one old programmes and one souvenirs

PREVIOUS
Leagues: Shropshire 1891-93, Birm 1893-96, 21-40, N Staffs 1896-1900, Cheshire 00-01, Birm Comb 00-12, 46-52, Cheshire Co. 52-69, N.P.L. 69-79, 83-85, Alliance Prem 79-83, GMVC 85-95
Grounds: Lammascotes, Stone Rd, Newtown, Doxey (until 1896)

CLUB RECORDS
Attendance: 8,536 v Rotherham Utd FA Cup 3rd Rd 75
Win: 11-0 v Dudley Town FA Cup 6.9.58 **Defeat:** 0-12 v Burton Town Birmingham Lge 13.12.30
Career Goalscorer: M Cullerton 176 **Career Appearances:** Jim Sargent
Transfer fee paid: £13,000 for S Butterworth from VS Rugby 90
Transfer fee received: £100,000 for Stan Collymore from Crystal Palace 1990

BEST SEASON
FA Trophy: Winners 1971-72 & 78-79. R-up 75-76
FA Cup: 4th Rd 74-75, 1-2 v Peterborough Utd. (H) League clubs defeated: Halifax, Stockport, Rotherham

HONOURS
Birm Comb Champ 12-13; Birm Lge Champ 25-26; N.P.L. Champ 71-72, 84-85, Champ Shield 84-85; FA Trophy 71-72, 78-79, R-up 75-76; Bob Lord Trophy 85-86; Wednesday Charity Cup 20-21; Mid F/light Cup 70-71; Jim Thompson Shield 86-87; Staffs Sen Cup 54-55 56-57 62-63 71-72 77-78 86-87 91-92 Dr.Martens Western Division 99-00

Players progressing: M Aleksic (Plymouth), J Arnold (Blackburn), R Williams/MCullerton/T Bailey (Port Vale), K Barnes (Man City), A Lee (Tranmere), ECameron (Exeter), W Blunt (Wolves), G Bullock (Barnsley), K Mottershead (Doncaster), McIlvenny (WBA), S Collymore (C Palace), P Devlin (Notts Co.),R Price (Birmingham C.)

Back Row, left to right: Allan Dodd,Danny Edwards, James Lindley, Dennis Pearce, Wayne Daniel, Will Smith, Glynn Blackhurst and James Dunnn. **Middle Row:** Eddie Silk (physio), Nicky Campbell, Richard Beale, Lee Downes, Craig Wilding, Paul Rutter, Marcus Jackson, and Chris Goodwin (Assdt. Physio). **Front Row:** Adam Yates, Craig Lovatt, Robert Heath, Phil Robinson (Manager), Neil Grayson, Gary Fife and Les Hines.

Date	Comp.	Opponents	Att.	Score	Goalscorers
16/08	LP	Eastbourne Borough	494	1 - 1	Wilding 32
19/08	LP	NUNEATON BOROUGH	1265	0 - 3	
23/08	LP	NEWPORT COUNTY	773	1 - 0	**Davidson 77**
25/08	LP	Hednesford Town	1288	2 - 1	Wilding 11, McAughtrie 73
30/08	LP	Welling United	507	1 - 2	**Davidson 61**
02/09	LP	MOOR GREEN	751	1 - 2	Daniel 71
06/09	LP	CHIPPENHAM TOWN	681	2 - 0	Goodman 45, **Davidson 71**
09/09	LP	Hinckley United	405	1 - 1	Goodman 68
13/09	LP	DORCHESTER TOWN	786	3 - 0	Goodman 45, **Davidson 53 57**
16/09	LP	Bath City	521	0 - 1	
20/09	LP	HAVANT & WATERLOOVILLE	707	2 - 1	**Davidson 38 82**
27/09	**FA Cup Q2**	**GRANTHAM TOWN**	797	1 - 2	**Davidson 12[p]**
04/10	LP	Weymouth	1357	1 - 0	**Davidson 78**
18/10	LP	Crawley Town	1023	0 - 2	
21/10	LP	MERTHYR TYDFIL	547	3 - 1	Wilding 33, McAughtrie 55, **Davidson 90**
25/10	LP	Havant & Waterlooville	514	2 - 2	**Davidson 32 83**
01/11	LP	TIVERTON TOWN	804	1 - 2	**Davidson 72**
15/11	LP	Chippenham Town	473	3 - 0	Colley 4, **Davidson 30**, Heath 40
22/11	LP	DOVER ATHLETIC	688	2 - 1	Gibson 40, Wilding 57
29/11	**FA Trophy 2**	**SPENNYMOOR UNITED**	152	2 - 1	**Davidson 25 27**
06/12	LP	Cambridge City	502	0 - 1	
13/12	LP	EASTBOURNE BOROUGH	616	**4 - 1**	**Davidson 19[p]**, Gibson 43, Wilding 66 77
26/12	LP	HEDNESFORD TOWN	**1974**	1 - 1	**Davidson 37[p]**
01/01	LP	Worcester City	1521	1 - 0	Heath 84
03/01	LP	GRANTHAM TOWN	806	0 - 1	
10/01	**FA Trophy 3**	**Scarborough**	1117	2 - 1	**Davidson 71,89**
17/01	LP	Nuneaton Borough	1077	0 - 0	
24/01	LP	HINCKLEY UNITED	936	2 - 0	Wilding 45, Fife 76
31/01	**FA Trophy 4**	**CANVEY ISLAND**	**1163**	**0 - 2**	
07/02	LP	Chelmsford City	337	2 - 1	McAughtrie 50, **Davidson 87**
10/02	LP	WESTON-SUPER-MARE	646	1 - 1	Lovatt 78
14/02	LP	Merthyr Tydfil	543	1 - 1	**Davidson 32**
21/02	LP	CAMBRIDGE CITY	737	1 - 1	Wilding 75
25/02	LP	Newport County	541	1 - 3	**Davidson 59[p]**
28/02	LP	CRAWLEY TOWN	952	0 - 1	
06/03	LP	Dorchester Town	486	0 - 0	
09/03	LP	WELLING UNITED	458	3 - 2	**Davidson 79[p]**, Gibson 80, Beale 90
13/03	LP	Moor Green	368	2 - 1	Grayson 2 33
20/03	LP	BATH CITY	298	2 - 0	Grayson 69 71
27/03	LP	Tiverton Town	557	0 - 0	
03 /04	LP	WEYMOUTH	788	1 - 2	Clarke 73[og]
10 /04	LP	Grantham Town	351	2 - 0	Heath 28, Fife 51
12 /04	LP	WORCESTER CITY	837	2 - 0	McAughtrie 22 Heath 82
24 /04	LP	CHELMSFORD CITY	866	2 - 1	Wilding 43 48
29/04	LP	Weston-super-Mare	217	**1 - 5**	Fife 86 (p)
01/05	LP	Dover Athletic	1003	0 - 0	

Average Home League Attendance: **802** 60-48 Top Goalscorer: **Danny Davidson 22** (17+1FAC+4FAT)

PLAYING SQUAD 2004-2005

Goalkeepers:
James Lindley (Hucknall), Will Smith (Heath Hayes)

Defenders:
Wayne Daniel (Boldmere), Richard Beale (Redditch), Craig McAughtrie (Carlisle), Dennis Pearce (Peterborough), Alan Dodd (Kidsgrove),

Midfield:
Phil Robinson (Hereford), Robert Heath (Stoke), Craig Lovatt (Leek), Mark Lowry (Hereford), Glyn Blackhurst (Youth team), Danny Edwards (Shrewsbury)

Forwards:
Robin Gibson (Wrexham), Lee Downes (Kidderminster), Neil Grayson (Forest Green), Nicky Campbell (Willenhall), Craig Wilding (York), Gary Fife (Youth team)

STALYBRIDGE CELTIC

CLUB OFFICIALS

President: Roy Oldham
Chairman: Peter Dennerly
Vice Chairman: Dorothy Norton
Directors:
B McCallum, G Crossley, G Greenwood, J Dillon, R Gorski, P Fenton,S.White
Club Secretary: Martyn Torr
Tel: 07860 841765
Football Sec. & Commercial Man.
John Hall
Tel: 0161 4560765(H) 0161 338 2828(W)
07813 864492 (M)
Press Officer: Keith Trudgeon
Tel: 0161205 7631 (B) 0161 304 8934 (H)
07767 404642

FOOTBALL MANAGEMENT TEAM

Manager: David Miller
Assistant Manager: Gerry Luczka
Captain: Kevin Parr
Sports Therapist: David Pover
Chief Scout: Ian Senior

2003-2004

Top Scorer & P.o.Y.: Phil Eastwood 20
+ P.o.Ys.: Barrie Keeling & Chris Denham

PROGRAMME

Pages: 40 Price: £1.50
Editor: Nick Shaw Tel: 0161 633 1117

FACT FILE

Formed: 1909
Nickname: Celtic
Sponsors: Stepan & Tameside T.M.B.C.
Club colours: Blue & white/blue/ white
Change colours:l Gold& Green
Midweek matchday: Tuesday
Reserves' League: None
Local Press: Manchester Evening News, Manchester Evening News Pink (Sun. a.m.), Ashton Reporter, Ashton Advertiser
Local Radio: G.M.R. (BBC Manchester), 96.2 The Revolution

GROUND Bower Fold, Mottram Road, Stalybridge, Cheshire SK15 2RT
Tel: 0161 338 2828 Fax: 0161 338 8256. Club Website: www.stalybridgeceltic.co.uk

Directions: From Stockport and South: M60,M67 to end of Motorway through large roundabout to traffic lights.Then left to mini roundabout and left again into Mottram Road.Follow signs to Stalybridge, down hill and ground is on left next to Hare & Hounds pub.

Capacity: 6,108 **Seats:** 1,200 **Cover:** 1,200

Clubhouse: Open matchdays only. Food available **Club Shop:** Contact Bob Rhodes Tel: 01457 764044 (H)

PREVIOUSLeagues: Lancashire Comb. 1911-12, Central League 12-21, Southern League 1914-15 Football League 21-23, Cheshire County Lge 23-82, North West Counties 82-87, Northern Premier 87-92, 98-01, Conference 92-98, 01-02

CLUB RECORDS **Attendance:** 9,753 v WBA, FA Cup replay, 22-23 **Defeat:**1-10 v Wellington Town 9.3.4
Career goalscorer: Harry Dennison 215 **Win:** 16-2; v Manchester NE 1.5.26 & v Nantwich 22/10/326
Career appearances: Kevin Booth 354 **Goalscorer (season):** Cecil Smith 77 1931-32
Fee paid: £15,000 to Kettering Town for Ian Arnold 95 **Fee received:** £16,000 for Lee Trundle from Southport

BEST SEASON **FA Cup:** Second Round 93-94, 1-3 v Carlisle Utd.(A); 99-00 1-2 v Chester City (H). League clubs defeated: None
FA Trophy: 6th Rd.v Stevenage Borough 0-1 2001 02 **League**: 12th Conference 92-93

HONOURS Northern Premier Lge Prem Div 91-92, 00-01; Div.1; NPL Cup 98-99 Presidents Cup 00- 01 02-03Challenge Shield 91-92 Cheshire County Lg 79-80, Lg Cup 21-22; Challenge Shield 77-78, N.W. Cos Lg 83-84, 86-8,Challenge Shield 83-84 Champions v Cup Winners Trophy 83-84; Lancs Div 2 11-12; Southern Div 15-16 Manchester Section 18-19Cheshire Snr Cup 52-53, 00-01; Manchester Snr Cup 22-23, Intermediate Cup 57-58, 68-69, Challenge Shield 54-55, 00-01 (Junior Cup 62-63); Lancs Floodlit Cup 88-89, Reporter Cup Edward Case Cup 77-78. S.E.LancsdLg Cup 37-38 Man/Lg Open Trophy 48-49 Ashton Challenge Cup Winners (13)Man.Junior Cup 62-63 Altrincham Cup 18-19

Players progressing: Too numerous to list. but includes recently Eamoon O'Keefe, John Anderson, Lee Trundle

Back row, left to right: Roy Barker (Kit Manager), Dave Miller(Team Manager), Darren Bowman, Lee Connell, Terry Bowker, Craig Dootson, Barrie Keeling, Paul Sykes, Dean Calcutt, Greg Pearce and Gerry Luzcka (Coach). **Front row**: Gary Williams, Andy Hayward, Ian Monk, Tony Whealing, Nathan Wharton, Kevin Parr(Club Captain), Danny Caldecott, Dave German and Ben Smith

Date	Comp.	Opponents	Att.	Score	Goalscorers
16/08	LP	GAINSBOROUGH TRINITY	504	2 - 0	Potts 4[p], Foster 90
19/08	LP	Radcliffe Borough	431	2 - 3	Mayers 27, Foster 45
23/08	LP	Barrow	1140	2 - 0	Salmon 33[og], Potts 90
25/08	LP	ASHTON UNITED	673	1 - 1	Foster 7
30/08	LP	Burscough	267	0 - 0	
02/09	LP	SOUTHPORT	801	2 - 1	Foster 52[p] 54
06/09	LP	WORKSOP TOWN	577	**0 - 3**	
09/09	LP	Alfreton Town	664	1 - 3	Parr 90
13/09	LP	SPENNYMOOR UNITED	415	0 - 2	
20/09	LP	Bradford Park Avenue	283	3 - 2	Mayers 20, Pearce 77, Potts 85
23/09	LP	HUCKNALL TOWN	416	1 - 2	Potts 28
27/09	**FA Cup Q2**	**Guisborough Town**	205	2 - 2	Wharton 45, Potts 50
30/09	**FA Cup Q2 rep**	**GUISBOROUGH TOWN**	305	3 - 1	Mayers 2, **Eastwood 31**, Potts 52
04/10	LP	Whitby Town	304	2 - 0	Mayers 61, Potts 89
07/10	LP	ALFRETON TOWN	441	3 - 0	**Eastwood 8**, Potts 19, Mayers 39
11/10	**FA Cup Q3**	**Gedling Town**	**210**	**1 - 0**	Mayers 52
13/10	LP	Droylsden	612	0 - 2	
18/10	LP	RUNCORN HALTON	524	2 - 2	Potts 70, Mayers 87
25/10	**FA Cup Q4**	**Ossett Albion**	621	1 - 0	Mayers 76
28/10	LP	LANCASTER CITY	413	**0 - 3**	
01/11	LP	HARROGATE TOWN	489	1 - 2	Eastwood 16
08/11	**FA Cup 1**	**Barnet**	1736	2 - 2	Keeling 45, **Eastwood 77[p]**
15/11	LP	RADCLIFFE BOROUGH	534	0 - 2	
18/11	**FA Cup 1 rep**	**BARNET**	1549	0 - 2	
22/11	LP	Frickley Athletic	190	2 - 1	Potts 60, Mayers 84
29/11	**FA Trophy 2**	**Redditch United**	**288**	3 - 0	Heald 17 56, Keeling 46
06/12	LP	BURSCOUGH	410	1 - 1	**Eastwood 64**
09/12	LP	Ashton United	413	1 - 2	Wharton 52
13/12	LP	WAKEFIELD & EMLEY	347	3 - 3	**DENHAM 5 31 78**
26/12	LP	Altrincham	795	3 - 3	**EASTWOOD 45 73[p] 90**
01/01	LP	ALTRINCHAM	**1022**	1 - 0	Denham 17
03/01	LP	Gainsborough Trinity	500	0 - 0	
10/01	**FA Trophy 3**	**Leigh RMI**	401	1 - 1	Mayers 30
		Tie awarded to Stalybridge Celtic for Leigh playing an ineligable player			
24/01	LP	BRADFORD PARK AVENUE	439	2 - 0	Pearce 53, Denham 76
31/01	**FA Trophy 4**	**MARINE**	614	1 - 1	Mayers 24
03/02	**FA Trophy 4 rep**	**Marine**	374	1 - 0	**Eastwood 67**
07/02	LP	Wakefield & Emley	211	3 - 1	Mayers 41 64[p], Heald 86
14/02	**FA Trophy 5**	**CANVEY ISLAND**	**832**	**0 - 0**	
17/02	**FA Trophy 5 rep**	**Canvey Island**	**761**	**0 - 4**	
21/02	LP	DROYLSDEN	654	2 - 1	Denham 66 71
24/02	LP	Worksop Town	398	1 - 2	Denham 50
06/03	LP	WHITBY TOWN	469	1 - 3	Monk 82
09/03	LP	Lancaster City	272	1 - 2	Potts 18
13/03	LP	Spennymoor United	151	3 - 1	Wharton 16, Hayward 45, Denham 65
16/03	LP	Marine	253	2 - 0	Potts 5, Denham 45
20/03	LP	BLYTH SPARTANS	424	2 - 0	Hayward 73, Denham 87
23/03	LP	FRICKLEY ATHLETIC	374	**5 - 0**	Denham 19, Hayward 47, Wharton 49, **Eastwood 57[p] 60**
30/03	LP	Blyth Spartans	343	1 - 0	Monk 71
03 /04	LP	Harrogate Town	389	3 - 4	Keeling 4, Hayward 78 88
06 /04	LP	Vauxhall Motors	241	1 - 1	Denham 5
10 /04	LP	VAUXHALL MOTORS	529	3 - 4	Hayward 44 55, German 80
12 /04	LP	Southport	923	3 - 2	Hayward 11Wharton 46 **Eastwood 53**
14 /04	LP	MARINE	357	1 - 1	**Eastwood 2**
17 /04	LP	Runcorn Halton	274	**0 - 3**	
20 /04	LP	Hucknall Town	316	3 - 1	Parr 10, Hayward 26, **Eastwood 80**
24 /04	LP	BARROW	555	2 - 2	Monk 80 90
		Average Home League Arrendances:	**517**	87-79	Top Goalscorer: **Phil Eastwood 13** (10+2FAC+1FAT)

PLAYING SQUAD 2004-2005

Goalkeepers:
Craig Dootson (Leigh RMI)

Defenders:
Danny Caldecott (Atherton LR), David German (Leigh RMI), Lee Todd (Mossley), Terry Bowker (Bamber Bridge), Tony Whealing (Radcliffe), Barrie Keeling (Radcliffe), Greg Pearce (Chesterfield)

Midfield:
Paul Sykes (Worksop), Darren Bowman (Rossendale), Ben Smith (Hollinwood), Dean Calcutt (Accrington Stanley), Kevin Parr (Glossop), Nathan Wharton (Radcliffe), Scott Bonsall (Harrogate), Lee Connell (Bury)

Forwards:
Andy Hayward (Bradford PA), Chris Denham (Radcliffe), Ian Monk (Leigh RMI), Phil Eastwood (Southport)

VAUXHALL MOTORS F.C.

CLUB OFFICIALS

President: Tony Woodley

Chairman: Alan Bartlam

Vice Chairman: Len Jones

Treasurer: Steve McInerney

Secretary: Carole Paisey, 31 South Road, West Kirby, Wirral CH48 3HG

Tel & Fax No: 0151 625 6936

FOOTBALL MANAGEMENT TEAM

Manager:Owen Berown
Assistant Manager: Clive Evans
Captain: Robbie Lawton

FACT FILE

Formed: 1963
Re-formed 1995
Nickname: The Motormen
Club Sponsors: Lookers Wirral
Colours: White/navy blue/white
Midweek Matchday: Tuesday
Reserves' Lge: Wset Cheshire Lge.
Club Website:www.vmfc.com

2003-2004

Leading Goalscore r& Player of the Year:
Terry Fearns

The Motorman
The official programme of
Vauxhall Motors F.C.

Lookers
WIRRAL
Nationwide

Nationwide North
VAUXHALL MOTORS
versus
DROYLSDEN
Tuesday, 17th August, 2004
Kick off 7.45 p.m.

Programme
£1.50

36 Pages
Programme Website Editor: Andy Wilson
Tel No; 077884 75516

GROUNDVauxhall Sports Ground, Rivacre Road, Ellesmere Port, South Wirrall. CH66 1Nj
Tel 7 Fax: 0151 328 1114 (Ground) 0151 327 2294 (Club)
Email: admin@vauxhallfc.co.uk

Directions: M 53 junction 5, take the A41 to Chester. At the first set of lights (at Chimneys pub) turn left into Hooton Green. Follow to end and turn left at T-junction. Follow to the end and take right at the T-junction into Rivacre Rd. Ground is 250 yards on right.
Floodlights: Yes Clubhouse: Yes Club Shop: Yes Ian Cowell (0151 625 7491)

HONOURS West Cheshire Lge Div 1 86, 95, 03 R-up 84, Div 2 84. W. Ches. Lge Bowl 68, Pyke Cup 2000, R-up 73, 01
N.W.C. Lge. 2nd Div 88-89 95-96; Raab Karcher Chall Cup 90-91;.NWC Challenge Cup 98-99, Division 1 99-00,
Unibond League Div 1 R-up 2001-02 Premier Division R-up 2001-2002
N.W.Co Floodlit Trophy Winners 99-00. Cheshire Amateur Cup R-up 87 ,94,2000
Wirral Senior Cup 87, R-up 83, 84, 95, 00; Wirrall Amateur Cup 86 R-up 87; Wirral Junior Cup 83

PREVIOUS **Leagues:** Ellesmer Port Lge., Wirral Combination, West Cheshire League 66-87, 92-95; North West Counties Lg 87-92, 95-00,
Names: Vauxhall Motors 63 -87, 93-95 Vauxhall GM 88-92, 95-99

BEST SEASON **FA Vase:** S-Final 99-00 v ChippenhamTown 0-1 aet (2 legs)
F.A.Trophy: 4th Round 2001-02 v Northwich Vics 0-4 & 2002-03 vWindsor & Eton (0-0 & 0-3)
F.A Cup: Second Round Proper v Macclesfield Town (0-2) after beating Q.P.R. (0-0 H, 1-1 A Won 4-3 after pens)

RECORDS **Attendance:** 1,500 v English F.A. XI, 1987

Date	Comp.	Opponents	Att.	Score	Goalscorers
16/08	LP	Lancaster City	343	0 - 0	
23/08	LP	WAKEFIELD & EMLEY	143	1 - 0	Cumiskey 41
25/08	LP	Marine	344	2 - 3	Cumiskey 13[p], Nesbitt 67
30/08	LP	BRADFORD PARK AVENUE	204	6 - 2	**FEARNS 53 80 90,** Cumiskey 57 73, Nesbitt 80
01/09	LP	Droylsden	232	1 - 2	Cumiskey 55[p]
06/09	LP	Blyth Spartans	383	6 - 3	**FEARNS6 17 36 48 80**, Lynch 88
09/09	LP	ALTRINCHAM	303	1 - 1	**Fearns 14**
13/09	LP	GAINSBOROUGH TRINITY	201	0 - 2	
20/09	LP	Radcliffe Borough	294	2 - 1	Young 80, McCann 90
23/09	LP	BURSCOUGH	203	3 - 2	Nesbitt 15, Cumiskey 40 73[p]
27/09	**FA Cup Q2**	**SOUTHPORT**	492	3 - 1	Cumiskey 13[p] 90[p], Robinson 69
04/10	LP	Worksop Town	555	3 - 4	Young 17, **Fearns 28 45**
07/10	LP	RUNCORN HALTON	242	**6 - 0**	Kissock 4, Cumiskey 57 60, **FEARNS 79 83 89**
11/10	**FA Cup Q3**	**Bradford Park Avenue**	321	1 - 1	**Fearns 82**
14/10	**FA Cup Q3 rep**	**BRADFORD PARK AVENUE**	278	1 - 3	Lawton 4
18/10	LP	BARROW	270	1 - 1	**Fearns 53**
25/10	LP	Spennymoor United	110	1 - 2	Young 2
28/10	LP	RADCLIFFE BOROUGH	168	**0 - 5**	
01/11	LP	Bradford Park Avenue	360	2 - 6	Lynch 24, Young 69
04/11	LP	DROYLSDEN	202	2 - 4	**Fearns 5 43**
08/11	LP	Runcorn Halton	229	1 - 1	Cumiskey 40
15/11	LP	Alfreton Town	404	1 - 5	Cumiskey 89
29/11	**FA Trophy 2**	**Alfreton Town**	181	1 - 1	Lawton 56
02/12	**FA Trophy 2 rep**	**ALFRETON TOWN**	147	2 - 4	Cumiskey 16[p] 56
06/12	LP	HUCKNALL TOWN	207	1 - 3	Cumiskey 2
13/12	LP	WORKSOP TOWN	227	1 - 1	Nesbitt 53
26/12	LP	Burscough	186	1 - 3	**Fearns 62**
03/01	LP	ASHTON UNITED	209	1 - 2	Robinson 37
10/01	LP	WHITBY TOWN	204	1 - 1	**Fearns 78**
17/01	LP	Harrogate Town	602	2 - 3	Cumiskey 39, **Fearns 90**
31/01	LP	SOUTHPORT	385	3 - 2	**Fearns 25**, Cumiskey 61 75
07/02	LP	Frickley Athletic	228	2 - 0	**Fearns 71**, Lawton 90
17/02	LP	Altrincham	570	1 - 3	**Fearns 33**
21/02	LP	LANCASTER CITY	204	2 - 1	Lynch 10, **Fearns 50**
28/02	LP	Southport	822	1 - 1	Cumiskey 67
02/03	LP	Hucknall Town	557	0 - 2	
06/03	LP	ALFRETON TOWN	232	2 - 0	Roberts 20, Cumiskey 26
09/03	LP	Barrow	1027	1 - 0	Cumiskey
13/03	LP	Whitby Town	243	1 - 1	**Fearns 37**
16/03	LP	HARROGATE TOWN	173	3 - 0	**Fearns 8 10,** McGivern 74
23/03	LP	Ashton United	202	1 - 0	**Fearns 56**
27/03	LP	Gainsborough Trinity	306	0 - 0	
30/03	LP	SPENNYMOOR UNITED	169	4 - 2	Cumiskey 31 44, **Fearns 53**, Lawton 62
03 /04	LP	FRICKLEY ATHLETIC	196	2 - 1	Cumiskey 56, Roberts 71
06 /04	LP	STALYBRIDGE CELTIC	241	1 - 1	**Fearns 45[p]**
10 /04	LP	Stalybridge Celtic	529	4 - 3	**Fearns 12 56[p]**, Roberts 45, Lawton 65
12 /04	LP	MARINE	339	1 - 0	**Fearns 86(p)**
17 /04	LP	BLYTH SPARTANS	**463**	2 - 1	Lawton 3, Cumiskey 50
24 /04	LP	Wakefield & Emley	129	1 - 0	Macauley 10
		Average Home League Attendance:	**235**	86-83	Top Goalscorer: **Terry Ferns 34** (33+1FAC)

PLAYING SQUAD 2004-2005

Goalkeeper:
Tim Dittmer (Liverpool)

Defenders:
James Glendenning (Droylsden), Mike Tomlinson (Runcorn), Phil Brazier (Northwich), Wayne McDermott (Leek), Alan Griffiths (Tranmere),Tony Hallam (Morecambe), Tony Allen (Blackpool)

Midfield:
Carl Spellman (Kidsgrove), Carl Nesbitt (Poulton Vics), Robbie Lawton (Caernarfon), Marvin Molyneux (Burscough), James Olsen (Macclesfield)

Forwards:
Peter Cumiskey (Leigh RMI), Tony Wright (Aberystwyth), Karl O'Donnell (Southport)

WORCESTER CITY

CLUB OFFICIALS

Chairman: Dave Boddy
Vice Chairman: Laurie Brown

Secretary: Graham Hill, 8 Dawson Close, Lower Wick, Worcester WR2 4DL

FOOTBALL MANAGEMENT TEAM

Manager: John Barton
Player Coach: John Snape
Physio: Archie Richards

FACT FILE

Formed: 1902 Nickname: The City
Sponsors: E.E.Engineering
Newsline: 09066 555 810
Colours:Blue/white/blue.
Change colours:White/blue/white
Midweek matchday: Monday
Res Lge: Midland Comb Res & Central Conf
Local Press: Worcester Standard, Worcester Evening News
Local Radio: Radio Wyvern,Classic Hits BBC Hereford & Worcester

2003-004

P.o.Y: Danny McDonnell
Top Scorer: Leon Kelly
2004-2005 Carl Heeley

PROGRAMME
Pages: 32 Price: £2.00
Editor: Graham Hill (0778 6992 272)

GROUND St George's Lane, Barbourne, Worcester WR1 1QT Tel: 01905 23003 Fax: 26668

Directions: M5 jct 6 (Worcester North), follow signs to Worcester, right at first lights, St Georges Lane is 3rd left. 1 mile from Foregate Street (BR)station

Capacity: 4,004 Cover: 2,000 Seats: 1,125 Floodlights: Yes

Clubhouse: Open every evening and Saturday and Sunday daytime. Cold snacks available
Club Shop: One outside - souvenirs, and one inside - programmes Contact club for details.

PREVIOUS **Leagues:** West Mids (Birmingham) 1902-38, Southern 38-79, Alliance Premier 79-85 Southern 1985-2004
Names: Berwick Rangers **Grounds:** Severn Terrace, Thorneloe, Flagge Meadow

CLUB RECORDS **Attendance:** 17,042 v Sheff Utd (lost 0-2), FA Cup 4th Rd 24/1/59
Win: 18-1 v Bilston, Birmingham League 21/11/31 **Defeat:** 0-10 v Wellington, Birmingham League 29/8/20
Career Goalscorer: John Inglis 189 (1970-77) **Career Appearances:** Bobby McEwan 596 (1959-75)
Transfer fee paid: £8,500 for Jim Williams (Telford United, 1981)
Transfer fee received: £27,000 for John Barton (Everton, 1979)

BEST SEASON **FA Cup:** 4th Rd 58-59. 1st Rd (12)
FA Trophy: QF 69-70 73-74 80-81 81-82 **Welsh Cup:** Semi-Final 78-79

HONOURS Southern Lg 78-79, Div 1 67-68, Div 1 Nth 76-77, Lg Cup R-up 45-46 59-60, Chal.Cup 39-40, Champs Cup 78-79; West Mids (B'ham) Lg(4) 13-14 24-25 28-30 (R-up (3) 31-34); Worcs Snr Cup (26) 07-14 28-30 32-33 45-46(jt) 48-49 55-59 60-61 62-63 64-65 69-70 77-78 79-80 81-82 83-84 87-88 96-97; B'ham Snr Cup 75-76; Staffs Snr Cup 76-77; Inter Lg Champs Cup 78-79

Players progressing: A Awford (Portsmouth 91), P King/K Ball (Cardiff C.60/65), JWilliams/M Gayle (Walsall 79/91), J Fairbrother (Peterborough 65), DTennant (Lincoln 66), R Davies (Derby 71), N Merrick (Bournemouth 74), J Barton(Everton 79), A Preece (Wrexham 90), D Lyttle (Swansea 92) M.Griffiths (Torquay United 99)

Back Row: Ray Woods, Allan Davies, Dan Parker, Barry Woolley, Dan Jones, Leon Kelly, Adam Webster, Stewart Hadley, Jon Holloway, John Morris Middle Row: Martin Obrey, Archie Richards, Kevin Halliday, Mitch Counsell, Shaun Hayes, Danny McDonnell, Lewis Skyers, Dean Smith, Liam McDonald, Mick Tuohy, Geoff Ashby. Front Row: Mark Owen, David Holmes, Paul Carty, John Snape, John Barton, Carl Heeley, Adam Wilde, Pat Lyons, Darren Middleton

Date	Comp.	Opponents	Att.	Score	Goalscorers
W16/08	LP	HAVANT & WATERLOOVILLE	1001	1 - 1	**Kelly 48**
19/08	LP	Merthyr Tydfil	653	2 - 0	**Kelly 16**, Wilde 34
23/08	LP	Welling United	485	1 - 0	Middleton 22
25/08	LP	MOOR GREEN	1258	3 - 0	**Kelly 51**, Owen58, Webster 59
30/08	LP	Crawley Town	864	0 - 4	
01/09	LP	HINCKLEY UNITED	1060	2 - 0	Holloway 33, Davies 83
06/09	LP	DORCHESTER TOWN	1048	1 - 0	Hadley 87
09/09	LP	Weston-super-Mare	450	0 - 1	
13/09	LP	TIVERTON TOWN	958	1 - 2	**Kelly 72**
16/09	LP	Hednesford Town	488	1 - 3	Middleton 50[p]
20/09	LP	BATH CITY	946	**7 - 0**	**HEDLEY6 32 60, Kelly 16 57**, Holloway 28, Wilde 89
27/09	**FA Cup Q2**	**Nuneaton Borough**	1352	0 - 1	
04/10	LP	Nuneaton Borough	1091	1 - 2	**Kelly 64**
18/10	LP	WEYMOUTH	1380	2 - 2	Webster 10, **Kelly 34**
21/10	LP	Hinckley United	281	0 - 0	
25/10	LP	Chippenham Town	435	2 - 1	Middleton 78, Carty 90
01/11	LP	NEWPORT COUNTY	1180	**1 - 5**	Webster 36
08/11	LP	Chelmsford City	403	2 - 2	Woolley 33, Middleton 89
15/11	LP	HEDNESFORD TOWN	1004	0 - 1	
22/11	LP	WESTON-SUPER-MARE	729	3 - 0	**Owen 61,73 ,79**
29/11	**FA Trophy 2**	**Marine**	339	0 - 2	
06/12	LP	Eastbourne Borough	519	3 - 1	Webster 18, **Kelly 48**, Carty 85
26/12	LP	Moor Green	643	1 - 1	**Kelly 75**
01/01	LP	STAFFORD RANGERS	1521	0 - 1	
03/01	LP	Dover Athletic	804	1 - 2	Owen 13
10/01	LP	Newport County	641	4 - 0	Heeley 37, **Kelly 57**, Owen 87, Wilde 90
24/01	LP	NUNEATON BOROUGH	1073	4 - 0	Carty 27, Owen 29, Heeley 53, Wilde 60
31/01	LP	WELLING UNITED	805	3 - 1	McDonald 24, Wilde 75, Holloway 82
03/02	LP	Bath City	486	1 - 1	**Kelly 67**
07/02	LP	Tiverton Town	529	1 - 1	Cousins 63[og]
14/02	LP	CHELMSFORD CITY	915	1 - 0	Owen 75
28/02	LP	Cambridge City	459	0 - 0	
06/03	LP	DOVER ATHLETIC	1001	5 - 1	**Kelly 42, WEBSTER 48 61 65[p],** Snape 52
13/03	LP	GRANTHAM TOWN	1068	4 - 1	Holloway 28, **Kelly 36,** Wilde 55[p], Stanley 58
16/03	LP	Weymouth	1403	1 - 3	Wilde 60
20/03	LP	Havant & Waterlooville	351	5 - 0	Wilde 4 71, **Kelly 12**, McDonald 64, Webster 85
27/03	LP	MERTHYR TYDFIL	1116	2 - 0	Davison 20, **Kelly 75**
29/03	LP	CRAWLEY TOWN	**1856**	0 - 1	
03 /04	LP	Dorchester Town	466	0 - 3	
10 /04	LP	CHIPPENHAM TOWN	1036	0 - 0	
12 /04	LP	Stafford Rangers	837	0 - 2	
17 /04	LP	EASTBOURNE BOROUGH	786	2 - 1	Woolley 85, Heeley 90
224 /04	LP	Grantham Town	305	3 - 4	Stanley 23(p), Owen 68, Woolley 87
01/05	LP	CAMBRIDGE CITY	991	0 - 2	
		Average Home League Attendance:	**1035**	71-53	Top Goalscorer: **Kelly 16**

PLAYING SQUAD 2004-2005

Goalkeepers:
Danny McDonnell (Halesowen), Lewis Skyers (Youth team)

Defenders:
Rob Warner (Tamworth), Carl Heeley (Sutton Coldfield), Barry Woolley (Ilkeston), Paul Carty (Hednesford), Dan Parker (Youth team), Allan Davies (Burton Alb), Colin Hoyle (Burton Alb)

Midfield:
Shabir Khan (Youth team), Liam McDonald (Youth team), Jai Stanley (Moor Green), Pat Lyons (Burton Alb), Les Hines (Hednesford), Nick Colley (Stafford R)

Forwards:
Christian Moore (Telford Utd), Adam Webster (Bedworth), Leon Kelly (Ilkeston), Mark Owen (Willenhall)

WORKSOP TOWN

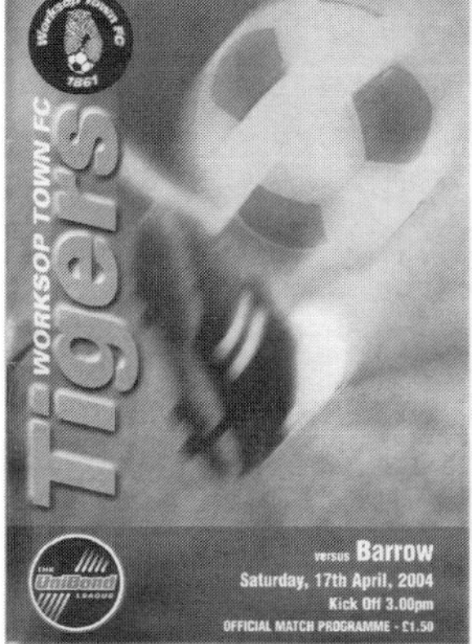

Pages: 28-40 Price: £1.50
Editor: Matt Halfpenny 01909 500491/500500

Local Press: Worksop Guardian, Worksop Star, Nottingham Football Post.
Local Radio: Radio Sheffield, Radio Hallam, Radio Lincoln,Trax FM

CLUB OFFICIALS

Chairman: Howard Raymond
Club Secretary: Keith Illett, 2 Mount Ave., Worksop, Notts (01909 487934)
Company Secretary: Chris Smith
Press Officer: Samantha Medlam

FOOTBALL MANAGEMENT TEAM

Team Manager: Ronnie G;lavin
Assistant Manager: Peter Price
Physio: Kerrry Spooner

FACT FILE

Formed: 1861
Nickname: The Tigers
Sponsors:Haizlewood Foods
Colours: All Amber
Change colours: All Blue
Midweek matchday: Tuesday
Youth Teams' Lge: Central Mid.Res
U18s: Notts Imp.

2002-2003

Leading Goalscorer: Gary Townsend 21
P.o.Y.: Paul Sykes
2004-2005 Captain: Mark Haran

GROUND

Babbage Way, off Sandy Lane, Worksop, Notts S80 1UJ (01909 501911).
Directions: M1 jct 31 (from north) jct 30 (from south), follow Worksop signs,join A57 and follow signs for Sandy Lane Industrial Estate - ground on left. 5mins walk from station.
Capacity: 3,000 Cover: 1,000 Seats:1,000
Clubhouse: 1861 Bar / Resaurant and Sportsman Bar.
Club Shop: `The Tigershop' 30 page catalogue from S.Medlam01909 501911

PREVIOUS **Leagues:** Midland (Counties)1896-98 1900-30 49-60 61-68 69-74, Sheffield Assoc. 1898-99 1931-33, Central Comb. 33-35, Yorkshire 35-39, Central All. 47-49 60-61, Northern Premier 68-69,74-
Grounds: Netherton Road, Bridge Meadow, Central Ave. (pre 1989), The Northolme (Gainsborough Trin. - shared) 89-92.

CLUB RECORDS **Attendance:** 2,100 v Chris Waddle XI Linden Whitehead's testimonial 0 7.05.01
Goalscorer: Kenny Clark, 287 **Appearances:** Kenny Clark 347
Win: 20-0 v Staveley, 1/9/1894 **Defeat:** 1-11 v Hull City Res., 55-56. **Unibond Highest** : 12-0 v Frickley Ath.
Fee Received: £47,000 for Jon Kennedy, Sunderland May 2000 **Paid:** £5,000 for Kirk Jackson to Grantham Town, 98-99

BEST SEASON **FA Cup:** 3rd Rd: 07-08 v Chelsea (A) 1-9, 21-22 v Southend (H) 1-2, 22-23 v Spurs (A) 0-0, 0-9, 55-56 v Swindon (A) 0-1. 2nd Rd: 25-26, 1st Rd: 20-21, 26-27, 61-62, 78-79. **League Clubs defeated:** Rotherham T. 1894-95, Grimsby T. 94-95, Nelson 1921-22, Chesterfield 22-23, Coventry C. 25-26, Bradford C. 55-56. **FA Trophy**: Q,Final 1-2 v Forest Green 00-01

HONOURS N.P.L. Presidents Cup 85-86 95-96, Unibond Div One Runners-up 97-98, Unibond Premier Div. Runners-up 98-99,Unibond Chairman"s Cup:2001-02 Sheffield Assoc. Lg 1898-99, Sheffield & Hallamshire Snr Cup 23-24 52-53 54-55 65-66 69-70 72-73 81-82 84-85 96-97, Mansfield Charity Cup 22-23; Midland Cos Lg 21-22 65-66 72-73 (R-up 62-6366-67 73-74).

Players P rogressing to Football League: J Brown (Sheff Wed), G Dale (Chesterfield 48), A Daley (Doncaster 50), K Wood (Grimsby 51), H Jarvis (Notts Co. 51),B Taylor (Leeds 51), S Rhodes 51, D Gratton 52, A Hodgkinson 53, J Harrison 67 (Sheffield Utd), S Lloyd & P Marshall (Scunthorpe 54),A Rhodes (QPR 54), R Moore (Rotherham 55), H Mosby (Crewe 56), L Moore (Derby 57), H Bowery (Nottm Forest 75), T Moore (Rochdale 84), S Adams (Scarborough 87), D Moss (Doncaster 93), Jon Kennedy (Sunderland 00), K Jackson (Darlington 01).

Date	Comp.	Opponents	Att.	Score	Goalscorers
19/08	LP	Wakefield & Emley	350	1 - 1	Roberts 64[p]
23/08	LP	Spennymoor United	275	1 - 1	Caudwell 29
25/08	LP	Harrogate Town	521	2 - 0	
30/08	LP	RUNCORN HALTON	518	0 - 1	
03/09	LP	Bradford Park Avenue	367	1 - 0	Bambrook 13[p]
06/09	LP	Stalybridge Celtic	577	3 - 0	Whitehead 19, Bowker 32[og], Davies 41
09/09	LP	FRICKLEY ATHLETIC	650	3 - 0	Whitehead 12, Sykes 54, Haran 59
13/09	LP	Blyth Spartans	463	3 - 3	Todd 8, Caudwell 30, Roberts 90
16/09	LP	SOUTHPORT	601	1 - 0	Bambrook 5
20/09	LP	LANCASTER CITY	624	0 - 0	
27/09	**FA Cup Q2**	**KING'S LYNN**	834	2 - 2	Bambrook 19, Caudwell 75
30/09	**FA Cup Q2 rep**	**King's Lynn**	1209	4 - 1	Whitehead 65 85, Peacock 89, Cauldwell 90
04/10	LP	VAUXHALL MOTORS	555	4 - 3	Caudwell 2 71, Bambrook 15, Davies 90
11/10	**FA Cup Q3**	**Farsley Celtic**	374	0 - 3	
14/10	LP	Hucknall Town	817	1 - 3	Bambrook 42
17/10	LP	Alfreton Town	903	1 - 2	Peacock 70
25/10	LP	MARINE	536	1 - 2	**Townsend 37**
28/10	LP	ASHTON UNITED	453	3 - 0	Whitehead 32, Haran 71, Todd 88
01/11	LP	Southport	801	3 - 2	Haran 36, Bambrook 81 88
04/11	LP	Radcliffe Borough	280	2 - 1	Sykes 28, Todd 78
08/11	LP	ALTRINCHAM	635	0 - 0	
11/11	LP	HARROGATE TOWN	603	1 - 0	Ward 89
15/11	LP	Barrow	1010	0 - 1	
22/11	LP	DROYLSDEN	519	1 - 3	Bambrook 84[p]
29/11	**FA Trophy 2**	**DROYLSDEN**	341	1 - 0	**Townsend 45**
06/12	LP	Runcorn Halton	253	3 - 2	**Townsend 82 89**, Todd 90
13/12	LP	Vauxhall Motors	227	1 - 1	Caudwell 78
26/12/03	LP	GAINSBOROUGH TRINITY	**1168**	0 - 0	
03/01	LP	Burscough	229	0 - 0	
10/01	**FA Trophy 3**	**Guiseley**	583	2 - 0	Davies 48, Taylor 64
17/01	LP	RADCLIFFE BOROUGH	476	4 - 1	**Townsend 19**, Callery 28, Sykes 52 85[p]
07/02	LP	BLYTH SPARTANS	501	1 - 0	Beardsley 67
11/02	**FA Trophy 4**	**Margate**	278	0 - 2	(at Ashford Town)
14/02	LP	WHITBY TOWN	376	1 - 1	Taylor 82
21/02	LP	Whitby Town	382	3 - 2	Sykes 6, Bambrook 11, **Townsend 22**
24/02	LP	STALYBRIDGE CELTIC	398	2 - 1	**Townsend 13,** Sykes 77
06/03	LP	BURSCOUGH	446	1 - 1	**Townsend 83**
16/03	LP	SPENNYMOOR UNITED	448	**4 - 0**	**Townsend 24**, Callery 44, Taylor 60, Sykes 62[p]
20/03	LP	Frickley Athletic	318	1 - 1	Bradshaw 90
23/03	LP	BRADFORD PARK AVENUE	374	1 - 2	Muller 31
30/03	LP	Lancaster City	273	0 - 2	
01 /04	LP	ALFRETON TOWN	657	0 - 0	
03 /04	LP	Droylsden	389	2 - 2	Sykes 5[p], Muller 35
06 /04	LP	WAKEFIELD & EMLEY	319	**4 - 0**	Taylor 14, **Townsend 30,** Sykes 48, Muller 63
10 /04	LP	HUCKNALL TOWN	841	**0 - 3**	
12 /04	LP	Gainsborough Trinity	708	1 - 2	
14 /04	LP	Ashton United	193	3 - 0	Taylor 33, Sykes 59, **Townsend 70**
17 /04	LP	BARROW	538	2 - 4	Sykes 28, Bambrook 85
20 /04	LP	Altrincham	484	1 - 2	**Townsend 11**
24 /04	LP	Marine	330	2 - 0	Bambrook 21, Cauldwell 69
		Average Home League Attendance:	556	78-58	Top Goalscorer: Gary Townsend 12 (11+1FAT)

PLAYING SQUAD 2004-2005

Goalkeepers:

Ian Bowling (Kettering), Matthew Ghent (Lincoln)

Defenders:

Kevin Davies (Telford Utd), Ryan Davis (Luton), Steve Nicholson (Farsley), James Dudgeon (Halifax), Mark Haran (Kettering), Paul Dempsey (Scarborough)

Midfield:

Simeon Bambrook (Wakefield-Emley), Linden Whitehead (Alfreton), Miles Thorpe (Wakefield-Emley), Mark Wilson (Wakefield-Emley), Brian O'Callaghan (Barnsley), Chris Davies (Hucknall)

Forwards:

Gary Townsend (Youth team), Dene Cropper (Boston Utd), Antony Jackson (Frickley), Blake Norton (Rossendale)

FOOTBALL LEAGUE

STEP 1

FOOTBALL CONFERENCE

STEP 2

CONFERENCE NORTH

CONFERENCE SOUTH

STEP 3

NORTHERN PREMIER

SOUTHERN PREMIER

ISTHMIAN PREMIER

STEP 4

NORTHERN PREMIER DIV.1

SOUTHERN LEAGUE NORTH

SOUTHERN LEAGUE SOUTH

ISTHMIAN DIVISION 1

STEP 5/6

STEP 7

BASINGSTOKE TOWN

CLUB OFFICIALS

Chairman: David Hunt
President: Rafi Razzack
Secretary: Richard Trodd
5 Lehar Close, Brighton Hill, Basingstoke
RG22 4HT Tel: 01256 413076
Press Officer: Ian Trodd
Commercial Manager: Ken Taylor

FOOTBALL MANAGEMENT TEAM

Manager: Ernie Howe
Asst Manager: Pete Peters
Coach: Steve Richardson
Physio: Mark Randall

PROGRAMME

Pages: 24 Price: £1.50
Editor: Linda Murfitt (07795 617314)

FACT FILE

Formed: 1896
Nickname: Stoke
Sponsors: Centerprise International
Colours:Blue &Yellow stripes/blue/blue&yellow
Change colours: Red&black stripes/black/black
Midweek home matchday: Tuesday
Reserves' League: Suburban (Prem Div)
Website: www.btfc.co.uk

Local Press: Basingstoke Gazette (461131)
Local Radio: Radio 210 (01189 413131),
Kestrel Radio (01256 694000)

2003-04

Captain:Scott Tarr
Leading Goalscorer:Craig McAllister
Player of Year: Neville Roach

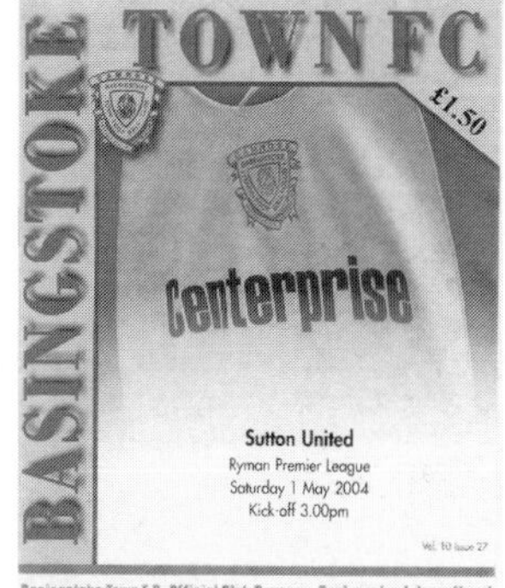

GROUND Camrose Road, Western Way, Basingstoke RG22 6EZ Tel: 01256 325063 or 01256 327575 Emai: info@btfc.co.uk

Directions: Exit 6 off M3 and follow A30 west, ground off Winchester Road. Two miles from bus and rail stations

Capacity: 6,000 Cover:2,000 Seats: 651

Clubhouse: Open every day (incl. lunchtime) Steward: Cheryl Fox (01256 464353)

Club Shop: Open daily 10-5pm, selling programmes, books, scarves, shirts, badges etc.

PREVIOUS **Leagues:** Hants 1900-40 45-71; Southern 71-87 **Ground:** Castle Field 1896-1947

CLUB RECORDS **Attendance:** 5,085 v Wycombe Wanderers, FA C 1st Rd replay 97-98
Win: 10-0 v Chichester City (H), FA Cup 1st Qualifying Rd, Sept. 1976
Defeat: 0-8 v Aylesbury United, Southern League, April 1979.
Appearances: Billy Coombs
Goalscorer: Paul Coombs 159 (Oct 91 99)
Transfer Fee Paid: £4,750 for Steve Ingham (Gosport Borough)
Transfer Fee Received: £6,750 for Steve Ingham (Bashley)

BEST SEASON **FA Trophy:** 3rd Rd 98-99, 0-2 v Yeovil T. (H) and 3rd Rd 2003-04 v Kings Lynn (A)
FA Cup: 2nd Rd replay 97-98, 3-4 pens aet 0 -0 v Northampton (H) after 1-1; 2nd Rd 89-90, 2-3 v Torquay U. (H)
League clubs defeated: Wycombe Wanderers 97-98

HONOURS Southern Lge Southern Div 85-86; Isthmian League Div 1 R-up 88-89 96-97; Hants League 67-68 69-70 70-71 (R-up 65-66 66-67 68-69, North Div 11-12 19-20); HantsSenior Cup 70-71 89-90 95-96 96-97

Players progressing: Tony Godfrey (Southampton 58), John Neale (Exeter 72), Mike Doherty (Reading 82), Micky Cheetham (Ipswich 88), Matt Carmichael (Lincoln), Tony Franklin (Exeter), Steve Welsh (Peterborough 90)

Date	Comp.	Opponents	Att.	Score	Goalscorers
16/08	LP	Canvey Island	579	1 - 3	Roach 20
19/08	LP	HENDON	452	1 - 4	**McAllister 23**
23/08	LP	FORD UNITED	280	1 - 0	Hemmings 90
25/08	LP	Hitchin Town	477	2 - 2	Lambert 17, **McAllister 88**
30/08	LP	HEYBRIDGE SWIFTS	329	1 - 1	Elad 76
02/09	LP	Aylesbury United	355	**3 - 0**	**McAllister 23 71**, Elad 33
06/09	LP	Harrow Borough	162	1 - 1	Roach 40
09/09	LP	ST ALBANS CITY	335	1 - 1	Ewin 32
13/09	LP	THURROCK	288	0 - 3	
16/09	LP	Bishop's Stortford	249	1 - 0	Elad 75
20/09	LP	HORNCHURCH	322	0 - 3	
22/09	LP	Carshalton Athletic	418	2 - 0	**McAllister 6,** Ewin 26
27/09	**FA Cup Q2**	**CRAY WANDERERS**	351	1 - 0	**McAllister 47**
04/10	LP	Maidenhead United	292	2 - 0	Roach 68, Ray 84
07/10	LP	GRAYS ATHLETIC	318	0 - 2	
11/10	**FA Cup Q3**	**BRACKNELL TOWN**	429	0 - 0	
14/10	**FA Cup Q3 rep**	**Bracknell Town**	375	0 - 1	
18/10	LP	KETTERING TOWN	338	2 - 2	**McAllister 14**, Bristow 70
21/10	LP	Hayes	232	1 - 2	Everitt 16[og]
25/10	LP	Braintree Town	192	1 - 0	**McAllister 70**
08/11	LP	BILLERICAY TOWN	284	0 - 1	
11/11	LP	NORTHWOOD	227	2 - 0	Bristow 26, Burgess 51
15/11	LP	Bedford Town	408	2 - 5	**McAllister 31**, Burgess 81
22/11	LP	Sutton United	437	2 - 2	**McAllister 21 62**
29/11	**FA Trophy 2**	**Chippenham Town**	466	1 - 1	Roach 18
02/12	**FA Trophy 2 rep**	**CHIPPENHAM TOWN**	237	1 - 0	**McAllister 72**
06/12	LP	KINGSTONIAN	351	2 - 1	Bristow 15, **McAllister 29**
13/12	LP	CANVEY ISLAND	352	1 - 2	**McAllister 4**
20/12	LP	Hendon	182	1 - 0	Elad 59
27/12	LP	BOGNOR REGIS TOWN	468	0 - 1	
10/01	**FA Trophy 3**	**King's Lynn**	1089	1 - 3	Bristow 86
17/01	LP	HARROW BOROUGH	272	0 - 1	
24/01	LP	Thurrock	227	0 - 0	
07/02	LP	BRAINTREE TOWN	279	**3 - 0**	Roach 76, **McAllister 82**, Levis 88
10/02	LP	Northwood	186	0 - 0	
14/02	LP	Kettering Town	785	**3 - 0**	Torres 66, Burgess 69, Roach 75 F
21/02	LP	BEDFORD TOWN	384	2 - 0	
24/02	LP	St Albans City	144	**3 - 0**	**McAllister 31 83**, Torres 42
28/02	LP	Billericay Town	393	1 - 3	**McAllister 62**
02/03	LP	HAYES	244	0 - 2	
06/03	LP	CARSHALTON ATHLETIC	334	1 - 2	Warner 55
09/03	LP	BISHOP'S STORTFORD	205	1 - 2	Bristow 19
13/03	LP	Hornchurch	482	0 - 2	
20/03	LP	MAIDENHEAD UNITED	314	2 - 1	**McAllister 24**, Roach 47
23/03	LP	Ford United	102	1 - 1	Burgess 50
27/03	LP	Grays Athletic	268	1 - 3	Lennox 85
03 /04	LP	Heybridge Swifts	180	**3 - 0**	Roach 19 75, Torres 57
10 /04	LP	HITCHIN TOWN	312	2 - 3	**McAllister 21**, Duffy 23[og]
12 /04	LP	Bognor Regis Town	402	3 - 1	Stamp 33, **McAllister 47 60**
17 /04	LP	AYLESBURY UNITED	342	2 - 0	Torres 8, **McAllister 76**
24 /04	LP	Kingstonian	318	0 - 2	
01/05	LP	SUTTON UNITED	**720**	**0 - 5**	
05/05	**Play-off SF**	**LEWES**	**310**	**1 - 4**	**McAllister 26**

Average Home League Attendance: **337** 63-73 Top Goalscorer:**Craig McAllister 24** (21+1C+1T+1PO)

Bold Print indicates 1) Cup Ties 2) Biggest victory 3) Biggest Defeat 4) Largest Attendance 5) Top scorer's goals
Opponent's name in CAPITALS denotes home games and goalscorer's names in **BOLD CAPITALS** denote hat tricks.

PLAYING SQUAD 2004-2005

Goalkeepers:

Scott Tarr (Yeading)

Defenders:

Jason Bristow (Reading), Steve Hemmings (Youth team), Ricky Allaway (Reading), Neville Stamp (Exeter), Ian Dickens (Youth team), David Ray (Youth team), Nathan Stamp (QPR)

Midfield:

Toby Sumner (Aldershot), Sergio Torres (Argentina), Stuart Tanfield (Aldershot), Brett Cooper (Aldershot)

Forwards:

Neville Roach (Slough), Cristian Levis (Argentina), Martin Whiddett (AFC Totton)

BISHOP'S STORTFORD

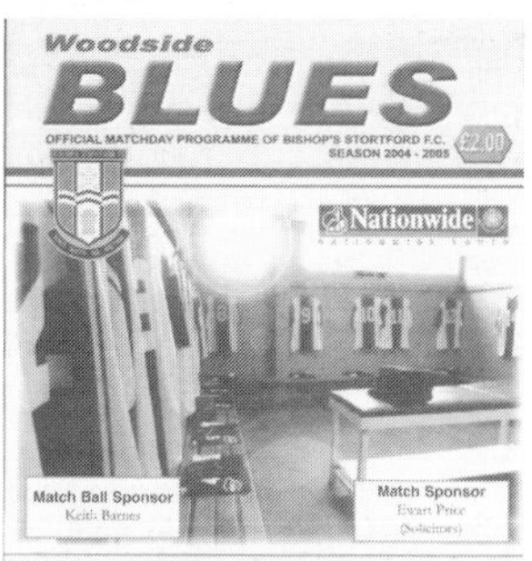

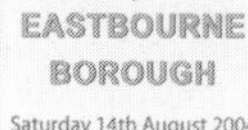

CLUB OFFICIALS

Chairman: John Goodwin
Secretary: Ian Kettridge,25 Cox Ley,Hatfield Heath,Bishop,s Stortford, Herts. CM22 7ER Tel No: 07904169017 (M)
Press Officer: Daniel Smart
Tel No: 07736 459052 (M)

FOOTBALL MANAGEMENT TEAM

Team Manager: Martin Hayes
Assistant Månager/Coach: Les Whitton
Physio: Peter Fox & David Jude

FACT FILE

Formed: 1874 Nickname: Blues or Bishops
Colours: Blue & white stripes/blue/blue
Change colours: Yellow/yellow/yellow
Midweek matchday: Tuesday
Local Press: B.Stortford Citizen, Herts & Essex Observer, Herald
Local Radio: BBC Essex, Essex FM, Breeze AM, Mercury FM,Three Counties

PROGRAMME

Pages: 72 Price: £1.50
Editor: Ian Kettridge (Secretary)

GROUND Woodside Park, Dunmow Road, Bishop 's Stortford (08700 339900)
Directions: M11 jct 8, A1250 towards town centre, left at first roundabout. Woodside is first on right opposite Golf Club. Entrance is between industrial units on right. By rail: British Rail: W. Anglia Line (London, Liverpool Str.-Cambridge)
Capacity: 4,000 Cover: 700 Seats: 298 Floodlights: Yes
Clubhouse: Open lunchtimes,evenings and matchdays Function room(seating 250) available for hire .
Club Shop: Full stock inc. scarves, badges and other souvenirs. Massive stock of programmes and books etc. Contact Adam Sydesvia club.

PREVIOUS **Leagues:** East Herts 1896-97, 02-06, 19-21; Stansted & Dist. Lg 06-19; HertsCounty 21-25 27-29; Herts & Essex Border 25-27; Spartan 29-51; Delphian 51-63;Athenian 63-73 and Isthmian 74-04

CLUB RECORDS **Attendance:** 6,000 v Peterborough Utd, FA Cup 2nd Rd 1972 & v Middlesbrough FACup 3rd Rd replay, 1983
Win: 11-0: Nettleswell & Butntmill, Herts Jun Cup 2nd Rd 1911 **Defeat:** 0-13 v Cheshunt (H), Herts Sen. Cup 1st Rd 9/1/26
Fee Paid: For Vinnie John to Grays Athletic (1999) **Fee Received:** Undisclosed for Glen Southam from Dagenham & Red(04)
Scorer: (Since 29) Jimmy Badcock 123 **Appearances:** Phil Hopkins 543

BEST SEASON **FA Amateur Cup:** Winners 73-74 **FA Trophy:** Winners 80-81
FA Cup: 3rd Rd rep. 82-83 (above) - League clubs beaten: Reading 82-83

HONOURS Isthmian Lg Div 1 80-1 94-5 (Lg Cup 88-9, Full Mem. Cup 90-1), Prem. Inter Lg Cup 89-90; Athenian Lg 69-70 (R-up 66-7, Div 1 65-6, Div 2 R-up 64-5); Delphian Lg 54-5; London Snr Cup 73-4; Herts Snr Cup 58-9 59-0 63-4 70-1 72-3 73-4 75-686-7; E Anglian Cup 81-2; Herts Charity Cup 62-3 65-6 73-4 81-2 82-3 84-5 87-8 96-7 02-03 03-04 Herts Charity Shield 54-5; Herts I'mediate Cup (res) 94-95; Eastern F'lit Cup 84-5; Essex F'lit Cup 67-8; Essex & Herts Border Comb 81-2 88-9 R-up (2) 92-4; Fred Budden Tphy R-up 78-9 90-1 92-3

Players progressing: P Phelan (Southend 61), M Hollow (Orient 62), P Phillips(Luton 69), T Baker (Colchester 86), T Sorrell (Maidstone, Colchester, Barnet 88), C Hoddle (Leyton O., Barnet 89), T English (Colchester 89), L Fortune-West (Gillingham 95), L Braithwaite (Exeter City 96)

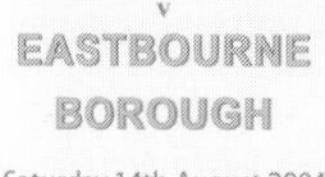

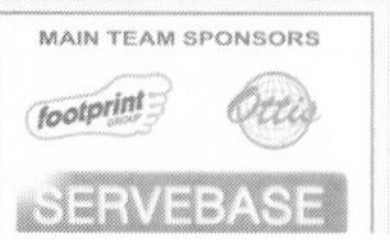

Back row, left to right: Les Whitton (Coach), Onaldo, Colin Taylor, Ray Taylor, Alex Riches, Richard Hayward, Vinnie John, Tim Langer, Lee Mitchell, Andy Keepence, Owen Beale and Tom Moylette (Coach) **Front row:** Martin Hayes (Player/Manager), Charlie Goodwin, Glen Southam, Mark McGibboin, Jimmy Sygrue, Freddie Hyatt, Troy Braham, Carl Allison, Danny Wolf, Rob French and Trevor Paul

Date	Comp.	Opponents	Att.	Score	Goalscorers
16/08	LP	Ford United	163	0 - 3	
19/08	LP	CANVEY ISLAND	512	2 - 0	Barnett 57, Essandoh 80
23/08	LP	CARSHALTON ATHLETIC	332	0 - 3	
25/08	LP	Hendon	325	5 - 2	**Southam 37**, **HOWELL 43 48 50,** Barnett 45
30/08	LP	BOGNOR REGIS TOWN	339	0 - 0	
02/09	LP	Grays Athletic	317	1 - 3	Renner 75
06/09	LP	MAIDENHEAD UNITED	275	2 - 1	**Southam 22[p]**, Langer 37
09/09	LP	Hornchurch	505	0 - 2	
13/09	LP	Sutton United	503	2 - 2	Barnett 87, Essandoh 90
16/09	LP	BASINGSTOKE TOWN	249	0 - 1	
20/09	LP	St Albans City	412	2 - 3	Renner 79, Rainford 80
23/09	LP	THURROCK	252	1 - 3	Cooper 84
27/09	**FA Cup Q2**	**Sutton United**	429	0 - 0	
30/09	**FA Cup Q2 rep**	**SUTTON UNITED**	347	1 - 1	Langer 81
04/10	LP	BILLERICAY TOWN	355	3 - 0	Cooper 22 32, **Southam 88**
07/10	LP	Bedford Town	473	3 - 0	**Southam 73**, Bunn 78, Langer 85
11/10	**FA Cup Q3**	**Maidstone United**	601	1 - 1	Bunn 74
14/10	**FA Cup Q3 rep**	**MAIDSTONE UNITED**	568	3 - 2	Renner 11, **Southam 57 90[p]**
18/10	LP	NORTHWOOD	304	**6 - 0**	Renner 13 45, Bullivant 20[og], Rainford 30 52, McKeown 50
25/10	**FA Cup Q4**	**GLOUCESTER CITY**	768	2 - 0	Renner 37, Barnett 68
28/10	LP	Kingstonian	255	1 - 1	Essandoh 72
02/11	**FA Trophy 1**	**Slough Town**	332	2 - 2	**Southam 15,** Essandoh 68
04/11	**FA Trophy 1 rep**	**SLOUGH TOWN**	217	2 - 1	Wiltshire 27, **Southam 52**
08/11	**FA Cup 1**	**Mansfield Town**	4679	0 - 6	
15/11	LP	Hayes	256	0 - 1	
18/11	LP	BRAINTREE TOWN	351	2 - 3	Essandoh 62, Barnett 86
22/11	LP	HEYBRIDGE SWIFTS	271	0 - 1	
29/11	**FA Trophy 2**	**Kingstonian**	358	2 - 0	Howell 30, Martin 31
06/12	LP	Harrow Borough	218	0 - 1	
09/12	LP	Aylesbury United	253	1 - 0	Barnett 14
13/12	LP	FORD UNITED	278	4 - 0	Morrison 45, McKeown 72, Essandoh 80, Barnett 88
19/12	LP	Canvey Island	441	**1 - 5**	Barnett 65
27/12	LP	HITCHIN TOWN	443	3 - 0	Morrison 49 75, Rainford 90
01/01	LP	Carshalton Athletic	424	2 - 1	Barnett 63, Howell 80
03/01	LP	KETTERING TOWN	**561**	4 - 1	Howell 29 57, Morrison 51 80
10/01	**FA Trophy 3**	**ALDERSHOT TOWN**	957	2 - 4	Cooper 61, **Southam 90**
17/01	LP	Maidenhead United	292	4 - 0	Cooper 5, Howell 39, Bunn 61, **Southam 67**
24/01	LP	SUTTON UNITED	457	1 - 1	Bunn 86
07/02	LP	KINGSTONIAN	489	2 - 1	Bunn 5, **Southam 28**
10/02	LP	Braintree Town	386	0 - 2	
14/02	LP	Northwood	234	3 - 2	Martin 36, Bunn 38, Barnett 90
17/02	LP	HORNCHURCH	349	2 - 1	Rainford 2 **Southam 68**
21/02	LP	HAYES	367	0 - 0	
28/02	LP	Kettering Town	821	2 - 3	Howell 58,71
02/03	LP	AYLESBURY UNITED	275	4 - 4	Bunn 14, **Southam 18[p]**, Essandoh 19, Martin 86
06/03	LP	Thurrock	294	1 - 1	Bunn 74
09/03	LP	Basingstoke Town	205	2 - 1	Barnett 45, Rainford 69
13/03	LP	ST ALBANS CITY	421	2 - 2	Martin 14, Bunn 30
20/03	LP	Billericay Town	450	0 - 1	
27/03	LP	BEDFORD TOWN	357	3 - 1	Bunn 45 68[p], Rainford 83
03 /04	LP	Bognor Regis Town	286	1 - 0	**Southam 37[p]**
10 /04	LP	HENDON	358	2 - 0	**Southam 70, 77**
12 /04	LP	Hitchin Town	438	2 - 0	Hayes 5, **Southam 85**
17 /04	LP	GRAYS ATHLETIC	363	1 - 2	**Southam 69**
24 /04	LP	HARROW BOROUGH	283	1 - 1	**Southam 49 (p)**
01/05	LP	Heybridge Swifts	305	0 - 1	
		Average Home League attendance:	358	**93-78**	Top Goalscorer: **Glen Southam 19** (14+2FAC+3FAT)

PLAYING SQUAD 2004-2005

Goalkeepers:
Andy Young (Hoddesdon), Rob Elliott (Charlton)

Defenders:
Anthony Allman (Woking), Anthony Fenton (Newtown), Rob Gillman (Ashford T), Ollie Blackwell (Braintree), Paul Kyriacou (Anorthosi (Cyp)), Gareth Gwillam (Farnborough)

Midfield:
Richard Howell (Stevenage), David Rainford (Ford Utd), Scott Forbes (Canvey Island), Alex Riches (Saffron Walden), Alex Marin (Sawbridgeworth)

Forwards: Ali Heselton (Northwood), Paul Hakim (Wingate & F), Ben Yiadom (Northwood), Mervin Abraham (Redbridge), Leon Green (Weymouth), Martin Hayes (Romford), Tim Langer (Aveley)

BOGNOR REGIS TOWN

CLUB OFFICIALS
Chairman: Tom Martin
President: S Rowlands
Secretary: Peter Helsby, c/o The Club.
02392 291388 or 01243 822325
Press Officer& Commercial Manager:
Jack Pearce

FOOTBALL MANAGEMENT TEAM
Manager: Jack Pearce
Coach:Graham Vick
Captain: M.Birmingham
Physio: Mel Henry

FACT FILE
Founded: 1883
Nickname: The Rocks
Sponsors: Wayne Windows
Colours: White (green trim)/green/white
Change colours: Blue/white/red
Midweek home matchday: Tuesday
Reserves ' League: None
Local Radio: Radio Sussex, Ocean Sound, Radio Solent, Southern Sound, Spirit FM
Local Press: Bognor Regis Journal & Guardian, Bognor Observer, Brighton Argus, Portsmouth News

PROGRAMME
Pages: 36 Price: £1.20
Editor: N.Folland 01243 822325

GROUND Nyewood Lane, Bognor Regis PO21 2TY Tel: 01243 822325
Directions: West along sea front from pier, past Aldwick shopping centre then turn right into Nyewood Lane
Capacity: 6,000 Cover: 3,800 Seats: 243 Floodlights: Yes
Clubhouse: Open every night, matchdays and Sunday lunchtimes. Hot food available
Club Shop: Selling programmes and normal club items

PREVIOUS **Leagues:** W Sussex Lge 1896-1926; Brighton, Hove & District Lge 26-27; Sussex County Lge 27-72; Southern Lge 72-81

CLUB RECORDS **Attendance:** 3,642 v Swansea FA Cup 1st Rd replay, '84
Goalscorer: Kevin Clements (206) **Appearances:** Mick Pullen, 967 (20 seasons)
Transfer Fee Paid: £2,200 Guy Rutherford 95-96
Fee Received: £10,500 for John Crumplin & Geoff Cooper (Brighton & Hove Alb, 87) & Simon Rodger (C Palace 89)

BEST SEASON **FA Amateur Cup:** 1st Round 71-72 **F A Trophy:** 3rd Round 95-96
F A Cup: 2nd Rd on four occasions - League clubs beaten: Swansea 84-85, Exeter 88-89
84-85 2-6 v Reading (A), 85-86 1-6 v Gillingham (A), 88-89 0-1 v Cambridge (H), 95-96 0-4 v Peterborough (A)

HONOURS: Isthmian Lg Div 1 R-up 81-82, (Lg Cup 86-87); Southern Lg R-up 80-81 (Lg Cup R-up 80-81), Merit Cup 80-81; Sussex Lg 48-49 71-72 (R-up 38-39 51-52), Div 2 70-71, Invitation Cup 40-41 49-50 62-63 71-72; Brighton Lg R-up 26-27; W Sussex Lg (5) 20-25 (R-up 1896-97, 25-26), Jnr Lg 10-11 13-14; Southern Co's Comb 78-79; Sussex Snr Cup(9) 54-56 79-84 86-87 94-95 (R-up 51-52 58-59 84-85 00-01); Sussex Prof. Cup 73-74, Sussex RUR Cup 71-72; Sussex I'mediate Cup 52-53, Littlehampton Hosp. Cup 29-30 33-34; Bognor Charity Cup(8) 28-29 30-31 32-33 37-38 47-48 58-59 71-73; Gosport War Mem. Cup (2) 81-83 (R-up 86-87); Snr Midweek F'lit Cup R-up 74-75

Players progressing: E Randall (Chelsea 50), J Standing (Brighton 61), A Woon (Brentford 72), J Crumplin & G Cooper (Brighton 87), Simon Rodger (C Palace 89)

2004-2005 Back row, left to right: G Rutherford, M Russell, D Wright, K Murphy, R Sansom, C Foster, C Stoner, P Lawrence, D Beck, J Rowland, T White, R Brown.
Front Row: R Hudson, J Howell, D Birmingham, L Savage, M Birmingham, S Sargent, J Price, D Piper.

Date	Comp.	Opponents	Att.	Score	Goalscorers
16/08	LP	BRAINTREE TOWN	328	4 - 1	Rutherford 24 Hudson65 Sargent 85 Beck88
19/08	LP	Sutton United	552	0 - 1	
23/08	LP	Northwood	217	2 - 1	D Birmingham 26, M Birmingham 39
25/08	LP	BILLERICAY TOWN	418	2 - 0	Sargeant 10, Savage 89
30/08	LP	Bishop's Stortford	339	0 - 0	
02/09	LP	HARROW BOROUGH	465	3 - 1	Beck 17, M Birmingham 59, Rowland 73
06/09	LP	HAYES	451	4 - 0	M Birmingham 5, Beck 69, Savage 85, Sansome 87
09/09	LP	Aylesbury United	335	0 - 1	
13/09	LP	Kettering Town	1012	1 - 3	Price 85
16/09	LP	GRAYS ATHLETIC	313	2 - 1	Stillman 30, Howell 85
20/09	LP	FORD UNITED	329	3 - 2	Howell 14, Beck 32 73
23/09	LP	Kingstonian	395	1 - 1	**Russell 86**
27/09	**FA Cup Q2**	**HAVANT & WATERLOOVILLE**	945	0 - 4	
04/10	LP	Hendon	226	2 - 2	**Russell 57,** Sansom 85
07/10	LP	CARSHALTON ATHLETIC	**551**	0 - 1	
11/10	LP	MAIDENHEAD UNITED	331	0 - 3	
18/10	LP	Hornchurch	474	0 - 3	
25/10	LP	HEYBRIDGE SWIFTS	280	2 - 0	D Birmingham 5, Collins 81
01/11	**FA Trophy 1**	**Uxbridge**	153	1 0	**Russell 85**
15/11	LP	ST ALBANS CITY	347	2 - 2	**Russell 11**, Browne 24[og]
22/11	LP	BEDFORD TOWN	276	0 - 0	
29/11	**FA Trophy 2**	**Weston-super-Mare**	270	0 - 1	
06/12	LP	Hitchin Town	315	2 - 2	**Russell 49,** Frater 82[og]
13/12	LP	Braintree Town	187	3 - 0	Hudson 14, Murphy 28, **Russell 80**
16/12	LP	Canvey Island	411	1 - 3	**Russell 87**
20/12	LP	SUTTON UNITED	277	0 - 2	
27/12	LP	Basingstoke Town	468	1 - 0	Sanson 71
01/01	LP	NORTHWOOD	420	5 - 2	Piper 31 66, Hudson 40, White 45, M Birmingham 62
06/01	LP	Thurrock	259	1 - 4	Collins 8
17/01	LP	Hayes	268	1 - 0	Murphy 56
24/01	LP	KETTERING TOWN	405	1 - 0	Rutherford 62
31/01	LP	Grays Athletic	295	0 - 6	
07/02	LP	Heybridge Swifts	205	2 - 1	**Russell 23**, Hudson 50
10/02	LP	THURROCK	326	**6 - 1**	Price 1, **RUSSELL 18 20 30 84,** Poate 59
21/02	LP	St Albans City	225	2 - 2	Parker 48 52
24/02	LP	AYLESBURY UNITED	324	4 - 0	Price 42, **Russell 45**, Murphy 75, Moss 90[og]
02/03	LP	Maidenhead United	192	2 - 0	**Russell 31,** Rowland 90
06/03	LP	KINGSTONIAN	460	2 - 0	**Russell 31 77**
09/03	LP	HORNCHURCH	262	1 - 3	**Russell 28**
13/03	LP	Ford United	119	0 - 2	
20/03	LP	HENDON	294	1 - 2	Birmingham 45
27/03	LP	Carshalton Athletic	530	1 - 1	**Russell 43**
03 /04	LP	BISHOP'S STORTFORD	286	0 - 1	
10 /04	LP	Billericay Town	405	1 - 1	M Birmingham 18
12 /04	LP	BASINGSTOKE TOWN	402	1 - 3	**Russell 31**
17 /04	LP	Harrow Borough	200	1 - 0	Rutherford 47
20 /04	LP	CANVEY ISLAND	325	0 - 0	
24 /04	LP	HITCHIN TOWN	435	2 - 0	**Russell 40 49**
01/05	LP	Bedford Town	444	**0 - 8**	
		Average Home League Attendance:	**361**	66-71	Top Goalscorer: **Matthew Russell 21** (20 +1FAT)

PLAYING SQUAD 2004-2005

Goalkeepers:

Craig Stoner (Portsmouth)

Defenders:

David Piper (Eastleigh), Kevin Murphy (Waterlooville), Jody Rowland (Arundel)

Midfield:

David Wright (Dorchester), Michael Birmingham (Portsmouth), Guy Rutherford (Worthing), David Birmingham (Bournemouth), Jamie Howell (Torquay), Tm White (Portsmouth)

Forwards:

Richard Hudson (Lewes), Matt Russell (Horsham YMCA), Louis Savage (Havant & Waterlooville), Daniel Beck (Brighton), Bikram Singh (Moneyfields)

CAMBRIDGE CITY

CLUB OFFICIALS

Chairman: Arthur Eastham

President: Sir Neil Westbrook, CBE MA FRICS

Secretary: Andy Dewey, 50 Dooggett Road, Cambridge, CB1 9LF

Tel No: 01223 245694

Press Officer: Chairman

email: arthur@cambridgecityfc.com

FOOTBALL MANAGEMENT TEAM

Manager: Gary Roberts

Captain: Matt Langston

Physio: Peter Corder

FACT FILE

Formed: 1908

Nickname: Lilywhites

Sponsors: Lancer UK

Colours:White /black/ white. Change All Sky

Midweek matchday: Tuesday

Reserves' League: Eastern Counties

Website: www.cambridgecityfc.com

2003-04

Player of the Year: Matt Langston

Leading Goalscorer: Danny Bloomfield

Cambridge City Football Club

Main Club Sponsors

LANCER

2003/04 Season

'Everyone at the club would like to welcome you to Milton Road'

Dr Martens League - Premier Division

City v Tiverton Town

£1.50 Saturday 24th April - Kick off 3.00pm Prog. 29

Pages: 44 Price: £1.50

Editor: Secretary

Local Press: Cambridge Evening News

Local Radio: BBC Radio Cambridge

GROUND City Ground, Milton Road, Cambridge CB4 1UY Tel: 01223 357973

Directions: Fifty yards on left from start of A1309, Cambridge to Ely Rd. (Behind Westbrook Centre). Thirty minutes walk from Cambridge BR

Capacity: 2000 Cover: 1,400 Seats:533 Floodlights: Yes

Clubhouse: 11am-11pm Mon-Sat, 12-3 & 7pm-10.30 Sun. Bingo, Dances, Pool, Darts

Club Shop: Sells badges, scarves, pennants, replica shirts and leisurewear. Contact Neil Harvey (01223 235991)

PREVIOUS **Leagues:** Bury & Dist. 08-13 19-20, East Anglian 08-10, Southern Olympian 11-14, Southern Amateur 1913-35, Spartan 35-50, Athenian 50-58 **Name:** Cambridge Town 1908-51

CLUB RECORDS **Attendance:** 12,058 v Leytonstone, FA Amateur Cup 1st Rd, 1949-50

Scorer: Gary Grogan **Appearances:** Mal Keenan

Fee Paid: £8,000 for Paul Coe (Rushden & Diamonds) **Fee Received:**£100,000 from Millwall for Neil Harris 1998

BEST SEASON **FA Amateur Cup:** Semi Final 27-28 **FA Trophy:** 2nd Rd. 86-87 87-88

FA Cup: 1st Rd; v Ashford 66, v Swindon 46, v Walthamstow Ave. 48, v Hereford 93, v Wigan Ath. 99, v Exeter City 01

HONOURS Southern Lg 62-63 (R-up 70-71, Southern Div 85-86, Div 1 R-up 69-70, Champ Cup62-63; E Anglian Cup (9); Eastern Prof Floodlit Lg 65-66 72-73, Cambs Prof Cup(6); Cambs Invitation Cup (8); Spartan Lg 47-48 48-49 (R-up 49-50); EasternDiv Champs 45-46); Southern Amat Lg 20-21 27-28 28-29 30-31 31-32; Bury & Dist.Lg (4); E Anglian Lg (6); AFA Snr Cup 30-31 46-47 47-48(shared) 48-49 49-50;AFA Invitation Cup 50-51; Hunts Prem Cup 62-63 64-65; Suffolk Sen Cup 09-10; Addenbrookes Hosp Cup 87-88; The Munns Youth Cup 82-83 83-84 84-85; ChilternYouth Lge Cup R-up 75-76; South Mids Lg Youth Trophy 82-83; Robinson Cup 87-8889-90; Jim Digney 89-90; Essex & Herts Youth Lg 89-90 Southern Lg Cup R-up 98-9

Players progressing: K Wright (West Ham 46), A Gallego(Norwich 47), A Stokes (Watford 61), D Weddle (Middlesbrough 61), D Hicksen(Bury 62), B Harvey (Blackpool 62), R Whitehead (Darlington 62), G Cummins(Hull 62), R Pearce (Peterborough 63), A Banks (Exeter 63), T Carroll (Ipswich66), Dominic Genovese (Peterborough 88), Roy Jones (Swindon), Winston Dubose(Oldham), K Wilkin (Northampton Tn 91), S Flack (Cardiff City 95), D Hedcock(Sheffield Wed 96), Neil Harris (Millwall 1998), Tesfaye Bramble, Shane Wardley (Southend United)

Back row, left to right: Paul Fewings, Tom Pell, Marc Abbott, Jamie Alsop, Luke Hughes, Mark Roper, Loz Church, Marcus Hering, Steve Shipley, Jim Wilson and Michael Gash. **Middle Row:** Glen Fuff, Rob Nightingale, Matt Langston, Alan Calton, Duncan Roberts, Dave Sadler, LeeSummerscales and Robbie Simpson **Front Row**: Craig Pope, Sam Swonnell, Dale Binns, Gary Roberts (Manager), Pete Corder)Dhysio), Richard Scott,Rob Miller and Carl Williams.

Date	Comp.	Opponents	Att.	Score	Goalscorers
16/08	LP	Weston-super-Mare	244	0 - 1	
19/08	LP	CHELMSFORD CITY	378	2 - 0	Nightingale 33, Quilter 47
23/08	LP	DORCHESTER TOWN	333	4 - 2	Pluck 8 51, Nightingale 55[p], Simpson 89
25/08	LP	Grantham Town	486	1 - 2	**Bloomfield 10**
30/08	LP	Bath City	558	2 - 1	Simpson 41, Nightingale 61
02/09	LP	WELLING UNITED	410	0 - 3	
06/09	LP	HAVANT & WATERLOOVILLE	367	2 - 3	**Bloomfield 11 80**
09/09	LP	Crawley Town	748	0 - 2	
13/09	LP	Weymouth	1454	1 - 2	Simpson 41
16/09	LP	DOVER ATHLETIC	290	2 - 1	Godbold 85, **Bloomfield 88**
20/09	LP	Chippenham Town	471	2 - 0	Itonga 49, Godbold 85
27/09	**FA Cup Q2**	**ILKESTON TOWN**	294	3 - 1	Riddle 53, Simpson 59, Gale 65
04/10	LP	MERTHYR TYDFIL	418	2 - 2	Simpson 53, **Bloomfield 66**
11/10	**FA Cup Q3**	**LOWESTOFT TOWN**	357	3 - 0	**BLOOMFIELD 27,34,75**
18/10	LP	Chelmsford City	364	1 - 1	Itonga 69
21/10	LP	CRAWLEY TOWN	307	**2 - 5**	**Bloomfield 65,** Itonga 90
25/10	**FA Cup Q4**	**FORD UNITED**	412	2 - 3	Itonga 75, Niven 88
01/11	**FA Trophy 1**	**Worthing**	406	0 - 0	
04/11	**FA Trophy 1 rep**	**WORTHING**	205	2 - 3	**Bloomfield 30,** Nightingale 78
08/11	LP	HINCKLEY UNITED	520	1 - 2	Nightingale 9
15/11	LP	Havant & Waterlooville	537	3 - 2	**Bloomfield 23 58**, Pluck 87
29/11	LP	Moor Green	204	1 - 1	**Bloomfield 85**
06/12	LP	STAFFORD RANGERS	502	1 - 0	**Bloomfield 1**
13/12	LP	Hednesford Town	459	2 - 2	Nightingale 63, Riddle 82
20/12	LP	Dorchester Town	508	2 - 0	Nightingale 18[p], **Bloomfield 57**
26/12	LP	GRANTHAM TOWN	519	1 - 1	Martin 49
01/01	LP	Nuneaton Borough	798	1 - 2	**Bloomfield 50**
03/01	LP	EASTBOURNE BOROUGH	419	0 - 0	
10/01	LP	Merthyr Tydfil	552	3 - 1	Langston 39, Martin 57, **Bloomfield 64**
13/01	LP	BATH CITY	299	0 - 0	
17/01	LP	NEWPORT COUNTY	494	0 - 2	
24/01	LP	Tiverton Town	795	1 - 1	Nolan 22
07/02	LP	WEYMOUTH	**811**	1 - 0	Nolan 68
14/02	LP	CHIPPENHAM TOWN	338	1 - 1	Nightingale 17
21/02	LP	Stafford Rangers	737	1 - 1	Simpson 89
24/02	LP	Hinckley United	218	0 - 0	
28/02	LP	WORCESTER CITY	459	0 - 0	
06/03	LP	Welling United	630	1 - 0	**Bloomfield 80**
20/03	LP	HEDNESFORD TOWN	384	0 - 1	
27/03	LP	Dover Athletic	751	1 - 0	Blackman 30[p]
03 /04	LP	MOOR GREEN	355	1 - 1	Miller 12
10 /04	LP	Eastbourne Borough	657	1 - 1	Battersby 63
12 /04	LP	NUNEATON BOROUGH	426	1 - 3	Blackman 26
17 /04	LP	Newport County	541	0 - 1	
20 /04	LP	WESTON-SUPER-MARE	307	1 - 1	Baillie 59
24 /04	LP	TIVERTON TOWN	653	**6 - 4**	Hughes 4, **BLOOMFIRELD 30 44 82,** Langston 33, Scott 54
01/05	LP	Worcester City	991	2 - 0	Baillie 81 **Bloomfield 87**
		Average Home Attendance:	**424**	64-60	Top Goalscorer:**Danny Bloomfield 22** (18+3FAC+1T)

PLAYING SQUAD 2004-2005

Goalkeepers:

Duncan Roberts (Newport Co), Alan Calton (Norwich)

Defenders:

Glenn Fuff (King's Lynn), Matt Langston (Stevenage), Lee Summerscales (Fakenham), Mark Roper (Norwich), Jamie Alsop (Ipswich), Lee Chaffey (Ipswich), Marcus Hering (Youth team), Steve Shipley (Norwich), James Wilson (Diss), Craig Pope (Barnet)

Midfield:

Lewis Baillie (Heybridge), Carl Williams (Hitchin), Sam Swonnell (Watford), Luke Hughes (Youth team), Richard Scott (Stevenage), Dale Binns (Hendon), Marc Abbott (Youth team), Lawrence Church (Youth team), Rob Miller (Bedford), Rob Nightingale (Youth team)

Forwards:

Paul Fewings (Kettering), Tom Pell (Peterborough), Robbie Simpson (Norwich), Dave Sadler (Hinckley Utd)

CARSHALTON ATHLETIC

CARSHALTON ATHLETIC
FOOTBALL CLUB
SEASON 2002/03
Ryman League
Division 1 South
Ryman
Programme £1.50
TOOTING & MITCHAM

CLUB OFFICIALS

Chairman: Victor Thompson
President: John Carpentiere
Vice Chairman:T.B.A.
Secretary: Kevin Powell, 35 Dale Dark Avenue,Carshalton, Surrey SM5 2ES
0208 773 1406 (H) 07884 246518 (M)
General Man: Tracey Wadsworth-Smith
Press Officer & Commercial Manager:
Roger Fear: 07747 842937(M)
email: rfear22222aol.com

FOOTBALL MANAGEMENT TEAM

Man: Billy Smith Asst Man:George Wakelin
Coach: Jimmy Dack
Physios: Tanya Clarke

FACT FILE

Formed: 1905
Nickname: Robins
Sponsors: Hyundai Belmont
Colours: White, maroon trim/maroon/white
Change colours: Maroon
Midweek matchday: ~Mondays
Reserve League: Suburban
Newsline: 0930 555 877
Local Press: Sutton Comet, Sutton Herald
Local Radio: BBC Southern Counties

GROUND War Memorial Sports Ground, Colston Av, Carshalton SM5 2PW
Tel: 0208 642 8658

Directions: Turn right out of Carshalton BR Station, and Colston Avenue is first left. Entrance 150 yards on right. London Transport bus 151 from Morden to Wrythe Green Lane

Capacity: 8,000 Cover: 4,500 Seats: 240 Floodlights: Yes

Clubhouse: Open every evening and lunchtime. Licenced bar, pool, darts,machines, discos on Saturday. Separate function hall (bookings taken). Food:sandwiches, rolls, burgers, hot dogs, teas, coffees and soft drinks. (0181 642 8658)

Club Shop: Sells hats, scarves, T-shirts, badges, programmes etc

PROGRAMME

Pages: 20 Price: £1.50p
Editor: Roger Fear
Tel No: 01737248066 (H))

PREVIOUS **Leagues:** Southern Sub (pre-1911); Surrey Snr 22-23; London 23-46; Corinthian46-56; Athenian 56-73
Grounds: Wrythe Recreation Ground 1907-14; Culvers Park 19-20

CLUB RECORDS **Attendance:** 7,800 v Wimbledon, London Senior Cup
Career goalscorer: Jimmy Bolton(242)
Career appearances: Jon Warden (504)
Transfer fee paid: £15,000 from Enfield for Curtis Warmington
Transfer fee paid £30,000 for Ian Cox (Crystal Palace)
Win: 13-0 v Worthing, Loctite Cup Third Round 28/2/91

BEST SEASON **F.A.Trophy :** 3rd Rd 95-96 lodst away at Hyde United (2-3)
FA Cup: 2nd Rd 82-83, lost 1-4 at Torquay. - League clubs defeated: None

HONOURS: Isthmian League Div 2 R-up 76-77, Corinthian League 52-53 53-54, Surrey Senior League R-up 22-23, Surrey Senior Cup(3) Runners-up (5) Surrey Senior Shield 75-76 Runners-up (2)), London Challenge Cup 91-92 Isthmian Lg Cup R-up 90-91

Players progressing: Roy Lunnes (Crystal Pal. 60), Les Burns (Charlton 67), Ron Walker (Watford), Nobby Warren (Exeter),Terry Stacey (Plymouth A.), Frank GeorgelLeyton Orient) ,Tommy Williams (Colchester U), Alan Eagles (Leyton Orient), Derek Razzell (Q.PR),Muray Jones Crystal Pal.) Gus Caesar (Arsenal), Darren Annon (Brentford) 94, Ian Cox (Crystal Pal.) 94, Carl Asaba (Brentford)

L-R - Back Row: Steve Lang (coach), Graham Baker (coach), Steve Darlington, Mark Costello, Berandeh Ouefio,Tutu Henriques, Mark Pye, Stuart Searle, Peter Wood, Gary Elliott, John Hamsher, Romuald Bouadji, John(JJ)Johnson (Kit Manager)
Front Row: Matt York, Byron Glasgow, Nigel Webb, Michael Johnson, Barry Gartell (Chief Executive), Graham Roberts (Manager), Steve Friend (Chairman), Keith Dublin (Captain), Tommy Williams, Baroan Tagro, Scott Todd

Date	Comp.	Opponents	Att.	Score	Goalscorers
16/08	LP	ST ALBANS CITY	367	1 - 1	Le Bihan 78[p]
19/08	LP	Thurrock	325	3 - 2	Le Bihan 35[p], **Marvell 61**, Todd 89
23/08	LP	Bishop's Stortford	332	3 - 0	York 44, Boateng 57, **Marvel 85**
25/08	LP	BEDFORD TOWN	439	2 - 1	**Marvel 55 70**
30/08	LP	Billericay Town	405	1 - 0	**Marvell 90**
01/09	LP	NORTHWOOD	454	1 - 0	Johnson 67
06/09	LP	KETTERING TOWN	571	3 - 2	Olusesi 45, Kane 89, Boateng 90[p]
09/09	LP	Grays Athletic	291	0 - 0	
13/09	LP	Aylesbury United	403	1 - 1	Olususi 10
15/09	LP	HAYES	432	2 - 0	Wood 45, Johnson 67
20/09	LP	Heybridge Swifts	273	0 - 4	
22/09	LP	BASINGSTOKE TOWN	418	0 - 2	
27/09	**FA Cup Q2**	**Enfield Town**	501	1 - 0	**Marvell 42[p]**
04/10	LP	HITCHIN TOWN	342	2 - 1	Wood 20, Russell 37
07/10	LP	Bognor Regis Town	551	1 - 0	Russell 23
11/10	**FA Cup Q3**	**Hornchurch**	611	0 - 5	
18/10	LP	Hendon	235	2 - 1	Bates 39[og], Russell 53
20/10	LP	HORNCHURCH	476	0 - 0	
01/11	**FA Trophy 1**	**BROMLEY**	495	3 - 1	York 5, Boateng 32, Kane 90
11/11	LP	Maidenhead United	255	0 - 0	
15/11	LP	CANVEY ISLAND	719	0 - 2	
29/11	**FA Trophy 2**	**THURROCK**	198	2 - 2	Boateng 7, Olusesi 71
02/12	**FA Trophy 2 rep**	**Thurrock**	103	0 - 1	
06/12	LP	BRAINTREE TOWN	272	2 - 1	McDonnell 33 83
13/12	LP	St Albans City	264	**4 - 0**	**Marvell 4**, Wood 70, Bolt 71, Boateng 84
15/12	LP	HARROW BOROUGH	279	3 - 2	**Marvell 8**, Boateng 58, York 78
20/12	LP	THURROCK	310	0 - 3	
27/12	LP	Sutton United	1213	**0 - 6**	
01/01	LP	BISHOP'S STORTFORD	424	1 - 2	Kane 88
06/01	LP	Kingstonian	379	1 - 0	McDonnell 28
10/01	LP	GRAYS ATHLETIC	400	0 - 2	
17/01	LP	Kettering Town	984	3 - 0	York 11, McDonnell 33 83
24/01	LP	AYLESBURY UNITED	381	3 - 0	Russell 24 **Marvell 51** Boatang 65
07/02	LP	Harrow Borough	184	0 - 0	
09/02	LP	MAIDENHEAD UNITED	276	3 - 2	**Marvell 5**, Boateng 20, York 32
14/02	LP	HENDON	359	1 - 3	York 87
17/02	LP	Ford United	141	1 - 2	Hawthorne 52
21/02	LP	Canvey Island	772	0 - 3	
28/02	LP	FORD UNITED	276	1 - 1	McDonnel 24l
06/03	LP	Basingstoke Town	334	2 - 1	Bouadji 2 Saunders 16
13/03	LP	HEYBRIDGE SWIFTS	314	4 - 1	**Marvell 23,** Stone 70, McDonnell 74, York 81
20/03	LP	Hitchin Town	282	3 - 0	**Marvell 11**, Stone 38, McDonnell 73
27/03	LP	BOGNOR REGIS TOWN	530	1 - 1	McDonnell 53
30/03	LP	Hayes	287	0 - 1	
03 /04	LP	BILLERICAY TOWN	282	2 - 1	McDonnell 20[p] 81
08 /04	LP	Hornchurch	394	0 - 2	
10 /04	LP	Bedford Town	403	0 - 1	
12 /04	LP	SUTTON UNITED	**1077**	2 - 2	Stone 8, Saunders 12
17 /04	LP	Northwood	221	**4 - 0**	Patterson 13 87, Bouadji 58, **Marvell 89**
24 /04	LP	Braintree Town	223	1 - 0	York 41
01/05	LP	KINGSTONIAN	517	2 - 1	Saunders 54, York 74
		Average Home League Attendance:	**431**	72-64	Top Goalscorer **Marvel 13** (12+1FAC)

PLAYING SQUAD 2004-2005

Goalkeepers:

Stuart Searle (Aldershot)

Defenders:

Romauld Bouadji (St Ettienne (France)), Mark Costello (Staines), Gary Elliott (Whyeleafe), Colin Hartburn (Tooting), Chris Head (Crystal Palace), Ellis Hooper (Crawley), Peter Wood (Hampton)

Midfield:

Des Boateng (St Leonards), Danny Carroll (Stevenage), Dale Marvel (Kingstonian), Marlon Patterson (Fisher), Sam Saunders (Ashford T), Kevin Watson (Team Bath), Matt York (Banstead)

Forwards:

Kevin Cooper (AFC Wimbledon), Billy Harding (Wycombe), Conrad Kane (Tooting), Nic McDonnell (St Albans), Adrian Stone (Ashford T)

DORCHESTER TOWN

CLUB OFFICIALS
Chairman: E. C. G. Belt
President: A. E. Miller
Vice Chairman: K. Miller
Comm Mgr: Brian Benjafield
Secretary: David Martin
21 Diggory Crescent, Dorchester
01305 262345
General Manager: Keith Kellaway
Press Officer: Rob Hodder(07971 225910)

FOOTBALL MANAGEMENT TEAM
Manager: Mark Morris
Physio: Geoff Dine

FACT FILE
Formed: 1880
Nickname: The Magpies
Sponsors: A.J.Dennis & Son
Colours: Black & white stripes/black/black
Change colours: All Yellow
Midweek games: Tuesdays (7.45)
Newsline (Magpies Hotline): 0839 664412
Reserves' League: Dorset Comb

2003-2004
Top Scorer: Mattew Groves
Player of the Year: Matty Holmes

Pages: 32 Price: £1.50
Editor: Melvin Cross (01305 848365)

Local Press: Dorset Evening Echo, Western Gazette, Western Daily Press
Local Radio: Radio Solent, Wessex FM

GROUND Avenue Stadium, Weymouth Avenue, Dorchester DT1 2RY Tel: 01305 262451

Directions: Situated at the junction of the town bypass (A35) and the Weymouth road (A354)
Nearest station: Dorchester South
Capacity: 5,009 Cover: 2,846 Seats: 697 Floodlights: Yes

Clubhouse: Dorchester Lounge Club - access via main entrance to stadium. Cold food and snacks
Club Shop: Sells replica shirts, badges, mugs, etc

PREVIOUS **Leagues:** Dorset; Western 1947-72
Grounds: Council Recreation Ground, Weymouth Avenue 1880-1929; The Avenue Ground, Weymouth Avenue 29-90

CLUB RECORDS **Attendance:** 4,000 v Chelsea, official ground opening 1990. Competitive: 4, 159 v Weymouth, Southern Lge Prem Div , 99
Goalscorer: Dennis Cheney 61 (in one season) **Appearances:** Derek (Dinkie) Curtis 458 50-66
Win: 7-0 v Canterbury (A), Southern Lge Southern Div 86-87
Defeat: 0-13 v Welton Rovers Western Lge 66
Fee Paid: £12,000 for Chris Townsend (Gloucester City, 1990)
Fee Received: £35,000 for Trevor Senior (Portsmouth, 1981)

BEST SEASON **FA Trophy:** 3rd Rd replay 71-72, 96-97
FA Cup: 2nd Rd Replay 81-82, 1-2 v A.F.C. Bournemouth after 1-1. 2nd Rd 54-55 57-58; 1st Rd8 times

HONOURS Southern Lg 85-85, R-up 79-80 Div 1 Sth R-up 77-78, Lg Cup 86-87 R-up 91-92; Western Lg 54-55 R-up 60-61, Div 2 R-up 49-50, Lge Cup 54-54; Dorset Snr Cup 50-51 60-61 67-68 68-69 71-72 93-94 94-95; Dorset Lg 37-38

Players progressing: Len Drake (Bristol Rov. 57), David Noake (Luton 59), Mike Turner (Swindon 61), Trevor Senior (Portsmouth 81), David West (Liverpool 83), Mike Squire (Torquay 84), Jeremy Judd (Torquay 84),Tony White (Bournem'th 85), Graham Roberts (Spurs, Chelsea, Rangers, England) who progressed via Weymouth. Darren Garner (Rotherham U, 95), Craig Taylor (Swindon),Syfyan Ghazghazi (Club African De Tunis 98)

Back row, left to right: Phil Simpkin (Reserve Team Manager), Geoff Dine (Physio), Warren Byerley, Joseba Barandiaran, Steve Legg, Carl Poore, Alex Browne, Mike Walker, Craig Bradshaw, Anthony Griffin, Mark Ormorod, Mike White, Justin Keeler, Andy Harris, Jamie Brown, Matthew Groves, Mark Jermyn, Simon Radcliffe, Steve Llewelyn, Brian Benjafield and Derek Taylor (kit Managert) **Front row:** Keith Kellaway (director), Steve Gould (Financial Director), David Martin (Secretary/Director), Albert Miller (President), Mark Morris (Manager), Eddie Belt (Chairman), Kevin Dove (Director), David Grassby (Director), Shaun Hearn (Director), Colin Clark (Vice Chairman) and Roger Murray (Director)

Photo: Dorset Evening Echo

Date	Comp.	Opponents	Att.	Score	Goalscorers
16/08/03	LP	HINCKLEY UNITED	521	1 - 1	Shepherd 25
18/08/03	LP	Havant & Waterlooville	501	2 - 3	Brown 65, Tubbs 69
23/08/03	LP	Cambridge City	333	2 - 4	Shepherd 20, Walker 66
25/08/03	LP	BATH CITY	633	1 - 0	Browne 76
30/08/03	LP	CHELMSFORD CITY	558	4 - 1	Tubbs 23, Keeler 44, Browne 80, Cooper 86
02/09/03	LP	Weston-super-Mare	339	1 - 1	Holmes 56
06/09/03	LP	Worcester City	1048	0 - 1	
09/09/03	LP	TIVERTON TOWN	632	1 - 0	Keeler 44[p]
13/09/03	LP	Stafford Rangers	786	0 - 3	
16/09/03	LP	EASTBOURNE BOROUGH	428	0 - 1	
20/09/03	LP	HEDNESFORD TOWN	529	3 - 4	Keeler 3 82[p], Browne 67
27/09/03	**FA Cup Q2**	**Weston-super-Mare**	293	1 - 4	Browne 88
04/10/03	LP	Moor Green	224	3 - 1	Hann 64, Brown 89, **Groves 90**
18/10/03	LP	HAVANT & WATERLOOVILLE	505	1 - 2	**Groves 64**
21/10/03	LP	Tiverton Town	494	1 - 1	O'Hagan 73
01/11/03	**FA Trophy 1**	**Leyton**	79	5 - 1	Keeler 2, Holmes 22, **Groves 29 66,** Cooper 76
08/11/03	LP	CHIPPENHAM TOWN	573	3 - 1	Davies 41[og], Cooper 69, Brown 72
15/11/03	LP	Newport County	637	0 - 0	
22/11/03	LP	Crawley Town	1023	3 - 2	O'Hagan 19, Brown 54 65
29/11/03	**FA Trophy 2**	**HARROW BOROUGH**	272	3 - 0	Brown 23, **Groves 41,** O'Hagan 69
06/12/03	LP	DOVER ATHLETIC	478	0 - 2	
020/12/03	LP	CAMBRIDGE CITY	508	0 - 2	
26/12/03	LP	Weymouth	3734	**0 - 8**	
01/01	LP	WEYMOUTH	**4116**	2 - 2	Browne 5, Hann 84[p]
03/01	LP	Merthyr Tydfil	376	0 - 1	
10/01	**FA Trophy 3**	**MARGATE**	392	2 - 2	**Groves 44 45**
17/01	LP	GRANTHAM TOWN	405	2 - 2	O'Hagan 53, **Groves 61**
20/01	**FA Trophy 3 rep**	**Margate**	278	0 - 2	(at Ashford Town)
24/01	LP	WESTON-SUPER-MARE	488	3 - 2	**Groves 5,** O'Hagan 71 88
27/01	LP	WELLING UNITED	331	2 - 0	**Groves 41**, Walker 76
31/01	LP	Eastbourne Borough	433	1 - 2	Playford 9[og]
07/02	LP	NUNEATON BOROUGH	522	0 - 0	
14/02	LP	Grantham Town	353	0 - 4	
21/02	LP	CRAWLEY TOWN	701	2 - 0	Rawlinson 26, Hann 53
24/02	LP	Welling United	390	1 - 6	O'Hagan 73
06/03	LP	STAFFORD RANGERS	486	0 - 0	
09/03	LP	Hinckley United	201	0 - 1	
13/03	LP	Chelmsford City	351	0 - 2	
20/03	LP	MOOR GREEN	429	0 - 1	
27/03	LP	Bath City	642	0 - 0	
03 /04	LP	WORCESTER CITY	466	3 - 0	Keeler 6, Browne 28, Brown 77
06 /04	LP	Hednesford Town	353	4 - 2	Keeler 4, Laws 34, Browne 38, **Groves 72**
10 /04	LP	MERTHYR TYDFIL	508	1 - 0	Laws 11
12 /04	LP	Chippenham Town	621	**6 - 1**	**GROVES 8,53,64** Laws 10, 45 Jermyn 44
17 /04	LP	Dover Athletic	741	2 - 1	Laws 80, Jermyn 90
24 /04	LP	NEWPORT COUNTY	771	1 - 2	Keeler 72[p]
01/05	LP	Nuneaton Borough	653	0 - 2	
03/05	**Play-off**	**Bath City**	1250	4 - 2	Holmes 28, Keeler 47, **Groves 54,** Brown 90
08/05	**Play-off**	**Tiverton Town**	1339	3 - 1	Holmes 2 56, Wood 36 (at Exeter City)
		Average home league attendance:	**695**	74-81	Top Goalscorer: **Matthew Groves 15** (9+5FAT+1PO)

PLAYING SQUAD 2004-2005

Goalkeepers:

Mark Ormerod (Woking), Craig Bradshaw (Portsmouth)

Defenders:

Anthony Griffin (Cheltenham), Gary Middleton (Reading), Alex Browne (Weymouth), Mark Jermyn (Torquay), Simon Radcliffe (Bridport), Andy Harris (Weymouth)

Midfield:

Jamie Brown (BAT Sports), Jose Barandiarna (UPV (Spain))

Forwards:

Justin Keeler (Bournemouth), David Laws (Portland), Matty Groves (Portsmouth), Juan Ugarte (Real Sociadad (Spain)), Steve Legg (Wareham Rangers)

EASTBOURNE BOROUGH

CLUB OFFICIALS

Chairman: Len Smith

President: J Stonestreet

Secretary: Mrs Myra Stephens,
9 Gwent Road,St James Rd.,Eastbourne,
BN22 7BX
Tel/Fax: 01323 642834 07754174406(M)
email: myra@stephens529.fsnet.co.uk

FOOTBALL MANAGEMENT TEAM

Manager: Garry Wilson

Coach: Nick Greenwood

Physio: Ray Tuppen

FACT FILE

Founded: 1966 Nickname: Sports

Sponsors: 1st Class Window Systems Ltd.

Colours: Red & Black

Change: Yellow/black/yellow

Midweek Matchday: Tuesday

Reserve League:Sussex Co.Prem Res.

2003-004

Top Scorer: Scott Ramsay

Ps o.Y: Lee Hook & Stuart Tuck

2004-2005 Captain: Daren Pearce

Beside The Seaside
The Matchday Magazine of Eastbourne Borough F.C.
EASTBOURNE BOROUGH
FOOTBALL CLUB
Season 2003/04
NUNEATON BOROUGH
Saturday 24th April 2004
1st Class Window Systems Ltd
Programme £1.50

76 Pages Price: £150
Programme Editor: Mike Spooner
Tel./Fax: 01323 471071(H)
Website: www.eastbourne borough fc.co.uk
Local Press: Eastbourne Gazette & Herald

GROUND Langney Sports Club, Priory Lane, Eastbourne, E, Sussex Tel: 01323 766265 or 01323 743561 Email Address: head@stoucrosse-sussex.sch.uk

Capacity: 3,000 Seats:500 Cover: 2,500 Floodlights: Yes

Directions: A22 to Polegate, A27 @ junction of A27/A22 new by-pass follow signs to cre matorium and then first right to Priory Lane
One mile from Pevensey & Westham(BR). Buses from Eastbourne

Clubhouse: Open every evening & lunchtime with adjoining sports hall, boardroom and matchday tea bar **Club Shop:** Yes

HONOURS Sussex County League Champions 99-00 R-up: 2002-03, Sussex Co. Lg R-up 91-92, Div 2 87-88, Lg Cup 89-90, Div 3 86-87, Div 3 Cup 86-87, 5-aside 1990; Sussex I'mediate Cup 85-86, Eastbourne Chall. Cup 85-86 86-87 99-00 00-01
Sussex Senior Cup 2001-02, Dr Martens Eastern Div R-up 02-03

PREVIOUS **League:** Eastbourne & Hastings, Unijet Sussex Oo League.**Name:** Langney Sports
Grounds: Princes Park, Wartling Rd, Eastbourne/ Adjacent pitch

RECORDS **Attendance:** 1703 Sussex Senior Cup Final v Crawley Town 2003
Goalscorer: Nigel Hole 146 **Appearances:** Darren Baker 500
Win: 10-1 v Haywards Heath Town, Sussex County Lg Div. 1 11/4/92
Defeat: 0-8, v Sheppey United (A), FA Vase Prel. Rd 9/10/93
v Peacehaven & Telscombe (A), Sussex County Lg Div. 1 9/11/93

Date	Comp.	Opponents	Att.	Score	Goalscorers
16/08	LP	STAFFORD RANGERS	494	1 - 1	Austin 6
19/08	LP	Welling United	629	2 - 1	Crabb 51, **Ramsay 89**
23/08	LP	Moor Green	239	1 - 0	Simmonds 37
25/08	LP	DOVER ATHLETIC	780	3 - 1	Pearce 81, **Ramsay 85**, Yates 89
30/08	LP	Nuneaton Borough	1303	**0 - 4**	
02/09	LP	CRAWLEY TOWN	**1239**	1 - 1	Simmonds 82
06/09	LP	HINCKLEY UNITED	543	0 - 2	
09/09	LP	Havant & Waterlooville	472	0 - 1	
13/09	LP	BATH CITY	476	1 - 1	**Ramsay 71**
16/09	LP	Dorchester Town	428	1 - 0	White 19
20/09	LP	Merthyr Tydfil	516	2 - 2	Smart 15, White 65
27/09	**FA Cup Q2**	**CHELMSFORD CITY**	608	2 - 2	Crabb 38, Pearce 61[p]
01/10	**FA Cup Q2 rep**	**Chelmsford City**	441	2 - 0	Austin 62, White 65
04/10	LP	GRANTHAM TOWN	590	1 - 0	White 56
11/10	**FA Cup Q3**	**Braintree Town**	351	4 - 0	Pearce 32, Smart 59, **Ramsay 67**, Goodwin 90
18/10	LP	Chippenham Town	435	1 - 0	**Ramsay 88**
21/10	LP	WELLING UNITED	456	1 - 1	**Ramsay 43**
25/10	**FA Cup Q4**	**STEVENAGE BOROUGH**	1305	2 - 2	**Ramsay 4 37**
28/10	**FA Cup Q4 rep**	**Stevenage Borough**	1205	0 - 1	
01/11	**FA Trophy 1**	**WELLING UNITED**	533	1 - 2	Simmonds 56
08/11	LP	NEWPORT COUNTY	451	1 - 2	**Ramsay 72**
15/11	LP	Weymouth	1159	0 - 1	
22/11	LP	CHELMSFORD CITY	514	1 - 1	**Ramsay 43**
29/11	LP	Grantham Town	272	**3 - 0**	Yates 11, **Ramsay 54 81**
06/12	LP	WORCESTER CITY	519	1 - 3	**Ramsay 49**
13/12	LP	Stafford Rangers	616	1 - 4	Crabb 49
20/12	LP	MOOR GREEN	400	0 - 1	
26/12	LP	Dover Athletic	1103	0 - 2	
03/01	LP	Cambridge City	419	0 - 0	
10/01	LP	Tiverton Town	540	3 - 2	Pulman 4, Rowland 16, **Ramsay 59**
17/01	LP	CHIPPENHAM TOWN	580	1 - 2	Pulman 4
24/01	LP	Hednesford Town	459	2 - 1	**Ramsay 24 77**
31/01	LP	DORCHESTER TOWN	433	2 - 1	Dell 6, **Ramsay 89**
07/02	LP	MERTHYR TYDFIL	577	1 - 1	Crabb 81
10/02	LP	HAVANT & WATERLOOVILLE	487	2 - 0	Tuck 43 **Ramsey 62**
14/02	LP	Crawley Town	1437	1 - 3	**Ramsay 55[p]**
21/02	LP	WEYMOUTH	839	2 - 1	Crabb 40, Tuck 58
28/02	LP	Weston-super-Mare	257	1 - 2	**Ramsay 48**
06/03	LP	HEDNESFORD TOWN	583	2 - 2	**Ramsay 37**, Tuck 45
13/03	LP	Bath City	603	0 - 2	
20/03	LP	TIVERTON TOWN	439	2 - 1	Crabb 14, Simmonds 41
27/03	LP	Hinckley United	330	2 - 2	Tuck 28, Pearce 34
03 /04	LP	WESTON-SUPER-MARE	577	1 - 0	Smart 67
10 /04	LP	CAMBRIDGE CITY	657	1 - 1	Rowland 23
12 /04	LP	Chelmsford City	399	1 - 3	Dowland 23
17 /04	LP	Worcester City	786	1 - 2	**Ramsay 13**
24 /04	LP	NUNEATON BOROUGH	893	0 - 0	
01/05	LP	Newport County	607	1 - 1	Goodwin 27
		Average Home League Attendance:	**596**	59-63	Top Goalscorer:**Scott Ramsay 22** (20+2FAC)

PLAYING SQUAD 2004-2005

Goalkeepers:

Lee Hook (Sittingbourne)

Defenders:

Matt Piper (Brighton), Ross Johnson (Worthing), Ben Austin (Eastbourne T), Darren Baker (Youth team), Stuart Playford (Hastings), Stuart Tuck (Worthing)

Midfield:

Matt Smart (Horsham), Danny Simmonds (Hastings), Ollie Rowland (Whitehawk), Stuart Myall (Hastings), Danny Chapman (Dover), Daren Pearce (East Preston), Paul Stevens (Burgess Hill)

Forwards:

Scott Ramsay (Dover), Richard Brady (Fisher), Matt Crabb (Eastbourne Utd), Mark Goodwin (Eastbourne T), Richard Harris (Wycombe), Simom Rowland (Whitehawk)

GRAYS ATHLETIC

Pages: 48 Price: £1.50
Editor: Jeremy Mason
Tel Nos: 01375 406540 (H)

CLUB OFFICIALS

Chairman: Alan Barnard
Secretary & Press Officer: Phil O'Reilly
102 Luxborough Lane,Chigwell,Essex IL7
5AA Tel: 07980 643832
Commercial Manager: Joanne Warren
Tel No: 07825 178405

FOOTBALL MANAGEMENT TEAM

Manager:Mark Stimson
Asst Man.: John Polston
Physio:Joe O'Reilly

FACT FILE

Formed: 1890
Nickname: The Blues
Sponsors: F.S.McKenzie
Colours: Sky Blue
Change cols: Purple &white/purple/purple
Midweek matchday: Tuesday
Local Press: Thurrock Gazette
Local Radio: BBC Essex, Radio Essex

GROUND Recreation Ground, Bridge Road, Grays RM17 6BZ (01375 391649)
Directions: Seven minutes walk from Grays station - turn right round one way system, right into Clarence Road, and at end into Bridge Road. Bus No. 370. By road - A13 towards Southend from London, take Grays exit and follow signs to town centre, keep left on one-way system, continue up hill for about 1/2 mile, turn right into Bridge Road, ground 1/2 mile on right
Capacity: 4,500 Cover: 1,200 Seats: 300 Floodlights: Yes
Clubhouse: Bar, pool, darts, bar snacks available. Indoor sports hall(.Steward: Chris Riley)
Club Shop: Sells `The First Hundred Years', sweaters, T-shirts, replica shirts, scarves, ties, etc. Contact Phil O'Reilly

PREVIOUS **Leagues:** Athenian 12-14, 58-83; London 14-24, 26-39; Kent 24-26; Corinthian 45-58

CLUB RECORDS **Attendance:** 9,500 v Chelmsford City, FA Cup 4th Qual. Round 1959
Win: 12-0 v Tooting (H) London Lge 24/2/23 **Defeat:** 0-12 v Enfield (A) Athenian Lge 20/4/63
Goalscorer: Harry Brand 269 (1944-52) **Appearances:** Phil Sammons, 673. 1982-97
Fee Paid: For Ian Durant (Canvey Island 85)
Fee Received: Undisclosed for Tony Witter (C. Palace), Dwight Marshall(Plymouth 1991) & Matthew Lawrence(Wycombe W)

BEST SEASON **FA Cup:** 1st Rd 51-52 88-89,00-01,01-02
FA Trophy: 4thRd 02-03, 01-02 **FA Amateur Cup:** 3rd Rd 63-64

HONOURS Isthmian Div 1 R-up 87-88 ,99-00(Div 2 Sth 84-85, Lg Cup 91-92); Athenian Lg R-up 82-83, Res. Sect. R-up 58-59 (Cup R-up 59-60); Corinthian Lg 45-46 (R-up 51-52 54-55 56-57), Lg Cup(2) 45-47, Mem. Shield(4) ; Essex Snr Cup 8(R-up 9; Essex SenTr 98-99; East Ang Cup 44-45 (R-up 43-44 54-55); Essex Thameside Tphy x 8 (R-up 7); Essex Elizabeth Tphy 76-77 (R-up 65-66); Claridge Tphy 87-88 88-89; Mithras Cup 79-80; Essex Int Cup(3) 56-57 58-60 (Jun Cup 19-20 (R-up 58-59); Essex & Herts ,Border Comb. East 87-88 (Ancillary Cup 78-79, Comb Cup 82-83); Fred Budden Tphy 86-87; Hornchurch Charity Cup 78-79 86-87; Neale Tphy 50-51; Ford Rate Tphy 83-84 85-86 87-88 (R-up 84-85 86-87); Stan Veness Mem. Tphy (8) 87-96

Players progressing: J Jordan (Spurs 47), R Kemp (Reading 49), B Silkman & TBanfield (Orient), G O'Reilly (Spurs), W Entwhistle (Bury 83), M Welch(Wimbledon 84), T Witter (C Palace 90), D Marshall (Plymouth 91), M Lawrence(Wycombe W. 96-97)

2003-04 Back Row (L-R): Danny Hipgrave. Tony Lock. Joe Bruce. Freddy Eastwood. Steve Robinson. Eddie Youds. Daniel Lunan. Ade Olayinka. Danny Hayzelden. **Middle:** Nicky Uglow(physio) Lee Williams. Wayne Vaughan. Matthew Woodward.(kit man) Martin Carthy. Dean Bradshaw. Donna Smith (physio). **Front:** Tobi Oshitola. Stuart Thurgood. Scott Barrett (asst/manager) Mel Capleton. Mark Stimsom (manager) Danny Kerrigan. Ram Marwa.
(Inset – Ellis Remy) (Inset- Leroy Griffiths)

Date	Comp.	Opponents	Att.	Score	Goalscorers
16/08	LP	BEDFORD TOWN	316	1 - 1	Lock 55
19/08	LP	Braintree Town	250	5 - 0	**EASTWOOD 26 36 69 85,** Lock 31
23/08	LP	Sutton United	489	0 - 1	
25/08	LP	NORTHWOOD	283	2 - 1	Stimson 88, **Eastwood 90**
30/08	LP	Hornchurch	626	0 - 2	
02/09	LP	BISHOP'S STORTFORD	317	3 - 1	**Eastwood 30,** Thurgood 70, Carthy 90
06/09	LP	Kingstonian	363	1 - 3	Carthy 78
09/09	LP	CARSHALTON ATHLETIC	291	0 - 0	
13/09	LP	HITCHIN TOWN	251	2 - 0	Carthy 41, Griffin 44
16/09	LP	Bognor Regis Town	313	1 - 2	**Eastwood 36**
20/09	LP	Aylesbury United	506	3 - 0	Carthy 34, Thurgood 47, Hayzelden 76
23/09	LP	KETTERING TOWN	350	1 - 1	Hayzelden 15
27/09	**FA Cup Q2**	**St Albans City**	420	4 - 2	Carthy 7, **Eastwood 37 70,** Thurgood 86
04/10	LP	HEYBRIDGE SWIFTS	280	4 - 0	Griffiths 49, Carthy 51, Hayzelden 60, Lock 90
07/10	LP	Basingstoke Town	318	2 - 0	**Eastwood 33 81**
11/10	**FA Cup Q3**	**HENDON**	**406**	**3 - 0**	**EASTWOOD 1 42[p] 68**
18/10	LP	Ford United	174	**0 - 3**	
21/10	LP	ST ALBANS CITY	226	**9 - 1**	**EASTWOOD 20[p] 28 56,** Griffiths 23 76, Carthy 43 67, Lock 65, Martin 89
25/10	**FA Cup Q4**	**MARGATE**	665	3 - 3	Griffiths 9 26, **Eastwood 81**
28/10	**FA Cup Q4 rep**	**Margate**	441	3 - 3	Thurgood 25 105, **Eastwood 106**
01/11	**FA Trophy 1**	**FISHER ATHLETIC**	387	2 - 2	Lock 5, Thurgood 90[p]
03/11	**FA Trophy 1 rep**	**Fisher Athletic**	164	3 - 0	Martin 32 59, Hayzelden 36
08/11	**FA Cup 1**	**ALDERSHOT TOWN**	1522	1 - 2	Griffiths 55
15/11	LP	HARROW BOROUGH	281	2 - 2	Youds 89, **Eastwood 90**
22/11	LP	Hayes	205	1 - 1	Carthy 45
29/11	**FA Trophy 2**	**Aylesbury United**	305	2 - 2	Carthy 50, **Eastwood 51**
02/12	**FA Trophy 2 rep**	**AYLESBURY UNITED**	243	0 - 1	
06/12	LP	BILLERICAY TOWN	316	1 - 1	Thurgood 40
13/12	LP	Bedford Town	373	4 - 0	Carthy 11, Griffiths 24, 81, Lunan 73
20/12	LP	BRAINTREE TOWN	271	1 - 1	**Eastwood 32**
01/01	LP	SUTTON UNITED	409	3 - 2	Thurgood 17[p], Youds 45, Williams 84
10/01	LP	Carshalton Athletic	400	2 - 0	**Eastwood 89, 90**
17/01	LP	KINGSTONIAN	365	1 - 0	**Eastwood 65[p]**
20/01	LP	HENDON	219	1 - 0	**Eastwood 59[p]**
24/01	LP	Hitchin Town	370	0 - 1	
31/01	LP	BOGNOR REGIS TOWN	295	6 - 0	Carthy 10, **EASTWOOD 24 67 86[p]**, Hayzelden 27, Griffiths
06/02 06/02	LP	Hendon	264	0 - 1	
10/02	LP	CANVEY ISLAND	**722**	1 - 1	Griffith 27
14/02	LP	FORD UNITED	319	2 - 0	Opara 19, Griffiths 67
17/02	LP	Maidenhead United	223	4 - 1	Opara 7 Carthy 73 Remy 89,90
21/02	LP	Harrow Borough	211	0 - 0	
02/03	LP	St Albans City	178	3 - 0	Hayzelden 22, **Eastwood 72, 83**
06/03	LP	Kettering Town	734	0 - 0	
09/03	LP	Canvey Island	732	1 - 1	Daly 83
13/03	LP	AYLESBURY UNITED	338	2 - 1	Opara 70, Bradshaw 85
16/03	LP	Thurrock	722	0 - 2	
20/03	LP	Heybridge Swifts	204	**0 - 3**	
27/03	LP	BASINGSTOKE TOWN	268	3 - 1	Thurgood 60, **Eastwood 75**, Carthy 88
03 /04	LP	HORNCHURCH	407	0 - 0	
06 /04	LP	MAIDENHEAD UNITED	134	1 - 1	**Eastwood 50**
10 /04	LP	Northwood	231	1 - 1	Daly 28
12 /04	LP	THURROCK	372	1 - 1	**Eastwood 75[p]**
17 /04	LP	Bishop's Stortford	363	2 - 1	Griffiths 14, Wild 35
24 /04	LP	Billericay Town	609	1 - 0	**Eastwood 43**
01/05	LP	HAYES	349	4 - 0	Carthy 40 65, **Eastwood 48**, Griffiths 70
		Average Home League Attendance:	**321**	103-54	Top Scorer: **Freddie Eastwood 36** (28+7FAC+1FAT) Including 4 hat tricks (3 x 3 and 1x 4)

PLAYING SQUAD 2004-2005

Goalkeepers:

Scott Barrett (Leyton Orient), Carl Emberson (Southend), Simon Overland (Gravesend)

Defenders:

Ade Olayinka (Barnet), Chris Wild (Harlow), Daniel Lunan (Southend), Eddie Youds (Huddersfield), Joe Bruce (Wingate & Finchley), Steve Robinson (Cheshunt)

Midfield:

Mark Stimson (Canvey Island), Danny Hazelden (Dagenham & Redbridge), Dean Bradshaw (Dulwich Hamlet), Martin Carthy (Bromley), Stuart Thurgood (Southend), John Nutter (Aldershot), Mitchell Cole (West Ham)

Forwards:

Ellis Remy (Lincoln), Freddy Eastwood (West Ham), Leroy Griffiths (Farnborough), Liam George (York)

HAVANT & WATERLOOVILLE

CLUB OFFICIALS

Chairman: David Crook

Vice Chairman: Peter Demott

Director of Football: Derek Pope

Directors: Trevor Brock, Ray Jones, John Carter, Sandy Peters, Ian Baird

Secretary & Press Officer: Trevor Brock, 2 Betula Close,Waterlooville, Hampshire. PO7 8 EJ Tel:02392 267276

Commercial Manager: Lisa Buckland (07717 871322)

2003-2004

Ps.o.Y:Dave Town & Chukki Eribenne

Top Goalscorer: Chukki Eribenne 19

FACT FILE

Formed: 1998

Nickname: Hawks

Sponsors: Conserv

Colours: All White with blue & yellow trim

Change colours: Gold & Navy Blue

Midweek matchday: Monday

Reserves' League:Duburban League Southern

FOOTBALL MANAGEMENT TEAM

Manager: David Leworthy

Assistant manager: Shaun Gale

Reserve Team Manager: Bobby De St Croix

Physio: Phil Ashwell

The Hawks
Havant and Waterlooville Football Club
Official Matchday Magazine
Saturday 14th August
Nationwide Conference South
Newport County A.F.C.
Match Sponsor:
Comserv
Nationwide
£2.00

Pages: 48 Price: £2.00

Editor: Simon Lynch

Tel Nos: 01489 790016(H) 07939 610071(M)

Local Media: News(Portsmouth) BBC Radio Solent,Power FM,The Quay

GROUND Westleigh Park, Martin Road, West Leigh, Havant PO9 5TH Tel: 02392 787822

Directions: Take B2149 to Havant off the A27 (B2149 Petersfield Rd if coming out of Havant). 2nd turning off dual carriageway into Bartons Road then 1st right into Martins Road. 1 mile from Havant station

Capacity: 4,500 Cover: 2,500 Seats: 560 Floodlights: Yes

Clubhouse: Open every day, lunchtime and evening. 2 bars, function suites. Hot & cold food available Club Shop: Sells various souvenirs & progs

PREVIOUS (Havant) **Leagues:** Portsmouth 58-71; Hants 71-86; Wessex 86-91. **Names:** Leigh Park; Havant & Leigh Park; Havant Town **Grounds:** Front Lawn 1958-83 (Waterlooville) **Leagues:** Waterlooville & District, Portsmouth 38-53, Hants1953-71. **Grounds:** Convent Ground 10-30, Rowlands Avenue Recreation Ground 30-63, Jubliee Park 63-98

CLUB RECORDS Attendance: 1,331 v Tamworth , F.A.Trophy Semi-Final Sexcond Leg 12.04.03

As Havant: Win: 10-0 x3; v Sholing Sports (H), FA Vase 4th Rd 85-86, v Portsmouth R.N. (H), Wessex League 90-91; & v Poole Town, Southern Lge Southern Div. 94-95. **Defeat:** 1-7 v Camberley Town (H), FA Vase 3rd Rd 88-89 **Career Goalscorer:** James Taylor 127 to date **Career Appearances:** James Taylor 222+ 29 to date

BEST SEASO (Havant) **FA Cup:** 1st Rd Proper (H) 1-2 2000-01 **FA Vase:** Qtr Final 85-86 **F.A.Trophy:** As H&WS-Final 2002-03 V Tamworth (Waterlooville) **FA Trophy:** 3rd Rd 98-99 (lost 0-1 at Worcester City) **FA Amateur Cup:** 1st Rd 59-60 **FA Cup:** 1st Rd 2nd replay 83-84, 0-2 v Northampton T. (A) after two 1-1 draws

HONOURS (Havant): FA Sunday Cup 68-69, Wessex Lg 90-91 R-up 88-89, Hampshire Lg Div 372-73 Div 4 71-72, Hampshire Sen. Cup 93-94,94-95 R-up 91-92 Hants.I'mediate Cup, Hants Junior Cup, Russell Cotes Cup 91-92, Portsmouth Sen. Cup 83-84 84-85 91-92, Gosport War Mem. Cup 74-75 91-92 92-93 94-95, Southern Cos F'lit Cup R-up 91-92, 00-01, Hants F'lit Cup 85-86, Portsmouth Lg. (Waterlooville): Southern Lg Div 1 Sth 71-72 Lg Cup 86-87, R-up 82-83, Hants Lg R-up 69-70 Div 2 59-60 64-65, Div 3 East R-up 53-54, Hants Sen. Cup 69-7072-73 84-85 R-up 75-76 90-91, 00-01, Russell Cotes Cup 88-89, Portsmouth Lg 49-50 50-51 51-52 Div 2 46-47, Div 3 38-39, Portsmouth Sen. Cup 68-69, Portsmouth Victory Cup 59-60 69-70,00-01
(H&W): Southern Lg.Southern 98-99, Capitol Lg R-up: 00-01 Hampshire Senior Cup R-up 00-01, 01-02

Back Row (L-R): Jason Chewins, James Ford, Dave Town, Gavin Holligan, Jamie Campbell, Neil Sharp, Alec Masson, Gareth Howells, Andy Poyser, Tom Jordan, James Taylor, Dean Holdsworth, Luke Byles, Neil Champion, Bobby Howe, Glenn Knight, Dean Blake and Geoff Pitcher.
Front: Shaun Gale(Asst Mgr), Phil Ashwell(Physio), Lisa Buckland(Commercial), Maurie Hibberd(President), John Carter(Director), Kevin Moore(Referees Liaison), Peter Demott(Vice-Chairman), Dave Leworthy(Manager), Dave Crook(Chairman), Derek Pope(Director), Trevor Brock(Director/Secretary), Ian Baird(Director), Peter Faulkner(Former Chairman), Bobby De St. Croix(Reserves Manager), Alan Smith(Asst Reserves Manager)

Date	Comp.	Opponents	Att.	Score	Goalscorers
16/08	LP	Worcester City	1001	1 - 1	**Eribenne 14[p]**
18/08	LP	DORCHESTER TOWN	501	3 - 2	Skelton 36, **Eribenne 38**, Town 88
23/08	LP	HEDNESFORD TOWN	459	1 - 2	**Eribenne 65[p]**
25/08	LP	Crawley Town	764	1 - 3	Howell 7
30/08	LP	Merthyr Tydfil	509	1 - 1	**Eribenne 80[p]**
01/09	LP	DOVER ATHLETIC	447	2 - 2	Taylor 60, **Eribenne 73**
06/09	LP	Cambridge City	367	3 - 2	Masson 10, Town 19, Blake 36
09/09	LP	EASTBOURNE BOROUGH	472	1 - 0	Taylor 83
13/09	LP	GRANTHAM TOWN	423	2 - 1	Taylor 28 90
16/09	LP	Welling United	477	1 - 1	**Eribenne 20**
20/09	LP	Stafford Rangers	707	1 - 2	Town 49
27/09	**FA Cup Q2**	**Bognor Regis Town**	945	4 - 0	Howe 1, Masson 27, Taylor 69, Ford 84
04/10	LP	TIVERTON TOWN	378	3 - 2	Skelton 54, Blake 80, Town 90
11/10	**FA Cup Q3**	**SALISBURY CITY**	494	3 - 4	Taylor 4 76, Town 59
18/10	LP	Dorchester Town	505	2 - 1	Skelton 38, **Eribenne 41**
21/10	LP	Weymouth	803	1 - 0	Blake 5
25/10	LP	STAFFORD RANGERS	514	2 - 2	**Eribenne 5, 77[p]**
01/11	LP	CHELMSFORD CITY	588	0 - 2	
08/11	LP	Nuneaton Borough	869	2 - 1	**Eribenne 11**, Town 29
15/11	LP	CAMBRIDGE CITY	537	2 - 3	Taylor 31, **Eribenne 56**
22/11	LP	MOOR GREEN	271	0 - 0	
29/11	**FA Trophy 2**	**FOLKESTONE INVICTA**	222	2 - 2	Taylor 21 32
02/12	**FA Trophy 2 rep**	**Folkestone Invicta**	337	0 - 1	
13/12	LP	CHIPPENHAM TOWN	321	1 - 1	Town 31
27/12	LP	CRAWLEY TOWN	583	1 - 3	Leworthy 67
03/01	LP	NEWPORT COUNTY	385	0 - 3	
17/01	LP	WELLING UNITED	455	1 - 1	Taylor 75
24/01	LP	Chippenham Town	553	0 - 3	
27/01	LP	Weston-super-Mare	207	0 - 2	
07/02	LP	HINCKLEY UNITED	418	2 - 0	Town 52 90
10/02	LP	Eastbourne Borough	487	0 - 2	
14/02	LP	Bath City	627	0 - 2	
21/02	LP	WESTON-SUPER-MARE	308	0 - 1	
24/02	LP	Hednesford Town	313	0 - 1	
28/02	LP	Tiverton Town	533	1 - 5	**Eribenne 51[p]**
06/03	LP	MERTHYR TYDFIL	349	4 - 2	**Eribenne 54, 65[p],** Masson 58, Town 68
20/03	LP	WORCESTER CITY	351	**0 - 5**	
27/03	LP	Chelmsford City	364	1 - 1	Town 75[p]
03 /04	LP	NUNEATON BOROUGH	461	**5 - 1**	Holligan 2 41, Town 39 56, **Eribenne 80**
10 /04	LP	WEYMOUTH	**855**	4 - 1	Holligan 27 53, Howe 40, Blake 74
12 /04	LP	Dover Athletic	801	2 - 0	Spiller (og)69 **Eribenne 90**
17 /04	LP	Hinckley United	303	2 - 2	**Eribenne 13,** Poate 78
20 /04	LP	Grantham Town	215	2 - 0	Taylor 72 89
24 /04	LP	BATH CITY	709	1 - 4	Taylor 53
28 /04	LP	Newport County	576	2 - 0	Masson 8, Skelton 69
01/05	LP	Moor Green	349	1 - 2	Taylor 17

Average Home League Attendance:**466** 68-77 Top Goalscorer: **Chucki Eribenne 17** (6 pens)

PLAYING SQUAD 2004-20005

Goalkeepers:

Gareth Howells (Aldershot), Andy Poyser (Michelton (Aust))

Defenders:

Neil Sharp (Swansea), Aaron Skelton (Luton), Shaun Gale (Exeter), Jason Chewins (Aldershot), Jamie Campbell (Woking), Luke Byles (Southampton), Tom Jordan (Forest Green), Alec Masson (Wick), Brett Poate (Southampton)

Midfield:

Geoff Pitcher (Brighton), James Ford (Bournemouth), Neil Champion (Aldershot), Glenn Knight (Youth team), Dean Blake (Bognor Regis), Bobby Howe (Swindon),

Forwards:

Dean Holdsworth (Wimbledon), Gavin Holligan (Wycombe), James Taylor (Bashley), David Town (Boston Utd)

HAYES

CLUB OFFICIALS
President Les Lovering
Chairman Derek Goodall
Vice Chairman Trevor Griffith
Financial Director Charles Mackintosh
Directors D Goodall, C Porter, E Stevens, T Griffith, C Mackintosh, A Bond, J Bond, N Griffith, T Gorman.
Football Secretary John Bond Jnr.
57 Austin Road, Hayes, Midd'xUB3 3DG
Tel No: 0208 581 8938(H)
07946 611369 (M)
General Manager & Commercial Manager:Willie Wordsworth
Tel No: 07977 815182 (M)
Press Officer Trevor Griffith
c/o the club Tel: 0208 573 2075

FACT FILE
Founded: 1909
Nickname: The Missioners
Club Sponsors: Taylor Woodrow
Club colours: Red & white shirts, black shorts, black socks
Change colours:
Light and dark blue stripes/sky/sky
Reserve team's league: Suburban Premier
Midweek home matchday: Tuesday
Local Press: Hayes Gazette
Local Radio: Capital Radio

FOOTBALL MANAGEMENT TEAM
Manager: Willy Wordsworth
Player/Asst Manager: Paul Holsgrove
Physio: T.B.A.

PROGRAMME
Pages: 32 Price: £1.50
Editor: Ken Green

GROUND Townfield House, Church Road, Hayes, Middx. UB3 2LE
Tel: 0208 573 2075
Directions: M25, M4, A312 (Hayes By-Pass), A4020 (Uxbridge Road) and Church Rd. is on the left.
Capacity: 6,500 **Seated:** 450 **Terracing - Covered:** 2,000 **Uncovered:** 4,050
CLUBHOUSE: Open Sat 12 - 11pm. Sun 12 - 3pm, 7 - 11pm. Midweek 6.30 - 11pm. Hot and cold snacks are available.
CLUB SHOP: Wide range of programmes & souvenirs. Contact Lee Hermitage, c/o the club.

PREVIOUS **Leagues:** Local leagues 1909-14; Gt. Western Suburban 19-22; London 22-24; Spartan 24-30; Athenian 30-71; Isthmian 71-96; Conference 96-02. **Names:** Bokwell Mission **Ground:** Botwell Common

CLUB RECORDS **Attendance:** 15,370 v Bromley, FA Amateur Cup, 10.2.51
Win: Unknown **Defeat:** Unknown
Career Goalscorer: Unknown **Career Appearances:** Reg Leather 701
Transfer Fee Paid: £6,000 for Gary Keen (Hendon) 1990 & for Joe Francis (Enfield) 1996
Transfer Fee Received: £30,000 for Les Ferdinand (Q.P.R.) 1987

BEST SEASON **FA Cup:** 2nd Round (replay) 72-73: 0-1 v Reading (H) after 0-0; 99-00: 2-3 aet v Hull City (A) after 2-2; also 2nd Round 90-91 & 91-92 League clubs defeated: Bristol Rov.72-73, Cardiff C.90-91, Fulham 91-92
FA Trophy: Quarter Final 78-79, 1-2 v Runcorn (A); 97-98, 0-1 v Cheltenham Town (A)
FA Amateur Cup: Runners Up 1930-31 **League:** 3rd Conference 98-99

HONOURS Isthmian League 95-96; Athenian League 56-57 Spartan League 27-28; Great Western Suburban League 1920-24 (x4)
Middlesex Senior Cup 19-20, 20-21, 25-26, 30-31, 35-36, 39-40, 49-50, 81-82, 95-96, 99-00;
London Senior Cup 31-32, 80-81; Middlesex Charity Cup - 15 Times; London Charity Cup 60-61

Players Progressing: Cyril Bacon (Orient 46), Phil Nolan (Watford 47), Dave Groombridge (Orient 51), Jimmy Bloomfield (Brentford 52), Derek Neate & Les Champleover(Brighton 56 & 57), Gordon Phillips (Brentford 63), Robin Friday (Reading 74), Les Smith (A Villa), Cyrille Regis (WBA 1977), Les Ferdinand (QPR 87),Derek Payne (Barnet 88), Paul Hyde (Wycombe 91), Dean Hooper (Swindon95), Jason Roberts (Wolverhampton W. 97)

L-R - Back: Paul Hamer, Peter Collins, Josiah Hunt, Danny Julienne, Mark Molesey, Chris Andrews, Bertrand Bossu, Sean O'Connor, Andrew Cooper, Peter Holsgrove, Ian Addele, Glen Harris. **Middle**: Caroline Bosley (Matchday asst.), John Case, Paul Johnson, Darren Crane, John Murphy, Jamie Jarvis, James Shipperley, Rob Bixby, Yiadom Yeboah, Leeyon Phelan, Elis Kodra, John Ellis, David Warner, Sarah Phillips (reserve team physio). **Front**: Mick Harvey (chief scout), Gary Austin, Dean Clark, Matt Gray, Justin Cochrane, Willy Wordsworth (manager), Derek Goodall (chairman), Paul Holsgrove (player/asst. manager), Ryan Williams, Richard Jolly, Kevin Warner, Ian Hodges, Mick Geraghty (reserve team man.).
Photo: Ray Peploe, HFC Photography

Date	Comp.	Opponents	Att.	Score	Goalscorers
16/08	LP	SUTTON UNITED	**393**	0 - 0	
19/08	LP	Hornchurch	427	2 - 0	**Holsgrove 11,** Demitrious 88
23/08	LP	Billericay Town	343	2 - 0	Case 13, Hastings 72
25/08	LP	HARROW BOROUGH	289	1 - 1	**Peter Holsgrove 90[p]**
30/08	LP	St Albans City	376	1 - 1	Hastings 85
02/09	LP	BRAINTREE TOWN	238	0 - 0	
06/09	LP	Bognor Regis Town	451	**0 - 4**	
09/09	LP	KINGSTONIAN	320	1 - 0	K Warner 31
13/09	LP	HENDON	282	3 - 1	Warner 7, Molesley 49, **Peter Holsgrove 71**
15/09	LP	Carshalton Athletic	432	0 - 2	
20/09	LP	Kettering Town	939	3 - 0	Thomas 29[og], Richards 43, Warner 67
23/09	LP	AYLESBURY UNITED	231	3 - 0	Forrester 36 50, **Peter Holsgrove 45**
27/09	**FA Cup Q2**	**TOOTING & MITCHAM UNITED**	272	4 - 2	**Peter Holsgrove 23 78,** Scott 65, Goodall 87
04/10	LP	NORTHWOOD	385	1 - 1	Everitt 87
07/10	LP	Hitchin Town	267	2 - 0	Forrester 12, **Peter Holsgrove 44**
11/10	**FA Cup Q3**	**BOREHAM WOOD**	350	1 - 1	Warner 60
14/10	**FA Cup Q3 rep**	**Boreham Wood**	268	1 - 3	Goodall 90
18/10	LP	Heybridge Swifts	205	2 - 1	Case 33, **Peter Holsgrove 90**
21/10	LP	BASINGSTOKE TOWN	232	2 - 1	Paul Holsgrove 44 80
08/11	LP	KETTERING TOWN	278	0 - 1	
11/11	LP	Ford United	132	0 - 0	
15/11	LP	BISHOP'S STORTFORD	256	1 - 0	D Warner 48
22/11	LP	GRAYS ATHLETIC	205	1 - 1	Scott 67
29/11	**FA Trophy 2**	**Halesowen Town**	458	3 - 1	Scott 36[p], **Holsgrove 48,** Warner 59
06/12	LP	Bedford Town	415	2 - 1	K Warner 21, Scott 52
20/12	LP	HORNCHURCH	253	1 - 1	Goodall 26
27/12	LP	Maidenhead United	425	0 - 1	
01/01	LP	BILLERICAY TOWN	287	1 - 1	Graham 50[og]
10/01	**FA Trophy 3**	**ARLESEY TOWN**	254	2 - 2	D Warner 1, Peter Holsgrove 25
13/01	**FA Trophy 3 rep**	**Arlesey Town**	282	1 - 1	Corbould 94[og] 3 4
17/01	LP	BOGNOR REGIS TOWN	268	0 - 1	
24/01	LP	Hendon	307	2 - 3	Case 35 Scott 82
27/01	LP	Kingstonian	253	0 - 1	
07/02	LP	Canvey Island	698	1 - 2	Case 12
10/02	LP	FORD UNITED	166	1 - 1	K Warner 46
14/02	LP	HEYBRIDGE SWIFTS	319	2 - 0	D Warner 17 44
21/02	LP	Bishop's Stortford	367	0 - 0	
24/02	LP	Sutton United	368	1 - 4	**Peter Holsgrove 69[p]**
28/02	LP	THURROCK	196	1 - 2	Case 29
02/03	LP	Basingstoke Town	244	2 - 0	Molesey 27, K Warner 64
06/03	LP	Aylesbury United	308	1 - 0	**Holsgrove P 45**
09/03	LP	Thurrock	137	0 - 2	
16/03	LP	CANVEY ISLAND	298	2 - 1	D Warner 33, Molesley 71
20/03	LP	Northwood	364	4 - 3	**PETER HOLSGROVE 16 57 64 90**
27/03	LP	HITCHIN TOWN	233	**5 - 1**	D Warner 11, Case 25, Molesley 66, **Peter Holsgrove 77 80**
30/03	LP	CARSHALTON ATHLETIC	287	1 - 0	Case 88
03 /04	LP	ST ALBANS CITY	263	1 - 0	D Warner 4
10 /04	LP	Harrow Borough	276	0 - 1	
12 /04	LP	MAIDENHEAD UNITED	274	0 - 1	
17 /04	LP	Braintree Town	201	2 - 1	Ayres 9[og], K Warner 83
24 /04	LP	BEDFORD TOWN	336	1 - 0	**Holsgrove P 24**
01/05	LP	Grays Athletic	349	**0 - 4**	
		Average Home League Attendance:	**273**	68-56	Top Goalscorer:**Peter Holsgrove 18** (14+2FAC+2FAT)

PLAYING SQUAD 2004-2005

Goalkeepers:
Kevin Davies (Aylesbury), Baboucarr Jallow (North Greeenford)

Defenders:
Jason O'Connor (Bournemouth), Rob Bixby (Youth team), Adam Everitt (Harrow), Yiadom Yeboah (Brook House), Peter Collins (Youth team), Jon Case (Youth team), Matt Gray (Barnet), Greg Woodcock (Youth team)

Midfield:
Kevin Warner (Brook House), Shane Demetrious (Chelsea), Dwayne Williams (Harefield Utd), Mark Molesley (Youth team), Kevin McKenna (Harrow), Dominic White (Youth team)

Forwards:
David Warner (Watford), Josh Scott (Youth team), Stuart Goodall (Uxbridge), Kieran Knight (Northwood), Abdulai Yoki (Harrow)

HORNCHURCH

CLUB OFFICIALS

Chairman: Gary Calder

Vice Chairman: Brian Davie

Secretary: Mick Ewen, c/o Hornchurch F.C.

Tel No: 01708 220080 (W)

07939 879295 (M)

Press Officer: Rob Monger c/o club

FOOTBALL MANAGEMENT TEAM

Manager: Gary Hill Captain: Paul McCartney

Physio: Richatrd Harper

FACT FILE

Founded: 1923 Nickname: Urchins

Sponsors: Premier Snacks

Colours: Red & white/red/red

Change: blue &white stripes/sky/sky

Midweek Matches: Tuesday

Reserve Lge: Essex & Herts Border Comb

Local Press: Romford Recorder

Local Radio: Essex Radio, Active FM

2003-2004

PLayer of the Year: Johnny Martin

Top Goalscorer: Vinnie John

PROGRAMME

16-20 pages with admission

Editor: Brian Davie 01708 445107

GROUND: The Stadium, Bridge Avenue, Upminster, Essex RM14 2LX
Tel: 01708 220080 Email: enquiries@urchins.org
Website: www.urchins.org

Directions: Fenchurch Street to Upminster (BR) then 10 mins walk.
Or tube to Upminster Bridge (LT), right outside station, 2nd right into Bridge Ave. ground 150yds on right.
By road Bridge Avenue is off A124 between Hornchurch and Upminster.
Buses 248, 348, 370, 373 from Romford or Upminster BR stations

Capacity: 3,000 Seats: 300 Cover: 350 Floodlights: Yes Club Shop: Yes,

Clubhouse: Mon-Fri 7.30-11, Sat 12-11, Sun 12-3. Cafeteria open matchdays

Club Shop: Yes, selling programmes, handbooks, scarves, hats, souvenirs etc.
Contact : Ron Quantock (01708 455529)

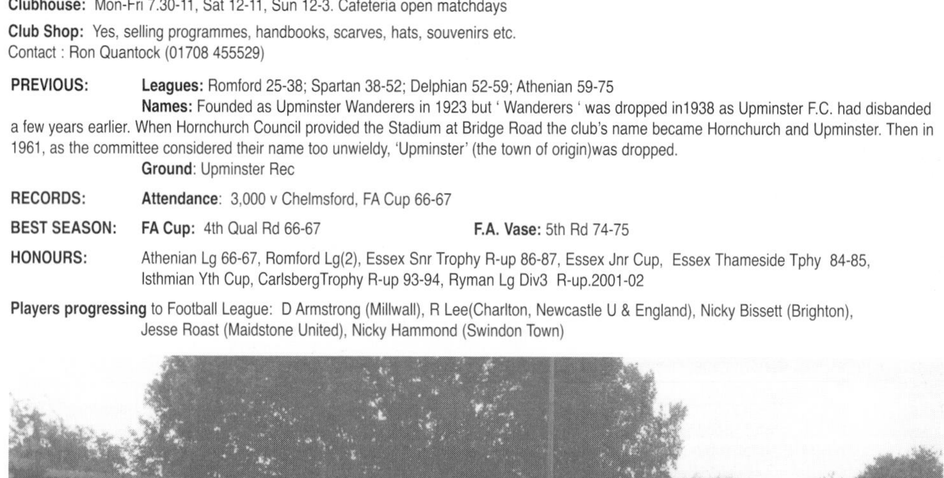

PREVIOUS: **Leagues:** Romford 25-38; Spartan 38-52; Delphian 52-59; Athenian 59-75

Names: Founded as Upminster Wanderers in 1923 but ' Wanderers ' was dropped in1938 as Upminster F.C. had disbanded a few years earlier. When Hornchurch Council provided the Stadium at Bridge Road the club's name became Hornchurch and Upminster. Then in 1961, as the committee considered their name too unwieldy, 'Upminster' (the town of origin)was dropped.

Ground: Upminster Rec

RECORDS: **Attendance**: 3,000 v Chelmsford, FA Cup 66-67

BEST SEASON: **FA Cup:** 4th Qual Rd 66-67 **F.A. Vase:** 5th Rd 74-75

HONOURS: Athenian Lg 66-67, Romford Lg(2), Essex Snr Trophy R-up 86-87, Essex Jnr Cup, Essex Thameside Tphy 84-85, Isthmian Yth Cup, CarlsbergTrophy R-up 93-94, Ryman Lg Div3 R-up.2001-02

Players progressing to Football League: D Armstrong (Millwall), R Lee(Charlton, Newcastle U & England), Nicky Bissett (Brighton), Jesse Roast (Maidstone United), Nicky Hammond (Swindon Town)

L-R - Back Row: John Lawrence, Ken Hunt, Ollie Adedeji, Chris Moore, Kevin Jopson, Mark Risley, Steve Jones, Richard Wray, Dmitri Kharine, Paul Wood, Vincent John, Chris Sorhaindo, Steve West, Andrew Martin, Scott Gooding, Adam Locke, John Gowens, George Borg.
Front Row: Glen Dyson, Paul Suton, Gavin McGowan, Steve Carter, Bradley Kite, Craig Cripps, Keith Rowland, Jamie Southon, John Keeling, Jon Bates, Nicky Lowery, Danny Cowley, Barry Fox, Andy Findlay, Garry Kimble, Dell Edkins, Terry Glen.

Date	Comp.	Opponents	Att.	Score	Goalscorers
16/08	LP	Hendon	287	0 - 1	
19/08	LP	HAYES	427	0 - 2	
23/08	LP	KETTERING TOWN	564	1 - 1	Gooding 2
25/08	LP	Aylesbury United	402	2 - 0	Keeling 54, A Martin 64
30/08	LP	GRAYS ATHLETIC	626	2 - 0	Martin 32, **John 55**
02/09	LP	Heybridge Swifts	301	1 - 1	Keeling 41
06/09	LP	Billericay Town	523	0 - 2	
09/09	LP	BISHOP'S STORTFORD	505	2 - 0	Martin 12, West 15
13/09	LP	HARROW BOROUGH	400	2 - 1	West 38, Allen 68
16/09	LP	Thurrock	441	3 - 1	Keeling 26, West 57, Martin 83
20/09	LP	Basingstoke Town	322	3 - 0	Southon 9, McGowan 17, Douglas 35
23/09	LP	ST ALBANS CITY	430	0 - 1	
27/09	**FA Cup Q2**	**BILLERICAY TOWN**	836	2 - 1	West 25, Southon 84
04/10	LP	SUTTON UNITED	503	3 - 0	Sterling 8, Graham 76, **John 81**
07/10	LP	Northwood	269	1 - 0	West 43[p]
11/10	**FA Cup Q3**	**CARSHALTON ATHLETIC**	611	5 - 0	Douglas 5, Martin 15 50, **John 30,** Locke 85
18/10	LP	BOGNOR REGIS TOWN	474	3 - 0	Martin 15, Lock 27, **John 88**
20/10	LP	Carshalton Athletic	476	0 - 0	
25/10	**FA Cup Q4**	**PAULTON ROVERS**	747	1 - 0	West 65
01/11	**FA Trophy 1**	**Wingate & Finchley**	160	2 - 0	Allen 38, Douglas 51
09/11	**FA Cup 1**	**DARLINGTON**	2186	2 - 0	West 43[p], **John 61**
11/11	LP	BEDFORD TOWN	562	1 - 0	**John 22**
15/11	LP	Braintree Town	300	3 - 1	Opara 10, Martin 59, West 85
22/11	LP	CANVEY ISLAND	**1168**	0 - 0	
29/11	**FA Trophy 2**	**NEWPORT COUNTY**	424	1 - 0	McGowan 59
06/12	**FA Cup 2**	**TRANMERE ROVERS**	3500	0 - 1	
16/12	LP	KINGSTONIAN	308	1 - 0	Allen 20
20/12	LP	Hayes	253	1 - 1	**John 80[p]**
26/12	LP	FORD UNITED	832	1 - 0	**John 46**
01/01	LP	Kettering Town	1212	2 - 3	**John 44[p]**, Allen 70
10/01	**FA Trophy 3**	**AYLESBURY UNITED**	549	2 - 0	**John 20,** Opara 54
17/01	LP	BILLERICAY TOWN	852	1 - 1	**John 30**
24/01	LP	Harrow Borough	220	0 - 0	
03/02	**FA Trophy 4**	**STEVENAGE BOROUGH**	741	1 - 0	Graham 49
07/02	LP	HITCHIN TOWN	495	4 - 0	Douglas 4, J Martin 36 88[p], Brayley 38
14/02	**FA Trophy 5**	**BURTON ALBION**	1205	2 - 1	Brayley 22, Keeling 90
17/02	LP	Bishop's Stortford	349	1 - 2	Martin 89(p)
21/02	LP	BRAINTREE TOWN	589	2 - 1	Matthews 19 Williams 42
02/03	**FA Trophy QF**	**Hednesford Town**	646	1 - 3	Brayley 39
06/03	LP	St Albans City	297	1 - 1	**John 8**
09/03	LP	Bognor Regis Town	262	3 - 1	**John 44,** Matthews 65, Brayley 82
13/03	LP	BASINGSTOKE TOWN	482	2 - 0	Graham 46, Douglas 85
16/03	LP	Maidenhead United	201	1 - 1	Abbott 63
20/03	LP	Sutton United	547	1 - 3	Douglas 41
23/03	LP	Hitchin Town	227	2 - 0	**John 20**, Southam 35
27/03	LP	NORTHWOOD	492	3 - 1	Martin 1, Gell 13[og], **John 87**
30/03	LP	HENDON	490	0 - 2	
03 /04	LP	Grays Athletic	407	0 - 0	
06 /04	LP	Bedford Town	261	1 - 2	Keeling 35
08 /04	LP	CARSHALTON ATHLETIC	394	2 - 0	Matthews 16, Martin 23
10 /04	LP	AYLESBURY UNITED	511	1 - 0	Southern 38
12 /04	LP	Ford United	268	0 - 0	
17 /04	LP	HEYBRIDGE SWIFTS	481	0 - 2	
20 /04	LP	THURROCK	410	2 - 0	Douglas 34 80
24 /04	LP	MAIDENHEAD UNITED	593	1 - 0	McGowan 50
27 /04	LP	Kingstonian	292	1 - 0	Douglas 62
01/05	LP	Canvey Island	911	2 - 3	Martin 44, McGowan 58
		Average Home League Attendance:	**547**	82-41	Top Goalscorer: **Vinnie John: 15** (12+2FAC+1FAT) **30 clean sheets** (7 in consecutive matches)

PLAYING SQUAD 2004-2005

Goalkeepers: Ashley Bayes (Woking), Mark Westhead (Stevenage), Jake Whincup (Brentford)

Defenders:

Tarkan Mustafa (Dagenham & Redbridge), Scott Gooding (Whyteleafe), Damon Searle (Forest Green), Jamie Stuart (Southend), Steve West (Dagenham & Redbridge), Lee Matthews (Dagenham & Redbridge), Paul McCarthy (Oxford)

Midfield:

Shaun Carey (Chester), Darren Caskey (Bristol C), Adam Locke (Luton), Simon Wormull (Stevenage), Steve Clark (Southend), Lee Elam (Yeovil), John Martin (Farnborough), Jamie Southon (Grays), Mark Graham (St Albans), Adrian Harris (Haverfordwest)

Forwards:

Kirk Jackson (Yeovil), Wayne Purser (Leyton Orient), Andy Douglas (Billericay), Danny Shipp (Dagenham & Redbridge), Charlie Taylor (Welling), Jean-Michel Sigere (Margate), Bertie Brayley (Canvey Island)

LEWES

CLUB OFFICIALS

President: T.B.A.**Chairman**: T. Parris

Secretary: Carole Bailey

Lewes F.C.,Westgate Street,Lewes.
East Sussex BN7 1YR
Tel: 01273 474518

FOOTBALL MANAGEMENT

Manager: Steven King
Captain : Marc Cable

2003-2004

Player of the Year: Danny Davis
Top Goalscorer: Lee Newman

FACT FILE

Founded: 1885
Nickname: Rooks
Colours: Red & Black /black/black
Change colours: Yellow & Blue
Midweek matches: Tuesday
Reserves' League: Suburban
Local Press: Evening Argus, Sussex Express
Local Radio:
Southern F.M.,B.B.C. Southern Counties

PROGRAMME

Pages: 32 pages Price: £1.50
Editor: Sean Trendall

GROUND: The Dripping Pan, Mountfield Road, Lewes BN7 1XN Tel: 01273 472100

Directions: Two minute walk from Lewes (BR) - turn left out of station and left into Mountfield Road. Ground 30 yards on right
Capacity: 3.000 Cover: 1,400 Seats: 400 Floodlights: Yes
Club Shop: Yes
Clubhouse: (01273 472100). Bar, tea bar

PREVIOUS: **Leagues:** Mid Sussex 1886-1920; Sussex Co 20-65; Athenian 65-77

RECORDS: **Attendance:** 2,500 v Newhaven, Sussex County Lg 26/12/47
Goalscorer: 'Pip' Parris 350 **Appearances:** Terry Parris 662
Transfer Fee Paid: £2,000 Matt Allen **Transfer Fee Received:** £2,500 for Grant Horscroft (Brighton)

BEST SEASON: **FA Cup:** 1st Rd Proper 2001-02 v Stoke City 0-2
FA Trophy: 3rd Rd Rd 02-03,03-04 **FA Amateur Cup:** 2nd Rd 67-68
FA Vase: Quarter Final 2001-02

HONOURS Isthmian Lg Div 1 South Champions 03-04 Play Off Winners for Confernce South 03-04 Div 2 Champions 01-02, R-up 79-80 91-92; Div 3 R-up 00-01. Ath'n Lg Div 1 69-70 (Div 2 67-68);Sussex Co. Lg 64-65 (R-up 24-25 33-34 58-59 63-64, Lg Cup 39-40); Mid Sussex Lg 10-11 13-14; Sussex Snr Cup 64-65 70-71 84-85 00-01(R-up 79-80 82-83 87-88); Sussex Royal Ulster Rifles Charity Cup(3) 61-63 64-65; Gilbert Rice Fl't Cup 82-83 88-89; Neale Tphy 68-69; Sussex F'lit Cup 76-77 (SF 83-84); Southern Counties Comb Div 1 80-81

Players progressing: (to Brighton unless stated) Don Bates(1950), Peter Knight (1964), Terry Stanley (1969), Colin Woffuden (1970), G Elphick & Steve Ford (Stoke 1981), Glen Geard, Grant Horscroft (1987), J Hammond (Fulham), S Funnell, L Allen (Wimbledon), M Rice (Watford)

2003-2004 back row (L-R): Jimmy Coleman, Peter Adeniyi, Luke Fontana, Dave Soutar, Tom Graves, Tony Chin, Steve King, Marc Cable, Paul Kennett, Julian Curnow, Dwain Clarke, Alan Pierce.
Front Row: Ahmet Suleymanoglu, Danny Davis, Marc Whiteman, Dominique Jean-Zephirin, Lee Newman, Paul Stokes, Junior Kadi.

Date	Comp.	Opponents	Att.	Score	Goalscorers
16/08	L1S	STAINES TOWN	352	1 - 1	Whiteman 55
19/08	L1S	Bromley	271	2 - 1	Whiteman 64, Adeniyi 73
23/08	L1S	Egham Town	156	4 - 2	Kadi 14, **Newman 31**, Fontana 88, Suleymanoglu 89
25/08	L1S	BRACKNELL TOWN	292	4 - 0	**FONTANA 46 53 58**, **Newman 85[p]**
30/08	**FA Cup P**	**Dorking**	222	5 - 3	**Newman 33, 42** Cable 69 Kadi 90 Fontana 90
06/09	L1S	Tooting & Mitcham United	282	4 - 0	**WHITEMAN 28 35 90[p]**, Fontana 45
09/09	L1S	HORSHAM	408	**6 - 1**	Kadi 4, **SULYEYMANOGLU 6 37 58,** Kennett 34, Fontana
13/09	**FA Cup Q1**	**Tonbridge Angels**	617	1 - 1	Adeniyi 80
16/09	**FA Cup Q1 rep**	**TONBRIDGE ANGELS**	468	2 - 1	**Newman 30 84**
20/09	L1S	Windsor & Eton	224	2 - 1	Kadi 36[p], Whiteman 90
23/09	L1S	CORINTHIAN CASUALS	268	3 - 2	Fontana 14, Whiteman 45, Suleymanoglu 85
27/09	**FA Cup Q2**	**Lowestoft Town**	317	1 - 2	**Newman 70**
30/09	L1S	Croydon Athletic	156	2 - 1	Davies 35, Fontana 69
04/10	**FA Trophy P**	**Dunstable Town**	213	2 - 1	Fontana 29, Kadi 53
11/10	L1S	Walton & Hersham	181	0 - 1	
14/10	L1S	DULWICH HAMLET	326	4 - 0	Kadi 2, Lovett 18, **Newman 45**, Adeniyi 83
18/10	L1S	MARLOW	360	3 - 0	**NEWMAN 14 40 52**
22/10	L1S	Molesey	141	2 - 2	Dwain 4, Murphy 19[og]
25/10	L1S	SLOUGH TOWN	360	3 - 2	**Newman 43,** Davis 67 88
01/11	**FA Trophy 1**	**NORTHWOOD**	370	4 - 2	Kadi 26 58, **Newman 70 90**
08/11	L1S	Metropolitan Police	161	4 - 1	Kennett 1, Davis 17, Adeniyi 54, Kadi 76
11/11	L1S	Epsom & Ewell	109	4 - 0	Dwain Clark 15 89, Kissi 47 51
15/11	L1S	ASHFORD TOWN (MIDDX)	340	2 - 0	Clark 64 69
25/11	L1S	WHYTELEAFE	255	2 - 1	Dean Clark 32, Watson 74
02/12	**FA Trophy 2**	**Cinderford Town**	148	3 - 3	**Newman 23[p] 29[p],** Watson 25
06/12	L1S	CROYDON	330	2 - 0	**Newman 62[p]**, Whiteman 90
09/12	**FA Trophy 2 rep**	**CINDERFORD TOWN**	343	4 - 3	Cable 17, Kennett 27, Tompkins 89[og], Whiteman 90
13/12	L1S	Staines Town	271	1 - 3	Fontana 32
30/12	L1S	EGHAM TOWN	315	4 - 1	**Newman 3,** Kadi 43[p] 75, Fontana 53
06/01	L1S	Banstead Athletic	85	**1 - 6**	Kadi 17
10/01	**FA Trophy 3**	**WEYMOUTH**	1077	5 - 8	Watts 14, Kadi 19, Davis 60 84, Adeniyi 69
13/01	L1S	Hampton & Richmond Borough	267	3 - 4	Watson 20, **Newman 74 83**
17/01	L1S	WALTON & HERSHAM	415	3 - 0	Whiteman 63, Cable 67, **Newman 87**
24/01	L1S	Marlow	190	2 - 1	**Newman 49** Whiteman 51
27/01	L1S	LEATHERHEAD	269	2 - 2	**Newman 61**, Kennett 69
07/02	L1S	Ashford Town (Middx)	155	3 - 2	**Newman 10, 44,** Whiteman 81
10/02	L1S	EPSOM & EWELL	260	2 - 0	**Newman 1,** Watts 14
14/02	L1S	METROPOLITAN POLICE	336	2 - 1	**Newman 5**, Whiteman 65
17/02	L1S	Dulwich Hamlet	388	1 - 4	**Newman 12**
21/02	L1S	Slough Town	419	0 - 1	
28/02	L1S	HAMPTON & RICHMOND BORO	440	2 - 2	Davis 18, 64
02/03	L1S	Whyteleafe	196	0 - 0	
06/03	L1S	Corinthian Casuals	120	4 - 2	Davis 13 Whiteman 55,63 Watts 87
09/03	L1S	MOLESEY	294	3 - 0	Whiteman 34, Kennett 36, Clarke 86
13/03	L1S	WINDSOR & ETON	728	1 - 2	Haughton 89
16/03	L1S	BROMLEY	314	3 - 1	Whiteman 49, Haughton 54 62
20/03	L1S	Leatherhead	205	4 - 5	**HAUGHTON 23 45 59,** Lovett 75
27/03	L1S	CROYDON ATHLETIC	371	1 - 2	Kadi 9
03 /04	L1S	TOOTING & MITCHAM UNITED	306	1 - 2	Haughton 55
10 /04	L1S	Bracknell Town	152	3 - 0	**Newman 19**, Haughton 57 82
12 /04	L1S	WORTHING	**932**	2 - 2	Whiteman 41, Rogers 56[og]
17 /04	L1S	Horsham	519	2 - 0	Haughton 51, **Newman 60**
20 /04	L1S	Worthing	872	3 - 0	Lovett 10, Haughton 23 36
24 /04	L1S	Croydon	208	4 - 0	Lovett 15 Whiteman 25,45 Adeniyi 39
01/05	L1S	BANSTEAD ATHLETIC	782	2 - 2	Moore 68, Adeniyi 71
03/05	**Play-off 1**	**Yeading**	**327**	**1 - 0**	**Whiteman 73**
05/05	**Play-off SF**	**Basingstoke Town**	**310**	**4 - 1**	**Davis 45, 83, Newman 46, Adeniyi 55**
08/05	**Play-off F**	**KINGSTONIAN**	**1062**	**1 - 0**	**Houghton 38**
		Average Home League Attendance	**350**	146-86	Top scorer:**Lee Newman 32** (22+FAC5+FAT4+PO1)

PLAYING SQUAD 2004-2005

Goalkeeper: Ademole Bankole (Crewe)

Defenders: Jay Lovatt (Farnborough), Joe Vines (Crawley), Francis Duku (Gravesend), Marc Cable (Burgess Hill), Max Hustwick (Kingstonian), Lee Fieldwick (Brentford)

Midfield:Barry Moore (Charleston Battery (USA)), Anthony Storey (Dunfermline), Danny Davis (Worthing), Paul Kennett (Worthing), Junior Kadi (Dulwich Hamlet), Dwain Clarke (Harrow), Peter Adeniyi (Dulwich Hamlet), Kirk Watts (Bromley)

Forwards:Luke Cornwall (Woking), Marc Whiteman (Weymouth), Lee Newman (Saltdean), Barrington Belgrave (Farnborough), Warren Haughton (Dulwich Hamlet)

MAIDENHEAD UNITED

CLUB OFFICIALS

Chairman: Jon Swan
Vice Chairman: Bob Hussey
President: Jim Parsons
Secretary: Ken Chandler
c/o Maidenhead United
Press Officer .:Jon Swan (07900 550601)
Commercial Manager: Paul Carney
Tel No: 07931 594517 (M)

FOOTBALL MANAGEMENT

Manager: John Dreyer
Asst. Manager: Phil Gray
Physio: Paul Lagerman

FACT FILE

Formed: 1870
Nickname: Magpies
Sponsors: C.F.Lake
Colours: Black & white stripes/black/black
Change colours: Yellow/green/yellow
Midweek matchday: Tuesday
Reserve League: Suburban
Local Press: Maidenhead Advertiser, Reading Evening Post, Slough Observer
Local Radio: 2-Ten FM, Star FM, Thames Valley FM, BBC Radio Berkshire

THE MAGPIE
2002-2003
£1.50
Ryman
IN TOWN TODAY
BEDFORD TOWN

PROGRAMME

Pages: 36 Price: £1
Editor: Steve Jinman 07909 655409

GROUND York Road, Maidenhead, Berks SL6 1SQ Tel: 01628 624739/636314
Directions: From Maidenhead BR station proceed eastwards down Bell St - 500 yds Ground is 5 miles from M4 in town centre.
Capacity: 4,500 Cover: 2,000 Seats: 400 Floodlights: Yes
Clubhouse: Open evenings & matchdays. Some hot food
Club Shop: Wide range of progs and club souvenirs. Contact Mark Smith 01753 854674

PREVIOUS **Leagues:** Southern 1894-1902; West Berks 02-04; Grt West Sub 04-22; Spartan 22-39; Grt West Comb 39-45; Corinthian 45-63; Athenian 63-73, Isthmian 1973-
Names: Maidenhead FC, Maidenhead Norfolkians. **Grounds:** Kidwells Park (Norfolkians)

CLUB RECORDS **Attendance:** 7,920 v Southall, FA Amat Cup Q/F 7/3/36 **Season's goalscorer:** Jack Palethorpe 66, 1929-30
Career appearances: Bert Randall 532, 1950-64 **Career goalscorer:** George Copas 270, 1924-35
Win: 14-1 v Buckingham Town (H), FA Amat. Cup 6/9/52 **Defeat:** 0-14 v Chesham United (A), Spartan Lge 31/3/23
Transfer fee paid: Undisclosed **Transfer fee received:** £5,000 from Norwich for Alan Cordice, 79

BEST SEASON **FA Cup:** Qtr Finals 1873-74 74-75 75-76 **F A Trophy:** 3rd Qual Rd **FA Amateur Cup:** Semi Final 35-36

HONOURS Isthmian Lg Div 2 Sth R-up 90-91,Promotion to Premier Division 99-00 Full Members Cup 96-97; Spartan Lg x3 R-upx2; Corinthian Lg 57-58 60-61 61-62 R-up 58-59 59-60, Mem. Shield 56-57 61-62,R-up x4, Neale Cup 48-49 57-58 60-61; Gt Western Suburban Lg 19-20 R-up 20-21; Berks & Bucks Snr Cup x 19, Berks & Bucks Benev. Cup x6 R-up x2; Mithras Cup R-up x4; Southern Comb. Cup R-up 81-82; Sub Lge West 97-98; Allied Counties Champ 97-98

Players progressing: A Cordice (Norwich 79), P Priddy (Brentford 72), D Kemp (Plymouth), L Sanchez (Reading),E Kelsey, J Palethorpe (Reading 30), B Laryea(Torquay), R Davies (Torquay), Mark Harris (C.Palace & Swansea C 1985),Ben Abbey (Oxford U via Crawley 99)

Back row,left to right: Paul Lagerman (Physio), Carl Levene, Nick Hart, Phil Heggie (Coach), Richard Barnard, Steve Croxford, Rickey Ibe, Lee Channell, Rob Saunders, Brian Connor, Adrian Allen, Orlando Jeffrey, Alan Devonshire (Manager) and Roger Coombs (Chairman). **Front row:** Richard Goddard (Reserve Team Manager), Adam Durrant, Andy Morley, Paul Kelly, Obinna Ulasi, Andy Rose, Chris Ferdinand, John Urry (Physio) with Dave Harrison (Coach) at the front. **Photo:** Maidenhead Advertiser

Date	Comp.	Opponents	Att.	Score	Goalscorers
16/08	LP	Heybridge Swifts	212	0 - 0	
19/08	LP	KINGSTONIAN	343	**0 - 4**	
23/08	LP	CANVEY ISLAND	259	0 - 0	
25/08	LP	Ford United	134	1 - 1	Currie 36
30/08	LP	HENDON	244	0 - 1	
02/09	LP	Kettering Town	958	1 - 3	**Yaku 13**
06/09	LP	Bishop's Stortford	275	1 - 2	Gallen 23
09/09	LP	HARROW BOROUGH	234	1 - 0	Boyce 5
13/09	LP	BRAINTREE TOWN	251	**4 - 0**	Lee 2, 4, **Yaku 39**, Gray 47
16/09	LP	St Albans City	220	2 - 1	Ashe 38, **Yaku 90**
20/09	LP	Thurrock	225	1 - 3	Lee 72[p]
23/09	LP	SUTTON UNITED	251	2 - 0	Boyce 14, Gray 16
28/09	**FA Cup Q2**	**Dover Athletic**	**703**	**0 - 4**	
04/10	LP	BASINGSTOKE TOWN	292	0 - 2	
07/10	LP	Billericay Town	257	1 - 0	Hale 60
11/10	LP	Bognor Regis Town	331	3 - 0	**Yaku 33 35,** Gallen 85[p]
18/10	LP	BEDFORD TOWN	285	2 - 1	Gallen 52, Ashe 65
25/10	LP	Northwood	273	0 - 0	
11/11	LP	CARSHALTON ATHLETIC	255	0 - 0	
15/11	LP	Hitchin Town	350	0 - 2	
22/11	LP	Aylesbury United	215	3 - 1	**Yaku 15 88**, Hale 43
29/11	**FA Trophy 2**	**Swindon Supermarine**	179	3 - 3	**Yaku 7,** Gray 84, Jenning 86
02/12	**FA Trophy 2 rep**	**SWINDON SUPERMARINE**	172	2 - 1	Hale 45, **Yaku 66**
13/12	LP	HEYBRIDGE SWIFTS	187	2 - 4	Hale 30 45
20/12	LP	Kingstonian	290	1 - 3	Farley 82
27/12	LP	HAYES	**425**	1 - 0	Brooks 49
01/01	LP	Canvey Island	684	1 - 3	Hale 31
10/01	**FA Trophy 3**	**Histon**	167	3 - 1	Hale 18 46, Farley 51
17/01	LP	BISHOP'S STORTFORD	292	**0 - 4**	
24/01	LP	Braintree Town	240	2 - 1	**Yaku 14** Costello 18
03/02	**FA Trophy 4**	**WEALDSTONE**	425	5 - 1	Hale 34, Sanders 51, **Yaku 55 85,** Gallen 90
07/02	LP	NORTHWOOD	231	3 - 1	Gallen 23, **Yaku 35**, Farley 47
09/02	LP	Carshalton Athletic	276	2 - 3	Boyce 38, **Yaku 39**
14/02	**FA Trophy 5**	**Halifax Town**	1345	2 - 0	Hale 9, **Yaku 89**
17/02	LP	GRAYS ATHLETIC	223	1 - 4	**Yaku 66**
21/02	LP	HITCHIN TOWN	217	2 - 1	**Yaku 10** Jennings 78
24/02	LP	Harrow Borough	104	1 - 1	Dugdale 12[p]
28/02	**FA Trophy QF**	**Canvey Island**	921	0 - 4	
02/03	LP	BOGNOR REGIS TOWN	192	0 - 2	
06/03	LP	Sutton United	191	3 - 0	Haworth 68 Hammond 80 Fleck 81
13/03	LP	THURROCK	188	1 - 4	Costello 24
16/03	LP	HORNCHURCH	201	1 - 1	Ashe 45
20/03	LP	Basingstoke Town	314	1 - 2	Gallen 50
23/03	LP	ST ALBANS CITY	190	4 - 2	Gallan 20 84[p], Hammond 33 81
27/03	LP	BILLERICAY TOWN	225	1 - 0	Haworth 59
30/03	LP	Bedford Town	367	2 - 1	Ashe 49, Haworth 69
03 /04	LP	Hendon	216	1 - 3	**Yaku 22**
06 /04	LP	Grays Athletic	134	1 - 1	Ashe 8
10 /04	LP	FORD UNITED	247	1 - 1	Ash 26
12 /04	LP	Hayes	274	1 - 0	**Yaku 52**
17 /04	LP	KETTERING TOWN	339	1 - 2	Ashe 47
24 /04	LP	Hornchurch	593	0 - 1	
01/05	LP	AYLESBURY UNITED	**425**	4 - 2	**Yaku 4, 71**, Ashe 55, Bolt 87
		Average Home League Attendance:	**260**	75-82	Top Goalscorer:**Laurence Yaku 21** (16 + 5 FAT)

PLAYING SQUAD 2004-2005

Goalkeepers: Nick Hart (Youth team)

Defenders:

Brendan Gallen (Sligo Rovers), Brian Connor (Marlow), Andy Dugdale (Egham), Steve Sanders (Chelmsford), Chris Elsegood (Northwood), Andy Jennings (Swindon Supermarine), Adam Durrant (Crystal Palace),

Midfield:

Jamie Cook (Stevenage), Barrie Matthews (Hornchurch), Kelvin McIntosh (Oxford C), Rob Saunders (Windsor), Julian Renner-Thomas (Windsor)

Forwards:

Craig O'Connor (Windsor), Lawrence Yaku (Northwood), Phil Gray (Chelmsford)

MARGATE

CLUB OFFICIALS
Chairman: Colin Page
President: Gordon Wallis
Vice Chairman: Keith Piperr
Director: K Piper
Secretary: Ken Tomlinson
65 Nash Road, Margate , Kent CT9 4BT
Tel & Fax: 01843 291040 (M) 07710033566
Executive Operations Manager:
David Canham Tel: 01843 299734
Press Officer: Secretary
Commercial Manager: Dave Canham
Tel No: 07719 703811 (M)

FOOTBALL MANAGEMENT
Manager: Chris Kinnear
Asst. Manager: Kevin Hales
Physio: M.Methanander

FACT FILE
Formed: 1896
Nickname: The Gate
Sponsors: A Gomez Ltd
Colours: Royal Blue shirts & shorts, white socks.
Change colours: Green&white/white/green
Midweek matchday: Tuesday
Reserve League: Suburban
Local Press: Isle of Thanet Gazette, Thanet Times, Thanet Extra
Local Radio: Radio Kent, Invicta Radio, TLR

PROGRAMME
Pages: 32 Price: £2
Editor: Keith Smith (07766 232071)

Margate Football Club
Season 2004-2005
£2
A.C.WELLARD
Nationwide
Bognor Regis Town
Saturday, 14th August 2004
Nationwide Conference South

GROUND Hartsdown Park, Hartsdown Road, Margate CT9 5QZ
Directions: A28 into Margate, turn right opposite Dog & Duck P.H. into Hartsdown Road, proceed over crossroads and ground is on left. Ten mins walk from Margate (BR).
Capacity: 6,000 Cover: 6,000 Seats: 1000 Floodlights: Yes
Clubhouse: Flexible hours, private functions, matchday facilities.
Club Shop: Contacts: Dave and Debra Canham (01843 221769)

PREVIOUS **Leagues:** Kent 11-23 24-28 29-33 37-38 46-59; Southern 33-37, 59-2001, Conference 2001-04
Names: Thanet Utd 1981-89 **Grounds:** Margate College;Dreamland, Northdown Rd; Garlinge

CLUB RECORDS **Attendance:** 14,500 v Spurs, FA Cup 3rd Rd 73 **Season's goalscorer:**
Career appearances: Bob Harrop **Career goalscorer:** Jack Palethorpe 66, 1929-30
Win: 8-0 v Stalybridge Celtic(H) 01-02, v Tunbridge Wells (H) 66-67, & v Chatham Town (H) 87-88
Defeat: 11-0 v AFC Bournemouth (A), FAC 1st Rd. 20.11.71
Transfer fee paid: £5,000 for Steve Cuggy (Dover Athletic 93)
Transfer fee received: Undisclosed for Martin Buglione (St Johnstone 92-93)

BEST SEASON **FA Cup:** Third Round 72-73 0-6 v Spurs (H), 36-37 1-3 v Blackpool (A)
League clubs defeated: Gillingham 29-30, Q.P.R., Crystal Palace 35-36, Bournemouth & Boscombe Ath. 61-62, Swansea 72-73, Leyton Orient 2002-03. **F A Trophy:** 6th Round 2001-2002

HONOURS **Southern Lge** 35-36, 00-01. Lge Cp 67-68,97-98, R-up 61-62 74-75,Div 1 62-63, R-up 66-67, Div 1 Sth 77-78, East Div R-up 33-34, Southern Div. R-up: 98-99. Merit Cup 66-67 77-78, Midweek Sect. 36-37, Kent Lge (4), R-up (5), Div 2 (4), Lge Cp 5), Kent Senior Cup (6), Kent Senior Shield (8), Kent F'lit Cp 62-63 66-67 75-76

2004-2005 Back Row (L-R): Aaron Barnett, Bill Edwards, Rocky Baptiste, Nejdet Hussen, Scott Ward, Greg Oates, Pat Gradley, Adrian Clarke, Mark Green. **Front Row:** John Keister, Che Stadhart, Peter Benevides, Darron Annon, Moses Jurju, Ian Pulman, Tamba Ngongou.

Date	Comp.	Opponents	Att.	Score	Goalscorers
9/08	Conf.	Shrewsbury Town	4015	1 - 1	Patmore 83
12/08	CONF.	ALDERSHOT TOWN	1005	1 - 2	McFlynn 85
16/08	CONF.	EXETER CITY	890	0 - 1	
23/08	CONF.	Tamworth	1056	1 - 1	Robinson 33[og]
25/08	CONF.	STEVENAGE BOROUGH	755	1 - 4	Pullman 59
30/08	Conf.	Forest Green Rovers	569	2 - 1	McFlynn 43, Stadhart 69
06/09	Conf.	CHESTER CITY	634	1 - 2	Sodje 39
13/09	Conf.	Accrington Stanley	1718	2 - 3	Omoyimni 27, Oates 31
20/09	Conf.	Halifax Town	1452	1 - 0	Sodje 40
23/09	Conf.	BARNET	780	0 - 1	
27/09	Conf.	NORTHWICH VICTORIA	478	3 - 1	Baltazar 1, Omoyinmi 55, Annon 74
04/10	Conf.	Telford United	1529	1 - 1	Porter 25
07/10	Conf.	Dagenham & Redbridge	1540	**0 - 4**	
11/10	Conf.	LEIGH RMI	429	2 - 0	Clarke 14, Simpson 68
18/10	Conf.	Scarborough	1263	1 - 0	Omoyinmi 63
25/10	**FA Cup Q4**	**Grays Athletic**	665	3 - 3	Clarke 45[p], Watson 89, **Saunders 90**
28/10	**FA Cup Q4 rep**	**GRAYS ATHLETIC**	441	3 - 3	**Saunders 81,** Leberl 112, Annon 117
01/11	Conf.	Morecambe	1499	3 - 3	**WATSON 36 66 79**
11/11	Conf.	WOKING	550	1 - 2	Sharpling 22[og] (at Ashford Town)
15/11	Conf.	Hereford United	2320	1 - 2	Porter 53
22/11	Conf.	BURTON ALBION	564	1 - 2	L Piper 78
29/11	Conf.	Chester City	1971	0 - 3	
06/12	Conf.	Farnborough Town	595	1 - 1	Piper 25
14/12	Conf.	SHREWSBURY TOWN	635	0 - 2	
20/12	Conf.	Aldershot Town	2529	2 - 0	Piper 45, Leberl 47
27/12	Conf.	GRAVESEND & NORTHFLEET	**1030**	1 - 3	Watson 12
01/01	Conf.	Gravesend & Northfleet	1725	1 - 2	Keister 30
04/01	Conf.	FOREST GREEN ROVERS	255	2 - 0	**Saunders 48,** Leberl 69
10/01	**FA Trophy 3**	**Dorchester Town**	392	2 - 2	**Saunders 52**, Keister 61
17/01	Conf.	Exeter City	3439	1 - 1	Omoyinmi 90
20/01	**FA Trophy 3 rep**	**DORCHESTER TOWN**	278	2 - 0	Clark 52, **Saunders 85** (at Ashford Town)
24/01	Conf.	Barnet	1591	1 - 3	Omoyinmi 55
08/02	Conf.	HALIFAX TOWN	391	2 - 0	Colley 10[og], Sigere 62
11/02	**FA Trophy 4**	**WORKSOP TOWN**	278	2 - 0	Clarke 24, Sodje 86 (at Ashford Town)
14/02	Conf.	Northwich Victoria	428	3 - 0	D Watson 21, Sigere 70, Clarke 85
17/02	**FA Trophy 5**	**Telford United**	1376	0 - 3	
21/02	Conf.	TELFORD UNITED	300	1 - 0	Baptiste 30
28/02	Conf.	Leigh RMI	302	2 - 4	Clarke 31, Watson 89
06/03	Conf.	DAGENHAM & REDBRIDGE	508	3 - 3	Baptiste 2, Clarke 7[p], Sigere 20
13/03	Conf.	Woking	2109	0 - 0	
16/03	Conf.	ACCRINGTON STANLEY	345	3 - 1	Baptiste 32, 47Sigere 86
20/03	Conf.	HEREFORD UNITED	604	1 - 3	Baptiste 89
27/03	Conf.	Burton Albion	1240	1 - 0	Stadhardt 19
03 /04	Conf.	FARNBOROUGH TOWN	386	**3 - 0**	Clarke 33 Stadhart 56 **Saunders 90**
10 /04	Conf.	TAMWORTH	448	3 - 2	Price 5[og], Stadhart 10, Porter 70
12 /04	Conf.	Stevenage Borough	1548	1 - 2	Porter 44
18 /04	Conf.	MORECAMBE	414	1 - 1	**Saunders 56**
24 /04	Conf.	SCARBOROUGH	404	0 - 2	

Average Home League Attendance: **562** 68-75 Top Goalscorer: **Jay Saunders 7**(3+2FAC+2FAT)

PLAYING SQUAD 2004-2005

Goalkeepers:
Scott Ward (Grays)

Defenders:
Greg Oates (Arsenal), Adrian Clarke (Stevenage), Billy Edwards (Sutton Utd), Darron Annon (Farnborough), Aaron Barnett (Bishop's Stortford), Mark Green (Gillingham)

Midfield:
John Keister (Stevenage), Pat Gradley (Boreham Wood), Peter Benevides (Rhode Island Stingrays (USA))

Forwards:
Rocky Baptiste (Stevenage), Ian Pulman (Chelsea), Che Stadhart (Gravesend)

NEWPORT COUNTY A.F.C.

CLUB OFFICIALS

Chairman: Chris Blight
Secretary: Mike Everett
c/o Cl;ub at Stadium Address
Club Website: www.newport-county.co.uk

Club's Email : hq.newportcounty@virgin.net

FOOTBALL MANAGEMENT TEAM

Manager: Peter Nicholas
Physio: John Fitzgerald
Kit Manager: Tony Gilbert

FACT FILE

Formed: 1989
Nickname: The Exiles
Sponsors: Acorn Recruitment
Colours: Amber shirts and black shorts
Change colours: All Navy Blue
Midweek matchday: Wednesday
Reserve League: Severnside League
Youth League: South West Counties Youth

2002-2003

Captain: Matt Rose
top Scorers:Jeff Ekhardt, Gary Lloyd,John Phillips all 8 goals

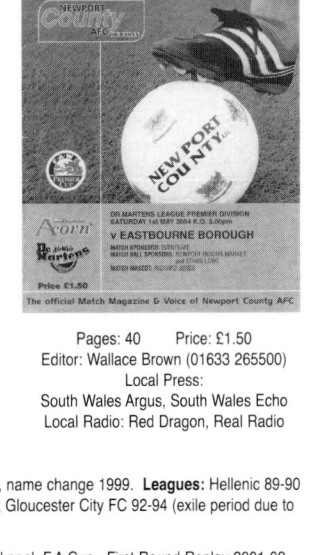

Pages: 40 Price: £1.50
Editor: Wallace Brown (01633 265500)
Local Press:
South Wales Argus, South Wales Echo
Local Radio: Red Dragon, Real Radio

GROUND Newport Stadium, Spytty Park, Langland Way, Newport, South Wales NP19 4PT
Fax 01633 666107 Tel: 01633 662262

Directions: From Severn Bridge on M4 take 1st exit signed Newport (jct 24), 1st left at r'bout follow signs for industrial area, left at r'bout after 2 1/2miles, over 2 r'bouts, next left for ground. Ample free parking available at ground
Capacity:4,300 Cover: 3,236 Seats: 1,236 Floodlights: Yes

Clubhouse: Small bar at ground with hot and cold snacks also available.
New social club open with breakfast menu on matchdays.

Club Shop: Open matchdays, sells a wide selection of souvenirs & programmes
Souvenires also available at club offices during the week.

PREVIOUS **Names:** Newport AFC were formed after the demise of Newport County in1988-89, name change 1999. **Leagues:** Hellenic 89-90
Grounds: London Road, Moreton-in-Marsh 89-90; Somerton Park, Newport 90-92; Gloucester City FC 92-94 (exile period due to dispute with FAW re League of Wales)

CLUB RECORDS **Attendance:** 4,300 (capacity) v Manchester United (friendly) 31.03.04 v Blackpool. F.A.Cup , First Round Replay 2001-02
Win: 9-0 v Pontlottyn Blast Furnace (A), Welsh Cup First Round 1/9/90
Defeat: 1-6 v Stafford Rangers (A) BHL 6/1/96, 1-6 v Wrexham F.A. of Wales Premier Cup Final 08/05/03
Career Goalscorer: Chris Lilygreen 93 **Career Appearances:** Mark Price 275 (222 Lg + 53 cup)
Transfer fee paid:£5,000 for Shaun Chapple from Forest Green Rovers £1,000 from RedditchU for Paul Burton
Transfer fee received: £5,000 from Merthyr Tydfil for Craig Lima

BEST SEASON **FA Cup:** First Round 2001-02 **FA Trophy:** 3rd Rd 99-00, 00-01, 02-03 **FA Vase:** N/A

HONOURS Hellenic Lge Prem Div 89-90 (Lge Cup 89-90); Glos Sen Cup Winners 93-94;Southern Lg. Mid Div Champions 94-95, R-up 98-99 Merit Cup Jnt Win 94-95, 98-99 Gwent FA Sen.Cup Winners 96-97,97-98,98-99,99-00,00-01,01-02 03-04 Herefordshire Sen Cup. 98-99, F.A.W. Premier Cup R-Up 2002-2003. S.W.Co Youth League 2002-03 2003-04 R-Up: 2000-01, 01-02

Insets: JAMIE MORALEE and CARL WILSON-DENIS. **Third Row:** KEVIN AHERNE-EVANS – DARREN JONES – ROGER FREESTONE (club captain) –SCOTT MORGAN – ANDREW THOMAS - RUSSELL JONES (Backroom Staff). **Second Row:** JOHN FITZGERALD (Physio) –PETER WHITE (Youth Team Physio) –LEE PHILLIPS –ASHLEY WILLIAMS – JONATHAN COATES - PETER NICHOLAS (Manager) – SCOTT YOUNG (captain) GLYN JONES (Head Coach) – SAM O'SULLIVAN –NORMAN PARSELLE (Youth Team Coach) – JOHN WHITE (Youth Team Manager) **Front Row:** BOBBY MORRIS (Backroom Staff)– TOM HOOPER– NATHAN DAVIES– JOHN PHILLIPS - GETHYN JONES – NEIL PASSMORE – JASON BOWEN – TONY GILBERT (Kit Manager)

Date	Comp.	Opponents	Att.	Score	Goalscorers
16/08/03	LP	WELLING UNITED	820	0 - 0	
19/08/03	LP	Weymouth	1453	1 - 2	Davis 26
23/08/03	LP	Stafford Rangers	773	0 - 1	
25/08/03	LP	MERTHYR TYDFIL	**935**	1 - 1	**Eckhardt 82**
30/08/03	LP	Grantham Town	423	1 - 2	Phillips 4
03/09/03	LP	CHIPPENHAM TOWN	751	2 - 2	Plant 53 64
06/09/03	LP	Nuneaton Borough	1097	0 - 2	
09/09/03	LP	Moor Green	296	1 - 1	**Eckhardt 62**
13/09/03	LP	CRAWLEY TOWN	632	1 - 2	Dickeson 43
17/09/03	LP	WEYMOUTH	658	1 - 1	Stevenson 86
20/09/03	LP	Hinckley United	480	4 - 1	**Eckhardt 4,33**, Shepherd 47, Dickeson 68
27/09/03	**FA Cup Q2**	**WEYMOUTH**	769	3 - 2	Lloyd 47[p], Mumford 55, Plant 76
04/10/03	LP	DOVER ATHLETIC	725	2 - 1	Davis 4, Mumford 60
11/10/03	**FA Cup Q3**	**MANGOTSFIELD UNITED**	667	3 - 6	Lloyd 10, Plant 38, **Eckhardt 50**
18/10/03	LP	Welling United	550	2 - 0	N Davis 54 70
22/10/03	LP	WESTON-SUPER-MARE	539	1 - 4	**Eckhardt 9**
25/10/03	LP	CHELMSFORD CITY	648	1 - 0	Morgan 78
01/11/03	LP	Worcester City	1180	**5 - 1**	Davis 26 54, J Phillips 77 79, G Phillips 30
08/11/03	LP	Eastbourne Borough	451	2 - 1	**Eckhardt 21**, Playford 66[og]
15/11/03	LP	DORCHESTER TOWN	637	0 - 0	
22/11/03	LP	Hednesford Town	565	2 - 1	**Eckhardt 12,** Davis 14
29/11/03	**FA Trophy 2**	**Hornchurch**	424	0 - 1	
06/12/03	LP	HINCKLEY UNITED	676	0 - 3	
13/12/03	LP	Tiverton Town	600	0 - 0	
6/12/03	LP	Merthyr Tydfil	871	1 - 1	Morgan 44
01/01/04	LP	BATH CITY	928	2 - 1	G Phillips 51, Moralee 76
03/01/04	LP	Havant & Waterlooville	385	3 - 0	Shepherd 23, G Phillips 53, J Phillips 84
10/01/04	LP	WORCESTER CITY	641	**0 - 4**	
17/01/04	LP	Cambridge City	494	2 - 0	Lloyd 52, Stevenson 90
31/01/04	LP	Chippenham Town	739	1 - 2	Lloyd 65
07/02/04	LP	GRANTHAM TOWN	560	2 - 2	O'Sullivan 69, Shephard 78
25/02/04	LP	STAFFORD RANGERS	541	3 - 1	Shephard 28, G Jones 64, Lloyd 77[p]
28/02/04	LP	Dover Athletic	902	0 - 2	
06/03/04	LP	TIVERTON TOWN	662	2 - 1	Davies 3, 5
09/03/04	LP	Weston-super-Mare	446	0 - 0	
27/03/04	LP	NUNEATON BOROUGH	644	1 - 2	Lloyd 87
03/04/04	LP	Chelmsford City	370	0 - 0	
10/04/04	LP	MOOR GREEN	566	1 - 1	**Eckhardt 38**
12/04/04	LP	Bath City	918	0 - 1	
17/04/04	LP	CAMBRIDGE CITY	541	1 - 0	L Phillips 54
21/04/04	LP	HEDNESFORD TOWN	523	1 - 1	Lloyd 52[p]
24/04/04	LP	Dorchester Town	771	2 - 1	Bowen 41 88
26/04/04	LP	Crawley Town	1669	2 - 1	Bowen 81, A Williams 90
28/04/04	LP	HAVANT & WATERLOOVILLE	576	0 - 2	
01/05/04	LP	EASTBOURNE BOROUGH	607	1 - 1	Bowen 20

Average Home League Attendance:**658** 58-59 Top Goalscorer:**Jeff Eckhardt 9** (8 + 1FAC)

PLAYING SQUAD 2004-2005

Goalkeepers:
Roger Freestone (Swansea)

Defenders:
Neil Passmore (Bristol R), Andrew Thomas (Youth team), Darren Jones (Forest Green), Scott Morgan (Forest Green), Lee Phillips (Forest Green)

Midfield:
Nathan Davies (Youth team), Ashley Williams (Youth team), Kevin Aherne-Evans (Merthyr Tydfil), Jason Bowen (Cardiff), Scott Young (Cardiff), Gethyn Jones (Youth team), Jonathan Coates (Swansea)

Forwards:
Sam O'Sullivan (Cardiff), John Phillips (Cardiff), Jamie Moralee (Forest Green), Carl Wilson-Denis (Fisher)

REDBRIDGE

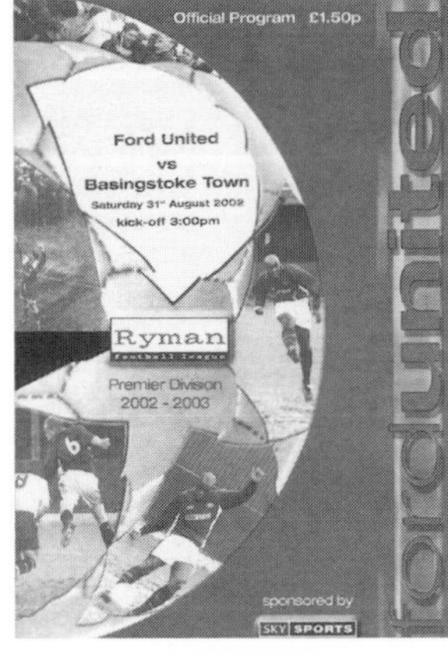

CLUB OFFICIALS

Chairman: Jimmy Chapman
President : Nick Scheeler
Secretary: Alan Wetherall, 23 Warley Avenue, Dagenham, Essex RM8 1JS
07802 226014/07958 947570 (M)
Chief Execs: John Rowe & George Adams

FOOTBALL MANAGEMENT TEAM
Manager: Craig Edwards
Coach: Lyndon Lynch
Assistant Coach: John Frosket
Physio.: Paul Baskin

FACT FILE
Formed: 2004
Nickname: Motormen
Sponsor: Sky Sports
Colours: Blue/blue/white
Change: Red/white/red
Midweek home matchday: Tuesday
Youth Section & Vets.Local Cups & Lgs

2003-2004
Top Scorer.: Glen Poole

PROGRAMME
Pages: 72 Price: £1
Editor:Mike Stephenson
Tel: 01268 402666 (W)
01268 684638 (H & Fax)
e-mail: deeps.steve@ blue yonder.co.uk

GROUND Oakside Stadium,Station Road, Barkingside, Ilford, Essex (0208550 3611)
Directions: From London Take A12 ,Eastern Avenue and turn left into Horns Road., Barkingside (Greengate). Right into Craven Gardens, right again into Carlton Drive and left into Station Road..Go over bridge and ground is on right next to Barkingside (Central Line). From Ilford BR station take 169 bus to Craven Gardens.
Capacity: 3,000 Seats: 316 Cover: 1000 Club Shop: Yes
Clubhouse: Large bar which is open every day 12.00 midday until 11.00 p.m.

HONOURS: London Snr Cup 55-56 56-57 94-95 97-98; 00-01 Essex Snr Lge 91-92 96-97,R-up 94-95, Essex Sen. Trophy 90-91 91-92,00-01 Essex Senior Cup 39-40 49-50 50-51 51-52 85-86, R-up Spartan Lg 49-50 50-51 55-56 56-57 57-58; London Lg 36-37 38-39; Essex Elizabethan 59-60 60-61 70-71; Gtr London Lg 70-71; Sportsmanship Award 77-78 79-80 80-81; Essex Thameside Trophy: 98-=99Essex & Herts Border Comb.(res) 94-95 (Lg Cup 94-95); Isthmian League Div 3 98-99, Promoted from Div 2 99-00, Promoted to Isthmian Premier 01-02

RECORDS: **Attendance:** 58,000 Briggs Sports v Bishop Auckland, at St James Park, Newcastle, FA Amateur Cup
Appearances: Roger Bond **Goalscorer:** Jeff Wood 196
Win: Unknown **Defeat:** Unknown

PREVIOUS: **Leagues:** Spartan, Spartan, Aetolian, Metropolitan, Essex Senior
Names: Brigg Sports (1934) & Ford Sports (1934) amalgamated in 1958. Ford United.
Grounds: Ford Sports & Social Club, Rush Green Road, Romford.

BEST SEASON: **FA Vase:** 98-99, 5th Round, 1-2 v Bedlington Terriers (H)
FA Amateur Cup: Semi-Final 53-54

Players progressing: Les Allen (Spurs), Mick Flanagan (QPR, Charlton, Crystal Palace), Jim Stannard (Fulham, Southend, Millwall), Nicky Hammond (Arsenal,Swindon), Laurie Abrahams (Charlton), Doug Barton (Reading, Newport)

2004-05

Date	Comp.	Opponents	Att.	Score	Goalscorers
16/08	LP	BISHOP'S STORTFORD	163	3 - 0	Abraham 3, Buffong 12, Reinelt 83
19/08	LP	St Albans City	315	0 - 2	
23/08	LP	Basingstoke Town	280	0 - 1	
25/08	LP	MAIDENHEAD UNITED	134	1 - 1	Cooper 59
30/08	LP	Sutton United	513	3 - 2	D Perkins 35, **Poole 66**, Edwards 68
02/09	LP	THURROCK	192	2 - 3	**Poole 1**, Abraham 15
06/09	LP	Braintree Town	201	2 - 1	Cooper 3 33
09/09	LP	HENDON	149	0 - 1	
13/09	LP	BILLERICAY TOWN	179	2 - 1	Abraham 24, Cooper 35
16/09	LP	Northwood	184	3 - 2	Abraham 13, **Poole 17[p]**, Reinelt 83
20/09	LP	Bognor Regis Town	329	2 - 3	**Poole 57**, B Lewis 90
23/09	LP	HITCHIN TOWN	101	3 - 0	Fiddes 17, Reinelt 59, Abraham 81
27/09	**FA Cup Q2**	**DIDCOT TOWN**	174	3 - 1	**ABRAHAM 9 51 71**
04/10	LP	BEDFORD TOWN	174	1 - 1	Abraham 80
07/10	LP	Heybridge Swifts	178	1 - 4	**Poole 89**
11/10	**FA Cup Q3**	**WORTHING**	167	3 - 2	Abraham 36, **Poole 42 90[p]**
18/10	LP	GRAYS ATHLETIC	174	3 - 0	Cooper 22, Carthy 58[og], Fiddes 73
21/10	LP	Kingstonian	228	2 - 0	O'Sullivan 55, Abraham 90
25/10	**FA Cup Q4**	**Cambridge City**	412	3 - 2	Perkins 38**, Poole 42,** Abrahams 73
01/11	**FA Trophy 1**	**Barton Rovers**	103	0 - 0	
04/11	**FA Trophy 1 rep**	**BARTON ROVERS**	83	1 - 0	Cooper 53
08/11	**FA Cup 1**	**Port Vale**	4016	2 - 2	Abraham 20, Fiddes 74
11/11	LP	HAYES	132	0 - 0	
15/11	LP	Kettering Town	771	3 - 0	**Poole 22,** Fenton 65, Reinelt 88
19/11	**FA Cup 1 rep**	**PORT VALE**	1374	1 - 2	**Poole 90**
22/11	LP	HARROW BOROUGH	84	1 - 3	**Poole 3**
29/11	**FA Trophy 2**	**CHELMSFORD CITY**	245	4 - 1	**Poole 19 53,** Cooper 70, Abraham 82
06/12	LP	Canvey Island	509	1 - 3	**Poole 90**
13/12	LP	Bishop's Stortford	278	**0 - 4**	
16/12	LP	Aylesbury United	220	2 - 3	Chandler 61, **Poole 82**
26/12	LP	Hornchurch	832	0 - 1	
10/01	**FA Trophy 3**	**Marlow**	235	1 - 3	Eberende 85
17/01	LP	BRAINTREE TOWN	112	3 - 0	Parkes 67, **Poole 74**, Fiddes 89
24/01	LP	Billericay Town	452	0 - 1	
07/02	LP	AYLESBURY UNITED	117	**4 - 1**	McLoud 31, Reinelt 49, Fenton 53, **Poole 90**
10/02	LP	Hayes	166	1 - 1	Reinelt 42
14/02	LP	Grays Athletic	319	0 - 2	
17/02	LP	CARSHALTON ATHLETIC	141	2 - 1	**Poole 2** Bradford 77(og)
21/02	LP	KETTERING TOWN	156	2 - 0	Edwards 5 Gordon 8 (og)
24/02	LP	Hendon	151	2 - 2	Edwards 5, McLeod 36
28/02	LP	Carshalton Athletic	276	1 - 1	Costello 31 (og)
02/03	LP	KINGSTONIAN	114	0 - 1	
06/03	LP	Hitchin Town	213	1 - 1	Reinelt 76
13/03	LP	BOGNOR REGIS TOWN	119	2 - 0	Fenton 24, Murray 85
16/03	LP	NORTHWOOD	129	3 - 0	**Poole 13[p]**, Lewis 25, Fiddes 34
20/03	LP	Bedford Town	374	1 - 1	Reinelt 27
23/03	LP	BASINGSTOKE TOWN	102	1 - 1	Reinelt 40
27/03	LP	HEYBRIDGE SWIFTS	136	5 - 3	Reinelt 13, **Poole 30 79**, Murray 78, Allen 89
30/03	LP	ST ALBANS CITY	182	2 - 2	**Poole 24,** Perkins 80
03 /04	LP	SUTTON UNITED	141	2 - 4	Allen 53, **Poole 88[p]**
10 /04	LP	Maidenhead United	247	1 - 1	**Poole 5**
12 /04	LP	HORNCHURCH	268	0 - 0	
17 /04	LP	Thurrock	171	0 - 0	
24 /04	LP	CANVEY ISLAND	**336**	0 - 3	
01/05	LP	Harrow Borough	150	1 - 1	**Poole 71**

Average Home League Attendance:**154** 89-76 Top Goalscorer: **Glenn Poole 25** (19 +4FAC + 2FAT)

PLAYING SQUAD 2004-2005

Goalkeepers:
Jamie Lunan (Grays), David Bull (Youth team)

Defenders:
Richard Halle (Grays), Chris Perkins (Canvey Island), Ben Lewis (Grays), Allan McLeod (Grays), Bobby Dinnen (Youth team), Kevin Stephens (Leyton Orient), Jordan Kelly (Southend), Simon Clarke (Chelmsford), Simon Ford (Bristol R)

Midfield:
Glenn Poole (Yeovil), Alex Fiddes (Grays), Yohance Lewis (Grays), Craig Edwards (Purfleet), Greg Lincoln (Northampton), Sam Taylor (Billericay)

Forwards:
Vil Powell (Retford Utd), Darryl Plummer (Southend), Deji Davies (Berkhamsted), Nathan Elder (Aveley), Jay Murray (St Albans)

St ALBANS CITY

CLUB OFFICIALS

Chairman: John Gibson

President: Cllr Malcolm MacMillan

Vice Chairman: Steve Carroll

Secretary & Press Officer:
Steve Eames c/o Club
01727 864296 (W) 01727 767252 (M)

FOOTBALL MANAGEMENT TEAM

Manager: Steve Castle
Physio: T.B.A.

FACT FILE

Formed: 1908
Nickname: The Saints
Colours: Yellow/blue yellow
Change colours: Red/white/red
Midweek home matchday: Tuesday
Newsline: 09066 555822
Club Website:http://www.sacfc.co.uk
E-Mail: info@sacfc.co.uk

GROUND: Clarence Park, York Rd, St Albans, Herts AL1 4PL Tel: 01727 864296
Directions: Left out of St Albans station - Clarence Pk 200yds ahead acrossHatfield Rd. M25, jct 21 to Noke Hotel island, straight on thru Chiswell Green towards St Albans, straight over 2 mini-r'bouts and one larger island, thru 2sets of lights and right at island at far end of city centre (St Peters St.) into Hatfield Rd, over mini-r'bout, left at 2nd lights into Clarence Rd, ground on left
Capacity: 6,000 Cover: 1,900 Seats: 904 Floodlights: Yes
Clubhouse: Open matchdays and available for functions. Manager:James Brewer
Tea bar within ground serves hot food
Club Shop: Club merchandise & League & non-League progs,magazines,videos etc
Managers:Barry Hillard c/o club

Programme: Pages: 32 Price: £1.50
Editor:Secretary (07985 524942).
Local Press: St Albans & District Observer, Herts Advertiser
Local Radio: BBC Three Counties, Chiltern Radio, Oasis

PREVIOUS **Leagues:** Herts County 08-10; Spartan 08-20; Athenian 20-23

CLUB RECORDS **Attendance:** 9,757 v Ferryhill Ath., FA Amtr Cup QF 27/2/26
Appearances: Phil Wood 900 (62-85)
Goalscorer: W H (Billy) Minter 356 (top scorer for 12 consecutive seasons 1920-32)
Win: 14-0 v Aylesbury United (H) Spartan Lge 19/10/12 **Defeat:** 0-11 v Wimbledon (H), Isthmian Lge 9/11/46.
Fee Paid: £6,000 for Paul Turner (Yeovil Town Aug 97) **Fee Received:** £92,750 for Dean Austin (Southend 90/Spurs 92)

BEST SEASON **FA Amateur Cup:** Semi final 22-23 24-25 25-26 69-70. **FA Trophy:** Semi-Final 1998-99 1-2 & 2-3 v Forest Green Rovers
FA Cup: 2nd Rd replay 68-69 (1-3 at Walsall after 1-1 draw), 80-81 (1-4 atTorquay after 1-1 draw), 96-97 (9-2 at Bristol City)

HONOURS: Isthmian Lg 23-24 26-27 27-28 (R-up 54-55 92-93), Div 1 85-86, Div 2 R-up 83-84, Lg Cup R-up 89-90, Res. Sect. R-up 48-49 60-61 61-62; Athenian Lg 20-21 21-22 (R-up 22-23); Spartan Lg 11-12 (R-up 12-13, East Div 09-10); Herts Co. Lg 09-10 (West Div 08-09, Aubrey Cup(res) 61-62); London Snr Cup 70-71 (R-up 69-70); AFA Snr Cup 33-34 (R-up 30-31 32-33 34-35); E Anglian Cup 92-93; Herts SnrCup(13) (R-up 10), Herts Snr Tphy 86-87, Herts Charity Cup(25) (R-up(18);Mithras Cup 64-65 71-72 (R-up 76-77); Wycombe F'lit Cup(2) 68-70; St AlbansHosp Cup 45-46; Hitchin Centenary Cup 70-71 (R-up 71-72); Victory Cup 25-26 27-28, Liege Cup 26-27; Billy Minter Invit. Cup (3) 90-93

Players progressing: A Grimsdell (Spurs 11), G Edmonds (Watford 14), R Burke(Man Utd 46), J Meadows (Watford 51), M Rose (Charlton 63), J Kinnear (Spurs 65), J Mitchell (Fulham 72), A Cockram (Brentford 88), D Austin (Southend 90),T Kelly (Stoke 90), M Danzey (Cambridge 92), D Williams (Brentford 93).

Back row left to right: Steve Cook (co-manager), Tom Upsher, Simon Martin, Ryan Moran, Derek Brown, Corey Campbell, Rob Smith, Richard Evans and Gary Roberts (co-manager). **Front row:** Richard Wilmot, Gary Wraight, Jon Rattle, Mike Bignall and Jimmy Sugrue.

Date	Comp.	Opponents	Att.	Score	Goalscorers
16/08	LP	Carshalton Athletic	367	1 - 1	Graham 23[p]
19/08	LP	FORD UNITED	315	2 - 0	McDonnell 43, De Souza 70
23/08	LP	HITCHIN TOWN	407	1 - 2	De Souza 52
25/08	LP	Heybridge Swifts	269	2 - 0	Campbell 21, Martin 87
30/08	LP	HAYES	376	1 - 1	Wraight 44
02/09	LP	Canvey Island	589	0 - 4	
06/09	LP	SUTTON UNITED	341	2 - 0	Wraight 9, Tomlinson 47
09/09	LP	Basingstoke Town	335	1 - 1	Bristow 49[og]
13/09	LP	Bedford Town	746	0 - 1	
16/09	LP	MAIDENHEAD UNITED	220	1 - 2	McDonnell 90
20/09	LP	BISHOP'S STORTFORD	412	3 - 2	Tomlinson 39[p], McDonnell 61, Oakes 81
23/09	LP	Hornchurch	430	1 - 0	McDonnell 29
27/09	**FA Cup Q2**	**GRAYS ATHLETIC**	420	2 - 4	Tomlinson 21[p], Oakes 44
04/10	LP	Harrow Borough	219	1 - 3	Martin 81
11/10	LP	KINGSTONIAN	318	0 - 1	
18/10	LP	BRAINTREE TOWN	301	0 - 0	
21/10	LP	Grays Athletic	226	**1 - 9**	S Martin 83
25/10	LP	Billericay Town	336	1 - 1	Tomlinson 71
08/11	LP	NORTHWOOD	358	3 - 0	Murray 49, Deacon 60, Martin 62
11/11	LP	KETTERING TOWN	334	0 - 1	
15/11	LP	Bognor Regis Town	347	2 - 2	Wraight 17, Murray 56
18/11	**Lge Cup 2**	**Heybridge Swifts**	122	1 - 2	Murray 47
29/11	**FA Trophy 2**	**CRAWLEY TOWN**	327	0 - 0	
02/12	**FA Trophy 2 rep**	**Crawley Town**	445	1 - 4	De Souza 8
06/12	LP	HENDON	295	0 - 4	
13/12	LP	CARSHALTON ATHLETIC	264	0 - 4	
26/12	LP	AYLESBURY UNITED	410	3 - 1	Tomlinson 21, Richards 38 43
10/01	LP	Hitchin Town	468	0 - 1	
17/01	LP	Sutton United	514	2 - 4	Brown 18, Willis 46
24/01	LP	BEDFORD TOWN	**422**	1 - 3	Willis 54
07/02	LP	BILLERICAY TOWN	341	0 - 2	
10/02	LP	Kettering Town	703	0 - 2	
14/02	LP	Braintree Town	291	4 - 2	Waite 3 10, **Clarke 19,** De Souza 61
21/02	LP	BOGNOR REGIS TOWN	225	2 - 2	De Souza 40 Wraight 84
24/02	LP	BASINGSTOKE TOWN	144	0 - 3	
28/02	LP	Northwood	305	4 - 3	Watts 24 Wraight 29Evans 48(og) **Clarke 70**
02/03	LP	GRAYS ATHLETIC	178	0 - 3	
06/03	LP	HORNCHURCH	297	1 - 1	**Clarke 42**
13/03	LP	Bishop's Stortford	421	2 - 2	Watts 75 80
20/03	LP	HARROW BOROUGH	195	0 - 1	
23/03	LP	Maidenhead United	190	2 - 4	Watts 35 45
27/03	LP	Kingstonian	351	2 - 1	Watts 49, Castle 82
30/03	LP	Ford United	182	2 - 2	**Clarke 13 60**
03 /04	LP	Hayes	263	0 - 1	
10 /04	LP	HEYBRIDGE SWIFTS	225	0 - 0	
12 /04	LP	Aylesbury United	357	2 - 0	Perkins 28, De Sousa 69
17 /04	LP	CANVEY ISLAND	341	**4 - 1**	**CLARKE 47 56 84**, Oakes 48
24 /04	LP	Hendon	422	1 - 1	**Clarke 15**
27 /04	LP	Thurrock	241	0 - 2	
01/05	LP	THURROCK	310	0 - 2	
05/05	**Play-off SF**	**Heybridge Swifts**	285	4 - 3	**PARKER 49 65 119,** De Souza 100
08/05	**Play-off F**	**Bedford Town**	1087	5 - 4	Deacon 11 Parker 59 **Clarke 65 (p)** De Souza 72 Watts 89
		Average Home League Attendance:	**305**	68-99	Top Goalscorer: **Lee Clarke 10**

PLAYERS SQUAD 2004-2005

Goalkeepers: Mel Capleton (Grays), James Robinson (Hitchin)

Defenders:

Chris Zoricich (Margate), Dean Hooper (Aldershot), James Ayres (Hitchin), Ben Martin (Swindon), Chris Seeby (Youth team)

Midfield:

Steve Castle (Stevenage), Adam Parker (Hitchin), Scott Oakes (Shelbourne), Matthew Hann (Dorchester), Rob Smith (Baldock), Greg Deacon (Youth team), Scott Cousins (Hendon), Gary Wraight (Barking), Darren Sarll (Bedford), Richard Thomas (Barking)

Forwards:

Neil Gough (Chelmsford), Miguel De Souza (Farnborough), Daniel McBreen (Universitatea Craiova (Romania)), Spencer Knight (Canvey Island), Lee Clarke (Peterborough), Ben Cogger (Oxford C), Gary Crawshaw (Farnborough)

SUTTON UNITED

CLUB OFFICIALS
Chairman: Bruce Elliott
President: Andrew W Letts
Secretary: Dave Farebrother, Borough Sports Ground
Tel No: 07734 719936
Press Officer: Tony Dolbear
Tel: Mobile 07966 507023
PR@suttonunited.net

FOOTBALL MANAGEMENT TEAM
Manager: John Rains
Asst.Man: Tony Rains **Coach:** Micky Cook
Physio: Jimmy Hendrie
Res Team Manager: Phil Dunne

FACT FILE
Formed: 1898 Nickname: The U's
Sponsors: Securicor
Colours:Amber & chocolate
Change colours: Green & white/black/black
Midweek matchday: Tuesday
Reserve League: Suburban League
Local Press: Sutton Advertiser, Sutton Guardian, Sutton Independent, Sutton Comet
Local Radio: Thames Radio, County Sound
2003 -2004
Captain: Eddie Akuamoah
Leading Scorers: Jon Nurse
Player Of the Year & Young Player o.Y.: : Nick Bailey

Pages: 48 Price: £2.00
Editor: Lyall Reynolds
Email: sutton editor@hotmail.com
Website: www.suttonunited.net

GROUND: Borough Sports Ground, Gander Green Lane, Sutton, Surrey SM1 2EY Tel: 0208 6444440 Fax: 0208 6445120 Website: www.btinternet.com/~suttonunited
Directions: Gander Green Lane runs between A232 (Cheam Road - turn by Sutton Cricket Club) and A217 (Oldfields Road - turn at`Gander' PH lights). Ground opposite `The Plough' 50 yards from West Sutton BR station. Bus 413 passes ground
Capacity: 7,032 **Seated**: 765 **Terracing - Covered:** 1,250 **Uncovered:** 5,000
Clubhouse: Open every day, food. Available for hire with five function rooms
Club Shop: Open matchdays selling a full range of souvenirs, etc, contact Tony Cove via club

PREVIOUS **Leagues:** Sutton Junior, Southern Sub 10-21, Athenian 21-63, Isthmian 63-86, 91-99, GMVC 86-91, 99-00
Names: Sutton Association, Sutton Guild Rovers **Grounds:** Western Road, Manor Lane, London Road, The Find.

CLUB RECORDS **Attendance:** 14,000 v Leeds United,FA Cup 4th Rd 24/1/70
Victory: 11-1 v Clapton 66, & leatherhead 82-83 **Defeat:** 13-0 v Barking 25-26
Scorer: Paul McKinnon (279) **Appearances:** Larry Pritchard 781 (65-84)
Fee Paid: to Malmo FF for Paul McKinnon 83 **Fee Received:** £100,000 for Efan Ekoku (Bournemouth 90)

BEST SEASON **FA Amateur Cup:** Runners-up 62-63 68-69; SF 28-29 36-37 67-68 **FA Trophy:** Runners-up 80-81; SF 92-93,99-00 **FA Cup:** 4th Rd-69-70, 0-6 v Leeds Utd (H); 88-89, 0-8 v Norwich C.(A), 3rd Rd 87-88 v Middlesbrough 1-1, 0-1, 93-94 v Notts Co(A)2-3

HONOURS Bob Lord Trophy 90-91; **Isthmian League** 66-67 84-86 98-99 R-up 67-68 70-71 81-82,03-04 Lge Cup (3) 82-84 85-86 97-98 R-up 79-80; Loctite Cup 91-92; Carlton Cup 95-96; **Athenian Lge** 27-28 45-46 57-58 R-up 46-47, Lg Cup 45-46 55-56 61-62 62-63, Res Sec 61-62 R-up 32-33; Anglo Italian Semi-Pro Cup 79 R-up 80 82; London Snr Cup 57-58 82-83; London Charity Cup 69-70 R-up 67-68 68-69 72-73; Surrey Snr Cup x15 R-up x 10, Surrey Premier. Cup x 5 R-up x6; Surrey Jnr Cup R-up 09-10; Surrey Snr Char. Sh. x3 R-up x6; Surrey Interm Char. Cup 31-32 R-up 34-35 38-39; Dylon Char. Sh. 84 R-up 80 82 83 85; Groningen Yth tournament 83 85 R-up 79 81 89 91; John Ullman Invit. Cup 88-89. Surrey Youth League Winners 2003-004

Past Players progressing: Numerous including the following since 1980 - S Galloway (C Palace 84), P McKinnon (Blackburn 86), R Fearon (Ipswich 87), PHarding (Notts Co), E Ekoku (Bournemouth 91), M Golley (Maidstone), A Barnes (C Palace 91), P Rogers (Sheff U 92), S Massey (C Palace 92), A & R Scott (Sheff U 93), O Morah(Cambridge 94), M Watson(West Ham 95), E Hutchinson (Brentford 000),T.Hutchinson(Dundee)

Back Row (L-R): John Rains (manager), Paul Honey, Matt Gray, Andrew Martin, Joff Vansittart, Phil Wilson, Bradley Thomas, Scott Corbett, David Kennedy, Scott Forrester, Tony Rains (assitant manager). **Front:** Micky Cook (coach), Lewis Gonsalves, Stuart Booth, Eddie Akuamoah, Kunle Olusesi, Nigel Brake, Peter Fear, Glenn Boosey, Sarah Capewell (physio).

Date	Comp.	Opponents	Att.	Score	Goalscorers
16/08	LP	Hayes	393	0 - 0	
19/08	LP	BOGNOR REGIS TOWN	552	1 - 0	Collins 78
23/08	LP	GRAYS ATHLETIC	489	1 - 0	Bolt 57[p]
25/08	LP	Kingstonian	781	2 - 1	Bailey 57, Hanlan 82
30/08	LP	FORD UNITED	513	2 - 3	Gray 31, Collins 64
02/09	LP	Hendon	309	2 - 0	Hodges 8, Gray 90
06/09	LP	St Albans City	341	0 - 2	
09/09	LP	THURROCK	431	**0 - 3**	
13/09	LP	BISHOP'S STORTFORD	503	2 - 2	Bolt 10[p] 81[p]
16/09	LP	Harrow Borough	110	4 - 2	Watson 10 40, Bailey 69, Bolt 77[p]
20/09	LP	CANVEY ISLAND	600	0 - 1	
23/09	LP	Maidenhead United	251	0 - 2	
27/09	**FA Cup Q2**	**BISHOP'S STORTFORD**	429	0 - 0	
30/09	**FA Cup Q2 rep**	**Bishop's Stortford**	347	1 - 1	Collins 76
04/10	**LP**	**Hornchurch**	503	0 - 3	
07/10	LP	BRAINTREE TOWN	411	1 - 2	Watson 58
18/10	LP	HITCHIN TOWN	499	**0 - 3**	
21/10	LP	Billericay Town	203	1 - 0	Fowler 10
08/11	LP	BEDFORD TOWN	518	1 - 1	Fowler 33
11/11	LP	AYLESBURY UNITED	414	2 - 2	Hanlan 16, Bailey 52
15/11	LP	Northwood	259	2 - 1	Bailey 6, Gray 45
22/11	LP	BASINGSTOKE TOWN	437	2 - 2	Bailey 19, Fowler 59
25/11	LP	Kettering Town	517	1 - 0	Nurse 43
29/11	**FA Trophy 2**	**BEDFORD TOWN**	356	2 - 0	Fowler 65, Nurse 72
06/12	LP	Heybridge Swifts	236	2 - 2	Bailey 45[p], Nurse 66
20/12	LP	Bognor Regis Town	277	2 - 0	Bailey 22, Nurse 75
27/12	LP	CARSHALTON ATHLETIC	1213	6 - 0	Nurse 9, Gray 27, **FOWLER 60 74 84,** Honey 80
01/01	LP	Grays Athletic	409	2 - 3	Quinton 4, Akuamoah 50
10/01	**FA Trophy 3**	**Forest Green Rovers**	701	0 - 4	
17/01	LP	ST ALBANS CITY	514	4 - 2	De Souza 39[og], Bailey 40, Nurse 44 54
24/01	LP	Bishop's Stortford	457	1 - 1	Boosey 85
03/02	LP	Thurrock	231	1 - 0	Jinuda 62
07/02	LP	KETTERING TOWN	586	2 - 1	Boosey 11, Nurse 90
10/02	LP	Aylesbury United	302	**6 - 0**	**FOWLER 16 43 59 66 90,** Nurse 81
14/02	LP	Hitchin Town	367	4 - 2	Bailey 41[p] 80[p], Fowler 45, Jinadu 51
21/02	LP	NORTHWOOD	537	0 - 0	
24/02	LP	HAYES	368	4 - 1	Fowler 7 20, Bailey 9, Boosey 74
28/02	LP	Bedford Town	458	1 - 2	Bailey 45
02/03	LP	BILLERICAY TOWN	491	1 - 1	Quinton 28
06/03	LP	MAIDENHEAD UNITED	191	**0 - 3**	
13/03	LP	Canvey Island	727	3 - 1	Jinadu 44, Bailey 61[p], J Nurse 88
20/03	LP	HORNCHURCH	547	3 - 1	J Nurse 28 72, Bailey 61[p]
23/03	LP	HARROW BOROUGH	412	3 - 0	Fowler 22, J Nurse 51, Gray 84
27/03	LP	Braintree Town	312	3 - 0	Bailey 11 52[p], C Nurse 63
03 /04	LP	Ford United	141	4 - 2	Bailey 15 77, J Nurse 56, Gray 87
10 /04	LP	KINGSTONIAN	710	4 - 1	Fowler 16, J Nurse 34, Boosey 70, Gray 77
12 /04	LP	Carshalton Athletic	1077	2 - 2	Bailey 24, Boosey 89
17 /04	LP	HENDON	613	2 - 0	Akuamoah 26, Boosey 65
24 /04	LP	HEYBRIDGE SWIFTS	603	5 - 1	**NURSE 38,48,51** Hanlon 55 Boosey 73
01/05	LP	Basingstoke Town	720	5 - 0	**QUINTON 4 18 47**, J Nurse 27, Honey 75

Average Home League Attendance:**528** 97-61 Top Goalscorers: **J.Nurse 19** (18 +1FAT) ?
& **Nick Bailey 19** (inc 6pens)

PLAYERS SQUAD 2004-2005

Goalkeepers:

Andy Iga (Hampton), Phil Wilson (Maidenhead)

Defenders:

Danny Brooker (Kingstonian), Craig Howard (Youth team), Mike Hollands (Brentford), Danny Hodges (Farnborough), Lewis Gonsalves (Youth team), Martin Dunne (Youth team), Danny Dray (Youth team),

Midfield:

Nigel Brake (Crawley), Graham Tydeman (Youth team), Chris Nurse (Kingstonian), Paul Honey (Youth team), Same Hewitt (Youth team), Matt Hanlan (Carshalton), Eddie Akuamoah (Kingstonian), Glenn Boosey (Chelsea), Dean Hamlin(YouthTeam)

Forwards:

Kunle Olulesi (Carshalton), Joff Vansittart (Crawley), Craig Watkins (Epsom & Ewell), Scott Forrester (Hayes), Andy Martin (Hornchurch)

THURROCK

CLUB OFFICIALS

Chairman: Grant Beglan
V/Chairman/Chief Exec: Tommy Smith
Secretary: Norman Posner, 1 Chase House Gardens, Hornchurch, Essex, RM11 2PJ, Tel: 01708 458301
Match Secretary/Press Officer: Norman Posner
Comm Mger: Tony Joy (01375 392906)

FOOTBALL MANAGEMENT TEAM

Manager: Colin McBride
Asst Manager: Jimmy McFarlane
Coach: Ronnie Hanley
Physio: Michelle Sheehan

FACT FILE

Founded: 1985
Nickname: Fleet
Sponsors: LakesideShopping Centre
Colours:Yellow &green/green/yellow & green
Change colours: All white
Midweek home matchday: Monday
Reserve's League: Essex & Herts Border

2003-2004

Captain: Jimmy McFarland
Top Scorer: Tresor Kandol 39
Player of the Year: Tresor Kandol

Pages: 60 Price: £1.50
Editor: Norman Posner (01708 458301 H)
Local Press: Romford, Thurrock Recorder, Thurrock Gazette
Local Radio: Essex Radio, BBC Radio Essex

GROUND: Thurrock Hotel, Ship Lane, Grays, Essex. 01708 865492 Fax: 01708 868863
Webside: www.purfleetfootballclub.com
Directions: M25 or A13 to Dartford tunnel r'bout. Ground is fifty yards on right down Ship Lane. Nearest station is Purfleet, two miles from ground
Capacity: 4,500 Cover: 1,000 Seats: 300 Floodlights: Yes
Clubhouse: Steward: Tommy South
Club Shop: Selling programmes & magazines. Contact Tommy South (01708 868901)

PREVIOUS **League:** Essex Senior 85-89 Isthmian 1989-2004. **Names**: Purfleet 1985-2003 **Grounds:** None

CLUB RECORDS **Attendance:** 2,572 v West Ham United, friendly 1998.
Goalscorer: George Georgiou 106. **Appearances:** Jimmy McFarlane 531
Win: 10-0 v Stansted (H) 86-87, v East Ham Utd (A) 87-88 (both Essex Senior League)
Defeat: 0-6 v St Leonards Stamco(A), FA Trophy 96-97. 0-6 v Sutton United(H) Isthmian Lge 97-98

BEST SEASON **FA Cup:** First Round Replay 2003-2004 (lost 1-3 away to Luton Town)
FA Trophy: Second Round Prop 95-96 (lost 1-2 away to Macclesfield Tn)

HONOURS: Isthmian Lg Div 2 91-92 Div 1 R-up 93-94, Div 2 Nth R-up 88-89, Associate Members Tphy 91-92; Essex Snr Lg 87-88 (Lg Cup (2) 86-88; Essex Snr. CupWinners 2003-04 R-up 97-98, 99-00, Stanford Charity Cup 87-88 (R-up 85-86); Essex Thames-Side Trophy 94-95; Essex Bus Houses Sen L/Cup 93-94; F Budden Trophy 94-95; Essex & HertsBorder Comb R-up 94-95; Full Members Cup R-up 99-00, 00-01.

Players progressing to Football League: Paul Cobb & Lee Williams (Leyton O.)

Back Row (L-R): Gary Redmond, David Collis, John O'Brien, Danny Lye, Steve Heffer, Michael Basham, Tresor Kandol, Martyn Lawrence, Cliff Akurang, Kris Lee, Danny Greaves, Mark Goodfellow.
Front Row: Lee Allen, Gary Howard, Chris Harvey, John Purdie, Paul Gothard, Paul Linger, Terry Bowes.
Inset: Jimmy McFarlane.

Date	Comp.	Opponents	Att.	Score	Goalscorers
16/08	LP	Kingstonian	354	1 - 1	Kandol 44[p]
19/08	LP	CARSHALTON ATHLETIC	325	2 - 3	Akurang 28 31
23/08	LP	HENDON	306	2 - 0	Akurang 28, Kandol 90
25/08	LP	Canvey Island	591	3 - 4	Kandol 72, Akurang 85[p]
30/08	LP	KETTERING TOWN	442	0 - 2	
02/09	LP	Ford United	192	3 - 2	Kandol 14, Akurang 42, Lee 47
06/09	LP	HEYBRIDGE SWIFTS	299	1 - 1	Pollard 90[og]
09/09	LP	Sutton United	431	3 - 0	Akurang 4, Linger 36, Lee 37
13/09	LP	Basingstoke Town	288	3 - 0	Kandol 26, Akurang 57, McFarlane 68
16/09	LP	HORNCHURCH	441	1 - 3	Kandol 72[p]
20/09	LP	MAIDENHEAD UNITED	225	3 - 1	Akurang 51 66, Allen 88
23/09	LP	Bishop's Stortford	252	3 - 1	Meah 19, McFarlane 55, Akurang 65[p]
27/09	**FA Cup Q2**	Buckingham Town	182	2 - 1	Akurang 85, Lawrence 87
04/10	LP	Braintree Town	177	0 - 1	
07/10	LP	HARROW BOROUGH	238	3 - 0	Akurang 58[p], Wareham 64, Collis 85
11/10	**FA Cup Q3**	**Bromley**	461	1 - 1	Linger 65
14/10	**FA Cup Q3 rep**	**BROMLEY**	231	3 - 0	Kandol 19, Linger 38, Bowes 71
18/10	LP	BILLERICAY TOWN	267	1 - 0	Kandol 73
21/10	LP	Hitchin Town	203	0 - 0	
25/10	**FA Cup Q4**	**DAGENHAM & REDBRIDGE**	957	2 - 1	Akurang 31, Kandol 46
01/11	LP	Bedford Town	466	0 - 0	
07/11	**FA Cup 1**	**LUTON TOWN**	1551	1 - 1	Bowes 80
15/11	LP	Aylesbury United	378	4 - 2	**AKURANG 18 43 55**, Kandol 22
18/11	**FA Cup 1 rep**	**Luton Town**	3667	1 - 3	Akurang 49
29/11	**FA Trophy 2**	**Carshalton Athletic**	198	2 - 2	Linger 14, Goodfellow 52
02/12	**FA Trophy 2 rep**	**CARSHALTON ATHLETIC**	103	1 - 0	McFarlane 80
06/12	LP	Northwood	155	3 - 0	Akurang 23, Collis 55, Kandol 57
13/12	LP	KINGSTONIAN	258	4 - 1	**KAANMDOL 29 38 44,** Akurang 40
20/12	LP	Carshalton Athletic	310	3 - 0	Linger 2 90, Kandol 22
01/01	LP	Hendon	297	1 - 1	Linger 37
06/01	LP	BOGNOR REGIS TOWN	259	4 - 1	Akurang 12, Bowes 30, Kandol 35 45
09/01	**FA Trophy 3**	**Wealdstone**	365	2 - 3	Akurang 5, Hummerdinger 73[og]
17/01	LP	Heybridge Swifts	240	3 - 0	Bowes 45, Linger 56 79
24/01	LP	BASINGSTOKE TOWN	227	0 - 0	
03/02	LP	SUTTON UNITED	231	0 - 1	
07/02	LP	BEDFORD TOWN	274	1 - 1	Howarth 84[og]
10/02	LP	Bognor Regis Town	326	**1 - 6**	Kandol 68
14/02	LP	Billericay Town	460	1 - 1	Kandol 35
21/02	LP	AYLESBURY UNITED	174	5 - 0	**KANDOL 11,20,23**, Martin 75 Davidson 80
28/02	LP	Hayes	196	2 - 1	Linger 24 Kandol 30
06/03	LP	BISHOP'S STORTFORD	294	1 - 1	Linger 17
09/03	LP	HAYES	137	2 - 0	Akurang 6, McFarlane 22
13/03	LP	Maidenhead United	188	4 - 1	Martin 6, Kandol 36, Akurang 51, Bowes 78
16/03	LP	GRAYS ATHLETIC	722	2 - 0	Kandol 6, Akurang 54
20/03	LP	BRAINTREE TOWN	201	0 - 1	
27/03	LP	Harrow Borough	160	2 - 1	Bowes 60, Allen 65
30/03	LP	HITCHIN TOWN	188	2 - 0	Kandol 29[p], Linger 79
03 /04	LP	Kettering Town	722	1 - 2	Akurang 23
09 /04	LP	CANVEY ISLAND	**1003**	1 - 2	Akurang 47
12 /04	LP	Grays Athletic	372	1 - 1	Martin 80
17 /04	LP	FORD UNITED	171	0 - 0	
20 /04	LP	Hornchurch	410	0 - 2	
24 /04	LP	NORTHWOOD	163	**6 - 0**	McFarland 42 Kandol 44 Martin 57 Akurandg 61(p) Linger87(p) Lee 88
27 /04	LP	ST ALBANS CITY	241	2 - 0	Martin 16, Akurang 90
01/05	LP	St Albans City	310	2 - 0	Kandol 74 90

Average Home League Attendance:**304** 102-57 Top Goalscorers: **Cliff Akurang 29** (25+3FAC+1FAT)
& **Tresor Kandol 28** (26 + 2FAC)

PLAYING SQUAD 2004-2005

Goalkeepers:

Paul Gothard (Dagenham & Redbridge)

Defenders:

Mark Goodfellow (Leyton Orient), Jason Broom (Dagenham & Redbridge), Craig Davidson (Canvey Island), David Collis (Ford Utd), John Purdie (Billericay), Jim McFarland (Clapton), Richard Goddard (Harrow), Steve Basham (Chelmsford)

Midfield:

Steve Heffer (Dagenham & Redbridge), Dwayne Plummer (Hendon), Martyn Lawrence (Concord R), Ryan Kirby (Harlow)

Forwards:

Tresor Kandol (Chesham Utd), Cliff Akurang (Hitchin), Kris Lee (Chelmsford), Lee Hodges (Bristol R)

WELLING UNITED

CLUB OFFICIALS
President: E Brackstone
Chairman: Paul Websdale
Vice Chairman: Steven Pain
General Manager: Graham Hobbins
Club Secretary: Barrie Hobbins
c/o the club
Tel: 0208 301 1196 Fax:0208 301 5676
Press Officer: Paul Carter
c/o the club

FOOTBALL MANAGEMENT TEAM
Manager: Paul Parker
Coach: Tim O'Shea
Captain: Lew Watts
Physio: Peter Green

FACT FILE
Founded: 1963
Nickname: The Wings
Club Sponsors:
E. Coomes, Bookmakers
Colours: Red/red/white
Change colours: Yellow/blue/white
Midweek home matchday: Tuesday
Welling Wingsline: 09068 80 06 54
Local Press: Kentish Times; Kent Messenger
Bexleyheath & Welling Mercury
Local Radio: Radio Kent;
Radio Invicta; R.T.M.

2003-2004
Leading Goalscorer: Paul Booth

PROGRAMME
Pages: 40 Price: £2.00
Editor: Gary McHolland-Pilcher

GROUND Park View Road Ground, Welling, Kent DA16 1SY
Tel: 0208 301 1196 Fax: 0208 301 5676
DIRECTIONS: M25, then A2 towards London. Take Welling turn-off, ground 1 mile.
By rail to Welling station (BR) - ground 3/4 mile.
CAPACITY: 4,000 **SEATED:** 1,070 **CLUBHOUSE:** Open on match days
CLUB SHOP: Sells programmes (League & non-League), scarves, mugs, caps, hats, badges, replica kits etc. Manager Peter Mason.

PREVIOUS **Leagues:** Eltham & Dt. Lge 1963-71, London Spartan Lge 1971-77, Athenian Lge 1977-79, Southern Lge 1979-86, 2001-04 Conference 86-2000 **Grounds:** Butterfly Lane, Eltham - 1963-78

RECORDS **Attendance:** 4,100 v Gillingham, FA Cup
Win: 7-1 v Dorking 1985-86 **Defeat:** 0-7 v Welwyn garden City 1972-73
Career Goalscorer: John Bartley - 533 **Career Appearances:** Nigel Ransom - 1,066 & Ray Burgess - 1,044
Transfer fee paid: £30,000 for Gary Abbott from Enfield
Transfer fee received: £95,000 from Birmingham City for Steve Finnan.1995

BEST SEASON **FA Cup:** Third Round 1988-89 0-1 v Blackburn Rovers League clubs defeated: Gillingham
FA Trophy: Quarter Final 1988-89 0-1 v Macclesfield

HONOURS London Spartan League 1978; Southern League Premier Division 1985/86; Kent Senior Cup 1985/86 98-99; London Senior Cup 1989/90; London Challenge Cup 1991/92, Runners-up 1993/94.

PLAYERS PROGRESSING: Paul Barron(Plymouth A), Andy Townsend (Southampton), Ian Thompson (AFC Bournemouth), John Bartley (Millwall), Dave Smith (Gillingham), Murray Jones (C. Palace), Kevin Shoemake (Peterborough), Tony Agana (Watford,), Duncan Horton (Barnet), Mark Hone (Southend), Steve Finnan & Steve Barnes (Birmingham City),Dean Standen (Luton Town)

L-R - Back Row: B Statham, J Farley, L Watts, T Hambley, J Ventor, G Knight, I Cousins, P Collins, T O'Shea, P Green.
Front Row: D Powell, B Burgess, A Rivere, D Standen, P Parker, D Slatter, A Berkley, P Booth, A Henry.

Date	Comp.	Opponents	Att.	Score	Goalscorers
16/08	LP	Newport County	820	0 - 0	
19/08	LP	EASTBOURNE BOROUGH	629	1 - 2	Powell 90
23/08	LP	WORCESTER CITY	485	0 - 1	
25/08	LP	Chelmsford City	474	1 - 0	Berkeley 76
30/08	LP	STAFFORD RANGERS	507	2 - 1	**Booth 77 90**
02/09	LP	Cambridge City	410	3 - 0	**Booth 15 55**, Powell 83
06/09	LP	MOOR GREEN	563	2 - 1	Berkeley 6, **Booth 9**
09/09	LP	Dover Athletic	806	1 - 3	Berkeley 17
13/09	LP	Hinckley United	327	1 - 2	Berkeley 65
16/09	LP	HAVANT & WATERLOOVILLE	477	1 - 1	Jinadu 31
20/09	LP	Grantham Town	412	0 - 2	
27/09	**FA Cup Q2**	**Slough Town**	465	1 - 1	Powell 87
30/09	**FA Cup Q2 rep**	**SLOUGH TOWN**	418	4 - 1	Standen 19, **Booth 44 81**, Beard 90
04/10	LP	CHIPPENHAM TOWN	546	1 - 3	**Booth 55**
11/10	**FA Cup Q3**	**Folkestone Invicta**	734	1 - 1	Beard 37
14/10	**FA Cup Q3 rep**	**FOLKESTONE INVICTA**	602	2 - 2	Powell 7, **Booth 95**
18/10	LP	NEWPORT COUNTY	550	0 - 2	
21/10	LP	Eastbourne Borough	456	1 - 1	Standen 56
25/10	**FA Cup Q4**	**WESTON-SUPER-MARE**	678	2 - 3	**Booth 69[p] 72**
01/11	**FA Trophy 1**	**Eastbourne Borough**	533	2 - 1	Slatter 11, **Booth 41**
15/11	LP	Moor Green	257	2 - 0	**Booth 54**, Brickell 69
29/11	**FA Trophy 2**	**DOVER ATHLETIC**	502	0 - 1	
06/12	LP	Chippenham Town	579	2 - 0	Berkeley 45, Collins 69
13/12	LP	BATH CITY	502	2 - 1	Collins 45, Riviere 66
27/12	LP	CHELMSFORD CITY	760	1 - 0	**Booth 14**
01/01	LP	Crawley Town	1640	0 - 0	
03/01	LP	WESTON-SUPER-MARE	539	2 - 1	Strouts 45, Collins 61
10/01	LP	NUNEATON BOROUGH	592	2 - 1	**Booth 55[p] 77**
13/01	LP	GRANTHAM TOWN	536	0 - 1	
17/01	LP	Havant & Waterlooville	455	1 - 1	Slatter 52
24/01	LP	MERTHYR TYDFIL	649	**0 - 3**	
27/01	LP	Dorchester Town	331	0 - 2	
31/01	LP	Worcester City	805	1 - 3	Taylor 9
07/02	LP	HEDNESFORD TOWN	550	2 - 0	**Booth 47[p] 69**
14/02	LP	Nuneaton Borough	647	2 - 2	Riviere 23, Acton 72[og]
21/02	LP	TIVERTON TOWN	487	4 - 0	Riviere 19 90, Collins 32, **Booth 35**
24/02	LP	DORCHESTER TOWN	390	**6 - 1**	Riviere 1, Watts 12, Strouts 33, **Booth 48,** Henry 74, Taylor 88
06/03	LP	CAMBRIDGE CITY	630	0 - 1	
09/03	LP	Stafford Rangers	458	2 - 3	Collins 30, **Booth 34**
13/03	LP	Weymouth	1702	2 - 1	Riviere 10 27
20/03	LP	HINCKLEY UNITED	622	2 - 3	Collins 15, **Booth 22**
30/03	LP	Merthyr Tydfil	418	0 - 2	
03 /04	LP	DOVER ATHLETIC	672	2 - 1	Collins 22, Tyne 47
10 /04	LP	Weston-super-Mare	308	1 - 2	Collins 28[p]
12 /04	LP	CRAWLEY TOWN	**1138**	**0 - 3**	
17 /04	LP	Tiverton Town	518	2 - 2	Tyne 14, Collins 58
24 /04	LP	WEYMOUTH	705	2 - 2	Tyne 7, Riviere 39
27 /04	LP	Hednesford Town	504	2 - 1	Henry 28, Collins 85
01/05	LP	Bath City	1188	0 - 2	
		Average Home League Attendance:	**596**	68-68	Top Goalscorer: **Paul Booth 22** (16+5FAC+1FAT)

PLAYING SQUAD 2004-2005

Goalkeepers:
Martin Brennan (Cambridge Utd)

Defenders:
Tony Browne (Dover), Ian Wiles (Chelmsford), Matthew Lee (Gravesend), Andy Arnott (Dover), Danny Slatter (Chelmsford), Lew Watts (Gravesend),

Midfield:
Lee Spiller (Dover), Jamie Day (Dover), Gareth Street (Chelmsford), Danny Lye (Thurrock),

Forwards:
Stephen Hughes (Brentford), George Lay (Chelmsford), Tommy Tyne (Dover), Paul Booth (Gravesend), Phil Collins (Margate)

WESTON-super-MARE

CLUB OFFICIALS

President: D A Usher

Chairman: Paul Bliss

Secretary/Press Officer: Stuart Marshall
c/o Weston Super Mare FC
Tel: 01934 621618
Commercial Manager & Press Officer:
Alan White 07966 755545 (M)

2003-2004

Leading Goalscorer: Marc McGregor
Player of the Year: Stuart Slater

FACT FILE

Formed: 1899
Nickname: Seagulls
Sponsors:
Colours: White/blue/blue
Change colours: All yellow
Midweek matches: Wednesday
Reserves' League: Somerset Senior

FOOTBALL MANAGEMENT TEAM

Manager: Frank Gregan
Assistant Manager: David Mehew
Captain: Billy Clark
Physio: T.B.A.

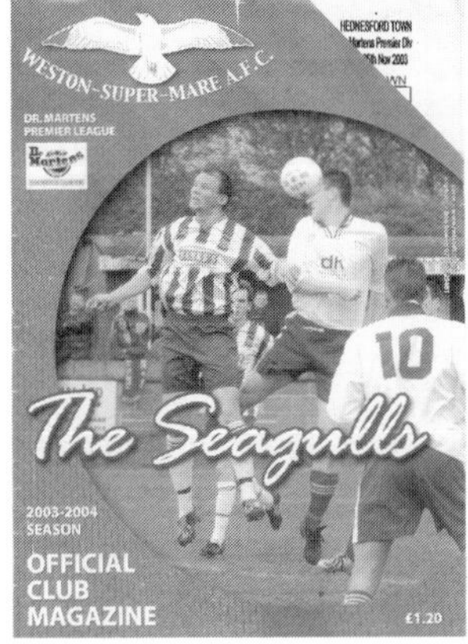

Pages: 32 Price: £1
Editors: Stuart Marshall & Phil Sheridan
Tel. 01934 621618

Local Press:
Bristol Evening Post, Western Daily Press
Local Radio: Somerset Sound, Radio Bristol

GROUND Woodspring Park, Winterstoke Road, Weston-super-Mare BS23 3YG
Tel: 01934 621618 FAX: 01934 622704

Directions: M5 Jct 21. A370 along dual carriageway to 4th roundabout.From South: M5 Jct 22, follow Weston signs for approx 7 miles, right at first r'bout(by Hospital), left at next r'bout, ground 1/2 mile on left. **From old ground take first pleft over mini roundabout along Winterstoke Road. Ground is half a mile on right.**

Capacity: 3,000 Seats: 278 Cover: 1,300

Clubhouse: Mon-Fri 7-11pm, Sat 12-11pm, Sun 12-3 & 7-11pm.
2 skittle alleys, 2bars. Bar meals and hot meals everyday

Club Shop: Sells a wide range of souvenirs & programmes.Contact Alan White at the club.

PREVIOUS
League: Western 1900-92 (Not continuous) **Name:** Borough of Weston-super-Mare
Grounds: The Great Ground, Locking Road 48-55, Langford Road 55-83 Woodspring Park 1984-2004

CLUB RECORDS
Attendance: 2,623 v Woking, FA Cup First Round Proper replay 23/11/93
At Langford Road: 2,500 v Bridgwater Town, FA Cup First Round Proper replay 1961-62
Win: 11-0 v Paulton Rovers **Defeat:** 1-12 v Yeovil Town Reserves
Career Goalscorer: Matthew Lazenby, 180 **Career Appearances:** Harry Thomas, 740
Transfer fee received: £20,000 Stuart Jones fromSheffield Wednesday 98 **Transfer fee paid:** None

BEST SEASON
FA Cup: 2nd Rd Proper 2003-04, 1-4 v Northampton Town (A)
FA Trophy: 4th Round 98-99, 03-04 **FA Vase:** Have not entered

HONOURS
Somerset Snr Cup 23-24 26-27; Western Lg Champions 91-92 (R-up 76-77), Lg Cup 76-77 (R-up 89-90), Merit Cup 76-77 77-78; Somerset Snr Lg (Reserves) Div 1 87-88 (R-up 90-91), Div 2 R-up 85-86, Div 3 84-85 Div 3 2000-01, Div 201-02.

Players progressing: Shaun Rouse (Carlisle United 94), Ian Maine, John Palmer(Bristol City),Wayne Brown(Chester City 97), Stuart Jones (Sheffield Wed 98), Ryan Souter (Bury 99)

Back Row (L-R): Luke Corbett, William Clark, Stuart Jones, Matthew Rose, Lee Jarman, Ian Howell.
Front Row: Jonathon French, David Gilroy, Lewis Hogg, Stuart Slater, Stephen Benton. Photo: Alan Coomes.

Date	Comp.	Opponents	Att.	Score	Goalscorers
16/08	LP	CAMBRIDGE CITY	244	1 - 0	McKeevor 56
19/08	LP	Bath City	809	1 - 3	Sorbara 30
23/08	LP	Dover Athletic	753	2 - 0	French 19, **Clark 80**
25/08	LP	CHIPPENHAM TOWN	432	1 - 2	Sorbara 90
30/08	LP	Moor Green	228	0 - 0	
02/09	LP	DORCHESTER TOWN	339	1 - 1	Sorbara 26
06/09	LP	Grantham Town	354	2 - 3	Davis 9, **Clark 77**
09/09	LP	WORCESTER CITY	450	1 - 0	McKeever 60
13/09	LP	NUNEATON BOROUGH	478	1 - 1	**Clark 72**
16/09	LP	Tiverton Town	505	0 - 2	
20/09	LP	WEYMOUTH	507	0 - 2	
27/09	**FA Cup Q2**	**DORCHESTER TOWN**	293	4 - 1	Davis 13, French 19[p], Sorbara 57, Slater 79
04/10	LP	Chelmsford City	329	0 - 0	
11/10	**FA Cup Q3**	**CHESHAM UNITED**	303	1 - 1	French 13
14/10	**FA Cup Q3 rep**	**Chesham United**	216	2 - 1	McKeevor 21, Sorbara 25
18/10	LP	HINCKLEY UNITED	243	2 - 2	Slater 65, Sorbara 87
22/10	LP	Newport County	539	4 - 1	McGregor 12[p] 78, Sorbara 19, French 58
25/10	**FA Cup Q4**	**Welling United**	678	3 - 2	**Clark 28,** McGregor 41 78
01/11	**FA Trophy 1**	**BROMSGROVE ROVERS**	265	1 - 1	French 25
04/11	**FA Trophy 1 rep**	**Bromsgrove Rovers**	233	3 - 0	Sorbara 19, Slater 68, Hodge 89
08/11	**FA Cup 1**	**Farnborough Town**	936	1 - 0	**Clark 5**
15/11	LP	TIVERTON TOWN	472	1 - 3	**Clark 7**
22/11	LP	Worcester City	729	**0 - 3**	
25/11	LP	HEDNESFORD TOWN	260	3 - 2	Slater 12, French 55, Simpkin 85[og]
29/11	**FA Trophy 2**	**BOGNOR REGIS TOWN**	270	1 - 0	Rose 10
06/12	**FA Cup 2**	**Northampton Town**	3948	1 - 4	**Clark 80**
13/12	LP	Weymouth	1156	0 - 0	
20/12	LP	DOVER ATHLETIC	252	0 - 1	
26/12	LP	Chippenham Town	641	1 - 1	Corbett 44
01/01	LP	MERTHYR TYDFIL	490	3 - 2	Corbett 26 67, **Gilroy 28**
03/01	LP	Welling United	539	1 - 2	Jarman 5
10/01	**FA Trophy 3**	**Gravesend & Northfleet**	670	2 - 2	**Gilroy 54**, Hunt 90
17/01	LP	BATH CITY	**599**	1 - 0	Hogg 32
20/01	**FA Trophy 3 rep**	**GRAVESEND & NORTHFLEET**	325	1 - 0	Corbett 87
24/01	LP	Dorchester Town	488	2 - 3	Corbett 61, Rose 76
27/01	LP	HAVANT & WATERLOOVILLE	207	2 - 0	**Gilroy 23[p]**, Friend 36
07/02	LP	Crawley Town	1426	0 - 2	
10/02	LP	Stafford Rangers	646	1 - 1	Rose 86
14/02	**FA Trophy 4**	**Telford United**	1095	2 - 4	Corbett 22 72
17/02	LP	Hinckley United	248	0 - 1	
21/02	LP	Havant & Waterlooville	308	1 - 0	**Gilroy 6**
28/02	LP	EASTBOURNE BOROUGH	257	2 - 1	Mings 29 76
06/03	LP	CHELMSFORD CITY	271	0 - 0	
09/03	LP	NEWPORT COUNTY	446	0 - 0	
16/03	LP	MOOR GREEN	258	2 - 3	McGregor 61, **Gilroy 85**
20/03	LP	Nuneaton Borough	656	1 - 1	McGregor 46
27/03	LP	GRANTHAM TOWN	272	2 - 0	Fudge 81, Hogg 90
03 /04	LP	Eastbourne Borough	577	0 - 1	
10 /04	LP	WELLING UNITED	308	2 - 1	Jarman 54 67
12 /04	LP	Merthyr Tydfil	607	2 - 1	NcGregor 60 **Clark84**
20 /04	LP	Cambridge City	307	1 - 1	**Gilroy 18**
24 /04	LP	Hednesford Town	526	2 - 2	McGregor 55, Cherry 88
29 /04	LP	STAFFORD RANGERS	217	**5 - 1**	**GILROY 9,29,72** McGregor 80 **Clark 88**
01/05	LP	CRAWLEY TOWN	579	1 - 2	McGregor 19
		Average Home League Attendance:	**361**	74-68	Top Goalscorers: **Billy Clark 9** (6+3FAC) & **Dave Gilroy 9**

PLAYING SQUAD 2004-2005

Goalkeepers:

Tony Malessa (Mangotsfield), Andy King (Odd Down)

Defenders:

Andy Robertson (Chippenham), Billy Clark (Newport Co), Lee Jarman (Barry), Steve Jenkins (Bath), Lewis Reed (Exeter)

Midfield:

Mark McKeever (Bristol R), Matthew Rose (Newport Co), Lewis Hogg (Barnet), Stuart Slater (Aberystwyth), Harry Kingston (Youth team), Bradley Thomas (Gloucester), Mark Cherry (Brislington)

Forwards:

Dave Gilroy (Bristol R), Jon French (Barry), Paul Hunt (Highworth), Adie Mings (Chippenham), Marc McGregor (Nuneaton), Ricky Hodge (Youth team)

WEYMOUTH

CLUB OFFICIALS

Chairman: Ian Ridley
President: Bob Lucas
Secretary: LizBell,106 WEsthill Road, Weymouth Dorset. DT4 9NF
Tel Nos: 01305 789705
or 07775 741077 (M)

FOOTBALL MANAGEMENT TEAM
Manager: Steve Claridge
Captain: Paul Buckle
Sports Therapist : Roger Hoare

FACT FILE
Formed: 1890 Nickname: The Terras
Sponsors: Style Holidays
Colours: Claret & sky/claret & sky
Change colours: White/claretr/white
Midweek matchday: Tuesday
Reserves' League: Pontins LeagueLcal
Press: Dorset Eve Echo Radio: Wessex FM

PROGRAMME
Pages: 64 Price: £2.00
Editor: Secretary

2003-2004
Player of the Year: Steve Tully
Top scorers: Lee Phillips & Steve Claridge

GROUND Wessex Stadium, Radipole Lane, Weymouth, Dorset DT4 9XJ Tel: 01305 785558

Directions: Arriving from Dorchester on A354, turn right following signs to Granby Industrial Estate at Safeway r'bout - ground on right as you enter estate
Capacity: 6,600 Cover: all sides Seats : 800

Clubhouse: Matchdays & functions. Hot & cold food available
Club Shop: Matchdays only. Progs & souvenirs. Contact Nigel Beckett (01305 813529

PREVIOUS **Leagues:** Dorset Lge, Western 1907-23 28-49, Southern 23-28 49-79, Alliance Premier 79-89
Ground: Recreation Ground (until 1987)

CLUB RECORDS **Attendance:** 4,995 v Manchester Utd, ground opening, 21/10/87
Career Goalscorer: W Farmer, Haynes. 275 **Career Appearances:** Tony Hobson 1,076
Transfer fee - Paid: £15,000 for Shaun Teale (Northwich) **Received:** £100,000 for Peter Guthrie (Spurs, 1988)

BEST SEASON **FA Cup:** Fourth Round 61-62, 0-2 v Preston N.E. (A). 1st rd on 29 occasions
League clubs defeated: Merthyr Town 24-25, Aldershot 49-50, Shrewsbury T. 56-57, Newport County 61-62, Cardiff C. 82-83
FA Amateur Cup: First Round 1900 **FA Trophy:** Fifth Round 2000-2001

HONOURS Alliance Prem Lg R-up 79-80, Lge Cup 81-82; Prem Inter Lg Cup R-up 87-88 QF 90-91; Southern Lge 64-65 65-66 R-up 54-55 77-78 ,03-04 Lg Cup 72-73 R-up x5, Southern Div R-up 91-92; Wstn Lg 22-23, Div 2 33-34 36-37, (R-up 35-36 47-48); Dorset Sen. Cup (27);Mark Frowde Cup (13)

Players progressing: A Smith (Accrington 61), G Bond/T Spratt/A Donnelly/M Cave(Torquay 61/65/67/68), P Leggett (Swindon 62), R Fogg (Aldershot 63), B Hutchinson (Lincoln 65), A Wool (Reading 71), A Beer (Exeter 74), B Iles(Chelsea 78), G Roberts (Spurs 80), T Gulliver/R Hill/N Townsend/P Morrell/JSmeulders (Bournemouth 66/67/79/83/84), T Agana (Watford), A Townsend/D Hughes(Southampton), S Claridge (C Palace), B McGorry/S Teale (Bournemouth), T Pounder/R Evans (Bristol Rvrs), R Pethick (Portsmouth 93)

2004/2005 - Back Row (L to R): Jamie Impey Lee Charles Robbie Pethick Simon Browne Matthew Bound Nathan Bunce. **Middle Row (L to R):** Roger Hoare (Sports Therapist) Joseba Barandiaran Lee Phillips Chuckki Eribenne Jason Mattthews Lee Philpott Dave Waterman Paul Gibbs Pete Dennis (Kit Man). **Front Row (L to R):** Steve Tully Martin Barlow Paul Buckle Steve Claridge (Player Manager) Gary Borthwick (Assistant Manager/Coach) Adam Wilde Ian Hutchinson Shaun Wilkinson.

Date	Comp.	Opponents	Att.	Score	Goalscorers
16/08	LP	Hednesford Town	610	0 - 0	
19/08	LP	NEWPORT COUNTY	1453	2 - 1	Hutchinson 25, Phillips 63
23/08	LP	NUNEATON BOROUGH	1379	1 - 1	**Claridge 24**
25/08	LP	Tiverton Town	873	2 - 1	Rees 45[og], Lamb 62
30/08	LP	Hinckley United	401	2 - 1	**Claridge 60**, Partridge 90
02/09	LP	BATH CITY	1567	3 - 3	**Claridge 4,** Tulley 7[p] 84[p]
06/09	LP	MERTHYR TYDFIL	1123	2 - 2	Lamb 22, Tully 28[p]
09/09	LP	Chippenham Town	704	3 - 1	**Claridge 3 39**, Nightingale 71
13/09	LP	CAMBRIDGE CITY	1454	2 - 1	**Claridge 19 37**
17/09	LP	Newport County	658	1 - 1	Nightingale 17
20/09	LP	Weston-super-Mare	507	2 - 0	Waldock 2, Philpott 30
27/09	**FA Cup Q2**	**Newport County**	769	2 - 3	**Claridge 39[p]**, Hutchinson 40
04/10	LP	STAFFORD RANGERS	1357	0 - 1	
18/10	LP	Worcester City	1380	2 - 2	Buckle 44, Nightingale 48
21/10	LP	HAVANT & WATERLOOVILLE	803	0 - 1	
25/10	LP	Bath City	882	2 - 0	Phillips 22, Tulley 33
01/11	**FA Trophy 1**	**MERTHYR TYDFIL**	994	5 - 2	Buckle 37 78, **Claridge 54 82,** Nightingale 75
08/11	LP	Merthyr Tydfil	451	4 - 0	Buckle 25, Partridge 49, Phillips 58 83
15/11	LP	EASTBOURNE BOROUGH	1159	1 - 0	**Claridge 59**
22/11	LP	HINCKLEY UNITED	1573	2 - 0	Phillips 19 43
29/11	**FA Trophy 2**	**ASHFORD TOWN (MIDDX)**	876	3 - 3	Partridge 9, Buckle 54[p], **Claridge 83**
02/12	**FA Trophy 2 rep**	**Ashford Town (Middx)**	405	3 - 1	**Claridge 67[p] 87,** Phillips 84
06/12	LP	Chelmsford City	505	3 - 1	Buckle 19, Hutchinson 31, **Claridge 55**
13/12	LP	WESTON-SUPER-MARE	1156	0 - 0	
26/12	LP	DORCHESTER TOWN	**3734**	**8 - 0**	Browne 6, **CLARIDGE 29 52 53**, **PHILLIPS 55 81 84[p],** Phillipott 90
01/01	LP	Dorchester Town	4116	2 - 2	**Claridge 46[p],** Nightingale 73
03/01	LP	CRAWLEY TOWN	2016	0 - 1	
10/01	**FA Trophy 3**	**Lewes**	1077	8 - 5	**Claridge 9 72**,Buckle 13,Nightingale 20 61 63, Phillips 80 89
17/01	LP	HEDNESFORD TOWN	1474	2 - 0	Pethick 70, Phillips 82
24/01	LP	Dover Athletic	1216	3 - 2	Pethick 43, Yetton 53, Phillips 70
31/01	**FA Trophy 4**	**ALTRINCHAM**	1722	0 - 2	
07/02	LP	Cambridge City	811	0 - 1	
21/02	LP	Eastbourne Borough	839	1 - 2	Philpott 17
28/02	LP	MOOR GREEN	1402	3 - 0	Phillips 1, 46, **Claridge 6**
02/03	LP	DOVER ATHLETIC	1358	3 - 0	**Claridge 7, 90**, Buckle 77,
06/03	LP	Crawley Town	4522	1 - 2	Tully 79
09/03	LP	Moor Green	383	2 - 1	Tully 75, Buckle 83
13/03	LP	WELLING UNITED	1702	1 - 2	Nightingale 68
16/03	LP	WORCESTER CITY	1403	3 - 1	Nightingale 10. 16, **Claridge 57**
20/03	LP	Grantham Town	398	1 - 1	**Claridge 85**
23/03	LP	Nuneaton Borough	836	3 - 4	Scott 44[og], **Claridge 60**, Phillips 75
27/03	LP	CHIPPENHAM TOWN	1416	0 - 1	
03 /04	LP	Stafford Rangers	788	2 - 1	Phillips 55, Nightingale 71
10 /04	LP	Havant & Waterlooville	855	**1 - 4**	Phillips 81
12 /04	LP	TIVERTON TOWN	1465	1 - 1	Wilkinson 26
17 /04	LP	CHELMSFORD CITY	1101	2 - 2	Phillips 15 89[p]
24 /04	LP	Welling United	705	2 - 2	Pethick 89, Lamb 90
01/05	LP	GRANTHAM TOWN	1188	1 - 0	Buckle 74
		Average Home League attendance:	**1,519**	99-68	Top Goalscorer: **Steve Claridge 28** (19+1FAC+7FAT)

PLAYING SQUAD 2004-2005

Goalkeepers: Jason Matthews (Clevedon),

Defenders:

David Waterman (Oxford Utd), John Waldock (Sunderland), Robbie Pethick (Brighton), Jamie Impey (Forest Green), Scott Dennis (Portland), Nathan Bunce (Stevenage), Matthew Bound (Oxford Utd), Simon Browne (Salisbury), Steve Tully (Torquay)

Midfield:

Lee Philpott (Hull), Ian Hutchinson (Halifax), Paul Buckle (Aldershot), Martin Barlow (Telford Utd), Lee Charles (Aldershot), Shaun Wilkinson (Havant & Waterlooville)

Forwards:

Steve Claridge (Millwall), Chukki Eribenne (Havant & Waterlooville), John Lamb (Youth team), Lee Phillips (Plymouth), Adam Wilde (Worcester)

FOOTBALL LEAGUE

STEP 1

FOOTBALL CONFERENCE

STEP 2

CONFERENCE NORTH

CONFERENCE SOUTH

STEP 3

NORTHERN PREMIER

SOUTHERN PREMIER

ISTHMIAN PREMIER

STEP 4

NORTHERN PREMIER DIV.1

SOUTHERN LEAGUE EAST

SOUTHERN LEAGUE WEST

ISTHMIAN DIVISION 1

STEP 5/6

STEP 7

NORTHERN PREMIER LEAGUE

SPONSORED BY: UNIBOND

President: N White F.S.C.A. **Chairman:** Peter Maude

Vice Chairman: Tom Culshaw **Chief Executive:** Duncan Bayley

Secretary & Treasurer: R D Bayley, 22 Woburn Drive, Hale, Altrincham, Cheshire WA15 8LZ Tel: 0161 980 7007 Fax: 0161 904 8850

Press Secretary: P Bradley, 7 Guest Road, Prestwich, Manchester M25 7DJ Tel: 0161 798 5198 Fax: 0161 773 0930

REVIEW OF THE SEASON

Last season highlighted a definite power swing from the traditional North West giants like Altrincham, Runcorn and Marine to new boys on the block from the East Midlands such as Hucknall Town, Alfreton Town, Harrogate Town and Worksop Town.

A couple of big names from the North West in Hyde United (champions of Division One) and Witton Albion (5th) had halted their personal slides but famous clubs such as ex Conference giants Altrincham and Runcorn were stuck in mid- table of the premier division while the East Midlands 'gang' certainly took advantage and made their presence felt.

Unfortunately for manager Steve Burr and his ex Macclesfield boss Peter Wragg, who was his assistant at Hucknall, the club's ground facilities just were not good enough for the Nationwide Conference and promotion as worthy champions was forfeited. This must have been a terrible anti climax for the management and their players and it's not surprising that there have been many personnel changes in the close season.

The new structure brought with it a series of play offs which created very exciting battles and often extra time and even penalties. Ashton United will have felt upset by not qualifying after remaining in the safety zone of the division until the last week of the season, but compared with Hereford United they couldn't complain. Bradford P.A.eventually beat Burscough in extra time to finish up in the Nationwide North but the system worked and was enjoyed by most.

Burscough, the F.A.Trophy holders started very slowly and looked doomed in the league. However, they rallied and although beaten by their Villa Park final opponents in their first defence of their Trophy title, their form improved and being involved in the exciting battles was a bonus. In fact the best Unibond challenges in the F.A.Trophy came from Altrincham who beat Runcorn, Southport and Southern League pacesetters Weymouth (away) before losing in the Fifth Round to Shrewsbury Town. With them in the Fifth Round were Stalybridge Celtic who had beaten Redditch United , Leigh RMI and Marine and then had been well beaten by Canvey Island.

The League were represented by five clubs in the First Round Proper of the F.A.Cup, but Bradford P.A, Gainsborough Trinity, Lancaster City, Stalybridge Celtic and Whitley Bay all failed at this stage.

Barrow were by far the best supported club and the League were once again given superb support from their main sponsors Unibond, who rewarded success, sportsmanship and goalscoring while Endsleigh Insurance also presented their goalscoring awards to Harrogate Town and Gateshead.

Although there have been structure changes, there will always be a long and arduous journey for clubs travelling from the north west to east and back again but the spirit still seems to be excellent and there is one aspect in which the Northern League definitely deserves credit - their weekly bulletin has the best statistics, is always ion time and contains everything that the public and media need. Thank you.

T.W.

PREMIER DIVISION FINAL LEAGUE TABLE 2003-04

		P	W	D	L	F	A	Pts
1.	Hucknall Town	44	29	8	7	83	38	95
2.	Droylsden	44	26	8	10	96	64	86
3.	Barrow	44	22	14	8	82	52	80
4.	Alfreton Town	44	23	9	12	73	43	78
5.	Harrogate Town	44	24	5	15	79	63	77
6.	Southport	44	20	10	14	71	52	70
7.	Worksop Town	44	19	13	12	69	50	70
8.	Lancaster City	44	20	9	15	62	49	69
9.	Vauxhall Motors	44	19	10	15	78	75	67
10.	Gainsborough Trinity	44	17	13	14	70	52	64
11.	Stalybridge Celtic	44	18	10	16	72	66	64
12.	Altrincham	44	16	15	13	66	51	63
13.	Runcorn FC Halton	44	16	13	15	67	63	61
14.	Ashton United	44	17	8	19	59	79	59
15.	Whitby Town	44	14	11	19	55	70	53
16.	Marine	44	13	12	19	62	74	51
17.	Bradford Park Avenue*	44	12	14	18	48	62	50
18.	Spennymoor United	44	14	6	24	55	93	48
19.	Burscough	44	10	15	19	47	67	45
20.	Radcliffe Borough	44	12	6	26	74	99	42
21.	Blyth Spartans	44	10	10	24	54	74	40
22.	Frickley Athletic	44	11	7	26	51	83	40
23.	Wakefield & Emley	44	8	6	30	45	99	30

Qualify for Conference North (positions 1–13)

* Promoted to Conference North via play off.

Bradford Park Avenue's Craig Smith hooks the ball over Burscough's Marvin Molyneux.

Photo: Darren Thomas

PLAY OFFS

QUARTER-FINALS

Ashton United 2 Hyde United 1
Marine 1 Burscough 3
Whitby Town 2 Radcliffe Borough 2
Bradford Park Avenue 3 Spennymoor United 1

SEMI-FINALS

Ashton United 1 Bradford Park Avenue 2
Radcliffe Borough 0 Burscough 2

THE FINAL

Bradford Park Avenue 2 Burscough 0

PREMIER DIVISION 03-04		1	2	3	4	5	6	7	8	9	10	11	12	13	14	15	16	17	18	19	20	21	22	23
1	ALFRETON TOWN		0-0	5-0	1-1	2-1	1-1	1-0	4-2	1-2	3-1	2-0	2-1	3-0	4-0	0-0	0-2	0-2	1-1	3-1	5-1	2-1	3-0	2-1
2	ALTRINCHAM	0-1		1-2	1-1	1-2	1-0	3-0	1-0	1-1	2-2	0-0	2-3	0-0	3-3	4-1	1-0	1-0	1-1	3-3	3-1	1-2	4-0	2-1
3	ASHTON UNITED	1-1	0-2		1-2	2-0	0-2	0-0	1-1	3-2	1-1	3-4	1-6	2-1	4-3	3-3	4-2	2-1	1-2	2-1	0-1	2-3	1-3	0-3
4	BARROW	1-2	2-1	3-0		3-0	4-0	3-3	2-1	3-1	3-0	1-2	1-0	4-3	1-1	2-0	1-0	1-1	2-0	0-2	0-1	3-2	0-0	1-0
5	BLYTH SPARTANS	1-0	2-2	2-0	0-2		0-0	0-1	1-5	1-3	1-1	3-4	1-2	0-0	5-0	1-0	3-3	1-4	0-2	0-1	3-6	1-0	1-1	3-3
6	BRADFORD PARK AVENUE	0-1	1-1	2-1	2-2	1-1		0-2	0-2	0-0	0-0	2-3	1-2	0-2	1-1	1-1	1-1	0-1	0-0	2-3	6-2	1-2	2-3	0-1
7	BURSCOUGH	4-1	3-1	1-2	1-1	1-2	1-1		1-3	3-1	0-0	1-0	0-1	0-1	0-0	3-6	1-3	0-3	2-1	0-0	3-1	1-1	1-1	0-0
8	DROYLSDEN	2-1	1-4	1-2	1-1	3-3	3-0	2-0		4-0	2-1	3-1	3-1	0-0	4-2	5-4	1-2	3-2	2-0	2-0	2-1	3-1	2-1	2-2
9	FRICKLEY ATHLETIC	0-3	1-1	1-2	4-2	2-1	0-1	2-0	0-3		0-0	0-0	0-1	0-2	4-3	3-0	1-2	1-2	3-2	1-2	0-2	2-1	3-1	1-1
10	GAINSBOROUGH TRINITY	2-4	2-3	3-0	0-0	2-0	3-3	4-1	1-2	3-0		2-0	2-1	3-2	2-0	6-2	0-1	1-2	3-1	0-0	0-0	3-0	2-2	2-1
11	HARROGATE TOWN	1-0	1-0	2-1	2-1	2-1	0-1	2-1	4-4	2-1	0-2		1-2	0-1	4-1	3-0	1-1	3-1	3-1	4-3	3-2	5-0	1-0	0-2
12	HUCKNALL TOWN	3-3	2-1	2-0	3-1	1-0	0-0	1-0	1-1	3-0	2-0	1-0		3-0	1-1	1-1	1-0	4-0	2-1	1-3	2-0	0-1	1-0	3-2
13	LANCASTER CITY	0-1	1-0	1-1	0-3	1-1	1-3	4-0	2-1	1-1	0-1	1-4	3-1		3-1	4-2	0-1	1-0	6-0	2-1	0-0	3-0	4-3	2-0
14	MARINE	0-1	0-1	0-2	1-2	1-0	2-0	4-0	1-2	2-1	3-1	2-2	1-1	1-1		3-2	1-3	1-1	1-3	0-2	3-2	3-0	2-2	0-2
15	RADCLIFFE BOROUGH	1-0	1-3	1-2	2-3	2-3	2-0	1-2	4-2	4-2	2-1	3-1	1-6	0-2	3-1		1-2	1-3	1-1	3-2	1-2	4-1	0-5	1-2
16	RUNCORN HALTON	2-2	0-3	1-2	0-0	1-0	1-2	0-0	2-2	2-0	2-2	4-1	1-2	0-1	0-2	2-2		1-1	1-2	3-0	1-1	5-3	1-1	2-3
17	SOUTHPORT	1-0	2-2	0-0	1-1	1-0	0-1	2-1	4-1	3-1	2-0	3-2	1-1	3-0	0-0	2-1	0-3		2-3	2-3	1-1	1-1	3-0	2-3
18	SPENNYMOOR UNITED	1-0	2-1	3-2	2-4	0-5	2-4	0-2	0-1	3-2	0-6	1-5	1-3	0-1	0-2	3-1	2-1	0-2		1-3	2-1	4-4	2-0	1-1
19	STALYBRIDGE CELTIC	3-0	1-0	1-1	2-2	2-0	2-0	1-1	2-1	5-0	2-0	1-2	1-2	0-3	1-1	0-2	2-2	2-1	0-2		3-4	3-3	1-3	0-3
20	VAUXHALL MOTORS	2-0	1-1	1-2	1-1	2-1	6-2	3-2	2-4	2-1	0-2	3-0	1-3	2-1	1-0	0-5	6-0	3-2	4-2	1-1		1-0	1-1	1-1
21	WAKEFIELD & EMLEY	0-3	2-0	1-2	2-5	1-2	0-1	2-2	0-2	0-2	0-2	0-2	0-3	1-0	0-4	2-1	3-5	0-1	2-0	1-3	0-1		0-3	1-1
22	WHITBY TOWN	0-4	2-3	0-1	3-2	2-1	0-1	1-1	1-2	2-1	2-1	0-2	0-0	2-1	1-2	1-0	1-0	0-5	1-0	0-2	1-1	2-1		2-3
23	WORKSOP TOWN	0-0	0-0	3-0	2-4	1-0	1-2	1-1	1-3	3-0	0-0	1-0	0-3	0-0	1-2	4-1	0-1	1-0	4-0	2-1	4-3	4-0	1-1	

LEAGUE CUP

FIRST ROUND

Ashton United	v	Leek Town	1-1* 6-5p
Bamber Bridge	v	Lancaster City	1-2
Bishop Auckland	v	Blyth Spartans	2-0
Burscough	v	Colwyn Bay	5-0
Guiseley	v	Wakefield & Emley	4-1
Hyde United	v	Altrincham	0-1
Kidsgrove Athletic	v	Matlock Town	0-2
Lincoln United	v	Gainsborough Trinity	2-1
Marine	v	Runcorn Halton	2-0
Ossett Town	v	Farsley Celtic	3-1
Rossendale United	v	Kendal Town	4-1
Stocksbridge P.S.	v	Frickley Athletic	1-3
Workington	v	Gateshead	2-1*

SECOND ROUND

Ashton United	v	Southport	1-3
Bradford Park Ave.	v	Bishop Auckland	1-6
Droylsden	v	Chorley	4-1
Frickley Athletic	v	Hucknall Town	4-5
Guiseley	v	Harrogate Town	2-1
Lancaster City	v	Radcliffe Borough	1-2
Lincoln United	v	Alfreton Town	2-1
Marine	v	Burscough	1-2
Matlock Town	v	Belper Town	1-0
Spennymoor Utd	v	Ossett Town	4-2
Stalybridge Celtic	v	Prescot Cables	1-2
Vauxhall Motors	v	Rossendale United	3-0
Whitby Town	v	Bridlington Town	2-1
Witton Albion	v	Barrow	4-1
Workington	v	Altrincham	0-0* 1-3p
Worksop Town	v	North Ferriby United	3-4

THIRD ROUND

Altrincham	v	Vauxhall Motors	1-2
Bishop Auckland	v	Prescot Cables	4-0
Burscough	v	Spennymoor United	4-2
Hucknall Town	v	Lincoln United	2-1
Matlock Town	v	North Ferriby United	2-1
Southport	v	Guiseley	2-3
Whitby Town	v	Radcliffe Borough	6-2
Witton Albion	v	Droylsden	0-1

QUARTER-FINALS

Bishop Auckland	v	Burscough	2-1*
Matlock Town	v	Guiseley	1-0
Vauxhall Motors	v	Hucknall Town	0-1
Whitby Town	v	Droylsden	1-2

SEMI-FINALS

Droylsden	v	Bishop Auckland	3-2
Hucknall Town	v	Matlock Town	2-1

THE FINAL

(1st leg 14th April)

Droylsden	v	Hucknall Town	2-0

(2nd leg 27th April)

Hucknall Town	v	Droylsden	1-2

PRESIDENT'S CUP

FIRST ROUND

Alfreton Town	v	Harrogate Town	0-2
Barrow	v	Bradford Park Avenue	3-1
Belper Town	v	Marine	1-3
Bridlington Town	v	Rossendale United	3-1
Chorley	v	Lancaster City	1-2
Ossett Town	v	Worksop Town	0-6
Stalybridge Celtic	v	Ashton United	3-4*
Workington	v	Frickley Athletic	3-1

QUARTER-FINALS

Ashton United	v	Barrow	0-0* 2-4p
Bridlington Town	v	Harrogate Town	0-3
Marine	v	Worksop Town	1-0
Workington	v	Lancaster	1-0

SEMI-FINALS

Marine	v	Barrow	0-2
Workington	v	Harrogate	4-4* 4-3p

THE FINAL

(First leg 7th April)

Barrow	v	Workington	3-2

(Second leg 27th April)

Workington	v	Barrow	4-3*

Barrow win on away goals

CHAIRMAN'S CUP

QUARTER-FINALS

Blyth Spartans	v	Kidsgrove Athletic	0-1
Hyde United	v	Wakefield & Emley	2-1*
Leek Town	v	Farsley Celtic	3-2
Stocksbridge P. S.	v	Gainsborough Trinity	0-3

SEMI-FINALS

Hyde United	v	Kidsgrove Athletic	3-1
Leek Town	v	Gainsborough Trinity	2-0

THE FINAL

(1st leg 7th April)

Hyde United	v	Leek Town	1-0

(2nd leg 14th April)

Leek Town	v	Hyde United	0-1

Gedlin Town defend in depth as **Alfreton Town**'s Grant Brown (No 5) heads goalwards. Photo: Bill Wheatcroft

Blyth Spartans keeper Craig Turns is covered by No 11 Ian Crutwell but they both fail to stop **Alfreton Town** ace goalscorer Mick Godber. Photo: Bill Wheatcroft

...ACTION EXTRA...ACTION EXTRA...ACTION EXTRA...

Ossett Town's Paul Fleming clears under pressure from **Workington**' Brian Dawson. Photo: Alan Watson

Emeka Nwadike is perfectly balanced to get his shot in for **Alfreton Town** against **Spennymoor United.**
Photo: Bill Wheatcroft

BAMBER BRIDGE

CLUB OFFICIALS

President: Arthur Jackson
Chairman: Nigel Webster
Directors: Nigel Webster, Dave Spencer, Dennis Allen, Gerry Lawson, Brian Gitty and Mike Boardman.
Secretary : George Halliwell, Irongate, Brownedge Road, Bamber Bridge, Preston PR5 6UX
Tel: 01772 454762 (H) 07929 231945 (M)
Commercial Manager: Keith Brindle

FOOTBALL MANAGEMENT TEAM

Manager: Paul Byron
Asst Manager: Andy Farley
Physio: Andy Hosgood

FACT FILE

Founded: 1952
Nickname: Brig
Sponsors: T.B.A.
Colours: White/black/black
Change Colours: Yellow/blue/yellow
Midweek Matches: Tuesday
Reserves' League: Lancashire Legue
Website: www.bamberbridge-fc,co.uk

GROUND Irongate Ground, Brownedge Road, Bamber Bridge, Preston, Lancs.PR5 6UX
Tel Nos: Club Office 01772-909690; Social Club 01772-909695; Fax No. 01772-909691

Directions: M6 Junct 29, A6 (Bamber Bridge Bypass) towards Walton-le-Dale, to r'bout, A6 London Road to next r'bout, 3rd exit signed Bamber Bridge (Brownedge Road) and first right. Ground 100 yds at end of road on left. Just over a mile from Bamber Bridge (BR).
Capacity: 3,000 Seats: 1008 Cover: 800 Club Shop: Yes
Clubhouse: On ground. Open all day Saturday matchdays, every evening and Sunday lunch. Refreshment cabin on ground serves hot & cold drinks & snacks etc during matches.

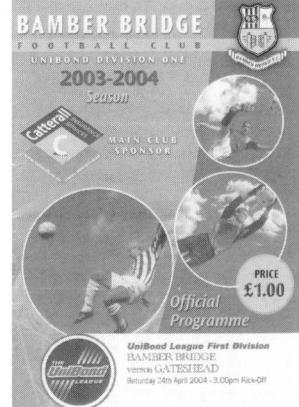

PROGRAMME

Pages: 36 Price: £1
Editor: Dave Rowland (01772 312987)

PREVIOUS **Leagues:** Preston & District 52-90; North West Counties 90-93.
Grounds: King George V Ground, Higher Walton 1952-86. **Names:** None

CLUB RECORDS **Attendance:** 2,300 v Czech Republic, Pre-Euro 96 Friendly.
Win: 8-0 v Curzon Ashton N.W.Co. 94-95. **Defeat:** Unknown
Fee Paid: £10,000 to Horwich R.M.I.for Mark Edwards.
Fee Received: £15,000 from Wigan Athletic for Tony Back, 1995.

BEST SEASON **FA Vase:** Semi Final 91-92 (lost 0-2 on agg to Wimborne Tn).
FA Cup: 2nd Round Proper, 99-00, v Cambridge United (A) Lost 0-1

HONOURS Nth West Co's Lge R-up 92-93 (Div 2 91-92, F'lit Cup R-up 91-92); Preston &Dist Lge(4) (R-up (3); Guildhall Cup 78-79 80-81 84-85 89-90, R-up 77-78 79-80 87-88; Lancs Amtr Shield 81-82, R-up 80-81 89-90; Lancastrian Brigade Cup 76-77 89-90 90-91; A.T.S.Lancs Trophy 94-95, R-Up 95-96, NPL Chall Cup 94-95; NPL 1st Div R-Up 94-95; NPL Prem Div Champ 95-96.

Back row, left to right: Billy Abbott, Stuart Shepherd, Jimmy King, Graham Bennett, David Hankin, Stuart Honor, Simon Woodward, Cyril Sharrock, Alex Porter, Andy Hosgood (physio) and Phil Brown.
Front row: Phil Robinson, Stewart Clitheroe, Mark Wane, Andy Farley (Assistant player-manager), Paul Byron (Manager), Dave Leaver, Danny Kent, Phil Miller and Jez Baldwin.

BISHOP AUCKLAND

Pages: 28 Price: £1.20
Editor: Bobby Wake (01388 609428)

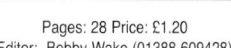

CLUB OFFICIALS

Chairman: Terry Jackson
Vice-Chairman: Tony Duffy.
Secretary/Press Off.: Tony Duffy, 90 Escomb Road, Bishop Auckland, Co. Durham, DL14 6TZ
Commercial Manager: Lynn Dentith.

FOOTBALL MANAGEMENT TEAM

Manager: Brian Honour
Asst Mgr: Tony Boylan
Physio: Alan Trennery

FACT FILE

Formed: 1886 Nickname: Bishops
Sponsors: EBAC
Colours: All Sky & Navy blue
Change colours: .
Midweek home matchday: Wednesday.
Reserve Team: None.
Local Press: Northern Echo, Evening Gazette, Newcastle Journal.
Local Radio: Radio Cleveland, Radio Metro, Radio Newcastle, Century Radio

2003-04

Top Scorer: Stuart Irvine
Ps.o.Y.:Stuart Irvine & Shaun Hope
2004-2005 Brian Rowe

GROUND DETAILS

Address: C/o Spennymoor United,Brewery Field, Durham Road, Spennymoor, Co.Durham.
Tel No: -1388 814100
Directions: As for Spennymoor United
Clubhouse: Yes, B.A. Social Club 0138 8603686

PREVIOUS **Leagues**: Northern Alliance 1890-91 and Northern League 1893-1988.

CLUB RECORDS **Attendance:** 17,000 v Coventry, FA Cup 2nd Rd 6/12/52. **Appearances:** Bob Hardisty.
Win: 12-3 v Kingstonian, Amateur Cup 55. **Defeat:** 0-7 v Halifax Tn FA Cup 2nd Rd 66-67.
Fee Paid: £2,000. **Fee Received:** £9,000 for David Laws from Weymouth.

BEST SEASON **FA Amateur Cup:** Winners 10 times **FA Trophy:** Quarter Finals 78-79, 88-89, 96-97, 99-00
FA Cup: 4th Rd 54-55, 1-3 v York City (H).
League clubs defeated: Crystal Palace, Ipswich 54-55, Tranmere 56-57.

HONOURS FA Amateur Cup 1895-96, 1899-1900 13-14 20-22 34-35 38-39 54-56 57-58 (R-up(8)01-02 05-06 10-11 14-15 45-46 49-51 53-54); Northern Lg(19) 1898-99 1900-02 08-10 11-12 20-21 30-31 38-39 46-47 49-52 53-5666-67 84-86, R-up (17) 78-79 86-87 96-97, Lg Cup(7) 49-51 53-55 59-60 66-67 75-76); D'ham Chall Cup 1891-92 98-99 1930-31 38-39 51-52 55-56 61-62 66-67 84-8585-86 87-88 96-97, 98-99 HFS Loans Lg Div 1 R-up 88-89. Plus tournaments in Isle of Man, Spain, Portugal etc

Players Progressing: B Paisley (Liverpool), F Richardson & S O'Connell (Chelsea 46 & 54), R Hardisty & K Williamson (Darlimgton 46 & 52), W Shergold (Newport 47), N Smith (Fulham 48), R Steel & K Murray (Darlington 50),A Adey (Doncaster 50), F Palmer & A Stalker (Gateshead 51 & 58), A Sewell(Bradford City 54), G Barker (Southend 54), J Major (Hull 55), H Sharratt(Oldham 56), F McKenna (Leeds 56), J Barnwell (Arsenal 56), D Lewis (Accrington Stanley 57), C Cresswell (Carlisle 58), W Bradley (Man Utd), L Brown(Northampton), P Baker (Southampton), M Gooding (Rotherham), K Nobbs & A Toman(Hartlepool), P Hinds (Dundee Utd), Jeff Smith (Bolton W.) 2001.Danny Mellanby (Darlington2001 M.Nelson (Bury) 2001

BLYTH SPARTANS

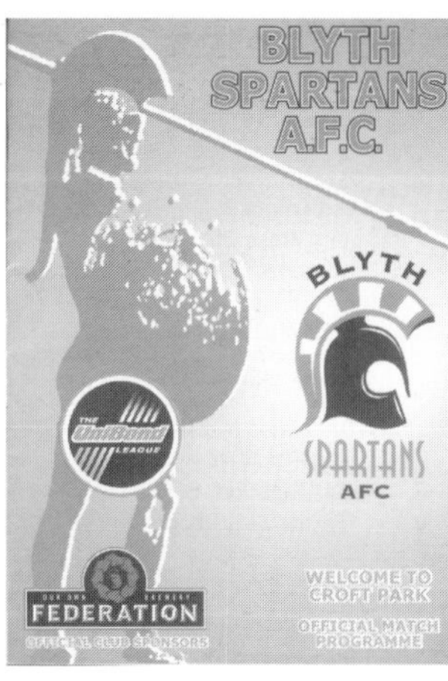

CLUB OFFICIALS

Chairman: Tommy Hedley

Secretary & General Manager:
Ian Evans, c/o Croft Park, Plessey Road, Blyth NE24 3 JE, NE24 2HJ. Tel: 01670 360820.

Match Day Secretary: Jeff Young

Press Officer: Brian Grey

FOOTBALL MANAGEMENT TEAM

Manager:Paul Baker

Assistant Manager: T.B.A.

FACT FILE

Formed: 1899 Nickname: Spartans

Sponsors: Federation Brewery.

Colours:Green & white stripes/black

Change colours: Yellow

Midweek Matches: Tuesday

Local Press:Newcastle Journal & Evening Chronicle.

2003-004

Top Goalscorer: Anthony Woodhouse

P.o.Y.: Craig Turns

2004-2005 Captain: Richard Forster

GROUND: Croft Park, Blyth, Northumberland. Tel: 01670 354818 FAX: 01670 545592
Website: www.spartans.freeserve.co.uk

Directions: Through Tyne tunnel heading north on A19, take Cramlington turn A1061, follow signs for Newsham/Blyth. Right fork at railway gates in Newsham, down Plessey Rd, ground can be seen on left. Buses X24, X25, X26, X1 from Newcastle.

Capacity: 6,000 Seats: 300 Cover: 1,000

Clubhouse: Open every night plus Saturday & Sunday lunch & matchdays. Available for wedding functions. Pies & sandwiches available.

Souvenir Shop: Large selection. Contact: Bob Bell (01670 369144)

Pages: 64 Price: £1
Editor: Brian Grey Tel: 0191 2650119

PREVIOUS Leagues: Northumberland 01-07; Northern Alliance 07-13, 46-47; North Eastern13-14 19-39 47-58 62-64; Northern Combination 45-46; Midland 58-60; Northern Counties 60-62; Northern 62-94. Names: None Grounds: None

CLUB RECORDS Fee Received: £30,000 for Les Mutrie (Hull City) 1979. Fee Paid:

BEST SEASON **FA Trophy:** Quarter-Final replay 79-80 82-83. **FA Amateur Cup:** Semi-Final 71-72.
FA Cup: 5th Rd replay 77-78 (lost to Wrexham). 1-1 (A) 1-2 (H) at Newcastle United

League clubs defeated Gillingham 22-23, Crewe Alexandra,Stockport County 71-72, Chesterfield, Stoke City 77-78, Bury 95-96.

HONOURS Nth Lg(10) 72-73 74-76 79-84 86-88 94-95, (R-up 71-72 73-74 77-78 84-85 94-95),Lg Cup(5) 72-73 77-79 81-82 91-92 94-95, Presidents Cup 96-97; Nth Eastern Lg35-36 (R-up 22-23, Lg Cup 49-50 54-55); Northumberland Lg 03-04; Northern All.08-09 12-13 (R-up 46-47); Northumberland Snr Cup (19); Shields Gazette Cup 95-96.

Players Progressing: William McGlen (Manchester Utd 46), Joe Roddom (Chesterfield 48), Henry Mills (Huddersfield 48), John Allison (Reading 49), James Kelly (Watford 49), Robert Millard (Reading 49), Jim Kerr (Lincoln 52), James Milner (Burnley 52), John Hogg (Portsmouth 54), John Allison(Chesterfield 55), John Inglis (Gateshead 57), John Longland (Hartlepool 58),Alan Shoulder (Newcastle 79), Les Mutrie (Hull City 79), Steve Carney(Newcastle 80), Craig Liddle (Middlesbrough 94), Paul O'Connor (Hartlepool 95). Gustavo Di Lella (Hartlepool 98)

BRIDLINGTON TOWN

CLUB OFFICIALS

Company & Club Secretary:
Chris Bemrose, 16 North Back Lane,
Bridlington, E. Yorks. YO16 7BA
Tel: 01262 604036 (H & F) 01262 676836(B)
e-mail Admin@brudtownafc.freeserve.co.uk

President: Barrie Garton

Chairman & Man.Director:
Gary Wilkinson
Tel: 07767 402745

Directors: D. Wilkinson, C. Webb & D Brewer

Match Sec.: Jonathon Bemrose
Tel: 01262 673995 (H) 01262 408224 (B)

FACT FILE

Founded: 1994
Sponsors: Barton Engineering,
PBS Construction (N.E.) Ltd
Wilkinson Caravans
Colours: All Red
Change Colours: All White
Midweek Matchday: Tuesday
Website: www.bridtownafc.freeserve.co.uk

2003-2004

Top Goalscorer: Paul Palmer 30
Players of the Year: Steve Robinson (Manager), Martin Thacker (Players) and Craug Suddaby (Supporters)

40 pages Price £1.00
Editor: Jonathon Bemrose

FOOTBALL MANAGEMENT TEAM

Team Manager: Billy Heath
Asst Manager: Mark Carroll
Coach: Pete Smurthwaite
Captain: Lee Harper

GROUND Queensgate Stadium, Queensgate, Bridlington YO16 7LN
Tel: 01262 606879

Capacity: 3,000 Seats: 742 Covered Standing 250 Executive Boxes: 2 Floodlights: Yes

Directions **From south on A165** - Pass golf course, straight over lights. Turn right at r'about by B&Q. Turn left at next lights & over rlwy bridge. At r'about bear left and then straight on up Quay Road. After lights turn right into Queensgate & ground is 800yds on right.
From south & west via A614 (formerly A166) - Straight on at lights (Hosp. on right). At r'about straight on to mini-r'about & take 2nd exit rt.. Over the first lights,left at next lights into Queensgate.Ground 800yds on rt.

Clubhouse: Open every evening & all day Sat & Sun

Club Shop: open on matchdays only

PREVIOUS **Leagues:** Driffield Lg.; East Riding County Lg., Northern Counties East -2003
Names: Grays Inn 1986, Greyhound F.C. 1988

CLUB RECORDS **Attendance:** 432 for an F.A. Sunday Cup Semi-Final 3.3.2000
Appearances: Neil Grimson 200+ (87-97)
Goalscorer: Neil Grimson
Win: 15-1 v Rudston (A), Driffield Lg Cup 94-95

BEST SEASON **FA Cup:** 4th Qual. Rd 02-03, 1-4 v Southport (A)
FA Vase: 6th Rd 02-03, 1-2 v Brigg Town (A)

HONOURS: E. Riding Sen. Co. Cup 96-97, 01-02. E Riding Co. Lg Div. 1 95-96, Sen. Cup 98-99; NCE Prem Div. Champions 02-03, Div1 R-up 2001-02, Presidents Cup R-up 01-02, Wilkinson Sword Trophy .01-02.

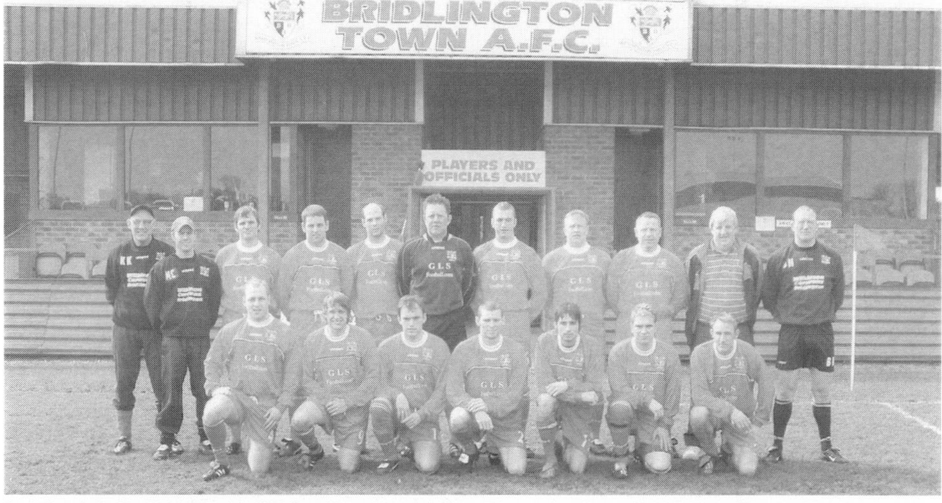

Back Row: L-R - Ken Knight (Physio), Mark Carroll (Asst Manager), Steve Robinson, Lee Harper, Stuart Baldwin, Chris Hill (GK), Craig Suddaby, JamieRichards, Wayne Lewis, Pete Smurthwaite (coach), Bill Heath (Manager).
Front L-R - Shaun Baker, Phil Harrison, Dave Ingram, Andy Thompson, Steve Underwood, Martin Thacker, Craig Burdick.

Photo: Jon Bemrose.

BURSCOUGH

CLUB OFFICIALS

Chairman: **Frank Parr**
Vice Chairman: **Stuart Heaps**
President: **Rod Cottam**
Secretary/:**Keith Maguire**, 218 Bescar Lane, Scarisbrick, Lancs. L40 9QT
TelNo: 01704 880587(H) 07970 030588 (M)
maguire@fadeal.co.uk
Press Officer: **Stan Strickland**

FOOTBALL MANAGEMENT TEAM

Manager: Mike Marsh
Asst Manager:Ian Bishop
Physio: Mel Singleton

FACT FILE

Founded: 1946
Nickname: Linnets
Sponsors: Nationwide Produce plc.
Colours: Green/white/green
Change colours:Sky blue /navy blue
.Midweek Matches: Tuesday
Reserves: Lancashire League

2003-004

Top Scorer: Darren Connell
Player of the Year: Stephen McNulty
2004-2005 Captain: Stephen McNulty

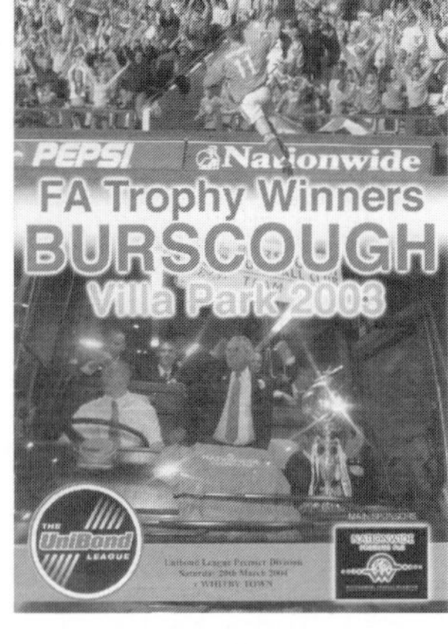

Pages:44 Price £1.50
Editor: Eric & Sue Berry

Local Radio: Radio Lancs,Red Rose.

GROUND: Victoria Park, Bobby Langton Way, Mart Lane, Burscough, Ormskirk, Lancs L40 0SD Tel: 01704 893237 Website: www.burscoughfc.co.uk
Directions: M6 Jct 27, follow signs thru Parbold A5209, right into Junction Lane (signed Burscough & Martin Mere) to lights, right onto A59 to Burscough Village, 2nd left over canal bridge into Mart Lane to ground. 200 yards from Burscough Bridge BR station (Wigan-Southport line). Half mile from Burscough Junction (Ormskirk Preston line)
Capacity: 2,500 **Seats:** 270 **Cover**:1,000 **Club Shop:** Yes: Margaret Manuel (01704893166)
Clubhouse: `Barons Club' (privately owned, access outside grd). Mon-Thurs 7-11pm, Fri 4-11pm, Sat 1-11pm, Sun noon-3 & 7-10.30pm. No food

PREVIOUS **Leagues:** Liverpool Co Comb. 46-53, Lancs Comb. 53-70, Cheshire Co.70-82, North West Cos 82-98, Unibond NPL98-01

CLUB RECORDS **Attendance:** 4,798 v Wigan Athletic,F.A.Cup 3rd Qual.Rd.1950-51
Goalscorer: Johnny Vincent 60 53-54. Most Goals in Game: Louis Bimpson 7. In Career: Wes Bridge 188
Win: 10-0 v Cromptons Recreation 1947 & v Nelson 1948-49, both Lancs. Comb.
Defeat: 0-9 v Earlstown, Liverpool County Comb.1948-49
Fee paid: £2,500 Stuart Rudd (Skelmersdale Utd 00-01)
Fee Received: £20,000 from Rochdale for Lee McEvilly 2001-02

BEST SEASON **FA Cup:** 1st Rd 59-60 77-78 79-80 80-81
FA Trophy: Winners 2002-2003 **FA Vase:** 1994-95 (Last 16)

HONOURS Liverpool Chall. Cup 47-48 50-51,54-55; George Mahon Cup 47-48; Liverpool County Comb Div 1, 49-50 (Div 2 53-54, 67-68); Lancs Comb.Div 2 53-54; Lancs Comb Div 1 55-56 69-70; Lord Wavertree Cup 67-68; Cheshire Co. Lge R-up 70-71, Lge Cup 74-75 R-up 73-74; Lancs Jnr Cup 47-4849-50 66-67; Liverpool Non-Lg Snr Cup 55/56, 71-72; N.W.C. Lge 82-83, Lge Cup 92-93 95-96 R-up 91-92, Chall. Shield 82-83, 95-96; Liverpool Sen. Cup R-up 92-93,95-96, 99-00., Liverpool Jun. Cup 00-01.

Players progressing: L Bimpson, B Parker (Liverpool 53), B Pilson (Stoke 53-54), A Green (Huddersfield), K Waterhouse (Preston), F Gamble (Derby 80), Tony Rigby (Bury), S Teale (Aston Villa), L Watson (Preston), K Formby A Russell (Rochdale 94),G Martindale (Bolton 94), S Perkins (Plymouth A. 97), M.Yates (Dundee 99), L. Trundle (Wrexham), R. Lowe (Shrewsbury T.), L McEvilly (Rochdale 02)

FARSLEY CELTIC

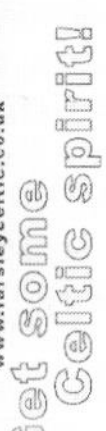

CLUB OFFICIALS

Chairman: Andrew Firbank

Directors: Andrew Firbank, Terry Deighton (MD), Martin Carrington (Co.Sec.), John Palmer and Paul Glover

Match Day Sec.: Martin Carrington, Throstle Nest, Newlands, Farsley, Leeds LS28 5BE

Tel : 0113 2298182 H) 07812 099838 (M)

FOOTBALL MANAGEMENT TEAM

Manager:Lee Sinnott

Reserves Manager: Gary Stokes

Coach: John Deacy

FACT FILE

Formed: 1908
Nickname: Villagers
Colours: All Royal Blue
Change colours: All Yellow
Midweek home matchday: Tuesday
Reserves' League: Lancashire
Local Press: Yorkshire Evening Post, Telegraph & Argus, Pudsey Times
Local Radio: Radio Leeds, Radio Aire, Radio Pennine

PROGRAMME

Pages: 32 Price £1
Editor: Helen Shepherd (0113 2561517)

GROUND: Throstle Nest, Newlands, Farsley, Pudsey, Leeds LS28 5BE Email: GRG LSL@aol.com
Directions: From North East: A1 south to Wetherby, A58 to Leeds, at 1st island (approx 8 miles) take 3rd exit (A6120 ring-rd), follow Bradford signs to 12th r'bout (approx 12 miles) - 1st exit (B6157 Stanningley). From M62 jct 26, M606 (Bradford) to r'bout, 4th exit (A6177) passing McDonalds on left, continue on Rooley Lane - Sticker Lane passing Morrisons store on left to lights (approx 3 miles) - right onto A647 (Leeds) to 2nd r'bout, 2nd exit (B6157 Stanningley). Continue 800yds passing Police & Fire Stations on left.Turn left down New Street at Tradex warehouse before turning right into Newlands. Ground at bottom of road. One mile from New Pudsey (BR)
Capacity: 4,000 Cover: 1,500 Seats: 300
Clubhouse: Lounge, games room and committee room Open every evening and Friday and weekend lunchtimes. New multi-purpose Leisure Centre available evenings and afternoons
Club Shop: League & non-League progs & magazines. Club badges, scarves,ties, sweaters, training suits, polo & T-shirts. Various souvenirs & photos. Contact: M.Pearson, 27 Rycroft Ct., Leeds LS13 4PE. 07798 865678 e-mail: clubshop@breathemail.net

PREVIOUS	**Leagues:** West Riding County Amateur; Leeds Red Triangle; Yorkshire 49-82; Northern Counties East 82-87
	Grounds: Red Lane, Farsley; Calverley Lane, Farsley (prior to 1948)
CLUB RECORDS	**Attendance:** 11,000 (at Elland Road) v Tranmere Rovers, FA Cup 1st Rd 1974
BEST SEASON	**FA Amateur Cup:** Third Round, 34-35
	FA Cup: 1st Rd 74-75 (see above). Lost 0-2. **FA Vase:** Quarter Final 87-88
HONOURS	West Riding County Cup 57-58 59-60 66-67 70-71 83-84 87-88 95-96 96-97 00-01; Yorkshire League 59-60 68-69 (R-up 57-58 58-59 70-71 71-72); Div 2 51-52;League Cup 62-63 63-64 66-67 96-97

Players progressing: Barry Smith (Leeds 1951), Paul Madeley (Leeds 1962),William Roberts (Rochdale 1988), Stuart McCall (Bradford City)

Back row left to right: Damien Place, Gary Shaw, Liam Sutcliffe, Damien Henderson, Paul Cuthbertson and Andy Lamb
Front row: Simon Brooker, Richard Hepworth, Liam Gray, Andy Shields and Chris Newton

FRICKLEY ATHLETIC

CLUB OFFICIALS

Chairman: Peter Bywater

Directors: Ken Day, Andrew Steel, Steve Pennock,Tony Corke, Brian Jackson Penny Wall, Neil Howden, Paul Graves,Roger Stanton, Paul Baines, John Hardcastle and Keith Donkin

Financial Secretary: A. Steele
Tel: 0114 2460218

Secretary: Steve Pennock, 3 Kingsley Crescent, Armthorpe, Doncaster DN3 3JG
Tel Nos: 01302 835956 (H)
07810 721860 (M)

FOOTBALL MANAGEMENT TEAM

Manager: Phil Sharpe

Assistant Manager: Mark Hancock

FACT FILE

Formed: 1910

Nickname: The Blues

Sponsors: T.B.A.

Colours: All blue with white stripe on shirt

Change colours: Yellow & black.

Midweek home matchday: Tuesday

Website: www.frickleyafc.co.uk

Local Press: South Yorks Times, Hemsworth & South Elmsall Express.

Local Radio: Radio Sheffield, Radio Hallam, Radio Leeds and Ridings F.M.

PROGRAMME

Pages: 40 Price: £1

Editor: Darren Haynes (01924 366462)

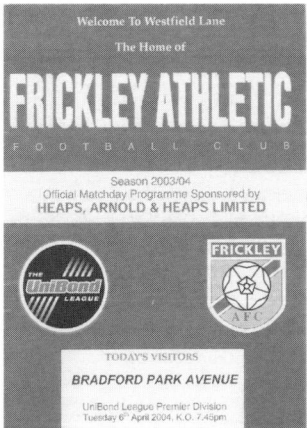

Welcome To Westfield Lane
The Home of
FRICKLEY ATHLETIC
FOOTBALL CLUB
Season 2003/04
Official Matchday Programme Sponsored by
HEAPS, ARNOLD & HEAPS LIMITED
THE UniBond LEAGUE
FRICKLEY AFC
TODAY'S VISITORS
BRADFORD PARK AVENUE
UniBond League Premier Division
Tuesday 6th April 2004, K.O. 7.45pm

GROUND Westfield Lane, South Elmsall, Pontefract Tel/Fax: 01977 642460 email: steve@ frickleyafc.co.uk

Directions: Follow signs for South Elmsall from A1 and A638. Left at Superdrug warehouse, right at T junction and immed. left up Westfield Lane. Left into Oxford Road (opposite Westfield Hotel) - ground at bottom on right. Two miles from South Elmsall (BR).

Capacity: 6,000 Cover: 2,500 Seats: 800

Clubhouse: On ground open matchdays, food available. **Club Shop:** Yes Contact: Secretary

PREVIOUS Leagues: Sheffield; Yorkshire 22-24; Midland Counties 24-33 34-60 70-76;Cheshire County 60-70; Northern Premier 76-80; GMV Conference (Alliance Premier) 80-87. Name: Frickley Colliery

CLUB RECORDS **Attendance:** 6,500 v Rotherham United, FA Cup First Round 1971.
Goalscorer: K Whiteley. **Defeat:** 0-12 v Worksop 2000-01 Unibond Premier **Fee Paid:** £1,800.
Fee Received: £12,500 for Paul Shirtliff (Boston Utd) & £12,500 for Russ Wilcox (Northampton)

BEST SEASON **FA Cup:** 3rd Rd 1985-86 (1-3 v Rotherham H).2nd Rd 84-85 (0-1 at Darlington). 1st Rd 36-37 57-58 63-64 71-72 73-74 83-84 86-87 88-89 00-01. League clubs defeated: Hartlepool United 85-86. **FA Trophy:** Quarter-Finals 84-85.

HONOURS Alliance Premier Lg R-up 85-86, Midland Counties Lg R-up 72-73 (Lg Cup 75-76),Yorkshire Lg R-up 23-24, Sheffield & Hallamshire Senior Cup 27-28 56-57 60-6162-63 66-67 78-79 85-86 87-88 89-90 99-00, Sheffield Assoc. Lg 20-21 (R-up 11-12).

Players Progressing: Dennis Smith & Jack Brownsword (Hull1946), Stan Scrimshaw (Halifax 1947), William Callaghan (Aldershot 1949), Leo Dickens 1950), John Ashley & Graham Caulfield (York 1950 & 67), Ron Barritt(Leeds 1951), John Pickup (Bradford PA 1955), Tom Hymers & Arthur Ashmore &Stewart Gray (Doncaster 1958 & 66 & 78), Colin Roberts (Bradford City 1959),Derek Downing (Middlesbrough 1965), Graham Reed & Russell Wilcox (Northampton1985 & 86), Will Foley (Swansea 1986), Gary Brook (Newport 1987), Wayne Scargill (Bradford City 94-95), Andy Hayward (Rotherham Utd.).

Back Row (L-R): Ronnie Akers (physio/coach), Lee Wilkinson, Antony Jackson, Steve Robinson, Nick richardson, Marc Shackleton, Phil Lindley, Lee Morris, Aaron Downes, Phil Sharpe (manager). **Front Row:** Michael Blythen, Dan Sheriffe, Duncan Richards, Craig Nelthorpe, Gary Hatto (player/assitant manager), Wayne Benn, Lee Pugh.

GATESHEAD

CLUB OFFICIALS

Chairman: Micrk Harland

Directors: Derek Bell and Phil Chambers

General Manager: John Young

Secretary: : Phil Chambers,
14 Kirkbride Place, Eastfield Dale,
Cramlington,Northumberland. NE23 2XG
Tel No; 07901 546929

Press Officer: Dean Ranyard
Tel No: 07715124588

2003-2004
Top Scorer: Paul Thompson 23
Player of the Year.: Paul Thompson

FACT FILE
Founded: 1930 Nickname: The Tynesiders
Sponsors: Veritas
Colours: White with black sleeves / black/ white
Change Colours: red with white sleeves / white / red
Midweek home matchday: Wednesday
Supporters' Unofficial Website:
Website: www..gateshead-fc.com

FOOTBALL MANAGEMENT TEAM
Manager: Derek Bell
Assistant Manager: Allan Ball
Coach: Eric Tait Captain: Paul Thompson
Physio: Bev Dougherty

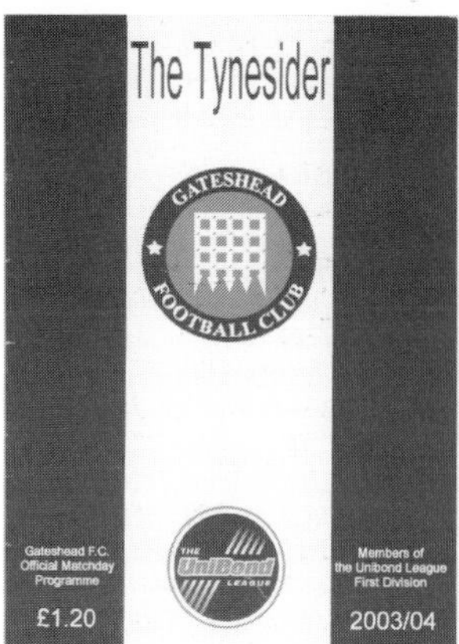

The Tynesider
GATESHEAD FOOTBALL CLUB
Gateshead F.C. Official Matchday Programme
£1.20
THE UniBond LEAGUE
Members of the Unibond League First Division
2003/04

Pages: 34 Price: £1.20
Editor: Dean Ranyard (0191 2580020)
Local Press: Gateshead Post, Newcastle Chronicle ,South Shields Gazette, Sunday Sun. Local Radio: BBC Radio Newcastle, Metro FM, Century Radio.

GROUND International Stadium, Neilson Road, Gateshead, NE10 0EF.
Tel: 0191 478 3883 Fax : 0191 427 5211.

Directions: From the South follow A1(M) to Granada services (Birtley),take right hand fork marked A194(M) (Tyne Tunnel, South Shields) follow A194 to first roundabout, turn left onto A184 - then 3 miles to stadium. Turn right at traffic lights into Neilson Road. BY RAIL to Newcastle Central Station,transfer to the Metro System and then to Gateshead Stadium.

Capacity: 11,795 Seats: 11,795 Cover: 3,300

Clubhouse: Bar inside Tyne & Wear stand open before, during and after matches

Club Shop: Sells full range of souvenirs, badges, programmes & fanzines. Contact: Gerald Crowe 0191 3016265 (W)

PREVIOUS **Leagues:** Football League - Div. 3 N. 30-58, Div.4 58-60, Northern Counties League 60-62, North Regional League 1962-1968, Northern Premier 68-70, 73-83,85-86, 87-90; Wearside 70-71; Midland Lge 71-72; Alliance Premier (Conference)83-85, 86-87, 90-98. **Grounds:** Redheugh Park - 1930-1971

CLUB RECORDS **Attendance:** 11,750 v Newcastle United (Pre-Season Friendly. 7th August 95)
Win: 8-0 v Netherfield, Northern Premier League. **Defeat:** 0-9 v Sutton United, 22.09.90, GMVC.
Career goalscorer: Bob Topping **Career appearances:** Simon Smith, 450, 85-94
Fee paid: £9,000 for Paul Cavell (Dagenham &Redbridge). **Fee received:** For Kenny Cramman from Rushden & D.

BEST SEASON **FA Cup:** Quarter Final, 1952-53. v Bolton W (H) 0-1 **FA Trophy:** Quarter Final, 0-1 v Wycombe W. (A) 13.3.93

HONOURS Football League Div. 3 North R-up 31-32, 49-50; Northern Premier - Champions82-83, 85-86; Runners-up 89-90; Northern Premier League Cup R-up 89-90; 02-03Multipart Shield 85-86.

Players Progressing: Osher Williams(Southampton, Stockport, Port Vale, Preston), John McGinley (Sunderland,Lincoln), Billy Askew (Hull City, Newcastle United), Lawrie Pearson (Hull City,Port Vale), Ian Johnson (Northampton Town), Ken Davies (Stockport), Kenny Lowe(Birmingham C., Barnet, Darlington, Stoke C.), Rob Jones (Stockport Coun ty)

Back row left to right: Michael Chilton, Michael Dickinson, Ben Ryan, Terry Burke, Taylor Keadle, James Curtis, Robert Southern and Richard Flynn.**Middle row:** Bev Dougherty (Physio), Ben Edusi, David Colvin, Neil Shotton, Stephen Harrison, Willie Moat, David Morgan, Eric Tait (Coach) and Tom Doleman (Kit Man). **Front row**: Mark Rasmussen, Ben Cattanach, Derek Bell (manager), Mike Coulson (former Chairman), Paul Thompson a nd Scott Mac Donald.

GUISELEY

CLUB OFFICIALS

Chairman: Philip Rogerson
Secretary: Bruce Speller
71 Oxford Avenue, Guiseley,
Leeds LS20 9BY
Tel: 01943 874534
Email: bruce.speller@virgin.net
Press Officer: John Martin
Tel: 01943 879473
Directors: P. Rogerson, S.Allen

FOOTBALL MANAGEMENT TEAM

Manager: Neil Parsley
Assistant Manager: Clive Freeman
Physio: Benn Gallagher
Captain: Richard Chattoe

PROGRAMME

Pages: 40 Price: £1 Edr: Rachel O'Connor

2003-2004

Player of the Year: Nathan Hay
Top Goalscorer: David Henry

FACT FILE

Formed: 1909
Colours:White/navy/white
Change Colours :Yellow/Navy
Midweek home matchday: Tuesday
Reserves' League: Lancashire League
Club Website: www.guiseleyafc.co.uk
Local Press: Yorkshire Evening Post, Bradford Telegraph & Argus, Airedale &Wharfedale Observer, Wharfe Valley Times

GROUND: Nethermoor, Otley Road, Guiseley, Leeds LS20 8BTTel: 0943 873223
Directions: Via M1 to M62 jct 28, follow Airport signs to junction of A65 at Horsforth. R-about turn left onto A65 through Rawdon to Guiseley centre. Ground 1/4 mile past traffic lights, on the right,entrance on A65 opposite Silver Cross factory. Further car parking available,frst right after ground, off Ings Crescent. 5 mins walk from Guiseley (BR/Metro) station.
Capacity: 3,000 Cover: 1,040 Seats: 427
Clubhouse: (01943 872872) Open before and after all games (closes 11pm). Snack bar within ground open before and during matches.
Club Shop: Sells programmes, various items of clothing, key rings, badges, mugs etc. Phone Jennifer Rogerson 01943 879236

PREVIOUS **Leagues:** West Riding Co. Amtr; West Yorks; Yorkshire 68-82; Northern Co's East82-91.

CLUB RECORDS **Attendance:** 2,486 v Bridlington Town, FA Vase Semi Final 1st Leg 89-90.

BEST SEASON **FA Cup:** First Round Proper 1994-95, 1-4 v Carlisle Utd. (at Valley Parade); 99-00, v Forest Green Rov. (A)
FA Vase: Winners 1990-91 (R-up 91-92, S.F. 94-95).
FA Trophy: Semi-Final 1994-95.

HONOURS FA Vase 90-91 (R-up 91-92), Northern Premier Lg Div 1 94-95 (Presidents Cup 94-95, Div 1 Cup 92-93), Northern Counties (East) Lg 90-91 (Lg Cup 90-91), West Riding County Cup(5 inc 94-95), Yorkshire Lg R-up 79-80 81-82 (Lg Cup 79-80).

Players Progressing: Keith Walwyn (York City), Frank Harrison (Halifax Town),Dean Walling (Carlisle United), Richard Annan (Crewe Alexandra). Dave Hanson (Halifax Town), Geoff Horsfield (Birmingham City)

Back row, left to right - Mark Stuart, David Henry, Scott Jackson, James Nettleton, Andrew Shuttleworth, David Cooke, Peter Sumner. **Front row,** left to right - Jeremy Illingworth, Richard Chattoe, Gary Shaw, John Lamb, Stewart Airdrie, Nathan Hay, Peter Atkinson.

HYDE UNITED

CLUB OFFICIALS

Chairman: Stephen Hartley
Secretary: Tony Beard,
30 Fishermans Close,Winterley, Sandbach,
Cheshire. CW11 4SW
Tel & Fax: 01270 212473
07778 792502 (M) See email below.
Commercial Manager: Paul Harrop
Tel No: 0161 368 1031

FOOTBALL MANAGEMENT TEAM

Manager: Steve Waywell
Assistant Manager: Tony Ellis
Physio: Danny Crawford
2003-2004
Leading Goalscorer: Neil Tolson
Player of the Year: Matty McNeil
2004-2005 Captain: John O'Kane
PROGRAMME
Pages: 32 Price: £1.
Editor: Mark Dring 0161 336 8076

FACT FILE

Formed: 1919 Nickname: The Tigers
Club Sponsors: Allen Mills Howard Ltd
Colours: Red/white/red
Change All Sky Blue
Midweek home matchday: Monday
Website: www.hydeunited.co.uk
Local Press: Tameside Advertiser
& Hyde Reporter.
Local Radio: GMR, Key 103 BBC ,GMR

GROUND Tameside Stadium, Ewen Fields, Walker Lane, Hyde SK14 2SB (0161 368 1031).
Directions: On entering Hyde follow signs for Tameside Leisure Park - in Walker Lane take 2nd car park entrance nr Leisure Pool, follow road
around to the stadium. Quarter of a mile from Newton (BR). Train from Manchester (15 minutes)
Capacity: 4,130 Cover: 2,000 Seats: 660
Clubhouse: (0161 368 1621). Open most nights, 150 seats. +Sponsors Lounge for 70
Club Shop: Yes, selling normal range of products. Contact Tony Beard 07778 792502 email: beard@fishermans.fslife.co.uk

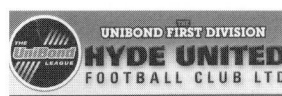

PREVIOUS **Leagues:** Lancs & Cheshire 19-21; Manchester 21-30; Cheshire County 30-68, 70-82; Northern Prem. 68-70

CLUB RECORDS **Att** 9,500 v Nelson, FA Cup 1952. **Scorer:** P O'Brien 247. **Appearances:** S Johnson 623.
Defeat: (as Hyde F.C.) 0-26 v Preston North End, F.A. Cup.
Fee Paid: £8,000 for Jim McCluskie (Mossley, 1989). **Fee Received:** £50.000 for Colin Little (Crewe Alexandra) 1995.

BEST SEASON **FA Cup:** 1st Rd 54-55(1-5 v Workington(A), 83-84 0-2 v Burnley (H), 94-95 1-3 v Darlington. (H)
FA Trophy: Semi Final 88-89 94-95 95-96

HONOURS Prem Inter-Lge Cup R-up (2) 88-90; NPL R-up(2) 87-89, 99-00 (Lg Cup 85-86 88-89 95-96(R-up 83-84 94-95), Chal. Shield 96-97, (R-up 86-87 90-91); Cheshire Co. Lg(3)54-56 81-82 (Lg Cup 33-34 52-53 54-55 72-73 81-82, Lg Chal. Shield(2) 80-82; Manchester Lg(5) 20-23 28-29 29-30 (Lg (Gilgryst) Cup(4) 27-29 49-50 70-71);Cheshire Snr Cup 45-46 62-63 69-70 80-81 89-90 96-97; Manchester Prem. Cup 93-94, 94-95, 95-96, 98-99,Snr Cup 74-75, Int Cup 55-56 56-57(jt), Jnr Cup 21-22 68-69;Lancs & Cheshire F'lit Cup(2) 54-56; Ashton Chal. Cup(6) 30-34 39-40 47-48;Hyde Chal Cup(2) 27-29; Reporter Cup(3) 72-74 75-76; Gavin Nicholson Mem Trophy79-80; Lancs F'lit Trophy(2) 86-88; Edward Case Cup(4), Unifilla Cup Winners: 99-00.
Players Progressing since 1980s: George Oghani (Bolton 1983), Kevin Glendon (Burnley 1983), Peter Coyne (Swindon 1984),Colin Little (Crewe Alex. 1995),Lutel James (Bury), Simon Yeo (Llincoln City 2002)

Back row left to right Steve Waywell (Manager) Phil Salt, Neil Tolson, Matty McNeil, Nicky Hill, Tim Mullock, Dale Johnson, Tony Ellis (Assistant Manager) Steve Clegg. **Front row** Danny Crawford (Physio) Andy Waine, Craig Buckley, John Gaynor, Chris Lynch, John O'Kane (Captain), Lee Brough, Wayne Dean, Carl Barrowclough.
Photo courtesy of Adrian Hunt.

LEEK TOWN

CLUB OFFICIALS

President: D.J.Bray

Chairman: Marvin Clarke

Directors:
Alan Clarke, Andy Wain and Dennis Bates

Non-Exec: Ray Bettany , Stan Trafford,
Dave Roberts and Brian Wain

Secretary: Christine Osmond
10 Corporation St, Stoke on Trent ST44AU
Tel: 01782 847936 (H) 07775567109 (M)

Commercial Manager: Paul Ogden.

Press Officer: MikeCope

2003-2004 Top Goalscorer: Dave Whittaker
Player of the Year: Steve Hodgson

FACT FILE

Founded: 1946 Nickname: The Blues
Club Sponsors: Kerrygold
Colours: Blue with white trim
Change colours: All Yellow
Midweek home matchday: Monday
Newsline: 0930 55 54 53
Press: Leek Post & Times, Eve. Sentinel
Local Radio: Radio Stoke, Signal Radio

FOOTBALL MANAGEMENT TEAM

Manager: Paul Ogden

Assistant Man: Benny Phillips

Physio: Dave Massey

Programme
Pages: 40 Price: £1.00
Editors: Steve Reynolds & Tracy Cope
01782 269040 (H) 07940370872 (Tracey)
07958046538 (Steve)
website: www.leektown.co.uk

GROUND Harrison Park, Macclesfield Road, Leek ST13 8LD
Tel: 01538 399278 Fax: 01538 399826

Directions: Opposite Courtaults chemical works on A523 Macclesfield to Buxton road half a mile out of Leek heading towards Macclesfield.

Capacity: 3,600 Seated: 625 Covered Terracing: 2,675

Club Shop: Contact: MarkGraham at club on 01538 386613

Clubhouse: `Blues' Bar openmatch days. Functions by request (01538 383734)

PREVIOUS **Leagues:** Staffs County, Manchester 51-54 57-73, West Mids (B'ham) 54-56,Cheshire County 73-82, North West Counties 82-87, Northern Premier 87-94 95-97,Southern League 94-95, Conference 97-99
Names: Abbey Green Rovers/ Leek Lowe Hamil. **Grounds:** None

CLUB RECORDS **Attendance:** 5,312 v Macclesfield Town, F.A. Cup Second Qualifying Round 73-74 **Win / Defeat:** Unknown
Transfer fee paid: £2,000 for Simon Snow (Sutton Town) **Transfer fee received:** £30,000 for Tony Bullock (Barnsley)
Career goalscorer: Dave Suttons 144 **Career appearances:** Gary Pearce 447.

BEST SEASON **FA Cup:** 2nd Rd 90-91, 0-4 v Chester (A) after 1-1 League clubs defeated: Scarborough 90-91.
FA Trophy: Runners-up 89-90, Q-F 85-86.

HONOURS FA Trophy R-up 89-90; Northern Premier Lg 96-97, R-up 93-94 (Div 1 89-90, Div 1Cup R-up 88-89, Presidents Cup R-up 93-94, Lg Shield 90-91); North West Co's LgCup 84-85 (Charity Shield 84-85); Cheshire County Lg 74-75 (Challenge Shield74-75); Manchester Lg 51-52 71-72 72-73 (Lg Cup 72-73); Staffs Snr Cup 95-96,R-up 54-55 81-82 95-96, Jnr Cup 51-52 70-71 (R-up 47-48 48-49 49-50)); StaffsCo. Lg 50-51 69-70 70-71 73-74 (R-up 47-48 49-50, Lg Cup 70-71 73-74); LeekPost Charity Shield 46-47; Leek Cup 47-48 52-53 70-71 71-72 (R-up 46-47); MayBank Cup 47-48 50-51 71-72; Hanley Cup 48-49 70-71 (R-up 49-5); Mid Cheshire LgDiv 2 87-88 (Div 2 Cup 87-88); Evans Halshaw Floodlit Cup Winners 93-94 94-95; Southern Lge Cup R-up 94-95; Unibond Lge Chall Cup R-up 95-96

Players progressing: Geoff Crosby (Stockport 52), Bill Summerscales (70), Mark Bright (81) & Martyn Smith (84) allto Port Vale, Paul Edwards (Crewe 89), Tony Bullock (Barnsley 97)

Back row, left to right: Steve Massey (Physio), Dave Whittaker, Ben Matthews, Shaun Cartwight, Steve Hodgson, Adam Martin, Matt Haddrell, Dean Butterworth, Dave McPherson and Ken Ashford (Kit Manager).**Middle row**: Martin Ridley, Richard Eye, Ross Clegg, Wayne Johnson, Ashley Wooliscroft, Tom Betts and Robert Hawthorn. **Front row**: Matt Bullock, Alex Brown, Carl Frost, Steve Taaffe, Paul Macari and Paul Buckley.

LINCOLN UNITED

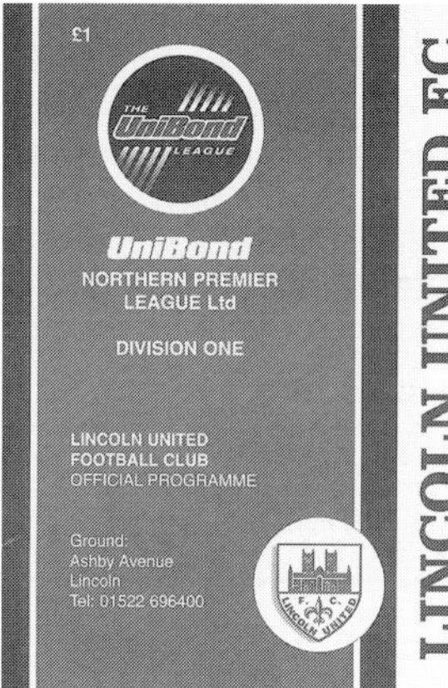

£1
THE UniBond LEAGUE
UniBond
NORTHERN PREMIER LEAGUE Ltd
DIVISION ONE
LINCOLN UNITED FOOTBALL CLUB OFFICIAL PROGRAMME
Ground: Ashby Avenue Lincoln Tel: 01522 696400
LINCOLN UNITED FC

CLUB OFFICIALS

Chairmen: Robin Taylor
President: Phil Morley
Directors: R.Taylor,D.Adkin, P.Day, C.Dennis and R.Parnham
General Manager: Roy Parnham
Secretary/Press Officer: Peter Doyle
4 Roxborough Close,Lincoln LN6 0QL
Tel No: 07971 034693 (M)
e-mail: peterdoyle@arcasys.com

FOOTBALL MANAGEMENT TEAM

Managers: John Wilkinson
Physio:Mark Hicks

FACT FILE

Formed: 1938
Nickname: United
Colours: All white
Change Colours: All light blue
Midweek home matchday: Tuesday
Reserves ' League: Lincolnshire

2002-2003

Captain: Paul Miller
Top Scorer: Ian Williams
Player of the Year: Karl Horswood

Programme
Pages: 40 Price:£1.00
Editor: Graham Wallhead (01522 871787)
Local Press: Lincolnshire Echo
Lincoln Standard
website: www..lincolnunitedfc.co.uk

GROUND Ashby Avenue, Hartsholme, Lincoln Tel: 01522 690674
Directions: From Newark A46 onto Lincoln relief road (A446), right at 2nd r'bout for Birchwood (Skellingthorpe Rd), go for 1 mile passing lake and Country Park, 1st right 10yds after 30mph sign into Ashby Ave., ground entrance200 yds, opposite Old Peoples home. From north follow A57 via Saxilby until reaching A46 Lincoln Relief Road - continue on this and turn left at r'bout signed Birchwood then as above. 3 miles from Loncoln Central (BR)
Capacity: 2,714 Seats: 400 Covered: 1,084
Clubhouse: Open daily normal licensing hours. Matchday snack bar -hot &cold food & drinks
Club Shop: Yes. Contact:Secretary

PREVIOUS
Leagues: Lincs 45-48 60-67; Lincoln 48-60; Yorks 67-82; Northern Co'sEast 82-86, 92-95; Central Mids 82-92
Grounds: Skew Bridge (40s); Co-op Sports Ground (to mid 60s); Hartsholme Cricket Ground (to 82)
Name: Lincoln Amateurs (until an ex-pro signed in 1954)

CLUB RECORDS
Attendance: 2,000 v Crook Town, FA Amateur Cup 1st Rd Proper, 1968
Scorer: Tony Simmons 215 **Appearances:** Steve Carter 447
Win: 12-0 v Pontefract Colls 95. **Defeat:** 0-7 v Huddersfield Town FA Cup 1st Round Proper16-11-91
Fee Paid: £1000 for Paul Tomlinson (Hucknall Town ,Dec 2000)
Fee Received: £3,000 for Dean Dye (Charlton Ath., 7.91)

BEST SEASON
FA Cup: First Round Proper 91-92 (0-7 at Huddersfield Town), 97-98 v Walsall (0-2 Away)
FA Trophy: 3rd 3Rd **F.A.Vase:**

HONOURS
Northern Counties East - Prem Div. 94-95, Div 1 92-93, Div 1 Sth 82-83,Div 2 85-86, Presidents Cup 94-95; Yorks Lg 70-71 73-74 (Lg Cup 70-71); Lincs Lg 63-64; Lincs Snr `A' Cup 72-73 85-86 95-96, R-up 91-92 94-95, `B' Cup 63-6470-71; Central Mids Lg 91-92 (Wakefield Cup 90-91); Evans Halshaw Floodlit Cup R-up 92-93; Lincs I'mediate Cup(7) 67-73 80-81; Blankney Hunt Inter Lge 95-96,Cup 95-96 Lincs Sen Cup: R-up 97-98 Unifila Div 1 Cup R-up 97-98

Back row, left to right: R.Taylor (Chairman), G.Goddard (Manager), D. Bent, G.Lewis, G Pawson, S Cherry, L.Cooper, B.Brown, P.Watts, K.Horswood, P.Tittcomb (Asst.Manager) and P.Morley (President). **Front row:** M.Hicks (Physio), P.Muser, G Walters, I.Williams, D.Hopgreaves., G.Buckthorpe and R.Armstrong.

MARINE

CLUB OFFICIALS

Chair: Paul Leary **Pres:** Dennis Hargreaves

Directors

Chairman, President , Sec, G. Kewley & M. Prescott (Treasurers), D.Rannard, M.Broderick,S Rawstrhorne, B.Lawlor, S.Rimmer,P.Hughes & P McCormack

Secretary: John Wildman
4 Ashbourne Avenue, Blundellsands, Liverpool L23 8TX Tel: 0151 924 5248

Press Off: Steve Rimmer (0151 928 9722)

Club Website: www.marinefc.com

FACT FILE

Formed: 1894 Nickname: The Mariners, or The Lilywhites Sponsors: Arriva

Colours: White/black/black

Change colours: Yellow/Green/Green

Midweek matchday: Tuesday

Reserves' League: Lancs. League Div. One

FOOTBALL MANAGEMENT TEAM

Manager: Roly Howard

Asst Mgr/Coach: Dave Thompson

Capt: James Connelly Physio: Anne Fisher

2003-2004

P.o.Y.: Eddie Hussin

Top Goalscorer: Steve Whitehall

GROUND Rossett Park, College Road, Crosby, Liverp'l L23 3AS (Tel: 0151 924 1743/4046)
Directions: College Road is off main Liverpool-Southport road (A565) in Crosby. Ground ten minutes walk from Crosby & Blundellsands (Mersey Rail). Bus No. 92
Capacity: 3,185 Cover: 1,400 Seats: 400

Clubhouse: Open daily. Concert Hall (250 seats), Members Lounge (100 seats).
Club Shop: Sells replica kit and range of souvenirs.Metal Badges in home and away colours. Contact: Joanne Cross (0151 929 3616)

Pages: 40 Price: £1.20
Editor: Dave Rannard (0151 4749848)
Local Press: Crosby Herald, Liverpool Echo, Daily Post Local Radio: BBC Radio Merseyside, Radio City

PREVIOUS **Leagues:** Liverpool Zingari; Liverpool Co. Comb.; Lancs Combination 35-39, 46-69; Cheshire County 69-79.
Name: Waterloo Melville **Ground:** Waterloo Park (1894-1903)

CLUB RECORDS **Attendance:** 4,000 v Nigeria, Friendly 1949
Goalscorer: Paul Meachin 200 **Win:** 14-2 v Rossendale Utd (A), Cheshire County Lge 25/2/78
Appearances: Peter Smith 952 **Defeat:** 2-11 v Shrewsbury Town F.A.Cup 1st Rd 1995
Fee Paid: £6,000 for Jon Penman (Southport Oct. 1995) **Fee Received:** £20,000 for Richard Norris (Crewe 96)

BEST SEASON **FA Trophy:** Semi Final 83-84, 91-92 **FA Amateur Cup:** Runners up 31-32 (SF 46-47)
FA Cup: 3rd Rd 92-93, 1-3 v Crewe Alex. (A) League clubs defeated: Barnsley 75-76, Halifax T. 92-93

HONOURS FA Amateur Cup R-up 31-32; Northern Prem Lg. 93-94 94-95, R-up 85-86 91-92, Lg Cup 84-85 91-92 02-03 R-up 80-81 85-86 Presidents Cup R-up 83-84 86-87; Cheshire Co. Lg73-74 75-76 77-78 R-up 72-73; Lancs Comb. R-up 46-47 Lg Cup 46-47 63-64 68-69; Liverpool Comb. 27-28 30-31 33-34 34-35 Lg Cup 30-31; Lancs Tphy 87-88 90-91 99-00; Lancs Jnr Cup 78-79; Lancs Amtr Cup (5); Liverpool Snr Cup 78-79 84-85 87-88 89-90 94-95 99-00; Liverpool Non-Lge Cup 68-69 75-76 76-77; Liverpool Chal. Cup 42-43 44-45 71-72.

Players Progressing: A Sharrock, S Brooks (Southport 73 &77), A Jones (Leeds 60), G Williams (Preston 72), J Lacy (Fulham), P Beesley (Sheffield Utd), M Kearney (Everton 81), A Finlay (Shrewsbury 81), P Cook (Norwich), P Edwards (Crewe), I Nolan (Tranmere), J McAteer(Bolton W.), R Norris (Crewe 96).

Back Row (L-R): Roger Patience (Asst. Manager), John Bradshaw (Physio), Gary Randles, Nicky Young, Paul McNally, Eddie Hussin, James Connolly, Peter Crookes, Paul Culshaw, Tommy Taylor, Lee Mullin, Roly Howard (Manager), Keith Johnson (Trainer).
Front Row: Anne Fisher (Physio), Dean thurston, Ben Kay, Steve Whitehall, Neil Murphy, Frank Heald, Richie Townsend, Paul Proctor, Will Dolan, Neil Black.

MATLOCK TOWN

CLUB OFFICIALS

Chairman: Darrell Holmes

Vice Chairman: Tom Wright

Directors: C.Britland (President), K.Brown, L.Bagshaw,C.Cresswell,Mrs.E.S Cresswell, G.Davies, S. Else, P.Eyre, S.Greenhough, T. Oliver, J.Parker, I Richardson, A.Smith, I Spencelley, G.Tomlinson, I.Waite and Mrs L.H.West

Chief Executive:: Keith Brown
`Barncroft', 1 Malvern Gardens
Matlock, Derbyshire DE4 3JH
01629 584231 (H) 07831 311427 (M)

Press Officer: Ian Richardson

Commercial Manager: Tom Wright

FACT FILE

Formed: 1885 Nickname: The Gladiators
Sponsors: T.Nutt & Sons (Carpets) Ltd. & Westons of Wiirksworth (TV & Radio)
Colours: All Royal Blue Change : All yellow
Midweek home matchday: Tuesday
Local Press: Matlock Mercury Derbyshire Times, Derby Evening Telegraph, Chesterfield Express & Sheffield Star
Local Radio: Radio Derby & Peak 107 F.M.

FOOTBALL MANAGEMENT TEAM

Managers:Ohil Brown & Gareth Williams
Physio: Michael Cunningham
Captain James Lukic
2003-2004 Top Scorer: Danny Holland
Player of the Year: Matt Taylor

GROUND Causeway Lane, Matlock, Derbyshire Tel: 01629 583866 (& Fax)

Directions: On A615, 500 yds from town centre and Matlock (BR)
Capacity: 5,500 Cover:1,200 Seats: 560

Clubhouse: Gladiators Social Club, on ground, open matchdays only

Club Shop: Yes. Contact: Sue Tomlinson (01629 583866)

PROGRAMME
Pages 40 Price £1.20
Editor: Mike Tomlinson (01629 583866)
Website: www.matlocktown.co.uk

PREVIOUS **Ground:** Hall Leys (last century). **Leagues:** Midland Counties 1894-96; Matlock & District; Derbys Senior; Central Alliance 24-25 47-61; Central Combination 34-35; Chesterfield & District 46-47; Midland Counties 1961-69

CLUB RECORDS **Attendance:** 5,123 v Burton Albion, FA Trophy 1975
Win: 10 v 0 Lancaster (A) **74** **Defeat:** 0-8 v Chorley (A) 71
Career **Goalscorer:** Peter Scott. **Career** **Appearances:** Mick Fenoughty
Fee Paid: £2,000 for Kenny Clarke1996 **Fee Received:** £10,000 for Ian Helliwell (York)

BEST SEASON **FA Trophy:** Winners 1974-75
FA Cup: 3rd Rd 76-77. 1st Rd 1885-86 86-87 86-8787-88 1959-60 74-75 75-76 89-90
League clubs defeated: Mansfield Town 76-77

HONOURS Northern Prem Lge R-up 83-84, Lge Cup 77-78, Shield 78-79 Div 1 R-up 03-04; Midland Counties Lge 61-62 68-69; Central All (North) 59-60 60-61, R-up 61-62 62-63,Div 1 Cup R-up 61-62, Div 2 59-60, Div 2 Cup 59-60 60-61; Derbyshire Sen Cup74-75 76-77 77 78 80-81 83-84 84-85 91-92, 2003-04 R-up: (10) Derbyshire Div Cup North) 61-62 R-up 62-63; Evans Halshaw Floodlit Cup 88-89 91-92; Anglo-Italian Non-League Cup 79

Players progressing: Keith Haines (Leeds 1959), Wayne Biggins (Burnley 1984),Darren Bradshaw (Chesterfield 1987), Les McJannet (Scarborough 1987), Ian Helliwell (York 1987)

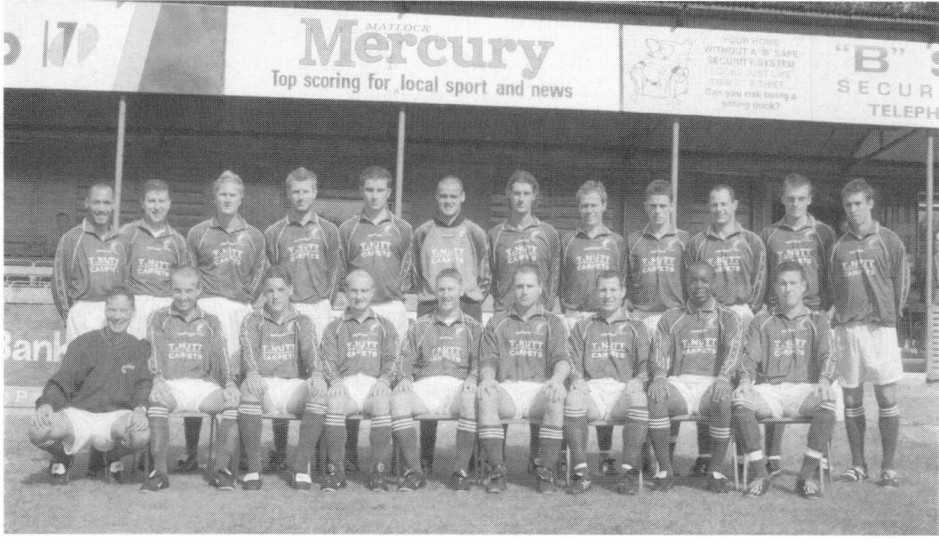

OSSETT TOWN

CLUB OFFICIALS

President: Paul Jervis

Chairman: Graham Firth

Football Chairman: Peter Wilkinson

Directors: Tim Asbury, Meg Coxhill, Graham Firth, David Huggins, Bruce Saull, Phil Thompson and Graham Willis

Commercial Manager: Graham Willis

Secretary: Bruce Saul, 42 Longlands Road, Ossett,W Yorks WF5 0QU

Tel Nos: 01924 277652 (H)01924 789347 (W) & 07962 0-35472 (M)

FACT FILE

Founded: 1936
Sponsors:: Builders Supply(Wakefield) Ltd
Colours:Red with white trim Change : All sky
Midweek matches: Tuesday
Reserves' League: Lancashire League
Website: www.ossetttown.org.uk
Local Press: Dewsbury Reporter, Wakefield Express

FOOTBALL MANAGEMENT TEAM

Manager: Gary Brook
Asst Manager: B. Crawther
Coach:Nigel Yarrow

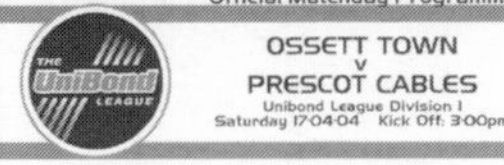

PROGRAMME

Pages: 56 Price: £1.00
Editor: Secretary

GROUND: Ingfield, Prospect Road, Ossett, Wakefield WF5 8AN Tel: 01924 272960

Directions: M1 jct 40, B6129 to Ossett, left into Dale Street, left again at lights opp. bus station on ring road, ground on left. Nearest stations Dewsbury or Wakefield Westgate - both three miles from. Buses 116, 117, 126 and127 from Wakefield, buses 116, 126 and 127 from Dewsbury, buses 117, 118 or 216 from Leeds

Capacity: 4,000 Seats: 360 Cover:1,000 Floodlights: Yes

Clubhouse: Open Fri & Sun lunchtimes, all day Sat and every evening. Pie & peas, chips, soup from tea bar

Club Shop: Yes (Graham Willis 01924 266393

PREVIOUS **Leagues:** Leeds 36-39; Yorkshire 45-82; N.C.E. 83-99
Ground: Fern House (pre-1958)

RECORDS **Attendance:** 2,600 v Manchester Utd, friendly 1988
Win: 10-1 v Harrogate RA (H), N.C.E. Lge Prem. Div. 27/4/93 **Defeat:** 0-7 v Easington Colliery, FA Vase 8/10/83
Fee received: £1,350 for Derek Blackburn (Swansea 1957)
Appearances: Steve Worsfold **Goalscorer:** Dave Leadbeater

HONOURS Northern Counties East - Lg Cup 89-90, Div 2 88-89, Res. Div 88-89, Res.Cup 87-88 88-89; West Riding County Cup 58-59 81-82.

Players progressing: Arnold Kendall (Bradford C.) 1949, Ron Liversidge(Bradford C.) 56, Derek Blackburn (Swansea) 57, Simon Lowe (Barnsley) 83, Gary Chapman (Bradford C.) 88, Mick Norbury (Scarborough) 1989, Mike Williams(Sheffield W.) 90, Dean Trott (Northampton) 98, Paul Cuss (Huddersfield Town) 98.

Back Row (L-R): John Kent (Physio), Steve Richards (Manager), Rob Nugent, James Walshaw, Mick Clark, Matt Daly, Ian Twitchen, Darren Leach, Richard Fidler, Steve Kittrick (Asst. Manager).
Middle Row: Steve Price, Tony Lennon, Ryan Gray, Rodney Rowe, Danny Brown.
Front Row: Robert bloomfield, Brook Newton, David Briggs, Andy Turner (Managing Director, First Choice Recruitment, Wakefield).
Photo: Courtesy of the Wakefield Express.

PRESCOT CABLES

CLUB OFFICIALS

President: G.Hayward**Chairman**: Ted Mercer
Vice Chairman: G.Hayward
Commercial Manager: A.Simpson
Secretary: Doug Lace
20 Cable Road, Prescott,
Merseyside L35 5AW

FOOTBALL MANAGEMENT TEAM

Manager: Tommy Lawson
Asst Manager: Andy Gray
Captain: Eddie Taylor

FACT FILE

Founded: 1886
Nickname: Tigers
Colours: Gold/black/blak
Change colours: All blue
Midweek Matches: Tuesday
Pages: 30 Price: £1.50

2003-2004

Player of the Year: David Chadwick
Top Goalscorer: Lee Cooper

GROUND Valerie Park, Hope Street, Prescot. L34 6HD
Tel: 0151 430 0507 email: kenderbyshire@blueyonder.co.uk

Directions: M62 Jct 7. A57 to Prescot. Take 3rd exit at roundabout after two and a half miles. Turn right after another 1/2 mile. Right at Hope & Anchor pub, into Hope Street..

Capacity: 4,400 Seats: 500 Cover: 800 Floodlights: Yes

Clubhouse: Refreshment bar, open matchdays/evenings for hot & cold refreshments

Club Shop: Yes withties & metal badges also available.

PREVIOUS **Leagues:** Liverpool Co. Comb.; Lancs Comb. 1897-98 18-20 27-33 36-67; Ches. Co. 33-36 78-82; Mid Cheshire 67-78; N.W.C. 82-2003
Names: Prescot Athletic; Prescot Cables 46-65 80-90; Prescot Town 65-80.

RECORD **Attendance:** 8,122 v Ashton National, 1932

BEST SEASON **FA Cup:** 2nd Rd 57-58 59-60 **FA Vase:** Last 16 2002-03

HONOURS N.W.C. Champions 2002-03; Lancs Comb. 56-57 (Lg Cup 47-48); Ches. Lg Div 2 76-77; Mid Ches. Lg 76-77; L'pool Non-League Cup (4) 51-53 58-59 60-61; L'pool Chal. Cup (5) 28-30 48-49 61-62 77-78; George Mahon Cup 36-37.

Photo: Mark Syder.

RADCLIFFE BOROUGH

CLUB OFFICIALS

Chairman: Bernard Manning (Junior)
President: Bernard Manning (Senior)
Directors: D. Murgatroyd, M Darlington, K.Glendon, Barney Hampson, B. Manning jr.
G Fielding (Company Secretary)
Football Secretary: Ian Hannay
Both c/o Radcliffe Borough

FOOTBALL MANAGEMENT TEAM
Manager: Kevin Glendon
Coach: Ronnie Evans
Physio: Roy Davies

FACT FILE

Formed: 1949 Nickname: Boro'
Sponsors: West-Tec.
Colours: Blue/blue/white
Change:Red & Black stripes/Black/Red & black
Midweek home matchday: Tuesday
Youth Team U18: Yes

2003--04
Top Scorer: Jody Banim 22
P.o.Y.: Danny Hurst
2004-05 Captain: Davy Luker

BORO REVIEW
OFFICIAL MATCHDAY PROGRAMME
£1.00
RADCLIFFE BOROUGH F.C.
UNIBOND PREMIER DIVISION
Saturday 24th April 2004 - Unibond League - BURSCOUGH

Pages: 28 Price: 80p
Editor: Roy Swinbank

Local Press: Radcliffe Times, Bolton Evening News, Manchester Evening News
Local Radio: GMR, Piccadilly Tower F.M. Bolton

GROUND: Stainton Park, Pilkington Road, Radcliffe, Lancs., M26 3PE 0161 724 5937 (club) 0161 724 8346 (Office) 0161 723 3178(Fax) Website: www.radcliffeborough.co.uk
Directions: M62 junction 17 - follow signs for Whitefield and Bury . Take A665 to Radcliffe. Thro' town centre, turn right into Unsworth St. (opposite Turf Hotel). Ground on left half mile Colshaw Close East. 1/2 mile from Radcliffe(BR)
Capacity: 3,000 Cover: 1,000 Seats: 350
Clubhouse: (0161 724 5937) `The Boro' - public house on ground with food available
Club Shop: Yes

PREVIOUS **Leagues:** South East Lancs; Manchester 53-63; Lancs Comb. 63-71; Cheshire County 71-82; North West Counties 82-87
Ground: Bright Street 1949-70.

CLUB RECORDS **Attendance:** 2,495 v York City (F.A.C 1st Round 2000-01)
Goalscorer: Ian Lunt **Appearances:** Chris Lilley.
Fee Paid: £5,000 for Gary Walker(Buxton, 1991). **Fee Received:** £20,000 from Shrewsbury Town for Jody Banim

BEST SEASON **FA Trophy:** 3rd Rd v Gateshead 1995-96
FA Cup: 1st Round Proper, 00-01 v York City 1-4)**FA Vase:** 4th Rd v Boston Town 93-94

HONOURS Unibond Lge Div One Champ 96-97; North West Counties Lg 84-85 (Div 2 82-83); Lancs Combination Lg. Cup 69-70; Manchester Lg R-up 55-56 (Lg Cup 58-59 joint); Manchester Prem. Cup R-up 97-98

Players progressing: Jim Hayman (Bury 50), Ian Wood (Oldham Athletic 65), Robert Hutchinson (Rochdale 74), Gary Haworth (Rochdale 84), Kevin Hulme (Bury 89), Neil Hardy (Stockport County) and Jody Banim (Shrewsbury Town)

Back Row (L-R): Kevin Glendon (Manager), Ronnie Evans (Asst. Manager), Simon Garden, Simon Kelly, Danny Hurst, Richard Landon, David Bean, Karl Marginson, Davy Luker, David Felgate, Roy Davies (physio).
Front Row: Tony Whealing, Steven Spencer, Richard Battersby, Jody Banim, Bernard Manning Jnr. (Chairman), Chris Denham, James Price, Jason Astley, Gary Simpson.

SPENNYMOOR UNITED

Chairman & Press Off: Barrie Hindmarch
Tel Nos 01388 815168 (H) 07951 720938 (M)
Vice Chairman: T. Metcalfe
Directors: S.Mottram, M.O'Donnell
Football Match Secretary
T.Metcalfe, 23 Tangmere,Spennymoor, Co.Durham DL16 6TU
Tel No: 01388 811561 (H)
Commercial Man: Des Beamson
General Sec.: Tom Metcalfe
Tel: 01388 811561

FACT FILE
Founded: 1904
Nickname: The Moors
Sponsors: T.B.A.
Club colours: Black & white stripes/black/white.
Change colours: All red
Midweek home matches: Tuesday
FOOTBALL MANAGEMENT TEAM
Manager: Tony Lee
Coach: Jason Ainsley
Captain: Phil Brumwell
Physio: Peter Carey
2003-04 Top Goalscorer; Danny Brunskill

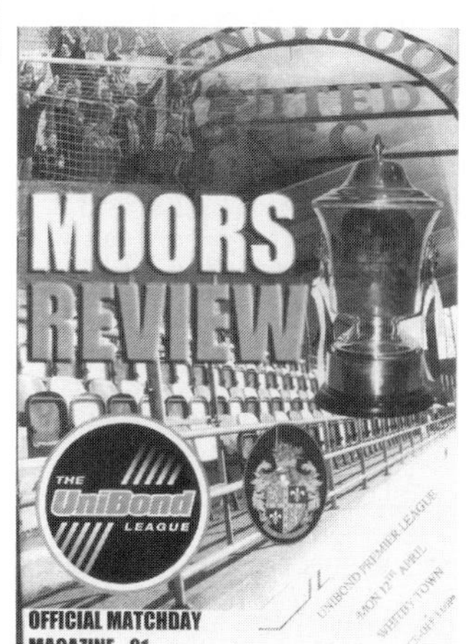

Pages: 44 Price: £1
WEbsite: www.spennymoorunited.fsnet.co.uk

Local Press: Northern Echo; The Journal

GROUND Brewery Field, Durham Road, Spennymoor, County Durham DL16 6JN Tel: 01388 811934 Directions: From South; A1(M), A167, A688,straight on at mini-r'bout, 3rd exit at next large r'bout (St Andrews church opposite), pass Asda on left, straight on at junction, pass Salvin Arms (Durham Rd), ground 200 yds on left. From A167North - leave at Croxdale (N.E.S.S. factory), right at cemetery on left - this is Durham Rd - ground half mile on right. Nearest rail stations are Durhamand Bishop Auckland (via Darlington)-buses from there.
Capacity: 7,500 **Seats:** 300 **Cover:** 2,000
Clubhouse: (01388 814100) Open eves. 7-11pm, Sat 12-11pm (matchdays only), Sun12-2 & 7-10.30pm. Bar snacks. Private functions. Tea bar in ground.

PREVIOUS **Leagues:** Northern 05-08 60-90; North Eastern 08-37 38-58; Wearside 37-38;Midland Counties 58-60; Northern Counties East 90-93. **Ground:** Wood Vue 1901-1904. **Names:** None.

CLUB RECORDS **Attendance:** 7,202 v Bishop Auckland, Durham County Challenge Cup 30/3/57.
Win: 19-0 v Eden Colliery, North Eastern Lge 6/2/37. **Defeat:** 0-16 v Sunderland`A', Durham Snr Cup 4.1.02 (H.T.: 0-10)
Goalscorer: Dougie Humble 200+ **Appearances:** Ken Banks 600+.
Fee Paid: £3,500 for Don Peattie (Gretna) **Fee Received:** £20,000 for Michael Heathcote (Sunderland, 88).

BEST SEASON **FA Trophy:** Semi Final 77-78
FA Cup: 3rd Rd 36-37, 1-7 v West Bromwich Albion(A). League clubs defeated : Hartlepool 27-28, Southport 75-76.

HONOURS Northern Premier Lg Cup 93-94 (Div 1 R-up 93-94); Northern Lg(6) 67-68 71-7273-74 76-79 (R-up(3) 74-75 79-81), Lg Cup(5) 65-66 67-68 79-81 86-87; Turney Wylde Cup 80-81; J R Cleator Cup 80-81 86-87; Northern Counties (East) Lg 92-93(Lg Cup 92-93); Durham Challenge Cup 29-30 44-45 45-46 53-54 62-63 67-68 72-7373-74 74-75 75-76 78-79 82-83 93-94 94-95 95-96 97-98; Durham Benevolent Bowl26-27 29-30 31-32 47-48 58-59 60-61; North Eastern Lg(4) 09-10 44-46 56-57 (Lg Cup 28-29).

Players Progressing: Over fifty, including: H. Hubbick (Burnley, 3.25), T .Dawson (Charlton, 3.39), T. Flockett (Charlton, 4.49), J. Smallwood(Chesterfield, 12.49), J. Oakes (Aldershot, 5.54), J. Adams (Luton Town, 53),Alan Moore (Chesterfield), Michael Heathcote (Sunderland, 5.87), Jason Ainsley(Hartlepool, 94), Richie Alderson (York City 97), Graeme Paxton (Newcastle Utd 97)

Back row, left to right: Peter Carey (Physio), Steve Bell, Michael Robson, David Goodchild, Martin Kearney, Jamie Pollock (Manager),Steve Hutt, Andy Shaw, Nicky Mohan, Leigh Grant and John Duffy (Assistant Physio). Front row: Ben Ryan, Stuart Brightwell, Jason Ainlsey (Assistant Manager), Chris Lynch, Steve Preen, Danny Brunskill, Neall Bishop and Anthony Woodhouse.

WAKEFIELD & EMLEY

CLUB OFFICIALS

Chairman: Peter Matthews.
President: Peter Maude
Director: Alan Blackman
Secretary: Ian Charlesworth, 62 Oakes Avenue, Brockholes, Holmfirth HD9 7EE
Tel : 01484 661780 (H) 07880 790701 (M)

FACT FILE
Formed: 1903
Nickname: 'The Pewits
Sponsors: Eurotrail
Colours: Claret & Sky/blue/claret
Change Colours. White/navy/navy
Mid week matchday: Tuesday
Reserves' Lge: N. Co's E
Web: www.emlyyafc.free-online.co.uk

2003-2004

FOOTBALL MANAGEMENT TEAM
Managers: Paul David & Ray Dennis
Physio: Daryl Brook.

GROUND Belle Vue Stadium, Doncaster Rd., Wakefield WF1 5HT
Tel. No: 01924 211611(office) 01484 661780 (Fax)
Directions: Jct 39 M1 ,follow A636 to Wakefield, then A638 Doncaster Road 1 mile from town centre.
Capacity: 11,000 Cover: 5,000 Seats: 1,050
Clubhouse: (01924 848398). Members' social club open seven nights a week and Saturday & Sunday. Bingo, discos, occasional cabaret.
Club Shop: Yes .Contact David Richardson Tel No: 01924 211611

Pages: 34 Price: £1
Editor: Jane Turner (01924 387056)
Local Press: Hudd'field Examiner, Hudd'field & Dist't Chronicle.,Wakefield Express
Local Radio: Radio Leeds, Radio Sheffield, Pulse FM, Huddersfield FM.,Ridings F.M.

HONOURS FA Vase Runners-up 87-88; Northern Premier Lge Div 1 R-up 90-91; Northern Counties E Lge 87-88, 88-89 (R-up 85-86); Yorkshire Lg 75-76 77-78 79-80 81-82(R-up(5) 72-74 76-77 78-79 80-81, Lg Cup 69-70 78-79 81-82, Div 2 R-up 69-0; Sheffield & Hallamshire Senior Cup 75-76 79-80 80-81 83-84 88-89 90-91 91-9297-98; Huddersfield Challenge Cup 82-83 83-84 85-86; Huddersfield Lg(4) 65-69.

PREVIOUS **Leagues:** Huddersfield; Yorkshire 69-82; Northern Counties East 82-89.
Names: Emley FC 1903-2002 **Grounds:** Emley Welfare Sports Ground

CLUB RECORDS **Attendance:** 5,134 v Barking, Amateur Cup 3rd Proper 1/2/69.
18,629 v West Ham Utd, at Upton Pk, 3rd Rd Proper 3/1/99.
Win: 12-0 v Ecclesfield Red Rose9-6-97 **Defeat:** 7-1 v Altrincham 25-4-98.
Goalscorer: Mick Pamment 305. **Appearances:** Ray Dennis 762.
Fee Received: £60,000 for Michael Reynolds (Ayr Utd 98)

BEST SEASON **FA Amateur Cup:** Third Round replay 69-70.
FA Vase: Runners-up 87-88 (Semi-Final86-87).
FA Trophy: Quarter Final 98-99
FA Cup: Third Round Proper 97-98 (1-2 v West Ham Utd) **League Club Defeated:** Lincoln City 1997-98

Players progressing: A Sweeney (Hartlepool Utd 79), G Cooper(Huddersfield Tn 84), J Francis (Sheffield Utd 88), S Smith (Crewe Alexandra1992), C Alcide (Lincoln City 95), C Hurst (Huddersfield Tn 97), G Hurst (Ayr Utd 98), M.Reynolds (Ayr United 1998)

Back row left to right: Daryl Brook (Physio), Ronnie Glavin (Manager), Paul David, Gary Hatto, Ryan Crossley, Mickey Norbury, Andy Wilson, Paul Cuss, Simeon Bambrook, Danny Day, Jimmy Martin (Assistant Manager) and John Peachey (Coach). **Front row:** Lee Ryan, Michael Reynolds, Steve Nicholson (Captain), Robert Tonks, MilesThorpe and Nicky Wood

WHITBY TOWN

CLUB OFFICIALS

Chairman: Graham Manser.

President: Brooks Mileson

Secretary: Mike Green

14 Linden Close, Briggswath, Whitby, North Yorks YO21 1RA Tel: 01947 811704Press Officer: Secretary

OTBALL MANAGEMENT TEAM

Manager: Harry A Dunn
Coach: Graham Robinson
Physio: Greg Henderson
Captain: Graham Robinson

FACT FILE

Formed: 1926
Nickname: Seasiders
Sponsors: Arnott Commercial
Colours: All Royal Blue
Change Colours: All white.
Midweek matchday: Wednesday
Reserve League: Teeside League

2003-2004

Top Scorer& Player of the Year:Craig Veart

GROUND Turnbull Ground, Upgang Lane, Whitby, North Yorks
Fax: 01947 603779 Tel: 01947 604847

Directions: Take the A174 road from town centre.
Ground on offside travelling towards Sandsend.

Capacity: 2,680 Cover: 1,143 Seats: 380

Clubhouse: Mon-Fri 7-11pm, Sat 12-11pm, Sun 12-2 & 7-10.30.

Club Shop: Yes Contact Alan McCluy 01947 603781

Pages: 40 Price: £1.20
Editor: Alison Booth 01947 820024

Local Press: Whitby Gazette, Northern Echo.
Local Radio: Yorkshire Coast Radio

PREVIOUS **Leagues:** Northern League 1926-97. **Name:** Whitby United (pre 1950). **Grounds:** None

CLUB RECORDS **Attendance:** 4,000 v Scarborough, N Riding Senior Cup 18.4.65
Win: 11-2 v Cargo Fleet Works 1950 **Defeat:** 3-13 v Willington 24.3.28
Career Goalscorer: Paul Pitman (382) **Career Appearances:** Paul Pitman (468)
Transfer Fee Paid: £2,500 for John Grady (Newcastle Blue Star 90)
Fee Received: £5,000 for Graham Robinson (Gateshead 97)

BEST SEASON **FA Vase:** Winners 97. **FA Amateur Cup:** Runner-up 1964-6 **FA Trophy:** QuarterFinals 1983-84
FA Cup: 2nd Round 83-84 v Wigan A (a) 0-1,1985-86 v York C (a) 1-3 League Clubs beaten: Halifax Town 1983-84

HONOURS : F.A Amateur Cup R-up 64-65; FA Vase 96-97; NPL Div 1 97-98; Northern Lge 92-93 96-97 (R-up 27-28 63-64 67-68 81-82 82-83), Lg Cup 28-29 63-64 69-70 76-77 84-85 95-96; Rothmans National Cup 75-76 77-78; Nth Riding SnrCup 64-65 67-68 82-83 89-90, 98-99; N Riding Bene Cup 92-93; J R Cleator Cup 84-85 92-93 95-96 96-97; Mickey Skinner Trophy [5], Unibond Presidents Cup R-up 99-00

Players Progressing: Malcolm Poskett (Hartlepool), Sammy Kemp (Huddersfield), Jimmy Mulvaney (Hartlepool, Barrow, Stockport), Bobby Veart (Hartlepool), Derek HamptonJ amie Burt, Trevor Smith, John Linacre & Phil Linacre (Hartlepool), Mark Hine (Grimsby). David Logan (Mansfield) Jamie Burt (Chesterfield).

Photo: Brian Murfield.

WITTON ALBION

CLUB OFFICIALS

President: T Stelfox

Chairman: Mike Worthington

Directors: Paul Worthington,Graham Edgeley Michael Miles, Mark Harris,Rob Sproson and Jiimmy Powell.

Secretary: Phil Chadwick
c/o GMB Stadium
Tel Nos: 01606 44845(H) 07860 227250 (M)

FACT FILE

Formed: 1887 Nickname: The Albion
Sponsors: Len Cooke Financial Consultants
Colours: Red & white stripes/ red/white
Change colours: All yellow
Midweek matchday: Monday
Reserve League: Altrincham Under 21

FOOTBALL MANAGEMENT TEAM

Manager: John Davison
Assistant Manager : Peter King
Physio: Shane Hoy

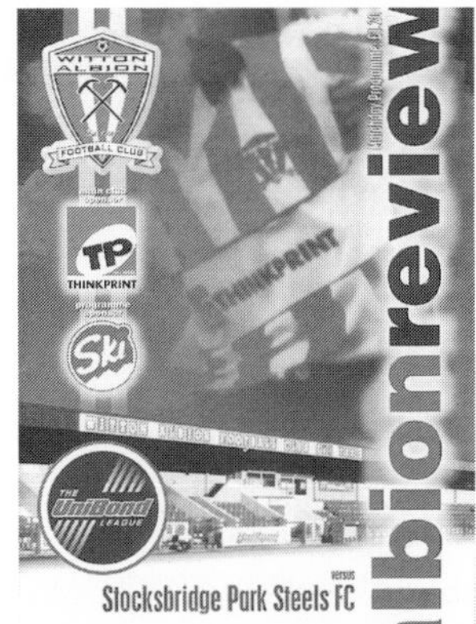

Pages: 32 Price: £1
Editor: Secretary

Local Press: Northwich Guardian, Northwich Chronicle
Local Radio: BBC GMR, BBC Radio Stoke

Website: www.wittonalbion.co.uk

GROUND "GMB" Stadium, Wincham Park, Chapel St, Wincham, Northwich.
Tel/Fax: 01606 43008 (office 01606 47117 club) Email: bp-uh-2000@aol.com

Directions: M6 junc 19. A556 towards Northwich, after 3 miles turn onto A559 at beginning of dual carriageway, after 3/4 mile turn left opposite Black Greyhound Inn, grd 1/2 mile on left immediately after crossing Canal Bridge

Capacity: 4,500 **Seated**: 650 **Cover**: 2,300 **Club Shop:**Yes Debbie Waterman(07960 058215)

Clubhouse: Concert room and Vice-Presidents room open matchdays, Tuesday,Thursday, Friday evenings. Food available for private functions

PREVIOUS
Leagues: Lancs Comb.; Cheshire County -79; Northern Premier 79-91, GMV Conference 91-94
Grounds: Central Ground, Witton Street, Northwich

CLUB RECORDS
Attendance: 3,940 v Kidderminster Harriers - FA Trophy Semi-Final 13.4.91 (Wincham Road)
9,500 v Northwich Victoria - Cheshire League 7.4.50 (Central Ground)
Win: 13-0 v Middlewich (H) NS Cup .**Defeat:** 0-9 v Macclesfield Town (a) 18.9.65
Fee Paid: £12,500 to Hyde Utd for Jim McCluskie 91 **Fee Received:** £11,500 for Peter Henderson from Chester City.
Goalscorer: Frank Fidler 175 (1947-1950) **Appearances:** Alf Ashley 556 (1946-1958)

BEST SEASON
FA Trophy: Runners-up 91-92, Semi-Finals 90-91, 92-93
FA Cup: 91-92 Second Round 91-92, 1-5 v Preston North End (A). League clubs defeated: Halifax Town91-92

HONOURS
Northern Prem Lge 90-91; Cheshire County Lge 48-49 49-50 53-54 (R-up 50-51),Lge Cup 53-54 75-76; Cheshire County Sen Cup (7); FA Trophy R-up 91-92 (SF 90-91 92-93)

Players progressing: P Henderson (Chester C.), Chris Nicholl (Burnley - ex-Southampton manager), Phil Power (Crewe), Neil Parsley & Mike Whitlow (Leeds), Geoff Horsfield (Halifax Town ,Fulham), Robert Trees (Bristol Rovers).

Back row,left to right: Simon Burton, Gary Furnival, Alex Kevan, Paul Gibson, Danny Webster, Andy Barlow, and Michael Bird. **Middle Row:** Shane Hoy (Physio), David Tickle, Dave Nolan, Brian Pritchard, Simon Hughes, Stuart Tulloch, John Stannard and Peter King (Assistant Manager). **Front row:**Darrell Dicken, Gareth Evans, Michael Yates, John Davison (Manager), Adam Foy, Mike Moseley and Lee Madin. Players absent: Craig Sargeson and Danny Salt.

WORKINGTON

CLUB OFFICIALS

Chairma: Dale Brotherton

President: Minnie Thexton

Vice Chairman: Humphrey Dobie

Match Sec.: Steve Durham (01946 61380)

Secretary: Dale Brotherton
Lime House, Holm Hill, Dalston, Carlisle
CA5 7BX Tel: 07977 759903

FOOTBALL MANAGEMENT TEAM

Manager:Tommy Cassidy

Asst. Man:Kenny Brown Captain: Will Varty

Physio:Gareth Livingstone

FACT FILE

Formed: 1884 (reformed 1921)
Nickname: Reds
Sponsors:Albany ARG Group
Colours: All Red
Change colours:All Blue.
Midweek matchday: Tuesday
Reserves' League: Lancashire League
Website: www.workingtonredsafc.co.uk

2003-2004

P.o.Y.: Mathew Henney
Top Scorer: Craig Johnston

,50Pages: 36 Price: £1
Press Off/ Ed: Steve Durham (01946 61380)

Local Press:
Evening News & Star, Times & Star
Local Radio: BBC Radio Cumbria, C.F.M

GROUND: Borough Park, Workington, Cumbria CA14 2DT Tel: 01900 602871

Directions: A66 into town, right at `T' junction, follow A596 for 3/4 mile - ground is then visible and signposted. Ground is north of town centre 1/4 mile from Workington (BR) station &1/2 mile from bus station

Capacity: 2,500 Cover:1,000 Seats: 350 Floodlights: Yes

Clubhouse: Open matchdays and for private functions. Food on matchdays restricted menu

Club Shop: Sells programmes, badges, magazines, pennants, photographs, replica kit, T-shirts. etc. Contact :John Crook (01946 832710)

HONOURS Football League: 5th in Div 3 65-66, 3rd Div 4 63-64, Cumberland County Cup 1886-91(x5) 95-00(x5) 1906-08(x2) 09-10 24-25 34-35 36-38(x2) 49-50 53-54 67-68 85-86 95-96, 99-00 (R-up 1885-86 91-92 1899-1901(x2) 02-03 08-09 11-12 23-24 26-27 29-30, 46-47 68-69 78-79) Football League Cup QF 63-64 64-65; N.P.L. Presidents Cup 83-84 R-up 03-04; North Eastern Lge R-up 38-39, Lge Cup 34-35 36-37 R-up 37-38; N.W. Trains Lg Div 1 98-99

PREVIOUS **Leagues:** Cumberland Assoc. 1890-94; Cumberland Sen. Lge 94-1901, 03-04; Lancashire Lge 1901-03; Lancashire Comb. 04-10; North Eastern 10-11, 21-51; Football League 51-77
Grounds: Various 1884-1921, Lonsdale Park 21-37

BEST SEASON **FA Cup:** 4th Rd 33-34. 1st Rd - 53 occasions.
FA Trophy: Q. Final 99-00 **FA Vase:** 6th Rd, 98-99 (1st season)

RECORDS **Attendance:** 21,000 v Manchester Utd, FA Cup 3rd Rd 4/1/58
Goalscorer: Billy Charlton 193 **Win:** 17-1 v Cockermouth Crusaders, Cumb-erland Sen. Lge 19/1/01
Appearances: Bobby Brown 419 **Defeat:** 0-9 v Chorley (A), NPL Prem. Div., 10/11/87
Fee Paid: £6,000 for Ken Chisholm (Sunderland,'56) **Fee Received:** £33,000 for Ian McDonald (Liverpool, '74)

Players progressing: Numerous, the best known being John Burridge.

Back Row (L-R): Tommy Cassidy (Manager), David Hewson, Mathew Henney, Will Varty, Neil Thompson, Simon Tucker, Craig Johnston, Paul O'Neill, Kenny Brown (Asst. Manager). **Front Row:** Alan Gray, Steve Archibald, Ryan McCluckey, Robert Ennis, Michael Farrer, Graham Goulding, Stuart Moffat.

...ACTION EXTRA...ACTION EXTRA...ACTION EXTRA...

Gainsborough Trinity winger Gareth Grant tackles **Guiseley's** Gary Birchall. Photo: Darren Thomas

Vauxhall Motors goalkeeper acrobatically saves against **Alfreton Town** Photo: Bill Wheatcroft

...ACTION EXTRA...ACTION EXTRA...ACTION EXTRA...

Neil Campbell of **Barrow** scores his side's fourth goal at **Worksop**. Photo: Bill Wheatcroft

Rob Pell of **Wakefield & Emley** challenges **Bradford Park Avenue**'s Craig Smith Photo: Darren Thomas

BAMBER BRIDGE
Goalkeepers: Andy Banks (Fleetwood)
Defenders: Steve Macauley (Macclesfield), Chris Blakeman (Chorley), Jamie Squires (Nuneaton), Mark Milligan (Fleetwood), Phil Robinson (Blackpool), Richard Fogarty (Great Harwood), Simon Woodward (Kendal)
Midfield: Brian Butler (Lancaster), Dave Leaver (Chorley), James Skeoch (Kendal), John Turner (Nuneaton)
Forwards: Brian Welch (Radcliffe), Chris Ward (Northwich), David Sutch (Congleton), Pual Ryan (Blackpool)

BISHOP AUCKLAND
Goalkeepers: Adam Clementson (Bedlington)
Defenders: Shaun Hope (Whitby), Steve Tobin (Shildon), Chris Neil (Brandon Utd), Brian Rowe (Bedlington),
Midfield: Steve Brackstone (York), Chris Moore (Hartlepool), Steve Salvin (Easington), Nicky Scaife (Bedlington), Kevin Dixon (Seaham)
Forwards: Paul Thompson (Gateshead), Stuart Irvine (Durham), Brian Ross (Hartlepool)

BLYTH SPARTANS
Goalkeepers: Craig Turns (Sunderland)
Defenders: Richard Forster (Hartlepool), Michael Laws (Whitby), Ian Dixon (Hartlepool), Ian Crutwell (Hull), Andy Leeson (Burnley), Mark Atkinson (Sunderland), Mark Evans (Whitley Bay), Paddy Atkinson (Queen of the South), Andy Armstrong (Tow Law)
Midfield: Paul Barrett (Wrexham), Gareth Williams (Whitley Bay), Christian Graham (Bedlington), Steve Richardson (Burnley), Gareth McAlinden (Gateshead), John Curran (Institute (N.Ireland)), Graham Fenton (Blackpool), Ben Summers (West Auckland)
Forwards: Anthony Woodhouse (Spennymoor), Wayne Phillips (Peterlee Newtown), Jamie Burt (Whitby), Lee George (Sunderland), Keith Graydon (Scarborough), Steve Preen (Spennymoor), Mark Sheeran (Whitby)

BRIDLINGTON TOWN
Goalkeepers: Gavin Kelly (Harrogate), Craig Wardale (Hall Road), Dave Bramley (Scarborough)
Defenders: Lee Harper (North Ferriby), Sam Sharman (Hull), Steve Robinson (Hall Road), Steve Heath (Alfreton), Wayne Lewis (Hall Road), Craig Suddaby (Hull)
Midfield: Martin Thacker (Hall Road), Shaun Baker (Goole), Craig Burdick (Goole), Kirk Blake (Recketts), Matthew Salvidge (Hall Road)
Forwards: Paul Palmer (North Ferriby), Kevin Smith (Harrogate Railway), Andy Thompson (North Ferriby), Phil Harrison (Hall Road)

BURSCOUGH
Goalkeepers: Matthew Boswell (Bradford PA), David Newnes (Youth team)
Defenders: Jeff Underwood (Southport), Danny Stone (Southport), Steve McNulty (Liverpool), Lee Dames (Youth team), Karl Bell (Rossendale), Ryan Bowen (Youth team), Dave McKearney (Morecambe), Michael White (Youth team)
Midfield: Matthew Parry (Prescot Cables), Martin Crowder (Everton), Liam Blakeman (St Helens), John Bluck (Youth team), Mark Byrne (Stockport),
Forwards: Gary Martindale (Telford Utd), David Eaton (Stafford R), Paul Gedman (Bangor C), David Rowan (Cheshire Lines)

FARSLEY CELTIC
Goalkeepers: Andy Woods (Chester)
Defenders: Lee Connor (Ashton Utd), Craig Hall (Leeds), Lee Beeton (Garforth), Chris Stabb (Ossett T), Steve Ball (Harrogate), Jon Dyson (Ashton Utd),
Midfield: Paul Rickers (Northampton), Gerard McCargo (Frickley), Andy Cooper (Huddersfield), Chris Howarth (Harrogate Railway), Gavin Bassinder (Gainsborough), Damian Place (Osterholz Sharnbeck (Germany)), Matt Smithard (Ossett T)
Forwards: Nathan Eno (Harrogate Railway), Curtis Bernard (Stocksbridge), Ray Stammar (SG Wattenscheld 09 (Germany)), Mark Bett (Wibsey), Michael Midwood (Ossett T)

FRICKLEY ATHLETIC
Goalkeepers: Marc Shackleton (Barnsley)
Defenders: Steve Robinson (Local football), Graeme Severn (Rossington Main), Chris Fawcus (Maltby Main), Lee Pugh (Brodsworth), Matthew Plant (Worksop)
Midfield: Dale Rimmington (Goole), Wayne Benn (Bradford PA), Gary Hatto (Wakefield-Emley), Phil Lindley (Bradford PA)
Forwards: Mark Vickerage (Bradford PA), Richard Tracey (Ossett T), James Walker (Rossington Main), Jamie Thompson (Bardsey)

GATESHEAD
Goalkeepers: Liam Connell (Youth team)
Defenders: Martin Smith (Darlington), James Curtis (Washington), Paul Buzzeo (Walker Central), Ben Edusei (Youth team), Paul Taylor (Seaham)
Midfield: Mark Atkinson (Blyth Spartans), Richard Flynn (Youth team), Richard Kent (Youth team), Mark Rasmussen (Burnley), Simon Colligan (Spennymoor)
Forwards: Craig Robson (Bishop Auckland), George Weatherley (Newcastle Benfield Saints), Paul Gibbs (Newcastle Benfield Saints)

GUISELEY
Goalkeepers: John Lamb (Thackley)
Defenders: Gary Shaw (Farsley Celtic), Keiron O'Brien (Frickley), Peter Atkinson (Harrogate), Richard Chattoe (Thackley), Clive Freeman (Goole), Neil Parsley (Witton), James Stansfield (Bradford PA), Kevin Graham (Goole)
Midfield: Dave Cooke (Local football), Jeremy Illingworth (Stocksbridge PS), Mark Stuart (Stalybridge), Ben Gallagher (Farsley Celtic), Nick Hey (Thackley), Neil Grayston (Droylsden), Dave Donaldson (Bradford PA)
Forwards: Simon Parke (Harrogate), Stewart Airdrie (Hednesford), Scott Jackson (Harrogate), Ryan Senior (Eccleshill), Curtis Bitton-Price (Harrogate)

HYDE UNITED
Goalkeepers: Tim Mullock (Kidsgrove)
Defenders: Lee Brough (Leek), Stephen Clegg (Milkwaukee Waves (USA)), Nicky Hill (Leigh RMI), Paul Jones (Oldham), Chris Lynch (Wigan), Neil O'Brien (Loughborough Dynamo)
Midfield: Carl Barrowclough (Leigh RMI), Craig Buckley (Bury), Keiran Delaney (Curzon Ashton), Wayne Dean (Curzon Ashton), John Gaynor (Bury), Jamie Milligan (Blackpool), John O'Kane (Blackpool), Phil Salt (Leigh RMI), Andrew Waine (Accrington Stanley)
Forwards: Tony Ellis (Mossley), Lee Evans (Stockport), Dale Johnson (Woodley Sports), Michael Meszoras (Macclesfield), Matty McNeil (Runcorn), Neil Tolson (Halifax)

LEEK TOWN
Goalkeepers: Steve Hodgson (Nuneaton)
Defenders: Shaun Cartwright (Stoke), Matt Haddrell (Macclesfield), Mike Heathcote (Colwyn Bay), Wayne Johnson (Congleton), Ben Johnson (Witton), Martyn Lancaster (Leigh RMI), Daniel Peake (Port Vale), Ashley Woolliscroft (Newtown), Adam Yates (Crewe)
Midfield: Alex Brown (Crewe), Matt Bullock (Buxton), Ross Clegg (Stalybridge), Richard Eyre (Kidsgrove), Rob Hawthorne (Crewe), Dave MacPherson (Stone Dominoes), Ben Matthews (Norton Utd)
Forwards: Dean Butterworth (Chorley), Carl Frost (Crewe), Paul Macari (Huddersfield), Steve Taaffe (Rocester), Dave Whittaker (Gresley R)

LINCOLN UNITED
Goalkeepers: Jamie Morgan (Lincoln Moorlands)
Defenders: Danny George (Grantham), Ben Brown (Youth team), Matt Roche (Kidsgrove), Duane Soar (Eastwood), Ian Wilkins (Grantham), Jason Barnett (Lincoln C), Joby Gowshall (Grantham), Gary Walters (Boston Utd), John Hibbins (Worksop),
Midfield: Brendan McDaid (Grantham), Charlie Trout (Lincoln C), Jason Minett (Grantham), Jon Hawley (Grantham), Kevin Riley (Gainsborough)
Forwards: Jamie Clarke (Grantham), Gary Bull (Grantham), Ian Williams (Spalding), Tony Simmons (Grantham), Rick Ranshaw (Grantham)

CORRECT AT TIME OF GOING TO PRESS

MARINE
Goalkeepers: Peter Crookes (Hyde)
Defenders: Chris Fitzsimmons (Rossendale), Neil Murphy (Altrincham), Paul Culshaw (Liverpool), Paul Proctor (Youth team), James Connolly (Southport)
Midfield: Ben Kay (Congleton), Will Dolan (Youth team), Paul McNally (Runcorn), Paul Byrne (Southport), Terry Anderson (St Helens), Michael Scully (Congleton)
Forwards: Steve Whitehall (Southport), Tommy Taylor (Local football), Neil Black (Tranmere), David Thompson (Southport), Dean Thurston (Macclesfield)

MATLOCK TOWN
Goalkeepers: Joel Armstrong (Staveley MW), Kevin Tye (Whitby)
Defenders: James Lukic (Youth team), Lee Handbury (Belper), Steve Circuit (Alfreton), Craig Holins (Gresley R)
Midfield: Ian Clarke (Staveley MW), James Lomas (Mansfield), Gareth Williams (Gainsborough), Mark Willgoose (Alfreton), Rocky White (Eastwood), Michael Sisson (Notts Co), Kris Bowler (Wakefield-Emley)
Forwards: Steve Taylor (South Normanton), Earl Alexander (Gresley R), Leroy Chambers (Droylsden), Phil Brown (Gainsborough), Simon Barrowclough (Rotherham)

OSSETT TOWN
Goalkeepers: Mick Clark (Ossett Alb)
Defenders: Niall Hudson (Belper), Danny Brown (Gainsborough), Steve Price (Goole), Matt Daly (Goole), Rob Nugent (Sheffield Utd), Adam Gray (Local football)
Midfield: Alex Callery (Worksop), David Briggs (Youth team), Brook Newton (Barnsley), Robert Bloomfield (Tadcaster), Ryan Gray (Gainsborough), Rob Hanby (Goole), Steve Gaughan (Barrow)
Forwards: Danny Davidson (Brighouse), Andy Evans (Ilkeston), Jamie Walshaw (Youth team), Rodney Rowe (Ashton Utd)

PRESCOT CABLES
Goalkeepers: Phil Priestley (Bangor C)
Defenders: Brian Holmes (Burscough), Colin Flood (Kidsgrove), Karl Clark (Kidsgrove), Mark Ashton (St Helens), Michael Peers (Vauxhall Motors), Lee Riley (St Helens)
Midfield: Adam Flynn (Liverpool), Gary Jensen (Rossendale), John Benson (Runcorn), Eddie Taylor (Nantwich)
Forwards: Steve Torpey (Port Vale), Steve O'Neill (St Helens), Kevin Garforth (Burscough)

RADCLIFFE BOROUGH
Goalkeepers: Danny Hurst (Cheadle)
Defenders: Richard Battersby (Oldham), Lee Duffy (Rochdale), James Price (Chorley), Gordon Armstrong (Accrington Stanley), Simon Kelly (Youth team), John Foster (Trafford), Paul Challinor (Droylsden)
Midfield: Andy Heald (Morecambe), Karl Marginson (Hyde), Steve Spencer (Leigh RMI), Davey Luker (Dalians), Gary Sampson (Accrington Stanley), Simon Carden (Accrington Stanley), Scott Wilson (Rossendale)
Forwards: Steve Foster (Stalybridge), Phil Denney (Ashton Utd), Rory Patterson (Rochdale), Jamie Baguley (Stockport)

SPENNYMOOR UNITED
Goalkeepers: Darren Horrigan (Lincoln C),
Defenders: John Butler (Washington Nissan), Anthony McStea (Brandon Utd), Steve Hutt (Bishop Auckland), Paul Talbot (Queen of the South)
Midfield: Curtis Taylor (Whitley Bay), Scott Emmerson (Pickering), Stuart Niven (Cambridge C), Mark Summerbell (Carlisle), Jon Cullen (Halifax)
Forwards: David Colvin (Gateshead), Michael Jack (Carlisle), Roy Allen (Bedlington), Tommy Raw (Scarborough), Danny Brunskill (Bishop Auckland)

WAKEFIELD-EMLEY
Goalkeepers: Paul Cuss (Huddersfield)
Defenders: Chris Kamara (Goole), Paul David (Bradley R), Nicky Wood (Bradford PA), Calum Selby (Barnsley), Scott Bairstow (Farsley Celtic), Dean Fearon (Stocksbridge PS), Richard Hirst (Ossett Alb), Gareth O'Reilly (Accrington Stanley)
Midfield: Adam Muller (Worksop), Robert Tonks (Local football), Andy Wilson (Ossett Alb), Chris Prasher (Youth team), Craig Hitchen (Youth team), Matthew Bland (Silsden), Martin Bland (Silsden)
Forwards: Rob Painter (Bradford PA), Rudi Coleano (Farsley Celtic), Scott Clarke (Youth team), Steve Kenworthy (Huddersfield), Max Joice (Brighouse), Lee Ryan (Garforth), JP Flynn (Youth team)

WHITBY TOWN
Goalkeepers: David Campbell (Guisborough)
Defenders: Paul Atkinson (Peterlee), Graeme Williams (Guisborough), Brian Linighan (Worksop), Chris Lynch (Thornaby)
Midfield: Craig Veart (Spennymoor), Alex Gildea (Scarborough), Graham Robinson (Gateshead), Scott Nicholson (Tow Law), Paul Campbell (Darlington), Danny Farthing (Goole)
Forwards: Steve Johnson (Darlington RA), David McTiernan (Peterlee), Anthony Ormerod (Scarborough), Liam Gildea (Scarborough), David Yale (Peterlee)

WITTON ALBION
Goalkeepers: Paul Gibson (Droylsden)
Defenders: Gareth Evans (Skelmersdale), Gary Furnival (Manchester C), Dave Tickle (Leigh RMI), Brian Pritchard (Southport), Danny Webster (Kidsgrove)
Midfield: Andy Barlow (Burscough), Dave Nolan (Marine), Adam Foy (Barnton), John Stannard (Marine), Alex Kevan (Droylsden), Darrell Dicken (Kidsgrove)
Forwards: Michael Yates (Lancaster), Mike Moseley (Runcorn), Lee Madin (Accrington Stanley), Craig Sargeson (Rossendale), Michael Bird (Northwich)

WORKINGTON
Goalkeepers: Adam Collin (Newcastle Utd)
Defenders: Paul O'Neill (Northwich), Anthony Wright (Carlisle), Alan Gray (Queen of the South), David Lynn (Carlisle), Neil Fitzhenry (Leigh RMI), Marc Green (Bamber Bridge), Will Varty (Carlisle)
Midfield: Craig Potts (Gretna), Matt Henney (Gretna), Rob Ennis (Parton), Tony Hopper (Barrow), Matthew Lea (Gretna)
Forwards: Ian Arnold (Barrow), Graham Goulding (Wilmington Hammerheads (USA)), Steve Archibald (Queen of the South), Gary Milne (Gretna), Craig Johnston (Carlisle)

NORTH PREMIER LEAGUE DIVISION ONE
LEVEL 4

FINAL LEAGUE TABLE 2003-04

		P	W	D	L	F	A	Pts
1.	HYDE UNITED	42	24	8	10	79	49	80
2.	MATLOCK TOWN	42	23	7	12	78	51	76
3.	FARSLEY CELTIC	42	20	14	8	78	56	74
4.	LINCOLN UNITED	42	20	11	11	73	53	71
5.	WITTON ALBION	42	17	12	13	61	56	63
6.	GATESHEAD (-4 pts)	42	21	4	17	65	68	63
7.	WORKINGTON	42	17	11	14	70	58	62
8.	LEEK TOWN	42	16	13	13	56	47	61
9.	GUISELEY	42	16	12	14	66	54	60
10.	BAMBER BRIDGE	42	16	12	14	64	53	60
11.	BRIDLINGTON TOWN	42	16	10	16	70	68	58
12.	PRESCOT CABLES	42	16	10	16	63	65	58
13.	BISHOP AUCKLAND	42	14	13	15	61	64	55
14.	OSSETT TOWN (-3 pts)	42	15	10	17	62	73	52
15.	ROSSENDALE UNITED	42	13	12	17	53	62	51
16.	COLWYN BAY	42	14	9	19	56	82	51
17.	NORTH FERRIBY UNITED	42	13	11	18	64	70	50
18.	CHORLEY	42	13	10	19	54	70	49
19.	STOCKSBRIDGE PS	42	12	12	18	57	69	48
20.	BELPER TOWN	42	9	15	18	44	58	42
21.	KENDAL TOWN	42	11	7	24	53	79	40
22.	KIDSGROVE ATHLETIC	42	10	9	23	45	67	39

Make up new Premier Division (positions 1–14)

Workington's Graham Goulding shoots for goal against **Kendal Town**. Photo: Alan Watson

	DIVISION ONE 03-04	1	2	3	4	5	6	7	8	9	10	11	12	13	14	15	16	17	18	19	20	21	22
1	Bamaber Bridge		2-1	1-3	2-0	0-0	1-1	1-2	0-2	1-2	2-3	5-1	3-0	0-0	1-0	4-4	1-1	0-0	2-2	2-1	4-0	1-2	2-0
2	Belper Town	2-1		1-1	0-2	2-0	2-0	1-1	1-1	1-0	0-1	3-0	1-1	0-2	0-1	0-2	0-3	3-0	2-2	0-0	1-0	0-0	1-1
3	Bishop Auckland	0-1	2-4		3-2	1-1	4-1	4-2	2-1	1-0	2-3	2-0	2-0	2-3	1-1	0-1	0-4	2-0	1-1	3-3	2-2	1-2	1-1
4	Bridlington Town	1-0	1-3	2-0		2-0	4-1	3-1	1-0	2-1	3-1	5-1	2-1	3-2	0-1	1-1	2-2	2-4	1-1	0-1	2-2	1-1	2-4
5	Chorley	0-1	1-1	2-1	1-1		3-2	1-2	4-1	1-2	1-0	2-2	2-1	1-0	2-3	2-0	1-2	1-2	4-2	2-0	1-3	1-1	4-1
6	Colwyn Bay	0-5	3-2	2-3	1-1	3-4		1-0	1-3	1-0	1-1	0-5	5-0	1-3	3-3	0-0	1-0	4-4	0-2	1-0	1-1	1-2	0-0
7	Farsley Celtic	1-1	2-2	4-0	2-2	1-0	5-0		3-3	5-3	1-3	2-1	1-1	0-0	2-2	1-2	5-0	2-1	0-2	1-0	3-1	1-0	2-1
8	Gateshead	2-1	2-1	0-3	2-3	1-0	1-2	3-4		1-5	2-1	2-1	2-1	4-2	1-0	1-3	3-2	0-2	1-1	2-0	4-1	1-0	2-3
9	Guiseley	1-1	3-0	1-1	2-1	1-3	1-2	2-0	4-2		0-1	4-0	2-0	1-1	1-2	3-1	1-2	1-1	0-1	2-1	0-0	2-2	3-1
10	Hyde United	4-0	3-1	1-1	3-1	0-0	4-0	1-1	0-2	1-0		1-0	1-0	0-1	2-0	2-1	4-0	5-2	4-1	2-0	1-1	0-1	3-1
11	Kendal Town	2-3	2-1	1-2	1-0	1-1	2-1	2-2	1-2	2-2	1-3		1-2	2-1	2-3	1-2	1-1	0-1	2-3	2-1	2-1	2-1	0-5
12	Kidsgrove Athletic	1-1	2-0	1-1	4-2	2-2	1-2	1-4	2-1	1-2	1-2	2-1		0-1	1-2	1-0	4-1	1-2	0-1	1-3	2-1	0-2	1-1
13	Leek Town	1-0	1-1	0-0	3-2	2-0	0-1	1-2	0-0	2-2	5-2	1-0	1-2		3-1	0-2	1-2	0-1	1-1	2-1	2-0	2-2	1-2
14	Lincoln United	1-1	0-0	0-0	2-0	4-1	2-1	0-1	0-1	2-2	2-0	4-3	2-1	1-1		5-2	3-3	0-0	1-0	4-0	0-0	4-1	1-0
15	Matlock Town	1-0	3-1	0-1	3-5	4-0	1-1	2-0	2-0	1-2	2-5	0-0	3-1	1-0	4-2		1-1	3-0	2-1	4-1	3-1	2-1	4-0
16	North Ferriby United	2-0	2-0	0-3	2-2	2-3	5-0	0-2	1-2	2-0	2-0	3-1	2-1	1-1	0-1	0-2		2-3	4-1	2-3	1-1	1-3	1-1
17	Ossett Town	2-3	2-0	0-0	0-1	1-0	4-1	1-2	4-0	1-2	2-2	0-2	1-1	0-2	3-1	0-4	2-2		2-2	0-0	3-0	2-3	1-2
18	Prescot Cables	2-3	1-0	4-2	1-1	4-1	0-2	0-1	2-0	1-0	0-1	2-1	2-1	1-3	1-0	0-2	3-1	5-3		0-1	2-3	3-0	0-2
19	Rossendale United	3-2	1-1	3-0	3-1	0-0	1-3	1-1	1-3	1-1	1-2	0-0	0-0	1-1	4-2	2-0	1-0	1-2	5-2		0-0	0-1	3-3
20	Stocksbridge Park Steels	1-3	3-3	2-1	2-0	4-0	0-3	2-2	3-0	1-1	2-2	0-2	2-1	0-2	3-2	2-1	3-0	1-2	3-1	2-4		0-1	0-1
21	Witton Albion	0-0	2-0	2-0	2-1	3-1	0-1	2-2	0-2	1-2	4-3	3-1	0-0	1-1	1-3	1-1	1-1	3-1	2-2	5-0	1-3		1-2
22	Workington	1-2	1-1	4-2	1-2	4-0	2-1	2-2	0-2	2-2	1-1	0-1	0-1	3-0	0-5	2-1	2-1	7-0	0-0	0-1	2-0	4-0	

AFC TELFORD

CLUB OFFICIALS

Chairman: Lee Carter
Tel Nos: 019052 410681(H)
01952 423043 (W) 07714 335873 (M)
Directors: L.Carter, Wyn Pryce, Mick Tranter, Ian Dosser, S.Shakeshaft and D.Topping
Club Safety Officer :
D.Topping Tel No: 01952 505979
Simon Shakeshaft, 16 Fernbrook, Dorrington, Shrewsbury SY5 7HY Tel Nos: 01743 719258 (H) 07970 659819 (M)

FOOTBALL MANAGEMENT TEAM

Manager: Bernard McNally
Player/Coach: Neil Howarth

FACT FILE

Formed: 2004

Sponsor: Capgemini

Colours:White with black trim/Black/Black
Change colours: Red with white trim/White/White

Midweek Matches: Tuesday

Ground: The New Bucks Head Stadium, The Bucks Way, Telford TF1 2TU
Tel.No: 01952 640064

Capacity: 4,101 **Seats:** 554 **Cover:** 2,960 **Floodlights:**

Directions: Leave M54 Jct.6 Take A5223 signposted Wellington. Over first island,second exit at second island and left at third. First turning right after railway gridge. Car park entrance on left. Officials make way to hotel car park by ground.

Clubhouse: Hotel.

PREVIOUS **Name:** Telford United
League: Conference

Pages: 48 Price: £2.00
Editors: Rollo Sheridan and James Baylis

Local Press: Stropshire Star, Wellington News

2004-2005 Back Row (L-R): Brin May (Physio), Gareth Jennings, Mark Briggs, Dion Scott, Charlie McKay, Andreas Kattos, Derek Wellings (Kit Manager). **Middle Row:** Glenn Tolley, Arron Lloyd, Alfie Carter, Andy Pryce, Stuart Brock, Tom Griffin, Ben Willetts, Tony Lacey (Supporter). **Front Row:** Luke McNally, Dean Craven, Neil Howarth (Player coach), Bernard McNally (Manager), Sean Parrish (Player Community Officer), Matt Johnson, Byron Benton.

BELPER TOWN

CLUB OFFICIALS

Chairman: Phil Varney
President: T.B.A.
Secretary: Bryan Rudkin
12 Crown Terrace,Bridger Street,Belper,
Derbyshire DE56 1BD Tel: 01773 825468
(H) 07710 444195 (M)
Press Officer: Nigel Oldrini

FOOTBALL MANAGEMENT TEAM

Manager: Gary Hayward
Asst Manager:Andy Freeman

FACT FILE

Formed: 1883
Nickname: Nailers
Colours: Yellow/black/black & yellow
Change colours: All white
Midweek home matchday: Wednesday
Reserves' League: Midlands Reg All
2003-2004
Captain: Steve Kennedy
Top Goalscorer: Sean Gummer
Player of the Year: Gary Ingham

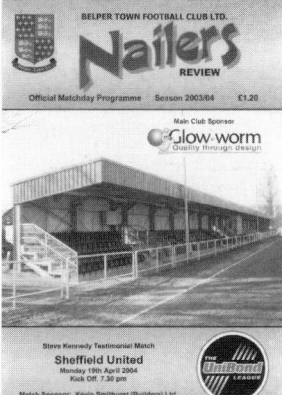

Pages:36 Price £1.20
Editor:Dave Laughlin 01773 856556

Local Press: Belper News, Derby Evening Telegraph, Belper Express
Local Radio: BBC Radio Derby

GROUND

Address: Christchurch Meadow, Bridge Street, Belper DE56 1BA (01773825549).
Directions: From M1 North, Jnct 28 onto A38 towards Derby, turn off at A610 (Ripley/Nottingham), then 4 exit at roundabout towards Ambergate. At junction with A6 (Hurt Arms Hotel) left to Belper. Ground on right past traffic lights. 400 yards from Belper (BR)
Capacity: 2,000 Cover:850 Seats: 488
Clubhouse: Open matchdays and for functions with bar and hot and cold food available.

PREVIOUS
Leagues: Central Alliance 57-61; Midland Co's 61-82, Northern Counies East 1982-97
Grounds: Acorn Ground prior to 1951
Names: None

CLUB RECORDS
Attendance: 3,200 v Ilkeston Town, 1955
Goalscorer: Mick Lakin 231
Appearances: Gil Rhodes
Fee Received: £2,000 for Craig Smith from Hinckley United
Fee Paid: £2,000 to Ilkeston Town for Jamie Eaton. 2001
Victory: 15-2 v Nottingham Forest 'A'1956
Defeat: 0-12 v Goole Town 1965

BEST SEASON
FA Vase: Semi-final 94-95
FA Amateur Cup: Not entered
FA Trophy: 3rd Qual Rd 97-98
FA Cup: 1st Rd Prop 1887-88 v Sheff Wed. (H) 2-3 (4th Qual. Rnd 1957-58, 00-01 ,01-02)

HONOURS
Northern Counties East Lge 84-85, Midland Counties Lg 79-80; Central Alliance Lge 58-59; Derbys Snr Cup 58-59 60-61 62-63 79-80

Players progressing: None

Back Row (L-R): Bob Elliott (Physio), Andy Freeman (Asst. Manager), Steve Kennedy, Jordan, Lambert, Anthony Tansley, Gary Ingham, Micky Allsop, Dominic Crookes, Tim Hogg, Gary Hayward (Manager). **Front Row:** Wayne Thornhill, Paul Hurrell, Matt Moran, Sean Gummer, Richie Butler, Lee Stratford, Paul Bennett (Kit Man), Neil Ashley.

BRIGG TOWN

CLUB OFFICIALS

President: Mike.Harness

Chairman: Mike Harness 01724 869893 (H)

Secretary: John Martin, Kingfisher Lodge,The Old Stackyard,Wrawby, Brigg, N.Lincs DN208RH Tel:01652 654526 (H) 07812 108195 (M)

FACT FILE

Formed: 1864 Nickname: Zebras

Colours: Black & white stripes/black/red

Change colours: Yellow/Blue

Midweek Matchday: Wednesday

FOOTBALL MANAGEMENT TEAM

Manager: Dave McLean

Ground: The Hawthorns, Hawthorn Avenue, Brigg (01652 652767) Office: 01652 651605

Directions: From M180 Junc 4 Scunthorpe East, A18 through Brigg leaving on Wrawby Rd, left into recreation ground and follow road into BTFC.

Capacity: 4,000 Seats: 250 Cover: 2 Stands Floodlights: Yes

Clubhouse: Licensed club open matchdays **Shop**: Contact: Kiron Brown (01652 656189)

PROGRAMME

Programme: 24 pages

HONOURS F.A. Challenge Vase 95-96; Northern Co's East Lg Presidents Cup R-up 91-92 92-93, R-up 95-96; Lincs Lg 49-50 53-54 73-74 75-76 (Div 1 68-69 69-70 70-71 71-72, Lg Cup 49-50 65-66 68-69 69-70 72-73); Mids Co's Lg 77-78 (Lg Cup 77-78); Lincs `A' Snr Cup 75-76 76-77 94-95 99-00; Lincs `B' Snr Cup (5), NCE (Premier) 00-01

PREVIOUS **Leagues:** Lindsey; Lincs 48-76; Midland Counties 76-82
Grounds: Manor House Convent, Station Rd (pre 1939); Brocklesby Ox 1939-59

BEST SEASON **FA Vase:** Winners 95-96, 02-03 **FA Cup:** 4th Rd Q

RECORD Attendance: 2,000 v Boston U. 1953 (at Brocklesby Ox)

Brigg Town Football Club Team 2004-2005 season at The Hawthorns.
Picture by Lee Beel/Scunthorpe Telegraphs

CHORLEY

CLUB OFFICIALS

Chairman: Ken Wright

Commercial Manager: T.B.A.

Secretary / Press Officer:
Mick Wearmouth
6 Avondale Rd, Chorley, Lancs. PR7 2ED
Tel: 01257 271395

FOOTBALL MANAGEMENT TEAM
Player - Manager: Jogn Hughes
Reserve Team Manager: Dave Haslam

FACT FILE
Formed: 1883
Nickname: The Magpies
Sponsors: Lex - Auto
Colours:White & black stripes/black/black
Change colours: All blue
Midweek matchday: Tuesday
Reserve League: Lancashire League
Local Press: Lancs Evening Post, Chorley Guardian.
Local Radio: Radio Lancs.
2003-2004
P.o.Y.: Billy McCartney
Top Scorer: Andy Mason
2004-2005 Captain: Ian Leather

PROGRAMME
Pages: 32 Price: £1.
Editor: John Newman

GROUND Victory Park, Duke Street, Chorley, Lancs Tel: 01257 263406
Directions: M61 jct 6, A6 to Chorley, going past Yarrow Bridge Hotel on Bolton Rd turn left at 1st lights into Pilling Lane, 1st right into Ashley St..,ground 2nd left. From M6; jct 27, follow signs to Chorley, left at lights,continue for 2 1/2 miles on A49, right onto B5251, on entering Chorley turn right into Duke Street 200yds after Plough Hotel. 1/4 mile from Chorley (BR).
Capacity: 4,100 Cover: 2,800 Seats: 900
Clubhouse: 01257 275662. Open every evening. Weekend entertainment, Snacks available
Club Shop: Yes.

PREVIOUS Leagues: Lancs Alliance 1890-94; Lancs 94-1903; Lancs Comb. 03-68, 69-70;Northern Premier 68-69, 70-72, 82-88; Cheshire County 72-82; GMV Conference 88-90.
Grounds: Dole Lane 1883-1901; Rangletts Park 01-05; St George's Park 05-20. Name: None

CLUB RECORDS **Attendance:** 9,679 v Darwen, 1931-32. **Goalscorer:** Peter Watson.
Fee Paid: Undisclosed to Marine for Brian Ross 1995. **Fee Received:** £22,500 for Paul Mariner (Plymouth, 1973).

BEST SEASON **FA Cup:** 2nd Rd 86-87 v P.N.E. (A) 0-5 after 2-2 at Blackburn, 90-91 v Shrewsbury Town (A) 0-1
League Clubs defeated in F.A. Cup : Wolverhampton W 1986-87 and Bury 1990-91 **FA Trophy:** Semi-Final 1995-96.

HONOURS Northern Premier Lg 87-88, Cheshire Co. Lg 75-76 76-77 81-82, Lancs Comb. 19-2022-23 27-28 28-29 32-33 33-34 45-46 59-60 60-61 63-64 (R-up 21-22 26-27 48-4962-63 64-65 65-66, Lg Cup 24-25 58-59 62-63), Lancs Lg 1896-97 98-99, Lancs Alliance 1892-93 (R-up 94-95), Lancs Jnr Cup 1894-95 1908-09 23-24 39-40 45-4657-58 58-59 60-61 63-64 64-65 75-76 79-80 81-82 82-83.

Players Progressing: Charles Ashcroft (Liverpool 1946),William Healey (Arsenal 49), Stan Howard (Huddersfield 52), Derek Hogg (Leicester 52), William Norcross (Southport 59), Micky Walsh (Blackpool 71),Paul Mariner (Plymouth 73), Graham Barrow (Wigan 76), Steve Galliers (Wimbledon77), Kevin Tully (Bury 80), Geoff Twentyman (Preston 83), Gary Buckley (Bury84), Chris Hunter (Preston 84).

Back Row (L-R): Lee Smith, Danny Mills, Anthony Hogan, Lee Bracey, Ian Leather, Keith Hill, Jim McBride (Coach), Neil Smith, Billy McCartney, Jamie Bates, Danny Queeley.
Front Row: Lee Ashcroft, Lee Pryers, Lee Clitheroe, David eatock, Andy Mason, Matt Edgington.

CLITHEROE

CLUB OFFICIALS

Chairman: David Burgess
Vice Chairman:John Robinson
Directors: Dolin Wilson, David Burgess, Colin Ball,Terry Nelson and Keith Lord.

Secretary: Colin Wilson, 4 Moss Street, Clitheroe, Lancs BB7 1DP
Tel/Fax: 01200 424370
Mobile: 07714 382232

FACT FILE

Formed: 1877. Nickname: The Blues
Colours: All Blue
Change colours: All yellow
Midweek matchday: Tuesday
Reserves' Lge: N.W.C.L
Website: www.clitheroefc.co.uk

FOOTBALL MANAGEMENT TEAM

Manager: Jimmy Mullen
Asst Manager: Bernard MackaY
Physio: Colin Edwards
Captain: James McIlvogue

GROUNDLlanelian Road, Old Colwyn, N.Wales. Tel: 01492 514581
Email Address:CBFC@MIKEROBS.COMDirections: M55 North Wales Coast - approaching Colwyn Bay take 1st exit signposted Old Colwyn, left at bottom slip road, straight over r'bout into Llanelian Rd - ground half mile on right. 2 miles from Colwyn Bar BR station.
Capacity: 2,500 Seats: 250 Cover: 700
Clubhouse: Open matchdays only.
Club Shop: Yes - contact: Matthew Motram (01492 515951) Metal Badges: Yes

Pages: 28 Price: £1
Editor: Aled Williams(07748 788168)
Local Press: North Wales Weekly News, North Wales Pioneer.
Club Website: www.cbfc.skynow.co.uk

PREVIOUS Leagues: Nth Wales Coast 01-21 33-35; Welsh National 21-30; Nth Wales Comb. 30-31; Welsh Lg (Nth) 45-84; North West Counties 84-91
Grounds: Eiras Park 1930-82; Llanelian Road 82-92; Northwich Victoria FC 92-93; Ellesmere Port Stadium94-95 (2 years in exile thro' dispute with FAW re League of Wales).

CLUB RECORDS **Attendance:** 5,000 (at Eiras Park) v Borough United, 1964.
Goalscorer: Peter Donnelly **Appearances:** Bryn A Jones

BEST SEASON **FA Trophy:** Quarter Finals 96-97.
F.A Cup: Second Round Proper 95-96 v Blackpool (A) 0-2. League club defeated: Wrexham(Welsh Cup)

HONOURS Northern Premier Lg Div 1 91-92 (Div 1 Cup 91-92); North West Counties Lg R-up90-91 (Div 3 R-up 83-84, Lg Cup 88-89, Floodlit Cup 90-91; Welsh Cup SF 91-92;Welsh National Lg R-up 27-28 29-30; Nth Wales Comb. 30-31; Welsh Lg Nth 64-6582-83 83-84 (R-up 35-36 45-46 63-64), Lg Cup 27-28; Alves Cup 63-64; Cookson Cup 73-74 79-80 80-81 81-82 83-84; Barritt Cup 79-80 81-82 83-84; Nth Wales Coast Chal. Cup 30-31 31-32 81-82 82-83 83-84 95-96 97-98; Nth Wales Coast Jnr Cup 1898-99. North Wst Coast Cup 99-00.

Players progressing: Peter Suddaby (Blackpool), Gareth Davies (Wrexham).

Back row, left to right: Keith Lord, Steve McCullough, Steve McDonald, John Paul Fagan, Russ Clark, Neil Spencer, Paul Stansfield, Barrie Hart, Andy Cowking, MartinAspinwall, Gary Jackson and MartinEatough. Front row: Stuart Todhunter, Kris Richens, Chris Whittingham, David Burgess, Lee Sculpher, Stewart Parkinson, Glyn Barker, Adam Gardner and Lee Cryer.

COLWYN BAY

CLUB OFFICIALS

Chairman: Henry Chapman

Directors:M.Roberts,R.Hayley,C.Chambers, Miss M Jones, Miss J.E.Jones

Commercial Manager: Carol Beard

Secretary : Mike Roberts,
18 Belgrave Road,Colwyn Bay, N.Wales
Tel Nos:01492 534724(H)
07887 782565 (M)

Press Officer: Andy Owens: 0161 4316938

FOOTBALL MANAGEMENT TEAM

Manager: Jimmy Mullen
Asst Manager: Bernard MackaY
Physio: Colin Edwards
Captain: James McIlvogue

FACT FILE

Formed: 1885
Nickname: Meredith & KirkhamSponsors: Bay View Centre
Colours: All Sky Blue.
Change colours: GoldReserve Team:
Midweek home matchday: Tuesday
Unofficial Club Website: www.cbfc.tk

2003-2004

P.o.Y.: Matthew Parry
Top Scorer: Matthew Johnson

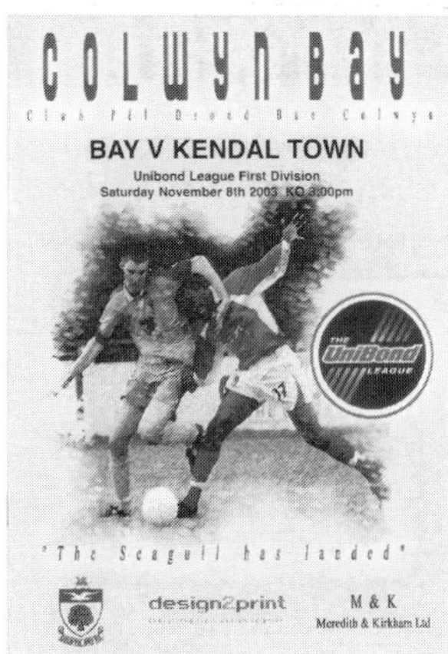

COLWYN BAY
BAY V KENDAL TOWN
Unibond League First Division
Saturday November 8th 2003 KO 3:00pm
'The Seagull has landed'
design2print
M & K
Meredith & Kirkham Ltd

Pages: 28 Price: £1
Editor: Aled Williams(07748 788168)
Local Press: North Wales Weekly News, North Wales Pioneer.
Club Website: www.cbfc.skynow.co.uk

GROUNDLlanelian Road, Old Colwyn, N.Wales. Tel: 01492 514581
Email Address:CBFC@MIKEROBS.COMDirections: M55 North Wales Coast - approaching Colwyn Bay take 1st exit signposted Old Colwyn, left at bottom slip road, straight over r'bout into Llanelian Rd - ground half mile on right. 2 miles from Colwyn Bar BR station.
Capacity: 2,500 Seats: 250 Cover: 700
Clubhouse: Open matchdays only.
Club Shop: Yes - contact: Matthew Motram (01492 515951) Metal Badges: Yes

PREVIOUS
Leagues: Nth Wales Coast 01-21 33-35; Welsh National 21-30; Nth Wales Comb. 30-31; Welsh Lg (Nth) 45-84; North West Counties 84-91
Grounds: Eiras Park 1930-82; Llanelian Road 82-92; Northwich Victoria FC 92-93; Ellesmere Port Stadium94-95 (2 years in exile thro' dispute with FAW re League of Wales).

CLUB RECORDS
Attendance: 5,000 (at Eiras Park) v Borough United, 1964.
Goalscorer: Peter Donnelly **Appearances:** Bryn A Jones

BEST SEASON
FA Trophy: Quarter Finals 96-97.
F.A Cup: Second Round Proper 95-96 v Blackpool (A) 0-2. League club defeated: Wrexham(Welsh Cup)

HONOURS
Northern Premier Lg Div 1 91-92 (Div 1 Cup 91-92); North West Counties Lg R-up90-91 (Div 3 R-up 83-84, Lg Cup 88-89, Floodlit Cup 90-91; Welsh Cup SF 91-92;Welsh National Lg R-up 27-28 29-30; Nth Wales Comb. 30-31; Welsh Lg Nth 64-6582-83 83-84 (R-up 35-36 45-46 63-64), Lg Cup 27-28; Alves Cup 63-64; Cookson Cup 73-74 79-80 80-81 81-82 83-84; Barritt Cup 79-80 81-82 83-84; Nth Wales Coast Chal. Cup 30-31 31-32 81-82 82-83 83-84 95-96 97-98; Nth Wales Coast Jnr Cup 1898-99. North Wst Coast Cup 99-00.

Players progressing: Peter Suddaby (Blackpool), Gareth Davies (Wrexham).

Back. James McIlvogue, Martyn Davies, Mick Heathcote, Matt Parry, Neil Coverley, Lloyd Roberts.

Front. Paul Wilson, Matt Johnson, Duncan Horler, Gareth John Williams (Mascot), Carl Dwyer, Ben Dews.

Photo Courtesy of: Ian Saunders Colwyn Bay Website http://cbfc.tk

EASTWOOD TOWN

CLUB OFFICIALS

President: George Belshaw
Chairman: Gary Hardy
Vice Chairman: Roy Cheatle
Secretary / Press Officer: Paddy Farrell, 7 Primrose Rise, Newthorpe, Notts. NG16 2BB Tel/Fax: 01773 786186
email: patriciafarrell777@hotmail.com

FOOTBALL MANAGEMENT TEAM

Manager: Bryan Chambers
Ass.Manager: Paul Cox
Physio: David Nicholls

FACT FILE

Formed: 1953
Nickname: The Badgers
Sponsors: T.B.A.
Colours: White with black trim/black/black
Change Colours: All Red or Blue
Midweek matchday: Tuesday

2003-2004

Captain: Paul Gould
Top Scorer: Jamie Morgan
Player of the Year:Danny Bryant

EASTWOOD TOWN FOOTBALL CLUB
5th Round The FA Vase
IS SPONSORED BY EUROCELL PROFILES LTD
euro cell
BUILDING PLASTICS
EASTWOOD TOWN v STONE DOMINOES
OFFICIAL PROGRAMME
PRICE £1

Programme: Pages: 50 Price: £1.00
Editor: Paddy Farrell 01773786186
Website: www.eastwoodtownfc.com

GROUND: Coronation Park, Eastwood, Notts. Tel: 01773 715823
Directions: From North - M1 jct 27, follow Heanor signs via Brinsley to lights in Eastwood. Turn left then first right after Fire Station - ground entrance on Chewton Street. From South - M1 jct 26, A610 to Ripley, leave at 1st exit(B6010), follow to Eastwood, left at lights, first left at `Man in Space' -ground entrance on Chewton Street. Nearest station - Langley Mill. Buses every10 mins (R11, R12 or R13) from Victoria Centre, Nottingham - approx 40 mins
Capacity: 5,500 Cover: 1,150 Seats: 650
Clubhouse: Social club open normal licensing hours (Sat 11am-11pm, midweek matches 6.30-11pm). Hot & cold food available. Steward; Jane Rowley
Club Shop: Sells programmes, mugs, scarves, badges etc. Contact R K Storer - 0115 9199596

PREVIOUS **Leagues:** Notts Alliance 53-61; Central Alliance 61-67; East Mids 67-71; Midland Counties 71-82; N.C.E. 82-88; N.P.L. 88-03

RECORDS: Attendance: 2,723 v Enfield, FA Amateur Cup, Feb 1965.

Appearances: Arthur Rowley, over 800 1st team games, but not a single booking, 1955-76

HONOURS: Northern Counties (East) Lg R-up 82-83 84-85; Midland Counties Lg 75-76 R-up 74-75 77-78, Lg Cup 77-78 79-80; Central Alliance 63-64 R-up 64-65; Notts Alliance 56-57 R-up x 6, Lg Cup 55-56; E. Mids Lg R-up 68-69; Notts Senior Cup x 9 R-up x 5; Evans Halshaw F'lit Cup 94-95 R-up 89-90 97-98; Mid Reg. All (Prem) 99-00 R-up 97-8, 98-9. MRA Chall. Cup 01-02

GRESLEY ROVERS

CLUB OFFICIALS
Chairman: Mark Evans
President: Gordon Duggins
Vice Chairman: George Sutton
Secretary / Press Officer: Neil Betteridge, 34 Thorpe Downs Road, Church Gresley, Swadlincote, Derbys DE11 9FB
Tel: 01283 226229
Commercial Director: Mark Evans

FACT FILE
Formed: 1882
Nickname: The Moatmen
Sponsors: Ashley Adams
Colours: Red/white/red
Change colours: White/black/white
Midweek matchday: Tuesday
Reserves' League: Midland Comb (Res. Div.)
Club Website: www.gresleyrovers.com

FOOTBALL MANAGEMENT TEAM
Manager: Gary Norton
Asst Manager: Alan Titterton
Physio: Jody Brooks Capt: Matt Smith

2003-2004
Top Scorer: Shaun Harrad
Player of the Year: Dale Belford

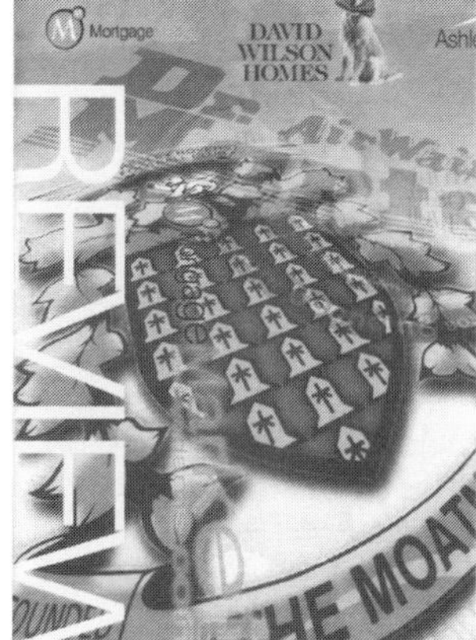

Pages: 32 Price: £1.00
Editor:Chairman

Local Press: Derby Evening Telegraph, Burton Mail, Burton Trader, SwadlincoteTimes
Local Radio: BBC Radio Derby

Ground Moat Ground, Moat Street, Church Gresley, Swadlincote, Derbys., DE11 9RE. Tel: 01283 216315
Directions: To A444 via either the A5, A38, A5121 or M42 , Junction 11. On reaching A444 head for Castle Gresley. Take exit at large island to Church Gresley, at next island 2nd exit (Church St), then 2nd left (School St) then 1st left into Moat St. 5 miles Burton-on-Trent (BR). Buses from Swadlincote and Burton
Capacity: 2,000 Cover: 1,200 Seats: 400 Floodlights: Yes
Clubhouse: Inside ground, open Mon & Thurs evenings & matchdays
Club Shop: Sells merchandise, programmes, metal badges etc.

PREVIOUS **Leagues:** Burton Lge 1892-95 97-01 09-10 43-45, Derbyshire Sen 1895-97 02-03,Leics Sen 1890-91 98-99 08-09 10-12 15-16 35-42 45-49, Notts 01-02, Midland 03-06, Central All 11-15 19-25 49-53 59-67, Birmingham Comb 25-33 53-54, Birmingham (now West Mids) 54-59 75-92, Central Comb 33-35, East Mids 67-75
Grounds: Mushroom Lane, Albert Village 1882-95, Church Str., Church, Gresley. 1895-1909

CLUB RECORDS **Attendance:** 3,950 v Burton Albion, Birmingham (now West Mids) Lg Division One 57-58
Win: 23-0 v Holy Cross Priory, Leics Jun Cup 1889-90 **Defeat:** 1-15 v Burton Crusaders 1886-87
Career Goalscorer: Gordon Duggins 306 **Career Appearances:** Dennis King 579
Transfer fee received: £30,000 for Justin O'Reilly (Port Vale 1996)
Transfer fee paid: £2,500 for David Robinson (Ilkeston Town 97)

BEST SEASON **FA Vase:** Runners-up 90-91, (SF 92-93) **FA Trophy:** Qtr Finals 95-96
FA Cup: 1st Rd Proper: 30-31 (1-3 at York City), 94-95 (1-7 at Crewe Alex.) League clubs defeated: None

HONOURS Southern Lge Champ 96-97; FA Vase R-up 90-91; West Mids Lg 90-91 91-92 (R-up 85-86 88-89); Lg Cup 88-89 R-Up. 86-87 91-92; Southern Lg Mid Div R-up 92-93; Derbys Snr Cup (7), (R-Up (3); Leics Snr Cup 1898-99 46-47 (R-Up 1899-90 45-46); Leics Sen Lg 00-01 46-47 47-48 R-Up (7); Coalville Charity Cup 46-47; Derby Senior Cup (S) (2) R-Up 00-01 01-02 Bass Vase (6); Cent All 64-65 66-67 R-Up(3) (Lg Cup 52-53); East Mids Reg Lg (2) R-Up (2); Dr.Martens (S Lge) Cup Fin 93-94

Players progressing: Phil Gee (Derby County 85), Mark Blount (Sheffield Utd 94), Colin Loss (Bristol City 94), Justin O'Reilly (Port Vale 96)

Back row, left to right: Jonathon Rowe, Chris White, Leon Doughty, Jamie Barrett, Emeka Ejiofor, Justin Rowe, Carl Slater, Jamie Hood, Mark Leesonand Donovan Rowe. **Middle row::** Richard Wardle, Liam Hebberd, Andy Simpson, Dale Belford, Brad Clarke, Karl Brown, Sean Gummer, and Gary White. **Front row:** Tom Guiney, Ian Bluck, Steve Hinks (Coach), Mark Evans (Chairman), Gary Norton (Manager), Alan Titterton (Asst.Manager), Ashley Dodds and John Branch.

ILKESTON TOWN

PROGRAMME

Pages: 32 Price: £1.50

Editors: Mic Capill

CLUB OFFICIALS

Acting Chairman: Dave Pullan

President: Robert Lindsay

Directors: Mike Tinkley (Co.Sec), Dave Morgan, Ian Brookes, Dave Pullan, Dave Harwood, Andrew Raisin, Robert Easton & Paul Millership

Secretary: Keith Burnand, 2 Woodland Grove, Clowne, Chesterfield S43 4AT

Tel: 01246 811063 (H) 07887 832125 (M)

Commercial Management:
J Sports Promotions Ltd

2003-04 Player of the Year & Top Scorer: Chris Freestone

FACT FILE

Re Formed: 1945
Nickname: The Robins
Sponsors: Ilkeston Co-op Travel
Colours: Red/blac/red
Change colours:All White
Midweek matchday:Tuesday
Reserves' League: Midland Reg. Alliance

FOOTBALL MANAGEMENT TEAM

Manager: Phil Stant
Asst Manager: Ernie Oliver
Reserves.Manager: Andy Worrall
Physio: Richard Barnes Captain: Mark Lever

GROUND New Manor Ground, Awsworth Rd, Ilkeston Tel: 0115 932 4094

Directions: M42 to M1 junc 23A, continue on M1 to junc 26, exit left onto A610 towards Ripley, take 1st exit signed Awsworth and Ilkeston (A6096), follow bypass signed Ilkeston A6096. Turn right after 1/2 mile signed Cotmanhay. Ground 200 yards on left

Capacity: 3,500 Seats: 270 Cover: 1,100 Floodlights: Yes

Clubhouse: Open Wed-Fri 7-11pm, Sat-Sun noon-3 & 7-11pm, and Mon or Tue if there is a match. Snacks behind bar. Large tea bar open matchdays 2-5pm (6.30-9pm for night games)

Club Shop: Sells wide range of souvenirs & programmes. Contact Manager Craig Lamont (0115 9305 622) or club secretary

PREVIOUS
Leagues: Midland 1894-1902 25-58 61-71; Notts & Derby Senior 1945-47; CentralAlliance 47-61; Midland Counties 1961-71 73-82; Southern League 1971-73; Northern Co.East 1982-86; Central Midlands 86-90; West Midlands (Regional) 90-94.
Ground: Manor Ground, Manor Rd (1945-92)

CLUB RECORDS
Attendance: 2,504 v Boston United FA Cup 1st Rd 15/11/97
Win: 14-2 v Codnor M.W 46-47: 13-0 v Swanwick OB 46-47
Defeat: 1-11 v Grantham T. 47-48: 0-10 v VS Rugby 85-86
Career Goalscorer: Jackie Ward 141. **Career Appearances:** Terry Swincoe 377
Season Goalscorer: Barry Jepson 62, 1952-53
Transfer fee paid: £7,500 Justin O'Reilly (Southport 1998) **Fee received:** £25,000 for Francis Green (Peterborough Utd)

BEST SEASON
FA Cup: 2nd Round - 1997-98 1-1, 1-2 v Scunthorpe Utd, 1999-00 0-3 (A) after 1-1 (H) v Rushden & Diamonds
FA Vase: 4th Round 88-89 1-2 v Tamworth
FA Trophy: 3rd Round 82-83 1-5 v Enfield, 94-95 2-2, 1-2 v Kidderminster H

HONOURS
Southern Lge, Midland Div 94-95, R-up 97-98; West Mids (Regional) Lg 93-94, Lg Cup 93-94, Div 1 91-92, Lg Cup 91-92; Central Mids Lg Cup 87-88; Midland Lg 67-68 R-up 1898-99; Midland Co Lg 67-68; Central Alliance 51-52 52-53 53-54 54-55 R-up 47-48 55-56 Derbyshire Senior Cup: Winners 1949, 53, 56, 58, 63, 83, 93 and 2000 Runners-Up: 2003-04

Back Row (L-R): Chris Thompson, Richard Lucas, Pascal Foreman, Ross Turner, Ryan Hindley, Jared Hather.
Middle Row: Chris Dawes (Kit Manager), Gilberto Palma, Steve Johnson, Liam Walshe, Tony Brown, Craig Swinscoe, Steve Chettle, Rick Brewer, Richard Barnes (Physio), Andy Worrall (Reserve Team Manager).
Front Row: Tom Mallinson, Paul Smith, Stuart Copnell, Dave Morgan (Director of Football), Ernie Oliver (Asst. Manager), Phil Stant (Manager), Keith Burnand (Secretary), Darren Knowles, Paul Eshelby, David Jervis.

KENDAL TOWN

CLUB OFFICIALS

Chairman: David Willan

Directors: D.Willan,C.Campbell, P.Knipe, B.Nicholson, G.O'Callaghan and J.Wharton

Secretary: Craig Campbell,
34 High Sparrowmire,Kendal,
Cumbria LA9 5PD
Tel: 01539 734209 (H)

Match Sec: John Wharton
3 Vickers Hill, Kendal, Cumbria.
Tel: 01539 734209

Press Officer: John Wharton

Website: www.kendaltownfc.co.uk

FACT FILE

F ormed: 1920 Nickname: Town

Colours: Black & white stripes/black/black

Change colours:All yellow

Midweek home matchday: Tuesday

Local Press: Westmorland Gazette
Lancaster Evening Post

Local Radio: Cumbria, The Bay. & Lakeland

MANAGEMENT TEAM

Manager: Tony Hesketh

Assistant Manager Barry Stimpson

Physio: Christian Chow Capt: Stuart Cuff

PROGRAMME

Pages 32 Price £1.00

Editor: Peter Hartley 01539 720448

GROUND Parkside Road, Kendal, Cumbria
Tel: 01539 727472 (office) 01539 722469 (Club)

Directions: M6 junction 36, follow signs for Kendal (South), right at lights, left at r-bout to `K' Village - Parkside Rd on right opposite factory main offices - ground 400 yds. A mile & a half from Oxenholme (BR) station - bus service to `K' village, No 41 or 41A

Capacity: 2,490 Cover: 1,000 Seats: 450

Clubhouse: The Park, open all matchdays. Pies & pasties available

Club Shop: Yes Manager Peter Knipe Tel No: 07979 555313

PREVIOUS **Leagues:** Westmorland; North Lancs; Lancs Combination 45-68; Northern Premier 68-83; North West Counties 83-87

CLUB RECORDS **Attendance:** 5,184 v Grimsby Town, FA Cup 1st Rd 1955
Goalscorer: Tom Brownlee. **Win:** 11-0 v Great Harwood 22/3/47. **Defeat:** 0-10 v Stalybridge Celtic 1/9/84
Fee Paid: Undisclosed for Tom Brownlee (Bradford C., 66). **Fee Received:** £10,250 for Andy Milner (Man. City 95)

BEST SEASON **FA Vase:** 3rd Rd 89-90 **FA Trophy:** 2nd Rd 80-81.
FA Cup: 2nd Rd replay 63-64, 1-4 v Chesterfield(A) after 1-1. 2nd Rd 49-50, 1st Rd 45-4648-49 52-53 54-55 55-56 64-65

HONOURS Lancs Comb. 48-49 64-65 (R-up 45-46 53-54 61-62 63-64, Lg Cup 55-56 60-61), Westmorland Snr Cup(12) 24-25 31-33 35-36 46-48 63-64 65-66 71-72 86-8789-89 90-91 Lancashire Senior Cup: 2002-2003

Players progressing: John Laidlaw (Carlisle 1946), Louis Cardwell (Crewe 1947),Herbert Keen (Barrow 1953), Alec Aston (Preston 1955), Horace Langstreth(Torquay 1956), John Simpson (Lincoln 1957), Dennis Rogers (Accrington 1959),Tom Brownlee (Bradford City 1965), Peter McDonnell (Bury 1973), Keith Silken(Workington 1973), Roger Wicks (Darlington 1981), Andy Milner (Man City)

Back row, left to right: Bruce Richardson (Ass Man), Adam Tower, Lee Pennington, Richard Close (Captain), Lee Ward, Philip Hodgson, Andy Owen, Damian Corcoran, Lee Bowen, Peter Smith (Manager) and Stan Casey (Trainer). **Front row:** James Sheppard, Chris Park, Mike McKechnie, Dave Foster, Ryan Close (Mascot), Gary Prosser, Gareth Jones, Jamie Close,Ian Simpson

KIDSGROVE ATHLETIC

CLUB OFFICIALS

Chairman: John Bailey

Vice Chairman: Stan Brown

Directors: John Bailey, Alan Thompson, Arthur Duckworth, John Rowley, Ernie Langford and Stan Brown

President: Ernie Langford

Secretary: Alan Thompson
7 Sandown Road, Crewe, Cheshire CW1 3TE
Tel: 01270 256588 (H) 07712 956400 (M)

FACT FILE

Formed: 1952
Nickname: "The Grove"
Colours: All Royal Blue with white trim
Change Colours: All yellow
Midweek Matches: Monday

FOOTBALL MANAGEMENT TEAM

Manager:Anthony Buckle
Physio: Graham Plant

KIDSGROVE
ATHLETIC F.C.
Out of the Blue
V Buxton F.C.
F.A. Cup 1st Round Preliminary
£1

PROGRAMME
Pages: 32 Price: £1
Editor: John Naisbett
Tel: 01270 874517 (H) 07881 511731(M)

GROUND: Clough Hall, Hollinswood Road, Kidsgrove, Stoke-on-Trent, Staffs
Tel: 01782 782412

Directions: M6 Jct 16, A500 towards Stoke, 2nd jctn onto A34 towards Manchester, turn right at 1st lights down hill,rt at lights into Cedar Rd , 2nd right into Lower Ash Rd, 3rd left into Hollinwood Rd to ground. BR Kidsgrove (5mins)
Capacity: 4,500 Seats: 400 Cover: 600 Floodlights: Yes

Clubhouse: Yes. Food matchdays. Seating 180 with Sky TV, Big Screen
Club Shop: Yes: Manager Ray Green Tel No: 01782 773640

HONOURS NWC Div. 1 97-98, 01-02; NWC Chall. Cup 97-98;
Mid Cheshire Lg 70-71,78-79 86-87 87-88, R-up 68-69 85-86; Lg Cup 67-68 69-70 85-86, R-up 84-85 86-87;
Staffs County Lge; Burslem & Tunstall Lge. Floodlit Trophy R-up: 1999

PREVIOUS **Leagues:** Burslem & Tunstall 1953-63, Staffordshire County 63-66, Mid Cheshire Lge. 66-90, North West Counties 90-2002.
Ground: Vickers & Goodwin 1953-60

BEST SEASON **FA Cup:** 1995, 1st Qualifying Round, 1-3 v Hinckley
FA Vase: Semi-Final 1997-98, 2-3 agg. v Tiverton Town

RECORDS **Attendance:** 1,903 v Tiverton Town, FA Vase S-F 1998.
Victory: 23-0 v Cross Heath W.M.C., Staffs Cup 1965
Transfer Fee Received: Richard Mitchell 2001-02 £3,000
Career Goalscorer: Scott Dundas 53 1997-98
Defeat: 2-7 v Glossop N.E., NWCL Div 1 93-94.

Players Progressing: Mark Bright (Crystal Palace), Ronnie Jepson (Port Vale).

L-R - Back Row: Dave Eaton, Darren Twigg, Chris Holmes, Wayne Mountford, Phil Traynor, Dale Hawtin.
Front Row: Paul Robertson, Steve Ashton, Danny Worthington, Steve Tobin, Andy Porter **Photo**: Bill Wheatcroft

MOSSLEY

CLUB OFFICIALS

Chair: Sam Rigby
President.: J Wharmby

Secretary: David Buckley, 18 Chellow Dene, Mossley, Ashton-under-Lyne, Lancs. OL5 0NB.
Tel: 01457 835989
Email:bobbuckley@mossleyafc.fsnet.co.uk

FACT FILE

Formed: 1903
Nickname: Lilywhites
Colours:White with black trim/black/black
Change: Yellow/blue/blue
Midweek matchday: Tuesday

FOOTBALL MANAGEMENT TEAM

Manager: Jason Beckford
Website: www.welcometo/mossleyafc
www.mossley.20m.com
Email: mossleyafc@hotmail.com

Ground: Seel Park, Market Street, Mossley, Lancs. (Grd 01457 832369), (Club 01457 836104)

Directions: From north; M60 J.23, then A635 to Ashton-U-Lyne, A670 Mossley to town centre Grd behind market place. From south; M6 Junc 19, A556, M56 to Junc 3, A5103 to M'chester, then Mancunian Way (A57M) to A635. Follow Ashton signs 5m, the Mossley signs via A670 to town centre. Rail: Mossley BR. Buses 153 from Manchester, 343 from Oldham, 350 from Ashton

Capacity: 4,500 Cover: 1,500 Seats: 200 Floodlights: Yes

Clubhouse: Open nights and matchdays **Club Shop**: Manager: Mike Charnley 01457 833736

PROGRAMME

28 Pages £1.00
Editor: John A. Cawthorne
Local Press : Oldham Evening Chronicle/ Mossley & Saddleworth Reporter/Manchester Evening News/Tameside Advertiser/Pink Final
Local Radio: BBC GMR/Key 103/ 96.2 Revolution

HONOURS FA Trophy Runners-up 79-80; Northern Premier League 78-79 79-80 (R-up 80-81 81-82 82-83, Chall Cup 78-79; NWC Floodlit Trophy R-up 95-96 NWTL Div 1 R-up 98-99

BEST SEASON **FA Cup:** 2nd Rd replay 49-50, also 2nd Rd 80-81 & 1st Rd 6 times.
FA Trophy: Runners-up 79-80
FA Vase: 6th Rd 96-97, 99-00

PREVIOUS **Leagues:** Ashton; South East Lancs; Lancs Comb. 18-19; Cheshire County 19-72; Northen Prem.
Names: Park Villa 03-04; Mossley Juniors 04-09.

RECORDS **Attendance:** 7,000 v Stalybridge 1950 **Fee Paid:** £2,300 **Fee Received:** £25,000 for Eamon O'Keefe (Everton, 1979)

2004-2005 Back Row (L-R): Steve Tobin, Billy McCartney, Rosa Martin (Physio), Jason Beckford (Manager), John Murphy (Asst. Manager), Tony Coyne, Paul Taylor, Steve Sheil, Gavinlee Ellison, Lee Bracey, Carl Rezai, Jordan Goodeve, Chris Downey. **Front Row:** Matty Taylor, Phil Drummond, Craig Fleming, Rhodri Giggs, Leon Mike, Josh Howard (Capt.), Adam Morning, Mario Daniel, Shaun Dootson.

NORTH FERRIBY UNITED

CLUB OFFICIALS

Pres: Brian Thacker **Chairman:** Les Hare

Press Officer: Dave Simmons

Secretary: Stephen Tather
39 Northfield, North Ferriby,
E Yorks HU13 0NYTel: 01482 634444 (H)

Directors: Les Hare, Steve Tather, Dave Simmons,D.Marshall, D.Searby, J.Garton,F.Fox, G. Branton, D,Thundercliffe, A.Hoyle, M.Bonwell & J.Parham

FOOTBALL MANAGEMENT TEAM

Manager: Brian France
Asst Mgr: Paul Olsson
Captain: Paul Farley
Physio: Ben Neves & Paul Bradford

FACT FILE

Founded: 1934
Nickname: United
Sponsors: Dransfield Developments
Colours: All white with green trim
Change colours: All yellow
Midweek matches: Tuesday
Reserves League: Humber Premier
Local Press: Hull Daily Mail

2003-2004

Player of the Year: Paul Foot
Top Goalscorer: Gary Bradshaw 17

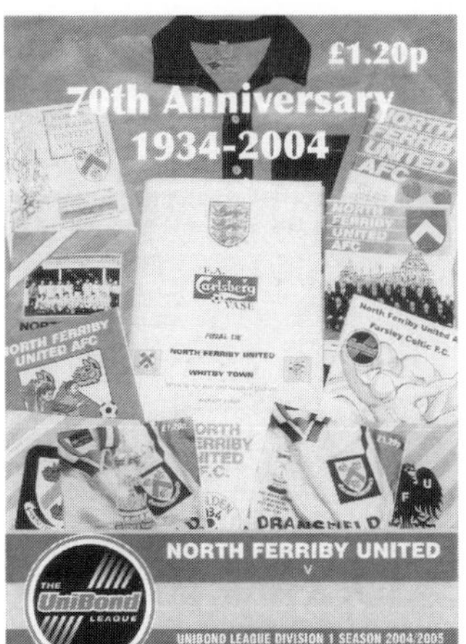

£1.20p
70th Anniversary
1934-2004
NORTH FERRIBY UNITED
v
THE UniBond LEAGUE
UNIBOND LEAGUE DIVISION 1 SEASON 2004/2005
OFFICIAL MATCHDAY PROGRAMME

PROGRAMME

Pages: 40 Price: £1.20
Editor: Dave Simmons Tel & Fax: 01482 632502

GROUND: Grange Lane, Church Road, North Ferriby HU14 3AA Tel: 01482 634601
Directions: Main Leeds-Hull road A63 or M62, North Ferriby is 8 miles west of Hull. Into North Ferriby, thru village passed the Duke of Cumberland Hotel, right down Church Rd, ground half mile on left. One mile from North Ferriby (BR)

Capacity: 3,000 Seats: 250 Cover: 1,000 Floodlights: Yes
Clubhouse: Bar, lounge, TV, pool open every night
Club Shop: Yes .Manager: Alan Beadle Tel No: 01482 634601

HONOURS FA Vase Finalist 96-97; Yorkshire Lg R-up 75-76, Lg Cup 74-75, Div 2 70-71; N.C.E. Prem Div : Champions 99-00 R-up 97-98, Div 1 85-86 (Lg Cup R-up) 90-91 97-98, Presidents Cup 90-91, 98-99, 99-00 Div 1 (North), R-up 82-83, Res. Div R-up 90-91; E. Riding Snr Cup (11), E. Riding Church Lg 37-38**PREVIOUS** **L eagues:** East Riding Church; East Riding Amateur; Yorks 69-82

BEST SEASON **FA Cup:** 3rd Q 97-98,98-99 **F.A.Trophy:** 4th Ropund 2001-02 **FA Vase:** R-up 96-97, SF 88-89, QF 89-90

RECORDS **Attendance:** 1,800 v Tamworth, FA Vase Semi-Final, 1989
Goalscorer: Andy Flounders 50, 98-99 Mark Tennison 161 **Appearances:** Paul Sharp 423 (1996-2004)
Win: 9-0 v Hatfield Main, N.C.E. Lge Prem 97-98. **Defeat:** 1-7 v North Shields,N.C.E. Lge Prem 91.
Fee received: £60,000 for Dean Windass (Hull City,1988)

Players progressing: T Hotte (Hull) 88, I Ironside (Halifax) 88, D France, D Windass & M Matthews (Hull) 91.

Back row, left to right: Chris Gowen, Danny Moore, Leon Wainman, Graham Botham, Dave Botham, Carl Wood, Rhys Pinder and Jamie Richards**:** Gary Hammond (Kitman), Rob Dewhurst, Craiig Elliott, Peter Sheldon, Paul Sharp, Paul Foot, Adam Lowthorpe, Steve Fisher and Paul Bradford (physio). **Front row:** Gareth Sewell, Steve Perrin, Steve Smith (Coach), Les Hare,(Chairman), Brian France (Manager), Joel Hartley and Peter Turnbull.

OSSETT ALBION

OSSETT ALBION
FOOTBALL CLUB
TASCA TANKERS LTD.
Main Sponsor TASCA TANKERS LTD.
V EASTWOOD TOWN

Prog: 44 pages Price: £1
Programme Sponsor:Champion Soccer
Editor: N Wigglesworth (01924 275630)
Website: www.pyke42.freeserve.co.uk

CLUB OFFICIALS

President: Miss Helen Worth
Chairman: Neville Wigglesworth
Vice-Chairman: Stuart Garside
Commercial Man.: D Riley 01924 240247
Press Officer: Neville Wigglesworth 01924 275630
Secretary: David Chambers, 109 South Parade, Ossett, Wakefield, WF5 0BE.Tel:01924 276004 (H)

FOOTBALL MANAGEMENT TEAM

Manager: Eric Gilchrist
Assistant Manager: Tony Passmore
Coach: Nigel Yarrow
Physio: Nicky Davies
Reserve Team Manager: Ashley Berry
Captain: Mick Norbury

FACT FILE

Founded: 1944 Nickname: Albion
Sponsors: TASCA TANKERS
Colours: Old gold & black/black/black
Change colours: All white
Midweek matches: Wednesday
Reserves' Lge: NCEL Res Div

2003-2004

Players of the Year: Adam Fretwell & Danny Toronczak
Top Goalscorer: Danny Toronczak 32
(Equal Top scorer in F.A.Cup 8)

GROUND: Queens Terrace, Dimple Wells, Ossett (01924 273618-club, 01924 280450-grd)
Directions: M1 jct 40. Take Wakefield road, right at Post House Hotel down Queens Drive. At end right then second left down Southdale Rd. At end right,then first left down Dimple Wells (cars only). Coaches take second left following the road for 200yds bearing left twice. Four miles from both Wakefield and Dewsbury BR stations. Buses 116 and 117
Capacity: 3,000 Seats: 250 Cover: 750 Floodlights: Yes
Clubhouse: 3 bars + function room, open 7 days per week - catering available
Club Shop: Selling various souvenirs & programmes. Contact : David Reilly

PREVIOUS **Leagues:** Heavy Woollen Area 44-49; West Riding Co. Amtr 49-50; West Yorks 50-57; Yorks 57-82. **Ground:** Fearn House

RECORDS **Attendance:** 1,200 v Leeds Utd, floodlight opening 1986
Win: 12-0 v British Ropes(H), Yorks. Lge Div. 2 6/5/59
Defeat: 2-11 v Swillington (A), W. Yorks. Lge Div. 1 25/4/56
F.A.Cup: 4th Qualifying Rd. 03-04 0-1 v Stalybridge Celtic
Goalscorer: John Balmer **Appearances:** Peter Eaton, 800+ (22 yrs)

HONOURS: Yorks Lg 74-75 R-up 58-59 61-62,R-Up: 59-60 61-62, Lg Cup 75-76, 76-77, Div 2 78-79, 80-81 R-up 58-59;73-74 N.C.E. Prem.Champions: 98-99 03-04 Div. R-up 00-01, League Cup R-Up: 95-96 President's Cup R-Up: 97-98 00-01 Div 1 86-87 Lg Cup 83-84;02-03 West Yorks Lg 53-54 55-56 Div 2 52-53, Lg Cup 52-53; W. Riding County Cup 64-65 65-66 67-68; 98-9 Wheatley Cup 56-57 58-59 96-97
Players progressing: Gary Brook (Newport, Scarborough, Blackpool) 1987, Ian Ironside (Barnsley, Middlesbrough, Scarborough) 1980.
Players Progressing: Chris Cornelly (Lincoln City 2001)
Steve Downes (Grimsby Town,York City 2002o
Local Media: Wakefield Express and Ridings FM Local Media

ROCESTER

CLUB OFFICIALS
Chairman: Alf.Hawksworth
Secretary: Gilbert Egerton
23 Eaton Rd, Rocester, Uttoxeter,
Staffs ST145LL. Tel: 01889 590101

FOOTBALL MANAGEMENT
Manager: Warren Campbell
Captain: Paul Ede

FACT FILE
Founded: 1876
Nickname: Romans
Colours: Amber & black/black/black
Change colours: All blue
Reserves' Lge: North Staffs (North)
Midweek matchday: Tuesday

2003-2004
Players of the Year: Craig Holland
& Andy Bostock
Top scorer:
Paul McMahon 50 (37 lg + 13 cup)

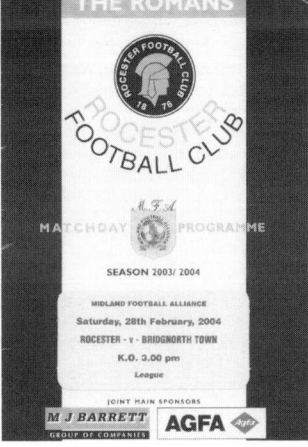

PROGRAMME
32 pages £1.00
Editor: Barry Brosnan Tel: 01889 567795

GROUND Hillsfield, Mill Street, Rocester, Uttoxeter, Staffs
Tel: 01889 590463 Email: rocester@floodlight org.uk
Directions: From A50 r'bout adjoining Little Chef at Uttoxeter take B5030 to Rocester & Alton Towers, right into Rocester village after 3miles over narrow bridge, in village centre bear right at sharp left-hand bend into Mill St., ground 500yds on left just past former cotton mill.
Capacity: 4,000 Seats: 230 Cover: 500 Floodlights: Yes
Clubhouse: On matchdays (normal licensing hours). Hot drinks & snacks. **Club Shop:** Yes

PREVIOUS **Leagues:** Ashbourne; Leek & Moorland; Cheadle & Dist; Uttoxeter Amateur; Stafford 53-57; Staffordshire County North 57-84; Staffordshire Senior 84-87; West Midlands 87-94; Midland Alliance 94-99 03-04; Southern 99-2003.

BEST SEASON **FA Cup:** 3rd Qual. Round 97-98, 1-2 v Bromsgrove Rovers (A)
FA Vase: 5th Round 86-87, 1-3 v Garforth Town (H) aet.

RECORDS **Attendance:** 1,026 v Halesowen T., FA Vase 4th Rd Jan.'87 (at Leek T.) 3-1 a.e.t.
Appearances: Peter Swanwick.(Goalkeeper who played for 20 years -1962-82)
Fee Received: £12,000 for Mark Sale from Birmingham City 1994

HONOURS West Mids Lg R-up 89-90 Div 1 87-88, Div 1 Cup 87-88, Staffs Senior Lg (x2) 85-87, Staffordshire FA Vase 85-86 87-88; Midland Alliance 98-99
League's GoldenBoot Winner 2003-2004: Paul McMahon

Back Row (L-R): Mick Ede (Physio), Kevin Millward, Chris Cipola, Paul Ridley, James Watson, RichardHewitt, Gavin Reynolds, Ben Skelton, and Warren Campbell (Manager). **Front row:** Andy Bostock, John Hassell, Craig Holland,Andy Marlow, Simon Wilshaw, Andy Colclough and Lee Owen.

Photo: Horace Wetton, The Sport Newspaper.

ROSSENDALE UNITED

CLUB OFFICIALS

Chairman: Declan Callan

V Chairmain: David White

President: David White

Press Officer: Kevin Procter

Secretary: Kevin Proctor
5 Booth Street, Waterfoot,
Rossendale, Lancs BB4 9AL
Tel: 01706 223405

FOOTBALL MANAGEMENT TEAM

Manager: Ashley Hoskins
Ass. Man.Hughie Bridge
.Physio: Cath Fitton

2003-2004

Captain: Dave Gamble
Top Scorer: Craig Sargeson & Chris Brooks
P.o.Y.: Chris Fitzsimmons

PROGRAMME

28 pages -£1.00
Editor: David Howarth

FACT FILE

Founded: 1898
Nickname: The Stags
Sponsors: Swinburne James Insurance
Colours: Blue & white stripes/blue/blue
Change colours: All Red
Midweek Matchday: Tuesday
Website: www.rosendaleunited.co.uk
Local Radio: Red Rose, Radio Lancashire.
Local Press: Lancs Evening Telegraph, Rossendale Free Press

GROUND Dark Lane, Staghills Rd, Newchurch, Rossendale, Lancs BB4 7UA
Tel: 01706 215119 (Ground); 01706 213296 (Club) Email: rossendaleunited@zen.co.uk

Directions: M60 Junc 18, M66 north following signs for Burnley, then A682 to Rawstenstall, take 2nd exit sign Burnley A682, at 1st lights turn right into Newchurch Rd, 1.5 miles turn right into Staghills Rd, grd 800 yards right

Capacity: 2,500 Cover: Yes Seats: 500 Floodlights: Yes

Clubhouse: Evenings & matchdays. Hot snacks. Pool, satellite TV, concert room **Club Shop:** Yes (Dave Rudge 01706 213296)

PREVIOUS **Leagues:** N.E. Lancs Comb.; Lancs Comb. 1898-99 1901-70; Central Lancs 1899-1901; Cheshire County 70-82; NWC 82-89 93-01; N.P.L. 89-93. **Grounds:** None

RECORDS **Attendance:** 12,000 v Bolton Wanderers FA Cup 2nd Rd 71
Appearances: Johnny Clarke 770, 1947-65 **Goalscorer:** Bob Scott
Fee Paid: £3,000 for Jimmy Clarke (Buxton, 1992)
Fee Received: £1,500 for Dave O'Neill (Huddersfield Town, 1974)
Win: 17-0v Ashton Town, Lancs Comb.1911-12
Defeat: 0-14 v Morecambe, Lancs Comb. 67-68

BEST SEASON **FA Cup:** 2nd Rd 71-72, 1-4 v Bolton W. at Bury FC. Also 1st Rd 75-76 Also 1st Rd 75-76, 0-1 v Shrewsbury T. (H)
FA Trophy : 2nd Rd 81-82 **FA Vase:** 5th Rd 86-87,88-89

HONOURS N.W.C. Lg Div 1 88-89 00-01(R-up 87-88 93-94), Div 2 R-up 85-86, Chall Cup 93-94

Players progressing: T Lawton, G Smith (Bradford C 52), E Hartley & W O'Loughton (Oldham 56/60), C Blunt (Burnley 64), F Eyre (Bradford PA 69), D O'Neill (Huddersfield), C Parker (Rochdale 92).

Taken before their friendly match v's Blackburn Rovers on Tuesday 20th July 2004. Rossendale Utd are wearing their change strip of all red as a gesture to the Premier League Club.

SHEPSHED DYNAMO

CLUB OFFICIALS

Chairman: Michael Voce

President: Gilbert Kinch

Directors: Michael Voce, Shaun Taylor, Peter Bull,David Wheatly, Eric Anderson and John Sharples.

Secretary: Peter Bull,17 Welland Rd, Barrow-on-Soar, Leicestershire LE12 8NA
Tel: 01509 413338 (H) 07974 214931 (M)

Press Offr: John BrindleyTel: 07971 339105

FOOTBALL MANAGEMENT

Team Manager: Peter McGurck

Coach:Anton Lambert Physio:Ian Davies

Captain: Duncan O'Brien(& P.O.Y.03-04)

FACT FILE

Re-formed: 1994
Nickname: Dynamo
Sponsors: Coalville Paints
Colours: Black & white stripes/black/black
Change colours: All Yellow
Midweek matchday: Wednesday
Reserves' League: Midland Comb.
Local Press: Loughborough Echo, Leicester Mercury, Coalville Times
Local Radio: Radio Leicester, Oak FM
Website: www.shepsheddyname.co.uk

PROGRAMME

Pages: 40 Price: £1.20
Editors: Andy Macmilllan (01509 822587) & Andy Reed
email: andy.macmillan@ntlworld.com

GROUND The Dovecote, Butthole Lane, Shepshed, Leicestershire Tel: 01509 650992
Directions: M1 J 23, A512 towards Ashby, right at first lights, right at garage in Forest Street, right into Butthole Lane opposite Black Swan. Five miles from Loughborough (BR)
Capacity: 5,000 Cover: 1,500 Seats: 400 Floodlights: Yes
Clubhouse: Takes 120 in main room, 50 in others **Club Shop:** Yes Manager: Steve Straw Tel. No: 01530810937

PREVIOUS
Leagues: Leicestershire Senior 07-16 19-27 46-50 51-81, Midland Counties 81-82, Northern Counties (East) 82-83, Southern 83-88, Northern Premier 88-93, Midland Combination 93-94, Midland Alliance 94-96
Names: Shepshed Albion 1890-1975 91-94, Shepshed Charterhouse 75-91
Grounds: Ashby Road (pre-1897), Little Haw Farm

CLUB RECORDS
Attendance: 2,500 v Leicester C. (friendly) 96-97
Win: 10-0 v Bloxwixh T. (H), Mid. Comb. 93-94 **Defeat:** 0-9 v Mangotsfield United (H) S.L. 2003-04
Career Goalscorer: Jeff Lissaman 104 (81-86) **Career Appearances:** Austin Straker 300
Transfer fee paid: £2,000 for Doug Newton (Charterhouse)
Transfer fee received: £10,000 for John Deakin from Birmingham City (Charterhouse)

BEST SEASON
FA Vase: Semi-Finalists 78-79 **FA Trophy:** 3rd Rd Replay v Emley 98-99
FA Cup: 1st Rd 82-83, 1-5 v Preston North End (A), 96-97 v Carlisle United (a) 0-6

HONOURS
Southern Lge Midland Div. R-up 83-84, N.C.E. Lge 82-83, Lge Cup 82-83; Midland Counties Lge 81-82, Lge Cup 81- 82; Leicestershire Senior Lge 10-11 20-21 78-79 79-80 80-81, R-up 21-22, Div 2 53-54 65-66 77-78, Div 2 Cup 77-78; Leicestershire Senior Cup (7); Loughborough Charity Cup 92-93 01-02; Midland Alliance Winners 95-96
Coalville Charity Cup Winners: 2003-04

Players progressing: Neil Grewcock (Burnley 84), Gordon Tucker (Huddersfield 87), Devon White (Bristol R. 87), John Deakin (Birmingham City)

2004-2005 Back row .left to right: I.Davies (Physio), G.West Asst. Man), L.Parker, M.Morran, C.Timms, R.Wilson, D.Wheatley (Gen Man.), P.McGurk (Team Manager), Peter Bull (Gen Sec.), M.Dorrian, A.Hook, D.Roberts, A.Lambert (Coach) **Front row:** M.Savage, P.Gamble, R.Lawrence, R.Keeling, A.Stevens (Capt), I.Roberts, W.Armstrong, C.Henson, C.McMorran, and D.O'Brien.

Photo: Steve Marriott Photographic Services

SPALDING UNITED

CLUB OFFICIALS

Chairman: Chris Toynton
Vice Chairman: Brett Maddison
President: John Chappell
Press Officer: Ray Tucker
Secretary: Graham Bowater, Chantrelle Cottage , Fern Drive, Spalding , Lincs. PE11 1GG
Tel Nos: 01775 714764 (H) 07977 918806(M)
John Franks, 2 Samworth Close, Castor, Peterborough PE5 7BQ (01733 380609)

FOOTBALL MANAGEMENT

Manager: Dick Creasey Asst Man: T.B.A.
Capt: Andy Lodge Physio: T.B.A.

FACT FILE

Founded: 1921Nickname: Tulips

Sponsors: Consumer First

Colours: Royal blue/white/royal blue

Change: Yellow/Blue/Yellow

Midweek matchday: Tuesday

Reserve League: Utd Counties Res Div 2.

PROGRAMME

36 Pages Price:£1.00

Editor:Audrey Fletche r& Ray Tucker

Website: www.spaldingunitedfc.co.uk

GROUND Sir Halley Stewart Playing Field, Winfrey Avenue, Spalding Tel: 01775 713328

Directions: Town centre off A16, adjacent to bus station. 250 yds from Spalding(BR) station

Capacity: 2,700 Seats: 300 Cover: ,500 Floodlights: Yes

Clubhouse: Open matchdays, and events **Club Shop:** Manager: Andy Gay (01775 710081)

PREVIOUS **Leagues:** Peterborough; U.C.L. 31-55 68-78 86-88 91-99; 03-04 Eastern Co's 55-60; Central Alliance 60-61; Midland Co's 61-68; N.C.E.F.L. 82-86; Southern 88-91, 99-03

RECORD **Attendance:** 6,972 v Peterborough, FA Cup 1952

BEST SEASON **FA Cup:** 1st Round 57-58, 1-3 v Durham City (A), 64-65, 3-5 v Newport Co. (A)

FA Trophy: 3rd Rd 99-00

FA Vase: Quarter-Finals 89-90, 1-3 v Guiseley

HONOURS Utd Counties Lg 54-55 74-75 87-88 98-99 R-up 50-53(x3) 72-73 75-76 96-97; KO Cup 54-55 94-95; N.C.E.Lg 83-84; Lincs Snr Cup 52-53; Hinchingbroke Cup 98-99 Lincs Snr `A' Cup 87-88, 98-99 R-up 97-98; Snr `B' Cup 50-51; Evans Halshaw F'lit Cup 89-90 E.Ang C .03-4

2003-2004 **Top goalscorer:** Lee Hudson

Player of the Year: Steve Appleby

Players progressing: Carl Shutt (Sheffield Wed.)

STOCKSBRIDGE PARK STEELS

CLUB OFFICIALS

President: J.Newton
Chairman: Allen Bethel
Vice-Chairman: M Grimmer
Secretary: Michael Grimmer
48 Hole House Lane, Stocksbridge
Sheffield S36 1BT Tel: 0114 288 6470
Press Officer: Edwin O'Sullivan
Commercial Manager: Andrew Horsley
Tel: 0114 288 3867

FOOTBALL MANAGEMENT TEAM

Manager: Peter RInkcavage
Asst Manager:Peter Bradshaw
Physio: John Megson Capt: Gary Middleton

FACT FILE

Formed: 1986
Nickname: Steels
Sponsors:John Crawshaw (Butchers)
Colours: Yellow/ blue/yellow
Change colours: All blue
Midweek matches: Tuesday
Reserves' League: SheffieldCounty Senior

2003-2004

Player of the Year: Gary Middleton

GROUND Bracken Moor Lane, Stocksbridge, Sheffield. Tel: 0114 288 2045
Fax: 0114 288 8305 Club Website: http://members.aol.com/spsfc/

Directions: M1 jct 35a (from S), 36 (from N), A616 to Stocksbridge.
On arrival in Stocksbridge turn left into Nanny Hill under the Clock Tower and continue up the hill for about 500 yds - ground on left

Capacity: 3,500 Cover: 1,000 Seats: 450

Clubhouse: Open 7 days (lunchtime & evenings). No food. Separate foodbar for matches

Club Shop: Mrs Janet Cartledge 01226 759023 badges, mugs, shirts, progs, scarves etc .

Pages: 28 Price:1.00
Editor: Edwin O'Sullivan
Tel: 0114 288 4218
Website: www.spsfc.com
Local Press:
Look local, Green'un, The Star

PREVIOUS **Ground:** Stonemoor 49-51 52-53 **Names:** Stocksbridge Works, Oxley Park;clubs merged in 1986
Leagues: Sheffield Amateur/ Sheffield Association/Yorkshire 49-82

CLUB RECORDS **Attendance:** 2,000 v Sheffield Wed., Floodlight opening Oct '91
Fee Received: £15,000 for Lee Mills (Wolves, 1992) **Fee Paid:** Nil
Win: 5-0 v Warrington Town NPL 96-97 **Defeat:** 2-7 Witton Albion 2001-02
Scorer: Trevor Jones (145) **Appearances:** Not known

BEST SEASON **FA Cup:** 4th Q 50-1, 56-7 **FA Trophy:** 3rd Q 96-97 **FA Vase:** 4th Rd 95-96.

HONOURS Northern Co's East Prem Div 93-94, R-up 95-96, Div 1 91-92, Lg Cup 94-95; Sheffield Snr Cup 92-93 95-96,98-99. Oxley Park F C: County Sen Div 1 85-86:Stocksbridge Works FC: Yorkshire Lge Div 1 51-52 54-55 55-56 56-57 57-58 61-62 62-63, Div 2 50-51 64-65, Div 3 70-71 74-75, Lge Cup 61-62 Sheffield Snr Cup 51-52

Players progressing: Peter Eustace (Sheffield Wednesday) 1960 (from Stocksbridge Works) , Lee Mills (Wolverhampton W.) 1992. Simon Marples 2002

Back row, left to right: Bates, Colley, Bullimore,Siddall, Middleton, Schofield, Ring and Riley **Front row:** Elam, Richards, Lucas, Maybury, Bradshaw, Rinkcavage, Megson, Smith, Bernard and Colliver

WARRINGTON TOWN

CLUB OFFICIALS

Chairman: Dave Hughes
President: Eric Shaw
Vice Chairman: Derek Holden
Press Officer: Colin Serjent

Secretary: Barry Thorpe, 46 Greenheys Road,Little Hulton,Manchester M389TP(01617901490)

FOOTBALL MANAGEMENT TEAM

Managers: Glenn Walker
Asst Man Derek Brownbill
Coach: Steve Pennington

FACT FILE

Formed: 194 8 Nickname: The Town
Colours: Blue & yellow/blue/blue
Change colours: Orange/black/black
Midweek matchday: Tuesday
Reserves' League: Mid-Cheshire

2003-2004

Top Scorers:
Mike Heverin & Graeme Mitchell 25 each
Players of the Year:
Phil Mitchell & Lee Riley

WARRINGTON TOWN AFC
The official match day magazine of Warrington Town AFC

Division 1
Season 2004/2005
Official Kit Sponsors
PRINT magic of WARRINGTON
Associate Sponsors
DJ Hughes Construction
Murraywood Construction

48-60 Pages £1.00
League Programme of the Year 2002-03
Editor: Paul Roach, 55 Moorcroft,
New Brighton, Mold, Flintshire CH7 6RU
Tel: 01352 752489, 07740 430190 (M))

Ground: Cantilever Park, Common Lane, Latchford, Warrington WA4 2RS
Tel: 01925 631932 (Club), 01925 653044 (office), 01925-653044 (FAX,only on matchdays).
Directions: M6 junction 20, then A50 towards Warrington. After 2 miles turn left immediately after swing bridge into Station Road, ground 600yds on left. From town centre travel 1 mile south on A49, left at lights into Loushers Lane, ground quarter mile on right. 2miles from Warrington Bank Quay (BR)
Capacity: 2,000**Cover:** 650 **Seats**: 350 **Floodlights:** Yes **Club Shop:** Yes (Barry Thorpe)
Clubhouse: Weekdays 1-11pm, Sat. 12-11pm, Sun. 12-11 p.m. Bar food on matchdays

PREVIOUS **Leagues:** Warrington & Dist. 49-52; Mid-Cheshire 52-78; Cheshire Co. 78-82; N.W.C. 82-90; N.P.L 90-97. **Name:** Stockton Heath 1949-62.

RECORDS **Attendance:** 2,600 v Halesowen T., FA Vase S-F 1st leg 85-86.
Goalscorer: Steve Hughes 167
Fee Received: £60,000 for Liam Watson (Preston N. E.) 92-93

BEST SEASON **FA Cup:** 4th Qual. Rd 94-95 replay with Hyde Utd..
FA Vase: Runners-up 86-87 **FA Trophy:** Quarter-Finalists 92-93

HONOURS: FA Vase R-up 86-87; N.W.C. Lge 89-90 (Lg Cup 85-86 87-88 88-89 (R-up 89-90), Div 2 00-01R-up 86-87, Div 3 R-up 82-83; Mid-Cheshire Lg 60-61 R-up 57-58, Lg Cup 54-55 55-56 11-12 72-73, Altrincham Amat. Cup 54-55,

Players progressing recently: M Leonard (Everton), N Whalley & L Watson (P.N.E.) 92-93.

WILLENHALL TOWN

CLUB OFFICIALS

President: Jack Williams
Chairman: JackWilliams
Vice Chairman: Edward Edmunds
Commercial Dept:
Adele Micklewright&Russ Brown with
Chris Myatt & Rob Fletcher
Secretary: Simon Haynes,
6 Ingledew Close, Briarsleigh, Walsall, West
Mid (01902 411758)

FOOTBALL MANAGEMENT TEAM
Manager: Rob Smith
Asst. Manager: Larry Chambers
Coach: Steve Wynn Captain: Martin Myers
Physios: Mick Andrews & Gary McHale.

FACT FILE

Founded: 1953 Nickname: Reds
Sponsors: Aspray Transport Ltd.
Colours: All Red
Change colours: Yellow & Blue/Blue/Blue
Midweek matchday: Tuesday.
Reserves League: Midland Comb.

2003-2004
Leading Scorer:John Quilt 32
Player of the Year: Jason Smith

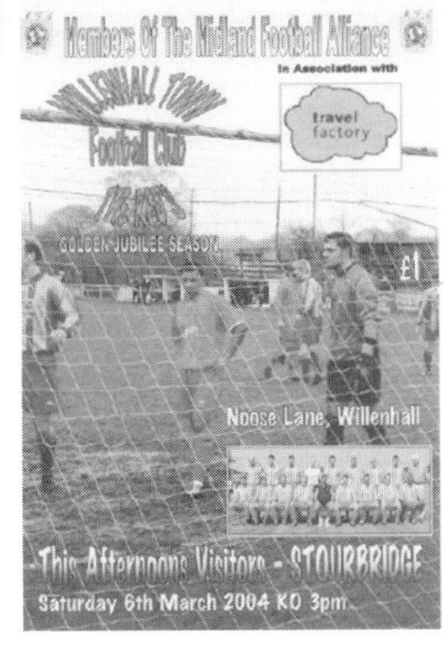

Members Of The Midland Football Alliance
In Association with
Willenhall Town
Football Club
travel factory
£1
Noose Lane, Willenhall
This Afternoons Visitors - STOURBRIDGE
Saturday 6th March 2004 KO 3pm

44-46 pages, £1.00
Editor: Russ Brown (01902 681011)

Ground: Noose Lane, Willenhall, West Midlands (01902 605132-club, 01902 636586-office).

Directions: M6 Jnc 10 follow 'new' Black Country route and then 'Keyway'. On leaving 'Keyway' follow signs to Wolverhampton(A454). At 'Neachells' P H house right into Neachells Lane, and first right again into Watery Lane. At island turn left onto Noose Lane, ground is 200yds on left.

Capacity: 5,000 **Seats**: 324 **Cover:** 500 **Floodlights:** Yes **Shop:** Yes

Clubhouse: Open Mon-Fri 12-2 & 7-12pm,Sat & Sun All Day Hot food available.

HONOURS FA Vase R-up 80-81; West Mids Lg 78-79, Div 1 75-76, Prem. Div Cup 79-80, Div 2 Cup 78-79(res); Southern Midland 83-84; Birmingham Snr Cup R-up 82-83; J W Hunt Cup 73-74., Mid Alliance Cup R-up 99-00, Rameses Invitation Cup 2000-01.

BEST SEASON **FA Vase:** Finalists 80-81 **FA Cup:** 1st Rd Proper v Crewe Alexander 1981

PREVIOUS **Leagues:** Wolverhampton Amateur/ Staffs County/ West Mids 75-82 91-94/ Southern 82-91. Mid.F.Alliance 94-02

RECORDS **Attendance**: 3,454 v Crewe Alexandra, FA Cup 1st Rd 1981.
Victory: 11-1 v Bridgnorth Town 2001-02
Goalscorer: Gary Matthews **Appearances**: Gary Matthews.

Players progressing: Sean O'Driscoll (Fulham), Joe Jackson (Wolves), Stuart Watkiss (Wolves), Tony Moore (Sheff U), Andy Reece (Bristol R.), Wayne O'Sullivan (Swindon), Adie Smith (Kidderminster H) & Peter Smith (Brighton & H)

WOODLEY SPORTS

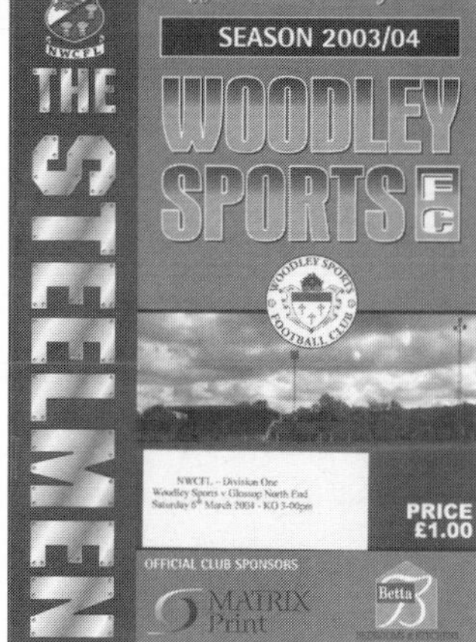

CLUB OFFICIALS

Chairman: Ian Campbell
20 Boundary Green,Denton, Manchester
M34 3BYTel No: 0161 336 2745

Secretary: Tony Whiteside, 4 Hayfield Road, Bredbury, Stockport, Cheshire SK6 1DE
0161 406 5599 (W) 077787 66382 (M)

FOOTBALL MANAGEMENT TEAM

Manager:Tony Hancock
Asst. Manager:Paul Kirkham
Captain: Mike Ryan Physio:Darrin Whittaker

FACT FILE

Founded: 1970
Colours: Royal Blue & Red
Change Colours:Yellow
Midweek Matchday: Tuesday

2003-2004

Top Scorer .: Mike Norton
Player of the Year;Mike Ryan

Pages: 48 Price:£1.00
Editor:Tony Whiteside

Ground: Lambeth Grove Stadium, Lambeth Grove, Woodley, Stockport. Tel: 0161 406 6896

Directions: M60 Jct 25, follow signs (A560) Bredbury, take left filter at lights which brings you onto A560 Stockport Road for approx 1 mile, turn left at pub, Lowes Arms into Mill Street which goes into Mill Lane. Over bridge take 2nd right into Woodlands Avenue, then 1st left into Lambeth Grove. Ground 200 yards ahead.
Floodlights: Yes

HONOURS NWC Div 2 99-00 Cheshgire Senior Cup 2003-04

RECORD **Attendance:** 1,500 v Stockport County

PREVIOUS **Leagues:** Lancashire & Cheshire, Manchester League.

BEST SEASON **FA Cup:** 99-00 **FA Vase:** 1st Round 1998-99

...ACTION EXTRA...ACTION EXTRA...ACTION EXTRA...

Worksop Town keeper Ian Bowling saves brilliantly against **Barrow.** Photo Bill Wheatcroft

Alfreton Town's first goal against **Ashton United** is scored by Tony Hemmings (falling on the edge of the six yard area) Photo: Bill Wheatcroft

...ACTION EXTRA...ACTION EXTRA...ACTION EXTRA...

Marine defend, but Mick Godber scores for **Alfreton Town.** Photo: Bill Wheatcroft

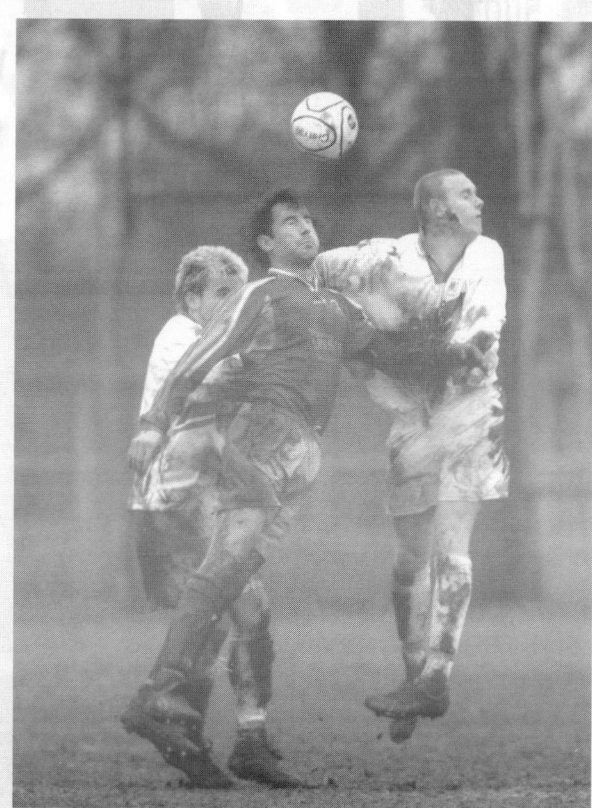

Robert Tonks of **Wakefield & Emley** is challenged Craig Smith and Michael Naylor of **Bradford P.A.**
Photo: Darren Thomas

FOOTBALL LEAGUE

STEP 1

FOOTBALL CONFERENCE

STEP 2

CONFERENCE NORTH

CONFERENCE SOUTH

STEP 3

NORTHERN PREMIER

SOUTHERN PREMIER

ISTHMIAN PREMIER

STEP 4

NORTHERN PREMIER DIV.1

SOUTHERN LEAGUE EAST

SOUTHERN LEAGUE WEST

ISTHMIAN DIVISION 1

STEP 5/6

STEP 7

SOUTHERN LEAGUE

SPONSORED BY: DR MARTENS

Chairman: D S R Gillard

Secretary: D J Strudwick

PO Box 90, Worcester WR3 8RX Tel: 01905 757509

Four clubs promoted; four clubs relegated; The Southern Football League receives Football Association approval to administer three Divisions in the proposed re-structured competitions; The Football Association sanction the re-structure of the National League System (in which the Southern League has played an active, positive role throughout); two new Directors elected to the Board; the Isthmian League mounts a challenge by way of Arbitration to the FA's decisions on re-structuring is defeated by a unanimous decision of the Arbitration Panel; Crawley Town win the Southern League Championship; offers from four Directors to resign from the League's Board are accepted; Hednesford Town reach the FA Trophy Final; Crawley Town retain the League Cup and become the first team since Wimbledon in the 1975/76 season to complete League & Cup double; six play-Off matches arranged and successfully staged; thirty-two new clubs join The Southern League by way of re-structure and promotion and Hednesford Town win the FA Trophy. It has been an exceptionally busy and eventful year.

Crawley Town started the new campaign as they finished the last. The Reds followed up their League Cup victory over Halesowen Town by trouncing League Champions (and Football Conference bound) Tamworth, 3-0 in the annual Championship Match. Their League campaign did not, however, open so sprightly. Four draws in their first seven games Crawley a little off the early pace, which was being set by Worcester City, Nuneaton Borough and Weymouth. But perhaps Crawley's eventual success was only being disguised by these early statistics. The four draws had all been gleaned away from home. The club's determination to avoid defeat 'on the road' was to prove significant.

The same objective was serving Weymouth well, too. Under the new control of Chairman Ian Ridley and Manager Steve Claridge, the Terras began a long spell on the top of the Table by November and remained undefeated away from home until their visit to Cambridge City on 7 February.

Meanwhile, in the Eastern Division, Tonbridge Angles began even more impressively. By 29 November, having lost none of their first seventeen matches, the Angels ascended to a seemingly impregnable fourteen point lead over King's Lynn. Histon were a further two points behind.

Redditch United were looking almost as comfortable in the Western Division. With the exception of one week in September, when Sutton Coldfield Town topped the Table after six games, Redditch led the pack throughout. Sutton, Rugby United and Solihull Borough all reduced Redditch's advantage to goal difference, at times, but at all other times the challengers trailed in the leader's wake.

As the fixture list proceeded full-steam ahead towards the important Christmas/New Year holiday programme, five Dr. Martens League clubs progressed to the F A Cup First Round Proper. Sadly, Grantham Town lost their encounter in the last minute against Leyton Orient, 2-1; Crawley Town crashed out at Telford United 3-2, after leading the Bucks 2-0; Histon lost 3-1 at Woking, after taking a 2nd minute lead and Salisbury City went out in courageous fashion at Sheffield Wednesday, 4-0, Weston-Super-Mare, though, defeated Farnborough Town 1-0 to earn a Second Round Tie at Northampton Town. This time, for Weston, the shoe was on the other foot; the Cobblers won 4-1.

Amid the final weeks of the campaign Crawley Town reached the League Cup Final, for the second successive season. Opponents Moor Green shocked the League Champions by taking a 44th minute lead in the First Leg at The Moorlands. Crawley recovered, however, to take a 2-1 advantage back to Sussex for the Second Leg. The Reds won the home tie 2-0 to retain the Worcester Vase 4-1 on aggregate.

The Cup victory climaxed a truly memorable year for Crawley Town. Four years after being brought out of Administration by the immensely modest John Duly, and under the guiding light of John's 'Chairman', Jo Gomm, Crawley Town had won five trophies (including the Sussex Senior Cup) in twelve months; five trophies for Manager Francis Vines - three in his first full season in charge of team affairs. It is such a pity one of the club's most dedicated servants, Stan Markham, whose contribution over many years was immeasurable, was unable to witness these later successes first hand. Stan passed away just before the season began. Have no doubt, though, he was watching from afar. And like us, Stan will be wishing Crawley the best of luck in the Football Conference next season.

Like them or loathe them, Play-Offs are here to stay. They were introduced this year to help create the format for next season's newly formed Leagues. Like them or loathe them, they were successful. Of the six Play-Off matches, five attracted 'best of season' gates. Over 2,000 spectators turned up at King's Lynn to watch the match between the First Division Champions, which Redditch United won 1-0. Redditch went on to complete Merthyr Tydfil's disappointing end to the season by defeating the Martyrs 3-0 to win a place in one of the new semi-national Divisions, where they will be joined by Dorchester Town and the 2nd to 13th placed Premier Division teams.

Banbury United won the Play-Off between the eighth placed clubs in the Regional First Division, against Sutton Coldfield Town, and will join the top seven from each of these Divisions at the newly constituted Premier Division level.

As a result of the re-structure 27 clubs from the Isthmian League and five from Feeder Leagues will join The Southern Football League for next season. The League's management extends a very warm welcome to all its new members. For some it is welcome back.

Thirty clubs will leave the League under re-structuring and one, Fleet Town, has been relegated. It is not easy to say farewell to so many friends but we hope it will not be long before our paths cross again. In the meantime, Good Luck to you all.

Even after the new Leagues and Divisions had been formed at Loughborough on 9 May, the season was far from over for Hednesford Town. Despite being in the bottom four of the Premier Division, the Pitmen defeated Aldershot Town of the Football Conference in the Semi-Final of the FA Trophy, to set up a Final against Canvey Island, the Champions of the Isthmian League. In a thriller at the Villa, Hednesford Town won the Trophy by the odd goal in five. But after the euphoria of such a fine win had diminished, the success must have brought little comfort for Manager Barry Powell who paid the price of relegation, with his job, one week after the Villa victory.

For at least one person, however, the Trophy win must have brought a great deal of personal satisfaction. Secretary Rod Hadley left Tamworth last season just a few months before the Lambs reached, but lost, the FA Trophy Final. To have gone one better with his new club must have ameliorated some of the sadness of an otherwise disappointing year.

With 2003/04 season completed, the League must now say goodbye to Dr. Martens. The second four-year sponsorship agreement has matured. During its eight-year liaison with the League, Dr. Martens has made it possible for the League to pass on, directly to clubs, nearly £750,000. Thank you Dr. Martens, and Max & Steven Griggs, in particular.

Thank you, too, to ICIS Clubwear, who have sponsored Bench Kit for three years and Match Balls for the past two years. We hope the Company's representatives, Roger Evans and Brian McCarthy, will enjoy the League's expression of appreciation at the Conference weekend in Torquay and will then hopefully make arrangements for the Match Ball sponsorship during the forthcoming season.

It is also true to say The Southern League will not be quite the same having lost its fifteen best placed clubs at the end of the season. But the Board of Directors consulted with, and delivered, what the majority of clubs wanted - a re-structure of the National League System. The Southern Football League has been in this position at least twice before. So now, with an infusion of new blood at club and Board level, the Grand Old Lady must rebuild itself again. As a newspaper reported during the season, the 20 year record of the Southern League's present administration "speaks for itself". With the help of current members, together with the new members mentioned above, the present administration promises to increase its efforts to restore its 'Grade 1 Listed League'. Top of the agenda is to locate a new main sponsor.

The Board of Directors Thursday 3 June 2004.

PREMIER DIVISION FINAL LEAGUE TABLE 2003-04

Qualify for Conference North/South (positions 2–13)

		P	W	D	L	F	A	Pts
1.	CRAWLEY TOWN	42	25	9	8	77	43	84
2.	WEYMOUTH	42	20	12	10	76	47	72
3.	STAFFORD RANGERS	42	19	11	12	55	43	68
4.	NUNEATON BOROUGH	42	17	15	10	65	49	66
5.	WORCESTER CITY	42	18	9	15	71	50	63
6.	HINCKLEY UNITED	42	15	14	13	55	46	59
7.	NEWPORT COUNTY	42	15	14	13	52	50	59
8.	CAMBRIDGE CITY	42	14	15	13	54	53	57
9.	WELLING UNITED	42	16	8	18	56	58	56
10.	WESTON-SUPER-MARE	42	14	13	15	52	52	55
11.	EASTBOURNE BOROUGH	42	14	13	15	48	56	55
12.	HAVANT & WATERLOOVILLE	42	15	10	17	59	70	55
13.	MOOR GREEN	42	14	12	16	42	54	54
14.	MERTHYR TYDFIL	42	13	14	15	60	66	53
15.	TIVERTON TOWN	42	12	15	15	63	64	51
16.	BATH CITY	42	13	12	17	49	57	51
17.	DORCHESTER TOWN*	42	14	9	19	56	69	51
18.	CHELMSFORD CITY	42	11	16	15	46	53	49
19.	DOVER ATHLETIC	42	12	13	17	50	59	49
20.	HEDNESFORD TOWN	42	12	12	18	56	69	48
21.	CHIPPENHAM TOWN	42	10	17	15	51	63	47
22.	GRANTHAM TOWN	42	10	15	17	45	67	45

*Qualified for Conference South via the play-offs.

PLAY OFF MATCHES FOR PLACES IN THE NEW SEMI-NATIONAL LEAGUES

SEMI-FINALS

King's Lynn 0 Redditch United 1 Att 2014

Tiverton Town 1 Chelmsford City 0 Att 569

Bath City 2 Dorchester Town 4 Att 1250

THE FINALS

Merthyr Tydfil 0 Redditch United 3

Att 907 (at Merthyr Tydfil)

Tiverton Town 1 Dorchester Town 3

Att 1339 (at Exeter City)

PLAY-OFF FOR PLACE IN SOUTHERN PREMIER DIVISION

Banbury United 2 Sutton Coldfield Town 1* Att 698

PREMIER DIVISION 03-04		1	2	3	4	5	6	7	8	9	10	11	12	13	14	15	16	17	18	19	20	21	22
1	Bath City		1-2	0-1	2-2	0-0	0-0	2-1	2-0	5-1	2-0	2-0	0-2	0-2	0-1	1-0	1-3	1-0	2-1	2-0	3-1	0-2	1-1
2	Cambridge City	0-0		2-0	1-1	2-5	4-2	2-1	0-0	1-1	2-3	0-1	1-2	2-2	1-1	0-2	1-3	1-0	6-4	0-3	1-1	1-0	0-0
3	Chelmsford City	0-0	1-1		1-3	0-4	2-0	0-0	3-1	0-0	1-1	2-0	0-3	3-1	1-0	0-0	1-2	1-2	3-3	0-1	0-0	1-3	2-2
4	Chippenham Town	1-1	0-2	0-0		0-1	1-6	0-0	0-1	2-2	3-0	0-0	2-1	3-3	4-0	2-1	1-1	0-3	1-1	0-2	1-1	1-3	1-2
5	Crawley Town	2-0	2-0	0-0	3-2		2-3	2-0	3-1	4-2	3-1	6-1	0-3	1-2	2-2	1-2	2-2	2-0	2-1	0-0	2-0	2-1	4-0
6	Dorchester Town	1-0	0-2	4-1	3-1	2-0		0-2	0-1	2-2	1-2	3-4	1-1	1-0	0-1	1-2	0-0	0-0	1-0	2-0	3-2	2-2	3-0
7	Dover Athletic	3-3	0-1	2-2	0-0	2-2	1-2		2-0	2-0	0-2	2-1	1-1	2-2	2-0	2-0	3-2	0-0	2-1	3-1	0-2	2-3	2-1
8	Eastbourne Borough	1-1	1-1	1-1	1-2	1-1	2-1	3-1		1-0	2-0	2-2	0-2	1-1	0-1	1-2	0-0	1-1	2-1	1-1	1-0	2-1	1-3
9	Grantham Town	1-1	2-1	1-3	0-2	1-0	4-0	2-2	0-3		0-2	1-1	1-1	0-1	0-1	2-1	0-5	0-2	1-1	2-0	3-2	1-1	4-3
10	Havant & Waterlooville	1-4	2-3	0-2	1-1	1-3	3-2	2-2	1-0	2-1		1-2	2-0	4-2	0-0	0-3	5-1	2-2	3-2	1-1	0-1	4-1	0-5
11	Hednesford Town	4-0	2-2	2-1	4-1	0-0	2-4	0-1	1-2	2-0	1-0		1-1	1-2	4-4	1-2	0-0	1-2	3-1	1-2	2-2	0-0	3-1
12	Hinckley United	1-2	0-0	1-2	0-0	4-0	1-0	3-1	2-2	0-1	2-2	4-0		1-2	0-0	1-4	1-1	1-1	2-0	2-1	1-0	1-2	0-0
13	Merthyr Tydfil	2-0	1-3	1-3	3-1	2-1	1-0	0-0	2-2	2-2	1-1	2-0	1-1		1-2	1-1	4-3	1-1	0-2	2-0	1-2	0-4	0-2
14	Moor Green	0-3	1-1	1-0	3-2	1-2	1-3	1-0	0-1	0-0	2-1	2-1	0-1	1-1		1-1	2-0	1-2	2-0	0-2	0-0	1-2	1-1
15	Newport County	2-1	1-0	1-0	2-2	1-2	0-0	2-1	1-1	2-2	0-2	1-1	0-3	1-1	1-1		1-2	3-1	2-1	0-0	1-4	1-1	0-4
16	NuneatonBorough	2-1	2-1	1-2	1-1	0-1	2-0	1-1	4-0	1-1	1-2	3-0	2-0	2-1	1-0	2-0		0-0	0-1	2-2	1-1	4-3	2-1
17	Stafford Rangers	2-0	1-1	2-1	2-0	0-1	3-0	2-1	4-1	0-1	2-1	1-1	2-0	3-1	1-2	1-0	0-3		1-2	3-2	1-1	1-2	2-0
18	Tiverton Town	1-1	1-1	3-3	3-1	2-2	1-1	1-0	2-3	1-1	5-1	2-3	3-0	2-1	2-1	0-0	0-0	0-0		2-2	2-0	1-2	1-1
19	Welling United	2-1	0-1	1-0	1-3	0-3	6-1	2-1	1-2	0-1	1-1	2-0	2-3	0-3	2-1	0-2	2-1	2-1	4-0		2-1	2-2	0-1
20	Weston-Super-Mare	1-0	1-0	0-0	1-2	1-2	1-1	0-1	2-1	2-0	2-0	3-2	2-2	3-2	2-3	0-0	1-1	5-1	1-3	2-1		0-2	1-0
21	Weymouth	3-3	2-1	2-2	0-1	0-1	8-0	3-0	1-0	1-0	0-1	2-0	2-0	2-2	3-0	2-1	1-1	0-1	1-1	1-2	0-0		3-1
22	Worcester City	7-0	0-2	1-0	0-0	0-1	1-0	5-1	2-1	4-1	1-1	0-1	2-0	2-0	3-0	1-5	4-0	0-1	1-2	3-1	3-0	2-2	

LEAGUE CUP

FIRST ROUND

Banbury United	v	King's Lynn	1-1* 2-3p
Bashley	v	Fleet Town	1-2
Bedworth United (w/o)	v	Atherstone United	
Bromsgrove R.	v	Halesowen Town	2-1
Dartford	v	Burgess Hill Town	0-3
Eastleigh	v	Burnham	3-1
Erith & Belvedere	v	Ashford Town	3-1
Gloucester City	v	Solihull Borough	1-4
Gresley Rovers	v	Shepshed Dynamo	2-1
Hastings United	v	Folkestone Invicta	2-6
Mangotsfield Utd	v	Cinderford Town	1-2
Newport IOW	v	Salisbury City	3-2
Rothwell Town	v	Histon	0-1
Rugby United	v	Ilkeston Town	2-1
Sittingbourne	v	Chatham Town	1-2
Stamford	v	Corby Town	2-1*
Stourport Swifts	v	Redditch United	1-1* 4-2p
Sutton Coldfield Tn	v	Evesham United	3-2
Swindon Supermarine	v	Taunton Town	0-3
Team Bath	v	Cirencester Town	2-3
Tonbridge Angels	v	Fisher Athletic	0-3
Yate Town	v	Clevedon Town	0-3

SECOND ROUND

Bedworth United	v	Solihull Borough	4-2
Cambridge City	v	Stamford	4-1
Chatham Town	v	Burgess Hill Town	1-0
Cinderford Town	v	Bromsgrove Rovers	1-3
Cirencester Town	v	Clevedon Town	3-0
Eastleigh	v	Newport IOW	2-1
Erith & Belvedere	v	Fleet Town	0-2
Folkestone Invicta	v	Fisher Athletic	3-2
Gresley Rovers	v	Stourport Swifts	3-2
King's Lynn	v	Histon	1-2
Sutton Coldfield Tn	v	Rugby United	2-1
Weymouth	v	Taunton Town	3-1*

THIRD ROUND

Bath City	v	Cirencester Town	3-0
Dorchester Town	v	Weston-super-Mare	2-0
Dover Athletic	v	Chatham Town	4-1
Eastleigh	v	Fleet Town	4-1
Folkestone Invicta	v	Chelmsford City	4-3
Grantham Town	v	Cambridge City	0-2
Havant & Waterlooville	v	Crawley Town	2-3*
Hednesford Town	v	Bedworth Utd	3-3* 4-2p
Hinckley United	v	Histon	3-0
Moor Green	v	Stafford Rangers	5-0
Newport County	v	Chippenham Town	0-4
Nuneaton Borough	v	Gresley Rovers	1-0
Tiverton Town	v	Bromsgrove Rovers	3-0
Welling United	v	Eastbourne Borough	2-1
Weymouth	v	Merthyr Tydfil	4-2*
Worcester City	v	Sutton Coldfield	1-1* 5-4p

FOURTH ROUND

Cambridge City	v	Nuneaton Borough	2-1
Crawley Town	v	Welling United	1-0
Dorchester Town	v	Eastleigh	1-2
Dover Athletic	v	Folkestone Invicta	2-0
Hinckley United	v	Hednesford Town	0-1
Tiverton Town	v	Chippenham Town	1-4
Weymouth	v	Bath City	2-0
Worcester City	v	Moor Green	0-2

QUARTER-FINALS

Cambridge City	v	Hednesford Town	1-0
Crawley Town	v	Dover Athletic	1-0
Eastleigh	v	Weymouth	5-2
Moor Green	v	Chippenham Town	3-1

SEMI-FINALS

Crawley Town	v	Eastleigh	2-0
Moor Green	v	Cambridge City	3-0

THE FINAL

1st LEG (6th April)

Moor Green	v	Crawley Town	1-2

2nd LEG (20th April)

Crawley Town	v	Moor Green	2-0

TOP GOALSCORERS - LEAGUE & LEAGUE CUP

Allan Tait	Crawley Town	22
Daniel Bloomfield	Cambridge City	20
Steve Claridge	Weymouth	20
Scott Partridge	Bath City	20
Lee Phillips	Weymouth	20
Daniel Davidson	Stafford Rangers	19
Chukkie Eribenne	Havant & Waterlooville	19
Charlie MacDonald	Crawley Town	19
Scott Ramsay	Eastbourne Borough	18
Cortez Belle	Merthyr Tydfil	17
Darren Edwards	Tiverton Town	17
Charles Griffin	Chippenham Town	17
Gerald Murphy	Nuneaton Borough	17
Craig Wilkins	Dover Athletic	17
Paul Booth	Welling United	16
Mark Danks	Hednesford Town	16
Leon Kelly	Worcester City	16
Neil Davis	Moor Green	13
James Mudge	Tiverton Town	13
James Constable	Chippenham Town	12
Kevin Wilkin	Nuneaton Borough	12

AYLESBURY UNITED

CLUB OFFICIALS

Chairman: Bill Carroll
Vice Chairman: Les Baycroft
Football Secretary: Peter Ash, 8 KeatsClose,Aylesbury HP21 7UT
01296 429775 (H) 01296 436350(W)
Press Officer: Tony Graham
Email: info@aylesburyutd.co.uk

FOOTBALL MANAGEMENT TEAM

Manager: Paul Curtis
Assistant Manager: Danny Nicholls
Physio: Gareth Styles

FACT FILE

Formed: 1897 Nickname: The Ducks
Sponsors: T.B.A.
Colours: Green & w hite/white/white
Change colours: Amber&black/black/amber
Midweek home matchday: Tuesday
Reserve Team's League: Suburban
Newsline: 0906 655 5811
Website: www.aylesburyunited.co.uk

2003-2004

Top Scorer Alvin Bubb 6
Captain& P.o.Y.: Matt Hayward

PROGRAMME

Pages: 36 Price: £1.50
Editor:Leon O'Sullivan
email: l.osullivan@btopenworld.com

Local Press: Bucks Herald, Bucks Advertiser
Local Radio: BBC Three Counties, Mix 96

GROUND The Stadium, Buckingham Road, Aylesbury HP20 2AQ Tel: 01296 436350
Fax: 01296 395667

Directions: On A413 to Buckingham, just off ring road opposite Horse & Jockey PH. Arriving from Buckingham ground is on left - from all other directions follow Buckingham signs and ground on right. Half hour walk from Aylesbury rail and bus stations

Capacity 4,000 Cover: 1000 Seats: 500 Floodlights: Yes

Clubhouse: Pub hours. Bar snacks available
Function room available for hire(01296 428000).

Club Shop: Sells programmes, magazines, leisurewear, badges etc.
Contact: 21 CD Club shop. c/o The Club

PREVIOUS **Leagues:** Bucks Contiguous 1897-1903, South Eastern 03-07, Spartan 07-51, Delphian 51-63, Athenian 63-76, Southern 76-88, GMV Conference 88-89 Isthmian Premier 89-2004
Grounds: Printing Works Ground 1897-1935, Sports Stadium, Wendover Rd (ground name changed to The Stadium, Turnfurlong Lane) 35-85, shared grounds 85-86 **Name:** Night School, Printing Works (merged in 1897)

CLUB RECORDS **Attendance:** 6,000 v England 1988 (at old ground: 7,500 v Watford, FA Cup 1st Rd1951)
Career goalscorer: Cliff Hercules **Career appearances:** Cliff Hercules
Transfer fee paid: £15,000 for Glenville Donegal (Northampton, 1990)
Transfer fee received: Undisclosed forJermaine Darlington (Q.P.R. 1999)

BEST SEASON **FA Trophy:** Semi-Final 2002-2003 **FA Cup:** 3rd Rd 95. League clubs defeated: Southend Utd 89-90

HONOURS Southern Lg 87-88 (Mids Div R-up 84-85, Sth Div R-up 79-80); Athenian Lg Div 2 R-up 67-68; Delphian Lg 53-54 (R-up 52-53, Lg Cup 59-60); Spartan Lg 08-09 (R-up 52-53), West Div 28-29 (R-up 45-46), Div 1 38-39 (R-up 34-35); Berks & Bucks Snr Cup 13-14 85-86 96-97; 99-00Isthmian League Cup 94-95, Isthmian Charity Shield 95-96 Isthmian League R-up 98-99

Players progressing: Ray Mabbutt (Bristol Rovers), Phil Barber (Crystal Palace 1986), Jermaine Darlington (Q.P.R. 99),Lee Cook (watford 00)

L-R - Back row: Greg Williams, Gary McCann, Scott Honeyball, Steve Cordery (Manager), Craig Maskell (Asst. player-manager), Adam Campion, Adam Wheeler, Mark Burgess.**Middle:** Peter Remnant (Reserve Team Man.), John Hay (Physio), Roni Joe, Steve McGrath, Gareth Risbridger, Phil Dicker, Chris Bangura, Tony Houghton, John Winter, Danny Grimsdell, Fiston Manuella, Ron Schmidt (Kit Man), Peter Wright (Director of Football). **Front:** Sam Sloma, Kesie Ibe, Daniel Gordon, Lewis Pritchard, Stuart Corbould, Rory Hunter, John Marsh, Danny Gray, Dwight Marshall

BANBURY UNITED

CLUB OFFICIALS

Chairman: Paul Saunders
Vice Chairman: Brian Kay
President: David Jesson
Commercial Mgr: Dave Bennett
Press Officer: Dave Bennett
Secretary: B Worsley, c/o Sol Systems, Unit 4 Mallorie Hse, Beaumont Rd,Banbury, OX16 1RH
Tel: 01295 265638 (H), 07941 267567
Email: bworsley@solsystems.freeserve.co.uk

FOOTBALL MANAGEMENT TEAM

Manager: Kevin Brock
Assistant Manager: Brian Robinson
Physio: Wally Hastie

FACT FILE

Founded: 1933 Reformed: 1965
Nickname: Puritans
Sponsors: Alex Lawrie Factors.
Colours: Red & gold/red/red
Change colours: White /white/white
Midweek matches: Tuesday
Reserves' Lge: Hellenic Res Div 1 East
Club Website: www.banburyunited.co.uk
Unofficial sites:
www..banbury-united.cityslide.com
www.expage.com.bufc

2003-2004
Top Scorer: George Redknapp
Player of the Year: George Redknapp
2004-2005 Captain:Keiran Sullivan

The Puritan
www.banburyunited.co.uk
Banbury United Football Club
Official Matchday Programme
2003/2004 Season
Banbury United
v
Burgess Hill Town
Dr. Martens Southern League Eastern Division
Saturday 6th March 2004
Kick off 3.00pm
Main Sponsors
Alex Lawrie Factors

Pages: 40 Price: £1.00
Editor: David Shadbolt
email:david@dshadbolt.fsnet.co.uk

GROUND Spencer Stadium, off Station Rd, Banbury, Oxon . OX16 5TA.
Tel: 01295 263354
Directions: M40 jct 11, follow signs for Banbury then BR station, turn right down narrow lane before entering station forecourt; eastern end of town
Capacity: 6,500 Seats: 250 Cover: 500 Floodlights: Yes
Clubhouse: Open match days & week-ends. Mid-week on hire.
Hot food available during after matches **Club Shop:** Yes

HONOURS Oxon Snr Cup 78-79 87-88,03-04 (R-up7); Birmingham Comb. R-up 47-48; Oxon Prof. Cup 52-53(jt) 70-71(jt) 72-73 77-78 79-80(jt); Hellenic premier Winners 99-00 Hellenic Lg.Cup R-Up 91-92; Birmingham Snr Cup R-Up 48-49 59-60 (S.F.46-47); Oxon Snr Lg. 34-35 39-4047-48 (res); Oxon Hosp. Cup 46-47 (R-up 45-46); Oxon Benev. Cup R-up 77-78 80-8182-83; Daventry Charity Cup 88-90 02-03; Smiths Mem. Cup 68-70 (R-up 66-68); Hitchin Centenary Cup 68-69 (R-up 67-68); Leamington Charity Cup 51-52; Bucks Charity Cup 00-01 Warks Comb. R-up 57-58 60-61, Presidents Cup R-up 60-61; Midland Floodlit Cup 67-68; Wallspan Comb. 85-86

PREVIOUS **Leagues:** Banbury Jnr 33-34; Oxon Snr 34-35; Birmingham Comb. 35-54; W.Mids 54-66; Southern 66-90
Name: Banbury Spencer

BEST SEASON **FA Cup:** 1st Rd replay 73-74 (Also 1st Rd 47-48 61-62 72-73) **FA Trophy:** 3rd Rd 70-71 73-74

RECORDS **Attendance:** 7,160 v Oxford City, FA Cup 3rd Qual.Rd, 30/10/48
Goalscorer: Dick Pike (1935-48), Tony Jacques (65-76) - both 222
Appearances: Ian Bowyer (557) Fee Paid : £2,000 for Phil Emsden (Oxford Utd, Jan 1980)
Fee Received: £20,000 Kevin Wilson (Derby, December 1979)
Win: 12-0 v RNAS Culham, Oxon Snr Cup 45-46
Defeat: 2-11 v West Bromwich Albion `A', Birmingham Comb. 38-39

Players progressing:
Ollie Kearns (Reading), Kevin Wilson & Richard Pratley(Derby), Mick Kearns & Terry Muckleberg (Oxford), Martin Singleton (Coventry)

Banbury celebrate winning the Senior Cup.

BATH CITY

CLUB OFFICIALS

Chairman: Stephen Hall
Directors: G.Todd,P.Weaver,M.Hughes. P.Williams and A Pierce

Secretary: Quentin Edwards c/o the club, 01225 423087 (B) & 07785 795532 (M)

Commercial Director: G.Todd
Safety Officer: J Watt
Press Officer:Q.Edwards

FOOTBALL MANAGEMENT TEAM

Manager: Gary Owers
Assistant Manager: Vaughan JonesPhysios:Dave Lukins

FACT FILE

Founded: 1889
Nicknames: The City or The Romans
Midweek home matchday: Tuesday
Colours: Black & white stripes/black/b & w
Change: Red/White/RedYouth League: South West Counties
Ladies Team: Yes
Unofficial Club Website:www.bathcityfc,com
2003-2004
Top ScorerScott Partridge
Player of the Year:Matt Coupe
2004-2005 Captain: Steve Jones

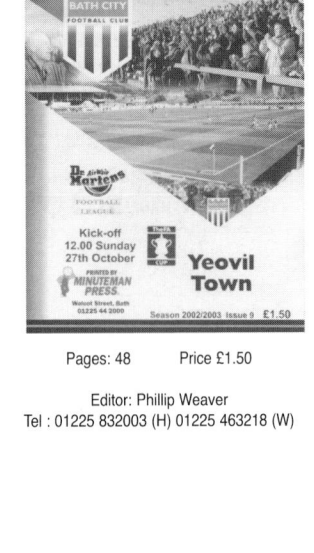

Pages: 48 Price £1.50

Editor: Phillip Weaver
Tel : 01225 832003 (H) 01225 463218 (W)

GROUND Twerton Park, Twerton, Bath Avon BA2 1DB. Tel: 01225 423087/313247
Fax: 01225481391 Email Address: mail@bathcityfootballclub.co.uk
Directions: Twerton Park is situated on the A4/A36 Lower Bristol Road - on theBristol side of Bath City Centre (Approx 2.5 miles). The area is serviced byJ18 on the M4. From the centre of Bath the bus route is No.5 - Twerton HighStreet
Capacity: 8,840 Seated: 1,017 Covered Terracing: 4,800
Clubhouse: Several bars open all week and full service with menu on match-days catering for up to 250 people Club Shop: Contact MrM.Brush

PREVIOUS
Grounds: The Belvoir Ground, Lambridge 1889-1932
Leagues: Southern League, Vauxhall Conference

CLUB RECORDS
Attendance: 18,020 v Brighton & Hove Albion, FA Cup.
Defeat: 9-0 Yeovil Town 46-47 **Victory:** 8-0 v Boston United 98-99
Career goalscorer: Paul Randall. **Career appearances:** David Mogg (530)
Transfer fee paid: £15,000 for Micky Tanner from Bristol City
Transfer fee received: £80,000 for Jason Dodd from Southampton

BEST SEASON
FA Cup: Third Round 63-64, 0-3 v Bolton W. (A) after 1-1: 93-94 **FA Trophy:** 4th Round, 89-90

HONOURS
Southern League Champions 59-60, 77-78; R-up 29-33, 61-62, 89-90; Southern League Cup 78-79; Somerset Premier Cup 51-52, 52-53, 57-58, 59-60, 65-66, 69-70, 77-78, 80-81, 81-82, 83-84, 84-85, 85-86, 88-89, 89-90, 93-94, 94-95;Anglo-Italian Cup R-up 76-77, 77-78

Players progressing: Alan Skirton (Arsenal),Tony Book (Plymouth A.), Kenny Allen (Bournemouth), Peter Rogers (Exeter C.), R Bourne (Torquay), Martyn Rogers (Exeter City)Dave Wiffil (Manchester C.), , Brian Wade (Swindon Town), Jeff Meacham (Bristol R.), Martin Hirst (BristolC.), Paul Bodin (Swindon), Graham Withey (Coventry), Jason Dodd (Southampton), Paul Adcock (Torquay) and Jamie Gosling (Yeovil Town)

Taken before their F.A. Cup 3rd Qualifying Round tie against Thame United.
Back Row (L-R): Scott Hendy, Matt Coupe, Steve Jenkins, Mark Bryant, Mitch Counsell, Jim Rollo, Drew Shore.
Front Row: Steve Tweddle, Frankie Bennett, David Cleverley, Andy Williams.

Photo: Arthur Evans.

BEDFORD TOWN

CLUB OFFICIALS

Chairman: David Howell

Directors:

Dave Redman, Tony Luff, Gerry Edmunds.

Secretary: Dave Swallow c/o club

01234 403889 (H) 01234 262616(W)

Company Secretary: Barry Stephenson

FOOTBALL MANAGEMENT TEAM

Manager: Nick Platnauer

Asst. Manager: Dave Randall

Captain: Lee Howarth

Captain: Lee Howarth

Physio: Brendon Skinner

2003-2004

Player of the Year:Ian Brown

Top Scorer: Drew Roberts

FACT FILE

Nickname: The Eagles

Founded 1908

Reformed: 1989

Sponsors: T.B.A.

Coaches and Charles Wells.

Colours: Blue with white trim

Change Colours: White with blue trim

Midweek Matchday: Tuesday

Reserves' League: Beds.Reserve Lg.

Supporters Website: www.bedfordeagles.net

Local Press:Beds Times, Beds on Sunday

Local Radio: Chiltern Radio,Three Counties

PROGRAMME

Pages: 40 Price: £1.50

Editor: Dave Swallow

email: bedford townfcalbtconnect.com

GROUND: The New Eyrie, Meadow Lane, Cardington, Bedford MK44. 3SB Fax: 01234 831990 Tel: 01234 838448.

Directions: BR station Bedford Midland 3miles from ground. Bus station 5 mins walk from BR station. Service 171 & 172 stop outside ground (Canvins stop). Trains from London Thameslink run every 30 mins to Bedford. By road:**A1** going north take L. turn Bedford A603 at Sandy r'abt. Over small bridge keep on this road for 5 miles, ground on right. **M1** going North A603. Next r'abt straight over to Cambridge A1 & Bedford A603. Take 3rd turn to Bedford. At r'abt take 4th exit to Sandy A603. Ground is half a mile on left.

Capacity: 3,000 Seats: 300 Cover: 1000 Floodlights: Yes

Clubhouse: Matchdays bar snacks **Club Shop:** Good range of merchandise Gerry Edmonds (01234 381213)

PREVIOUS **Leagues:** South Midlands 91-94 (predecessors: Utd Co's 08-39; Southern 46-82 Isthmian 94-2004
Grounds: Allen Park, Queens Park, Bedford (park pitch) 1991-93
(predecessors: London Rd; Gasworks; Queens Pk; The Eyrie, Raleigh Street)

CLUB RECORDS **Attendance:** 3,000 v Peterborough Utd, ground opening 6/8/93.
Career scorer: Jason Reed **Career appearances:** Jason Reed
Win: 9-0 v Ickleford, and Caddington **Defeat:** 0-5 v Hendon

BEST SEASON **FA Cup:** 1st Rd proper 01-02 **FA Vase:** 5th Round 1998-99, 1-2 v Tiverton Town (H) **F.A.Trophy:** 4th Rd v Yeovil Town 99-00

HONOURS: Isthmian League: Div 1 R-up. 00-01 Div. 2 98-99; South Midlands Lg 94-95 (Div 1 92-93, F'lit Cup 94-95); Hinchingbrook Cup 94-95 94-95; Beds Sen Cup 94-95.
(Predecessors: Southern Lg 58-59 (Div 1 69-70), Utd Co's Lg 30-31 32-33 33-34 (R-up 7 Times)Vandanal Cup 97-8 Beds Prem , Beds Premier Cup 97-98 **FA Cup** 4th Rd 63-64 65-66. **FA Trophy** Semi-Final 74-75.

Players progressing: Bill Garner (Southend 69), Nicky Platnaeur (Bristol Rovers 77). Ray Bailey/Derek Bellotti/Billy Brown/Bert Carberry/PeterHall/Dave Quirke/Bobby Fold (Gillingham 56-67), Phil Driver (Wimbledon 78), Joe Dubois (Grimsby T 53), Ted Duggan (Luton T 56), Harry Duke (Noprwich C 46),John Fahy (Oxford U 64), Ken Flint (Spurs 47), Joe Hooley (Accrington 61), Joe Kirkup (Reading 55), Graham Moxon (Exeter C 75), Bela Olah (Northampton 58),Gary Sergeant (Peterborough U 77), Neil Townsend (Southend U 73)

Back Row (L-R): Daniel Purzycki, Daniel French, Liam Folds, Lee Howarth, Steve Jackman, Ian Brown, Rene Howe, James Taylor, Eddie Lawley, Craig Rydeheard, Julian Capone, danny Liqourice (GK Coach).
Front Row: Brendon Skinner (Physio), Dave Randall (Asst. Manager), Drew Roberts, Chris Dillon, Nick Platnauer (Manager), Darren Sarll, Neil Lazarus, Kym Davis (Coach), Noel Quinn.

CHESHAM UNITED

CLUB OFFICIALS

President: Bill Wells
Chairman: Phillip Morgan
Secretary: David Stanley , 17 Old Vicarage gdns, Markyate, St.Albans, Herts AL3 8PW 01582 840707 (H) 07766 761862(M)
Commercial Manager: T.B.A.
Press Officer: Phil Morgan

FOOTBALL MANAGEMENT TEAM

Manager: Steve Bateman
Capt: Peter Clifford **Physio:** Jude Monteath

FACT FILE

Formed: 1886 Nickname: The Generals
Sponsors: T.B.A.
Colours:
Claret & sky blue/claret & sky blue/ claret
Change colours: White/white/sky blue
Midweek home matchday: Tuesday
Reserve Team's League: Capital
Match information: 09068 335505

2003-21004

Player of the Year & Top goalscorer:
Garry Sippetts

THE MEADOW
matchday magazine
Ryman Division One (North)
CHESHAM UNITED
v
EAST THURROCK UNITED
Saturday 10th April 2004
Kick-off 3.00pm
Ryman
matchday magazine £1.50

Pages: 52 Price: £1.50
Editors: Alan Calder
(01442 230420 [H])

Local Radio: Three Counties
Local Press: Bucks Examiner, Bucks Advertiser, Bucks Free Press

GROUND: The Meadow, Amy Lane, Amersham Road, Chesham, Bucks. HP5 1NE
Tel: 01494 783964 (ground clubhouse) Fax: 01494 782456 Club Website: www.cheshamunitedfc.co.uk Email Address: jimchamberschesham@talk21.com

Directions: M25 junction 18, A404 to Amersham, A416 to Chesham - go down to r-about at foot of Amersham Hill, then sharp left. 10 mins walk from Chesham station (Metropolitan Line)
Capacity: 5,000 Cover: 2,500 Seats: 284 Floodlights: Yes

Clubhouse: Open every evening & matchdays. Bar snacks. Available for hire(business training meetings, weddings etc)
Club Shop: Open matchdays Metal Badges: Yes

PREVIOUS **Leagues:** Spartan 17-47; Corinthian 47-63; Athenian 63-73 Isthmian 73-2004

CLUB RECORDS **Attendance:** 5,000 v Cambridge Utd, FA 3rd Rd 5/12/79
Goalscorer: John Willis **Appearances:** Martin Baguley (600+)
Record Fees - Paid & Received: Undisclosed (club policy)

BEST SEASON **FA Cup:** 3rd Rd 79-80. 1st Rd 66-67 68-69 76-77 82-83
FA Amtr Cup: R-up 67-68 **FA Trophy:** 3rd Rd 92-93 (1-3 v Sutton United [H])

HONOURS: FA Amtr Cup R-up 67-68, Isthmian Lg 92-93 (Div 1 90-91 96-97), Div 2 Nth 86-87, Associate Members Cup R-up 90-91, Charity Shield 94-95; Athenian Lg Div 1 Cup 63-64 68-69; Corinthian Lg R-up (2) 60-62 (Lg Cup 60-61); Spartan Lg(4) 21-23 24-25 32-33 (R-up 26-27 29-30 33-34); Berks & Bucks Snr Cup 21-22 25-26 28-29 33-34 47-48 50-51 64-65 66-67 75-76 92-93. 00-01 03-04(R-up 94-95, 01-02)

Players progressing: Bill Shipwright & Jimmy Strain (Watford 53 & 55), StewartScullion (Charlton 65), John Pyatt (L'pool 67), Brian Carter (Brentford 68),Kerry Dixon (Spurs 78), Tony Currie (Torquay 84), Dwayne Plummer (Bristol Rovers)

Chesham's players celebrate after beating Bracknell Town in the Berks & Bucks Senior Cup at Wycombe Wanderers in May 2004.

CHIPPENHAM TOWN

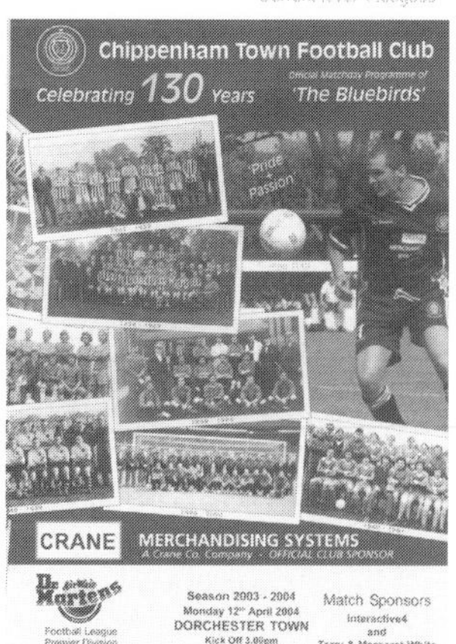

Chippenham Town Football Club
Celebrating 130 Years
Official Matchday Programme of 'The Bluebirds'
Pride
Passion
CRANE
MERCHANDISING SYSTEMS
A Crane Co. Company - OFFICIAL CLUB SPONSOR
Dr Martens
Football League Premier Division
Season 2003 - 2004
Monday 12th April 2004
DORCHESTER TOWN
Kick Off 3.00pm
Issue 23 £1.50
Match Sponsors
Interactive4
and
Terry & Margaret White

PROGRAMME
Pages: 32 Price: £1.50
Editors: Secretary

CLUB OFFICIALS

President: Doug Webb
Chairman: T.B.A.
Vice-Chairman: T.B.A.**Secretary:** Chris Blake, 28 Sadlers Mead, Chippenham, Wilts SN15 3PB
Tel: 01249 658212(H &W) 07713 502116(M)
Press Officer: Chris Blake
Com. Man: Lauren McKel (01249 705912)

FOOTBALL MANAGEMENT TEAM

Manager: Steve White
Physio:Ronnie Needham

FACT FILE

Formed: 1873
Nickname: The Bluebirds
Club Sponsors: D.L.Windows, Costcutters, Shoestrings, Crane Merchandising Systems,
Club colours:Royal Blue/Royal Blue/white
Change colours:All white or All yellow
Midweek matches: Tuesday
Local Press: Chippenham News, Wilts Gazette, Wiltshire Chronicle

2003--2004

Leading Goalscorer: Charlie Griffin
Player of the Year: Scott Walker

GROUND Hardenhuish Park, Bristol Road, Chippenham SW 14 6LR Tel: 01249 650400
Website: www.chippenhamtownfc.co.uk email: chrisblake@chiptownfc.freeserve .co.uk

Directions: M4 jct 17, A350 into Chippenham, follow signs for Trowbridge/Bath until r'about, left onto A420 into town, ground 800yds on left 15 mins walk from railway station on main A420 Bristol Road

Capacity: 4,000 Seats: 300 Cover: 1,000 Floodlights: Yes
Clubhouse: Yes, open matchdays. Food available **Club Shop:** Yes

PREVIOUS **Leagues:** Hellenic, Wiltshire Senior, Wiltshire Premier, Western League
Grounds: Westmead, Lowden, Little George Lane, Malmesbury Rd

RECORD **Gate:** 4,800 v Chippenham Utd, Western League 1951
Goalscorer: Dave Ferris **Appearances:** Ian Monnery

BEST SEASON **FA Cup:** 1st Round 51-52 **FA Vase:** Finalists 99-00

HONOURS F.A. Vase R-up 99-00, Western Lg 51-52 R-up 00-01, Div 1 80-81, Div 2 52-53 (Res) 80-81. Wilts Senior Cup; Wilts Senior League; Les Phillips Cup (Western Lg Cup) 99-00 00-01, Wilts Premier Shield 2001-02. Dr Martens Division 1 Western Division: Runners-Up 2001-02

L-R - Back Row: Colin Towler, James Constable, Elia Wilmot, Mark Hervin, Lee Davidson, Martin Paul, Sam Allison, Scott Walker and Gary Horgan.**Front row:** Simon Charity, Charlie Griffin, Andy Roberston and Rene Regis. **Photo:** Wiltshire Gazette & Herald

CIRENCESTER TOWN

CLUB OFFICIALS

Chairman: Steven Abbley,

17 Dianmer Close, Hook, Swindon. SN4 8ER.
Tel: 01743853293 (H) 01793 884900 (B)

Secretary: Jim Saunders,
16 Arnold Way Cirencester, Glos. GL7 1TA
Tel: 01285 659002 (H) 01285 654474 (FAX)

e.mail:jim@lynn16wanadoo.co.uk

Commercial Manager: Stephen Abbley

Press Officer: Jim Saunders

FOOTBALL MANAGEMENT TEAM

Manager: Brian Hughes

Physio: T.B.A.

FACT FILE

Founded: 1889
Nickname: Centurians
Sponsors: P.H.H./Cheltenham Windows
Colours: Red & black/ black/ red
Change colours: Blue & white
Midweek Matchday: Tuesday
Reserves' League: Cirencester & District
Local Press:
Standard, Western Daily Press
Local Radio:
BBC Radio Gloucester, Severn Sound

PROGRAMME

Pages: Varies   Price: £1
Editor: Steve Mattos
01285 654543(W) 01285 654474(FAX)
emaill: jim@lynn16wanadoo.co.uk

CIRENCESTER TOWN FOOTBALL CLUB
SEASON 2004/05
SOUTHERN FOOTBALL LEAGUE
PREMIER DIVISION
CIRENCESTER TOWN
V
HEDNESFORD TOWN
Tuesday 24th August 2004
Kick Off 7.30pm
Matchday Programme
Team Sponsors
Match Sponsors
£1-20p

GROUND Corinium Stadium,Kingshill Lane, Cirencester Tel: 01285654543

Directions: Leave by-pass at Burford Road roundabout to the left. Then right at lights,laft at junction first left and ground is 250 yards on right.
Capacity: 4,500 Seats: 550 Cover: 550 Floodlights: Yes

Clubhouse: Open Tuesday - Friday evenings & Saturday. Snacks are available onmatchdays. Club Shop: None

PREVIOUS **Leagues:** Hellenic League Names: None. Grounds: Smithfield Stadium

CLUB RECORDS **Attendance:** 2,600 v Fareham 1969
Win: Unknown **Defeat:** Unknown
Career Goalscorer: Unknown **Career Appearances:** Unknown
Transfer fee paid: None **Transfer fee received:** None

BEST SEASON **FA Trophy:** 1st Qual. Round 1996-97 (1st season in comp.)
FA Vase: Never past the 1st Round **FA Cup:** 4th Qualifying Round, 2001-02

HONOURS Gloucestershire Senior Amateur Cup 89-90; Hellenic League Div One Challenge Cup 90-91; Hellenic League Prem Div 95-96, League Cup 95-96; Gloucestershire County Cup 95-96

Players progressing: None

Back row, left to right: Gary Wooton, Gareth Hopkins, Mike Davies, Paul Thompson, Adam Mayo, Kevin Halliday, Nathan Edwards, Alan Bird, Tom Cole, Neil Arndale.
Front Row: Ben Fitch, Stuart Fraser, Shaun Wimble, Scott Griffin, Steve Tapp (Asst. Manager), Brian Hughes (Manager), Darren Robison (Coach), Adam Hemmings, Nick Stanley, Michael Jackson.

DUNSTABLE TOWN

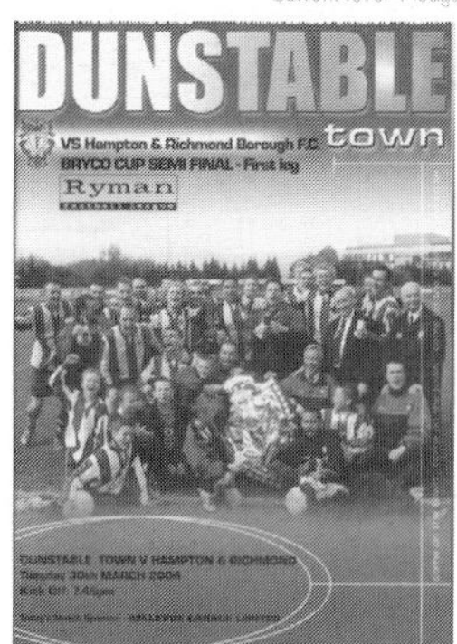

Programme Editor:
Derek Tripney: 0771 319 1400

CLUB PERSONNEL
Chairman: Tony Potter
President:Barry Fry
Directors: Roger Dance, Derek Tripney, Steve Kay
Secretary: Malcolm Aubrey,
25 Copperfields Close, Houghton Regis, Dunstable, Beds. LU5 5TE
Tel: 01582 667555 (H) 0771 8580625 (M)
email: malcolmaubrey@btopenworld.com
Press Officer: Derek Tripney
Match Secretary: Malcolm Aubrey

FOOTBALL MANAGEMENT TEAM
Manager: Darren Croft
Captain: Grant Carney
Physio: John Bell

FACT FILE
Formed: 1998
Nickname : The Blues
Colours:Blue & white stripes/blue/blue & white
Change Colours:Red & black hoops/black/red & black
Midweek Matchday: Tuesday
Youth League:Southern Floodlit Youth Lg.

2003-2004

Player of the Year: Julian Old
Top Goalscorer: Grant Carney

GROUND: Creasey Park Stadium, Creasey Park Drive, Dunstable, Bedfordshire LU6 1DNN
Tel No: 01582 667555

DIRECTIONS: Travel north on A5, through centre of Dunstable, then left at traffic lights into Brewers Hill Road and straight over mini roundabout. Ground is on the right.

CAPACITY :2,400 Cover: Yes Seating: 240 Floodlights Yes

CLUBHOUSE: Open six days a week and may be used by away supporters in match days.

SNACK BAR: in ground and open on match days for all supporters withusual refreshmants available.

PREVIOUS **Leagues:** Spartan South Midlands 1998-2003 & Isthmian 2003-2004

HONOURS: S.S.M. Champions 2002-03 & Beds Sen Cup 03-04 Bryco Cup Runners-Up 03-04, S.Mids Lg Challenge Trophy R-Up 02-03, S.Mid Sen Div R-up 2000-01, Beds Senior Cup Runners-up 2000-01
S.Mid Div 1 Champions 99-00, Div1 Lg Cup 99-00

Back row, left to right: Grant Carney, Gareth Seeley, Bernie Christie, Paul Taylor,Tony Francis, Matt Baldry, Thomas Hayes, Chris Harvey and Marc Kefford. **Front Row:** Tony Burgess, Robbie Keen, Julian Old, Dean Walker, Darren Croft (Manager), Sponsor Tony Potter, Paul Reeves (Manager), Neil Pugh, Jonathon Barnett, Chris Hemmings and John Bell (Physio).

GLOUCESTER CITY

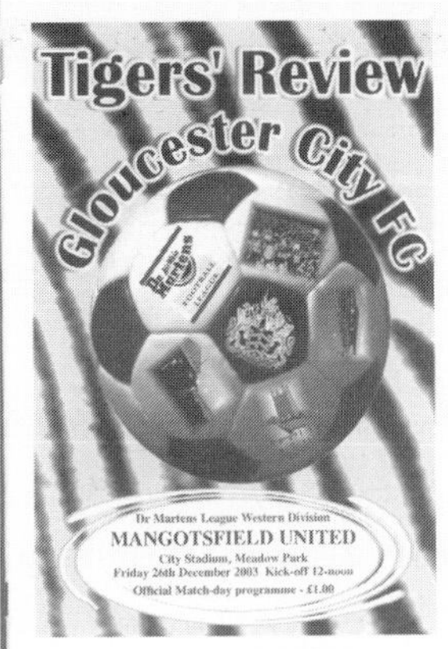

CLUB OFFICIALS

Chairman: Colin Gardner

President: R F Etheridge

Secretary: Jason Mills
25 Hewlett Road, Cheltenham,
Gloucestershire GL52 6AD
Tel/Fax: 01242 700496 Mob: 07768 750590
Club Email: mills.jason@virgin.net

Press Off: Ashley Loveridgel
Tel: 07760 417119

FOOTBALL MANAGEMENT TEAM

Manager: Chris Burns

Assistant Manager: Mike Cook

Coaches: Chris Gardner & Karl Bayliss

Physio: Adrian Tandy

FACT FILE

Formed: 1889
Nickname: The Tigers
Sponsors: Keyway
Colours: Yellow & black stripes/ black/black
Change colours: All White
Midweek games: Tuesday
Local Press: Gloucester Citizen, Western Daily Press
Local Radio: Severn Sound, BBC Radio Gloucestershire

PROGRAMME

Pages: 44 Price: £1.00
Editor: Mike Dunstan Tel: 01242 701662

GROUND Meadow Park, Sudmeadow Road, Hempsted, Gloucester GL2 6HS Tel: 01452 421400
Directions: From North: A40 then then A4301 towards City Centre & Historic Docks, right into Severn Road over swingbridge, right into Llanthony Road/Hempsted Lane, 2nd right into Sudmeadow Road, ground 50yds on left
Capacity: 3,500 Cover:2,500 Seats: 560 Floodlights: Yes
Clubhouse: Meadow Park Sports & Social Club in ground. Normal licensing hours. **Club Shop:** Yes

PREVIOUS **Leagues:** Bristol & Dist. (now Western) 1893-96, Gloucester & Dist. 97-1907, NorthGlos. 07-10, Glos. North Senior 20-34, Birmingham Comb. 1935-39
Grounds: Longlevens 1935-65, Horton Road 65-86 **Name:** Gloucester Y.M.C.A

CLUB RECORDS **Attendance:** 4,000 v Dagenham & Redbridge, FA Trophy S-F 2nd Leg, 12.4.97
Win: 10-0 v Sudbury Town (H), FA Cup 3rd Rd Q., 17.10.98
Defeat: 1-12 v Gillingham 9.11.46
Goalscorer: Reg Weaver, 250 **Appearances:** Stan Myers & Frank Tredgett in 1950s
Fee Paid: £25,000 for S Fergusson (Worcester City), and D Holmes (Gresley R.)
Fee Received: £25,000 Ian Hedges (AFC Bournemouth, 1990)

BEST SEASON **FA Cup:** 2nd Rd 89-90 **FA Trophy:** Semi-Final 1996-97

HONOURS Southern Lg R-up 90-91, Lg Cup 55-56 R-up 81-82, Midland Div 88-89), Glos NthSen Lg 33-34, Glos Sen. Cup 37-38 49-58 65-66 68-69 70-71 74-75 78-79 79-80 81-82 82-83 83-84 90-91 92-93; Sen Amat Cup (Nth) 31-32)

Players progressing: Numerous including - William Teague (61) & Rod Thomas (64) to Swindon, John Layton (Hereford 74), Ian Main (Exeter 78), Mike Bruton (Newport 79), Mel Gwinnett (Bradford C. 84), Steve Talboys (Wimbledon 91)

GRANTHAM TOWN

DR MARTEN'S LEAGUE - Premier Division
Welcome to the home of...
GRANTHAM TOWN FC
CRYSTAL
Grantham
2002-2003 Official Matchday Programme - £1.50
CRYSTAL
Journal
Follow Town every Friday

Programme: 38 pages £1.50
Ed:Andy Sutton 01476 419391 (H)
Local Press: Grantham Journal, Nottingham Evening Post, Melton & GranthamTrader, Grantham Citizen, Lincolnshire Echo
Local Radio: Radio Lincolnshire, Lincs FM

CLUB OFFICIALS

Chairman: Barry Palmer
President:George Freeston
Secretary: Pat Nixon
72 Huntingtower Road, Grantham,
Lincs NG31 7AU
Tel: 01476 419391 FAX: 01476 419392

FOOTBALL MANAGEMENT TEAM

Manager:Dave Norton
Assistant Manager: Phil Turner
Physio: Nigel Marshall Capt: Adrian Speed

FACT FILE

Formed: 1874
Nickname: Gingerbreads
Sponsors: Downtown (Home)
Gladwish Landsales (Away)
Colours: Black & White stripes/black/black
Change: Yellow/black or white/yellow
Midweek matchday: Tuesday
Reserve League: Central Conference
Club Website: www..granthamtownfc.co.uk
www.cheiroa.domon.co.uk/gtfc
2003-2004
Player of the Year: Mario Ziclard

GROUND South Kesteven Sports Stadium, Trent Road, Grantham, Lincs Tel: 01476 402224
Directions: Midway between A1 and A52 on edge of Earlesfield Industrial Estate; from A1 take A607 to Earlsfield Ind. Est and continue into Trent Rd
Capacity: 7,500 Cover: 1,950 Seats: 750 Floodlights: Yes

Clubhouse: (01476 402225) Open evenings and weekends. Bar, darts, pool etc.Frequent live entertainment. Available for functions **Club Shop:** Programmes and a wide range of souvenirs. Contact club number.

PREVIOUS **Leagues:** Mid Amat All, Central All. 11-25 59-61, Midland Co's 25-59 61-72,Southern Lge 72-79, Northern Prem. 79-85
Names: Grantham FC, pre-80. Grounds: London Rd up to 90

CLUB RECORDS **Attendance:** 3,695 v Southport. F.A.Trophy Quarter Final 97-98
Win: 13-0 vRufford Colliery (H), FA Cup Preliminary Rd 15/9/34
Defeat: 0-16 v Notts County Rovers (A), Midland Amateur All. 22/10/1892
Career Goalscorer: Jack McCartney 416
Career Appearances: Chris Gardiner 664
Transfer Fee - Paid:undisclosed for Mario Ziccari **Received:** £20,000 for Gary Crosby (Notts Forest 87)

BEST SEASON **FA Cup:** 3rd Rd 1883-84 86-87 1973-74. Comp Proper on 24 occasions
FA Trophy: Quarter Final 1971-72, 97-98

HONOURS Southern Lg R-up 73-74 (Div 1 Nth) 72-73 78-79, Merit Cup 72-73), Southern Lg Mid Div Champions 97-98. Eastern Division R-up. 2001-02 Midland Co's Lg(3) 63-64 70-72 (R-up 37-38 64-65 69-70, Lg Cup 68-69 70-71), Midland Amtr Lg10-11 (Lg Cup R-up 10-11), Central All. 24-25 (Southern Div R-up 59-60), Lincs Snr Cup 1884-851936-37 (R-up(5) 34-36 39-40 45-47), Lincs Co. `A' Cup(3) 53-54 60-62 (R-up 49-50 52-53 57-58), Lincs Co. Snr Cup 71-72 82-83 (R-up 80-81)

Players progressing: E Morris (Halifax 50), P Thompson/R Cooke (Peterborough 64/80), J Rayner (Notts County 64), D Dall (Scunthorpe 79), N Jarvis/H Wood (Scunthorpe 80), D White (Bristol Rvrs 86), T Curran (Grimsby 87), G Crosby (Nottm Forest 87), A Kennedy (Wrexham 87), R Wilson (Lincoln 87)

Grantham line up before a 2004-2005 fixture.

HALESOWEN TOWN

CLUB OFFICIALS

Chairman: Nigel Pitt **Pres:** Laurence Wood

Vice Chairman: Paul Floud

Secretary: Stewart Tildesley
83 Bloomfield Street, Halesowen B63 3RF
Tel: 0121 5508443(H) 07710 434708(M)

Commercial Manager: Nigel Pitt

General Manager & Press Officerr:
Colin Brookes

FOOTBALL MANAGEMENT TEAM

Man: Paul Holleran Physio:Gavin Blackwell

Captain: Darren Grocutt

2003-2004

Player of the Year.: Asa Charlton

Top Scorer: Jason Moore 27

FACT FILE

Formed: 1873
Nickname: Yeltz
Sponsors: T.B.A.
Newsline: 09066 555818
Colours: Blue with white trim
Change colours: White & Black
Midweek home matchday:Tuesday
Reserve's League: None
Local Press: Sports Argus, Express & Star, Birmingham Mail, Halesowen News, Stourbridge & Halesowen Chronicle
Local Radio: BBC West Midlands, B.R.M.B., Beacon

PROGRAMME

Pages: 44 Price: £1.50p
Editor: Bob Peppere-mail: rjp1@onetel.com

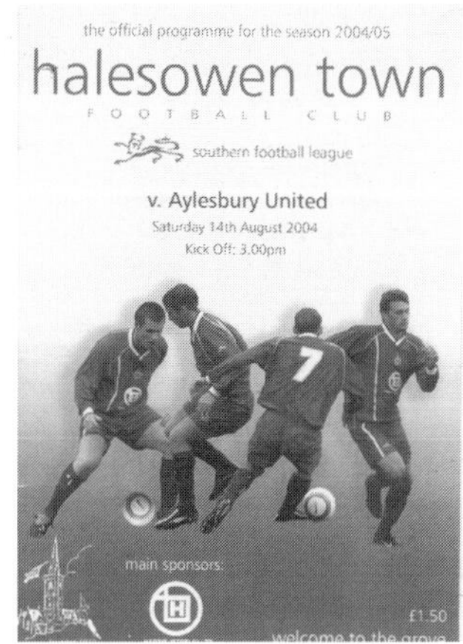

the official programme for the season 2004/05
halesowen town
FOOTBALL CLUB
southern football league
v. Aylesbury United
Saturday 14th August 2004
Kick Off: 3.00pm
main sponsors:
£1.50

GROUND The Grove, Old Hawne Lane, Halesowen, West Midlands B63 3TB Fax: 01902 714221 Tel: 0121 550 2179
Directions: M5 jct 3, A456 (signed Kidderminster) to 1st island turn right (signed A459 Dudley), left at next island (signed A458 Stourbridge), at next island take 3rd left into Grammar School Lane, then Old Hawne Lane - ground 400 yds on left
Capacity: 5,000 Cover: 1,518 Seats: 518 Floodlights: Yes
Clubhouse: (0121 602 2210) 12-2.30 & 7-11 (10.30 Sun) pm daily.Cold snacks served.
Club Shop: Sells replica strips, T-shirts, waterproof tops, coats, scarves, progs, badges etc

PREVIOUS **Leagues:** West Mids 1892-1905 06-11 46-86, Birmingham Comb. 11-39

CLUB RECORDS **Attendance:** 5,000 v Hendon F.A. Cup 1st Rd Proper 1954, (18,234 v Southall,1986 FA Vase Final at Wembley)
Goalscorer: Paul Joinson 369 **Appearances:** Paul Joinson 608
Win: 13-1 v Coventry Amateurs, Birmingham Senior Cup, 1956
Defeat: 0-8 v Bilston, West Midlands League, 7/4/62
Fee Paid: £7,250 for Stuart Evans (Gresley 1996)
Fee Received: £40,000 for Jim Rodwell (Rushden & Diamonds 96)

BEST SEASON **FA Vase:** Winners 84-85, 85-86 R-up 82-83 **FA Trophy:** 3rd Round Proper 94-95
FA Cup: 1st Rd 9 times: 54-55 then each season from 84-85 to 91-92

HONOURS Southern Lg Premier Div R-up 96, Southern Lg Midland Div 89-90, Western Division 01-02 W Mids Lg(5) 46-47 82-85 85-86 (R-up 64-65, Lg Cup 82-83 84-85 R-up 02-03),B'ham Snr Cup 83-84,97-98 (R-up 51-52 67-68), Staffs Snr Cup 88-89 (R-up 83-84), FA Vase (2) 84-86 (R-up 82-3) Worcs Snr Cup 02-03 Winners 51-52 61-62 (R-up 87-88), Midland Comb. Res Div 89-90

Players progressing Arthur Proudler (A. Villa), Cyril Spiers (A. Villa), Billy Morris (Wolves), Dean Spink (A. Villa), Stuart Cash (Nottm Forest), Andrew Pearce, Tim Clarke & Sean Flynn (Coventry), Dean Stokes (Port Vale), Frank Bennett (Southampton), Julian Alsop (Bristol R.)

2004-2005 - L-R - Back Row: Ryan Robinson-Little (Kit), Lewis Baker, Steven Pope, Niki Preston, Richard Williams, Mark Sheils, Daniel Jones, Jason Moore, Asa Charlton, Alex Cowley, and Colin Brookes (General Manager) **Front Row**: Paul Danks, Ian Cooper, Richard Colwell, Simon Forsdick, Ben Steane, Darren Grocutt, Paul Holleran (Manager), Jimmy Harhoff, Stuart Skidmore, David Haywood, Richard Burgess and Gavin Blackwell (physio).

HEDNESFORD TOWN

CLUB OFFICIALS

Directors: Steve Price & Carole Price

Chairman: Steve Price

Managing Director: Terry Brumpton

Secretary: Rod Hadley (01827 66786)

email: rod.hadley@btopenworld.com

Press Officer: Neil Holden

FOOTBALL MANAGEMEN TE AM

Manager:Chris Brindley
Assistant Manager: T.B.A.

FACT FILE

Founded: 1880
Nickname: The Pitmen
Club Sponsors: Extra Personnel
Club colours: White/black/red&black
Change colours: Sky Blues
Midweek home matchday: Monday
Reserves' league: Central Conference,
Web site: www.hednesfordtownfc.co.uk
Hotline Number: 09066 555880

Season 2003-2004

Leading Scorer: Mark Danks 22
P.o.Y.: Carl Palmer
Captain: Steve Palmer

Pages: 32 Price: £1.50
Editor: Lee Kempson
Local Press: Express & Star; Sporting Star; Chase Post; Cannock Mercury; Birmingham Evening Mail &Birmingham Post; Sports Argus; The Chronicle **Local Radio**: Radio WM; BRMB; WABC;Beacon; Signal; BBC Radio Stoke, Rivioum Capital Gold

GROUND Keys Park,Keys Park Road, Hednesford, Cannock, Staffordshire WS12 2DZ
Tel:015 43 422870, **Fax**: 01543 428180, **Hotline:** 0930 555880 **e-mail:** contact@ hednesfordtown.fsnet.co.uk
SIMPLE DIRECTIONS: M6 Jct 11 to Cannock (or M6 toll jct T7), Follow signs for A460 (Rugeley). After crossing A5 at Churchbridge Island continue to follow A460(Rugeley)- five islands-pick up signs for HTFC , Keys Park.
CAPACITY: 6,039 **SEATED:** 1,010 **COVERED TERRACING:** 4,324
CLUB SHOP: Open throughout the week
SOCIAL FACILITIES: Strikers Bar - Open matchdays and every evening 7-11 except Sunday. Chase Suite holds functions and conferences

PREVIOUS **Leagues:** Walsall & District; Birmingham Combination 08-15, 45-53; West Midlands 19-39, 53-72, 74-84; Midland Counties 72-74; Southern League 84-95; Conference 95-01.
Grounds: The Tins (behind Anglesey Hotel) until 1904, Cross Keys until 1995. **Names:** None

HONOURS F.A.Trophy Winners 2003-2004,Welsh Cup R-up 91-92; Southern League - Prem. Div. 94-95; Midland Div. R-up 91-92, Lge. Cup R-up 86-87; West Midlands. Lge 77-78, R-up 83-84; Lge. Cup 83-84; Birmingham Comb. 09-10 50-51, R-up 12-13 52-53; Staffs SeniorCup 69-70, 73-74; R-up 92-93; Birmingham Sen. Cup 35-36; R-up 93-94.

CLUB RECORDS **Attendance:** (at Cross Keys) 10,000 v Walsall F.A.Cup 1919-20 (at Keys Park): 3,169 v York City F.A.Cup 13.01.97
Win: 12-1 v Birmingham City, B'ham Wartime Lge Cup 40-41, 12-1 v Redditch United, B'ham Comb. 52-53
Defeat: 0-15 v Burton, B'ham Comb. 52-53
Career goalscorer: Tosh Griffiths, Joe O'Connor (post-war) 230 in 430 apps **Career apps:** Kevin Foster 463
Transfer fee paid: £12,000, for Steve Burr (Macclesfield Town 1991)
Transfer fee received: £50,000, for Dave Hanson (Leyton Orient)

BEST SEASON **FA Cup:** Fourth Round 1996-97 2-3 v Middlesbrough (A)
League clubs defeated: Blackpool 96-97, York City 96-97, Hull City 97-98, Barnet 98-99
FA Trophy: Winners 2003-2004 3-2 v Canvey Island **League:** 3rd, Conference 95-96

Players Progressing (Post War): Brian Horton (Port Vale 70), Vernon Allatt (Halifax T. 79); Chris Brindley (Wolverhampton W. 86), Scott Cooksey (Shrewsbury T. 98), Dave Hanson (Leyton Orient), Paul Ware (Macclesfield T.), Keith Russell (Blackpool 97) and Ashley Williams (Stockport County)

HEMEL HEMPSTEAD TOWN

CLUB OFFICIALS

Chairman: David Boggins

President: Brendan Glynn

Vice President: Dave Lloyd

Secretary: Bob Jackson, 39 Hobbs Hill Rd
Hemel Hempstead HP3 9QA
01442 263074 (H) 01707 352305 (W)

Press Officer: Harry Kelly

FACT FILE

Founded: 1885 Nickname: TheTudors
Sponsors: Haven
Colours: All red with white trim
Change colours: Green & White
Midweek Matches: Tuesday

FOOTBALL MANAGEMENT TEAM

Manager: Tony Kelly
Asst Manager: Chris Walton
Coach: Ninny Ryan Physio:John Burt

PROGRAMME

Pages: 48 Price: 80p
Editor/Press Off.: Bob Jackson
e-mail: Bob.Jackson@hemeltownfc.com
Local Press: Hemel Gazette, Herald
Local Radio: Sports Talk, Chiltern, Three Counties Radio

GROUND: Vauxhall Ground, Adeyfield Rd, Hemel Hempstead HP2 4HW
Tel: 01442 259777 e-mail: info@hemeltownfc.com

Directions: Euston to Hemel Hempstead Station.
H2 or H3 bus to Windmill Rd., Longlands

Capacity: 3,152 Seats: 250 Covered Standing : Yes Floodlights: Yes

Clubhouse: Open 7-11pm weekdays, 12-11pm weekends & Bank Hols.
Tea bar with hot snacks open matchdays. Tel: 01442 259777.

Club Shop: None

PREVIOUS **Leagues:** Spartan 22-52; Delphian 52-63; Athenian 63-77Isthmian 77-04
Names: Apsley 1885-1947; Hemel Hempstead Town (merged with Hemel Hempstead Utd in1947)
Grounds: Crabtree Lane (til '71)

CLUB RECORDS **Attendance:** 2,000 v Watford 1985 (at Crabtree Lane: 3,500 v Tooting, FA AmtrCup 1st Rd 1962)
Goalscorer: Dai Price **Appearances:** John Wallace, 1012

BEST SEASON **FA Cup:** Never past Qualifying Rounds
FA Vase: 4th Rd 98-99 v Taunton Town

HONOURS Ryman Lge Div 3 98-99; Herts Snr Cup 05-06 07-08 08-09 25-26 61-62 65-66 91-92,
Herts Charity Cup/Shield 25-26 34-35 51-52 63-64 76-77 83-84 (R-up 90-91), Spartan Lg 33-34,
Herts Intermediate Cup 54-55 65-66 83-84, West Herts St Mary Cup 70-71 75-76 82-83 85-86 90-91 91-92 93-94,
Athenian Lg Div 1 R-up 64-65 (Res Cup 65-66), Delphian Lg (res) 54-55 (Res Cup 54-55 61-62)

L-R - Back Row: Chris Walton (coach), Lee Graves, Rene Street, Darren Grieves, Robbie Simpson, Danny Turner, Mat Rawdon, Fergus Moore, Paul Lamb, Darren Bonfield, James Hannington, Daniel West, Gary Fitzgerald, Steve Baker, Marvyn Watson, John Simon White. **Front Row**: Joe Narty, Marcelle Bruce, Nick Jackson, Bobby Highton, Danny Adams, Vinnie Ryan (coach), Tony Kelly (manager), Bryan Hammett, Vinnie Somers, Chris Watters, Richard McDonagh

HISTON

CLUB OFFICIALS

Chairman: Gareth Baldwin

President: Peter Betson

Secretary: Mrs Lisa Baldwin,
5 Caxton Lane, Foxton,
Cambridge CB2 6SR Tel: 01223 872989(H)
0845 3455472 (W)
email: lisa.baldwin@intervivo.net

Press Officer: Steve Wells (01353 862367)
Email:stevenwells1@ composerve.com

FOOTBALL MANAGEMENT TEAM

Manager: Steve Fallon
Coach: Chris Tovey
Captain: Neil Andrews
Physio: Lee Petrucci

FACT FILE

Founded: 1904
Nickname: 'The Stutes'
Sponsors:Webster Building & Civil Engineers
Colours: Red and blackstripes/black/black
Change colours: Sky & Navy/navy/sky
Midweek Matches: Tuesday
Reserves League: Ridgeons Premier
Youth Team: Southern Co. Floodlit Lg.
'A' Team: Kershaw Premier League
Website: http://.histonfootballclub.tripod.com

2003-04

Leading Goalscorer: Neil Kennedy 34
Player of the Year: Colin Vowden

GROUND Bridge Rd, Impington, Cambridge
Tel: 01223 237373 Fax: 01223 237373
email: gareth@corporate innovations.co.uk

Directions: Leave A14 northern Cambridge bypass on B1049 (signposted Histon and Cottenham). Ground half a mile on right.
5 miles from Cambridge (BR). Bus No.104

Capacity: 3,250 Seats: 450 Cover: 2000 Floodlights: Yes

Clubhouse: Bar/lounge open matchdays only. Snacks and hot food available

PROGRAMME

42 pages £1.50
Editor: Steve Wells 07876 746795)(W)
email:StevenWells1@compuserve.com
Local Press : Cambridge Evening News
Local Radio: Q103, Star FM
BBC Radio Cambridgeshire

HONOURS
Eastern Co's Lg - Prem. Div. 99-00, Div 1 R-up 96-97, Cup 90-91;
Cambridgeshire Professional Cup: 2001-02, 02-03, 03-04 (Retained for three years)
Cambridge Invitation Cup 77-78 79-80 96-97,00-01 R-up 50-51 52-53 53-54 2001-02 02-03 03-04.
Spartan Lg Div 1 (East) 50-51; Cambs Chall Cup; Cambs Lg Section;
Kershaw Prem Lge 00-01R-up 97-98, Sen Lge A 96-97 R-up 03-04, Cup 96-97;00-01
Auto Trader Lge & Cup (U18) 96-97 Kershaw Champions Co Cup (U18) 98-99, Colts League (U17) Champions 98-99
Under 18 Munnns Cup Winners: 96-97, 98-99, 2001-02, 2003-2004.

PREVIOUS
Leagues: Cambridgeshire 04-48; Spartan 48-60; Delphian 60-63; Athenian 63-65; Eastern Counties 66-00
Name: Histon Institute 04-51

BEST SEASON
FA Cup: 1st Rd Proper 2003-04 v Woking (A) **FA Vase:** 4th Rd 96-97, 97-98 **F.A .Trophy:** 4th Round 2000-2001
In Southern League: 2003-04 Eastern Division Runners-up, Merit Cup as Top Goalscorers (96) and Fair Play Winners

RECORD
Attendance: 6,400 v King's Lynn, FA Cup 1956

Back Row (L-R): Steve Fallon Manager, Roscoe Hipperson, Colin Vowden, Paul Barber, Ossie Mintus, Louie Farrington, Neil Kennedy, Ian Cambridge, Lee Petrucci (Physio). **Front:** Neil Coburn, Mark Abbs, Peter Munns, Wayne Goddard, Matthew Haniver, Adrian Cambridge, Neil Andrews (Captain) Robbie Nightingale, Tony Beck.

HITCHIN TOWN

CLUB OFFICIALS

Chairman: **Terry Barratt**

Secretary: **Roy Izzard**

2 Bedford Road, Ickleford, Hitchin, Herts

Tel: 01462 433171

Media Officer: **Neil Jensen**

Tel: 01462 454678 0207 5457921

Email: jensenneilf@aol.com

FOOTBALL MANAGEMENT TEAM

Manager: Kerry Dixon

Assistant Manager: Ian Donnelly

Captain: Paul Covington

Physio: Peter Prince

FACT FILE

Formed: 1865 Reformed 1928

Nickname: The Canaries

Sponsors: Alma Engineering

Colours: Yellow/green/green

Change colours: All BlueMidweek match-day: Tuesday

Clubcall Line: 09066 555 817

Website: www.hitchintownfc.co.uk

2003-2004

Top Scorer: Chris Dillon 12

Ps o.Y. : Richard Wilmot & Stuart May

Hitchin Town
2003-04
FOOTBALL CLUB
Tuesday September 16 7.30pm
Hitchin Town v Canvey Island
Ryman League Premier Division
Matchball Sponsor: Bedford Dave
Hitchin Town are sponsored by ALMA ENGINEERING £1.50

Pages: 40 (A5) Price: £1.50

Editor: Neil Jensen (neil.Jenson@db.com)

Local Press: Hitchin Comet, Herts on Sunday

Local Radio: Chiltern, BBC Three Counties

GROUND: Top Field, Fishponds Road, Hitchin SG5 1NU (01462434483) + 01482 459028 on match days only **Directions:** On A505 near town centre opposite large green. 1 mile from Hitchin(BR). From A1(M) Jct 8,A602 towards Bedford into Hitchin.Over two roundabouts through lights on one way system. Turn right at next roundabout for Fishponds Road.

Capacity: Cover: 1,250 Seats: 500 Floodlights: Yes

Clubhouse: (01462 434483). Members bar, Function Hall (available for hire). Open every-day. Steward: Eamonn Watson

Club Shop: Yes, Contact - Chris Newbold on chris@bewvikd013.freeserve.co.uk

PREVIOUS **Leagues:** Spartan 28-39; Hert & Middx 39-45; Athenian 39,45-63 Isthmian League 1964-2004

CLUB RECORDS **Attendance:** 7,878 v Wycombe Wanderers, FA Amateur Cup 3rd Rd 18/2/56

Win: Spartan Lge 29-30 13-0 v Cowley, 13-0 v RAF

Defeat (Isthmian Lge): 0-10 v Kingstonian (A) 65-66, v Slough T. (A) 79-80

Career Appearances: Paul Giggle 769 (68-86) **Career Goals:** Paul Giggle, 214

Fee paid: £2,000 Ray Seeking Potton United, July 1989 **Fee received:** £30,000 Zema Abbey to Cambridge Utd Jan 00

BEST SEASON **FA Trophy:** 5th Rd 98-99 **FA Amateur Cup:** Semi Final 60-61, 62-63

FA Cup: 2nd Rd on four occasions - v Swindon 1-3 (A) 76-77, v Boston Utd, 0-1 (A) 73-74, v Wycombe Wand. 0-5 (H) 94-95, v Gillingham 0-3 (A) 95-9

HONOURS: Isthmian Lge R-up 68-69Div 1 92-93 R-up 98-99, Spartan Lge 34-35; AFA Sen Cup 30-31; Herts Snr Cup (19-record); London Sen Cup 69-70 (R-up 72-73); E Anglian Cup 72-73; Herts Charity Cup(17), Herts I'mediate Cup (8); Woolwich Trophy 82-83; Televised Sport International Cup 88-89 90-91; Southern Comb. Senior Floodlit Cup 90-91

Back row, left to right: Chris Harvey, Matt Nolan (now Peterborough), Matt Childs, Dean McElroy, Anthony Francis(Now Dunstabe), Ryan Frater, Lawrence Yaku and Craig Rydeheard (now Bedford T) **Middle Row:** Peter Prince (physio), Kerry Dixon (manager), Jon Bone, Ian Scott, Joe Bruce (now Grays A), James Robinson, Adam Parker (now St Albans C), Carl Williams (Now Cambridge City), Dean Brennan (Stevenage B),Ian Donnelly (Ass. Manager) and Syd Springett (Kit Man). **Front Row:** Tony Huckle (President), Kevin Evans, James Ayres (now BraintreeT), Stuart Maynard, Ribbie O'Keefe (ex Manager), James Osborn,Carl Drew (now Arlesey T), Wayne Mills and Terry Barratt (Chairman).

KING'S LYNN

CLUB OFFICIALS

Chairman: Colin Nichols
President: Jim Chandler
Secretary: Nigel Link
58 Hall Lane, West Winch,
Kings Lynn PE33 0PP
Tel:01553 841089 (H) 07885 144039 (M)

FOOTBALL MANAGEMENT TEAM

Director of Football: Kevin Boon
Managers:
Darren Bloodworth &Kevin Boon
Physio: Dave Edgeley

FACT FILE

Formed: 1879 Nickname: The Linnets
Sponsors: Lynn News
Colours: Royal Blue with gold trim/Blue/Blue & Gold hoops
Change : White with blue & gold trim
Midweek home matchday: Tuesday
Reserves League: Jewson Eastern Div 1

PROGRAMME

Pages: 24 Price: £1.20
Editor: Secretary

GROUND The Walks Stadium, Tennyson Road, King's Lynn PE30 5PB Tel: 01553 760060 **Directions:** At mini r-about arriving from A10/A47 take Vancouver Avenue. Ground on left after a half mile. Quarter mile from King's Lynn (BR), half mile from bus station
Capacity: 8,200 Cover: 5,000 Seats: 1,200 Floodlights: Yes
Clubhouse: Normal licensing hours, with extension on matchdays **Club Shop:** Sells metal badges and other merchandise

PREVIOUS **Leagues:** Norfolk & Suffolk; Eastern Co.s 35-39 48-54; UCL 46-48; Midland Co.s54-58; NPL 80-83
Name: Lynn Town **Ground**: None

CLUB RECORDS **Attendance:** 12,937 v Exeter, FA Cup 1st Rd 50-51
Win: 17-0 v Beccles 29/30 **Defeat:** 0-11 v Aston Villa FA Cup 1905/6
Career Appearances: Mick Wright 1,152 (British Record) **Career Goalscorer:** Malcolm Lindsay 321
Transfer Fee Paid: Shaun Keeble Wisbech 98-99 **Transfer Fee Received:** Mark Paul , Southampton.98-99

BEST SEASON **FA Cup:** 3rd Rd 61-62 (0-4 at Everton). Competition Proper on 14 occasions; 05-06 37-38 49-50 51-52 58-63 64-65 68-69 71-72 73-74 84-85. Rd 2 97-98 League clubs defeated: Aldershot 59-60, Coventry 61-62, Halifax 68-69
FA Trophy: 2nd Rd 78-79 **FA Vase:** 5th Rd 94-95 (0-2 at Diss Town **FA Amateur Cup:** R-up 1900-01

HONOURS FA Amateur Cup R-up 1900-01, Southern Lg R-up 84-85 (Div 1 R-up 63-64), NPLPresidents Cup 82-83, Eastern Co's Lg 53-54 (R-up 49-50 52-53 (Lg Cup 53-54),Norfolk & Suffolk Lg(8)(R-up(6)), E Anglian Lg R-up(2), Norfolk Snr Cup(19)(R-up(20), Norfolk Invitation Cup 94-95, Norfolk Premier Cup 68-69(jt) 73-74, EastAnglian Cup(4)(R-up(3), Eastern Prof Floodlit Lg 68-69, Southern Lg Midland R-up 95-96 ,U.C.L. Reserve Division, League & Cup 'double', 99-00. Southern League Cup. R-up: 2001-02
Players progressing: N Rowe (Derby 1949), B Taylor & P Ward (Bradford P. A. 54& 55), T Reynolds (Darlington 54), G Reed (Sunderland 55), P McCall (Bristol C55), J Neal (Swindon 57), T Dryburgh (Oldham 57), J Hunter (Barrow 59), JStevens (Swindon), G Catleugh (Watford), George Walters (Chesterfield 64), PMcNamee (Notts County 1966), W Biggins (Burnley), Jackie Gallagher(Peterborough 80), Andy Higgins (Rochdale 83), Neil Horwood (Grimsby 86),Darren Rolph (Barnsley 87), Mark Howard (Stockport 88), Andy Hunt, Malcolm Lindsay

Back Row (L-R): Adam Jones, Chris Bacon, Jack Defty, Danny Hammond, Tony Battersby, Mark Burrows, Nick Perks (physio). Middle: Richard Simper (kit-man), Mark Angel, Lee Stevenson, Steve Wilson, Charlie Defty, Aaron Osborne, Robbie Harris, Mark Camm, Dave Edgley (physio). **Front:** Nicky Blake, Danny Bloomfield, Kevin Boon (joint manager), Gary Setchell, Darren Bloodworth (joint manager), Craig Fishlock, Carl Holmes.

Photo: Lynn News.

MERTHYR TYDFIL

CLUB OFFICIALS

Chairman: Wyn Holloway
Vice Chairman: Paul Sugrue
Football Sec: Anthony Hughes,4 BrynmorlaisSt.,Penydarren, Merthyr Tydfil CF47 9YE
Tel: 01685 359921 (H&F)
07958006911 (M)
Press Off. Mike Donovan

FOOTBALL MANAGEMENT TEAM
Manager: John Relish

FACT FILE

Formed: 19445
Nickname: The Martyrs
Sponsors: Rainbow Print
Colours: Black & white stripes/black/black
Change colours:Red with yellow trim
Midweek home matchday: Tuesday
Reserves' League: None
Club Website: www.themartyrs.com
Local Press: Merthyr Express
Local Radio: Valleys Radio

GROUND Penndarren Park, Merthyr Tydfil, Mid Glamorgan
Tel: 01685 384102 Email: pughy@tinyonline.co.uk
Directions: (South) A470 Express Way to Merthyr Centre to Pontmorlais (traffic lights) turn left then first right, first right at Catholic Church and right again into Park Terrace . (North) Heads of theValley road to Town Centre, to Pontmorlais(traffic lights) turn right, then as above
Capacity: 10,000 Seats: 1,500 Cover: 5,000 Floodlights: Yes
Clubhouse: Open Mon. to Sun. 6.30 - 11.00pm. 2 club cafes open on matchdays for hot food
Club Shop: Sells replica kits, club souvenirs & programmes.
Contact Mel Jenkins01443 692336

PROGRAMME
Pages: 36 Price: £1.50
Editor:Mike Donovan 07788 185149 (M)

PREVIOUS **Leagues:** Southern League 46 -89 (Southern League 46-59, 1st Division 59-61, 64-71, !st Div. North 72-79, Premier Div. 61- 64, 71-72, 88-89, Midland Div. 79-88), G M Conference 89-95.
Names: None **Grounds:** None

CLUB RECORDS **Attendance:** 21,000 v Reading FA Cup 2nd Rnd 1949/50
Win: 11-0 v Rushden 1987 **Defeat:** 9-2 v Altrincham 1993
Transfer fee paid: £10,000 to Cardiff City for Robbie James 1992
Transfer fee received: £12,000 for Ray Pratt from Exeter City 1981

BEST SEASON **Welsh FA Cup:** Winners 48-49 50-51 86-87
FA Trophy: 3rd Rd v Northwich Vic 95-96
FA Cup: 2nd Round on six occasions. League clubs defeated: Bristol Rovers

HONOURS Welsh FA Cup 48-49, 50-51, 86-87; Southern League 47-48, 49-50, 50-51, 51-52, 53-54; Southern League (Midland) 87-88; Southern League (Premier) 88-89;Southern League Cup 47-48, 50-51

Players Progressing : Syd Howarth (Aston Villa), Cyril Beech, Gilbert Beech,Bill Hullet, Ken Tucker (Cardiff City), Nick Deacy (Hereford United), Gordon Davies (Fulham), Ray Pratt (Exeter City), Peter Jones, Paul Giles (Newport County)

Bakc Row (L-R): Jane Price (physio), Jeff Eckhardt, Jason Eaton, Chris Holloway, Dale Griffiths, Dai Griffiths (kit man).
Middle Row: Andrew York, Gethin Jones, Kristian Whitcombe, Ashley Morris, Chris Bale, Lee Howells, Richard French.
Front Row: Ryan Dorrian, Steve Williams, Garry Shephard, John Rellish (coach), Danny Carter (captain), Addie Britten (Asst. coach), Paul Keddle, Craig Steins. Photo: Robert Prosser - Merthyr Express.

RUGBY UNITED

CLUB OFFICIALS
Chairman: Brian Melvin
Secretary: Doug Wilkins,
298 Rocky Lane, Great Barr,
Birmingham B42 1NQ
Tel: 0121 681 1544 (H 0121 686 4068 (F)
Press Officer: Alan Turner
Tel: 01788 567181
Commercial Manager:Lisa Melvin

FOOTBALL MANAGEMENT TEAM
Manager:Tony Dobson
Asst Manager: Steve Shea
Physio: Bob Gardner

FACT FILE
Formed: 1956 Nickname: The Valley
Sponsors: Rugby Telegraph & Melbros Ltd
Colours: Sky Blue/White/White
Change colours: All Red
Midweek matchday: Tuesday
Club Newsline: 0930 555971
Reserves' League: Midland Combination
Website: www.rugbyutd.co.uk

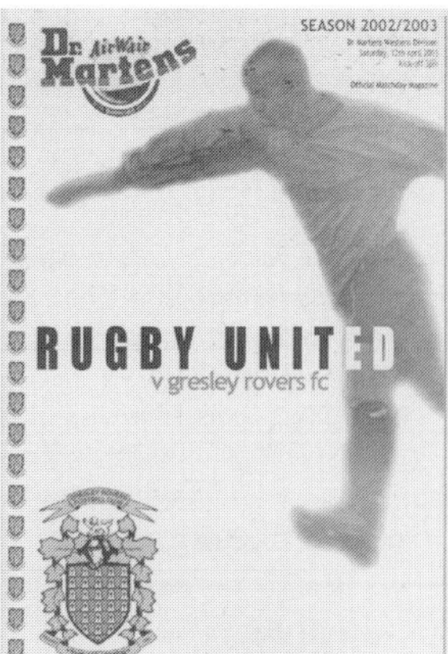

Pages: 36 Price: £1.50
Editor: Neil.Melvin 01788 567717

Local Press: Rugby Advertiser, Coventry Evening Telegraph, Rugby Observer
Local Radio: Mercia Sound, CWR

GROUND: Butlin Road, Rugby, Warks. CV21 3ST Tel: 01788 844806
Directions: The ground is situated off Clifton (B5414) on the north side of Rugby. 1 mile walk from the station Club Call Line: 09066 555971
Capacity: 6,000 Cover: 1,000 Seats: 750 Floodlights: Yes
Clubhouse: Open every night and weekend lunchtimes. Entertainment Saturday nights. Excellent facilities include Long Alley Skittles, darts and pool
Club Shop: Yes

PREVIOUS **Name:** Valley Sports, Valley Sports Rugby
Leagues: Rugby & District 1956-63, Coventry & Partnership, North Warks 63-69, United Counties 69-75, West Midlands 75-83

CLUB RECORDS **Attendance:** 3,961 v Northampton FA Cup 1984 **Defeat:** 1-11 v Ilkeston Town (A) 18.4.98
Win: 10-0 v Ilkeston Tn FA Trophy Preliminary Rd 4/9/85 *All-time record FA Trophy win
Career Goalscorer: Danny Conway, 124 **Career Appearances:** Danny Conway, 374
Transfer fee paid: £3,500 R Smith, I Crawley, G Bradder **Transfer fee received:** £15,000 T Angus (Northampton)

BEST SEASON **FA Cup:** 2nd round 87-88, plus 1st Rd 84-85 85-86 86-87 94-95 League clubs defeated: None
FA Trophy: **FA Vase:** Winners 82-83

HONOURS Southern Lg Midland Div 86-87 (R-up 94-95, Lg Cup 89-90), FA Vase 82-83,Mid Floodlit Cup 84-85 89-90 98 -00(R-up 86-87), Birmingham Snr Cup 88-89 91-92, Utd Co's Lg Div 3 Cup 69-70.

Players progressing: S Storer (Birmingham 1985), S Bicknell (Leicester), S Norris (Scarborough), T Angus (Northampton Town), Ashley Walker (Peterborough), Ian King (Stoke City)

Back Row (L-R): Steve Townsend (general assistant), Jon Douglas, Andy Commander, Andy Rutherford, Jermaine Gordon, Craig Dutton, Paul Shepherd, Dean Thomas, Rory Squire, Gary Redgate, Neil Melvin, Danny Hall, Kevin Charley, Bob Gardner (physiotherapist). **Front:** Steve Evans, Gary Moran, Robbie Beard, Dave Pearson, Steve Shea (assistant manager), Tony Dobson (manager), Justin Marsden, Adam Hart, Richard Wesley, Jamie Williams.

SOLIHULL BOROUGH

CLUB OFFICIALS

Chairman : Trevor Stevens

President: Joe McGorian

Secretary: Joe Murphy, 25 Coombe Drive, Nuneaton, Warwicks. CV10 9DD

Tel No: 02476 373103 (H)
Tel: 079711 89952 (M) Fax: c/o club

Press Officer: Richard Crawshaw
Tel: 01564 702746 or 07795 388647(M)

FOOTBALL MANAGEMENT TEAM

Manager: Guy Rusell

Assistant Manager:Robin Judd

Physio: Graham Jones

FACT FILE

Formed: 1953 Nickname: Boro
Sponsors: Carling Black Label
Colours: Red/white/red
Change colours: Blue/Black/Black
Midweek matchday: WednesdayLocal Press: Solihull Times, Solihull News, Sunday Mercury, Sports Argus
Local Radio: Radio WM, BRMB
Website: www.solihullborougfh-fc-co.uk
2003-2004 Captain: Nick Amos
Players of the Year:
Paul Hunter, Mark Gayle & Niki Preston
Top Scorer: Paul Hunter 15

PROGRAMME

Pages: 44 Price: £1.50
Editor:Andy Walker 07811 443865 (W)

Ground: Damson Park, Damson Parkway, Solihull, W. Mids B91 2PP Tel: 0121 705 6770 Fax: 0121 711 4045
Directions: Leave M42 at Jnct 6. A45 for 2 miles towards B'ham.Past Honda Garage and opp Forte Posthouse Hotel, left at filter to traffic lights into Damson Parkway.(Signpost Landrover/Damsonwwod) Go round roundabout, down other side of dual crriageway for 100 jds .Ground on left. From Coventry use A45 to Posthouse. Solihull,A41 into Hampton Lane and Yew Tree LaneLane.
Capacity: 3,050 Cover: 1,000 Seats: 280 Floodlights: Yes
Clubhouse: Country Club facilities and all type of functions can be booked.(0121 705 6770)

PREVIOUS **Leagues:** Mercian; Midland Combination 69-91
Name: Lincoln FC **Grounds:** Widney Stadium, Solihull 65-88,Moor Green 88-98,Redditch 98-00

CLUB RECORDS **Attendance (at new ground):** 2,000 v Birmingham City Friendly 2002-03
Win: 9-0 v Glossop North End (H) F.A.Cup 1st Q Rd 2002-03
Defeat: 1-6 v Tiverton Town (A) Southern League (Western) 99-00
Career Goalscorer: Joe Dowling 138 **Career Appearances:** Darrel Houghton 360
Transfer fee paid: £15,000 for Recky Carter, from Kettering Town
Transfer fee received: £30,000 from Coventry City for Andy Williams

BEST SEASON **FA Cup:** 1st Rd 97-98; 1-1,3-3 (2-4pen) v Darlington and 92-93, 2-2,2-3 v V.S.Rugby
FA Vase: 5th Rd 74-75 **FA Trophy:** 4th Rd Prop 97-98 and 2001-02

HONOURS Southern Lg Midland Div 91-92; Midland Comb. R-up 84-8590-91, Chall Cup R-up 73-74 90-91, Presidents Cup R-up 69-70; Lord Mayor of Birmingham Charity Cup 91-92 92-93 94-95 96-97; Worcs Sen. Cup R-up 92-93 96-97 97-98; 99-00Birmingham Sen. Cup 94-95

Players Progressing: Kevin Ashley (Birmingham C.), Andy Williams (Coventry C.), Geoff Scott . Danny Conway ,Nicky Cross and Alan Smith (LeicesterC.), Dean Spink (Aston Villa), John Frain (Northampton T.), Jamie Campbell (Walsall) and John Gayle (Birmingham City)

Back Row (L-R): Morton Titterton, Leon Mitchell, Guy Hadland, Nick Amos, Mark Gayle, Paul Bonar, Michael Swan, Adam Cooper, Jamie Petty, Richard Kavanagh.
Front Row: Dean Peer, Mark Faulds, Mark Lowry, Matt Hawker, Robin Judd (Assistant Manager), Guy Russell (Manager), Pete Barry, Martin Hier, Dean Tilley, Mark Shepherd.

STAMFORD

CLUB OFFICIALS

Chairman: Ken Joynson
Vice-Chairman: Richard Jacobs
Secretary & Press Officer: Jeremy Biggs
`The Essendine', Essendine, Stamford, Lincs., PE9 4LD Tel: 01780 763048(H)
01780 763048(W) 01778 380020(F)
jeremybiggs@essendine70.freeserve.co.uk

FOOTBALL MANAGEMENT TEAM

Manager:Billy Jeffrey
Assistant: Nick Ashby
Coach: Andy Drummond
Captain: Andy Peaks Physio: Pete Foskett

FACT FILE

Founded: 1896 Nickname: Daniels
Sponsors: V.Couzens(Stamford) Ltd, Newflame and H.P.C.(Homes) ltd.
Colours: Red
Change Colours: Yellow & green
Midweek matchday: Tuesday

2003-004

Top Scorer: Kevin Byrne 25
Players of the Year: Ludec Michalik and Andy Peake (Players)

STAMFORD
PROGRAMME AFC
Southern League Football (Eastern Division)
At the Newflame Stadium
SEASON 2003 – 2004

Pages : 44 Price:£1.20
Editor: John Burrows(07710290000(W)
Local Press: Stamford Mercury, Peterborough Evening Telegraph,Rutland Times & Herald & Post
Local Radio: Rutland Radio, LincsFM Radio Lincolnshire & Radio Cambridgeshire

GROUND Newflame Stadium, Kettering Road,, Stamford, Lincs
Tel: 01780 763079 (Clubhouse) 01780 766027 (Pressbox)

Directions: Off A43 Kettering Rd, 1 mile east of A1. 200 yds from station
Capacity: 5,000 Seats: 250 Cover: 1,250 Floodlights: Yes
Clubhouse: Open matchdays and functions
Food available matchdays - hot and cold
Club Shop: Wide range of Lge + non-Lge progs & club souvenirs.

PREVIOUS **Leagues:** Peterborough; Northants (UCL) 08-55; Central Alliance 55-61; Midland Co's 61-72; UCL 72-98
Grounds: None **Names:** None

CLUB RECORDS **Attendance:** 4,200 v Kettering, FA Cup 3rd Qual Rd 53
Win: 13-0 v Peterborough Reserves, Northants Lge 29-30 **Defeat:** 0-17 v Rothwell,FA Cup 27-28
Appearances: Dick Kwiatkowski 462 **Goalscorer:** Bert Knighten 248

BEST SEASON **FA Cup:** 12-13 5th Qual. Round
FA Vase: Winners 79-80, R-up 75-76 83-84 **FA Trophy: 00-01** (1st season) 2nd Round

HONOURS FA Vase 79-80 R-up 75-76 83-84; Utd Co's Lg 75-76 77-78 79-80 80-81 81-82 96-97 97-98 KO Cup 51-52 75-76 79-80 81-82 85-86); Northants Lg 11-12; Lincs Snr`A' Cup 78-79 82-83 97-98, 00-01; Lincs Snr `B' Cup 51-52 53-54; William Scarber Mem. Cup 70-71 82-83 85-86 88-89 93-94 94-95; Stamford Chal. Cup 89-90; Lincs Jnr Cup 48-49 Hinchingbrooke Cup 1906-07, 07-08, 97-98

Players progressing: A Birchenall (Chelsea), R Chester(Aston Villa), T Tye (Chelsea), G Fell (Brighton), C Chapman (Wolves), S Collins (Peterborough), K Alexander (Grimsby), A Tillson (Grimsby), B Stubbs (Notts Co.), D Genovese (Peterborough), J Johnson, C MacCartney (Notts Co), B McNamara (Northampton), D Norris (Bolton), M.Clifford (Boston United) and S.Corry (Oldham Athletic)

Stamford celebrate their winning promotion to the Southern League Premier Division on the final day of the season.**Back row** (left to right):Andy Drummond, (Coach), Danny Steadman, Malcolm Ndekwe, Nick Ashby, Ludek Michalik, Kevin Byrne, Ryan Nash, Rob Maddox, Kevin Ainslie, Matt Green, Dennis Rule, Garath Ptichard and Billy Jeffrey (Manager). **Front row:** Pete Foskett (physio), Andy Peaks, Robbie Blowers, Warren Donald and Ian Edge.
Photo: Stamford Mercury

TEAM BATH

CLUB OFFICIALS

Chairman:Matt Birch c/o Univ. of Bath, Sports Development,
Claverton Down, Bath BA2 7AY
Tel: 01225 386339

Secretary: Phil Searle
12 Chepstow Close, Chippenham SN14 0XP
Tel: 01249 460857 (H)
01225 384246 (W)
email:phil@matchtight.co.uk

FOOTBALL MANAGEMENT TEAM

Manager: Ged Roddy Tel: 01225 826339
Coach: Paul Tisdale Captain: Chris Holland
Physio: Ian Andrews

FACT FILE

Formed: 2000
Colours: Yellow & Blue/blue/yellow
Change colours: All blue
Midweek Matchday: Monday

PROGRAMME

Editor: Phil Searle

2003-2004

PLayer of the Year: Ali Kines
Top Scorers: Paul Tisdale & Luke Prince

GROUND University of Bath, Sports Training Village, Claverton Down, Bath.
Tel: 01225 826339

Directions: Follow signs to Claverton Down and Park & Ride (University).
Take the Norwood Ave. entrance to the campus and as you drive towards the university you will approach two "hanger" like buildings on the right.
This is the Sports Training Village. Follow signs to free car park.

PREVIOUS **Leagues:** Western 2000-03
CLUB RECORDS **Attendance:** 5469 v Mansfield Town, FA Cup 1st Round
BEST SEASON **FA Vase:** 01-02 - 3rd Round, 0-1 v Arlesey Town (H)
FA Cup: 02-03 -1st Round proper, 2-4 v Mansfield Town (H)
HONOURS Western Lge Div. 1 00-01, Premier Division 02-03
Players Progressing: Barry Lavety 03 (St Mirren, Bertrand Covic 03 (Cheltenham Town)
Karl Keiniger 03 (KSV Hessen Kassel)

TIVERTON TOWN

CLUB OFFICIALS

President: Dr Gavin Haig F.R.C.S.
Chairman: Dave Wright
Vice-Chairman: Pete Buxton
Directors: John Fournier, Chris Fisher,Ian Moorcroft and Alan Smith
Football Secretary: Ramsay Findlay
35 Park Road, Tiverton, Devon EX16 6AY Tel: 01884 256341(h) 01884 254949 (W)
Treasurer: Kim Smith
General Secretary: John Smith

2003-2004

Top Goalscorer: Jamie Mudge
Player of the Year: Rob Cousins

FACT FILE

Formed: 1920 Nickname: Tivvy
Colours: Yellow/black/yellow
Change colours: All white
Midweek matches: Wednesday
Youth Team: Somerset Floodlit Youth Lg

FOOTBALL MANAGEMENT TEAM

Manager: Martyn Rogers
Assistant Manager: Pete Conning
Physio: Dai Morgan
Assistant Physio: Mike Perry
Captain: Rob Cousins

GROUND: Ladysmead, Bolham Road, Tiverton, Devon EX16 8SG Tel: 01884 252397
Website: www.tiverton-town-fc.co.uk

Directions: Leave M5 at Jct 27. Take second Tiverton turn off A361, at end of dual carriageway . Turn left and then cross over new roundabout after 500 yards. Carry on again straight over mini roundabout and ground is on right after 200 yards.
Capacity: 3,500 Seats: 520 Cover: 2,300
Clubhouse: Lunctimes, evenings. All day Sat during season. 3 bars. Food(burgers, chips etc)
Club Shop: Yes

Pages: 56 Price: £1.50 (with colour)
Editor/ Press Officer: John Fournier
Tel: 01884 32654 (H) & 07980 54363(W)
email:johnfournier@eclipse.co.uk

PREVIOUS **League:** Devon & Exeter; Western League **Ground:** The Elms, Blundell Road 1920-39

RECORD **Attendance:** 3,000 v Leyton Orient, FA Cup First Round Proper 1994-95
Career Goalscorer: Phil Everett
Record Win: (DML) 7-1 v Cirencester 2001 **Record Defeat:** (DML) 2-6 v Stafford Rangers (A) 2001-02

BEST SEASON **FA Vase:** Winners 97-98 98-99, R-up 92-93 **FA Cup:** 1st Round 90-91 91-92 94-95 97-98

HONOURS FA Vase 97-98 98-99; Western Lg 93-94 94-95 96-97 97-98 (R-up 92-93 95-96 98-99); Les Phillips Cup 92-93 94-95 95-96 96-97 97-98; Amateur Trophy 77-78 78-79, Div 1 R-up 88-89; Devon St Lukes Cup 90-91 91-92 92-93 94-95 96-97 (R-up 89-90); Devon & Exeter Lg 51-52 66-67 70-71 84-85; Devon Snr Cup 55-56 65-66; East Devon Snr Cup 35-36 37-38 52-53 55-56 60-61 62-63 66-67; North Devon Charity Cup 72-73 86-87. Devon St Luke's Bowl 99-00; Dr. Martens Western Div. R-up 2000-01

Players progressing: Jason Smith (Coventry City 93 & Swansea City 98), Mark Saunders (1995) & Kevin Nancekivell (2000) Plymouth Argyle

L-R - Back: Luke Vinnicombe, Ben Harris, Danny Haines, James Mudge, Steve Ovens, Shaun Goff. **Middle**: Dai Morgan (Physio), Matthew Aubrey, Steve Peters, Stuart Fraser, David Steele, Rob Cousins, Kevin Nancekivell, Mike Perry (Asst. Physio). **Front**: Richard Pears, Steve Winters, Martyn Rogers (Manager), Jason Rees, Martyn Grimshaw (Asst. Man.), Chris Holloway, Paul Chenoweth

AYLESBURY UNITED
Goalkeepers:
Jack Rashid (St Neots)
Defenders:
Jason Burnham (Brackley), Matt Hayward (Oxford C), Daniel Mead (Watford), Kai Ridley (Brackley), Stuart Smeathers (Raunds), Greg Williams (Thame), John Winter (Etoile Caruage (Switz)
Midfield:
Tom Alabaster (Youth team), Neil Champelovier (Oxford C), Dean Cracknell (Northampton), Jay Gould (Youth team), Paul Lamb (Brackley), Dean Powles (Youth team)
Forwards:
Mesach Cole (Buckingham), Paul Edgweworth (Newport Pagnell), Danny Gray (Youth team), Leon Gutzmore (Arlesey), Ryan Wiffen (Haywood Utd)

BANBURY UNITED
Goalkeepers:
Simon Tricker (Abingdon Utd)
Defenders:
Jason Allen (Brackley), Mark Essex (Hook Norton), Ady Fuller (Ford Sports), Keiran Sullivan (Racing Club Warwick), Andy Wallbridge (Didcot)
Midfield:
Dave Billington (Oxford C), Kevin Brock (Oxford C), Paul Eldridge (Brackley), Chris Jackson (Aylesbury), Liam O'Neill (Ford Sports), Chris Potter (Abingdon T), Les Robinson (Hednesford), Ollie Stanbridge (Aylesbury)
Forwards:
Wayne Blossom (Highfield OB), Howard Forinton (Farnborough), Matty Gooderick (Oxford C), Jody McKay (Hook Norton), George Redknap (North Leigh), Andrew Stidder (Youth team)

BATH CITY
Goalkeepers:
Paul Evans (Rushden & Diamonds)
Justin Shuttlewood (Frome)
Stuart Frazer (Tiverton)
Defenders:
Steve Jones (Forest Green), Matt Coupe (Forest Green), Mike Trought (Bristol R), Graeme Power (Tiverton), Grant Monelle (Bristol C)
Midfield:
Jim Rollo (Clevedon), Gary Owers (Forest Green), Bobby Ford (Oxford Utd), Russell Milton (Cheltenham), Dean Stevens (Torquay), Jimmy Benefield (Torquay), Yan Klukowski (Youth team)
Forwards:
Scott Partridge (Weymouth), John Williams (Kidderminster), Steve Tweddle (Forest Green), Ricky Hulbert (Youth team), Reinier Moor (Exeter)

BEDFORD TOWN
Goalkeepers:
Ian Brown (Kempston R)
Defenders:
Ashley Blake (Berkhamsted), James Taylor (Watford), Noel Quinn (Youth team), Richard Weale (Harrow), Steve Jackman (Raunds), Matt Childs (Hitchin), Lee Howarth (Kettering)
Midfield:
Jason James (Barton R), Andre Juraszek (Youth team), Craig Rydeheard (St Albans), Dean McElroy (Hitchin), Derwayne Stupple (Berkhamsted), Richard Challinor (Corby), Simon Gooderham (Marlow)
Forwards:
Danny Purzycki (Gornick Leczna (Poland)), Rene Howe (Youth team), Chris Dillon (Hitchin), Tommy Hayes (Dunstable), Mike McKenzie (Kettering)

CHESHAM UNITED
Goalkeepers:
Bradley Hughes (Grimsby)
Defenders:
Peter Clifford (Berkhamsted), Simon Sweeney (Berkhamsted), Matt Skinner (Chalfont), Steve Bateman (Berkhamsted)
Midfield:
Mark Dawber (Berkhamsted), Andy Adebowale (Berkhamsted), Dave Fotheringham (Youth team), Steve Miles (Marlow), Steve Sinclair (Boreham Wood), John Richardson (Berkhamsted)
Forwards:
John Lawford (Berkhamsted), Ben Smith (Hitchin), Gary Sippetts (Berkhamsted), Andre Scarlett (Hitchin)

CHIPPENHAM TOWN
Goalkeepers:
Chris Gianangelo (Forest Green), Mark Hervin (Cirencester)
Defenders:
Ian Herring (Swindon), Gary Thorne (Merthyr Tydfil), Wayne Thorne (Clevedon),
Midfield:
Mark Badman (Bath), Simon Charity (Paulton R), Gary Horgan (Bath), Andy Kirk (), Matthew McEntegart (Cirencester), Scott Walker (Newport Co), Ellis Wilmot (Mangotsfield)
Forwards:
Sam Allison (Salisbury), James Constable (Cirencester), Martin Paul (Newport Co), Rene Regis (Waltham Forest)

CIRENCESTER TOWN
Goalkeepers:
Paul Thompson (Mangotsfield)
Defenders:
Kevin Halliday (AFC Newbury), Gary Wotton (Boreham Wood), Alan Bird (Weston-super-Mare), Andy Minturn (Bath), Lee Stevens (Lewisburg College (USA)), Matthew McEntegart (Youth team), Neil Arndale (Bristol R), Stuart Fraser (Eastbourne T), Thomas Cole (Youth team)
Midfield:
Shaun Wimble (Oxford C), Michael Jackson (Weston-super-Mare), Adam Mayo (Youth team), Darren Robison (Newport Co), Marc Richards (Cinderford), Mike Davis (Mangotsfield), Nathan Edwards (Chippenham)
Forwards:
Gareth Hopkins (Cheltenham), Ben Fitch (Youth team), Adam Hemmings (Gloucester), Andy McCabe (North Leigh), Jody Bevan (Weston-super-Mare), Nick Stanley (Youth team), Scott Griffin (Cinderford)

DUNSTABLE TOWN
Goalkeepers:
Paul Taylor (Letchworth)
Defenders:
Dean Walker (Letchworth), Marc Kefford (Toddington R), Julian Old (Chertsey), Ryan Frater (Hitchin),
Midfield:
Adam Turner (Buckingham), Jason Huntly (Leighton), Robbie Kean (Boreham Wood), Tony Fontanelle (Arlesey), Junior George (Buckingham)
Forwards:
Grant Carney (Letchworth), Karl Spring (Arlesey), Jonathan Barnett (Hitchin)

GLOUCESTER CITY
Goalkeepers:
Matt Bath (Whitminster)
Defenders:
Marvin Thompson (Cheltenham), Dan Avery (Cheltenham), Adie Harris (Cinderford), Adam Howarth (Bath), Neil Griffiths (Longlevens)
Midfield:
Dave Wilkinson (Brockworth), Chris Thompson (Northampton), Chris Burns (Forest Green), Keith Knight (Cirencester), Neil Mustoe (Yeovil), Tom Webb (Luton)
Forwards:
Jimmy Cox (Weston-super-Mare), Andy Hoskins (Brockworth), Karl Bayliss (Clevedon), Kenny Stiles (Wellington), Lee Smith (Youth team)

GRANTHAM TOWN
Goalkeepers:
Mario Ziccardi (Lincoln Utd)
Defenders:
Adrian Speed (Holbeach), Stuart Reddington (Gainsborough), Dave Robinson (Tamworth), Neil Spafford (Youth team), Tim Wooding (Cambridge C)
Midfield:
Fabien Smith (Ilkeston), Willis Francis (Notts Co), Brett Darby (Tamworth), Anton Burke (Radcliffe Olympic), Jamie McGowan (Kidsgrove), Darren Standage (Sandiacre), Peter Sutton (Harrogate), Andy Teare (Youth team)
Forwards:
Scott Huckerby (Kidsgrove), Dominic Hallows (Leicester), Darren Collins (Nuneaton), Darren Connell (Burscough)

HALESOWEN TOWN
Goalkeepers:
Mark Gayle (Solihull), Mark Shiels (Gresley R)
Defenders:
Neil Smith (Stafford R), Asa Charlton (Worcester), Dan Jones (Worcester), Darren Grocutt (Tamworth), Josh Skidmore (Cheltenham), Steve Pope (Bromsgrove), David Haywood (Solihull), Nick Preston (Solihull)
Midfield:
Lewis Baker (Stourbridge), Stuart Skidmore (Causeway Utd), Ben Steane (Bedworth), Andy Spencer (Boldmere), Shaun Wray (Stourbridge), Richard Kavanagh (Studley), Simon Forsdick (Shepshed)
Forwards:
Jason Moore (Coventry), Richard Burgess (Redditch), Alex Cowley (Redditch), Jimmy Haarhoff (Moor Green)

CORRECT AT TIME OF GOING TO PRESS

HEDNESFORD TOWN
Goalkeepers:
Ryan Young (Hucknall)
Defenders:
Chris Brindley (Stafford R), Lee Barrow (Stafford R), Richard Teesdale (Hereford), Ross Adams (WBA), Tom Griffiths (Youth team)
Midfield:
Carl Palmer (Rushall Olympic), Anthony Maguire (Torquay), Craig Dean (Gresley R), Lee Williams (Telford Utd), Danny McGhee (Rushall Olympic), Grant Beckett (Bromsgrove), David Berks (Rocester), Matthew Turner (Koge Boldklub (Denmark))
Forwards:
Damian Charie (Youth team), Steve Anthrobus (Aberystwyth), Chris Gray (Sutton Coldfield), Leon McSweeney (Hucknall), Damian Jarrett (Tamworth), Andy Bell (Wycombe)

HEMEL HEMPSTEAD TOWN
Goalkeepers:
Clint Drake (Boreham Wood), Martin Peat (Leyton)
Defenders:
Daniel West (Wimborne), Tom Neill (Chesham), Nick Leach (Yeading), Andy Cook (Northwood)
Midfield:
Tony Kelly (Berkhamsted), Danny Grieves (Aylesbury), Bobby Highton (Boreham Wood), Chris Harvey (Dunstable), Mark Jones (Aylesbury), Dean Palmer (Boreham Wood), Paul Kelly (Hampton & Richmond B), Daniel Braithwaite (Chesham)
Forwards:
Bryan Hammatt (Wealdstone), James Bent (Chesham), Alex Stewart (Thame), George Fowler (Farnborough)

HISTON
Goalkeepers:
Paul Barber (Newmarket)
Defenders:
Neil Coburn (Cambridge C), Louie Farrington (Baldock), Colin Vowden (Cambridge C), Roscoe Hipperson (Spalding), Steve Willis (Soham)
Midfield:
Neil Andrews (Cambridge C), Jamie Barker (Youth team), Adie Cambridge (Cambridge C), Wayne Goddard (Mildenhall), Matt Haniver (Cambridge Utd), Erhan Okay (Cambridge Utd), Ossie Mintus (Rothwell), Leigh Meddows (Cambridge Utd)
Forwards:
Ian Cambridge (Chelmsford), Peter Munns (Wisbech), Neil Kennedy (Newmarket), Charles Libam (Ivory Coast)

HITCHIN TOWN
Goalkeepers:
Richard Wimot (Dagenham & Redbidge), Neil Cheek (Ware), Ian Taylor (St Albans)
Defenders:
Gordon Barr (Hoddesdon), Paul Covington (Aylesbury), Matt Baldry (Dunstable), Jim Duffy (Youth team), Jake Meah (Arlesey), James Kidd (Leighton), Mark Burke (Luton), Lee McCulloch (Old Dunstablians)
Midfield:
Kevin Evans (Youth team), Stuart Maynard (Enfield), Ian Scott (St Albans), Gavin Jaggard (Bedford), Ben L'Honore (Stevenage), Glem Lamacraft (Youth team)
Forwards:
Josh Sozzo (Bedford), Ricky Case (Bishop' Stortford), Darran Hay (Biggleswade), Mark Bridge (Ware)

KING'S LYNN
Goalkeepers:
Steve Wilson (Bedford), Aaron Osborne (Norwich)
Defenders:
Gary Setchell (Tamworth), Danny Hammond (Cambridge Utd), Mark Burrows (Rothwell), Adam Jones (Mansfield), Nicky Blake (Youth team), Charlie Defty (Youth team)
Midfield:
Jack Defty (Youth team)
Carl Holmes (Stamford), Lee Stevenson (Sheffield Wed), Mark Camm (Lincoln C), Craig Fishlock (Bradford C), Daryl Sutch (Boston Utd)
Forwards:
Tony Battersby (Cambridge C), Danny Bloomfield (Cambridge C), Mark Angel (Boston Utd), Robbie Harris (Wisbech), Chris Bacon (Youth team), Tom Doughty (Swaffham)

MERTHYR TYDFIL
Goalkeepers:
Ashley Morris (Youth team)
Defenders:
Paul Keddle (Rhayader), Kristian Witcombe (Caerleon), Gethin Jones (Cardiff), Steve Williams (Newport Co), Andy York (Carmarthen), Jeff Eckhardt (Newport Co)
Midfield:
Danny Carter (Barry), Dean Clarke (Barry), Grant Thomas (Swansea), Ryan Dorrian (Newport Co), Richard French (Newport Co), Lee Howells (Cheltenham), Chris Holloway (Tiverton), Dale Griffiths (Swansea)
Forwards:
Craig Steins (Leeds), Garry Shepherd (Newport Co), Jason Eaton (Bath), Chris Bale (Cinderford)

RUGBY UNITED
Goalkeepers:
Jason Pearcey (Forest Green), Dean Thomas (Shepshed), Paul Shepherd (Bedford)
Defenders:
Andy Commander (Shepshed), Craig Herbert (Hayes), Gary Redgate (Atherstone), Adam Hart (Atherstone), Andy Rutherford (Barwell), Gary Moran (Gresley R), Richard Wesley (Yth team)
Midfield:
Jamie Williams (Hucknall), Danny Hall (Coventry), Craig Dutton (Sutton Coldfield), Neil Melvin (Derby), Rory Squire (Youth team), Steve Evans (Hednesford)
Forwards:
Justin Marsden (Youth team), Robbie Beard (Bedworth), Dave Pearson (Shepshed), Jermaine Gordon (Corby), Jon Douglas (Tamworth), Kevin Charley (Bedworth)

SOLIHULL BOROUGH
Goalkeepers:
Mark Gayle (Halesowen), Chris Taylor (Hinckley Utd), Craig Johnson (K'minster)
Defenders:
Peter Barry (Atherstone), Adam Cooper (Nuneaton), Martin Heir (Bedworth), Dean Peer (Moor Green)
Midfield:
Nick Amos (Hednesford), Mark Faulds (Youth team), Guy Hadland (Bedworth), Matt Hawker (Romulus), Richard Kavanagh (Stourport Swifts), Aengus Martin (Molesey), Jamie Petty (Moor Green), Dean Tilley (Earlswood), Morton Titterton (Hinckley Utd
Forwards:
Aaron Farrell (Kidderminster), Junior Hewitt (Bedworth), Leon Mitchell (Halesowen), Mark Shepherd (Redditch)

STAMFORD
Goalkeepers:
Darren Watts (Ford Sports), Paul Warnecki (Daventry T)
Defenders:
Nick Ashby (Raunds), Andy Peaks (Raunds), Glen Gibb (Ford Sports). Dennis Rhule (Gainsborough), Delroy Gordon (Kettering)
Midfield:
Robbie Maddox (Corby), Kevin Ainslie (Bourne), Glen Thompson (Kettering), Michael Boyle-Chong (Kettering), Gary Butterworth (King's Lynn), Matthew Green (Rothwell), Danny Steadman (Wisbech), Ian Edge (Bedford), Ryan Nash (Rothwell)
Forwards:
Jason Turner (Rothwell), Gareth Pritchard (Wisbech), Kevin Byrne (Corby), Malcolm Ndekwe (King's Lynn), Dale Watkins (King's Lynn)

TEAM BATH
Goalkeepers:
Ryan Northmore (Woking), Ali Hines (Gloucester), Darren Chitty (Melksham)
Defenders:
Alex Ball (Bristol C), Peter Tisdale (AFC Newbury), Dean Smith (Purfleet), Chris Holland (Exeter)
Midfield:
Matt Warner (Basingstoke), Marc Canham (Bournemouth), Jon Nicholls (Torquay), Danny Maye (Corby), Neil Saunders (Harlow)
Forwards:
Carl Heiniger (Newcastle Benfield Saints), Matt Lewis (Cardiff), Tomas Jaukovic (None)

TIVERTON TOWN
Goalkeepers: Mark Ovendale (York)
Defenders:
Rob Cousins (Forest Green), Shaun Goff (Exeter), Nathan Rudge (Chippenham), Ian Patchett (Yeovil), Steve Winter (Basingstoke), Chris Vinnicombe (Wycombe)
Midfield:
David Steele (Youth team), Kevin Wills (Torquay), Matt Locke (Team Bath), Mike Booth (Taunton), Dave Hallett (Wimbledon), Iain Harvey (Yate)
Forwards:
Paul Milsom (Bath), Darren Edwards (Mangotsfield), Carl Cliff-Brown (Clyst R), Tom Stocco (Team Bath), Jamie Mudge (Exeter), Jamie Densham (Exmouth)

SOUTHERN LEAGUE DIVISION ONE WEST
STEP 4

FINAL LEAGUE TABLE 2003-04

WESTERN DIVISION		P	W	D	L	F	A	Pts
1.	Redditch United	40	25	9	6	75	30	84
2.	Gloucester City	40	24	7	9	77	46	79
3.	Cirencester Town	40	24	4	12	73	40	76
4.	Halesowen Town	40	20	13	7	64	40	73
5.	Rugby United	40	21	8	11	57	40	71
6.	Team Bath	40	21	6	13	62	41	69
7.	Solihull Borough	40	19	9	12	50	31	66
8.	Sutton Coldfield	40	16	15	9	52	38	63
9.	Bromsgrove Rovers	40	16	11	13	60	48	59
10.	Ilkeston Town	40	16	10	14	58	59	58
11.	Clevedon Town	40	16	5	19	55	59	53
12.	Gresley Rovers	40	15	7	18	52	60	52
13.	Mangotsfield United	40	14	8	18	70	70	50
14.	Evesham United	40	15	5	20	56	57	50
15.	Taunton Town	40	14	8	18	50	55	50
16.	Yate Town	40	11	9	20	51	79	42
17.	Swindon Supermarine	40	10	9	21	41	69	39
18.	Stourport Swifts	40	9	11	20	43	62	38
19.	Bedworth United	40	8	12	20	39	61	36
20.	Cinderford Town	40	7	9	24	50	94	30
21.	Shepshed Dynamo	40	5	13	22	31	87	28

NB: Atherstone withdrew from the league. Results shown in grid opposite but records expunged from above table.

TOP GOALSCORERS - LEAGUE & LEAGUE CUP

Andrew Hoskins	Gloucester City	28
David Seal	Mangotsfield United	25
Gareth Hopkins	Cirencester Town	22
Dean Perrow	Sutton Coldfield	19
Richard Ball	Stourport Swifts	18
Robert Beard	Rugby United	18
Jason Moore	Ashby/Halesowen	18
Matthew Rawlins	Yate Town	18
James Cox	Gloucester City	17
Paul Szewczyk	Bromsgrove Rovers	17
Chris Freestone	Ilkeston Town	16
Anthony Lynch	Taunton Town	16
Paul Hunter	Solihull Borough	15
Richard Leadbeater	Redditch United	15
Martin Myers	Redditch United	14
Jack Pitcher	Mangotsfield Town	14
Jody Bevan	Cirencester Town	12
Richard Kear	Cinderford Town	12
Scott Griffin	Cirencester Town	11
Justin Miller	Swindon Supermarine	11
Craig Pountney	Evesham United	11
Mark Shepherd	Redditch United	11

	WESTERN DIVISION 03-04	1	2	3	4	5	6	7	8	9	10	11	12	13	14	15	16	17	18	19	20	21	22
1	Atherstone United		2-0	-	-	0-1	-	-	-	-	-	-	-	-	-	-	-	-	-	-	-	-	-
2	Bedworth United	-		0-0	1-0	0-1	0-0	1-2	1-2	0-0	0-1	2-1	2-1	0-1	0-0	0-1	0-0	0-0	0-1	3-1	1-2	1-1	0-3
3	Bromsgrove Rovers	-	1-2		2-2	0-0	3-0	2-1	0-1	0-2	3-3	3-0	1-1	0-1	1-3	5-1	0-1	2-0	2-1	3-0	2-1	3-3	3-2
4	Cinderford Town	-	4-1	1-2		1-8	0-1	0-3	0-2	0-4	1-2	1-0	1-3	2-0	1-5	1-1	1-3	0-1	0-2	4-3	2-2	3-3	0-1
5	Cirencester Town	-	2-3	2-0	5-0		0-0	2-0	2-1	2-0	0-1	2-1	1-2	0-3	3-0	4-1	1-2	3-2	0-2	3-1	2-1	1-0	1-0
6	Clevedon Town	-	3-1	0-0	1-1	2-3		2-4	0-2	2-0	2-0	2-3	3-0	0-3	0-2	2-1	1-2	2-0	1-2	0-1	2-3	0-1	4-0
7	Evesham United	-	3-0	0-1	2-1	0-0	2-3		4-2	1-1	1-2	0-1	0-1	2-0	0-1	0-2	1-0	3-0	1-3	1-0	4-0	0-1	2-1
8	Gloucester City	4-1	2-1	1-0	4-0	2-0	3-1	3-1		3-3	2-2	0-1	2-2	1-1	0-1	5-2	2-2	1-0	2-1	3-1	3-1	4-3	1-2
9	Gresley Rovers	-	2-0	0-3	1-2	0-3	0-2	2-0	1-2		1-0	0-2	2-0	2-3	2-3	3-0	1-0	3-3	1-1	2-1	1-4	1-1	4-1
10	Halesowen Town	-	6-3	0-0	1-1	2-1	3-0	0-2	0-0	2-0		2-2	6-0	0-0	1-0	1-1	1-0	2-2	1-0	6-0	3-1	1-0	1-0
11	Ilkeston Town	-	2-0	2-2	2-2	2-2	3-5	2-3	0-3	1-2	0-0		4-2	0-6	0-4	5-1	1-0	1-3	2-1	0-1	3-1	1-2	5-1
12	Mangotsfield United	-	2-1	4-3	6-2	1-5	1-2	3-1	3-2	1-2	4-0	2-4		2-3	0-3	0-1	0-0	3-1	0-0	5-2	0-0	1-1	4-1
13	Redditch United	5-0	1-1	4-0	5-2	2-1	1-0	3-1	0-1	2-0	0-2	1-1	3-0		1-0	1-0	1-2	1-1	1-1	2-0	0-0	2-1	4-0
14	Rugby United	-	4-1	1-5	2-1	2-1	1-1	3-2	1-0	2-1	1-0	0-1	1-0	2-3		1-0	1-2	1-1	1-1	2-1	2-0	0-1	2-2
15	Shepshed Dynamo	-	0-0	1-1	2-2	1-3	1-2	2-1	0-6	0-3	2-2	0-0	0-9	0-0	0-0		0-4	1-1	0-2	1-0	1-1	2-3	0-4
16	Solihull Borough	-	3-2	0-1	3-0	1-2	3-1	3-1	0-0	0-1	0-1	0-0	0-0	1-1	2-0	3-0		2-1	0-1	2-1	0-1	0-1	4-1
17	Stourport Swifts	-	1-1	1-2	1-4	0-1	2-0	0-1	1-2	1-1	0-2	0-1	2-1	0-4	3-0	2-1	2-0		0-3	1-1	2-0	0-2	2-0
18	Sutton Coldfield Town	-	2-2	1-1	1-0	2-0	1-0	2-1	0-1	2-0	3-1	1-1	3-1	1-0	0-0	2-2	1-1	2-2		0-0	2-3	1-2	1-1
19	Swindon Supermarine	-	0-3	1-0	2-2	1-0	3-1	1-1	0-2	2-1	4-2	0-1	3-2	1-2	0-0	1-1	0-1	2-1	1-1		0-0	1-0	1-1
20	Taunton Town	-	0-1	1-2	2-0	1-3	1-2	3-1	5-0	2-0	1-1	0-1	1-3	0-2	1-0	1-0	1-1	3-1	0-0	4-1		0-1	2-0
21	Team Bath	-	2-1	1-0	4-0	0-1	1-2	0-0	1-3	1-2	1-2	2-1	1-0	1-2	0-2	3-0	0-1	2-1	2-0	3-1	4-0		3-0
22	Yate Town	-	3-3	2-1	0-5	0-2	1-3	3-3	2-1	5-0	1-1	0-0	0-0	1-5	1-3	3-1	0-1	1-1	4-1	2-1	1-0	0-3	

ASHFORD TOWN (Middlesex)

CLUB OFFICIALS

Chairman: Robert Parker
Vice Chairman: Mark Vaughan
President: T.B.A.
Secretary: Alan Constable
3 Craigwell Close, Chertsey Lane,
Staines, Middx. TW18 3NP
Tel: 01784 440613 (H) 07956 930719 (M)
01784 451614 (Fax) Email: alanc52@aol.com
Press Secretary: Terry Ryan

FOOTBALL MANAGEMENT TEAM

Manager: Nathan Wharf
Captain: Ross Davidson

FACT FILE

Formed: 1964
Nickname: Ash Trees
Colours: Tangerine & white/black/tangerine
Change colours:All Blue
Midweek matchday: Wednesday

2003-2004

P.o.Y.: Russell Canderton
Top Scorer: Richard Butler 21

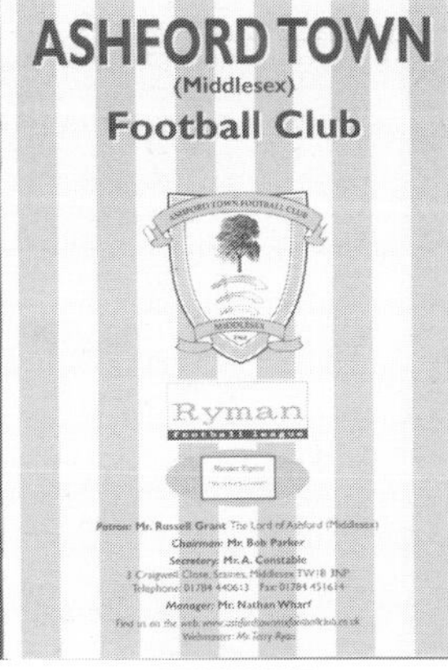

PROGRAMME

Pages:40 Price: £1.50
Editor: Jon Gooding
email:jontheref1@hotmail.com

GROUND Short Lane, Stanwell, Staines, Middx Tel: 01784 245908
Club Website: www.ashfordtownmxfootballclub.co.uk

Directions: M25 jct 13, A30 towards London, 3rd left at footbridge after Ashford Hospital crossroads - ground signposted after 1/4 a mile on right down Short Lane. 2 miles from Ashford (BR) & Hatton Cross (tube) stations. Bus route - Westlink 116

Club Shop: No

Capacity: 2550 Seats: 150 Cover: 300 Floodlights: Yes

Clubhouse: Open 7 days a week. Refreshments always available - hot food on matchdays

PREVIOUS
Ground: Clockhouse Lane Rec
Leagues: Hounslow & Dist. 64-68; Surrey Intermediate 68-82; Surrey Premier 82-90 Combined Counties League 90-00 Isthmian 2000-01 - 03-4

CLUB RECORDS
Appearances: Alan Constable 650
Attendance: 750 v Brentford, friendly 29/7/86
Goalscorer: Andy Smith

BEST SEASON
FA Vase: 4th Round 2000-2001
FA Trophy: 2nd Rd 2003-04 **FA Cup:**1st Qual. Rd. 1996-1997

HONOURS:
Combined Co's Lg Champions 94-95, 95-96, 96-97, 97-8, 99-00; Chall Cup R-up 92-93 94-95, Lg Vase Cup R-up 91-92 94-95; Surrey I'mediate Lg, Surrey Prem. Cup 89-90; Middx Prem. Cup R-up 89-90; Southern Comb Cup 95-96, R-up 01-02 World Wide Carpets Prem Ch Cup 98-99 Aldershot Senior Cup: 2002-2003, Middsx Charity Cup 2000-01

BEDWORTH UNITED

CLUB OFFICIALS

Chairman: Kevin Hateley
Vice Chairman: Sue Harrison
Secretary: Graham J Bloxham
43 Mount Pleasant Road, Bedworth,
Warwicks CV12 8EX
Mobile: 07748 640613
Press Officer: John Harris

FOOTBALL MANAGEMENT TEAM

Manager: Mark Hallam **Assistant Manager**: Russell Dodd **Club Doctor**: Philip Earl
Physio: Nigel Clemmet **Capt**: Neil O'Sullivan

2003-04

Leading Goalscorer: Lee Mioore
Player of the Year: Jamie Richardson

FACT FILE

Formed: 1896 Nickname: Greenbacks
Sponsors: Brose
Colours: Green & white stripes/Green/Green.
Change colours: Yellow /green/yellow
Midweek matchday: Tuesday
Youth League :Midland Floodlit
Club website:www.bedworthunited.fwsi.com
Local Press: Heartland Evening News, Weekly Tribune, Bedworth Echo, Coventry Evening Telegraph
Local Radio: Mercia Sound, BBC CWR

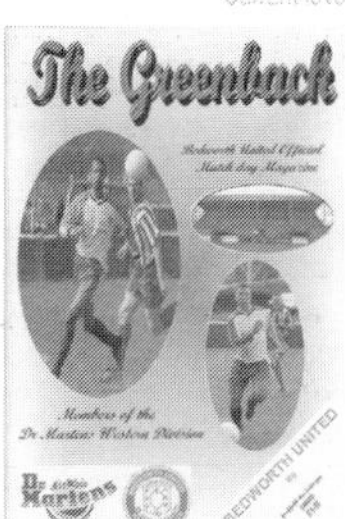

PROGRAMME

Pages: 60 Price: £1.20
Editor: James Earl
01905 755692

GROUND The Oval, Miners Welfare Park, Coventry Road, Bedworth CV12 8NN Tel: 02476 314302 Email: ronald@dkemp.3freeservice.co.uk
Directions: M6 jct 3, into Bedworth on B4113 Coventry to Bedworth road, ground200yds past past Bedworth Leisure Centre on this road. Coaches should park at this Leisure Centre. Buses from Coventry and Nuneaton pass ground
Capacity: 7,000 Cover: 300 Seats: 300 Floodlights: Yes
Clubhouse: Social club open every day 7.30-11pm & w/e noon-3pm. Hot and cold bar food
Club Shop: Selling a wide range of souvenirs & programmes. Contact : Ron Kemp 01203 318014

PREVIOUS **Leagues:** Birmingham Comb. 47-54; West Mids (at first Birmingham) Lg 54-72
Name: Bedworth Town 47-68 **Ground:** British Queen Ground 11-39

CLUB RECORDS **Attendance:** 5,127 v Nuneaton Borough, Southern Lg Midland Division 23/2/82
Win: 11-0 **Defeat:** 1-10
Career Goalscorer: Peter Spacey (1949-69) **Career Appearances:** Peter Spacey
Transfer fee paid: £1,750 for Colin Taylor (Hinckley Town, 1991-92)
Transfer fee received: £30,000 for Richard Landon (Plymouth Argyle, January 1994)

BEST SEASON **FA Trophy:** Second Round 80-81 **FA Cup:** 4th Qualifying Rd 1983/89/90

HONOURS Birmingham Comb.(2) 48-50, Birmingham Snr Cup(3) 78-79 80-82, Midland Floodlit Cup 81-82 92-93

Players progressing: Phil Huffer (Derby County 1953), Geoff Coleman(Northampton Town 1955), Ian Hathaway (Mansfield Town 1989), Richard Landon(Plymouth Argyle 1994),Robert Oddy (Coventry City 2002), Dan Pitham (Burnley 2002), Inderpaul Khela , Ashley Pringle and Phil Garner (all Kidderminster Harriers), Tom Bates (Coventry C. 2003)

Taken before last game of 2003-2004 season. Back Row (L-R): Robert Scott, Stephen Olanipekun, Scott McGragor, Russell Dodd (Asst. Manager), Gary Hateley, Mark Hallam (Manager), James Earl, Philip Male, James Richardson, Scott Hadland, Darren Massingham. **Front Row:** Jack Manning (Coach), Tom Bates, Tom Stevenson, Kirk Smith, Neil O'Sullivan (Capt.), James Wood, Chris Goodman, Lee Moore, Simon Benn (Coach).

BRACKLEY TOWN

CLUB OFFICIALS

Managlng Director: Ray Styles
Chairman:Phil Lines President: Mike Bosher
Com. Man: Ray Styles: 0772 040587
Press Officer: Brian Martin

Secretary/Press Officer: Pat Ashby,
2 Barrington Court, Ward Road,
Brackley, NN13 7LE
Tel: 01280 840900(O) 07969 825636(M)

FOOTBALL MANAGEMENT TEAM
Manager: Tim Fowler
Asst.Man: Pete Salt

Formed: 1890
Nickname: Saints
Colours:Red /white/white
Change colours: All Yellow
Midweek matchday: Wednesday

2003-04
Leading Goalscorer:Ben Milner
Captain:Paul Lamb
Player of the Year:Andy Baird

Ground: St James Park, Churchill Way, Brackley, Northants NN13 7EJ. Tel: 01280 704077
Office: 01280 703652: Club Website: www..brackleytownfc.co.uk
Club Email: btfc1890@aol.com
Directions: Churchill Way, east off A43, south end of town
Capacity: 3,500 Cover: 150 Seats: 300
Floodlights: Yes
Clubhouse: Fully licensed. Lounge & main hall. Food available. Open all week.
Club Shop: Yes, selling club merchandise,programmes and badges etc.

PROGRAMME
Price: £1
Editor: Brian Martin(01280 706619)
Local Press: Brackley Advertiser,
Banbury Guardian, Herald & Post
Milton Keynes Citizen - Local Radio: Fox FM

PREVIOUS **Leagues:** Banbury & District; North Bucks; Hellenic 77-83; United Counties 83-94; Hellenic 94-97,Southern 97-99

Names: None

Ground: Banbury Road, Manor Road, Buckingham Road (up to 1974)

CLUB RECORDS **Attendance:** 720 v Kettering, Northants Senior Cup 1989

Fee Received: £2,000 for Phil Mason from Oxford City 98

BEST SEASON **FA Trophy:** 1st Qual Rd 97-98

FA Cup: 2nd Qual Rd 97-98

HONOURS United Counties R-up 88-89 (Div 1 83-84); Northants Snr Cup R-up 88-89; Buckingham Charity Cup (3); Hellenic Lg Prem 96-97, 2003-04 Div 1 Cup 82-83.

Players progressing: Jon Blencowe (Leicester) **Transfer Fee Paid:** None

BRACKNELL TOWN

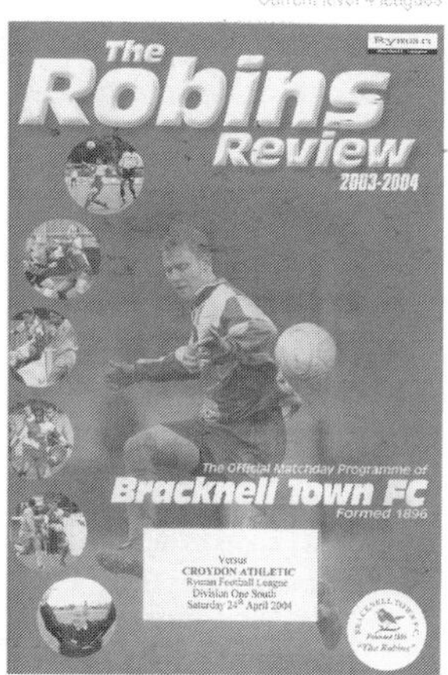

CLUB OFFICIALS

Chairman: Chris Nixon
President: Jack Quinton
Vice-Chairman & Match Secretary:
Malcolm Hutt, 3 Livingstone Gardens,
Woodley, Reading RG5 3LT
01189 694946 (H) 07977 822148 (M)

Secretary: David Mihell, 51 Upshire Gdns.,
The Warren,Bracknell, Berks RG12 9YZ
Tel: 01344 488369 (H) 07712 489415 (M)
Press Off.: Robert Scully 01344 640721

FOOTBALL MANAGEMENT TEAM

Manager: Alan Taylor
Physio: Richard Lansiquot

FACT FILE

Founded: 1896
Nickname: Robins
Colours: Red & white quarters/red/red
Change colours: All Blue
Sponsors: GAME (www.game.uk.com)
Midweek Matchday: Tuesday
Reserve's League: Suburban (west)

GROUND Larges Lane, Bracknell RG12 9AN.
Tel: 01344 412305 (club), 01344 300933 (office- T & Fax)
Directions: Off A329 just before Met Office r'bout by Bracknell College, ground 200 yards. From Bracknell (BR)/bus station - right out of station, follow pathover bridge, left down steps and follow cycle path ahead, after 300yds follow curve over footbridge, right and follow lane to end, left and ground on leftafter bend
Capacity: 2,500 Seats: 190 Cover: 400 Floodlights: Yes
Clubhouse: Members' bar open 11am-11pm Mon-Sat, 12-3 & 7-10.30pm Sun.
Club Shop: Yes, selling metal badges, programmes, scarves, club sweaters, club ties

PROGRAMME

Pages: 48 Price: £1.00
Editor: Robert Scully 01344 640721
Local Press: Bracknell News

PREVIOUS **Leagues:** Great Western Comb.; Surrey Snr 63-70; London Spartan 70-75
Grounds: None **Names:** None

CLUB RECORDS **Attendance:** 2,500 v Newquay, FA Amateur Cup 1971
Career Goalscorer: Richard Whitty **Career Appearances:** James Woodcock

BEST SEASON **FA Cup:** 1st Round Proper, 00-01 (0-4 v Lincoln City)

HONOURS: Isthmian Lg Div 3 93-94; Berks & Bucks Snr Cup R-up; Spartan Lg 74-75, (Lg Cup 81-82 82-83); Surrey Snr Lg 68-69 (Lg Cup 68-69 69-70)

Players progressing: Willie Graham (Brentford)

Back row (L-R): Chris Nixon (Chairman), Tony Hardy (Committee), Mike Savage (Coach), Neil Baker, Gavin Smith, Jon Underwood, Lee Edwards, Jon Palmer, Paul Gower, James Glynn, Danny Hayward, Jack Quinton (President), Ken Ballard (Coach), Alan Taylor (Manager), Malcolm Hutt (Vice Chairman)
Front row (L-R): Richard Lansiquot (Physio), Adam Crittenden, Neil Selby, Derek Walters, Ben Edwards, Stuart Hammonds, Mike Cook, Martin Douglas, Mark Tallentire (Assistant Manager)

BROMSGROVE ROVERS

CLUB OFFICIALS

Chairman: Herbert Brakenthwaite

President: Charles W Poole

Secretary: G.J.Bayley,14 Orchard Rd.,Bromsgrove B61 8HZ

01527 877559 (H& FAX)

07837 105368 (W)

Fixture Secretary: Brian Hewings

Tel No: 01527 831182 (H)

Commercial Managers: Helen Jones

FOOTBALL MANAGEMENT TEAM

Manager:Joe Jackson

Captain:Ross Collins

Physios: LStuart Ellwell

FACT FILE

Formed: 1885

Sponsors: Banks's

Nickname: Rovers or Greens

Colours: Green & White stripes/green/black

Change colours: Red/black/black

Midweek matchday: Tuesday

Reserves' league: Central Conference. & Midland Combination Reserves

2003-2004

Top Goalscorer: Paul Szewczyk

Player of the Year: Steve Hillman

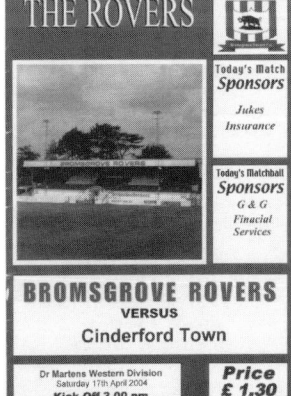

THE ROVERS

Today's Match Sponsors

Jukes Insurance

Today's Matchball Sponsors

G & G Finacial Services

BROMSGROVE ROVERS

VERSUS

Cinderford Town

Dr Martens Western Division

Saturday 17th April 2004

Kick Off 3.00 pm

Price £ 1.30

Pages: 40 Price: £1.30

Editor: Helen & Andy Jones

01527 882682 (H) 07830 286991 (W)

GROUND: Victoria Ground, Birmingham Road, Bromsgrove, Worcs, B61 0DR
Tel: 01527 876949

Directions: Ground is situated on the north side of Bromsgrove on the Birmingham Road, off the A38 Bromsgrove by pass. The M5 and M42 join theA38 to the north of the town making it easy to get to the ground without havingto go into town.

Capacity: 4,893 **Seated:** 394 **Covered Terracing:** 1,344

Clubhouse: Victoria Club (01527 878260) - Serves hot & cold food. Big screenTV, pool table & darts. Open matchdays and week-day evenings.

Club Shop: Selling replica clothing & souvenirs. Contact Tracy Kite (01527 876949)

PREVIOUS **Leagues:** Birmingham Lge 1898-08 53-65, Birmingham Comb. 1908-53, West Midlands 65-72, Southern Lge - Northern Div. 73-79, Midland Div. 79-86, Premier Div. 86-92, GMVC 92-97, Southern 97-01, Midland Alliance 01-02
Grounds: Old Station Road 1885-87, Recreation Ground 87-88, Churchfields 88-97,Well Lane 1897-1910.

CLUB RECORDS **Attendance:** 7,389 v Worcester City - 1957
Career - Goalscorer: Chris Hanks 238, 83-94 **Appearances:** Shaun O'Meara 763, 75-94
Win: 11-0 - v Hinckley Ath. 1970, v Halesowen Town `A' 1939 **Defeat:** 0-12 v Aston Villa `A' 1939
Fee paid: £3,000 for Recky Carter (Solihull B.) 93-94 **Fee received:** Undisclosed for Scott Cooksey (Peterborough) Dec. 93

HONOURS Vauxhall Conference R-up 92-93, Lge Cup 94-95 95-96; Southern Lge Prem 91-92, R-up 86-87, Cup 92-93, R-up 86-87, Midland Div 85-86, Merit Cup 85-86, Cup 85-86, R-up 73-74 87-88; Bill Dellow Cup 85-86; Worcester Sen Cup (8), R-up (10); Birmingham Sen Cup 46-47, R-up 47-48 88-89; W Mid Lge R-up 67-70, Cup 67-68 70-71; Birminham Lge 59-60, R-up 04-05 56-57 60-61; Birmingham Comb 46-47, R-up 49-50 50-51; Hereford Charity Chall Cup 46-47, R-up 47-48.

Players progressing: M McKenna (Northampton 46),R Hartle (Bolton 52), A McLean (Bury 53), A Smith (A.Villa 54), M Deakin (CPalace 54), B Puster (Leicester 58), Tom Smith (Sheff Utd 1978), MalcolmGoodman (Halifax 1979), Steve Smith (Walsall 1980), Gary Hackett (Shrewsbury 1983), Bill McGarry, Martyn O'Connor (C Palace 1992), Scott Cooksey (Peterborough 1993), Steve Taylor (Crystal Palace 1995).

Back row, left to right: Brian Hewings (Secretary), Lewis Churchill, Barrie Day (Associate Director), Dany Lennon, Terry Brown (Associate Director), Steve Frost, PaulSzewczyk, Ian Gandy, Ross Colins, Garth Palmer, Mark Bellingham, Brian Kite (Associate Director), Jonathon Daniels, Stuart Elwell(Physio) and Troy Douglin.**Front row:** Alec Hodgkiss (Associate Director), Riad Erraji, Mark Benbow, Steve Hillman, Joe Jackson (Manager), Tom Herbert (Chairman), Tom Stokes (Coach), Dave Benton,Ryan Mahon, Arthur Appleton and Geoff Bayley (Company Secretary)

BURNHAM

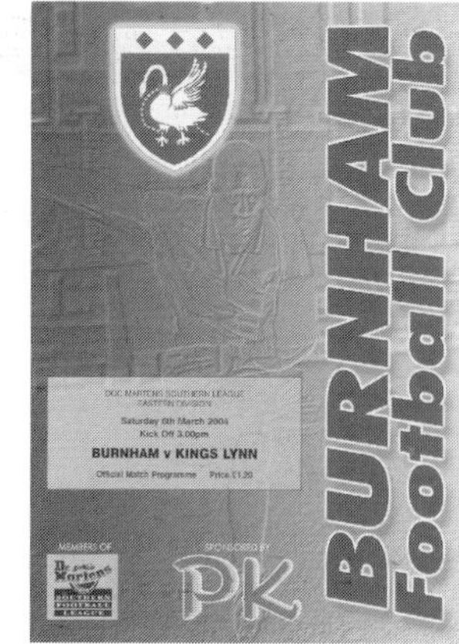

32 pages Editor: Cliff Sparkes(01753 642490)

Local Press:
Slough Observer, South Bucks Express,
Maidenhead Advertiser, Buckingham Advertiser
Local Radio:
Star FM, BBC Thames Valley, Swan F.M.

CLUB OFFICIALS

Chairman: Malcolm Higton
Vice Chairman: Rod Saunders
Secretary: Alan King, 41 Underwood Road, High Wycombe, Bucks. HP 13 6YD
Press Officer: Alan King
(01494523920 (H) 078999 41414(M)

FOOTBALL MANAGEMENT TEAM

Manager: Steve Mellor
Assistant Manager:Roger Emms
Coach:Steve Mellor
Captain: Paul Brett
Physio: Lisa McKnney

FACT FILE

Founded: 1878
Sponsors: T.B.A.
Colours: Blue & white/blue/white
Change colours: Yellow/yellow/black
Midweek matchday: Tuesday 7.30
Reserve Team's Lge: Suburban

2003-2004
Captain: Paul Brett
Top Goalscorer: Michael Bartley
Player of the Year: Jon Horsted

Ground: The Gore, Wymers Wood Road, Burnham, Slough SL1 8JG
Tel: 01628 602467

Directions: North west of village centre, 2 miles from Burnham BR station, 2miles from M4 junction 7, 5 miles from M40 junction 2, 100yds north of Gorecrossroads - fork right into Wymers Wood Rd and ground is immediately on right

Capacity: 2,500 Cover: 250 Seats: 250 Floodlights: Yes

Clubhouse: Open every evening and w/e lunch.
Darts and pool, two bars, usual matchday food **Club Shop:** Yes

PREVIOUS **Leagues:** Sth Bucks & East Berks; Maidenhead Intermediate; Windsor, Slough & Dist; Gt Western Comb. 48-64; Wycombe Comb. 64-70; Reading Comb. 70-71; Hellenic 71-77; Athenian 77-84; London Spartan 84-85; Southern 85-95; Hellenic 95-99
Name: Burnham & Hillingdon 1985-87 **Ground:** Baldwin Meadow (until 20's)

RECORD **Attendance:** 2,380 v Halesowen Town, FA Vase 2/4/83
Scorer: Fraser Hughes 65, 69-70 **Win:** 18-0 v High Duty Alloys, 70-71
Defeat: 1-10 v Ernest Turners Sports, 63-64

BEST SEASON **FA Cup:** 3rd Qualifying Rd **FA Vase:** Semi-Final 82-83, Q-F 77-78.
FA Trophy: 4th Round Replay 99-00

HONOURS Athenian Lg R-up(2) 78-80, Hellenic Lg 75-76 98-99 Div 1 R-up 72-73, Lg Cup 75-76 98-99, Div 1 Cup 71-72, London Spartan Lg 84-85 Lg Cup 84-85, Reading Comb. Lg Cup 70-71 All Champions Cup 70-71, Wycombe Comb. R-up (4) 65-67 68-70

Players progressing: D Hancock (Reading), R Rafferty (Grimsby Town), D Payne (Barnet)

Back row:
Steve Lockhart, Arron Lennon, Roger Emms, Michael Bartley, terrence Mitchell, Chris Ferdinand.

Front Row:
John Horsted, Steve Noakes, Steve Smith, Daryl Jones, Adam Logie.

Photo: Alan Coomes.

CINDERFORD TOWN

CLUB OFFICIALS

Chairman: Ashley Saunders
President: S Watkins
Vice Chairman: Ray Reed

Secretary: Chris Warren
9c Tusculum Way, Mitcheldean,
Glos GL17 0HZ
01594543065 (H) 01594 592202
Press Officer: Scot randell-Wilce

FOOTBALL MANAGEMENT TEAM

Manager: Phil Mullen
Asssitant Mnager/Coach: Paul Davies
Capt: Quentin Townsend
Physio: Keith Marfell

FACT FILE

Formed: 1922 Nickname: Town
Sponsors: 'The Forester'
Colours: Black & white stripes/black/black
Change :Green & white stripes/white/white
Midweek matchday: Tuesday
Reserves' League: No reserve team

2003-2004

Top Goalacsorer: Richard Kear
Player of the Year: Andy Fisher

PROGRAMME

Pages: 50 Price: £1.00
Editor: Dave Roberts Tel: 01594 824365
Local Radio: Radio Glos,Severn Sound
Local Press:The Forester, Glos Citizen,
Westerren Daily Press

GROUND The Causeway, Hilldene, Cinderford, Glos. Tel: 01594 827147 or 822039

Directions: From Gloucester take A40 to Ross-on-Wye, then A48 - Chepstow. In 8miles turn right at Elton garage onto A4151 signed Cinderford, thru Littledean, up steep hill, right at crossroads, second left into Latimer Rd. Ground 5 minswalk from town centre

Capacity: 2,500 Cover: 1,000 Seats: 250 Floodlights: Yes

Clubhouse: Open every day. 2 bars, kitchen, 2 skittle alleys, darts, dancehall,committee room

Club Shop: Souvenirs, club badges (£3.00), ties, mugs , scarves and pennants (Contact: Dave Gettings)

PREVIOUS **Leagues:** Glos Northern Snr 22-39 60-62, Western 46-59, Warwickshire Comb 63-64,West Midlands 65-69, Gloucestershire County 70-73 85-89, Midland Comb. 74-84,Hellenic 90-95
Names: None **Grounds:** Mousel Lane, Royal Oak

CLUB RECORDS **Attendance:** 4,850 v Minehead, Western League, 1955-56
Win: 13-0 v Cam Mills 38-39 **Defeat:** 0-10 v Sutton Coldfield 78-79
Career Appearances: Russell Bowles 528 **Career Goalscorer:** Unknown

BEST SEASON **FA Cup:** 2nd Rd v Gravesend 95-96 **FA Trophy:** 2nd Qual Rd
FA Vase: 2nd Rd 91-92 **FA Amateur Cup:** 3rd Qual Rd 52

HONOURS Hellenic Lg Premier Champions 94-95, Premier Lg.Cup 94-95, Floodlit Cup 93-94,Div 1 90-91; Glos Northern Snr Lg Div 1 38-39 60-61, R-up (6); Nth Glos Lg Div1 38-39 60-61; Glos Snr Amtr Cup (Nth) (6), R-up (3); Western Lg Div 2 56-57; Warwickshire Comb. 63-64; W Mids Lg Prem Div Cup 68-69; Glos Jnr Cup (Nth) 80-81; Midland Comb. 81-82; Glos Co. Lg R-up 69-70 71-72 73-74; Glos FA Trophy R-up 92-93; Hungerford Cup 94-95, Glos.Sen Cup Winners 00-01

Players Progressing:Nick McKernon (Mansfield Town), Wayne Hatswell (Kidderminster Harriers via Forset Green), Dave Bird (Cheltenham T) and Darren Campbell (International Athlete) 95-96

CLEVEDON TOWN

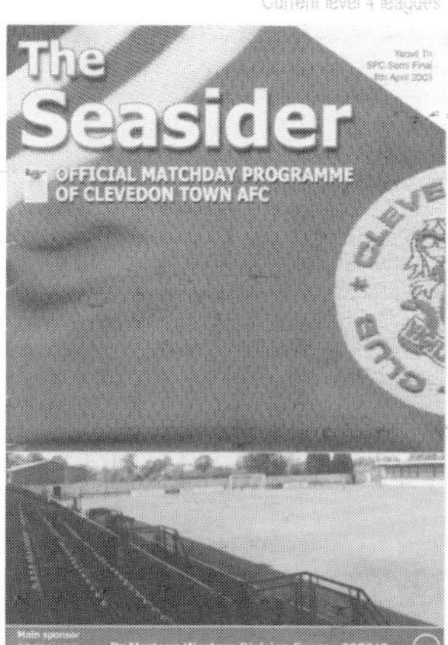

The Seasider
OFFICIAL MATCHDAY PROGRAMME
OF CLEVEDON TOWN AFC
Dr Martens Western Division Season 2002/3

Pages: 34 Price:£1.30
Editor: Russell Isaac (01275 343000)

Local Radio: Radio Bristol, Star 107.7 FM
Local Press: Clevedon Mercury
Evening Post, Western Daily Press

CLUB OFFICIALS

Chairman: John Croft

Directors: R.J.Ayers, B.W.Bradshaw, S.T.Haas, T Walsh and G,Thomas

Secretary: Steve Batt, 1st Floor Flat, ,Courtyard Cottage, Haberfield Hall, Happerton Lane, Easton in Gordano, Bristol BS20 0QH
Tel Nos: 01275 813868 (H) 07817 397677 (M)

Commercial Manager: Gary Bradshaw (M) 07768 270718

FACT FILE

Formed: 1880
Nickname: The Seasiders
Sponsors: Bradshaw Group
Colours: Blue & white stripes/blue/blue
Change colours: All yellow or all green
Midweek Matches: Tuesday
Youth Team: Som Youth Floodlit, SWCo
Web-site: www.clevedontownafc.co.uk

FOOTBALL MANAGEMENT TEAM

Manager: Steve Fey
Coach: David Mogg Physio: Steve Tregale
Youth Team Manager:Barry Dudbridge

GROUND Ha nd Stadium, Davis Lane, Clevedon email: info@handstadium.co.uk
Fax: 01275 871601 Tel: 01275 871600(ground) 01275 341913 (office)

Directions: M5 Jct 20 - follow signs for Hand Stadium; first left into Central Way (at island just after motorway), 1st left at mini-r'bout into Kenn Rd, 2nd left Davis Lane; ground half mile on right. Or from Bristol(B3130) left into Court Lane (opposite Clevedon Court), turn right after 1mile, ground on left. Nearest BR station: Nailsea & Backwell. Buses from Bristol
Capacity: 3,650 Seats: 300 Cover: 1,600 Floodlights: Yes
Clubhouse: Open every day and evening. Separate function suite & lounge bar.Hot food available. Matchday refreshment bar within ground sells confectionary, teas & hot food
Club Shop: Sells all types of souvenirs, programmes and replica kit. Exchanges welcome. Contact Stev Small **Supporters Club Chairman:** Russell Coneybeare

PREVIOUS
Leagues: Weston & District, Somerset Senior, Bristol Charity, Bristol & District, Bristol Suburban, Western 74-93
Grounds: Dial Hill ('till early 1890's); Teignmouth Road ('till 1991)
Names: Clevedon FC, Ashtonians (clubs merged in 1974)

CLUB RECORDS
Attendance: 1,600 v Bristol City, Friendly. 27/7/98 Ground Record: Bristol Rovers v Ipswich Town 24/7/02
(At Teignmouth Road: 2,300 v Billingham Synthonia, FA Amateur Cup, 52-53)
Win: 18-0 v Dawlish Town (H), Western League Premier Division 24/4/93
Defeat: 13-3 v Yate YMCA (A), Bristol Comb 67-68

BEST SEASON
FA Cup: 3rd Qual. Rd 2nd replay 92-93 v Newport AFC, 2-4 after two 1-1
FA Amateur Cup: 3rd Round Proper, 52-53 **FA Vase:** 6th Round 87-88, v Sudbury Town (A) **FA Trophy:** 2nd Round 98-99

HONOURS Southern League, Midland Division 98-99, Western League 92-93 (R-up 91-92), League Cup (R-up 92-93), Bristol Charity League 37-38,40-41, Somerset Senior Cup 01-02 04-05 28-29 , 00-01,01-02 Somerset Snr League 36-37, Div 1(Res.) 92-93, Bristol & suburbanLeague 25-26,27-28,28-29, Weston & District League: 39-40,43-44,44-45, Somerset Premier Cup;86-87,98-99, 00-01,01-02 Somerset Junior Cup 1897-98,Somerset Medal Competition: 87-88, Clevedon Charity Cup 26-27,30-31.

Players Progressing: Jason Eaton (Bristol City) and Jonathon Gould (Halifax Town)

Back row (L-R): Shaun Penny (asst. manager), Peter Beadle, Rob Scott, Paul Heywood, Graham Cheeseman, Dave Horsman, Peter Trego, Jordan Conti, Greg Dando, Graham Gee, Simon Hill, Jack Pilcher, Mike Regan, Steve Tregale (physio). Front row: Adrian Needs, Lee Vickerman, Tom Jacobs, Leon Hapgood, Chay Harris, Rob Norris, James Springett, Andy McClennon. Photo courtesy of the Independent. Photographer - Bob Bowen.

CORBY TOWN

CLUB OFFICIALS

Chairman: James Kane C.B.E.

President: Vacant

Secretary: Gerry Lucas, 8 Richmond Avenue, Kettering, Northants NN15 5JG

Tel: 01536 513507 (H) 07932 633343 (M)

FOOTBALL MANAGEMENT TEAM

Manager: Lee Glover

Assistant Manager:Rob Dunion

Physio: Rob Earley

Captain: Bobby White

FACT FILE

Formed: 1948

Nickname: The Steelmen

Sponsor:Corus

Colours: White/black/black

Change colours:All Yellow

Midweek matchday: Wednesday

2003-2004

Player of the Year: Steven Julian

Top Scorer: Michael Sneddon

Pages: 32 Price: £1

Editor: David.Tilley (01536 403667)

Local Press: Northampton Evening Telegraph

Local Radio: BBC Radio Northampton, Hereward, Connect F.M.

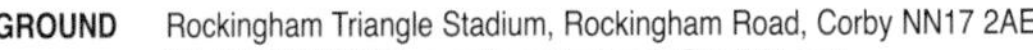

GROUND Rockingham Triangle Stadium, Rockingham Road, Corby NN17 2AE
Tel: 01536 406640 email : corbytownfc@ talk21.com

Directions: On northern outskirts of town at junction of A6003 and A6116,opposite entrance to Rockingham Castle grounds. Nearest Station: Kettering (rail bus to Corby)

Capacity: 3,000 Cover: 1,150 Seats: 960 Floodlights: Yes

Clubhouse: Trackside Bar open matchdays and during the week for hot food etc.

Club Shop: Sells badges, progs etc.(Before & half time) C .Woolmer Tel: 01536 260900

PREVIOUS **Leagues:** United Counties 35-52, Midland 52-58

CLUB RECORDS **Attendance:** 2,240 v Watford, pre-season friendly 86-87
At Old Ground; 10,239 v Peterborough Utd, FA Cup 3rd Qual. Rd 52-53
Win: 14-0 v Gainsborough Trinity, 56-57 **Defeat:** 0-10 v Paget Rangers, 95-96
Career Goalscorer: David Hofbauer 141 (84-95) **Career Appearances:** Derek Walker600 (78-92)
Transfer fee - Paid: £2,700 for Elwyn Roberts (Barnet, 81) **Received:** £20,000 for Matt Murphy (Oxford U. 93)

BEST SEASON **FA Cup:** 3rd Rd 65-66 (lost to Plymouth). 1st Rd on five occasions; 54-55 63-6667-68
League clubs defeated: Luton Town 65-66 **FA Trophy:** 3rd Rd, 1986-87

HONOURS UCL 50-51 51-52 (R-up 37-38), Midland Lg R-up 52-53, Southern Lg Midland Div R-up 90-91 (Merit Cup 63-64 90-91), Northants Snr Cup 6; Maunsell Cup 83-84, Daventry Charity Cup 94-95, Midland Floodlit Cup 74-75, Evans Halshaw F'lit Cup 91-92, Anglia Floodlit Trophy 68-69 72-73, Chelmsford Invitation Cup 63-64 64-65 65-66 (jt), Kettering & Dist Samaritan Cup 60-61(joint) 68-69, Wellingborough Charity Cup 50-51, Desborough Nursing Cup 48-49 50-51 (joint), Bob Cumning Cup 6

Players progressing: A McCabe (Chesterfield 55), L Chalmers (Leicester C. 56), K Brown (Nottm Forest 56), P Kearns (Aldershot 62), N Dean (Southampton 63), H Curran (Millwall 64), D McNeil/A McGowan/G Reilly (Northampton69/75/76), P Chard (Peterborough 79), T Morley (West Ham), J Flower (SheffieldUtd), M Murphy (Oxford Utd 93), C McKenzie (Hereford 94)

Back row, left to right: LIam Carson, Steven Julian, Andrew Brown, Jim Le Masurier, Jamie Hawthorn, Michael Stanton, Liam Harrold and Wayne Spencer.**Front Row:** Michael Sneddon, Richard Lavin, Lee Glover (Manager), Gary Kennedy, Danny Marlow & Scott Marshall **Photo:David Tilley.**

EGHAM TOWN

CLUB OFFICIALS

Chairman: Peter Atkins

Vice Chairmen:

Peter Barnes & Brian Askew

President: Peter Barnes

Press Officer: Secretary

Club Administrator:

Alison Thompson, 138A Thorpe Lea Rd,
Egham, Surrey. TW20 8BL
Tel: 01784 463562

FOOTBALL MANAGEMENT TEAM

Manager:Peter Burdett

Coaches: Alf Coulton Physio: Ken Weaver

FACT FILE

Founded: 1877

Nickname: Sarnies/Town

Colours: Yellow/green/yellow

Change colours: All blue

Midweek Matches: Tuesday

Reserves' League: Suburban

Local Press: Herald & News

Local Radio: County Sound

The Sarnies
Egham Town
Football Club
SPONSORED BY
COURAGE
RYMAN DIVISION 1
SOUTH
Ryman
PROGRAMME SPONSOR
A
ARENA MECHANICAL HANDLING GROUP LTD
OFFICIAL PROGRAMME SEASON 2002-2003

GROUND: Runnymeade Stadium, Tempest Road, Egham, Surrey TW20 8HX
Tel: 01784 435226 Club email: eghamtownfc.co.uk

Directions: M25 jct 13, follow signs to Egham, under M25 at r'bout, left to end, left at mini r'bout, over railway crossing, left to end (Pooley Green Rd), right, Tempest Rd. 2nd right. Bus 41 43 441 from Staines to Pooley Green Rd. 30 mins from Egham or Staines (BR)

Capacity: 5,635 Seats: 335 Cover: 1,120 Floodlights: Yes Club Shop: No

Clubhouse: (01784 435226) 7-11pm daily & weekend lunchtimes. Function hall

PROGRAMME

Pages: 40 Price: £1

Editor: Mark Ferguson

Tel: 01784 210703 (H)

PREVIOUS **Leagues:** Hounslow & District 1896-1914; Surrey Intermediate 19-22; Surrey Senior 22-28 65-67; Spartan 29-33 67-74; Parthenon 64-65; Athenian 74-77

Names: Runnymede Rovers 1877-1905; Egham FC 05-63

Grounds: Anglers Rest 1877-1914; Manorcroft Rd 19-26; Vicarage Rd 26-27 28-39;Green Lane 27-28

RECORD **Attendance:** 1,400 v Wycombe Wanderers, FA Cup 2ndQual Rd 72

Scorer: Mark Butler 50 (91-92) Career record scorer as well **Appearances:** Dave Jones 850+

Win: 10-1 v Camberley, 81-82 **Defeat:** 0-10 v Fisher Ath. (A), Parthenon League 64-65

Transfer Fee Paid: £3,000 for Mark Butler, 1990

Transfer Fee Received: £4,000 for Mark Butler (Wycombe Wanderers, 1988)

BEST SEASON **FA Cup:** 4th Qual Rd 90-91, 0-2 v Telford Utd (A)

HONOURS Isthmian Lg Assoc Members Tphy R-up 91-92; Spartan Lg 71-72 (Lg Cup R-up 67-68); Athenian Lg R-up 75-76 (Div 2 74-75); Surrey Snr Cup R-up 91-92, Surrey Snr Lg 22-23, Lg Charity Cup 22-23 (R-up 26-27 34-35); Surrey Intermediate Lg 20-21, Charity Cup 19-20 20-21 (R-up 26-27); North West Surrey Charity Cup 20-21;
Egham Twinning Tournament 67-68 71-72 74-75 75-76 76-77 80-81; S.Comb. F'lit Cup 77-78 (R-up 83-84).
Promotion to Div 1.

Left to right

Back row:
Gary Duffy
Alan Jordan,
Paul de Luca,
Michael Bolger,
Andy Bugdale and
Jack McKinlay

Front row:
Andy Durbin,
Paul Reed,
Reece White and
Matt Edwards

Grant Eaton is missing

Photo:
Alan Coomes.

EVESHAM UNITED

CLUB OFFICIALS

Chairman: **Jim Cockerton**

Vice Chairman: **Steve Lane**

President: **M E H Davis**

Treasurer: **Dave Wright**

Secretary/Press Officer: Roger Westmacott, 67 Digby Road, Evesham, Worcs. WR11 1BW Tel No: 01386 47849 (H)

FOOTBALL MANAGEMENT TEAM

Manager: David Busst

Asst Manager: Paul West

Physio:Phil Greenway

Captain: Lee Knight

FACT FILE

Formed: 1945 Nickname: The Robins
Sponsors; Dane Valley/Banks's
Colours: Red & white stripes/black/black
Change Colours: All blue
Midweek matches: Tuesday
Reserves' League: No reserve team
Local Press: Evesham Journal,
Worcester Evening News, Gloucester Echo
Local Radio: Classic Gold
BBC Hereford & Worcester, FM102 The Bear

2003-004

Top Scorer Craig Pountney
P.o.Y.: Andy Smith

PROGRAMME

Pages: 58 Price: £1
Editor: Mike Peplow (01684 561770))

EVESHAM UNITED Football Club
OFFICIAL PROGRAMME
SEASON 2003/04
£1.00
MATCH SPONSOR THE QUEMINET PARTNERSHIP North St, Sudbury
MATCHBALL SPONSOR WHITEHEAD ALLOYS Buck St, Middlesbrough
MAIN SPONSOR
Dr Martens Western Division
EVESHAM UNITED v SWINDON SUPERMARINE
Monday 12th April 2004 Kick Off 3.00 pm

GROUND Common Road, Evesham, Worcestershire WR11 4PU Tel: 01386 442303
Directions: From Evesham High Street turn into Oat St, and join one-way system,turn right between Willmotts factory called Conduit Hill into Common Rd, ground 200yds down on right just before railway bridge. 5 minutes walk from Evesham BR station
Capacity: 2,000 Seats: 350 Cover: 600 Floodlights: Yes
Clubhouse: Open matchdays and training nights. Cold food available in club, and hot food from tea hut on matchdays
Club Shop: Contact John Hawkins c/o the club

PREVIOUS **Leagues:** Worcester, Birmingham Combination, Midland Combination 51-55 65-92, West Midlands Regional 55-62
Name: Evesham Town **Ground:** The Crown Meadow (pre-1968)

CLUB RECORDS **Attendance:** 2,338 v West Bromwich A., friendly 18/7/92
Win: 11-3 v West Heath United **Defeat:1-8 v Ilkeston Town**
Career Goalscorer: Sid Brain **Career Appearances:** Rob Candy
Transfer fee paid: £1,500; to Hayes for Colin Day, 1992
Transfer fee received: £5,000 for Simon Brain (to Cheltenham Town)

BEST SEASON **FA Vase:** Quarter Finals 1991-92 **FA Amateur Cup:** Runners-up 1923-24
FA Trophy: 3rd Qual Rd 96-97 **FA Cup:** 2nd Qual Rd 96-97

HONOURS FA Amateur Cup R-up 23-24, Worcestershire Snr Urn(2) 76-78 (R-up 90-91), Midland Comb.(6) 52-53 54-55 65-66 67-69 91-92 Chal. Cup 53-54 87-88 91-92 R-up (5) 54-55 71-72 83-84 88-90, Worcestershire Comb. 52-53 54-55; B'gham Combination R-up 30-31, Evesham Hosp. Cup 89-90, Tony Allden Mem. Cup 1973 19881992

Players progressing: Billy Tucker, Gary Stevens (Cardiff 77), Kevin Rose(Lincoln 78), Andy Preece (Northampton 86), Simon Brain (Hereford, via Cheltenham Town), Billy Turley (Northampton Tn)

Back row, left to right: Lawence O'Shaugnessey (kit man), Linton Bailey, Gavin O'Toole, Iain Langstone, Lee Ross, Tim Clarke, Jermaine Clarke, David Cairns, Marc Burrow, Steve Duncon, Antony Watson and Phil Greenway (physio) **Front row:** Leon Thomas, Danny Williams, Stuart Hamilton, Grant Pinkney, Lee Knight (Captain), Paul West (Assistant Mannager)Andy Smith, Leon Blake, Tobias McIntosh and Simon Fitter. **Photo: The Journal Series**

MANGOTSFIELD UNITED

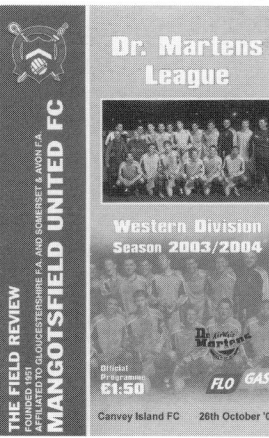

CLUB OFFICIALS

President: Richard Davis

Chairman: Roger Pullin

Vice Chairman: Len Street

Secretary: Steve Porter,40 Colliers Break, Emersons Green, Bristol BS16 7EE

Tel Nos:0117 9873394(H) 0117 9497749 (W)

FOOTBALL MANAGEMENT TEAM

Manager: Martyn Grimshaw

Assistant Manager: Nigel Webb

Captain: Scott Hendy

FACT FILE

Founded: 1950
Nickname: The Field
Sponsors: Flo Cas
Colours: Sky & maroon/maroon/sky
Change colours:White/maroon/maroon
Midweek matchday: Tuesday 7.45
Reserve League: Somerset County

2003-004

Top Scorer: David Seal
Player of the Year:Gary Warren

PROGRAMME

Pages: 32 Price: £1.50
Editor: Bob Smale (0117 9401926)

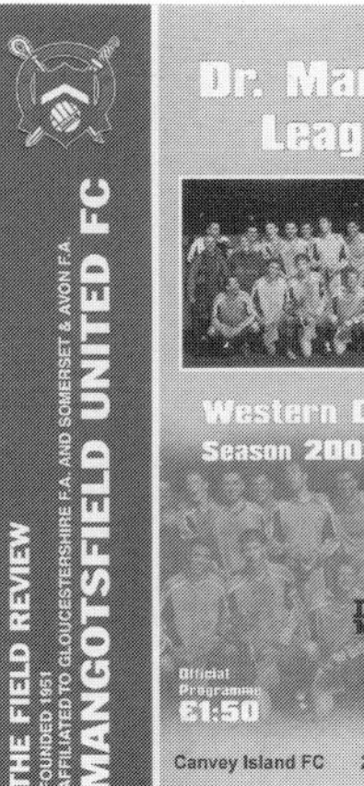

GROUND Cossham Street, Mangotsfield, Bristol BS17 3EW Tel: 0117 956 0119

Directions: M4 jct 19, M32 jct 1; A4174 marked Downend, through lights, over double mini-r'bout to Mangotsfield, left by village church onto B4465 signposted Pucklechurch, ground quarter mile on right. From central Bristol take A432 thru Fishponds, Staple Hill, to Mangotsfield and turn right by village church onto B4465. From Bath/Keynsham follow A4175, right at island at Willsbridge onto A431, then rejoin A4175 at next island (Cherry Garden Hill) to Bridge Yate, straight over double mini-r'bout and take 1st left, right into Carsons Rd after 1 mile and follow to Mangotsfield village & turn right by church onto B4465

Capacity: 2,500 Seats: 300 Cover: 800 Floodlights: Yes

Clubhouse: Open 11-11. Snacks - hot food on matchdays. Lounge bar for functions etc **Club Shop:** Yes

PREVIOUS **Leagues:** Bristol & District 50-67; Avon Premier Combination 67-72; Western League 72-00

RECORD **Attendance:** 2,386 v Bath City, FA Cup 77-78

Goalscorer: John Hill **Appearances:** John Hill 600+

Win: 14-0 v Dawlish (a) 1993 Western League **Defeat:** 3-13 v Bristol City United (Bristol & District Div 1)

& 17-0 v Hanham Sports (Bristol & District League `Div 6)

HONOURS Western Lg 90-91r-up 99-00, Lg Cup 73-74 r-up 86-87, Div 1 r-up 82-83; Somerset Prem. Cup 87-88, r-up 88-89 95-96; Glos Snr Cup 68-69 75-76 02-03; Glos FA Trophy 84-85 86-87 90-91 94-95 96-97; Hungerford Invitation Cup 74-75; Rothmans Nat. Cup r-up 77-78; Hanham Invit. Charity Cup 84-85 85-86; Youth honours: Glos Yth Shield 81-82 84-85 (R-up 82-83); Somerset Floodlit Yth Lg 81-82 82-83 83-84 84-85 87-88 98-99; Somerset Yth Shield 76-77

Reserve honours Somerset Snr Lg (Res.) Div 1 98-99 Div 2 97-98 75-76, Div 3 74-75; Somerset Comb. Cup 74-75

BEST SEASON **FA Vase:** Semi Final 95-96 **FA Cup:** 4th Qualifying Rd Replay v Lewes 0-0 (H) 0-2 (A) 2001-02

Players progress ing: G Megson, S White, G Penrice, P Purnell, N Tanner, M Hooper

(including): Martyn Grimshaw (manager), Bryant, Pendry, Summers, Hendy, Drysdale, Price, Hallett, Lane, Zabec, Loydon, Haines, Shore, Warren, Hobbs, Peart, Seal, Claridge, Davis, Patterson.

Photo courtesy of the Independent. Photographer - Neil Phillips.

MARLOW

FOOTBALL CLUB

Oak Tree Road, Marlow SL7 3ED

Building for the future with

NORTH WEST ESTATES PLC

-pleased to be part of Marlow's future-

Ryman

CLUB OFFICIALS

Chairman: Terry Staines

Secretary: Paul Burdell,
69 Wycombe Rd., Marlow. SL7 3HZ
Tel: 01628 890540

Press Off./Comm. Man.: Terry Staines

FACT FILE

Formed: 1870
Nickname: The Blues
Sponsors: North West Estates
Colours: Royal Blue, white trim/royal/royal
Change colours: All Red
Midweek matchday: Tuesday
Reserves' League: Suburban Premier

FOOTBALL MANAGEMENT TEAM

Manager: Tim Cook
Coach:T.B.A.
Physio: Mark Skoyles

2003-2004

Top Scorer: Yash Romeo
Player of the Year:Keiron Drake

PROGRAMME

Pages: 40 Price: £1
Editor: Terry Staines
Local Press: Bucks Free Press, Maidenhead Advertiser, Evening Post
Local Radio: Radio Berkshire, Thames Valley Radio

GROUND: Alfred Davis Memorial Ground, Oak Tree Road, Marlow SL7 3ED
Tel: 01628 483970 Information Line (normal call rates): 01932 710215

Directions: A404 to Marlow (from M4 or M40), then A4155 towards town centre. Turn right into Maple Rise (by ESSO garage), ground in road opposite (Oak Tree Rd).
1/2 mile from Marlow (BR). 1/4 mile from Chapel Street bus stops

Capacity: 3,000 Cover: 600 Seats: 250 Floodlights: Yes

Clubhouse: Open matchdays & most evenings. Snack bar open matchdays

PREVIOUS: **Leagues:** Reading & Dist.; Spartan 1908-10 28-65; Great Western Suburban;Athenian 65-84
Name: Great Marlow **Grounds:** Crown Ground 1870-1919); Star Meadow 19-24

CLUB RECORDS: **Attendance:** 3,000 v Oxford United, FA Cup 1st Rd 1994.
(Ground - 8,000 SloughT. v Wycombe W., Berks & Bucks Snr Cup Final, 1972)
Goalscorer: Kevin Stone 31
Appearances: Mick McKeown 500+
Fees - Paid: £5,000 for Richard Evans (Sutton Utd. 94)
Received: £8,000 for David Lay from Slought Town 94

BEST SEASON: **FA Cup:** Semi-Finals 1882; 3rd Rd 94-95 (0-2 v Swindon), 92-93 (1-5 v Tottenham);
1st Rd - 19 times -1871-85 86-88 92-93 1991-92 94-95
FA Trophy: 4th Rd 2003-2004 **FA Vase:** 5th Rd replay 74-75, 5th Rd 00-01

HONOURS: Isthmian Lg Div 1 87-88, Div 2 South R-up 86-87, Lg Cup 92-93, Associate Members Trophy: 2000-01; SpartanLg Div 1 37-38 (Div 2 West 29-30); Berks & Bucks Sen Cup (11)

Players progressing: Leo Markham (Watford 1972), NaseemBashir (Reading)

Back row left to right: Jim Melvin (coach) Paul Woodhouse, James Hinchin, Ian McTaggart, John Isaac, Tim Cook (Player-manager) , Stuart English, Seb Neptune, Matthew Rodney, Steve Croxford and Mark Skoyles (Physio). **Front Row:** Mattie Glynn, Simon Teague, Yashwa Romeo, Simon Herbert, Robert Gibson, John Beale (captain), James Pritchard, Jeff Lamb and Micky Floyd.

OXFORD CITY

CLUB OFFICIALS

Chairman:BrianCox
President: T.B.A.
Vice Chairman: Colin Taylor**Press Officer/Secretary:** John Shepperd
20 Howe Close, Wheatley, Oxford OX33 1SS
Tel: 01865 872181 (& Fax)
07748 628911 (M)

FOOTBALL MANAGEMENT TEAM

Manager: Andy Sinnott
Asst Manager:Peter Lamont
Physio: Neil Greig Captain: Martin Brown

FACT FILE

Formed: 1882
Nickname: City
Sponsors: S.M.C.
Colours: Blue & white hoops/blue/blue
Change colours: All Yellow
Midweek Matchday: Tuesday
Reserves Lge: Suburban
Website: oxfordcityfc.co.uk

2003-2004

Captain: Julian Dark
Top Gopalscorer: Colin Simpson
Player of the Year:Andy Ballard

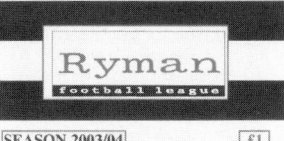

OXFORD CITY
FOOTBALL CLUB
CIVITAS OXONIENSIS
FORTIS EST VERITAS
Founded 1882
Ryman
football league
SEASON 2003/04 £1

PROGRAMME

Pages: 60 Price: £1
Editor: Colin Taylor 07764 386658 (M)
Local Press: Oxford Mail
Local Radio: Radio Oxford FM, Fox FM

GROUND Court Place Farm, Marsh Lane, Marston, Oxford.OX3 0NQ.Tel& Fax: 01865 744493.
Directions: From London M40/A40, ring-road to North, take 1st slip road, follow signs to John Radcliffe hospital and Court Place Farm Stadium, ground on left after leaving flyover. From the north same ring-road.
Capacity: 3,000 Seats: 300 Cover: 400 Floodlights: Yes
Clubhouse: Open matchdays, most refreshments available
Club Shop: Yes, open matchdays, selling souvenirs. Contact Clare Hutchins

PREVIOUS **Leagues:** Isthmian 07-88; South Midlands 90-93
Grounds: The White House 1882-1988; Cuttleslowe Pk 90-91; Pressed Steel,Romanway 91-93

CLUB RECORDS **Attendance:** 9,500 v Leytonstone, FA Amateur Cup 50
Win: 9-0 v Harlow Town, Isthmian League 9/10/76
Defeat: 0-8 v Wycombe Wanderers, Isthmian League - date unknown
Scorer: John Woodley **Appearances:** John Woodley
Fee Paid: £3,000 for S Adams (Woking) **Fee Received:** £17,500 for Howard Forinton (Yeovil T. 1.97)

BEST SEASON **FA Amateur Cup:** Winners 05-06 Runners-up 02-03 12-13 **FA Vase:** Runners-up 94-95
FA Cup: Second Round 69-70, 1-5 v Swansea City (H) **FA Trophy:** 1st Rd Prop 96 v Merthyr Tydfil

HONOURS FA Amateur Cup 05-06 (R-up 02-03 12-13); F.A.Vase R-Up 94-95; Isthmian Lg R-up 34-35 45-46, Div 1 95-96 R-up 77-78 South MidlandsLg 92-93; Oxon Senior Cup - 28 times

Players progressing: A Blakeman (Brentford 46), C Holton (Arsenal 50), K Savin(Derby 50), R Adams (Blackpool 48), A Jeffries (Brentford 49), P James (Luton 49), D Gordon/E Wilcox (WBA 47/48), V Mobley (Sheffield Wed 63), J Varney (Hull 50), P Lee (Hereford 73), H Poole (Port Vale 55), G Parker (Luton 81), M Keown(Arsenal 84), D Meeson (Wolves 52) S.Nelson (Doncaster Rovers) Jermaine McSporran(Wycombe W)

Back L-R Cameron Abbassi, Julian Dark (asst manager), Jermaine Ferreira, Colin Simpson, Jack Smillie, Robert Cruse, Neil Crosby, Robin Antonowicz, Martin Brown, Andy Ballard, Mark Baker, Danny Riley, Neil Greig (physio), Andy Sinnott (manager).
Front L-R Peter Lamont (coach), Chris Harper, Adam Doyle, Neil Champelovier, Steve Benbow, Sam Shepherd, Justin Lee, Andy Prescott, Chris Perkins.

PAULTON ROVERS

President: L.Rogers
Chairmen: David Bissex and Andrew.Chappell
Secretary: Tracy Curtis, 12 Linden Close,Waterford Park, Westfield, Radstock, BA3 3EJ
Tel Nos: 01761 420659 (H) 07760 377302 (M)
email: tracycurtis.2000@tesco.net
Press Officers: Matt Bissex & Tony Walsh

FOOTBALL MANAGEMENT TEAM
Manager: Darren Perrin
Assistamt Manager: Ian Hedges
Coach: Mike Gilgour
Captain: Richard perry
Physio: Bob Stokes & Dave Tyrrell

FACT FILE
Founded: 1881
Nickname: Rovers
Sponsors: Barons Property Centre/Bass Breweries
Colours: White & maroon/maroon/maroon
Change colours: Yellow/navy/navy
Midweek matches: Monday
Reserves' League: Somerset Snr

Website: www.paultonroversafc.co.uk

2003-2004
Top Goalscorer Graham Colnourne
Player of the Year: Scott Woodman

Programme: 20 pages, £1.00
Editor: D Bissex (01761 412463)
Local Press: Bath Evening Chronicle, Bristol Evening Post, Western Daily Press Somerset Guardian

GROUND: Athletic Ground,Winterfield Road, Paulton, SomersetBS397RF. Tel No: 01761 412907
Directions :From A39 at Farrington Gurney,follow A 362 marked Radstock for two miles. Turn left at roundabout, take B3355 to Paulton and ground is on right.
Capacity: 5,000 **Seats**: 253 **Cover** 2,500 **Floodlights** :Yes
Clubhouse:Three bars, lounge, skittle alley and dance hall with catering faciliies (available for hire). Capacity 300.
Club Shop: Contact Chairman: 07793 908616 (M)

HONOURS: Western League Premier Runners-Up: 2003-04, Div 2 R-Up: 1900-01 Somerset Senior Cup:(12) Somerset Senior League (70 Somerset Flodlit Yoputh League 96-97.
PREVIOUS Leagues: Wiltshire Premier and Somerset Senior
Grounds: Chapel Field, Cricket Ground and Recreation Ground 1946-48
RECORD Attendance: 2,000 v CRewe Alexandra F.A.Cup 1906-07
Appearances: Sreve Tovey
Goalscorer: Graham Colbourne

Back row (L-R): Steve Casey, Simon Ford, Alex Brain, Graham Colbourne, Nathan Brown, Krtis Sage, Andrew Catley.
Front row: Chris Lewis, Ross Padfield, Steve Bridges, Kye Palmer, Steve Tovey, Danny Allen.
Photo courtesy of the Independent. Photographer - Philip Waite.

ROTHWELL TOWN

CLUB OFFICIALS

Chairman: **Keith Johnson**
President: **Ken Cheney**
Secretary: **Roger Barratt**
18 Norton St., Rothwell, Northants NN14 2DE
Tel: 01536 507744
Press Officer : **Mark Southon**
Tel: 07870 551428

FOOTBALL MANAGEMENT TEAM
Manager: D.Williams
Physio: Bob Bramah

FACT FILE
Founded: 1895
Nickname: The Bones
Sponsors:Springfir Country Homes
Colours: Blue & black with white /blue/blue
Change : Red, black & white trim, black/red
Midweek matchday: Tuesday
Newsline: 0930 555 829
Reserves' League: Utd Counties Res Div

Rothwell Town
Football Club
Matchday Programme £1.00

Dorchester Town

Pages: 48 Price: £1.00
Prog Ed:David Rudkin 01536 711976

Local Press: Northants Evening Telegraph, Chronicle & Echo, Herald & Post
Local Radio: BBC Radio Northants, KCBC

GROUND **Home Close,** Cecil Street, Rothwell, Northants NN14 2EZ Tel: 01536 710694
Directions: A14/A6 to Rothwell. At town centre r'about turn into BridgeStreet (right if north-bound, left if southbound), take 3rd left into TreshamStreet, ground is at top on left.
3 miles from Kettering (BR); Rothwell is served by Kettering to Market Harborough buses
Capacity: 3,500 Seats: 264 Cover: 1,264 Floodlights: Yes
Clubhouse: Rowellian Social Club, open every evening and weekend lunchtimes.Crisps and rolls available on matchdays (hot food and drinks available in ground). `Top of the Town Ballroom', lounge seats 200
Club Shop: Sells various souvenirs incl. metal badges.

PREVIOUS **Leagues:** Northants 1896-1911 21-33, Kettering Amateur 11-21 33-48, Leics.Senior 48-50, United Counties 50-56 61-94, Central Alliance 56-61 **Grounds:** Harrington Rd, Castle Hill **Name:** Rothwell Town Swifts

CLUB RECORDS **Attendance:** 2,508 v Irthlingborough Diamonds, United Counties League 1971
Win: 17-0 v Stamford, FA Cup Preliminary Round replay 1927
Defeat: 1-10 v Coalville Town, Leicestershire Sen Lge 1949
Transfer fee paid: Undisclosed for Andy Wright (Aylesbury 1992)
Transfer fee received: Undisclosed for Matty Watts (Charlton 1990)

BEST SEASON **FA Cup:** Fourth Qualifying Round 99-00
FA Trophy: Second Round Proper 94-95 **FA Vase:** Fifth Round 92-93 (1-2 v Bridlington Town)

HONOURS Northants Lg1899-1900 (R-up 1895-96 96-97 97-98), Northants Snr Cup 1899-1900 23-24 59-60 88-89 95-96 01-02 (R-up 24-25 71-72 87-88), United Counties Lg 92-93 94-95 (R-up 69-70 70-71 87-88 89-90 90-91), KO Cup 55-56 70-71 71-72 91-92 92-93 (R-up 77-78 79-80 82-83), Div 2 52-53 53-54, Div 2Cup 52-53 53-54, Benevolent Cup 92-93 94-95 (R-up 89-90 90-91) Southern League Mid Div R-up 96-97

Players progressing: Lee Glover (Nottingham Forest) 1987, Matty Watts (CharltonAth.) 1990, Mathew Lawrence (Wycombe Wanderers) and Chris McKenzie (Leyton Orient)

Back row, left to right: Danny Potter, Carl Lake, Reece Lester, Kevin Brooks, Danny Spencer, Paul Rice, John Hughes.

Front Row: Martin Flanagan, Lee Quincy, Jonathan Mitchell, Joe Hanney.

Photo: Alan Coomes

STOURPORT SWIFTS

CLUB OFFICIALS

Chairman: Chris Reynolds

President: Roy Crowe

General Manager: John McDonald

Secretary & Matchday Contact
John McDonald
65 Princess Way, Stourport
Worcs. DY13 0EL
Tel: 01299 82088

FOOTBALL MANAGEMENT TEAM

Manager: Dave Titterton

Asst Manager/Coach: Kevin Sweeney

Physio: T.B.A. Captain: Steve Ulfig

FACT FILE

Founded: 1882 Nickname: Swifts

Sponsors: Reynolds of Rushock

Colours: All Yelow

Change colours: All WhiteMidweek match-day: Tuesday

Website: www.fly.to/swifts

2003-004

Top Scorer: Richard Ball

Players of the Year: Craig Webb

PROGRAMME

68 pages £1.50

Editor: Leighton Jones

email: swifts-fanzine@yahoo.co.uk

GROUND Walshes Meadow, Harold Davis Drive, Stourport-on-Severn.
Tel: 01299 825188

Directions: Follow one-way system through Stourport sign posted Sports Centre.Go over River Severn Bridge, turn left into Harold Davies Drive. Ground is at rear of Sports Centre. Nearest rail station is Kidderminster.

Capacity: 2,000 Seats: 250 Cover: 150 Floodlights: Yes

Clubhouse: Open matchdays. Hot snacks available. Licensed bar. **Club Shop:** No

PREVIOUS **Leagues:** Kidderminster/ Worcester/ West Midland Regional, Midland Football Alliance 1998-2001
Grounds: Bewdley Rd; Moor Hall Park; Feathers Farm; Olive Grove; Hawthorns.

RECORDS **Attendancee:** 4,000 v Birmingham, charity match.
Goalscorer: Gary Crowther **Appearances:** Ian Johnson
Win: 10-0 **Defeat:** 1-7

BEST SEASON **FA Cup:** 3rd Q Rd 2001-02 **F.A.Vase:** 6th Rd 20001 **FA Trophy:** 2nd Rd.

HONOURS West Mids Prem Div R-Up 94-95 96-97 97-98, Lg Div 1 R-up 87-88, Prem Div Cup 92-93, Div 2 Cup R-up 82-83; Worcs Snr Urn 92-93 93-94 94-95 97-98 Worcs Infirmary Cup 94-95 95-96 97-98; MFA 2000-01

Included in the team photo are : O'Malley, Mark Jones, Small, Webb, Powell, Shirley, Lloyd, Hayward, Crisp, Willetts, Checketts, Green, Childs, A.Jones, Atkinson, Dave Titterton (Manager), and Kevin Sweeney (Assistant Manager). **Photo: Keith Clayton**

SUTTON COLDFIELD TOWN

CLUB OFFICIALS

Chairman: Tom Keogh

Secretary: The Rev Ken Hawkins
70 Holifast Rd.,Wylde Greem
West Midlands B721AE
Tel: 01213501630(H) 07812 771365(M)

FOOTBALL MANAGEMENT TEAM

Manager: Chris Keogh

Asst Man: Brian Kenning

Physio: Ed Judge

FACT FILE

Formed: 1897
Nickname: Royals
Colours: All Blue
Change colours: All Yelow
Midweek matchday: MondayFeeder Team:
Sutton Town(Mid Comb)
Local Press:
Sutton Coldfield News, Sutton Observer
Local Radio: BRMB, Radio WM

PROGRAMME

Pages: 28 Price: £1.20
Editor:Terry Coley 0121 240 4521 (H)

GROUND Central Ground, Coles Lane, Sutton Coldfield B72 1NL
Fax/Tel: 0121 354 2997 or 0121 355 5475 email: alan.fleming1@btinternet.com

Directions: A5127 into Sutton, right at Odeon cinema (Holland Rd), then first right into Coles Lane - ground 150 yds on left. 10 mins walk from SuttonColdfield (BR), bus 104 from Birmingham

Capacity: 4,500 Cover: 500 Seats: 200 Floodlights: Yes

Clubhouse: Brick built lounge & concert room, fully carpeted and extensively decorated Open daily, food available

Club Shop: Selling metal badges, scarves, hats, pens, rosettes, progs. Contact: Bill Portman

PREVIOUS
Leagues: Central Birmingham, Walsall Sen., Staffs Co., BirminghamComb. 50-54, West Mids (Regional) 54-65 79-82, Midlands Comb. 65-79
Name: Sutton Coldfield FC 1879-1921
Grounds: Meadow Plat 1879-89/ Coles Lane (site of current ambulance station) 90-1919

CLUB RECORDS
Attendance: 2,029 v Doncaster Rovers, F.A. Cup 80-81 (Receipts £2,727)
Career Goalscorer: Eddie Hewitt 288
Career Appearances: Andy Ling 550
Fee paid: £1,500 twice in 1991, for Lance Morrison (Gloucester) , Micky Clarke(Burton A.) and Steve Farmer (Atherstone U)
Fee received: £25,000 for Barry Cowdrill (WBA 1979)

BEST SEASON
FA Cup: 1st Rd 80-81, 0-1 v Doncaster R (H), 92-93, 1-2 v BoltonWanderers (A)
FA Trophy: 1st Round replay 1989-90
FA Amateur Cup: 2nd Round 1970-71

HONOURS Southern Lg Midland Div R-up 82-83, West Mids Lg 79-80 (Lg Cup 80-81 81-82), Midland Comb.(2) 77-79 (R-up(2) 69-71, Lg Cup 69-70), Walsall Senior Lg 46-47, Walsall Sen. Cup(3) 77-80 (R-up 80-81), Staffs Sen. Cup R-up 89-90, Lord Mayor of Birmingham Charity Cup 95-96, R-up 93-94, Worcs Sen. Cup SF 88-89, Walsall Challenge Cup R-up 46-47 47-48, Sutton Charity Cup 46-47 65-66 71-72 86-87 89-90 90-91, Express & Star Cup 44-45 Dr Martens Cup 98-99

Players progressing: Arthur Corbett (Walsall 49), Paul Cooper (Manchester C.), Noel Blake (Leeds), Steve Cooper (Barnsley), Peter Latchford (WBA), Mark Smith (Wolves), John Barton (Everton), Barry Cowdrill (WBA 79),Colin Dryhurst (Halifax 79), Dale Belford (Notts Co. 87), Ellis Laight (Torquay 92)

Back Row,left to right: R. Richardson (Coach),K. Murragh, C.Ferguson, D. Massingham, M.Gray, S.Farmer, E. Ejiofor, D.Baker, J. Bray, B. Burns, W. Dyer, K. Jones, D.Shaw and E.Judge (physio) **Front Row:** K.Thompson, L.B ailey, D. Burrows, A. Ling, C. Keogh (Manager), B. Kenning (Assistant Manager),S. Tucker, M. Smioz, M. Gardiner, S. Randall and A. Hughes

SWINDON SUPERMARINE

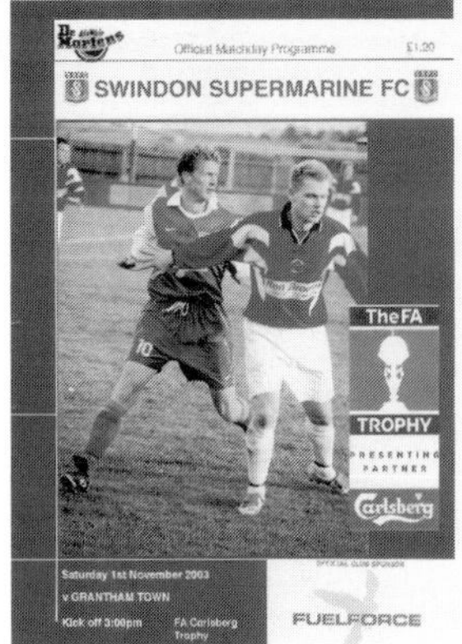

CLUB OFFICIALS

Chairman: Mick Parsons

President: Cliff Puffett

Secretary: Judi Moore,
Chardon Rise, Bell Lane,
Liddington,Swindon, SN4 0HH
Tel: 01793 828778

Press Officer: Leigh Moore
01793 790685

FOOTBALL MANAGEMENT TEAM

Manager: Mark Collier

Physio: Wayne Roberts

FACT FILE

Founded: 1992
Nickname: 'Marine'
Sponsors: Fuelforce
Colours: Blue & white hoops/blue/blue
Change colours: Red & White/Red/Red
Midweek Matchday: Tuesday

PROGRAMME

Pages: 40 Price: £1.00
Editor: Keith Yeomans
Tel: 07721 885728 01793 487461

GROUND Hunts Copse, South Marston, Swindon
Tel: 01793 828778. E-mail: supermarinefc@aol.com.

Directions: On A361 Swindon/Highworth road, adjoining South Marston Ind. Estate. Six miles from Swindon (BR) - buses in direction of Highworth, Fairford & Lechdale. If lost ask for Honda.

Capacity: 3,000 Seats: 300 Cover: 300 Floodlights: Yes

Club Shop: Opening this season - contact Andy Garrett **Clubhouse:** Yes

PREVIOUS **Leagues:** Wiltshire Lge., Hellenic League to 2001
Names: Vickers Armstrong 46-81,Supermarine 82-91 (merged 1992), Penhill Youth Centre 70-84, Swindon Athletic 84-89 (merged)
Ground: Supermarine: Vickers Airfield (until mid-1960s); Swindon Ath.: Merton 70-84; `Southbrook', Pinehurst Road 84-92

RECORD **Attendance:** 1,550 v Aston Villa

HONOURS: Hellenic Lge - Premier Div. 97-98, 00-01, R-up 95-96 98-99; Div. One 85-86 86-87; Reserve Section 96-97; Lge Cup 96-97,99-00; Floodlit Cup 97-98.,99-00, 00-01. Wiltshire Senior Cup 82-83, 86-87, 89-90. Wilts Premier Shield 96-97.Wilts Youth Cup 01-02, Hellenic Challenge Cup 96-97, 99/00.

Back row (L-R): Alan Young, Dave Gee, Russell Jones, Tom King, Dean Miles, Marc Jones, Simon Futcher, Steve Bennet, Sam Collier. **Front row:** Ryan Jones, Steve Jenkins, James Hambridge, Giles Harris (Capt), Mark Collier (manager), Chris Copp, Matty Goodwin, Tony Joyce. Photo courtesy of the Independent.

TAUNTON TOWN

CLUB OFFICIALS

Chairman: T F Harris

Secretary & Press Officer:
Martin Dongworth
c/o the club
Tel: 01823 322850 (H)

FOOTBALL MANAGEMENT TEAM
Manager: Russell Musker
Asst. Man: David Mogg
Captain: Alex Watson
Physio: Graham Webster

FACT FILE
Formed: 1947 Nickname: Peacocks
Club Sponsors: T.G.Roofing
Colours: All Sky Blue
Change colours: All Gold
Midweek matches: Wednesday
Reserves ' League: None
Local Radio: Orchard FM, Radio Bristol
Local Press: Somerset County Gazette

PROGRAMME
Pages: 48 Price: £1
Editor: Martin Dongworth
T.B.A.Newsline: 09066 555 849

2003-2004
Player of the Year & Top Scorer:
Antony Lynch

Ground: Wordsworth Drive, Taunton, Somerset TA1 2HG Tel: 01823 278191
Directions: Leave M5 Jct 25, follow signs to town centre, at 2nd set of lights turn left into Wordsworth Drive; ground on left. 25 mins walk from Taunton (BR); turn left out of station and follow road right through town centre bearing left into East Reach. Follow road down and turn right into Wordsworth Drive shortly after Victoria pub
Capacity: 4,000 Seats:400 Cover: 1,000 Floodlights: Yes
Clubhouse: Social club to accommodate 300, full bar facilities. Separate bar & hall for private functions
Club Shop: Yes

PREVIOUS
Leagues: Western 54-77; Southern 77-83, Western 83-2002
Grounds: Several prior to 1953

CLUB RECORDS
Attendance: 3,284 v Tiverton Town, **FA Vase:** Winners 00-01
Appearances: Tony Payne **Scorer** (in a season) : Reg Oram 67
Win: 12-0 v Dawlish Town (A), FA Cup Prel. Rd, 28/8/93
Defeat: 0-8 v Cheltenham Town (A), FA Cup 2nd Qual. Rd, 28/9/91

BEST SEASON
FA Cup: 1st Rd Proper 81-82, 1-2 v Swindon T. (A)
FA Trophy: 1st Rd Proper 80-81, 1-5 v Hendon at Q.P.R
FA Vase: Winners 00-01, R-up 93-94, S-F 97-98 98-99

HONOURS
FA Vase Winners 00-01 R-up 93-94, Western Lge Champions 68-69 89-90,95-6,98-9,99-00, 00-01 (R-up 93-94 97-98, Les Phillips R-up 93-94 97-98, Alan Young Cup 73-74 75-76 (jt with Falmouth), Charity Chall. Cup 49-50, 50-51), Somerset Snr Lg 52-53, Som Prem.Cup R-up 82-83 89-90 92-93 98-99

Players progressing: Charlie Rutter (Cardiff), Stuart Brace (Southend), Steve Winter (Torquay) Kevin Maloy (Exeter C.)

Back row (L-R): Nick Skinner, Martin Douglas, Mark Forrester, Jason Heath, Gary Fisher, Eubio Rosario, Alex Watson, Kenny Griffiths, Dale Peckham, Danny Harris, David Heath, Simon Lyons, Leandro Naldoni.
Front row: Paul Chenoweth, Steve Campbell, Gary Phell, Andy Neal, Leigh White, James Hughes, Jason Wood, Mark Smith, Matt Rawlings. Photo courtesy of the Independent. Photographer - Ian Beech.

THAME UNITED

CLUB OFFICIALS

Chairman: Jim Tite

Vice Chairman: Bernard Wakelin

Secretary: Fred Saulsbury, 86 Station Road, Chinnor,Oxon. OX39 4HA Tel No: 01844 351073

FOOTBALL MANAGEMENT TEAM

Manager:Mark West
Assistant Manager: Brett Chowns
Captain: James Saulsbury

FACT FILE

Founded: 1883
Sponsors:T.B.A.
Nickname: United
Colours: Red & black/black/red & black.
Change colours: Green & white
Midweek Matchday: Tuesday
Reserves' League: Suburban

2003-2004

Top Scorer: John Mitchell
Player of the Year: Andy Williams

Thame United FC
at Windmill Road
Ryman
Tarmac

Pages: 24 Price: £1
Editor: Wendy Garrad 01844 213017 (W)
Local Press: Oxford Mail, Thame Gazette, Bucks Free Press
Local Radio: Radio Oxford, Fox FM, Mix 96

GROUND: Windmill Road, Thame, Oxon OX9 2DR (01844 213017)
Club Website: www.thameunitedfc.co.uk

Directions: Into Nelson Street from Market Square. 3 miles from Haddenham &Thame Parkway (BR). Nearest bus stop at Town Hall (half mile away)

Capacity: 3,600 Seats: 284 Cover: 850 Floodlights: Yes

Clubhouse: Open every evening and weekend lunch times **Club Shop:** No -
Banqueting facilities for 200 (weddings, dinners, dances etc)

PREVIOUS **Leagues:** Oxon Senior; Hellenic 1959-87; South Midlands 1987-91, Isthmian 1991-2004
Name: Thame FC **Ground:** None

CLUB RECORDS **Attendance:** 1,035 v Aldershot, Isthmian Div 2 4/4/94
Win:11-3 v Barton Rovers 16/09/01 **Defeat:** 2-11 v Hungerford, FA Cup Prelim. Rd 1984
Career Goalscorer: Not known **Career Appearances:** Steve Mayhew

BEST SEASON **FA Cup:** Third Qualifying Round 91-92, 0-4 v Salisbury
FA Vase: Semi Final 1998/99

HONOURS Isthmian Lg Div 2 94-95, Div 2 R-up 98-99 Div 3 R-up 92-93; Hellenic Lg 61-62 69-70, Premier Div Cup (4); Sth Mids Lg 90-91; Oxon Snr Cup 1894-95 05-06 08-09 09-10 75-76 80-81 92-93;00-01,01-02. Oxon Interm Cup 76-77 78-79 91-92,99-00 02-03; Oxon Charity Cup

Players progressing to the Football League: None

Back row, left to right: Andy Williams, Tony Joyce, Steve Smith, Alex Stewart, Mark Avery.

Front Row: Nando Perna, Justin Merritt, James Saulsbury (Capt.), Jon Gardner, Mark Jones, John Mitchell.

Photo: Arthur Evans

YATE TOWN

YATE TOWN
Football Club
Dr. Martens's Southern Football League
Western Division
2003-04
Main Club Sponsor
THE ERH GROUP
E.R. Hemmings (Building) Ltd.
ERH Communications Ltd.
A B Johnson
Official Programme
£1.00

CLUB OFFICIALS

Chairman: Peter Jackson

President: Roger Hawkins

Secretary: Terry Tansley
1 Tyning Close, Yate, Bristol. BS37 5PN
Tel: 01454 324305

Press Officer: Secretary

FOOTBALL MANAGEMENT TEAM

Manager : Richard Thompson

Physio: Steve Carter

FACT FILE

Formed: 1946
Nickname: The Bluebells
Colours: White/navy/white
Change colours: All Yellow
Midweek matchday: Tuesday
Reserve Team's League: Glos County Lg
Website: www.yatetownfc.com

2003-2004

Captain: Ben Trotman
Top Scorer: Matt Rawlings 18
Player of the Year: Dave Elsey

PROGRAMME

Pages: 40 Price: £1
Editor: Terry Tansley c/o Club

GROUND Lodge Road, Yate, Bristol BS37 7LE Tel: 01454 228103

Directions: M4 jct 18, A46 towards Stroud, then A432 to Yate. Turn right into Green Goose Way. at 1st R'bout into link road and Yate shopping centre. Turn right at third main traffic lights into North Road. 1st left into lodge Road. Five miles from Bristol Parkway BR main line station, half mile from Yate BR station. Buses 329, X68 and 328

Capacity: 2,000 Cover: 400 Seats: 236 Floodlights: Yes

Clubhouse: Open every night & weekend lunchtimes. Skittles, darts, pool, live entertainment

Club Shop: Selling programmes & usual souvenirs. Contact: Secretary

PREVIOUS **Leagues:** Gloucestershire County 68-83; Hellenic 83-89, 00-03; Southern Lge 89-00
Name: Yate YMCA 1946-70 **Grounds:** Yate Aerodrome 50-54, Newmans Field 54-60, Sunnyside Lane 60-84

CLUB RECORDS **Attendance:** 2,000 for Bristol Rovers v Bristol Rovers Past, Vaughan Jones testimonial 90
Win: 13-3 v Clevedon, Bristol Premier Comb 67-68
CareerGoalscorer: Kevin Thaws **Career Appearances:** Gary Hewlett
Transfer fee - Paid: £2,000 to Chippenham Town for Matt Rawlings(2003) **BEST SEASON FA Vase:** Fifth Round 1991-92

HONOURS Hellenic Lg (x2) 87-89 Premier R-up 02-03 Lg Cup Winners 02-03 Div 1 R-up 84-85, Lg Skol Cup R-up 87-88), Glos Chall. Trophy 88-89, 00-01 (R-up x2), Glos Snr Amtr Cup Sth 77-78 91-92 (res) 92-93 (res), Glos Snr Chal. Cup (Nth) R-up 89-90 92-93 94-95, Stroud Charity Cup R-up 74-75 81-82 84-85 (Sect. A Winners(6) 76-78 79-80 82-83 87-89), Berkeley Hosp. Prem.Cup(3) 73-75 80-81, S.W. Co's Sutton Vase 85-86 Dr.Martens Fairplay award 98-99, 99-00

Players Progressing:
Richard Thompson (Newport Co.), Phil Purnell (Bristol R.), Darren Tilley (York C.), Steve Winter (Walsall), Mike Davis (Bristol R. 93)

Back Row (L-R): Lee Barless (Asst. Manager), Mike Wyatt, Phil Ward, Dave Lee (transfered to Mangotsfield), Darren Hobbs, Richard Thompson (Manager), Tony Court, Tony Bennett, Nick Brooks, Paul Metheringham, Steve Carter (Physio). **Front Row:** Marc Hughes, Kevin Coles, Andy Neal, Dave Bright (transfered to Bath City), Mark Smith, Gary Powell, Dave Elsey, Leigh Williams (transfered to Brislington).

SOUTHERN LEAGUE DIVISION ONE EAST
STEP 4

FINAL LEAGUE TABLE 2003-04

EASTERN DIVISION		P	W	D	L	F	A	Pts
1.	King's Lynn	42	28	7	7	90	35	91
2.	Histon	42	26	10	6	96	41	88
3.	Tonbridge Angels	42	27	7	8	82	46	88
4.	Eastleigh (-3 pts)	42	27	4	11	88	40	82
5.	Folkestone Invicta	42	20	15	7	91	45	75
6.	Salisbury City	42	21	11	10	73	45	74
7.	Stamford	42	20	11	11	63	45	71
8.	Banbury United*	42	19	10	13	65	57	67
9.	Burgess Hill Town	42	19	7	16	67	54	64
10.	Sittingbourne	42	18	8	16	61	55	62
11.	Bashley	42	18	7	17	66	58	61
12.	Ashford Town	42	15	9	18	51	53	54
13.	Chatham Town	42	13	10	19	49	67	49
14.	Fisher Athletic	42	13	10	19	61	81	49
15.	Corby Town	42	12	9	21	44	75	45
16.	Dartford	42	13	6	23	48	81	45
17.	Burnham (-3 pts)	42	12	11	19	52	76	44
18.	Hastings United	42	12	7	23	60	91	43
19.	Newport IoW	42	11	7	24	42	69	40
20.	Rothwell Town	42	9	11	22	30	47	38
21.	Erith & Belvedere	42	7	10	25	45	84	31
22.	Fleet Town	42	5	7	30	35	114	22

*Promoted to Southern Premier Division via play-off match.

TOP GOALSCORERS - LEAGUE & LEAGUE CUP

Player	Club	Goals
Paul Sales	Eastleigh	29
Nicholas Sullivan	Burgess Hill	23
Kevin Byrne	Stamford	22
Neil Kennedy	Histon	22
James Dryden	Folkestone Invicta	22
Steven Harper	Burgess Hill Town	21
David Staff	King's Lynn	20
Matthew Tubbs	Salisbury City	19
Carl Holmes	King's Lynn	18
George Redknap	(Banbury United)	18
Akpol Sodje	Erith & Belvedere	18
Richard Brady	Fisher Athletic	17
Brendan Cass	Tonbridge Angels	17
Carl Rook	Hastings United	16
Nicholas Banger	Eastleigh	15
Hamid Barr	Fisher Athletic	15
Joby Thorogood	Ashford Town	15
Adrian Cambridge	Histon	14
Shaun Hales	Fleet Town	14
Tostao Kwashi	Dartford	14

	EASTERN DIVISION 03-04	1	2	3	4	5	6	7	8	9	10	11	12	13	14	15	16	17	18	19	20	21	22
1	Ashford Town		1-1	2-1	2-2	1-2	1-1	2-1	2-1	0-1	1-1	0-2	1-1	2-1	3-1	1-2	3-1	1-0	0-0	0-2	1-2	1-0	0-2
2	Banbury United	1-0		1-0	4-1	1-1	3-1	4-0	1-1	1-2	2-1	3-0	1-0	4-3	1-0	0-4	0-3	2-1	1-0	0-1	3-1	1-0	1-3
3	Bashley	1-0	1-1		1-0	1-1	2-2	3-2	3-3	4-1	2-0	2-0	7-0	3-0	5-0	0-3	1-2	0-2	0-1	2-4	0-1	0-0	0-6
4	Burgess Hill Town	1-0	2-1	1-2		0-1	0-2	5-2	0-1	5-2	3-1	4-1	3-0	2-2	6-2	0-1	0-3	1-1	0-0	1-0	2-0	2-1	0-1
5	Burnham	2-2	0-4	0-1	1-2		0-2	1-1	0-3	1-2	2-2	2-2	3-0	0-4	3-1	0-2	0-3	4-3	2-0	2-1	2-5	0-4	1-2
6	Chatham Town	1-1	0-1	3-1	0-3	1-1		3-2	3-0	1-2	3-2	0-3	0-0	0-3	0-1	0-1	1-0	2-1	0-2	2-3	1-1	2-2	0-1
7	Corby Town	0-5	0-2	1-0	2-3	1-1	2-1		3-0	1-0	2-1	1-0	2-2	0-4	2-3	3-3	2-1	0-1	0-0	2-1	0-4	3-1	1-2
8	Dartford	0-2	2-2	1-3	2-1	2-1	1-1	0-1		1-5	1-3	3-1	3-0	1-6	3-0	0-5	1-0	2-0	2-0	0-3	1-0	0-1	2-3
9	Eastleigh	1-2	6-1	3-1	4-0	3-0	2-0	4-1	5-0		5-1	3-1	3-0	2-1	6-2	0-2	0-0	2-1	1-0	1-2	1-2	0-1	0-0
10	Erith & Belvedere	0-2	2-1	1-3	1-1	0-3	2-1	0-0	2-0	1-2		4-1	3-4	0-4	1-1	0-3	0-5	3-0	0-2	0-3	1-1	1-2	1-3
11	Fisher Athletic	1-2	1-2	3-1	1-3	1-0	1-0	2-0	2-1	2-1	1-1		1-2	1-1	2-2	2-1	0-2	0-3	0-0	2-1	1-4	1-4	3-7
12	Fleet Town	1-1	1-1	1-5	0-3	0-2	1-2	1-0	0-0	0-3	0-3	2-5		2-6	3-0	2-5	0-1	1-1	1-3	1-5	0-3	0-4	1-2
13	Folkestone Invicta	3-1	3-2	1-2	2-1	1-1	5-1	0-0	1-0	1-2	0-0	3-0	6-1		2-0	1-1	2-2	3-0	0-0	2-2	1-0	2-2	1-1
14	Hastings United	2-0	1-0	1-1	1-2	2-2	1-2	3-1	0-3	0-1	4-0	4-4	4-1	1-2		1-4	0-2	0-2	1-0	1-4	2-2	3-0	1-5
15	Histon	0-2	2-2	1-1	2-0	6-1	2-1	3-0	6-0	1-0	1-1	2-0	5-1	2-2	1-2		1-4	6-1	2-1	2-1	2-1	0-0	1-1
16	King's Lynn	1-0	4-1	1-0	2-1	1-2	6-0	2-0	4-1	1-1	1-0	2-2	4-1	1-1	4-2	1-0		4-0	1-0	0-2	5-2	3-1	4-1
17	Newport IOW	3-2	0-4	0-2	1-1	1-0	1-2	0-1	3-0	0-3	3-1	2-2	2-1	0-3	1-2	1-1	0-0		0-2	1-1	1-2	2-0	2-0
18	Rothwell Town	2-0	1-0	0-1	2-2	0-1	0-2	0-1	2-2	0-1	1-1	0-3	0-1	1-4	2-3	1-2	1-1	2-0		0-2	0-0	0-2	0-1
19	Salisbury Town	2-1	1-1	5-1	0-1	1-1	1-1	2-0	3-1	0-4	3-0	2-1	1-0	1-1	3-2	0-0	0-3	2-0	1-1		3-0	1-1	1-1
20	Sittingbourne	1-2	0-0	2-0	0-2	4-1	0-0	4-2	1-3	1-0	3-1	0-1	3-1	2-1	2-2	1-3	1-2	1-0	0-3	1-0		0-0	0-2
21	Stamford	4-1	3-3	1-0	1-0	2-1	5-3	0-0	1-0	1-1	2-1	2-2	5-0	0-0	1-0	1-2	2-3	1-0	1-0	2-0	1-0		1-3
22	Tonbridge Angels	1-0	3-0	0-2	1-0	1-3	0-1	1-1	1-0	0-2	2-1	2-2	2-1	1-2	2-1	4-3	2-0	2-1	4-0	2-2	1-3	3-0	

ARLESEY TOWN

CLUB OFFICIALS

Chairman: Bryan Ellis (01462 682612)
Vice-Chairman: Chris Albon (01462 628565)
President: Maurice Crouch
Secretary: Keitgh Broughton
9 Davis Row,Arlesey , Beds. SG15 6RB
Email: secretary@arleseytown.co.uk

FOOTBALL MANAGEMENT TEAM

Manager: Nicky Ironton
Asst Man:Keith Barrett Coach:Andy Theodosiou Physio: Eric Turner

FACT FILE

Founded: 1891
Nickname: The Two Blues
Colours: Sky & navy quarters/navy/navy
Change Colours: All white.
Midweek matchday: Tuesday
Reserves' Lge: S. Midlands Lge Res Div 1
Club Website: www.arleseyfc.co.uk

2002-2003

Captain: Stuart Beevor
P.o.Ys.: Steve Magona,Dean Harding & Martyn Patching
Top Scorers:
Marvin Samuel & Wayne Cort

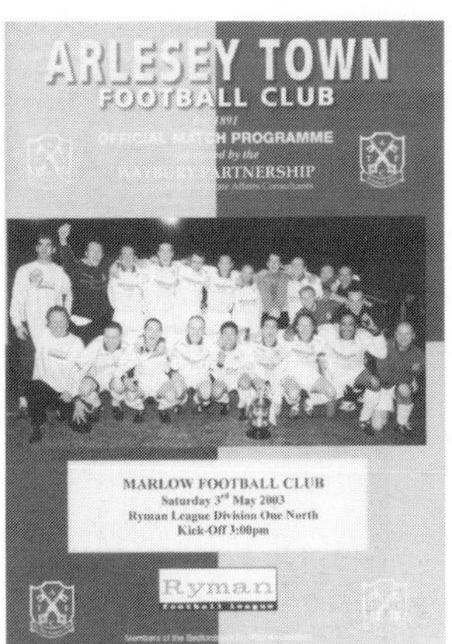

PROGRAMME

Price: £1.00
Editor: Pete Brennan (01462 834455)

GROUND: Hitchin Rd, Arlesey, Beds SG15 6RS
Tel: 01462 734504 and www.arleseyfc.co.uk

Directions: A1 take A507 to Shefford, at 3rd roundabout turn left, 1st left follow road through village, ground 1.5 miles on left

Capacity: 2,920 Seats: 150 Cover: 600 Floodlights: Yes

Club Shop: Yes Old programmes, leisure wear,replica hits andd various souvenirs

Clubhouse: Open daily 7- 11.00, Sat 12p.m.-11.30, Sun 12-2.30 7-11.30
Members bar ,wide screen for Sky TV, function suite and hot food available.

PREVIOUS: **Leagues:** Biggleswade & Dist.; Beds. Co. (S. Mids) 22-26 ,27-28; Parthenon; London 58-60; Utd Co's 33-36 82-92. Spartan South Midlands 92-99

RECORDS: **Attendance:** 2,000 v Luton Town Reserves, Beds Senior Cup 1906
Appearances: Gary Marshall

BEST SEASON: **FA Vase:** Winners 94-95 **FA Cup:** 4th Qual.Round 2002-2003 v Hererford United (0-1)

HONOURS: FA Vase Winners 1994-5; Isthmian League (Ryman) Div 3 Champions 00-01, Beds Sen Cup 65-66 78-79 96-97, Prem Cup 83-84, 01-02, Interm Cup 57-58; S Mids Lge Prem Div 51-52 52-53 94-95 95-96.99-00, Div 2 29-30 31-32 35-36, Chall Trophy 79-80, Prem Shield 64-65, O'Brien Prem Cup 93-94, F'litCup 90-91; Utd Co Lge Prem Div 84-85, KO Cup 87-88; Hinchingbrooke Cup 77-78 79-80 81-82 96-97; Biggleswade KO Cup 77-78 80-81

Players Progressing: Roland Legate (Luton), Pat Kruse (Brentford, Leicester) & Dave Kitson (Camb U)

L-R - Back row: James Dillnutt, Shaun Marshall, Matt Corbould, Steve Magona, Tony Fontenelle, Keith B arrett (Asst Manager), Andy Theodosiou (player coach), Martyn Patching, Craig Reynolds, Dave Hatchett, Eric Turner, (Physio), Margaret Brabrook (physio) and Nicky Ironton (Manager). **Front row:** Stuart Beevor, Mitch Barrett, Jamie Lever, Harry Ironton (Mascot), Dean Harding, Simeon Bird (mascot), Matt Turnbull, George Ironton, Barry Dellar, Bradley Poole, Lee Tekell, Sam Parratt and Karl Spring.

AVELEY

CLUB OFFICIALS

Chairman: Graham Gennings
President: Ken Clay
Press Officer: Terry King
Secretary: Craig Johnston
10 San Juan Drive, Chafford Hundred,
Grays, Essex RM16 6LQ.
Tel: 01375 650220 (H) 07946 438540 (M)

FOOTBALL MANAGEMENT TEAM

Manager : Brian Horne
Assistant Manager : David Guiver
Physio : Paul Wilson

FACT FILE

Founded: 1927
Sponsors: Freightmaster
Colours: All Royal blue
Change: All Red
Midweek matches: Wednesday
Reserves' Lge: Essex Business House

A warm welcome is extended to all our visitors
This is 'Mill Field' the home of
THE 'MILLERS' REVIEW
AVELEY F.C.
What on earth has the Waltham Forest goalkeeper unearthed in his 6 yard box during the first half of last Saturday's league encounter ? Our eagle eyed photographer capturing a rare foray !
Match Sponsor :- BESPOKE LOGISTICS
Match Ball Sponsor :-
Ryman football league
Today's Opponents
Tilbury FC
Ryman Isthmian League Division One North
Saturday 6th March 2004.
£1.50

Pages: 48 Price: £1
Editor: Terry King& Craig Johnston
Local Press: Thurrock Gazette
Romford Recorder
Local Radio: Radio Essex, Essex Radio

GROUND: `Mill Field', Mill Road, Aveley, Essex RM15 4TR
Tel: 01708 865940

Directions: London - Southend A1306, turn into Sandy Lane at Aveley.
Rainham or Purfleet BR stations then bus No. 723 to the ground. Bus from Rainham No 324

Capacity: 4,000 Cover: 400 Seats: 400 Floodlights: Yes

Clubhouse: Normal pub hours. Bar snacks and hot food available
Club Shop: No

PREVIOUS **Leagues:** Thurrock Com 46-49; London 49-57; Delphian 57-63; Athenian 63-73

RECORDS **Attendance:** 3,741 v Slough T., FA Amateur Cup 27.2.71
Goalscorer: Jotty Wilks, 214 **Appearances:** Ken Riley, 422
Win: 11-1 v Histon, 24/8/63
Defeat: 0-8 v Orient, Essex Thameside Trophy, 11/4/85

BEST SEASON **FA Cup:** 1st Rd 70-71, 0-1 v Yeovil League clubs defeated: None
FA Amateur Cup QF 70-71 **FA Trophy** 3rd Qual Rd replay 74-75 **F.A.Vase** 3rd Rd 89-90

HONOURS: Isthmian Lg Div 2 (North) R-up 89-90, Lg (AC Delco) Cup 89-90; London Lg 51-5254-55 (R-up 55-56, Lg Cup 53-54); Delphian Lg R-up 57-58 (Lg Cup 61-62);Athenian Lg 70-71 (Div 2 R-up 68-69); Essex Junior Cup 47-48 48-49; Essex Thameside Trophy 79-80 R-up 97-98; Hornchurch Charity Cup 81-82 (R-up 83-84); East Anglian Cup 88-89, R-up 97-98 Essex Senior Cup Finalists 2002/03

Players progressing: David Case & Alan Hull (Orient), Alan Parkinson (Orient 1967), Yilmaz Orhan (W Ham 1972), Keith Day (Colchester 1984), Paul Williams (Charlton, Sheff Wed & C.Palace) Paul Wilson (Barnet), David Morrison (Peterborough U), Tony Sorrell (Maidstone Utd), Steve Crane (Gillingham), David Matthews (Walsall, Southend United)

2004-2005 Back row,left to right: Chris Wolf, Steve Dickinson, Gary Moulding (Asst.Manager), Kevin Head (Physio), Amin Levitt (Manager), Nicky Lowery, Manzeidi Mbala, Des Gallen, Graham Hill, Marc Palmer, Chris Sorhaindof, Luke Baulkham, Jimmy Stevens, Daniel Johnson, Tolo Mas, Danny Curran, Kevin Hoddy (Coach) and Michael Lenahan. **Front row:** Luke Moore, Kevin Marsden, Jermain Hughes, Steve Pashley, Mark Risley, Ben Fuller, Rob Scott, Jordan Kelly, Rio Alderton and Jon Whitaker.

BARKING & EAST HAM UNITED

CLUB OFFICIALS

Chairman: Peter Webster

Secretary: Roger Chilvers
50 Harrow Rd, Barking, Essex IG11 7RA Tel: 020 8591 5313

Press Officer: Derek Pedder
Tel: 020 85292 483

FOOTBALL MANAGEMENT TEAM

Manager: Deninis Elliott
Coaches: Jay Devereux & Terry Beck
Captain: Jay Devereux
Reserves' Manager:Tony Myers
Goalkeeping Coach: Marc Baker
Physio: Donna Read

FACT FILE

Founded: 1880 Nickname: The Blues
Main Sponsors: Star Bookmakers
Colours: Blue & white
Change Cols: White
Midweek matchday: Tuesday
Reserves' Lge: Essex & Herts Border Prem.
Ladies Lg: S.E.Combination
Youth League: Eastern Junior Alliance
Club Website: www.barkingfc.co.uk

2003-2004

Player of the Year & Top Scorer:
Billy Read

GROUND Mayesbrook Park, Lodge Avenue, Dagenham RM8 2JR Tel: 020 8595 6900/6511
Email Address: john@capitalcair.co.uk

Directions: Off A13 on A1153 (Lodge Ave), and ground 1 mile on left.
Bus 162 from Barking station or Nos 5 or 87 to Robin Hood. Nearest tube Becontree.

Capacity: 2,500 Cover: 600 Seats: 200 Floodlights: Yes
Clubhouse: 2 large bars, open daily 11am-11pm (Sundays Noon-11pm).
Hot & cold food and drinks. **Club Shop:** Yes. Manager: Brad Robinson

PROGRAMME

Pages: 16 Price: £1.00
Editor: Mark Harris & Derek Pedder
Local Press: B arking & Dagenham Post
B & D Recorder.
Local Radio: Active FM

PREVIOUS **Grounds:** Eastbury Field, Kennedy Estate,Movers Lane,Barking Recreation Ground Merry Fiddlers,Vicarage Field (until 1973)
Names: Barking Rovers,Barking Woodville, Barking Institute,Barking Town and Barking
Leagues: London 1896-98 09-23, South Essex 1898-21, Leyton & Dist 1899-1900,Athenian 12-13 + 23-52 S.E.Combination 39-40 Isthmian 1952-2004

CLUB RECORDS **Attendance:** (At Mayesbrook) 1,972 v Aldershot FA Cup 2nd Rd 78
Win: 14-0 v Sheppey Utd Mithras Cup 69-70 **Defeat:** 0-8 v Marlow.
Fee received: £6,000 for Alan Hull (Orient) **Fee paid:** None over £1,000
Goal scorer: Neville Fox 241 (65-73) **Appearances:** Bob Makin 566

BEST SEASON **FA Vase**: 96-97 5th Rd **FA Amateur Cup:** Runners-up 26-27 **F.A.Trophy:** 2nd Rd 79-80
FA Cup: 2nd Rd rep. 81-82 1-3v Gillingham (A) after 1-1. Also 2nd Rd 78-79 79-80 83-84, and 1st Rd 26-27 28-29 78-80.
League clubs defeated: Oxford Utd 79-80.

HONOURS FA Amateur Cup R-up 26-27; Isthmian Lg 78-79 (Lg Cup R-up 76-77); Athenian Lg 34-35 (R-up 24-25); London Lg 20-21 (Div 1 (A) 09-10); South Essex Lg Div 1 (2),R-up (3), Div 2 (4); London Senior Cup (4), R-up (3); Essex Senior Cup (7), R-up (8); Dylon Shield 79-80; Eastern Floodlit R-up (3); Essex Elizabethian 66-67, R-up (2); Essex Thameside (4), R-up (5); London Charity Cup 61-62 R-up 21-22; London Intermediate Cup (3) ,R-up(1); East Anglian Cup 37-38 53-54;Mithras Cup (3), R-up (2); Premier Midweek (2). Vandanel Trophy R-up 99-00

Players progressing:40 players to date including: - 1956; Peter Carey (Orient 57), Lawrie Abrahams (Charlton 77), Kevin Hitchcock (Nottm Forest83 & Chelsea), Dennis Bailey (Fulham 86), Alan Hull (Orient 87) Joe Sibley1939, Hedley Sheppard 1932, Paul Wilson (Barnet) John Still (Ex-Manager Barnet), Mark Lazarus (Leyton O),J.Tresarden 1922 (West Ham U & England) and H.j.Holse,1908 (Manchester U & England), Darren Purse
In 1900 Billy Quash won a Gold Medal in the Olympic Games.

BARTON ROVERS

CLUB OFFICIALS
Chairman: Trevor Capon
President: Pat Howarth
Vice Chairman: Richard Carey
Football Secretary: Owen Clark,
c/o Barton Rovers F.C.
Tel: 01582 882398
Press Officer: Nick Rhodes
Tel: 01582 881865

FOOTBALL MANAGEMENT TEAM
Manager:Gordon Guile
Assistant Manager: Geoff Livingstone
Physio: Mark Boulding

FACT FILE
Formed: 1898
Nickname: Rovers
Sponsors: Hillson Builders
Colours: All royal blue with white trim
Change colours: All yellow
Midweek Matchday: Tuesday
Reserves' League: None
Local Press: Luton News, Herald,
Beds on Sunday
Local Radio: Radio Chiltern, Radio Beds
Three Counties Radio

GROUND Sharpenhoe Road, Barton-le-Clay, Bedford MK45 4SD
Tel: 01582 707772

Directions: M1 Jct 12, from London exit turn right, take 2nd right through Harlington and Sharpenhoe. Entrance to ground 44 yds on right down concrete drive entering village. 41/2 miles from Harlington (BR), 6 miles from Luton (BR), good bus or taxis service from Luton
Capacity: 4,000 Seats: 160 Cover: 1,120 Floodlights: Yes

Clubhouse: Noon-3pm weekends (no football), noon-11pm (matchdays), 7-11pm weekdays. Real ale, hot & cold snacks, pool, darts, gaming machines
Club Shop: Yes (contact 01582 751013)

PROGRAMME
Pages: 64 Price: £1.20
Editor: Sec & Nick Rhodes (01582 881865)

PREVIOUS **Leagues:** Luton & Dist. 47-54; Sth Midlands 54-79
Grounds: Church Pitch 1898-1912; Barton Cutting 1912; Sharpenhoe Rd 12-33; Faldo Rd 33-38; Barton Rec. 46-75

CLUB RECORDS **Attendance:** 1,900 v Nuneaton, FA Cup 4th Qual. Rd 1976
Win: 17-1 v Flitwick Athletic (H), S Midlands Lge Div 1 55-56
Defeat: 1-11 v Leighton United (H), S Midlands Lge Prem Div 62-63
Scorer: Richard Camp 152, 1989-98 **Appearances:** Tony McNally 514 (1988-2000)
Fees - Paid: £1,000 for B Baldry (Hitchin Town, 1980) **Received:** £1,000 for B Baldry (Bishop's Stortford, 1981)

BEST SEASON **FA Cup:** 1st Round 1980-81, 0-2 v Torquay United (A)
FA Vase: Runners-up 77-78 (SF 76-77 81-82, QF 75-76 78-79)
FA Trophy: 2nd Rd 98-99, 99-00

HONOURS: Sth Mids Lg(8) 70-73 74-79 (R-up 67-68), Div 1 64-65 (R-up 55-56), Div 2 54-55, Lg Shield 57-58 60-61 68-69, Chal. Tphy 71-72 74-75 77-78 78-79; Beds Snr Cup (7), R-up (5); Beds Premier Cup 95-96, R-up 81-82 83-84 88-89, 99-00 01-02 Beds Intermediate Cup 53-54; Luton & Dist. Lg Div 3 47-48; North Beds Charity Cup 72-73 74-75 76-77 77-78 79-80 80-81 (R-up 70-71); Isthmian Lge Div 2 R-Up 94-95, Assoc. Members Trophy R-up 92-93; South Midlands Floodlight Cup 98-99. Hinchingbroke Cup 2001-02 R-up: 98-99,99-00

Players progressing: Kevin Blackwell (Huddersfield T.)

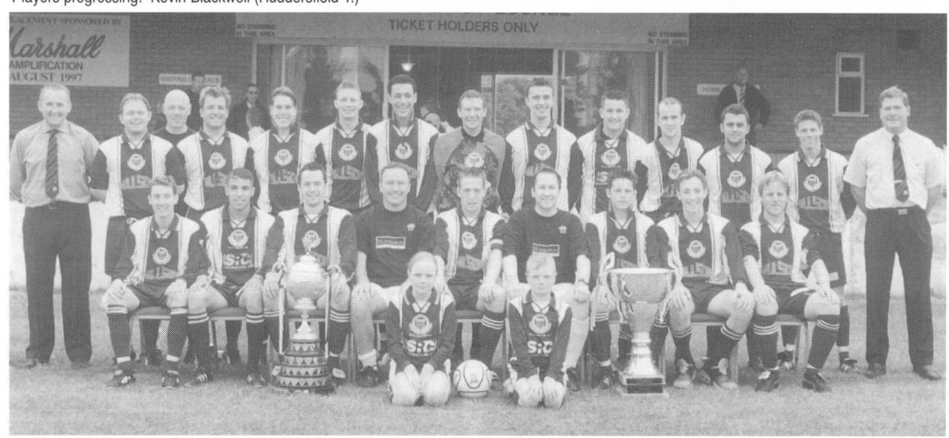

L-R - Back Row: Kevin Thoburn (u18 Manager), Paul Donnelly, Mark Boulding (Physio), Steve Turner, Keiran Carey, Dave Cook, Leon Cashman, Brad Gillham, Brett Donnelly, Chris Payne, Danny Kennoy, Robert Messina, Matt Endersby, Owen Clark (secretary)
Front: Dave Brown, Jermaine Daley, Keith Coughlin, Ian Allinson (Manager), Stuart Lochhead (Cpatain), Geoff Livingstone (Asst. Manager), Drew Roberts, Paul Ayling, Richard Fisher

BEACONSFIELD SYCOB

CLUB OFFICIALS

President: D Piercy
Chairman: Fred Deanus
Director of Football: Colin Barnes

Secretary: Ken Barrett, 31 Stockey End, Abingdon, Oxon OX14 2NF. Tel: 01235202058 (H), 01235 537080 (B)
Email: beacsrams@aol.com

FOOTBALL MANAGEMENT TEAM

Manager/Coach: Peter Scott
Physio: Phil Gray

FACT FILE

Founded: 1994

Nickname: The Rams

Colours:Red &white quarters/black/

red & white

Change colours: All Yellow

Midweek Matches: Monday

Reserves' League: Suburban Premier

GROUND: Holloway Park, Slough Road, Beaconsfield, Bucks (01494 676868).
Directions: M40 (Jct 2), 1st exit to A355. Club 100yds on right. 1.5 miles from Beaconsfield BR Bus 441Slough/ High Wyc'be**PREVIOUS NAMES:** SloughYCOB & Beaconsfield U merged 1994
Capacity: 3,000 Cover: 400 Seats:: 250 Floodlights: Yes C lub Shop: Clu **Clubbhouse:** Open eves & matchdays. Bar, Committee Room, Hall, Kitchen, Changing Room l

PROGRAMME
Pages: 64 Price: £1
Editor: Grant Hastie
Tel No:02083742175(H,W & Fax)

HONOURS: As Slough : Chilt.Lg R-up: 93-4,Lg Cup 92-3 Slough T Cup R-up 91-2. Champions Spartan South Midlands 2000-01, 2003-2004 Berks& Bucks Sen Trophy 2003-04

Leagues: Beaconsfield Utd: Wycombe & District; Maidenhead. Slough YCOB: Windsor, Slough & District; East Berks; Chiltonian (pre 1994) Spartan South Midlands.

Previous Grounds:

As Slough: Haymill Community Centre,Burnham Lane,slough (pre 1944)

Record Gate:

300 Beaconsfield Utd v Chesham Utd, Berks & Bucks Sen Cup 1985

BEST SEASONS:

FA Cup: 3rd Q Rd 98-998

FA Vase: Beaconsfield: 1st Rd 83-84 85-86 87-88

BERKHAMSTED TOWN

CLUB OFFICIALS

Chairman & Secretary:

5 Brackenhill, Berkhamsted, Herts HP42PU

Tel : 01442 878118 (H) 07711 719600(W)

e-mail: djfgl@hotmail.com

Press Officer: Bob Sear
Tel: 01442 864547 (H & B)

FOOTBALL MANAGEMENT TEAM

Manager: Simon Lane
Coach: Mark Pearson
Physio: Bryan Hardy

FACT FILE

Formed: 1895
Nickname: Lilywhites
Sponsors: T.B.A.
Colours: White/black/black
Change Colours: All Gold
Midweek Matchday: Tuesday
Reserves' Lge: Suburban League Prem Div
Local Press: Berkhamsted Herald, Berkhamsted Gazette
Local Radio: Chiltern Radio, Mix '96', Three Counties Radio
Website: www.berkhamstedfc.co.uk

GROUND Broadwater, Lower Kings Road, Berkhamsted, Herts HP4 2AA
Tel: 01442 862815

Directions: Adjacent to Berkhamsted station (Euston-Birmingham line). A41 toBerkhamsted town centre traffic lights, left into Lower Kings Road

Capacity: 2,500 Seats: 170 Cover: 350 Floodlights: Yes

Clubhouse: Open 7 days a week. Pool & darts - Big screen

Club Shop: Contact Doug Pearcey

PROGRAMME

Pages: 64 Price: £1
Editor: Grant Hastie
Tel No:02083742175(H,W & Fax)

PREVIOUS
Leagues: Herts Co. 1895-1922; Herts Co: 1921,Spartan 22-51, 66-75; Delphian 51-63; Athenian 63-66, 83-84; London Spartan 75-83
Grounds: Sunnyside Enclosure 1895-1919, Sports Ground 1919-83
Name: Bekhamsted Comrades 1919-22

CLUB RECORDS
Attendance: 1,732 v Bedlington Terriers F.A.Vase Semi Final 2nd Leg 2001
Career appearances: Ray Jeffrey (612)
Victory: 14-0 **Defeat:** 2-12

BEST SEASON
FA Cup: 3rd Qual Rd v Barnet 87-88, v Slough 91-92, v Chesham U. 92-93, v Burton Albion 2001-02
FA Vase: Finalists 2000-01
FA Trophy: 1st Rd v Kidderminster Harriers 97-98

HONOURS
Herts Senior Cup 52-53; London Spartan Lge 79-80 (Div 2 26-27);Herts Charity Cup: 2001-02
Herts Charity Shield 50-51(jt) 73-74 79-80 84-85 90-91; Herts Senior County Lge Aubrey Cup 52-53; St Marys Cup(13); Apsley Senior Charity Cup (9); Southern Comb 84-85(F/lit Cup 84-85)

Players progressing: Frank Broome(Aston Villa & England), Maurice Cook (Fulham), Keith Ryan(Wycombe), Maurice Telling (Millwall)

BOREHAM WOOD

CLUB OFFICIALS

Chairman: Danny Hunter

President: W F O'Neill

Secretary: Peter Smith, 26 Briarwood Road, Stoneleigh, Epsom, Surrey KT17 2LY Tel: 020 8393 2902(H) 0771 1745987(W)

Press Officer: John D Gill (020 8723 6407)

FOOTBALL MANAGEMENT TEAM

Manager: Ian Allinson
Asst Manager: Geoff Livingstone
Physio: Chris Barton

FACT FILE

Formed: 1948
Nickname: The Wood
Sponsors: Oinnacle
Colours: White/black/black
Change:Sky Blue/White/White
Midweek matchday: Monday
Local Radio: Chiltern Radio
Local Press: Boreham Wood Times, Watford Observer, Herts Advertiser

PROGRAMME

Pages: 44 Price: £1.00
Editor: John Gill (020 8723 6407)

2003-2004

Top Scorer & P.O.Y.: Sammy Winston

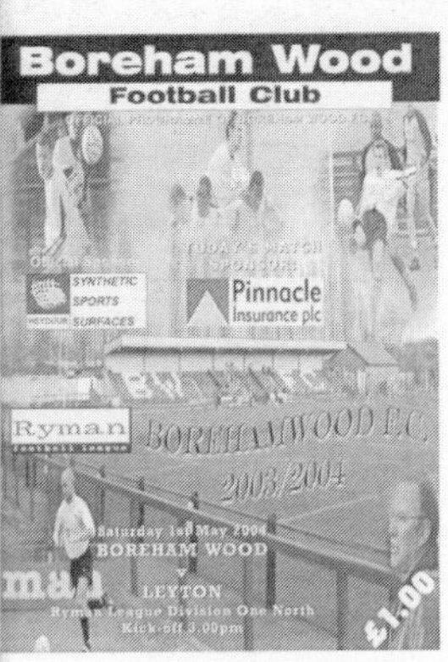

GROUND: Meadow Park, Broughinge Rd, Boreham Wood,Herts WD6 5AL (020 8953 5097)
Directions: A1 towards London from M25, 1st turn for Boreham Wood, head for town centre, into Brook Rd at r'bout before town centre, Broughinge Rd is 1st right. 1 mile from Elstree & Boreham Wood station (Thameslink),or bus 292 or107 to McDonalds (5 minutes walk)
Capacity: 4,502 Cover: 1,568 Seats: 600 Floodlights: Yes
Clubhouse: (020 8953 5097). Open during normal licensing hours. Snacks available. Function room (250) available for hire
Club Shop: Sells good selection of souvenirs & programmes. Contact: Jeff Weston

PREVIOUS **Leagues:** Mid Herts 48-52, Parthenon 52-57, Spartan 56-66, Athenian 66-74
Ground: Eldon Avenue 1948-63 **Names:** Boreham Wood Rovers and Royal Retournez, amalgamated in 1948
CLUB RECORDS **Attendance:** 4,030 v Arsenal 13-07 01 Friendly **Goalscorer:** Micky Jackson, 208 **Appearances:** Dave Hatchett, 714
BEST SEASON **FA Amateur Cup:** 3rd Rd. replay 70-71 **FA Trophy:** 3rd Rd 1995-96. Replay at Chorley 3-4, 3rd Rd replay 97-98
FA Cup: 2nd Round v Luton Town 1996-97. v Cheltenham Town 97-98
HONOURS: Isthmian Lg.Prem Div R-Up 97-98 Div I 94-95, 00-01 Isthmian Lg Div 2 76-77 (Yth Cup R-up 80-81), Isthmian Lge. Cup 96-97; R-Up 94-95,95-96 ,98-99 Athenian Lg 73-74 (Div 2 68-69, Div 1 R-up 69-70), Spartan Lg R-up 65-66, Herts Senior Cup 71-72 ,98-99 01-02 (R-up 66-67 74-75 79-80 87-88,96-97,97-98 03-04), Herts Junior Cup 51-52, Parthenon Lg 55-56 (R-up(2) 53-55 56-57, Herts Charity Shield 64-65, Herts Interm Cup 69-70, Herts Charity Cup (5) 80-81 83-84 85-86 88-90 (R-up 71-72 84-85 86-87 90-91 91-92 92-93), London Senior Cup R-up89-90, London Intermediate Cup 70-71, Neale Trophy 69-70, Essex & Herts BorderComb 72-73 (Lg Cup 72-73, Western Div R-up 82-83 89-90), Mithras Cup 76-77, Middx Border Lg 81-82 (Lg Cup 79-80), Wallspan Floodlit 86-87, London Challenge Cup 97-98
Players progressing: Colin Franks (Watford & Sheff Utd), Charles Ntamark (Walsall), Dean Samuels (Barnet 96), Justin Gentle (Colchester U), Kenny Veysey (Plymouth Argyle) and Matthew Brady (Wycombe Wanderers)

Back row(L-R): Steve Gracie (Physio), Joe Baker, Leon Ettienne, Olujimi Oshin, Pat Gradley, Clint Drake, Deji Davies, Scott Chalmers-Stevens, Gary Dixon, Dave Cook, Fergus Moore, Ryan Moran, Dominic Grime, Noel Imber, Daniel Hunter (Kit Manager). **Front row:** Kevin Lucas (reserve Team Manager), James Hawes, Rob Kean, Sammy Winston (Capt.), Geoff Livingstone (Asst. Manager), Ian Allinson (Team Manager), Stuart Reeks, Nick Grime, Tony Okolie, Paul Wood.
Photo: John D, Gill.

CHATHAM TOWN

CLUB OFFICIALS

Chairman: Frank Skinner

Secretary: Brian Burcombe
4 Hallwood Close, Parkwood, Rainham,
Kent ME8 9NT
Tel: 01634 363419

FACT FILE
Founded: 1882
Nickname: Chats
Sponsors: Topps Scaffolding
Colours: Red & black/black/black
Change Colours: All Blue
Midweek matchday: Tuesday

FOOTBALL MANAGEMENT TEAM
Manager: Clive Walker
Asst Manager: Phil Miles

56 pages Price: £1.00
Editor: Graham Byott 07733 131982(M)

GROUND Maidstone Road Sports Ground, Maidstone Road, Chatham, Kent
Tel: 01634 812194

Directions: M2, A229 Chatham turn-off, follow signs to Chatham, ground one and a half miles on right opposite garage. 1 mile from Chatham (BR).
Capacity: 5,000 Seats: 500 Cover: 1,000 Floodlights: Yes

Clubhouse: Matchdays and functions

PREVIOUS **Names:** Chatham FC; Medway FC (1970s)
Leagues: Southern (several spells); Aetolian 59-64; Metropolitan 64-68;Kent (Sev. spells),
Ground: Great Lines, Chatham 1882-90

RECORD **Gate:** 5,000 v Gillingham, 1980

BEST SEASON **FA Cup:** QF 1888-89 (incl 2-0 v Nottm Forest 2-0)
FA Trophy: 3rd Rd 70-71

HONOURS Kent Lg (9) 1894-95 03-05 24-25 26-27 71-72 73-74 76-77 79-80 00-01 R-up 02-03 23-24 25-26 70-71 74-75 80-81,
Lg Cup 71-72 76-77 (R-up(3), Thames & Medway Comb.(5) 1896-97 04-06 19-20 23-24,
Kent Snr Cup 1888-89 1904-05 10-11 18-19, Kent Snr Shield 19-20

Back Row Left to Right : Richard Sykes, Glenn Billinness, Nick Berkhauer, Richard Smith, Ollie Cotton, Lewis Green, Andy Boyle, Kevin Spriggs, Danny Larkin.
Middle Row : Mark Brookes, Gary Stock, Kenny Dyer, Clive Walker (manager), Steve Best, Steve Binks (asst manager), Andy Forster, Tom Binks, Gerrard Cunningham.
Front Row : Matt Bourne, Martin Di Fede, Craig Beckwith, Garry Tilley, Frannie Collin, John Sesan, Matt Nicholl

DARTFORD

CLUB OFFICIALS

Chairman: David Skinner
Vice Chairman: Bill Archer
Secretary: Peter Martin,10 Pembroke Place,Sutton-at-Hone, Dartford, Kent DA4 9HR (01322 864038)
CommercialManager.: Bill Archer

FOOTBALL MANAGEMENT TEAM

Manager: Tommy Sampson
Ass Man:Martin Farnie Coach: Paul Sawyer
Captain: Tommy Osborne
Physio:Dave Phillips

FACT FILE

Formed: 1888
Nickname: The Darts
Colours: White & black/black/black
Change colours: All Red
Midweek home matchday: Tuesday
Res League:Go Travel Kent Div 1
Website: www.darfordfc.co.uk

2003-2004

Player of the Year & Top Scorer:
Tostao Kwashi

Pages: 40 Price: £1.50
Editor: Tony Jaglo Tel No: 01322 222081
Press: Dartford Times, Dartford Messenger
Local Radio: Radio Kent.

GROUND c/o Gravesend & Northfleet FootballClub
Directions: From Dartford Town Centre: Take A226 to Gravesend/Swanscombe for 4 miles until Swansccombe. At bottom of Galley Hill through lights and ground is immediately on left.
From A2 coastbound: Take Bluewater/Greenhithe exit (B255) and at second roundabout, with McDonalds onright) turn right towards Swanscombe junction with A226 . Then as above.
British Rail: Northfleet Station two minutes from ground
Dartford F.C. Email Address: info@dartfordfc.co.uk

PREVIOUS **Leagues:** Kent League 1894-96 1897-98 1899-1902 1909-14 21-26 93-96; Southern League 1896-98, 1899-1900, 26-81, 82-84, 86-92; GMVC 81-82, 84-86
Grounds: The Brent/ Westgate House, Potters Meadow, Engleys Meadow, Summers Meadow, Watling St, then groundshares with Cray Wanderers, Erith & Belverdere & Purfleet

CLUB RECORDS **Attendance:** 11,004 v Leyton Orient FA Cup 48
Career Appearances: Steve Robinson 657
Win: 11-1 v Faversham Tn Kent Snr Cup 65 **Defeat:** 0-10 v Guildford City SouthernLge 46
Transfer fee paid: £6,000 for John Bartley (Chelmsford 88) **Received:** £25,000 forAndy Hessenthaler (Redbridge Forest)

BEST SEASON **FA Trophy:** Runners-up 74 **FA Vase:** 2nd Qual Rd 95/96
FA Cup: 3rd Rd Prop 35-36 & 36-37 League clubs defeated: Cardiff (1935), Exeter(1961), Aldershot (1968)

HONOURS Southern Lg 1930-31, 31-32, 73-74, 83-84, R-up 87-88, 88-89, Eastern Div 30-31,31-32, Southern Div 80-81, Southern Lg Div 2 1896-97, Lg Cup 76-77, 87-88, 88-89, Championship Shield 83-84, 87-88, 88-89; Kent Lg 1995-96, Lg Cup 24-25,Kent Snr Cup 29-30, 34-35, 38-39, 69-70, Snr Trophy 95-96, Inter Lg Chall 1974;FA Trophy R-up 1974

Players progressing: Idris Hopkins (Brentford 32), Fred Dall(West Ham 36), Riley Cullum/Fred Alexander/Ted Croker (Charlton 47/48/48) Frank Coombs (Bristol C 49), James Kelly (Gillingham 51), Tom Ritchie (Grimsby 58), Dave Underwood (Watford 60), Derek Hales (Luton 72), Andy Hessenthaler (Watfordvia Redbridge F),Jimmy Bullard (West Ham United)

Back row left to right: Dave Phillips (Physio), Mark Horam, Kwabena Amaning, Brad Potter, Richard Avery, Chris Tedder, Jimmy Simpson, James Tedder, Lee Coburn, Jimmy Carter, Eddie McClements, Tostao Kwashi, MikeWhybrow (Kit Man) and Dave Skinner (Chairman). **Front row:** Luke Cuthbert, Tommy Martin, Tommy Planck, Paul Sykes (Club Captain), Tommy Sampson(Manager), Paul Sawyer (Coach), Tommy Osborne (Team Captain), Ted Ansell, Cris Nunn and Barry Gibson.

EAST THURROCK UNITED

CLUB OFFICIALS

Chairman: Wayne Bennett

Club Secretary: Mick Stephens: 39 New Park Road, Benfleet, Essex SS7 5UR

Tel Nos: 01268 458571(H)07979 214350 (W)

FAX: 01268 458571

FOOTBALL MANAGEMENT TEAM

Manager: Lee Patterson
Assistant Manager.: Dave Card
Coach: John Coventry
Physio: T.B.A.

FACT FILE

Founded: 1969
Nickname: Rocks
Colours: Amber&black/black/black
Change: Blue/white/white
Midweek Matchday: Tuesday
Reserves' Lge: Essex/Herts Border Comb.

East Thurrock United
FOOTBALL CLUB
www.eastthurrockunited.com
season 2003-2004
Ryman football league

GROUND: Rookery Hill, Corringham, Essex Tel: 01375 644166-club

Directions: A13 London-Southend, take 1014 at Stanford-le-Hope for two and a half miles - ground on left. Two miles from Stanford-le-Hope and Basildon BR stations

Capacity: 4,000 Seats: 160 Cover:1,000 Floodlights: Yes

Clubhouse: Open all day seven days a week. Hot and cold snacks

Club Shop: No

PROGRAMME

36 pages £1.00
Editor: Alex Dywer 07956 651645
Local Press:
Thurrock Gazette/ Thurrock Recorder
Local Radio: BBC Essex

PREVIOUS

Leagues: Sth Essex Comb.; Gtr London; Metropolitan 72-75; London Spartan 75-79; Essex Snr 79-92
Grounds: Billet, Stanford-le-Hope 70-73 74-76; Grays Athletic 73-74; Tilbury FC 77-82; New Thames Club 82-84
Name: Corringham Social (pre-1969 Sunday side)

CLUB RECORDS

Attendance: 1,250 v Woking in F.A. Cup 2003
Goalscorer: Graham Stewart 102 **Appearances:** Glen Case 600+
Win: 7-0 v Coggeshall (H) 1984
Defeat: 0-9 v Eton Manor (A) 1982, both Essex Snr League
Transfer Fee Received: £22,000 for Greg Berry (Leyton Orient)

BEST SEASON

FA Cup: 4th Qualifying Round v Woking 2003-2004

HONOURS:

Metropolitan Lg Div 2 72-73, Essex Snr Lg R-up 88-89 (Lg Cup 88-89 91-92, Harry Fisher Mem. Tphy 83-84 90-91, Sportsmanship Award 81-82 86-87 89-89), Essex SnrTphy R-up 91-92 95-96, Fred Budden Tphy R-up 89-90, Essex & Herts Border Comb.89-90,01-02 (Lg Cup 89-90) , Isthmian League Div. Three 99-00 East Anglian Cup Winners 2003

Players progressing to Football League: Greg Berry (Leyton Orient & Wimbledon)

ERITH & BELVEDERE

CLUB OFFICIALS
Chairman: John McFadden
President: L O'Connell
Vice Chairman: Peter Bird
Secretary: Kellie Discipline, 23 Stuart Evans Close, Welling, Kent DA16 1SM
TelNos: 01322 526184(H) 07932 756837(M)
e-mail: kelliedt@tinyworld.co.uk
Press Off./Com Man.: Martin Tarrant
Tel: 01322 400722

FOOTBALL MANAGEMENT TEAM
Manager: Barry Lakin
Asst Manager: Steve Robinson
Captain: Lewis Tozer
Physio: Rob Couldwell

FACT FILE
Formed: 1922
Nickname: Deres
Colours:Blue & whitequarters/blue/blue
Change colours: All RedMidweek home matchday:Tuesday
Reserves' League:Kent League Div1

2003-2004
Top Goalscorer: Atpo Sodje
Player Of the Year: Joni Seitsonen

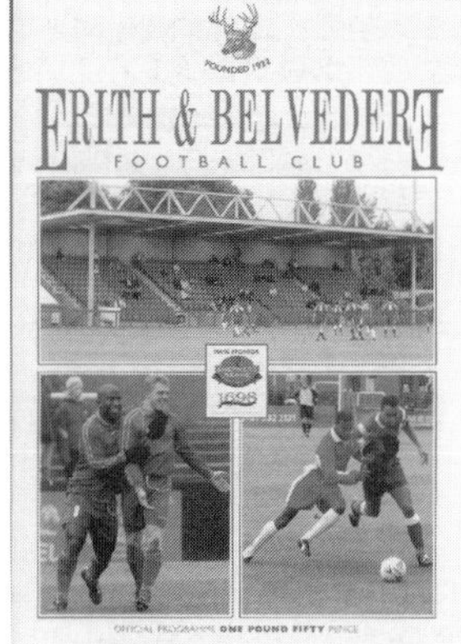

Pages: 30 Price: £1.50p
Editor: Martin Tarrant & Brian Spurrell
Tel No: 01322 400722 (H07713 189912 (W)
Local Press:
Kentish Times, Kentish Independent
Local Radio: Radio Kent, Radio Mellenium

GROUND: Park View Rd Ground, Welling, Kent DA16 1SY Tel: 0181 301 1196
Email: kelliedt@tinyworld.co.uk
Directions: As for Welling United F.C.:M25,then A2 towards London.Take Welling turn-off, ground one mile. By rail to Welling stationBR (BR) ground 3/4 mile.
Capacity: 1,500 Cover: 1,000 Seats: 500 Floodlights: Yes
Club Shop: Sells programmes, badges and pens
Clubhouse: Licensed social club open matchdays and weekends. Cold snacks available. Separate canteen provides hot food on matchdays

PREVIOUS
Leagues: Kent 22-29 31-39 78-82, London 29-31, Corinthian 45-63, Athenian 63-78
Names: Belvedere & District FC (Formed 1918, restructured 1922)

CLUB RECORDS
Attendance: 5,573 v Crook Colliery Welfare Amt Cup 3rd Rd 1949
Win: 14-2 v Royal Marines, Kent Lge 18/11/33. (16-2 v RAF Friendly 4/9/41) **Defeat:** 0-15 v Ashford, Kent Lge 28/4/37
Career Appearances: Dennis Crawford 504, 56-71 **Career Goalscorer:** Colin Johnson284, 61-71

BEST SEASON
FA Amateur Cup: Runners-up 1923-24, 37-38 **FA Trophy:** Third Qualifying Round second replay 89-90
FA Vase: Third Round 76-77 **FA Cup:** 4th Qual Rd 1924-25 (Equiv to 1st Rd Prop). League clubs defeated: None

HONOURS
FA Amat Cup R-up 23-24 37-38; Athenian Lge Div 1 R-up 70-71 Lge Cup 73-74, Memorial Shield 67-68; Corinthian Lge R-up 62-63, (Lge Cup 47-48 48-49 49-50); Kent Lge 81-82, (Lge Cup R-up 81-82); London Sen Cup 44-45 (R-up 38-39); Kent Amat Cup 6, (R-up 4); Kent F/lit Lge R-up 67-68; Kent Interm Cup R-up 90-91; Kent Jun Cup 67-68; Kent County Yth Lge 90-91; Kent Yth Cup 87-88. Bromley Hosp Cup 38-39; Essex & Herts Border Comb Cup 73-74.

Players progressing: John Coshall (West Ham 28), Fred Ford 36/ Cyril Hammond 46/ KeithPeacock 62 (Charlton), Tommy Ord (Chelsea 72), Sean Devine (Barnet 95)

Back row, left to right:
Junior Samuels,
Richard Vercesi,
Jani Seitsonen,
Ray Aboagye,
Steve Sodje,
Mark Horan.

Front Row:
Stuart Abbott,
Darren Adams,
Paul Roberts,
Ryan Briggs,
Scott Saunders.

Photo: Alan Coomes

FISHER ATHLETIC (LONDON)

CLUB OFFICIALS

Chairman : Sam Muduroglu

Secretary: John Leyden,33 Carew Close,Chafford100,Nr Grays,Essex

Tel No: 01375 481224

General Manager: Elaine O'Keefe

FOOTBALL MANAGEMENT TEAM

Manager:Wayne BurnettPlayer-Coach: Tony Dolby

Physio: Joe Miller

FACT FILE

Formed: 1908

Nickname: The Fish

Colours: Black & white stripes/white/white

Change colours: All Blue

Midweek matchday: MondayReserves'

League: Suburban Premier

Local Press: Southwark News, South London Press

Local Radio: Capital & Capital Gold

FISHER ATHLETIC (LONDON) FOOTBALL CLUB

VERSUS

TILBURY F.C.

SATURDAY 21ST AUGUST 2004
3.00 P.M.

Champion Hill Stadium
Edgar Kail Way
Dog Kennel Hill
London SE22 8BD

Official Match Day Programme: Price £1.00

GROUND The Surrey Docks Stadium, Salter Road, London SE16 5LH
Tel: 0207 231 5144 Fax:0207 2520060

Directions: 8 mins walk - Rotherhithe(tube).2 miles - London Bridge (main line). Buses 381,225

Capacity: 5,300 Cover: 4,283 Seats: 400 Floodlights: Yes

Clubhouse: None **Club Shop:** None

PROGRAMME

Pages: 40 Price: £1.50

Editor: Teresa Watson(07776 138982(M)

PREVIOUS **Leagues:** Parthenon, West Kent, Kent Amateur, London Spartan 76-82, Southern 82-87, GMV Conference 87-91
Names: Fisher Athletic 08-93, Fisher`93 93-96 **Ground:** London Road, Mitcham

CLUB RECORDS **Attendance:** 4,283 v Barnet, GMV Conference 4/5/91
Win: 7-0 v Lewes Sept 95, FA Cup **Defeat:** 1-8 v Clevedon (away) 10.03.01
Career Goalscorer: Paul Shinners 205 **Career Appearances:** Dennis Sharp 720
Transfer fee paid: £2,500 for Ben Taylor (Sittingbourne)
Transfer fee received: £45,000 for Paul Gorman (Charlton 1991)

BEST SEASON **FA Cup:** 1st Rd 84-85 (0-1 at home to Bristol City), 88-89 (0-4 at BristolRovers)
FA Trophy: Third Round replay 87-88 **FA Vase:** Second Round replay 82-83 **FA Amateur Cup:**

HONOURS Southern Lg 86-87 (R-up 83-84, Southern Div 82-83, Lg Cp 84-85, Championship Cup 87-88, Merit Cup), London Spartan Lg 80-81 81-82 (R-up 78-79, Senior Div77-78, Div 2 R-up 76-77), Parthenon Lg 61-62 (Lg Cup 63-64 65-66), Kent AmateurLg 73-74 74-75 (R-up 72-73),Kent Intermediate 97-98.98-99 London Senior Cup 84-85 87-88 88-89, LondonIntermediate Cup 59-60 (R-up 75-76), Kent Senior Cp 83-84, Kent Senior Trophy 81-82 82-83, Surrey Inter Cup 61-62,Southern Lg. Eastern Div 99-00

Players progressing:John Bumstead (Chelsea), Trevor Aylott (Bournemouth), Paul Shinners (Orient 84), Dave Regis (Notts Co. - via Barnet), Paul Gorman(Charlton 91), Sean Devine (Barnet via Okonia Nicossia), George Barry (LeytonOrient), Dean Martin (West Ham Utd), Jason Lee (Charlton), Ken Charlery (Barnet), Steve Watts (Leyton Orient)

GREAT WAKERING ROVERS

CLUB OFFICIALS
Chairman: Roy Kettridge
Vice-Chairman: Nobby Johnson
President: Eddie Ellis
Secretary: Roger Sampson
37 Lee Lotts, Gt. Wakering, Essex
Southend SS3 0HA Tel: 01702 218794
Press Officer: Nobby Johnson
Tel: 01702 468243

FOOTBALL MANAGEMENT TEAM
Manager:Tony Cross
Coaches: Gary Heywood & Del Robinson
Physio: Clive Taylor

FACT FILE
Founded: 1919
Nickname: Rovers
Sponsors:I.M.S.
Colours:Green & whitestripes /white/green
Change Coours: Red/Blue/Red
Midweek Matchday: Tuesday
Reserves' Lge: Essex & Herts Border Comb

2002-2003
Top Scorer: Dan Trenkel 21
2003-2004
Captain Danny Scopes

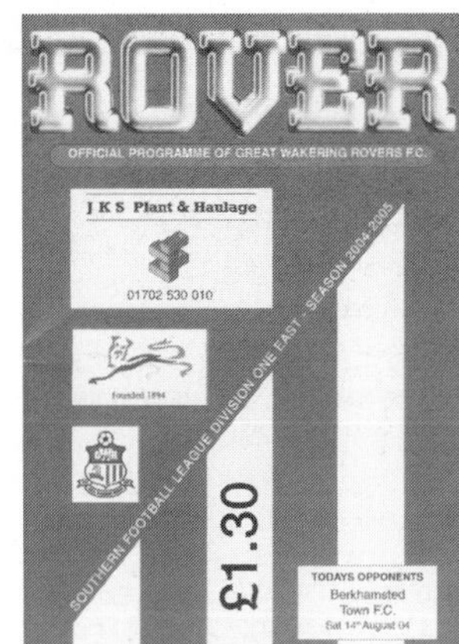

PROGRAMME
Pages: 24-32 Price: £1.30
Editor: Nobby Johnson (01702 468243)
Website: great wakeringroversfc.co.uk

GROUND: Burroughs Park, Little Wakering Hall Lane, Gt. Wakering, Southend SS3 OHQ
Tel: 01702 217812

Directions: 4a bus from Shoeburyness (BR), 4a or 4b from Southend - alight at British Legion in Gt Wakering alongside which runs Little Wakering Hall Lane. A127 past Southend signed Gt Wakering. In Gt Wakering, .5 mile past large Total garage along High Street is Little Wakering Hall Lane, ground 250 yds along on left

Capacity: 2,500 Cover: 300 Seats: 150 Floodlights: Yes
Clubhouse: Open every eve., Sat 11-11, Sun 12-3 & 7.30-10.30.
Hot meals, snacks etc matchdays only **Club Shop:** No

PREVIOUS **Leagues:** Southend & Dist. 19-81, Southend All. 81-89, Essex I'mediate 89-92, Essex Senior 1992-1999,Isthmian 1999-2004
Ground: Gt Wakering Rec

RECORDS **Attendance:** 659 v Potters Bar FA Vase 5th Rd 7-2-98
Win (in Senior Football): 9-0 v Eton Manor 27/12/93
Defeat (in Senior Football): 1-7 v Bowers Utd, Essex Snr Lge 1-4-98

BEST SEASON **FA Cup:** 2nd Qual 98-99
FA Vase: 5th Round 97-98, 01-02

HONOURS Isthmian League div. 3 R-iup 99-00; Essex I'mediate Cup 91-92, Essex I'mediate Lg Div 2 91-92, Div 3 90-91, Lg Cup 91-92, Southend Charity Shld 90-91 91-92, Essex Snr Lg. 94-95, Lg Res. Sect. 94-95
(Wirral Programme Essex Sen. Lg. Award 92-93 94-95)

Players progressing: Les Stubbs (Southend, Chelsea) 1947, Jackie Bridge(Southend Utd) 1948, Kevin Maddocks (Maidstone Utd)

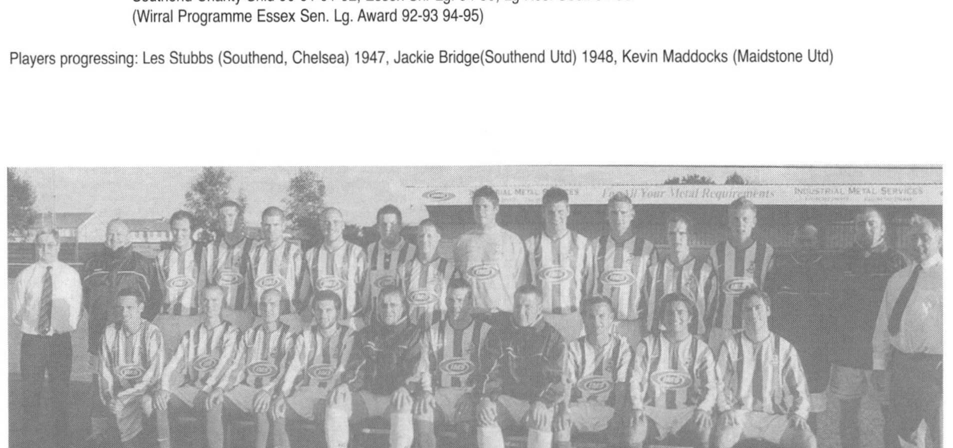

Back row left to right: Roy Kettridge (Chairman), Cleve Taylor (Physio), Paul Wheeler, Brendan Walshe, Jason Tolan, Dan Trenkel, Dan Wornham, Gary Ewers, Dale Brightly, Craig Dennis, Danny Heale, Terry Harris, Sam Lake, Del Robinson (Coach), Ryan Wilkinson (Coach), Roger Burroughs (Club benefactor). **Front Row:** John Heffer, Daren Twidell, Darren Brown, Paul Harrison, Tony Cross (Manager), Danny Scopes (Capt.), GaryHeywood (coach), Lee Guiver. Danny Pitts, Simon Deakin. Photo: Dave Henderson.

HARLOW TOWN

CLUB OFFICIALS

Chairman: Steve Ray

President: Ron Bruce

Press Officer: T.B.A.

Secretary: Martin Haines, 23 Wood Hill, Harlow, Essex CM12 0XA

Tel No: 01279 454453(H) 07729 967876(W)

FOOTBALL MANAGEMENT TEAM

Manager: Tom Cunningham

Coaches: Paul Wickenden & Ian Green

FACT FILE

Founded: 1879

Nickname: Hawks

Sponsors: BritSec Int. Ltd

Colours: Red & white/white/white

Change: White / Black/ Black

Midweek Matchday: Wednesday

Reserves' Lg: Essex & Herts Border Comb.

Website:www.harlowtown.co.uk

Local Press: Harlow Citizen, Harlow Star, Harlow Herald & Post

Local Radio: Essex Radio, BBC Essex, Ten 17

PROGRAMME

36 pages £1.00

Editor: Mark Kettlety 07940 322612(M)

GROUND Harlow Sports Centre, Hammarskjold Rd, Harlow CM20 2JF Tel: 01279 445319 Email: jeff.bothwell@ britsec.co.uk

Directions: Near town centre, 10 mins walk from Harlow Town (BR) station

Capacity: 10,000 Cover: 500 Seats: 400 Floodlights: Yes

Club Shop: Yes **Clubhouse:** Open daily 11-11 (10.30 Sundays). Hot & cold food available

PREVIOUS **Leagues:** East Herts (pre-1932); Spartan 32-39 46-54; London 54-61; Delphian 61-63; Athenian 63-73; Isthmian 73-92; Inactive 92-93

Grounds: Marigolds 1919-22; Green Man Field 22-60

CLUB RECORDS **A ttendance:** 9,723 v Leicester, FA Cup 3rd Rd replay 8/1/80

Goalscorer: Jeff Wood (45 in 88-89) **Appearances:** Norman Gladwin 646 (1949-70)

Win: 12-0 v Hertford Ath. (H), E. Herts Lge 5/10/29 **Defeat:** 0-11 v Ware (A), Spartan Lge Div. One (East) 6/3/48

BEST SEASON **FA Amateur Cup:** 2nd Rd 72-73 **FA Trophy:** 2nd Rd(2) 80-82 **FA Vase:** 3rd Rd 88-89

FA Cup: 4th Rd 79-80 (lost 3-4 at Watford). Also 1st Rd 80-81 81-82 League clubs defeated: Southend, Leicester 79-80

HONOURS Isthmian Lg Div 1 78-79 (R-up 82-83, Div 2 Nth 88-89, Yth Cup 77-78), Ath'n LgDiv 1 71-72, E Angl. Cup 89-90, 01-02Knight F'lit Cup R-up 87-88, Essex Snr Cup 78-79, Essex F'lit Competition R-up 71-72, London Lg Chal. Cup 59-60, Spartan LgCup 52-53, Epping Hosp. Cup (3) 46-49, Essex & Herts Border Comb Cup 75-76, Fred Budden Trophy 88-89 89-90, Chelmsford Yth Lg 86-87 (Lg Cup 86-87 87-88)

Players progressing: Jeff Wood (Charlton 75), Neil Prosser (B'mouth 80)

Back Row (L-R): Ryan Oliva, Danny Chapman, Viegbe Ganyo, Theo Daniels, Oliver Monksfield, Gregg Williams. **Middle:** Paul Wickenden (coach), Kevin Warren, Neil Moore, Stephen Mensah, Glenn Jackson, Charlie Hasler, Gabriel Fanibuyan, Tobi Ositola, Adam Dangerfield, Ian Green (coach). **Front Row:** Marvin Hong, Mark Taylor, Marc Salmon, Tommy Cunningham (Manager), Leon Lalite, Ricky Goldblatt, Jon Renaut.

LEIGHTON TOWN

CLUB OFFICIALS
Secretary: Roy Parker c.o L.T.F.C.
email: reds@leightontownfc.co.uk
Chairman: Iain S McGregor
President: M.Hide
Press Officer: Iain McGregor

FACT FILE
Founded: 1885
Nickname: Reds
Colours: Red & whitestripes/red/red
Change colours: Orange & black
Midweek Matchday: Tuesday
Reserves' League: Suburban

2003-2004
Player of the Year & Leading Goalscorer:
Matt Rawdon

FOOTBALL MANAGEMENT TEAM
Manager: Paul Burgess
Captain: Jason Haggerwood
Physio: Geoge Lathwell & Eddie Kerr

Welcome to Bell Close...

Official Matchday Programme
Leighton Town
football club
Price £1.00

PROGRAMME
£1.00
Editor: James Ullyett 07932 764734 (H)
Local Press:
Leighton Buzzard Observer, The Citizen
Local Radio: Three Counties Radio,
Radio Chiltern, Mix 96
Website: www.leightontownfc.co.uk

GROUND:

Address: Bell Close, Lake Street, Leighton Buzzard, Beds
Tel: 01525 373311

Directions: From bypass (A505) take A4146 (Billington Rd) towards Leighton Buzzard, straight overfirst roundabout then straight over mini-r'bout .After aprox 50 yards take first left into car park which is opposite the Safeways petrol stattion.
Half a mile from Leighton Buzzard (BR) station.
Buses from Luton, Aylesbury and Milton Keynes

Capacity: 2,800 Seats: 155 Cover: 300 Floodlights: Yes

Club Shop: No

Clubhouse: Normal licensing hours.
Snack bar on matchdays - full range of hot snacks & drinks

HONOURS Isthmian Lge Div 2 Champions 03-04 Div 3 R-up 95-96; Sth Midlands Lg 66-67 91-92, Lg Cup 90-91, O'Brien Tphy 90-91, Reserve Div 1 87-88 91-92 94-95, Res Div 2 76-77, Res Challenge Cup 93-94 94-95; Beds Snr Cup 26-27 67-68 68-69 69-70 92-93; Bucks Charity Cup 94-95;98-99 Spartan Lg Div 2 23-24 27-28; Leighton & District Lg, Beds Intermediate Cup (res) 90-91; Beds Yth Cup 91-92 92-93,94-95 94-95; Chiltern Youth Lg 94-95, Lg Cup 93-94; East Anglian Yth. Cup 94-95; Assoc Mem. Cup 96-97.98-99, S.E. Co.Youth F'lit Lge (Corinthian Div.) 99-00, 01-02

BEST SEASON **FA Cup:** Third Qual. Round 70-71, 1-2 v St Albans City (A)
FA Vase: 2nd Round 1980-81, 94-95, 95-96, 00-01

PREVIOUS **Leagues:** Leighton & Dist; South Midlands 22-24 26-29 46-54 55-56 76-92; Spartan 22-53 67-74; United Counties 74-76
Name: Leighton United 1922-63 **Ground:** Wayside

CLUB RECORDS **Attendance:** 1,522 v Aldershot T., Isthmian Lg Div 3, 30/1/93
As Leighton Utd. **Win:13-0** v Met. Railway 1925/6 (H) Spartan League
Defeat: 0-12 v Headington Utd (A) 18.10.47 Spartan League
As Leighton Town **Win:10-1** v Skefko(H) 31.12.66 **Defeat: 0-8** v Electrolux(A) 16.10.65 & **0-8** v Harpenden 1965/66 4.11.65

MALDON TOWN

CLUB OFFICIALS

Chairman:Mike Kirkham

Secretary: Phil Robinson,
9 Lyndhurst Drive, Bicknacre,
Essex CN3 4XL
Tel No: 01245 222633 (H) 07759 066636 (M)
Email Address: robbophil@hotmail.com

FOOTBALL MANAGEMENT TEAM

Manager: Colin Wallington
Physio:Ian Jenkins

FACT FILE

Founded: 1946
Nickname: 'The Town'
Colours: Blue & white hoops/blue/blue
Change colours: Red & black hoops/black/black
Midweek Matchday: Tuesday

2002-03

Leading Goalscorer:Terry Warwick
Captain:Nicky Smith
Player of the Year: Paul Goodacre

Ground: Wallace Binder Ground, Park Drive, Maldon CM9 5XX (01621 853762)
Capacity: 2,500 Seats: 250 Cover: 500 Floodlights: Yes

Programme:24 pages £1.00
Editor: Alan Drewer
Club Website: http://www.maldontownfc.co.uk

HONOURS Essex Snr Lg 84-85 (Sportsmanship Award 87-88,88-89,94-95, Res Shield 93-94), Res Cup:94-95, Essex & Suffolk Border Lg 55-56 (Cup 64-65),Essex Intermediate Cup 51-52, Tolleshunt D'Arcy Cup 93-94,99-00, Eastern Div 1 R-Up 96-97

PREVIOUS **Leagues:** Mid Essex, N. Essex, Essex & Suffolk Border, Essex Senior
Ground: Fambridge Road (pre-1994)

BEST SEASON **FA Cup:** 2000-01 **FA Vase:** 20003 Semi- Final v AFC Sudbury

RECORDS **Attendance:** 1,163 v AFC Sudbury April @003

SITTINGBOURNE

CLUB OFFICIALS

Chairman: Andy Spice

President: Jim Clarke

Secretary:John Pitts, 4 Silverdale Grove Sittingbourne, Kent ME10 1UY (Tel No: 01795 476809 Fax 07092 112833)
email: John@bourne.plus.com

Commercial Manager: John Cooper

FOOTBALL MANAGEMENT TEAM

Manager: Mark Beeney

Assistant Manager/Coach: Steve Nolan

Physio: Gary Wisdom

FACT FILE

Formed: 1881 Nickname: Brickies

Sponsors: Hidsons Kia

Colours: Red with blacktrim/red/black

Change colours: All yellow

Midweek matchday: Tuesday

Reserves' league: Go Travel Kent

2003-2004

Top Scorers: Jon Neal & Michael Missen 13

Players of the Year:Jamie Coyle

2004-2005s

Captain: Jamie Coyle

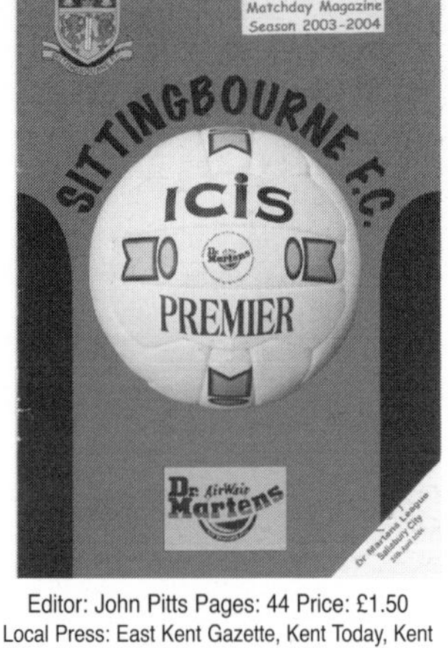

Editor: John Pitts Pages: 44 Price: £1.50
Local Press: East Kent Gazette, Kent Today, Kent Messenger Extra, Sittingbourne & Sheppy Adscene. Kent on Sunday
Local Radio: Invicta Supergold, BBC Radio Kent, K.M.F.M.,Invicta FM,Medway, Mercury F.M. Swale Sound

GROUND Bourne Park, Central Park Stadium, Eurolink, Sittingbourne, Kent ME10 3SB Tel: 01795 435077/420444 Fax: 01795 420444 Email Address: club@sittingbournefc.co.uk
Directions: Through Sittingbourne on main A2, club signposted clearly and regularly from both east and west. 1 mile from Sittingbourne BR station.
Capacity: 3,000 Cover: 600 Seats:300 Floodlights:Yes
Clubhouse: 'The Clubhouse' (01795 435077)
Club Shop: Sells a wide selection of souvenirs etc. Open matchdays or contact Ann Morrison (01795 664436) Official Club Website: www.sittingbournefc.co.uk

PREVIOUS **Leagues:** Kent 1894-1905 09-27 30-39 46-59 68-91, South Eastern 05-09, Southern 27-30 59-67
Grounds: SittingbourneRec. Ground 1881-90, Gore Court Cricket Ground 90-92, The Bull Ground1892-1990
Names: Sittingbourne United 1881-86

CLUB RECORDS **Attendance:** 5,951 v Tottenham Hotspur, friendly 26/1/93
Transfer fee paid: £20,000 to Ashford Town for Lee McRobert, 1993.
Transfer fee received: £210,000 from Millwall for Neil Emblen and Michael Harle, 1993

BEST SEASON **FA Cup:** 2nd Rd 25-26 (0-7 at Swindon Town), 28-29 (1-2 at Walsall), plus 1st Rd26-27 30-31 62-63

HONOURS Southern Lg Southern Div 92-93 95-96; Kent Lg 1897-98 1902-03 57-58 58-59 75-76 83-84 90-91 (Lg Cup 25-26 58-59 73-74 80-81, Div 2 Cup 54-55 57-58 83-84 86-8787-88); Kent Senior Cup 01-02 28-29 29-30 57-58; Kent Senior Shield 25-26 27-28 53-54; Kent Senior Trophy 89-90; Thames & Medway Cup 55-56 58-59; Thames & Medway Comb 02-03 07-08 11-12 24-25 25-26; Chatham Charity Cup 03-04 19-20;" Kent Midweek Lg(res) 91-92 (Lg Cup 90-91).

Players progressing: Jason Lillis (Walsall 93), Neil Emblen & Michael Harle 93, Steve Forbes 94, Lee McRobert 95 (Millwall) Jimmy Case (Brighton 93), Lee Harper (Arsenal 94)

TILBURY

CLUB OFFICIALS

Chairman: Robin Nash
Vice Chairman: Daniel Nash
Secretary / Press Officer: Lloyd Brown
52 Lionel Oxley House,New Road,
Grays, Essex RM176PP
Tel: 01375 409938 (H)
0776 232 6519 (M)

FOOTBALL MANAGEMENT TEAM

Manager: Paul Joynes
Physio: Steve Bell
Captain: Dean Cleaver

FACT FILE

Founded: 1900
Nickname: Dockers
Colours: Black& white stripes,black,black
Change: Red & white stripes,white,red
Midweek Matches: Tuesday

2003-2004
Captain: John Scarboroough
Top scorers: Nial Ritchie & Chris Stevens 9
Playerof the Year.: Niall Ritchie

Ryman League Division 1 North
TILBURY F.C.
Ryman football league
SEASON 2003/04 £1

PROGRAMME
36 Pages Price: £1.00
Editor: Lloyd Brown

Local Press: Thurrock Gazette, Thurrock Recorder
Local Radio: Essex Radio, BBC Essex

GROUND: Chadfields, St Chad's Rd, Tilbury, Essex RM18 8NL Tel: 01375 843093
Directions: BR from Fenchurch Street to Tilbury Town then one mile walk.
By road: M25 (jct 30 or 31) - A13 Southend bound, Tilbury Docks turn off after 4 miles, Chadwell St Mary turn off (left) after another 1.5 miles, right after 400 metres, rt at r'bout (signed Tilbury), right into St Chad's Rd after .5 mile, 1st rt into Chadfields for ground.
Capacity: 4,000 Seats: 350 Cover: 1,000 Floodlights: Yes **Club Shop**: No
Clubhouse: Open evening, all day Fri. & Sat. and Sun. lunchtimes. Hot &cold food

PREVIOUS **Leagues:** Grays & Dist.& Sth Essex (simultaneously); Kent 27-31; London 31-39 46-50 57-62; Sth Essex Comb. (war-time); Corinthian 50-57; Delphian 62-63; Athenian 63-73
Grounds: Green & Silley Weir Ground 1900-11; Orient Field 19-38 **Names:** None

RECORDS **Attendance:** 5,500 v Gorleston, FA Cup 4th Q Rd 19/11/49
Goalscorer: Ross Livermore 282 (in 305 games, 1958-66) **Appearances:** Nicky Smith 424 (1975-85)
Fee received: £2,000, Tony Macklin to Grays A. 1990 & for Steve Conner to Dartford, 1985
Win: 17-0 v No.9 Coy Royal Artillery (H), South Essex Lg 4/10/02.
In Senior Football; 13-2 v Chalfont National (A), London Lg 28/4/92
Defeat: 1-10 - v Maidstone U. (A), Corinthian Lge 4.9.62 & v Met. Police (A), Isthmian Lg. 6.5.95

BEST SEASON **FA Cup:** 3rd Rd 77-78, 0-4 v Stoke City (A)
FA Amateur Cup: Quarter Final v Wimbledon 46-7
FA Vase: Round 4 v Cowes Sports (a) 99-00

HONOURS: Isthmian Lg Div 1 75-76, (Div 1 Cup 74-75), Div 3 Prom.: 91-92, 99-00; Athenian Lg 68-69 (Div 2 62-63); London Lg 58-59 59-60 60-61 61-62, Lg Cup 58-59 60-61 61-62, R-up (3); DelphianLg 67-68 (Div 2 62-63); Essex Snr Cup 60-61 63-64 72-73 74-75 (R-up 46-47 47-48 69-70 71-72 78-79);

Players progressing to Football League: L Le May, T Scannell, T Oakley, JEvans

Other HONOURS: Essex Professional Cup 75-76; Mithras Cup 72-73 75-76 76-7778-79 (R-up 71-72 74-75); Essex Elizabethan Tphy 63-64 68-69 (R-up 55-56 59-60 64-65 67-68 70-71); Essex F'lit Comp. 68-69, Anglo-Italian Barassi Cup R-up 75-76; Essex Jnr Cup 08-09 24-25 (R-up 03-04); Stanford Charity Cup 62-63 92-93;Grays & Dist. Lg(numerous); Neale Trophy 65-66; Memorial Shield R-up 87-88

L-R - Back Row: C.Ware, G.Durrant, I. Hillaire, M.Neufille, L.Forbes, E.Styles, S.Miller, D.Hudson, P.Woods, J.Ray, D.Harris and C.Wall. **Front row:** J.Hannis, K.Ayres, D.Cleaver, J.Moore, M.Hart, K.Wilson, P. Cobb and T.Davey.

UXBRIDGE

CLUB OFFICIALS

Chairman: Alan Holloway
President: Alan Odell
Secretary: Roger Stevens, 9 Bourne Avenue, Hillingdon, Middlessex UB8 3AR
Tell No: 01895 236879
Match Sec: Mick Burrell Tel: 01895 443094
Match Sec Res:PeterGranville 01595 233208
Commercial Manager: Derek Marshall
Press Officer: David Gill
Youth Team Sec: David Gill 0208 581 6517

FACT FILE

Formed: 1871
Nickname: The Reds
Sponsor:
Colours: Red/white/red
Change: All Sky navy blue.
Midweek matchday: Tuesday
Reserves' League: Suburban (North Div)

2003-2004

P.O.Y.: Michael Swaysland
Top Goalscorer: Michael Swaysland

2004-2005 Captain: Stuart Bamford.

FOOTBALL MANAGEMENT TEAM

Manager: George Talbot Ass. Manager: Sean Dawson
Coach: Mark Gill Physios: Ian Doubleday & Paul Donnell
Res Manager: Phil Granville Youth Manager: Robert Frape

Pages: 44 Price: £1.00
Editor: BB Publications
E-mail: bbpublications@tiscali.co.uk
Local Press: Uxbridge Gazette & Leader, Uxbridge Recorder
Local Radio: Capital, G L R, Star FM

GROUND Honeycroft, Horton Road, West Drayton, Middx UB7 8HX Tel: 01895 443557
Directions: From West Drayton (BR) turn right then 1st right (Horton Road).Ground 1 mile on left. From Uxbridge (LT) take 222 or U3 bus to West Drayton station, then follow as above. By road, ground 1 mile north of M4 jct 4 takingroad to Uxbridge and leaving by first junction and turning left into Horton Rd- ground 500yds on right. Nearest Railway station: West Drayton.
Capacity: 3,770 Cover: 760 Seats: 339 Floodlights: Yes
Clubhouse: Open every evening and weekend/bank holiday lunchtimes. (01895 443557)
Hot & cold snacks available on matchdays Large clubhouse with bar and function room availablefor hire.

PREVIOUS **Leagues:** Southern 1894-99; Gt Western Suburban 1906-19, 20-23; Athenian 1919-20, 24-37, 63-82; Spartan 37-38; London 38-46; Gt Western Comb. 39-45;Corinthian 46-63
Name: Uxbridge Town 23-45 **Grounds:** RAF Stadium 23-48, Cleveland Rd 48-78
CLUB RECORDS **Attendance:** 1,000 v Arsenal, opening of floodlights 1981
Career Scorer: Phil Duff, 153 **Career Appearances:** Roger Nicholls, 1054
BEST SEASON **FA Trophy:** 2nd Rd.1998-99, 99-00, 00-01 **FA Vase:** 4th Rd 83-84
FA Cup: 2nd Rd 1873-74. Also 1st Rd 1883-84 84-85 85-86 **FA Amateur Cup:** Runners-up 1897-98
HONOURS FA Amateur Cup R-up 1897-98; London Chall. Cup 93-94 96-97 98-99, R-up 97-98; IsthLge Div 2 S. R-up 84-85; Athenian Lge Cup R-up 81-82, Res. Sect. 69-70, Res. Cup R-up 68-69; Corinthian Lge 59-60 (R-up 48-49), Lge Mem. Shield 50-51 52-53; Middx Sen.Cup 1893-94 95-96 1950-51, 2000-01 R-up 97-98; Middx Sen. Charity Cup 07-08 12-13 35-36 81-82 (R-up 69-70 82-83 85-86); Middx PremCup 95-96 (R-up 2000-01; Allied Counties Yth Lge [East] 92-93 (Lge Cup R-up 86-87), Lge Shield 88-89 92-93, R-up 97-98; AC Delco Cup R-up 85-86; Suburban Lge North Div 95-96 97-98, R-up 96-97; Middx Sen Yth Cup 96-97
Players progressing: William Hill (QPR 51), Lee Stapleton (Fulham 52), Gary Churchouse (Charlton A.), Tony Witter (QPR), Guy Butters (Spurs), Michael Meaker (QPR)

2004-05 Back Row (L-R): S Dawson, G Talbot, S Lake, M Saysland, J swift, R Francis, J Beckford, C O'Leary, K swift, M Gill, P Donelly.
Front: N Rundell, S Bamford, J Cleary, H Howells, S Walters, A Sweet, T Thunder.

WALTHAM FOREST

CLUB OFFICIALS

Chairman: Harry Ramis

Vice-Chairman: Altan Kemal

President: George Cross

Secretary / Press Officer: Andy Perkins
4 Chestnut Drive,Wanstead, London E11 2TA
Tel: 02085304551

FOOTBALL MANAGEMENT TEAM

Team Manager Hakan Heyrattin

Asst.Man : Eddie Styein & Hasan Oktay
Physio: Mike Gordon

FACT FILE

Formed: 1995
Nickname: Lilywhites
Sponsors:Eds Transport Services.
Colours: White/black/white
Change colours: Yellow/blue/blue
Midweek home matchday: Tuesday
Reserves' Lge: Suburban & Capital
2003- 2004Captain: Ian Barnes
Top Scorers: Dewayne Clarke

Season 2003-2004
Waltham Forest Football Club
v
Oxford City Football Club
RYMAN LEAGUE DIVISION ONE (NORTH)
SATURDAY, 10TH APRIL 2004 KO 3pm
MAIN SPONSORS
E.D.S TRANSPORT SERVICES
Nationwide Storage & Distribution
Ryman
E.P.S Heating Ltd

Pages: 32 Price: £1
Editor: Andy Perkins
Local Press: Waltham Forest Guardian,
Local Radio: LBC
Website: www.waltham forestfc.com

GROUND: Wadham Lodge Sports Ground,Kitchener Road, Walthamstowe,London E17
Tel: 020 8527 2444 **Email:** andyperkins@walthamforestfc.com
Directions: Take the North Circular Road to The Crooked Billet,then turn right into Chingford Road and into Brookscroft Road , ground is in Kitchener Road first on left .Walthamstowe Central (Victoria Line tube) is one mile away then buses W21 or 256
Capacity: 2,000 Cover: 600 Seats: 200 Floodlights: Yes
Clubhouse: Open 11-11 Mon-Sat 12-3 & 7-10-30 Sun. Tel: 0208 527 2444
No hot food but snacks available on match days from tea bar.
Club Shop: Sells progs, pennants, scarves, badges etc. Contact Ian Ansell c/o club

PREVIOUS **Name:** Walthamstow Pennant (64-95), Leyton Pannant (1995-2003)

HONOURS London Challenge Cup Runners-Up 1995-96, 1996-97

Back Row (L-R): Cevdet Ezel, Dave Salmon, Altan Kemal, Dave Crabb, David Field, Simon Tickler, Rick Brown, Ian Barnes, Peter Goodman, Gavin King, Paul Salmon, Robert Carter, Liam Baptiste, John Lawford, Andy Perkins, Tony Brazior, George Gross, Harry Ramis.
Middle Row: Billy Reid, Jay devereax, Tony Samuels, Kemi Kemal, Hakan Ramis, Wayne Brown, Onder Acil, John Morgan, SAS.
Front Row: Hasan Oktay, Ryan Lee, Warren Ryan, Paul Adolphe, Chris Cashman, I SOS, Ryan Fishendon, Warren Hackett.

WINGATE & FINCHLEY

CLUB OFFICIALS

Chairman: Michael Brown

Presidents:David Pleat & Harvey Ackerman

Press Off.:Adam Rynhold
Tel: 020 8888 7530 (H) 079561 43291(M)

Secretary: Maurice Hanover,c/o Club.
Tel : Club - as below.
020 8501 0607(H) 07976 265588(M)

FOOTBALL MANAGEMENT TEAM

Manager: Adam Lee
Coach: AdamJeff Bookman

FACT FILE

Founded: 1991
Nickname: Blues
Colours: SkyBlue & white stripes/white/white
Change Colours: All yellow
Midweek matches: Tuesday
Reserve's Lge: Sub Lge U18

PROGRAMME

32 pages Price: £1.50
Editor: Peter Rebak (0208 8609 0001)

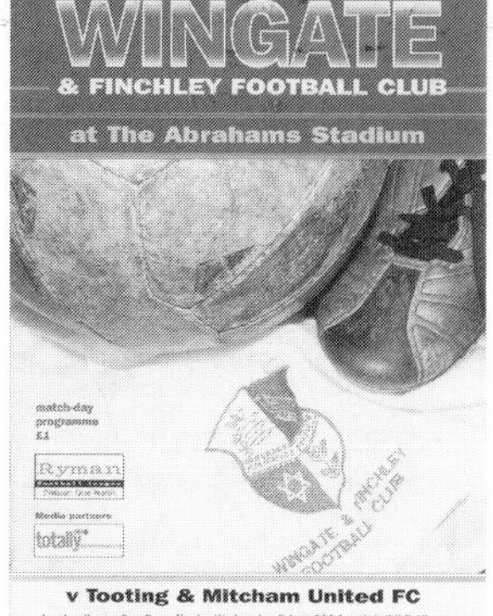

GROUND: The Abrahams Stadium, Summers Lane, Finchley, London N12 0PD
Tel: 0208 446 2217 Fax: 020 8343 8194

Directions: North Circular (A406) to junction with High Road Finchley (A1000).
Go north and Summers Lane is 200 yds on right - parking for 80 cars. Bus 382 passes ground
Tube to East Finchley (Northern Line) and then 263 bus to Summers Lane towards North Finchley

Capacity: 8,500 **Seats:** 500 **Cover:** 500 **Floodlights:** Yes **Club Shop:** No

Clubhouse: Open during matches. Also tea-bar selling most refreshments

PREVIOUS: **Names:** Wingate (founded 46), Finchley (founded late 1800s) merged in 91
Leagues: (as Wingate & Finchley) South Mids 89-95Finchley: London 02-12 14-15 23-25 30-39; Athenian 12-14 29-30 45-73; Isthmian73-91Wingate: Middx 46-52; London 52-62; Delphian 62-63; Athenian 63-75; Barnet Yth,Hendon & Dist. Sunday 75-84; Herts 84-89 Isthmian 94-04

CLUB RECORDS: **Attendance:** 9,555 - Finchley v Bishop Auckland, F.A. Amat Cup QF 49-50
Career Goalscorer: Marc Morris 578 **Career Appearances:** Marc Morris 587(1975-93)
Win: 9-0, Wingate v Sarratt, Herts Co. Lge Div. 1, 20/4/85
Defeat: 0-9 v Edgware,Ryman League Division Two. 15.1.2000

BEST SEASON **FA Vase:** 74-75 Quarter Final (Wingate)
FA Amateur Cup: Semi-Final (Finchley)

HONOURS: Isthmian League Div. 3 R-up 98-99, Promoted (7th) 2001-02, London Senior Cup winners 94-95

Previous Honours Finchley: London Snr Cup, London Charity Cup, FA Amtr Cup SF, Athenian Lg 53-54(R-up 63-64 65-66), London Lg 36-37 (R-up 35-36, Div 2 06-07(jt with Enfield),Lg Cup 34-35, Park Royal Cup 37-38)
Wingate: Middx Lg(2)(R-up(1), Lg Cup), London Lg R-up(2)(Lg Cup(1)), Middx SnrCup SF, Athenian Lg Div 2 69-70, Herts Co. Lg Div 1 84-85 (Aubrey Cup 85-86),Herts I'mediate Cup 84-85, Herts Snr Tphy 86-87, Sth Mids Lg Div 1 R-up 89-90(Lg Cup SF 89-90), Barnet Yth Lg 75-76, Pete Morrison Cup 82-83 83-84 (R-up 79-80 84-85), Hendon & Dist. Int. Div 79-80. Win & Fin: London Sen Cup 79-80

Back row, left to right: Adam Lee, Marcus Davis, A Newman, Andy Walker, Daniel Boateng, Steve Forwell and Robert Donn
Front row: Daniel Nielson, Daniel Fitzpatrick, John Butterfield, Dean Williams, Paul Wood, Daniel Berg, Clive Wilson and Guy Morris.
Photo: Arthur Evans

WIVENHOE TOWN

CLUB OFFICIALS

Chairman: Phil Reeve
Secretary / Press Officer: Mike Boyle,
15 Daniell Drive, Colchester, Essex
Tel: 01206 573223

FOOTBALL MANAGEMENT TEAM
Manager: Steve Pitt

FACT FILE
Formed: 1925 Nickname: The Dragons
Colours: Royal blue/white/white
Change colours: Orange/black/black
Reserves' League: Essex & Suffolk Border
Midweek matchday: Tuesday
2003-2004
P.o.Y.: Ray Turner
Top Goalscorer: Ray Turner
2004-2005
Captain: David Gregory

40 Pages Price: £1.00
Editor: M.Boyle
Local Press: East Anglian Daily Times, Colchester Evening Gazette
Local Radio: BBC Radio Essex, S.G.R.

GROUND: Broad Lane Ground, Elmstead Road, Wivenhoe CO7 7HA
Tel: 01206 825380

Directions: Coming out of Colchester towards Clacton take first turning (right) towards Wivenhoe, then 1st left and the ground is clearly visible on the right at the cross-roads. 1 mile from Wivenhoe (BR)

Capacity: 3,000 Cover: 1,300 Seats: 250 Floodlights: Yes

Clubhouse: Open normal pub hours. Tel: 01206 825380
Club Shop: A full range of souvenirs etc

PREVIOUS: **Leagues:** Brighlingsea & District 1927-50; Colchester & East Essex 50-71; Essex & Suffolk Border 71-79; Essex Senior 79-86
Name: Wivenhoe Rangers
Grounds: Spion Kop; Broomfield (twice); Claude Watcham's Meadow; Vine Farm; King George V Playing Fields; Essex University

CLUB RECORD **Attendance:** 1,912 v Runcorn, FA Trophy 1st Rd, Feb 1990
Transfer fee received: £5,875 for Bobby Mayes (Redbridge Forest)
Win: 18-0 v Nayland. **Defeat:** 0-8 v Carshalton A. (H), Isthmian Lg 28/8/93
Career goalscorer: Paul Harrison, 258 in 350 games **Career appearances:** Keith Bain, 536

BEST SEASON **FA Cup:** 4th Qual Rd 89-90 2-3 v Halesowen Tn (A), 94-95 1-2 v Enfield (H)
FA Trophy: 2nd Rd replay 89-90 **FA Vase:** 5th Rd 82-83;

HONOURS Isthmian Lg Div 1 89-90 (Div 2 Nth 87-88); Essex Snr Lg R-up 79-80 81-82 85-86(Harry Fisher Tphy 83-84 85-86); Essex & Suffolk Border Lg 78-79, Div 1 72-73,Div 2 71-72, Lg Cup R-up(2); Colchester & East Essex Lg 52-53 55-56 (R-up 70-71), Div 1 59-60 69-70, Div 2 R-up 68-69, Lg KO Cup 51-52 52-53 54-55 55-56 (R-up 59-60), Challenge Cup 52-53); Brighlingsea & Dist Lg Div 1 35-36 36-37 47-48(R-up 37-38), Lg KO Cup 36-37 37-38 47-48, Challenge Cup 36-37; Essex Snr Tphy87-88 Essex Jnr Cup R-up 55-56 78-79; Amos Charity Cup(7) (R-up 72-73); StokesCup(3); Wivenhoe Charity Cup (4), (R-up [4]); Cristal Monopole Cup (5), (R-up 2); Sidney James Mem. Tphy 69-70 (R-up 72-73), Tolleshunt D'Arcy Mem. Cup(3)(R-up 2); Walton & District Charity Cup 73-74 78-79; Coggeshall Brotherhood Cup80-81; Brantham Charity Cup R-up 82-83; Worthington Evans Cup 81-82 (R-up 80-8185-86); Harwich Snr Cup R-up 84-85; Woodbridge Chal. Cup 91-92; Mat FowlerShield 92-93 94-95

Players progressing: Robert Reinelt (Gillingham) 1993

FOOTBALL LEAGUE

STEP 1

FOOTBALL CONFERENCE

STEP 2

CONFERENCE NORTH

CONFERENCE SOUTH

STEP 3

northern premier

SOUTHERN PREMIER

ISTHMIAN PREMIER

STEP 4

NORTHERN PREMIER DIV.1

SOUTHERN LEAGUE EAST

SOUTHERN LEAGUE WEST

ISTHMIAN DIVISION 1

STEP 5/6

STEP 7

ISTHMIAN LEAGUE

Ryman
football league

SPONSORED BY: RYMAN

Chairman: A C F Turvey, MCIM

Secretary: N R Robinson, Triumph House, Station Approach, Sanderstead Road, South Croydon Surrey CR2 0PL

Tel: 020 8409 1978 (H) 020 8651 5053 (B) secretary@isthmian.co.uk

Last season was not a happy time for the Isthmian League. The whole campaign was played under the shadow of re structuring and questioning whether the League officers were representing the majority view of their clubs in the national debate, conducted under the jurisdiction of the Football Association.

Did they really want to be part of it? The clubs intimated that they did .

Were they happy about the 1-2-3-4 structure of leagues at the top ? They probably didn't mind, but they definitely thought that two of the four should be theirs.

Those were two of the very basic points in a much more complicated discussion, but the headlines and politics were unsettling for everyone involved in the competition.

While the dust was swirling to obscure matters off the field, the championship was never in doubt on it. Canvey Island finally secured promotion after three near misses and thoroughly deserved their place in the Conference. They surprisingly didn't complete the league and Trophy double but, with Lee Boylan fabulous goalscoring ability in front of a quality squad, the whole club will be looking forward to challenging the top teams and also moving into a special new ground.

Where would the rest of the Ryman clubs be placed in the end of season shuffle? That was the problem for just about every other club so it made the season very special indeed. Some would be in Conference South, others would stay where they were (but that would really be going down a level in the pyramid).

It was also possible that a club in their old Division One could achieve a mini miracle and find themselves in one of the Conference Divisions and out of the Isthmian family all together. As Division One South champions they beat Yeading away 1-0.and then faced Basingstoke Town from the lower regions of Ryman Premier. They won 4-1 away again and qualified to face Kingstonian and celebrated a famous promotion with a 1-0 victory and a place in the Conference.

With six clubs gaining automatic promotion behind their champions, Yeading and Lewes, in the Divisions One North and South respectively, there were obviously a lot of happy supporters. Clubs such as Windsor & Eton, Hemel Hempstead, Dunstable Town, Cheshunt and Leyton will enjoy life in a Premier Division and it's good to see Wealdstone, Dulwich Hamlet and Slough Town on the way back. Leighton Town and Dorking also timed their good season to perfection and they will feel released away from football at Step 5 level.

Apart from providing an F.A.Trophy finalist in Canvey Island, the county of Essex certainly provided the Ryman League with an impressive line up in the F.A.Cup competition proper. Thurrock featured on Sky TV in their live tie against Luton Town and of course Canvey again obliged but lost to neighbours Southend United were joined in the First Round by Grays Athletic, Hornchurch and Ford United with neighbours Boreham Wood also involved.

Hopefully, the spirit of the Isthmian League, a great competition, will help it regroup and strengthen as the dust settles after an unpleasant couple of years. Many old friends have moved on and new names have arrived. Hopefully, the future will be a happy and successful one with the Isthmian League playing its part in creating a healthy and positive new structure .

PREMIER DIVISION FINAL LEAGUE TABLE 2003-04

			P	W	D	L	F	A	Pts
	1.	Canvey Island	46	32	8	6	106	42	104
Qualify for Conference North/South	2.	Sutton United	46	25	10	11	94	56	85
	3.	Thurrock	46	24	11	11	87	45	83
	4.	Hendon (stay in Premier Div.)	46	25	8	13	68	47	83
	5.	Hornchurch (-1pt)	46	24	11	11	63	35	82
	6.	Grays Athletic	46	22	15	9	82	39	81
	7.	Carshalton Athletic	46	24	9	13	66	55	81
	8.	Hayes	46	21	11	14	56	46	74
	9.	Kettering Town	46	20	11	15	63	63	71
	10.	Bognor Regis Town	46	20	10	16	69	67	70
	11.	Bishop's Stortford	46	20	9	17	78	61	69
	12.	Maidenhead United	46	18	9	19	60	68	63
	13.	Ford United	46	16	14	16	69	63	62
	14.	Basingstoke Town	46	17	9	20	58	64	60
	15.	Bedford Town	46	14	13	19	62	63	55
	16.	Heybridge Swifts	46	14	11	21	57	78	53
	17.	Harrow Borough	46	12	14	20	47	63	50
	18.	Kingstonian	46	12	13	21	40	56	49
	19.	St Albans City *	46	12	12	22	55	83	48
	20.	Hitchin Town	46	13	8	25	55	89	47
	21.	Northwood	46	12	9	25	65	95	45
	22.	Billericay Town	46	11	11	24	51	66	44
	23.	Braintree Town	46	11	6	29	41	88	39
	24.	Aylesbury United	46	5	14	27	41	101	29

*Qualified for Conference South via the play-offs.

PLAY OFF MATCHES FOR PLACES IN THE NEW SEMI-NATIONAL LEAGUES

FIRST ROUND

(contested by Division One North and South champions)

(3rd May at Yeading)

Yeading 0 **Lewes** 1 **Att** 327

SEMI-FINALS

(8th May at grounds of first named clubs)

Basingstoke Town 1 **Lewes** 4 **Att** 310

Bedford Town 3 Hitchin Town 1 **Att** 703

Harrow Borough 0 **Kingstonian** 0 aet (3-4p) **Att** 268

Heybridge Swifts 3 **St Albans City** 4* **Att** 285

THE FINALS

Bedford Town 4 **St Albans City** 5 **Att** 1087

Lewes 1 Kingstonian 0 **Att** 1062

PLAY-OFF FOR PLACE IN ISTHMIAN PREMIER DIVISION

Dulwich Hamlet 2 Wealdstone 2* 4-5p

Att 582

PREMIER DIVISION 03-04		1	2	3	4	5	6	7	8	9	10	11	12	13	14	15	16	17	18	19	20	21	22	23	24
1	Aylesbury United		0-3	3-3	3-2	0-1	1-0	0-0	0-2	1-1	3-2	0-3	0-1	0-1	1-1	0-0	1-4	0-2	0-2	0-0	1-3	1-2	0-2	0-6	2-4
2	Basingstoke Town	2-0		2-0	0-1	1-2	0-1	3-0	1-2	1-2	1-0	0-2	0-1	0-2	1-4	1-1	2-3	0-3	2-2	2-1	2-1	2-0	1-1	0-5	0-3
3	Bedford Town	4-1	5-2		2-1	0-3	8-0	2-0	2-4	1-0	1-1	0-4	2-0	1-2	0-2	3-1	1-2	2-1	2-3	0-0	1-2	1-4	1-0	2-1	0-0
4	Billericay Town	2-2	3-1	0-0		1-0	1-1	0-1	0-3	0-1	1-0	0-1	0-1	0-2	1-2	1-2	1-3	2-0	3-1	1-2	0-1	1-4	1-1	0-1	1-1
5	Bishop's Stortford	4-4	0-1	3-1	3-0		0-0	2-3	2-0	0-3	4-0	1-2	1-1	0-0	2-0	0-1	3-0	2-1	4-1	2-1	2-1	6-0	2-2	1-1	1-3
6	Bognor Regis Town	4-0	1-3	0-0	2-0	0-1		4-1	0-0	0-1	3-2	2-1	3-1	4-0	1-2	2-0	2-0	1-3	1-0	2-0	0-3	5-2	2-2	0-2	6-1
7	Braintree Town	2-0	0-1	0-2	2-2	2-0	0-3		0-3	0-1	1-2	0-5	0-2	1-2	1-3	1-3	2-0	1-3	0-1	0-1	1-2	2-5	2-4	0-3	1-0
8	Canvey Island	4-0	3-1	3-1	0-2	5-1	3-1	4-1		3-0	3-1	1-1	1-1	2-1	1-0	2-0	4-0	3-2	1-1	6-1	3-1	1-1	4-0	1-3	4-3
9	Carshalton Athletic	3-0	0-2	2-1	2-1	1-2	1-1	2-1	0-2		1-1	0-2	3-2	2-0	1-3	4-1	2-1	0-0	3-2	2-1	3-2	1-0	1-1	2-2	0-3
10	Ford United	4-1	1-1	1-1	2-1	3-0	2-0	3-0	0-3	2-1		3-0	1-3	0-0	0-1	5-3	3-0	0-0	2-0	0-1	1-1	3-0	2-2	2-4	2-3
11	Grays Athletic	2-1	3-1	1-1	1-1	3-1	6-0	1-1	1-1	0-0	2-0		2-2	4-0	1-0	4-0	2-0	0-0	1-1	1-0	1-1	2-1	9-1	3-2	1-1
12	Harrow Borough	0-2	1-1	2-1	2-1	1-0	0-1	2-3	0-1	0-0	1-1	0-0		1-0	1-2	0-0	0-2	0-0	1-2	0-1	1-1	2-2	3-1	2-4	1-2
13	Hayes	3-0	2-1	1-0	1-1	1-0	0-1	0-0	2-1	1-0	1-1	1-1	1-1		3-1	2-0	5-1	1-1	0-1	1-0	0-1	1-1	1-0	0-0	1-2
14	Hendon	1-1	0-1	1-0	3-0	2-5	2-2	1-0	1-0	1-2	2-2	1-0	2-0	3-2		0-1	3-0	1-0	1-2	2-0	3-1	1-1	1-1	0-2	1-1
15	Heybridge Swifts	1-2	0-3	0-0	1-4	1-0	1-2	1-2	1-4	4-0	4-1	3-0	2-3	1-2	0-0		4-2	1-1	1-0	0-2	0-0	3-2	0-2	2-2	0-3
16	Hitchin Town	2-2	2-2	1-3	2-5	0-2	2-2	2-0	1-3	0-3	1-1	1-0	3-2	0-2	1-4	1-2		0-2	1-1	3-0	2-0	1-2	1-0	2-4	0-0
17	Hornchurch	1-0	2-0	1-0	1-1	2-0	3-0	2-1	0-0	2-0	1-0	2-0	2-1	0-2	0-2	0-2	4-0		1-1	1-0	1-0	3-1	0-1	3-0	2-0
18	Kettering Town	2-2	0-3	0-0	1-0	3-2	3-1	1-2	1-4	0-3	0-3	0-0	1-1	0-3	4-1	4-1	1-1	3-2		1-1	3-1	2-1	2-0	0-1	2-1
19	Kingstonian	0-0	2-0	0-0	0-0	1-1	1-1	2-2	1-2	0-1	0-2	3-1	1-1	1-0	0-1	1-1	1-1	0-1	1-0		3-1	0-1	1-2	1-2	1-1
20	Maidenhead United	4-2	0-2	2-1	1-0	0-4	0-2	4-0	0-0	0-0	1-1	1-4	1-0	1-0	0-1	2-4	2-1	1-1	1-2	0-4		3-1	4-2	2-0	1-4
21	Northwood	1-1	0-0	3-1	4-5	2-3	1-2	3-1	1-5	0-4	2-3	1-1	3-1	3-4	0-1	2-1	1-0	0-1	1-2	2-0	0-0		3-4	1-2	0-3
22	St Albans City	3-1	0-3	1-3	0-2	3-2	2-2	0-0	4-1	0-4	2-0	0-3	0-1	1-1	0-4	0-0	1-2	1-1	0-1	0-1	1-2	3-0		2-0	0-2
23	Sutton United	2-2	2-2	1-1	1-1	2-2	1-0	1-2	0-1	6-0	2-3	1-0	3-0	4-1	2-0	5-1	0-3	3-1	2-1	4-1	0-3	0-0	4-2		0-3
24	Thurrock	5-0	0-0	1-1	1-0	1-1	4-1	0-1	1-2	2-3	0-0	2-0	3-0	2-0	2-0	1-1	2-0	1-3	0-2	4-1	3-1	6-0	2-0	0-1	

LEAGUE CUP

FIRST ROUND

Arlesey Town	v	Abingdon Town	3-0
Banstead Athletic (w/o)	v	Tring Town	
Bracknell Town (w/o)	v	Clapton	
Chalfont St Peter	v	Ware	5-1
Dorking	v	Worthing	0-1
Dunstable Town	v	Wivenhoe Town	7-1
East Thurrock Utd	v	Croydon	2-1
Epsom & Ewell	v	Waltham Forest	0-1
Flackwell Heath	v	Egham Town	1-5
Great Wakering R.	v	Barton Rovers	2-1
Harlow Town	v	Hertford Town	2-0
Kingsbury Town	v	Wealdstone	0-8
Leatherhead	v	Croydon Athletic	1-4
Leighton Town	v	Ashford Town (Middx)	0-2
Marlow	v	Barking & East Ham Utd	2-2* 5-4p
Metropolitan Police	v	Corinthian Casuals	2-1*
Molesey	v	Windsor & Eton	3-1
Oxford City	v	Cheshunt	1-3
Staines Town	v	Witham Town	4-4* 4-5p
Tooting & Mit' Utd	v	Leyton	1-2*
Wembley	v	Camberley Town	0-1
Wingate & Finchley	v	Chertsey Town	2-0
Wokingham Town	v	Tilbury	2-4
Yeading	v	Edgware Town	5-1

SECOND ROUND

Arlesey Town	v	Hornchurch	0-2
Basingstoke Town	v	Aylesbury United	2-0
Bedford Town	v	Bognor Regis Town	1-0
Berkhamsted Town	v	Ashford Town (Middx)	0-2
Billericay Town	v	East Thurrock United	1-2
Bracknell Town	v	Chalfont St Peter	5-0
Braintree Town	v	Thurrock	1-2
Camberley Town	v	Northwood	0-1
Canvey Island	v	Hendon	0-3
Carshalton Athletic	v	Harlow Town	0-1
Chesham United	v	Lewes	1-0
Dulwich Hamlet	v	Hampton & Richmond	3-3* 3-4p
Egham Town	v	Tilbury	4-2
Ford United	v	Bishop's Stortford	2-1
Great Wakering R.	v	Banstead Athletic	2-1
Harrow Borough	v	Bromley	2-0
Heybridge Swifts	v	St Albans City	2-1
Horsham	v	Witham Town	2-1
Kingstonian	v	Croydon Athletic	2-0
Leyton	v	Enfield	4-1
Maidenhead Utd	v	Hayes	3-2
Marlow	v	Boreham Wood	3-2
Molesey	v	Walton & Hersham	0-0* 4-2p
Slough Town	v	Cheshunt	1-4
Sutton United	v	Metropolitan Police	2-0
Thame United	v	Hitchin Town	1-2
Uxbridge	v	Dunstable Town	1-2
Waltham Forest	v	Aveley	0-2
Whyteleafe	v	Grays Athletic	0-2
Wingate & Finchley	v	Wealdstone	2-0
Worthing	v	Kettering Town	2-0
Yeading	v	Hemel Hempstead Town	2-1

THIRD ROUND

Aveley	v	Hornchurch	0-5
Basingstoke Town	v	Ashford (Middx)	0-0* 2-3p
Bracknell Town	v	Hendon	4-3*
Chesham United	v	Molesey	6-1
East Thurrock Utd	v	Wingate & Finchley	1-2
Egham Town	v	Grays Athletic	0-1
Ford United	v	Northwood	0-1
Harlow Town	v	Great Wakering Rovers	3-1
Heybridge Swifts	v	Harrow Borough	3-2*
Hitchin Town	v	Marlow	1-3
Horsham	v	Bedford Town	0-3
Leyton	v	Hampton & Richmond Boro'	1-2
Sutton United	v	Dunstable Town	2-3
Thurrock	v	Kingstonian	1-0
Worthing	v	Maidenhead United	2-0
Yeading	v	Cheshunt	4-4* 8-9p

FOURTH ROUND

Bracknell Town	v	Worthing	2-1*
Chesham United	v	Ashford Town (Middx)	2-0
Dunstable Town	v	Grays Athletic	1-0
Hampton & Rich' B.	v	Wingate & Finchley	4-2
Heybridge Swifts	v	Cheshunt	3-4
Hornchurch	v	Harlow Town	0-0* 2-4p
Marlow	v	Northwood	2-0
Thurrock	v	Bedford Town	4-1

QUARTER-FINALS

Bracknell Town	v	Hampton & Richmond Boro'	1-2
Dunstable Town	v	Harlow Town	4-1*
Marlow	v	Cheshunt	1-2
Thurrock	v	Chesham United	2-1

SEMI-FINALS (played over two legs, home & away)

			1st	2nd
Cheshunt	v	Thurrock	0-2	2-1
Dunstable Town	v	Hampton & Rich'B.	2-1	3-1

THE FINAL (7th August)

Thurrock	v	Dunstable Town	5-1

BILLERICAY TOWN

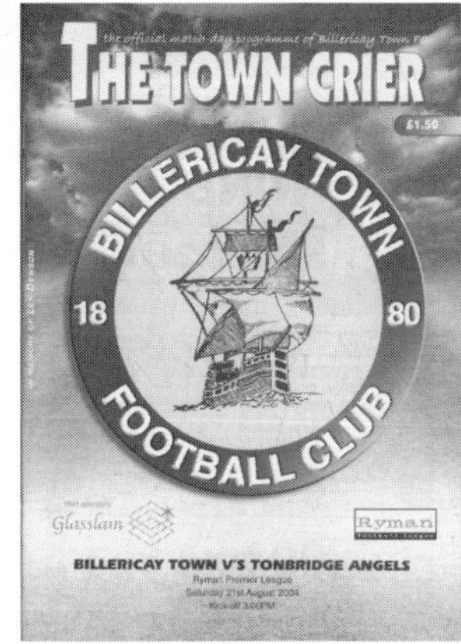

CLUB OFFICIALS
Chairman: Steve Kent
President: Jim Hall
Secretary: Ian Ansell c/o B.T.F.C.
Tel No: 0208 500 9778 (H)
Hon.Admin Secretary: Len Dewson
Press Officer: Simon Williams

FOOTBALL MANAGEMENT TEAM
Manager: Justin Edinburgh
Assistant Manager.: Matt Jones
Youth Developement: Martin Godbold
Physio: Gary Lynn

2003-2004
Top Goalscorer: Danny Hockton
Player of the Year: Jamie Dormmer

FACT FILE
Formed: 1880
Nickname: The Town
Sponsors:Stadia Management Ltd.
Colours: Royal Blue/White/ Royal Blue
Change colours: Yellow/black/yellow
Midweek Matches: Tuesday
Local Press: Evening Echo, Billericay Gazette, Billericay Recorder
Local Radio: BBC Radio Essex, Essex Radio, Essex FM

PROGRAMME
Pages: 32 .Price: £1.50
Editor: Simon Williams

GROUND: New Lodge, Blunts Wall Rd, Billericay CM12 9SA. 01277 652188 Club Website: www.billericaytownfc.co.uk
Directions: From Shenfield (A129) right at 1st lights then 2nd right. FromBasildon (A129) over 1st lights in town, then left at next lights and 2nd right. Half mile from Billericay (GER) (London Liverpool St. - Southend line). 5 mins walk from buses 222, 251, 357, 255, 551
Capacity: 3,500 Seats: 424 Cover: 2000 Floodlights: Yes
Clubhouse: Open every evening 8-11pm (except Monday)(1pm-11pm Sat) and weekendlunch times noon-2.30pm. Discos, live entertainment
Club Shop: Open matchdays for souvenirs, metal badges, old progs, programme swaps Andrew Turner (01277 631476)

PREVIOUS **Leagues:** Romford & Dist. 1890-1914; Mid Essex 18-47; South Essex Comb. 47-66; Essex Olympian 66-71; Essex Snr 71-77; Athenian 77-79 **Grounds**: Laindon Road (pre-1971).

CLUB RECORDS **Attendance:** 3,841 v West Ham Utd, Floodlight opener 77. Comp match: 3,193 v Farnborough Tn, FA Vase SF 1st leg 76
Win: 11-0 v Stansted (A), Essex Senior League 5/5/76
Defeat: 3-10 v Chelmsford City (A), Essex Senior Cup 4/1/93
Goalscorer: (career) F Clayden 273, (season) Leon Gutmore 51 (97-98) **Appearances:** J Pullen 418
Fees - Paid: Undisclosed **Received:** £22,500+ increments for Steve Jones (West Ham, Nov. 1992)

BEST SEASON **FA Cup:** 1st Rd Proper 97-98 **FA Vase:** Winners - 75-76, 76-77 & 78-79
FA Trophy: 5th Rd 00-01 **FA Amateur Cup:** 3rd Qual Rd 73-74

HONOURS: Essex Snr Lg 72-73 74-75 75-76, R-up 71-2 73-4, Lg Cup 71-72, Challenge Cup 72-73, 76-77 (R.up 74-75); Isthmian Lge Div 2 79-80, Div 1 R-up 80-81, 97-98; Athenian Lg 77-79 (Lg Cup 77-78); East Anglian Cup R-up 79-80 84-5; Essex Snr Cup 75-76 R-up 85-6 93-4,4-5,5-6; Essex Snr Tphy 77-78 79-80; Essex Thameside Tphy 86-87 91-92 R-up 90-1; Essex F'lit Tphy 77-78; Phillips F'lit Tphy 76-77; Rothmans Merit Award 1978

Players progressing: D Westwood (QPR) 75, A Hull, D Carter (Peterborough,Orient), D Cass (Orient) 88, D Ludden (Orient) 92, S Jones (West Ham) 92

BRAINTREE TOWN

CLUB OFFICIALS

Chairman: Lee Harding
Vice Chairman: Barry Shepherd
President: Ron Webb
Secretary: T A Woodley, 19a Bailey Bridge Rd., Braintree, Essex CM7 5TT
Tel: 01376 326234
Press Officer: Ron Webb Tel: 01376 325338

FOOTBALL MANAGEMENT TEAM

Manager: George Borg
Coach:Gary Abbott
Physio: Tony Brightwell

FACT FILE

Founded: 1898
Nickname: The Iron
Sponsors: Westdrive
Colours:Yellow
Change colours: White
Local Radio: BBC Essex (103.5 fm), Essex Radio (102.6 fm)

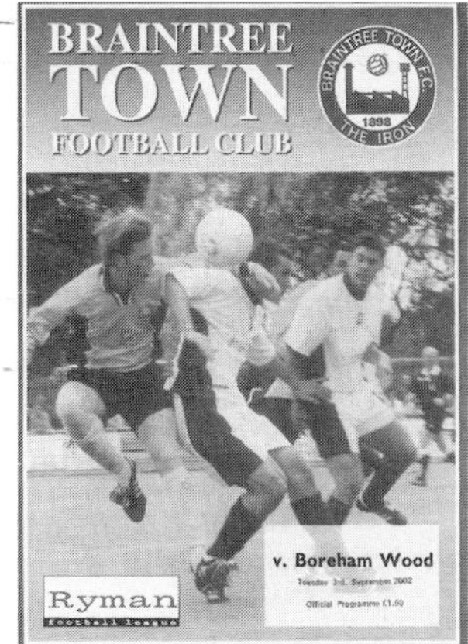

PROGRAMME

Pages: 40 Price: £2.00
Editor: Len Llewellyn (01277 363103 T/Fax)

GROUND Cressing Road Stadium, Clockhouse Way, Braintree, Essex (01376 345617)
Directions: From Braintree by-pass, turn into Braintree at the McDonalds r'bout, follow signs for East Braintree Ind. Est. - floodlights on left 3/4 mile into town just past. Orange Tree Pub. Entrance next left in Clockhouse Way, then left again. 1 mile from Braintree & Bocking (BR). Bus 353 from Witham or town centre. Town centre 20 mins walk
Capacity:3,050 Cover 1,500 Seats 250 Floodlights:Yes
Clubhouse: Open evenings 7-30-11, Sun 12-3, Sat matchday 12.00- 11.00 Full bar facilities
Club shop: ContactTom Marshallc/o club (75 year History of Braintree £15.99)

PREVIOUS **Leagues:** North Essex 1898-1925; Essex & Suffolk Border 25-28 55-64; Spartan 28-35; Eastern Co's 35-37 38-39 52-55 70-91; Essex Co. 37-38; London 45-52; GtrLondon 64-66; Metropolitan 66-70; Southern 91-96
Names: Manor Works 1898-1921; Crittall Ath. 21-68; Braintree & Crittall Ath. 68-81; Braintree FC 81-82
Grounds: The Fair Field 1898-1903; Spaldings Meadow, Panfield Lane 03-23

CLUB RECORDS **Attendance:** 4,000 v Spurs, charity challenge match, May 1952
Career Goalscorer: Chris Guy 211, 63-90. **Seasonal Record Scorer:** Gary Bennett 57, 97-98
Career Appearances: Paul Young 524, 66-77 **Fee Paid:** £2,000 for Shane Bailey (Sudbury Town)
Fee Received: £10,000 Matt Metcalf (Brentford 93) & John Cheesewright(Colchester 93)
Win: 15-3 v Hopes (Birmingham Friendly 39), 12-0 v Thetford Tn (Eastern Lge 35-36)
Defeat: 0-14 v Chelmsford City A (Nth Essex Lge 23)

BEST SEASON **FA Cup:** 4th Qual. Rd 69-70 85-86 94-95 97-98

HONOURS: Isthmian Lge Div 2 R-up 97-98, Div 3 R-up 96-97; Guardian Insurance Cup R-up 96-97; Eastern Counties Lg 36-37 83-84 84-85 (R-up 86-87 87-88 88-89 90-91), Lg Cup 87-88 (R-up 35-36 74-75); Essex County Lg R-up 37-38; London Lg (East) R-up 45-46, Lg Cup 47-48(jt) 48-49 51-52 (R-up 49-50); Metropolitan Lg Cup 69-70; Essex Elizabethan Tphy R-up 68-69; E. Anglian Cup 46-47 68-69 95-96; Essex Sen.Tphy 86-87 (R-up 90-91); Essex & Suffolk Border Lg 59-60 84-85 (Lg Cup 59-60); Nth Essex Lg 05-06 10-11 11-12; Essex Sen Cup 95-96 R-up 96-97; Essex Jnr Cup R-up 04-05 05-06 22-23; RAFA Cup 56-57; Gtr Lon. Ben. Cup 65-66; Worthington Evans Cup (3) R-up (4); Eastern F'lit Cup 85-86 96-97 (R-up 94-95 97-98); Anglian F'lit Lg 69-70; Jan Havanaar Inter. Tour. 94-95 (R-up 92-93)

Players progressing: J Dick (West Ham 53), S Wright (Wrexham 83), J Cheesewright (Birmingham C. 91), G Bennett, M Metcalf (Brentford 93),R Reinelt (Gillingham 93), M de Souza (Birmingham C.), G Culling (ColchesterU 94) , S.Forbes (Southend U), S.Brown (Tottenham H) and D.Theobald (Brentford)

Back row: Andrew Potter, Paul Catley, Gavin Cowan, Tommy Noble, Adam Gillespie and Mark Jones.

Front row: Matt Hayter, Brett Girling, Neil Cousins, Dean Parratt and Nicky Hayden.

CHELMSFORD CITY

CLUB OFFICIALS

Chairman: **Trevor Wright**

Secretary: **David Clarke**
186 The Avenue, Lowestoft, Suffolk.
NR33 7LW
Tel 01502 580079 or
0781 8267555

FOOTBALL MANAGEMENT TEAM
Manager: Steve Mosely
Asst.Man: Keith Day Coach: Amin Levitt
Captain: Ian wiles
Physio: Paul Smith

FACT FILE
Formed: 1878(Turned Pro 1938)
Nickname: City or 'The Clarets'
Sponsors:T.B.A.
Colours: All Claret with white trim
Change colours: All white with claret trim
Midweek matches : Monday
Club Website: www.chelmsfordcityfc.com

2003-2004
Captain: Mike Rutherford
Top Scorer: Lloyd Blackman
Player of the Year: Paul Nicholls

THE CLARET

Pages: 52 Price: £1.50
Editor: Chris Evans (07799 030669)
Local Press: Essex Chronicle,
Chelmsford Weekly News,
East Anglian Daily Times, Evening Gazette
Local Radio: Essex Radio/Breeze AM,
BBC Essex, Chelner FM

GROUND Ground Share with Billericay Town
New Lodge, Blunts Wall Road, Billericay CM12 9SA Tel: 01277 652188

Directions: From Shenfield (A129) right at 1st lights then 2nd right. FromBasildon (A129) over 1st lights in town, then left at next lights and 2nd right. Half mile from Billericay (GER) station (London Liverpool St. - Southend line). Ground 5 mins walk from buses 222, 251, 357, 255, 551
Capacity: 3,500 Seats: 424 Cover: 600 Floodlights: Yes

Clubhouse: Open eves 8-11pm (except Mon),1pm-11pm Sat & w/e lunch noon-2.30pm.
Club Shop: Sells progs, badges, scarves, mugs etc. Contact Sharon Chantryvia club

PREVIOUS **Leagues:** None **Grounds:** New Writtle Street 38-97, Maldon Town 97-98
Name: None (Brentwood Town were incorporated in 1970)

CLUB RECORDS **Attendance:** 16,807 v Colchester, Southern League 10/9/49
Goalscorer: Tony Butcher, 287 (1957-71) **Appearances:** Derek Tiffin, 550 (1950-63)
Win: 10-1 v Bashley (H) Dr Martens Leagu 26/4/2000
Defeat: 2-10 v Barking (A), FA Trophy, 11/11/78
Fee - Paid: £10,000 for Tony Rogers (Dover Athletic, 1992) **Received:** £50,000 for David Morrison (Peterborough 94)

BEST SEASON **FA Cup:** 4th Rd, 1938-39 (v Birmingham City). 1st Rd 26 times
FA Trophy: Semi-final 69-70 v Telford Utd

HONOURS Southern Lg 45-46 67-68 71-72 (R-up 48-49 60-61 63-64 65-66); Southern Div 88-89, R-up 97-98, Lg Cup 45-46 59-60 (R-up 60-61); Merit Cup 71-72; Southern Lg War-Time (East) 39-40); Essex Prof Cup 5; Essex Snr Cup 85-86 88-89 92-93; Non-League Champs Chall Cup 71-72; E Anglian Cup 48-49; Eastern Co's Lg(3) 46-49(Lg Cup 59-60); Eastern F'lit Comp 6, (Cup 72-73 74-75); Metropolitan Lg 67-68, Lg Prof Cup 67-68, Autumn Shield 70-71; Essex Snr Lg Cup 84-85; Harry Fisher Mem. Tphy 88-89

Players progressing: G Merton (Watford 48), G Adams (Orient 49), W O'Neill(Burnley 49), B Farley/S McClellan/L Dicker/P Collins (Spurs 49/49/51/68), O Hold (Everton 50), R Marden (Arsenal 50), C McCormack (Barnsley 50), D Sexton(Luton 51), W Bellet & R Mason & A Nicholas (Orient 61 & 63 & 65), R Gladwin(Norwich 66), B King (Millwall 67), J O'Mara (Bradford City 74), N Spink (Aston77), M Dziadulewicz (Wimbledon 79), M Cawston (Southend 84), P Coleman (Exeter84), J Keeley & A Owers (Brighton 86 & 87), I Brown (Bristol C 93), D Morrison (Peterborough 94)

Back row, left to right: Keith Day (Assistant Manager), Steve Butterworth, Ian Wiles, Russ Edwrads, Darren Smith, Rio Alderton, Paul Nicholls, Matt Jones, Wes Faulkner, Simon Clarke, Dale Watkins and Steve Mosely **Front row:** Paul Smith (Physio), Ray Taylor, Jack Wignall, Garry Cross, Carl Allison, Gareth Street, George Lay, Steve Nirman, Danny Curran, Amin Levitt (COach).

CHESHUNT

CLUB PERSONNEL

Chairman: Vince Satori
Vice Chairman: Kevin Sands
President: Paul Philips
Secretary & Press Officer:
Robert Brassett
561 Hertford Rd., Enfield Wash, Enfield,,
Enfield, Middl'x EN3 5UQ
Tel: 0208 805 6132 (H) 0788 0603108 (M)
email: rob@brassett.net

FOOTBALL MANAGEMENT

Manager: Andy Leese
Asst Manager: John Meakes
Coaches: Kevin Mudd & Gary Berry
Physio: Sarah StimpsoR
Res.Managers: Shaun Good & Dave Chappell

FACT FILE

Founded: 1946
Nickname: Ambers
Sponsors: T.B.A.
Colours: Amber & black/Black/Black
Change colours: Sky Blue & Navy Blue
Midweek matchday: Tuesday
Reserves' Lge:Suburban
Youth Team: S Co Floodlit Youth League.
Website:http://www.cheshuntfc.comt

Programme

Pages: 56 Price: £1.50
Editor: Jim Tuite
Local Press: Herts Mercury, Enfield Gazette, Herald (Free paper),Welwyn & Hatfield Times & Lee Valley STar (Free)

GROUND **Address:** The Stadium, Theobalds Lane, Cheshunt, Herts. Tel: 01992 626752
Directions: M25 J 25, A10 north towards Hertford, next r'about 3rd exit to next r'about, turn left proceed under railway bridge, turn left, ground approx 400 yards on right. 400yds from Theobalds Grove BR station, Buses 310, 242, & 311 to station
Capacity: 2,500 Seats: 285 Standing Cover: 350 Floodlights: Yes
Clubhouse: 120 Bar + 170 Function Hall **Club Shop:** No **Parking**: 150

PREVIOUS **Name:** Cheshunt Sports 46-47
Leagues: London 46-51 55-59; Delphian 51-55; Aetolian 59-62; Spartan 62-64;Athenian 64-77; 87-93 Isthmian 77-87 94-
Grounds: Gothic Sports,Theobalds Lane 1946, College Rd. 46-49 Cheshunt Stadium 49-50, 52-53 Brookfield Lane 50-58

RECORDS **Attendance:** 5,000 v Bromley, F.A. Amateur Cup 2nd Rd 28.01.50
Victory: 11-0 v Royal Ordinance Factories (a) 1946-47 London Lg. Div.1
Defeat: 0-10 v Eton Manor London League 17.04.56
Record All Time Goalscorer: Eddie Sedgwick 128 **Most all time Appearances:** John Poole 526

BEST SEASON **FA Vase:** Quarter Final 81-82 v Blue Star 0-1 after 1-1 **FA Cup:** 4th Qual. Rd (4) **F.A.Amateur Cup** 3rd Rd 49-50, 69-70

HONOURS Athenian Lg 75-76 R-up 73-74, Div 1 67-68, Div 2 R-up 65-66, Lg Cup 74-75 75-76; Spartan Lg 62-63, Lg Cup 63-64 92-93, R-up 89-90; London Lg 49-50 R-up 56-57, Div 1 47-48 48-49 R-up 46-47, Div 1 Cup 46-47, Lg Cup R-up 58-59, Park Royal Cup 46-47; Isthmian Lg Div 2 Champions 2002-03, R-up 81-82 Div 3 R-up 94-95; Herts Snr Cup 23-24 R-up 48-49 49-50 68-69 69-70 71-72 73-74; Herts Charity Cup 00-01 05-06 R-up 70-71 74-75 80-81; Herts Charity Shield 46-47 65-66 R-up 52-53 53-54 54-55 63-64 64-65; Herts Snr Centenary Tphy 91-92; E. Anglian Cup 74-75 R-up 75-76; Mithras F'lit Cup 69-70 R-up 75-76; London Charity Cup 73-74; Roy Bailey Tphy 90-91 94-95 97-98 98-99 99-00

Players progressing: Ian Dowie, Ruben Abgula, Steve Sedgeley, Lee Hodges, Paul Marquis, Steve Terry, Neil Prosser, Mario Walsh

It's celebration time at Cheshunt, after clinching promotion to the Isthmian Premier Division.

DOVER ATHLETIC

CLUB OFFICIALS
Chairman:Mike Kemp
Directors:Steve Cattermole & John Farringdon
Secretary: Denise Farringdon c/o Club
Tel No 0770 9748001 (M)
Press Officer: M.Kemp
Commercial Manager
Dave Scoggins Tel: 01304 240041

FOOTBALL MANAGEMENT TEAM
Manager:Richard Langley
Assistant Manager: Paul Hyde
Reserve Team Manager: Richard Langley
Physiotherapist: T.B.A.
Club Doctor: Dr. J.P.Allingham

FACT FILE

Founded: 1983
Nickname: The 'Whites'
Club Sponsors: Hoverspeed
Club colours:White/Blackwhite
Change colours:Yellow/blue/yellow
Yellow shirts yellow shorts, yellow socks
Reserve team's league: Kent League Div. 1
Midweek home matchday: Tuesday
email: dover.athletic@virgin.net

Pages: 38 Price: £1.50
Editor: Chris Collins
Tel: 01233 504278
email: dover.athletic@virgin.net

Local Press: Dover Express; Dover Mercury
Local Radio: Radio Kent; Invicta FM
KFM Radio

GROUND Hoverspeed Stadium,Crabble Athletic Ground, Lewisham Road, River, Dover, Kent. CT17 0JB Telephone No : 01304 822373 Fax: 01304 821383
Directions: Follow the A2 from Canterbury until you pass the Forte Posthouse on your left and approach a r-about with McDonalds & petrol station on your left. Turn right signed 'Town Centre' & follow down the hill.
Capacity: 6,500 Covered Terracing: 4,900 Seats: 1,000
Clubhouse: Social Club open 7 days a week. Meals available. **Contact:** Gavin Hughes 01304 822306/01304 822373
Club Shop: At the ground. Open matchdays for general souvenirs. Contact 01304 822373

PREVIOUS — **Leagues:** Kent League, Southern League, Conference
Grounds: None **Names:** Dover FC

CLUB RECORDS — **Attendance:** 4,186 v Oxford United (FAC1st Rd) Nov .02
Win: 7-0 v Weymouth 03.04.1990 **Defeat:** 1-7 v Poole Town
Career Goalscorer: Lennie Lee 160 **Career Appearances:** Jason Bartlett 359
Transfer Fees Paid: £50,000 for David Leworthy (Farnborough Town) Aug. 93
Received: £50,000 for Ricky Reina (Brentford) '97

BEST SEASON — **FA Cup:** Fourth Qualifying Round x 8
(as Dover FC) 2nd Round 75-76 1-4 v Southend Utd. (A) League club defeated Colchester Utd.
FA Trophy: Semi-Final 97-98 **FA Amateur Cup:** Did not compete
League: 6th Conference 99-00

HONOURS — Southern League - Premier Division 89-90, 92-93; Southern Division 87-88; Championship Match 1990, 1983; Premier Inter League Cup 90-91; Challenge Cup 91-92. Kent Senior Cup 90-91, R-up 93-94, 96-97

Players progressing: Ricky Reina (Brentford) 1997

Back Row (L-R): Craig Wilkins, Chris Wright, Shaun Welford, Dale Skelton, Matt Carruthers, Dean Readings, Nick Humphrey, Craig Cloke. Middle Row: Robin Hastie (Kit Manager), Jack Tanner, Michael Smissen, James Rogers, Tom Hickman, Pat Mullin, Paul Rogers, Shane Hamshare, Danny Welch, Laurence Ball, Billy Bone, Frank Clark (Physio). Front Row: Sam Vallance, Ricky Spiller, Steve Cattermole (Director), Richard Langley (Head Coach), Mick Kemp (Chief Executive), John Farringdon (Director), James Farrier, Micky Lane.

EASTLEIGH

CLUB OFFICIALS

Chairman: Roger Sherwood

President: Clive Wilson

Secretary: John Dunn
21 Vale Drive, Midanbury,
Southampton SO18 4SW
Tel: 023 8032 2884 (H) 07730 734044 (M)

Director of Football: Mark Dennis

Commercial Manager: Pat Mallon

FOOTBALL MANAGEMENT TEAM

Manager:Paul Doswell

Coach: David Hughes & Mark Dennis
Physio: Bert Wyatt

FACT FILE

Founded: 1946

Nickname: None

Sponsors: Southern Exhaust Services

Colours: White & Navy/Navy /White & Navy

Change colours: All red

Midweek matches: Wednesday

2003-2004

Captain: Riob Marshall

Top GOalscorer: Robbie Matthews

PROGRAMME
32 pages with admission
Editor: Mark Pearce & Tommy Whale
Press Officer: Malcolm Clarke

GROUND `Ten Acres', Stoneham Lane, North Stoneham, Eastleigh SO50 9HT
Tel: 02380 613361

Directions: M27, J 5, to r'bout - exit marked Stoneham Lane. Carry on to r'bout & come back down Stoneham Lane, turning right opp. Concord Club. Ground 400 yds on left. Bus 48 (S'hampton-Winchester) to Stoneham Church stop Southampton Parkway (BR) 3/4 mile.

Capacity: 2,300 Seats: 175 Cover: 210 Floodlights: Yes

Club Shop: No

Clubhouse: 11-11 Mon-Sat plus Sundays. Extensive function facilities. All catering undertaken

PREVIOUS

Leagues: Southampton Jnr & Snr 46-59, Hampshire 50-86, Wessex 86-2003
Names: Swaythling Ath. 46-73; Swaythling 73-80
Grounds: Southampton Common 46-47; Walnut Avenue, Swaythling 47-75

CLUB RECORDS

Gate: 2,500 v Southampton, floodlight opener 30/9/75
Scorer : Johnny Williams, 177 **Appearances** : Ian Knight, 611
Win: 12-1 v Hythe & Dibden (H) 11/12/48 **Defeat:** 0-11 v Austin Spts (A) 1/1/47

BEST SEASON **FA Vase:** 4th Round 82-83, 90-91, 94-95

HONOURS Wessex Lg Cup R-up 91-92, Hants Lg Div 2 69-70 R-up 54-55 60-61 62-63 64-65 (Res), Div 3 (W) 50-51 53-54 70-71(Res), Comb.(Res) (3) R-up 96- Hants Comb Cup (Res) 96-7, 97-8 Midweek F'lit Cup 78-79, Southampton Snr Lg (W) 49-50 R-up 51-52(Res), Div 1 56- 57 57-58 (Res), Russell Cotes R-up 76-77 80-81 89-90, Hants I'mediate Cup 50-51 56-57(Res) 74-75 (Res) R-up 73-74 (Res), Soton SnrCup (Res) 74-75 78-79 87-88 96-97 R-up (7) 55-56 57-59 60-61 66-67 71-72 80-81 87-88), Soton Jnr Lg Div 2 47-48 (Res), Reg Mathieson Tphy (Res) 74-75 78-79 87-88

Back row, left to right: John Dunn, Rob Marshall, Paul Sales, Lee Bright, Rob Ashford, David Walsh, Colin Matthews, Wayne Shaw, Robbie Matthews, Charlie Balfe, Phil Walner, Danny Rolfe and Roger Sherwood. **Front row**: David Asker, Tyrone Bowers, Nicky Banger, Albert Wyatt, Mark Dennis, Paul Doswell, David Hughes, Darren Colvin.Lee Pragnell, Kevin Gibbons, Martin Beck and Shea Saunders.

FOLKESTONE INVICTA

CLUB OFFICIALS

Chairman: **Bob Dix**

President: **Bill Hewson**

Secretary: **Ritchie Murning,**19 Barley Way, Kingsworth,Ashford, Kent TN23 3JA

FOOTBALL MANAGEMENT TEAM

Manager: Neil Cugley
Asst Manager: Dave Williams
Physio: Lee Dyson

FACT FILE
Founded: 1936
Sponsors: Eurotunnel (Le Shuttle) & Silver Spring
Colours: Amber & black stripes/black/amber
Change Colours:white/blue/white
Midweek matchday: Tuesday
Reserves League: Winstonlead Kent Div 1
Club Website: www.folkestoneinvicta.co.uk
2003-2004
Top Goalscorer: Allan Tait
P.o.Y.: James Dryden
2004-2005
Captain: Scott Lindsey

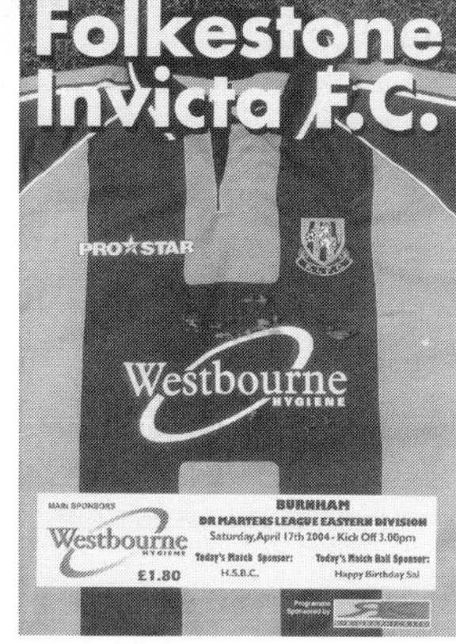

Pages: 60 Price: £1.50
Editor: Richard Murrill (01303 276517)

Local Press: Folkstone Herald
Local Radio: K.M.F.M., Invicta Radio

GROUND Westbourne Stadium, Cheriton Road, Folkestine, Kent CT20 5JU
Tel: 01303 257461 FAX:01303 255541

Directions: On the A20 behind Safeway foodstore, midway between Folkestone Central & West BR stations

Capacity: 6,500 Seats: 900 Cover: 3,500 Floodlights: Yes

Clubhouse: Yes, Stripes Club & Invicta Club
Club Shop: Yes (01303 257266)

PREVIOUS **Ground:** South Rd, Hythe (pre-1991). Kent County Lg matches were played on council pitches
Leagues: Kent County (pre-1991-98)

CLUB RECORDS **Attendance:** 2,332 v West Ham Utd Friendly Nov 96
Ground Record: 7,881 Folkestone Town v Margate, Kent Snr.Cup 1958
Win: 9-0 v Crockenhill WHL Div 1 **Defeat:** 0-7 v Crockenhill WHL Div 1

BEST SEASON **FA Vase:** Last sixteen 97-98
FA Cup: 3rd Rd 2003-2004 Leagues Clubs Defeated: None

HONOURS (since joining Winstonlead Kent League) Kent Lge R-up 97-98, Kent Senior Trophy R-Up 93-94, 94-95,98-99,99-00
Dr.Martens League ,Eastern Division Runners-up: 99-00 Promotion to Dr.Martens Premier Division 1999-2000

HAMPTON & RICHMOND BOROUGH

CLUB OFFICIALS

Chairman: Graham Wood
President: Alan Simpson OBE
Vice Chairman: Michael Holland
Press Officer: Les Rance
Football Secretary:

FOOTBALL MANAGEMENT TEAM

Manager: Alan Devonshire
Coach: Carl Taylor

FACT FILE

Formed: 1921
Nickname: Beavers/Borough
Sponsors: M.M Cox.Properties Ltd.
Colours: Red & blue/blue/red
Change Colours: White/red/blueMidweek
Matchday: Tuesday
Website: http://www.hrbfc.co.uk
Local Press: Middx Chronicle, Surrey Comet, Richmond & Twickenham Times, The Informer

Hampton & Richmond Borough FC
Ryman
The Beveree Review
2003-2004 Season
Main Sponsor M.M Cox Properties Ltd

PROGRAMME

Pages: 28 Price: £1.50p
Editor: Stefan Rance

2003-2004

Captain: Dudley Gardner
Top Scorer: AdrianAllen
Player of the Year: Allen Inns

GROUND: Beveree Stadium, Beaver Close, off Station Rd, Hampton TW12 2BX
Tel: Office 020 89412838 (matchdays only) Club: 020 8979 2456
Boardroom: 020 8941 2838

Directions: A3 out of London, fork left (signed Staines/Esher/Sandown Pk) onto A243, A309 Staines exit to Hampton Ct at `Scilly Isles' r'bout, left at r'bout after Hampton Court Bridge onto A308, after 1 mile right into Church St (A311), left after White Hart after 200yds into High St, Station Rd on right just before junction with A308

Capacity: 3,000 Seats: 300 Cover: 800 Floodlights: Yes

Clubhouse: (020 8979 2456). Lounge bar and hall, open on matchdays and training nights. Hall available for hire.

Club Shop: Sells various souvenirs & prog. Contact: Adrian Mann (020 8773 0858)

PREVIOUS
Leagues: Kingston & District 21-33; South West Middx 33-59; Surrey Snr 59-64; Spartan 64-71; Athenian 71-73
Grounds: Hatherop Rec (until 1959)

CLUB RECORDS
Win: 11-1 v Eastbourne Utd, Isthmian Lge Div 2 (S), 90-91 **Defeat:** 0-13 v Hounslow Town, Middlesex Senior Cup 62-63
Goalscorer: Peter Allen (176) 1964-73 **Appearances:** Tim Hollands (750) 1977-95
Fees - Paid: £3,000 for Matt Flitter (Chesham United) June 2000
Fees - Received: £40,000 for Leroy Griffiths from Q.P.R.May 2001

BEST SEASON
FA Cup: 1st Rd Proper 00-01 (1-2 v Barnet) **FA Amateur Cup:** 1st Rd Prop 73-74 (2-4 v Leytonstone)
FA Trophy: 4th Rd 01-02 .1-4 v Hereford United (A)
FA Vase: 3rd Rd 91-92 (0-1 v Newport IOW), 95-96 (0-1 v Colllier Row)

HONOURS: London Snr Cup(2) 86-88; Spartan Lg(4) 64-67 69-70, (R-up 67-68), Lg Cup(4) 64-68 (R-up 2); Surrey Snr Lg 63-64 (Lg Cup R-up 60-61); Middx Charity Cup 69-70 95-96 97-98,98-99 (R-up 68-69 71-72 89-90 94-95); Middx Snr Cup R-up 71-72 76-77 95-96; Athenian Lg Div 2 R-up 72-73; Southern Comb. Cup 68-69 71-72 76-77 81-82 83-84 85-86 96-97 (R-up 77-78 79-80 97-98); Isthmian Lge promotion from Div 1 97-98, Div 2 95-96, Div 3 91-92. Isthmian Lg.Cup Finalists 01-02

Players progressing: Andy Rogers (Southampton), Dwight Marshall (Plymouth), Paul Rogers (Sheffield Utd via Sutton Utd), Derek Bryan Brentford 97), Darren Powell (Brentford 98), Julian Charles (Brentford 99.), Leroy Griffiths (Q.P.R. 01)

Back Row (L-R): Michael Currie, Steve Omonua, Jamie Jarvis, Adrian Blake, Orlando Jeffrey, Alan Inns, Sam Okafor.
Front Row: Marcello Fernandes, Lee Channell, Richard O'Connor, Andy Morley.

Photo: Les Rance.

HARROW BOROUGH

CLUB OFFICIALS

Chairman: Jim Ripley **President:** T.B.A.
Secretary: Peter Rogers,
21 Ludlow Close, South Harrow, Middx HA2 8SR (0208 248 8003H)(0208 4230157W)
Commercial Manager:
The Secretary c/o the club
Press Officer: Paul Carter (07971 848385)

FOOTBALL MANAGEMENT TEAM

Manager:David Howell
Asst Manager: Phil Gridelet
Physio: Jenny Mullen

2003-04

Captain: Kevin McKenna
Top Scorer: Ross Fitzsimon 12
Player of the Year: Richard Goddard

FILE

Formed: 1933
Nickname: The Boro
Sponsors:T.B.A.
Colours: Red, white trim/red/red, white hoops
Change cols: White/navy blue trim/navy/navy
Midweek matchday: Tuesday
Website: www.harrowboro.com
Local Press: Harrow Observer and Harrorw Times

PROGRAMME

Pages: 32 Price: £2,00
Editor: T.B.A.

FACT

GROUND: Earlsmead, Carlyon Avenue, South Harrow, Middx HA2 8SS Tel: 0208 422 5221. Email: paul@harrowboro.co.uk
Directions: Underground to Northolt (Central Line) then 140 bus to Northolt Park BR, or 282 bus, to Eastcote Arms or to South Harrow (Piccadilly Line) then 114 or H10 to Kings Rd.Junction. By road leave A40 at Macdonalds roundabout towards Northolt station (A312 north), left at lights, right at next island (Eastcote Arms pub), ground 5th turning on right.
Capacity: 3,070 Cover: 1,000 Seats: 350 Floodlights: Yes
Clubhouse: Open daily, normal pub hours. 4 bars, games room, equipped for social events. Hot and cold food available, buffets by prior request
Club Shop: Sells progs, scarves, badges, T-shirts, etc. Contact c/o club

PREVIOUS **Leagues:** Harrow & Dist 33-4; Spartan 34-40, 45-58; W Middx Comb 40-1; Middx Sen41-45; Delphian 58-63; Athenian 63-75; **Names:** Roxonian 1933-8; Harrow Town 38-66 **Ground:** Northolt Road 33-4

CLUB RECORDS **Attendance:** 3,000 v Wealdstone, F.A. Cup 1st Qualifying Rd 1946 **Fee Received:** £16,000 for Lee Endersby (Enfield 97)
Scorer: Dave Pearce, 153 **Appearances:** Steve Emmanuel 522 (1st team only), Les Currell 582, Colin Payne 557
Fee Paid: Unspecified to Dagenham for George Duck & Steve Jones, Summer 81
Win: 13-0 v Handley Page (A), Middlesex Snr Lg 18/10/41. **Defeat:** 0-8 5 times: Wood Green T. (A) Middx Lge 40, Met Police (A) Spartan Lg 52, Briggs Spts (A) Spartan Lg 53, Hertford T. (A) Spartan Lge 53, Hendon (A) Middx Snr Cup 65

BEST SEASON **FA Trophy:** Semi final 82-83 **FA Cup:** 2nd Rd 83-84 (1-3 at home to Newport Co)

HONOURS: Isthmian Lg 83-84 (Div 1 R-up 78-79); Athenian Lg Div 2 R-up 63-64; Spartan Lg R-up 57-58 (Div 2 West 38-39 (R-up 37-38); Middx Senior Cup 82-83 92-93; Harrow & Dist. Lg Div 1 R-up 33-34; Middx Charity Cup 79-80 92-93 (R-up 78-79); Middx Intermediate Cup 55-56,R-up 75-76, Middx Premier Cup 81-82,R-up 82-83, Harrow Sen Cup 95 97, London Interm'te C 78-79

Players progressing: D.Russell (Arsenal), M.Lucas (L.Orient), R.Shaw (Torquay U), T.Eden (Raith R), T. Carpenter (Watford), M Bottoms (QPR 60), C Hutchings (Chelsea 80), R Holland (Crewe 85), J Kerr (Portsmouth 87), D Howell, A Pape & E Stein, (Barnet), D .Byrne (Gillingham), R.Rosario (Norwich), D Kemp (Crystal Palace), M Doherty (Reading), D Bassett (Wimbledon), G Borthwick (Bournemouth), B.Shaw, (Torquay U),T.Evans (Scunthorpe U), L.Charles (Q.P.R.), P.Barrowcliff (Brentford) M.Richardson (Camb Utd & Torquay U).
Internationals: K Karamoko(Mali) and O.Roberts (Grenada)

2004 -2005 - Back Row L-R: Daniel McGonigle, Paul Hamer, Brian Haule, Steve Dogbe, Craig Nicholson, Keita Karamoko, Dean Marney, John Bacon, Clinton Lamb and Matk Henry. **Middle row:** Mark Wakeling (Goalkeeping Coach), Mick Martin (Kit Manager), Paul Killick, Wesley Baynham, Steve Brockett, Clemente Lopez, Stan Patrick, Steve Mills (Coach), Jenny Mullen (Physio), Phil Gridelet (First TeamCoach).**Front row:** Paul Johnson, Rob Sterry, Fabio Valenti, Daniel Dyer, Dave Howell (Manager), Perry Norman, Wayne Walters, Osman Hasan and Carl Hunt. **Photo Paul Carter**

HENDON

CLUB OFFICIALS

Chairman: Ivor Arbiter

Secretary: Graham Etchell, c/o Hendon FC.
Tel: 020 8201 9494(Club)

Marketingl Manager:Martyn Kempson
Press Officer: David Ballheimer

FOOTBALL MANAGEMENT TEAM

Man: Tony Choules Ass.Man:Gary Farrell
Player/Coach: Warren Kelly
Physio: Michael Rayner

FACT FILE

Formed: 1908 Nickname: Dons or Greens
Sponsors: UK Packaging
Colours: Green /white/white
Change Colours: Sky & Navy Blue/navy/sky
Midweek matchday: Tuesday
Reserve League: Capital Football League
Club Line: 09066 555 836
Club Website: www.hendonfc.net

2003-004

Captain: Jon Barrie-Bates
Ps.o.Y: Eugene Ofori
Top Scorer: Eugene Ofori

Hendon
OFFICIAL MATCHDAY MAGAZINE £1.50
Saturday 24th April 2004
Ryman Football League Premier
St ALBANS CITY
Kick Off 3.00pm

Pages: 40 Price: £1.50p
Editor: Secretary
Local Press: Hendon Times, Willesden & Brent Chronicle
Hampstead & Highgate Express
Local Radio: Capital, GLR, LBC

GROUND: Claremont Road, Brent Cross, London NW2 1AE.
Tel: 020 8201 9494 Fax: 020 8905 5966

Directions: From Brent Cross station (Northern Line) to the east take first left after flyover on North Circular - Claremont Rd is then left at 4th mini-r'bout. Buses 102, 210, 226 and C11 pass ground

Capacity: 3,029 Cover: 601 Seats: 329 Floodlights: Yes

Clubhouse: (contact Sue Damary 020 8455 9185). Two banqueting suites,conference centre, room hire, restaurant & bars open licensing hours 7 days aweek. Hot & cold food, pool, darts, bingo, members club, satelite TV,entertainments Contacts Beryl Elsley & Lorraine Hartnett

Club Shop: Sells football souvenirs (Contact: Chris Rogers)

PREVIOUS **Leagues:** Finchley & Dist. 08-11, Middx 10-11, London 11-14, Athenian 14-63.
Names: Christ Church Hampstead to 08, Hampstead Town to 26, Hampstead to 33,Golders Green to 46
Grounds: Kensal Rise 08-12; Avenue Ground, Cricklewood Lane 12-26

CLUB RECORDS **Attendance:** 9,000 v Northampton, FA Cup 1st Rd 1952
Goalscorer: Freddie Evans 176 (1929-35) **Appearances:** Bill Fisher 787 (1940-
Defeat: 2-11 v Walthamstow Ave. (A), Athenian Lge 9/11/35 **Win:** 13-1 v Wingate (H), Middx Senior Cup 2/2/57
Fee Paid: Paul Whitmarsh (undisclosed) **Fee Received:** £30,000 for Iain Dowie (Luton)

BEST SEASON **F.A. Cup:** First Rd 20 times, Second Rd 5 times **F.A.Trophy:** 5th Rd 98-99

HONOURS: European Am Champions 72-3; Isthmian Lg 64-5 72-3 (R-up 63-4 65-6 73-4) Lg Cup 76-7 (R-up 86-7), Full Members Cup 94-5 97-8 98-99, Premier Inter-Lge Cup R-up 86-7; Middx Lge 12-3 13-4; Athenian Lg 52-3 55-6 60-1 (R-up 28-9 32-3 47-8 48-9 51-2); London Lg Div 1 R-up 12-13 (Amtr Div 13-4); Finchley & Dist. Lg 10-1; London Snr Cup 63-4 68-9 (R-up 35-6 50-1 54-5 58-9 71-2); Middx Snr Cup (14) (R-up 83-4), Middx Interm 64-5 66-7 72-3, Middx Charity Cup(14); London IntermCup (4) (R-up (2); Suburban Lg 92-3 (R-up 84-5 97-8) George Ruffell Mem.Trophy: 2001-02, R-Up 98-9 02-03

Players progressing: Peter Shearing (WHU 60), Iain Dowie (Luton 88), PeterAnderson (Luton), Jeff Harris (Orient), Phil Gridelet (Barnsley 90), GerrySoloman (Leyton O 91), Junior Hunter & Micah Hyde (both Cambridge 94-95),Simon Clark (Peterboro' 94-95),Junior Lewis(Gillingham 99-00)

HEYBRIDGE SWIFTS

CLUB OFFICIALS

Chairman: Andrew Barber
President: T.B.A.
Vice Chairman: Michael Gibson
Secretary: Liz Creasy c/o club
Match Secretary: Terry Stowers
74 Wood Road, Heybridge, Maldon,
Essex CM9 8JA Tel: 01621 857226
Press Offr: Tony Foster (M) 07931 330756
(H) 01621 858171
Treasurer: Chris Daines

FOOTBALL MANAGEMENT TEAM

Manager: Keith Martin
Asst. Manager: Colwyn Rowe
Physio: Glenn Churchet

FACT FILE

Formed: 1880 Nickname: Swifts
Sponsors: Towermaster.
Midweek matchday: Tuesday
Colours: Black & white stripes/black/black
Change colours: All Red or Amber/ white
Reserves' Lge: Essex & Herts Border Comb
Club Website: www.heybridgeswifts.com

PROGRAMME

Pages: 52 Price: £1.50
Editors: Tony Foster & MK Publications

2003-004

Top Scorer: Neil Cousins
Players.o.Y: Lee Kersey & John Pollard
2004-2005 Captain John Pollard

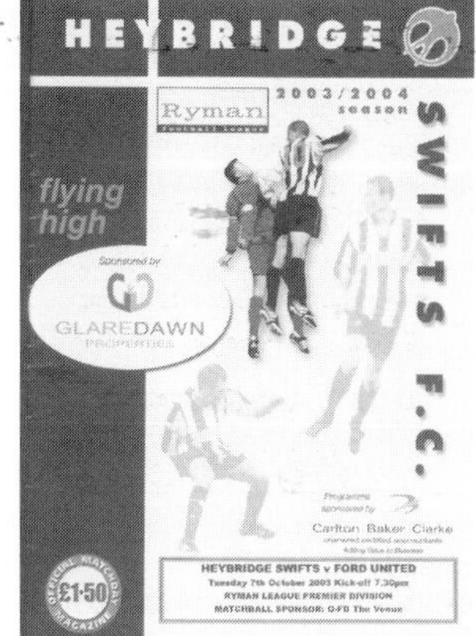

GROUND: Scraley Road, Heybridge, Maldon, Essex CM9 8JA Tel: 01621 852978
Directions: Leave Maldon on the main road to Colchester, pass through Heybridge then turn right at the sign to Tolleshunt Major (Scraley Road). The ground on the right. Six miles from nearest station (Witham). By bus via Chelmsfordand Maldon
Capacity: 3,000 Cover: 1,200 Seats: 550 Floodlights: Yes
Clubhouse: Two bars open every night. Games room, boardroom, kitchen (on matchdays)
Club Shop: Open matchdays, sells club sweaters, shirts, scarves, baseball hats, enamel badges, old progs etc. Contact Tony Foster, c/o club.

PREVIOUS **Leagues:** Essex & Suffolk Border, North Essex, South Essex, Essex Senior 1971-84

CLUB RECORDS **Attendance:** 2,477 v Woking FA Trophy 97 and pre season v West Ham United , 3,000 +, 99-00.
Goalscorer: Julian Lamb 115 (post war), Dave Matthews 112 (Isthmian)
Appearances: Hec Askew 500+, John Pollard 496
Fee Paid: £1,000 Dave Rainford, Lee Kersey **Fee Received:** £35,000, Simon Royce (Southend Utd)

BEST SEASON **FA Trophy:** Qtr finals v Woking 22/3/97 (lost 0-1)
FA Cup: First round 0-2 v Gillingham 11/11/94, 0-3 v Bournemouth 15.11.97 **League clubs defeated:** None

HONOURS: Isthmian Lg Div 1 R-up 95-96, Div 2 North 89-90; Essex Senior Lg 81-82 82-83 83-84, Lg Cup 82-83, Trophy 81-82; JT Clarke Cup 82-83; Thorn EMI National Floodlit Competition R-up 82-83; Eastern Floodlit Cup 93-94; East Anglian Cup 93-94 94-95; Essex & Suffolk Border Lge 31-32; Essex Jun Cup 31-32; North Essex Lge 46-47 Ryman League Cup 00-01

Players progressing: Simon Royce (Southend United & Charlton Athletic), Peter Cawley & Ben Lewis (Colchester Utd), Alan Hull (Leyton Orient), Jonathan Hunt (Birmingham City), Dominic Naylor (Leyton Orient), Haken Hayrettin (Doncaster Rovers), Derek Payne & Tom Meredith (Peterborough Utd), Ben Barnett, Eddie Stein & Tim Alexander (Barnet), Ashley Vickers (Peterborough United), James Pullen (18 year old ,goal-keeper to Ipswich Town) 99-00.

Back L to R: Andy Jesney (coach), Glenn Churchett (Physio), Paul Abrahams, Lewis Baillie, Ollie Blackwell, Dave Culverhouse, Tim Bruce, Kingsley Banks, Kevin Budge, Dave Rainford, John Pollard, Dean Curtis (Assistant Manager), Ricky Clarke (coach) **Front**: Jamie Window, Chris Payne, Leon Hunter, Scott Lovett, Dave Greene (manager), Andy Tomlinson, Danny Barber, Paul Cobb, Danny Wornham.

KINGSTONIAN

CLUB OFFICIALS
Chairman: Rajesh Khosla
Chief Executive: Anup Khosla
Directors : Rajesh Khosla & Anup Khosla,
Club Secretary & Press Officer:
Graham Richards, 1 Bridge Court, Bridge Street, Leatherhead, Surrey KT22 8BW
Tel No: 01372 377076 or 07775 656694
e-mail g.richards@virgin.net
Commercial Manager: Tom Dixon

FOOTBALL MANAGEMENT TEAM
Manager: Kim Harris
Coach: Scott Steele Physio: Greg Rowland

FACT FILE
Founded: 1885
Nickname: The Ks
Sponsors: Cherry Red Records & Easy Way
Club Colours: Red & white hooped shirts, black shorts, black socks
Change Colours: Blue/white/blue
Midweek matchday: Monday
2003-004
Top Score: Stafford Browne
P.o.Y.: Lance Key
2004-05 Captain: Peter Barnsby

Kingstonian
www.kingstonian.net
Official Matchday Programme - £1.50
Kingstonian F.C.
Ryman
RYMAN LEAGUE PREMIER DIVISION 2003-2004
KINGSTONIAN
v
NORTHWOOD
MONDAY 12TH APRIL
KO 3pm
is proud to support Kingstonian FC

Pages: 32 Price: £1.50
Editor: Robert Wooldridge Tel: 020 8669 3824

Local Press: Surrey Comet 020 8546 2261
Local Radio: County Sound; Southern Counties

GROUND: Kingsmeadow Stadium, Kingston Road, Kingston-upon-Thames, Surrey. KT13PB
Tel: 0208 547 3335/6 Fax: 0208 974 5713
DIRECTIONS: From town centre - Cambridge Rd on to Kingston Rd (A2043) to Malden Rd. From A3, turn off at New Malden, turn left on to A2043 - grd 1 mile on left. Half mile from Norbiton (BR)
CAPACITY: 4,262 **COVERED TERRACING:** 2,538 **SEATED:** 1,080
SOCIAL FACILITIES: Banqueting centre, open 7 days. 3 bars capacity 400.
Contact : Gary Winters (as below)
CLUB SHOP: Sells programmes, shirts, badges etc.
Contact Sandra & Gary Winters 0208 747 3336

RECORDS **Win:** 15-1 v Delft, friendly 5/9/51; Competitive 10-0 v Hitchin (H) Isthmian Lge 19/3/66)
Attendance: 4,582 v Chelsea (Friendly) 22.7.95 **Defeat:** 0-11 v Ilford (A) Isthmian Lge 13/2/37
Fee Paid: £18,000 for David Leworthy to Rushden & Diamonds '97 **Goalscorer:** Johnny Whing 295
Fee Received: £150,000 for Gavin Holligan from West Ham Utd. '99 **Appearances:** Micky Preston 555

PREVIOUS **Leagues:** Kingston & Dist.; West Surrey; Southern Suburban; Athenian 1919-29; Isthmian League 29-98; Conference 98-01
Names: Kingston & Surbiton YMCA 1885-87, Saxons 87-90, Kingston Wanderers 1893-1904, Old Kingstonians 08-19
Grounds: Several to 1921; Richmond Rd 21-89

HONOURS FA Trophy 98-99 99-00; Isthmian League 33-34, 36-37, 97-98, R-up 47-48 62-63, Div 1 R-up 84-85, League Cup 95-96; Athenian Lge 23-24 25-26, R-up 26-27; London Senior Cup 62-63 64-65 86-87, R-up x 5; Surrey Senior Cup x 9, R-up 90-91.

BEST SEASON **FA Amateur Cup:** Winners 32-33 R-up 59-60 **FA Trophy:** Winners 98-99 99-00
FA Cup: 4th Round replay 00-01, 0-1 v Bristol City (H), after 1-1 **League:** 5th Conference 99-00
League clubs defeated: Brighton & H.A. 94-95, Brentford & Southend Utd. 00-01

PAST PLAYERS: C Nastri (C Palace), H Lindsay (Southampton 65), G Still (Brighton 79), D Byrne (Gillingham 1985), J Power (Brentford 87), Jamie Ndah (Torquay), Gavin Holligan (West Ham '99)

2004-2005 - Back to front, left to right: F Muscat, M Rhodes, B Alimi, R Savage, M Ahmad, T Cass, M Bradford, M Lee, J Ignatidis
P Ferrie, M Williams, A Graham, J Hinds, L Key, B Marchena, J Francois, D Cunningham, J Frimpong, M Beard, J Street
D Timothy, M Scotchford, M Pattison, A Gilbert, L Collins, S Steele, G Ball, D Souyana, B Asante

LEYTON

CLUB PERSONNEL
Chairman: Costa Sophocleous
Hon. Life President: Doug Digby
President: Laurie Aldridge
Football Consultant: Peter Shreeves

Secretary / Press Officer / Match Sec.
Tony Hampford
282 Lea Bridge Rd, Leyton,
London E10 7LD
Tel: 0208 539 5405 (B)
07904 012402 (M)

FOOTBALL MANAGEMENT
Manager: Costa Sophocleous
Assistant Manager: Stuart Hibberd
Coach: Alan Payne Captain: Ben Wood
Physio: Simon Purton

FACT FILE
Founded: 1868
Nickname: Lilywhites
Colours: White/ blue/ white
Change colours: Blue/ white/ blue
Midweek Matches: Tuesday
Reserves' Lge: Essex & Herts Border Comb

Programme
36 pages Price £1.00
Editor: Tony Hampford

2003-2004
Leading Goalscorer: Trevor Paul
Players of the Year:Ben Wood

GROUND

Address: Leyton Stadium, 282 Lea Bridge Road, Leyton, London E10 7LD Tel: 0208 539 5405 email: enquiries@leytonfc.co.uk
Directions: Lea Bridge Rd. is the A104, ground next to Hare & Hounds PH.
Leyton (Central Line) thence bus 58 or 158 to Lea Bridge Road.
Clapton (BR) Walk 100 yds to Lea Bridge Rd. roundabout, buses 48, 55, 56 to ground.
Bus 48 runs direct to ground from London Bridge (BR) station

Capacity: 2,500 Seats: Yes Cover: Yes Floodlights: Yes
Clubhouse: Lounge Bar open week days and Saturdays 11am-11pm Sunday 11pn-10.30 pm
Club Shop Contact Tony Hampford 020 8539 5405

PREVIOUS

Leagues: Ryman Div 2, Essex Senior 02; Essex Intermediate; London Spartan

RECORDS

Attendance: 100,000 for 1952 F.A.Amateur Cup Final v Walthamstowe A. at Wembley

BEST SEASONS

FA Cup: 1st Rd Proper 84-85 v Swanseaa City (A)
FA Amateur Cup: Winners 1926-27,1927-28, R-up 1951-52

HONOURS FA Amateur Cup 26-27 27-28

2004-2005 - Back row left to right: Peter Shreeves (Consultant) Alan Payne (Head Coach), Vas Soteriou, Simon Peddie, George Georgiou, Scott Honeyball, James Hasell, James Courtnage, Scott Curley, Chris Bangura, Danny Jones, Des Thomas, Trevor Paul, Victor Renner, Paul Golby, Stuart Hibberd (Asst. First Team Manager), Rowly Cray (Director of Football).

Front row left to right: Lee Taylor (Club Physiotherapist), Alan Hyde (Matchday physio), Ian Bass, Troy Braham, Manny Williams, Paul Armstrong, Ben Wood (Captain), Mark Sophocleous, Leli Bajada, Roy Parkyn, Brett Freeman, Danny Honeyball, George Gregoriou.

NORTHWOOD

CLUB OFFICIALS

Chairman: Andy Johnson

Vice Chairman: Martin Ellis

President: Lothar Hahn

Secretary: Alan Evans,48 Webster Gardens,Ealing W5 5ND

Tel No: 07960 744049

Press Off: Robin Piper (01928 840069)

FOOTBALL MANAGEMENT TEAM

Manager: Matt HarveyCoaches:Gary Farrell & John Toogood

Physio: George Price

FACT FILE

Founded: 1899 Nickname: Woods

Sponsors: Don Bruse Bookmakers

Colours: All red Change colours: All yellow

Midweek Matches: Tuesday

Reserve League: Suburban

Local Press: Ruislip & Northwood Gazette, Watford Observer

Website: www.northwoodfc.com

2002-2003

Captain: Chris Gell

Top Scorers:Chris Moore,Scott Fitzgerald 29

Players of the Year:

Dave Sargent & Danny Butler

PROGRAMME

Pages: 60 Price:£1.00

Editor: A Evans (020 8566 2880)

GROUNDNorthwood Park, Chestnut Avenue, Northwood Tel: 01923 827148 Email:alan.evansfc@btopenworld.com

Directions: A404 (Pinner-Rickmansworth) - Chestnut Ave. on left by large grey iron railway bridge. Third of a mile from Northwood Hills station (Metropolitan Line) - right out of station to r'bout, left into Pinner Rd, left into Chestnut Ave after 300yds. Buses 282 and H11 to Northwood Hills

Capacity: 3,075 Seats:307 Cover:932 Floodlights: Yes **Club Shop:** No

Clubhouse: Weekends & most eves from 6pm. Bar. Hot and cold food. Pool

HONOURS: Isthmian Lg Associate Members Cup 92-93,99-00; London Spartan Lg 91-92 (R-up 89-90), Lg Cup 89-90 91-92;Hellenic Lg Div 1 78-79 (Prem Div Cup R-up 81-82); Middx Lg 77-78 (R-up 72-73 76-77), Div 1 R-up 71-72, Challenge Cup 74-75 76-77 77-78; Middx Snr Charity Cup R-up 93-94; Middx Snr Cup SF 91-92 92-93 98-99; R-up 99-00 Jnr Cup 46-47 47-48 48-49; Harrow & Wembley Lg (9); Middlesex Premier Cup 94-95 Finallists 99-00, 01-02Isthmian League Div 1 North Champions 2002-03. Isthmian Div 2 R-up 99-00, Isthmian League Cup Winners 2001-02 Isthmia CharityShield Winners 2002

PREVIOUS: **Leagues:** Harrow & Wembley 32-69; Middlesex 69-78; Hellenic 79-84; London Spartan 84-92 **Names:** Northwood Town

CLUB RECORDS: **Attendance:** 1,642 v Chelsea Friendly July 1997

Goal Scorerin Season: Lawrence Yaku 61 (99-00) **Career Appearances:** Chris Gell (493 current total)

Win: 15-0 v Dateline (H) Middlesex Inter Cup 1973 **Defeat:** 0-8 v Bedfont (Middlesex Lg.1975)

BEST SEASON: **FA Cup:** 4th Qual Rd 00-01 **F.A.Trophy:** 3rd Rd 00-01 **FA Vase:** Quarter Final 96-97

Players progressing: Gavin Maguire, Derek Payne (Barnet), Warren Patmore (Cambridge United),Scott Fitzgerald (Watford)

Back row. left to right; Scott Fitzgerald, Wayne Carter, Lee Holman, Gary Williams, Chris Moore, Rob Bullivant, Danny Butler, Kieran Knight, Dave Sargent and George Price (Physio). **Middle row:** Craig McIntosh, Garry Farrell (Coach), John Toogood (Coach), Tony Choules (Manager), Andy Johnson (Chairman), Alan Merison (Gen-Manager), Daryl Craft and Ben Porter.
Front row: Gavin Hart, Dave Nolan, Chris Gell and Craig Totton. **Photo:** Paul Evans

SALISBURY CITY

Chairmen: Neville Beal
Director: Stuart McGlashan
Secretary: Douglas Ferraro, The Wardens House,Husey's Almhouses,Salisbury Wilts SP1 3SZ Tel No: 07803 247874 or 01722 322535 Email douglasfJ@aol.com
Press Off: Alec Hayter Tel: 02380 867195
Youth Dev Off: Symon Pickett **Football in Com Offs.:** Andy Cook& Craig Davies
Commercial Manager: Trevor Cross

FOOTBALL MANAGEMENT TEAM
Manager: Nick Holmes
Asst. Player Manager: Mark Kelly
Youth Coach: Terry Hatt
Trainer: Conrad Parrott

ACT FILE
Formed: 1947
Nickname: The Whites
Sponsors: In-Excess
Colours: White/black/white
Change colours:Red/navy/navy
Midweek matchday: Tuesday
Reserve Team's League: Wessex Comb
Club Line: 'City Line' 0906 555 864
Website:www salisburycity-fc.co.uk

2003-004
Top Scorer:Matthew Tubb
Player of the Year: Kevin Sawyer
2004-2005 Captain: Scott Bartlett

the WHITES
Dr. Martens League Eastern Division
SALISBURY CITY v. CHATHAM TOWN
Saturday 1st May 2004 3.00pm
Matchday Programme Sponsor ALLAN TROWBRIDGE
Main Team Sponsor IN-EXCESS
2003/2004 Matchday Programme £1.50

Pages: 48 Price: £1.50
Editors: Alec Hunter

Local Press: Salisbury Journal, Evening Echo & Sports Echo, Western DailyPress
Local Radio: BBC Wiltshire Sound, Spire F.M

GROUND The Raymond McEnhill Stadium, Partridge Way, Old Sarum, Salisbury SP4 6PU Tel:01722 326454, Fax 01722 323100 Club Website: www.salisbury-city-fc.com
Directions: The Stadium is situated off A345 (Salisbury - Amesbury) road on the northern edge of the city 2 miles from the City centre. Continue on this road, turn right onto A338 signed Old Sarum Business Park, Partridge Way & ground on left (well signposted)
Capacity: 3,740 **Cover**:2,247 **Seats:** 457 **Floodlights**: Yes
Clubhouse: On ground, . Hot & cold snacks. Hospitality Boxes available for hire.
Club Shop: Sells replica shirts, memorabilia, programmes, scarves, metal badges, souvenirs. Open all week. Contact Lynn Robinsonr, Commercial Office (01722 326454)

PREVIOUS **Leagues:** Western 47-68 **Name:** Salisbury FC, 47-92 **Ground:** Hudson Field 47-48, Victoria Park 48-97

CLUB RECORDS **Attendanceat Victoria Park:** 8,902 v Weymouth, Western League 48 New Ground: 2,570 v Hull City F.A. Cup 1998.
Win: 11-1 v R.A.F Colerne (H) Western League Div 2 1948 **Defeat:** 0-7 v Minehead, Southern League 1975
Career Goalscorer: Royston Watts 180 (59-65) **Career Appearances:** Barry Fitch 713 (63-75)

Transfer fee paid: £15,000 for Craig Davis from Bashley 2003. **Transfer fee received:** £20,,000 for Adrian Randall (Forest Green Rovers)

BEST SEASON **FA Trophy:** 2nd Rd 96-97 (lost to Dorchester Town)
FA Amateur Cup: 2nd Rd 49-50 (lost to Dulwich Hamlet)) **FA Cup:** 2nd Rd 59-60 (lost to Newport County)

HONOURS Southern Lg Southern Div Champ 94-95, R-up 85-86 92-93; Western Lg 57-58 60-61,R-up 58-59 59-60 61-62 67-68; Div 47-48 Lg Cup 55-56 Hants Senior Cup 61-62 63-64; Wilts PremierShield(12) Western Co Floodlit Cup: 1982-83 Hospital Cup (10)

Players progressing: Eric Fountain (Southampton 48), Cyril Smith (Arsenal 48), Tony Alexander (Fulham 65), John Evans (Stockport County 67), Graham Moxon (Exeter 75), Eric Welch (Chesterfield 76), Ian Thompson (Bournemouth 83), Trevor Wood (Port Vale 88), Denny Mundee (Bournemouth 88), Matthew Carmichael (Lincoln 90), Frank Monk (Southampton 47),George Marks 49), Joe Stocks (Millwall 64), Jason Matthews (Exeter C), James Hayter (Bournemouth 1999) and Steve Mildenhall (Swindon Town 1997)

Salisbury City F.C. before their 1st Round F.A. Cup tie at Sheffield Wednesday.
Back Row: Stuart James, Steve Witt, Tommy Killick (Asst. Player Manager), Leigh Phillips, Dean Bowden, Darren Crook, Andy McGlashan, Aaron Turner, Michael Cooper, Mathew Davies, Kevin Sawyer, Stuart Brown, Josh Thomas.
Front Row: John Harris (Reserve Team Manager), Craig Davis, John Purches, Andy Cook, Steve Strong, Matthew Tubbs, Adam Wallace, Scott Bartlett (capt.), Wayne Turk, Gary Funnell, Roger Emms, Matthew Holmes.

Photo: A Hayter SCFC.

SLOUGH TOWN

Pages: 36 Price: £1.50
Editor: John Tebbit

Local Press: Slough Observer Slough Express
Local Radio: Thames Valley FM, Star FM
Radio Berkshire

CLUB OFFICIALS

Chairman: Martin Deaner
Secretary / Press Off.: Roy Merryweather
Tel: 01753 860656 (Ground)
01753 554833(W)
01189 722871(H)
01753 533949 (Fax)

FOOTBALL MANAGEMENT TEAM

Manager: Eddie Denton
Coach: Micky Lewis
Captain: Steve Daly
Physio: Kevin McGoldrick

FACT FILE

Formed: 1890
Nickname: The Rebels
Sponsor:Coldseal
Colours: Amber/navy blue/amber
Change colours: All white
Midweek home matchday: Tuesdays
Website: www.sloughtownfc.net

2003-2004

Top scorer: Ian Hodges 35 League
Player of the Year: Ian Hodges

GROUND: Groundsharing with Windsor & Eton F.C.
Details and Directions as for Windsor & Eton F.C.
Club Shop: Contact: Emma Gammon (07989 434371 *M)

PREVIOUS **Leagues:** Southern Alliance 1892-93; Berks & Bucks 1901-05; Gt Western Suburban1906-19; Spartan 1920-39; Herts & Middx 1940-45; Corinthian 1946-63; Athenian1963-73; Isthmian 1973-90, 94-95; Alliance Prem. (GMVC) 90-94
Grounds: Dolphin Playing Fields & Stadium, Chalvey Rd Sports Grd, YorkRd Maidenhead 1920, Centre Sports Ground 36-42

CLUB RECORDS **Attendance:** 8,000 - Schoolboys u15 Final Slough v Liverpool - 1976
Win: 17-0 v Railway Clearing House - 1921-22 **Defeat:** 1-11 v Chesham Town 1909/10
Fee Paid: £18,000 for Colin Fielder from Farnborough - 1991 **Career appearances:** Terry Reardon 458 - 64/81
Fee Received: £22,000 from Wycombe W. for Steve Thompson **Career goalscorer:** E.J.C. Tory Norris 84 - 25/26

BEST SEASON **FA Cup:** 2nd Round Proper, 79-80 (Yeovil T), 82-83 (Bishop's Stortford), 85-86 (Leyton O.), 86-87 (Swansea C.).
League clubs defeated: Millwall, 1-0 (H) Jan. 1983
FA Trophy: Semi-Final 1976-77, 2-6(agg) v Dagenham; 97-98, 1-2(agg) v Southport

HONOURS: FA Amateur Cup R-up 72-73; Great Western Suburban League R-up 19-20: Spartan League R-up 20-21 21-22 31-32 32-33 38-39; Herts & Middx League R-up 43-44; Corinthian League 50-51 (R-up 45-46 46-47 57-58); Athenian League 67-68 71-72 72-73 (R-up 68-69),LgCup 71-2 72-3 Div 1 64-65, Memorial Shield 64-65 71-72 72-73); Isthmian League 80-81 89-90 R-up 94-95, (Div 2 R-up 73-74),Lg Cup 75-76 80-81 R-up 94-95 Lge Shield 89-90 ; Berks & Bucks Sen Cup (10) 02-03 19-20 23-24 26-27 35-36 54-55 70-72 76-77 80-81

2003-2004 Back Row (L-R): Alex Haddow, Adrian Browne, Lee Riddell, Martin Moller, Alan Foster, Matt Seedel, Ryan Spencer, Danny Steer, Michael Murphy. **Middle Row:** Kevin McGoldrick (physio), Ryan Williams,Paul Barrowcliff, Josias Carbon,Matt Miller, Mark Bartley, Tony Boot, Freddie Hyatt, Paul Lillywhite (Kit man). **Front Row:** Veli Hakki, Darron Wilkinson, Steve Daly (capt), Eddie Denton (Manager), Michael Gilkes (Asst. Manager), Nick Gyoury, Ian Hodges, Glen Harris.

STAINES TOWN

CLUB OFFICIALS

Chairman: Alan Boon
Vice Chairman: Ken Williams
Secretary: Steve Parsons
3 Birch Green, Staines, Middx TW18 4HA
Tel: 01784 450420
General Manager: Chris Wainwright
Commercial Manager: Ken Williams
Press Officer: Stuart Moore (01784 421118)

FOOTBALL MANAGEMENT

Manager: Steve Cordery
Asst Man: Craig Maskell
Physios: Gareth Workman & Geoff Dadswell

PROGRAMME

Pages: 44 Price: £1.50
Editor: Sec. & Stuart Moore (01784 421118)

FACT FILE

Formed: 1892
Nickname: The Swans
Sponsors: The Exchange Nightclub
Colours: Old gold (blue trim)/royal/royal
Change colours: All white
Midweek matchday: Tuesday
Reserve league: Sutton & District Vets Lg.
Local Press: Staines & Ashford News, Middx Chronicle, Informer,Staines Gaurdian
Local Radio: County Sound, GLR, Capital, Star FM, Radio Wey.

2002-03

Leading Scorer: Neil Selby - 14
P.o.Y.: Steve battams

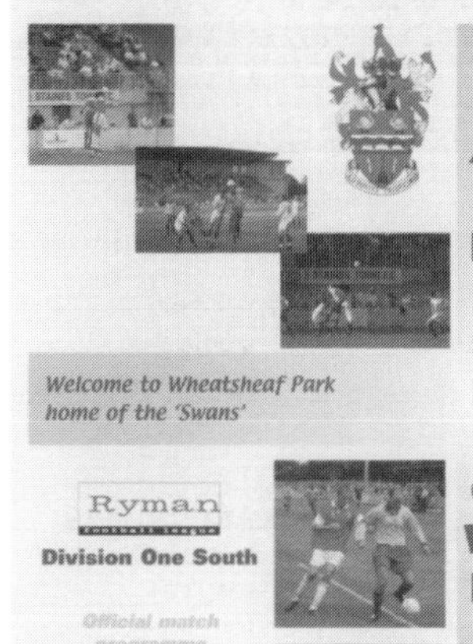

Welcome to Wheatsheaf Park home of the 'Swans'
Ryman
Division One South
Official match programme

GROUNDWheatsheaf Park, Wheatsheaf Lane,Staines,Middlesex TW18 2PD(01784 455988)
Directions: M25 Jct13 to A30 Staines by-pass to Crooked Billet roundabout.Take town centre exit(A308) and left into South St., at iron bridge. Pass bus staion and bear left into Laleham Rd. Wheatsheafe Lane is 1km on right Buses 481, 570,and 573 pass Wheatsheaf Lane.
Capacity: 3,000 **Cover:** 850 **Seats:** 300 **Floodlights**:Yes **Food:** Rolls and snacks available
Club HQ & Clubhouse: Staines Town FC, Wheatsheaf Lane, Staines Modern sports bar.
Club Shop: Souvenirs available from Ray Moore c/o STFC.

PREVIOUS **Leagues:** W London All (pre-1900), W London, W Middx (pre-1905), Gt WesternSuburban 05-13 20-24, Gt Western Comb, Munitions Lg (World War 1), London Works(World War 1), Hounslow & Dist 19-20, Spartan 24-35 58-71, Middx Sen 43-52; Parthenon 52-53, Hellenic 53-58, Athenian 71-73
Names: Staines Albany and St Peters Institute (merged) in 1895, Staines 05-18,Staines Lagonda 18-25, Staines Vale (2nd World War)
Grounds: Edgell Rd (St Peters Inst); The Lammas, Shortwood Common, Mill Mead(Hammonds/Wicks/Pursers Farm); Shepperton Road (to 51); Wheatsheaf Lane - From 51-except g/share Chertsey Town (1996-8), Walton & Hersham (2001-02) & Egham Town (2002-Feb 03)

CLUB RECORDS **Attendance:** 2,750 v Banco di Roma (Barassi Cup) 1975 (70,000 saw 1st leg in Rome)
Goalscorer: Alan Gregory 122 **Appearances:** Dickie Watmore 840
Win: 14-0 v Croydon (A), Isthmian League Div. 1 19/3/94 **Defeat:** 1-18 v Wycombe Wands. (A), G West Sub Lge 27.12.09
Fee Paid: For R Teale (Slough 81) **Fee Received:** For Scott Taylor (Millwall 95-96)

BEST SEASON **FA Amateur Cup:** 3rd Rd 23-24 **FA Trophy:** 2nd Rd 2nd Replay 76-77l (Last 32)
FA Cup: 1st Rd 84-85, 0-2 v Burton Alb (A) & 1879-80 & 80-81 (as St Peters Institute)

HONOURS Isthmian Lg Div 1 74-75 88-89 (Div 2 74-75); Athenian Lg Div 2 71-72 (Div 1 R-up 72-73); Spartan Lg 59-60 (R-up 70-71), Lg Cup 68-69 (R-up 60-61 70-71); Hellenic Lg R-up 55-56 (Lg Cup R-up 53-54 55-56); Gt Western Suburban Lg Div 1R-up 11-12 22-24 (Div 2 (Middx) 20-21); W London All Div 1 1899-1900; W LondonLg Div 1 00-01; W Middx Lg 04-05 (R-up 03-04); London Snr Cup R-up 76-77 80-81; Middx Snr Cup(7), (R-up 09-10 32-33 79-80), Snr Charity Cup 94-95; Barassi Cup76; Southern Comb. Chall. Cup 64-65 66-67 68-69 94-95 96-97,(R-up 67-68 94-95,99-00);W Middx Cup 23-24; Staines Cottage Hosp Cup 24-25; Merthyr Middx Charity Shield 90-91,(R-up 94-95); El Canuelo Trophy 92-93 94-95 94-95; Carlsberg Cup 94-95; Melksham Middx Charity Shield 96-97 Jim Lawford Memorial Cup 99-00, Midd'x Bowl 2001-2 (shared)
Players progressing: R.Bennett (Southend 72), J.Love (Crystal Palace 75), P.Shaw (Charlton A77). E.Young (Wolves) , G.Hill (Millwall), W.Stemp (Brighton), M.Ferney)Fulham), S.Taylor (Millwall & Bolton W)

Staines Town celebrate promotion having beaten Met Police 4-2 at Wheatsheaf Park. The squad, roughly left to right: Jermaine Hunter, Gavin Tomlin, Jon Henry-Hayden, Kezie Ibe, Roni Joe, Jon McDonald, Richard Gell, Trent Phillips (coach), Gareth Risbridger, Matt Lovett, Mark Jones, Peter Barnsby, Matt Flitter, Dean Pitcher, Danny Thomas, Paul Ellis, Mark Pye, Nick Taylor (Kit Man), Craig Maskell, Steve Codery (manager), Andre DeLisser, Danny Rocco and Steve Battams. Missing from the picture were Julian Sills and Emilien Mendy.

TONBRIDGE ANGELS

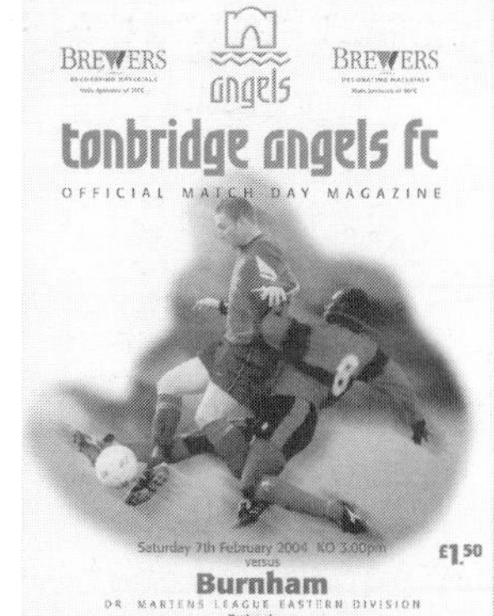

BREWERS
angels
BREWERS
tonbridge angels fc
OFFICIAL MATCH DAY MAGAZINE
Saturday 7th February 2004 KO 3.00pm
versus
Burnham
£1.50
DR MARTENS LEAGUE EASTERN DIVISION

CLUB OFFICIALS

Chairman: Paul Dainty
Vice Chairman:T.B.A.
Secretary: Charlie Cole
30 Faraday Ride,Tonbridge TN10 4RL
Tel No: 01732 354985
Press Officer:T.B.A.
Commercial Manager:Tamsin Jeffrey

FOOTBALL MANAGEMENT TEAM

Manager: Tony Dolby
Physio: Chris Dunk

FACT FILE

Founded: 1948
Nickname: The Angels
Sponsors: T.B.A.
Colours: Royal Blue with white trim
Change Colours: Yelow/Black/Yellow
Midweek matchday: Tuesday
Reserves League: Suburban

2003-2004
Player of the Year:Craig Roser
Top Scorer:Brendon Cass
2004-2005 Captain:Lloyd Hume

GROUND Longmead Stadium, Darenth Avenue, Tonbridge, Kent TN10 3JW
Tel: 01732 352417

Directions: From Tonbridge BR station, through High Street, north up Shipbourne Rd (A227 Gravesend road) to 2nd mini-r'bout ('The Pinnacles' pub), left into Darenth Avenue, ground at bottom of Avenue, far side of car park

Capacity: 5,000 Seats: 202 Cover: 400 Floodlights: Yes

Clubhouse: Open Mon-Sat evenings and Sunday lunchtimes.
Hot food on matchdays from burger bar

Club Shop: Yes, progs, replica kits etc, contact Lorraine Parks (01732 350865)

Pages: 38 Price: £1
Editor:Maurice Brown c/o Club

Local Press: Kent Messenger, Courier, Sevenoaks Leader
Local Radio: Mercury, Radio Kent, K,F.M.

PREVIOUS **Leagues:** Southern 48-89, Kent 89-93
Ground: The Angel 48-80 **Names:** TonbridgeAngels, Tonbridge F.C., Tonbridge A.F.C

CLUB RECORDS **Attendance:** 1,463 v Yeovil Town, FA Cup 4th Qualifying Round 26/10/91.
At theAngel Ground: 8,236 v Aldershot, FA Cup 1st Round 1951
Win: 11-1 v WorthingFA Cup 1951 **Defeat:** 2-11 v Folkstone, Kent Sen Cup 1949
Career Goalscorer: Unknown **Career Appearances:** Mark Gillham, 520 to date
Transfer fee paid: **Transfer fee received:** £7,500 for Paul Emblen (Charlton Ath 97)

BEST SEASON **FA Cup:** First Round (proper) 50-51 51-52 52-53 67-68 72-73

HONOURS Kent League 94-95 (League Cup (2)), Southern League Cup Runners-up (2) (SF(1)), Kent Senior Cup 64-65 74-75 Runners-up x2, Kent Senior Shield 51-5255-56 57-58 58-59 63-64

Players progressing: R Saunders, M McMcDonald, T Burns, I Seymour, G Moseley, T Morgan, Neil Emblen, Paul Emblen.

Back Row (L-R): Michael Clarke, Craig Roser, Nick Barnes, Michael Holder, Sam Tydeman, Luke Anderson, Ryan Royston, Keith Moore, Jonathan Heath, Kieron Wilson.**Front Row:** Damien Hodge, John Beales, Mascot, Luke Piscina, Steve Searle, Brendon Cass, Rick Bryce.

WEALDSTONE

CLUB OFFICIALS

Chairman: Nick Symmons
Vice Chairman: Nick DuGard
Secretary: Roger Slater, c/o 31 Jersey Avenue,Stanmore,Middlesex HA7 2JG
Tel: 01992 509 105
Commercial Director: Howard Krais
Press Officer: Steve Paull
Company Secretary: Graham Clark

FOOTBALL MANAGEMENT TEAM

Manager: Gordon Bartlett
Assistant Manager: Leo Morris
Coach: Fred Cummings Capt: Robin Tucker
Physio: Becky Price

FACT FILE

Formed: 1899
Nickname: The Stones
Sponsors: Carthium Group Ltd
Colours: Blue & white quarters
Change colours: Navy & Yellow Quarters
Midweek matches: Tuesday
Reserves' League: Suburban
Club Website: http://come.to/wealdstonefc

2003-2004

Top scorer:Richard Jolly 34
Player of the Year: Richard Jolly

we are the
stones
match magazine 2003-4
WEALDSTONE v CHESHAM UNITED
wealdstone football club news, views, interviews £1.50
Fleetline

Pages: 36-40 Price: £1.50
Editor: Terry Dollman
Local Press:
Harrow Observer, Harrow Times
Local Radio: None give reports
W.F.C..Clubcall Line: 90901 560 7001

GROUND: (Sharing with Edgware FC) White Lion Ground, High Street,Edgware,Middlesex (Ground Tel No: 020 8952 6799) Email Address: roge@ dircon.co.uk
Directions: Left out of Edgware station(Northern Line), left again at crossroads and ground is on right , 300 yards down Edgware High Street opposite Warwick Wright behind Premier Lodge Hotel

Clubhouse: New clubhouse at Edgware Town F.C. to open soon.

PREVIOUS **Leagues:** Willesden & Dist. 1899-1906 08-13; London 1911-22; Middx 13-22; Spartan 22-28; Athenian 28-64; Isthmian 64-71; Southern 71-79 81-82,88-95; GMVConference 79-81 82-88
Grounds: College Farm 03-10; Belmont Rd 10-22; Lower Mead Stad 22-91; Vicarage Rd (Watford FC) 91-93; The Warren (Yeading F.C.) 93-95

CLUB RECORDS **Attendance:** 13,504 v Leytonstone FA Amateur Cup Fourth Round replay 5/3/49
Goalscorer: George Duck, 251 **Appearances:** Charlie Townsend, 514
Win: 22-0 v The 12th London Regiment (The Rangers)(H), FA Amateur Cup 13/10/23
Defeat: 0-14 v Edgware Town (A), London Senior Cup 9/12/44
Fees Paid: £15,000 for David Gipp (Barnet, 90) **Received:** £25,000 for Stuart Pearce (Coventry City 83); for Sean Norman (Chesham, 1989)

BEST SEASON **FA Amateur Cup:** Winners 1965-66 **FA Trophy:** Winners 1984-85
FA Cup: Third Round 77-78, 0-4 v Q.P.R. (A). 1st Rd on 13 occasions. League clubs defeated: Hereford Utd and Reading, 77-78

HONOURS: FA Trophy 84-85; FA Amateur Cup 65-66; GMV Conference 84-85; Isthmian Lge - Div3 96-97; Southern Lg Southern Div 81-82, Div 1 South 73-74, Lg Cup 81-82; Athenian Lg 51-52 (R-up 52-53 58-59 60-61); Spartan Lg R-up 22-23; London LgDiv 2 12-13 (R-up 11-12); London Snr Cup 61-62 (jt) (R-up 39-40 51-52 60-61); Middx Snr Cup (11); Middx Senior Charity Cup (12); Capital League 84-85 86-87

Players progressing: Stuart Pearce (Coventry City 83), Vinnie Jones(Wimbledon 86), Danny Bailey (Exeter 89), Phil White (Orient 53), Tom McGhee & John Ashworth (Portsmouth 54 & 62), Charlie Sells (Exeter City 62), Eddie Dilsworth (LincolnCity 67), Colin Franks (Watford 69)

Wealdstone celebrate after their promotion play-off success against Dulwich Hamlet. Photo: Graham Smith.

WINDSOR & ETON

CLUB OFFICIALS
Chairman: Peter Simpson
President: T.B.A.
Secretary: Steve Rowland,
c/o Football Club
Tel: 07887 770630 (M)
Press Officer: Secretary

FOOTBALL MANAGEMENT TEAM
Manager: Dennis Greene
Asst Manager:Colin Ferguson

FACT FILE
Founded: 1892
Nickname: Royalists
Colours: All red with green trim
Change colours: Blue
Midweek matches: Tuesday
Reserves' League: Suburban (South)
Local Press: Windsor & Eton Express,
Windsor & East Berks Observer,
Evening Post
Local Radio: BBC Radio Berkshire,Star FM

PROGRAMME
28 pages Price: £!.00
Editor: Malcolm Williams

GROUND Stag Meadow, St Leonards Road, Windsor, Berkshire SL4 3DR (01753 860656)
Directions: A332 from M4 junct 6. Third left at r'bout , left into St Leonards Rd at lights on T-junction, ground 500 yards on right on B3022 opposite Stag &Hounds PH. 1 mile from town centre -
BR to Windsor Central station (from) Slough or Windsor Riverside (change at Staines from Waterloo)
Capacity: 4,500 Cover: 650 Seats: 400 Floodlights: Yes
Clubhouse: Yes **Club Shop:** Yes

PREVIOUS **Leagues:** Southern 1895-96; West Berks; Great Western Suburban 1907-22; Athenian 22-29 63-81; Spartan 29-32; Great Western Comb; Corinthian 45-50; Metropolitan 50-60; Delphian 60-63 **Ground:** Ballon Meadow 1892-1912

CLUB RECORDS **Attendance:** 8,500 (Charity match) **Appearances:** Kevin Mitchell
Fee Paid: £9,000 for Keith White (Slough Town)
Fee Received: £45,000 for Michael Banton & Michael Barnes (Barnet)

BEST SEASON **FA Amateur Cup:** 4th Rd 21-22 **FA Vase:** Semi-Final 80-81 (QF 79-80) **FA Trophy:** 3rd Rd 88-89
FA Cup: 2nd Rd replay 83-84. 1st Rd 7 times 25-26 80-81 82-86 91-92. League clubs defeated: None

HONOURS Isthmian Lg Div 1 83-84 Div 2 R-up 82-83 2000-01,
Athenian Lg 79-80 80-81 Lg Cup 79-80 R-up 78-79 80-81, Div 2 Cup 63-64 R-up 68-69, Spartan Lg R-up 36-37 37-38 Div 1 30-31,
Metropolitan Lg R-up 53-54 Lg Amtr Cup 51-52 52-53, Lg Cup 52-53 R-up 53-54 54-55, Gt Western Suburban Lg R-up 21-22,
Berks & Bucks Snr Cup (11) 10-11 36-38 40-45 61-62 87-89 R-up 07-08 24-25 26-27 38-39 46-47 62-63,
Berks & Bucks Benev. Cup 35-36 37-38 46-47 62-63 R-up 38-39 47-48 49-50

Players progressing: Reg Dare (Southampton 1949), Steve Adams (Charlton 1979), Dave Barnett (Colchester 1988), Vic Woodley (Chelsea & England), Billy Coward (QPR, Walsall), Ken Groves (Preston), Dave Regis (Notts County), Damian Spencer (1998)

Back Row (L-R): Dave Tilbury, Dave Carroll, Jason Cousins, Chuck Martini, Leon Townley, Tony Reid.
Front Row: Ryan Parsons, Jermaine Lowe, Craig O'Connor, Kieran Gallagher, Spencer Walsh.

Photo: Alan Coomes.

WORTHING

CLUB OFFICIALS

Chairman: Beau Reynolds
President: Morty Hollis
Vice Chairman: Ray Smith

Secretary/Press Off.: Paul Damper
19 Fletcher Road, Worthing,
West Sussex BN14 8EX
Tel: 01903 210290

FOOTBALL MANAGEMENT TEAM

Manager: Alan Pook
Assistant Manager:Danny Bloor
Physio: Alan Robertson

FACT FILE

Formed: 1886 Nickname: The Rebels
Colours: Red, with white trim/red/red
Change : White withbluetrim/ white/white
Midweek matches: Tuesday
Local Press: Evening Argus, Worthing Herald,Worthing Guardian
Local Radio: Southern FM,Splash F.M. Southern Counties Radio

2003--2004

Top Scorer: Sam Francis
Player of the Year: Sam Francis
2004-2005 Captain; Paul Rogers

PROGRAMME

Pages: 48 Price: £1.50
Editor: Alistair McKail

GROUND Woodside Road, Worthing, West Sussex BN14 7HQ (01903 239575)
Directions: Follow A24 to town, at end of Broadwater Rd having gone over railway bridge, 1st right into Teville Rd, right into South Farm RD, 2nd left into Pavilion Rd, Woodside Rd is first right. Half a mile fromWorthing (BR)
Capacity: 4,500 Seats: 450 Cover: 1,500 Floodlights: Yes
Clubhouse: Open 2 hrs before kick-off & closes 11pm. Hot & cold food available
Club Shop: Yes

PREVIOUS **Leagues:** West Sussex Sen 1896-04, 05-14, 19-20; Brighton, Hove & Dist 19-20; Sussex County 20-40, 45-48; Corinthian 48-63; Athenian 63-77 **Names:** Worthing Association pre 1899 **Grounds:** Homefield Park, Beach House Park

CLUB RECORDS **Attendance:** 3,600 v Wimbledon F.A.Cup 14th November 1936
Transfer fee paid: Undisclosed fee forMarc Rice (Havant & Waterlooville1998)
Transfer fee received: £7,500 for Tim Read (Woking, 1990)
Win: 25-0 v Littlehampton (H) West Sussex Lge 1911-12 **Defeat:** 0-14 v Southwick (A), Sussex County Lge 1946-47
Career Goalscorer: Mick Edmonds 276 **Career Appearances:** David Bloom 397

BEST SEASON **FA Vase:** 5th Rd 78-79**FA Trophy:** 3rd Rd Replay 85-86 **FA Amateur Cup:** Quarter-Final replay 07-08
FA Cup: 2nd Rd 82-83, 0-4 v Oxford Utd; 1st Rd 36-37, 94-95 (1-3 v AFC Bournem'th), 99-00 (0-3 v Rotherham United)

HONOURS Isth.Lg R-up (2) 83-85 (Div 1 82-83, Div 2 81-82 92-93);Isth Full members Cup r-up98-99, Athenian Lg Div 1 R-up 63-64, Div 2 R-up 71-72, Lg Cup R-up 72-73, Mem. Shield R-up 63-64; SussexSnr Cup (21); Sussex RUR Char. Cup (13); Sussex Co. Lg(8)W Sussex Lg (7); Brighton Char. Cup(10) Worthing Char. Cup (11); AFA Invit. Cup 63-64 68-69 73-74 75-76 (Snr Cup R-up 36-37 46-47 48-49); Corinth. Lg Mem. Shield R-up 49-50 (NealeTphy 58-59); Roy Hayden Mem. Tphy 75(jt), 77 78,99. Don Morecraft Tphy 72 73 76 8182; Sussex F'lit Cup(3) 88-90 97-98; Sussex I'mediate Cup 34-35 64-65; BrightonChal. Shield 29-30 31-32

Players progressing: Ken Suttle (Chelsea 48), Alan Arnell & Fred Perry (Liverpool 54), Craig Whitington (Scarborough, via Crawley Town) 93, Darren Freeman (Gillingham), Paul Musselwhite (Scunthorpe), Trevor Wood (Port Vale), Richard Tiltman (Brighton), David Cameron (Lincoln C), Charlie Webb (Brighton 1908),Vince Taylor (Arsenal), Eric Parsons (West Ham U & Chelsea), E.G.D.Wright (Hull City)

Back Row (L-R):
Graham Martin (no longer at club),
Ben Carrington,
Chris Dicker,
Glenn Davies,
Tom Graves (no longer at club),
Ross Standen,
Andrew Beech,
Paul Rogers,
Darren Freeman,
Gavin Geddes.

Front Row:
Ross Johnson,
Mark Knee,
Owen Hill,
Mascot,
Mark Pulling,
Wesley Lopez,
Sam Francis.

YEADING

CLUB OFFICIALS

Chairman: Philip Spurden

Secretary: Bill Gritt, Fourwinds,182 Cherry Tree Road, Beaconsfield, Bucks.HP9 1BA

Tel. Nos :01494 674188 (H) 07710102004(M)

Commercial Manager: Bill Perryman
Tel: 020 8756 1200

Press Officer: Tim Fuell (0778 2284164)

FOOTBALL MANAGEMENT TEAM

Managers: Johnson Hippolyte
Asst. Manager: Dereck Brown
Coaches: Erskine Smart & Jason Tucker

FACT FILE

Formed: 1965
Nickname: The Ding
Colours: Red & black stripes/black/black
Change colours: All white
Midweek matchday: Tuesday
Reserves League: Capital
Website: www.yeadingfc.co.uk
Local Newspapers: Hayes Gazette, Hillingdon Times

2002-2003

Captains: Steve Ashley & Nevin Saroya
Top Scorer: Matt Miller 30
Players of the Year: Keith Newby & Emond Protain

Yeading
Official Matchday Publication £1.50
at The W

Programme - Pages: 36 Price: £1.50
Editor: Tim Fuell

GROUND The Warren, Beaconsfield Rd.Hayes, MiddlesexUB4 0SL
Tel: 020 8848 7362 Fax: 020 8756 1200 email: yeading@yeadingfc.co.uk
Directions: 2 miles from Hayes (BR) - take Uxbridge Road and turn right towards Southall, right into Springfield Rd and then left into Beaconsfield Rd. Bus 207 stops 1/2 mile from ground
Capacity: 3,500 Cover: 1,000 Seats: 250 Floodlights: Yes
Clubhouse: Open normal pub hours.' The Warren' Conference & Banquetting suite available for hire.
Club Shop: No Metal Badges: Yes

PREVIOUS Leagues: Uxbridge & Dist. 65-67; W. Middx. Comb. 67-68; S W Middx 68-74; Middx 74-84; Spartan 84-87

CLUB RECORDS **Attendance:** 3,000; v Hythe Town, FA Vase SF 1990; v Tottenham Hotspur, friendly
Career Goalscorer: Dave Burt 327 **Career Appearances:** Norman Frape 457
Fee Paid: £3,000 for Matt Edwards to Hucknall Town **Fee Received:** £45,000 for Andrew Impey (QPR)

BEST SEASON **FA Cup:** First Round Proper 93-94 & 94-95
FA Vase: Winners 89-90 **FA Trophy:** 2nd Round 97-98, 98-99, 00-01

HONOURS FA Vase 89-90; Isthmian League Div 2 Sth 89-90 (Div 1 R-up 91-92) League Cup 2002-03;Spartan League 86-87 (R-up 85-86, Senior Div R-up 84-85, League Cup 85-86 86-87); Middlesex Snr League (6) 71-73 74-76 81-82 83-84 (R-up 73-74 74-75 78-79, LeagueCup (6) 72-73 75-76 79-83); South West Middlesex League (2) 69-71; Middlesex Snr Cup 89-90 91-92, Middlesex Prem. Cup 80-81, Middlesex I'mediate Cup (5) 70-7274-76 77-78, Middlesex Jnr Cup (4) 68-69 70-72 74-75; Uxbridge League 66-67; Middlesex Border League Cup 86-87 (AJA Cup 86-87); Suburban League Nth 87-88; Allied Counties Yth League 89-90 (Lge Cup 89-90)

Players progressing: Andrew Impey (Leicester City ,West Ham United , QPR and England U 21) and Lee Charles (Q.P.R.via Chertsey Town) Charlie Oatway(Cardiff C)

Yeading F.C. Ryman League Division One North Champions 2003/04

(Left to Right) Jason Tucker, Daniel Hawkesworth, Jonathan Hippolyte (Mascot), Darti Brown (Captain), Delroy Preddie, Dean Harper, Alex Stanley, Emond Protain, Keith Newby, Leon Woodruffe, Bradley Quamina, DJ Campbell

BILLERICAY TOWN
Goalkeepers:
Dave McCartney (Millwall)
Defenders:
Danny Kerrigan (Grays), Robin Trott (Gravesend), Pat Sappleton (Farnborough), Matthew Game (Leyton Orient), Dave McSweeney (Southend)
Midfield:
Matt Jones (Chelmsford), Gary Henty (Barking), Jamie Dormer (Barking), Steve Forbes (Hendon), Leon Hunter (Heybridge Swifts), Keiran Gallagher (Hendon)
Forwards:
Danny Hockton (Crawley), Neil Cousins (Heybridge Swifts), Chris Stowe (Hampton & Richmond), Ross Wareham (Leyton Orient), Bradley Allen (Hornchurch)

BRAINTREE TOWN
Goakeepers:
Danny Gay (Hornchurch), Paul Rutherford (Tottenham)
Defenders:
Paul Lorraine (Erith & Belvedere), Ollie Adedeji (Hornchurch), Ollie Blackwell (Heybridge Swifts), Louis Riddle (Stevenage)
Midfield:
Gavin McGowan (Hornchurch), Billy Burgess (Welling), Andy Porter (St Margaretsbury)
Forwards:
Gary Abbott (Walton & Hersham), Brad Quinton (Bishop's Stortford), Steve Good (Romford), Louis Evans (Gravesend)

CHELMSFORD CITY
Goalkeepers:
Paul Nicholls (Havant & Waterlooville)
Defenders:
Garry Cross (Slough), Iain O'Connell (Margate), Russell Edwards (Welling), Wes Faulkner (Aveley), Ian Cousins (Welling), Russell Penn (East Thurrock), Kevin Watson (Team Bath)
Midfield:
Steve Butterworth (Youth team), Steve Norman (Dover), Liam Hopkins (Youth team), Sam Cooper (Redbridge)
Forwards:
Steve Bennett (Youth team), Gary Ansell (East Thurrock), Lee Williams (Grays), Fabian Forde (Hendon)

CHESHUNT
Goalkeepers:
Bradley Hughes (Grimsby), David Lovell (Aylesbury), Russell Ling (Leyton Pennant)
Defenders:
Andy Keepence (Bishop's Stortford), Matt Waldron (Enfield), Same Ledger (Somersett Ambury), Ryan Harris (Leyton Pennant), Mark Brewer (Billericay), Owen Coll (Hitchin)
Midfield:
Carl Ashton (Potters Bar), Ross White (Grays), Steve Wales (Broxbourne Borough), Steve Obeng (Edgware), Marvin Walker (Boreham Wood), Glenn Adams (Aveley),
Forwards:
Leon Archer (Somersett Ambury), Darrell Cox (St Margaretsbury), Chris Bangura (Kingstonian), Chris Watters (Hemel Hempstead), Andy Aransiba (Tilbury), Henry Haastrup (Hillingdon)

DOVER ATHLETIC
Goalkeepers:
Dave Wietecha (Folkestone), Paul Hyde (Leyton Orient)
Defenders:
Craig Cloke (Youth team), Craig Wilkins (Gravesend), Dean Readings (Youth team), Nicky Humphrey (Tonbridge),
Midfield:
Matt Carruthers (Newport IoW), Tom Hickman (Youth team), Billy Bone (Gravesend), James Rogers (Youth team)
Forwards:
Michael Smissen (Sittingbourne), Rob Smidmore (Youth team), Danny Welch (Youth team)

EASTLEIGH
Goalkeepers:
Colin Matthews (Newport IoW), Wayne Shaw (AFC Totton)
Defenders:
Danny Rofe (Newport IoW), Lee Bright (Youth team), Tyrone Bowers (Salisbury), Danny Woods (Bournemouth FC), Sam Wyeth (Youth team
Midfield:
Danny Smith (Winchester), David Hughes (Southampton), Martin Thomas (Exeter), Christer Warren (Bristol C), Neil Davis (Havant & Waterlooville), Jamie Stokoe (AFC Bournemouth
Forwards:
Andy Forbes (Winchester), Martin Beck (Winchester), Nicky Banger (Woking), Paul Sales (Bashley), Robbie Matthews (Salisbury), Robbie Chamberlain (Youth team)

FOLKESTONE INVICTA
Goalkeepers:
Tony Kessell (Dartford), Dan Morrin (Maidstone)
Defenders:
Adam Flanagan (Hastings), John Guest (Sittingbourne), Paul Lamb (Maidstone), John Walker (Youth team), Drew Watkins (Cray Wanderers)
Midfield:
Scott Lindsay (Welling), Martin Chandler (West Ham), Mark Munday (Margate), Mark Rook (Bearsted), Michael Everitt (Youth team)
Forwards:
James Dryden (Youth team), Simon Glover (Dover), Ian Pulman (Margate)

HAMPTON & RICHMOND BOROUGH
Goalkeepers:
Adrian Blake (Maidenhead), Kieran Drake (Marlow), Matt Pollard (Chalfont)
Defenders:
Matt Elverson (Kingstonian), Orlando Jeffrey (Maidenhead), Jeremy Jones (Leatherhead), Sammy Okafor (Enfield), Steve Omonua (Barking), Dean Wells (Brentford)
Midfield:
Henry Cook (Youth team), Dudley Gardner (Slough), Alan Inns (Wokingham), Craig Lewington (Kingstonian), Andy Morley (Maidenhead), Lee O'Leary (Brook House), Obinna Ulassi (Maidenhead)
Forwards:
Adrian Allen (Maidenhead), Michael Currie (Maidenhead), Luke Fontana (Banstead), Graham Harper (Whyteleafe)

HARROW BOROUGH
Goalkeepers:
Keita Karamoko (Wembley)
Defenders:
Wayne Walters (Wembley), Perry Norman (Chertsey), Dean Marney (Greenwich), Rob Sterry (youth team), Paul Johnson (Tooting)
Midfield:
Fabio Valenti (Edgware), Steve Dogbe (Chesham), Osman Hasan (Hounslow)
Forwards:
Brian Haule (Hampton & Richmond B), Daniel Dyer (Wembley), Danny McGonigle (Wembley)

HENDON
Goalkeepers:
Dave King (Hastings), Luke Thornton (Ware)
Defenders:
James Burgess (Youth team), Danny Butler (Wealdstone), Will Davies (Matlock), Jazz Rose (Youth team), Dave Sargent (St Albans), Rene Street (Northwood)
Midfield:
Ricardo Alves (Fiorentina (Italy)), Wayne Carter (Northwood), David Hunt (Ware), Danny Julienne (Northwood), Richard McDonagh (Hemel Hempstead), Dave Nolan (Northwood), Martin Vrhovski (Wingate & Finchley), Scott Williams (Northwood)
Forwards:
Usif Bangura (Wakefield-Emley), John Frendo (Ware), Mark Nicholls (Northwood), Eugene Ofori (Liberty Professionals (Ghana)), Anthony Robinson (Stourport Swifts)

HEYBRIDGE SWIFTS
Goalkeepers:
Darren Placid (Southend)
Defenders:
Danny Barber (Clacton), Daryl Bourgeois (Cambridge Utd), Erdem Artun (Woodbridge), Alan Kimble (Dagenham & Redbridge)
Midfield:
John Pollard (St Albans), Adam Gillespie (Braintree), Russell Williamson (Braintree), Michale Shinn (Youth team), Jamie Baker (Woodbridge), Ergun Artun (Halstead)
Forwards:
Sean Marks (Youth team), James Robinson (Youth team), Carl Griffiths (Harlow), James Rowe (Histon), Dwayne Edwards (Woodbridge)

CORRECT AT TIME OF GOING TO PRESS

KINGSTONIAN
Goalkeepers:
Lance Key (Northwich), Barry Marchena (Brentford)
Defenders:
Fraser Muscat (Youth team), Matt Bradford (Brighton), Jermaine Hinds (Dorking), Dean Souyana (Youth team), Bernard Asante (Youth team), Anthony Savage (Aveley), Leon White (Youth team)
Midfield:
Bashiru Alimi (Millwall), Martyn Lee (Maidenhead), Dave Timothy (Carshalton), Mark Scotchford (Youth team), Matt Pattison (Farnborough), Scott Steele (Woking)
Forwards:
Reggie Savage (Youth team), Mazin Ahmad (Youth team), Martyn Williams (QPR), Adrian Graham (Youth team), Josh Francois (Youth team), Liam Collins (Walton & Hersham), Greg Ball (Walton & Hersham)

LEYTON
Goalkeepers:
James Hassell (Harlow), Jamie Hussey (Fisher), James Courtnage (Enfield)
Defenders:
Ian Bass (Waltham Forest), Terry Brooks (Priory Court), Paul Golby (Barkingside), Scott Honeyball (Enfield), Ross McPherson (Youth team), Roy Parkyn (Arlesey), Simon Peddie (Enfield), Vas Soteriou (Enfield), Carl Fannon (Aveley), Ben Wood (Ford Utd)
Midfield:
Troy Braham (Bishop's Stortford), Scott Curley (Braintree), Koin Hosobuchi (Crown & Manor), Mark Sophocleus (Plymouth), Victor Boyle-Renner (Bishop's Stortford)
Forwards:
Leli Bejada (Bishop's Stortford), George Georgiou (East Thurrock), George Gregoriou (Enfield), Trevor Paul (Bishop's Stortford), Andrew Thomas (Youth team), Manny Williams (Bowers Utd), Paul Armstrong (Enfield)

NORTHWOOD
Goalkeepers:
Rob Bullivant (University), Dean Lindsay (Hendon)
Defenders:
Steve Dell (Hornchurch), Mark Dennison (Brook House), Luke Evans (Windsor), Stuart Reeks (Boreham Wood), Gary Meakin (Hendon), Lee Gardner (Southall T)
Midfield:
Danny Yeoman (Uxbridge), Dean Clark (Hayes), Richard Morton (Newcastle T), Chris Glynn (Southall T), Gavin Hart (Southall T), Jonny Moore (St Albans)
Forwards:
Dean Papali (Brook House), Kevin Chakodza (Brook House), Kieron Keane (Southall T), Brian Fitzgerald (QPR), Anthony Finn (Edgware), Eric Kwake (Hampton & Richmond B)

SALISBURY CITY
Goalkeepers:
Kevin Sawyer (Cirencester)
Defenders:
Scott Bartlett (Cirencester), Tim Bond (AFC Bournemouth), Andy Cook (Millwall), Michael Cooper (Yeovil), Andy McGlashan (Youth team), Josh Thomas (Weymouth), Aaron Cook (Bashley), Mark Lisk (Bashley)
Midfield:
Matt Davies (Woking), Wayne Turk (Cirencester), Mike Harris (Bashley), Steve Strong (Lymington & New Milton), Craig Davis (Bashley), Glen Davies (Newport IoW), Matt Holmes (Bemerton Heath Harlequins)
Forwards:
Stuart Brown (Jomo-Cosmo (South Africa)), Adam Wallace (Southend), Leigh Phillips (Lymington & New Milton), Matt Tubbs (Dorchester)

SLOUGH TOWN
Goalkeepers:
Michael Parkin (Torquay)
Defenders:
Steve Daly (Boreham Wood), Michael Murphy (Windsor), James Saulsbury (Thame), Nick Gyoury (Chelmsford), Danny Steer (Eastleigh), Josias Carbon (Oxford Utd)
Midfield:
Darron Wilkinson (Hayes), Veli Hakki (Boreham Wood), Sam Shepherd (Oxford C), Christian Metcalfe (Northwood), Alex Haddow (Aldershot), Glen Harris (Hayes), Ryan Spencer (Hayes)
Forwards:
Ian Hodges (Hayes), Matt Miller (Yeading), Matt Seedel (Youth team), Andrew Deaner (AFC Newbury)

STAINES TOWN
Goalkeepers:
Matt Hodson (Yeading), Matt Lovett (Youth team)
Defenders:
Peter Barnsby (Kingstonian), Darren Deegan (Hampton & Richmond B), Matt Flitter (Kingstonian), Danny Gordon (Aylesbury), Jon McDonald (Youth team), Sam Okikiolu (Clyde)
Midfield:
Paul Ellis (Aylesbury), Richard Gell (Aylesbury), Mark Jones (Kingstonian), Jake Newton (Youth team), Mark Pye (Carshalton), Gareth Risbridger (Aylesbury), Danny Rouco (Hampton & Richmond B), Julian Sills (Kingstonian), Danny Thomas (Brentford)
Forwards:
Andre Delisser (Hendon), Jon Henry-Hayden (Kitchener Spirit (Canada)), Jermaine Hunter (Walton & Hersham), Ronnie Joe (Bedford), Craig Maskell (Aylesbury), Dean Pitcher (Youth team), Gavin Tomlin (Aylesbury)

TONBRIDGE ANGELS
Goalkeepers:
Jamie Turner (Gravesend)
Defenders:
Tony Dolby (Fisher), John Beales (Youth team), Andy Larkin (Maidstone Utd), Craig Roser (Chatham), Keiron Wilson (Youth team)
Midfield:
Mike Rutherford (Welling), Luke Anderson (Welling), Sam Tydeman (Fisher), Steve Searle (Fisher), Jon Heath (Youth team)
Forwards:
Brendan Cass (Youth team), Luke Piscina (Youth team), Paul Emblen (Wycombe), David Powell (Welling), Pat Blackman (Youth team)

WEALDSTONE
Goalkeepers:
Andy Carter (Hemel Hempstead), Charlie Leary (Youth team)
Defenders:
Robin Tucker (Buckingham), Rob Courtnage (Dulwich Hamlet), Matt Carvell (Grantham), Danny Wolf (Braintree), Chris Cahill (Brook House), Lyndon Duncan (Exeter), James Shipperley (Hayes), James Fisher (Wembley), Leon Henderson (Wembley)
Midfield:
Tommy Williams (Carshalton), Martin Carter (Aylesbury), Andy Myhill (Viking Sports), Danny Tilbury (Hayes), Jason Shaw (Hampton & Richmond B), Gary McKeown (Bishop's Stortford), Mitch Hahn (Southend), Brian Jones (Hemel Hempstead)
Forwards:
Marvin Morgan (Youth team), Richard Jolly (Hayes), Ben Alexander (Watford), Jermaine Beckford (Youth team), Danny Clarke (Enfield T)

WINDSOR & ETON
Goalkeepers:
Chuck Martini (Bromley)
Defenders:
Ian Dickens (Basingstoke), Lee Kersey (Heybridge Swifts), Ryan Parsons (Wycombe), Justin Skinner (Weston-super-Mare), Dave Tilbury (Yeading), Leon Townley (St Albans)
Midfield:
Kieran Adams (Purfleet), Dave Carroll (Aldershot), Lewis Cook (Wycombe), Morgaro Gomis (Chelsea), Paul Holsgrove (Hayes), Terry O'Connor (Egham), Spencer Walsh (Andover)
Forwards:
Peter Holsgrove (Hayes), Tony Reid (Hampton & Richmond B), Keith Scott (Dagenham & Redbridge), Dennis Greene (Heybridge Swifts)

WORTHING
Goalkeepers: Will Packham (Farnborough)
Defenders:
Ian Payne (Crawley), Stewart Holmes (Easbourne B), Chris Dicker (Withdean), Lamont (), Marc Pullan (Crawley), Chris Hibberd (Worthing Utd)
Midfield:
Paul Rogers (Sutton Utd), Mark Knee (Lewes), Marc Pulling (Withdean), Roy Pook (Withdean), Youness Nabil (Windsor), Clay Lamont (Withdean), Nko Ekoku (Leatherhead)
Forwards:
Phil Ruggles (Leatherhead), Sam Francis (Withdean), Ben Carrington (Eastbourne T)

YEADING
Goalkeepers: John Armand (Youth team), Delroy Preddie (Chesham)
Defenders: Mark Kleboe (Aldershot), Marc Leach (Wingate & Finchley), Nev Saroya (Brentford), Alex Stanley (Farnborough), Danny Hawksworth (Northwood), Jason Tucker (Chertsey), Leon Woodruffe (Hendon)
Midfield: Karl Bailey (Ashford T (Middx)), Darti Brown (Willesden Constantine), Derek Brown (Chesham), David Clarke (Harrow), Keith Newby (Harrow), Brad Quamina (Youth team), Ryan McIntosh (QPR)
Forwards: Errol Telemarque (Hayes), Johnson Hippolyte (Chesham), Davis Haule (Woking), DJ Campbell (Billericay), Michael Barima (Harrow)

ISTHMIAN LEAGUE DIVISION ONE
STEP 4

FINAL LEAGUE TABLE 2003-04

Qualify for Isthmian/Southern Premier Division

DIVISION ONE NORTH		P	W	D	L	F	A	Pts
1.	Yeading	46	32	7	7	112	54	103
2.	Leyton	46	29	9	8	90	53	96
3.	Cheshunt	46	27	10	9	119	54	91
4.	Chesham United (Sth)	46	24	9	13	104	60	81
5.	Dunstable Town (Sth)	46	23	9	14	86	61	78
6.	Hemel Hempstead Town (Sth)	46	22	12	12	75	72	78
7.	Wealdstone*	46	23	7	16	81	51	76
8.	Arlesey Town	46	23	7	16	95	70	76
9.	Boreham Wood	46	20	13	13	82	59	73
10.	Harlow Town	46	20	10	16	75	51	70
11.	Wingate & Finchley	46	19	13	14	68	63	70
12.	East Thurrock United	46	19	11	16	62	54	68
13.	Uxbridge	46	15	14	17	59	57	59
14.	Aveley	46	15	14	17	67	71	59
15.	Thame United	46	16	9	21	72	83	57
16.	Waltham Forest (-3pts)	46	15	13	18	62	60	55
17.	Wivenhoe Town	46	15	10	21	79	104	55
18.	Barton Rovers	46	16	6	24	52	80	54
19.	Oxford City	46	14	11	21	55	65	53
20.	Berkhamsted Town	46	12	10	24	66	88	46
21.	Great Wakering Rovers	46	10	13	23	47	97	43
22.	Tilbury	46	10	9	27	56	100	39
23.	Barking & East Ham Utd	46	8	7	31	37	100	31
24.	Enfield	46	5	7	34	44	138	22

*Qualified for Isthmian Premier Division via play-off.

Qualify for Isthmian Premier Division

DIVISION ONE SOUTH		P	W	D	L	F	A	Pts
1.	Lewes*	46	29	7	10	113	61	94
2.	Worthing	46	26	14	6	87	46	92
3.	Windsor & Eton	46	26	13	7	75	39	91
4.	Slough Town	46	28	6	12	103	63	90
5.	Hampton & Richmond	46	26	11	9	82	45	89
6.	Staines Town	46	26	9	11	85	52	87
7.	Dulwich Hamlet	46	23	15	8	77	57	84
8.	Bromley	46	22	10	14	80	58	76
9.	Walton & Hersham	46	20	14	12	76	55	74
10.	Croydon Athletic	46	20	10	16	70	54	70
11.	Tooting & Mitcham Utd	46	20	9	17	82	68	69
12.	Ashford Town (Mx)	46	18	13	15	69	62	67
13.	Leatherhead	46	19	9	18	83	88	66
14.	Bracknell Town	46	19	6	21	81	87	63
15.	Horsham	46	16	11	19	71	69	59
16.	Marlow	46	16	11	19	50	64	59
17.	Whyteleafe	46	17	4	25	66	93	55
18.	Banstead Athletic	46	15	8	23	56	73	53
19.	Molesey	46	12	6	28	45	84	42
20.	Metropolitan Police	46	9	14	23	58	84	41
21.	Croydon	46	10	10	26	57	88	40
22.	Egham Town	46	8	8	30	55	92	32
23.	Corinthian Casuals	46	6	6	34	48	110	24
24.	Epsom & Ewell	46	5	8	33	40	117	23

*Qualified for Conference Division One via play-offs.

	DIVISION ONE NORTH 03-04	1	2	3	4	5	6	7	8	9	10	11	12	13	14	15	16	17	18	19	20	21	22	23	24
1	Arlesey Town		4-2	4-2	0-1	1-4	1-0	3-2	2-2	2-1	1-0	1-2	9-0	0-1	1-0	4-1	1-0	4-2	3-1	2-0	2-0	0-2	1-1	3-2	5-0
2	Aveley	4-0		0-0	1-0	1-0	1-2	0-0	1-1	5-1	0-0	1-1	2-1	4-1	0-0	1-2	0-0	0-2	4-2	0-0	0-0	3-1	1-0	1-1	1-1
3	Barking & East Ham United	1-2	2-0		0-0	2-1	0-3	0-4	0-2	2-6	2-0	0-0	0-0	0-3	0-1	0-4	2-3	1-2	2-0	1-1	0-1	1-4	1-2	0-3	1-2
4	Barton Rovers	3-2	2-1	1-0		2-3	1-1	1-1	1-5	0-1	0-3	4-0	3-2	1-3	0-2	0-2	3-1	2-1	0-2	2-1	1-0	1-1	0-2	3-1	0-3
5	Berkhamsted Town	4-3	1-5	2-2	2-1		1-2	1-1	0-5	0-2	2-4	1-1	1-2	3-2	1-2	1-1	0-1	5-0	1-2	2-1	2-1	0-0	2-2	3-4	3-4
6	Boreham Wood	4-0	2-1	1-2	2-0	4-0		1-1	1-3	3-1	4-0	2-1	0-2	1-1	2-2	1-2	1-0	0-1	6-0	3-1	1-1	3-2	2-0	4-3	1-3
7	Chesham United	1-3	3-1	5-0	3-0	4-2	1-1		1-0	1-2	5-1	1-1	7-0	1-0	5-2	2-0	1-4	6-1	1-1	4-0	1-0	1-3	2-0	8-2	0-0
8	Cheshunt	3-0	2-3	5-0	3-0	0-2	2-0	1-2		2-2	4-1	4-2	4-0	1-3	5-0	3-1	2-0	1-1	1-0	4-2	1-1	3-2	1-2	6-3	2-1
9	Dunstable Town	1-1	4-0	5-0	1-2	2-1	0-2	2-1	2-2		1-1	2-1	2-3	1-3	0-1	3-1	1-0	2-1	3-1	0-0	1-2	2-0	4-1	5-1	0-1
10	East Thurrock United	1-1	3-1	5-0	2-1	0-1	3-3	4-0	1-3	0-1		3-0	2-0	1-0	1-0	1-0	1-2	3-1	2-0	0-1	3-0	0-2	0-1	2-3	3-2
11	Enfield	0-6	1-2	3-1	3-2	1-1	2-4	2-7	1-3	1-5	1-1		0-0	0-6	1-2	1-2	3-2	0-5	1-4	1-7	0-4	0-8	0-4	0-1	1-4
12	Great Wakering Town	0-1	2-2	4-0	3-3	4-1	0-2	0-0	1-4	1-3	0-3	2-1		2-1	0-3	1-1	0-3	1-1	1-2	2-1	0-0	0-0	1-1	0-2	2-3
13	Harlow Town	0-2	0-1	0-1	1-0	2-0	3-2	4-0	3-0	0-2	0-0	4-0	3-1		1-1	0-0	2-3	2-1	1-3	0-0	0-1	0-1	1-1	1-1	1-1
14	Hemel Hempstead Town	1-0	1-1	1-0	4-0	0-3	0-0	3-1	3-7	3-3	3-2	3-2	4-0	2-4		2-4	0-1	1-1	1-5	1-0	2-2	2-1	1-2	2-1	1-1
15	Leyton	4-3	1-0	3-2	0-1	3-1	1-0	2-4	2-1	0-0	1-1	2-1	3-3	3-3	1-1		2-1	3-0	3-2	4-1	1-0	1-0	0-0	5-1	1-2
16	Oxford City	1-0	2-3	2-1	0-1	0-0	2-1	1-2	1-1	2-2	0-1	3-1	0-1	2-4	1-2	1-3		2-1	2-2	1-1	1-1	1-3	1-3	1-1	1-1
17	Thame United	4-3	2-1	3-0	0-3	2-0	2-0	1-3	0-0	1-2	0-0	8-0	3-0	1-0	2-3	0-2	1-2		4-3	1-0	2-2	0-3	1-2	2-1	2-2
18	Tilbury	3-4	2-0	1-2	0-1	1-1	1-1	0-2	1-1	0-3	0-0	3-2	1-2	0-4	0-3	1-3	2-1	3-0		0-4	0-0	0-2	1-6	1-2	1-2
19	Uxbridge	0-0	3-2	1-1	2-0	2-1	1-1	1-0	0-5	1-0	0-0	3-0	0-0	1-0	1-1	0-1	0-1	2-2	6-1		0-0	1-3	2-0	2-0	0-2
20	Waltham Forest	1-6	4-1	3-1	2-0	3-0	3-0	2-4	0-2	1-1	0-1	3-2	3-0	0-1	0-1	1-2	2-0	1-1	2-2	1-2		1-1	0-3	5-2	3-1
21	Wealdstone	0-0	1-0	1-2	2-1	2-2	1-2	3-1	0-4	5-0	3-1	2-0	5-0	0-1	0-2	1-2	2-2	3-0	1-0	2-1	1-0		3-1	0-2	1-2
22	Wingate & Finchley	1-0	4-4	2-1	2-2	2-0	4-4	2-1	1-1	2-1	0-0	1-0	1-1	1-4	0-1	1-5	2-0	0-4	0-0	0-2	1-3	2-0		0-1	1-2
23	Wivenhoe Town	4-4	2-3	2-0	3-2	0-4	1-1	0-3	2-6	0-2	0-1	1-2	4-2	1-1	3-3	0-4	0-0	4-1	2-1	2-2	4-1	0-1	1-1		3-2
24	Yeading	3-0	7-2	2-1	6-0	2-0	1-1	2-0	2-1	3-1	4-0	3-1	2-0	3-0	6-1	0-1	1-0	5-1	7-0	3-2	2-1	3-2	0-3	3-2	

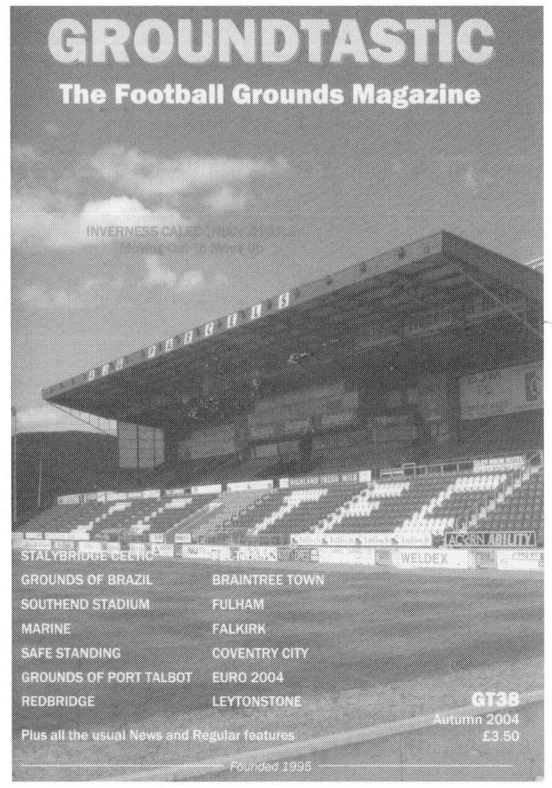

	DIVISION ONE SOUTH 03-04	1	2	3	4	5	6	7	8	9	10	11	12	13	14	15	16	17	18	19	20	21	22	23	24
1	Ashford Town (Middlesex)		2-0	4-1	1-1	2-1	0-2	2-0	1-1	1-0	2-0	0-0	1-2	2-2	2-3	1-1	3-1	1-2	1-2	0-2	2-3	2-2	4-2	3-0	1-1
2	Banstead Athletic	0-1		1-0	1-2	0-1	1-4	1-1	1-1	5-1	4-1	0-1	1-2	1-3	6-1	1-0	1-1	0-2	1-2	0-1	2-1	0-1	2-0	0-3	1-1
3	Bracknell Town	0-0	3-0		0-1	5-0	5-4	1-0	1-2	3-2	2-0	0-4	2-1	1-3	0-3	1-1	0-3	4-0	4-2	3-4	0-6	2-1	10-1	0-0	4-2
4	Bromley	2-3	1-1	4-0		3-0	2-0	2-2	2-2	1-2	2-0	2-0	1-3	2-0	1-2	0-2	1-1	4-0	0-4	2-1	1-0	0-3	2-2	1-0	0-0
5	Corinthian Casuals	0-2	1-6	0-3	0-1		0-4	1-3	0-3	4-2	0-1	1-1	1-1	3-2	2-4	2-4	1-1	0-1	4-1	0-0	0-3	1-2	0-5	0-3	1-3
6	Croydon	2-2	3-1	0-2	0-1	4-3		0-2	2-2	0-2	0-2	0-3	4-2	3-1	0-4	2-4	0-1	3-1	1-0	0-4	2-2	1-1	0-1	0-1	1-1
7	Croydon Athletic	1-0	3-0	1-2	0-2	3-2	1-0		2-2	2-1	3-0	2-4	1-2	3-2	1-2	2-0	4-2	4-1	1-0	0-3	0-2	2-0	5-1	0-0	0-0
8	Dulwich Hamlet	4-0	1-2	2-2	0-4	3-2	2-0	1-0		1-0	3-1	2-1	1-0	4-2	4-1	3-1	1-1	1-3	2-4	2-2	1-1	1-4	1-3	2-2	2-1
9	Egham Town	2-2	1-2	1-2	1-4	1-1	3-2	1-3	0-0		1-0	2-2	0-2	2-3	2-4	0-0	3-0	1-2	2-3	2-1	1-1	0-1	2-3	0-1	0-2
10	Epsom & Ewell	0-5	1-1	0-2	1-1	4-1	1-2	1-1	0-2	1-2		0-2	0-3	1-2	0-4	0-3	2-5	2-0	1-4	0-2	2-3	0-3	0-1	2-4	2-2
11	Hampton & Richmond Borough	1-0	2-1	1-1	1-3	2-0	2-0	1-1	1-3	1-1	2-1		1-0	1-2	4-3	1-0	3-0	3-1	4-0	2-0	2-1	1-1	2-2	0-1	1-2
12	Horsham	1-0	3-1	4-1	1-2	1-1	2-2	1-2	0-1	1-3	5-0	3-1		2-3	0-2	3-0	2-2	5-0	1-4	0-3	2-3	0-0	1-0	0-1	1-2
13	Leatherhead	2-2	6-0	2-2	0-5	2-0	2-2	3-2	0-2	2-1	1-2	0-3	0-1		5-4	3-1	3-3	2-2	2-3	1-0	1-0	2-2	0-1	1-0	0-1
14	Lewes	2-0	2-2	4-0	3-1	3-2	2-0	1-2	4-0	4-1	2-0	2-2	6-1	2-2		3-0	2-1	3-0	3-2	1-1	1-2	3-0	2-1	1-2	2-2
15	Marlow	0-2	0-1	2-1	1-0	4-3	2-0	0-0	0-0	1-1	4-1	1-1	2-0	3-4	1-2		2-0	0-1	0-0	3-1	1-0	1-2	1-0	0-0	0-5
16	Metropolitan Police	0-1	0-2	1-2	1-3	2-0	1-1	1-1	0-0	2-0	2-2	1-3	1-1	1-2	1-4	1-1		1-0	1-3	1-3	2-2	1-2	6-2	2-2	0-2
17	Molesey	0-2	1-0	4-3	1-2	2-3	1-1	0-2	0-0	2-0	2-0	0-1	1-1	0-2	2-2	3-0	0-2		0-3	0-2	0-3	1-1	0-2	0-1	0-2
18	Slough Town	1-1	5-1	4-1	4-2	2-1	3-1	1-0	1-2	3-1	7-1	1-1	3-2	3-1	1-0	1-2	3-0	3-1		2-2	2-0	1-1	3-1	1-3	1-1
19	Staines Town	5-1	0-0	3-0	3-1	0-2	5-2	1-0	3-2	1-0	2-0	1-0	0-0	3-2	3-1	3-0	4-2	2-1	1-3		1-2	0-0	2-1	1-1	3-3
20	Tooting & Mitcham United	2-3	2-0	3-2	4-3	3-0	0-0	2-1	1-2	4-1	3-3	0-2	2-2	4-0	0-4	0-1	2-1	1-3	0-2	2-0		2-1	2-1	1-1	1-2
21	Walton & Hersham	0-0	0-1	2-0	3-3	3-2	2-1	2-1	0-1	3-1	8-0	1-3	1-1	1-1	1-0	3-0	2-0	2-1	3-1	2-4	1-1		3-0	0-1	0-2
22	Whyteleafe	1-2	1-3	0-2	1-1	2-1	2-1	1-4	0-3	3-2	5-2	1-4	2-3	1-2	0-0	2-0	0-1	3-2	2-0	1-2	3-2	2-0		1-3	1-3
23	Windsor & Eton	5-1	0-1	2-0	1-0	1-0	2-0	1-1	0-0	4-2	1-1	0-1	3-1	4-2	1-2	0-0	2-0	2-0	1-4	2-0	3-1	5-3	2-0		1-1
24	Worthing	2-1	4-0	2-1	2-1	2-0	4-0	1-0	1-2	2-1	1-1	1-3	1-1	2-0	0-3	4-0	4-1	2-1	2-0	2-0	3-2	2-2	0-1	2-2	

AFC WIMBLEDON

CLUB OFFICIALS
President: **Dickie Guy**
Chairman: **Kris Stewart**
0208 540 7396 (B) 07970 702798 (M)
Finance Director: **Erik Samuelson**
Commercial Director:**Ivor Heller**
Secretary: **Trevor Williams,**
110B Cavendish Road, Colliers Wood,
London SW19 2EZ
Tel: 07817 480 505 (M) 0208 547 3528 (B)
email:trevor.williams@afcwimbledon,co,uk
Press Officer: **Charlie Talbot**:07768114 452

FOOTBALL MANAGEMENT TEAM
Manager:Dave Anderson
Asst Manager:John Turner
Coach:Warren Kelly
Physio: Mike Rayner
Sports Therapist: John Harris

FACT FILE
Founded: 2002
Nickname: The Dons or Wombles
Sponsors: SI Games & Sports Interactive
Colours: Blue with yellow trim
Change colours:Yellow with blue trim
Midweek home matchday: Tuesday
Reserves' League: Suburban League
2003-2004
Top Scorer: Kevin Cooper
P. o.Y:Matt Everard
2004-2005 Captain: Joe Sheerin

Pages 48 (full colour) **Price**: £2.
Editor: Charlie Talbot
Club Website:www.afcwimbledon.co.uk
Local Press:Surrey Comet South London Press **Local Radio**:County Sound and Southern Counties

GROUND Kingsmeadow Stadium, Jack Goodchild Way, 422a Kingston Rd., Kingston-upon-Thames, Surey KT1 3PB
Tel: 0208 547 3335/6 0208 974 5713 (Fax)
Clubhouse : open matchdays and evenings. Two function rooms for hire.

Directions: From town centre - Cambridge Rd on to Kingston Rd (A2043) to Malden Rd. From A3, turn off at New Malden, turn left on to A2043 - ground 1 mile on left. Half mile from Norbiton (BR)

Capacity: 4,262 **Covered :** 2,200 **Seating:** 1,047 **Shop:** Yes **Floodlights:** Yes

PREVIOUS **Names:** Formed as Wimbledon F.C. in 1889
Leagues: Combined Counties.

CLUB RECORDS **Attendance:** 4,262 v Chipstaed and Raynes Park Vale 2003-2004
Goalscorer: Kevin Cooper 107
Appearances: Kevin Cooper 110

BEST SEASON **FA Vase:** 4th Round 2003-2004
FA Cup: N/A

HONOURS Combined Counties League and Cup Winners 2003-04.

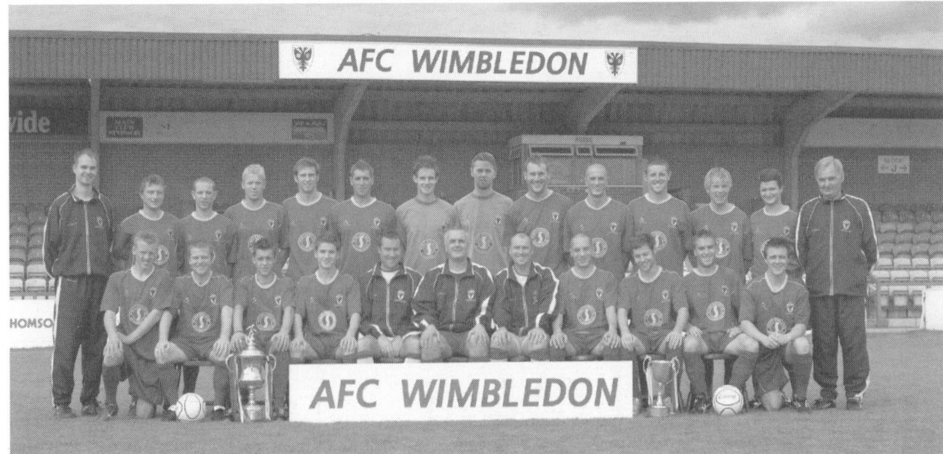

Back Row (L-R): Mike Rayner (physio) Jon-Barrie Bates, Martin Randall, Steve Butler, Antony Howard, Joe Sheerin, Paul Smith, Danny Naisbitt, Matt Everard, Michael Woolner, Gavin Bolger, Richard Butler, Simon Bassey, Dennis Lowndes (Kit manager).
Front: Lewis Taylor, Gareth Graham, Steve Gibson, Jamie Taylor, John Turner (assistant manager), Dave Anderson (manager) Warren Kelly (coach), Ryan Gray, Robert Ursell, Chris Gell, Paul Quinn.

ASHFORD TOWN

CLUB OFFICIALS

Chairman: Tim Thorogood
President: Ashley M Batt
Secretary/Press Officer: Elaine Osbourne,The HomelandsAsshford Rd., Kingsnorth,,Ashford, Kent.TH261NJ, 01233646713 (H) 07759889152(M)
Commercial Director: Peter Young
Tel: 01233 611838(Ground)

FOOTBALL MANAGEMENT TEAM

Manager: Tim Thorogood
Asst Manager: Gary Anderson
Coach: Tim Thorogood
Physios: George Sargeant& Stuart Unthank

FACT FILE

Formed: 1930
Nickname: Nuts & Bolts
Colours: Green/navy/green
Change colours: White&green/green/white
Midweek home matchday: Tuesday
Reserves' League: Go Travel Kent Lge

2003-2004

Captain: Ian Gibbs
Top Scorer: Adrrian Stone 23
Players of the Year: Ian Gibbs & John Whitehouse

Pages: 32 Price: £1.50
Editor: Shelley Jenner

Local Press: Kentish Express& Adscene
Local Radio: Radio Kent, Invicta Radio

GROUND The Homelands, Ashford Road, Kingsnorth, Ashford, Kent TN26 1NJ
Tel: 01233 611838
Directions: M20 jct 10, follow A2070 signs towards Brenzett & Lydd airport, dual carriageway to junction of old A2070, ground 1 mile on left thro' village of Kingsnorth. 4 miles south of Ashford
Capacity: 3,200 Cover: 1,250 Seats: 500 Floodlights: Yes
Clubhouse: Open matchdays and for special functions. Licensed bar, function room. Limited food - sandwiches & simple snacks.
Club Shop: Sells old progs, pennants, scarves, badges etc. Contact: Sue Brown at Ground

PREVIOUS **Names:** Ashford United, Ashford Railway, Ashford F.C.
Leagues: Kent 30-59. Ground: Essella Park, Essella Rd 30-87

CLUB RECORDS **Attendance:** 6,525 (at Essella Park, previous ground), v Crystal Palace, FA Cup 1st Rd 1959.
3,363 (at current ground), v Fulham FA Cup 1st Round 1994.
Goalscorer: Dave Arter 197. **Appearances:** Peter McRobert 765
Win: 10-1 v Bury Town, February 1964. **Defeat:** 0-8 v Crawley Town, November1964
Fee Paid: £7,000 for J Ross & D Arter (Sittingbourne, March 94)
Fee Received: £25k for Jeff Ross & Dave Arter (Hythe Tn, 90). Individually: £20k for Lee McRobert (Sittingbourne, 93)

BEST SEASON **FA Trophy:** Semi Final 72-73, 96-97 2nd Rd
FA Cup: 2nd Rd 61-62, 0-3 v QPR (H), 66-67, 0-5 v Swindon (A). 1st Rd 7 times. League clubs defeated: None.

HONOURS FA Trophy SF 72-73; Southern Lg Southern Div R-up 86-87 95-96; Kent Lg 48-49(R-up 31-32), Lg Cup 38-39; Kent Senior Cup 58-59 62-63 92-93 95-96

Players progressing: Ollie Norris (Rochdale 61), HowardMoore (Coventry 66), Tony Godden (WBA 75), Lee McRobert (Millwall 94)

Back row, left to right: Gary Anderson (Asst.Man), Stuart White, Paul O.Brien, Simon Elliott, Dave Hassett, John Whitehouse, Martin Anderson, Ian Gibbs, Dean Hill and Stuart Unthank (Physio).**Front row:** George Sergeant (Asst.physio, standing), Sam Saunders, Barry Gardner, Adrian Stone, Lee McRobert, Kevin Skinner, Ian Ross, Aaron O'Leary and Tim Thorogood (Manager, standing). **Photo:** D. F. West.

BANSTEAD ATHLETIC

PROGRAMME

Pages: 38 Price: £1.00
Editor: Tom Maslona
01737 350982

CLUB OFFICIALS

Chairman: Terry Molloy
President: Gordon Taylor
Press Officer: Ray Best**ecretary:** Gordon Harrison
69 Chipstead Lane, Lower KIngswood, Surrey KT20 6RD (01737 833817)

FOOTBALL MANAGEMENT TEAM

Manager: Bob Langford
Ass't Manr: Ray Best Coach:Robin Lewis
Captain: James Greenaway
Physio: John Steerwood

FACT FILE

Founded: 1944
Nickname: A's
Sponsors: PDM Marketing
Colours: Amber/amber/amber
Change colours: All red
Midweek Matchday: Tuesday
Club Website: www.bansteadathletic.co.uk

2003-2004

Top Scorer: Stuart White
Player of the Year: Aaron Day

GROUND Merland Rise, Tadworth, Surrey KT20 5JG (01737 350982)

Directions: Follow signs to Tattenham Corner (Epsom racecourse), then to Banstead Sports Centre. Ground adjacent to swimming pool.
Half a mile fromTattenham Corner (BR)
Bus 420 from Sutton stops outside ground.
Also buses 406 & 727 from Epsom

Capacity: 3,500 Seats: 250 Cover: 800 Floodlights: Yes

Clubhouse: All week 11am-11pm. 2 bars, real ale, bar snacks

Club Shop Yes

PREVIOUS **Leagues:** Surrey Int., Surrey Snr 49-65, Spartan 65-75, London Spartan 75-79, Athenian 79-84

CLUB RECORDS **Attendance:** 1,400 v Leytonstone, FA Amateur 1953

Win: 11-0 **Defeat:** 0-11

Career goalscorer: Harry Clark **Career appearances:** Dennis Wall

Transfer fee received: None **Transfer fee paid:** None

BEST SEASON **FA Cup:** 3rd Qual.Rd. 86-87. 00-01 FA Vase: Semi - finals 96-97

HONOURS: Surrey Snr Lg(6) 50-54 56-57 64-65, R-up(5) 49-50 54-56 57-59, Lg Cup 57-58, Charity Cup 52-53 58-59; London Spartan Lg R-up 77-78 (Lg Cup(2) 65-67);Surrey Prem. Cup R-up 91-92, 95-96; Surrey Snr Shield 55-56; Gilbert Rice F'lit Cup 81-82 86-87 (R-up(4) 82-86); Athenian Lg Cup(2) 80-82 (R-up 82-83 (SF 79-80); Surrey Int. Lg(2) 47-49, Cup 46-47 54-55; E. Surrey Charity Cup (4) 59-6066-67 76-78, R-up 79-80, I'mediate Sect. 75-76 (R-up 76-77), Jnr Sect. 81-82;Southern Comb. Cup R-up 69-70; Suburban Lg R-up 86-87; Carlton T.V. Trophy R-Up 95-96

Players Progressing: W Chesney & B Robinson (Crystal Palace)

Back Row (L-R): Dean Walker, Graham Knight, Stuart White, Steve Shaw, Warren Aburn, Gary Morgan (Kit Sponsor), Jamie Ribolla, James Greenaway, Warren Burton, Aaron Smith. **Front Row:** Wayne Finnie, Lee Cormack, Andy Briant, Mark Leahy (Capt.), Marcel Dennis, Richard Laming, Danny Wright, Grant Hutchison, Simon Mitchell, Aaron Day. Photo courtesy of Surrey Mirror.

BASHLEY

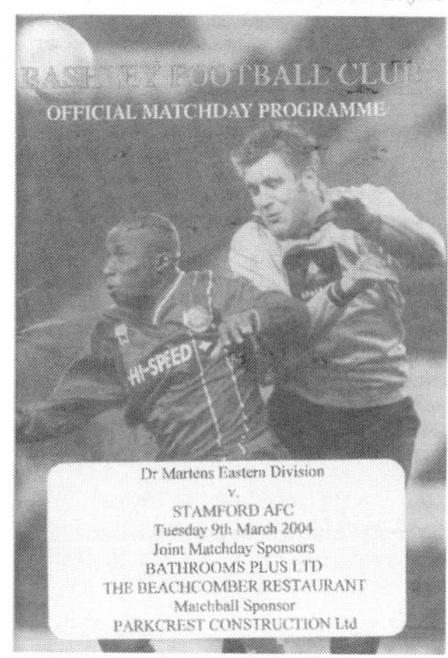

Pages: 36 Price: £1
Editor: Secretary

CLUB OFFICIALS

Chairman: Gary Parsons
President: Trevor Adams
Vice Chairman: Derick Binns
Secretary: Pete Plowman,
c/o Bashley F.C.
Mobile:07944 629383

FOOTBALL MANAGEMENT TEAM

Manager:Barry Blanckley
Assistant Manager: Fraser Quirk
Reserves Manager: Chris Collinge

FACT FILE

Formed: 1947
Nickname: The Bash
Sponsors: Spaceage
Colours: Gold/l;ack/Black
Change colours: Blue & white
Midweek matchday: Tuesday
Reserves' League: Wessex Comb
Local Press: Bournemouth Echo, Southern Pink, New Milton Advertiser
Local Radio: 2CR, Solent, Ocean Sound

GROUND Recreation Ground, BashleyRd., New Milton,Hampshire BH25 5RY.
Tel: 01425 620280 FAX: 01425 638376

Directions: A35 Lyndhurst towards Christchurch, turn left down B3058 towards New Milton, ground on left in Bashley village. Half hour walk from New Milton (BR) station .New Cargo Bus service C32 (NewMilton-Lymington)

Capacity: 4,250 Cover: 1,200 Seats: 300 Floodlights: Yes

Clubhouse: Usual licensing hours. Snacks available **Club Shop:** Open matchdays

PREVIOUS **Leagues:** Bournemouth 50-83; Hants 83-86; Wessex 86-89

CLUB RECORDS **Attendance:** 3,500 v Emley, F.A. Vase S.F. 1st Leg 87-88
Win: 21-1 v Co-operative (A), Bournemouth Lge, 64
Defeat: 2-20 v Air Speed(A), Bournemouth Lge, 57
Career Goalscorer: Colin Cummings
Career Appearances: John Bone
Transfer fee paid: £7,500 for J Stagg from Andover **Transfer fee received:** £7,500 for Darren Powell from Weymouth 95

BEST SEASON **FA Cup:** 2nd Rd Proper 1994-95, 0-1 v Swansea City
FA Vase: Semi Final 87-88, Qtr Final 88-89 FA Trophy: 2nd Round 91-92

HONOURS Southern Lg Southern Division 89-90 (Lg Cup SF 89-90), Wessex Lg 86-87 87-88 88-89, Hants Lg Div 3 84-85, Hants Lg Combination 88-89, Russell Cotes Cup 88-89 90-91 92-93

Players Progressing : Wayne Brown (Bristol C 1994), David Billington Peterborough 1996), Ryan Young (Plymouth 1997), Dean Higgins (Torquay 1998), Danny Smith (Bournemouith 1998), Craig Davies (Cardiff City 1998), Tony Wallis (Cardiff C 1999), Wade Elliott (AFC Bouremouth 2000)

Back Row, Left To Right: Glen Botterill (Reserve Physio), John Clare (1st Team Physio), Lee Harvey, Paul Wilson, Derek Brown, Gary Williams (Reserve Manager), James Heeps, Andy Lomas (Assistant Manager), Steve Jackman, Eddie Lawley, Paul Turner, Kevin Slinn, Steve Gee (Reserve Team Assistant), Kenny Mist (Chief Scout) **Front Row:** Grant Haley, Carl Adams, Josh Sozzo, Paul Covington, Roger Ashby (Manager), Ian Edge, Rob Miller, Mark Paul, Steve Berry.

BROMLEY

CLUB OFFICIALS

Chairman: Jerry Dolke
Secretary: Colin Russell
2 Burrlands, 5 Overbury Avenue,
Beckenham, Kent BR3 6PZ

email: info@bromleyfc.net

FOOTBALL MANAGEMENT TEAM

Manager:Stuart McIntyre
Ass.Manager/Coach:Mark Qatts

FACT FILE
Formed: 1892
Nickname: The Lilywhites
Colours: White/black/black
Change colours: All red
Midweek home matchday: Tuesday
Reserve's League: Kent Div 2
Youth League: Kent Youth League
Newsline: 0930 555 838
2003-2004
Captain: John Myatt
Player of the Year: Mark Willy
Top Goalscorer:Adolph Amoako

Pages: 32 Price: £1.50
Editor: Iona Bartlett

Local Press: Bromley Times
Local Radio: Radio Kent,
Bromley Local Radio
Website: www.bromleyfc.net

GROUND Hayes Lane, Bromley, Kent BR2 9EF Tel: 0208 460 5291 or 0208 313 3992

Directions: One mile from Bromley South (BR). Buses 314, 146 and 119 pass ground.
Junction 4 off M25, then A21 towards London
Capacity: 5,000 Cover: 2,500 Seats: 1,300 Floodlights: Yes
Clubhouse: Open matchdays. Food available
Club Shop: Yes. contact Jim Brown

PREVIOUS **Leagues:** South London - 1894; Southern 94-96; London 96-98 99-1901; West Kent 01-04; Southern Suburban 04-07; Kent 1898-99, 11-14; Spartan 07-08; Isthmian 08-11; Athenian 19-52
Grounds: White Hart Field Cricket Ground, Widmore Rd & Plaistow Cricket Field (pre-1904), Hayes Lane 1904-37

RECORDS **Attendance:** 12,000 v Nigeria, 1950
Goalscorer: George Brown 570 (1938-61) **Appearances:** George Brown
Win: 13-1 v Redhill, Athenian League 1945-46 **Defeat:** 1-11 v Barking ,Athenian League 1933-34
Fee Paid: Unknown **Fee Received:** £50,000 for Jon Goodman (from Millwall 90)

BEST SEASON **FA Amateur Cup:** Winners 10-11, 37-38, 48-49
FA Trophy: Second Round 91-92 **FA Cup:** 2nd Rd replay v Scarborough 37-38, Lincoln 38-39, Watford 45-46

HONOURS: Isthmian League(4) 08-10 53-54 60-61 (R-up 52-53 55-56 87-88), Div 1 R-up 79-80 5-86 90-91, Prince Phillip 5-a-side Cup 1979; Athenian League 22-23 48-49 50-51 (R-up 35-36); London League Div 2 1896-97; Spartan League 07-08; Kent Senior Cup 49-50 76-77 91-92 96-97; Kent AmateurCup (12) 07-08 31-32 35-36 36-37 38-39 46-47 48-49 50-51 52-53 53-54 54-55 59-60; London Challenge Cup 1995-96. London Senior Cup: 09-10, 45-46, 50-51, 02-03

Players progressing: Roy Merryfield (Chelsea), Stan Charlton (Arsenal 52), RonHeckman (Orient 55), John Gregory (West Ham 51), Bill Lloyd (Millwall 56), Brian Kinsey (Charlton 56), Harold Hobbs (Charlton & England), Matt Carmichael (Lincoln 90), Leslie Locke (QPR 56), Jon Goodman (Millwall 90), Dean Wordsworth (Crystal Palace 97), Landry Zahana-ONI (Luton Town 98)

Photo: www.MPAphotography.co.uk

BURGESS HILL TOWN

BURGESS HILL TOWN FOOTBALL CLUB

DR MARTENS SOUTHERN LEAGUE EASTERN DIVISION

SEASON 2003 - 2004

MATCHDAY PROGRAMME

£1

CLUB PERSONNEL

Chairman: Eddie Benson**Patron**: Jack Lake

Secretary: Roger Puttick
48 Maple Drive,Burgess Hill RH15 8AW
Tel: 01444 243080
Email : bhtfcsocial@ aol.com

FOOTBALL MANAGEMENT

Manager: Gary Croydon

FACT FILE

Founded: 1882
Nickname: Hillians
Sponsors: Time 24
Colours: Yellow& black quarters/black/yellow
Change colours: All red
Midweek matchday: Wednesday

GROUND Leylands Park, Burgess Hill, West Sussex RH15 8AW
Tel: 01444 242429 Website: www.bhtfc.org.uk

Capacity: 2,000 Seats: 307 Cover: Yes Floodlights: Yes

Directions: Turn east from A273 London Road into Leylands Road, take 4th left signposted Leyland Park. Nearest station Wivelsfield

Clubhouse: Bar & social facilities. Tea bar

Club Shop: Yes Club badges available

PROGRAMME
Pages: 60 Price: £1

PREVIOUS **Leagues:** Mid Sussex League, Sussex County >03

CLUB RECORD **Attendance:** 1,598 v Tiptree United F.A.Vase 6th Round

BEST SEASON **FA Cup:** 4th Qual. Rd. 99-00, 1-4 v Hereford United
F.A.Vase: Quarter -Final v Tiptree United 2001-02

HONOURS Sussex County Lg 75-76, 96-97, 97-98, 98-99; 01-02, 02-03; Lg Cup 73-74 79-80 97-98 98-99 (R-up 90-91), Div 2 74-75 (Cup 73-73), F/lit Cup 96-97, Res 76-77 77-78 91-92, Res. Sect. East 77-78 82-83 84-85, Res. Cup 82-83 98-99, 02-03; Yth Sect. West 91-92 East 95-96 96-97 97-98 98-99 North 96-97 97-98, 02-03; Sussex Fives 80; Mid-Sussex Lg 1900-01 03-04 39-40 46-47 56-57 Div 2 03-04 (res), Div 3 20-21 36-37, Div 4 (res) 56-57; Mid Sussex Snr Cup 94-95 96-97; 01-02 Montgomery Cup 39-40 56-57; Mowatt Cup 45-46; Sussex RUR Charity Cup 91-92; Sussex I'mediate Cup 76-77; Sussex Yth Lge 96-97 97-98, Cup 91-92 97-98

Back row, left to right:Nick Bridle, Kevin Townsend, Darin Killpatrick, Shaheen Sadough, Ben Andrews, Steve Harper, Mattt Hurley, John Sullivan, Chris White (assistant manager) and Pat Gannon. **Front row**: Sean Edwards, Nicky Sullivan, Darren Smith, Lloyd Cotton, Adie Downey (Captain), Alex Robinson, Jack Holdroyd, Matt Stares and Matt Geard.

CORINTHIAN CASUALS

CLUB OFFICIALS

Chairman: Geoff Hewitson

President: Jimmy Hill

MatchSec Michael Maidment, I Market Lane,Langley Bucks.SL3 8BQ01753 546330

Secretary: Phillip Pepperell,54 Ruskin Drive, Worcester Park,Syrrey.KT4 Tel.No: 0208255 8656

Press Off: Nick Overend (01730 825418)

FOOTBALL MANAGEMENT TEAM

Manager: Mickey Stephens
Captain: Simon Shergold

FACT FILE

Founded: 1939
Sponsors: T.B.A.
Colours: Chocolate & Pink/sky/sky
Change colours: White/navy/white
Midweek Matchday: Tuesday
Reserves' League: Suburban

2003-2004

Players of the Year:
John Eldred & Gavin Cartwright
Top Goalscorer: John Eldred 12

CORINTHIAN-CASUALS F.C.
2003/04
RYMAN LEAGUE • DIVISION ONE SOUTH
Ryman

PROGRAMME

Pages: 24-48 Price: £1
Editor: Nick Overend
23 South Acre, South Harling,West Sussex GU31 5 LJ (01730 825418)
Club Website:
www.corinthian-casuals.co.uk

GROUND King George's Field, Hook Rise South, Tolworth, Surrey KT6 7NA
Tel: 020 8397 3368 Email Address:info@corinthian-casuals.co.uk

Directions: A3 to Tolworth r'bout (The Charrington Bowl). Hook Rise is slip road immediately after the Toby Jug pub. Turn left under railway bridge after a 1/4mile - grd on right. Half mile from Tolworth (BR); turn left, continue to Toby Jug, then as above.

Capacity: 2,000 Seats: 161 Cover: 700 Floodlights: Yes Club Shop: Yes

Clubhouse: Evenings, matchdays, Sun lunchtimes. Hot & cold snacks matchdays

PREVIOUS **Leagues:** Isthmian 39-84, Spartan 84-96; Combined Counties 96-97

HONOURS R-up 55-56 (SF 56-57), London Spartan Lg R-up 92-93 (Lg Cup R-up 91-92); Combined Counties Lg R-up 96-97

as CASUALS FA Amateur Cup Winners, 1935-36 London Senior Cup R-Up: (4) London Charity Cup (6) Surrey Senior Cup 29-30 Isthmian League Ruynners Up 1936-37

CLUB RECORDS

Career Records: Goals Cliff West 219 **Appearances** Bruce Martin 504

BEST SEASON **FA Cup:** 1st Rd 65-66 1st Rd replay 85-86 **FA Vase:** 5th Rd 83-84
FA Amateur Cup: Runners-up 55-56 **FA Trophy**: 2nd Rd 02-03 (1st year in competition)

Players progressing: Peter Phillips (Luton Town), Andy Gray, Tony Finnegan, Alan Pardew (Crystal Palace), Leroy Griffiths (Q.P.R.)

L to R -

Back row :
Micky Stephens
Tony Jupp
Elliott Lyward
Nathan Jupp
Chris Roberts
Ashley Martin
Iain Waghorn
Justin Georgiou
Gavin Cartwright
Dave Roberts
Bob Mapleson
Brian Adamson

Front Row:
R Jim Taylor
Andy Gibbons
Jamie Byatt
Lyndon Buckwell
Jamie White
Tony Blunt
Simon Shergold
Paul Midwinter

CRAY WANDERERS

CLUB OFFICIALS

Chairman: Gary Hillman
President: Bill Faulkner

Secretary: Brian Olley,
3 Corbett Close, New Addington,
Surrey CR0 0JS

FOOTBALL MANAGEMENT TEAM

Manager: Ian Jenkins
Asst.Manager: Joe Francis
Reserve Team Manager: Sam Wright

FACT FILE

Founded: 1860
Nickname: Wands
Sponsors: Hillman
Colours: Amber & black
Change Colours: Blue
Midweek matchday: Tuesday

2003-04

Leading Goalscorer:Jamie Kempster
Captain:Phil Turner
Player of the Year:Ian Rawlings

The Official Matchday Magazine of Cray Wanderers F.C.
THE WANDERER
Mark Johnson
Founded 1860
CRAY WANDERERS
versus
AFC SUDBURY
Saturday February 21st 2004 - Kick Off 3.00pm
F.A. Challenge Vase - Sixth Round
Sponsored by Hillman Contractors £1

Programme: 32 pages, 50p
Editor/Press Officer: Greg Mann
Tel: 0181 318 9604(H) 0171 500 4496B)

Ground: Bromley F.C. Hayes Lane, Bromley, Kent BR2 9EF (0181 460 5291 or 0181 313 3992)
Websites: http://www.craywands.co.uk
Directions: One mile from Bromley South (BR). Buses 316, 146 and 119 passground. Junction 4 off M25, then A21 towards London
Capacity: 5,000 Cover: 2,500 Seats: 1,300 Floodlights: Yes
Clubhouse: Open pub hours (freehouse). Hot & cold food available **Club Shop:** Yes

HONOURS London Lg(2) 56-58 (Lg Cup 54-55), Aetolian Lg 62-63 (Lg Cup 63-64), GtrLondon Lg 65-66 (Lg Cup(2) 64-66), Metropolitan Lg Cup 70-71 (Amtr Cup(2) 66-68), London Spartan Lg(2) 76-78, Kent Lg 01-02,03-04 80-81 02-03 03-04(R-up 79-80 90-91) Lg Cup 83-84 02-03 03-04, Kent Snr Tphy 92-93, 03-04 Kent Amtr Cup(4) 30-31 62-65, Kent Intermediate Cup 03-04

PREVIOUS **Leagues:** Kent 1894-1903 6-7 9-14 34-38; W Kent 03-06 07-09; London 20-34 51-59; Kent Amtr 38-39 46-51; S London All 43-46; Aetolian 59-64; GtrLondon 64-66; Metropolitan 66-71; London Metropolitan 71-75; London Spartan 75-78

Grounds: Star Lane; Tothills; Twysden; Fordcroft; Grassmeade, St Mary Cray

CLUB RECORDS

Gate: 1,523 v Stamford, F.A. Vase QF 79-80

Goalscorer: Ken Collishaw, 274 **Appearances:** John Dorey c500, 61-72

Win: 15-0 v Sevenoaks, 1894-95 **Defeat:** 1-11 v Bromley, 20-21

Winners: Kent League Premier Division championship, Kent Senior Trophy, Kent League Division One & Two Cup; Kent Intermediate Cup
Back row L to R: John de Palma (Physio), Paul Foley, Robert Browning, Danny Evans, John Mayall, Micky Simmons, David Gray, James Taylor, Richard Dimmock, Danny Whelan, Ian Rawlings, John Allwright.
Front row: Andy Silk, Jamie Wood, Sam Wood, Adam Heaslewood, Joe Francis (Assistant Manager), Gary Hillman (Chairman), Ian Jenkins (Player-Manager), Jamie Kempster, Ross Lover, Matt Woolf, Ricky Bennett.

CROYDON

CLUB OFFICIALS

Chairman: Jim Moody

Secretary: Gordon Tennant, 21 Sharonelle Court,Station Road, Wokingham,Berks.RG40 2AX Tel Nos: 01189891357(H) 07775 740838(M)

Press Off: Simon Hawkins (07710 459858)

FOOTBALL MANAGEMENT TEAM

Manager: Mick Read

Asst. Manager: Dickson Gill

Captain: Warren Burton

Coach & Physio: Micky Gillam

2003-2004

Top Scorer: Craig Dundas

P.o.Y.: Warren Burton

FACT FILE

Formed: 1953
Nickname: The Trams
Sponsors: T.B.A.
Colours: Sky &navy
Change colours: Red & White
Midweek home matchday: Wednesday
Youth Team's League: Southern Youth
Local Press: Croydon Advertiser,

PROGRAMME

Pages: 20 Price: £1.00
Editor:Vince Mitchell (01892 542671(H)

GROUNDCroydon Sports Arena, Albert Rd, S.Norwood,. SE25 4QL Tel: 0208 654 3462/8555
Directions: From Portland Rd turn down either Belmont Rd or Grasmere Rd. and the Stadium is off Albert Rd inn South Norwood.Train to East Croydon or Norwood Junction, then bus 197 to either Belmont or Dundee Road. Walk down either - ground at bottom.2 mins walk fromArena tram stop (Croydon Tram Link)
Capacity: 6,000 **Cover:** 1,000 **Seats**: 450 **Floodlights**: Yes
Clubhouse: Open every evening and lunchtime, snacks available. Dancing & discos, Lounge bar available for private hire **Club Shop:** Yes

PREVIOUS **Leagues:** Surrey Senior 53-63; Spartan 63-64; Athenian 64-74
Name: Croydon Amateurs 1953-74

CLUB RECORDS **Attendance:** 1,450 v Wycombe, FA Cup 4th Qualifying Rd 1975
Career appearances: Alec Jackson (1977-88) 452 + 111goals and Tony Luckett(1962-73) 411 appearances
Transfer fee paid: Steve Brown **Transfer fee received:** Peter Evans (to Sutton Utd)

BEST SEASON **FA Cup:** 2nd Round replay 79-80, 2-3 v Millwall after 1-1 **F.A.Vase:** 4th Round 1994-95
FA Trophy: 2nd Round 81-82, 82-83 **FA Amateur Cup:** 3rd round 71-72 **F.A.Youth Cup**: 4th Round 1976-77

HONOURS Isthmian Lg Div. 1 99-2000, R-up 75-76 Div 2 95-96, Lg Cup: R-up 74-75, 00-01 FM Cup 99-2000; Surrey Snr Cup 81-82 (R-up 76-77 99-00), Surrey Prem Cup 86-87, Spartan Lg 63-64, Athenian Lg R-up 71-72 Div 2 65-66 (R-up 70-71)), Surrey Snr Lg R-up 56-57 60-61 62-63 (Lg Cup 60-61), Charity Cup 53-54 62-63, Res Section 57-58), London Senior Cup Winners 2001-02 R-up 77-78, Suburban Lg South 86-87(Lg Cup(2), Southern Yth Lg 85-86 (Lg Cup 85-86 87-88), Berger Yth Cup 78-79, Southern Youth Lg Cup 96-97. Womens F.A.Cup 95-6,99-00 R-up 97-98 Premier Lg 99-00

Players progressing: Alan Barnett (Plymouth 1955), Peter Bonetti (Chelsea), Leroy Ambrose (Charlton 1979), Steve Milton (Fulham - via Whyteleafe), Murray Jones (Crystal Pal. - via Carshalton and)John Bailey (Bournemouth via Enfield and Dagenham)

L-R - Back: John Finch (coach), Ian Fairs (Physio), Chris Walsh, Mark Tompkins, Jamie White, Oliver Hunt, Danny Moody, Matt Martin, Stuart Read, Craig Dundas, Roy Newman, Roger Hoyte (Reserve Team Man.), Mick Read (Manager). **Front:** Trevor Reddick, James Cecil, Shane Sutherland, Michael Ebanks, Danny Edwards, Jiim Moody (Chairman), Kris Hollidge, Darren Hall, Rob Fraser.

CROYDON ATHLETIC

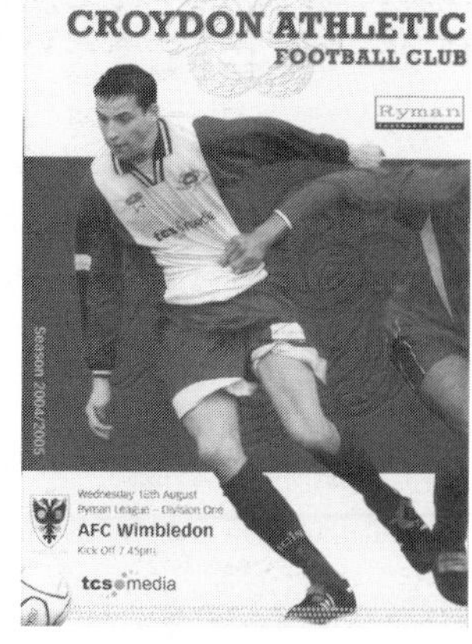

CLUB OFFICIALS

Chairman: Keith Tuckey
V Chairman/ Press Officer: Clive Thompson
Chief Executive: Dean Fisher
153 Chipstead Valley Road,
Coulsdon, Surrey CR5 3BQ
Tel: 020 8407 3296 (H & Fax)
020 7556 6092

FOOTBALL MANAGEMENT TEAM

Manager: Hayden Bird
Asst Man.: Peter Thomas
1st Team Coach: Jeff Evans
Chief Scout: Simon Liddle
Physio: Mick Reed

FACT FILE

Founded: 1990 Sponsors: T.C.S. Media

Colours: Maroon & white/maroon/maroon

Change colours: Yellow/royal/royal/royal

Midweek matches: Wednesday

Reserve League: Suburban (S)

2003-2004

Top Goallscorer: Billy Jackson

Player of the Year: James Hall

2004-2005

Captain: Dean Davenport

GROUND Mayfields, off Mayfield Road, Thornton Heath, Surrey, CR7 6DN.
Tel: 0208 6648343: Email: dfisher@croydonathletic.co.uk

Directions: Follow A23 from London & continue on A23 into Thornton Road. After roundabout take !st on right into Silverleigh Road, left fork into Trafford Road which continues into Mayfield Road. To end and turn left and follow narrow road to ground. 1 mile from Norbury (BR). Buses 109, 60

Capacity: 3,000 Seats: 163 Cover: 660 Floodlights: Yes
Clubhouse: Open every evening & weekends **Club Shop:** Yes

PROGRAMME
Pages: 52 Price: £1.50
Editor: Dean Fisher
Club Website:
www.croydonathletic.co.uk

PREVIOUS **Leagues:** None

RECORDS **Attendance:** 550
Goalscorer: John Fowler
Appearances: Graham Edginton/ Paul Gall/Leon Maxwell

BEST SEASON **FA Vase:** 4th Rd 00-01 FA Trophy:
FA Cup: 2nd Qual. Rd 94-95

HONOURS: London Spartan Lg 94-95, R-up 88-89 93-94, (Reserve Div 88-89, R-up 88-89); London Snr Cup R-up 91-92; Southern Youth Lg 92-93; Bearman Harber MemTrophy 87-88; Wirral Prog 86-87 96-97; Umbro Fair Play 97-98; Isthmian League Div 3 2001-02

Players progressing to Football League: Jamie Ndah (Torquay Utd)

DORKING

CLUB OFFICIALS

Chairman: Jack Collins

President: Ingram Whittingham

Vice-Chairman: Ray Collins

Co. Sec.: Martin Collins

Secretary: Ray Collins

11 Richmond Way, Fetcham,

Surrey KT22 9NP

Tel: 01372 453867

Press Officer: Bryan Bletso

FOOTBALL MANAGEMENT TEAM

Manager: Steve Lunn

Assistant Manager: Andy Lunn

Coach: Brian Cottingham

Catain: Peter Maynard

Physio: Bennie Fishlock

FACT FILE

Formed: 1880

Nickname: The Chicks

Colours: Green & white hoops/green/green

Change colours: All navy blue

Midweek matches: Tuesday

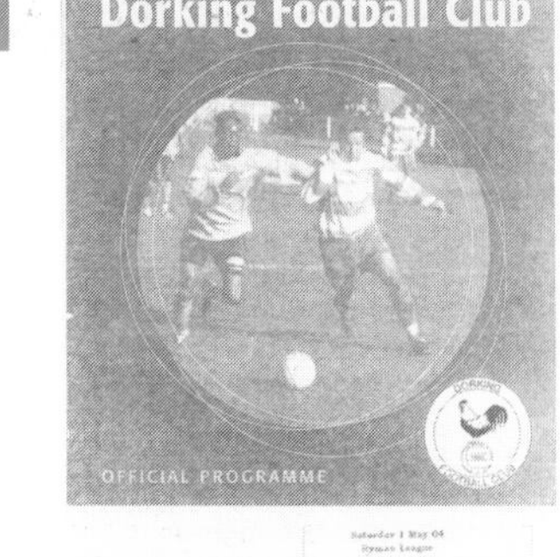

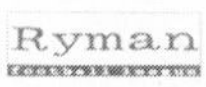

Programme48 pages £1 Edr: Bryan Bletso
Local Press: Dorking Advertiser, Surrey Mirror, Surrey Advertiser
Local Radio: County Sound, BBC Southern Counties, Radio Mercury

GROIUND **Address:** Meadowbank, Mill Lane, Dorking, Surrey RH4 1DX
Tel: 01306 884112

Directions: Mill Lane is off Dorking High St. next to Woolworths and Marks &Spencers, & opposite the White Horse pub. Fork right in Mill Lane past the Malthouse pub. 1/2 mile from both Dorking and Deepdene (BR) stations

Capacity: 3,600 Cover: 800 Seats: 200 Floodlights: Yes

Club Shop: Yes

Clubhouse: All week &Sun. 4-11 p.m. Sats 12-11pm Hot & cold food on matchdays

PREVIOUS

Ground: Prixham Lane (until 1953)

Leagues: Surrey Senior 22-56 77-78; Corinthian 56-63; Athenian 63-74 78-80; Southern 74-77

Names: Dorking Town 77-82; Guildford & Dorking United (when club merged with Guildford in1974)/

CLUB RECORDS

Attendance: 4,500 v Folkestone Town, FA Cup 1st Qual. Rd 1955 and v Plymouth Argyle 1st Rd F.A.Cup 92-93

Goalscorer: Andy Bushnell **Appearances**: Steve Lunn

Win: 7-0 v Barking, Isthmian Lge Div. One, 31/10/92

BEST SEASON

FA Cup: 1st Round Proper 92-93, 2-3 v Plymouth A. (H)

FA Vase: 5th Round 2001-2002 **FA Trophy:** 2nd Rd 91-92

Players progressing to Football League:

Steve Scrivens & John Finch (Fulham), Andy Ansah (Brentford 1989)

DULWICH HAMLET

CLUB OFFICIALS

Chairman: Martin Eede
President: Tommy Jover
Vice Chairman: Jack Payne
Secretary:: John Leahy, 58 Newquay House, Black Prince Road, Kennington, London S.E.11 6HL Tel: 0207 582 9296
Press Officer: John Lawrence
Tel: 020 8761 2091

FOOTBALL MANAGEMENT TEAM

Manager: Martin Eede
Captain: Alex Brown Physio: Danny Keenan

FACT FILE

Formed: 1893
Nickname: The Hamlet
Sponsors: H.R.Jennings for Insurance
Colours: Navy blue & pink stripes/navy/navy
Change: Red & light blue squares/red/red

Midweek matchday: Tuesday
Reserve League: Suburban
Local Press: South London Press, Southwark News

PROGRAMME
Pages: 48 Price: £1.20
Editor: John Lawrence

2003-04
Top Scorer & P.O.Y. : Omari Coleman

GROUND: Champion Hill Stadium, Edgar Kail Way, East Dulwich, London SE22 8BD Tel: 020 7274 8707
Directions: East Dulwich station, 200yds. Denmark Hill station, 10 mins walk. Herne Hill station then bus 37 stops near grd. Buses 40 & 176 from Elephant & Castle, 185 from Victoria
Capacity: 3,000 Cover: 1,000 Seats: 500 Floodlights: Yes
Clubhouse: Open 7 days a week. Function rooms & meeting room available for hire Health Club,Gymnasium,Squash courts (020 7274 8707)
Club Shop: Sells programmes, pennants, badges, scarves, baseball caps, replica shirts (by order only).

PREVIOUS **Leagues:** Camberwell 1894-97; S/thern Sub 1897-1900 01-07; Dulwich 00-01; Spartan 07-08
Grounds: Woodwarde Rd 1893-95; College Farm 95-96; Sunray Avenue 96-1902; Freeman's Ground, Champion Hill 02-12; Champion Hill (old ground) 1912-92; Sandy Lane (groundshare with Tooting & Mitcham F.C.) 91-92

CLUB RECORDS **Attendance:** 20,744, Kingstonian v Stockton, FA Am Cup Final 1933 (at refurbished ground): 1,835 v Southport FAC 98-99
Career Goalscorer: Edgar Kail 427 (1919-33) **Career Appearances:** Reg Merritt 571 (50-66)
Fee Paid: T Eames (Wimbledon), G Allen (Carshalton Ath 80) **Fee Received**: E Nwajiobi (Luton 83)
Win: 13-0 v Walton-on-Thames, 37-38 **Defeat:** 1-10 v Hendon, 63-64

BEST SEASON **FA Amateur Cup:** Winners 19-20 31-2 33-4 36-7 **FA Trophy:** Quarter Final 79-80
FA Cup: 1st Rd replay 30-31 33-34. 1st Rd on 14 occasions

HONOURS: Isthmian League 19-20 25-26 32-33 48-49, (R-up(7) Div 1 77-78; London Senior Cup 24-25 38-39 49-50 83-84 03-04 (R-up 05-06 07-08 20-21 27-28); Surrey Senior Cup 14 (R-up -6); London Chal. Cup 98-9 R-up 91-92; 99-00 London Charity Cup(12); Surrey Senior Shield 72-73; Surrey Centen. Shld 77-78; Sth of the Thames Cup (4) 56-60; Southern Comb Cup 73-74

Players progressing: W Bellamy (Spurs), A Solly (Arsenal), L Fishlock/A Gray/APardew (C Palace), J Moseley & E Toser (Millwall), R Dicks (Middlesborough), GJago/J Ryan (Charlton Ath 51/63), G Pearce (Plymouth), R Crisp (Watford 61), ENwajiobi (Luton 83), C Richards & J Glass (Bournemouth), P Coleman (Millwall86), A Perry (Portsmouth 86), N Kelly (Stoke City), C Emberson (Rotherham), CAsaba (Brentford)S.Watts (Leyton O), M.King (Barnet),J Darlington (Q.P.R.), D.McEwen (Spurs)

FLEET TOWN

CLUB OFFICIALS

Chairman: Martn Griffiths

President: Tony Frost

Vice Chairman: Jon Goodyear

Secretary: John Goodyear
25 Velmead Road,Fleet,Hants GU52 7LJ
Email: goodyear.john@btinternet.com

Press Officer: Steve Cantle 07801845643

FOOTBALL MANAGEMENT TEAM

Manager:Mark Dennis

Asst Man: Dave Skilton

Coach: Jesse Bone & Mervyn Grifiths

Physio: David Keir

FACT FILE

Founded: 1890

Re-Formed: 1947

Nickname: The Blues

Sponsors: Southern Coating Contractors Ltd.

Colours: Navy & sky stripes/sky/navy & sky

Change: Red & Black/black/red&black

Midweek Matches: Tuesday

Reserves' League: Suburban(Wednesdays)

Website: www.fleettownfc.co.uk

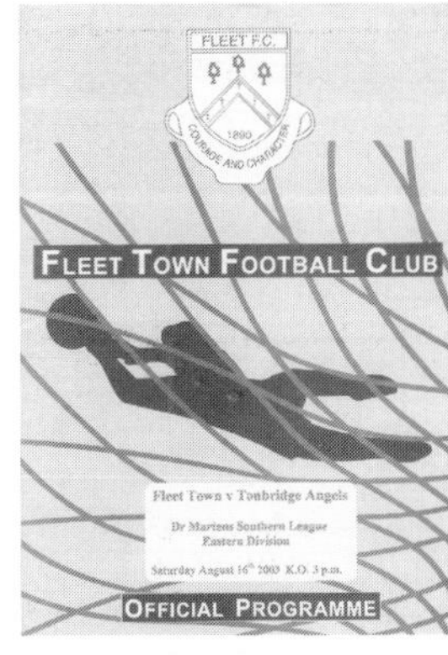

PROGRAMME

20 Pages Price: £1.00

Editor: Steve Cordingly

01252 626474

GROUND: Calthorpe Park, Crookham Road, Fleet, Hants Tel: 01252 623804

Directions: Leave the M3 at Junction 4A. Follow signs to Fleet via A3013. At 5th round about (a T-junction), turn left over railway bridge.
Carry on past `Oatsheaf' pub on the right - ground is 1/4 mile further on right.

Capacity: 2,000 Seats: 200 Cover: 250 Floodlights: Yes

Clubhouse: Yes. Hot & cold food served

Club Shop: Yes

PREVIOUS
Leagues: Hampsire 61-77, Athenian, Combined Co's, Chiltonian, Wessex 89-95, Southern 95-00, Wessex 00-02
Names: None **Grounds:** None

CLUB RECORDS
Win: 15-0 Pertersfield 26.12.94 **Defeat:** 0-6 v Margate 1999
Attendance: 1,050 v Coventry City 1995 (Pre-Season Frirerndly)
Transfer fee paid: £3,000 to Aldershot Dec 99 for Mark Russell 1991
Career Goalscorer: Mark Frampton 428 **Appearances:** Mark Frampton250

BEST SEASON
F.A.Cup: 2nd Q 97-98 F.A.Trophy: 2nd Rd 97-98 F.A.Vase: 3rd Rd 94-95

HONOURS
Wessex Lg 94-95 Runners-Up 01-02, Lg Cup R-up 92-93, 01-02; Hants Lg Div 2 R-up 61-62 (Div 1 R-up 60-61), Aldershot Snr Cup 92-93, 99-00; Simpsonair Challenge Shield 1993, Hants Yth Lg Div 3 92-93.

January 2004 - Back Row (L-R): Bruce Kendall (Asst. Manager), Ed Hare, Craig Anstey, Dan Jeffrey, Calvin Sparshatt, Anthony Millerick, Steve Black, Ian Saunders (Capt.), Mick Catlin (Manager). **Front Row:** Steve Whitcher, Nick Clark, Jamie Proctor, Ben Buckland, Shea Saunders. Not in picture: Shaun Hale. Photo: Steve Cantle.

HASTINGS UNITED

CLUB OFFICIALS

Chairman:David Walters
President: Mick Maplesden
Vice Chairman: David Ormorod
Secretary : R A Cosens
22 Baldslow Road, Hastings TN34 2EZ
01424 427867 (H) 01424 444635 (B)
0771 2634288 (M)

FOOTBALL MANAGEMENT TEAM

Steve Lovell & Vince Moorton

2003-04

Captain: Jimmy Elford
P.o.Y.:Carl Rook
Top scorer:Carl Rook 15

FACT FILE

Formed: 1894
Nickname: The Arrows
Colours: Claret & Blue
Change colours:Yellow
Midweek matchday: Tuesday
Reserves' League: Go Travel Kent Div 1
Newsline: 09066 555 879
Local Press: Hastings Observer, Evening Argus
Local Radio: BBC Southern Counties
Southern Sound, Arrow FM

PROGRAMME

Pages: 76 Price: £1.50
Editor: David Bealey Tel: (01797 253310)

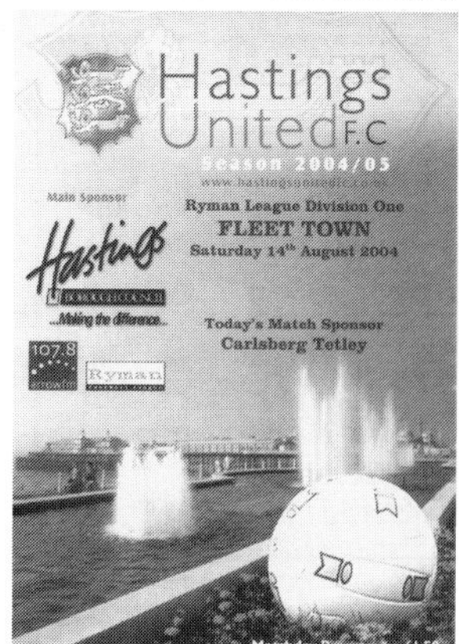

GROUND The Pilot Field, Elphinstone Road, Hastings TN34 2AX Tel: 01424 444635

Directions: From A21 turn left at 3rd mini-r'bout into St Helens Rd, left after 1 mile into St Helens Park Rd, this leads into Downs Rd, at end of Downs Rd (T-junction) turn left, ground 200yds on right. From town centre take Queens Road (A2101). Right at roundabout into Elphinstone Road - ground 1 mile on right. 1 1/2 miles from Hastings BR station - infrequent bus service fromtown centre to ground

Capacity: 4,050 Cover: 1,750 Seats: 800 Floodlights: Yes

Clubhouse: Open matchdays and every evening

Club Shop: Sells replica kits, scarves, programmes, pens, key-rings, badges etc

PREVIOUS
Leagues: South Eastern 04-05, Southern 05-10, Sussex County 21-27 52-85,Southern Amateur 27-46, Corinthian 46-48
Name: Hastings & St Leonards Amateurs **Ground:** Bulverhythe Rec Gd (pre 76)

CLUB RECORDS
Attendance: 4,888 v Notts Forest, friendly 23/6/96. Competitive: 1,774 v DoverAthletic, Southern Lge Prem. Div. 12/4/93
Goalscorer: (Season) Terry White (33) 99-00
Transfer Fee Paid: £8,000 for Nicky Dent from Ashford **Received:** £50,000 for Paul Smith from Notts Forest

BEST SEASON
FA Cup: 1st Round Proper 2002-2003 v Stevenage Bor. (A) 0-1 **FA Trophy:** 3rd Rd 1998-99
FA Amateur Cup: 3rd Rd. 38-39 **FA Vase:** 5th Rd. rep. 90-91

HONOURS
Southern Lg Cup 94-95, Southern Div 91-92, Div 2 R-up 08-09, Div 2(B) 09-10; Sussex Co Lg R-up 21-22 25-26, Lg Cup 80-81, Div 2 79-80 (R-up 59-60), Div 2Cup 79-80; Sussex Sen Cup 35-36 37-38 95-96 97-98; AFA Snr Cup 37-38; Gilbert Rice F/lit Cup 89-90

Players progressing: Peter Heritage (Gillingham), Paul Smith (Nottm Forest)

Back Row (L-R): Lee Hockey, Simon Stickney, Steve Ringwood, Will Toal, Ryan Peters, Stuart Mayall.
Front Row: Carl Rook, Russell Eldridge, Jimmy Elford, Mitchell Sherwood, Ricky Spiller.

Photo: Alan Coomes.

HORSHAM

CLUB OFFICIALS

Chairman: Frank King

Vice Chairman: Tim Hewlett

President: Geoff Holtom

Press Officer: Jeff Barrett (01403 267730)

Secretary: Jef Barrett, 3Bunting Close, Horsham, West Sussex RH13 5PA.
Tel: 01403 267730
Email : jeff.barrett@btinternet.com

FOOTBALL MANAGEMENT TEAM

Manager: John Maggs
Asst Mgr/Coach:Ali Rennie
Physio: Geoff Brittain

FACT FILE

Founded: 1885
Nickname: Hornets
Club Sponsors: Sunley Homes
Colours: Amber & Green
Change colours: Maroon & Lincoln Green
Midweek Matches: Tuesday
Local Press: West Sussex County Times:
Market Square, Horsham (01403 253371

2003-2004

Captain & Player of the Year:
Eddie French
Top Scorer: Gavin Geddes

PROGRAMME

Pages: 40 Price: £1.20
Editor:Adam Hammond (01403 217316)

GROUND: Queen St, Horsham RH13 5AD Tel: 01403 252310 E mail address : c/o Sec

Directions: From the station turn left into North Street. Pass the Arts Centre to lights and turn left. At next set of lights (200 yards) turn left again into East Street. East St. becomes Queen Street after the Iron Bridge and the ground lies opposite Queens Head pub.

Capacity: 3,000 Seats: 300 Cover:1,400 Floodlights: Yes

Clubhouse: Matchdays only. Hot and cold snacks. Dancehall **Club Shop:** Yes

PREVIOUS

Leagues: W Sussex Sen; Sussex County 26-51; Metropolitan 51-57; Corinthian 57-63; Athenian 63-73
Grounds: Horsham Park, Hurst Park, Springfield Park

CLUB RECORDS

Attendance: 8,000 v Swindon, FA Cup 1st Rd, November 1966
Victory: 16-1 v Southwick Susussex Co Lg 1945-46
Defeat: 1-11 v Worthing Sussex Sen Cup 1913-14

BEST SEASON

FA Cup: 1st Rd 47-48 (lost 1-9 at Notts County), 66-67 (lost 0-3 v Swindon)
F.A. Trophy: 1st Rd Proper Replay 76-77 **F.A.Vase:** 4th Rd Replay 85-86

HONOURS

Sussex Snr Cup 33-34 38-39 49-50 53-54 71-72 73-74 75-76; Sussex RUR Cup (13); Sussex Floodlight Cup 77-78;01-02 Sussex County Lg (7), R-up (4), Lg Cup 45-46 46-47; Metropolitan Lg 51-52; Ryman League Div 2 R-up 2001-02 Athenian Lg Div 1 72-73, Div 2 69-70 72-73; West Sussex Sen Lge (4); ICIS Div 3 95-96

Players progressing: Jamie Ndah (Barnet), Darren Freeman (Fulham)

Back row, left to right: Jeff Barrett (Secretary), Geoff Brittain (Physio), Eddie French (Captain), Ian Chatfield, Gavin Geddes, John Kirby, Steffan Ball, Lee Butcher, Matt Ottley, David Flemming, Scott Kenward, Stuart Hardy, John Maggs (Manager) and Frank King (Chairman).
Front row: Barrie Westgate, Gary Charman, James Grant, Ali Rennie (Asst. Manager),Lee Carney, Carlo Castrechino and Andy Salako.

LEATHERHEAD

CLUB OFFICIALS

Chairman: Tim Edwards
Secretary: Gerald Darby
Ranmore, 31 Harriots Lane, Ashtead, Surrey, KT21 2QG
Press Office/Comm. Director: Stev e Dennis

FOOTBALL MANAGEMENT TEAM

Manager:Paul Harford
Youth Team Manager:Martin Bullen
Physio: Steve Young

FACT FILE

Founded: 1946
Nickname: Tanners
Sponsors: The Beer Seller
Colours: Green and White/green/green
Change colours: Blue & white
Midweek Matchday: Tuesday

2003-2004

Captain: Danny Lavender
Top Scorer: Phil Ruggles
PLayer of the Year: Michael Webb

Pages: 40 Price: £1.40
Editor: Dave Pope
Local Press: Leatherhead Advertiser, Surrey Advertiser
Local Radio: County Sound

GROUND Fetcham Grove, Guildford Rd, Leatherhead, Surrey KT22 9AS
Tel: 01372 360151, Fax: 01372 362705

Directions: M25 jct 9 to Leatherhead; follow signs to Leisure Centre, ground adjacent.
Half mile from Leatherhead (BR)
London Country Buses 479 and 408 - ground opposite bus garage

Capacity: 3,400 Seats: 200 Cover: 445 Floodlights: Yes

Clubhouse: Bar open 12-11pm matchdays. Full catering. Tel: 01372 360151

Club Shop: Yes. Tel: 01372 362705

PREVIOUS **Leagues:** Surrey Snr 46-50; Metropolitan 50-51; Delphian 51-58; Corinthian 58-63; Athenian 63-72

CLUB RECORDS **Attendance:** 5,500 v Wimbledon, 1976
Win: 13-1 v Leyland Motors 46-47 Surrey Sen Lge
Defeat: 1-11 v Sutton United
Career goalscorer: Steve Lunn 96-97 (46)
Career appearances: P Caswell 200
Fee paid: £1,500 to Croydon (B Salkeld)
Fee received: £1,500 from Croydon (B Salkeld)

BEST SEASON **FA Amateur Cup:** Semi finalists 70-71 73-74
FA Trophy: Runners-up 77-78
F A Cup: 4th Round 74-75, 2-3 v Leicester C.(A). Also 2nd Rd 75-76 76-77 78-79,1st Rd 77-78 80-81
League clubs defeated: Colchester, Brighton 74-75, Cambridge Utd 75-76,Northampton 76-77

HONOURS FA Trophy R-up 77-78; Isthmian Lg Cup 77-78; Corinthian Lg 62-63; Athenian Lg Div 1 63-64; Surrey Snr Cup 68-69 (R-up 64-65 66-67 74-75 78-79); Surrey Snr Lg 46-47 47-48 48-49 49-50(Lg Cup 49-50), Snr Shield 68-69, Charity Cup 46-47 49-50); E. Surrey Charity Cup 68-69 (R-up 67-68); London Snr Cup R-up 74-75 77-78; Surrey Inter Cup 89-90; Southern Comb. Cup 89-90

Players progressing: Chris Kelly (Millwall), B Friend (Fulham), L Harwood (Port Vale), John Humphrey (Millwall), Ali Chaaban (Farnborough T)

Back Row (L-R): John Lloyd, Dante Alighier, Phil Ruggles, Mick Johnston, Marc Charles-Smith, Nko Ekoku.
Front Row: Paul McKay, Danny Lavender, Alex Inglethorpe, Adam Gray, Iain Hendry..

Photo: Alan Coomes.

METROPOLITAN POLICE

CLUB OFFICIALS

Chairman: Des Flanders QPM
Vice Chairman: Ian Carter
President: Sir John Stevens QPM
Secretary: Tony Brooking
15 Westmoreland Ave,
Hornchurch, Essex. RM112EJ.
Tel: (01708 450715)

FOOTBALL MANAGEMENT TEAM

Manager: Jim Cooper
Physio: Dick Pierce

FACT FILE

Founded: 1919 Nickname: Blues
Club Sponsors: Copleys Lyd,' News of the World' Chatterbox and Hatch Associates
Colours: All blue
Change colours:White
Midweek Matches: Tuesday
Reserves' League: Suburban

2003-2004

Top Scorer:Scott Bennetts
Capt: Jon Daley
P.O.Y.Jon Daly

Pages: 10 Price: Free
Editor/ Press Officer:
Cliff Travis (01932 782215)

Local Press: Surrey Comet, Surrey Herald
Local Radio: County Sounds

GROUND: Metropolitan Police Sports Ground, Imber Court, East Molesey Tel: 0208 398 7358)

Directions: From London: A3 then A309 to Scilly Isles r'bout, right into Hampton Court Way, left at 1st r'bout into Ember Court Rd - ground faces in 300yds. From M25 jct 10: A3 towards London for 1 mile, A307 through Cobham, left immd. after Sandown Park into Station Rd - ground 1 mile on left.
Half mile from either Thames Ditton or Esher BR stations

Capacity: 3,000 Seats: 297 Cover: 1,800 Floodlights: Yes **Club Shop:** No

Clubhouse: (0181 398 1267). Four bars, dancehall, cafeteria open 9am-11pm. Hot & cold food

PREVIOUS: **Leagues:** Spartan 28-60; Metropolitan 60-71; Southern 71-78
Grounds: None **Name:** None

CLUB RECORDS: **Attendance:** 4,500 v Kingstonian, FA Cup 1934
Goal Scorer: Mario Russo
Appearances: Pat Robert
Win: 10-1 v Tilbury 1995
Defeat: 1-11 v Wimbledon, 1956

BEST SEASON **FA Cup:** 1st Rd - 32-33, 0-9 v Northampton T. (A); 84-85, 0-3 v Dartford (H); 94-95, 0-3 v Crawley T. (H)

HONOURS: Isthmian Lg Div 2 R-up 77-78 87-88; Spartan Lg 28-29 29-30 36-37 38-39 45-46 53-54 54-55, (R-up 47-48), Lg Cup 59-60 (R-up 57-58); Middx Snr Cup 27-28;Surrey Snr Cup 32-33, Charity Shield 38-39; Metropolitan Lg Cup 68-69 (Amtr Cup 68-69 69-70); London Snr Cup R-up 34-35 40-41; Herts & Middx Comb. 39-40;Diadora Lg Carlsberg Trophy 94-95

Back row, left to right: Gavin McPherson (coach), Chris Rose, Steve Flynn, Jon Daly (captain), Dave Newman, Stuart Mackenzie, Mark Harper, Scott Bennetts, Micky Parma and Jim Cooper (manager). **Front row:** Lee Cormack, Stayrt Harte, Ian Batten, Paul sears, Neil Williams and Koti Davis.

MOLESEY

CLUB OFFICIALS

Chairman: Keith Knight

President: T.B.A.

Pres Officer: Peter Bowers

Secretary : Fiona Bowers (c/o the club)

FOOTBALL MANAGEMENT TEAM

Manager: Steve Beeks
Asst Man/Coach: Dave Skilton
Reserve Team Manager:Steve Webb.
Youth Team Manager: Ross Teague

2003-2004

Captain: Lee Richardson
Top Scorer: Lee Richardson 14
Player of the Year: John Murphy

FACT FILE

Formed: 1952 (as senior club)
Nickname: The Moles
Colours: White/black/black
Change colours: All Yellow
Midweek home matchday: Tuesday
Reserve Team's League: Suburban
Youth Team: Southern Yth Lge
Local Press: Surrey Comet, Surrey Herald, Molesey News
Local Radio: Thames 107.8 FM
Hospital Radio, County Sound, Three Counties, Star FM.

PROGRAMME

Pages:28 Price: £1.20
Editor: Pete Bowers c/o the club

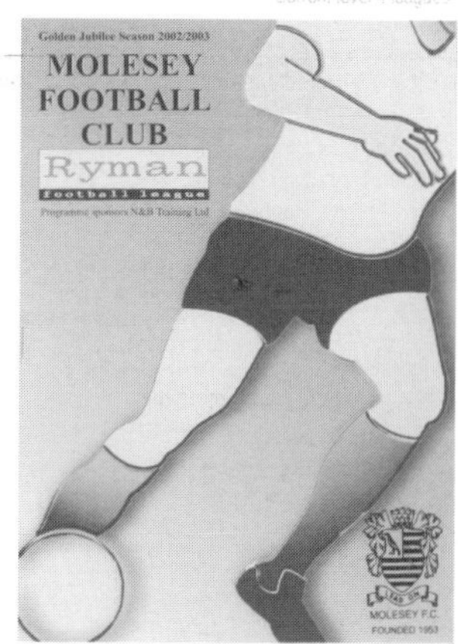

GROUND **Address:** 412 Walton Road, West Molesey, Surrey KT8 0JG Tel: 0181 941 7989 (Boardroom) 0181 979 4823 (Clubhouse)
Directions A3 from London to Hook, thenA309 to Marquis of Granby pub, right to Hampton Court station, turn left forWest Molesey, ground one mile on left
Capacity 4,000 Cover: 600 Seats: 400 Floodlights: Yes
Clubhouse Open every evening and weekend lunchtimes 2 bars, discos, live artists, darts, bingo, pool. Steward: John Chambers
Club Shop: Contact John Chambers

PREVIOUS **Leagues:** Surrey Intermediate 53-56; Surrey Snr 56-59; Spartan 59-72; Athenian72-77
Name: Molesey St Pauls 1950-53. **Grounds:** None

CLUB RECORDS **Attendance:** 1,255 v Sutton United, Surrey Senior Cup Semi-Final 1966
CareerGoalscorer: Michael Rose, 139
Career Appearances: Frank Hanley, 453
Transfer fee paid: £500 for Chris Vidal (Leatherhead 88)
Transfer fee received: £5,000 for Chris Vidal (Hythe Town 89)

BEST SEASON **FA Vase:** 6th Rd 81-82. **FA Trophy:** 1st Rd replay 90-91
FA Cup: First Round Proper 94-95, 0-4 v Bath City (H)

HONOURS Isthmian Lg Div 1 R-up 92-93, Div 2 South R-up 89-90, Lg Cup R-up 92-93, Surrey Senior Lg 57-58, Lg Charity Cup 56-57, Spartan Lg R-up 59-60. Lg Cup 61-62 R-up 63-64, Surrey Senior Shield R-up 74-75, Southern Combination Cup 90-91 94-95

Players progressing: John Finch (Fulham), Cyrille Regis (WBA, Coventry &England)

Back row, left to right: A.Ismani, S.Franklin. P.Williams, A Creamer, M.Tacey, W.Aburn, M.Frampton, J.Murphy and S Braburn
Front row: L. O'Leary, A Mansueto, S.Lampard, L.Richardson, S.Beeks, F.Allebuosi, P. Caughter and M.Griffiths.

NEWPORT I.W.

CLUB OFFICIALS

Chairman: Bill Manuel **Pres:** W Bunday
Secretary: David Bartlett, 10 Eastcliff Court,Crescent Road, Shanklin, I.o.W. PO37 6EJ Tel: 01983 865059 or 07717 251839
Office Manager: Pauline Crisp

FOOTBALL MANAGEMENT TEAM

Manager: John Linnington
Assistant Manager: Roger McCormack
Coach: Steve Brougham
Physio: Chris Cheverton

FACT FILE

Formed: 1888 Nickname: The Port
Colours: Yellow/Blue/Yellow
Change colours: Blue/White/Red
Midweek matchday: Wednesday
Reserves' League: Isle of Wight League
Clubcall: 09066 555 890
Local Press: Portsmouth Evening News, I.o.W. County Press, Southampton Evening Echo
Local Radio:
Solent, Isle of Wight Radio, Ocean Sound

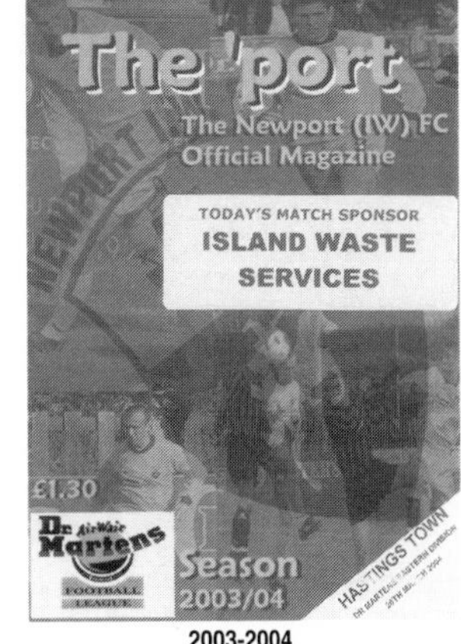

2003-2004

Captain.: Simon Pilcher
Leading Goalscorer: Ashley Wright
Player of the Year: Joe McCormack

PROGRAMME

Pages: 28 Price: £1.30
Editor: Alan Phillips (07830365264)

GROUND: St. George's Park, St George's Way, Newport, Isle of Wight, PO30 2QH. Tel: 01983 525027

Directions: Roads from all ferry ports lead to Coppins Bridge R-abt at eastern end of town. Take Sandown/Ventnor exit, go to small r-about, St George's way is 1st exit, ground on left 5 mins walk from Newport Bus station along Church Litten (past old ground) turn left then right at r-about.

Capacity: 5,000 Cover: 1,000 Seats: 300 Floodlights: Yes

Club Shop: Sells souvenirs & progs. Contact Roger Sanders 01983 825925

Clubhouse: Open every evening & weekend lunch times. 2 bars, full range of hot and cold bar snacks. Snack Bar inside ground

PREVIOUS **Leagues:** Isle of Wight 1896-1928; Hants 28-86; Wessex 86-90
Ground: Church Litten (previously Well's Field) 1888-1988

CLUB RECORDS **Attendance:** 2,270 v Portsmouth (Friendly) : 7th July 2001 and 2,217 FA Cup 1st Rd Nov 1994 v Aylesbury U.,
Win: 14-1, v Thornycroft Athletic (H),Hampshire Lge Div. One, 22.12.45
Defeat: 1-11 v Emsworth(A) Hampshsire Div. Lge 1926-27 **Career Appearances:** Jeff Austin 540 (69-87)
Career Goalscorer: Roy Gilfillan 220 1951-57 **Record Goalscorer:** Frank Harrison 62 1929-30
Fee paid: £5,000 for Colin Matthews (Bognor Regis Town 00) **Fee received**: £2,250 for Mick Jenkins (Havant) 92-3

BEST SEASON **FA Trophy:** 4th Rd 99-00 **FA Vase:** Fifth Round 91-92, 92-93
FA Cup: 2nd Rd 35-36 45-46. 1st Rd another 8 times - 52-53, 53-54, 54-55, 56-57, 57-58, 58-59, 94-95, 95-96
League clubs defeated: Clapton Orient 45-46

HONOURS Dr. Martens Lge Eastern Div. 00-01, Wessex Lg R-up 89-90, Comb. 91-92, 99-00 (res 2.) League Cup 01-02 (res); Hants Lg (11), R-up (7), Div 2 R-up 70-71, Hants Snr Cup (8); Russell Cotes Cup (3); Pickford Cup (4); Isle of Wight Snr (Gold) Cup (34); Hants F'lit Cup 76-77 77-78; Isle of Wight Lg (4) 07-09 23-24; Hants I'mediate Cup 31-32 96-97; Hants Comb. Cup 38-39

Players progressing: Gary Rowatt (Cambridge United)

Back Row (L-R): Simon Picher, Justin Hughes, Lee Wood, Mark Isaacson, Joe McCormack, Chris Bridges, Jon Holmes, Jamie White, Dean Raynor.
Front Row: Alex Perry, Ian Buckman, Kevin Youngs, Iain Stevens, Darren Thorpe, Danny Hatcher.

TOOTING & MITCHAM UTD

CLUB OFFICIALS

Chairman: John Buffoni
President: Cliff Bilham
Vice Chairman: Alan Simpson

Secretary: Les Roberts, 91 Fernlea Road, Mitcham, Surrey CR4 2HG (01816 465275)

Commercial Manager: John Pollard
Press Officer: Steve Taylor c/o club

FOOTBALL MANAGEMENT TEAM

Manager: Richard Cadette
Coach: Peter Shaw
Physio: Danny Keenan

FACT FILE

Formed: 1932
Nickname: Terrors
Sponsors: Claremont Coaches
Colours: Black & white stripes/black/white
Change colours: All red
Midweek matchday: Tuesday
Reserve League: Suburban
Local Press: Mitcham News, South London Press, South London Guardian
Local Radio: Capital

TOOTING & MITCHAM UNITED FOOTBALL CLUB SEASON 2002-3 Ryman football league

PROGRAMME

Pages: 24 Price: 80p
Editor: Steve Taylor

GROUND: Imperial Fields, Bishopsford Road, Morden, Surrey SM4 6BF
Tel Nos: 020 8648 3248 (ground) 020 8685 9229 (board room)
Directions: Phone club please.
Capacity: 8,000 Cover: 1,990 Seats: 1,990 Floodlights: Yes
Clubhouse: Open every evening and weekend lunchtimes. Wide variety of food available
Club Shop: Sells souvenirs & confectionary

PREVIOUS: **Leagues:** London 32-37, Athenian 37-56 **Ground:** None **Name:** None

CLUB RECORDS: **Attendance:** 17,500 v QPR, FA Cup 2nd Rd 56-57
Goalscorer: Alan Ives 92 (1972-78) **Appearances:** Danny Godwin 470
Win: 11-0 v Welton Rovers, FA Amateur Cup 62-63
Defeat: 1-8 v Kingstonian, Surrey Snr Cup 66-67 v Redbridge Forest (H), LoctiteCup 3rd Rd 19/2/91
Fee Paid: £9,000 for Dave Flint (Enfield) **Fee Received:** £10,000 for Herbie Smith (Luton)

BEST SEASON: **FA Trophy:** 2nd Qualifying Rd Replay 71-72 81-82
FA Amateur Cup: 1st Rd replay 22-23 **FA Vase:**
FA Cup: 4th Rd 75-76, 1-3 v Bradford C. (A) 3rd Rd 58-59; 2nd Rd 56-57 76-77;1st Rd 5 other occasions
League clubs defeated: Bournemouth & Boscombe Ath, Northampton 58-59, Swindon 75-76

HONOURS: Isthmian League 57-58 59-60 (Full Members Cup 92-93); Athenian League 49-50 54-55; London Challenge Cup R-up 59-60; Surrey Senior Cup 37-38 43-44 44-45 52-53 59-60 75-76 76-77 77-78; Surrey Senior Shield 51-52 60-61 61-62 65-66 London Senior Cup 42-43 48-49 58-59 59-60 (R-up 43-44 44-45); South Thames Cup 69-70;

Players progressing: Trevor Owen (Orient 58), Dave Bumpstead (Millwall 58), Paddy Hasty (Aldersot 58), Walter Pearson(Aldershot), Richie Ward & Alex Stepney (Millwall 62 & 63), Vic Akers(Watford 75), Paul Priddy (Wimbledon 78), Carlton Fairweather & Brian Gayle(Wimbledon 84)

WALTON & HERSHAM

CLUB OFFICIALS

Chairman: Alan Smith
President: Allen Batsford
Secretary: Michael Groom,15 Windsor Walk, Weybridge, Surrey KT13 9AP
Tel No: 01932 842982
Press Officer: Mervyn Rees
Tel: 01932 245756

FOOTBALL MANAGEMENT TEAM

Manager: Ian Hazell
Physio: T.B.A.

FACT FILE

Formed: 18960 Nickname: Swans
Sponsors: Beales
Colours: All red
Change colours: Yellow/Green/yellow
Midweek home matchday: Tuesday
Reserve Team's League: Suburban
Club Website: waltonandhershamfc.org.uk

2003-2004

Captain:& P.o.Y.: Francis Dean
Top Scorer: Scott Edgar

Official Match Day Programme
Walton Hersham F.C.
The Ryman Football League
£1.50

GROUND: Sports Ground, Stompond Lane, Walton-on-Thames Tel: 01932 245263 (club)

Directions: From North: Over Walton Bridge & along New Zealand Ave., down 1-way street and up A244 Hersham Rd - grd 2nd right. From Esher: Down Lammas Lane then Esher Rd, straight over 1st r'bout, 4th exit at next r'bout (WestGrove) 2nd left at end of Hersham Rd and Stompond Lane 1/2 mile on left.Ten min walk Walton-on-Thames (BR). Bus 218 passes grd

Capacity: 6,500 Cover: 2,500 Seats: 500 Floodlights: Yes
Clubhouse: (01932 245263). Open every night. TV, darts, pool, refreshments on matchdays
Club Shop: Open matchdays. Contact Richard Olds c/o the club

Pages: 36 Price: £1.50
Editor: Mark Massingham Tel: 01932 885814

Local Press: Surrey Herald, Surrey Comet
Local Radio: County Sound, BBC Southern Counties

PREVIOUS **Leagues:** Surrey Senior; Corinthian 45-50; Athenian 50-71

CLUB RECORDS **Attendance:** 10,000 v Crook Town, FA Amateur Cup Quarter Final 1951-52
Scorer: Reg Sentance 220 in 11 seasons **Appearances:** Terry Keen 449 in 11 seasons
Win: 10-0 v Clevedon, FA Amateur Cup 1960 **Defeat:** 11-3 v Kingstonian Surrey Sen Shield 58
Transfer fee paid: £6,000 **Transfer fee received:** £150,000 for Nathan Ellington 99

BEST SEASON **FA Trophy:** 4th Round 99-00 **FA Amateur Cup:** Winners 72-73, (SF 51-52, 52-53)
FA Cup: 2nd Rd 72-73 (v Margate), 73-74 (v Hereford). League clubs defeated: Exeter 72-73, Brighton 73-74

HONOURS: Isthmian Lg R-up 72-73, Barassi Cup 73-74; Athenian Lg 68-69 (R-up 50-51 69-70 70-71, Lg Cup 69-70); Corinthian Lg 46-49 (R-up 49-50), Premier Midweek F'litLg 67-69 70-71 (R-up 71-72); Surrey Snr Cup 47-48 50-51 60-61 61-62 70-71 72-73 R-up (6); London Snr Cup R-up 73-74; SouthernComb. Cup 82-83 88-89 91-92; 99-00 00-01Surrey Comb.Cup 49-50 91-92.

Players progressing: Dennis Pacey (Leyton O 1952), Keith Amos (Arsenal1952),Mike Whitear (Crystal Palacr), Andy McCulloch (QPR 1970), Mick Heath (Brentford 1971),Paul Priddy (Brentford 1972), Richard Teale (Q.P.R. 1973), SteveParsons (Wimbledon 1977), Stuart Massey (Crystal Palace), Ross Davidson(Sheffield Utd), Nathan Ellington (Bristol Rovers), Paul Smith (Brentford),Tommy Williams (West Ham United) and Basir Savage (Reading)

Back row, left to right: Stuart Smith (physio), Luke Gerrard, Lee O'Donnell, Chris Whelan, Nicky Andrews, Scott Edgar, Alan Dowson, Tristan Frontin and Jamie Laister **Front row:** Adam Thompson, Marcus Rose, Adam Fennell, Paul Harkness, Ben Loney, Francis Dolan, Wes Goggin and mascot Ali Crawford

WHYTELEAFE

CLUB OFFICIALS

Chairman: Mark Coote
Secretary: Graham Douce c/o W.F.C.
Press Secretary: Brian Davis,
Tel: 020 8651 2999
Commercial Manager: T Douce
Tel: 01883 343450
Match Secretary: Edward Lucas:
Braeside,Johns Road,Tatsfield,Westerham,
Kent TN16 2AP
.Tel No: 01959 577361 (H)

FACT FILE

Formed: 1946 Nickname: Leafe
Sponsors: Custom cables
Colours: Green & white hoops/green
Change colours: Yellow /green/green
Midweek matchday: Tuesday
Reserve Team's League: Suburban
2003-04
Top Goalscorer & Player of the Year:
Mark Tompkins

Programme
Pages: 36 Price: £1.00
Editor: Chris Layton (01883 381169)
Local Press: Croydon Advertiser
Local Radio: Mercury

FOOTBALL MANAGEMENT TEAM

Manager:Stuart Massey Assistant Manager : Bernie Donnelly
Captain: Ali Reeve Physio: John Knapton

GROUND 15 Church Road, Whyteleafe, Surrey CR3 0AR
Tel: 020 8660 5491 (Ground) 020 8645 0422 (Boardroom)

Directions: Five minutes walk from Whyteleafe (BR) - turn right from station, and left into Church Road

Capacity: 5,000 Cover: 600 Seats:400 Floodlights: Yes

Clubhouse: Every evening & lunches at w/e. Hot & cold food, pool, darts, gaming machines
Clubshop: Yes

PREVIOUS **Leagues**: Caterham & Edenbridge, Croydon, Thornton Heath & Dist., SurreyIntermediate (East) 54-58, Surrey Senior 58-75, Spartan 75-81, Athenian 81-84
Names: None **Grounds:** None

CLUB RECORDS **Attendance:** 2,210 v Chester City F.A.Cup 1st Rd 99-00.
Transfer fee paid: £1,000 for Gary Bowyer (Carshalton)**Transfer fee received:** £25,000 for Steve Milton

BEST SEASON **FA Vase:** 5th Rd 80-81 85-86
FA Trophy: 4th Rd 98-99 v Kingstonian **FA Cup:** First Round proper, 99-00 v Chester City (H)

HONOURS Isthmian Lge Div 2 South R-up 88-89; Surrey Senior Lge 68-69 (Lge Cup R-up 68-69, Lge Charity Cup 71-72, Res Sect 62-63 (Chall. Cup 62-63 (R-up 59-60); Surrey Sen. Cup 68-69 (R-up 87-88); Surrey Prem. Cup R-up 84-85; E. Surrey Charity Cup 79-80 (R-up 76-77 77-78); Thornton Heath & Dist Lge 51-52(Lge Cup 51-52) Div 4 R-up 51-52; Edenbridge Charity Cup 51-52; Caterham & Purley Hospital Cup 51-52; Surrey County Interm Lge East Sect 1 55-56; Surrey Jun. Cup R-up 51-52; Caterham & Edenbridge Lge Div 3 51-52; Borough of Croydon Charity Cup 56-57; Southern Yth Lge 89-90 (R-up 88-89), Lge Cup 88-89 89-90; Southern Counties M'week F'lit Cup 95-96
Players progressing: Steve Milton (Fulham), Ian Cox and Alan Pardew (Crystal Palace)

Back row, left to right: Bernie Donnelly, Kevin Smith, Mark Dickinson, Paul Scott, Lee Richardson (Manager), Danny Rose, Mark Coote (Chairman), Nigel Golley, Ian Peddle, Pater Garland, Stuart Massey, John Knapton (Physio) and Colin Turner (Director of Football)
Front row: Andre Robinson, Ryan Gray, Kenny Lowhing, Luke Basford, Ali Reeve, Graham Brett, Danny Bowere and Tim Strong (Kit Manager).

ISTHMIAN LEAGUE DIVISION TWO
STEP 5

FINAL LEAGUE TABLE 2003-04

		P	W	D	L	F	A	Pts
1.	Leighton Town	42	28	7	7	111	36	91
2.	Dorking	42	27	8	7	87	47	89
3.	Hertford Town	42	24	9	9	74	35	81
4.	Chertsey Town	42	22	9	11	75	53	75
5.	Flackwell Heath	42	22	5	15	71	53	71
6.	Witham Town	42	20	10	12	75	54	70
7.	Kingsbury Town	42	14	11	17	60	64	53
8.	Ware	42	14	10	18	67	60	52
9.	Abingdon Town	42	15	6	21	83	81	51
10.	Camberley Town	42	15	6	21	51	71	51
11.	Wembley	42	13	9	20	46	67	48
12.	Wokingham Town	42	12	7	23	55	94	43
13.	Edgware Town	42	12	6	24	62	88	42
14.	Chalfont St Peter	42	12	6	24	57	89	42
15.	Clapton	42	8	5	29	47	129	29

2003-04	1	2	3	4	5	6	7	8	9	10	11	12	13	14	15
1 Abingdon Town		3-2	3-0	0-2	7-1	2-2	2-4	3-1	2-3	5-5	2-7	2-1	5-3	4-1	0-0
2 Camberley Town	2-1		3-2	0-0	2-3	1-3	0-1	2-1	0-2	2-1	1-0	1-1	0-1	1-2	1-3
3 Chalfont St Peter	1-1	2-4		1-1	4-3	1-3	2-3	0-2	0-1	2-2	0-1	2-1	2-2	0-2	7-2
4 Chertsey Town	4-1	2-1	0-1		0-4	0-1	2-2	1-0	1-1	1-0	2-1	1-1	3-0	2-3	1-0
5 Clapton	0-5	1-2	3-0	0-6		1-7	0-2	2-4	1-6	3-1	0-4	1-7	0-1	0-1	1-2
6 Dorking	2-1	3-0	2-1	4-1	3-2		6-1	1-0	5-3	3-0	1-2	1-0	3-0	1-0	4-0
7 Edgware Town	6-3	0-1	1-3	2-6	10-0	2-2		0-1	0-4	0-2	0-3	0-0	0-1	1-1	1-2
8 Flackwell Heath	1-0	3-1	1-0	1-3	3-3	4-1	1-0		1-0	3-1	2-2	3-2	4-0	1-3	3-1
9 Hertford Town	3-0	0-1	1-2	1-0	2-0	1-1	3-0	2-1		4-1	0-1	0-0	2-0	2-0	2-1
10 Kingsbury Town	2-0	2-2	0-1	0-3	3-0	2-2	0-1	0-0	2-4		0-2	2-1	0-0	2-0	3-1
11 Leighton Town	3-2	8-0	3-0	3-1	9-0	2-1	4-1	1-0	1-1	1-2		3-2	3-2	2-0	9-0
12 Ware	0-1	2-2	1-2	3-1	1-2	1-1	2-1	0-1	0-1	5-1	1-0		3-1	2-3	4-1
13 Wembley	1-0	0-0	2-0	1-4	4-0	0-1	1-0	0-2	0-1	1-0	0-5	0-2		5-0	1-4
14 Witham Town	3-1	5-1	4-2	1-2	6-1	1-1	5-0	1-0	1-0	1-1	1-1	3-0	2-0		3-0
15 Wokingham Town	0-2	4-0	0-2	2-4	4-0	0-0	1-4	0-3	0-2	1-0	1-1	2-0	1-4	2-1	

TEAMS PLAYED EACH OTHER THREE TIMES.

2003-04	1	2	3	4	5	6	7	8	9	10	11	12	13	14	15
1 Abingdon Town		1-2	-	0-1	-	1-2	-	1-2	-	2-0	-	1-2	-	1-1	-
2 Camberley Town	-		2-0	-	4-0	-	0-1	-	0-2	-	0-1	-	0-0	-	2-0
3 Chalfont St Peter	0-3	-		6-1	-	0-4	-	2-3	-	0-3	-	1-1	-	0-3	-
4 Chertsey Town	-	2-0	-		1-1	-	2-1	-	1-0	-	2-2	-	1-1	-	1-2
5 Clapton	1-1	-	3-0	-		1-1	-	0-3	-	0-2	-	2-2	-	1-3	-
6 Dorking	-	1-0	-	3-2	-		3-1	-	0-3	-	0-2	-	1-0	-	1-0
7 Edgware Town	3-4	-	1-2	-	2-1	-		1-3	-	1-1	-	3-2	-	3-1	-
8 Flackwell Heath	-	0-4	-	0-1	-	0-1	-		1-3	-	3-1	-	3-1	-	1-1
9 Hertford Town	0-3	-	1-1	-	0-2	-	4-0	-		1-1	-	1-1	-	3-1	-
10 Kingsbury Town	-	3-0	-	1-4	-	4-1	-	2-1	-		3-2	-	3-0	-	1-1
11 Leighton Town	1-0	-	8-0	-	1-2	-	2-0	-	1-1	-		1-1	-	2-0	-
12 Ware	-	2-4	-	0-1	-	1-3	-	2-1	-	1-0	-		4-2	-	4-1
13 Wembley	2-0	-	3-2	-	1-0	-	1-1	-	0-0	-	1-2	-		1-1	-
14 Witham Town	-	2-0	-	1-1	-	3-1	-	3-3	-	1-1	-	0-1	-		1-1
15 Wokingham Town	4-7	-	1-3	-	2-1	-	4-1	-	1-3	-	0-3	-	2-2	-	

ABINGDON TOWN

GROUND
Address: Culham Road, Abingdon OX14 3HP (01235 521684)
Directions: On A415 road to Dorchester-on-Thames half a mile south of town centre. Nearest rail station is Culham. Main line: Didcot Parkway or Oxford. Buses from Didcot,Oxford & London
Capacity: 3,000 Cover: 1,771 Seats: 271 Floodlights: Yes
Clubhouse: (01235 521684). 7.30-11pm. 6pm matchdays. 12.30-2.30, 4-11 Sat. Hot food on matchdays. Pool, darts, jukebox, canteen
Club Shop: Selling programmes, magazines, scarves. Metal Badges: £2
HONOURS
Berks & Bucks Sen Cup 58-59 (R-up 88-89 92-93); Isthmian League Div 2 (Sth) 90-91 (Assoc. Mem. Tphy R-up 90-91); London Spartan Lg 88-89 Hellenic Lge(4) 56-57 58-60 86-87, R-up(3) 70-72 87-88,Lg Cup 57-58 70-71 81-82 (R-up 83-84 86-87), Div 1 75-76, Div 1 Cup 75-76,Res. Div(3) 69-71 86-87, Res. Div Cup 70-71 85-86, Res. Div Suppl. Cup 74-75;Oxford & Dist. Lg (3) 1898-1901; Reading & Dist. Lg 47-48; Berks & Bucks Jnr Cup 06-07; Abingdon Centenary Cup 58-59; Joan Lee Mem. Cup 69-70 70-71 86-87
PREVIOUS
Leagues: Oxford & Dist.; West Berks; Reading Temperance; North Berks; Reading & Dist. 1927-50; Spartan 50-53; Hellenic 53-88; London Spartan 88-89
Name: Abingdon FC (merged with St Michaels in 1899).
CLUB RECORDS
Attendance: 4,000 v Swindon Town (Maurice Owen Benefit game) 1950s
Career appearances: Roger Charles
BEST SEASONS
FA Vase: Fifth Round, replay, 1989-90.
FA Cup: 4th Qualifying Round
60-61 0-2 v Hitchin, 89-90 1-3 v Slough(H), 92-93 1-2 v Merthyr T.(A) after 0-0
Players progressing: Maurice Owen (Swindon Town), George Buck (Stockport County& Reading), Sammy Chung (Reading, Norwich City, Watford & WolverhamptonWanderers), Jermaine McSporran (Wycombe Wanderers via Oxford City), Howard Forinton (Birmingham City,Plymouth Argyle via Oxford City and Yeovil Town)

FACT FILE
Formed: 1870
Nickname: The Abbotts
Sponsors: T.B.A.
Colours: Yellow & green/green/yellow
Change colours: Black & white
Programme: Pages: 40 Price:£1.00
Editor: Kevin Rowland(01235 522115)
Midweek Matchday: Tuesday
Reserves ' League: Suburban (North)
Local Press: Oxford Mail, Oxford Times, Abingdon Herald, South Oxon Guardian

CLUB PERSONNEL
Chairman: Phil Evans
President: Dr Tim Reynolds
Secretary: Ted Quail,
107 Park Lane, Thatcham,
Newbury, Berks RG18 3BZ
Tel: 01635868967
Press Off : Roger Nichols
Tel: 07768 427268 (M)

Management Team
Manager: Paul Berry
Asst Manager: Ray Hayward
Captain: Scott Davies
Physio: T.B.A.

2003-2004
Player of the Year: Chris Johnson
Top Goalscorer: Joey Beauchamp

BROOK HOUSE

Secretary: Barry Crump, 19 Bradenham Road, Hayes, Middlesex UB4 8LP.
Fax & Tel: 0208 841 3959 (H), 07966 468029(B)

Ground: Farm Park, Kingshill Avenue, Hayes, Middlesex (0208 842 1448)
Directions: From North Circular road: A40 Western Ave. to Target r'about, left towards Hayes (A312), over White Hart r'about towards Yeading/Hayes, right at traffic lights in to Kingshill Ave, ground 1 mile on right. Nearest BR stationis Hayes & Harlington, then bus 90 or 195 to Brook House pub. Nearest tube is Northolt (central line), then bus to ground
Capacity: 2,000 Cover: 100 Seats: 120 Floodlights: Yes Club Shop: No
Clubhouse: Open weekdays 7-11pm, Sat noon-11pm, Sun noon-11.00pm
PREVIOUS:
League: Spartans South Midlands
HONOURS: SSM Prem South 97-98, Prem Div R-Up 99-00, Lge Cup 99-00 ,91-92.
BEST SEASON:
FA Vase: 3rd Round Proper 97-98
FA Cup: 1st Qual Rd 93-94
Players progressing: Neil Shipperley (Crystal Palace), MarkHyde (Orient), Mark Perry (QPR) David Warner (To Watford for £10,000) and Anthony Charles (To Crewe Alexandrafor £6,000)

FACT FILE
Founded: 1974
Colours: Blue & white stripes/blue/blue
Change colours: Red & Black
Midweek matchday: Tuesday
Reserve League: Suburban League
Programme: 28 pages, £3 with entry
Editor: Dave Swann

CLUB PERSONNEL
President: Victor Kirby
Chairman: Mick Ralph
Vice-Chairman: JohnHandell
Press Officer: Lawrie Watts
Manager: Bob Strutton Ass Man: Joe Mitchell

CAMBERLEY TOWN

GROUND

Address: Krooner Park, Krooner Road, off Frimley Rd, Camberley, Surrey, GU15 2QP. Tel: 01276 65392

Directions: M3 Jct 4, follow signs to Frimley, then B3411 towards Camberley, ground on left opposite `The Standard' pub

Capacity: 3,000 Seats: 195 Cover: 280 Floodlights: Yes Club Shop: Yes **Clubhouse**: Open matchdays & 2 evenings. Food available from burger bar matchdays

HONOURS:
Isthmian Lg Div 2 R-up 78-79; Surrey Snr Lg 30-31 31-32 32-33 (R-up 46-47 61-62), Lg Charity Cup 37-38 51-52 (R-up 31-32 36-37 54-55 72-73); Surrey Snr Cup 78-79 (R-up 35-36); W. Surrey Lg 13-14 (R-up 12-13); Ascot & Dist Lg 03-04; Surrey Jnr Charity Cup R-up 08-09; Surrey Jnr Cup 1897-98 1909-10 (R-up 07-08); Aldershot Snr Lg 12-13 (Lg Charity Cup R-up 21-22); Southern Comb. Cup 80-81 (R-up 78-79 85-86 87-88); Aldershot Sen Cup 96-97 97-98

PREVIOUS **Leagues:** Ascot & District; West Surrey; Aldershot Snr; Surrey Snr 22-73 Spartan 73-75; Athenian 75-77 82-84; Isthmian 77-82
Names: Camberley & Yorktown 1896-1946; Camberley FC 46-67
Grounds: London Rd Rec 1898-1905 12-18/ Southwell Park Rd 05-09/ Martins Meadow 09-12

CLUB RECORDS: **Attendance:** 3,500 v Crystal Pal. friendly 14.10.74
Competitive: 2,066 v Aldershot Town, Isthmian Lge Div. 3, 10.11.92
Appearances: Brian Ives
Win: 15-0 v Royal Engineers, friendly, 20/9/19
Defeat: 0-11 v Abingdon Town (A), Isthmian Lge Div. 2 (South) 25/8/90

BEST SEASON: **FA Vase:** Quarter Final 85-86, 98-99 v Woodbridge
FA Cup:1st Rd Prop 98-99 v Brentford 4th Qual. 32-33 33-34 97-98

FACT FILE
Founded: 1896
Nickname: Krooners, Reds or Town
Colours: Red & white stripes/red/red
Change :Green & white hoops'black/black
Midweek Matches: Tuesday
Reserve's League: Suburban
Programme: 24 pages, £1
Local Press: Camberley News
Bracknell News

CLUB PERSONNEL
Chairman: Ian Waldren
Press Office & Prog.Ed,: Andy Vaughan
Secretary: David Clifford
63 Inglewood Ave, Camberley,
Surrey. GU15 1RS
Tel & Fax: 01276 516613
Website: www.cambrleytownfc .co.uk

MANAGEMENT TEAM
Manager: Ken Ballard
Asst.Mans: Steve Atkins
Captain: paul Dadson
Physio: Mike Hatton

2003-2004
Top Scorer: Scott Holman
P.o.Y.:Edgar Pestana (GK)

CHALFONT ST. PETER

GROUND
Address: Mill Meadow, Amersham Road, Chalfont St Peter SL9 7BQ
Tel: 01753 885797

Directions: A413 from Uxbridge (London) to Chalfont. Turn left 100 yds after 2nd major roundabout (between Ambulance station and Community Centre.
Just under two miles from Gerrards Cross (BR)
Regular buses from Slough & Uxbridge

Capacity: 4,500 Cover: 120 Seats: 220 Floodlights: Yes Club Shop: No

Clubhouse: Open every evening, Saturday afternoons and Sunday lunchtimes

PREVIOUS **Leagues:** Great Western Combination 1948-58; Parthenon 58-59; London 60-62; Spartan 62-75; London Spartan 75-76; Athenian 76-84

BEST SEASON **FA Trophy:** 3rd Qual Rd 89-90 91-92
FA Vase: 4th Rd 87-88
FA Cup: 3rd Qual Rd85-86 (wins over Banbury, King's Lynn and Barking)

HONOURS Isthmian Lg Div 2 87-88; Athenian Lg R-up 83-84 (Lg Cup 76-77 82-83); London Spartan Lg Div 2 75-76; Berks & Bucks Intermediate Cup 52-53; Berks & Bucks Benevolent Cup 64-65

CLUB RECORDS **Attendance:** 2,550 v Watford, benefit match 1985
Career Goalscorer: Unknown **Career Appearances:** Colin Davies
Transfer Fee Paid: £750 to Chertsey (Steve Church, March 1989)

Players progressing to Football League: Paul Barrowcliff (Brentford), Dean Hooper (Swindon)

FACT FILE
Founded: 1926
Nickname: Saints
Colours: Red, green,red.
Change colours:All Blue
Midweek matchday: Tuesday
Reserves' League:
Programme: Pages: 30 Price: £1.00
Editor: Nigel Orr
Local Press: Bucks Advertiser,
Bucks Examiner, Bucks Free Press,
Wycombe Midweek
Local Radio: Chiltern Radio

CLUB PERSONNEL
Chairman:Denis Mair
Press Officer: Nick Simon (0776 5963184)
Secretary: Migel Orr,Trio Nicol Road,Chalfont St Peter, Bucks Sl9 9NF
Tel No: 01753 887209
Manager: Martin Dean

2002-2003
Captain: Kevin Powell
Players of the Year: Mark Needham & Peter Weirich Top Scorer: Barry Brosnan.

CHERTSEY TOWN

GROUND

Address: Alwyns Lane, Chertsey, Surrey KT16 9DW

Tel: 01932 561774 Email: ctfc.freeserve.co.uk

Directions: Alwyns Lane is off Windsor Street at north end of shopping centre. 10 mins walk from Chertsey (SWT). Buses from Staines and Woking

Capacity: 3,000 Seats: 250 Cover: 1000 Floodlights: Yes

Clubhouse: Open weekday evenings and weekend lunchtimes

Club Shop: Open matchdays, selling club & football souvenirs. Contact Daniel Dullaway

PREVIOUS

Leagues: West Surrey (pre-1899); Surrey Jnr 1899-1920; Surrey Intermediate 20-46; Surrey Snr 46-63; Metropolitan 63-66; Gtr London 66-67; Spartan 67-75; London Spartan 75-76; Athenian 76-84; Isthmian 84-85; Combined Counties 85-86.

Grounds: The Grange (pre-World War 1), The Hollows (pre-1929)

CLUB RECORDS

Attendance: 2,150 v Aldershot, Isthmian Lge Div. 2 4/12/93

Goalscorer: Alan Brown 54, 1962-63

Win: 10-1 v Clapton (H), Isthmian Lge Div. 3, 91-92

Defeat: 1-12 v Bromley (H), FA Cup Preliminary Rd, 82-83

Transfer fee received: £67,500.

BEST SEASON

FA Vase: Quarter Final 87-88 91-92

FA Cup: 3rd Qual. Rd 92-93, 1-3 v Kingstonian (H)

FA Trophy: 2nd Qual Rd 95-96

FA Amateur Cup: 3rd Qual Rd 61-62

HONOURS

Isthmian Lge Cup 94-95 (Assoc. Members Trophy 94-95), Div 2 R-up 94-95, Div 3 R-up 91-92; Surrey Snr Lge 59-60 61-62 62-63 (Lge Cup 59-60 61-62); Combined Co's Lge R-up 85-86 (Concours Tphy 85-86); Surrey Snr Cup R-up 85-86; Spartan Lge & Lge Cup R-up 74-75

Players progressing:

Rachid Harkouk (Crystal Palace), Peter Cawley (Wimbledon 87), Lee Charles (Q.P.R. 95)

FACT FILE

Formed: 1890

Nickname: Curfews

Sponsors: T.B.A.

Colours: Blue & white stripes/white/blue

Change colours: Yellow & Black

Midweek Matchday: Tuesday

Club Website: www.curfews.co.uk

Programme

Pages: 36 Price: £1

Editor: Chris Gay (01276 20745)

Local Press: Surrey Herald

Local Radio: BBC Southern Counties, County Sound

CLUB OFFICIALS

Chairman: Steve Powers

President: Cllr Chris Norman

Vice Chairman: Sav Ramayon

Press Officer / Secretary:

Ben O'Conner

2 Monaveen Gardens, West Molesey, Surrey KT8 1SB Tel: 0208 224 1387

FOOTBALL MANAGEMENT TEAM

Manager:Mark Stowe

Asst Manager: Mark Turner

Physio: Peter Chessman

CLAPTON

GROUND

Address: The Old Spotted Dog, Upton Lane, Forest Gate, London E7 9NP
Tel: 0208 4720822

Directions: BR to Forest Gate.Tube to Plaistow (District Line).
Official entrance in Upton Lane.
Docklands Light Railway to Prince Regent then 325 bus to ground

Capacity: 2,000 Seats: 100 Cover: 180 Floodlights: Yes

Club Shop: No

Clubhouse: Match days. Light snacks available. To hire please contact club

HONOURS: FA Amateur Cup: 06-07 08-09 14-15 23-24 24-25 (R-up 04-05); Isthmian Lg 10-11 22-23 (R-up 05-06 07-08 09-10 24-25), Div 2 82-83; Essex Thames-side Tphy(2); A.F.A.Invitation Cup (2); London Snr Cup (2); London Charity Cup; Essex Snr Cup (4); Middlesex Snr Cup; Essex Sen Trophy; First English team to play on the continent, beating a Belgian Select XI over Easter 1890.

PREVIOUS **Leagues:** Southern 1894-96 (founder members); London 1896-97
Grounds: None

CLUB RECORDS **Attendance:** 12,000 v Tottenham Hotspur, FA Cup 1898-99
Defeat: 0-14 v Nottingham Forest (H), FA Cup 1st Rd 1890-91

BEST SEASON **FA Cup:** 3rd Rd Proper 25-26 (lost 2-3 to Swindon at Upton Park)
League clubs defeated Norwich City 25-26.
FA Amateur Cup: 06-07 08-09 14-15 23-24 24-25 (R-up 04-05);

Players progressing to Football Lge: Numerous over past 116 years. Currently:, Gary Charles (West Ham)

FACT FILE

Founded: 1878

Nickname: Tons

Sponsors: T.B.A.

Colours: Red & white stripes/black/black

Change colours: Yellow/black/black

Midweek Matchday: Tuesday

Programme: up to 12 pages £1.00

Editor: Barbara Walton

CLUB PERSONNEL

Chairman: Duwayne Brooks

Chief Executive: Vince McBean

Secretary: Colin Walton, 2 Mansfield Road, Ilford, Essex IG1 3AZ

Boardroom & Club Hospitality: Jenny Oli

MANAGEMENT TEAM

Manager:Colin Walton

Assistant Manager: Trevor Dewbury

Captain: Jamie Barry

Physios:Lucelta Eugene

2003-2004

Leading Goalscorer: Darryl Wilson

Player of the Year: Jamie Barry

EDGWARE TOWN

GROUND
Address: White Lion Ground, High Street, Edgware HA8 5AQ. Tel: 0181 9526799

Directions: Left out of Edgware tube station (Northern Line), left again at crossroads and ground is 300yds on right in Edgware High St. . Buses 32, 288 142

Capacity: 5,000 Seats: 220 Cover: 1,500 Floodlights: Yes
Club Shop: No
Clubhouse: Open nightly and Fri, Sat, Sun lunchtimes.
Hot & cold food matchdays, cold food lunchtimes

HONOURS: Isthmian Lg Div 3 91-92; London Spartan Lg 87-88 89-90 (Lg Cup 87-88); Corinthian Lg R-up 53-54, Memorial Shield 52-53 61-62; Athenian Lge R-up 81-82; Middx Snr Lg 40-41 41-42 42-43 43-44 44-45, Cup 47-48 (R-up 73-74 94-95); London Snr Cup R-up 47-48; Middx Border Lg Cup 79-80; Suburban Lg Div R-up 89-90

PREVIOUS **Leagues:** Corinthian 46-63; Athenian 64-84; London Spartan 84-90
Names: Edgware F.C. **Grounds:** None

CLUB RECORDS **Attendance:** 8,500 v Wealdstone, FA Cup 1948
Career Appearances: John Mangan
Career Goalscorer: Steve Newing

BEST SEASON **FA Vase:** 5th Round, 1991-92

Players progressing: Brian Stein (Luton), Dave Beasant (Wimbledon), Scott McGleish (Charlton 94)

FACT FILE

Founded: 1939
Nickname: Wares
Colours: Green & white quarters/green/green
Change colours: All yellow
Midweek Matchday: Tuesday
Reserve League: Suburban
Sponsor: Philiam Construction

Programme:
Pages: 16 Price: 50p
Editor: Paul Gregory (0181 959 2535)
Website: www.edgwaretownfc.com

CLUB PERSONNEL

Chairman: Paul Karaiskos
President: Mr V Deritis
Patron: Russell Grant

Secretary: Peter Evans,
5 Windmill Ct., Windmill Lane, Bushey,
Herts WD23 1NG
Tel: 0208 420 4750
Fax: 0208 950 8924

Manager: John Harding
Asst Manager: Noel Blackwell
Physio: Sarah Gow

2003-2004
Leading Goalscorer:
Captain:
Player of the Year:

ENFIELD

GROUND: Meadow Park, Broughinge Rd, Boreham Wood, Herts WD6 5AL. Tel: 0208 9535097 Email: efcltd@lineone.net
Directions: A1 towards London from M25, 1st turn for Boreham Wood, head for town centre, into Brook Rd at r'bout before town centre, Broughinge Rd is 1st right. 1 mile from Elstree & Boreham Wood station (Thameslink), or bus 292 or 107 to McDonalds (5 minutes walk)
Capacity: 4,502 Cover: 1,568 Seats: 500 Floodlights: Yes
Club Shop: Alan Farmer (0208366 6066)
PREVIOUS **Leagues**: Tottenham & Dist 1894-95; Nth Middx 96-1903; London 03-13 20-21; Middx 08-12, 19-20;
Athenian 12-14 21-39 45-63; Herts & Middx Comb 39-42; Isthmian 63-81; GMV Conference 81-90
Name: Enfield Spartans 1893-1900 **Grounds:** Baileys Field 1893-96; Tuckers Field 96-1900; Cherry Orchard Lane1900-36
CLUB RECORDS **Attendance:** 10,000 (10/10/62) v Spurs, floodlight opener Southbury Road 1936-1999
Win: 18-0 v Stevenage FA Cup 2nd Qual 22/10/27 (H)
Defeat: 0-12 v Woolwich Polytechnic, London Lge Div 2 27/4/04
Fee Paid: for Gary Abbott (Barnet)
Fee Received: for Paul Furlong (Coventry City)
Scorer: Tommy Lawrence, 191 1959-1964.
Appearances: Steve King 617 (77-89)
BEST SEASON **FA Amateur Cup:** Winners 66-7 69-70 R-up 63-4 71-2
FA Trophy: Winners 81-2 87-8
League clubs beaten: Wimbledon, Northampton 77-78, Hereford, Port Vale 80-81, Wimbledon 81-82, Exeter 84-85, Orient 88-89, Aldershot 91-92, Cardiff City 94-95, Torquay Utd 94-95, Chesterfield 99-00

HONOURS: Alliance Premier Lge 82-83 85-86 (R-up 81-82), Lg Cup R-up 81-82; IsthmianLg(8) 67-70 75-78 79-80 94-95 (R-up 64-65 71-72 74-75 80-81 90-92 95-96), LgCup(2) 78-80 (R-up 91-92 94-95); Athenian Lg(2) 61-63 (R-up 34-35); London LgDiv 1 11-12 (R-up 04-05 06-07); Middx Snr Cup 13-14 46-47 61-62 65-66 68-71 77-81 88-89 90-91 97-98, (R-up 10-11 20-21 47-48 51-52 57-60 62-63 66-67 72-73 75-76 84-85); London Snr Cup 34-35 60-61 66-67 71-73 75-76 (R-up 63-64 67-68 70-71); Middx Lg (West) 09-10 (R-up 10-11); European Amtr Cup Winners Cup 69-70

Players progressing: Terry McQuade (Millwall 61), Roger Day (Watford 61), Jeff Harris (Orient 64), Peter Feely (Chelsea 70), Carl Richards & Jon Bailey (B'mouth 80 & 95), Paul Furlong (Coventry 91), Andy Pape (Barnet 91), GregHeald (Peterborough 94), Lee Marshall (Norwich City 97)

FACT FILE
Formed: 1893
Nickname: The E's
Sponsors: T.B.A.
Colours: White/blue/white
Change colours: All Yellow
Midweek matchday: Monday
Reserves' League: Middlesex Co.
Local Press: Enfield Gazette, Enfield Advertiser, Enfield Independent
Website: www.enfieldfc.com

PROGRAMME
Pages: 48 Price: £1.50
Editor: Derek Bird

CLUB OFFICIALS
Chairman: A Lazarou
President: R.Prosser
Secretary & Match Sec: Derek Bird,
17 Fishers Close, Waltham Cross,Herts.
Tel: 01992 301741 07765 837246 (M)
07992 066605 (Fax)

FOOTBALL MANAGEMENT
Manager: Terry Back

2003-2004
Captain:
Top Scorer & P.o.Y.:

EPSOM & EWELL

GROUND:GROUND:
Groundshare with Banstead Athletic FC. Merland Rise, Tadworth, Surrey KT20 5JG
Tel: 01737 350982
Directions: Follow signs to Tattenham Corner (Epsom racecourse), then to Banstead Sports Centre. Ground adjacent to swimming pool.
Half a mile fromTattenham Corner (BR)
Bus 422 from Sutton stops outside ground.
Also buses 460 from Epsom
Capacity: 3,500 Seats: 250 Cover: 800 Floodlights: Yes
Clubhouse: Normal licensinghourd, food available **Club Shop:** No
PREVIOUS **Leagues:** Surrey Snr 24-27 73-75; London 27-49; Corinthian 49-63; Athenian 63-73 75-77
Grounds: Horton Lane, Epsom 1925-26 and West Atreet, Ewell 1926-93
Names: Epsom Town (previously Epsom FC) merged with Ewell & Stoneleigh in 1960
CLUB RECORDS **Attendance:** 5,000 v Kingstonian, F.A. Cup 2nd Qual. Rd, 15/10/49
Record Goalscorer: Tommy Tuite
BEST SEASON **FA Cup:** 1st Round 33-34 **FA Trophy:** 2nd Roundd 81-82
FA Vase: Runners-up 74-75
HONOURS FA Vase R-up 74-75; London Lg 27-28, R-up (5); Corinthian Lg Memorial Shield 59-60 (R-up 51-52 56-57);
Athenian Lg Div 2 R-up 75-76 (Lg Cup R-up 76-77, Div2 Cup R-up 67-68); Isthmian Lg Div 2 77-78 (Div 1 R-up 83-84),
Div 2 S . Promotion 01-02 Vandanel Ass Members Trophy R-up 97-98;
Surrey Snr Lg 25-26 26-27 74-75 (R-up 73-74),
Lg Cup 73-74 74-75, Charity Cup 26-27 (R-up 73-74), Surrey Snr Cup 80-81 (R-up 3); Surrey Snr Shield 32-33 54-55;
Surrey Interm'te Cup 29-30,Charity Cup 57-58; S Comb. Cup 79-80 (R-up 82-83 92-93)
Players progressing: Matt Elliott (Leicester), Chris Powell(Derby), Paul Harding (Notts County, Birmingham), Murray Jones (Grimsby),
Alan Pardew (Charlton), Mick Leonard (Chesterfield)

FACT FILE
Founded: 1917
Nickname: E's
Colours: Royal & white
Change: All yellow
Midweek Matches: Tuesday
Reserves' League: Suburban
2003-2004
Captain:
Leading Goalscorer:
Player of the Year:

PROGRAMME
Pages: 28/32 Price: £1.50
Editor: Stella Lamont (01737 356245)

Club Website www.eefc.net

CLUB OFFICIALS
President: Stella Lamont
Chairman: Peter Lumm
Vice Chairman: Derick Hayles
Secretary: D Wilson, 33 Delaporte Close, Epsom, Surrey KT17 4AF
Tel: 01372 729817
email: d.wilson@nbad.co.uk

FOOTBALL MANAGEMENT TEAM
Manager: Ray Purvis
Coaches: Barry Barnes & Mark Freeborough
Physio: Kevin Taylor

FLACKWELL HEATH

GROUND:
Address: Wilks Park, Heath End Rd, Flackwell Heath, High Wycombe. HP10 9EA
Tel: 01628 523892

Directions: M40 jct 3 Wycombe East, follow signs for F/Heath left up Treadway Hill & right at top of hill at roundabout. Wilks park 800yds on right, grd at rear of Magpie (PH). Bus 301 either from bus station or High Street near bottom of Crendon Street which comes from BR station. Ask for Oakland Way

Capacity: 2,000 Seats: 150 Cover: Yes Floodlights: Yes

Club Shop: No
Clubhouse: Open every night 6.30-11pm & before & after matches. Hot food in tea bar

HONOURS: Gt Western Combination 57-58 62-63; Hellenic Lg Div 1 R-up 76-77; Berks & Bucks Snr Cup SF 85-86 Wycombe Senior Cup (12)

PREVIOUS: **Leagues:** Wycombe & District; Gt Western Comb.; Hellenic 76-82; Athenian 82-84

RECORDS: **Attendance:** 4,500 v Oxford U., charity game 1986
(competitive: 700 v Aldershot Town, 27/10/92)
Goalscorer: Tony Wood **Appearamces:** Lee Elliott
Win: 6-0 v Clapton & v Petersfield (both away)
Defeat: 0-7 v Aveley (H)

BEST SEASON: **FA Cup:** 4th Qual. Rd 1-4 v Crawley Town 2002-2003

FACT FILE
Founded: 1907
Colours: All Redk
Change colours: All Gold
Midweek Matches: Tuesday
Programme: 18 pages £1
Editor:

CLUB PERSONNEL
Chairman: T Glynn
Vice Chairman: G.Turner
President: Ken Crook
MANAGEMENT TEAM
Manager:
Coach;
Physio:

Secretary: Mrs Christine Hobbs
23 Southfield Rd., Flackwell Heath, Bucks. HP10 9BT
Tel: 01628 521051

2003-2004
Leading Scorer:& Player of the Year:
Leigh Mason
Captain:Ashley Smith

HERTFORD TOWN

GROUND
Address: Hertingfordbury Park, West Street, Hertford Tel: 01992 583716

Directions: Rail to Hertford Nth (from Moorgate) or Hertford East (LiverpoolStr.); both 15 mins walk. Green Line bus to town centre then 10 mins walk.
By road; off bypass heading east, turn off at Ford garage
Capacity: 6,500 Seats: 200 Cover: 1,500 Floodlights: Yes
Club Shop: Souvenirs
Clubhouse: Yes

PREVIOUS
Leagues: Herts Co.; Spartan 21-47 48-59; Delphian 59-63; Athenian 63-72; Eastern Co's 72-73
Names: None
Grounds: None

BEST SEASON
FA Cup: 4th Qual. Rd. 73-74 (lost 1-2 at Hillingdon Borough)

CLUB RECORDS
Gate: 5,000 v Kingstonian, F.A. Amateur Cup 2nd Rd 55-56
Appearances: Robbie Burns

HONOURS
Herts Char. Cup 72-73, 89-90, Herts Snr Cup 66-67, Hertford Char.Shd 19-20 20-21 35-36 49-50 55-56 59-60, Eastern Co's Lg Cup 72-73, East Anglian Cup 62-63 69-70, Southern Co's Comb. F-lit Cup 94-95, Mithras Cup SF 85-86, Ryman Div 3 R-up 97-98

Players progressing to Football League: G Mazzon (Aldershot), J.Hooker (Brentford)

FACT FILE
Founded: 1908
Nickname: The Blues
Sponsors: Bayeux
Colours: Blue & yellow stripes/blue/blue
Change colours: Red
Midweek Matches: Tuesday
Reserves' Lge: Herts Senior County Reserve League
Website: www..hertfordtownfc.co.uk

PROGRAMME
Pages: 24 Price:£1.00
Editor: Elaine Waumsley (01992 302110)
Local Newspapers: Hertfordshire Mercury

CLUB OFFICIALS
President: John Hedley
Chairman: Ray Hill

Secretary & Press Officer:
Stephen Hedley
29 Upper Field Road, Wewyn Garden City, Herts AL7 3LP
Tel: 01707 333712

FOOTBALL MANAGEMENT
Manager: Brian Owen
Physio: Lee Pickering

ILFORD

Secretary: Bill Robertson, 2 Humphrey Close, Clayhall, Ilford, Essex JG5 0RW
Tel: 0208 550 6680 (H) 07930 104076 (W)
(All club correspondance to ground please)

Ground: Cricklefield Stadium, High Road, Ilford, Essex. IG1 1UB Tel: 0181 514 0019

Directions: 5 min walk from Seven Kings Station. Opposite 'TheCauliflower' publ, Or 86 Bus

Capacity: 5,000 Seats: 216 Cover: Yes Floodlights: Yes

Clubhouse: Open lunch and evening evry day. Snacks available

PREVIOUS Leagues: Spartan 87-95, Essex Senior 95-04

HONOURS: FA Amateur Cup: 28-29 29-30, R-up 35-36 57-58 1973-74
Isth. Lge Champ. 06-07 20-21 21-22 R-up 11-12 26-27 31-32 37-38 38-39 03-04
Essex Senior Cup x14 (record nos. of wins), R-up x5; London Sen. Cup: x7 R-up x5
London Charity Cup: x 6 R-up x 7: Essex I'mediate Cup R-up x1;
London I'mediate Cup R-up x1; Eastern F'lit Comp. Group Winners 96-97

BEST SEASON
FA Cup: 73-74 2nd Rd, 0-2 v Southend Utd. (H)
FA Vase: 99-00 2nd Rd 1-2 v Watton United (a)

CLUB RECORDS
Attendance: 17,000 Ilford Boys v Swansea Boys (Schools Trophy Final)

FACT FILE
Founded: 1881 Re-Formed: 1987
Sponsor: Netbusters
Colours: Blue & white hoops/blue/blue & white
Change colours: Red & white hoops/red/r+w
Midweek matches: Monday or Wednesday
Prog Editor: Len Llewellyn(01277 363103)

CLUB PERSONNEL
Chairman: George Hogarth
Vice Chairman: Melvin Attwell
President: Lord John Taylor of Warwick
Manager: Allan Fenn Asst.Man: Chris Woods
Captain: Allan Fenn

2003-2004 Top Scorer: Daniel Clarke 18
Player of the Year: Dave McCartney

KINGSBURY TOWN

GROUND:

Address: Silver Jubilee Park, Townsend Lane, Kingsbury, London NW9 7NE
Tel: 0208 2051645 Website:www.madasafish.com/~kingsbury-town

Directions: Underground to Kingsbury, cross road and take bus 183 to TownsendLane (2 miles) - ground in far left-hand corner of Silver Jubilee Park

Capacity: 2,500 Seats: 165 Cover: 400 Floodlights: Yes

Club Shop: Sells club ties, pennants, metal badges
Contact Allan Davies (01895 443761)

Clubhouse Mon-Fri 7-11, Sat 12-11, Sun 12-2.30 & 7-10.30. Food on matchdays

HONOURS: Isthmian Lg Div 2 Nth R-up 85-86; Spartan Lg Cup R-up 59-60 64-65; Parthenon Lg 51-52 (Prem Charity Cup 52-53 53-54; Snr Charity Cup 53-54); Middx Snr Cup R-up 88-89; Middx Charity Cup 85-86 (R-up 88-89); Middx Lg Charity Cup (3) 44-47; Willesden & Dist. Lg R-up 30-31 (Div 2 34-35)

PREVIOUS: **Leagues:** Hellenic 27-30 (as Davis Sports); Willesden & District 30-43; MiddxSnr 44-47; Parthenon 47-59; Spartan 59-76 78-81; Athenian 76-78 81-84
Grounds: None **Name**: Davis Sports

RECORDS: **Attendance:** 1 ,300 v Wealdstone, FA Amateur Cup 1971
Appearances: Mick Coffey (goalkeeper)
Win: 8-0 v Eastbourne United, 91-92. Defeat: ?????
Record Fees - Paid: £500 **Received**: £600

BEST SEASON: **FA Vase:** 4th Rd 74-75
FA Cup: 3rd Qual. Rd. 87-88, 0-1 v Leytonstone-Ilford (H)

Players progressing to Football League: Billy Dare (Brentford & West Ham), JohnMeadows, Dave Underwood, Dwight Marshall (Plymouth (via Grays Ath.), Ashley Bayes (Leyton Orient)

FACT FILE
Founded: 1927
Nickname: Kings
Sponsors:
VPA Entertainment Technology
Colours: Royal blue & White/white/royal
Change colours: Yellow/navy/yellow
Midweek Matches: Tuesday
Reserves' League: Suburban

Programme
16-20 pages 50p
Editor: Dave Thomas
Local Press: Harrow Observer, Willesden Chronicle, Allsport Weekly, Edgware & Finchley Times

CLUB PERSONNEL
Chairman: Mark Harrt
Press Officer: Dave Thoomas
Secretary: David Thomas,
9 Hillview Gardens, Kingsbury, NW9 0DE

Manager: Toni Kelly
Physio: Ann Bryan

2003-2004
Leading Goalscorer:
Captain:
Player of the Year:

WARE

GROUND:

Address: Wodson Park, Wadesmill Road, Ware Herts SG12 0HZ
Tel: 01920 463247

Directions: A10 off at junction A602 & B1001 (Ware North), turn right at roundabout 300yds, and follow Ware sign, past Rank factory, turn left at main round about onto A1170 (Wadesmill Rd). After 3/4 mile stadium on right

Capacity: 3,300 Seats: 312 Cover: 500 Floodlights: Yes

Club Shop: Yes

Clubhouse: Licensed bar open matchdays. Light snacks at refreshment bar

HONOURS: Herts Snr Cup 1898-99 03-04 06-07 21-22 53-54, Herts Char. Shield 26-27 56-57 58-59 62-63 85-86, Herts Char. Cup R-up 64-65 65-66 78-79 89-90, Spartan Lg 52-53 (Div 1 Sect.B 51-52, Div 2 Sect.A 26-27), Athenian Lg Div 2 Cup 65-66 72-73,East Anglian Cup 73-74, Herts Co. Lg 08-09 21-22, East Herts Lg 04-05 06-07 (LgCup 06-07), Perry Cup 26-27 28-29 37-38 51-52 52-53 53-54 55-56, Dunkels Cup 52-53, Rolleston Cup 39-40 51-52

PREVIOUS: **Leagues:** East Herts; North Middx 07-08; Herts County 08-25; Spartan 25-55;Delphian 55-63; Athenian 63-75
Grounds: Highfields; Canons Park; London Rd, Presdales Lower Park 1921-26

RECORDS **Attendance:** 3,800 v Hendon Amt Cup 56-57
Career Goalscorer: M Hibbert 229.
Goalscorer (season): George Dearman 98(1926-27)
Career Appearances: Gary Riddle 654
Win: 10-1 v Wood Green Town **Defeat**: 0-11 v Barnet

BEST SEASON: FA Cup: First Round Proper 68-69, 1-6 v Luton Town.

Players progressing: Derek Saunders (Chelsea), Ken Humphrey (QPR)

FACT FILE
Founded: 1892
Nickname: Blues
Sponsors: M.C.PlumbingColours: Blue & white stripes/blue/blue
Change colours: Amber/black
Midweek Matchday: Tuesday
Reserves' Lge:
Essex & Herts Border Comb

Programme: 24 pages, 50p
Editor : K.Mynott (01992 551605
Local Press: Herts Mercury, Herts Star, Herald & Post

CLUB PERSONNEL
Chairman: Aiden MynottPress Officer:
Secretary

Secretary: Ian Bush,
42 Burnett Square, Hertford SG14 2HD
Tel: 01992 587334

Manager: Jim Clemo
Assistant Manager: Barry Mason
Coach: Glen Alzapiedi
Physio: Frank Roberts

2003-2004
Leading Goalscorer:John Frendo 29
Players of the Year:John Frendo,Nicky Burt and Kevin Kilroy

WEMBLEY

GROUND

Address: Vale Farm, Watford Road, Sudbury, Wembley HA0 4UR Tel: 0181 908 8169

Directions: Sudbury Town station (Underground) 400 yds, or 10 mins walk from North Wembley (BR) station. Buses 18, 92, 245 & 182

Capacity: 2,000 Cover: 350 Seats: 350 Floodlights: Yes

Clubhouse: Open every night & weekend lunchtimes. Hot food on matchdays (0181 904 8169)

Club Shop: No

PREVIOUS

Leagues: Middx 46-49; Spartan 49-51; Delphian 51-56; Corinthian 56-63; Athenian 63-75

CLUB RECORDS

Attendance: 2,654 v Wealdstone, FA Amateur Cup 52-53

Career goalscorer: Bill Handrahan 105 (1946-52)

Career appearances: Spud Murphy 505 (78-88)

Win: 11-1 v Hermes, London Senior Cup 1963

Defeat: 0-16 v Chelsea, London Challenge Cup 59-60

Fee received: £10,000 for Gary Roberts (Brentford, 1981) **Transfer Fee paid:** Nil

BEST SEASON

FA Trophy: 1st Round proper 91-92 **FA Amateur Cup:** 2nd Round 66-67, 68-69

FA Cup: 1st Round Proper 1980-81, 0-3 v Enfield (A)

HONOURS

Middx Sen Cup 83-84 86-87 (R-up 55-56 68-69 78-79 87-88 91-92 92-93 98-99); Middx Lge 47-48 (Lge Cup 46-47), Middx Charity Cup 67-68 (jnt) 80-81(jnt) 82-83 86-87 94-95,(R-up 83-84 87-88 96-97); Middx Invitation Cup 56-57; Athenian Lge R-up 74-75 (Div 1 R-up 67-68); Corinthian Lge Mem Shield R-up 58-59; Delphian Lge R-up 55-56; Spartan Lge Div 1 West 50-51 (Dunkel Trophy 50-51 jnt); London Sen Cup R-up 55-56; Hitachi Cup SF 83-84; Suburban Lge North 85-86, Lge Cup 84-85 (R-up 83-84)

Players progressing

Keith Cassells (Watford 1977), MikeO'Donague (Southampton 1979), A McGonigle (Olympiakos), Gary Roberts (Brentford1980), Richard Cadette (Orient 1984)

FACT FILE

Formed: 1946
Nickname: The Lions
Sponsors: G & B Builders
Colours: Red & white/red/red
Change colours: All gold
Midweek matchday: Tuesday
Reserves' League: Suburban

Programme

Pages: 28 Price: £1
Editor: Richard Markiewicz
(0208 902 0541 - before 9pm)
Local Press: Wembley & Harrow Observer
Local Radio: Capital, G.L.R

CLUB OFFICIALS

Chairman: Brian Gumm
President: Eric Stringer
Commercial Manager: Nick Bennett

Secretary: Mrs Jean Gumm
14 Woodfield Avenue, North Wembley, Middx. HA0 3NR Tel: 0208 908 3353
Press Officer: Richard Markiewicz
Tel: 0208 902 0541 before 9pm

FOOTBALL MANAGEMENT

Manager: Scott Cousins
Asst. Manager: Roger Linton

WITHAM TOWN

Ground: Spa Road, Witham, Essex CM8 1UN
Tel: 01376 511198 (lounge) 500146 (reception) 520996 (boardroom)

Directions: From Witham BR (network S.E.) station; through pub car park and follow road to Faulkbourne, at main r'bout turn left and ground is on the right.
By road: Off A12 at Witham sign, left at 1st lights (Spinks Lane), right at end of road, follow road under railway bridge - ground 100yds on left

Capacity: 2,500 Seats: 150 Cover: 300 Floodlights: Yes

Clubhouse: Open every night and weekend lunctimes.Hot bar snacks.

Club Shop: No

HONOURS: Essex Snr Lg 70-71 85-86 (R-up 84-85 86-87), Tphy 85-86 (R-up 88-89); Essex Thameside Trophy R-up 95-96; Loctite Tphy SF 90-91

PREVIOUS: **Leagues:** Mid Essex; Essex & Suffolk Border; Essex Senior 71-87
Ground: Spa Road **Names:** None

CLUB RECORDS **Attendance:** 800 v Billericay Town, Essex Senior League, May 1976
Win: 7-0 v Banstead 27/9/94 **Defeat:** 0-9 v Collier Row 21/10/95
Goalscorer: Colin Mitchell **Appearances:** Keith Dent (16 years)
Fee received: for Steve Tilson (Southend)

BEST SEASON: **FA Vase:** 5th Round, 85-86
FA Cup: 2nd Qual. Rd 87-88 (v Gravesend), 88-89 (v B. Stortford), 89-90 (v Dartford)

Players progressing to Football League: Steve Tilson (Southend)

FACT FILE

Founded: 1947 Nickname: Town
Colours: All White
Change colours: Blue & white
Midweek Matchday: Tuesday
Reserves' Lge: Essex & Suffolk Border League Division 2
Prog: 24 pages, 60p Editor: Nigel Dudley
Local Press: Witham & Braintree Times, Essex Chronicle, East Anglian DailyTimes, Evening Gazette
Local Radio: BBC Essex, Essex Radio, Chelmer Radio

CLUB PERSONNEL

Chairman: Alan Collins
President: B Olley
Press Officer: G Vale (01376 513861)
Secretary: Jim Claydon, 58 Silver Street, Silver End, Witham, Essex CM8 3QG
Tel: 01376 584086 (H)
01376 583241 x 426 (B)

MAMAGEMENT TEAM

Manager: Tony Last
Assistant Manager: & Physio: Stuart Bevis
Captain: Simon Roberts

2003-2004

Player of the Year: Justin Pearce
Top Goalscorer: Kevin Hawes

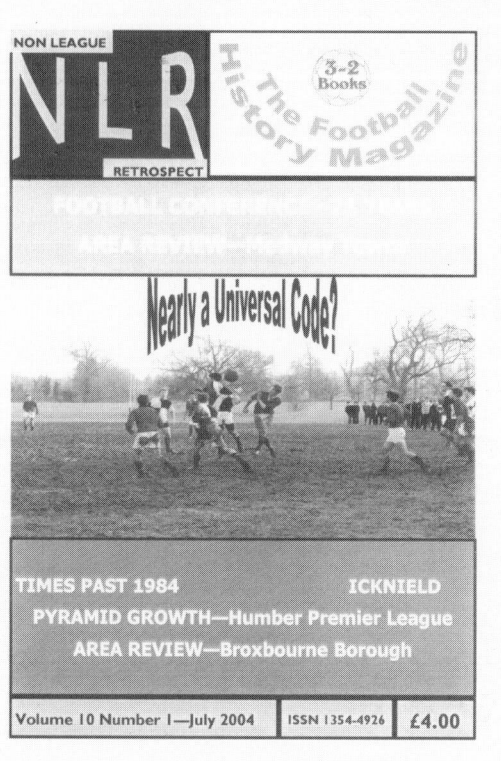

FOOTBALL LEAGUE

STEP 1

FOOTBALL CONFERENCE

STEP 2

CONFERENCE NORTH | CONFERENCE SOUTH

STEP 3

NORTHERN PREMIER | SOUTHERN PREMIER | ISTHMIAN PREMIER

STEP 4

NORTHERN PREMIER DIV.1 | SOUTHERN LEAGUE EAST | SOUTHERN LEAGUE WEST | ISTHMIAN DIVISION 1

STEP 5/6

STEP 7

COMBINED COUNTIES

President: Ron Monkley **Chairman:** John Bennett
General Secretary: Alan Constable
Tel: 01784 440613

FINAL LEAGUE TABLE 2003-04

PREMIER DIVISION	P	W	D	L	F	A	Pts
1. AFC Wimbledon	46	42	4	0	180	32	130
2. AFC Wallingford	46	32	7	7	114	43	103
3. Reading Town	46	28	10	8	79	46	94
4. Southall	46	29	5	12	121	55	92
5. Sandhurst Town	46	27	11	8	109	60	92
6. Bedfont (+3pts)	46	26	11	9	94	62	92
7. Walton Casuals	46	25	9	12	112	64	84
8. Chipstead	46	26	6	14	92	57	84
9. Ash United	46	23	11	12	103	68	80
10. Chessington & Hook United	46	21	8	17	94	75	71
11. Godalming & Guildford	46	20	9	17	65	61	69
12. Merstham	46	20	9	17	63	67	69
13. Feltham	46	19	6	21	82	67	63
14. North Greenford United	46	18	6	22	80	91	60
15. Hartley Wintney (-3 pts)	46	17	7	22	77	111	55
16. Raynes Park Vale	46	12	9	25	72	94	45
17. Horley Town	46	12	8	26	67	94	44
18. Cobham	46	12	8	26	57	114	44
19. Westfield (-3 pts)	46	11	10	25	53	88	40
20. Frimley Green	46	9	10	27	53	109	37
21. Withdean (+3 pts)	46	8	7	31	62	115	34
22. Farnham Town	46	8	4	34	44	125	28
23. Chessington United	46	7	6	33	52	140	27
24. Cove	46	7	5	34	50	137	26

PREMIER	1	2	3	4	5	6	7	8	9	10	11	12	13	14	15	16	17	18	19	20	21	22	23	24
1 AFC Wa		1-2	3-1	4-0	4-2	5-0	4-1	5-1	2-0	6-0	3-1	3-2	1-2	3-2	2-0	4-0	1-0	2-3	3-1	2-4	3-1	1-0	4-1	W-L
2 AFC Wi	1-1		2-0	8-0	7-0	6-0	0-0	5-1	8-0	4-1	1-0	4-0	4-0	6-0	2-0	3-2	3-0	7-0	3-3	4-1	4-2	5-2	3-0	6-0
3 Ash Utd	2-2	3-5		3-0	4-0	3-1	3-2	0-1	3-1	4-0	4-3	3-0	5-0	1-1	2-2	1-0	0-0	1-3	4-0	3-3	3-3	0-3	3-1	4-2
4 Bedfont	2-1	1-6	3-3		2-4	1-1	0-0	3-0	4-1	5-0	1-1	2-0	1-0	3-4	2-1	4-1	3-0	3-1	2-1	1-1	2-0	1-1	3-1	2-1
5 Ches Utd	0-6	0-9	1-5	3-2		0-3	0-2	4-2	5-2	2-1	1-2	2-2	0-1	1-3	1-3	1-2	0-0	2-2	0-3	3-5	1-5	1-2	0-0	0-8
6 Ches&Ho	1-1	3-5	2-1	0-3	3-0		1-2	1-3	3-0	5-0	0-0	1-1	0-1	3-3	2-0	3-1	2-4	1-2	5-3	1-2	1-1	2-1	3-2	2-0
7 Chipstead	0-0	0-3	1-1	1-3	7-0	2-3		1-0	4-0	2-1	1-3	4-0	3-2	2-0	6-0	3-1	2-4	7-4	1-2	3-4	2-0	1-2	1-1	1-0
8 Cobham	3-2	0-4	2-1	0-2	4-0	0-4	1-1		3-0	1-0	3-2	1-3	2-4	1-3	1-1	0-0	3-0	2-1	0-1	2-5	1-9	0-6	0-0	2-2
9 Cove	0-2	0-2	1-3	0-7	2-5	0-2	0-1	1-2		4-1	0-2	0-0	1-4	1-2	0-0	1-2	2-1	2-4	1-4	1-1	0-2	1-6	2-1	2-4
10 Farnham	1-4	0-4	2-3	3-4	2-1	1-1	0-2	1-3	5-3		2-4	2-1	0-1	2-1	1-0	0-1	2-1	1-1	0-1	0-2	0-5	1-7	1-4	3-1
11 Feltham	0-2	0-2	1-2	0-3	4-0	1-0	0-3	4-1	4-4	3-0		6-0	0-2	9-0	0-3	1-1	6-0	1-1	0-2	2-4	0-1	2-1	0-0	5-0
12 Frimley	1-2	1-3	2-2	0-2	2-1	1-4	1-2	4-1	1-0	0-0	0-2		0-2	0-5	0-0	2-4	1-0	3-2	1-3	0-4	1-2	1-7	1-1	3-3
13 Godalming	0-2	1-4	1-1	1-0	0-0	2-1	1-2	4-1	1-2	3-0	0-1	3-2		5-0	0-2	0-0	1-0	3-6	2-4	1-0	0-1	0-3	4-0	4-1
14 Hartley	1-3	0-2	0-3	1-1	3-1	0-3	1-2	3-0	1-3	2-1	3-1	1-1	2-1		4-1	0-5	4-2	5-1	0-2	1-2	3-7	1-5	3-2	0-1
15 Horley	1-3	2-4	0-5	0-2	4-2	1-7	1-2	0-0	3-0	3-1	0-1	5-2	0-1	7-1		0-2	2-3	1-4	2-3	0-2	2-2	2-3	1-2	4-1
16 Merstham	0-4	0-6	1-0	2-2	1-0	1-1	0-1	2-1	1-2	2-0	1-0	0-1	0-2	4-2	0-0		1-2	3-1	0-1	1-3	1-2	2-2	3-1	3-2
17 N.Greenf.	0-3	1-2	1-4	1-1	4-2	5-1	3-1	2-0	3-1	4-0	1-0	5-2	0-0	2-3	6-2	3-5		2-1	0-1	0-5	1-5	0-4	5-1	3-4
18 Raynes PV	0-1	2-3	0-1	0-3	4-1	1-0	1-3	3-3	3-1	1-1	1-2	3-0	1-1	0-1	0-3	0-1	2-4		0-1	1-1	3-2	1-2	2-3	0-0
19 Reading	1-1	0-2	2-1	0-1	1-1	3-1	1-0	3-0	5-1	3-0	0-2	1-0	2-2	0-0	0-0	1-2	2-1	2-1		1-1	1-0	1-1	4-0	1-0
20 Sandhurst	1-1	2-2	4-2	2-2	2-1	0-2	0-3	4-1	8-0	3-1	3-0	3-1	2-0	2-3	2-0	0-0	0-0	3-2	1-2		0-4	1-1	3-1	4-0
21 Southall	1-1	0-4	5-2	1-2	2-0	2-3	1-0	3-1	3-0	3-0	5-0	3-1	2-0	4-1	5-0	0-1	4-0	2-0	0-0	1-3		5-1	3-2	6-0
22 Walton C	0-2	0-3	1-1	1-1	4-0	3-1	3-2	5-1	1-3	5-1	2-1	2-4	2-2	2-0	4-2	2-0	0-2	1-1	1-1	3-2	0-2		4-0	2-0
23 Westfield	0-3	0-3	0-1	2-1	3-0	0-7	0-3	4-1	1-1	0-2	3-1	2-2	0-0	0-0	0-1	1-2	2-2	0-1	0-1	0-2	4-1	2-0		2-0
24 Withdean	3-1	2-4	0-1	0-1	1-3	1-3	1-2	1-1	7-3	5-3	0-4	1-2	0-0	3-3	1-5	1-1	0-2	2-1	2-4	0-2	0-3	1-4	0-3	

FINAL LEAGUE TABLE 2003-04

PREMIER DIVISION	P	W	D	L	F	A	Pts
1. AFC Guildford	34	26	5	3	98	26	83
2. Colliers Wood United	34	25	3	6	93	27	78
3. Bookham (+7pts)	34	20	8	6	73	35	75
4. Hersham RBL	34	20	4	10	76	37	64
5. Coney Hall	34	19	7	8	81	43	64
6. Merrow	34	19	6	9	76	50	63
7. Farleigh Rovers	34	16	11	7	56	32	59
8. Staines Lammas (-1 pt)	34	16	6	12	80	49	53
9. Worcester Park	34	17	2	15	63	53	53
10. Ditton	34	15	6	13	82	66	51
11. Monotype	34	13	7	14	59	68	46
12. Seelec Delta (-4 pts)	34	12	9	13	60	57	41
13. Crescent Rovers	34	12	4	18	51	71	40
14. Shottermill/Haslemere	34	9	5	20	48	67	32
15. Netherne Village	34	9	4	21	40	72	31
16. Chobham & Ottershaw	34	4	6	24	26	105	18
17. Sheerwater (-3 pts)	34	3	4	27	40	120	10
18. Cranleigh (+3 pts)	34	2	1	31	29	153	10

DIVISIION ONE	1	2	3	4	5	6	7	8	9	10	11	12	13	14	15	16	17	18
1 AFC Guildford		2-1	4-0	2-0	1-0	9-0	4-0	2-1	3-0	1-0	1-0	5-1	1-0	1-0	7-0	1-0	2-1	7-2
2 Bookham	1-4		1-0	0-2	3-2	4-0	3-0	3-2	3-0	1-0	1-1	4-0	3-0	2-2	0-0	4-2	1-0	3-0
3 Chobham & Ottershaw	1-3	1-1		2-1	1-5	3-1	0-2	0-2	0-0	0-9	2-2	1-5	3-2	1-1	3-2	1-1	0-4	0-3
4 Colliers Wood United	2-1	3-0	8-0		2-1	6-0	1-2	5-1	1-1	3-0	0-1	4-3	5-0	1-1	4-1	5-0	3-1	0-1
5 Coney Hall	1-1	2-2	5-0	0-2		9-0	3-1	3-1	1-1	0-1	4-3	1-1	2-1	5-1	4-2	2-1	3-2	2-1
6 Cranleigh	2-8	0-3	2-0	2-7	2-4		0-1	0-5	0-3	0-6	0-1	2-6	1-4	1-7	3-3	2-1	3-4	0-2
7 Crescent Rovers	0-3	2-2	0-0	1-2	1-1	4-2		2-1	0-2	1-3	1-4	2-0	0-1	2-1	4-2	2-0	1-6	4-3
8 Ditton	2-3	0-3	4-1	1-3	1-5	7-0	5-2		2-2	3-4	4-0	0-0	5-0	1-1	4-0	1-0	1-1	2-1
9 Farleigh Rovers	2-2	1-2	2-1	0-0	0-1	6-0	3-0	2-2		1-1	0-0	4-0	3-1	2-1	2-0	1-1	1-0	0-2
10 Hersham RBL	0-0	0-1	1-0	0-3	2-2	11-0	1-0	3-1	0-3		3-2	1-2	4-1	2-0	3-0	3-0	4-0	1-4
11 Merrow	2-1	1-1	2-1	1-3	0-1	4-2	3-3	6-1	1-3	1-2		2-1	3-1	3-1	5-2	2-0	4-3	0-0
12 Monotype	3-3	1-2	5-2	2-1	1-4	2-0	1-0	2-5	0-2	2-2	2-4		2-0	2-1	2-1	1-1	2-4	0-0
13 Netherne Village	0-3	0-3	5-0	0-6	2-1	2-0	1-3	1-3	1-2	1-3	0-1	1-0		1-1	3-3	1-2	2-1	0-1
14 Seelec Delta	0-0	3-2	6-0	0-1	1-2	1-0	3-1	2-2	0-0	2-0	2-9	4-1	2-1		2-4	3-1	1-4	1-3
15 Sheerwater	2-4	1-10	4-0	0-2	0-3	6-2	1-4	1-5	0-2	0-3	0-3	1-3	1-2	1-3		0-5	1-1	0-7
16 Shottermill & Haslemer	0-6	2-1	4-0	1-2	2-2	2-1	4-2	2-4	2-0	0-1	1-3	1-2	3-3	1-3	5-0		0-2	2-1
17 Staines Lammas	1-3	0-0	4-1	1-4	2-0	7-0	3-2	4-0	2-1	2-0	0-1	1-1	1-1	0-0	7-0	4-1		1-4
18 Worcester Park	1-0	1-2	4-1	0-1	1-0	5-1	2-1	2-3	2-4	0-2	3-1	2-3	0-1	0-3	3-1	1-0	1-6	

LEAGUE CUP

FIRST ROUND

AFC Guildford	v	Godalming & Guildford	0-2
(at Godalming & Guildford)			
Bedfont	v	Feltham	1-0
Chessington Utd	v	Withdean	1-2
Cobham	v	Bookham	1-0
Crescent Rovers	v	Coney Hall	0-4
Hartley Wintney	v	Staines Lammas	4-2
Merrow	v	Chessington & Hook United	0-3
(Chessington & Hook United expelled)			
Merstham	v	AFC Wimbledon	1-5
(at AFC Wimbledon)			
Netherne	v	Monotype	0-2
Raynes Park Vale	v	Farleigh	6-2

SECOND ROUND

AFC Wallingford	v	Ash United	1-1* 4-1p
AFC Wimbledon	v	Walton Cas.	5-4
Bedfont	v	Worcester Park	3-1
Cobham	v	Withdean	6-0
Cove	v	Hersham RBL	4-0
Ditton	v	Hartley Wintney	4-1
Farnham Town	v	Westfield	3-5
Godalming & Guildford	v	Chobham & Ottershaw	2-1
Horley	v	Frimley Green	4-2
Monotype	v	Colliers Wood	1-5*
Raynes Park Vale	v	Merrow	5-1
Reading Town	v	Shottermill & Haslemere	2-0
Sandhurst Town	v	Coney Hall	1-3
Seelec Delta	v	North Greenford United	1-1*2-3p
Sheerwater	v	Chipstead	1-2*
Southall	v	Cranleigh	12-0

THIRD ROUND

Bedfont	v	Cobham	0-1
Chipstead	v	AFC Wimbledon	1-3
Cove	v	AFC Wallingford	0-4
Ditton	v	North Greenford United	1-3*
Godalming & Guildford	v	Raynes Park Vale	4-4* 4-5p
Horley Town	v	Colliers Wood United	0-2
Reading Town	v	Coney Hall	0-2
Southall	v	Westfield	3-0

QUARTER-FINALS

AFC Wallingford	v	Colliers Wood United	2-1
AFC Wimbledon	v	Raynes Park Vale	5-0
North Greenford U.	v	Cobham	5-1
Southall	v	Coney Hall	1-6

SEMI-FINALS

Coney Hall	v	AFC Wimbledon	0-5
North Greenford U.	v	AFC Wallingford	3-2

THE FINAL (30th April at Woking)

North Greenford U	v	AFC Wimbledon	1-4

Former Wimbledon player Laurie Sanchez presents AFC Wimbledon's Matt Everhard with the 'Man of the Match' award for his performance during their 4-1 win over North Greenford United in the League Cup final.

Photo: Eric Marsh.

AFC GUILDFORD

Secretary: Paul Milton, 38 South Lane, Ash, Aldershot, Hampshire GU12 6NG
Tel Nos: 01252 658473 (H) 07803 169499 (M)
email: paul.x.milton2baesystems.com

Ground: Snoxall Playing Fields, Knowle Lane, Cranleigh, Surrey.
Tel No: 01483 275925
Nearest Railway Station: Guildford **Bus** Arriva 56,63

FACT FILE

Formed: 1996
Colours: Red & white/black/black

CLUB PERSONNEL
Chairman: Jim Betts
Tel Nos: 01483 429193 (H) 07885 903371 (M)

Match Secretary: Tony Shaw
01483 472248 (H) 07810 125802 (M)

AFC WALLINGFORD

Secretary: Richard may, 27 Chiltern Crescent, Wallingford, Oxon OX100PG
Tel Nos: 01491 837391 (H) 01491 823612 (W) 07748 828574(M)
Ground: Wallingford Sports Park, Hithercroft Road,Wallingford,Oxon.(Tel:01491 835044
Directions : Nearest Railway station: Cholsey & Moulsford. Bus - Thames Transit.
Capacity: 1,500 Cover: 100 Seats: 40 Floodlights: Yes
Clubhouse: Open evenings 7.30-11.00, Sat & Sun Tea & snacks available 01491 835044
HONOURS: Chiltonian Prem Lge 97-98; Bon Accord Trophy 95-96 Combined Counties League Premier Division Champions 01-02,Runners Up 2000-01, Berks & Bucks Senior Trophy : Winners 01-02 Finalists 2000-01, North Bucks Nairne Paul Cup Winners 2000-01
RECORDS: **Attendance:** 280 v Reading Town **Goalscorer:** Carl Henry 62, 97-98
In Career: Steve Wood 130 92-98 **Appearances**: Anthony Hill 243
PREVIOUS: **Leagues:** Chiltonian Lge 95-98

FACT FILE
Founded: 1995
Colours: Red & black hoops/black/red & black
Change colours: Blue & white
Midweek matchday: Tuesday
Programme: 20 pages; price 50p
Editor: Andy Ham (01491 837608)

CLUB PERSONNEL
President: Ken Lester
Chairman: Lindsay Townsend
Tel: 01491 839103 (H)
Match Secretary: G Lee
21 Orchard Close, Brightwell, Wallingford, Oxon. Tel: 01491 836921 (H)
Manager: Dave Crowdy

ASH UNITED

Secretary: James Avenell, 82 Ewins Close,Ash,Aldershot, Hants. GU12 6SB
Tel/FAX No: 01252 321528
Email: garethwatmore@hotmail.com
Ground: Youngs Drive, off Shawfield Rd, Ash, Nr Aldershot Tel: 01252 745757
Directions: A323 towards Ash, left into Shawfield Rd, left into Youngs Drive
1 mile from both Ash and Ash Vale BR stations. Bus - Stagecoach 20A, 550
Capacity: 1,500 Seats: None Cover: Yes Floodlights: Yes
HONOURS: Prem Chall Cup 97-98; Comb Co Lge 81-2, 86-7, 98-99; Aldershot Sen Cup 98-99,01-02
CLUB RECORDS **Attendance;**914 v AFC Wimbledon .League 2002-2003
Goalscorer: Shaun Mitchell 44 **Appearances:** Tommy Burton 540
BEST SEASON **FA Cup:** 2nd Qual Rd v Walton & Hersham 98-99
FA Vase: 4th Rd v Tiverton Town 98-99 & v Tow Law 2001-02
PREVIOUS **Ground:** Ash Common Rec. 70-71 **Leagues:** Surrey Snr, Aldershot Snr.

FACT FILE
Founded: 1911
Colours: Green with red trim/green/red
Change colours: All blue
Midweek Matchday: Tuesday
Prog: 36 pages, £1.00 Editor: Secretary

CLUB PERSONNEL
Pres; Paul Murray Chairman: Robert J Atkins
Vice-Chairman: Jerry Kerrigan
Press Off: Gareth Watmore (07739 657994)
Manager: TerryEames

2003-2004
Top Scorer: James BLason 24
Player of the Year: Paul Bonner

BEDFONT

Secretar Les King, 14 Harlequin Close, Isleworth, Middlesex. TW7 7LA
Tel No: 0208 894 5525 (H) 0208 392 3021 (W)
Ground: The Orchard, Hatton Rd, Bedfont, Middx. Tel: 0208 8907264
Directions: Turn down Faggs Rd opposite Hatton Cross (Picadilly Line) station on Great South Western Rd (A30), then sharp right into Hatton Rd. Ground opposite Duke of Wellington pub. Bus - Westlink 203
Capacity:2,000 Seats: 100 Cover: 50 Floodlights: Yes Clubhouse: Yes
HONOURS Comb. Co's Chal. Vase 92-93 (Res. Div R-up 88-89, Res. Cup R-up 89-90, Grant McClennan Yth Cup 91-92), Middx Lg 73-74 76-77 (Div 1 (Res) & Div 1 Cup 71-72 78-79 79-80, Surrey Prem. Lg 84-85 86-87, Middx I'mediate Cup 69-70 76-77, Inter. Contois Tour. 1992, Liege Euromann Tour. 89, Harold Clayton Cup 90-91, Hounslow & Dist. Div 1 (Res) 86-87
PREVIOUS **Names:** Bedfont Inst.(1900), Bedfont Rangers(1950) & Fairholme Utd(1953) merged 1968. Club later merged with Interharvester(1973) & Bedfont Eagles(1988). **Ground:** Bedfont Rec.

FACT FILE
Founded: 1968
Colours: Yellow & blue stripes/blue/blue
Change colours: All red or White/navy/navy
Midweek matches: Tuesday
Programme: 20 pages, 50p. Editors: Les King (020 8891 1985)

CLUB PERSONNEL
President: Roger Cooper
Chairman: Mick Carroll
Manager: John Morris
Coach: Ron Griffin
Asst. Man.: Mark Wilson

CHESSINGTON & HOOK UNITED

Secretary: Alan Warwick, 38 Hartfield Road, Chessington, Surrey. KT9 2PW
Tel:020 8397 1843(H)

Ground: Chalky Lane, Chessington, Surrey. Tel: 01372 745777

Directions: Turn off A243 into Chalky Lane opposite Chessington World of Adventure Theme Park Railway - Chessington South. Bus - London Transport 71.

Floodlights: Yes

HONOURS: Combined Counties Lge Prem Cup R-up 97-98, Surrey County Lge Prem Div R-up 96-97, Div 1 70-71, Combination Cup 2001-02

PREVIOUS **Leagues:** Middx Lge 68-69, Surrey County 69-72, Home Counties 72-78 Comb Co 78-81, Surrey Prem, Surrey Comb, Surrey Prem.

2003-2004 Player of the Season: Mark Russell Top Goalscorer: Neil Wicks

FACT FILE
Founded: 1968
Colours: All blue
Change colours: Yellow/black/yellow or Red and Black
Midweek Matchday:
Programme: Yes Price: £1.00

CLUB PERSONNEL
President: Ray Hall Chairman: Graham Ellis
63 Stormont Way, Chessington, Surrey. KT9 2QW
Tel: 020 8391 4829(H)
Manager: Paul Ellis 020 8397 8499 (H)
Captain: Tom Duffell

CHESSINGTON UNITED

Secretary: John Carleton, 22 Dawson Road, Kingston upon Thames, Surrey KT1 3AT
Tel No: 0208546 8266 & 0208241 8461 FAX: 0208241 8461
Mobile: 07785 986943
Email: carleton-john@ hotmail.com

Ground: Fetcham Park, off Randalls Road,Leatherd, Surrey KT22 0AQ
Tel No: 01372 370208

Directions: .
Nearest B.R. Leatherhead
Buses: London Country 465 & 479

FACT FILE
Formed:
Colours: All white
Change Colours: All Blue

Programme: Price: Pages:
Editor:

CLUB PERSONNEL

Chairman/Secretary:Terry Parmenter
90 Somerset Avenue,Chessington,Surrey.
Tel No: 02028287 5643 or 07940387041
terryparmenter@blueyonder.co.uk

Chessington United - Back Row (L-R): Joshua Smith, Danny Greenleaf, Richard Powell, Wayne Clifton, Salluie Matusa, Ryan Adams.
Front Row: Robbie Burns, David Whitehead, Niko Maroushaz, Adam McCullagh, Mike Green.
Photo: Alan Coomes.

CHIPSTEAD

Secretary: Geoff Corner, 20 Sunnymede Avenue, Carshalton Beeches, Surrey SM54JF Tel: 0181 642 0827 (H)

Ground: High Road, Chipstead, Surrey. Tel: 01737 553250

Directions: Brighton Road northbound, left into Church Lane, left into HogcrossLane, right High Road. 1 1/2/ miles from Chipstead (BR). Bus -London County 405, 407

Capacity: 2,000 **Seats:** 30 **Cover:** 100 **Floodlights**: Yes

HONOURS Surrey Premier Lg R-up 82-83 83-84 85-86 (Lg Cup 82-83 84-85 85-86), Combined Co's Lg 89-90 (R-up 90-91 92-93, Lg Cup 86-87 90-91 92-93, Elite Class Cup R-up 89-90, Reserve Section Cup 92-93)

BEST SEASON **FA Cup:** 1998-99 **FA Vase:** 1998-99

CLUB RECORDS **Attendance:**1,770

Goalscorer: Mick Nolan 124 Appearances:

PREVIOUS **Leagues:** Surrey Intermediate 62-82; Surrey Premier 82-86

FACT FILE

Founded: 1906 Nickname: Chips

Colours: Green & white/black/black

Change colours: All Red

Midweek matchday: Tuesday

Programme: 36 pages Price: 50p

Editor:Terry Antell

CLUB PERSONNEL

President: Dave Argent

Chairman: Don.Faircloth,156 St Andrews Rd, Coulsdon,Surrey CR5 3HF(0208 668 8348)

Manager: Perry Gough

2003-2004

Captain & P.o.Y.: Darrel Teesdale

Top Scorer: Mick Nolan

COBHAM

Secretary: Ken Reed, 29 Waterer Gardens,Tadworth, Surrey KT20 5PS (01737 352641)

Ground: Leg O'Mutton Field, Anvil Lane, Downside Bridge Rd, Cobham, Surrey Tel: 01932 865959

Directions: A3 turnoff A245, A307 (Portsmouth) towards Leatherhead, right intoBetween Streets, rt into Downside Rd then rt opposite car park. Cobham & StokeD'Abernon (BR) 2 miles. Bus - Green Line 715, London Country 501, 513

Capacity: 2,000 Seats: None Cover: Yes Floodlights: Yes Club Shop: No Clubhouse: Yes

HONOURS Combined Co's Lge Cup 01-02, League R-Up: 98-99 Reserves Lge (3)

BEST SEASON **FA Cup:** 1st Q 02-03 **FA Vase:** 1998-99 3rd Rd.

CLUB RECORDS **Attendance:** 2,000 v Showbiz XI, charity game 1975

PREVIOUS **League:** Surrey Senior **Grounds:** Cobham Rec

FACT FILE

Founded: 1892

Nickname: Hammers

Sponsor:Prestege Couriers

Colours: Red & Black Hoops /black/black

Change colours:All white

Midweek matchday: Tuesday

Programme: Yes

CLUB PERSONNEL

Chairman: Chris Woolston

President: David Robinson

Manager: Matt Alexander

Coach: Ian Savage

Physio: C Bird

COLLIERS WOOD UNITED

Secretary: Tony Hurrell, 1 Inglewood, Pixton Way, Forestdale, Croydon, Surrey Tel: 0208 651 3259 (h) 0208 942 8962 (w) 07956 983947 (m)

Ground: Croydon FC, Croydon Sports Arena, Albert Road, South Norwood, SE25 4QL Tel: 0208 654 3462

Directions: From Portland Rd turn down either Belmont Rd or Grasmere Rd. and the Stadium is off Albert Rd inn South Norwood.Train to East Croydon or Norwood Junction, then bus 197 to eitherBelmont or Dundee Road. Walk down either - ground at bottom.2 mins walk fromArena tram stop (Croydon Tram Link)

Capacity: 6,000 **Cover:** 1,000 **Seats**: 450 **Floodlights**: Yes

Clubhouse: Open every evening and lunchtime, snacks available. Dancing & discos, Lounge bar available for private hire **Club Shop:** Yes

FACT FILE

Founded: 1874

Nickname: The 'Woods'

Colours: Blue & black/black/black

CLUB PERSONNEL

Chairman: John Stanton

President: Ron Palmer

COVE

Secretary: Graham Brown, 6 Longfield Close,Haley Estate, Farnborough. GU14 8HQ Tel: 01252 650920 - Club Email: covefc1897@aol.com

Ground: Oak farm Fields,7 Squirrels Lane, Farnborough, Hants GU14 8PB. Tel.: 01252 543615

Directions: Farnborough (BR) 2 miles; right into Union Street, right at lights into Prospect Rd, left into West Heath Rd, right into Romayne Close and follow signs to Cove FC. Or, M3 jct 4, follow A325 signed Aldershot & Farnham, right into Prospect Rd. (signed Cove FC & Farnborough Town FC), then as above

Capacity: 3,500 Seats: 75 Cover: 475 Floodlights: Yes Club Shop: No

Clubhouse: Mon-Fri 7-11, Sat 12-11, Sunday 12-3 & 7-11. Hot food on matchdays

HONOURS: Surrey I'mediate Lg; Surrey Prem. Lg x5, R-up x3, Lg Cup x3, Res.Section x4 ,R-up x4, Res. Cup x2; Combined Co's Lg Cup 81-82; Hants Lg Div 3, Div 4, Div 2 R-up; Aldershot - Snr Cup x5, R-up, Snr Shield x4, Snr Lg, Div 2x3, Div 2 Cup, Div 4Cup

PREVIOUS Leagues: Aldershot Jnr; Aldershot I'mediate 45-48; Surrey I'mediate 48-71; Surrey Snr 71-73; Hants 74-81; Combined Counties 81-90 &95-01; Isthmian 90-95;

CLUB RECORDS **Attendance:** 1,798 v Aldershot, Isthmian Lg Div 3, 1/5/93

BEST SEASON **FA Cup**: 2nd Rd 2000-01 **FA Vase:** 5th Rd 00-01 2-3 v Chippenham Tn. (H)

FACT FILE

Founded: 1897

Sponsors: Sunnyside Removals

Colours: Yellow & black stripes/yellow/yellow

Change colours: Red & white stripes/red/red

Midweek Matches: Tuesday

Reserves' League: Comb. Cos. 1st Div

Programme: 30 pages, 50p

Editor: Graham Brown (01252 650920)

CLUB PERSONNEL

Chairman: P.Wentworth

President: Ron Brown

FARNHAM TOWN

Secretary: CharlieWhite,37 Upper Way, Farnham, Surrey GU9 8RL Tel No: 01252 726303 (H)
Ground: Memorial Ground, West Street, Farnham, Surrey (01252 715305)

Directions: From A31, direction Winchester, take 2nd turning into town at Coxbridge roundabout. Follow West Street until you come to new mini roundabout - the Memorial Ground is on the right.

Capacity: 2,000 Seats: 30 Cover: 150 Floodlights: Yes
Clubhouse: Open every evening and match daysClub Shop: No

HONOURS Combined Counties Lg 90-91 91-92, Challenge Cup Prem Div 95-96, Challenge Tphy 91-92 (R-up 89-90).
CLUB RECORDS **Attendance:** 1,138 v A.F.C.Wimbledon, League 2002-2003
PREVIOUS **Leagues:** Surrey Intermediate; Surrey Snr 47-71: Spartan 71-75: London Spartan 75-80: Combined Counties 80-92.
BEST SEASON **FA Cup:** Never past Qualifying Rounds

FACT FILE
Founded: 1921 Nickname: The Town
Sponsors:T.B.A.
Colours: Claret & blue stripes/white/sky blue
Change: All Yellow
Midweek Matchday: Tuesday
Reserve League: Comb Counties Res Div
Programme: 32 pages 50p
Editor: T,B,A,

CLUB PERSONNEL
Chairman: Keith Haskell
President; Paul Cooper
Press Officer: Charlie White
Manager: Andy Nunn
Asst Manager: Dave Ward
Coach: Simon Musslewhite

FELTHAM

Secretary: John Cronk,Flat 8 Wyvern Court, 24 Gordon Rd, Ashford, Middsx TW15 3EZ
Tel: 01784 243122 (H) 0208 839 2104 (B) Website: http://www.felthamfc.freeserve.co.uk/
Ground: Feltham Arena(All weather surface), Shakespeare Ave., Feltham, Middx.Tel: 0208 890 6164 (club), 0208 890 6905 (ground)
Directions: BR to Feltham & 5 mins walk thro' Glebelands Park. Buses 90, 285,117, 237, H24 or H25 to Feltham station, or 116 to top of Shakespeare Ave. By car: M3, M4, A312 Staines road towards Bedfont, 2nd left is Shakespeare Ave
Capacity: 10,000 Seats: 650 Cover: 1,500 Floodlights: Yes
Clubhouse: Open 7 days a week. 2 bars, dancehall available for hire Club Shop: No
HONOURS Surrey Snr Lg R-up 65-66 (Lg Cup 65-66, Charity Cup 63-64 65-66),Southern Comb. Cup(2)(R-up(2)), Middx Summer Cup, Isthmian Div 2 80-81, Comb.Cos. Lge Co. 96-97
PREVIOUS **Leagues:** Feltham: West Middx Sunday; Staines & Dist.; Hounslow & Dist.; Surrey Snr 63-68; Spartan 68-73; Athenian 74-77; Isthmian 78-95
CLUB RECORDS **Attendance:** 1,9 38 v Hampton,Middlesex Senior Cup 1968
Goalscorer: Paul Clarke 130 **Appearances:** Paul Clarke 326
BEST SEASON **FA Cup:** 3rd Qual.Rd.77-78, 1-4 v Tilbury; 82-83, 0-1 v Chesham U

FACT FILE
Founded: 1946 Sponsors: Feltham first
Colours: Royal blue & white halves/blue/blue
Change colours: Red /White or Blue/White
Midweek Matches: Wednesday
Programme: 20 pages, 50p
Editor:Chris Thompso
Email: cjthompson-uk@yahoo.co.uk

CLUB PERSONNEL
Chairman: Brian Barry
Prsident/Patron: Andy Lonsdale
Press Officer: Secretary
Managers: Sammy Boyd & Dave Patience
Players progressing:Rachid Harkouk,Tony Witter(CrystalP) Andy Pape (QPR), Pat Gavin (Gillingham) Bobby Wilson (Brentford)

FRIMLEY GREEN

Secretary: Mark O'Grady, 8 Rokes Place, Yateley, Hants. GU46 6FF
Tel: 01252 879883 (H) 01923 234300 (B) 07812 026390 (M)
email: mogradyuk@yahoo.co.uk

Ground: Frimley Green Recretarion Ground, Frimley Green Road, Frimley Green, Camberley, Surrey GU16 Tel: 01252 835089

Travel: Nearest railway station: Frimley or Farnborough (North)
Bus: Stagecoach, Hants & Surrey 49, 50 & 530

FACT FILE
Founded: 1919
Colours: Blue & white halves/white/blueChange

CLUB PERSONNEL
President: Paul Grace
Chairman: Craig Fennell
Tel: 01252 317325 (H) 07831 248260 (M)

2003-2004
Player of the Year: Tom Tyler
Top Scorer: Scott Brighty

GODALMING & GUILDFORD

Secretary: Eddie Russell, 31 Harts Gardens, Guildford, Surrey GU2 9QB. 01483 535287 (H & B)

Ground: Weycourt, Meadrow, Godalming, Surrey (01483 417520)
Directions: A3100 from Guildford - past Out & About Hotel on left, then 'Save' petrol station on right, then 1st right 50 yards on. From Godalming on A3100, grd on left by Leathern Bottle pub. Three quarters of a mile from Farncombe BR station

Capacity: 3,000 Seats: 200 Cover: 200 Floodlights: Yes Club Shop: No
Clubhouse: Open Tues, Thurs eves, matchdays. Hot & cold snacks available
HONOURS Combined Co's Lg 83-84, Lge Chall. Trophy 82-83, Res Lge 95-96 96-97, Res Chall Cup 92-93 97-98, Chall Shield 96-97: Southern Comb Chall Cup 97-98
PREVIOUS **Leagues:** Guildford & Dist 50-71; Surrey Intermediate 71-78; Surrey Co. Senior 78-79
RECORDS **Attendance:** 1,305 v A.F.C. Wimbledon 5.10.02
Goalscorer: Sean Gorman 127 **Appearances:** Paul Monger 356
BEST SEASON FA Cup: 2nd Q.Rd. **FA Vase:** 2nd Rd.
Players progressing: John Humphreys (MIllwall)

FACT FILE
Founded: 1950 Nickname: The Gees
Colours: Yellow/green/green
Change colours: Blue & white/white/blue.
Midweek matchday: Tuesday Prog Yes

CLUB PERSONNEL
Chairperson: Jane Phillips
Life President: Bill Kyte
Press Officer: Secretary
Manager: Roger Steer
Asst Managers: Mick Wollen
Coach: Dave Ward Physio: Jan Eaton

HARTLEY WINTNEY

Secretary: Gerry Wykes, 140A Middlemoor Road, Frimley, Camberley, Surrey
Ground: Memorial Playing Fields, Green Lane, Hartley Wintney, Hants
Tel: 01252 843586
Directions: A30 west through Camberley, left at parade of shops at beginning of village then sharp right - ground on right. Or from M3 Jct 4A 6 miles to Green Lane
Two miles from Winchfield (BR)
Buses: Stagecoach 200, Bee Line 111, 112
Capacity: 2,000 Seats: None Cover: Yes Floodlights: Yes
HONOURS: Aldershot Senior League winners: 73-74,74-75,75-76. Alderhot Senior Cup Winners 76-77,80-81 CoCo.League Winners 82-83,R-up 80-81
BEST SEASON **FA Cup:** 1st Qualifyong Round **FA Vase:** 3rd Rd 1992-93
PREVIOUS **Leagues:** Basingstoke/ Aldershot

ACT FILE
Founded: 1897
Nickname: The Row
Colours: Orange & black/black/black
Change colours: White/orange/white
Midweek matchday: Tuesday
Programme: Yes

CLUB PERSONNEL
Chairman: Kevin Donegan
Vice Chairman: Luke Mullen
President: W A Mitchell
Treasurer: Nick FlintPress Officer: Luke Mullen
(07860 729608 (M)

HORLEY

Secretary: Mrs Maureen Turner, 81 Chequers Drive, Horley, Syrrey RH6 8DX
Tel No: 01293 406783

Match Secretary: Victoria Burtenshaw Tel No: 01293 781362

Ground: The New Defence, Court Lodge Road, Horley, Surrey RH6 8RS
Tel : 01293 406783
Nearest Railway Station: Horley **Bus:** 100, 526

FACT FILE

Formed:1896
Colours: Claret/Blue/Blue

CLUB PERSONNEL

Chairman: Graham McLaren
Tel Nos: 01293 416822 (H) 07801 319162 (M)

Press Officer:Jim Bletchley
Tel Nos: 01293 773297 (H) 07714 837568 (M)

MERSTHAM

Secretary: Richard Baxter, 2 Wood Street, Merstham, Surrey. RH1 3PF
Tel: 01737 645748 (H) 01293 450809 (B) Email: the.baxters@virgin.net
Ground: Merstham Rec., Weldon Way, Merstham, Redhill, Surrey RH1 3QB (01737 644046)
Directions: Leave Merstham village (A23) by School Hill, take 5th right (WeldonWay), clubhouse and car park 100m on right. 10 mins walk from Merstham (BR);down School Hill, under railway bridge, then 5th turning on right into WeldonWay. Bu98-99s - London Country 430, 432 & 435
Capacity: 2,500 Seats: 100 Cover: 100 Floodlights: Yes Club Shop: No
Clubhouse: Open p.m. Mon-Fri and matchdays All day Sat & Sun. Snacks available.
HONOURS Combined Co's Lg R-up 87-88 89-90 (Elite Class Cup 89-90 (R-up 90-91), Res. Sect. 90-91), Spartan Lg 79-89 (Lg Cup 79-80), Surrey Snr Lg 71-72, Surrey Snr Char. Cup 79-80, E. Surrey Char. Cup 80-8 98-99, Surrey I'mediate Lg 52-3.Fair Play & Prog Awards 01-02
CLUB RECORDS **Attendance:** 1,587 v AFC Wimbledon 9.11.02
BEST SEASON **FA Cup:** 3rd Q Rd **FA Vase:** 4th Rd.
PREVIOUS **Leagues:** Redhill & Dist; Surrey Co.S.E. Intermediate; Surrey Snr 64-78; London Spartan 78-85 **Grounds:**None

FACT FILE
Founded: 1892
Club Sponsors: The Tiling Company
Colours: Amber & black stripes/black/amber
Change colours:White,navy, red.
Midweek matches: Tuesday/Thursday
Programme: Yes Editor:Mrs S Fish

CLUB PERSONNEL
Chairman:Ted Hickman President: Bill Lawton
Press Officer: Roger Peerless
Manager: Mick Sullivan
Ass.Manager: Rees Williams
2003-2004 P.o.Y.: Chris Boulter
Top Scorer: Marc Rollings
2004-2005 Captain: Shane Traynor

NORTH GREENFORD UNITED

Secretary: Mrs B Bivens, 1 The Green, sarratt, Hertfordshire WD3 6AY
Tel: 01923 270057 (H & Fax)
Ground: Berkeley Fields, Berkeley Avenue, Greenford, Middlesex UB6
Tel: 0208 422 8923

Travel: Nearest railway station: Greenford (Central Line) & Sudbury Hill (Piccadilly)
Bus: Metro Link 92

FACT FILE
Founded: 1944
Colours: Blue & white/blue/blue

CLUB PERSONNEL
President: John Bignell
Chairman: Mick Hardwick
Tel: 0208 423 0702 (H)
Press Secretary: John Bivens
Tel No: 01923 270057
2003-2004
P.o.Y.: Nelto Cornwall
Top Scorer: Paul reed
2004-2005 Captain: James Perrie

RAYNES PARK VALE

Secretary: Paul Armour, 9 Banstead Road, East Ewell, Surrey KT17 3EP
Tel:07980 914211 (M) Fax: 0207 492 1132
e-mail: paul.armour2bt.com

Ground: Prince George's Playing Field, Raynes Park. SW20 9NB Tel: 07714 339747
Capacity: 2,000 Covered Seating: 200 Covered Standing: 100 Floodlights: Yes

Directions: Bus - London Transport 163 & 152
Nearest railway station - Raynes Park.

HONOURS: Div 1 Champions 2002-03 Combined Counties Lg: Div 1 Cup R-up 02-03, Div 1 Challenge Shield 02-03

Club Records Attendance: 1,871 v AFC Wimbledon (played at Carshalton Ath F.C.)

2003-2004 **Player of the Year**: Doug Morrow **Top Goalscorer**: Rawle Kendall

FACT FILE
Formed 1995 Nickname: The Vale
Sponsors:Korea Foods Company Ltd.
Colours: Red & blue/red/blue
Change cols: Yellow/blue/yellow
Midweek Matchday:Tuesday
Programme: Pages: 32 Price:£1.00
Website: http://raynesparkvalefc.tripod.com.

CLUB PERSONNEL
President: Robert Hallett
Chairman: Syd Toulson
Vice Chairman:Nigel Thorn
Director of Football: Steve Smith
Managers:Lee Dobinson & Brian Imms
Captain: Lee Cox
Coach: Gary Clark

READING TOWN

Secretary & Fixture Sec: Richard Grey, 6 Milestone View Court, Lowfield Road, Caversham Park, Reading RG4 6ND Tel: 0118 948 4920 Email:richardigrey@aol.com

Ground: Reading Town Spts Ground, Scours Lane, Tilehurst, Reading, Berks (0118 945 3555)

Directions: Out of Reading on Oxford road (A329), past Battle Hosp. Scours Lane 1st right after roundabout ,Nearest station - Tilehurst or Reading (General). Bus -Reading Bus 17(Tilehurst)

Capacity: 2,000 Seats: No Cover: Yes Floodlights: Yes Clubhouse: Yes

PREVIOUS Leagues: Chiltonian 89-95, Reading 66-89 **Ground**:Adwest Spts Grd,Kings Meadow
Names: Lower Burghfield, XL United, Vincents Utd, Reading Garage, ITS Reading Town

CLUB RECORDS **Attendance:** 1,067 v AFC Wimbledon 2002-03
Defeat: 0-10 v Feltham(A) 96-97
Win: 7-0 v Cranleigh/Viking Spts/AFC Wallingford all Home 97-98

BEST SEASON **FA Cup:** 1st Qual. Rd. 00-01 **FA Vase:** 4th Rd 96-97

HONOURS Comb. Counties Lge R-up 97-98; Chiltonian Lge Champions 94-95, Berks &Bucks Sen. Trophy 95-96, R-up 96-97

FACT FILE
Founded: 1968
Colours: Red & white stripes/black/white
Change colours: Yellow/red/red
Midweek Matchday: Tuesday
Programme: 20 pages 50p
Editor: Richard Grey

CLUB PERSONNEL
Chairman: Roland Ford, 103 Little Heath Road, Tilehurst, Berkshire RG31 5TG
Tel: 0118 941 2270
Manager:Colin Millard

2002-2003
P.o.Y.: Clyde Masson
Top Scorer: Ashaine Murray 23
2004-2005 Captain: Andy Sharratt

SANDHURST TOWN

Secretary Mike Elsmore, 67 Avocet Crescent, Sandhurst, Berks GU47 0XW
Match Sec Tel Nos: 01252 768217 (W) 01344 778145 (H)

Ground: Bottom Meadow, Memorial Ground, Yorktown Rd, Sandhurst (07831 366140)

Directions: M3 Jn4- A331 -A321 or M4 Jn10 -A329 -A321. Park in main council offices car park off A321. Walk down tarmac path to ground. Nearest station: Sandhurst. Buses: 174,193 & 194

Capacity: 2,500 Seats: Eight Cover: Yes Floodlights: Yes Clubhouse: Yes

PREVIOUS Leagues: Reading & Dist.; East Berks; Aldershot Snr 79-84; Chiltonian84-90

CLUB RECORDS **Attendance:** 2,449 v AFC Wimbledon 187.08.02 League
Win: 9-1 v Cranleigh (08.01.2000) **Defeat:** 0-8 v Cobham 26.10.1991)
Goalscorer: Glenn Price **Appearances:** John Parker

BEST SEASON **FA Vase:** 2nd Rd 01-02,02-03 **FA Cup:** 1st Rd Qualifying

HONOURS Combined Co's Lge Chal. Vase R-up 92-93 (Reserve Chal. Cup R-up 91-92), Chiltonian Lg R-up 86-87, Aldershot Snr Lg R-up 83-84; Berks & Bucks Sen.Trophy R-up 92-93 Aldershot Senior Cup: 00-01 , Co.Co. Res Cup 00-01, 01-02

FACT FILE
Founded: 1910
Nickname: Fizzers
Colours: Red/black/black
Change colours: Yellow,blue,yellow
Midweek matchday: Tuesday
Programme: Yes

CLUB PERSONNEL
Chairman:T.B.A.
President: Malcolm Watts
Manager:Peter Browning

2003-2004
Top Scorer: Mark Anderson 20

SOUTHALL

Secretary: Geoff Harrison, 241 High Street South,Dunstable, Beds. LU6 3HY
Tel Nos: 01582 658603 (W) 07879 4035&2 (M)

Ground: Ground share with Chesham United F.C. Tel No: 01494 783964

Directions: M25 jct 18, A404 to Amersham, A416 to Chesham. Go to roundabout at foot of Amersham Hill, then sharp left. Ten minutes walk from Chesham station (Metropolitan Line).

Capacity: 5,000 Cover: 2,500 Seats: 284 Floodlights: Yes

PREVIOUS: **Leagues**: Southern 1896-1905; Gt West'n Suburban 1907-14; Athenian19-73 Herts & Middx 1939-45; Isthmian 73-00

CLUB RECORDS **Crowd:** 19,094 v Watford F.A.C 3Rd 1936 **Goals** Ken Merry **Apps**. Reg Short

BEST SEASON: **FA Cup:** 3rd Round 35-36, 1-4 v Watford (H) & First Round (5)
FA Vase: Runners-up 85-86 **FA Amateur Cup:** Runners-up 24-25

HONOURS: FA Amateur Cup R-up 24-25, FA Vase R-up 85-86, Isth Lg Div 2 R-up 74-75 Gt Western Suburban Lg 12-13, Athenian Lg 26-27 R-up 54-55, Middlesex Snr Cup x12, Middlesex Charity Cup x 9 and West Middx Cup x10.

FACT FILE
Founded: 1871 Nickname: The Hall
Colours: Red & white /black/red
Change: All Blue
Midw'k Matchday:Tues.Res Lg: Middx County
Prog: 20 pages, £1 Ed: Geoff Harrison
Local Press: Southall Gazette

CLUB PERSONNEL
Chairman: B.S.Gill President: S.S.Dhami
Manager: Frank Gill Physio:Simon SokelClub
Website: www.southallfootballclub.co.uk
Club Email: secf@southallfootballclub.co.uk
2003-2004 P.o.Y.: Andre Robinson
Top Scorers: Donal O'Sullivan & A Robinson
2004-2005: Captain: Chris Barrett

WALTON CASUALS

Secretary: Stuart Roberts, 47 Foxholes, Weybridge, Surrey. KT13 0BN. Tel: 01932845923
Email: sroberts@cattronuk.com

Ground: Franklyn Road Sports Ground, Waterside Drive, Walton-on-Thames, Surrey KT12 2JG
Tel No: 01932 787749 Website: http://www.waltoncasualsfc.co.uk
Directions: Next to Elmbridge Leisure Centre, left off Terrace Rd at first roundabout out of Walton centre. Hersham (BR), then bus 564 to Elmbridge Leisure Centre.

Capacity: 1,500 Seats: None Cover: 80 Floodlights: Yes
Clubhouse: Matchdays only. Hot food available from Tea Bar Club Shop: No

HONOURS Suburban Lge (South) 82-83, (R-up 83-84); Surrey Prem Lge R-up 94-95, S.P.L. Chall Cup 93-94, (R-up 94-95); Surrey Premier Cup R-up 86-87,CoCo Lg Cup 99-00 R-up 00-01

BEST SEASON **FA Vase:** 1Rd Proper 00-01 **FA Cup:** PrelimRd 2000-01,01-02

PREVIOUS **Leagues:** Surrey Premier, Surrey Senior, Surrey Intermediate, Suburban.

CLUB RECORDS **Attendance:** 178 v Pagham FA Vase 96/97

FACT FILE
Founded: 1948
Nickname: The Stags
Sponsors: Browns Building Centre
Colours: Tangerine/black/tangerine
Change colours: All Blue
Midweek Matchday: Tuesday
Programme: 28 pages70p
Editor/Press Officer: Stuart Roberts

CLUB PERSONNEL
Chairman:Graham James (01932 227921)
General Manager: David Symonds
President: Grahan James
Manager: Ray Noad

WESTFIELD

Secretary:
GROUND Woking Park, Kingfield, Woking, Surrey Tel: 01483 771106

Directions: (Adjacent to Woking FC.)
M25 J10 or 11, signposted from outskirts of Town.Ground 1 mile.
Woking B.R.Station & buses from Woking
Capacity: 1,000 Seats: None Cover: Yes Floodlights: Yes
Clubhouse Yes - open matchdays when snacks are available.
Club Shop No
HONOURS
PREVIOUS **League:** Surrey County Senior League

FACT FILE
Founded: 1953
Colours:Yellow/black/yellowChange colours:Yellow/Black/Yellow
Midweek Matchday:Tuesday
Programme: No

CLUB PERSONNEL
President: Richard Hill
Chairman: Steven Perkins
Tel: 01252 547900 (B)
Press Officer: Pat Kel;ly (07710 305200 (M)
Manager: John Cassidy
Asst. Managers:
Alan Morton & Brian Hennessy

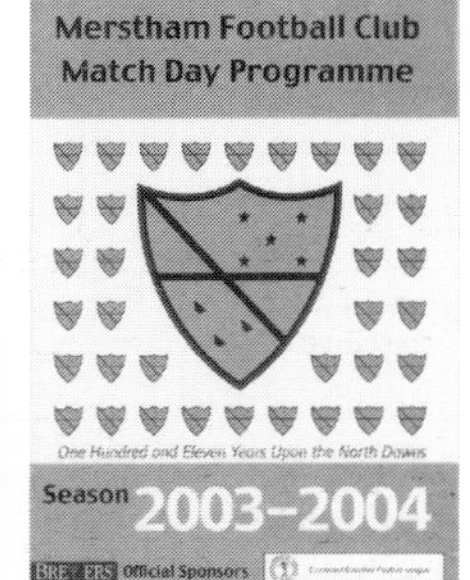

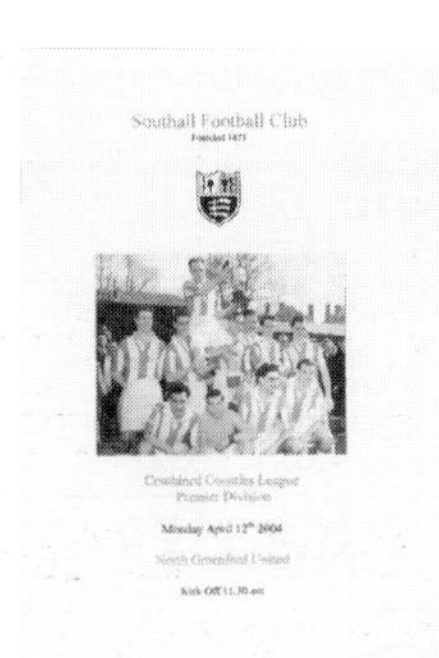

BEDFONT GREEN

Secretary: Stewart Cook, 22 Denman Drive,
Ashford, Middlesex TW15 2AR
Tel (h) 01628 622678 (b) 01189 341313
(b) 01189 349828 (m) 07831 412 412539
Email: stewart.cook@bedfrontgreenfc.co.uk

Colours: Blue/White

Ground: Ashford Recreation Ground Clockhouse Lane, Ashford,
Middlesex TW15 2HH
Tel 01784 252586

BOOKHAM

Secretary: Paul Chapman, 22 Strathcona Avenue,
Bookham, Surrey KT23 4HP
Tel (h) 01372 450764 (b) 01372 378666
(f) 01372 379667 work (m) 07729 626024
Email: paul2chappers@aol.com

Colours: Yellow/Black

Ground: Chrystie Recreation Ground,
Dorking Road, Bookham KT23
Tel 01372 459482

CHOBHAM

Secretary: Deborah Bexon, 40 Newton Way,
Tongham, Farnham, Surrey GU10 1BY
Tel (h) 01252 318276

Colours: Black & White/Black

Ground: Chobham Recreation Ground, Station Road, Chobham,
Surrey GU24 8AZ
Tel 01276 857876

CONEY HALL

Secretary: Mrs Jeanette Goddard,
12 Wrights Road, South Norwood, London SE25 6RY
Tel (h) 0208 771 6708 (m) 07956 842372

Colours: Red & Black Stripes/Black

Ground: Tiepigs Lane, West Wickham, Bromley,
Kent BR4 9BY
Tel 0208 462 9103

CRANLEIGH

Secretary: Steve Dawe, 2 Seltops Close,
Cranleigh, Surrey GU6 7JW
Tel (h) 01483 276639 (b) 01306 627481
(f) 01306 627561 (m) 07771 973134
Email: steve.dawe@thebrickbusiness.com

Colours: Blue

Ground: Snoxall Playing Fields, Knowle Lane, Cranleigh, Surrey
Tel 01483 275925

CRESCENT ROVERS

Secretary: Michael Bishop, 64 Wolsey Crescent,
New Addington, Croydon, Surrey CRO OPF
Tel (h) 01689 842996 (b) 020 8667 8380
Email: michael@bishop842.freeserve.co.uk

Colours: Green, White & Black/Black

Ground: Wallington Sports & Social Club,
34 Mollison Drive, Wallington, Surrey SM6 9BY
Tel 020 8647 2558

DITTON

Secretary: Colin Owens, 2 Lynton Close,
Chessington, Surrey KT9 1HB
Tel (h) 020 8397 5928 (f) 020 8397 5928
(m) 07710 290276
Email: ozzieowens@aol.com

Colours: Yellow/Green

Ground: Long Ditton Recreation Ground, Windmill Lane, Long Ditton,
Surbiton.
Tel 020 8873 0204

FARLEIGH ROVERS

Secretary: Mrs Val Wilcocks, 238 The Glad,
Shirley, Croydon, Surrey CRO 7UJ
Tel (h) 0208 406 3493 (m) 07754 626364

Colours: Black & Red/Black

Ground: Parsonage Field, Harrow Road,
Warlingham CR6 9EY
Tel 01883 626483

Monotype F.C. - Back Row (L-R): Dave Basher (Manager), Danny Hall, Andrew Page, James Wastell, Ben Savage, Dave Roffey, Richard Grover, John Penalver, Richard Eastoe.
Front Row: Steve Smith, Steve Searle, Adam Bentley, Sean Sharkey, Colin Brazil, Andy Smith.
Photo: Gordon Whittington.

Sheerwater F.C. Photo: Gordon Whittington.

HERSHAM ROYAL BRITISH LEGION

Secretary: Ron Shields, 17 Back Green,
Hersham, Surrey KT12 4HZ
Tel (h) 01932 246724 (b) 01483 462322
(f) 01483 462306 (m) 07742 167150
Email: rons@early.co.uk

Colours: Red & Black.Black

Ground: West End Recreation Groundm, West End Lane, Esher, Surrey
Tel 01372 463535

MERROW

Secretary: James Moseley, 27 Watersmeet Close,
Weybrook Park, Guildford, Surrey GU4 7NQ
Tel (h) 01483 301468 (m) 07736 518426

Colours: Red

Ground: The Urnfield, Downside Road,
Guildford, Surrey GU4 8PH
Tel 01483 567545

MONOTYPE

Secretary: Paul Robinson, 44 Copsleigh Avenue,
Salfords, Redhill, Surrey RH1 5BG
Tel (h) 01737 771571 (m) 07979 596073

Colours: Black & Gold/Black

Ground: Perry Wood Sports & Social Club, Honeycrock Lane, Salfords,
Redhill, Surrey RH1

Tel 01737 766645

NETHERNE VILLAGE

Secretary: Mrs Dorothy Eason
37 Tollers Lane, Old Coulsdon, Surrey CR5 1BF
Tel (h) 01737 554446 (f)01737 554446 (m) 07774 849144

Colours: Green & White/White

Ground: Woodplace Lane, Coulsdon, Surrey CR5 1NF
Tel 01737 557509

SEELEC DELTA

Secretary: Roger Brown, PO Box 136,
Dorking, Surrey RH4 2YP
Tel (f) 01306 881824 (m) 0-7931 482129
Email: backroomrogerbrown@hotmail.com

Colours: Black & Red/Black

Ground: Dorking FC, Mill Lane, Dorking, Surrey RH4 1DX
Tel 01306 884112

SHEERWATER

Secretary: Trevor Wenden.
14 Byrefield Road, Guildford, Surrey GU2 9UH
Tel (h) 01483 838578 (m) 07791 612008
Email: trevor.wendon2@ntlworld.com

Colours: Royal Blue

Ground: Sheerwater Recreation Ground,
Blackmore Crescent, Sheerwater Estate,
Woking, Surrey GU21 5QJ
Tel 01932 348192

SHOTTERMILL & HASLEMERE

Secretary: Colin Clement, 17 Fir Tree Avenue,
Haslemere, Surrey GU27 1PL
Tel (h) 01428 641447 (m) 07778 025937

Colours: Navy Blue & White/Navy Blue

Ground: Woolmer Hill Sports Ground, Haslemere, Surrey GU27 1QA
Tel 01428 643072

STAINES LAMMAS

Secretary: Bob Parry. 18 Hurstdene Avenue,
Staines, Middlesex TW18 1JQ
Tel (h) 01784 453886 (b) 0208 344 0309
(f) 01784 469196 (m) 07771 947757

Colours: Blue

Ground: Laleham Recreation Ground,
The Broadway, Laleham
Staines, Middlesex TW18 1RZ
Tel 01784 465204

WARLINGTON

Secretary: Les Badcock,
29 Verdayne Gardens, Warlingham,
Surrey CR6 9RP
Tel (h) 01883 626287 (b) 020 8409 8851
(m) 07890 589030
Email: lesbadcock@hotmail.com

Colours: Black & White Stripe/Black

Ground: Verdayne Playing Fields, Warlingham, Surrey CR6
Tel 01883 626287

WORCESTER PARK

Secretary: Tony McCarthy
25 Lutyens House, Churchill Road,
London SW10 3AB
Tel (h) 0207 834 7544 (m) 07961 829070

Colours: Blue

Ground: Skinners Field, Green Lane,
Worcester Park, Surrey
Tel 020 8337 4995

ESSEX SENIOR LEAGUE

SPONSORED BY: EASTWAY

President: Vacant **Chairman & Publicity:** Robert Errington

Secretary: David Walls, 2 Hillsfield Cottage, Layer, Breton, Essex CO2 0PS. Tel & Fax: 01206 330146

Email: EssexSenior@wallsd.freeserve.co.uk

THE ISLAND OF DREAMS

Concord Rangers were worthy League Champions thus making it a glorious double for the **Island of Canvey** in the Thames Estuary with their neighbours being the first ever former Essex Senior League club to reach the Conference League. Manager, **Ben Embery** and his Assistant, **Steve Jackson** were also the first ever to achieve a Championship with two different clubs, having been previously successful with **Canvey Island** in 1987. Concord's prolific striker, **Danny Heale**, easily won the Don Douglas Trophy as the Leading Scorer.

The season commenced with a welcome to newcomers **London APSA** who proved to be a breath of fresh air and made friends everywhere they played. Their crowning glory came in the Gordon Brasted Memorial Trophy when they knocked out **Enfield Town** 1-0 with their only shot of the game.

The League were extremely grateful to **Eastway Construction** and to Costas Sophocleous of Leyton FC for his very generous sponsorship.

Once again, a form ESL club has done remarkably well with their third promotion in a row. **Enfield Town** were worthy League Cup winners in a thrilling match with **Sawbridgeworth Town** played at Ilford. In their League campaign they broke the previous record for away games without defeat but their adverse home record meant only fourth place in a very keen competition for the minor places. This was to prove a very contentious final placing when the League were subject to an extraordinary situation after the FA chose to sanction its National Non-League System Committee to allow the Isthmian League to make up its number in its Division Two to 16 at the expense of our own constitution.
In the meantime with no club being eligible for promotion to the new Southern League Division One, the Isthmian League "chose" **Enfield Town**, our Hospitality winners, only to change their mind just before our AGM and take second place **Ilford**. Enfield Town's ground transformation was remarkable and even more so as most of the work was accomplished by Supporters. It was a great shock to the League and for our Cup Winners, still reducing the League by one to fifteen clubs and was testament to the problems that can be caused when rules are amended at a stroke without considered thought or consultation.

The Gordon Brasted Trophy was a triumph for **Romford** who outplayed **Ilford** on the day with, arguably, the best performance of the season. Sportsmanship winners were **Stansted**, members since our inception in 1971 and the **Secretary of the Year** was **John Taylor of Barkingside** with the League Chairman pointing out that it was the whole Taylor family who personified the game at our level with the amount of time and work put into the running of that particular club.

Their was sadness in the season with the passing of our President, **Arthur Dimond,** a colossus of the football world in Essex. His calming influence on the League was such that he is a very difficult act to follow and will be remembered with great affection. The League now look forward to a very interesting transitional time in football and hope that the continuing and curious anomaly of County based clubs being in two separate Leagues at the same level will be sorted out for the good of the game.

Robert Errington - Chairman

FINAL LEAGUE TABLE 2003-04

		P	W	D	L	F	A	Pts
1.	Concord Rangers	30	22	4	4	75	26	70
2.	Ilford	30	19	8	3	66	23	65
3.	Sawbridgeworth Town	30	19	6	5	60	29	63
4.	Enfield Town	30	18	9	3	60	35	63
5.	Romford	30	18	4	8	66	39	58
6.	Waltham Abbey	30	16	6	8	50	37	54
7.	Basildon United	30	15	4	11	67	42	49
8.	Bowers United	30	13	4	13	41	51	43
9.	Eton Manor	30	9	8	13	43	52	35
10.	Southend Manor	30	9	7	14	42	50	34
11.	Barkingside	30	9	6	15	46	62	33
12.	Burnham Ramblers	30	7	10	13	42	58	31
13.	Stansted	30	7	5	18	33	72	26
14.	Brentwood	30	5	5	20	31	60	20
15.	London APSA	30	5	5	20	34	76	20
16.	Hullbridge Sports	30	2	3	25	28	72	9

		1	2	3	4	5	6	7	8	9	10	11	12	13	14	15	16
1	Barkingside		1-1	2-4	4-0	3-4	0-1	0-3	0-4	2-1	1-1	3-1	2-1	2-6	1-2	2-0	1-2
2	Basildon United	1-1		0-1	3-0	0-0	0-3	1-3	7-0	5-2	0-3	2-0	1-2	0-2	1-2	3-1	1-0
3	Bowers United	2-1	3-1		1-2	2-1	1-0	0-2	0-2	3-2	1-3	0-3	1-2	1-6	2-1	4-0	0-1
4	Brentwood	1-1	3-1	0-1		1-1	1-2	5-5	1-0	4-1	1-3	0-2	1-2	0-1	0-1	0-2	1-2
5	Burnham Ramblers	6-1	1-7	2-2	2-0		0-3	3-4	5-1	0-0	0-3	3-3	0-6	0-1	2-1	1-1	0-1
6	Concord Rangers	0-1	3-3	4-1	3-0	5-0		1-1	3-1	2-1	2-1	2-0	4-0	1-2	3-0	5-2	0-2
7	Enfield Town	1-0	1-4	1-0	2-0	2-0	3-3		1-1	2-0	2-2	2-1	1-2	0-0	1-1	2-0	0-1
8	Eton Manor	0-1	1-2	2-2	5-2	1-3	1-3	1-4		2-0	0-0	3-2	0-1	2-2	1-1	1-2	1-1
9	Hullbridge Sports	1-3	0-4	0-1	0-1	1-0	1-3	2-3	1-2		0-1	0-1	0-2	0-2	3-3	5-1	2-4
10	Ilford	3-0	3-0	3-0	1-0	4-0	0-2	2-2	0-0	4-1		3-0	2-1	1-1	4-1	3-0	3-0
11	London APSA	1-3	1-6	0-0	3-3	0-6	0-6	0-3	0-1	4-0	2-4		1-5	0-2	2-2	2-2	2-1
12	Romford	2-1	3-1	6-0	2-2	1-1	1-2	2-2	0-1	6-3	0-2	2-0		1-1	2-1	3-0	0-4
13	Sawbridgeworth	4-3	1-2	2-0	1-0	0-0	0-3	2-3	3-1	1-0	2-2	2-1	2-3		1-0	2-0	7-0
14	Southend Manor	4-1	1-2	0-1	2-0	3-0	1-3	1-2	2-2	1-1	1-0	3-0	1-5	1-2		3-3	0-3
15	Stansted	1-1	0-7	0-5	2-1	1-1	2-3	0-1	0-4	1-0	1-3	6-2	0-2	1-0	1-2		2-4
16	Waltham Abbey	4-4	0-1	2-2	4-1	0-0	0-0	0-1	3-2	4-0	2-2	1-0	2-1	1-2	1-0	0-1	

LEAGUE CUP

FIRST ROUND (over two legs home & away)

Barkingside	v	Stansted	3-3 0-0r* 3-5p
Basildon	v	Waltham Abbey	3-2 1-0
Brentwood	v	Eton Manor	0-0 2-0
Burnham Ramblers	v	Enfield Town	2-3 2-4
Concord Rangers	v	Ilford	2-2 3-2
London APSA	v	Bowers Utd	2-2 2-7
Sawbridgeworth	v	Romford	1-1 3-1
Southend Manor	v	Hullbridge	0-0 4-2
Hullbridge Sports	v	Southend Manor	0-0 2-4

QUARTER-FINALS (over two legs home & away)

Brentwood	v	Basildon United	1-2 0-3
Concord Rangers	v	Sawbridgeworth Town	2-2 0-1
Enfield Town	v	Bowers Utd	2-1 1-0
Southend Manor	v	Barkingside	0-0 1-5

SEMI-FINALS (over two legs home & away)

Enfield Town	v	Barkingside	5-1 1-0
Sawbridgeworth T.	v	Basildon United	1-2 2-1* 4-3p

THE FINAL (3rd May at Ilford)

Enfield Town	v	Sawbridgeworth Town	3-2

BARKINGSIDE

Secretary: John Taylor, 2 Courage Close.Hornchurch, Essex RM11 2BJ (01708 456373)
Ground: Oakside, Station Road, Barkingside, Ilford, Essex Tel: 020 8550 3611
Directions: From London A12 Eastern Ave to Green Gate, left into Hurns Rd to Barkingside, right into Craven Gardens, right Carlton Drive to Station Rd, under bridge and grd on right. Next to Barkingside station (Central Line). From Ilford station (BR) take 169 Bus to Craven Gardens
Capacity: 3,000 Seats: 350 Cover: 850 Floodlights: Yes Club Shop: No
Clubhouse: Saturdays 1pm-12. midweeek matchnights 6.30-11pm. Rolls, hotdogs,hamburgers
HONOURS: Spartan Lge. Prem. Div. 96-97, R-up 90-91 (Harry Sunderland Shld 83-84 (R-up 84-85); London Sen. Cup 96-97; S. Essex Lge R-up 46-47, L'don Lg R-up 49-50 (Lg Cup 55-56 (R-up 52-53 62-63)), Gtr L'don Lg 64-65,S.S.Mids Premier 98-99.Harry Fisher Mem Trophy 00-1
PREVIOUS: Leagues: Ilford & Dist. 1898-1925 44-47; Ilford Minor 25-44; Sth Essex 47-48; Walthamstow 48-50; London 50-64; Gtr London 64-71; Metropolitan-London 71-75; Spartan 76- South Midlands 1996-99 **Grounds:** Fulwell Cross PF 1898-1921; Clayhall Rec 21-29; Hainault PF 29-33; Barkingside Rec 33-57 **RECORDS: Gate:** 957 v Arsenal Res., London Lg 1957

FACT FILE
Founded: 1898
Colours: SkyBlue/navy blue/navy blue
Change colours: All Red
Midweek matchday: Monday
Programme: Yes
Editor: John Taylor

CLUB PERSONNEL
Chairman: John Taylor
Manager: Rod Stringer
Physio: Paul Baskin

2003-2004
P.o.Y. & Top Scorer: Paul Carr

BASILDON UNITED

Secretary: C.Thomas, 57 Lansdowne Road, Lowestoft, Suffolk NR33 7ES
Tel.Nos: 01502 586951 (h) 07801 427513 (M)
Ground: Gardiners Close, Gardiners Lane, Basildon, Essex SS14 3AW Tel: 01268 520268

Directions: A176 off Southend arterial (A127), left at r'bout into Cranes FarmRoad, proceed to end of duel carriageway, left at lights, Gardiners Close is 1st left (Football Club signed). Two and a half miles from Basildon BR station
Capacity: 2,000 Seats: 400 Cover: 1,000 Floodlights: Yes
Clubhouse: Open lunchtimes, evenings, weekends. Hot food sold Club Shop: No

HONOURS Isthmian Lge Div 2 83-83; Essex Senior Lge (5) 76-80 93-94, Lg Cup 77-78 93-94 97-98, Res. Cup 92-93; Essex Senior Trophy 78-79; Res. Lge &Shield 94-95
PREVIOUS **Leagues:** Grays & Thurrock; Gtr London 68-70; Essex Snr 70-80; Athenian 80-81; Isthmian 81-91 **Name:** Armada Sports **Ground:** Grosvenor Park 63-69
CLUB RECORDS **Attendance:** 4,000 v West Ham, ground opening 11/8/70

FACT FILE
Founded: 1963
Sponsors: T.B.A.
Colours: Amber & black stripes/black/black
Change:Green & white hoops/white/g&w
Midweek Matches: Wednesday
Programme: 16 pages, £1.00
Editor:John Moran (07801 461605)

CLUB PERSONNEL
President: J Oakes
Chairman: Dennis Taylor
Press Officer: Frank Ford (07789 534174)
Manager:John Doyle

Basildon United - Back Row (L-R): Martin Lawrence, Greg Heighway, Rob Jones, Louis Green, Simon Dawson, Neil Curtis.
Front Row: Lee Murray, Nikki Beale, Neil Richmond, Ben Coleman, Danny Wilson.

Photo: Alan Coomes.

BOWERS PITSEA F.C.

Secretary: Lee Stevens, 59 Cross Green, Lee Chapel South, Basildon, Essex SS16 5Q
Tel No: 01268 548 493 (H)
Ground: Len Salmon Stadium, Crown Avenue, off Kenneth Rd,Pitsea, Basildon (01268 452068)
Directions: Turn into Rectory Rd from Old London Rd (B1464) at Pitsea Broadway into Kenneth Rd, right at top Crown Ave. 1.25 miles Pitsea (BR). Bus 5& 42 toRectory Rd, Bowers Gifford
Capacity: 2,000 Seats: 200 Stand: Yes Floodlights: Yes
Clubhouse: Open every night Club Shop: No
PREVIOUSLeagues: Thurrock & Thameside Comb.; Olympian**Ground:** Gun Meadow, Pitsea
HONOURS Thurrock & Thameside Comb. 58-59; Essex Snr Lg 80-81,98-99 R-up 83-84 Div 1 Cup 90-91,Lg Cup Winners 81-82,98-99 R-up (3) Harry FisherMem Trophy 91-92 R-up (4) E.S.L. Charity Cup 99-00
BEST SEASON **FA Cup:** 1st Rd Q 98-99 **FA Vase:** 4th Rd 98-99
CLUB RECORDS **Attendance:** 1,800 v Billericay F.A.Vase
Players progressing: Steve Tilson (Southend Utd)

FACT FILE
Founded: 1946
Colours: All CLaret
Change colours:All Sky BlueMidweek Matches:Wednesday7.30
Res League: Essex & Herts Border Co. Comb
Programme: 30pages £1.00
Editor:Lee Stevens
CLUB PERSONNEL
Chairman:Barry Hubbard
Vice Chairman: Vacent
Manager: Marc Massey
2003-2004
Player of the Year: Anthony Reeve
Top Scorer: Anthopny Reeve

BRENTWOOD TOWN

Secretary: Colin Harris, 56 Viking Way, Pilgrims Hatch, Brentwood, Essex CM15 9HY
Tel: 01277 219564 (H) Email Address: info@brentwoodtownfc.co.uk**Ground:** Brentwood Centre, Doddinghurst Rd, Brentwood, Essex. 01277 215151 Ext.713
Directions: From east end High St (Wilsons Corner) turn north into Ongar Rd. 3rd mini-round-about ,Right into Doddinghurst Rd, Centre half mile on right after A12 Bridge, ground far right.
Capacity: !,000 Cover: 100 Seats: 50 Floodlights: Yes
Clubhouse: Open Tues & Thur evening & matchdays Club Shop: No
PREVIOUS **Names:** Manor Ath. 55-70, Brentwood Ath. 70-72 Brentwood F.C. 72-2004
Grounds: King George, Hartswood, `Larkins', Ongar (pre-92), East Thurrock 92/93
Leagues: Romford & Dist., Sth Essex Comb., London & Essex Border,Olympian
HONOURS Olympian Lg Cup 67-68, Essex Inter. Cup 76-77, Essex Lg Cup 75-76 78-79 90-91; Harry Fisher Mem. Trophy 95-96 ,Essex Senior League 2000-01, League Sportsmanship Award 00-01,01-02
BEST SEASON **FA Vase:** 3rd Rd Prop 95-96

FACT FILE
Founded: 1955 Nickname: Blues
Sponsor: CLC Construction
Colours: Sky blue/navy blue/sky blue
Change colours: All Yellow
Midweek Matches: Tuesday
Programme: 50p Editor Ken Hobbs
e-mail: KenHobbs@brentwoodtownfc.co.uk)
Club Website:www.brentwoodtownfc.co.uk
CLUB PERSONNEL
Chairman: Terry Smith
Manager: Paul Delea (H) 01708 550630
2003-2004 Top Scorer: Jeff Thomas 10
2004-2005 Captain: Dave Stittle

BURNHAM RAMBLERS

Secretary: Shaun Pugh
Ground: Leslie Fields Stadium, Springfield Rd, Burnham-on-Crouch CM0 8TE (01621 784383)
Club Website: www.burnhamramblersfc.co.uk
Directions: On B1010 from South Woodham Ferrers, trt,1/2 mile before town.
10 mins -Burnham on Crouch railway station
Capacity: 2,000 Seats:156 Stand: Yes Floodlights: Yes Club Shop: No
Clubhouse: Mon-Fri 7-11pm, Sat 12noon -11pm, Sun 12-3 & 7-9.30pm. Hot meals & snacks available
HONOURS Olympian Lg 65-66; Essex I'mediate Cup R-up 81-82; Essex Snr Lg Cup R-up 86-87 89-90 97-98, (Reserve Cup 89-90 (R-up 92-93), Reserve Shield R-up 90-91; Harry Fisher Mem. Trophy 96-97, R-up 97-98 99-00; Sportsmanship Award 96-97
PREVIOUS **Leagues:** N Essex, Mid-Essex, Olympian, S.E. Essex
Grounds: Wick Rd ,Millfields and Saltcourts
BEST SEASON **FA Vase:** 5th Rd 88-89
CLUB RECORDS **Gate:** 1,500 v Arsenal at opening of new stand

FACT FILE
Founded: 1900 Nickname: Ramblers
Colours: AllBlue
Change colours: All Yellow
Midweek matches: Tuesday
Reserves' Lge: Essex Senior Reserves
Prog: 32 pages, £1.00 Editor: Martin Leno
CLUB PERSONNEL
Chairman:Ron Hatcher V- Chair: Shaun Pugh
President: R J Cole, Esq
Press Officer: Nigel Radcliffe, 07774412634
Manager: Mike Everett Physio:Tom Riley
Captain: Shaun Hull
2003-04
P.o.Y.: Lee Perry Top Scorer: Ricky Holmes

CONCORD RANGERS

Secretary: Eddie Crace, 71 Tilburg Road, Canvey Island, Essex, SS8 9ER. Tel: 01268 681868H 07889 904109M 01268 2950288W E-mail: eddie.crace@cnh.com
Ground: Thames Road, Canvey Island, Essex. SS8 0HP 01268 691780 / 515750
Website: www.concordrangersfc.co.uk Email: ecrace@newholland.com
Directions: Follow A130 onto Canvey Island and turn right into Thorney Bay Road, then right again into Thames Road.
Capacity: 1,500 Cover: Yes Seats: Yes Floodlights: Yes
HONOURS Southend & Dist. Lge - Lge & Cup 84-85; Southend Alliance - Lge & Cup 87-88; Essex Intermediate Lg Div 2 90-91; Essex Sen Lge 97-98 03-04, R-Up 02-03 Cup 96-97;Eastern Jnr Alliance Cup Winners 2002 Essex & Herts Lg 03-04 R-Up 02-03 Wirral Programme Award 93-94, Harry Fisher Trophy 99-00 ESL Charity Cup 00-01
PREVIOUS **Leagues:** Southend & Dist. All., Essex I'mediate (pre-1991) **Ground:** Waterside
CLUB RECORDS **Gate:** 1,500 v Lee Chapel North, FA Sunday Cup 89-90
Win: 12-1 v Woodford, Essex Snr Lge 00-01

FACT FILE
Founded: 1967
Colours:Yellow & blue/blue/yellow
Change colours: Red/black/red
Midweek Matches: Tuesday
Clubhouse: Evenings & weekends
Programme: 20 pages, 50p
Editor: Chris Symes (01206 851627)
CLUB PERSONNEL
President: Albert Lant
Chairman: Antony Smith
Manager: Mark Jenkins Captain: Adrian Owers
2003-2004
Player of the Year: Adrian Owers
Top Goalscorer: Darren Bethell

Cadbury
Carlsberg
Nationwid
FREE!
Kitbag
with every
full kit
ordered
JJB

Sawbridgeworth Town - Back Row (L-R): Richard Goodchild, Ryan Williams, Shaun O'Neil, Mark Aken, Martin Sedgwick, Matt Hayter.
Front Row: Steve Robbins, Chris Webb, Dan Wardle, Matt Lilley, Mark Pearcy.

Photo: Alan Coomes.

London APSA - Back Row (L-R): Asim Choudhury, Bai-Mass Lette, Steve Nicholas, Fahim Shah, Sam Whitby, Shawn Baptiste, Bilal Bapu, Patrick Nkenda.
Front Row: Urfat Hussian, Zaheer Saleh, Zabeer Khan, Danny Sinfield, John Langton, Furkan Anwar, Dean Davis, Mohoudin Elwali.

Photo: Alan Coomes.

ENFIELD TOWN

Secretary: Peter Coath, 33 Ashford Crescent.,Enfield Middx EN3 7HX
Tel.Nos: 020 8292 4495 (H) 07949 378931 (M) **Website:** www.etfc.co.uk
Press Officer: Ciaran Glennon, 42 Cecil Avenue,Enfield, Middlesex EN1 1PP (07730 953813)
Fixture Sec.: Keith Wortley, Greenways, Appleby Street, Cheshunt, Herts EN7 6QZ
Tel nos: 01992 201690 (H) 07732 319897 (M)
Ground: Brimsdown Sports & Social Club, Goldsdown Road, Enfield Tel: 020 8804 5491
Capacity: 2000 Covered Seats: 150 Covered Standing: 300 Floodlights: Yes
Clubhouse: Yes
Directions: BR from Liverpool Street to Brimsdown (half mile away) or Southbury Road. By road off Green Street, itself off Hertford Road (A1010). Buses 191 or 307
Honours: Essex League Champions 02-03 R-up: 01-02 Lg Cup Winners 01-02,03-04 Cherry Red Books Trophy 01-02, Gordon Brasted Mem Trophy 02-03 Middlx SenCup R-up 02-03
Apps & Goals: Daniel Clarke: 100apps 68 goals **Best Victory:** 7-0 v Ilford (away) 28.04.03
Record Attendance: 562v Enfield Middx Charity Cup 03-04

FACT FILE
Founded: June 2001
Nickname ETs or Towners
Sponsor: Direct Boot & Embroidery
Colours: White/blue/white Change:All yellow
Midweek Matchday: Tuesday
Programme: Price: £1.50 Pages:32
Editor: Ciaran Glennon
CLUB PERSONNEL
Chairman: David Bryant
Fixture Sec: Keith Wortley (07732 319897)
Manager: Jim Chandler
Captain: Graeme Hall
2003-2004
Top Scorer: Billy Cove
Player of the Year: Lee Smith

ETON MANOR

Secretary: Larry mcDonald, 20 Heynes Rd, Dagenham, Essex RM8 2SX Tel No: 0208 5902863
Ground: Waltham Lodge Sports Ground,Kitchener Rd.,Walthamstowe London E17 4JP(020 8527 2444)
Directions: Sharing with Tilbury F.C.
Capacity: 1,000 Seats: 60 Cover: 60 Floodlights: Yes
Clubhouse: Yes
HONOURS Essex Snr Cup R-up 37-38, London Lg 33-34 37-38 52-53 53-54 (R-up 48-49 57-58, Lg Cup 55-56 (R-up 46-47 54-55)), Greater London Lg 64-65, Essex Intermediate Cup 64-65,London Intermediate Cup R-up 33-34 66-67, Essex Snr Lg Sportsmanship Award 75-76 (Div 1 Cup 90-91, Res. Div 76-77, Res. Div Cup 91-92).
PREVIOUS Leagues: London 33-59; Aetolian 59-64; Greater London 64-69; Metropolitan 69-75.
Grounds: Wildness, Hackney; GUS Sports Ground, Clapton; Walthamstow Ave. FC; Norwegian Ground, Barking; Roding Lane, Buckhurst Hill, ThurrockHotel **Name:** Wilderness Leyton.
CLUB RECORDS **Gate:** 600 v Leyton Orient, opening of floodlights at Roding Lane.
Goalscorer: Dave Sams

FACT FILE
Founded: 1901 Nickname: The Manor
Colours: Sky/navy/navy
Change: Yellow/dark blue/light blue
Midweek Matches: Tuesday
Prog: 12 pages with entry
.CLUB PERSONNEL
Chairman & Prog Ed.: Reg Curtis
Man:Kirk Whitelock Gen Man: Alex Lee
Coach: Brian Partridge.
Physio: Sue Abercrombie
2002-2003
Player of the Year:Tony Marsh
Top Scorer: Asa Pamplin
2004-2005 Captain:Gary Scales

HULLBRIDGE SPORTS

Secretary: Mrs.Beryl Petre, 58 Grasmere Ave., Hullbridge, Essex SS5 6LF
Tel: 01702 230630 (H) 01702 552211 (B)
Ground: Lower Road, Hullbridge, Hockley, Essex SS5 6BJ Tel: 01702 230420
Directions: Turn into Rawreth Lane from A130 (left if arriving fromChelmsford), down to mini-r'bout, left, across next mini-r'bout, up hill, ground signed on right just past garage
Capacity: 1,500 Seats: No Cover: Yes Floodlights: Yes Club Shop: No
Clubhouse: Lounge bar, function hall with bar & changing rooms - set in 16 acres
HONOURS Essex Intermediate Snr Div Cup 87-88, Southend & District Lg Div 1 65-66 (Div 2 51-52, Div 3 56-57), French Cup 51-52, Essex Snr Lg Sportsmanship Award 91-92 92-93 93-94
PREVIOUS **Leagues:** Southend & Dist., Alliance, Essex I'mediate
Grounds: Pooles Lane Rec

RECORD ATTENDANCE: 800 v Blackburn Rovers F.A.Youth Cup 99-00

FACT FILE
Founded: 1945
Sponsor: Thermo Shield
Colours: Royal Blue & white/blue/white
Change colours: Red & white/black/black
Midweek matches: Tues/Thursday
Programme Editor: T.B.A.
Website: www.sportsworldwide.co.uk

CLUB PERSONNEL
Chairman: Terry Scourfield
Manager: Jayson Stephens

LONDON APSA

Secretary: Zabir Bashir

Ground: Aveley FC, `Mill Field', Mill Road, Aveley, Essex RM15 4TR
Tel: 01708 865940. Fax: 01708 680995

Directions: London - Southend A1306, turn into Sandy Lane at Aveley. Rainham or Purfleet BR stations then bus No. 723 to the ground. Bus from Rainham No 324

Capacity: 4,000 Cover: 400 Seats: 400 Floodlights: Yes

Clubhouse: Normal pub hours. Bar snacks and hot food available

Previous League: London Intermediate Lge >2003
2003-2004 **Player of the Year:** Peter Allen **Top Goalscorers**: Mahammed Dakri & Patrik Nkenda **Captain**: Mohammed Dakri

Concord Rangers - Back Row (L-R): Steve Knott, Jamie Gold, Lee Goodwin, Dave Brightley, Brendan Walsh, Dave Cannon, Danny Stanley.
Front Row: Darren Brown, Ian Wastell, Danny Heale, Danny Greaves.

Photo: Alan Coomes.

ROMFORD(2002)

Secretary: Colin Ewenson,71 Riversdale Rd.,Romford, RM52NR (07973 717075)
Ground: Ford Sports & Social Club,Rush greeen Road, Romford RM5 2NR (01708 745678) Club Call: 09066 555 841 Website: www.romfordfc.co.uk
Directions: The Ground is on the A124 between Romford & Dagenham.Take the A12 from London as far as the Moby Dick junction.Turn left and then right at the 1st r'about into Collier Row Rd. The ground entrance is signposted 200 yards on the right. Nearest station is Romford (BR). From directly outside the station the London bus 247 passes the ground.
Capacity: 2,500 Cover: 300 Seats: 175 Floodlights: Yes
Previous Leagues: Essex Senior 92-96, Isthmian 96-02
Grounds: Hornchurch 92-95, Ford Utd 95-96 ,Sungate 1996-2001
Club Records - Att.: 820 v Leatherhead (IL2) 15/4/97; **Career Goalscorer:** Danny Benstocks 61; **Season goalscorer:** Vinny John 45 (97-98); **Career Appearances:** Start Horne 234
Best Season: FA Vase: 5th Rd 96-97 v Bedlington Terriers 2-1F.A.Cup: 4th Q Rd 97-9 & 99-00
HONOURS Essex Senior Lge 95-96, Lge Cup 95-96; Isthmian Div 2 96-97; East Anglian Cup 97-98 Gordon Brasted Mem Trophy 03-4

FACT FILE
Reformed: 1992 Nickname: The Boro
Colours:All blue with two gold hoops on chest
Change colours: All white with two blue hoops
Midweek home matchday: Tuesday (7.45)
Reserves' Lge: Essex & Herts Border Prem
Programme: Pages: 40 Price: £1.20
Editor: Derek RobinsonTel: 01708 349595
Local Press: Romford Recorder

CLUB OFFICIALS
Chairman & Press Officer:Steve Gardener
Press Officer: Steve Gardener
Manager:Mark Reed Captain: Micky Rogan
Physio: Peter Shepherd
2003-04 P.o.Y. & Top Scorer: Jason Friend 29

SAWBRIDGEWORTH TOWN

Secretary: Mrs Leslie Atkins,41 The Orchards,, Sawbridgeworth.CM21 9BB (01279 725665)
Ground: Crofters End, West Road, Sawbridgeworth, Herts. CM21 0DE (01279 722039)

Directions: Three quarters of a mile from the station; up Station Road then into West Road.
Capacity: 1,500 Seats: None Cover: 250 Floodlights: Yes Club Shop: No

HONOURS Essex Olympian Lg 71-72; Essex Snr Lg R-up 92-93 94-95; Harry FisherMem. Cup 87-88; Lg Cup 94-95 R-up 92-93 93-94, Res. Div 91-92 92-93 (R-up 93-94), Res. Shield R-up 92-93); Herts Snr Tphy 90-91 93-94 (R-up 92-93);Herts Charity Shield 92-93 94-95 95-96; Uttlesford Charity Cup 92-93; Herts Intermediate Cup R-up 93-93(res); S. Midlands F'lit Cup R.up 94-95; Res. Sect S.M Lge & Lg.Cup R-Up 94-95
PREVIOUS Leagues: Essex Olympian, Spartan 36-53
CLUB RECORDS Attendance: 610 v Bishop's Stortford.
PREVIOUS GROUNDS: Hyde Hall, Pishiobury, Hand & Crown.

FACT FILE
Founded: 1890
Nickname: Robins
Colours: Red & black stripes/black/black
Change colours: Sky Blue & White
Midweek Matchday;
Prog Editor: T.B.A

CLUB PERSONNEL
Chairman: Barry Hodges
President: Ron Alder
Manager:Don Watters
Physio: T.B.A.
2003-2004
P.o.Y.: Stefen Szajenski
2004-2005: Captain: Martin Sedgwick

Sawbridgeworth Town - Back Row (L-R): Tim O'Reilly, Paul Hammick, Richard Goodchild, Martin Comber, Martin Sedgewick, Steffan Szajewski.
Front Row: Mark Pearcey, Danie Wardle, Alex Martin, Gregg Pike, Christian Wheeler.

Photo: Alan Coomes.

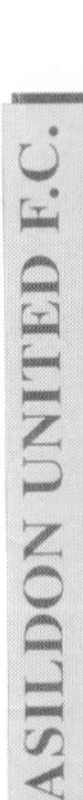

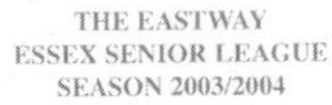

THE EASTWAY
ESSEX SENIOR LEAGUE
SEASON 2003/2004

Sponsored by

ANGLO ENVIRONMENTAL TYRE RECYCLING

The Stadium
Gardiners Close
Basildon
Essex

Tel: 01268 520268 Official Programme £1

STANSTED
Football Club
MATCHROOM
The Eastway
Essex Senior Football League

SOUTHEND MANOR

Secretary: Steve Durrant, 11 Clayton Rd.,Southend on Seas, Essex SS25DL (01702 301572)
Ground: Southchurch Park Arena, Lifstan Way, Southend-on-Sea. Tel: 01702 615577
Directions: A127 then A1159 for 1 mile turn right at second roundabout by Invisible Man PH, then due south for 1 mile, ground on right near sea front
Capacity: 2,000 Seats: 500 Cover: Yes Floodlights: Yes
Clubhouse: Open every evening Club Shop: No
HONOURS Essex Sen Trophy 92-93; Essex Interm'te Cup 78-79; Essex Sen League 90-91, R-Up: 99-00 Essex Sen League Cup 87-88, R-Up:99-00,00-01 Challenge Cup 89-90;Harry Fisher Mem Trophy 90-91 92-93 (R-up 91-92) Essex Sen Cup 2001-02 , ESL Charity Cup 2001-02
PREVIOUS **Leagues:** Southend Borough Combination, Southend Alliance
Grounds: Victory Spts/ Oakwood Rec
RECORDS **Attendance:** 1,521 v Southend Utd, 22/7/91, floodlight opener
BEST SEASON **FA Vase:** 1996-97

FACT FILE
Founded: 1955 Nickname: The Manor
Sponsors: Info-Line
Colours: Yellow/black/yellow
Change colours: All white
Midweek Matchday: Tuesday
Reserves Lge: Essex & Herts Border Comb
Programme: 10 pages, 50p
Editor/Press Off: Chris Hunt 01702 615897
Website: www.southendmanor.co.uk

CLUB PERSONNEL
Chairman: Robert Westley
Vice-Chairman: Geoff Gorham
Manager::Steve Sinnett
Coach: Andy Dixon

STANSTED

Secretary: Terry Shoebridge ,2 Dawson Close,Saffron Walden ,Essex CB10 2AR
Tel Nor: 01799 -527937 (H)
Ground: Hargrave Park, Cambridge Road, Stansted, Essex. (01279 812897)
Directions: B1383 north of Bishops Stortford on west side of Cambridge Rd. Stansted (BR) - 1/2 mile
Capacity: 2,000 Seats: 200 Cover: Yes Floodlights: Yes
Clubhouse: Matchdays till 11pm. Sandwiches available. Club Shop: No
HONOURS FA Vase Winners 83-84; Essex Snr Lg R-up 82-83; Essex Snr Lg Cup 83-84, (R-up 72-73 94-95); Harry Fisher Mem Cup 82-83 84-85 (R-up 92-93 93-94); E. AnglianCup 83-84; Eastern F/lit Cup 83-84 R-up 01-02; Uttlesford Char. Cup 93-84 86-87 88-89 94-95 97-98 01-02
PREVIOUS **Leagues:** Spartan; London; Herts Co. **Grounds:** Greens Meadow; ChapelHill
RECORD **Attendance:** 828 v Whickham (FA Vase 83-84)
Best Seasons **FA Cup:** 97-98 **FA Vase:** Winners 83-84

FACT FILE
Founded: 1902 Nickname: The Blues
Sponsor: BBL Medical Locums
Programme 50p Editor: Dave Ryan
Colours: Blue /Blue/White
Change: Yellow & Black/Black/Yellow
Midweek matches: Tuesday
Reserves League:Essex Senior Res Section

CLUB PERSONNEL
Chairman: Terry Shoebridge
President: Bob Marin
Manager: Alan Penfold Gen Man: Tony Mercer
Captain: Paul Dennis

2003-2004
P.o.Y.: ErkanYusuf Top Scorer: Luis Frota

WALTHAM ABBEY

Secretary: Dave Hodges, 13 Rosebank,Waltham Abbey, Essex EN9 3DE
Tel Nos: 07956 570408 (M) 01992 651594(H) 01992 719333(W)
FAX: 019902 768111

Ground: Capershotts, Sewardstone Road, Waltham Abbey, Essex. Tel: 01992 711287
Directions Nearest Bus: Waltham Abbey Nearest Station: Waltham Cross

Previous League: Essex & Herts Border Comb.

FACT FILE
Formed:
Colours:A;ll Green & White

Change Colours: All Red & Black

CLUB OFFICIALS
Chairman: Joe Collins (01992 467375)

EASTERN COUNTIES LEAGUE

SPONSORED BY: RIGEONS

Founded 1935

Hon. Patron: Derek Needham **President:** Roger Pauley

Secretary: B Badcock, 41 The Copse, Southwood, Farnborough, Hants GU14 0QD Tel: 01252 518 586 www.jewsonleague.co.uk

FINAL LEAGUE TABLE 2003-04

PREMIER DIVISION		P	W	D	L	F	A	Pts
1.	AFC Sudbury	42	32	5	5	123	30	101
2.	Maldon Town (Promoted)	42	30	6	6	107	35	96
3.	Wroxham	42	29	8	5	108	36	95
4.	Diss Town	42	27	5	10	104	54	86
5.	Soham Town Rangers	42	24	8	10	88	62	80
6.	Clacton Town	42	19	14	9	65	54	71
7.	Halstead Town	42	19	9	14	77	54	66
8.	Lowestoft Town	42	19	8	15	66	68	65
9.	Bury Town	42	17	11	14	86	82	62
10.	Newmarket Town	42	18	7	17	76	78	61
11.	Norwich United	42	17	10	15	51	58	61
12.	Mildenhall Town	42	16	12	14	72	61	60
13.	Histon Res.	42	14	10	18	70	77	52
14.	Wisbech Town (-1 pt)	42	13	8	21	64	82	46
15.	King's Lynn Res.	42	11	11	20	63	71	44
16.	Great Yarmouth Town	42	10	13	19	59	67	43
17.	Woodbridge Town	42	12	6	24	52	78	42
18.	Dereham Town	42	10	9	23	42	85	39
19.	Stowmarket Town	42	11	6	25	42	88	39
20.	Gorleston	42	9	10	23	56	86	37
21.	Tiptree United	42	9	7	26	40	95	34
22.	Fakenham Town	42	2	5	35	30	140	11

PREMIER DIVISION	1	2	3	4	5	6	7	8	9	10	11	12	13	14	15	16	17	18	19	20	21	22
1 AFC Sudbury		2-1	4-0	5-0	2-2	9-0	2-0	2-0	0-0	4-0	1-1	1-0	2-0	3-2	1-2	5-1	4-1	7-0	4-0	3-1	5-0	0-2
2 Bury Town	0-3		3-3	3-1	0-4	3-0	5-1	1-1	4-2	1-2	1-0	2-0	2-2	0-0	5-6	0-2	2-2	4-0	0-1	4-2	2-0	1-2
3 Clacton Town	0-2	1-0		1-1	3-2	3-2	2-2	3-0	0-0	2-0	1-0	1-1	2-1	4-1	2-3	2-1	2-5	3-2	3-1	6-0	0-3	2-1
4 Dereham Town	0-1	1-2	1-0		1-4	2-2	1-2	1-0	2-2	2-2	1-1	4-3	0-4	0-0	0-4	0-1	1-0	4-0	2-1	1-1	0-3	1-2
5 Diss Town	0-4	2-2	0-2	4-0		4-0	6-2	3-2	3-1	4-0	6-1	4-0	0-1	1-1	3-1	4-1	0-2	0-2	2-0	3-0	4-3	1-3
6 Fakenham Town	0-3	1-3	1-1	1-3	1-3		2-1	0-2	0-8	1-6	0-4	1-3	1-2	0-0	1-4	1-2	0-5	0-0	0-1	1-4	2-1	1-1
7 Gorleston	0-4	3-4	0-1	1-0	1-1	4-0		2-3	2-2	1-1	1-0	5-0	1-1	1-1	1-0	1-2	1-2	1-2	5-2	0-0	1-1	1-2
8 Great Yarmouth	1-3	1-1	1-1	2-1	1-2	4-0	3-4		1-0	4-1	1-2	0-1	1-2	5-2	1-1	1-2	1-2	2-1	0-0	2-2	1-3	2-2
9 Halstead Town	0-2	0-3	0-1	4-0	1-1	2-1	5-2	3-1		0-2	2-0	1-2	0-3	3-0	3-1	1-1	2-3	3-2	2-1	0-0	0-1	1-1
10 Histon Reserves	0-3	5-6	2-2	3-0	1-5	4-0	2-0	2-2	3-2		0-2	0-1	0-3	3-1	2-3	0-0	0-0	2-0	2-2	2-1	3-1	2-2
11 King's Lynn Res.	1-3	1-2	0-1	1-0	1-2	5-1	5-0	1-2	0-2	3-4		3-2	1-4	2-2	1-0	1-1	1-1	1-0	1-1	4-0	5-2	2-3
12 Lowestoft Town	1-6	3-0	0-0	4-1	0-2	5-1	1-1	3-1	1-2	2-1	4-3		3-1	1-1	1-4	2-1	2-2	2-1	1-0	1-1	2-1	0-0
13 Maldon Town	1-1	5-1	1-1	2-0	5-0	8-0	7-2	1-1	1-0	3-1	3-0	0-0		1-2	4-0	2-0	3-2	7-2	1-2	1-0	2-0	2-1
14 Mildenhall Town	3-1	7-2	0-0	2-0	0-1	5-0	2-1	2-0	2-1	1-1	2-0	3-1	0-3		1-2	2-0	1-2	2-2	4-0	3-1	2-2	0-1
15 Newmarket Tn	0-2	1-1	1-1	6-2	4-2	5-3	1-0	4-3	3-5	1-0	1-1	1-3	0-3	0-3		1-0	1-2	2-2	1-1	1-3	0-1	1-2
16 Norwich United	1-6	5-0	0-0	1-1	2-4	1-0	1-0	0-0	0-0	1-1	2-1	1-0	0-2	3-2	1-2		1-4	1-0	1-3	2-0	4-2	0-2
17 Soham Town R.	1-0	3-1	1-1	3-0	0-5	3-2	2-2	1-0	2-4	2-1	2-2	1-0	1-4	3-2	2-0	2-2		2-0	4-0	1-3	6-0	1-2
18 Stowmarket Tn	0-6	2-2	2-1	0-1	1-2	2-0	1-0	3-2	0-4	2-0	2-0	1-2	0-2	1-4	1-1	1-1	2-5		1-0	2-1	0-1	1-2
19 Tiptree Town	0-2	0-6	0-3	1-2	0-3	3-2	1-2	0-2	1-2	1-3	2-2	4-1	1-4	1-1	1-0	0-1	0-2	1-0		1-3	1-1	1-4
20 Wisbech Town	1-2	2-2	2-0	6-3	1-0	2-0	2-1	1-1	0-3	2-4	1-1	2-3	0-2	2-3	0-1	1-3	1-0	4-0	7-1		3-0	0-6
21 Woodbridge Tn	2-2	2-3	0-1	0-1	0-3	5-1	2-0	1-1	0-2	2-1	1-1	3-1	0-2	1-0	2-5	0-1	1-2	0-1	2-3	2-1		0-2
22 Wroxham	5-1	1-1	7-2	0-0	1-2	4-0	4-0	0-0	1-2	2-1	4-1	0-3	4-1	5-0	5-1	1-0	5-1	3-0	6-0	6-0	1-0	

FINAL LEAGUE TABLE 2003-04

DIVISION TWO		P	W	D	L	F	A	Pts
1.	Cambridge City Res.	38	25	8	5	76	40	83
2.	Harwich & Parkeston	38	24	8	6	89	48	80
3,	Leiston	38	22	8	8	74	40	74
4.	Stanway Rovers	38	20	10	8	69	43	70
5.	Kirkley	38	18	10	10	84	60	64
6.	Whitton United	38	19	5	14	85	57	62
7.	Godmanchester Rovers	38	17	8	13	54	52	59
8.	Ipswich Wanderers (-2 pts)	38	17	9	12	51	36	58
9.	Swaffham Town	38	15	13	10	62	54	58
10.	Ely City	38	19	1	18	60	58	58
11.	Haverhill Rovers	38	17	5	16	73	66	56
12.	Cornard United	38	15	7	16	53	60	52
13.	Long Melford	38	14	8	16	62	66	50
14.	Needham Market	38	14	5	19	67	73	47
15.	Felixstowe & Walton United	38	12	9	17	52	63	45
16.	March Town United	38	12	5	21	70	99	41
17.	Downham Town	38	9	7	22	43	79	34
18.	Hadleigh United	38	6	13	19	42	57	31
19.	Thetford Town	38	6	6	26	38	85	24
20.	Somersham Town	38	4	5	29	34	102	17

NB: Warboys Town withdrew during the season. Their results remain in the result grid below but have expunged from the league table.

DIVISION TWO		1	2	3	4	5	6	7	8	9	10	11	12	13	14	15	16	17	18	19	20	21
1	Cambridge City R		1-1	2-1	0-3	2-0	1-0	2-1	2-0	2-2	4-1	3-1	1-1	4-1	0-2	2-0	2-1	0-0	1-1	4-1	2-1	2-1
2	Cornard United	0-2		3-2	2-1	2-1	0-2	1-2	2-0	0-4	1-0	1-2	2-0	4-2	7-2	1-2	0-0	0-1	0-0	1-0	-	2-0
3	Downham Town	0-3	0-2		0-1	2-1	0-1	1-0	1-2	2-3	1-0	0-6	2-2	3-0	3-1	0-1	5-1	1-1	1-1	2-1	-	2-5
4	Ely City	1-4	1-0	1-0		1-0	3-1	2-1	1-2	2-0	3-0	2-3	1-2	2-1	2-0	2-1	4-0	0-3	1-0	4-1	3-2	4-0
5	Felixstowe & W.	0-2	0-1	2-0	3-1		1-3	3-1	1-1	0-1	3-1	2-2	1-3	0-3	2-3	2-1	1-2	1-1	2-0	2-2	-	2-2
6	Godmanchester R.	1-5	3-2	2-0	0-1	0-0		3-0	1-2	5-1	0-4	1-4	3-1	6-1	0-0	2-2	1-0	0-2	3-0	1-0	7-0	0-3
7	Hadeigh United	2-2	1-3	2-2	3-1	2-2	0-0		1-2	1-2	1-1	3-3	0-2	2-2	1-1	2-1	6-0	0-0	0-2	2-2	5-0	0-1
8	Harwich & Parke.	3-0	1-1	3-3	2-0	4-0	2-0	1-0		5-0	0-0	1-4	5-2	2-1	2-1	7-4	6-2	3-0	1-1	6-1	-	3-1
9	Haverhill Rovers	5-0	3-0	0-1	1-3	2-3	1-2	1-1	3-4		0-0	0-2	1-1	6-0	7-1	4-3	3-0	1-4	1-1	4-1	-	0-4
10	Ipswich Wanderers	0-1	7-0	2-1	3-0	0-2	0-0	1-0	0-1	2-1		0-0	1-0	5-1	2-3	2-0	1-0	1-1	1-1	0-1	-	2-1
11	Kirkley	1-1	2-1	2-0	2-1	3-4	0-2	2-1	3-4	3-0	0-1		2-2	0-2	5-3	3-0	1-0	2-2	3-0	4-1	-	1-3
12	Leiston	2-0	2-0	6-0	2-0	2-0	3-0	1-0	1-0	1-3	3-0	1-1		0-0	3-1	0-2	4-0	3-1	1-2	4-3	1-1	2-1
13	Long Melford	2-3	5-2	0-0	2-1	1-1	6-2	2-0	3-1	3-1	0-1	1-4	1-2		7-1	1-1	3-0	0-0	0-1	3-0	10-0	1-2
14	March Town Utd	1-2	5-1	8-2	2-1	1-1	1-2	2-1	0-1	1-3	1-4	4-2	0-2	2-2		0-2	4-2	2-0	1-2	3-2	-	0-2
15	Needham Market	0-2	2-1	4-0	1-1	0-1	1-1	0-1	0-3	0-1	2-1	2-2	1-6	4-0	7-2		5-0	4-2	1-2	4-0	-	0-2
16	Somersham Town	0-3	1-1	2-2	0-3	2-3	1-2	2-1	1-1	0-1	0-1	2-3	0-3	0-1	3-2	1-3		1-6	0-2	1-0	-	2-5
17	Stanway Rovers	1-1	0-3	1-0	4-1	2-0	0-0	3-1	2-2	1-2	0-2	3-1	2-0	2-0	6-2	0-2	4-2		1-0	3-1	5-4	3-1
18	Swaffham Town	1-2	0-0	3-2	5-3	3-2	2-0	0-0	0-4	3-1	2-2	3-2	1-1	1-1	2-2	9-3	3-3	1-2		3-1	-	3-2
19	Thetford Town	1-5	2-2	0-1	2-1	1-2	0-2	0-1	2-2	1-2	0-1	1-1	0-0	0-2	1-3	1-0	2-1	1-3	2-1		-	2-0
20	Warboys Town	-	-	-	-	1-8	-	-	-	-	-	1-3	-	-	-	0-3	-	-	-	-		-
21	Whitton UNited	1-3	1-3	4-0	5-0	3-1	2-2	1-1	3-0	3-2	1-1	2-2	2-3	0-1	5-2	6-1	4-1	1-2	1-0	4-1	3-2	

LEAGUE CUP

PRELIMINARY ROUND

Cornard United	v	Needham Market	3-0
Dereham Town	v	Thetford Town	1-1* 4-3p
Great Yarmouth Tn	v	Bury Town	0-1*
Harwich & Parke.	v	Tiptree United	2-1
Haverhill Rovers	v	Cambridge City Res.	1-8
Kirkley	v	Diss Town	3-5
Maldon Town	v	Swaffham Town	2-0
March Town United	v	Somersham Town	2-0
Mildenhall Town	v	Whitton United	2-2* 3-2r
Newmarket Town	v	Godmanchester Rovers	1-0
Woodbridge Town	v	Stanway Rovers	3-1*

FIRST ROUND

Bury Town	v	Woodbridge Town	5-4
Cambridge City R.	v	Diss Town	4-3
Dereham Town	v	Soham Town Rangers	0-1*
Ely City	v	Warboys Town	4-1
Felixstowe & W.U	v	Fakenham Town	2-1
Hadleigh United	v	AFC Sudbury	1-4
Histon Reserves	v	Long Melford	2-1
Ipswich Wanderers	v	March Town United	0-0* 5-4p
King's Lynn Res.	v	Halstead Town	1-6
Leiston	v	Stowmarket Town	0-2
Lowestoft Town	v	Downham Town	7-2
Maldon Town	v	Gorleston	3-2
Newmarket Town	v	Harwich & Parkeston	0-2
Norwich United	v	Mildenhall Town	1-0
Wisbech Town	v	Cornard United	5-1
Wroxham	v	Clacton Town	2-0

SECOND ROUND

AFC Sudbury	v	Harwich & Parkeston	2-2* 4-2r
Halstead Town	v	Wroxham	1-4
Lowestoft Town	v	Cambridge City Res.	0-4
Maldon Town	v	Felixstowe & Walton United	1-0
Norwich United	v	Bury Town	1-2
Soham Town R.	v	Ely City	4-1
Stowmarket Town	v	Ipswich Wanderers	2-1
Wisbech Town	v	Histon Res.	2-3

QUARTER-FINALS

AFC Sudbury	v	Wroxham	3-0
Bury Town	v	Cambridge City Reserves	3-2
Histon Res.	v	Soham Town Rangers	1-2
Maldon Town	v	Stowmarket Town	4-0

SEMI-FINALS

Bury Town	v	Maldon Town	0-1
Soham Town R.	v	AFC Sudbury	2-0

THE FINAL (8th May at Diss Town)

Maldon Town	v	Soham Town Rangers	2-1*

DIVISION ONE CUP

PRELIMINARY ROUND

Felixstowe & W.U.	v	Harwich & Parkeston	2-2* 10-9p
Hadleigh United	v	Ipswich Wanderers	0-1
Stanway Rovers	v	Long Melford	2-1
Swaffham Town	v	Ely City	2-2* 3-4p
Warboys Town	v	Godmanchester Rovers	0-2

FIRST ROUND

Cambridge City R.	v	Somersham Town	8-0
Downham Town	v	Godmanchester Rovers	0-1
Ely City	v	Thetford Town	2-0
Felixstowe & W.U.	v	Ipswich Wanderers	0-0* 3-4p
Kirkley	v	Needham Market	5-0
March Town United	v	Haverhill Rovers	0-1
Stanway Rovers	v	Cornard United	1-0
Whitton United	v	Leiston	0-0* 5-4p

QUARTER-FINALS

Ipswich Wanderers	v	Haverhill Rovers	2-3
Kirkley	v	Ely City	1-0
Stanway Rovers	v	Cambridge City Res.	2-2* 6-5p
Whitton United	v	Godmanchester Rovers	2-1*

SEMI-FINALS

Kirkley	v	Stanway Rovers	2-1
Whitton United	v	Haverhill Rovers	0-1

THE FINAL (3rd May at Diss Town)

Haverhill Rovers	v	Kirkley	2-0

AFC SUDBURY

Ground: Kingsmarsh Stadium, Brundon Lane, Sudbury, Suffolk CO10 1WQ (01787 376213)
Directions: From Sudbury centre follow Halstead/Chelmsford signs for about 1mile. 1st right after railway bridge at foot of steep hill, and 1st right after sharp left hand bend
Capacity: 2,500 Seats: 200 Cover: 150 Floodlights: Yes
Clubhouse: Matchdays/ training nights Shop: Yes Contact: Darren Witt (M) 0402 159375)

HONOURS WANDERERS - Eastern Co's Lg Div 1 92-93, Ess. & Suff. Border Lg(2) 89-91 (R-up 88-89), Suffolk Snr Cup 90-91**TOWN:**Southern Lge -Lge Cup 93-94, R-up 97,Champonship 93-94, Southern Div (Post War)R-up 93-94; Eastern Counties Lg x 7, R-up x 6, Lg Cup x 6, Suffolk Prem.Cup x 13, R-up x 8, Suffolk Sen. Cup (2); E. Anglian Cup 85-86 91-92, R-up 83-84 95-96; Essex Suff Border Lg x 5; E.S.B.L.Cup 49-50, R-Up 46-47; East F'lit Group -94 & 95 A.F.C.: Eastern League Champiuons 2001-02 Suffolk County Premier Cup Winners 2001-02

PREVIOUS **Names:** Sudbury Town (1885) & Sudbury Wanderers (1958) merged 1999
Leagues: Wanderers- Essex & Suffolk Border. Town Suffolk & Ipswich; Essex & Suffolk Border; Eastern Co 55-90; Southern 91-97 Eastern Co. 98-99
BEST SEASON **FA Vase:** 2002-03, 03-04 FA Vase Final (as A.F.C.)
FA Cup: 1st Round Proper, 00-01 (1-6 v Darlington)
TOWN **FA Vase:** Runners-up 88-89 **FA Trophy:** 3rd Rd.Proper 95-96
FA Cup: 2nd Rd Proper 96-97, 1-3 v Brentford. Played at Colchester Utd. F.C.

FACT FILE
Founded: 1st June,1999
Colours: Yellow/blue/yellow
Change Colours: All Red
Midweek Matchday: Tuesday
Programme: 48 + pages £1
Editor:Peter Scott (01787 379123)
Local Press : Suffolk Free Press, East Anglian Daily Times

CLUB PERSONNEL
Joint Chairmen: Nick Smith & Phil Turner
Secretary: David Webb
6 Melford Road, Sudbury, Suffolk CO10 1LS
Tel: 01787 372352 (H) 01787 886000 x6223 (B)
Manager: Gary Harvey

BURY TOWN

Secretary: Mrs Wendy Turner, 64 Winthrop Rd., Bury-St-Edmunds, Suffolk. IP333UF
Tel Nos: 01284 753688 (H) 01284 762291 (W) Club Website: www.burytownfc.co.uk
Ground: Ram Meadow, Cotton Lane, Bury St Edmunds, Suffolk IP33 1XP Tel: 01284 754721
Directions: Leave A14 at sign to Central Bury St Edmunds, follow signs to town centre at exit r'bout, at next r'bout 1st exit into Northgate St, L. at `T' junct (lights) into Mustow St, left immediately into Cotton Lane - ground 350 yds on right, through `Pay & Display' car park. 10 mins from station
Capacity: 3,500 Cover: 1,500 Seats: 300 Floodlights: Yes
Clubhouse: Members'/Public Bars open at matchdays **Club Shop:** Yes
HONOURS Eastern Counties Lg 63-64, R-up 37-38, Lg Cup 61-62 63-64; Metropolitan Lg 65-66, R-up 67-68 70-71, Lg Cup 67-68, Professional Cup 65-66; Suffolk Premier Cup (9); Suffolk Senior Cup 36-37 37-38 38-39 44-45 84-85
PREVIOUS **Leagues:** Norfolk & Suffolk; Essex & Suffolk Border; Eastern Co's 35-64 76-87; Metropolitan 64-71
Names: Bury St Edmunds 1895-1902; Bury Utd 02-06, Bury Town(1995) Ltd.
BEST SEASON **FA Cup:** 1st Rd replay 68-69, 0-3 v AFC Bournemouth (A) after 0-0
FA Vase: Qtr Finals 88-89 **FA Trophy:** 2nd Rd 70-71
CLUB RECORDS **Attendance:** 2,500 v Enfield, FA Cup 3rd Qual. Rd 1986
Goalscorer: Doug Tooley 58 **Appearances:** Doug Tooley **TransferFee Paid**: £1,500 for Mel Springett (Chelmsford 1990) **Fee Received**: £5,500 forSimon Milton (Ipswich)
Players progressing: D Lewis (Gillingham), L Carberry T.Pearce+S.Milton(Ipswich), T Bly (NorwichCity) + G Stevens (Brighton),

FACT FILE
Formed: 1872
Nickname: The Blues
Colours: All blue
Change colours:White/black/black
Midweek matchday: Tuesday
Programme: 40 pages £1.00
Editor: Chris Ward

CLUB PERSONNEL
Chairman: Russell Ward
Vice Chairman: Adrian LewisPresident: Cyril Elsey
Manager: Richard Wilkins
Asst Manager: Trevor Collins
Captain:Andrew Eady
Physio: Darren Gibbs

2003-04
Leading Goalscorer:James Tatham
Player of the Year:Ian MIller

CAMBRIDGE CITY RESERVES

Secretary: Stuart Hamilton, 55 Crowhill, Godmanchester, Huntingdon, Cambs
Tel: 01480 382675

Ground: City Ground, Milton Road, Cambridge CB4 1UY Tel: 01223 357973
Directions: 50 yards on left from start of A1309, Cambridge to Ely Rd. 30 minswalk from Cambridge BR
Capacity: 5,000 Cover: 1,400 Seats:423 Floodlights: Yes

Clubhouse: 11am-11pm Mon-Sat, 12-3 & 7pm-10.30 Sun. Bingo, Dances, Pool, Darts

Club Shop: Sells programmes, club history, badges, scarves, pennants, replica shirts etc. Contact Neil Harvey (01223 235991)

FACT FILE
Colours: White & black halves/black/white & black hoops
Change colours: Green & Yellow halves,green,green& yellow hoops
Midweek matchday: Monday
Programme Editor: Secretary

CLUB PERSONNEL
Chairman: Dennis Rolph
Fixtures Sec.: Andy Dewey
50 Doggett Rd., Cherry Hinton, Cambridge
01223 245694 (H) 01223 555410 (Bus. Fax)
Manager:Jeremy George
Tel; 01954 782484

AFC Sudbury Back Row (L-R): Andrew Claydon, Paul Betson, David Head, Dean Greygoose, Chris Howlett, Chris Tracey, Gary Harvey (Manager).
Front Row (L-R): Neil Calver, Shane Wardley, Gary Bennett, Brett Girling, AAron Gardiner.

Photo: Alan Coomes.

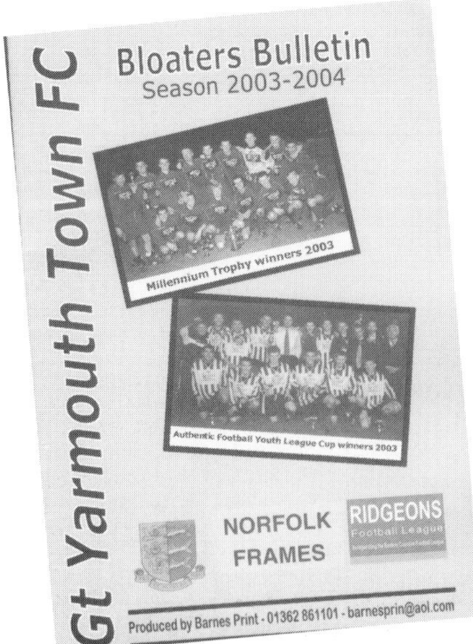

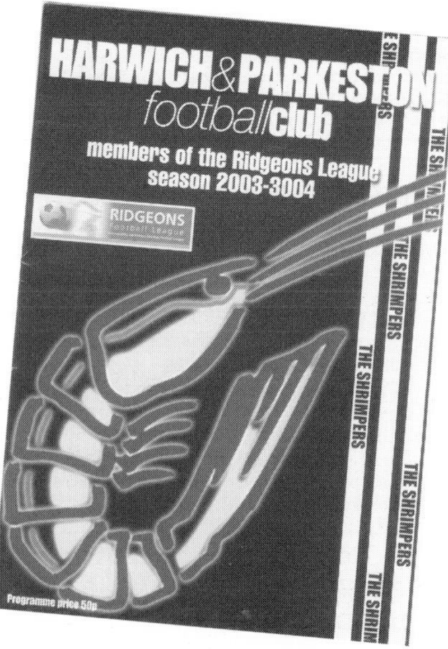

CLACTON TOWN

Secretary: Mrs Linda Pigeon c/o Club Tel: 01255 476133
email: Linda.ctfc@btopenworld.com
Ground: The Rush Green Bowl, Rushgreen Road, Clacton-on-Sea, Essex CO16 7BQ
Tel/Fax: 01255 432590 email: supporters@clacton-town.com
Directions: A133 to Clacton, at r'bout right into St Johns Rd, 4th left CloesLane, 3rd right Rushgreen Rd, ground approximately half mile on right. From B1027 take main Jaywick turn off (Jaywick Lane), then 2nd left after about half a mile into Rushgreen Rd. Ground 400 yds. 2 miles from Clacton (BR), buses 3, 5or 5a to Coopers Lane/Rushgreen Rd
Capacity: 3,000 Seats: 200 Cover: Yes Floodlights: Yes Club Shop: Yes
Clubhouse: Licensed club. Open 7-11pm Mon-Fri, all day Sat & Sun.
Hot & cold food available at all times.

HONOURS Southern Lg Div 1 59-60; Eastern Co's Lg R-up 36-37 53-54 64-65 74-75 (Lg Cup 73-74), Div 1 98-99 (Lg Cup 98-99); Eastern F/lit Cup 95-96; East Anglian Cup 53-54,99-00; WorthingtonEvans Cup 56-57 67-68 74-75.
PREVIOUS **Leagues:** Eastern Co's 35-37 38-58; Southern 58-64
Grounds: Clacton Stadium, Old Road 06-87; Gainsford Av (temp)
RECORD **Attendance:** 3,505 v Romford, FA Cup 1st Qual. Rd 1952 (at Old Road)
BEST SEASON FA Vase: 4th Rd 74-75,99-00 ,**FA Cup:** 1st Rd,1-3 v Southend U. (H) 60-61
Players progressing: Vivian Woodward (Spurs), Mick Everitt (Arsenal), Christian McLean (Bristol R.)

FACT FILE
Founded: 1892
Nickname: Seasiders
Colours: White/white/royal blue
Change colours: yellow/yellow/royal blue
Midweek Matches: Tuesday
Programme: 40 pages. £1.50
Editor: Karl Fuller 07930 104454
Local Press: Clacton Gazette
web site: www.clacton-town.co.uk

CLUB PERSONNEL
Owner: John Shuffleworth
Chairman: Mick Brpoadbent
Team Manager: Allan Dilloway

2003-04
Leading Goalscorer:Keith Hertherington
Captain:
Player of the Year: Darren Gould

DEREHAM TOWN

Secretary Ray Bayles, 62 Church View Close, Sprowston, Norwich NR7 8QA
Tel NO: 01603 789905
Ground: Aldiss Park, Norwich Road, Dereham, Norfolk NR20 3AL
Tel/Fax: 01362 690460
Capacity: 3,000 Seats: 50 Cover: 500 Club Shop: (01362 690460)
Directions: **From Swaffham** (A47) turn off to Bawdeswell/Swanton Morley, pass Little Chef on left and Ground is on right. **From Dereham** town centre follow A47. Aldiss Park is onleft before A47 **From Norwich** (A47)turn offas above ,left at ist T jct then right at 2nd Jct Ground on left.

HONOURS Anglian Combination 97-98, Jewson Eastern Div 1 R-up 2000-01
Jewson League Cup R-Up: 2001-2002

PREVIOUS **Leagues:** Dereham & Dist., East Anglian, Anglian Combination >98
Names: Dereham, Dereham Hobbies
Grounds: Recreation Ground 1890-1998

RECORD **Defeat:** 0-13, v Gorleston, Norfolk Sen. Cup 9.1.1926

FACT FILE
Formed: 1890
Nickname: The Magpies
Colours: Black & white/black/white
Change colours: all Red
Midweek matchday; Tuesday
Programme - 20 pages 50p
Editor: Barnes Print
Tel: 01362 860781 Fax: 01362 860977
Website: www.derehamtownfc.com

CLUB PERSONNEL
Chairman: George Hayes Tel: 01362 860922
Manager:Simon Barnes
Captain: Graham Barrett

2003-2004
TopGoalscorer:Graham Barrett
Player of the Year: Graham Challen

DISS TOWN

Secretary: Steve Flatman, 31 Aldrich Way, Roydon, Diss, Norfolk.IP22 4FJ (01379 641406)
Ground: Brewers Green Lane, Diss Tel: 01379 651223
Directions: Off B1066 Diss-Thetford Rd, near Roydon School.1.5 miles from Diss (BR)
Capacity: 2,500 Seats: 280 Cover: Yes Floodlights: Yes
Club Shop: Yes, including pennants
Clubhouse: Open evenings (except Sunday), Sat/Sun lunchtimes, and matchdays
HONOURS FA Vase 94-95; Eastern Co's Lg Div 1 91-92, Anglian Comb. 76-77 78-79(R-up 74-75, Div 1 67-68 73-74, Lg Cup 67-68 79-80 81-82), Norfolk & Suffolk Lg R-up 55-56 (Applegate Cup 56-57 57-58(joint)(R-up 55-56)), Norfolk Snr Cup 74-75 95-96, Norfolk Jnr Cup 1891-92, Jewson Prem Lge R-up 95-96 R-up Millennium Trophy 2001
PREVIOUS **Leagues**: Norwich & District; Norfolk & Suffolk 35-64; AnglianComb. 64-82
Ground: Roydon Road 1886-1982
BEST SEASON **FA Vase:** Winners 94-95, QF 91-92
RECORDS **Attendance:** 1,731 v Atherton LR, FA Vase SF 1st leg 19/3/94
Players progressing A Thurlow (Man City), M Cawston (Norwich), T Whymark(Ipswich), C Stafford, P Gibbs (Colchester United)

FACT FILE
Founded: 1888
Nickname: Tangerines
Sponsors: Apple Garages
Colours: Tangerine/navy/tangerine
Change colours: Sky blue/navy/navy
Midweek Matches: Tuesday
Reserve's League: Anglian Combination
Programme: 16 pages £1.00
Editor: Gary Enderby (01379 608767)

CLUB PERSONNEL
Chairman: Des Tebble
President: Michael Gooderham
Match Secretary: Pam Flatman
Treasurer: Tony Collins
Manager: Robert Fleck and P.Tong
Leading Goalscorer: Coreen Hardy

GORLESTON

Secretary: David House, 9 Magdalen Way,Gorleston, Norfolk NR31 7BW (01493 661600)
e.mail: dh@david house.co.uk

Ground: Emerald Park, Woodfarm Lane, Gorleston, Great Yarmouth Tel: 01493 602802

Directions: On Magdalen Estate - follow signs to Crematorium, turn left and follow road to ground. Five and a half miles from Great Yarmouth Vauxhall (BR)

Capacity: 5,000 Seats: 2000 Cover: 4,000 Floodlights: Yes

Clubhouse: Bar, colour TV, snacks. Matchday Tea, coffee,cold drinks, burgers, hotdogs, rolls
Club Shop: No

HONOURS Eastern Co's Lg 52-53 72-73 79-80 80-81; Lge Cup 55-56; Norfolk Snr Cup x 13, R-up x 25; Anglian Comb. 68-69, Norfolk & Suffolk Lg x 7; E Anglian Cup (3);Jewson Lge Div 1 95-96

PREVIOUS **Leagues:** Gt Yarmouth & Dist; Norfolk & Suffolk; Anglian Comb

BEST SEASON **FA Cup:** 1st Rd. 51-52, 57-58

RECORD **Attendance:** 4,473 v Orient, FA Cup 1st Rd 29/11/51

Players progressing: J Joblins (Norwich), M Bailey (Wolves), D Stringer(Norwich), R Carter (Aston Villa), D Carter (Man City), A Brown (Charlton), S Morgan (Cambridge), P Gibbs (Colchester)

FACT FILE

Founded: 1884
Nickname: Greens
Colours: Green & White/whitw/white
Change colours: All blue
Midweek Matchday: Tuesday
Programme: 56/60 pages £1.00
Editor:Simon Barnes Printing

CLUB PERSONNEL

Chairman & President: Jimmy Jones

Manager: Martin Sinclair

GREAT YARMOUTH TOWN

Secretary: Brian Smith, The Bungalow, Humberstone Farm, Cobholm, Great Yarmouth, Norfolk NR31 0AZ. Tel & Fax: 01493 656099

Ground: Wellesey Recreation Ground, Wellesey Road (01493 843373)

Directions: Just off Marine Parade, 200yds north of Britannia Pier.1/2 m from Vauxhall BR(BR)

Capacity: 3,600 Seats: 500 Cover: 2,100 Floodlights: Yes Club Shop: Yes

Clubhouse: (01493 843373). Committee Room, Sky TV, darts, pool. Hot & cold food

HONOURS Eastern Co's Lg 68-69 (R-up 56-57 67-68 77-78 78-79), Lg Cup 37-38 74-75 80-81; East Anglian Cup(3); Norfolk Senior Cup x 12, R-up x 22; Norfolk Premier Cupx 2 jt; Norfolk & Suffolk Lg 13-14 26-27 27-28; Anglian Comb. Cup 65-66(res); E Anglian Lg 56-57(res)

PREVIOUS **Leagues:** Norfolk & Suffolk

BEST SEASON **FA Cup:** 2nd Rd 52-53, 1st Rd 47-48 **FA Vase:** Semi-Final 82-83

RECORD **Attendance:** 8,944 v Crystal Palace, FA Cup 1st Rd 52-53
Appearances: Mark Vincent 673 games (1984-2003)
Scorer: Gordon South 298 (1927-47)
Win: 14-0, 2.2.10

Players progressing: R Hollis (Norwich), M Blyth & N Keeley (Scunthorpe), S Davy (West Ham), K Ready (Aston Villa), G Butcher (Blackburn)

FACT FILE

Founded: 1897
Nickname: Bloaters
Colours: Amber & black stripes/black/black
Change colours: All blue
Midweek Matches: Tuesday
Programme: 40 pages, #1.00
Editorial: Barnes Print, Dereham

CLUB PERSONNEL

Acting Chairman: John Baldry
Manager: T.B.A.
2002-03
Leading Goalscorer:Robert George
Player of the Year: Tony Spearing
2004-2005
Captain:Mark Vincent

HALSTEAD TOWN

Secretary: Stephen Webber, 12 Ravens Ave, Halstead, Essex CO9 1NZ
Tel: 01787 476959 (H) 01284 767278 (B)

Ground: Rosemary Lane, Broton Ind Est, Halstead, Essex CO9 2HR Tel: 01787 472082

Directions: A131 Chelmsford to Braintree - follow signs to Halstead.
In Halstead, 1st left after Police Station, then 1st right, and left to ground

Clubhouse: Open evenings and matchdays

PREVIOUS **Leagues:** North Essex; Halstead & District; Haverhill; Essex & Suffolk Border; Essex Senior 80-88
Grounds: Three Gates 1879-1948, Coggeshall Pieces, Ravens Meadow, King George Pl'y Field

RECORD **Attendance:** 4,000 v Walthamstow Avenue, Essex Senior Cup 1949

HONOURS Eastern Co's Lg 94-95 95-96, R-up 93-94 (Div 1 R-up 89-90), Cup 95-96; Essex Senior Trophy 94-95 96-97; Knight Floodlit Cup R-up 90-91; Essex &Suffolk Border Lg 57-59 77-78 94-95 (res), (R-up 49-50 54-55 60-61), Div 1 (res) 94-95); Essex Snr Lg Cup R-up 79-80; Essex Jnr Cup 01-02 46-47 (R-up 00-01)

Players progressing Steve Allen (Wimbledon Physio)

2003-2004: **Top Scorer**: Dave Barefield **P.o.Y.:** Glen Revell

FACT FILE

Founded: 1879
Nickname 'The Town'
Colours: White /black/white
Change colours:Red/white/red
Midweek Matches: Tuesday
Programme: Page 24 Price £1.00
Editor: Paul Downes Tel: 01787 477320 (H)
Local Press : Halstead Gazette

CLUB PERSONNEL

Chairman: Tony Lister
Vice-Chairman: T.B./A.
President: Michael Gage
Fixture Sec.: Steve Webber
Manager: Andy Clark
Physio: B Dunster
Captauin: Tony English

HISTON RESERVES

Secretary: Mick W Collis, 22 Haddows Close, Longstanton, Cambridge CB4 5DJ
Tel: 01954 201083 (H)

Ground Bridge Rd, Impington, Cambridge
Tel: 01223 232301 Fax: 01223 237373
Club Website: Website: www.histonfootballclub.tripod.com
EMAIL Address: gareth@corporate innovations.co.uk

Directions: Leave A14 northern Cambridge bypass on B1049 (signposted Histon and Cottenham). Ground half a mile on right.
5 miles from Cambridge (BR). Bus No.104

Capacity: 3,250 Seats: 250 Cover: 250 Floodlights: Yes

Clubhouse: Bar/lounge open Tues-Sun eves, Sun lunch and matchdays.Snacks available

HONOURS Eastern Co's Lg Div 1 R-up 01-02, Div.1 Lge Cup R-up 01-02.

FACT FILE

Founded: 1904
Colours: Red & black stripes/black/red & black
Change colours: Sky & navy/navy/sky & navy
Midweek matches: Wednesday

CLUB PERSONNEL

Chairman: Gareth Baldwin
President: G P Muncey
Manager: Nacer Relizani

2002-03
Leading Goalscorer:
Captain:
Player of the Year:

HARWICH & PARKESTON

Secretary: Andy Schooler, 21 The Vineway, Harwich, Essex CO12 4AX
01255 504590 (H) 01255 509700 (B) 01255 509718 (Bus. Fax)

Ground: Royal Oak, Main Road, Dovercourt, Harwich CO12 4AA Tel: 01255 503649

Directions: On main road into Dovercourt. 600 yds from Dovercourt (BR)

Capacity: 5,000 Seats: 350 Cover: 1,000 Floodlights: Yes

Clubhouse : Open every day. Dances, bingo, darts, pool, function room **Club Shop:** No

PREVIOUS **Leagues:** Eastern Co's 35-37 38-64; Essex County 37-38; Athenian 64-73 83-84; Isthmian 73-83 **Ground:** Phoenix Field, Seafront

RECORD **Attendance:** 5,649 v Romford, FA Amat Cup 4th Rd 1938

BEST SEASON

FA Vase: Q-F 90-91

FA Amateur Cup: R-up 1898-99, 52-53

HONOURS: FA Amateur Cup R-up 1898-99 52-53; Eastern Counties 35-36(jt) Lg Cup 35-36 36-37 96-97; Essex County 37-38; Athenian Div 1 R-up 65-66 Div 2 64-65, Lg Cup 64-65; Essex Sen. Cup 1898-99 36-37; Essex Sen. Trophy 89-90; AFA Senior Cup 35-36 36-37; Worthington Evans Cup 80-81

FACT FILE

Founded: 1875 Nickname: Shrimpers
Colours: White & black/black/black
Change colours: All Red
Midweek Matches: Tuesday
Reserves: Essex & Suffolk Border Lge Prem. Div
Programme: 28 pages, 50p
Editor: Carl Allen Tel: 01255 552510
Website: mysite.freeserve.com/the shrimpers

CLUB PERSONNEL

Chairman:Tony Armstrong
Pres:Terry Rowlands Press Off: Carl Allan
Manager: Mitchell Springett
2003-04 Leading Goalscorer: Matt Carmichael
P.o.Y.: Lee Neale
2004-05 Captain: Nathan Munson

KING'S LYNN RESERVES

Secretary: Norman Cesar, 42 Woodlands Gardens,North Wootton, Kings Lynn, Norfolk.
Tel No: 01553 631336

GROUND The Walks Stadium, Tennyson Road, King's Lynn PE30 5PB
Tel: 01553 760060

Directions: At mini r-about arriving from A10/A47 take Vancouver Avenue. Ground on left after a half mile. Quarter mile from King's Lynn (BR), half mile from bus station

Capacity: 4,000 Cover: 2,700

Clubhouse: Normal licensing hours, with extension on matchdays

Club Shop: Stocks a wide range of clothing and associated goods (01553 631336)

FACT FILE

Colours: Yellow with blue trim
Change colours: All white
Midweek matches: Tuesday

CLUB PERSONNEL

Manager: Robert Taylor

2003/2004
P.o.Y.: Charlie Defty
Top Scorer: Simon Bush

LEISTON

Chairman: Andrew Crisp, 14 Huntingfield Road, Leiston,Suffolk IP164DH (01728 833913)

Secretary: David Rees, 7 Hancocks Close, Leiston, Suffiolk Ip16 4LD
Tel No: 01728 833549 e-mail: gagrees@aol.com

Ground: LTAA, Victory Road, Leiston, Suffolk IP16 4LD
Tel: 01728 830308

Directions:

Capacity: Covered Seating: 53 Covered Standing: 400 Floodlights: Yes

Honours: Jewson Eastern League Div 1 Cup Winners 2002

Record **Attendance:** 269 v Kirkley 27.12.03

2003- 2004 **Player of the Year:** Tim Sparks **Top Scorer:** Glen Driver 26

FACT FILE
Formed: 1880
Colours: Navy & white/navy/navy
Change colours: Yellow/black/white
Midweek matches: Wednesday
Programme: Yes
Editor: Pat ChallisTel: 07980 186223

Manager: Steven Wright
Tel: 01728 688618
Captain: Carl Chenery

LOWESTOFT TOWN

Secretary: Terry Lynes, 31 Avondale Road Lowestoft, Suffolk NR32 2HU
Tel: 01502 564034 (H) 07930 872947(M)
E-mail:terry@ltfcblues.freeserve. co. uk
Ground: Crown Meadow, Love Rd, Lowestoft Tel: 01502 573818
Directions: Just off A12, 10 mins from Lowestoft (BR)
Capacity: 3,000 Seats: 466 Cover: 500 Floodlights: Yes
Clubhouse: Pub hours, Snacks available **Club Shop:** Yes (incl metal badges)

HONOURS Eastern Co's Lg(8) 35-36(jnt) 37-38 62-63 64-65 67-68 69-71 77-78, Lg Cup(8) 38-39 54-55 65-67 68-69 75-76 83-84; 00-01Norf. & Suffolk Lg(8) 1897-99 1900-04 28-29 30-31; Suffolk Prem. Cup(7) 66-67 71-72 74-75 78-80; 99-00,00-01Suffolk Snr Cup(10) 02-03 22-24 25-26 31-32 35-36 46-49 55-56; E Anglian Cup(10); Anglian Comb. (Res.) 77-78 79-80 (Lg Cup 76-77); E Anglian Lg (Res.) 57-58 63-64

PREVIOUS **League:** Norfolk & Suffolk 1897-1935
BEST SEASON **FA Cup:** 1st Rd 26-27 38-39 66-67, 67-68, 77-78
RECORDS **Attendance:** 5,000 v Watford, FA Cup 1st Rd 67
Goalscorer: M Tooley 383 **Appearances:** C Peck 629
Win: 19-0 v Thetford Town (H), Eastern Counties League

Players progressing: Eddie Spearitt (Ipswich 1965), Nigel Cassidy (Norwich1967), Richard Money (Scunthorpe 1973), Graham Franklin (Southend 1977)

FACT FILE
Founded: 1885
Nickname: Blues
Sponsors: CWA Group
Colours: Royal Blue/white/blue
Change colours: White & Navy
Midweek Matches: Tuesday
Reserves' Lge: Anglian Combination
Programme:44 pages £1.00
Editor: Shaun Cole (07946 438298)
Website: www.lowestofttownfc.co.uk

CLUB PERSONNEL
Chairman: Shaun Cole
President: Roy Harper
Manager: Micky Chapman

MILDENHALL TOWN

Secretary: Val Clarke, Crundale House,Manor Road, Mildenhall,Suffolkl IP28 7EL
Tel No: 01638 718324
Ground: Recreation Way, Mildenhall, Suffolk (01638 713449)

Directions: Next to swimming pool/carpark, quarter of a mile from town centre

Capacity: 2,000 Covered Seats: 50 Covered Standing: 200
Floodlights: Yes

Clubhouse: Open matchdays & functions. Light refreshments available

HONOURS Suffolk Junior Cup 1899-1900

PREVIOUS **Leagues:** Bury & District; Cambs Lg 2B, 1B & Premier

RECORD **Attendance:** 450 v Derby County. Friendly July 2001

2003-04

Leading Scorer: Owen Paynter Player of the Year:Graham Rush

FACT FILE

Founded: 1890
Nickname: The Hall
Colours: Amber/black/black
Change colours:All RedMidweek Matchday: Tuesday
Programme: £1.00
Editor: Frank Marshall (01638 720616)
Local Press : Bury Free Press, Newmarket Journal, Cambridge Evening News,East Anglian Daily Times,Green 'Un
CLUB PERSONNEL
Chairman: Martin Tuck
Vice Chairman: Bill Flynn
Fixture Sec:Eric Lloyd Tel: 01638 718324

Managers: Trevor Munns

Captain: Mark Reeder

NEWMARKET TOWN

Fixture Secretary: Elaine Jeakins, 140 New Cheveley Road,Newmarket CB88BY
Tel Nos: 01638 602525 (H) 01638 750201 (W) 07801 815682 (M)
Ground: Cricketfield Road, off New Cheveley Road, Newmarket (01638 663637)

Directions: 400 yds Newmarket (BR) - turn right into Green Rd, right at cross roads New Cheveley Rd, ground at top on left
Capacity: 1,750 Seats: 144 Cover: 150 Floodlights: Yes
Clubhouse: Matchdays only. Refreshments available

HONOURS Suffolk Snr Cup 34-35 93-94; Cambs Invitation Cup 58-59; Cambs Chall. Cup 21-22 26-27; Cambs Snr Lg, 19-20; Ipswich Snr Lg 30-31 31-32 32-33 33-34; Peterborough Lg 57-58; Suffolk Premier Cup 93-94 94-95 96-97

PREVIOUS **League:** Bury Snr; Ipswich Snr; Essex & Suffolk Border; Utd Co's 34-37; Eastern Co's 37-52

BEST SEASON **FA Cup:** 4th Qual. Rd 92-93, 0-2 v Hayes (H)
FA Vase: 4th Round 91-92
RECORD **Attendance:** 2,701 v Abbey Utd (now Cambridge Utd), FA Cup 1st Qual.Rd 1/10/49

Players progressing: Mick Lambert (Ipswich), M Wright (Northampton), G Tweed(Coventry), R Fuller (Charlton), Colin Vowden (Camb.Utd.) and A Rhodes (Brentford)

FACT FILE
Founded: 1877
Nickname: Jockeys
Colours: Yellow & navy/navy/yellow
Change Colours: All Red
Midweek Matches: Tuesday
Programme:£1.00
Editor: Tony Pringle (01638 669438)

CLUB PERSONNEL
Chairman: Alan Collen
President: M J Nicholas
Manager: Chris Nunn

NORWICH UNITED

Secretary: Keith Cutmore,42 Desmond Drive,Old Catton, Norwich NR6 7JN
Tel. No.: 01603 407148 (H) 07946033588 (M)

Ground: Plantation Road, Blofield, Norwich, Norfolk NR13 4PL
Tel: 01603 716963
Website:www.norwichunited.fsnet.co.uk

Directions: Half a mile from Blofield village - coming from Norwich on Yarmouth Rd turn left in Blofield at Kings Head pub & follow to Plantation Rd (grd on right after bridge over bypass). 1/2 hour Brundall BR (Norwich-Yarmouth line)
Capacity: 3,000 Seats: 100 Cover: 1,000 Floodlights: Yes
Clubhouse: Matchday food & drink: Tea, coffee, cold drinks, hotdogs, burgers, soup, sandwiches, rolls
Club Shop: Yes incl. metal badges & pennants

HONOURS Eastern Co's Lg Div 1 90-91 01-02, R-up 89-89, Lg Cup 91-92, Anglian Combination 88-89. Jewson League Div 1 2001-02
PREVIOUS **Ground:** Gothic Club, Heartsease Lane, Norwich (until end of 90-91)
RECORD **Attendance:** 401 v Wroxham, League match, 2/10/91
Goalscorer: M Money **Appearances:** Tim Sayer

FACT FILE
Founded: 1903
Nickname: Planters
Colours: Yellow&blue/blue/blue
Change colours: All red.
Midweek Matches: Tuesday
Programme: 24 pages, 50p
Editorial Office:Barnes Print (01362 861101)
Local Press : Eastern Counties Newspapers

CLUB PERSONNEL
Chairman: John Hilditch, Pres Michael Miles
Vice-Chairman: Peter Bowyer
Manager: Paul Franklin Physio: Martyn Parker

SOHAM TOWN RANGERS

Secretary: Chris Abbott, 6B Broad Piece, Soham, Ely Cambs. CB7 5EL (07760 222487)
Ground: Julius Martin Lane, Soham, Ely , Cambs.CB7 5DE Tel: 01353 720732

Directions: A142 between Newmarket and Ely, at roundabout at northern end of by-pass turn left towards town centre and then right at the corner shop into Julius Martina Lane. Ground is on left
Capacity: 2,000 Seats: 250 Cover: 1,000 Floodlights: Yes Shop: Yes

Clubhouse: Function Room, Lounge Bar, Stud Bar, Public Bar.Available for private hire
Clubhouse Manager: M.Howe **Club Shop:** No.**HONOURS**
Eastern Co's Lg Div 1 R-up 92-93; Peterborough & District League (3), Milleniuim Cup 2000-01, Cambs Invitation Cup 1990-91, 97-98, 98-99
PREVIOUS **Leagues:** Peterborough & Dist
Ground: Soham Rangers: Brook Street 1919-47
Names: Soham Town and Soham Rangers merged in 1947
RECORD **Attendance:** 3,000 v Pegasus, FA Amateur Cup 1963
BEST SEASONS **F.A.Cup:** 3rd Q v Kings Lynn (A) 70-71
F.A.Vase: 4th Round v Aldershot Town (A) 93-94

FACT FILE
Founded: 1947
Nickname: Town or Rangers
Main Sponsor: C.J.Murfitt
Colours: Green/ black/green
Change colours: Blue/black/ black
Midweek Matchday: Tuesday
Reserves ' League: Cambs Senior. A
Prog: £1.00 Editor:Fred Parker 01353 624500
Local Press : Ely Standard, Newmarket Journal, Cambridge Evening News

CLUB PERSONNEL
Chairman: Colin Murffitt Pres: Vinnie Jones
Manager Kevin Pritchard
Ass.Manager : Brett Natthews
Coach: Shawn Sowden Physio: M. Drury

2003-04
Leading Goalscorer:Steve Bugg
Ps o.Y: Peter Hinde & Michael Simpson

2004-2005
Captain: Peter Hinde

STOWMARKET TOWN

Secretary: Mr Mark Bolton,45 Primrose Way, Needham Market, Suffolk.
Tel Nos: 01449 721394 (H) and 07866 17802 (M)

Ground: Green Meadows Stadium, Bury Road, Stowmarket
Tel: 01449 612533

Directions: About 800 yds from Stowmarket BR station - turn right at 1st lights and head out of town over r'bout into Bury Road - ground on right
Capacity: 2,000 Seats: 200 Cover: 450 Floodlights: Yes

Clubhouse: Bar open 6.30pm onwards Mon-Fri, weekends 12.0pm onwards.
Matchday food available Club Shop: No.

HONOURS Eastern Co's Lg R-up 91-92, Suffolk Premier Cup(4), Suffolk Snr Cup(10)
Suffolk Jnr Cup., Churchman Cup: 99-00.91-92,92-93

PREVIOUS **Leagues:** Ipswich & Dist.; Essex & Suffolk Border 25-52
Grounds: The Cricket Meadow, 1883-1984
Names: Stowupland Corinthians; Stowmarket Corinthians; Stowmarket FC

BEST SEASON **FA Cup: 2nd Q Rd 1992** **FA Vase:** 4th Rd 1983-84

RECORD **Attendance:** 1,200 v Ipswich Town, friendly July 1994
At Cricket Meadow: 3,800 v Romford, FA Amtr Cup 1st Rd 15/12/51

Players progressing: Craig Oldfield (Colchester), Les Tibbott, Ted Phillips & Brian Klug (Ipswich)

FACT FILE
Founded: 1883
Nickname: Stow
Colours: Gold & black/black/black
Change colours: All Red
Midweek Matches: Wednesday
Reserves' Lge: Essex & Suffolk Border
Programme: 20 pages,£1.00
Ed: Brian Seaman (01449 775166)
Local Press: East Anglian, Bury Free Press

CLUB PERSONNEL
Chairman: Andrew Horrex
President: John Bultitude
Fixture Sec: Christine Gillingham
23 Windermere Road,Stowmarket, Suffolk
Tel& Fax: 01449 674507(H) 07880 732416(M)
Manager: Mark Barnard Coach: Mark Barnard
Physio: Deeann Kirton

2003-04
Top scorer: Paul Nozedar P.o.Y.: Richard Butler

2004-2005
Captain:Kevin Barker

WISBECH TOWN

Secretary: Colin Gant, 5 Oxford Olace, Terrington-St-Clement Kings Lynn , Norfolk 01553 828600 **Ground**: Fenland Park, Lerowe Road, Wisbech, Cambs Tel: 01945 584176
Directions: Follow A47 bypass to the West Walton turn off roundabout where there is a Little Chef, turn left for Wisbech, Lerowe Road is first left after 30mph sign. Entering town from north along A1101 cross Freedom Bridge, atroundabout go straight over sign Walsoken/West Walton
Capacity: 3,800 Seats: 284 Cover: 1,000 Floodlights: Yes
Clubhouse: Open every evening. Matchday food & drink - Tea, coffee, cold drinks, confectionary, burgers, hotdogs, soup, sandwiches, rolls Club Shop (open matchdays): Contact Secretary

PREVIOUS **Leagues:** Peterborough 1920-35; Utd Co's 35-50; Eastern Co's 50-52 70-97; Midland 52-58; Southern 58-70, 97-02

CLUB RECORDS Attendance: 8,004 v Peterborough United, Midland League 25/8/57
Goalscorer: Bert Titmarsh 246 (31-37) **Appearances**: Jamie Brighty (731)

BEST SEASON **FA Cup:** 2nd Rd 57-58, 97-98 League clubs defeated: Colchester
FA Trophy: 3rd Qual Rd. 97-98 **FA Vase:** Semi-Finals 84-85, 85-86

HONOURS Southern Lg Div 1 61-62; Utd Co's Lg (3) 46--47-48 49-50+ 61-62 (res) (R-up 48-49, Lg Cup 35-36 (R-up 46-47); Midland Lg R-up 57-58; Eastern Co's Lg 71-72 76-77 90-91, R-up 70-71 73-74 83-84 92-93 96-97, Lg Cup x4, R-up x3; Cambs Invit Cup x8; E Anglian Cup 87-88 (R-up 40-41 48-49); Peterborough Lg x5; Peterborough Snr Cup 32-33 76-77 89-90 97-98

2003-2004 **Player of the Year**: Scott Johnson **Top Scorer**: Andy Furnell

FACT FILE
Founded: 1920 Nickname: Fenmen
Newsline: 09066 555865
Colours: Red/white/red
Change colours: Yellow/Green/Yellow
Midweek Matchday: Tuesday
Programme: Pages: 44 Price: £1
Editor:Spencer Larham
01945 581200 or 07793863849

CLUB PERSONNEL
Directors
Chairman: Barry Carter
Vice Chairman: George Campion
C.Gant, D.Parson, T.Wright, D.Vincent, C.Garwood and T.Close.
President: J W A Chilvers
Press Off.: Chris Smith (01945 476325)
Manager:Jackie Gallagher & Roy McManus
Reserve Team Manager: Stuart Webb
Youth Manager:: Trevor Melton

WOODBRIDGE TOWN

Secretary: Eric Smy,10 Peterhouse Crescent,Woodbridge, Suffolk IP12 4HT
Tel No: 01394 384213

Ground: Notcutts Park, Seckford Hall Road, Woodbridge, Suffolk IP12 4DA Tel: 01394 385308

Directions: Turning into Woodbridge off last rounda'bout from Lowestoft, or first roundabout from Ipswich. Take first turning left and first left again. Drive to ground at end of road on left.

Capacity: 3,000 **Seats:** 50 **Cover:** 200
Floodlights: Yes

Clubhouse: Visitors bar, lounge bar, function hall.Matchday Tea, coffee, cold drinks, hotdogs, soup, burgers, sandwiches, rolls.

HONOURS Suffolk Sen Cup(4), Jun Cup (4); Eastern Co Lg Cup 93-94 97-98, Lge Div 1 R-up 93-94; Ipswich Sen Lge (2)

PREVIOUS **Leagues:** Suffolk & Ipswich Ground: Kingston PF

BEST SEASON **FA Cup:** 3rd Rd Q 97-98 & 00-01 **FA Vase:** 6th Round 98-99

RECORD **Attendance:** 3,000 v Arsenal, floodlight opener 2/10/90

FACT FILE
Founded: 1885
Nickname: The Woodpeckers
Sponsors: Brafe Engineering
Colours: Black & white stripes/black/black
Change colours: Yellow/blue/yellow
Midweek Matchday: Tuesday
Reserves League: Essex & Suffolk Border
Programme: 20-24 pages ,50p
Match Secretary & Programme Editor:
D Crowley(07766 952997)
Local Press : East Anglian Daily Times

CLUB PERSONNEL
Chairman: Keith Dixon
President:Andrew Dalby
Football Sec: David Crowley (01394 384853)
Commercial Manager: Andy Leech
Manager: Mick Stockwell

2003-04
Leading Goalscorer:Aren Howell
Player of the Year: Mark Bailey

WROXHAM

Secretary : Chris Green, 24 Keys Drive, Wroxham, Norfolk NR12 8S Tel: 01603 783936 (H) 079412385 (M) Email Address: secretary@wroxhamfc.com
Ground: Trafford Park, Skinners Lane, Wroxham, Norfolk Tel: 01603 783538

Directions: Arriving from Norwich turn left at former Castle PH and keep left to ground. One and a half miles from Wroxham + Hoveton (BR). Buses 722, 724 and717
Capacity: 2,500 Seats: 50 Cover: 250 Floodlights: Yes
Clubhouse: Bar, pool, darts etc. Drinks, hot & cold food Club Shop: No

HONOURS Eastern Co's Lg 91-92 92-93 93-94 96-97 97-98, 98-99, R-Up x 3. Lg.Cup 92-93, 99-00, 92-93 R-up 90-91), Div 1 88-89; Norfolk Snr Cup 92-93 96-97 97-98;99-00,01-2 03-4 Anglian Comb(6) (LgCup(7); Res did the double in 94-95.Jewson Res K.O. Cup 00-01

PREVIOUS **Leagues:** Norwich City; East Anglian; Norwich & Dist.; Anglian Comb. 64-88
Grounds: Norwich Road; The Avenue; Keys Hill (all pre-1947)

BEST SEASON **FA Vase:** Quarter Final v Durham City 2001-02

RECORDS **Attendance:** 1,011 v Wisbech Town, E. Counties Lge Prem. Div. 16/3/93
Goalscorer: Matthew Metcalf. Appearances: Stu Larter
Win: 15-2 v Thetford Town (H), E. Counties Lge Prem. Div. 17/1/92
Defeat: 1-24 v Blofield (A), Norwich & District League, early 1960s

Players progressing: Matthew Metcalf (Brentford) 93, Paul Warne (Wigan Athletic) 97

FACT FILE

Founded: 1892
Nickname: Yachtsmen
Colours: All Blue
Change colours: All Red
Midweek Matchday: Tuesday
Reserves ' League: Anglian Comb Prem Div
Programme: 20 pages
Editor: Matt Carpenter
Local Press : North Norfolk
Eastern Football (Norwich 628311)
Web-site:www.wroxhamfc.com

CLUB PERSONNEL

Chairman: Pat Pen President: Les King
Press Officer: Secretary
Manager: Bruce Cunningham
Physio: Martin Parker

2003-04

Leading Goalscorer: Russell Stock
Captain:Justin Fox
Player of the Year: Martin McNeil

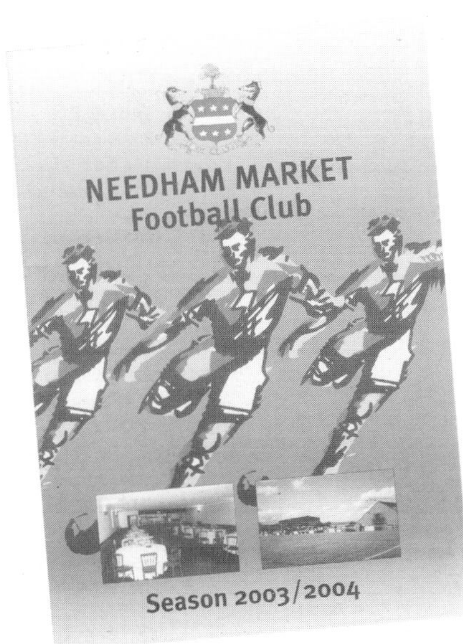

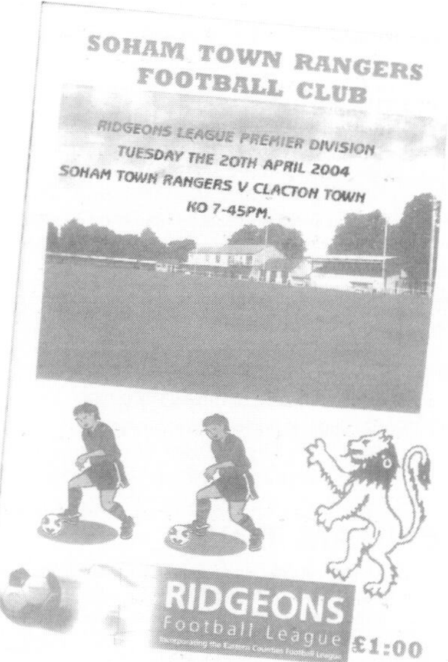

SOHAM TOWN RANGERS
FOOTBALL CLUB
RIDGEONS LEAGUE PREMIER DIVISION
TUESDAY THE 20TH APRIL 2004
SOHAM TOWN RANGERS V CLACTON TOWN
KO 7-45PM.
RIDGEONS
Football League
£1:00

CORNARD UNITED

Secretary: Chris Symes, 22 Greenacres, Mile End, Colchester, Essex CO4 (01206 851627)
Ground: Blackhouse Lane Sportsfield, Great Cornard, Suffolk (01787 376719)
Directions: Left off r'bout on A134 coming from Ipswich/Colchester intoSudbury, follow signs for Country Park - ground is immediately opposite along Blackhouse Lane
Capacity: 2,000 Seats: 250 Cover: 500 Floodlights: Yes Club Shop: No
Clubhouse: Open matchdays & Sunday lunchtimes. Matchday Tea, coffee, colddrinks, & snacks
HONOURS Eastern Co's Lg Div 1 89-90 (Lg Cup R-up 92-93), Essex & Suffolk BorderLg 88-89 (Lg Cup 88-89), Suffolk Snr Cup 89-90, Suffolk Jnr Cup R-up 84-85, Harwich Senior Charity Cup 2001-02, Eastern Floodlight League Cup 2001-02
PREVIOUS Leagues: Sudbury S/day 64-65; Bury St Edmunds & Dist 65-72; Colchester71-78; Essex Suffolk Bord 78-89. Grounds: Cornard Rec 64-71; Great CornardUpper School 71-85
RECORDS: Appearances: Keith Featherstone **Goalscorer :** Andy Smiles
Attendance: 400 v Colchester Utd 1997 **Win:** 18-2 v St Peters House, Colchester Lge 14/9/72
Defeat: 4-10 v Finningham, Bury Lge 7/2/68

FACT FILE
Founded: 1964 Nickname: Ards
Sponsors: Pizza Town
Colours: All Navy Blue
Change colours: White/Navy Blue/White
Midweek Matches: Tuesday
Reserve League: Essex & Suffolk Border
Prog:16 pages Ed:Neil Cheese(01787311368)
Local Press : Suffolk Free Press,
East Anglian Daily Times
CLUB PERSONNEL
Chairman: Michael Ford
Vice-Chair: Mike Ford
Manager: Chris Symes
Ass.t Manager:Jason Stalker Physio: Mike Ford

DOWNHAM TOWN

Secretary: F. Thorne, 6 Maple Rd., Downham Market, Norfolk, PE38 9PY. (01366 382563)

Ground: Memorial Field, Lynn Road, Downham Market, Norfolk (01366 388424)

Directions: One and a quarter miles from Downham Market (BR) - continue to townclock, turn left and ground is three quarters of a mile down Lynn Road
Capacity: 1,000 Seats: 60 Cover: Yes Floodlights: Yes
Clubhouse: Bar open matchdays, refreshments & snacks available

HONOURS Peterborough Lg (5) 62-63 73-74 78-79 86-88;
Norfolk Senior Cup 63-64 65-66 (R-up(3) 66-69)

PREVIOUS Leagues: Peterborough

RECORD Attendance: 325 v Wells Town Norfolk Senior Cup, 1998-99

FACT FILE
Founded: 1881
Nickname: Town
Sponsor: Lynwere Engineering
Colours: Red/white/red
Change colours: Sky/Navy/sky
Midweek Matches: Tuesday
Programme: Yes, with entry
Editor: Chairman

CLUB PERSONNEL
Chairman: John Fysh
President: Louis Barker
Manager: Robin Sainty

ELY CITY

Secretary: Derek Oakey, 11 Frederick Talbot Close, Soham, Nr. Ely Cambs, CB7 5EY
Tel: 01353 722141 (H) 01353 722179 (W) email: derk.oakey@tesco.net
Ground: Unwin Sports Ground, Downham Road (01353 662035)
Directions: A10 Ely by-pass turn off for Downham. 3 miles (approx) from Ely(BR)
Capacity: 1,500 Seats: 150 Cover: 350 Floodlights: Yes
Clubhouse: Open matchdays, refreshments available
Club Shop: Metal Badges: Yes
HONOURS Cambs Snr Cup 47-48, Eastern Co's Lg R-up 69-70 (Lg Cup 79-80)
Jewson Eastern Div 1 Winners 1996-97,R-up 1999-00,Cup Winners 99-00
PREVIOUS Leagues: Peterborough; Central Alliance 58-60
Grounds: Paradise Ground (1890 1986)
BEST SEASON FA Cup: 1st Rd 56-56 (2-6 v Torquay)
RECORD Gate: 260 v Soham, Eastern Co's Lg Div 1, 12/4/93
At old ground: 4,260 v Torquay, FA Cup 56-57

FACT FILE
Founded: 1885Nickname: Robins
Colours: All red with white trim
Change colours: All Blue
Midweek Matches: Tuesday
Programme: 24 pages- 50p
Editor: Derek Oakley
Local Press: Ely Standard (01353 667831)
Club Website: elycityfc.com
CLUB PERSONNEL
Chairman: Robert Button
Manager: Steven Taylor
2003-2004
Player of the Year & Top Scorer: Jon Hawes

FAKENHAM TOWN

Secretary: Eddie Linnell, 40 Warren Avenue, Fakenham, Norfolk. NR21 8NP
Tel Nos: 01328 855445 (H&W) 07939 171254 (M)
Ground: Clipbush Lane, Fakenham NR21 8SW Tel/Fax: 01328 856222
Directions: Corner of A148 & Clipbush Lane
Capacity: 3,000 Seats: 264 Cover: 500 Floodlights: Yes

Clubhouse: Bar, TV. Refreshments available Tel: 01328 855859 Club Shop: Yes
HONOURS Norfolk Snr Cup 70-71 72-73 73-74 91-92 93-94 94-95;,98-99 Eastern Co's Premier Division R-up: 98-99, Lg Div1, R-up 91-92; Anglian Comb. Cup 78-79
PREVIOUS Leagues: N Norfolk 1884-1910; Norwich & Dist 10-35; Norfolk & Suffolk 35-64; Anglian Comb 64-87
Grounds: Hempton Green 1884-89; Star Meadow 89-1907; Barons Hall Lawn 1907-96
BEST SEASON FA Vase: 98-99 3rd Rd **FA Cup:**
RECORD Gate: 1100 v Watford-official opening of new ground
Players progressing Nolan Keeley (Scunthorpe)

FACT FILE
Founded: 1884
Nickname: Ghosts
Sponsors:Warner Paperbacks
Colours: Amber & black/black/amber
Change colours: All White
Midweek Matchday: Tuesday
Reserves' League: Anglian Comb
Programme: 32 pages, 50p
Editor: John Cushion
Tel: 01328 862548
Local Press : Dereham & Fakenham Times

CLUB PERSONNEL
Chairman: Tim Amos
President:Tony Fisher
Press Officer: J Cushion
Commercial Manager: T.Vertigan
Managers: Stuart Woodhouse

FELIXSTOWE & WALTON UNITED

Secretary: Chris& Jane Ryan,43 Brook Lane,Felixstowe,Suffolk IP11 7LG
Tel No: 01394 275873

Ground: Dellwood Avenue, Felixstowe IP11 9HT Tel: 01394 282917
Email:felixstowe@btinternet.com **Web**: http:/www.felixstowe,btinternet.co.uk

Directions: A14 to Felixstowe. Turn right at 3rd r'bout then 1st left - ground100 yds on left. 5 mins walk from Felixstowe (BR) and town centre

Capacity: 2,000 Seats: 200 Cover: 200 Floodlights: Yes

Clubhouse: Bar, snack bar, TV, **Club Shop:** Yes, including enamel badges

HONOURS Suffolk Senior Cup 66-67, 74-75 and 98-99 (as Walton United)

PREVIOUS **Leagues:** Essex & Suffolk Border; Ipswich & District
Names: Felixstowe Port & Town, Felixstowe Town, Felixstowe United
Merged with Walton United in 2000 **Grounds:** Tennis Club,Ferry Road.

RECORD **Attendance:** 1,500 v IpswichTown, floodlight inauguration 25/1/91

AWARD Wirral Eastern Counties Programme of the Year 2003-2004

FACT FILE
Founded: 1890 Nickname: Seasiders
Colours: Red & white stripes/black/red
Change: Yelow & Blue/yellow/yellow
Midweek Matches: Tuesday
Programme: 48 pages, £1.00
Editor: Phil Griffiths Tel: 01394 277156
Local Press: East Anglia Daily Times

CLUB PERSONNEL
Pres: Dave Ashford Chairman: Tony Barnes
Fixture Sec: Chris Ryan (01394 275873)
Manager: Paul Adams (01473 404559)

2003-004
Top Scorer: Liam Hunn 14
P.o.Y.: Jimmy Andrews
2004-2005 Captain: Nicky Barker

GODMANCHESTER ROVERS

Secretary: Roger Coxhead, 28 Dovehouse Close, Godmanchester, Cambs PE29 2DY
Tel: 01480 383357 Fax: 01480 395137 e-mail: secretary@goddy.co.uk

Ground: Bearscroft Lane, Godmanchester, Cambs.PE29 2LQ (07950 367417)

Directions: From A14 turn off for Godmanchester. Take A1198 towards Wood Green Animal Shelter,Bearscroft Lane is half mile from A14 on left down

Capacity: **Cover:** 150 **Floodlights:** Yes **Club Shop**: No

Clubhouse: Temporary portacabins. New clubhouse to be opened in Spring 2005

Previous League: Cambridgeshire League and Hunts County League.

Honours: Hunts Junior Cup 1938-39 and 1988-89
Kershaw Premier League Cup 1994-95

Club Records: **Attendance**: 138 v Cambridge City Reserves Dec.2003.

Season 2003-2004 Player of the Year: Steve Thompson
Top Goalscorer: Chris Ewles

FACT FILE
Founded: 1911 Nickname: Goddy/Rovers
Sponsors: Ace Cabs,Notleys and Sears
Colours: Sky blue/navy/navy
Change: Green/white/black
Midweek Matches: Tuesday
Programme: 16 pages + entry £1.00
Editor: Secretary.

CLUB PERSONNEL
President: Mrs Jackie Hills
Chairman: Keith Gabb
Manager: Eric Cheesewright
Ass Mans: Howard Kemp and Paul Allgood
Coach: Errol McCammon
Captain: Stuart Wood
Physio: Sandra Holmes
General Manager: Daryl Potter

HADLEIGH UNITED

Secretary: Peter Hutchings, 3 Mowlands, Capel St Mary, Ipswich. IP9 2XB Tel: 01473 311093

Ground: Millfield, Tinkers Lane, Duke Street, Hadleigh, Suffolk Tel: 01473 822165

Directions: Turn off A12 approx halfway between Ipswich & Colchester. Take B1070 & follow signs to Hadleigh. Duke Street is off the High Street - turn left by Library

Capacity: 3,000 Seats: 250 Cover: 500 Floodlights: Yes

Clubhouse: Open matchdays. **Website**: hadleigh-utd.co.uk

HONOURS Ipswich & Dist./Suffolk & Ipswich Lg 53-54 56-57 73-74 76-77 78-79
(Mick McNeil) Lg Cup 76-77 80-81 81-82 86-87;
Suffolk Senior Cup 68-69 71-72 82-83.03-04 Eastern Co.Lg Champions 93-94

PREVIOUS **Leagues:** Suffolk & Ipswich (prev. Ipswich & D.)(pre-1991)
Grounds: Grays Meadow, Ipswich Road

RECORD **S - Gate:** 518 v Halstead Town, FA Vase Replay 17.1.95
Win: 8-1 v Chatteris(A) 17/1/95
Defeat: 0-7 v Harwich & Parkston (H) 12/10/96, & Wisbech (H) 26/4/97

FACT FILE
Founded: 1892 Nickname: Brettsiders
Colours: White & navy/navy/navy
Change colours: All claret
Midweek Matches: Tuesday
Reserves' Lge: Essex & Suff. Border
Programme: 12 pages, 50p
Editor: Peter Hutchings (01473 311093)

CLUB PERSONNEL
Prest: K.Grimsey Chairman: Rolf Beggerow
Manager: Louis Newman
2003-2004 Top Scorer:Tony Cracknell
Ps.o.Y.: Miles Donovan (Players) ,Kevin Godbold (Managers) and Tony Cracknel(fans)
2004-05 Captain Archie Arnold

HAVERHILL ROVERS

Secretary: Chris Rice, 23 Ovington Place, Haverhill, Suffolk. CB9 0BA
Tel: 01440 712748 (H) 07904 705803 (M)

Ground: Hamlet Croft, Haverhill, Suffolk Tel: 01440 702137

Directions: Centre of Haverhill

Capacity: 3,000 Seats: 200 Cover: 200 Floodlights: Yes

Clubhouse: Open matchdays and functions. Snacks available

HONOURS Eastern Co's Lg 78-79 Lg Cup 64-65; Essex & Suffolk Border Lg 62-63 63-64; East Anglian Cup 90-91; Suffolk Sen Cup 96-97

PREVIOUS **League:** Essex & Suffolk Border

RECORD **Attendance:** 1,537 v Warrington Town, FA Vase QF 86-87

Players progressing: R Wilkins (Colchester)

2003-2004 **Player of theYear:** Ed Campbell **Top Goalscorer:** Paul Jenkin

FACT FILE
Founded: 1886 Nickname: Rovers
Colours: All red Change :All yellow
Midweek Matches: Tuesday
Programme: 24 pages,50p
Editor: Ray Esdale (01440 704670)
Local Press : Haverhill Echo, Cambridge Evening News

CLUB PERSONNEL
Chairman: Terry McGerty
President: N Haylock
Press Officer: Steven Esdale (01440704670)
Manager: Paul Goodman Physio: Nel Franklin
Captain: Marcis Hunt

IPSWICH WANDERERS

Secretary: Dennis Miller, Saracen's House. 25 St Margaret's Green, Ipswichh IP4 2BN
Email address: dennis@dennismiller.co.uk

Ground: Humberdoucey Lane, Ipswich, Suffolk Tel: 01473 728581

Directions: Take Woodbridge Road out of Ipswich,then left fork into Playford Road. Take first left into Humberdoucy Lane Ground 300yds on right

Capacity: 2,000 Seats: 50 Cover: Yes Floodlights: Yes

Clubhouse: Bar,Tea, coffee, cold drinks, confectionary, burgers, hotdogs,sandwiches, rolls

PREVIOUS **Leagues:** Little David Sunday **Name:** Loadwell Ipswich

RECORD **Attendance:** 335 v Woodbridge, ECL Div 1 4/4/94

BEST SEASON **FA Cup:** 2nd Qual Rd 2000-01
FA Vase: 1st Round 2002-03

HONOURS Eastern Lge Div 1 97-98

FACT FILE
Founded: 1983
Nickname: Wanderers
Sponsors: N.T.L.
Colours: All Blue
Change colours: Red & black/black/red & black
Midweek Matches: Tuesday
Prog. Ed.:John Murphy (01473 723382)
Web site: ipswichwanderersfc.co.uk
Local Press: East Anglian Daily Times, Evening Star

CLUB PERSONNEL
Chairman: Alan.Haste
President: P.Emmerson
Manager: Jason Dozell

KIRKLEY

Secretary: Simon West, 34 Nidderdale,Calton Colville, Lowestoft. NR33 8UG
Tel No: 07787 805 493 (M)

Ground: Kirkley Recreation Ground, Walmer Road, Lowestoft, Suffolk
Tel: 01502 513549

Directions: From A12 to Lowestoft town centre and go over roundabiout at Teamways Garage and past Teamways Pub. Take next left into Walmar Road.

Capacity: 1,000 Clubhouse: Yes Club Shop: No

PREVIOUS **Leagues**: Anglian Combination >2003

HONOURS Anglian Combination Prem.Champions 99-00, 01-02, 2-03, Lge Senior Cup R-up: 00-01,02-03 Div 1 (2), Div 2 78-9 Suffolk Sen Cup (5) Sen K.O. Cup 01-02 Suffolk Jnr Cup (3) Halesworth Charity C (4)

FACT FILE
Formed: 1886
Colours: Royal Blue
Change colours: Red
Midweek Matchday: Wednesday
Programme - 20 Pages 50p Price
Editor:S.West

CLUB PERSONNEL
Chairman:Bob Jenkerson
Manager: N.Shorten
Captain: Leon Harewood

2003-2004
Player of the Year & Top Scorer:Daniel Stokeld

LONG MELFORD

Secretary: Colin Woodhouse, 10 Church Walk, Long Melford, Sudbury, Suffolk CO10 9DO Tel Nos: 01787 372966 (H) 07720 598479 (W)

Ground: Stoneylands, New Road, Long Melford, Suffolk. Tel: 01787 312187

Directions: Turn down St Catherine Road off Hall St (Bury-Sudbury road) and then turn left into New Road.

Capacity: Covered Seating: 106 Covered Standing: 406 Floodlights: Yes/No

Clubhouse: Licensed bar with smart function facilities for parties of a hundred. Contact: Michelle (01787 312187)

Club Shop:

Previous Leagues: Essex & Suffolk Border Lge. until 2002

Honours: Suffolk Senior Cup (8) , Essex & Border League Champions (5) Runners-Up (3) Border League Cup Winners (3) Runners -Up (4)

Season 2003-2004 Player of the Year: Tony French
Top Goalscorer: Darren Judd

FACT FILE
Formed: 1868
Nickname : The Villagers
Colours:Black & White stripes /black/black
Change Colours: All white
Midweek Matchday:Tuesday
Programme: Price: £1 Pages: 32 (all colour)
Editor: Richard Kemp (01787 378149)

CLUB PERSONNEL
Chairman: Colin Woodhouse
Vice Chairman: Simon
GardenPresident:Richard Kemp
Manager: Darren Pratt
Captain: Jason Haygreen
Reserve Team managers; Wes Stalker and Jim Walker Physio:Sue Hopkins

MARCH TOWN UNITED

Secretary: R S Bennett, 47 Ellingham Ave, March, Cambs PE15 9TE (01354 658901)

Ground: GER Sports Ground, Robin Goodfellows Lane, March (01354 653073)

Directions: 5 mins from town centre, 10 mins from BR station

Capacity: 4,000 Seats: 500 Cover: 2,000 Floodlights: Yes

Clubhouse: On ground, seating 150. Light refreshments available

HONOURS Eastern Co's Lg 87-88 (Lg Cup 60-61), Utd Co's Lg 53-64, Cambs Invitation Cup 54-55, East Anglian Cup 53-54 (jt withBarking)

PREVIOUS **Leagues:** Peterborough; Isle of Ely; Utd Co's 48-54
Ground: The Avenue (prior to 1946)

BEST SEASON FA Cup 1st Rd53-54 77-78,

RECORD **Gate:** 7,500 v King's Lynn, FA Cup 1956

FACT FILE
Founded: 1885
Nickname: Hares
Club colours: Yellow/blue/yellow
Change colours: Black & white/black/black
Midweek Matches: Tuesday
Programme: 30p
Editor: G.Wesley
Local Press : Cambs Times, Fenland Advertiser, Peterborough Evening Telegraph

CLUB PERSONNEL
Chairman: Gary Wesley
President: D Wilkinson

NEEDHAM MARKET

Secretary: D Bloomfield, 33 Quinton Road, Needham Market, Suffolk IP6 8DA
Tel: 01449 720693

Fixture Secretary: P Collier, 9 The Knoll, Framlingham, Woodbridge IP13 9DH
Tel: 01728 724108

Ground: Bloomfields, Quinton Road, Needham Market, Suffolk
Tel: 01449 721000

Directions: Quinton Road is off Barretts Lane which in turn is off Needham Market High Street.

Capacity: 1,000 Seats: 250 Cover: 250 Floodlights: Yes

Club Shop: No

PREVIOUS **Leagues:** Ipswich & District; Suffolk & Ipswich until 1996
Grounds: Youngs Meadow; Crowley Park until 1996
Names: None

HONOURS Suffolk & Ipswich Lge 95-96

FACT FILE

Founded: 1927
Nickname: N/A
Colours: Red & Black
Change Coloures: Blue and YellowMidweek
Matchday: Tuesday
Programme Editor: Ian Verneau
Tel No: 01473 413957

CLUB PERSONNEL

Chairman: Nicky Francis
Manager: M.Morsely
2003-04
Leading Goalscorer:M.Wake
Player of the Year: Danny Phillips

SAFFRON WALDEN TOWN

Secretary: Peter Rule, 48 Church Rd., Saffron Walden, Essex CB10 1JQ (01799 522417)

Ground: The Meadow, Catons Lane, Saffron Walden,Essex CB10 2DX (01799 522789)

Directions: Into Castle St off Saffron-W High St. Then left at T jct and 1st left by Victoria Pub.

Capacity: 3,500 **Seats:** 274 **Cover:** 120 **Floodlights:** Yes **Clubhouse** : Yes Club **Shop**: No

Previous Leagues: Haverhill & Dist, Stansted & Dist,Cambs Sen,Herts * Essex Border,North Essex,Essex& Suffolk Border,Spartan, Parthenon, Herts Co, Essex Sen(71-74) (96-03) Eastern Co(74-84) and Isthmian (84-96) **Ground:** Saffron Walden Common 1872-1890

CLUB RECORDS: Attendance: 6,000 v Rainham Ath. Essex Junior Cup Final at Braintree

Scorers: Alec Ramsey 192, William Barker 178 Appearances: Les Page 538 David Argent 483

Best Season F.A.Cup: 2nd Q Rd Replay 84-85 1-2 v Kings Lynn **F.A.Vase** 5th Rd 90-1

Honours:Since 1990: E.Anglian CupR-Up 94-5,E.Floodlit C 91-2,92-3,99-00,Essex Lg Sportsmanship 98-9,99-00,00-01,Essex Sen Lg 73-74 &9-00 Lg Cuo 99-00S.Mid F't C 99-0

FACT FILE

Formed: 1872(Oldest club in Essex)
Nickname: The Bloods
Sponsor:Coxys.com PC Furniture
Colours: Red & Black/Black/Black
Change colours:Blue & Yellow/yellow/yellow
Midweek Matches: Wednesday
Prog.48 pages 50p Editor:Carole Butchart

CLUB PERSONNEL

Chairman:John Butchart Manager: Marc Das
Coach: Peter Summers Capt: Tommy Butchart
2003-4 P.o.Y.: T Butchart Top Scorer: Benes

STANWAY ROVERS

Secretary: Colin Moorcroft,7 Miles Close, Stanway, Essex CO3 0JB
Tel No: 01206 5774200 Fax: 01206 363940 e-mail: colin@moorcroft29.freeserve.co.uk

Ground: `Hawthorns', New Farm Road, Stanway, Colchester, Essex CO3 0PG (01206 578187)

Directions: Leave A12 at Jct 26 to A1124. Turn right(from London)or left from Ipswichonto Essex Yeomanry Way. A1124 towards Colchester 1st right into Villa Rd,then left into Chaple Rd, and left into New Farm Rd. Ground 400 yds on left.Nearest BR station is Colchester North

Capacity: 1,500 Seats: 100 Cover: 250 Floodlights: Yes Shop: No

Clubhouse: 6.45-11pm eves, 12-11pm Sats. Rolls, soup, tea, coffee etc available matchdays

Club Shop: Pennants & ties (Club website:lineone.net/ m alan brierley

HONOURS Essex Intermediate Cup R-up 89-90 90-91, Essex & Suffolk Border Lg R-up 91-2 (Div 1 86-87, Div 2 81-81 85-86), Essex Junior Cup R-up 74-75

PREVIOUS **Leagues:** Colchester & E Essex; Essex & Suffolk. Border (pre-1992)
Ground: Stanway Secondary School, Winstree Road (20 years)

RECORD **Gate:** 210 v Harwich & P ECL Div 1 04 **Win:** 10-0 v Thetford Town 3.11.01 and v March Town 9.12.00 ECL Div 1 **Defeat:** 0-10 v Sudbury Townt (A), E.C.L. Cup

FACT FILE

Re-Formed: 10.7.56 Nickname: Rovers
Sponsors: R.J.Brett Contracts
Colours: Gold& black/black/black& gold
Change : Navy, red & white/navy/navy & red
Midweek matchday: Wednesday
Reserves' Lge: Essex & Suff. Border
Programme: 12 pages, 50p
Editor: Mick Norfolk
Local Press: Essex Co.Standard, Eve Gazette

CLUB PERSONNEL

Chairman: Alan Brierley
President: Richard Deguille
Manager:James McIntyre
Physio: John Chandler

SWAFFHAM TOWN

Secretary: David.Ward, 14 Mount Close,Swaffham. PE37 7BX
Tel: 01760 722516 (H) 01760 720130 (Fax) 07771 960863 (M)
Email Address: pepward@aol,com

Ground: Shoemakers Lane, Swaffham, Norfolk (01760 722700)
Capacity: 2,000 Seats: 50 Cover: 250 Floodlights: Yes

Clubhouse: Open Tuesday, Thursday, Saturday plus functions

HONOURS Norfolk Snr Cup (2), Anglian Comb. 89-90 (Div 1 88-89)
Jewson Divison 1 Champions 00-01

PREVIOUS **Leagues:** Dereham, Anglian Combination

RECORD **Attendance:** 250 v Downham Town, Eastern Co's League Cup 3/9/91

2002-03
Leading Goalscorer: Captain: Player of the Year:

FACT FILE

Founded: 1892
Nickname: Pedlars
Midweek Matchay: Tuesday
Colours: Black & white stripes/black/black
Change: REd/Blue/Blue
Programme: 36 pages, Free
Editor: Simon Barnes, Barnes Print
Tel No: 01362 861101

CLUB PERSONNEL

Chairman:Steve Tanskley
President: Stewart Collins
Manager: MARCCURSON

Wisbech Town F.C.
Season 2003/04
Ridgeons League
Premier Division
Official Programme

RIDGEONS
Football League
FOUNDED 1911

THETFORD TOWN

Secretary: R.Richards, 60 Nunnery Drive, Thetford, Norfolk IP243EN
Tel Nos: 01842 764282 (H) 01284 701121 (W)
Email Address: omwgh@lineone.net

Ground: Mundford Road, Thetford, Norfolk Tel: 01842 766120

Directions: Off bypass (A11) at A143 junction - ground 800yds next to sports ground
Capacity: 2,000 Seats: 400 Cover: 400 Floodlights: Yes
Clubhouse: Bar, teas, refreshments, light meals & snacks **Club Shop:** No
HONOURS Eastern Co's Lg R-up 89-90, Norfolk & Suffolk Lg 54-55;
Norfolk Senior Cup 47-48 90-91
PREVIOUS **Leagues:** Norfolk & Suffolk **Grounds**: None
RECORD **Attendance:** 394 v Diss Town, Norfolk Snr Cup 91
Players progressing: Dick Scott (Norwich C.), Kevin Seggie (Leeds U.),Simon Milton (Ipswich T.)
Local Press: Thetford & Watton Times, Bury Free Press

FACT FILE
Founded: 1883
Sponsors: Thetford Garden Centre
Colours: Claret & blue//claret/claret
Change: Yellow & blue
Midweek Matches: Tuesday
Reserves League: Anglian Comb
Programme: 50p Editor: Secretary
Club Website: thetford townfc.fsnet.co.uk

CLUB PERSONNEL
Chairman: Mike Bailey Vice-Chair: Denise Jones
Press Officer: Paul Stevenson
Manager: Peter Jones Captain: Glen Sharp

2003-2004
P.o.Y.: Gary Hockins
Top Goalscorer: Glen Sharp

TIPTREE UNITED

Secretary: John Wisbey, 103 Peace Road, Stanway, Colchester, Essex
Tel Nos: 01206 564222 (H) 07703 585814 (M)
Email: johnwisbey@tiptreeunited.com
Ground: Chapel Road, Tiptree, Essex Tel: 01621 815213
Directions: Enter town on B1023 - Chapel Road is left at second crossroads, ground 200yds on left. 3 miles from Kelverdon (BR).
Served by Eastern NationalColchester to Maldon bus
Capacity: 2,500 Seats: 150 Cover: 300 Floodlights: Yes
Clubhouse: Open daily 7-11pm (all day Fri & Sat) & 12-2.30, 7-10.30 Sun.
Large bar, two snooker tables, pool, darts, netball, badminton, pigeon club, bingo. Dance hall seats 180, small hall seats 60. **Club Shop:** No
HONOURS Essex Snr Tphy 80-81, Eastern Co's Lg 81-82 (Lg Cup 81-82 84-85),
Essex Snr Lg R-up 75-76 77-78, Harwich Charity Cup (4),
Jewson Eastern Div 1 Champions 99-00 and F.A.Vase Finalists 2001-2002
PREVIOUS **Leagues:** Essex & Suffolk Border; Essex Senior 78-84
RECORD **Attendance:** 1,920 for F.A.Vase Semi-Final v AFC Sudbury 2002

FACT FILE
Founded: 1933
Nickname:The Jam -Makers
Sponsors: Gralostar
Colours: Red& blackstripes/black/black
Change colours: Yellow/blue/white
Midweek Matchday: Tuesday
Reserves: Essex & Suffolk Border Premier
Programme: 32 pages ,£1 Editor: Secretary
Local Press : Colchester Evening Gazette, Essex County Standard'
Southern Pitch of the Year Award+
Website: www.tiptreeunited.com

CLUB PERSONNEL
Chairman: Fred Byles
President: Peter Fidge
Manager:Jody Brown

2003-04
Leading Goalscorer & P.o.Y.: John Watson

2004-2005
Captain:Michael Bovester

WALSHAM-LE WILLOWS

Secretary: Gordon Ross, 2 Palmer Street, Walsham -le- Willows, Bury St Edmonds , Suffolk IP31 3BZ Tel Nos: 01359 259474 (H) 07742 111892 (M)

Ground: Walsham Sports Club, Summer Road, Walsham-le-Willows, Suffolk IP31 3AH
Tel No: 01359 259298

Directions: From Bury - Diss road (A143) turn off down Summer Lane in Walsham -le - Willows and ground is on the right

Clubhouse: Yes

FACT FILE

Colours: Blue & Yellow/blue/blue

Change colours:Red & black/red/red

Midweek Matches: Wednesdays

CLUB PERSONNEL

Chairman: Mike Powles (07971 613933)

Manager: Paul Smith

Programme Editor: Chairman

WHITTON UNITED

Secretary: John Green, 48 Leggatt Drive, Bramford, Ipswich Ip8 4EX
Tel Nos: 01473 742920 (H) -7702 262224)M_
Ground: King George V Playing Field, Old Norwich Road, Ipswich, Suffolk. Tel: 01473 464030

Directions: Turn off A14, junction A1156 approx 3 miles west of A12/A14junction
Capacity: 600 Seats: No Cover: 100 Floodlights: Yes
Club Shop: No
Clubhouse: Licensed Bar. Hot & Cold Food available

HONOURS Suffolk Senior Cup 58-59 62-63 92-93; Suffolk & Ipswich Lge 46-47 47-48
65-66 67-68 91-92 92-93, Jewson Fairplay Trophy 96-97, 97-98

PREVIOUS **Leagues:** Suffolk & Ipswich Grounds: Old Norwich Rd, Ipswich

RECORD **Attendance:** 528 v Ipswich Town 29/11/95
League 244 v Ipswich Wanderers13/1/96

FACT FILE
Formed: 1926 Nickname: None
Sponsors: Speedyhire
Colours: Green & white quarters /green/green
Change colours: Blue & white /white/white
Midweek Matches: TuesdayYouth's League: U18 Eastern Jun Alliance
Programme: 24pages- 50p
Editor: MIck Norfolk 01206 734435 (H)

CLUB PERSONNEL
Chairman: Jeff Crane President: Russell Woodward
Fixture Sec: Alan Elliott (01473 461931)
Manager: Ruel Fox

HELLENIC LEAGUE

SPONSORED BY: GLADWISH LAND SALES

Patron: Sir Henry Cooper OBE, KSG. (2001)

Chairman: Michael Broadley

Secretary: Brian King, 83 Queens Road, Carterton, Oxon OX18 3YF

Tel: 01993 212738 **Fax:** 01993 212775 **E-mail:** hellenic_league_office@ntlworld.com

FINAL LEAGUE TABLE 2003-04

PREMIER DIVISION		P	W	D	L	F	A	Pts
1.	Brackley Town	42	28	8	6	106	36	92
2.	Southall Town	42	28	8	6	104	42	92
3.	Bishops Cleeve	42	27	8	7	94	36	89
4.	Slimbridge	42	26	11	5	85	29	89
5.	Didcot Town	42	28	4	10	90	35	88
6.	Hungerford Town (-1pt)	42	25	6	11	90	45	80
7.	Carterton Town	42	22	9	11	63	45	75
8.	North Leigh	42	21	6	15	70	51	69
9.	Highworth Town	42	19	11	12	66	45	68
10.	Fairford Town (-3 pts)	42	21	8	13	74	63	68
11.	Abingdon United	42	19	11	12	54	49	68
12.	Chipping Norton T.	42	15	9	18	57	68	54
13.	Tuffley Rovers	42	11	13	18	43	49	46
14.	Bicester Town	42	11	6	25	32	64	39
15.	Henley Town	42	11	6	25	44	82	39
16.	Wootton Bassett Town	42	11	5	26	38	73	38
17.	Pegasus Juniors	42	11	5	26	45	105	38
18.	Pewsey Vale	42	10	7	25	58	99	37
19.	Shortwood United	42	11	4	27	53	95	37
20.	Hook Norton (Relegated)	42	8	12	22	42	76	36
21.	Almondsbury Town	42	10	5	27	33	86	35
22.	Gloucester United	42	4	8	30	40	108	20

PREMIER DIVISION	1	2	3	4	5	6	7	8	9	10	11	12	13	14	15	16	17	18	19	20	21	22
1 Abingdon Utd		1-1	1-0	0-2	0-2	2-0	1-1	2-0	2-1	2-2	3-2	2-0	1-1	2-0	0-6	5-0	1-0	1-0	3-3	0-0	0-2	0-0
2 Almondsbury T.	0-3		3-0	0-3	0-4	0-1	1-0	0-3	0-4	3-1	1-1	0-1	1-0	0-0	0-2	1-2	1-4	0-4	0-3	0-5	2-1	1-2
3 Bicester Town	1-1	1-0		1-5	2-1	1-1	1-3	0-1	1-1	0-1	0-1	1-0	0-2	0-2	0-2	0-0	2-0	2-2	1-2	0-3	1-4	1-0
4 Bishops Cleeve	4-1	2-1	2-1		1-1	1-0	4-1	1-2	7-0	2-1	2-2	4-0	3-2	2-1	1-2	3-2	3-0	2-0	0-1	0-0	2-0	2-0
5 Brackley Town	1-1	5-0	1-0	2-1		2-0	2-0	1-3	0-2	4-0	6-1	1-1	1-1	2-1	1-2	3-0	3-0	5-0	1-2	3-2	3-0	7-2
6 Carterton Town	1-0	0-1	1-1	2-2	0-1		0-2	2-1	3-2	3-0	1-1	2-0	1-1	1-0	2-1	4-1	2-1	2-1	1-1	4-1	2-1	3-0
7 Chipping N. Tn	0-1	2-1	1-0	2-2	0-1	0-5		0-0	0-2	2-1	1-2	0-1	1-2	4-3	2-0	1-1	1-1	3-1	2-2	0-5	1-0	3-0
8 Didcot Town	3-0	1-1	1-0	0-1	0-2	4-0	5-1		7-1	2-0	3-0	0-0	4-0	1-2	0-1	7-0	5-0	3-0	3-0	0-2	3-1	1-3
9 Fairford Town	0-0	4-1	2-0	1-0	2-6	1-0	1-1	0-2		6-0	2-1	0-0	1-2	3-1	2-3	2-1	1-0	5-2	0-2	2-1	1-1	4-0
10 Gloucester Utd	0-1	2-3	1-3	0-0	1-5	0-2	2-3	3-7	1-2		0-2	0-5	1-1	1-3	0-3	2-3	3-0	2-3	2-2	1-3	0-0	1-2
11 Henley Town	0-2	1-2	2-0	0-3	0-3	1-2	0-2	0-1	0-2	2-1		1-6	2-0	0-3	0-1	3-1	5-1	3-1	0-4	1-1	0-2	0-1
12 Highworth Town	2-0	3-0	1-0	0-3	1-1	2-2	2-1	1-0	2-0	4-0	1-1		1-1	0-2	3-0	6-0	3-1	1-0	2-0	0-2	2-0	2-0
13 Hook Norton	0-2	0-2	0-1	0-3	0-2	1-2	1-1	1-2	1-4	3-0	1-2	1-1		1-2	2-1	2-1	3-3	1-1	0-0	1-1	1-1	1-0
14 Hungerford Tn	3-0	1-0	1-0	1-0	3-1	1-0	3-2	1-2	3-0	10-0	3-0	2-2	2-1		1-1	2-0	5-2	3-0	1-1	3-2	1-1	4-0
15 North Leigh	1-2	2-3	0-1	1-5	0-2	3-1	1-0	1-3	1-1	3-1	3-0	2-2	4-0	1-0		4-0	3-0	3-1	0-2	2-3	0-0	1-0
16 Pegasus Juniors	1-1	3-1	0-3	1-1	0-7	1-2	1-3	1-4	0-0	2-3	3-1	3-1	2-1	1-5	2-5		0-2	0-3	0-4	0-2	1-0	2-1
17 Pewsey Vale	0-1	3-0	5-2	3-6	2-3	1-2	2-1	1-1	1-4	1-1	3-1	3-4	1-2	1-1	4-1	1-2		1-0	0-8	0-2	0-0	1-0
18 Shortwood Utd	0-4	4-1	1-2	1-4	1-4	0-2	2-2	0-1	0-1	1-0	4-1	2-1	3-2	2-4	2-1	0-4	6-3		0-4	0-4	0-3	0-3
19 Slimbridge	1-0	1-1	4-0	2-0	1-1	3-1	3-0	1-2	1-2	2-0	4-2	2-0	4-0	2-0	0-0	1-0	2-0	0-0		0-1	2-0	2-0
20 Southall Town	7-3	3-0	2-0	1-1	2-2	0-0	3-1	4-0	5-2	1-1	1-0	2-0	5-1	2-1	1-2	3-1	7-3	4-1	2-3		2-1	3-0
21 Tuffley Rovers	1-0	2-0	1-2	0-2	0-0	0-1	1-2	0-1	3-2	1-1	1-1	2-2	1-0	2-1	1-0	4-0	1-1	1-3	1-1	1-2		0-2
22 Wootton Bas. T.	0-2	1-0	2-0	0-2	1-3	2-2	1-4	0-1	1-1	1-3	0-1	1-0	5-1	2-4	0-0	1-2	0-2	2-1	0-2	1-2	1-1	

FINAL LEAGUE TABLE 2003-04

DIVISION ONE WEST		P	W	D	L	F	A	Pts
1.	Purton	34	24	10	0	83	25	82
2.	Ross Town	34	22	8	4	73	34	74
3.	Shrivenham	34	22	6	6	78	26	72
4.	Witney United (Promoted)	34	18	9	7	63	34	63
5.	Ardley United (Promoted)	34	17	10	7	68	46	61
6.	Easington Sports	34	12	16	6	49	40	52
7.	Quarry Nomads	34	14	7	13	71	59	49
8.	Old Woodstock Town	34	14	7	13	53	60	49
9.	Winterbourne United	34	13	8	13	62	52	47
10.	Headington Amateurs	34	12	8	14	59	66	44
11.	Harrow Hill	34	12	6	16	45	61	42
12.	Kidlington	34	10	11	13	66	69	41
13.	Cheltenham Saracens	34	11	8	15	47	53	41
14.	Malmesbury Victoria	34	11	6	17	41	52	39
15.	Cirencester United	34	8	9	17	51	66	33
16.	Middle Barton	34	7	5	22	34	81	26
17.	Adderbury Park	34	5	3	26	34	95	18
18.	Clanfield	34	3	5	26	37	95	14

FINAL LEAGUE TABLE 2003-04

DIVISION ONE EAST		P	W	D	L	F	A	Pts
1.	Wantage Town	32	23	7	2	85	16	76
2.	Letcombe	32	19	10	3	60	27	67
3.	Milton United (Promoted)	32	16	11	5	71	45	59
4.	Eton Wick	32	15	9	8	64	45	54
5.	Binfield	32	15	8	9	52	38	53
6.	Rayners Lane	32	14	9	9	73	51	51
7.	Chalfont Wasps	32	15	4	13	54	51	49
8.	Finchampstead	32	12	9	11	54	42	45
9.	Martin Baker Sports	32	12	3	17	49	73	39
10.	Penn/Tylers Green	32	9	11	12	46	54	38
11.	Chinnor	32	10	5	17	46	57	35
12.	Bisley Sports	32	9	8	15	38	52	35
13.	Prestwood	32	9	6	17	63	75	33
14.	Badshot Lea	32	9	6	17	50	73	33
15.	Englefield Green Rovers	32	8	7	17	44	76	31
16.	Hounslow Borough (-1pt)	32	8	5	19	45	80	28
17.	Holyport	32	6	8	18	42	81	26

LEAGUE CUP

PRELIMINARY ROUND

Almondsbury Town	v	Witney United	1-2
Bicester Town	v	Eton Wick	0-5
Chalfont Wasps	v	Wantage Town	2-1
Cheltenham Saras	v	Adderbury Park	3-0
Cirencester United	v	Pegasus Juniors	2-3
Drayton Wanderers	v	Didcot Town (w/o)	
Easington Sports	v	Wootton Bassett Town	1-1* 3-4p
Fairford Town	v	Ardley United	2-1*
Gloucester United	v	Clanfield	6-1
Headington Am.	v	Englefield Green Rovers	3-1
Henley Town	v	Bisley Sports	0-0* 4-1p
Holyport	v	Badshot Lea	1-2
Hook Norton	v	Letcombe	1-2
Hounslow Borough	v	Hungerford	0-3
Kidlington	v	Finchampstead	4-4* 10-9p
Malmesbury Vics	v	Winterbourne United	1-3
Middle Barton	v	Chipping Norton	1-3
Milton United	v	Chinnor	2-0
Old Woodstock	v	Brackley Town	0-6
Penn & Tylers G.	v	Martin Baker	0-1
Pewsey Vale	v	Shrivenham	2-5
Prestwood	v	Quarry Nomads	3-2*
Rayners Lane	v	Binfield	3-4
Ross Town	v	Harrow Hill	2-1
Slimbridge (w/o)	v	New College Academy	
Southall Town	v	Carterton Town	1-3
Tuffley Rovers	v	Purton	2-2* 6-7p

FIRST ROUND

Abingdon United	v	Bishops Cleeve	0-5
Badshot Lea	v	Binfield	4-2*
Brackley Town	v	Didcot Town	1-1* 5-6p
Chalfont Wasps	v	Prestwood	1-2
Chipping Norton T.	v	Eton Wick	6-0
Henley Town	v	Carterton Town	1-4
Highworth Town	v	Purton	1-2
Letcombe	v	Kidlington	4-2
Martin Baker Sp.	v	Headington Amateurs	2-6
Milton United	v	Hungerford Town	1-3

First Round continued....

Pegasus Juniors	v	Witney United	1-1* 5-4p
Ross Town	v	North Leigh	3-2*
Shrivenham	v	Shortwood United	1-0
Slimbridge	v	Fairford Town	0-1
Winterbourne Utd	v	Gloucester United	0-2
Wootton Bassett T.	v	Cheltenham Saracens	1-2*

SECOND ROUND

Badshot Lea	v	Carterton Town	2-4*
Cheltenham Sar.	v	Didcot Town	0-2
Chipping Norton T.	v	Shrivenham	3-1
Gloucester United	v	Bishops Cleeve	0-1
Headington Am.	v	Purton	0-3
Hungerford Town	v	Fairford Town	2-0
Pegasus Juniors	v	Ross Town	2-2* 3-5p
Prestwood	v	Letcombe	3-2

QUARTER-FINALS

Bishops Cleeve	v	Chipping Norton Town	5-0
Hungerford Town	v	Carterton Town	2-0
Prestwood	v	Purton	0-1
Ross Town	v	Didcot Town	1-3

SEMI-FINALS (played over two legs)

			1st	2nd
Bishops Cleeve	v	Purton	4-0	1-1
Hungerford Town	v	Didcot Town	1-1	1-2*

THE FINAL (8th May at Fairford Town)

Didcot Town	v	Bishops Cleeve	3-1

Didcot Town after winning the League Cup.

ABINGDON UNITED

Secretary: John Blackmore,91 Gainsborough Green, Abingdon, Oxon OX14 5JL(01235 202124)
Ground: Northcourt Road, Abingdon OX14 1PL Tel: 01235 203203
Capacity: 2,000 Seats: 52 Cover: 120
Floodlights: Yes

Directions: From north (Oxford) leave A34 at Abingdon north sign and Northcourt Rd is 1st major turning after r'bout. From South, East or West leave Abingdonon A4183 and turn left into Northcourt Rd after 1 mile. 2 miles from Redley (BR)
Clubhouse: Two bars, food available. Open normal pub hours every day

HONOURS N Berks Lg 53-54 (Lg Cup R-up 53-54), Charity Shield 52-53;
Hellenic Lge - Prem Div R-up 96-97, Div 1 R-up 76-77 81-82, Res. Div 97-98, F/Lit Cup 96-97, Lg Cup R-up 89-90, Div 1 Cup 65-66 81-82 R-up 66-67, Reserve Cup 98-99 R-up 93-94;
Berks & Bucks Senior Cup R-up 83-84,Berks & Bucks Senior Trophy 97-98 R-up 93-94 96-97

PREVIOUS **League**: North Berks
Grounds: None

RECORD **Gate:** 1,500 v Oxford Utd 1994
Appearances: D Webb

FACT FILE
Founded: 1946
Nickname: The U's
Colours: All yellow
Change colours: All Blue
Midweek matchday: Tuesday
Reserves' Lge: Suburban
Programme: 50p
Editor: W Fletcher, ACJI (01235 203203)
Website: abingdonunitedfc.co.uk

CLUB PERSONNEL
Chairman: Derek Turner
General manager: John Blackmore
Manager: Andy Slater
Coach: Mark O'Hara
Physio: Chris Janes
Press Officer: Bill Fletcher (01235 203203)

2003-2004
Leading Goalscorer:Richard Pierson
Player of the Year: Carl Wilkins
2004-2005 Captain:Richard Pierson

ALMONDSBURY TOWN

Secretary: Roger Perry, 61 Brookbridge House, Standfast Road, Henbury, Bristol BS10 7HW
Tel No: 0117 959 0309 (H) 07834 083437 (M)

Ground: Oakland Park, Gloucester Rd., Almondsbury, Bristol BS12 4AGTel: 01454 612220

Directions: Adjacent to M5 junction 16 - follow A38 Thornbury - ground first left. Four miles from Bristol Parkway (BR). County bus services to Thornbury, Stroud and Gloucester
Capacity: 2,000 Seats: None Cover: No
Floodlights: Yes
Clubhouse: 7 days, all sports, refreshments, function room, entertainment,skittles

HONOURS Glos Co. Lg(4) 76-78 79-81 (R-up 75-7681-82), GFA Chal. Tphy 78-79 (R-up 80-81), Avon Prem. Comb. 74-75, Glos SnrAmtr Cup 87-88, Hellenic Lg 83-84 (R-up 82-83, Lg Cup(2) 83-85)

PREVIOUS **Leagues:** Bristol Weslyan; Bristol Suburban; Bristol Premier Comb.; GlosCo
Ground: Almondsbury Rec. (until 1986)

BEST SEASON **FA Vase:** R-up 78-79, SF 77-78
RECORD **Gate:** 2,100,Hellenic Cup Final replay 89-90 (Newport AFC v Abingdon U)

FACT FILE
Founded: 1897
Nickname: Almonds
Colours: Navy & sky blue/navy/navy
Change colours: Red/black/black
Midweek Matchday: Tuesday
Programme: 20 pages 25p
Editor: Will Bundy
Tel: 0117 959 0309

CLUB PERSONNEL
Chairman: Bob Jenkins
President: Peter Howarth
Manager: NIck Tanner
Coach: Micky Jefferies & Shaun Heyes
Physio: Peter Allen & Brian North

2002-03
Leading Goalscorer: Craig Davidge 13
Captain:
Player of the Year:

ARDLEY UNITED

Secretary: Norman Stacey, Ardkey House, Somerton Rd., Ardley.OX27 7NS
Tel Nos: 01869 345597 (H) 01869 241542 (W) 01869 249049 (F)
Ground: The Playing Fields, Oxford Road, Ardley OX27 7PA (01869 346429)

Directions: M40 junc 10 take B430 towards Middleton Stoney on the right after1/2 mile. From Oxford take B430 through Weston-on-the-Green & Middleton Stoney and ground is on the left hand side after chirch in village.

Clubhouse Capacity: Cover: Seats: Floodlights

HONOURS Oxon Snr Lg R-up 92-93 (Pres. Cup R-up 90-91 91-92) Hellenic League Div One 96-97,97-98 Division One Cup 94-5,95-6,96-7,97-98

PREVIOUS **Leagues:** Oxon Senior (pre1993)

RECORD **Attendance:** 120 v Oxford City (1999)

FACT FILE
Founded:
Colours: Sky/sky/navy
Change colours: All yellow
Midweek matchday: Wednesday
Programme Yes Ed: Mandy Reed

CLUB PERSONNEL
President: Ben Gow
Chairman & Press Officer: Norman Stacey
Manager: Paul Spittle
Coach: Tony Blossom
Physio: Clive Wright

2003-2004
Top Scorer: Gary Lawton 20

BICESTER TOWN

Secretary: Phil Allen, 38 Bassett Avenue, Bicester, Oxon. OX26 4TZ
Tel Nos: 01869 252125 (H) 01869 343688 (W)
e-mail: philip@bassett38.freeserve.co.uk

Ground: Sports Ground, Oxford Rd, Bicester Tel: 01869 241036 (office& fax)
Capacity: 2,000 Seats: 250 Cover: 550 Floodlights: Yes

Directions: From Oxford; past Tescos on outskirts of Bicester - ground on right
From Aylesbury; turn left at first island on outskirts of Bicester onto bypass, right at next island, pass Tescos & ground on right.

Clubhouse: One bar

HONOURS Hellenic Lg 60-1 77-78 (Lg Cup 90-91 (R-up 92-93), Div 1 76-77)

PREVIOUS **League**: Oxon Senior
Name: Slade Banbury Road (pre-1923)

RECORD **Attendance:** 955 v Portsmouth, floodlight inauguration 1/2/94

FACT FILE
Founded: 1876
Nickname: Foxhunters
Cols: Red & white/white/red
Change: Blue & black
Club's Email:philip@bassett38,freeserve,co.uk
Midweek Matchday: Tuesday
Reserves' league: Hellenic Lge Res. Div.
Programme: With entry
Editor:Bill Evans (01869 600256)

CLUB PERSONNEL
Chairman: David Simpson
Vice Chairman: John PrpaPresident: Michael Kinane
Fixture Secretary: Phil Allen
Press Officer: David Simpson
Tel No: 07703 347338
Manager: Kevin Leach Coach: Barry Grant
Physio: Ray Huntley

2003-2004
Top Goalscorer: John-Paul Hannaway 16

BISHOPS CLEEVE

Secretary: Phil Tustain, 36 Hardy Road, Bishops Cleeve, Cheltenham GL52 4BN
Tel: 01242 697281 (H) 01242 673333 x 2287 (B)

Ground: Kayte Lane, Bishops Cleeve, Cheltenham GL52 3PD 07778 859722
or ,on matchdays 07969 680984

Capacity: 1,500 Covered Seating: 50 Floodlights: Yes

Directions: North of Cheltenham on the A534, pass Racecourse then turn right at traffic lights and then left into Kayte Lane, ground half a mile on the left.

Clubhouse: Full facilities, bar, dance area

HONOURS Hellenic Lg Cup R-up 90-91, Helleneic Div 1West R-up: 2001-02

PREVIOUS **Leagues:** Cheltenham, Nth Glos
Grounds: The Skiller (pre-1913), Village Field (pre-1950)

RECORD **Attendance**: 1,000 v Newport AFC

FACT FILE
Founded: 1892
Nickname: Skinners
Colours: Green/green/black
Change colours: White/white/green
Midweek Matchday: Wednesday

CLUB PERSONNEL
President: John Davies
Chairman: David Walker

Press Officer:Will Pember
Tel: 01242 673800
Programme Editor: John Pickup
Tel No: 07763 861192
Coach:John Banfield
Physio: Will Pember
Captain: Andy Tucker

2003-2004
Top Goalscorer: Andy Keveran 20
Player of the Year: Richard Clark

CARTERTON F.C.

Secretary: John McCarthy, 13 Lord Close Carterton, Oxon. OX18 3PF (01993 213003)

Ground: Kilkenny Lane, Carterton, Oxfordshire (01993 842410)

Directions: Enter Swinbrook Rd which is off the Burford-Carterton road, proceed into Kilkenny Lane (one track road), ground car park 200yds on left before sharp corner. Hourly buses to Carterton from Oxford
Capacity: 1,500 Seats: 75 Cover: 100 Floodlights: Yes

Clubhouse: Lounge & fully licensed bar open every day 7.00-11pm, Sat & Sun: noon-11pm Sat 4-6pm. Snacks & meals available

HONOURS Oxon Junior Shield 85-86; Oxon Snr Cup R-up 90-91 96-97 98-99 Witney & Dist.Lg 65-66 (Div 1 84-85 76-77); Hellenic Lg Div 1 89-90 93-94 (Reserve Div 1989-90 (R-up 93-94)); Oxon Intermediate Cup R-up 93-94(res.)Hellen Supplementary Cup 99-00, Hellenic League Challenge Cup 2000-01, Reserves Division 1. 2001-02

PREVIOUS Leagues: Witney & District

RECORD **Gate:** 650 v Swindon Town July 2001 **Goalscorer:** Phil Rodney

FACT FILE
Founded: 1922
Reformed: 1946/1983
Colours: Red with green trim/green/red
Change colours: Black &white/black/black
Midweek matches: Tuesday
Programme: 20 pages 50p
Editor: Tracey Stacker
Website: www.cartertontownfc.co.uk

CLUB PERSONNEL
Presidents: K.Trethowan & R Ferryman
Chairman: Nick Truman
Match Secretary: Glyn Yates

Press Officer: Dave Stock(01993 843126)
Manager: Bill Pirie
Physio: T.B.A. Coach:Terry Merriman
Captain:J.Butt

2003-04
Leading Goalscorer: Mark Threlfall 15
Player of the Year:G.Smales

CHIPPING NORTON TOWN

Secretary: Bob Tanner, 36 Fox Close, Chipping Norton, Oxon. OX7 5BZ
Tel: 07881 712624

Match Secretary: Terry Maycock, 31 Newlands, Witney, Oxon. OX28 3JL
Tel: 01993 778260 (H) 07747 742239 (M)

Ground: Walterbush Road, Chipping Norton, OX7 5DP
Tel: 01608 645311 or 01608 642562

Capacity: 2,000 Covered Seating: 50 Covered Standing: 150 Floodlights: Yes

Directions: From South – A361 to Chipping Norton, past school on right, take 1st left turning into Walterbush Road.
From North – drive through town and take A361 towards Burford by Kings Arms, past fire station on left, then take 1st right into Walterbush Road.

RECORD **Attendance:** 1000 v Wolverhampton Wanderers 1981

HONOURS Hellenic Lge. Div.1 West R-up 02-03

FACT FILE
Re-formed 2001
Nickname: The Magpies
Colours:
Black & white stripes/black/black & white
Change colours: Yellow/blue/yellow
Midweek fixtures: Tuesday

CLUB PERSONNEL
Chairman: Nigel Harrison
email: happyhaulier@btinternet.com
Tel: 01993 703319
Press Off./Program Editor: Terry Maycock
Tel: 01993 778260

Manager: Alan Dore
Assistant Manager: Richard Archer

2003-2004
Top Goalscorer: Mark Odom 21

DIDCOT TOWN

Secretary: Simon Kelly c/o Loop Meadow Stadium

Ground: Loop Meadow Stadium, Bowmont Water, Didcot, OX11 7GA. (01235 813138)
Website: http://users.tinyoline.co.uk/stevetclare/DTFC1/
Capacity: 5,000 Seats: 250 Cover: 500 Floodlights: Yes

Directions: From Town Centre: Take station road (old ground) and turn right under bridge just before station into Cow Lane. Left by Ladygrove Pub into Tamar Way. Then first left at roundabout. From A34: leave at Milton interchange and take Didcot road for approximately one mile. At roundabout take perimeter road Cross three more roundabouts and turn right at third into Avon Way

Clubhouse: Every evening and 12 noon to close at weekends and national holidys.

HONOURS Hellenic Lg 53-54,Lg Cup 1965-66 66-67 92-9397-98 03-04
Div 1 76-77,Div1 Cup 76-7,
Supplementary Cup 2002-03 Berks & Bucks SeniorTrophy 2000-01, 2002-03

PREVIOUS **Leagues:** Hellenic 53-54; Metropolitan League 57-63

RECORD **Attendance:** 825 v Oxford United, 2001

FACT FILE
Founded: 1907
Nickname: Railwaymen
Colours:Rerd & white/white/red* white
Change colours: All yellow
Midweek Matchday: Tuesday
Programme: £1.00
Editor: Steve Clare

CLUB PERSONNEL
Chairman: John Bailey
Press Officer: Simon Kelly
e-mail: didcot1907@aol.com
Manager:Stuart Peace
Ass.Managar: Paul Noble
Captain: AndyCooper
Physio: Mark Roberts

2003-2004
Top Scorer: Ian Concannon
Player of the Year: Grant Goodhall

FAIRFORD TOWN

Secretary: William Beach, 33 Park Close, Fairford, GL7 4LF Tel: 01285 712136 (H)
Email address: william@beach747.freeserve.co.uk

Ground: Cinder Lane, London Road, Fairford, Cirencester Tel: 01285 712071

Directions: Entering Fairford on A417 from Lechlade turn left down Cinder Lane150yds after 40mph sign. From Cirencester on same road, follow thru village andturn right down Cinder Lane 400yds afterRailway Inn.
Buses from Swindon,Lechlade and Cirencester
Capacity: 2,000 Seats: 100 Cover: 150 Floodlights: Yes

Clubhouse: Open each evening, weekend lunches & before and after all games

Club Shop: Yes

HONOURS Glos Challenge Trophy 79-80, 98-99 02-03 (R-up 82-83); Hellenic Lg R-up 78-79 79- 80 90-91 94-95, (Premier Div Cup 78-79, Div 1 71-72, Div 1 Cup 71-72); Glos Jnr Cup 62-63; Swindon & Dist Lg 64-65 68-69 ,Hellenic floodlit Trophy: 2001-02

PREVIOUS **Leagues:** Cirencester & District (pre-1946)/ Swindon & District 46-70
Grounds: None

RECORD **Attendance:** 1,525 v Coventry City, friendly July 2000
Goalscorer: Pat Toomey **Win:** 9-0 v Moreton T **Defeat:** 0-9 v Sharpness

FACT FILE
Founded: 1891 Nickname: Town
Colours: Red/white/red
Change colours:All Blue
Midweek matchday: Wednesday
Reserves' League: Hellenic Reserve section
Prog: 20 pages Editor/Press Officer: President
Club Website: www.fairfordtownfc.co.uk

CLUB PERSONNEL
President: Michael Tanner
Manager: Mark Webb
Physio: Ian Watkins
Captain Lee Clark

2003-2004
Leading Scorers:Lee Stoddart& Neil Matthews
Player of the Year: Neil Matthews

Almondsbury Town - Back Row (L-R): Chris Barnes, Justin Cattle, Danny Thorpe, Stuart Woods, Marcus Mapstone, Ian Howse, Phil Walsh. **Front Row (L-R):** Paul King, Craig Davdge, Leon Moloney, Russell Knight, Joe Howe, Carl Rutter (capt). Photo: Arthur Evans

Chipping Norton Town - Back Row (L-R): Steve Wright, Gary Wright, Richard Barrett, Leon Canning, Ben Adcock, Richard Archer, Michael Bolton. **Front Row (L-R):** Craig Dore, Jason Court, Matthew Jefferey, Robbie Wyatt, Mark Odom, Darren Mills. Photo: Gordon Whittington.

Shortwood United - Back Row (L-R): T Oakley, J Lane, M Williford, M Haddock, E Prentice, C Greenhough, C Wilson. **Front Row (L-R):** C Phillips, L Pritchard, P groves, K Pritlove, R Evans, M Beckingham, P Ralph. Photo: Gordon Whittington.

HENLEY TOWN

Secretary: Tony Kingston, 50 Birdhill Avenue Reading Berks. RG2 7JU
Tel: 01189 670196(H) 07712139502 (M); 01189 844496 (B);
Fax: 01189 842201; E-mail: june.Kingston@btinternet.com

Ground: The Triangle, Mill Lane ,Henley-on-Thames
Tel: 01491 411083

Directions: From Henley Town Centre take the A4155 Reading Road.
Mill Lane is approx. 1 mile on the left past the Newtown Ind. Est. and immed. before the Garage and roundabout for Tesco.
The ground is on the left, over the railway bridge.
Henley-on-Thames Railway Station ten minutes walk.
Buses 328 Reading or 329 Wycombe

Capacity: 2,500 **Seats:** 60 + disabled **Cover:** 160 **Floodlights:** Yes

Clubhouse: Open lunchtimes & evenings weekdays plus all day Sat,Sun

Record Gate: 2000+ v Reading, 1922 at old Reading Road ground

Recent Honours: Hellenic Lge Div1 East 00-01 Oxon Senior Cup (5)

Best Season: **FA Vase:** **FA Cup:**

2002-2003: **P.o.Y.:** Stuart Gosby **Top Scorer:** Danny Seaward

FACT FILE

Founded 1871
Nickname: The Lillywhites or TheTown
Colours: White /black/black
Change cols.: Yellow & Green /green/yellow
Midweek fixtures: Tuesday 7.30
Prog Ed: Mike Trendall (01491 577075)
Web site: www.henleytown.co.uk

CLUB PERSONNEL

Chairman: Andrew Bryan
Press Officer: As Secretary
Director of Coaching:Keith Stiles
Manager:Dennis Bainborough
Captain: Carl Thomas
Assistant Manager: T.B.A.
Physio: Richard Ellis
Youth Development: Bobby Wilkinson

HIGHWORTH TOWN

Secretary: Fraser Haines, 222 Windrush, Highworth, Swindon SN6 7EB
Tel Nos: 01793861109 (H) 07939 032451 (M)

Ground: Elm Recreation Ground, Highworth. SN6 7DD (01793 766263)

Directions: Enter on A361 from Swindon, past Simpsons Garage, straight over island, next sharp left into The Green by Vet's Surgery -ground & car park 60yds on left next to Sports Hall.

Capacity: 2,000 Seats: 50 Cover: 250 Floodlights: Yes Club Shop: No

Clubhouse: Sat 12-2.30 & 4.30-11pm. Mon to Fri 7-11pm. Rolls & Hot food

HONOURS Wilts Snr Cup 63-64 72-73 95-96 97-98(R-up 88-89), Hellenic Div 1 Cup 88-89,Arthur Shipway Cup 88-89 93-94, Swindon & District Lg 63-64 64-65 65-66 68-69 Hellenic Supplementary Cup Winners: 98-99, Hellenic Reserve Division Two Winners 98-99, Hellenic Premier Division R-Up 9-00

PREVIOUS **Leagues:** Wilts; Swindon & Dist

RECORD **Attendance:** 2,000 v QPR opening Floodlights
Scorer: Kevin Higgs **Appearances:** Rod Haines
Win: 12-0 v Beeches, Arthur Shipway Cup 1992
Defeat: 2-8 v Milton United, Hellenic Lge Div. 1, 1987

FACT FILE

Founded: 1893
Nickname: Worthians
Sponsors: Logic Builders
Colours: Red /red/black
Change: Sky blue & white/white/skywhite/blue
Midweek matchday: Tuesday
Reserves Lge: Hellenic Reserve Div
Programme: 16 pages, 60p
Editor: Mike Markham (01793 763462)

CLUB PERSONNEL

President: Alan Vockins
Chairman: CliveWebb
Match Secretary: Dave Evans (01793 763548)
Press Officer: Secretary Manager: John Fisher
Coach: Dave Webb Physio:Alan Jenning
Captain:John Reeves

2002-03

Leading Goalscorer: Matty Jack 18

HUNGERFORD TOWN

Ground: Town Ground, Bulpit Lane, Hungerford RG17 0AY
Tel: 01488 682939 (club) 01488 684597 (boardroom) 01488 684597 (Fax)

Directions: M4 jct 14 to A4, right and left at Bear Hotel, through town centre on A338, left into Priory Rd, second left into Bulpit Lane, over crossroads, ground on left. 3/4 mile from Hungerford BR station

Capacity: 3,000 Seats: 300 Cover:320 Floodlights: Yes **Club Shop**: Yes

Clubhouse: Open eves & lunchtimes including Sunday. Two bars, dancehall, boardroom/ committee room, darts, pool, fruit machines. Hot & coldsnacks. Steward: Dianne Tanner (01488 682939)

HONOURS: Berks & Bucks Snr Cup 81-82 (R-up 75-76 76-77); Hellenic Lg Div 1 70-71, Prem Div Cup 77-78, Div 1 Cup 70-71, Benevolent Cup 60-61; Hungerford Cup 96-97, Isthmian Lge Representatives in Anglo-Italian Tournament 81.

PREVIOUS **Leagues:** Newbury & D.; Swindon & D.; Hellenic 58-78 Isthmian 1978-2003

CLUB RECORDS **Attendance:** 1,684 v Sudbury Town, FA Vase SF 1st leg 88-89
Scorer: Ian Farr (268) **Appearances:** Dean Bailey (approx 400)
Transfer Fee Paid: £4,000 for Joe Scott (Yeovil T.)
Received: £3,800 for Joe Scott (Barnstaple T.)

BEST SEASON **FA Cup:** 1st Rd 79-80, 1-3 v Slough T. (A)
FA Vase: Semi-Final 77-78 79-80 88-89

Players progressing to Football League: Steve Hetzke (Reading, Blackpool,Sunderland), Bruce Walker (Swindon, Blackpool), Des McMahon (Reading), Brian Mundee (Bournemouth, North'ton)

FACT FILE

Founded: 1886 Nickname: Crusaders
Club Sponsors: Kerridge Insurance
Colours: White/navy blue/blue
Change colours: All yellow
Midweek Matchday: Tuesday
Reserves' League: Hellenic
Programme: 24 pages, 50p
Editor:Martyn Leach (01488 683682)

CLUB PERSONNEL

Chairman: Alan Holland
Vice Chairman: Ron Tarry
President: Sir Seton Wills
General Secretary: Norman MatthewsMatch Match Secretary: Ken Holmes
Press Officer: Ron Tarry (01488 682539)
Manager: Gary Ackling (01793 764983)
Asst.Man: Tim North
Physio: Richard Fox

2003-04

Top Goalscorer & P.o.Y.:Darren Howell

2004-2005

Captain.: Darren Howell

MILTON UNITED

Secretary: Sue Walker, 122 High St, Sutton Courtney, Abingdon, OX14 4AX Tel: 01235 847158 (H)

Ground: The Sportsfield,Milton Hill, Potash Lane,Milton Heights,Oxon Tel:01235 832999

Directions: Exit A34 at Milton, 10 miles south of Oxford & 12 miles north of J 13, M4. A4130 towards Wantage, after 100m 1st left, then 1st right into Milton Hill. Entrance 200m on left.

Capacity: Covered Seats: 50 Floodlights: Yes Club Shop: No

Clubhouse: On ground, open matchdays

HONOURS Hellenic Lg 90-91 (Div 1 89-90 R-Up.94-95)), Nth Berks Lg(4) 85-86 87-89(R-up 84-85 86-87, Lg Cup(3) 84-86 88-89, Div 2 80-81, Charity Shield(4) 84-86 87-89 (R-up 82-83), Nth Berks War Mem. Cup(3) 83-85 87-88, Berks & Bucks Intermediate Cup 90-91

RECORD **Attendance:** 500 v Almondsbury Picksons, Hellenic Lg 90-91
Goalscorer: Nigel Mott

FACT FILE
Founded: 1926
Colours: Sky & claret/claret/sky & claret
Change colours: Orange/white/white
Midweek matchday: Tuesday
Programme Editor / Press Officer:
David Taylor (01235 816376)

CLUB PERSONNEL
Chairman: Ken Tull President: John Cannon
Match Secretary: Sid Tindall (01491 835630)
Manager: Paul Biddle
Coach: Nigel Mott
Physio: John Belcher

NORTH LEIGH

Secretary: Mike Burnell, 49 Ashfield Road, Carterton, Oxford OX18 3QZ
Tel Nos: 01993 845507 (H) 01635 577018 (W) 07760 171762 (M)
Match Secretary: Keith Huxley, The Orchard, Cote, Bampton, Oxon. OX18 2EG
Tel: 01993 851497 (H) 0118 913 3223 (B)
email: keith_huxley@fwuk.fwc.com
Ground: Eynsham Hall Park Sports Ground, North Leigh, nr Witney, Oxon OX8 6PW
Tel: 01993 881427
Directions: Ground is situated off A4095 Witney to Woodstock road 3 miles east of Witney. Entrance to ground is 300yds east of Main Park Entrance
Capacity: 2,000 Seats: 100 Cover: 200 Floodlights: Yes
Clubhouse: Bar open matches. Snacks available **Club Shop:** No

PREVIOUS **Leagues:** Witney & District 08-89

CLUB RECORDS **Attendance:** 326 v Andover F.A.Vase 4th Rd. 17.01.04 **Scorer:** P Coles **Appearances:** P King

HONOURS Hellenic Lg Div 1 R-up 92-93 (Reserves Cup 93-94), Oxon Jnr Shield 56-57 83-84, Oxon Charity Cup 84-85 88-89, Witney & Dist. Lg(13) 50-57 84-90 LgCup (10) 47-48 51-52 53-55 56-57 81-82 85-89), Oxon Yth Cup 93-94 94-95,OxonYth u17 Lg & Cup 93-94. Oxford Sen. Cup R-Up 94-95. Marriott Cup 95-96; Oxon U-16 Youth Cup 98-99, Allied Counties Under 18 Youth (West Div)Winners

FACT FILE
Founded: 1908
Nickname: None
Sponsors: Various
Colours: Yellow /black or red/yellow or black
Change colours: All claret & blue
Midweek matches: Tuesday
Programme: 20 pages, £1 with entry
Editor: Steve Smith(07736 637097)

CLUB PERSONNEL
President: Mrs Christine Smith
Chairman: Peter King
Press Officer: Barry Norton
Tel: 01993 881777
Manager: Mark Gee
Asst Manager: David Ebsworth
Physio: Andrew Davidson

2003-2004
Top Goalscorer: Andrew Caton 30

PEGASUS JUNIORS

Secretary: Trevor Jones, 219 Ledbury Road, Hereford, HR1 1QE (01432 351459)

Ground: Hereford Leisure Centre, Holmer Road,Hereford (01432 278178)
Directions: A49 Ross Road over Greyfriars Bridge, Victoria Street to end of Edgar Street, then turn left to next mini roundabout and then right.Leisure Centre 500 yds on left.
Capacity: 1,000 Seats 50 Cover : Yes Floodlights: Yes
Clubhouse: 48 St Owens Street

HONOURS Herefordshire Snr Amtr Cup 71-72; Worcs Senior Urn 85-86; Herefordshire Co. Chal. Cup (6) 81-83 84-85 87-88 89-90, 98-99, R-up 93-94; Hellenic Lg Div 1 84-85 98-99, R-up 93-94, Div 1 Cup R-up 93-94)

PREVIOUS **Leagues:** Leisure Centre

RECORD **Attendance:** 1,400 v Newport AFC 89-90

FACT FILE
Founded: 1955
Colours: All red
Change colours: All blue
Midweek Matchday: Wednesday
Programme: Included with admissian (£3.00)
Editor: Kevin Bishop (07931971765))

CLUB PERSONNEL
President: Mark Ellis
Chairman: Roger Hesten.
Press Officer: Chris Wells
(01432 358345)
Manager: Chris Hyde
Physio: T.B.A.Captain:Darren Braithwaite

2003-04
Leading Goalscorer:Gavin Stone 13
Player of the Year: Darren Braithwaite

PEWSEY VALE

Secretary: Liz Montague, 39 Swan Meadow, Pewsey, Wilts, SN9 5HP
Tel Nos: 01672 563664 (H) 07739 138297 (M)
E-mail: montymadhouse@tiscali.co.uk

Ground: Recreation Ground, Ball Rd, Tel: 01672 562990

Directions: From A345 take first right into Co-0p car park. Park top left hand side next to Bowls & Tennis club and walk through to pitch.

Capacity Unlimited Cover: Yes Floodlights: Yes

Clubhouse:

PREVIOUS **League:** Wiltshire County (pre-1993), Western League 93-01
Name: Pewsey Y.M. (until late 1940s)

HONOURS Wiltshire County League 92-93

RECORD **Attendance:** 107 v Purton 27.08.01

FACT FILE
Nickname : 'Vale'

Colours: Black & White]/Black/Black
Change colours:
Navy & lime green/navy/lime green & navy
Midweek matchday: Wednesday
Programme Editor: Chairman

CLUB PERSONNEL
Chairman: Rob Thompson
Manager: Steve Wootton

2003-2004
Top Goalscprer: Barry Flippance 18

SHORTWOOD UNITED

Secretary: Mark Webb, 2 Green View Cottage, Shortwood, Nailsworth, Stroud, Glos GL60SE
Tel: 01453 836233 (H) 0781 2842724 (M)

Ground: "Meadow Bank", Shortwood, Nailsworth, Gloucestershire (01453 833936)

Directions: In Nailsworth turn into Spring Hill then first left. Continue pastshop and and keep left past "Britannia" (signposted Shortwood) - continue toend for ground. 4 miles from Stroud (BR)
Capacity: 5,000 Seats: 50 Cover: 150 Floodlights: Yes
Club Shop: No

Clubhouse: Mon-Sat 7-11pm, Sun 12-2 & 7-10.30pm.. Hot food kitchen on matchdays

HONOURS Glos.Co.Lg 81-82 (R-up 80-81), Glos Tphy 83-84 91-92,94-95,(R-up 79-80), Hellenic Lg 84-85 91-92 (R-up 85-86 89-90 94-95, Div 1 R-up 83-84, Div 1Cup83-84), Prem Lge Cup R-up 95-96, Hungerford Merit Cup, Glos Snr AmCup 85-86,99-00 R-up 79-80), Stroud Charity Cup 91-92 92-93 94-95 00-01, 03-04 (R-up 95-96), Stroud Lg 27-28 (Div 2 26-27 64-65(res), Div 3 25-26 49-50(res) 62-63(res)), Glos Northern Snr Lg R-up (4)res)(Div 2 62-63 80-81(res) 90-91(res)), Arthur Shipway Cup 78-79 79-80, Supp'tary Cup R-up 98-99, Glos N. Sen 2 R-up 98-99

PREVIOUS **Leagues:** Stroud; Glos Northern Snr; Glos Co
Ground: Table Land, Wallow Green

RECORD **Attendance:** 1,000 v Forest Green Rovers, FA Vase 5th Rd 81-82
Goalscorer: Peter Grant **Appearances:** Peter Grant
Win: 11-0 **Defeat:** 0-9 **Fee Received:** Paul Tester (Cheltenham, 80-81)

FACT FILE
Founded: 1900 Nickname: The Wood
Sponsors: Ecotricity
Colours: Red & white,red,white
Change: Blue/Blue/Yellow
Midweek matchday: Tues or Wed
Reserves' League: Glos Northern Snr 1
Programme: 18 pages, 50p
Editor:Kenton Posthlethwaite

CLUB PERSONNEL
Chairman: Peter Webb
Vice C'men: W Stratford, W Lewis
President: R T Tanner
Press Officer: Mark Webb
Tel: 01453 83 5094 (H) 07816205152 (M)
Managers: Mark Sumpter & Ian Freebrey.

2003-2004
Top Scorer:Chris Davis
Player of the Year: Ewen Prentice

2004-2005
Captain:Rich Evans

Pegasus Juniors - Back Row (L-R): Chris Hyde (Manager), Cory Hyde, Adriano Girolami, Laurence Helme, Matthew Tayler, Steve Aubrey, Peter Wallace, Neal Hotchkiss. **Front Row (L-R):** Alan Trumper (physio), Darren Preece, Gavin Stone, Darren Braithwaite, darren Jones, Matthew Gray.

Slimbridge - Back Row (L-R): Carl Wait (Goalkeeping coach), Matt Green, Craig Cole, Richard Moore, Ashley Thomas, Andy Pritcher (capt.), Ryan Chandler, Adam Paul, Gary Marshall, John Hamilton (physio), John Evans (coach), Doug Gray (manager). **Front Row (L-R):** Leon Stirling, Bradley Thomas, Ross Casey, Julian Freeman, Jon Embling, Edward Ward, Steve Badham.

Photo: Arthur Evans.

SLIMBRIDGE

Secretary: & Press Officer David Phillips, 14 Woodcock Close Abbeydale Gloucester GL4 4WT
Tel: 01452 414766 (T & F) 07754 088063 (Match Days Only)

Ground: Wisloe Road, Cambridge, Glos. GL2 7AF Tel: 01453 890361

Directions: From the A38 take the A 4135 to Dursley ground is 100 yards on left.

Clubhouse:

HONOURS: Hellenic Lge Div.1 West 02-03, Hellenic Brian Wells Cup 02-03
Hellenic Floodlit Cup 03-04 G.F.A.Trophy 03-04R-up 01-02

PREVIOUS **League:** Gloucestershire County Lge.

RECORD **Attendance:** 525 v Shortwood United 24.8.03 (Hellenic Premier)

FACT FILE
Founded:
Colours: Blue/blue/white
Change: Red/red/black
Programme Editor: Martin Tudor
07989 442139
Midweek matchdays: Tuesday

CLUB PERSONNEL
Chairman: John Mack
Tel: 01453 899211
Manager: Doug Gray
Tel: 01453 544306
Coach: John Evans
Physio: John Hamilton

2003-2004
Leading Goalscorer: Julian Freeman 33
P.o.Y.: Andy Pritchett

2004-2005
Captain: Andy Pritchett

TUFFLEY ROVERS

Secretary: Graham Moody, 50 Giles Cox, Quedgeley, Gloucester GL2 4YL
Tel: 01452 724083 (H & Fax) 01452 522009 (B)

Ground: Glevum Park, Lower Tuffley Lane, Gloucester Tel: 01452 423402

Directions: Follow Gloucester city ring-rd to traffic lights signed M5 South & Bristol. Turn right signed Hempsted & city centre, after 200 yds turn right (McDonalds on corner) into Lower Tuffley Lane, ground 400yds on left
Capacity: Seats: 50 Cover: Yes Floodlights: Yes

Clubhouse: 800 yds from ground. Open before & after matches, and normal pub hours at other times. Snacks available. Club Shop: No

HONOURS Hellenic Lg Div 1 92-93 (Div 1 Cup 92-93, F'lit Cup 98-99), Glos Co. Lge 90-91, Glos SnrAmtr Cup 87-88, Stroud Lg 72-73,94-95, Glos Northern Sen. Lg. Div 1 87-88 98-99 (res) Div2 79-80.

PREVIOUS **Leagues:** Stroud; Glos Northern Senior; Glos County (pre-1991)
Grounds: Stroud Rd, Gloucester; Randwick Park, Tuffley

RECORD **Attendance:** 150 v Cinderford Town 94-95

FACT FILE
Founded: 1929
Nickname: Rovers
Club Sponsors: Albell Construction
Colours: All Claret
Change colours: All Sky Blue
Midweek Matchday: Wednesday
Reserve League: Glos.Northern Senior Lge
Programme: approx 10 pages with entry
Editor: Graham Moody

CLUB PERSONNEL
President: T.B.A.
Chairman: Graham Moody
Press Officer: Roy Craddock
(01452 413720)
Manager: Doug Foxwell
Coach: Rob Whittington
Physio: Sean Tracey

2003-21004
Top Goalscorer:Carl Cresswell 14

WANTAGE TOWN

Secretary: Alan Parker, Little Orchard, Manor Rd, Wantage, OX12 8DW Tel: 01235 763842(H & F)

Ground: Alfredian Park, Manor Road, Wantage, Oxon Tel: 01235 764781

Directions: Take Hungerford Road from Wantage (A338) The ground is signposted on right opposite recreation ground **Capacity**: 1,500 Seats: 50 Cover: 300 Floodlights: Yes

Clubhouse: Mon-Fri 7.30-11pm, Sat noon-2.30, 4-7pm **Club Shop:** No

Programme: 28 pages, 50p Editor: Tony Woodward (01367 241328)

PREVIOUS **Leagues:** Swindon & Dist. 1901-12 30-35 47-56; N Berks 12-22 38-40 46-47; Reading & D. 22-30 35-38

RECORD **Attendance:** 550 v Oxford Utd July 03.

HONOURS Hellenic R-up 81-82, Div 1 80-81 R-up 69-70 87-88 91-92 95-96, Div1 Cup R-up 91-92; Oxon Snr Cup 82-83; Berks & Bucks Intermediate Cup 54-55; Swindon & Dist. x4

FACT FILE
Founded: 1892 Nickname: Alfredians
Colours: Green &white/white/white
Change Colours: Blue& white/black/white
Midweek Matchday:Tuesday
Prog. Ed.:Dave Broadis 01235 769300

CLUB PERSONNEL
Chairman: Tony Woodward
President: John Hutchings
Match Sec.: Colin Blunsden 01235 768605 (H)
1st Team Manager: Stuart Peace
Coach: Terry Delaney
Physio: Ian Howard
Top Goalscorer 03-04: Steve Tucker 24

WITNEY UNITED

Secretary: Adrian Bircher 13 Colwell Drive Witney Oxon OX28 5NJ
Tel: 01993 200913 (H) 01865 393361(B) 07747 123411 326074 (M)
e-mail: adrian1.bircher@ntlworld.com

Ground: Marriotts Stadium, Downs Road, Witney OX8 5LY
Tel: 01993 702549

Directions: From West: A40 eastbound towards Oxford. At Minster Lovell r'about, take the first exit towards Minster Lovell. After two miles turn right into Downs Road (signposted for Witney Lakes Golf Club), ground half a mile on right. From Witney town centre: head west down Welch Way, at r'about take 3rd exit into Curbridge Road. At r'about, take 3rd exit into Deer Park Road, at traffic lights turn left into Range Road, at end turn left ground is 400 yards on right.

Capacity: 3,500 Cover: 2,000 Seats: 280 Floodlights: Yes

FACT FILE
Formed 2002
Colours: Gold/black/black
Change: All Green
Midweek matchday: Tuesday
Programme Editor: Richartd Wickson
Tel No: 07834352543

CLUB PERSONNEL
Chairman: Steve Lake
Tel: 01993 700664 (H) 07790197474 (M)
V-Chairman: John Bircher
Manager:Alan Clark Ass.Man: Steve Paish
Physio: Bob Haydon

WOOTTON BASSETT TOWN

ecretary: Rod Carter, 14 Blackthorn Close, Wootton Bassett, Swindon SN4 7JE
Tel: 01793 851386 (H); 01793 494367 (B); 01793 494355 (F);
07946 034999 (M) Email: rod.carter@woolworths.co.uk

Ground: Gerard Buxton Sports Ground, Rylands Way, Wootton Bassett, Swindon 01793 853880

Directions: M4 jnct 16 to Wootton Bassett (A3102), left at 2nd r'bout (Prince of Wales pub on right), 2nd left into Longleaze (just after Mobil garage) and Rylands Way is 3rd right by shops, ground 100yds on right. From Calne/Devizes direction proceed thru town centre and turn right into Longleaze after Shell petrol station on right - Rylands Ave. is 3rd left. Coming from Malmesbury take last exit off r'bout by Prince of Wales pub and Longleaze is 2nd left

Capacity: 4,000 Seats: None Cover: 350 Floodlights: Yes Club Shop: No
Clubhouse: Open every matchday. Matchday refreshments - teas, coffees, soups & light snacks

PREVIOUS **Leagues:** Wilts (pre-1988) **Grounds:** None
RECORD **Gate:** 2,103 v Swindon T., friendly 7/91 **Win:** 11-2 **Defeat:** 0-9
Scorer: Brian (Toby) Ewing **Appearances:** Steve Thomas
Attendance: 2,103 v Swindon Town July 1951
HONOURS Hellenic Lg Div 1 Cup 89-90 93-94, Wilts Lg 87-88 (Div 2 84-85,Subsidiary Cup 78-79), Wilts Snr Cup R-up 02-03 03-04 87-88, Ghia Snr 83-84,Ghia Jnr Cup R-up 88-89, FA Amateur Cup QF 26-27

FACT FILE
Founded: 1882
Colours: Blue & yellowstripes /blue/yellow
Change colours: Maroon & Yellow
Midweek matchday: Tuesday
Reserve's League: Wiltshire
Programme: 12 pages, free
Editor: Fred Doherty (07771 860309)

CLUB PERSONNEL
Chairman: Paul Harrison
President: Keith Lodge
Press Officer: Rod Carter (see Sec)

Manager: Peter Yeardley
Coach: Mike Byrne
Physio: TBA

ADDERBURY PARK

Secretary Clive Boddy 5 Coppice Close Banbury Oxon OX16 9SW
Tel: 01295 255641 (H) 01295 225004 (B) 01295 225005 (F)

Ground: Adderbury Park Playing Fields, Round Close Road, Oxford.
Tel: 07788 867532

Directions: Take the A4260 from Oxford, enter village and turn left at village green into High Street, then into New Road, turn sharp left into Round Close Road. Ground entrance is 100 yards on left.

Clubhouse:

Previous League: Oxfordshire Senior Lge.>2002

2003-2004 **Player of the Year:** Mike Kenny **Top Goalscorer:** Adam Daley

FACT FILE
Formed: 1983
Colours: Emerald & white white/whiteChange: Red/black/black
Midweek matchday: Tuesday
Program Editor: Tony Luckett 07774255193
email: jimbo111@tinyworld.co.uk

CLUB PERSONNEL
Chairman: Jim Hay 01295 263466
email: peejay@supanet.com
Press Officer: John Daley 01295 257231
email: Topstriker69@aol.com

Manager: Jim Hay
Coach/Physio: Dennis Horrocks
Captain: Mike Kenny

CHELTENHAM SARACENS

Secretary & Press Officer: Robert Attwood, 179 Arle Road, Cheltenham GL51 8LJ
Tel: 01242 515855 (H) 01242 241819 (B) 01242 222994 (Fax)

Ground: Petersfield Park, Tewkesbury Road, Cheltenham GL51 9DX(01242 584134)

Directions:

Clubhouse: 2 mins away at 16-20 Swindon Rd, Cheltenham

HONOURS Glos Snr Cup 91-92 Glos Primary Cup 71-72, Winners Hellenic Div 1 99-00

PREVIOUS **League:** Cheltenham 1964-86

RECORD **Attendance:** 327 v Harrow Hill 31.8.03

Players progressing: S Cotterill (Wimbledon) 88, K Knight (Reading) 89

FACT FILE
Founded: 1964 Nickname: Saras
Colours: Blue&yellow/blue/yellow
Change colours: Green/black/black
Midweek Matchday: Wednesday
Reserves League: Hellenic Reserve section
Programme : 20 pages, 50p
Editor: Robert Attwood 01242 690405

CLUB PERSONNEL
Chairman: Chris Hawkins (01242 692332)
Man:Gerald Oldham Physio: Chris Hawkins

2003-2004
P.o.Y.: Anders Harvey
Top Scorer: Ross Constantine
2004-2005 Captain: Nick Locke

CIRENCESTER UNITED

Secretary/Press Officer: Gordon Varley, 95 Vaisey Rd, Cirencester, Glos GL7 2JW
Tel: 01285 657836 (H) 0973 631650 (M) 01367 718259 (B)
Ground: Grounnd sharing with Cirevncester Town
Directions: As for Corinium Stadium
Capacity: 4,500 Seats: 550 Cover: 550 Floodlights: Yes Club Shop: No
Clubhouse: Training nights & matchdays. Rolls & sundries available
HONOURS Glos Snr Amtr Cup R-up 86-87 89-90; Cirencester Lg 72-73 74-75 (Div 2(3)71-73 74-75, Lg Cup 74-75, Res. Cup 74-75); Cheltenham Lg 76-77 83-84 (Div 275-76, Lg Cup 83-84 (R-up 86-87), Snr Charity Cup 86-87); Stroud Charity Cup86-87 (Section A 82-83 83-84); Arthur Shipway Cup 86-87 (R-up 87-88 92-93);Fairford Hospital Cup R-up(4) 83-85 90-91 92-93; Hellenic Res Div 95-96, Cup96-97
PREVIOUS **Leagues:** Cirencester & Dist.(4 yrs); Cheltenham (8 yrs)
RECORDS **Scorer:** M Day **Appearances:** J.Stratford 310
2003-2004 **Top Goalscorer & Player of the Year:** G.Robinson

FACT FILE
Founded: 1970 Nickname: Herd
Colours: Red & black/black/red
Change colours: All Blue
Midweek Matchday: Wednesday
Programme: 40 pages, 50p
Editor: N Warriner (01285 656187)

CLUB PERSONNEL
President:R.Trinder
Chairman: Paul King
Press Officer: As Secretary
Manager: Ivor Probert
Coach: J.Stratford
Captain: Mark Warrinerxxx
Physio: R.Stratford

CLANFIELD

Secretary: Jenny Fisher, 62 Mill Lane, Clanfield, Oxon. Tel No: 01367 810471
Ground: Radcot Road, Clanfield, Oxon Tel: 01367 810314

Directions: Situated on the A4095, 8 miles west of Witney & 4 miles east of Faringdon, at the southern end of Clanfield. Buses from Witney - contact Thames Transit for details
Capacity: 2,000 Seats: No Cover: 300 Floodlights: No
Clubhouse: Every evening & Sat/Sun lunch Club Shop: No

HONOURS Oxon Jnr Shield 32-33, Oxon I'mediate Cup 67-68, Witney & Dist. Lg 66-67 (Div 1 65-66, Div 2 64-65), Hellenic Lg Div 1 69-70 (Premier Div Cup 72-73, Div1 Cup 69-70 85-86), Jim Newman Mem. Tphy 83-84 87-88, Faringdon Thursday Memorial Cup 69-70 71-72 96-97

PREVIOUS **Leagues:** North Berks; Witney & District
RECORD **Attendance:** 197v Kidlington August 2002

FACT FILE
Founded: 1890 Nickname: Robins
Sponsors: Olphert & Lamb
Colours: All red
Change colours: Yellow & Black/black/black
Reserves' League: Hellenic Lge Res. section
Prog: 8 pages, with admission Ed: Secretary

CLUB PERSONNEL
President: B Wallis Chairman: J Osborne
Manager: Jason Court & Peter Osborne
Press Officer & Physio: Trevor Cuss

2003-2004
Leading Goalscorer: A Winney 14
Player of the Year: John Mason

EASINGTON SPORTS

Secretary: Matthew Wiggins, 26 Victoria Place, Banbury, OX16 3NN. Tel: 01295 256714
Ground: Addison Road, Banbury, Oxon, OX16 9DH (01295 257006)
Club Email: matt@wiggins1.freeserve.co.uk

Directions: From Oxford A423. After passing under flyover on the outskirts of Banbury take first turning left into Grange Road then third right into AddisonRd. Ground at top on left. One and a half miles from Banbury (BR)
Capacity: 1,000 Seats:0 Cover: 30 Floodlights: No
Programme: Yes

Clubhouse: Changing rooms, showers, bar facilities and food

HONOURS Oxon Snr Cup R-up, Oxon Intermediate League & Cup, Oxon Snr Lg

PREVIOUS **Leagues:** Banbury Jnr; Oxon Snr; Warwick Combination
Ground: Bodicote

RECORD **Attendance:** 250 v Witney Town 68

FACT FILE
Founded: 1946
Colours: Red & white/black/red & white
Change colours: Blue/ white
Midweek Matchday: Wednesday
Reserves' League: Hellenic Res. section

CLUB PERSONNEL
Chairman: T.B.A.
President: Bob Cogbill
Manager/Coach: Andy Maguire
Physio: Bernie Jarvis
Press Officer: T.B.A.

HARROW HILL

Secretary/Match Sec: Robert Partridge, 20 Littledean Hill Road, Cinderford, Glos., GL14 2BE
Tel: 01594 825360 (H) 01594 825225 (B)
Club Email: harrowhillafc@aol.com
Ground: Larksfield Road, Harrow Hill , GL17 9PB Tel: 01594 543873

Directions: Take A40 west out of Gloucester, follow A40 for 8 miles then takeA4136 to Longhope, pass by on the outskirts of Michealdean, up steep hill(Plump Hill), then second turn on the right signed Harrow Hill. At phone box onthe left turn right into Larksfield Road, ground on right at top of hill.
Capacity: Seats: Cover Floodlights: Yes
Shop:

RECORD **Attendance:** 350 v Cinderford Town 1992
Previous Leagues:
HONOURS:

FACT FILE
Founded: 1932 Nickname: Harry Hill
Colours: claret & blue/claret/claret
Change Colours:Blue & black/black/blue
Midweek Matchday: Wednesday

CLUB PERSONNEL
Chairman: Reg Taylor
Press Officer:Mark Rawlings
markrawlings@drybrook.freeserve.co.uk
Manager: Neil Walding
Coach:Steve Boseley Physio: Martin Burford

2003-2004
Ps.O.Y.: Paul Frowen & Tom Burford
Top Scorers: Carl Woodroffe 17
2004-2005: Captain: Paul Frowen

HEADINGTON AMATEURS

Secretary: Stephen Giles, 67 Lucerne Ave.,Bure Park,Bicester, Oxon.OX26 3EG
Tel No: 01869 246141 Email Address: steve.giles3@ btinternet.com
Ground: Barton Rec., Barton Village Road, Barton, Oxon Tel: 01865 760489
Directions: From Green Rd r'bout, Headington, (on A40) take Barton/Islip exit(1st exit coming from Witney, last coming from London), turn left into NorthWay, follow road for half mile - ground at bottom of hill on left Seats: None Cover: None Floodlights: No Club Shop: No
Clubhouse: Tues & Thurs 6-11, Sat matchdays 4.45-11. Rolls, chips,burgers, hot dogs, etc
HONOURS Oxon Snr League(4) 72-74 75-77 (R-up 71-72 74-75 77-78 81-82 84-85, Div1 68-69, Presidents Cup(2) 72-74 (R-up 71-72 77-78 84-85)), Oxon Charity Cup75-76 (Intermediate Cup 88-89), Hellenic League Div 1 R-up 87-88 (Res. Sect.92-93, Res. Cup 91-92)
PREVIOUS Leagues: Oxford City Junr 49-66; Oxford Sen 67-88 **Grounds:**Romanway,Cowley
RECORDS **Attendance:** 250 v Newport AFC 91 **Scorer:** Tony Penge **Appearances:**Kent Drackett **Win:** 6-0 v Carterton (H) 91 **Defeat:** 0-9 Highworth Town (a) 2002 RPM Records Cup
Player Progressing: James Light (Oxford United) 1970s

FACT FILE
Founded : 1949 Nickname: A's
Sponsors: Shaun Bradford Decorating & Construction
Colours: All red
Change: Yellow/blue/white
Midweek matchday: Tuesday
Programme: 8 pages, £1 with entry
Editor: James Light (01865 750126)

CLUB PERSONNEL
Pres: Shaun.Bradford Chairman: Donald Light
Press Officer: Donald Light
Manager: Dean Fitzgerald
Coach/Physio:Michael Maciak

2003-2004
P.o.Y.: Neil Drewett Top Scorer: Matt Phillips
2004-2005 Captain: Mark Evans

HOOK NORTON

Secretary: Geoff James, Speedwell, Brick Hill, Hook Norton, Oxon
Tel No: 01608 737476
Ground: The Bourne, Hook Norton OX15 5PB 01608 737132
Capacity: 500 Covered Seating: no Covered Standing: no Floodlights: no
Directions: From Oxford – A44 to junction with A361 turn right, take 1st left to a 'T' junction, turn right & enter village, after 30 MPH turn left then 1st right into 'The Bourne', take 1st left into ground.
Clubhouse: On ground
Previous League: Oxfordshire Senior League
Record Gate: 244 v Banbury United 12th Dec 1998
Honours: Oxford Senior League Champions 1999-2000
Hellenic Lge Div.1 West Champions 01-02
Oxfordshire Senior Cup Runners-Up 2002-2003
Best Season FA Vase: 2nd Qualifying Round.

FACT FILE
Founded: 1901
Nickname: Hooky
Sponsors: Gladwish Land Sales
Colours: Sky Blue /Emerald Green
Change colours: Maroon and silver
Midweek fixtures: Wednesday
Program Editor: Mark Willis 01608 664101
email: repro@kmslitho.co.uk

CLUB PERSONNEL
Chairman: Michael Barlow
Deputy Chairman: Michael Barlow
Press Officer: Geoff James 01608 737476
Manager Anton Sambrook and Ben Spiro
Coach: Matty Haycock
Physio: Steve Slaughter & Louisa White

2003-2004
Top Scorer: Jody McKay P.o.Y.:Jake Tyrrell
2004-2005
Captain: Jake Tyrrell

Middle Barton F.C. Photo: Gordon Whittington.

Shrivenham - Back Row (L-R): Tony Garland (Asst. Manager), Alan Jennings (Physio), Carl Watkins, Neil Sutton, Jon Peters, Chris Webb, Mark Peters, Rich Tilling, Alex Green, Alan Dyton (Manager).
Front Row (L-R): Matty Wood, Teg Jones, Steve Winchcombe, Matthew Hampson (capt.), Liam Thompson, Tom Jones, Michael Kitchen.

Photo: Gordon Whittington.

KIDLINGTON

Secretary: David Platt, 57 Cherry Close,Kidlington, Oxon OX5 1HHJ (01865 370266 (H) 01865 244161(W) EMail Address: david.platt@environment-agency.gov.uk

Ground: Yarnton Rd, Kidlington, Oxford Tel: 01865 375628 Floodlights: No

Clubhouse: Two bars open after matches

Directions: From Kidlington r'bout (junction of A4260 & A34) A423 north toKidlington; after 3rdlights take 2nd left (Yarnton Road), ground is 200yds onthe left ,just passes the turning to Morton Avenue.

HONOURS Oxon Snr Lg 53-54 (R-up 47-48), Hellenic Lg Cup 74-75 (R-up 68-69 73-7474-75, Div 1 R-up 63-64 78-79), Oxon Intermediate Cup 52-53 84-85 (R-up 68-69 73-74 74-75), FA Vase 5th last sixteen 76-77

PREVIOUS **League**: Oxon Snr 47-54

RECORD **Attendance:** 2500 v Showbiz XI 1973

FACT FILE
Founded: 1909
Colours: : Green /green/ red
Change colours: Red & white stripes/red/red
Midweek Matchday:Tuesday/Wednesday
Programme: 32pages £2.00
Editor: Chairman

CLUB PERSONNEL
President: Gordon Norridge
Chairman: Geoff Talboys (07970 245888)
Manager: Kevin Walton

2003-2004
P.o.Y.: Tom Green, Luke Holden
Leading Goalscorer: Luke Holden 34

MALMESBURY VICTORIA

Secretary: Sue Neale, 30 Gastons Road, Malmesbury, Wilts. SN16 0BE
Tel: 01666 823560 E-Mail: sue@paulneale.freeuk.com

Ground: Flying Monk Ground, Gloucester Road, Malmesbury
Tel: 01666 822141

Website: www.malmesbury-victoria.com

Directions: From A429 (sign for Tetbur), pass Nurdens to roundabout and go past school then take next left B4014 signposted Sherston. Go down hill to mini roundabout, straight over roundabout. Go past Somerfield's super store, narrow right turning into ground behind super store.

Previous Leagues: Wiltshire Premier League

Honours: Wiltshire League Champions 99-00 Wiltshire Senior Cup 01-02

2003-2004 **Player of the Year**: R.Trowbridge **Top Goalscorer**: A.Mitchell

FACT FILE
Founded:
Nickname: The Vic's
Colours: Black & white stripes/black/red
Change colours: Yellow/Blue/Yellow
Midweek fixtures: Tuesday or Wednesday

CLUB PERSONNEL
Chairman: Paul Neale 01666 823560
Press Officer: John Wilkins 01666 824112
Prog Ed: Sarah Neale 01666 823560
Manager:
Graham Learmouth 01249 460069
Coach: Paul Rose

MIDDLE BARTON

Secretary: Julie Reed, 5 Hillside Road, Middle Barton, Oxon OX7 7EY
Tel: 01869 347388

Match Secretary: Jeane Beale, 3 Dorne Closer, Middle Barton, Oxon OX7 7HD
Tel: 01869 340753

Ground: Worton Road, Middle Barton, Oxon. Tel: 01869 347597

Directions: Middle Barton village is situated on the B4030, 5 miles east of Enstone. 200 metres passed the Fox PH turn left at cross roads, ground 200 metres on right.

Clubhouse: Open every evening

Previous League: Oxfordshire Senior League

Honours: Oxfordshire Sen. Lge R-up 98-99

FACT FILE
Founded: 1952
Midweek Matchday: Wednesday
Colours: Blue & white/blue/white
Change colours: Yellow/black/black
Programme: Yes, first season

CLUB PERSONNEL
President: Derrick Jarvis
Chairman: John Hanks
Press Officer: Phil Smith (01869 347471)
Manager/Coach: Tim Fowler
Physio: Lucy Waring

PURTON

Secretary: Alan Eastwood, 12 Hylder Close,Woodhall Park,Swindon,Wilts. SN2 2SL
Tel: 01793 729844 **Email Address:** eastwood@hylder.fsnet.co.uk

Ground: The Red House, Purton, Tel: 01793 770262 (Saturday afternoons only)

Directions: Purton is on B4041 Wootton Bassett to Cricklade Road. Ground nearvillage hall

Capacity: Unlimited Seats: None Cover: None Floodlights: No

Clubhouse: Open after matches and before matches on Saturdays

HONOURS Wiltshire Lg Div One 48-49 85-86, Div 2 83-84, Div 3 86-87; Wilts Senior Cup (6) 38-39 48-49 50-51 54-55 87-88, 88-89,94-95 Wilts Yth Cup 77-78 85-86 88-89, Fairford Hosp. Cup (3) 87-89 93-94 Hellenic Lg. Div One 95-96, Divison One West Champions 2003-04, Hellenic Supplement Cup 2001-02

RECORD **Attendance:** 508 v Dorcan 5.5.85

PREVIOUS **Leagues:** Wiltshire Premier

FACT FILE
Founded: 1923 Nickname: The Reds
Sponsors: The Care Company
Colours: All red Change colours: All purple
Midweek Matchday: Wednesday
Programme: 36--40 pages
Editor: Alan Eastwood (01793 729844)

CLUB PERSONNEL
President: Alan Eastwood
Chairman: Tony Brown
Press Officer: Alan Eastwood
Manager: Chris Pethick

2003-2004
P.o.Y.: Kenny Hughes
Top Goalscorer: Eushell Fearon

QUARRY NOMADS

Secretary: Amanda Blake, 43 Merton Way, Yarnton, Oxford. OX5 1NN (01865 841282)
Match Sec.: Keith Dolton, 58 Pitts Road Headington Oxford OX3 8AZ (01865 450256)

Ground: Margaret Road, Headington, Oxford OX3 8NQ Tel: 07860 408769

Directions: Exit M40 J 8, then A40 towards Oxford to Green Road r'about (McDonalds on left), straight over towards Headington.Take third left into Wharton Road, then at T junction turn left into Margaret Road. Ground on left.

Clubhouse: Small licensed bar with food and drinks on match days Contact: Mrs Dolton.

RECORD **Attendance:** 334 v Headington Amateurs 25.08.03

PREVIOUS **League**: Chiltonian

HONOURS Hellenic League Div.1 (East) Champions 2002-03

2003-2004 **Player of the Year**: Llam Callaghan **Top Goalscorer:** Aniclet Obhaimbo

FACT FILE
Formed: 1936
Web Site: www.qnfc.co.uk
Colours: Black & whitehoops/black/black
Change colours: All yellow or all red
Midweek fixtures: Tuesday
Prog. Editor: Andrew Molden 01865 433686
E-mail: ac.mold@hotmail.com

CLUB PERSONNEL
Chairman: Richard Lawrence 01865 873258
Press Officer:KeithDolton 01865 768970
Manager: Liam O'Callaghan
Captain: Liam Callaghan
Physio: Paul Dolton

ROSS TOWN

Secretary: Alan Bridges, Re-adel, Willowbrook,Greytree,Ross-On-Wye HR9 7JS.
Tel: 01989 564432 (H) 01594 542421 x 1276 (W)

Ground: Cinderford Town FC, Causeway Ground, Hilldene, Cinderford (01594822039)

Directions: From Gloucester take A40 to Ross-on-Wye, then A48 - Chepstow. In 10miles turn right at Elton garage onto A4151to Cinderford, thru Littledean, up steep hill, right at crossroads, and left into Latimer Rd.(F.C signposted).
Ground 5 mins walkfrom town centre

Capacity: 3,500 Cover: 1,000 Seats: 250 Floodlights: Yes

HONOURS Hereford Lge 94-95, Charity Shield 95-96; Hereford FA Charity Bowl 94-95; Worcester & Dist Lge 95-96, Baylis Cup 95-96; Hereford FA County Chall Cup 97-99 R-up 95-96; 98-99 Pershore Hospital Charity Cup R-up 95-96, Hellenic Lg Cup R-up: 99-00

PREVIOUS **Leagues:** Hereford Lg, Worcester & District League.

RECORD **Attendance:** 147 v Harrow Hill 26/3/97

FACT FILE
Founded:1993
Nickname: Riversiders
Colours: Red /black/black
Change colours:Green/Green/White
Midweek Matchday: Tuesday/Wednesday

CLUB PERSONNEL
Patron: Dave Sexton
Chairman: Geoff Jones
Director of Football and
Press Officer: Chris Parsons (01989 566712)
Manager: Martin Thomas
Coach: Chris Parsons
Physio: Sylvia Durham

SHRIVENHAM

Secretary: Matthew Hampson, 12 Grange Drive, Swindon, Wilts SN3 4LD
Tel: 01793 330983(H) 01793 423033 (B 07748 804593 M
E-mail: Matthew.Hampson@atlworld.com

Match Secretary: Robb Forty, 7A Devizes Rd., Swindon, Wilts
Tel: 01793 484455(H) 07767 371414 (M)

Ground: The Recreation Ground, Shrivenham SN6 8BJ Tel: 01793 784453

Directions: 'Off Highworth Road, Shrivenham' Village is signposted off A420, six miles east of Swindon, four miles west of Faringdon

Previous League: North Berks League

Record Gate 800 v Aston Villa X1 21st May 2000

Honours North Berks League Champions 00-01

FACT FILE
Founded:
Colours: Blue & white hoops/blue/white.
Change colours: Yellow/black/yellow
Midweek fixtures: Tuesdays
Programme: Yes
Editor: Dan Prescott (Press Officer)

CLUB PERSONNEL
Chairman: Ian Richardson 01793 782033
Press Officer: Dan Prescott 07989 603948
Managers:Alan Dyton and Tony Garland
Coaches: Alan Dyton and Neiil Batten
Physio: Alan Jennings

TROWBRIDGE TOWN

Secretary: Nigel Armstrong, 23 Chelwood Close, Chippenham, Wilts. SN14 0SA
Tel Nos: 01249 654588 (H) 01225 814402(W)

Ground: Wood Marsh, Bradley Road, Trowbridge, Wilts.

Capacity: 1,500 **Floodlights:** No (Floodlit cup matches at Westbury United)

Directions: From A350 Trowbridge by pass go towards Westbury and turn tight after a mile at Yarnbrook roundabout towards Trowbridge. Under railway bridge and take North Bradley exit at next roundabout. Continue to Marsh Turn and ground is 50 yards on left.

Record
Attendance: 220 v Southbrook August 1999

FACT FILE
Colours: Yellow with black stripe/black/black
Change colours: Red & Green/green/green
Midweek Matches: Tuesday
Programme: Yes
Editor: Andrew Neaden
Tel No: 01373 827788

CLUB PERSONNEL
Chairman: John Fitchen
Manager: Neil Kirkpatrick

TYTHERINGTON ROCKS

Secretary: Graham Shipp, 21 Elmdale Crescent, Thornbury, Bristol BS35 2JQ
Tel Nos: 07811 318424 (M) 01179365377 (W)

Ground: Hardwicke Playing Field, Tytherington
Tel No: 01454 416798

Capacity: 1,500 **Floodlights:** No

Directions: M5 Jct 14 take A38 for Bristol. Tytherington turn off is approx five miles. Enter the village and ground is signposted.

Previous League: **Glos.County League**

FACT FILE

Colours: mber & Black/black/black
Change colours: Green & Black/black/black
Midweek Matches:Wednesday
Reserves' Lge:
Programme:Yes
Editor: Ron Holpin
Tel No: 01454 614303

CLUB PERSONNEL

Chairman: Ted Travell
Manager: Andy Mathias

WINTERBOURNE UNITED

Secretary: John Lloyd, 9 Stanford Close, Frampton Cotterell, Bristol. BS36 2DG
Tel: 01454 775841(H) 0117 9552048(B) E-mail john-lloyd@1-nil.co.uk

Ground Parkside Avenue, Winterbourne, Bristol BS36 1LX 01454 850059

Directions Leave Junction 1 of M32 turn left then left again at traffic lights, sign posted Yate. Keep on road for two miles into Winterbourne After Ridings High School turn right into Parkside Avenue, ground on right.

Clubhouse:

Previous League: Gloucester County League

Honours: Gloucester County League Champions 00-01

Record Attendance:

FACT FILE

Formed:
Nickname: The Bourne
Colours: White/red/red
Change colours: Red/white/white or red
Midweek fixtures: Tuesday or Thursday

CLUB PERSONNEL

Chairman: Robyn Maggs
Tel: 01454 887338
Press Officer: as Chairman
Program Editor: John Lloyd 01454 775841
Manager Stuart Jones
Coach: Richard Dunn
Physio: Ken Purnell

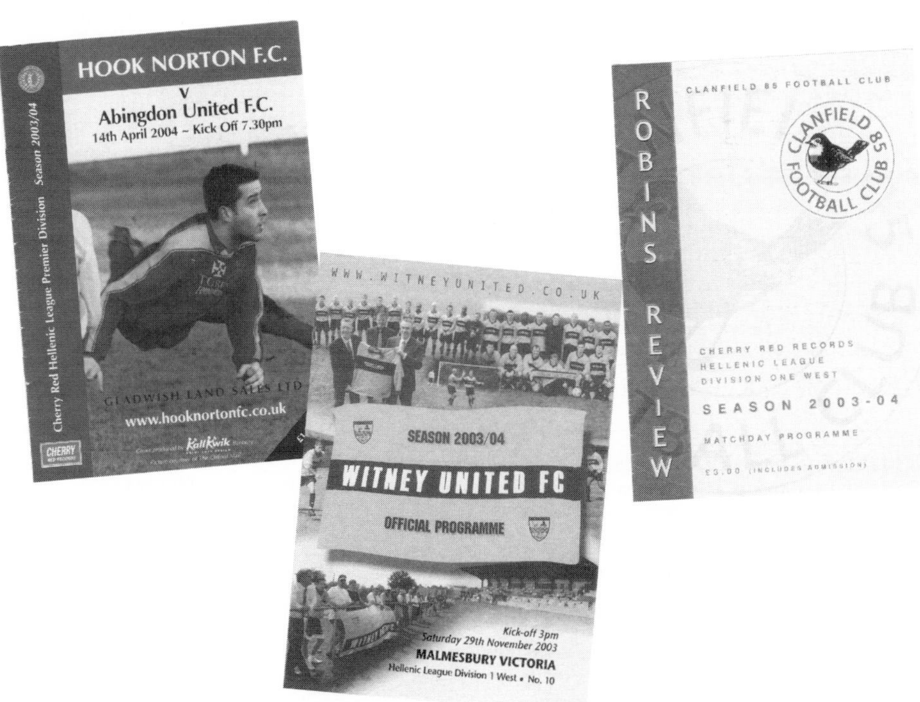

BADSHOTT LEA

Secretary: Mark Broad, 57 Lambourne Way, Tongham, Surrey GU10 1AB
Tel Nos: 01252 659990 (H) 07743 694930 (M)
email: badshotleafc@aol.com

Ground: Recreation Ground,The Green, Badshot Lea, Farnham,Surrey GU9 9LB
Tel No: 01252 316076

Capacity: 1,500 **Floodlights:** No (Floodlit Cup matches played at Farnham Town FC.)

Directions: From M3 Jct 4 take A331 towards Farnham for 5 miles. Turn off towards Aldershot on A323 and then left after 400 yards at first junction. At Badshot Lea village crossroads, go over lights then left into The Green after 150 yards and drive round green to car park. **2003-2004** **Top Goalscorer**: Bradley Smith

FACT FILE
Nickname: The Baggiy's
Colours:Sky Blue/Claret/Claret
Change colours:Royal Blye/white/white
Midweek Matches: Tuesday
Programme: Yes
Editor: Secretary

CLUB PERSONNEL
Chairman: Stuart Page
Tel No: 01420 489107
email: stpagw@02.co.uk
Manager: David Ford
Assistant Manager:Gary Tompkins

BANBURY UNITED RESERVES

Ground: The Stadium, off Station Approach, Banbury, Oxfordshire
Tel: 01295 263354 / 261899

BINFIELD

Secretary: Vernon Bradshaw, 21 Audley Way Ascot Berks SL5 8EE
Tel: 01344 886144 (H); 01344 356651 (B)

Ground: Stubbs Lane Binfield 01344 860822

Directions From A329 Bracknell to Wokingham Road, turn by the Travel Lodge into St. Marks Road, through the village into Terrace Road South & North, then at T junction by All Saints' Church turn right & then left into Stubbs Hill.

Record Gate: 268 v Englefield 2001-02
Previous League: Chiltonian

FACT FILE
Colours: All reded.
Change colours:All Blue
Midweek fixtures: Tuesday
Nickname: Moles

CLUB PERSONNEL
Chairman: Bob Alloway
Press Officer: Glen Duggleby
Programme Editor: Rob Jones
Manager:Richard Witty
Coach: T.B.A.

BISLEY SPORTS

Secretary Michael Clement, 3 Lower Guilford Road, Knaphill, Woking, Surrey, GU21 2EE
Tel: 01483 475003 (H) 01483 736286 (B) E-mail: mclem0@aol.com

Ground: Burghfield Sports Grnd, Church Lane, Bisley GU24 9EB
Tel: 07796 094941

Directions: Exit M3 at Junction 3. Head southbound on A322 towards West End & Bisley. Go over two roundabouts then turn left opposite the Hen & Chicken P. House into Church Lane, ground is about 400 yards on left hand side.

FACT FILE
Colours:Shirts – Blue & black/black/black
Change colours: All red
Midweek fixtures: Tuesday

CLUB PERSONNEL
Chairman: Peter Lucas
email: sales@carfiles.co.uk Tel: 01276 671314
Press Officer: See Secretary
Program Editor: Bruce Henderson
Tel: 01483 472432
Manager: Andy Clement Tel: 01276 24374
Coaches: John Cook & Bruce Henderson

CHALFONT WASPS

Secretary: Bruce Keen, 25 Albion Crescent, Chalfont St Giles, Bucks. HP8 4ET
Tel: 01494 875129 (H) email: bruce.keen@tesco.net

Match Sec/Press Off. & Prog. Editor.: Bob Isherwood 01494 871445 (H)

Ground: Crossleys, Bowstridge Lane, Chalfont. HP8 4QN Tel: 01494 875050

Directions On entering Chalfont St. Giles Village from A413 (Aylesbury - Uxbridge Road), turn left into Bolostridge Lane immediately after the shops. After a quarter of a mile turn right into Crossleys by a small green. Ground is directly ahead through the gates

Record Attendance: 50 v Harrow Hill Rovers 00-01
Previous League: Chiltonian

FACT FILE
Colours: Yellow & black striped/black/black.
Change colours: All Green
Midweek fixtures: Tuesday
Nickname: The Stingers

CLUB PERSONNEL
Chairman: Steven Waddington
Manager: John Franks
Coach: Denis Higgs

CHINNOR

Secretary: Richard Carr, 1 Harrison Place, Thame, Oxon. OX9 3TB
Tel Nos: 01844 217501 (H) 07786 115089 (M) 01844 215110 (FAX)

Ground: Station Road, Chinnor, Oxon OX39 4PV
Tel No: 01844 352579

Capacity: 1,500 **Floodlights:** No

Directions: M40 Jct 6 and follow B34009 towards Princes Riisborough. Enter Chinnor after 3 miles and turn left at The Crown Pub roundabout. Ground is 400 yards on right.

2003-2004 Top Goalscorer: Ryan Davis 16

FACT FILE

Colours: Orange/orange/black
Change colours:All Royal Blue
Midweek Matches: Tuesday
rogramme: Yes
Editor: James Matthews (07740 167512
james.matthews@waterstones.co.uk

CLUB PERSONNEL

Chairman: Richard Carr
Press Officer: Neil Pearson
Tel No: 07720 401077
Manager: Richard Carr
Assistant Manager: John Hathaway

Chinnor F.C. Photo: Gordon Whittington.

Chalfont Wasps - Back Row (L-R): Barry Leather (Asst. Manager), Steve Crook, Jon Hammersley, Paul Crook, Jamie Hill, Sam Woodward, Leighton Brooks, Jamie Skerritt, John Franks (Manager).
Front Row (L-R): Craig Herridge, Ryan McIntosh, Micky Poole, Jason Watson, Marcus Fearon.
Photo: Gordon Whittington.

ENGLEFIELD GREEN ROVERS

Secretary Jon West, 74 Lindsay Road, New Haw, Surrey KT15 3BE
E-mail Jon.west2@ntlworld.com

Ground: Coopershill Lane Englefield Green 01784 43566

Directions: Leave M25 at junction 13, A30 by passing Egham, at top of Egham Hill turn right at traffic lights. After passing Village Green on the left take 2nd turning right at the north east of green. Ground on right after half a mile.

Record Gate: 100 v Eton Wick, 1999

2003-2004: Alan Sewell

FACT FILE
Colours: All green & white
Change cols.: Red & white halves/white/white
Midweek fixtures: Tuesday
Nickname: The Rovers

CLUB PERSONNEL
Chairman: Paul Solari
Manager:T.Chapman
Captain: R.Banks
Coach: G.Kelly
Physio, Press Off & Prog Ed: Peter Casey

ETON WICK

Secretary : Barrie Shurville, 21 The Wheat Butts, Eton Wick, Berks., SL4 6JH.
& Press Officer 01753 862969 (H) 07860262614 (B)
& Prog Editor

Ground: Tel No: 01753 852749

Directions: From M4 junction 7 follow A4 to Maidenhead. At first roundabout (Sainsbury's) take B3026 towards Eton Wick. Ground is on the right after theparade of shops. From Eton take B3026 and ground is on the left after the Catholic church.

Honours:

Record Gate 500 v Andover, 1993 FA Vase

Previous League: Chiltonian League

2003-2004: Player of the Year: Richard Sanford Top Scorer: Peter Wayth

FACT FILE
Nickname: The Wick
Cols:Amber/black/black Change:All white
Midweek matchday: Tuesday

CLUB PERSONNEL
Chairman: Micky Foulkes 01753 733629
Man/Coach: Paul Gillow 01753 851877
Captain: Mick McManus
Physio: Ully Walsh

FINCHAMPSTEAD

Secretary: David Hobbs, 57 Welford Road, Woodley, Berkshire RG5 4QS
Tel : 01189 696195 Web Site: www.finchampsteadfc.co.uk

Match Sec.: Michael Husk, 16 Sadlers Lane, Winnersh, Berks RG41 5AJ
01189 785949 (H)

Press Officer: Stephen King 01189 732890 E-mail:
Stephen@kingsb.fsnet.co.uk

Ground: Finchhampstead Memorial Park, The Village, Finchampstead RG114JR
Tel: 01189732890

Directions: A321 from Wokingham, then fork right onto B3016. At the Greyhound pub turn right onto the B3348. The ground is 200 yards on the right.

Record Gate 425 v Sandhurst, 1958/ 9 **Previous League:** Chiltonian

FACT FILE
Formed:
Nickname: Finch
Colours: Sky blue & white/black/black
Change colours: All red
Midweek fixtures: Wednesday

CLUB PERSONNEL
Chairman: Kieron Brown (01344 452007)
E-mail: aquaspec@globalnet.co.uk
Manager: Steven McClurg
Coach : Willie Graham

HOLYPORT

Secretary: Eddie Pearce 1 Australia Ave Maidenhead Berks SL6 7DJ
Tel: 01628 673554 (H) 01628 680680 (B) 01628682700 (F)
E-mail: EddieP@Maidenads.co.uk

Ground: Braywick Sports Centre, Braywick Road, Maidenhead, Berks.
Tel: 01628 627066

Floodlights: No

Directions: From M4 exit at junction 8/9 take Maidenhead Central road, at roundabout take 1st left, follow dual carriageway for 300 yards and turn right into complex, signed Maidenhead Rugby club. In sports park follow road to the end, main pitch is on the left with changing rooms in front of you.

Previous League: East Berks. Lge >2002

FACT FILE
Colours: Claret/green/yellow
Change: Blue/red/red
Midweek matchday: Wednesday

CLUB PERSONNEL
Program Editor: Mark Burton
Tel: 01494 436331
Chairman: Norman House
Tel: 01628 626882
Manager: Mark Burton

HOUNSLOW BOROUGH F.C.

Secretary: Stefano Poulos, 7 Fairways, Thornbury Road, Isleworth Middlesex TW7 4NS Tel Nos: 0208 560 9763 (H); 0208 5800591 (B); 0208 560 1295 (F) 7765305003 (M) E-mail hounslowborough.f.c@lineone.net

Ground: Conquest Club, Wood Lane, Isleworth, Middlesex TW7 5EJ 0208 560 2892

Capacity: Covered Seating: Covered Standing: Floodlights: Yes/No

Directions: From M25 onto M4 at junction 3 then follow signs to Central London. At Gillett Corner turn left into Syon Lane. Ground 100 metres on the left.From A40 turn at Target Roundabout and follow A312 Hayes by pass to A4 then follow signs to Central London until Gillett Corner, turn left and ground on the left.

Record Gate 120 v Letcombe, 2003 **Previous League:** Chiltonian League

2003-2004 Player of the Year: Michael Smith Top Goalscorer: Adam Lock 17

FACT FILE
Colours: Blue & white /blue/blue
Change cols.: Red & blue/red/red
Midweek matchday: Tuesday
Prog Editor: Fiona Price (0208 5802718)
Web site: www.sportworldwide.com

CLUB PERSONNEL
Chairman: James Stefanopoulos
Manager:Chris Sparks
Captain: Jamie Sparks
Coach:Ray Gyrvan

KINTBURY RANGERS

Secretary: Peter Angell, 34 Queensway, Kinfbury, Berkshire RG17 9XD
Tel No: 01488 658445

Ground: Recreation Ground, Inkpen Road, Kintbury, Berks RG17 9TY
Tel No: 01488 657001

Capacity: 1,500 **Clubhouse**: Yes. **Floodlights:** Yes

Directions **From East**: M4 Jct 13, take A34 South then exit A4 to Hungerford then left at Kentbury crossroads.**From West**: M4 exit Jct 14 to Hungerford. Turn left at A4 and then right at Kintbury cross roads. In village follow road to shops and turn left. Ground is 200 yards on right.

Honours: North Berks League Champions 2003-2004

FACT FILE
Colours: Amber & Black/Black/Black
Change colours: Green & Black/Black/Green
Midweek Matches: Wednesday
Programme: Yes
Editor: Craig Angell
Tel No: 01488 658445

CLUB PERSONNEL
Chairman: Bert Newman
Manager & Press Officer: Jim Greenwood
Tel No: 01635 281293
Safety Officer: Mark Annetts (01488 658846)

LETCOMBE

Secretary: Des Williams, 8 Larkdown, Wantage, Oxon OX12 8HE
Tel No: 01235 764130
email: deswilliams@larkdown.fslife.co.uk

Ground: Bassett Road, LetcombeRegis Oxon OX12 9JU
Tel No: 07765 144985

Capacity: 1,500 **Floodlights:** No

Directions: Take B4507 from Wantage (Signposted White Horse) and turn left to Letcombe Regis aftyer half a mile. Ground on far side of village on right.

2003-2004 Top Goalscorer: Richard Claydon 29

FACT FILE
Colours: Purple/Navy/Navy
Change colours: Green/Red/Red
Midweek Matches:Tuesday
Programme: Yes
Editor: Russell Stock

CLUB PERSONNEL
Chairman: Dennis Stock
Manager: Matt Goddard
Assistant Manager: Kevin Bailey

OLD WOODSTOCK TOWN

Secretary: Ian F. Lenegan
c/o Workplace Systems plc.,Precedent Drive, Rooksley, Milton Keynes MK13 8PP
Tel:08362 42300(H), 01908 251301or 251311 (W) 01908 201287 (Fax)

Ground: New Road, Woodstock

Directions: A44 from Oxford into centre of Woodstock, turn right opposite The Crown into Hensington Road. After half a mile the road bends to the right, take the first turning right into New Road, ground half-way along on the left.

HONOURS Oxfordshire Sen. Lge 98-99

PREVIOUS **Leagues:** Oxfordshire Senior League

FACT FILE
Founded:
Midweek Matchday: Tuesday
Colours: Blue & red/blue/ red
Change colours: White/green/blue
Programme : Yes Ed: Mike Harris

CLUB PERSONNEL
President: Ian F Lenagan
Chairman: Ted Saxton
Press Officer: Mick Harris (01865 376018)
Manager: Andrew Townsend
Coach:Trevor Stokes
Physio: Graham Bowerman

PENN & TYLERS GREEN

Secretary: Malcolm James, Woodlands, Forty Green Rd, Forty Green, Beaconsfield HP9 1XS
Tel: 01494 677311 (H) 0207 777 0602 (B) email: malcolm.d.james@chase.com

Ground: Elm Road, Penn, Bucks HP10 8LF Tel: 01494 815346

Directions: Entrance to ground is off the main Hazlemere to Beaconsfield road. From Beaconsfield follow the road through Penn towards Hazlemere, pass the pond on green & ground entrance is on the right before going downhill.

Record Attendance: 125 v Chalfont Wasps 00-01

Previous League: Chiltonian

FACT FILE
Colours: Blue & white striped/blue/white
Change colours: All yellow
Midweek fixtures: Tuesday
Program Editor: Neil Bellamy 01494 812492

CLUB PERSONNEL
Chairman & Match Secretary:
Robert Dalling 01494 671424
Press Officer: Neil Bellamy
Manager: Richard Mikurenda

PRESTWOOD

Secretary: Paul Mullen, 16 Maybush Gardens, Prestwood, Bucks HP 16 9EA
Tel No: 01494 864048 EMail: paul.mullen @the-fa,org

Ground: Prestwood Sports Centre 01494 865946

Directions: From the Chequers Public House in the Centre of Prestwood, take the road signposted to Great Hampden. The ground is approximately half a mile on the left.

Previous Leagues: Chiltonian League

Record Attendance:

Honours:

FACT FILE
Formed:
Colours: Claret / claret
Change colours: orange/ blck/orange
Midweek fixtures: Tuesday

CLUB PERSONNEL
Chairman:
Manager:Steven Simmons 01494 725217
Reserves Manager: A Henney
01494 712544

RAYNERS LANE

Secretary: Tony Pratt, 4 Stirling Close Cowley Uxbridge Middx. UB8 2BA
01895 233853 (H)

Ground: Tithe Farm Social Club,151 Rayners Lane, South Harrow HA2 0XH
Tel No: 0208 8648724

Directions: From A40 Polish War Memorial (First junction after Northolt Aerodrome) turn left into A4180 (West End Road), approx. 500m turn right into Station Approach, at lights turn right into Victoria Road Sainsbury's on the right). At next roundabout continue straight on to lights at junction with Alexandra Avenue (Matrix pub/restaurant on left). Continue straight on over lights and take 2nd turning on left into Rayners Lane. Ground is approx. half a mile on left.

Record Gate 550 v Wealdstone, 1983 Season 2000/2001: Member of the Hellenic Lg

2003-2004 Top Scorer and Player of the Year: Tommy Metcalfe 23

FACT FILE
Nickname: The Lane
Colours: Yellow/green/yellow
Change colours: White/blue/white
Midweek fixtures: Tuesday

CLUB PERSONNEL
Chairman: Richard Mitchell 020 8422 6340
Press Off/Prog.Ed: Tom Lynn
0208 868 4671
Manager/Coach: Danny Mills
07970 402299
Physio: Andy Gushkes Captain: Steve Bird

WOKINGHAM & EMMBROOK

Secretary: Mick Franklin, 27 Quartz Close, Woosehill, Wokingham RG41 3TS
Tel Nos: 0118 9629349 (H) 07836 298186 (M)

Ground: Lowther Road, Wokingham RG141 1JB
Tel No: 0118 9780209

Capacity: 1,500 **Floodlights:** No

Directions: Turn off Reading Road in Wokingham into Forest Road and then turn right into Lowther Road. Entrance is on the right.

PREVIOUS League: Isthmian League

PREVIOUS Names: Wokingham Town. Emmbrook Sports.
Leagues: Isthmian League (Wokingham).
Reading League (Emmbrook Sports).

FACT FILE
Formed: 2004 Changed name after merger
Colours: Orange/black/black
Change colours: White/white/orange
Midweek Matches: Tuesday
Programme: Yes
Editor: T.B.A.

CLUB PERSONNEL
Chairman:Mark Ashwell
Manager: Glen Duggleby

KENT LEAGUE

SPONSORED BY: GO TRAVEL

President: D D Baker **Chairman:** P C Wager

Vice Chairman: D Richmond

Hon. Secretary & Treasurer: A R Vinter, Bakery House, The Street, Chilham, Nr Canterbury, Kent CT4 8BX

Tel: 01227 730457 Fax: 01227 738880

FINAL LEAGUE TABLE 2003-04

PREMIER DIVISION		P	W	D	L	F	A	Pts
1.	Cray Wanderers	32	22	4	6	88	35	70
2.	Thamesmead Town	32	22	3	7	72	38	69
3.	VCD Athletic	32	21	5	6	65	29	68
4.	Maidstone United	32	19	10	3	71	30	67
5.	Whitstable Town	32	19	5	8	77	52	62
6.	Hythe Town	32	17	7	8	51	41	58
7.	Erith Town	32	17	2	13	53	45	53
8.	Greenwich Borough	32	14	8	10	57	53	50
9.	Ramsgate	32	11	11	10	49	46	44
10.	Herne Bay	32	11	7	14	50	49	40
11.	Sevenoaks Town	32	12	1	19	40	57	37
12.	Beckenham Town	32	9	8	15	39	53	35
13.	Lordswood	32	9	5	18	34	68	32
14.	Tunbridge Wells	32	8	6	18	30	57	30
15.	Slade Green	32	7	8	17	42	47	29
16.	Deal Town	32	5	4	23	37	71	19
17.	Sporting Bengal United	32	1	2	29	26	110	5

PREMIER DIVISION		1	2	3	4	5	6	7	8	9	10	11	12	13	14	15	16	17
1	Beckenham Town		0-2	4-0	0-2	0-2	1-1	0-0	1-2	0-7	1-1	3-0	0-0	4-1	3-0	1-2	0-1	1-3
2	Cray Wanderers	3-1		4-0	1-0	1-3	2-1	3-1	3-0	2-3	4-1	2-0	2-0	10-0	3-1	1-1	1-1	2-3
3	Deal Town	0-0	1-5		0-2	1-3	1-2	0-2	1-3	1-2	2-4	0-2	2-1	7-0	2-5	0-2	0-1	0-3
4	Erith Town	3-0	1-4	2-1		4-2	2-0	1-1	0-2	3-2	1-4	2-1	2-1	6-0	1-1	2-0	1-3	3-0
5	Greenwich Borough	1-3	0-4	3-3	1-0		3-1	0-3	2-0	1-0	1-0	2-1	3-1	2-0	1-1	1-1	1-1	2-2
6	Herne Bay	3-1	0-2	3-3	4-2	4-0		0-1	3-0	1-2	0-3	3-1	0-1	1-0	1-1	1-0	0-1	0-2
7	Hythe Town	1-3	1-1	3-2	1-0	2-1	3-1		3-1	1-4	3-0	4-1	1-0	2-0	0-4	0-0	2-1	1-0
8	Lordswood	1-1	1-5	2-1	0-2	3-3	0-4	1-3		1-1	0-0	0-1	1-0	3-0	0-3	0-0	0-5	2-4
9	Maidstone United	0-0	2-1	5-0	1-0	2-0	2-2	1-1	4-0		2-2	1-1	3-2	2-1	1-0	0-0	2-1	1-1
10	Ramsgate	1-1	1-2	0-3	0-2	2-2	1-1	1-1	2-1	1-1		1-0	0-0	6-0	4-3	3-1	0-0	1-4
11	Sevenoaks Town	1-2	0-3	2-1	3-0	1-3	1-0	2-1	3-1	0-3	1-4		3-0	3-2	0-3	0-1	1-2	3-2
12	Slade Green	0-2	2-2	2-0	1-2	3-3	2-2	1-4	4-0	1-1	0-1	0-1		4-1	0-2	1-1	1-2	6-1
13	Sporting Bengal United	0-2	2-3	0-2	2-4	0-5	1-1	0-3	0-1	1-5	2-2	0-3	1-4		1-4	2-5	1-3	0-5
14	Thamesmead Town	2-0	3-2	2-1	1-0	2-0	3-0	4-0	4-2	0-4	2-0	4-1	1-0	3-2		3-2	1-0	2-4
15	Tunbridge Wells	3-2	0-3	0-1	0-2	1-4	3-2	2-1	2-3	1-3	1-3	1-0	0-3	0-4	0-1		0-4	0-4
16	VCD Athletic	4-0	1-3	2-1	5-0	2-0	2-5	5-0	1-0	1-2	2-0	2-1	0-0	3-2	3-2	1-0		4-1
17	Whitstable Town	6-2	4-2	0-0	3-1	4-2	2-3	1-1	2-3	3-2	2-0	4-2	3-1	2-0	0-4	1-0	1-1	

PREMIER DIVISION CUP

PRELIMINARY ROUND

VCD Athletic	v	Hythe Town	2-4

FIRST ROUND

Cray Wanderers	v	Tunbridge Wells	2-1
Deal Town	v	Sporting Bengal United	6-2
Erith Town	v	Slade Green	1-0*
Greenwich Boro'	v	Thamesmead Town	0-1
Lordswood	v	Hythe Town	0-1
Maidstone United	v	Beckenham Town	6-1
Sevenoaks Town	v	Herne Bay	1-2
Whitstable Town	v	Ramsgate	0-1

QUARTER-FINALS

Deal Town	v	Herne Bay	0-1
Erith Town	v	Cray Wanderers	0-1
Hythe Town	v	Maidstone United	0-1*
Thamesmead Town	v	Ramsgate	3-0

SEMI-FINALS (played over two legs)

			1st	2nd
Herne Bay	v	Cray Wanderers	1-4	2-0
Thamesmead Town	v	Maidstone United	2-0	3-4

THE FINAL (8th May at Folkestone Invicta)

Cray Wanderers	v	Thamesmead Town	0-1

Herne Bay - Back Row (L-R): Jon Warden (coach), Dave Briggs (physio), Wes Hammond, Jack Delo, Steven Lloyd, Sam Denly, Jamie Cook, Simon Bryant (manager). **Front Row (L-R):** Robbie Summers, Jamie Wynch, Andy Thompson, Lee Jones, Alex Hossick, John Utterson, Leigh Bremner.

BECKENHAM TOWN

Secretary: Peter Palmer,36 Inglewood,Pixton Way, Selsdon, Surrey CR0 9LP
Tel: 020 86513363 Mobile 07774 728758
Website: www.beckenhamtownfc.co.uk

Ground: Eden Park Avenue, Beckenham, Kent Tel: 07774 728758

Directions: M25, A21 to Bromley then follow signs to Beckenham.
Ground 1 mile west of town off A214.
2 mins walk from Eden Park (BR) station - trains from London Bridge. Bus 264

Capacity: 4,000 Seats: 120 Cover: 120 Floodlights: Yes

Clubhouse: All day opening at weekends.
Hot & cold food, teas, etc. Bar & dance area.

Club Shop: Yes

HONOURS London Spartan Lg Cup R-up 77-78 78-79, Kent Snr Tphy R-up 81-82 93-94, Kent Lg Cup R-up 84-85 92-93 (Div 2 Cup R-up 90-91)

PREVIOUS **Leagues:** S. E. London Amtr 71-73; Metropolitan 73-75; London Spartan 75-82
Ground: Stanhope Grove, Beckenham (60 yrs)

RECORD **Gate:** 720 v Berkhamstead F.A.Cup 94-95
Scorer: Ricky Bennett **Appearances:** Lee Fabian 985

FACT FILE

Reformed: 1971
Nickname: Reds
Colours:All Red
Change Colours:Yellow/blue/blue
Midweek matchday: Tuesday
Programme: 16 pages, 31.00
Editor:Secretary

CLUB PERSONNEL

Chairman: John Weatherhead
Vice Chairman: B Hollaway
Manager: Kevin Sugrue
Asst Manager: Jason Taylor

2002-03

Leading Goalscorer: Jason Claws
Captain:Matthew Belton
Player of the Year:David Weatherhead

DEAL TOWN

Secretary: Colin Adams,156 Mill Hill, Deal, Kent CT149JA (01304 372784)

Ground: Charles Sports Ground, St Leonards Road, Deal, Kent Tel: 01304 375623
Directions: A258 through Walmer, left into Cornwall Road, continue intoHamilton Road, veer left into Mill Rd, follow round to right into Manor Road, right into St Leonards Road, ground 100 yards on right. 1 mile from both Walmerand Deal BR stations. Local buses stop near ground
Capacity: 2500 Seats: 180 Cover: 180 Floodlights: Yes

Clubhouse: Matchdays & functions. Bar. Tea bar with hot & cold food Club Shop: Yes

HONOURS F.A.Vase Winners 99-00, Kent Lg 53-54,99-00 (R-up 88-89,98-99) Lg Cup 57-58, 81-82 , 98-99 (R-up 94-95), Kent Snr Tphy 94-95 , 99-00 R-up 82-83 90-91, Gtr London Lg Cup 67-68, Aetolian Lg R-up 59-60

PREVIOUS **Leagues:** Kent 09-59; Aetolian 59-63; Southern 63-66; Gtr London 66-71

RECORDS **Gate:**(Competitive) 2,495 v Newcastle Town F.A.Vase, S-Final 2nd Leg. 26.3.00
Scorer: Joe Brayne 175
Appearances: Alan Barrow 544 (recent times)

Player progressing: Danny Wallace (Southampton)

2003-04

Leading Goalscorer: Lee Marjoram 12 Players of the Year: Ben Laslett and Danny Smith

FACT FILE

Founded:1908
Nickname: Town
Sponsors: DEal Electrical
Colours: Black & white hoops/black/black
Change: Red & black stripes/black/red
Midweek matchday: Tuesday
Reserves' Lge: Go Travel Kent Div 1
Programme: 36/40 pages, £1.00
Editor: Colin Adams (01304 372784)

CLUB PERSONNEL

Chairman: David Saunders
Vice-Chairman: Bob Chivington
Fixture Sec: Colin Adams (01304 372784)
Manager:Derek Hares
Asst. Man.Andy Bigginton
Physio:Brenton Duke

ERITH TOWN

Secretary: Jim Davie, 6 Dashwood Close, Broomfield Road, Bexleyheath, Kent. DA6 7NU
Tel: 020 8306 7068

Ground: Erith Sports Stadium, Avenue Road, Erith, Kent DA8 3AJ (01322 350 271)
Directions: Off the A206 at Erith, into Victoria Road, then left at T junction into Avenue Road. First right along driveway which leads to leisure car park, stadium on left.600 yards from Erith BR.
Capacity: 1,450 Seats: 1,006 Cover: 60 Floodlights: Yes (156 lux)
Clubhouse: Use Leisure Facilities Shop: No

PREVIOUS **Leagues:** London Metropolitan Sunday 1959-91, London-Spartan 1991-96
Names: Woolwich Town 1959-89 and 1990-97 Woolwich Heathway 1989-90

CLUB RECORDS **Appearances:** Alan Hanlon 192 (8)
Victory: 7-2 v Canterbury City, Kent Sen. Trophy 20.12.00
Defeat: 0-8 v Deal
Goalscorer: Ben Hackett 42 **Goals in Season:** Dean Bowey 18 00-01
Attendance: 325 v Charlton 11.08.01Athletic x1 (Friendly)

HONOURS: Met Sunday Lge: Senior Section 1966, 1971, 1975.
London Spartan Lge: Intermediate Cup R-up 1994 & 1995. Div 1 R-up: 1995.
London F.A. Intermediate Cup R-up 1995. London F.A. Senior Cup R-up 2000

FACT FILE

Founded: 1959
Nickname: The Dockers
Colours: Red& blackstripes/black/black
Change Colours: White/red/red
Midweek matchday: Monday
Reserve League: Kent League(Go Travel) Div 1
Programme: 40-52 pages £1.00 (Ian Birrell)

CLUB PERSONNEL

Chairman: Albert Putnam
Vice Chairman: Phil Legg
President: Cyril Rebak
General Manager: Ian Birrell
Press Secretary: Matthew Panting
Manager: Willie O'Sullivan
Coach Nicky Johns

2003-04

Top Goalscorer:Glen McTaggart 24 (club record)
Player of the Year: Chris Arnold
2004-2005: Captain: Alan Hanlon

GREENWICH BOROUGH

Secretary: Janet Hogg(Letters c/o club)
Tel Nos: 0207 3543509 07970 986537M

Ground: Harrow Meadow, Eltham Green Rd, Eltham, London SE9 Tel: 0208 8595788

Directions: South Circular (A205) to McDonalds, grd opposite.
1 mile from both Eltham and Kidbrooke BR stations

Capacity: 2,500 Seats: 5o Cover: 50 Floodlights: Yes

Clubhouse: Yes

HONOURS London Spartan Lg 79-80 (Lg Cup 82-83), Kent Lg 86-87 87-88 (Lg Cup 84-85 86-87), Kent Snr Tphy 84-85, FA Vase 5th Rd 89-90

PREVIOUS **Leagues:** South London Alliance; Kent Amateur; London Spartan 77-84
Ground: Erith & Belvedere F.C. 1992-93
Name: London Borough of Greenwich

RECORD **Gate:** 2,000 v Charlton, floodlight opening, 1978
Defeat : 0-8 v Faversham Town, August 1989

FACT FILE
Founded: 1928
Nickname: Boro
Colours: All Red
Change Colours: All blueMidweek matchday: Tuesday
Programme: 16 pages, £1.00
Editor: Keith Harmer
Tel: 07930 618911 (M)

CLUB PERSONNEL
Chairman: T. Hassan

Manager: L. Hussein
Asst Manager: K. Crowhurst

2002-03
Leading Goalscorer:
Captain:
Player of the Year:

HERNE BAY

Secretary: Simon Harris 72 Station Road, Herne Bay, Kent CT6 5QH
Email: roland@hernebay,co.uk

Ground: Winch's Field, Stanley Gardens, Herne Bay, Kent Tel: 01227 374156

Directions: Leave new Thanet Way at Herne Bay/Canterbury exit. Follow signs toHerne Bay via Canterbury Road. After railway bridge (1/2 mile), take first left into SpencerRoad, then first left into Stanley Gardens, Ground on left **Clubhouse:** Open matchdays

Club Shop: Yes

Capacity: 4,000 Seats: 200 Cover: 1,500 Floodlights: Yes

HONOURS Kent Lg 91-92 94-95 96-97 97-98, (R-up 92-93 00-01), Div 2 62-63 63-64, R-up92-93(res) 94-95(res), Lg Cup 96-97, R-up 78-79 97-98, Div 2 Cup 53-54; Kent Snr Tphy 78-79, 96-97; Kent Amtr Cup 57-58 (R-up 58-59 63-64 68-69 72-73); Aetolian LgDiv 2 62-63 63-64 (Lg Cup R-up 62-63), Div 2 Cup 62-63 63-64; Athenian Lg Div 2 70-71 (Lg Cup 66-67); Kent Amtr Lg Cup 53-54 54-55; Thames & Medway Comb. CupR-up 61-62; FA Cup 4th Qual. Rd 70-71 86-87.

PREVIOUS **Leagues:** East Kent, Faversham & Dist, Canterbury & Dist, Kent Amateur, Kent 53-59, Aetolian 59-64, Athenian 64-74 **Ground:** Memorial Park 1886-1953

RECORDS **Attendance:** 2,303 v Margate, FA Cup 4th Qual. Rd 70-71
Win: 19-3 v Hythe 1900 **Defeat**: 0-11 v RAF Manston, Kent Amateur Lge 1935
Fee received: £3,000 for Mark Munday (Gravesend) 1994

FACT FILE
Founded: 1886Nickname: The Bay
Colours: Blue & white Change Colours: Red & black halves
Midweek matchday: Tuesday
Reserves' League: Kent Lge Div One
Programme: 36 pages, £1.00
Editor/Press Off.: Doug Smith (01227742182)
Website: www.hernebayfc.co.uk

CLUB PERSONNEL
Chairman: J Bathurst
Vice Chairman: W Dordoy
President: R. Whateley Bates.
Manager: Jason Lillis
Asst. Manager: Paul Haylock
Physio: Dave Silman
2002-03
Leading Goalscorer:Leigh Bremner
Player of the Year: Steven Lloyd

HYTHE TOWN (2001)

Secretary: Martin R Giles, 21 Wych Elm Way, Hythe, Kent. CT21 6QE
Tel: 01303 265962 (H) 01303 267619 (B)
Email Address: infohythetownfc.co.uk

Ground: Reachfields Stadium, Fort Rd, Hythe, Kent. Tel: 01303 264932 or 238256

Directions: On A259 west out of Hythe, turn left after light railway lights (Fort Road), entrance at end
Capacity: 3,000 Seats: 400 Cover: 2,400 Floodlights: Yes

Clubhouse: Bar open weekends/matchdays & training nights

Club Shop: No

HONOURS None as Hythe United or Hythe Town (2001)

PREVIOUS **Leagues**: Kent County and Southern
Names: Hythe Town and Hythe Town 1988 Ltd

BEST SEASON **FA Vase:** Semi-Final 89-90 **FA Cup:** 4th Q Rd v Hayes 1989-90

RECORD **Attendance**: 2,147 v Yeading 1990 F.A.Vase Semi-Final

FACT FILE
Founded: 1992
Sponsors: Carr Construction, Saga Group and Portex
Colours: All Red
Change Colours:Blue & White
Midweek Matchday: Tuesday
Programme: 60p
Website: www.huthetownfc.co.uk
Editor: Martin Whybrow

CLUB PERSONNEL
Chairman: Paul Markland
President: Rt Hon Michael Howard QC
Press Officer: Richard Giles
Manager: Paul Fisk
Physio: Dave Garlinge
Catain: Ian Hayes

2003-04
Top Goalscorer: & P.o Y.: Roy Godden

Greenwich Borough - Back Row (L-R): Lee Macken, Matt Norris, Mark Dudley, Michael Holden, Steve McKenzie, Damian Scannell. **Front Row (L-R):** Joshua Olabaul, Marcos Perona, Kwabena Amaning, Keiron Collins, Wesley Cain. Photo: Alan Coomes.

Hythe Town - before their Kent Senior Trophy final with Cray Wanderers.

Photo: Roger Turner.

LORDSWOOD

Secretary: Steve Lewis, Sunnybrook, Gorsewood Road, Hartley, Longfield, Kent DA3 7DF
Tel: 01474 708233 (H) 01233 822300 (B) 07775 541573 (M)
Email: stev_lewis@southernharvesters.co.uk

Ground: Lordswood Sports & Social Club Tel: 01634 669138
North Dane Way, Walderslade, Chatham, Kent ME5 9XX
Website: www.lordswoodfc.co.uk

Capacity: 600 Seats: 125 Cover: No Floodlights: Yes

Clubhouse: Yes
Club Shop: No

HONOURS None

PREVIOUS **Leagues:** Kent County Lge 68

RECORD **Attendance:** 650

FACT FILE
Founded: 1968
Nickname: Lords
Colours: Orange/black/black
Change Colours: Maroon
Midweek Matchday: Wednesday
Reserve or Youth League: Both
Programme: Yes Editor: T.B.A.

CLUB PERSONNEL
Chairman: R.Constantine
Vice Chairman: R.Johnson.
Press Officer: D.Harman
Manager: P.Piggott
Asst. Man./ Coach:W.Barlow

2003-04
Captain:Sam Colyer
Player of the Year: Sam Colyer

MAIDSTONE UNITED

Secretary: Adrian Hubbard
Ground: Ground share with Sittingbourne FC - Bourne Park Eurolink Industrial Park, Church Road, Sittingbourne ME10 3SB Tel: 01795 435077
Website: www.maidstoneunited.co.uk Hotline 09068 800691
Directions: Through Sittingbourne on main A2, club signposted clearly and regularly from both east and west. 1 mile from Sittingbourne BR station.
Capacity: 8,000 Cover: 3,300 Seats: 2,000 Floodlights: 420 lux
HONOURS Kent Lg 01-02 R-up 02-03 Kent Lg Cup 02 Kent LG Shield 02 Kent Sen Trophy 03 Kentb Junior Cup 95Kent Co Lg Div 1 99,Div2 95 Div4 94 West kent Challenge Shield 94,99 R-up 95 Tunbridge Wells Charity Cup 94 Weald of Kent Cup 00,01
PREVIOUS **Names:** Maidstone Invicta
Grounds: London Rd 92-01 Central Park 01-02
Leagues: Kent County League 93-01
BEST SEASON **FA Vase:** 2nd Rd 01-02 0-3 v Mildenhall
FA Cup: 2nd Q Rd 02-03 v Boreham Wood
RECORDS **Attendance:** 1,589 v Gillingham (friendly) 12.03.02 937 v Boreham Wood F.A.Cup 29.09.02 **Victory**: 12-1 v Aylesford K Co Lg Div 1 26.03.94
Defeat: 2-8 v Scott Sports Kent Co Lg Div 1 24.0296

FACT FILE
Founded: 1966 Nickname: The Stones
Reformed 1992
Sponsors: joebec.com
Colours: Amber/black/gold
Change Colours: All white
Midweek matchday: Tuesday
Programme: Yes Editor Ian Tucker
Editor: Steve Hemsley Tel: 01892 514006

CLUB PERSONNEL
Chairman: Paul Bowden-Brown
Vice Chairman:Richard Bowden-Brown
Life President:George Gray
Manager:Jim WardCoach:Mal Watkins
Physio:Simon Kavanagh
2002-2003 Capt: Paul Foley
P.o.Y.: Neil Davey
Top Scorer: Richard Sinden 26

RAMSGATE

Secretary: Martin Able, 1 Parkside Villas,Tivoli Rd., Margate, Kent CT9 5PZ (01843 290272)
Ground: Southwood Stadium, Prices Avenue, Ramsgate, Kent Tel: 01843 591662

Directions: From London on A229, A253 into Ramsgate - left into Netherhill atr'bout, right into Ashburnham Rd, right into Southwood Rd. 15 mins walk from Ramsgate BR station; walk thru Warre Recreation Ground, along St Lawrence HighStr., left at `St Lawrence Tavern', follow Southwood Rd and turn right into PricesAvenue

Capacity: 5,000 Seats: 400 Cover: 600 Floodlights: Yes

Clubhouse: Open matchdays & private functions. Two bars, two pool tables,darts. Hot & cold food on matchdays Club Shop: Yes (First team home matches)

HONOURS Kent Lg 49-50 55-56 56-57 98-99(Lg Cup 48-49 92-93 93-94 94-95 00-01) Kent I'mediate Cup 54-55, Kent Snr Cup 63-64, Thames & Medway Cup 60-61, KentSnr Shield 60-61, Kent Floodlit Tphy 69-70, Kent Snr Tphy(3) 87-89 98-99 Kent Lg Charity Shield 97-98

PREVIOUS **Leagues:** Southern 59-75
Name: Ramsgate Athletic

RECORDS **Gate:** 5,200 v Margate, 56-57
Scorer: Mick Williamson
Win:11-0(H) & 12-1 (A) v Canterbury City, Kent League 2000-01

FACT FILE
Founded: 19469 (1898 as Ramsgate Town)
Nickname: Rams
Sponsors: Thanet Waste
Colours: Red & white stripes/red/red
Change Colours: Green/green/yellow
Midweek matchday: Tuesday
Reserves' League: Kent Lge Div. One
Programme: 28 pages
Editor: Steve Redford (01843 596138)

CLUB PERSONNEL
Chairman: Richard Lawson
Vice Chairman: Paul Jefcoate
President: Tom Pendry
Commercial Manager: Martin Power
Tel: 01843 597703
Manager: Peter Hook Asst Man: Lee Bosham
Physio: Gallvic Walker
2002-03 Capt: Paul Downey
Po.yY:Danny Twyman
Top Scorer: Mo Takaloobighashi

SEVENOAKS TOWN

Secretary: Edwin Diplock, 23 Holly Bush Lane, Sevenoaks, Kent TN13 3TH
Tel: 01732 454280

Ground: Greatness Park, Seal Road, Sevenoaks Tel: 01732 741987
Directions:

Capacity: Seats: 110 Cover: 200 Floodlights: Yes
Clubhouse: **Club Shop:**

Previous League: Kent County League until 2003

Honours Kent County League Champions (3), Local Charity Cup Winners (12)

FACT FILE
Founded: 1883
Colours:
Azure & black stripes/black/black
Change colours:
Navy & scarlet quarters/navy/navy

CLUB PERSONNEL

2003-04
Player of the Year: James Townsend
Top Goalscorer: David Forster
2004-2005
Captain: David Norbury

Sevenoaks Town - Back Row (L-R): Sim Johnston, Richard Kennedy, Steve Clarke, Darren Smart, Dave Norburn, James Townsend. **Front Row (L-R):** Mark Abbott, Brad Mortimer, Jon Cooke, Robbie Jenner, Wayne Balmer.
Photo: Alan Coomes.

SLADE GREEN

Secretary: Bruce Smith, 15 Gumping Rd, Orpington, Kent BR5 1RX Tel: 01689 858782

Ground: The Small Glen, Moat Lane, Slade Green, Erith, Kent Tel: 01322 351077

Directions: Off A206 between Erith & Dartford.
400 yards from Slade Green BR station. Buses 89 & B13
Capacity: 3,000 Seats: 150 Cover: 400 Floodlights: Yes
Clubhouse: Yes; Hall, Directors Lounge & Canteen Club Shop: No

HONOURS Kent Snr Tphy 91-92 (R-up 80-81); Kent Lg Cup 82-83; Kent Amtr Lg 52-53 53-54 60-61 (Lg Cup 60-61); Kent Intermediate Cup 61-62; Kent Benevolent Cup46-47; West Kent 60-61 65-66; Dartford Lg R-up 48-49 (Lg Cup 47-48 (R-up 46-47)); Erith Hospitals Cup 46-47 48-49; Gtr London Lg R-up 68-69; Plumstead Challenge Cup 48-49

PREVIOUS Leagues: Dartford 46-52; Kent Amateur 52-62; Greater London 62-70
Name: Slade Green Athletic 46-86

RECORDS **Attendance:** 3,000 v Millwall, friendly 25/7/92
Goalscorer: Colin Dwyer **Appearances:** Colin Dwyer
Win: 14-0 v Island Social, Kent Amtr Lge 1953 **Defeat:** 1-9 v Whitstable Greater London 64-65

Players progressing : Roy Dwight (Nottm Forest), Alan Clark (Charlton) , Fred Lucas (Charlton)Tommy Tuite (Millwall Jan. 1999)

FACT FILE
Founded: 1946 Nickname: The Green
Sponsor: Threes and Fours
Colours: Green
Change Colours: WhiteMidweek matchday: Tuesday
Reserve League:
Programme: 44 pages, incl. with admission
Editor: Robert Smith (01322 287982)

CLUB PERSONNEL
Chairman: Brian Smith
President: P.Johnson
Press Officer: Robert Smith (01322 339748)
Manager: Phil Miles
Coach: Peter Little
Physio: Graham Barber

2002-03
Player of the Year:Lee Barbe
2004-2005
Captain:Darren Upson

SPORTING BENGAL UNITED

Secretary: Sana Miah, 11 Shadwell Gardens,Cable Street, London.E1 2QG

Tel No: 07951 115656

Ground: MIle End Stadium, Rhodeswell Road, Off Burdett Riad,London E14

Tel No: 0208980 1885

Directions: From M2/A2 continue onto A102 through Blackwell Tunnell. Left onto A13 towards centre of London.Turn right into Burdett Road (A1205) then left at the second set of traffic lights into St Pauls Way leading onto Rhodeswell Road. Ground is on right.

PREVIOUS Leagues: Asian League until 1999

London Intermediate 1999-2000

RECORD **Attendance:** 4,235 v Touring Phalco Mohammedan S.C.

2003-2004 **Player of the Year:** Younes Ben Messaood **Top Scorer**:Prince Pipim

FACT FILE

Formed: 1996

Colours:All Royal Blue

Change colours: Gold/Black/Black

Midweek Matches:Wednesday

Programme Editor: Nasyar Miah

CLUB PERSONNEL

Chairman: Suroth Miah

Manager: Micky Leslie

Captain: Adrian Edward

THAMESMEAD TOWN

Secretary: David Joy, The Cottage, Halcot Avenue, Bexleyheath, Kent Da6 7QB (01322 558429)
Ground: Bayliss Avenue, Thamesmead, London SE28 8NJ Tel: 0181 311 4211

Directions: By road: From Dartford tunnel A2 to London, exit Danson Interchange and follow signs for Thamesmead and Abbey Wood. From Blackheath tunnel exit on south side and follow signs to Woolwich, to Plumstead and then to Thamesmead

From Abbey Wood (BR) north east along Harrow Manor Way, into Crossway at 3rd r'bout, Bayliss Av. is 3rd right (Bexley bus 272 stops in Crossway near Bayliss Av.

Capacity: 400Seats: 125 Cover: 125 Floodlights: Yes Club Shop: No

Clubhouse: Mon-Fri 6-11pm, Sat 12-11pm, Sun 12-3 & 7-10.30pm. Double bar,lounge, dance-floor, children's games room, video machines, hot & cold food.New members Bar

HONOURS Spartan Lg Div 3 79-80 (Lg Cup 84-85 86-87; I'mediate champs 85-86);Kent I'mediate Cup 83-84 94-95; 4 promotions & 9 trophies (inc London & Kent FA Cups) in progress thru Spartan I'mediate Divs, 1980-87; Kent Lge Div 2 94-95, Div 2 Cup 94-95

PREVIOUS **Leagues:** London Spartan 80-91
Ground: Meridian Sports Ground, Charlton

RECORDS **Attendance:** 400 v Wimbledon, ground opening 1988
Appearances: Delroy D'Oyley **Win** : 9-0 v Kent Police, Kent League 19/4/94

FACT FILE
Founded: 1970
Nickname: The Mead
Sponsors: Courage Brewery
Colours: Green& White/Green/Green
Change Colours: All blue
Midweek matchday: Tuesday
Reserves League: Winstonlead Kent D2
Programmes: Yes. £1.00
Editor: Albert Panting

CLUB PERSONNEL
Chairman: Nicky O'Keefe
Vice Chairman: John Kelly
President: Albert Panting
Press Officer: Keith McMahon
Manager: Paul Blade
Physio: Allen Martin

2003-04
Leading Goalscorer & P.o.Y.: Michael Power

2004-2005
Captain:Dean Kearley

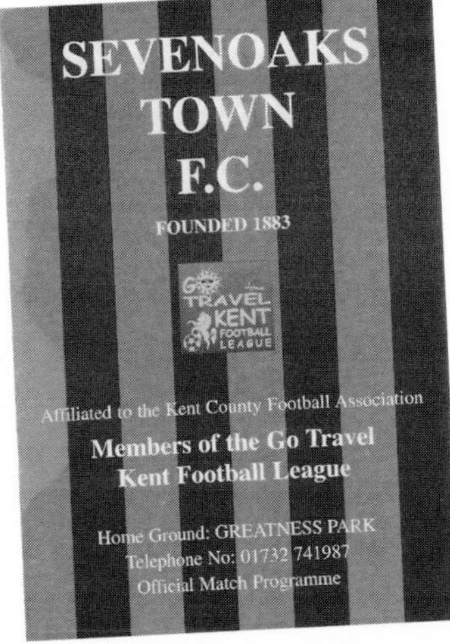

Lordswood - Back Row (L-R): Neil Crust, Andy Doerr, Darren Watson, Glen Cook, Ray Broad, Paul Piggott (Player Manager). **Front Row (L-R):** Craig Allen, Ronan O'Connor, Sean Hetterley, Sam Colyer, James Day, Gary Beggs. Photo: Alan Coomes.

Maidstone United - Back Row (L-R): Paul Foley, Nick Davis, Scott Appleton, Neil Davy, Elliot Bradbrook, Kevin Hudson, Richard Sinden. **Front Row (L-R):** Aaron Lacy, Jason Bartlett, Mark Horan, Daniel Kedwell. Photo: Alan Coomes.

TUNBRIDGE WELLS

Acting Secretary: N.Sales, 10 Oakwood Rise, Tunbridge Wells, Kent TN2 3HQ
Ground: Culverden Stadium, Culverden Down, Tunbridge Wells, Kent TN4 Tel: 01892 520517

Directions: Leaving town on main Tonbridge rd (A26), turn left into Culverden Down ground half mile. 1 mile from Tunbridge Wells Central(BR). Served by any Tunbridge Wells-Tonbridge bus - to St Johns
Capacity: 3,750 Seats: 250 Cover: 1,000 Floodlights: Yes
Clubhouse: Open matchdays and as required Club Shop: No

HONOURS Kent Lg 84-85 (R-up 68-69, Lg Cup 74-75 77-78 85-86 87-88) Kent SnrTphy R-up 85-86 91-92
PREVIOUS **Names:** None. predecessors: T . Wells FC 1886-1910 47-50 T. Wells Rgrs 03-09 63-67; T. Wells Utd 51-62
Grounds: Down Lane 1906; Combley Park 06-10; Swiss Cottage 06-14;Down Farm 19-39; St Johns 47-50; Eridge Road 50-67
RECORDS **Attendance:** 967 v Maidstone United, FA Cup 1969
Goalscorer: John Wingate 151 **Appearances:** Tony Atkins 410
Win: 10-0 v Deal (H), May'86
Defeat: 1-11 v Deal Town (H), 20/2/93

FACT FILE
Founded: 1886
Reformed: 1967
Nickname: Wells
Colours: Red/Red/White
Change Colours: Blue/Blue/White
Midweek Matchday: Tuesday
Prog: 40 pages, 50p Editor: Mat Harris
Web: www.@team2.com/tunbridge wellsfc

CLUB PERSONNEL
Chairman: N.Sales
Vice Chairman:J Farnie
President: P.Wager
Manager: K.Metcalfe

2003-04
Player of the Year: Matthew Bromby
2004-2005
Captain: Lee Skinner

VICKERS CRAYFORD, DARTFORD ATHLETIC

Secretary: Brian Norris,Peelers Lodge ,21 St Edith's Road, Kemsing,Sevenoaks, Kent TN15 6PT. Tel No: 01689 854302
Ground: Thamesmead Town FC, Bayliss Avenue, Thamesmead, London, SE28 8NJ Tel: 0208 311 4211 (Temporary Groundshare)
Home Ground (Pending floodlights) Oakwood, Old Road, Crayford, Kent, DA1 4DN.
Home clubhouse: Lounge Bar every day and evening. Plus snack bar on matchdays.
Directions: From Abbey Wood (BR) north east along Harrow Manor Way, into Crossway at 3rd r'bout, Bayliss Av. is 3rd right (Bexley bus 272 stops in Crossway near Bayliss Av. By road: From Dartford tunnel A2 to London, exit Danson Interchange and follow signs for Thamesmead and Abbey Wood. From Blackheath tunnel exit on south side and follow signs to Woolwich, to Plumstead and then to Thamesmead.
Capacity: 400 **Seats:** 125 **Cover:** 125 **Floodlights**: Yes

PREVIOUS **League:** Kent County.
Grounds: Flamingo Park, Sidcup (pre 1994); VCD Sports & Social Club,Old Road, Crayford
RECORD **Victory:** 10-1 v Canterbury City 14.5.01 **Defeat:** 0-5 v Deal Town 20.4.02

HONOURS Kent County Cup 61-62, 63-64, 94-95, R-Up: 84-85, 89-90. Kent County Lg Div One 96-97 Kent County Premier 96-97. West Kent Cup 87-88.Kent Lge Cup: Winners 99-00 ,Runners up 98-99, 02-03. Kent Intermediate Shield (2) R-up(1), Erith Hosp Cup x4, R-Up x4; Kent Sen, Tphy. R-up 00-01

FACT FILE
Founded: 1916
Nickname: The Vickers
Sponsors: MB Fire Protection
Colours: Green & white/green/green
Change Colours: Blue & white/blue/blue
Midweek matchday: Wednesday
Programme: 40 pages 50p

CLUB PERSONNEL
Chairman: Michael Bonello
Vice Chairman:
President:
Manager:Martin Ford
Asst. Man.: Peter Burke
Coach: Roy Passey
Physio: Peter Burke

2002-03
Leading Goalscorer:
Captain:
Player of the Year:

WHITSTABLE TOWN

Secretary: George Corney, 46 Elizabeth Way, Herne Bay, Kent CT6 6ET (01227 363496)
Ground: Belmont Road, Belmont, Whitstable, Kent Tel: 01227 266012

Directions: From Thanet Way (A299), left at Tescos r'bout and down MillstroodRd - ground at bottom of road, 400yds from Whitstable (BR) station. Car park at Grimshall Rd entrance
Capacity: 2,000 **Cover:** 1,000 **Seats:** 500 **Floodlights:** Yes **Club Shop**: Yes
Clubhouse: Social & recreation purposes, open all matchdays. Bar. Hot food &drinks at tea-bar

HONOURS Kent Lg Div 2 27-28 33-34 49-50 (Lg Cup 79-80 (R-up 89-90 91-92)), KentAmtr Lg East 60-61, Kent Amtr Cup 28-29, Kent Snr Tphy R-up 78-79 89-90 92-93,Gtr London Lg Cup R-up 65-66, Kent Amtr Cup 28-29, Kent Midweek Lg Cup 92-93
PREVIOUS **Leagues:** E. Kent 1897-1909; Kent 09-59; Aetolian 59-60; Kent Amtr 60-62 63-64; S E Anglian 62-63; Gtr London 64-67; Kent Premier 67-68 (also in New Brompton, Thanet & Faversham & Dist. Lges over the years)
Names: Whitstable Utd (pre-1886); Whitstable Swifts 93-95; WhitstableTown 95-1905; Whitstable FC 08-66
GroundsSaddleston's Field 1885-94; Westmeads (Cromwell Rd) 94-95; Joy Lane 95-1908; Church Rd 08-09
RECORDS **Gate:** 2,500 v Gravesend & N, FA Cup 3rd Q. Rd,19/10/87
Goalscorer: Barry Godfrey **Appearances:** Frank Cox 429 (1950-60)
Win: 18-0 v Greenstreet (H), Faversham & Dist. Lge 20-21
Defeat: 0-10 v Sittingbourne (A), FA Cup 1st Qual. Rd 62-63

FACT FILE
Founded: 1885
Nickname: Oystermen, Reds, Natives
Sponsors: D & J Tyres
Colours: Red & White/ white/Red
Change colours: Yellow/blue/yellow
Midweek matchday: Tuesday
Programme: 48 pages, £1.00
Editor/Press Off:Jon Homer
Website: whitstabletownfc.co.uk

CLUB PERSONNEL
Chairman: Joe Brownett V-Chair: Alan Gower
President: George Gifford
Fix Sec:Bruce Smith (01227 274138)
Manager: Matt Toms
Asst. Managers: Marc Seager & Mark Lane
Physio: Graeme Brown Capt: Marc Seager

2003-04
Leading Goalscorer:Andy Constable
Player of the Year:Scott Price

MIDLAND FOOTBALL ALLIANCE

SPONSORED BY: TRAVEL FACTORY

President: Bernard Davis **Chairman:** Pat Fellows

Secretary: Peter Dagger, 32 Drysdale Close,
Wickhamford, Worcestershire WR11 7RZ
Tel: 01386 831763 Fax: 01386 833488
E-mail: PDagger@talk21.com

FINAL LEAGUE TABLE 2003-04

		P	W	D	L	F	A	Pts
1.	Rocester	46	28	12	6	96	45	96
2.	Willenhall Town	46	27	13	6	114	49	94
3.	Stratford Town	46	28	8	10	89	45	92
4.	Quorn	46	26	12	8	84	47	90
5.	Studley	46	26	7	13	96	52	85
6.	Oadby Town	46	23	8	15	90	56	77
7.	Chasetown	46	22	11	13	68	50	77
8.	Coalville Town	46	20	12	14	87	61	72
9.	Stourbridge	46	19	15	12	74	52	72
10.	Bridgnorth Town	46	20	12	14	76	66	72
11.	Oldbury United	46	19	14	13	72	55	71
12.	Racing Club Warwick	46	20	9	17	64	63	69
13.	Westfields	46	20	6	20	67	61	66
14.	Rushall Olympic	46	15	16	15	58	55	61
15.	Boldmere St Michaels	46	17	9	20	76	77	60
16.	Biddulph Victoria	46	16	12	18	66	74	60
17.	Causeway United	46	15	11	20	66	82	56
18.	Barwell	46	15	9	22	63	75	54
19.	Alvechurch	46	12	14	20	67	87	50
20.	Ludlow Town	46	12	11	23	56	84	47
21.	Grosvenor Park	46	9	9	28	53	79	36
22.	Cradley Town	46	8	12	26	60	92	36
23.	Pelsall Villa	46	7	7	32	46	132	28
24.	Stafford Town	46	1	5	40	27	176	8

	1	2	3	4	5	6	7	8	9	10	11	12	13	14	15	16	17	18	19	20	21	22	23	24
1 Alvechur		3-3	1-3	2-1	0-3	1-2	1-1	0-4	1-5	4-2	2-1	0-0	0-1	2-1	1-1	1-2	1-1	2-3	3-1	1-1	2-2	0-2	1-1	5-2
2 Barwell	1-1		1-0	0-2	2-0	1-1	0-0	2-1	4-2	3-1	2-1	1-2	1-3	3-0	0-1	0-0	0-4	1-0	4-0	2-0	0-2	1-0	2-1	0-3
3 Biddulph	0-3	5-3		2-2	2-2	1-2	0-1	3-0	1-1	1-0	0-2	1-5	0-1	1-1	5-2	0-0	0-4	0-0	3-2	3-2	0-2	4-3	1-0	1-1
4 Boldme.	3-2	1-0	4-1		1-2	3-1	2-1	2-1	3-0	0-2	1-1	2-3	1-1	4-1	1-2	0-2	0-1	2-4	5-0	0-1	2-3	1-1	0-3	0-5
5 Bridgno.	2-0	4-1	1-3	0-3		3-1	1-2	3-2	2-1	2-0	1-1	2-1	3-1	4-2	1-1	1-0	0-1	1-2	0-0	0-3	4-1	0-1	3-1	0-2
6 Caus.	2-1	2-1	1-1	1-1	1-4		2-3	1-1	1-3	0-1	3-0	1-2	0-1	1-3	2-1	2-1	0-0	1-1	6-0	1-0	1-5	1-1	4-2	2-2
7 Chaset.	3-1	2-1	0-1	2-1	1-2	1-1		1-0	1-0	0-1	0-1	1-3	2-2	2-0	0-1	0-0	2-2	0-0	3-1	3-3	0-1	1-2	1-0	1-0
8 Coalville	2-2	1-1	2-2	2-2	1-1	6-3	2-0		3-2	1-0	3-1	2-0	2-0	7-0	1-2	2-3	2-4	3-3	4-0	2-0	1-0	0-1	0-2	1-0
9 Cradley	1-3	4-3	2-2	1-3	4-4	0-0	0-2	0-4		2-1	0-1	3-1	0-3	6-2	0-1	0-1	2-2	0-0	4-0	2-2	0-2	0-1	0-3	0-7
10 Grosv.	0-0	1-0	1-3	0-3	2-2	2-1	0-2	3-4	2-2		0-1	0-2	0-0	1-1	1-2	1-1	1-2	0-3	4-0	1-2	1-1	2-3	1-2	1-5
11 Ludlow	3-1	3-0	0-2	0-2	0-1	3-1	0-2	1-2	1-1	0-5		5-4	1-3	1-1	1-3	2-0	1-2	1-1	3-2	0-4	1-3	1-3	0-0	2-4
12 Oadby	1-1	1-1	0-1	1-6	6-0	1-2	0-1	0-3	2-0	2-1	1-0		0-3	12-0	0-1	4-1	0-4	2-1	5-0	1-1	0-1	2-1	3-0	2-0
13 Oldbury	1-1	0-0	0-0	2-4	0-0	2-1	0-0	1-1	3-2	0-4	3-0	1-3		2-1	1-3	5-0	2-0	2-1	5-0	1-3	0-1	2-2	3-1	1-2
14 Pelsall	1-2	1-3	1-4	1-1	1-3	0-1	1-3	1-1	0-3	5-1	2-2	0-5	0-3		1-0	3-1	3-1	2-3	2-1	0-6	1-4	0-3	0-1	0-2
15 Quorn	4-0	3-2	3-1	0-0	2-1	2-1	4-3	4-1	3-1	2-1	1-1	0-1	1-1	0-1		4-0	0-1	0-0	9-1	1-1	1-1	3-2	2-1	2-2
16 RacW	0-3	4-1	4-1	2-0	0-0	2-1	0-1	1-2	5-2	3-1	0-0	0-0	1-0	5-1	0-2		1-0	2-0	1-1	1-0	2-1	0-2	0-2	1-3
17 Rocest.	1-3	3-0	2-0	3-0	1-1	4-1	1-1	3-3	1-0	1-0	3-1	1-0	1-0	2-1	2-2	6-4		6-0	8-0	1-3	0-2	2-1	1-1	2-2
18 RushO	2-0	4-0	2-0	1-3	2-2	1-1	2-0	0-0	0-0	3-2	4-3	0-0	1-1	1-0	0-1	0-2	1-2		4-0	0-1	3-2	0-3	2-0	1-2
19 Stafford	2-3	0-5	1-4	2-1	0-4	3-4	2-7	0-4	0-0	1-2	1-5	0-4	1-7	1-1	2-4	1-2	0-3	0-0		1-2	0-2	0-8	0-3	0-6
20 Stourbr.	5-3	0-3	1-1	1-1	0-1	1-2	1-3	0-0	2-0	2-1	5-0	1-1	1-3	4-0	2-1	1-1	1-3	0-0	1-0		2-2	2-1	1-2	1-1
21 Stratford	4-0	1-0	2-1	2-0	2-1	2-0	1-1	1-2	2-0	1-1	1-1	1-0	5-0	3-1	2-1	2-1	0-1	1-0	7-0	1-1		0-1	2-1	1-2
22 Studley	2-1	1-1	4-1	5-1	3-3	5-0	4-2	2-1	2-1	2-0	2-0	2-3	0-0	5-1	0-1	0-4	0-0	2-1	6-0	0-2	0-4		3-0	0-1
23 Westf	2-0	2-1	1-0	3-0	3-1	2-1	0-1	1-0	1-1	1-0	0-1	1-2	1-1	6-1	0-0	0-2	1-2	1-0	4-0	0-1	5-3	1-4		4-5
24 Willenh	2-2	4-2	1-0	6-1	2-0	1-2	2-4	2-0	4-2	1-1	2-2	2-2	3-0	5-0	0-0	4-1	1-1	1-1	4-0	0-0	3-0	1-0	4-0	

LEAGUE CUP

FIRST ROUND

Barwell	v	Westfields	1-0
Biddulph Victoria	v	Coalville Town	2-5
Boldmere St Michaels	v	Racing Club Warwick	2-0
Cradley Town	v	Oldbury	2-1
Oadby Town	v	Stratford Town	1-2
Pelsall Villa	v	Bridgnorth Town	2-5
Stafford Town	v	Quorn	1-4
Stourbridge	v	Chasetown	4-0

SECOND ROUND

Alvechurch	v	Boldmere St Michaels	1-3*
Barwell	v	Grosvenor Park	1-2*
Causeway United	v	Stourbridge	0-1
Coalville Town	v	Bridgnorth Town	1-1* 9-10p
Cradley Town	v	Rocester	1-3*
Ludlow Town	v	Studley	0-5
Stratford Town	v	Quorn	3-2*
Willenhall Town	v	Rushall Olympic	0-1

QUARTER-FINALS

Bridgnorth Town	v	Boldmere St Michaels	1-1* 4-3p
Rushall Olympic	v	Grosvenor Park	2-1
Stourbridge	v	Rocester	1-1* 4-3p
Stratford Town	v	Studley	2-0

SEMI-FINALS (played over two legs)

			1st	2nd
Bridgnorth Town	v	Rushall Olympic	0-0	1-2
Stratford Town	v	Stourbridge	3-2	0-0

THE FINAL (7th August)

Rushall Olympic	v	Stratford Town	1-3*

Stourbridge League Cup Semi-finalists Back Row (L-R): Tim Langford, Matt Southwick, Scott Gennard, Jim Conway, Andy Higgs, Leon Broadhurst, Jon Ford. **Front Row:** Adam Bastable, Nathan Broadhurst, Jamie Rogers, Tim Nicholls, James Taylor. Photo: Marshall's (Birmingham) 01 384 274877

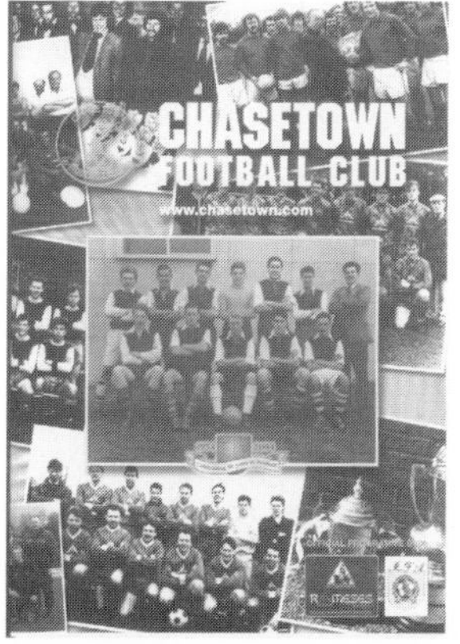

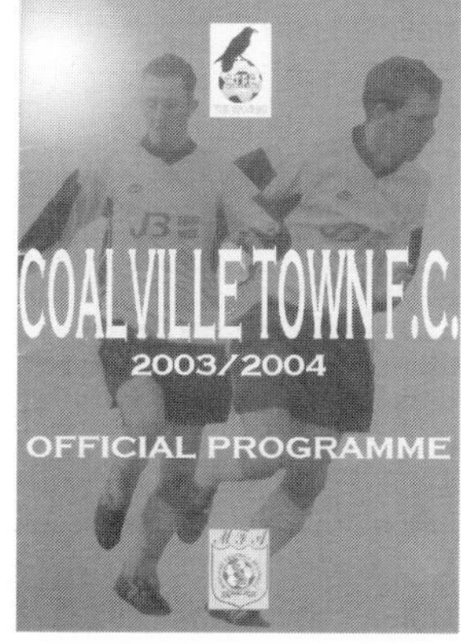

ALVECHURCH F.C.

Secretary: Stephen Denny, 11 Shawhurst Croft, Hollywood, Birmingham B47 5PB Tel: 01564 822302

Ground: Lye Meadow, Redditch Rd, Alvechurch, Worcs Tel: 0121 445 2929

Directions: M42 jct 2, follow signs to Redditch, taking dual carriageway. At island turn right (signed Alvechurch) ground approx one mile on right. Ground is actually on Redditch Road, just south of Alvechurch village

Capacity: 3,000 **Seats**:100 **Cover:**Yes **Floodlights**:Yes

Clubhouse: Open evenings and matchdays **Club shop:** No

HONOURS Mid Comb Prem Div 2002-03, Chall Cup R-up 95-96, Smedley Crooke Cup R-up 94-95

CLUB RECORDS **Goalscorer:** Dean Meyrick **Appearances:** Dean Meyrick

PREVIOUS **Leagues:** Midland Combination 1994-2003

Name: None (predecessors, Alvechurch FC, founded 1929, folded in 1992)

FACT FILE

Founded: 1994

Nickname: The Church

Sponsors: Centreprint

Colours: Gold/black/black

Change colours: Black &White,white/black

Midweek matchday: Wednesday

CLUB PERSONNEL

Chairman: Michael Rowley

Director of Football: Lee Shaw

Patron: Roy Yardley

Manager: Mick Preece

BARWELL

Secretary: Mrs Shirley Brown, 101 Eskdale Road, Hinckley, LE10 0NW (01455 446048)
Email address: steven.brown16@ntlworld.com

Ground: Kirkby Rd, Barwell, Leics (01455 843067)
Directions: M42 jct 10 (Tamworth Services), A5 towards Nuneaton. Remain on A5for approx 11 miles, go straight on at traffic lights at the Longshoot Motelthe 400 yards at r/about take 1st exit left sign A47 Earl Shilton, in 3 milesat traffic lights go straight ahead and in 1 mile at r/about take first leftexit sign Barwell in village centre 1/2 mile go straight over mini r/about, 20yards turn right into Kirkby Rd, ground 400 yards on right.
Capacity: 2,500 Seats: 256 Cover: 750 Floodlights: Yes
Clubhouse: Evenings & lunchtimes. Snacks available. **Club Shop:** No

HONOURS: Barwell Ath.: Leics Snr Lg Tebbutt Brown Cup 91-92, Leics Sen Cup 96-97.

PREVIOUS **Names:** Barwell Athletic F.C., Hinckley F.C. - amalgamated in 1992.
Leagues: Midland Combination 92-94
(Barwell Ath.: Leics Senior. Hinckley: Central Midlands 86-88)
Ground: Barwell Ath.: Kirkby Road pre 1992, Hinckley: groundshare at Hinckley Ath. pre-'92

RECORDS **Goalscorer:** Andy Lucas
Appearances: Adrian Baker

FACT FILE
Founded: 1992.
Nickname: The Kirkby Roaders
Sponsors: Radio Corner
Colours: Yellow/green/yellow
Change colours: All blue with white trim
Midweek matchday: Tuesday
Programme: 36 pages #1.00
Editor: I Backhouse
CLUB PERSONNEL
Chairman: David Laing.
Vice Chairman: Colin Burton
President: Derek Withers
Press Officer: Merv Nash.
Manager: Bob Steel
Asst Manager: Steve Greenhill
Physio: Viv Coleman Captain: Scott Clamp
2003-2004
Leading Goalscorer:Andy Tiday
Player of the Year:Andy Tiday

BIDDULPH VICTORIA

Secretary: John A Shenton, 27 Portland Drive, Biddulph, Stoke-on-Trent ST8 6RY.
Tel: 01782 251058 Email: secretary@biddulphvictoriafc.co.ukk
Ground: Tunstall Road, Biddulph, Stoke-on-Trent, (01782 522737 club).
Directions: From South, M6 J15 join A500 to 7th Exit to A50 (Tunstall & Kidsgrove). Follow new road up the hill past Focus DIY to traffic island. Turn right towards Tunstall in half a mile turn left into Furlong Rd. at church. At bottom of road bear left onto A527. Continue up hill to island. Straight ahead for approx 2 miles and ground is on the right. **From the North** M6 J18. Follow signs to Congleton and then to Biddulph on the A527. Continue through Biddulph town to the traffic lights. Straight over and ground is 250 yards on the left.
Capacity: 1,200 Seats: 224 Cover: 224 Floodlights: Yes **Club Shop:** No
Clubhouse: Open from 1pm Saturdays, 7pm weekdays. Hot snacks at tea bar
HONOURS Industrial Rewinds Lge Cup 97-98 R-up 99-00; Joe McGorian Cup 1998; West Mids Lg Div 1 92-93, Staffs Snr Lg 84-85, Lg Cup 84-85 85-86; Staffs Co. Lg R-up 79-80, Staffs FA Vase 83-84 86-87; Sentinel Cup 86-87; Leek & Moorlands Lg 72-73, Div 2 71-72.
BEST SEASON **FA Cup** 4th Qual Rd 97-98 **FA Vase:** 2nd Rd Proper 97-98
PREVIOUS **Leagues:** Leek & Moorlands 69-78; Staffs Co. (North) 78-83; Staffs Sen 83-90; W Midland (Reg) 90-94. **Names:** Knypersley Victoria >2002
RECORDS Attendance: 1,100 v Port Vale, friendly 1989 **Fee paid:** £1,000 M Biddle Congleton
Goalscorer: John Burndred 128 **Appearances:** Terry Stanway 681
Defeat: 0-9 v Meir KA, Staffs Sen. **Win:** 10-0 v Clancey Dudley, West Mids Reg. Div. 1 90-91

FACT FILE
Founded: 1969 Nickname: The Vics.
Sponsors: tba
Colours Sky blue & maroon
Change Colours: Yellow & navyl blue
Midweek matchday: Tues/Thurs
Reserve League: None
Programme: 40 pages £1.00
Editor/ Press Officer: Secretary
Website: www.biddulphvictoria fc.co.uk
CLUB PERSONNEL
Chairman: Terry Greer
Vice Chairman: John Shallcross
Commercial Dept: T.B.A.
Manager; Terry Greer Ass.Man: Matt Beeby
Physio: W. Harrison
2003-2004
Top Scorer: James Marrow 30
P.o.Ys.: Brett Barlow & Matt Davenport
2004-2005
Captain: Steve Callear

Barwell - Back Row (L-R): Tim Green, Nico Moore, Trev Hughes (Res. team Manager), Adam Cheater, Ashley Picker, Tom Rossell. **4th Row:** Mitch Ball, Scott Brown, Phil Coleman (physio), Justin Quelch, Sam Hanson, Harpeet Chettra, Wayne Cooke, Ashley Boulter, Nathan Adams, Danny Coleman. **3rd Row:** Adie Baker, Mark Taft, Dave Coleman, Lea Tatton, Dave Sharpe, Matt Boyles, Mike McLarnon, Adam Turner, Dave Hart, Kev Julian (Asst. Manager). **2nd Row:** Viv Coleman (physio), Andy Rutherford, Matt Willcock, Simon Willcock, Keith Morris, Carl Gilbert, Jason Percival, Alan Hussey (Manager), Frank Williamson (coach). **Front Row:** Stuart Wilson, Mario Kyriacou, Michael Skubala, Andy Tiady, Scott Clamp, Rich Walker, Dlae Turner, Ross Blockley, Martyn Keatley-Lill.

Boldmere St Michaels - Back Row (L-R): Alan Parsons (Manager), Ian Jones, John Daniels, Jon Price, Steve Behan, Sam Williams, Gareth Murphy, Andy Bagley, Tim Lane, Mick Talbot (physio). **Front Row (L-R):** Mick Hawkins (Asst. Manager), Alan Wright, Nathan Gough,Guy Maraine, Paul welburn, Mike Burgess, Tim Gould. Photo: Peter Barnes.

Causeway United

Back Row (L-R): Neil Smith, Aaron Dunn, Matt Sidaway, Chris Busby, Danny Cox, Matt Aston

Front Row (L-R): Chris Papworth, Inderjit Rai, Matt Stock, Simon Dixon, Paul Parker. Photo: Marshall's (Birmingham) 01 384 274877

BOLDMERE St. MICHAEL

Secretary: Peter Yates, 8 Crome Road, Great Barr, Birmingham B43 7NL
Tel Nos: 0121 360 1611 (H) 07903 154374 (M)

Ground: Trevor Brown Memorial Ground,Church Road, Boldmere, Sutton Coldfield
Tel: 0121 373 4435 or 0121 384 7531

Directions: A38 & A5127 from City towards S. Coldfield, left at Yenton lights onto A452 (Chester Rd), Church Rd is 6th turning on the right.
Nearest station: 400yds from Chester Road (BR).

Capacity: 2,500 **Seats:** 230 **Covered**: 400 **Floodlights:** Yes

Clubhouse: Bar & lounge, every evening and four lunchtimes.

HONOURS: Birmingham AFA 36-37; Birmingham AFA Snr Cup; Birmingham Jnr Cup, FA Amtr Cup SF 47-48; AFA Snr Cup 47-48; Central Amtr Lg 48-49; Midland Comb 85-86 88-89 89-90, Challenge Cup 77-78 89-90; Tony Allden Mem.Cup 78-79 88-89 91-92; Challenge Trophy 86-87; Sutton Charity Cup 96-97. Midland Comb. Reserve Div 2001-02

PREVIOUS: **Leagues:** West Mids 49-63; Midland Combination 63-94.

Players Progressing: John Barton (Everton, Derby County),Kevin Collins (Shrewsbury), Jack Lane (Birmingham City, Notts Co.), John Lewis(Walsall), Don Moss (Cardiff, C Palace), Harry Parkes (Aston Villa), Wally Soden (Coventry). Mike Griffiths (Torquay Un ited) , Robin Elmes, Jimmy Quiggin (Hereford United) and Paul Devlin (Birmingham City)

FACT FILE

Founded: 1883 Nickname: Mikes.
Sponsor: Swift Forwarding
Colours: White/black/black
Change Colours: Yellow/yellow/yellow
Midweek matches: Tuesday
Programme: 32 pages, £1.00
Editor: D.Holvey (0121 3536321)

CLUB PERSONNEL

Chairman: Keith Fielding
Match Secretary: as secretary
Manager: Rob Mallaband
Captain: Andy Dale

2003-2004

Leading Goalscorer: Nathan Gough
Player of the Year: Alan Wright

BRIDGNORTH TOWN

Secretary: Nick Clarke, 26 Greenfields Drive, Bridgnorth, Shropshire WV16 4JR

Ground: Crown Meadow, Innage Lane, Bridgnorth, Salop WV16 6PZ (01746 762747)

Directions: Follow signs for Shrewsbury (A458) over river bridge on by-pass,turn right for town centre at island, right at T junction, 1st left into Victoria Road, right at cross-road, follow road into Innage Lane, ground on left.

Capacity: 1,600 Shop: Yes Seats: 250 Cover: 700 Floodlights: Yes

Clubhouse: Evenings & weekend lunches, Dancehall, darts, pool, hot food on matchdays

Record Fee Recieved: £10,000 for Delwyn Humphries from Kidderminster Harriers

Players Progressing: Roger Davies (Derby county) and Paul Jones (Wolves via Kidd'ter H)

HONOURS: Midland Comb 79-80 82-83 (R-up 76-77 80-81); Lg Cup 78-79, Tony Allden Mem Cup R-up, Kidderminster & Dist Lge,Shropshire Snr Cup 85-86; Shropshire County Cup 70-71 75-76 76-77 78-79 79-80;Welsh Amt Cup 70-71; Shropshire County Jun Cup 98-99.

BEST SEASON: FA Cup: 3rd Qual Rd 64-65FA Vase: 5th Rd 75-76, 94-95

PREVIOUS Leagues: Kidderminster & Dist until 68; Midland Comb 68-83; Southern Lge, Midland Div. 83-96 Names: St Leonards Old Boys pre 46

RECORDS Goalscorer: Roger Davies 157 Appearances: Kevin Harris 426
Attendance: 1,600 v South Shields FA Vase 5th Rd 1976

FACT FILE

Founded: 1946 Nickname: The Town
Colours: All Blue
Change colours: All white
Midweek matchday: Tuesday
Prog: 24 pages,60p Editorsr: Committee
Local Press : Shropshire Star, Bridgnorth Journal, Express & Star.. Local Radio: Beacon, BBC Radio Shropshire
Youth League: West Mids Regional Regional

CLUB PERSONNEL

Chairman: Harold Broome
Vice Chairman: Mick Tranter
President: Mike Williams
Manager:Kevin Hestletine
Asst Manager: Bernard Mackay
Physios: Chris Harkson & Jenny Stretton
Captain: Phil Bates

2003-04

Top Goalscorer: Steve Clifford
P.o.Y: Tim Crann

CAUSEWAY UNITED

Secretary: Frank Webb, 10 Moorfield Drive, Halesowen, West Midlands B63 3TG
Tel: 0121 550 5219 (H) 0121 550 9916 (B)

Ground: Groundshare with Halesowen Town F.C., The Grove, Old Hawne Lane, Halesowen
Tel: 0121 550 2179

Directions: M5 jct 3, A456 (signed Kidderminster) to 1st island turn right (signed A459 Dudley), left at next island (signed A458 Stourbridge), at next island take 3rd left into Grammar School Lane, then Old Hawne Lane - ground 400 yds on left.

Club Colours: Blue/black/blue **Change Colours:** All red

Capacity: 5,000 Cover: 1,420 Seats: 420 Floodlights: Yes

Clubhouse: (0121 602 2210) 12-2.30 & 7-11 (10.30 Sun) pm daily. Cold snacks served.

Club Personnel

Chairman:Steven Hulston
Vice Chairman:John Truscott
Committee: M.Powell, KBoote. J.Caulwell
Manager: Alan Moore
Coach:Rob and Steve Sjilvcock
Physio: Lee Rhodes

2003-2004
Player of the Year: Matt Hollis
Top Scorer: Simon Dixon
2004-2005
Captain Matt Hollis

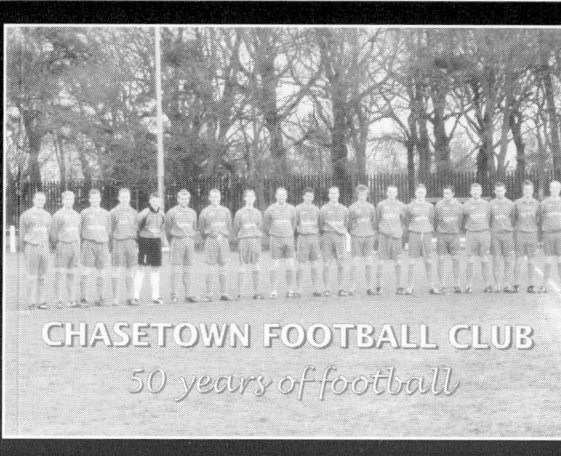

CHASETOWN

Secretary: Jonathan Booker, Flat J., Lichfield Court, Lichfield Road, Walsall, W MidlandsWS4 2DX

Ground: The Scholars, Church Street, Chasetown, Walsall WS7 8QL Tel: 01543 682222/684609

Directions: Follow Motorways M5, M6 or M42 and follow signs for A5. A5 to White Horse Road/Wharf Lane, left into Highfields Rd (B5011), left into Church Street at top of hill, ground at end just beyond church. Buses 394 or 395 W Mids Travel, 94 Chase Bus,from Walsall, 860 Midland Red from Cannock.

Capacity: 2,000 Seats: 112 Cover: 250 Floodlights: Yes **Club Shop:** Yes

Clubhouse: Mon-Fri 7.30-11pm, Sat 11.30am-11pm, Sun 8-10.30pm. Basic snacks

HONOURS West Mids Lg R-up 90-91 92-93 (Lg Cup 89-90 90-91, Div 1 77-78 (R-up73-74 74-75 75-76 80-81 82-83), Div 1 Cup R-up 80-81 82-83, Div 2 R-up 87-88,Div 2 Cup R-up 86-87); Walsall Snr Cup 90-91 92-93; Staffs Snr Cup R-up 91-92.

PREVIOUS **Name:** Chase Terrace Old Scholars 54-72 Ground: Burntwood Rec Cte (pre'83)
Leagues: Cannock Yth 54-58; Lichfield & Dist. 58-61; Staffs Co. 61-72; West Mids 72-94.

RECORDS **Attendance:** 659 v Tamworth, FA Cup 2nd Qual Rd 1/10/88.
Appearances: A Cox 469 (+15) **Win:** 14-1 v Hanford (H), Walsall Snr Cup 17/10/92.
Goalscorer: T Dixon 172 **Defeat:** 1-8 v Telford U Res., West Mids (Reg.) Lge Div. 1

FACT FILE
Founded: 1954.
Nickname: Scholars
Sponsors:Rameses Associates Ltd
Colours: All blue
Change Colours: All Red.
Sponsors: Aynsley Windows
Midweek matchday: Tuesday
Reserves League: Midland Comb
Programme: 26 pages, £1.00p
Editor: Loz Hawkes Tel No: 01543 686238

CLUB PERSONNEL
Acring Chairman: Alan Smith
President: Brian Baker
Press Officer: Paul Mullins
Manager: Charlie Blakemore
Asst Manager: Brian Fox
Physio: E Highfield.

COALVILLE TOWN

Secretary: Robert Brooks, 17 Ashland Drive, Coalville, Leics LE67 3NH
Tel: 01530 833269

Ground: Owen Street Sports Ground, Owen Street, Coalville
Tel: 01530 833365

Directions: From M1 J22 take A511 towards Coalville. At 3rd r'about take 3rd exit, then at 4th r'about bear left to Coalville centre. 2nd lights, left into Belvoir Rd and 2nd right into Owen St. Ground is on left at top of road

Capacity: 1000 Seats: 24 Cover:200 Floodlights: Yes

Clubhouse Open matchdays & training nights.

PREVIOUS **Names:** Ravenstoke Miners Ath 26-58; Ravenstoke FC 58-95; Coalville FC 95-98
Leagues: Coalville & Dist Amateur 1926-29, 33-35, 46-74 North Leicester 74-91; Leicestershire Senior 1991-2003
Grounds: Recreation Ground, Ravenslea, Ravenstone.

HONOURS: As Coalville Town:
Leics Sen Lg Prem. Div. 2001-02 02-03; Leics Sen Cup 99-00 R-up 01-02; Coalville Charity Cup 99-00, R-up 01-02

FACT FILE
Founded: 1926
Nickname: The Ravens
Colours: Black & white/black/red
Change Colours: All Light BlueMidweek match-day: Tuesday
Reserves League: Leics Comb Div 2
Programme
36 pages
Editor: Dan Gallagher

CLUB PERSONNEL
Chairman: Glyn Rennocks
Vice-Chairman: Steve Price
President: Mick Jordan
Press Officer: Dan Gallagher
Manager: Lee Harriman.
Captain: Ashley Brown

2003-2004
Player of the Year: Richard Williams
Top Goalscorer: Richard Saunders

CRADLEY TOWN

Secretary: David Attwood, 4 Birch Coppice, Quarry Bank, Brierley Hill, W Midlands DY5 1AP Tel: 01384 637430

Ground: Beeches View, Beeches View Ave, Cradley, Halesowen, B63 2HB. (01384 569658)

Directions: M5-jct3.A456 right at 2nd island into Hagley Rd. Third left to Rosemary Rd. Straigh into Lansdowne Rd/Dunstall Rd then left at T jct into Huntingtree Rd/Lutley Mill Rd.Left at next T jct into Stourbridge Rd and left into Beecher Rd East.First left into Abbey Rd and right into Beeches View Avenue at end .Ground entrance is between houses 48 & 50,20yyds on left. **Capacity:** 3,000 **Seats:** 200 **Cover:** 1,500 **Floodlights:** Yes

Clubhouse: Open matchdays only. Food available Club Shop: No

HONOURS West Mids Lg Div 1 90-91, Midland Comb. Div 2 72-73 R-up 75-76 77-78, Presidents Cup 74-75 75-76, Invitation Cup 72-73); Metropolitan Lg 70-71, Wednesbury Charity Cup 90-91, Dudley Guest Hosp. Cup 71-72 72-73 75-76 90-91

PREVIOUS Leagues: Metropolitan; Brierley Hill; Kidderminster; West Mids Amtr; Midland Comb. 71-82; West Midlands 82-99 **Name:** Albion Haden United **Grounds:** None

RECORDS Gate: 1,000 v Aston Villa, friendly **Goalscorer:** Jim Nugent **Apps:** R J Haywood **Win:** 9-1 v Wolverhampton U (H), West Midlands Lge 1990 **Defeat:** 0-9 v Paget Rangers (A) Invitation Cup 97 **Transfer fee paid:** £1,000 for Darren Marsh (Oldswinford, 1992) **Received:** £20,000 for John Williams (Swansea, 1991)

Players progressing: Alan Nicholls (Plymouth), John Williams, Jon Ford, Andy McFarlane (all Swansea), Duane Darby (Torquay)

FACT FILE
Founded: 1948
Nickname: HammersSponsors:Stables Solicitors
Colours: Red/black/black
Change colours: All Sky BlueMidweek match-day: Tuesday
Programme: Yes

CLUB PERSONNEL
President: Roy Kirton
Chairman:Trevor Thomas
Vice Chairman: Peter WilkesPress Officer: Trevor Thomas (01384 569658)
Manager: Steve Mole
Assistant Manager:Wayne Billingham
Physio: Lee Phodes

2003-2004
Leading Goalscorer:Lee Booth
Player of the Year: Stephen Thomas
2004-2005 Captain:Craig Hancox

LOUGHBOROUGH DYNAMO

Secretary: Max Hutchinson, 3 Wythburn Close, Loughborough, Leics LE11 3SZTel: 01509 266092

Ground: Nanpanton Sport Ground, Loughborough Tel: 01509 612144 **Club shop:** No

Capacity: 1,500 **Seats**: 250 **Cover:**Yes **Floodlights**:Yes **Clubhouse:** Open match days only

BEST SEASON **FA Vase:** 2003-04 **FA Cup:** N/A

HONOURS: Leics. Sen. Lge: Prem Div 03-04 Div. 1 01-02, Sen Lg.Cup 03-04 Cobin Trophy 62-63, 63-64, 64-65, County Medals R-up 60-61; District Lg Div 1 69-70, Div 2 64-65 Div 3 59-00 Three Sons Trophy 80-81; Charity Cup 87-88 03-04 Leics Sen.Cup: 02-03 03-04 Leics Presidents Trophy 03-04

2003-2004 **Player of the Year**: Ian Gaunt **Top Goalscorer**: Dave Burraway

FACT FILE
Founded: 1955
Nickname: The Moes
First Competitive Season: 57-58
Colours: Gold/black/black
Change colours:All Blue
Midweek matchday: Tuesday
Programme: Yes

CLUB PERSONNEL
Chairman: Frank Fall
Managers: James Ellis & Will Royall
Captain: Dave Hunt

LUDLOW TOWN

Secretary: Mrs T Bistow, 68 Dahn Drive, Ludlow, Shropshire SY8 1YX

Ground: The Coors Stadium, Bromfield Road, Ludlow, Shrops.(01584 876000)

Directions: From Kidderminster and West Midlands, take A4117 and turn right at roundabout onto A49 to Shrewsbury. Then exit on B4361 to Ludlow after one and a half miles, Ground is on right after passing under bridge . From South, follow A49 to north end of Ludlow by-pass and turn right onto B4361. From north,Telford and Shrewsbury, at northern approach to Ludlow, exit left from A49 onto B4361.

Capacity Unlimited Seats: 200 Cover: 150 Floodlights: Yes

Clubhouse: Yes Official opening at beginning ofthe season 2003-2004

HONOURS: West Mids. Lg. Prem Div. 00-01, Div. 2 78-79, Lg. Cup R-up 94-95. Div 1 Cup 90-91; Shropshire Co. Cup: 73-74, 93-94, 94-95, 96-97; Presteigne-Otway Cup 90-91.94-95:

PREVIOUS: **Leagues**: Kidderminster League 1961-63, Shropshire Co. Lg.: 1963-1978, West Midlands Lge 1978-2001
Ground: Riddings Park, Riddings Road, Ludlow, Shropshire

BEST SEASON **F.A.Vase:** 1st Q Rd. 98-99 (1st season) **F.A.Cup:** 1st □ Rd 2002-2003

FACT FILE
Formed: 1890
Colours: Red & white/black/black
Change colours: Yellow/Royal Blue
Midweek Matchdays: Tuesday
Reserve League: West Midlands
Programme: Yes

CLUB PERSONNEL
Chairman: Peter Gwilliam
Vice Chaiman: T.B.A.
Football Development Officer: Les Bristow
Asst Manager: Rob Jones
Coach: Paul Blakeley
Physio: Peter Ayling

2003-04
Leading Goalscorer:Andy Jones
Player of the Year:David Andrewartha
2004-2005 Captain:Steve Moore

MALVERN TOWN

Secretary: Margaret Caldicott, 20 Nixon Court, Callow End, Worcester WR2 4UU 01905 831327

Ground: Langland Stadium, Langland Avenue, Malvern, Worcs Tel: 01684 574068

Directions: From Worcester take A449 to Malvern.Turn left at roundabout signposted B4208 to Welland. Left at traffic lights into Pickersleigh Road. Turn left at Longford Arms Pub, into Maddesfield R oad. 2nd left into Langland Ave., ground 100yds on right. 1 mile from Malvern (BR)

Capacity: 4,000 **Seats:** 140 **Cover:** 310 **Floodlights:** Yes **Shop:** No

Clubhouse: 2 bars, large dance area, teabar matchdays **Best F.A.Vase Season:** 99-00 2nd Rd

HONOURS Worcester/ Midland Comb. 55-56 Mid Comb Cup R-up 75-76, WFA Senior Urn (7), WFA Sat Junior Cup Winners (4) Banks's Brewery Premier League Cup R-up 87-88 WFA Nursing Cup Winners 97-98, Robert Biggart Cup Winners 97-98, 98-99 ,Evesham Hosp Cup 99-00

PREVIOUS League: Midland Comb. 55-79 **RECORD** **Gate:** 1,221 v Worcester, FA Cup

FACT FILE

Founded:1947
Sponsors: Malvern Instruments
Colours: Claret and Sky Blue
Change:White/black/maroon
Reserves League: Banks's Brewery Div 1 S
Midweek Matchday: Tuesday
Prog: 28 pages 50p Editor: Mark Caldicott

CLUB PERSONNEL

Chairman: Geoff Brewer President: R Box
Manager: Neil Hunt
Gen Manager: Richard Anson
2002-03 Leading Goalscorer:D.Roberts/D.Cox
Captain:Dean Roberts
Player of the Year: Rik Halion

OADBY TOWN

Football Sec. Ken Farrant c/o Club. Tel Nos: 01455 557674 (H) 07790 728384 (M)
Match Day Sec: Ken Farrant,115 Foxhunter Drive, Oadby,Leics LE2 5FH (M) 0798 6359646
Ground: Topps Park, Wigston Rd,Oadby, Leics LE2 5QG Tel: 0116 271 5728
Club house (Available for hire) 0116 2718885 (Contact Mr M.V.Burton)
Directions: M69/M1 Jct 21. Follow A46 to Leicester take 4th turning off roundabout towards Narborough/ Enderby.Turn left on the outer ring road A563 ,towards Oadby.Turn right at lights after 4.5 miles towardsWigston.One mile to roundabout turn left first exit to Oadby follow Oadby road for another mile ground on right opposite Leicester Tigers Oval Park
Capacity: Unlimited Cover: 224 Seating: 224 Floodlights: Yes
Clubhouse: Yes - Open matchdays 11.00 am-11.00pm Shop: Yes
Best Seasons: **F.A.Cup**: 2nd Q.Rd 20002-03 **F.A.Vase**: 2002-03
HONOURS Leicestershire Senior Lge: (8) Midland Football Alliance 99-00
Div. 2 51-52; Lge Cup 77-78 93-94 94-95;
Leics Senior Cup 62-63 63-64 75-76 76-77 80-81
Charity CupsRolleston 58-59 59-60 68-69 74-75 88-89 93-94 96-97 97-98;
Coalville 60-61 63-64 65-66 69-70; Harborough 83-84 88-89; Oadby 70-71;
Battle of Britain 93-94 94-95 96-97

PREVIOUS **Leagues:** Leicestershire Senior League

FACT FILE

Founded:1939
Colours: All red
Change colours: All blue
Midweek matchday: Wednesday
Programme Editor: Kevin Zupp (01858 881023)

CLUB PERSONNEL

Chairman: Martin Reid
Vice Chairman: Nigel Swatland
Directors: K.G.Farrant., M.V.Burtion,
I Lockhead and L..C.Adam
President: David Bonner V-Pres: Terry Peat
Club Secretary: T.B.A.
Manager: Lee Adam
Coach: Ali Mauclan
Assistant Manager: Wayne North
Physio: Martin Almen

2003-04

Leading Goalscorer: Curtis.Warner
Captain: D.Poultney
Player of the Year: S.Towers

OLDBURY UNITED

Secretary: Lee Tomkinson, 36 Bryan Road, Walsall,WS2 9DW
Tel. Nos: 01922-447834 (H) 0121 3034468 (W) 07790 295141 (M)

Ground: The Cricketts, York Road, Rowley Regis, Warley, West Midlands (0121 5595564)

Directions: M5 jct 2, follow Blackheath & Halesowen signs, first left at lights and fourth right into York Road (turning before motorway flyover), ground 200yds on left.
One and a half miles from Sandwell & Dudley and Rowley Regis BR stations.
Bus 404 from West Bromwich, Oldbury and Blackheath.
Capacity: 3,000 Seats: 300 Cover: 1,000 Floodlights: Yes
Clubhouse: Mon-Fri 7.30-11pm, Sat-Sun 12-2.30 (12-11pm Sat matchdays).
Snacks available on matchdays. **Club Shop:** No

HONOURS West Mids Lg 92-93, Staffs Snr Cup 87-88, Midland Comb. R-up 78-79(Presidents Cup 72-73(res), Div 3 R-up 82-83(res), Chal. Vase 82-83(res)),Walsall Snr Cup 82-83, B'ham Snr Amtr Cup, Oldbury Lg Div 2 61-62, Worcs Snr Urn 86-87, Sandwell Charity Cup 86-87, Interlink Invitation Cup 96-97. Industrial Rewinds League Cup: 98-99
PREVIOUS **Leagues**: Oldbury 58-62/ Warwick & W Mids All. 62-65/ Worcs (later Midland) Comb. 65-82/ Southern 82-86.**Names:** Queens Colts 58-62/ Whiteheath Utd 62-65
Grounds: Brittania Park 61-63/ Newbury Lane (Oldbury Stadium) 63-78.
RECORDS **Attendance:** 2,200 v Walsall Wood, Walsall Snr Cup Final 1982.
Win: 10-1 v Blakenall **Defeat:** 1-9 v Moor Green.

FACT FILE

Founded: 1958
Nickname: Cricketts,The Blues.
Sponsors: Beswick Paper Group, Oldbury.
Colours: Navy with sky trim/blue/blue
Change colours: All amber
Midweek matchday: Tuesday
Programme: 28 pages, 60p
Editor: Football Secretary.

CLUB PERSONNEL

Chairman: Roy Keeling.
Vice Chairman: Ken Harris.
Press Officer: Ian Whitmore

Manager: Bob Green
Asst Mgr: Russell Dodd
Physio: Paul Millard

Oldbury United. Photo: Marshall's (Birmingham) 01 384 274877

QUORN

Secretary: Ms Margaret Berry, 214 Barrow Rd., Sileby, Leics.LE12 7LR
Tel: 01509 813259

Ground: Farley Way, Quorn, Leics (01509 620232)

Directions: From M1 jct 23 follow signs for A512 Loughborough. Turn right at roundabout (A6004) before town and pick up A6 (leicester).Three ,iles at large roundabout straight on to Quorn.Left at next lights ground on left.

Floodlights:Yes

HONOURS Leics Sen.Cup Winners 1940,1952,1954 Leicestershire Senior Lge 2002, Leics Sen. Lg. Premier Div Winners: 2000-01Div.1 Winners 1950-51,1987-88,1995-96Div 2: Winners 1949-50 Beacon Bitter League Cup Winners 2000-01

FACT FILE
Founded: 1924
Colours: Red/white/red
Change colours: Yellow & Blue.

CLUB PERSONNEL
Chairman: Stuart Turner

President, Commercial Manager, Press Officer etc.

Manager: Bob Steel
Asst. Man. / Coach:
Physio:

RACING CLUB WARWICK

GROUND: Townsend Meadow, Hampton Road, Warwick CV34 6JP Tel: 01926 495786
Directions: On the B4189 Warwick to Redditch road (via Henley in Arden) next to owners' & trainers' car park of Warwick Racecourse. From M40 jct 15 (1 1/2 miles) take A429 into Warwick, left into Shakespeare Ave., straight over island, right at T-junction into Hampton Rd, ground 300yds on left. 2 miles from Warwick BR station
Capacity: 1,000 Cover: 200 Seats: 250 Floodlights: Yes
Clubhouse: 01926 495786 Open every evening & Sat &Sun lunchtimes
Club Shop: Scarves, mugs, badges, programmes - contact Secretary
PREVIOUS Leagues: Birmingham & West Mids All., Warwickshire Comb., West Midlands (Regional) 67-72, Midland Comb. 72-89, Southern 89-2003 **Names**: Saltisford Rovers 1919-68
CLUB RECORDS Attendance: 1,000 v Halesowen Town, FA Cup 1987
Transfer fee paid: £1,000 for Dave Whetton (Bedworth United) **Win:** 9-1 v Knowle
Fee received: £5,000 for Ben Foster (Stoke City) **Defeat:** 0-7 v Redditch United
Career Goalscorer: Steve Edgington 200 **Career Appearances:** Steve Cooper 600
BEST SEASON FA Vase: 4th Round 77-78 **FA Cup:** 3rd Qual Rd 92-93
HONOURS: Midland Comb. 87-88 R-up 88-89; Warwick Lg 33-34 34-35 35-36; Birmingham & West Mids Alliance 48-49; Birmingham & Dist Alliance Senior Cup 49-50; Leamington & Dist Lg 37-38 45-46 46-47 47-48; Leamington Hospital Cup 37-38; Warwick Cinderella Cup 35-36 36-37 37-38 38-39 46-47; T G John Cup 36-37; Leamington Junior Cup 38-39 46-47

FACT FILE
Formed: 1919
Nickname: Racers
Colours: Gold & black
Change colours: Red/red/red
Midweek matchday: Tuesday
Youth's League: Mid F/Lit Yth Lge
Programme
Pages: 20 Price: £1.00
Editor: Graham Yoney**CLUB OFFICIALS**
Chairman: Jim Wright
Secretary: Pat Murphy
Tel: 01926 612675

FOOTBALL MANAGEMENT
Manager:Marcus Law

ROMULUS

Secretary: Andy Fitchett, 7 Saveker Drive, Sutton Coldfield, Birm. B76 1FT Tel: 0121 3111115H 07768 852784M

Ground: Vale Stadium, Farnborough Road, Castle Vale, Birm. B35 7BE. Tel: 0121 7476969 Fax: 0121 7476868 Email: information@romulus-fc.co.uk Website: www.romulus-fc.co.uk

Capacity: 2,000 Seats: 500 Cover: 600 Floodlights: Yes

Directions: From Birmingham City Centre take No. 67 bus alight at terminus. Ground is 3 mins walk. Train - exit at New Street station. Catch No. 67 bus from City centre. If travelling by car contact the secretary for directions.

Founded: 1979

Colours: Red & white stripes/red/red

Change colours: White/white/black

Chairman: John Matthews

Tel: 01827 899583 (H) 0121 693 4747 (B)

RUSHALL OLYMPIC

Secretary: Peter Athersmith, 46 Blakenall Lane, Leamore, Walsall, W Mids WS31HG
Tel: 01922 712632 (H) 0121 553 5525 (W) 07909 792422(M)
Ground: Dales Lane, off Daw End Lane, Rushall, Nr Walsall (01922 641021).
Directions: From Rushall centre (A461) take B4154 signed Aldridge. Approx., 1mile on right, directly opposite Royal Oak P.H., in Daw End Lane. Grd on right. 2 miles Walsall (BR) station.
Capacity: 2,500 Seats: 200 Cover: 200 Floodlights: Yes **Club Shop:** No
Clubhouse: Bar/lounge, every night 8-11pm, Sat matchdays, Sun noon-2.30pm
HONOURS West Mids Lge Div 1 79-80; Walsall Amtr Lge Div 1 55-56, Div 2 52-53, Snr Cup 54-55 55-56, Jabez Cliff Cup 55-56 ; Staffs Co. Lge Div 1(4) (Div 2 56-57); Walsall Charity Cup 52-53; Walsall Chal.Cup (2).Walsall Mem. Charity Cup (x7) 55-62; W Preston Chal. Cup 56-57; Cannock & Dist. Charity Cup 56-57; Wednesbury Snr Cup (3) Sporting Star Cup (5) J W Edge 62-63 66-67; Walsall Snr Cup 64-65;99-00 Lichfield Charity64-65 66-67; Staffs Yth Cup 81-82. Mid Alliance R-up 00-01,02-03 Lg.Cup Winners 2001-02
PREVIOUS **Leagues:** Walsall Amateur 52-55/ Staffs County (South) 56-78/ West Midlands (Reg) 78-94. **Grounds:** Rowley Place 51-75/ Aston University 76-79.
RECORDS **Attendance:** 2,000 v Leeds Utd Old Boys **Goalscorer:** Graham Wiggin
Appearances: Alan Dawson (400+ apps) **Players progressing:** Lee Sinnott (Watford), Lee Palin (Aston Villa),Stuart Watkiss (Walsall), Steve Taylor (Crystal Palace via Bromsgrove £1,500 + £18,000 sell on-record club fee)

FACT FILE
Founded: 1951 Nickname: Pics.
Sponsors:Williams Bookmakers
Colours: Amber with black trim/black/amber
Change colours: White & Black/white/white
Midweek matchday: Tuesday
Youth League: Miidland.Flloodlit League.
Programme: 60 pages, £1.00
Editor/ Press Officer: Darren Stockall (01922 379153).

CLUB PERSONNEL
Chairman: John Allen
Vice Chairman: Gary Cooper
President: Brian Greenwood.
Manager: Kevin Hadley
Asst Manager: Dave Beasley
Physio: Gary McHale, Mick Andrews

2002-03
Leading Goalscorer:Lee Booth 28
Captain:Richard Brown
Players of the Year: Lee Booth & Davifd Read

STOURBRIDGE

Secretary: Hugh Clark,10 Burnt Oak Drive, Stourbridge, W. Mids DY8 1HL Tel: 01384 392975

Ground: War Memorial Ath. Grd, High St., Amblecote, Stourbridge DY8 4HN (01384 394040)

Directions: Take A491, signposted Wolverhampton, from Stourbridge ring-road -ground 300yds on left immediately beyond traffic lights and opposite `RoyalOak' pub. Buses 311, 246 from Dudley, and 256 from Wolverhampton, pass ground. 1 mile from Stourbridge Town (BR)
Capacity: 2,000 Cover:750 Seats: 250 Floodlights: Yes
Clubhouse: Open most evenings from 8pm and Sunday lunchtimes
Club Shop: Programmes & souvenirs. Contact Nigel Gregg

PREVIOUS Name: Stourbridge Standard **Leagues:** West Midlands (prev. Birmingham) 1892-1939 54-71, Birmingham Comb. 45-53, Southern 71-00

HONOURS Welsh Cup R-up 73-74; Southern Lg Midland Div 90-91 (Lg Cup 92-93), Div 1 North73-74, Merit Cup 73-74; West Mids (prev. B'ham) Lg 23-24 (R-up 4); B'ham Comb. R-up 51-52; B'ham Snr Cup 49-50 45-46 75-76 (R-up 3); Worcs Snr Cup 9, (R-up 12); Herefordshire Snr Cup 54-55; Camkin Cup R-up 69-70; Camkin Presidents Cup 70-71; Albion Shield 43-44; Keys Cup 37-38 62-63, Worcs Comb. R-up 27-28; Worcs Jnr Cup R-up 27-28; Tillotson Cup R-up 39-40, MFA Davis League Cup 00-01. Joe McGorian Cup 01-02,02-03 Midland Alliance:01-02,02-03

BEST SEASON **FA Cup:** 4th Qual Rd: 67-68, 84-85 85-86 98-99
FA Trophy: Qtr Final 70-71

CLUB RECORDS **Career Goalscorer:** Ron Page 269 **Career Appearances:** Ron Page 427

FACT FILE
Formed: 1876 Nickname: The Glassboys
Sponsors: Stourbridge College
Colours: Red & white stripes
Change colours: Yellow & blue
Midweek matchday: Tuesday
Programme: Pages: 32 Price: £1.20
Editors: Hugh Clark & Nigel Gregg

CLUB PERSONNEL
Chairman: Stephen Hyde
Press Officer: Nigel Gregg
Managers:Jon Ford & Gary Hackett
Physio: Simon Ward.
Captain:Morgan Brookes

2003-04
Leading Goalscorer: Scott Gennard
Player of the Year: Jim Conway

STRATFORD TOWN

Secretary: Robin Lamb,14 Regal Close, Scimitar Park, Two Gates, Tamworth B77 1GT
Ground: Masons Road, off Alcester Road, Stratford-upon-Avon, Warks (01789 297479).
Directions: Follow the signs for Alcester/Worcester A422 from the town centre.
Masons Road is the 1st right afterthe railway bridge.
400 yards from Stratford-on-Avon (BR)station.
Local buses for West Green Drive.
Capacity: 1,100 Seating/Cover: 200
Floodlights: Yes

Clubhouse: Open every night **Club Shop:** Yes.Badges, Programmes,Scarves, Hats etc

HONOURS Midland Comb 56-57 86-87; Chal. Cup 86-87 88-89 (R-up 55-56); Chal. Vase 81-82; Jack Mould Tphy 81-82; Tony Allden Mem. Cup 86-87; B'ham Snr Cup62-63.

PREVIOUS **Leagues:** W Mids 57-70/ Mid Com. 70-73 75-94/ Hellenic 70-75.
RECORDS **Attendance:** 1,078 v Aston Villa, Birmingham Snr Cup, Oct 1996

Players progressing: Martin Hicks (Charlton '77), Roy Proverbs (Coventry, '56)

FACT FILE
Founded: 1944
Nickname: The Town
Sponsors: Sitel
Colours: Blue & White
Change Colours:Tangerine & Black
Midweek Matchday: Tuesday

Programme: 24 pages, £1.00
Editor:Alan Hawkins

CLUB PERSONNEL
Chairman:Craig Hughes
Vice-Chairman: Phil Day
Manager: Lennie Darby
Assistant Managers: Ian Britton & Rick Smith
Captain: Nigel Niblett

2003-2004
Leading Goalscorer: Scott Darroch
Player of the Year: Nigel Niblett

STUDLEY

Secretary: Mark Sealey c/o club.

Ground: Beehive, Abbeyfields Drive, Studley, Warwicks B80 7BE
Tel: 01527 853817
Directions: M42 Jct.3 onto A435 to Redditch.Over island at Dog Pub on left continue towards Studley. Ground on left signposted to Abbeyfields.
Capacity 1,500 **Seats:** 200 **Cover:** Yes **Floodlights**:Yes
Clubhouse Yes, on ground - Mon-Fri 7-11 fri-Sat 11am -11pm Sun 12-5(if dining) 7-10.30

HONOURS Midland Comb.: Prem Div R-up 2000-01,Div 1 91-92, Chall Cup R-up 91-92,
MFC Challenge Vase 87-88 R-up 88-89 WFA Senior Urn 2000-01,01-02,02-03
Presidents Cup R-up 91-92, Div2 Cup 87-88;
Smedley Crooke Char. Cup 90-91 91-92; Jack Mould Trophy R-up 1987-88
Birmingham Vase R-up 96-97, Tony allden memorial Cup: 2001-02

PREVIOUS **League:** Redditch & South Warwickse Sunday Comb 71-87 Mid Comb
Name: BKL Works

CLUB RECORDS **Appearances:** Lee Adams 523
Goalscorer: Brian Powell
Attendance: 810 v Leamington 2003-2004

FACT FILE
Founded: 1971
Nickname: Bees
Sponsors: Persimmon Hom
Colours: All Skyblue & navy blue.
Change colours: All Yellow
Programme: 50p Editor: Alec James
CLUB PERSONNEL
Chairman: David Robinson
Vice-Chairman: Alec JamesPress Officer: Dave Chiswell
Manager:K.Rowlands
Asst Manager: T.Whittington
Coach: Steve Cooper
Physio: Darren Oldrwy
2002-03
Leading Goalscorer:Craig Pountney
Captain:Steven Hands
Player of the Year:T.B.A.
2003-2004
Player of the Year: Vaughan Thomas
Leading Goalscorer: Mark Crisp

WESTFIELDS

Secretary & Chief Exec: Andrew Morris, 17 Fayre Oaks Green, Kings Acre, Hereford HR4 0QT Tel: 01432 264711
Ground: Allpay Park, Widemarsh Common, Hereford Tel: 07860410548
Directions: Just off A49 at Widemarsh Common
Capacity: 2,000 Seats: 150 Cover: 150 Floodlights: Yes Club Shop: Yes
Clubhouse: On ground
Previous Leagues: Herefordshire Sunday 66-74; Herefordshire 72-74; Worcester & Dist. 74-77
West Midlands League 1977-2003
Record **Attendance:** 518 v Rushden & Diamonds FA Cup 96
Goalscorer: Paul Burton **Appearances:** Jon Pugh

HONOURS West Midlands Champions 02-03, League Div 1 86-87, Div 2 R-up 83-84, Div 2 Cup 79-80 83-84, Hereford County Senior Cup 85-86 88-89 91-92 95-96 01-202-03, Youth Cup 92-93 95-96, Kington Challenge Cup x 5; Kington Invitation Cup x 4; Presteigne Ottway Cup x 4, Worcs Junior Cup 79-80, Wye Guild Cup x 2, Hereford Sunday League Premier 75-76 76-77, Div 1 71-72, Div 2 76-77, Div 3 75-76, Premier Division Cup x 3, Div 1 Cup x 2, Div 3 Cup 72-73, Smart Brown Cup 67-68, Fair Play Cup 67-68. D.Hartland Memorial Trophy 95-6,99-00 00-01R.Biggart Trophy 95-6,99-00, West Midlands League Cup 2002
Players progressing: Alex Sykes (Mansfield Town 92), Gary Bowyer (Nottingham Forest 89), John Layton (Hereford Utd 74)

FACT FILE
Founded: 1966
Nickname: The Fields
Sponsors: Left Bank Village
Colours: Maroon & sky/sky/sky
Change colours: Sky/white/ maroon
Midweek matchday: Tuesday
Programme: Yes Editor: Andy Morris

CLUB PERSONNEL
Chairman: John Morgan
Vice .Chaiman: Brian Jones
President: Graham Preece
Managers: Sean Edwards & Darren lynch
Coach: Jim Clyde
Physio: Mark Newman

2003-04
P.o.Y.: Scott Jackson
Top Scorer: Mark Hibbard
2004-2005
Captain: Roy Jordan

Malvern Town F.C.

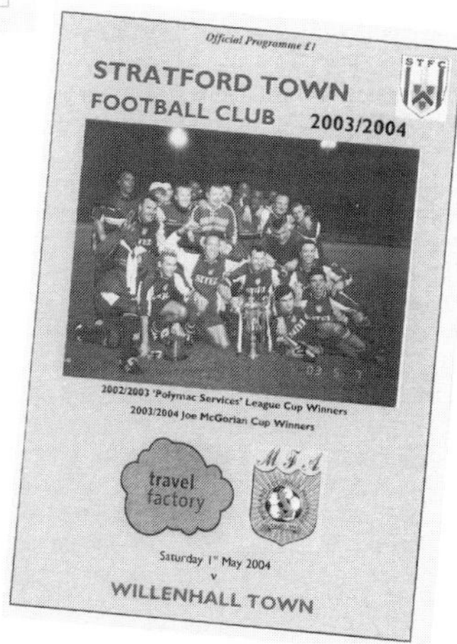

NORTHERN LEAGUE

SPONSORED BY: ALBANY

Founded 1889

President: George Courtney MBE **Chairman:** Mike Amos
Hon. Secretary & Treasurer: A Golightly, 85 Park Road North, Chester-le-Street, Co Durham DH3 3SA Tel: 0191 388 2056 Fax: 0191 3891 1385
E-mail: tonygol@northernlge.fsnet.co.uk

The far North faces the real danger of being frozen out completely. The FA's restructuring exercise, ill-conceived and catastrophically carried through, looks like it will forever deny the world's second oldest league and its clubs a meaningful part in the National League System.

The FA have, as we say in these parts, been tellt and better tellt. We warned for three years that, unless the geographical problems of the North-East were sympathetically addressed the league could be cast adrift through no fault of its own. Now it has been.

The promotion route, more of a mad march, is via the Unibond first division - the Northern Premier League. Northern? Had any Albany Northern League club taken promotion to the Unibond first in 2004-05, the nearest "derby" would have been in Ossett, in West Yorkshire - twice as far as their longest journey now.

Many other games would involve round trips of up to 500 miles - Telford in Shropshire, Willenhall near Walsall, Colwyn Bay, Rocester (somewhere near Uttoxeter racecourse), Kidsgrove (Staffordshire), Shepshed (Leicestershire)..... and so the magical mystery tour would progress. Any North-East club in the Unibond first would have further to travel in a season than any club now in the new Conference north and further than most in the Premiership.

Those who fly on automatic pilot, those who are blinkered or blind or who simply refuse to look at the facts, will claim that it is simply another example of the ANL's lack of ambition. What's ambitious about suicide? To take that parlous promotion route would not only require a massive financial injection - players' expenses as well as travelling costs - but undermine the cohesion and the community spirit of every one of our clubs.

For what? Thanks to the introduction of the Conference second divisions, "promotion" would simply be a return to the level/step at which they played in 2003-04 - and in case that sounds like the sort of restructuring which might be essayed with building blocks in the reception class of a kindergarten, remember the FA's oft-stated aims for the exercise.

They included introducing greater fairness and more consistency and reducing travelling costs. That all those fine principles have not only been ignored but reversed is a national scandal which will blight this League for ever..If only we would get the FA to admit it, and to be big enough to think again.

Which parts of "fairness", "consistency" or "economics" apply to the Albany Northern League?

Away from the wretched world of football politics, our clubs continue proudly - often heroically - as champions of their communities. Though the Vase proved disappointing. **Shildon** reached the first round of the FA Cup - by no means alone in seeing off opposition from nominally higher leagues - **Tow Law** played their 2,563rd Northern League game, a record, and **Billingham Synthonia** played their 2000th.

Dunston Federation Brewery, a club patiently constructed and enthusiastically run, won a League and Cup double that was applauded throughout the League and beyond, **Bobby Scaife** unsurprisingly collecting the "Manager of the Year" award. Relegated after just one season in the top flight, **Penrith** are joined in the second division by **Washington** and **Marske United.**

Ashington, something of a yo-yo club, won the second division from **Newcastle Benfield Saints** - in their first season - and **Consett**, returning to the first after just a year's absence. **Shotton Comrades** and **Murton** are relegated, the latter on ground criteria, replaced by **North Shields** and **West Allotment Celtic**, champions respectively of the Wearside League and Northern Alliance.

Newcastle Blue Star won the Craven Cup, for second division clubs, while **Billingham Town** and **Bedlington Terriers** won their respective County cups, again with several victories over teams from "higher" leagues. Another remarkable achievement was **Chester-le-Street** youth team's progress to the last 32 of the FA Youth Cup, where finally they lost to West Ham United at Upton Park - a truly memorable occasion.

No one took promotion to the Unibond. They're probably mightily relieved....

The League continues to be much blessed in its relationship with the Albany RTA Group, our handsome sponsors in perpetuity. Group chairman **Brooks Mileson**'s generosity increases annually and is guaranteed throughout his lifetime and that of his children, a uniquely munificent arrangement. Several other sponsors continue generously.

The Northern League Club, which serves football fans throughout the country, continues to grow as it has done every year since its inception. Benefits - for an annual subscription of just £10, falling to £7.50 - include a monthly newsletter and copies of the League magazine, discounts at grounds, 40 page grounds guide and a splendid lapel badge - that's the extra £2.50. Details of the Club from **Martin Haworth**, 17 The Turn, Morpeth, Northumberland NE61 2DU (www.northernleagueclub.co.uk).

Once again in 2004-05, the League will attempt to take action on what has become known as the curse of swearing. All but three clubs have agreed to a voluntary code of conduct which, in the absence of firmer action from the FA and match officials, will again see to eradicate gratuitously offensively language from pitch and dug-out.

No one's getting carried away, but few doubt the need for action if families ad other decent people are to return. Language becomes "offensive" if anyone's offended, and many are. The new initiative will be supported by posters for referees' room, dug-outs and clubhouse, and we hope for significant success.

There are some things of course, which could make even a God fearing league chairman swear, but we've said enough about those already....

Mike Amos, Chairman, June 22 2004

FINAL LEAGUE TABLE 2003-04

DIVISION ONE		P	W	D	L	F	A	Pts
1.	Dunston Fed. Brewery	40	25	9	6	76	32	84
2.	Durham City	40	23	9	8	90	53	78
3.	Bedlington Terriers (-3 pts)	40	25	5	10	104	58	77
4.	Shildon (-3 pts)	40	21	11	8	82	52	71
5.	Billingham Town	40	20	10	10	83	62	70
6.	Jarrow Roofing BCA	40	19	6	15	98	90	63
7.	Peterlee Newtown	40	17	9	14	82	67	60
8.	Brandon United	40	17	7	16	71	77	58
9.	Billingham Synthonia	40	16	9	15	75	65	57
10.	Whitley Bay	40	16	6	18	71	76	54
11.	Morpeth Town (-3 pts)	40	16	8	16	70	59	53
12.	Thornaby (-3 pts)	40	14	12	14	56	61	51
13.	West Auckland Town	40	14	8	18	63	96	50
14.	Guisborough Town	40	13	10	17	59	57	49
15.	Esh Winning	40	13	9	18	52	68	48
16.	Tow Law Town	40	13	8	19	63	78	47
17.	Chester-le-Str. Town	40	14	4	22	74	85	46
18.	Horden CW	40	11	11	18	58	81	44
19.	Washington	40	10	6	24	55	97	36
20.	Marske United	40	8	9	23	46	76	33
21.	Penrith	40	8	8	24	45	83	32

DIVISION ONE	1	2	3	4	5	6	7	8	9	10	11	12	13	14	15	16	17	18	19	20	21
1 Bedlington Terries		0-3	1-2	3-0	4-2	1-3	5-3	2-0	0-1	5-0	3-5	3-2	3-1	0-0	4-2	5-0	4-2	2-1	5-0	7-2	0-0
2 Billingham Synthonia	1-4		1-0	9-0	2-1	2-1	1-0	1-1	2-2	1-1	4-3	2-0	1-0	4-5	2-4	3-4	2-0	3-0	4-0	1-2	2-2
3 Billingham Town	3-3	3-2		2-0	4-2	0-2	4-3	2-2	0-0	4-0	3-1	2-0	0-2	2-2	3-1	3-4	0-0	2-0	4-1	4-1	0-1
4 Brandon United	0-1	1-1	2-2		1-4	2-3	1-2	1-0	1-0	3-0	1-2	4-3	0-4	5-1	1-1	2-2	2-0	3-0	2-1	3-1	0-4
5 Chester-Le-Street	3-4	1-0	1-3	2-4		1-3	0-3	0-2	3-2	3-1	0-1	6-2	2-1	5-1	3-4	2-1	0-2	4-4	0-0	3-0	1-0
6 Dunston Fed. Brewery	2-0	0-1	3-2	3-2	3-1		0-2	2-2	1-1	4-0	2-0	2-0	1-1	1-0	2-0	0-0	4-0	3-1	4-0	1-2	4-1
7 Durham City	1-1	1-1	5-1	3-2	3-1	0-2		0-0	2-3	3-1	4-1	7-2	1-1	2-1	2-1	1-3	2-1	1-1	5-3	4-0	2-0
8 Esh Winning	1-2	2-0	3-2	1-3	4-1	0-3	1-1		0-1	2-2	1-5	1-2	2-2	2-0	3-2	0-3	1-1	0-1	2-0	0-3	1-0
9 Guisborough Town	1-4	1-0	1-2	0-1	2-0	0-1	1-1	3-1		0-2	2-2	0-2	2-3	2-2	1-1	2-3	0-2	4-1	2-0	0-0	0-3
10 Horden Colliery Wel.	3-1	2-1	2-4	1-3	4-4	0-0	2-1	4-0	1-1		1-2	0-1	2-1	2-1	1-1	0-0	1-1	0-1	1-2	1-1	3-0
11 Jarrow Roofing B. CA	1-4	1-1	2-3	2-1	1-2	3-2	2-3	4-1	4-1	4-3		1-1	3-2	2-1	4-3	4-3	3-4	0-2	4-3	1-3	2-4
12 Marske United	1-0	2-2	1-3	0-0	0-1	0-2	1-4	0-0	0-5	0-1	1-1		2-1	5-0	0-2	1-2	0-1	3-0	3-4	1-1	1-4
13 Morpeth Town	2-3	3-1	0-1	0-2	2-2	1-2	3-1	1-2	0-0	5-1	1-1	2-1		2-0	3-1	0-2	2-0	1-1	2-1	5-0	1-0
14 Penrith	0-1	1-2	2-0	2-2	1-2	0-3	0-2	0-2	3-1	1-1	3-3	1-0	1-1		3-2	1-2	1-1	1-3	1-2	0-2	0-1
15 Peterlee Newtown	3-2	3-0	3-3	2-1	4-1	1-1	1-3	2-0	2-1	3-0	3-5	3-0	1-2	1-2		0-1	4-2	4-2	2-0	2-2	3-2
16 Shildon	1-1	4-1	2-1	2-3	2-1	1-1	0-2	5-1	2-1	5-2	1-2	0-0	3-1	5-1	0-0		0-1	3-0	2-0	5-1	0-0
17 Thornaby	2-4	0-2	1-3	3-3	1-0	0-0	1-1	0-4	1-3	1-1	3-2	2-2	3-1	4-0	0-0	0-0		4-1	3-1	1-0	3-2
18 Tow Law Town	1-2	5-4	1-1	3-1	0-6	2-3	1-3	3-0	0-2	6-1	4-2	2-4	3-0	0-1	2-0	1-1	0-0		1-0	1-2	1-2
19 Washington	1-4	1-3	1-1	3-5	2-1	0-1	1-1	1-3	0-4	3-1	3-2	1-0	1-3	3-1	0-4	3-3	3-1	3-3		1-3	3-2
20 West Auckland Town	1-6	1-1	2-3	1-3	4-0	0-0	1-2	1-3	3-2	1-5	1-3	1-0	5-4	3-2	0-3	1-5	1-0	1-1	2-2		3-7
21 Whitley Bay	1-0	3-1	1-1	3-0	3-2	2-1	1-3	2-1	1-4	1-4	2-7	2-2	1-3	0-2	3-3	3-0	1-4	1-3	2-1	3-4	

FINAL LEAGUE TABLE 2003-04

DIVISION TWO		P	W	D	L	F	A	Pts
1.	Ashington	38	27	7	4	91	28	88
2.	Newcastle Benfield Saints	38	26	7	5	106	42	85
3.	Consett	38	25	8	5	84	35	83
4.	Newcastle Blue Star (-3 pts)	38	24	6	8	87	53	75
5.	Washington Nissan	38	21	6	11	81	47	69
6.	Prudhoe Town	38	18	4	16	73	70	58
7.	Northallerton Town	38	15	12	11	73	57	57
8.	Hebburn Town	38	16	6	16	64	58	54
9.	Kennek Ryhope CA	38	15	8	15	65	55	53
10.	Whickham	38	14	10	14	66	57	52
11.	Alnwick Town	38	15	6	17	50	59	51
12.	South Shields	38	14	8	16	61	68	50
13.	Seaham Red Star	38	11	10	17	73	78	43
14.	Evenwood Town	38	13	4	21	43	58	43
15.	Murton (Relegated)	38	11	9	18	58	68	42
16.	Crook Town	38	11	8	19	61	79	41
17.	Willington	38	11	5	22	50	104	38
18.	Norton & Stockton Ancients	38	10	5	23	49	89	35
19.	Easington Colliery	38	8	3	27	41	119	27
20.	Shotton Comrades	38	6	6	26	47	99	24

DIVISION TWO		1	2	3	4	5	6	7	8	9	10	11	12	13	14	15	16	17	18	19	20
1	Alnwick Town		0-0	0-4	3-2	4-1	3-1	1-3	1-0	1-1	1-3	1-2	2-1	1-2	3-2	0-2	1-0	3-0	1-1	0-0	3-0
2	Ashington	3-2		1-1	3-0	2-1	2-0	1-0	3-1	1-0	1-1	1-2	1-1	4-1	1-0	4-1	6-2	0-0	2-1	4-0	1-0
3	Consett	2-0	1-1		4-0	3-2	4-0	0-1	0-2	2-0	0-4	3-1	3-2	3-0	1-2	2-0	3-2	1-1	4-0	1-0	4-1
4	Crook Town	0-1	0-1	0-3		2-3	1-0	2-0	2-1	1-1	1-2	0-2	0-2	0-4	2-3	2-5	4-0	1-3	2-4	2-1	3-3
5	Easington Colliery	2-1	2-5	1-3	0-4		0-2	1-4	0-8	2-1	0-4	1-5	0-6	2-3	2-3	2-2	1-0	2-1	1-6	1-2	0-1
6	Evenwood Town	0-2	2-3	1-1	0-0	0-0		3-1	3-1	0-1	1-2	3-0	0-1	4-1	0-1	1-0	2-1	1-0	1-2	4-2	0-3
7	Hebburn Town	4-2	0-2	0-0	1-2	3-1	1-0		1-1	1-4	1-2	1-0	0-0	5-1	5-2	3-2	1-2	2-4	0-0	0-2	1-0
8	Kennek Ryhope CA	0-1	0-1	2-2	2-1	8-0	1-0	0-1		2-1	2-2	3-3	0-1	2-1	2-1	1-1	4-2	2-3	2-0	1-0	5-1
9	Murton	1-1	0-2	1-3	1-4	1-2	2-0	0-3	1-3		3-5	3-4	2-2	3-0	3-1	1-0	6-4	2-1	3-0	1-1	1-2
10	Newcastle B'field St.	3-0	0-3	1-2	5-2	4-1	4-0	3-2	3-0	4-0		4-2	3-0	5-1	1-1	5-0	6-1	1-1	2-1	2-1	9-0
11	Newcastle Blue Star	2-1	1-0	1-0	4-0	8-2	4-2	2-3	1-1	1-1	0-1		1-1	2-1	2-1	3-1	3-1	2-2	2-0	2-0	2-1
12	Northallerton Town	1-1	2-2	0-2	2-2	4-2	0-1	0-0	4-0	1-1	3-4	1-3		3-1	2-0	2-3	2-2	4-2	2-4	3-1	1-0
13	Norton & Stockton A.	2-0	0-7	0-2	1-3	1-0	1-2	3-2	3-0	3-2	0-0	0-2	0-5		4-5	1-1	0-3	1-3	0-4	0-2	1-2
14	Prudhoe Town	4-1	3-2	2-3	6-0	1-1	1-0	2-0	0-2	2-1	2-0	3-1	1-2	1-5		3-3	3-1	1-1	4-1	0-5	4-1
15	Seaham Red Star	0-1	0-6	0-3	3-3	3-0	3-4	5-2	1-1	0-2	3-1	1-4	3-1	1-1	2-3		4-0	3-0	2-3	2-2	7-1
16	Shotton Comrades	2-3	0-3	0-4	2-2	0-1	1-0	4-3	1-1	1-1	2-3	1-2	1-3	2-0	1-3	0-0		4-2	0-3	0-3	2-3
17	South Shields	2-0	1-3	2-2	1-4	2-1	2-1	2-1	0-2	1-2	1-5	2-3	2-2	2-2	3-0	4-1	1-0		0-3	4-0	3-2
18	Washington Nissan	3-0	0-2	0-0	1-1	3-0	2-2	1-3	3-0	2-0	1-0	3-2	3-1	2-3	2-0	3-1	6-0	0-1		3-0	3-0
19	Whickham	2-1	2-1	2-4	1-1	8-0	3-0	0-4	4-1	2-2	1-1	2-2	1-2	0-0	2-1	2-2	4-0	2-0	2-2		3-0
20	Willington	1-3	0-6	2-4	0-5	1-3	1-2	1-1	2-1	3-2	1-1	1-4	3-3	2-1	2-1	1-5	2-2	2-1	1-5	3-1	

LEAGUE CUP

FIRST ROUND

Dunston Fed.	v	Guisborough	2-0
Easington	v	Washington Nissan	0-7
Evenwood	v	Benfield Saints	0-2
Hebburn Town	v	South Shields	2-3*
Jarrow R. B. CA	v	Bedlington Terriers	0-0* 5-6p
Marske United	v	Billingham Town	2-0
Norton & Stock. A.	v	Kennek Ryhope CA	0-3
Peterlee Newtown	v	Crook Town	3-2
Prudhoe Town	v	Ashington	1-3

SECOND ROUND

Alnwick Town	v	Benfield Saints	2-1*
Consett	v	Washington	1-2
Dunston Fed.	v	Bedlington	2-1
Durham City	v	Tow Law Town	5-1
Esh Winning	v	Willington	2-1
Horden (at Murton)	v	Murton	1-3
Marske United	v	Chester-le-Street	6-2
Northallerton Town	v	Kennek Ryhope CA	4-1
Penrith	v	Ashington	2-1
Seaham	v	Billingham Synthonia	1-2
Shildon	v	Brandon United	1-2
South Shields	v	Newcastle Blue Star	2-1
Thornaby	v	Peterlee Newtown	3-0
West Auckland T.	v	Washington Nissan	1-2
Whickham	v	Shotton Comrades	4-1
Whitley Bay	v	Morpeth Town	0-1

THIRD ROUND

Alnwick Town	v	South Shields	2-1
Brandon United	v	Murton	1-0
Dunston Fed.	v	Whickham	2-1
Durham City	v	Thornaby	1-0*
Esh Winning	v	Northallerton Town	3-0
Penrith	v	Marske United	2-2* 5-4p
Washington	v	Billingham Syn.	0-1*
Washington Nissan	v	Morpeth	3-5

QUARTER-FINALS

Brandon United	v	Durham City	1-2
Esh Winning	v	Billingham Synthonia	1-2
Morpeth	v	Dunston Federation	0-2
Penrith	v	Alnwick Town	0-0* 5-4p

SEMI-FINALS

Durham	v	Billingham Synthonia	3-2
Penrith	v	Dunston Federation	0-3

THE FINAL (5th May at Whitley Bay)

Dunston Feds	v	Durham City	2-1*

CRAVEN CUP

FIRST ROUND

Alnwick (w/o)	v	Easington Colliery	
Consett	v	Murton	3-1
Newcastle B. S.	v	Kennek Ryhope CA	5-1
Shotton Comrades	v	Prudhoe Town	3-0

SECOND ROUND

Alnwick Town	v	Consett	1-2*
Evenwood Town	v	Shotton Comrades	1-2*
Hebburn Town	v	Crook Town	2-3*
Newcastle B. S.	v	Washington	3-2*
Seaham Red Star	v	Northallerton Town	1-2
South Shields	v	Newcastle Blue Star	0-3
Whickham	v	Ashington	1-2
Willington	v	Norton & Stockton A.	2-3* aet

QUARTER-FINALS

Ashington	v	Consett	1-0
Crook	v	Northallerton Town	2-3
Newcastle B. S.	v	Newcastle Blue Star	1-3
Shotton Comrades	v	Norton & Stockton Ancients	1-0

SEMI-FINALS

Newcastle B. S.	v	Shotton Comrades	6-1
Northallerton Town	v	Ashington	0-1

THE FINAL (5th May at Prudhoe Town)

Newcastle B. S.	v	Ashington	1-1* 5-6p

ASHINGTON

Secretary: Brian Robinson, 80 Milburn Road, Ashington, N/thumberland NE63 0PG

Tel: 01670 852832 (H) 01670 521212 (B) Fax: 01670 852832

Ground: Portland Park, Ashington NE63 9XG (01670 811991 Social Club)

Directions: 200 yds north at traffic lights in centre of town

Capacity: 2,000 **Seats:** 350 **Cover**: 2,200 **Floodlights**: Yes **Club Shop**: Yes at ground

Clubhouse: Open 6-11 eves & from11am Tues (market day), closed Wed & Sun. Snacks.

.PREVIOUS **Leagues:** Northern All. 1892-93 1902-14 69-70; Football League; North Eastern 14-21 29-58 62-64; Midland 58-60; Northern Counties 60-62; Wearside 64-65; N.P.L. 68-69.,

RECORD **Attendance:** 13,199 v Rochdale, FA Cup 2nd Rd 9/12/50

BEST SEASON **FA Cup:** 3rd Rd 26-27 **FA Amateur Cup** SF 73-74

HONOURS Northumberland Snr Cup x9, N'berland Chall. Bowl x6, Midland Lg 58-59, North Eastern Lg Cup 33-34(jt) 39-40; Northern Alliance x 4, R-up x 6 Lg Cup 47-48, Craven Cup 98-99 and R-up 03-04 Northern League Division Two Champions 2003-04

FACT FILE

Formed: 1883 Nickname: The Colliers

Club colours: Black & white stripes/black/black

Change colours: Blue & white/blue/blue

Midweek Matches: Tuesday

Prog: 50pEd: A Marchett (01670 854585)

CLUB PERSONNEL

Chairman: Jim Lang Joint Presidents: Sir Bobby Charlton & Jackie Charlton OBE

Press Officer: Brian Bennett (01670 856606)

Manager: Tony Harrison Asst.Man Jimmy Harmison Physio: Ken Barton

2003-2004

P.o.Y.: Paul Simpson (GK)

Top Scorer: Alan Hogg

2004-05 Captain: Lee Picton

BEDLINGTON TERRIERS

Secretary: Alan Turnbull, 78 Rothesay Terrace, Bedlington, Northumberland. NE22 5PU
Tel Nos: 01670 822492 (H) 07904908847 (M)

Ground: Welfare Park, Park Rd., Bedlington, Northumberland. Tel: 01670 825485

Directions: Into Bedlington, turn left at `Northumberland Arms' on Front St., then 2nd Right, ground on right 100 yds . Club Website: www.btfc.fsnet.co.uk

Capacity: 3,000 Seats: 300 Cover:500 Floodlights: Yes

Clubhouse: Open every evening, 7-11pm Sat. & Sun lunch. Pool, darts etc Club Shop: Yes

Record Att: 2,400 v Colchester Utd **Record Seasons Scorer:** John Milner 63 , 98-99

HONOURS Northern League Div One 97-98 98-9 99-00 00-01 01-02 R-up: 85-86 9596 Div 2 94-95 (R-up 84-85), Northern Alliance 66-67 (R-up 67-68 69-70 71-72) Lg Cup 57-58 66-67 69-70 81-82, Lge Chall Cup 96-97 00-01,Northumberland Sen Cup 96-97. 97-98 01-02 03-04. Cleator Cup 97-88, 98-99, 99-00

PREVIOUS **Leagues:** Northern Alliance **Names:** Bedlington Mechanics 49-53; Colliery Welfare 53-56; Mechanics 56- 61; Bedlington United 61-65; Bedlington Colliery 65-68; Bedlington Town 68-74.

BEST SEASON
FA Cup: 2nd Rd v Scunthorpe(a) 0-1
FA Vase: Final 98-9 VTiverton T 0-1

RECORDS **Attendance:** 1,013 v Blyth Spartans, Northern Lg 85-86
Win: 11-0 v West Auckland, (H) Lge 96-97 **Scorer:** John Milner63

FACT FILE

Formed: 1949

Colours: Red & white/red&white/white

Change colours: Blue & whitw/blue&white/blue

Midweek Matches: Wednesday

Programme: 50 pages, £1.00

CLUB PERSONNEL

Chairman: David Perry (0468 195350)

Vice Chairman: John Feary

Press Officer:Jeff King

Tel Nos: 01670 735824 or 07730285558

Managers: Keith Perry & Tony Lowrey

Coach: Melvyn Harmison

Captain: Ian Dixon

Physio: Dave Robertson

2003-2004

Player of the Year: Robbie Cockburn

Top Goalscorer: Roy Allen 35

BILLINGHAM SYNTHONIA

Secretary: Graham Craggs, 10 Embleton Grove, Wynard,Stockton on TeesTS22 5SY
Tel No: 01740 645367

Ground: The Stadium, Central Avenue, Billingham, Cleveland (Press Box 01642 532348)

Directions: Turn off A19 onto A1027 signposted Billingham, Norton (this applies from either north or south), continue straight on along Central Avenue, ground on left opposite office block. 1 mile from Billingham (BR)

Capacity: 1,970 Seats: 370 Cover: 370 Floodlights: Yes

Clubhouse: On the ground. Normal club hours **Club Shop:**Yes(Lapel Badges)

HONOURS Northern Lg 56-57 88-89 89-90 95-96, R-up 49-50 50-51 51-52, Lg Cup 51-52 87-88 89-90, Div 2 86-87, Teeside Lg 36-37 (Lg Cup 34-35 38-39), Durham Chall. Cup 88-89 90-91, North Riding Snr Cup 66-67 71-72, North Riding Amat. Cup 38-39 56-57 62-63 63-64.

PREVIOUS **League:** Teeside (1923-War) **Name:** Billingham Synthonia Recreation

BEST SEASON
FA Amateur Cup 4th Rd 48-49 **FA Vase:** 3rd Rd 01-02
FA Trophy: Q-F replay 93-94, 1-2 v Woking after 1-1 (A)
FA Cup:1st Rd 48-49 51-52 56-57 57-58 87-88 89-90

RECORDS **Attendance:** 4,200 v Bishop Auck. 6/9/58
Scorer: Tony Hetherington **Appearances:** Andy Harbron

FACT FILE

Founded: 1923

Nickname: Synners

Sponsors: Darlington Building Society

Colours: Green & White quarters/white/white

Change colours: Yellow

Midweek Matches: WednesdayProgramme: 20 pages (+ads),50p

Editor: David Lealman (01642 559540)

CLUB PERSONNEL

Chairman: Stuart Coleby

President: Frank Cook

Press Officer: Secretary

Manager: Stuart Coleby

Physio: Tommy Cushley

Coach: Lenny Gunn

Captain: Craig Perry

2003-2004

Leading Goalscorer & Player of the Year: David Wells 32

BILLINGHAM TOWN

Secretary: Glenn Youngman,13 Blackthorne Grove, fairfield, Stockton, Cleveland TS19 7DG Tel/Fax: 01642 655516 and Tel: 01642 862058

Ground: Bedford Terrace, Billingham, Cleveland. Tel: 01642 560043

Directions: Leave A19 on A1027 (signed Billingham). Turn left at 3rd r/bout,over bridge 1st left, 1st left again to grd

Capacity: 3,000 Seats: 176 Cover: 600 Floodlights: Yes

Clubhouse: Open matchdays. Hot & cold food **Club Shop:** No

HONOURS Durham Cup 76-77 77-78, 03-04 R-up: 01-02Teesside Lg 77-78 81-82, Nth Riding Snr Cup R-up 76-77 81-82, Stockton & Dist. Lg (3)

PREVIOUS **Leagues :** Stockton & Dist. 68-74; Teesside 74-82.
Name: Billingham Social Club (pre-1982) **Ground:** Mill Lane (pre-1974)

BEST SEASON **FA Cup:** 1st Rd Proper 55-56
FA Vase: 5th Rd Proper

RECORDS **Attendance:** 1,500 v Manchester City, FA Youth Cup 1985
Scorer: Paul Rowntree 396 (1990-2001)
Appearances: Paul Rowntree 505 (including 2000-01)

Players progressing: Gary Pallister (Middlesbrough), Gerry Forrest (Southampton), Dave Robinson (Halifax), Tony Barratt (Hartlepool), Mark Hine (Grimsby), Tony Hall(Middlesbrough), Graham Hall (Arsenal).

FACT FILE
Founded: 1967 Nickname: The Social
Colours: All Blue
Change colours: Yellow/green/green
Midweek Matches: Tuesday
Programme: 28 pages, 50p
Editor:Peter Martin

CLUB PERSONNEL
Chairman: Tommy Donnelly
Hon. President: F Cook M.P.
President: G A Maxwell
Press Officer: Tom Donnelly
(01642 555332(H) 01642 370101(W)
Fax : 01642 651033
Manager: Alan Robinson
Asst Manager: Michael Watson
Coaches: Lee Tucker
2003-04
Captain: Richard Ward
Player of the Year: David Turner

BRANDON UNITED

Secretary: Brian Richardson, Flat 2, 30 Commercial St, Brandon, Durham DH7 8PL Tel: 0191 378 1373

Ground: Welfare Ground, rear of Commercial St., Brandon, Durham Tel: 0191 378 2957

Directions: A690 - 3 miles west of Durham City. Bus 50 from Durham

Capacity: 3,000 Seats: 200 Cover: 300 Floodlights: Yes **Club Shop:** No

Clubhouse: Open every day, lunch & evening. Pool Entertainment at weekends

HONOURS Northern Lg Div 1 Champions 2002-03 Div 2 84-85 99-00 Northern All.(2) 77-79, Lg Cup 77-78 79-80 Sunderland Shipowners Cup 81-82, Durham Co. Sunday Cup 73-74 75-76 76-77,Durham & Dist Sunday Lg(4) 73-77 (Div 2 69-70, Div 3 68-69), Staffieri Cup 75-76 FA Sunday Cup 75-76, Cleator Cup Winners 2003-2004

PREVIOUS **Leagues:** Durham & Dist. Sunday 68-77; Northern All. 77-80; Northern Amtr 80-81; Wearside 81-83.

BEST SEASON **FA Cup:** 1st Rd replay 88-89 (lost to Doncaster). Also 1st Rd 79-80
FA Vase: QF 82-83 83-84 **FA Trophy:** 3rd Qual. Rd 87-88 89-90

RECORD **Gate:** 2,500, FA Sunday Cup SF **Record Goalscorer:** Tommy Holden
Most Appearances: Derek Charlton 1977-86

Players progressing: Bryan Liddle (Hartlepool 1984) Dean Gibb (Hartlepool 1986), Paul Dalton (Manchester Utd 1988), Neil Richardson (Rotherham).

FACT FILE
Founded: 1968
Nickname: United
Sponsors: Bramble Down Landscapes
Colours: All red Change colours: All blue
Midweek Matches: Wednesday
Programme: Gree Teamsheet

CLUB PERSONNEL
Chairman: Neil Scott
Vice Chairman: John Dickinson
President: Brian Hewitt
Press Officer: Secretary
Manager: Ken Lindoe
.Physio: Keith Glendenning

2003-2004
Player of the Year: Mark Patterson
Top Goalscorer: Steven Hughes

CHESTER-LE-STREET TOWN

Secretary: Melvyn Atkinson, 1 St Marys Close, Chester-le-Street, Co Durham DH2 3EG Tel: 0191 288 3664

Ground: Moor Park, Chester Moor, Chester-le Street, County Durham (0191 388 3363)

Directions: Ground lies approx 2 miles south of town on A167 (C.-le-S. to Durham). Regular buses from C.-le-S. and Durham pass ground. Railway station 2 miles distant in town centre

Capacity: 3,500 Seats: 150 Cover: 1,500 Floodlights: Yes

Open Matchdays- midweek 6.30p.m.- 11.00 p.m. Saturday 12.00p.m.-7.00.Open Monday 7..30-11.00pm **Club Shop:** No, but old programmes available from editor

GROUNDS Ravensworth Welfare, Low Fell 72-73; Riverside Pk 73-78; Sacriston Welfare 78-79.

HONOURS Northern Lg Div 2 83-84 97-98; Wearside Lg 80-81 (R-up 82-83); Monkwearmouth Cup 80-81 81-82; Washington Lg; Durham Minor Cup; Washington AM Cup.

PREVIOUS **Leagues:** Newcastle City Amtr 72-75; Washington 75; Wearside 77-83
Names: Garden Farm 72-78

BEST SEASON **FA Cup:** 4th Qual. Rd. 86-87, 2-3 v Caernarfon Town (H)
FA Vase : 5th Rd v Fleetwood Town 84-85 (1-1,2-2,0-3)

RECORD **Gate:** 893 v Fleetwood FA Vase 18/2/85,
(3000 Sunderland v Newcastle,Bradford appeal match 85)
Appearances: Colin Wake 361
Win: 9-0 v Washington N.L. 28/2/98 **Defeat:** 0-7 v Consett 6/11/96

FACT FILE
Founded: 1972 Nickname: Cestrians
Colours: Blue & white hoops/white/white
Change colours: All yellow
Midweek Matches: Tuesday
Programme: 40 pages, 50p
Editor: K.Greener
email:keith@ greener82fsnet.co.uk
Club Website: chester-le-street-townfc.co.uk

CLUB PERSONNEL
Chairman: John Tomlinson
Vice Chairman: Jack Thornback
President: John Holden
Press Off.: Jack Thornback (0191 3883554)
Manager: Stuart Sherwood
Asst Manager: tony Heslop Stuart Sherwood
Physio: Mark Parkinson
2002-2003
Captain:ColinWake
Player of the Year: David Turner
Top gaolscorer: Steve Cuggy 14

...ACTION EXTRA...ACTION EXTRA...ACTION EXTRA...

Craig Armstrong 'scores' for Hebburn at Washington Nissan but is adjudged offside. Photo: Alan Watson

Opposite: Peterlee's Gary Clarkson relieves the pressure against Horden Colliery Welfare.
Photo: Alan Watson

...ACTION EXTRA...ACTION EXTRA...ACTION EXTRA...

Penrith's Phil Thornton heads clear against Marske United. Photo: Alan Watson

CONSETT

Secretary: Ian Hamilton, 29 Grange St. Delves Lane, Consett, Co. Durham DH87AG
Tel: 01207 509366 (H) 07947 130726 (M) email: thesecretarycafc@aol.com

Ground: Belle Vue Park, Ashdale Road, Consett, County Durham (01207 503788)

Directions: Quarter of mile north of town centre - along Medomsley Rd, left down Ashdale Rd, ground 100m yards on left. Follow signs for Sports Centre and Baths

Capacity: 4,000 Seats: 400 Cover: 1,000 Floodlights: Yes

Clubhouse: Matchdays, and evenings on request. Darts & pool **Club Shop:** No

PREVIOUS **Leagues:** Northern Alliance 19-26 35-37; North Eastern 26-35 37-58 62-64; Midland 58-60; Northern Counties 60-62; Wearside 64-70

BEST SEASON
FA Cup: 1st Rd 58-59, 0-5 v Doncaster Rov. (A)
FA Trophy: 2nd Rd 78-79

HONOURS North Eastern Lg 39-40 Div 2 26-27, Lg Cup 50-51(jt) 53-54, Durham Challenge x5 R-up x2, Northern Lg R-up 76-77 Div 2 88-89, Lg Cup 78-79 80-81, Northern Counties Lg 61-62, Sunderland Shipowners Cup 67-68, Monkwearmouth Charity Cup 67-68, Wearside Lg R-up 68-69 69-70.

FACT FILE
Founded: 1899 Nickname: Steelmen
Colours: Red with black & white trim/black/red
Change colours: Sky blue/dark blue/sky blue
Midweek Matches: Wednesday
Programme: 16 pages, 30p
Programme Editor: Andrew Pearson

CLUB PERSONNEL
Chairman: Derek .Nicholls
Vice Chairman: Stuart Moffat
President: John Hirst
Press Officer: Andrew Pearson, 01207 506194
Manager: Colin Carr
Physios: Brian Nicholson & Jim Vipond

DUNSTON FEDERATION BREWERY

Secretary: Bill Montague, 12 Dundee Close, Chapel House, Newcastle-upon-Tyne NE51JJ
Tel: 0191 2672250

Ground: Federation Park, Wellington Road, Dunston, Gateshead Tel: 0191 493 2935

Directions: Dunston/Whickham exit off A1(M), grd 400 yds north. along Dunston Rd on L. 1 mile from Dunston or Metrocentre stations. Buses from Gateshead & Metrocentre stop outside ground

Capacity: 2,000 Seats:120 Cover: 400 Floodlights: Yes

Clubhouse: Matchdays only. Hot & cold snacks. **Club Shop:** No

HONOURS Northern Lge Div 1 Champions 03-04 R-up 00-01, Div 2 92-93, Challenge Cup (4) Northern Amtr Lg 77-78 R-up 2, Lg Cup 77-78 78-79 R-up 75-76, Lg Shield 78-79 79-80, Wearside Lg 88-89, 89-90. R-up 90-91, Lg Cup 90-91, N. Comb. 86-87 R-up 3, Lg Cup 83-84, 86-87 R-up 3, Sunderland Shipowners Cup 87-88, Durham Co Tphy 81-82 R-up 2, Minor Cup 79-80 R-up 78-79, Gateshead Chy Cup 77-78 80-81, Heddon Homes Cup 80-81. Cleator Cup 00-01

PREVIOUS **Ground:** Dunston public park 75-86
Names: Whickham Sports; Dunston Mechanics Sports

BEST SEASON
FA Cup: 4th Qual. Rd 03-04, 0-1v Lancaster City.
FA Vase: Quarter-Finals 92-93, 0-2 v Gresley Rov. (A)

RECORDS **Attendance:** 1,550 - Sunderland Shipowners Cup Final 1/4/88
Win: 13-0 v Crook T. (H), Northern Lge Div. 1, 00-01 **Scorer:** Paul King
Defeat: 1-6 v Billingham Synthonia (A), Northern Lge Div. 1, 94-95 **Appearances:** Paul Dixon

FACT FILE
Founded: 1975 Nickname: The Fed
Sponsors: Federation Brewery
Colours: All blue with white trim
Change colours :All red
Midweek matchday: Tuesday
Reserve s' League : None
Programme: 28 pages 50p
Editor: Ian McPherson (0191 420 5583)

CLUB PERSONNEL
Chairman: Malcolm James
Vice-Chairman: Fred Fowles
President: John Smart
Press Officer: Ian McPherson (0191 420 5583)
Commercial Secretary: Malcolm James
Manager: Bobby Scaife
Asst Man: Perry Briggs Captain: Billy Irwin
Physio: Matt Annan

2003-2004
P.o.Y.: Steven Holmes
Top Goalscorer: David Southern

DURHAM CITY

Secretary: Kevin Hewitt, 21 Cherrytree Drive, Langley Park,Co Durham DH7 9FX
& Press Officer Tel: 0191 3733878 (H & FAX) 0191 383 4200 (W)

Ground: Archibalds Stadium, Durham Tel No: 0191 3869616

Directions At J62 on A1M take A690 towards Durham City. Follow signposts for Belmont Industrail Estate.

Capacity: **Seats:** 300 **Cover:** 700 **Floodlights: Yes**

HONOURS Northern Lg 94-95 (R-up 70-71, Div 2 R-up 30-31 91-92), Durham Benevolent Bowl 55-56, Northern Div 2 Champions 98-99, Div 2 Champions 98-99 Durham Challenge Cup R-up (3)

PREVIOUS **Leagues:** Victory 18-19; N Eastern 19-21 28-38; Football Lge 21-28; Wearside 38-39 50-51.
Grounds: Holliday Park 21-38; Ferens Park 49-94. NB club disbanded in 1938

BEST SEASON
FA Cup: 2nd Rd 25-26 57-58 (Also 1st Rd 27-28 55-56)
FA Vase: SF 01-02, QF 87-88
FA Amateur Cup: 2nd Rd rep. 57-58
FA Trophy: 1st Rd 83-84, 94-95

RECORD **Appearances:** Joe Raine, 552

Players progressing: Harry Houlahan (Newcastle 51), Derek Clark (Lincoln 51), Leo Dale & David Adamson (Doncaster 54/70), Stan Johnstone (Gateshead 54), Dennis Coughlan (Barnsley 57), John Wile (Sunderland 66), Brian Taylor(Coventry 68),Paul Malcolm (Rochdale 84), Gary Pearson (Darlington 02)

FACT FILE
Reformed: 1949 Nickname: City
Sponsors: Archibalds and Arnotts
Colours: Blue & gold halves/blue & gold stripe/ blue with gold top socks
Change colours: Red & black stripes
Midweek Matches: Tuesday
Progr: 50 pages Editor: Gordon Wright
Local Press: Northern Echo, Sunderland Echo, Evening Chronicle

CLUB PERSONNEL
President&Chairman: Stewart Dawson
Vice Chairman: David Asbery
Commercial Manager: Richrd Rodden
Press Officer: Secretary
Manager: Billy Cruddas
Asst Manager/Coach: Richard Ord
Justin Keegan
Physio: Simon Williamson

2003-2004
Player of the Year:Chris Mudd
Top Goalscorer: Glen Robson 27

ESH WINNING

Secretary: Roli Bell,12 Park Rd.Central, Chester-le-Street, Co Durham 0191 388 1458 (H)

Ground: West Terrace, Waterhouses, Durham Tel: 0191 373 3872 (Fax: 0191 387 1983)
Directions: Durham to Ushaw Moor, to Esh Winning; ground 1 mile further at Waterhouses
Capacity: 3,500 Seats: 160 Cover: 500 Floodlights: Yes
Clubhouse: Open daily. Snacks served **Club Shop:** No

HONOURS Durham & Dist. Sunday Lg 78-79 79-80, Durham Co. Sun. Cup R-up 78-79, Staffieri Cup 74-75, Guards Cup 72-73, N. Durham Yth Lg 94-95, Auckland Yth Lge 94-95.

PREVIOUS **Leagues:** Durham & Dist Sunday; Northern Alliance 81-82.
Grounds: None **Names:** Esh Winning Pineapple (pre-1982)

BEST SEASON
FA Cup: 2nd Qual Rd 90-91 **FA Vase:** 2nd Round 83-84

RECORDS **Gate:** 900 v Liverpool Fantail, FA Sunday Cup 1982
Goalscorer: Mark Drake **Appearances:** Paul Hewitson 40
Win: 11-0 v Norton (H) **Defeat:** 0-10 v Shotton Comrades
Fee Paid: £1,000 for Steven Burns **Received:** £500 for Paul Ward (Brandon U)

FACT FILE
Formed: 1967
Nickname: 'Stags'
Sponsors:Lumsden & Carroll
Colours: Yellow/green/green/ green
Change colours: Green & Navy
Midweek Matches: Wednesday
Programme: 20 pages, 50p
Editor: Nigel Quinn

CLUB PERSONNEL
Chairman: Charles Ryan
Vice Chairman: David Parkinson
President: Jack Lumsden
Press Officer: Secretary
Manager:Barrie Fleming
Physio:Trevor Best

2003-04
P.o.Y.: Craig Marron
Leading Scorer: Stephen Burns

2004-2005
Captain: Phil Coxall

GUISBOROUGH TOWN

Secretary: Keith Smeltzer, 212 Woodhouse Road, Guisborough, Cleveland TS14 6LP
Tel: 01642 226181 (W) 01287 201561 (H) 07811 850388 (M)
Ground: King George V Ground, Howlbeck Rd, Guisborough, Cleveland (01287 636925)
Directions: From west: bear left at 2nd set of lights, left into Howlbeck Rd after quarter mile, ground at end. Buses from Middlesbrough
Capacity: 3,500 Seats: 150 Cover: 400 Floodlights: Yes Club Shop: Yes
Clubhouse: Open evenings & weekends. Hot & cold snacks & drinks from kitchen on matchdays

HONOURS FA Vase R-up 79-80; Northern Lg Cup 87-88 (Div 2 R-up 86-87), Northern Alliance 79-80 (R-up 78-79, Lg Cup 78-79); N. Riding Sen. Cup 89-90 90-91 91-92 92-93 94-95.

PREVIOUS **Leagues:** Middlesbrough & District; South Bank; Northern Alliance 77-80; Midland Counties 80-82; Northern Counties (East) 82-85.

BEST SEASON
FA Cup: 1st Round Proper 88-89, 0-1 v Bury
F.A.Vase: Finalists 79-80
FA Trophy: 1st Rd Proper 90-91 91-92 92-93

CLUB RECORDS **Gate:** 3,112 v Hungerford, FA Vase SF, 1980
(at Middlesbrough FC - 5,990 v Bury, FA Cup 1st Rd 1988)
Goalscorer: Mark Davis 341 **Appearances:** Mark Davis 587
Win: 6-0 v Ferryhill & v Easington **Defeat:** 0-4 v Billingham Synthonia

FACT FILE
Founded: 1973 Nickname: Priorymen
Sponsors: Hensons Windows & Conservatories
Colours: Red & white stripes/Black/Red
Change colours:Yellow
Midweek matchday:Wednesday
Reserves ' League: Teesside Strongarm
Programme: 32pages, 50p
Editor: Stuart Burns
Local Press: Northern Echo, Middlesbrough Evening Gazette

CLUB PERSONNEL
Chairman: Richard Corden
Vce Chairman: Keith Watson
Press Officer: Stuart Burns
Manager: Steve Corden
Asst Manager: Tiger Wyke
Physio: Gary Hinchley

2002-03
Leading Goalscorer,Captain & P.oY.
Darren Mowdray

HORDEN COLLIERY WELFARE

Ground: Welfare Park , Park Rd, Horden, Peterlee, Co. Durham
Tel: 0191 587 3549 (Club)
Directions: A19 to Peterlee, signposted from there
Capacity: 3,000 Seats: 220 Cover: 370 Floodlights: Yes
Clubhouse: Open during normal licensing hours. Hot & cold snacks, darts, pool

HONOURS Northern Lge. Div. 2 R-up 02-03; North Eastern Lg 37-38 63-64 (`Non-Reserve' Medal 50-51)Durham Challenge Cup 35-36 63-64 80-81 81-82, 02-03 sDurham Benevolent Cup 33-34,
Wearside Lge 11-12 12-13 13-14 33-34 64-65 67-68 69-70 70-71 71-72 72-73, Lg Cup 33-34 49-50, Monkwearmouth Charity Cup 12-13 23-24 32-33 69-70 72-73, Sunderland Shipowners Cup 65-66 72-73, .

PREVIOUS **Leagues:** Wearside 07-35 63-75; N. Eastern 35-58 62-64; Midland (Co's) 58-60; Northern Co's 60-62. **Names:** Horden Athletic

BEST SEASON **FA Cup:** 2nd Rd 38-39, 2-3 v Newport Co. (H)
Also 1st Rd 25-26 52-53 53-54 54-55 81-82

RECORD **Attendance:** 8,000 - FA Cup 1937

Players progressing: Paul Dobson (Hartlepool Utd), Stan Anderson (Sunderland), Colin Bell (Bury), Tommy Garrett (Blackpool), Bob Taylor (Leeds Utd)

FACT FILE
Reformed : 1980
Nickname: Colliers
Colours: Red/black/red
Change colours:Green/white/greenReserves League: Wearside Div 2
Midweek Matches: Wednesday
Programme: 25pages £1.00

CLUB PERSONNEL
Chairman: Norman Stephens
Secretary: Rob Jones
1 York Road,Peterlee, Co.Durham SR8 2DS
Tel: 0191 587 0949 (H) 07932 951842 (M)
Press Officer: Secretary

JARROW ROOFING BOLDON C.A.

Secretary/Manager: Richard McLoughlin, 8 Kitchener Terrace, Jarrow NE32 5PU
Tel: 0191 489 9825

Ground: Boldon CA Sports Ground, New Road, Boldon Colliery (0191 519 1391)

Directions: A19 to junction with A184 (Sunderland/Newcastle). Follow signs to Boldon Asda stores, then to North Road Social Club. Ground behind. East Boldon(BR) 800 yds.

Capacity: 3,500 Seats: 150 Cover: 800 Floodlights: Yes Club Shop: Yes

Clubhouse: Open eves.& w/e lunchtimes. Hotdogs, burgers etc from tea bar on matchdays

HONOURS Wearside Lg Div 2 R-up 91-92 95-96; Sunderland Shipowners Cup R-up 93-94, 94-95; Tyneside Amtr Lg R-up 90-91, Chal. Shield 90-91 (R-up 89-90); Bill Dixon Cup 90-91; Mid-Tyne Lg 87-88; Fred Giles Cup R-up 87-88; Gateshead Charity Cup SF 90-91; Monkwearmouth Cup 94-95; Craven Cup 96-97, Northern League Div One Cup R-Up 98-98

PREVIOUS **Leagues:** Mid-Tyne; Tyneside Amtr 88-91; Vaux Wearside

RECORD **Attendance:** 500 v South Shields
Appearances: Mick Haley **Goalscorer:** Paul Chow

FACT FILE

Founded: 1987Nickname: Roofing
Sponsors: Jarrow Roofing Co
Colours: Yellow with Blue trim shirts, Royal Blue & Yellow sjhorts and socks
Change colours: Red & Black
Midweek matchday: Tuesday
Programme: 20 pages, free with entry
Editor: Brian Marshall (0191 4217011)

CLUB PERSONNEL

Chairman: Richard McLoughlin
Press Officer/Treasurer: Rose McLoughlin
Manager/ Secretary: Richard McLoughlin
Coaches: Colin Myers, Tony Metcalfe
Physio: John Cullen

2003-04

Leading Goalscorer: Paul Chow
Player of the Year:Ged Quinn
2004-2005 Captain: Chris McCabe

MORPETH TOWN

Secretary: Les Scott,1 Bennetts Walk, Morpeth, Northumberland NE61 1TP
Tel: 01670 517390 (H) 0780 3483509 (M) e-mail: les@craikpark.fsnt.co.uk

Ground: Craik Park, Morpeth Common, Morpeth, Northumberland
Tel: 01670 513785

Directions: Morpeth is signed off the A1 onto A197.
Take the B6524, right at Mitford sign, then right after about a mile into the ground, next to Morpeth Common

Capacity: 1000 Seated: 150 Cover: 150 Floodlights Yes

Clubhouse: Yes **Club Shop**: No

PREVIOUS **Leagues:** Northern Alliance pre 1994
Ground: Storey Park, Morpeth. pre 1992

BEST SEASON

FA Cup: 4th Q Rd v Burton Albion 1998-99

HONOURS Northern Alliance 83-84, 93-94 (R-up 37-38, 65-66, 73-74, 81-82, 84-85); Challenge Cup Winners 38-39, 85-86, 93-94 (R-up 36-37, 62-63, 73-74).

FACT FILE

Colours:
Amber & black stripes/black/black
Change colours: Blue,white,blue
Midweek Matchday: Tuesday
Programme: Yes

Chairman: Keith Jewitt
Tel.: 01670 518787 (H)
07730 983227 (M)
Press Officer: Les Scott (Secretary)

2003-2004

Player of the Year: Steve Walker
Top GoaLacorer: Paul Beaugrs
Captain: Iain Nickalls

NEWCASTLE BENFIELD SAINTS

Secretary: Tony Baird, 13 Queensway, Tynemouth, Tyne & Wear NE30 4ND

Ground: Benfield Park, Benfield Road, Newcastle-upon-Tyne.
Tel: 0191 265 9357

Directions: From Newcastle towards coast take 2nd exit after Corner House pub lights, right into Benfield Rd, ground on left opp. Walkergate Hosp. & adjacent to school.

FACT FILE

Colours: Black & White Quarters/Black/Black
Change colours:All White

Chairman: Jimmy Rowe

Manager: Keith Sheardown
Coach: Lee Boyle

PETERLEE NEWTOWN

Secretary: Arnie Church, 38 Hatfield Place, Peterlee, Co. Durham SR8 5SS (0191 586 4804)
Ground: Eden Lane, Peterlee, County Durham (0191 586 3004)

Directions: From town centre Asda, turn left into Edenhill Rd, then right into Robson Avenue. Left at the next junction and ground is on the right

Capacity: 6,000 Seats: 50 Cover: 200 Floodlights: Yes

Clubhouse: Open normal licensing hours. Sandwiches etc available **Club Shop:** No

HONOURS Northern Lg Div 2 82-83, North Eastern F'lit League, 4th Qual Rd FA Cup
PREVIOUS **Leagues:** Northern Alliance 76-79; Wearside 79-82

RECORD **Attendance:** 2,350 v Northern, Hillsborough Fund match 1989
Scorer : Keith Fairless **Appearances** : Keith Bendelow

BEST SEASON
FA Cup: 4th Qual. Rd replay 85-86 **FA Vase:**

Players progressing: Keith Fairless (Scarborough) 1986, Brian Honour(Hartlepool) 1988)
Nathan Jameson (Walsall)

FACT FILE
Formed: 1976 Nickame: Newtowners
Sponsors: Artix Ltd
Colours: Yellow/black/yellow
*Midweek Matches: Wednesday
Programme: 10 pages, 30p
Editor: Secretary
Local Press: Hartlepool Mail, Sunderland Echo, Northern Echo

CLUB PERSONNEL
Chairman: Rob Huntington
Vice-Chairman: Colin Austin (07817 707565)
President: David Brown
Press Officer: Ray Matthews (07720 548424)
Manager: Andrew Toman
Asst Manager: Tim Campbell
Physio: Ron Lamdrel
Ca[tain: Steven Cochrane
2003-2004
Leading Goalscorer: Paul Hinton
Player of the Year: Chris Emms

SHILDON

Secretary /Press Officer: Mike Armitage, 22 Hambleton Court, Byerley Park, Newton Aycliffe, Co.Durham DL5 7HR Tel: 01325 316322
Ground: Dean Street, Shildon, County DurhamTel: 01388 773877 **Directions:** In the town centre 1 mile from BR station and 300yds from Darlington-Bishop Auckland bus stop
Capacity: 4,000 Seats: 480 Cover: 1000 Floodlights: Yes **Club Shop:** No
Clubhouse: .Matchdays only.

HONOURS Northern Lg 33-34 34-35 35-36 36-37 39-40 (R-up 32-33 38-39, Div 2 Champions 2001-02 Lg Cup 33-34 34-35 37-38 38-39 39-40 52-53 2002-03), Durham Challenge Cup 07-08 25-26 71-72, Durham Amateur Cup 01-02 02-03, Durham Benevelopment Bowl 24-25.

PREVIOUS **Leagues:** Auckland & District 1892-96; Wearside 96-97; North Eastern 07-32.

BEST SEASON
FA Cup: 2nd Rd 36-37 1st Rd 27-28 29-30 34-35 36-37 55-56 59-60 61-62
FA Trophy: 3rd Qual. Rd 74-75 **FA Amateur Cup:** 4thRd 58-59 **FA Vase:** 1st Rd 86-87

RECORDS **Attendance:** 13,000 - Leeholme v Perkinsville, schoolboys game, 1920s. (Shildon game); 11,000 Shildon v Ferryhill Ath., Durham Sen. Cup 1922
Appearances: Bryan Dale **Goalscorer:** Jack Downing, 61 (1936-37)
Players progressing: Ken Whitfield (Wolves 47), James Smith(Chelsea 51), Mike Peacock, Philip Shute, Nigel Bolton (Darlington 60, 84, 95), Kevin Stonehouse (Blackburn 79), Alan White (Middlesbrough 93).

FACT FILE
Founded: 1890
Nickname: Railwaymen
Sponsors:Ashfield
Colours:All Purple
Change: White/black/white
Midweek Matches: Wednesday
Programme: 48 pages, 50p
Editor: Secretary

CLUB PERSONNEL
Chairman: Gordon Hampton
Vice Chairman: G. Elliott
President: John Atkinson
Manager: Ray Gowan
Assistant Manager: David Bayles
Physio: Neil Jennings
2003-2004
P.o.Y.: Garry Barnes
Leading Goalscorer: Garry Barnes 53
Captain: Danny Key

THORNABY

Ground: Teesdale Park, Acklam Road, Thornaby, Stockton-on-Tees TS17 8TZ Tel: 01642 606803
Directions: A19 to Thornaby turn off, ground half mile on right. One mile fromThornaby BR station. Any Stockton-Middlesbrough bus - stop at Acklam Rd,Thornaby
Capacity: 5,000 Seats: 150 Cover: 350 Floodlights: Yes
Clubhouse: 150+ seater social club with concert room, pool/games room and bar. Open every night and Sunday lunchtimes and all day Saturday. Sandwiches avail. in bar, canteen in ground sells pies, burgers, soup, drinks etc
Club Shop: No
PREVIOUS **Leagues:** Stockton & District 80-81; Wearside 81-85.
Names: Stockton Cricket Club 65-80; Stockton 80-99: Thornaby-on-Tees 99-00
Grounds: Grangefield Youth & Community Centre, Stockton 80-82; Tilery Sports Centre 82-83.
RECORD **Attendance:** 3,000 v Middlebrough, pre-season friendly August 1986
Appearances: Michael Watson
Win: 11-0 v Horden C.W.(H) Buchanan Cup 94-95
BEST SEASON **FA Vase:** 3rd Rd 89-90 **FA Trophy:** 3rd Rd 92-93
FA Cup: 4th Qual. Rd replay 92-93,1-2 v Blyth (H) after 1-1
HONOURS Northern Lg Div 2 87-88 91-92, Nth Riding Co. Cup 85-86, Inaugralwinners of Craven Cup (Northern Div 2 clubs) 94-95..

FACT FILE
Formed: 1980
Colours:Yellow and blue/Navy & white/yellow
Change colours: All sky
Midweek Matches: Wednesday
Reserves' Lge: Wearside & Teesside Lgs
Programme: 24 pages, 50p
Editor: Peter Morris (01642 585625)
Local Press: Northern Echo, Evening Gazette

CLUB PERSONNEL
Chairman: Lol Lyons
Press Officer: Paul Beards ()1642 897861)
Secretary: Peter Morris
20 Wheatear Lane, Ingleby Barwick, Stockton-on-Tees, Cleveland TS17 0TB
Tel: 01642 760779

Manager: Michael Watson
Asst Mgr: Peter May
Coach: Paul Sharkey

Dunston Federation Brewery - Back Row (L-R): M Annan (Sports Therapist), S Holmes, M Taylor, B Thompson, T Phillips, S Dawson, P Hogg, M Robson, S Pickering, D Burke.
Front Row (L-R): D Shore, D Southern, R Pitt, R Scaife (Manager), B Irwin (Captain), P Briggs (Asst. Manager), A March, K Young, M Farry.
Squad members missing from photo: S Brown, P Hollier, C Coates, A Snaith.

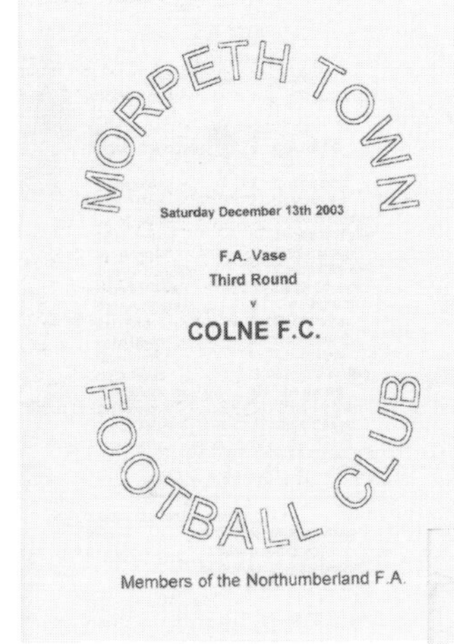

MORPETH TOWN
Saturday December 13th 2003
F.A. Vase
Third Round
v
COLNE F.C.
FOOTBALL CLUB
Members of the Northumberland F.A.

newcastle
benfield saints
football club
season 2003 - 2004
fifty pence
BENFIELD SAINTS F.C.
albany northern league
division two

THORNABY FOOTBALL CLUB
EST 2000
ALBANY NORTHERN LEAGUE
DIVISION 1
2003 - 2004 SEASON
OFFICIAL PROGRAMME
THORNABY FC V GUISBOROUGH TOWN

TOW LAW TOWN

Secretary: Bernard Fairbairn, 3 Coppice Walk, Mowden Park, Darlington, Co. Durham DL3 9DP Tel: 01325 350743

Ground: Ironworks Road, Tow Law, Bishop Auckland Tel: 01388 731443

Directions: Just of High Street in Tow Law town centre

Capacity: 6,000 Seats: 200 Cover: 300 Floodlights: Yes

Clubhouse: Every evening 8.30 -10.30 **Club Shop:** Yes

HONOURS **FA Vase R-up 97-98;** Rothmans National Cup 1977, Northern League Champions 23-24 24-25 94-95, R-up 28-29 88-89, Lg Cup 73-74; Rothmans Overseas Cup 76-77, Durham Chal. Cup 1895-96, Durham Amtr Cup 1892-93.

PREVIOUS **Leagues:** None

BEST SEASON
FA Cup: 2nd Rd rep. 67-68, 2-6 v Shrewsbury T. (A) after 1-1. Also 1st Rd 68-69 84-85 89-90. League Clubs defeated:Mansfield Town 67-68
FA Amateur Cup: 3rd Rd rep. 70-71 **FA Trophy:** 2nd Rd rep. 82-83
FA Vase: Runners-up 1997-98

RECORD **Gate:** 5,500 v Mansfield Town, FA Cup 1967

Players progressing: Reuben Cook & Ralph Guthrie (Arsenal 1951 & 53), Gordon Hughes, Terry Melling & Chris Waddle (Newcastle 1956 & 65 & 80), EricJohnstone & Kevin Dixon (Carlisle 1963 & 83), Keith Adamson (Barnsley 1966),Tom Henderson (Bradford PA 1969), Vincent Chapman (Huddersfield 1988)

FACT FILE
Founded: 1890
Nickname: Lawyers
Colours:
Black & white stripes/black/black & white
Change colours: Red & white
Midweek Matches: Tuesday
Programme: Yes
Editor:Chairman
Local Press : Northern Echo

CLUB PERSONNEL
Chairman: John Flynn
Press Officer: John Flynn (01388 730525)
Manager: Graeme Forster
Assistant Manager: Andy Sinclair

WEST AUCKLAND TOWN

Secretary: Allen Bayles, 11 Edith Terrace, West Auckland, Co.Durham.DL14 9JT Tel: 01388 833783 (H) & FAX, 01388 605221 (B) 01388 661366

Ground: Darlington Road, West Auckland, Co.Durham Tel: 01388 834403

Directions: Leaving West Auckland take A68-ground on right before leavingvillage. Bus route via Bishop Auckland fron Newcastle or Darlington

Capacity: 3,000 Seats: 250 Cover: 250 Floodlights: Yes **Club Shop:** No

Clubhouse: On Gound. (The Thomas Lipton Trophy is on display at the local Working Mans Club five minutes away). Tel No: 01388 661366

HONOURS FA Amateur Cup Finalists 60-61; Northern League Champions 59-60, 60-61 Div 2 90-91,Lg Cup 59-60,62-639r-UP;48-49,61-62,63-64) Durham Challenge Cup 63-64 Durham Benevolent Bowl 62-63; Sir Thomas Lipton Tphy`First World Cup'(as featured in `The Captains Tale') 1909, 1911.

PREVIOUS **League:** Auckland & District
Names: St Helens Utd (1919 only), West Auckland Town.

BEST SEASON **FA Cup:** 1st Rd 58-59, 61-62,98-99
FA Trophy: 3rd Rd. 77-78
FA Vase: 4th Rd. 2001-02 **FA Amateur Cup:** Runners-up 60-61; Q-F 59-60

RECORD **Gate:** 6,000 v Dulwich Hamlet, FA Amateur Cup 58-59
Victory: 11-0 in Durham County Cup

FACT FILE
Founded: 1892
Nickname: West
Sponsors:Rushlift Mechanical Handling and F.Hudson Transport
Colours: White with black & amber band s and amber collar & cuffs/white/white
Change Colours: All Yellow
Midweek Matches: Tuesday

CLUB PERSONNEL
Chairman: Jim Polfreyman
Press Officer:Stuart Alderson (01388 834211)
Manager: Alex Mathie
Assistant.Manager : David Hodgson

2003-2004
Player of the Year: Brian Fairhurst
Top Scorer: Philip McGuire

2004-2005
Captain: Brian Fairhurst

WHITLEY BAY

Secretary: Derek Breakwell 27 Kings Rd, Whitley Bay, Tyne & Wear, NE26 3BD 0191 252 7940
e-mail: derek.breakwell@blueyonder.co.uk

GROUND Hillheads Park, Rink Way off Hillheads Road, Whitley Bay, Tyne& Wear NE25 8HR 0191 291 3637 Club. Fax & matchday office 0191 291 3636
Website: www.whitleybayfc.com

Directions: 1 mile walk from bus station - leave St Pauls Church southward, turn right at r-about, around 3rd left at rear of ice rink.Whitley Bay (25mins from Newcastle) or Monkseaton metro stations, both 1 mile.

Capacity: 4,500 Cover: 650 Seats: 450

Clubhouse: Open 6-11pm Mon-Fri, 12pm 11pm Sat and Sun Bar,Darts,Pool.functions

Club Shop: Sells progs, scarves, hats, metal badges etc. Contact Tom Moody (0191 291 1618)

PREVIOUS **Leagues:** Tyneside 09-10, Northern All. 50-55, North Eastern Lge 55-58, Northern Lge 58-88; N.P.L. 88-00 **Name:** Whitley Bay Athletic 1950-58

CLUB RECORDS **Attendance:** 7,301 v Hendon, FA Amateur Cup 1965

Win: 12-0 v Shildon 1961 **Defeat:** 1-8 v Bishop Auckland 1979 **Goalscorer:** Billy Wright 307

Appearances: Bill Chater 640 **Fee Paid:**£3,000 for Craig Melrose from Bedlingtobn Terriers

Fee Received: £10,000 for Kevin Todd from Berwick Rangers

BEST SEASON **FA Amateur Cup:** Semi Final 65-66 68-69 **FA Trophy:** 3rd Rd 86-87

FA Cup: 3rd Rd 89-90 (0-1 v Rochdale [A]). **F.A.Vase:** Winners 2001-02

HONOURS: Northern Premier Lg Div 1 90-91 (Div 1 Cup 88-89 90-91), Northern Lg 64-65 65-66 (R-up 59-60 66-67 68-69 69-70), Lg Cup 64-65 70-71 (R-up 67-68); Northern Alliance 52-53 53-54 (Lg Cup 52-53 53-54); Northumberland Sen. Cup x 10, R-up x 8

FACT FILE
Formed: 1897
Nickname: The Bay
Colours: Blue & white stripes/white/white
Change colours: Red/blue/blue
Midweek home matchday: Tuesday
Programme Pages: 24 Price: £1.00
Website: www.whitleybayfc.co.uk

CLUB PERSONNEL
Chairman: Paul McIlduff
President: Sid Cope V- Chairman:Peter Siddle
Press Officer: Peter Fox (0773 982 7237 (M)
Manager:Ian Chandler Asst: Terry Burke
Coach: Steve Cuggy Captain: Leon Ryan
Physio: Glen Martin.

2003-2004
Top Scorer: Wayne Edgcumbe
Player of the Year: Leon Ryan

2004-2005
Captain: Patrick Little

ALNWICK TOWN

Secretary: Darren Middleton, 1 Fire Station Houses, Alnwick, NE66 2PB(1665 603781)
Ground: St James' Park, Alnwick, Northumberland Tel: 01665 603162
Directions: 35 miles north of Newcastle on A1, take the slip road to Alnwick,then first left. At roundabout turn left, ground is then on your left.
Capacity: 2,500 Seats: 100 Cover: 200 Floodlights: Yes
HONOURS Northern Lg Div 2 R-up 88-89, Northern Alliance 37-38 62-63 63-64 65-66 67-68 68-69 69-70 70-71 71-72 (R-up 59-60 61-62 66-67 72-73, Lg Cup 61-62 65-6667-68 68-69 70-71, Subsidiary Cup 80-81), Durham Central Lg Cup 64-65, Northumberland Benevolent Bowl 86-87, Northumberland SNR Cup R-up 61-62,Northumberland Amtr Cup 71-72.
PREVIOUS **League:** Northern Alliance 35-39 46-64 64-82
Names: Alnwick United Services; Alnwick United.
BEST SEASON
FA Cup: 3rd Qual. Rd 51-52 (3-4 at Blyth), 57-58 (4-6 at Easington Coll.).
FA Trophy: 3rd Qual. Rd 90-91.
RECORD **Attendance:** 600 v Bedlington Terriers, Northern Alliance 1971.

FACT FILE
Founded: 1879
Colours: Black & white stripes/black/black
Change colours: Green and yellow
Midweek Matches: Tuesday

Local Press: Northumberland Gazette

CLUB PERSONNEL
Chairman: Alan Wilcox
Manager: Malcolm Beusle
Press Officer: Secretary
Players progressing: George Turnbull (Grimsby 1950) and Brian Pringle (1973)

CROOK TOWN

Secretary/Press Officer: Kieron Bennett, Flat 4, Robertson Court, Salisbury Ave,,Chester le Street, Co.Durham. DH3 3FB Tel Noi: 0191 3875078
Ground: Millfield Ground, West Road, Crook, County Durham (01388 762959)
Directions: 400 yds west of town centre on Wolsingham Road (A689). Nearest BR station is Bishop Auckland (5 miles). Buses 1A & 1B from Bishop Auckland or X46& X47 from Durham
Capacity: 3,500 Seats: 400 Cover: 300 Floodlights: Yes
Clubhouse: Lic Bar open matchdays. Hot & Cold Food available from Shop **Club Shop:** Yes
PREVIOUS **Leagues:** Auckland & Dist. 1894-96; Northern 1896-28 29-30; Durham Central 28-29; North Eastern 30-36; Wartime Durham & Northumberland 40-41;Durham Cen. 41-45.
BEST SEASON **FA Trophy:** 3rd Rd 76-77 **FA Cup:** 3rd Rd, v Leicester 31-32. 2nd Rd (4), 1st Rd.(10) **FA Vase:** 4th Rd 99-00 **FA Amateur Cup:** Winners 5 times, plus S-F x 3
HONOURS FA Amateur Cup Winners 00-01 53-54 58-59 61-62 63-64; Northern Lg (5) (R-up 4) Lg Cup(3), (R-up 4); Durham Chall. Cup (4); Durham Ben't Bowl (6); E Armstrong Mem Tr. 97.
2003-2004 Player of the Year and Top Scorer: David Snow.

FACT FILE
Formed: 1889 Nickname: Black & Ambers
Sponsors: S.T.C.H.Colours: Amber/black/black
Change colours: All White
Midweek Matches: Wednesday
Programme: Yes Editor: Secretary

CLUB PERSONNEL
Chairman: Stephen Buddle
Vice-Chairman:Eddie Ryan
Chief Executive: Tom Chopra
President: Sir Tom Cowie O.B.E.
General Manager: David Buchanan
Manager: Alan Oliver
Asst. Manager: Dennis Pinkney
Physio: Stephen Hanson

EASINGTON COLLIERY

Secretary: Alan Purvis, 12 Wark Crescent, Jarrow, Tyne & Wear, NE32 4SH (0191 489 6930)
Ground: Easington Colliery Welfare Ground, CW Park, Easington, Co Durham. (0191 527 3047)
Directions: A19 Easington turn-off, B1284 thru Easington to 'Derby' PH (next to zebra crossing), ground on the right**Clubhouse:** Normal licensing hours. Pies, soup and sandwiches.
Capacity: 2,450 Seats: 175 Cover: 475 Floodlights: Yes **Club Shop:** No
HONOURS Northern Lg Div 2 R-up 85-86; Wearside Lge 29-30 31-32 32-33 47-48 48-49, R-up 28-29 46-47 73-74, Lg Cup 32-33 45-46 61-62; Monkwearmouth Cup 30-31 47-48 75-76; Sunderland Shipowners Cup 74-75 79-80.
PREVIOUS **Leagues:** Wearside 13-37 39-64 73-88
BEST SEASON **FA Cup:** 1st Round Proper 55-56
FA Trophy: 2nd Qual. Rd replay 88-89 **FA Vase:** 4th Rd replay 82-83
RECORD **Attendance:** 4,500 v Tranmere Rovers, FA Cup 1st Round 1955
Scorer: Andrew McKenna **Appearances:** David Howard **Ex Players**:: Ron Greener (Newcastle 1951), Frank Wayman (Darlington1957), John Langridge (Hartlepool 1982).

FACT FILE
Founded: 1913 Nickname: The Colliery
Colours: Green & white stripes/green/green
Change colours: Yellow/black/yellow/green
Midweek Matches: Tuesday
Programme: Yes Editor: Charlie Dodds

CLUB PERSONNEL
Chairman: Allan Barkas
Press Officer: Alan Purvis
Manager: Steve Todd
Asst Manager: Rob Barret

2003-2004
Top Scorer: Lee Johnston
Player of the Year: Kevin Osmond

2004-2005
Captain: Andrew Clark

EVENWOOD TOWN

Secretary: The Football Secretary, Evenwood Town F.C.c/o Evenwood Sports & Social Club, Stones End, Evenwood, Co.Durham
Ground: Welfare Ground, Stones End, Evenwood, County Durham Tel: 01388 832281
Directions: In village centre by Sports & Social club in StonesEnd
Capacity: 3,500 Seats: 150 Cover: 350 Floodlights: Yes
Clubhouse: Open lunch & evening every da except Monday
HONOURS Northern Lg 48-49 69-70 70-71 (Lg Cup 35-36), Durham Challenge Cup 69-70.
PREVIOUS **Leagues:** Barnard Castle & Dist. 1894-95; Auckland & Dist. 1894-96 1903-04 08-23 28-31; Wear Valley 1896-99 1904-06 24-25; Gaunless Valley 06-07; South Durham 27-28. Names: None
BEST SEASON **FA Cup:** 1st Rd 1936 FA Vase:
RECORD **Gate:** 9,000 v Bishop Auckland, FA Amtr Cup 1931
2002-2003: **Captain:** S.Moore **Player of the Year:** C.Warburton **Top Scorer:** K.Dinhey

FACT FILE
Founded: 1890
Nickname: The Wood
Sponsors: C A Roofing
Club colours: All blue
Change:Yellow
Midweek Matches: Tuesday
Programme: 50p Editor: Rev .Frank Campbell

CLUB PERSONNEL
Chairman: Craig Latcham
President: N Colegrove
Press Officer: Secretary
Manager: Ken Houlahan
Assistant Manager:Andy Turner

HEBBURN TOWN

Secretary: Tom Derrick, 63 Staneway, Felling, Gateshead, NE10 8LS.Tel: 0191 442 1563
Tel Nos: 0191 4421563 (H & Fax) 0191 2251444 (W)
Ground: Hebburn Sports & Social Ground, Victoria Road West, Hebburn Tel: 0191 483 5101
Directions: On the main road through the town about 1 mile from railway station. Hebburn lies on the Metroline - excellent bus service from Heworth Metro **Clubhouse:** 7-11 mon,11am-1pm Sat and 12-2.0 p.m. Sun.Pool ,darts etc.**Ground Capacity:** 2,000 **Seats**:153 **Cover:**420 **Lights**:Yes
PREVIOUSLeagues: Jarrow & Dist. Jnr 12-14; S Shields Comb. 19-22; Tyneside Comb. 22-27; Tyneside 27-39; Northern Comb. 41-44 45-59; North Eastern 44-45 59-60; Wearside 60-89.
Names: Reyrolles; Hebburn Reyrolles (pre-1988), Hebburn 88-00 **Club Shop:** No
HONOURS Shields Gazette Cup 91-92, Wearside Lg 66-67 (Monkwearmouth Charity Cup 68-69), Durham Challenge Cup 42-43 91-92, Tyneside Lg 38-39, Northern Comb. 43-44, Gateshead Charity Cup 35-36 37-38, Palmer Hospital Cup 27-28, Hebburn Aged Miners Cup 35-36, Heddon Homes Cup 42-43, Hebburn Infirmary Cup 35-36 36-37 37-38 38-39, Craven Cup 99-00.
BEST SEASON FA Vase: 2nd Rd 91-92 **FA Cup:** 2nd Qual. Rd rep. 89-90, 0-3 v South Bank (A)
RECORD Attendance: 503 v Darwen, FA Cup Prel. Rd replay 7/9/91 **Win:** 10-1 **Defeat** 3-10

FACT FILE
Founded: 1912 Nickname: Hornets
Colours: Yellow& navy stripes /navy blue yellow & navy blue.
Change colours:All white
Midweek Matches: Wednesday
Prog: 24 pages, 30p Ed: Steve Newton

CLUB PERSONNEL
Chairman: Bill Laffey **V-Chair**: Brian Errington
Press Officer: Alan Armstrong 0191 483 2046
Man: Tony Robinson **Ass.Man**: Vin Pearson
Coach: Norman Dryden
Captain: Paul Donaghy

2003-2004
Player of the Year: Paul Clegg
Top Scorer: Robert Marsden

KENNEK RYHOPE C.A.

Secretary: & Press Off Owen Haley, 34 Charter Drive, East Herrington, Sunderland SR3 3PG
Tel No: 0191 5200827 (H) 07957 621364 (M)

Ground: Meadow Park, Stockton Road, Ryhope, Sunderland (0191 523 6555)
Directions: Ground on Waterworks Road near Ryhope & Cherry Knowle Hospitals. From Sunderland follow signs for A19 South
Capacity: 2,000 Seats: 150 Cover: 200 Floodlights: Yes

HONOURS Northern League Div 2 R-Up 1981 and Northern Alliance League Cup1981.

PREVIOUS **Names:** Ryhope Community Association F.C. amalgamted with Kennek Roker from Wearside League in 1999

Leagues: S. C. Vaux: Tyne & Wear; NOrthEastern Amateur

BEST SEASON **FA Cup** 4th Q Rd 88-89 **FA Vase** 2nd Rd 1985 **F.A.Trophy:** 3rd Rd 86

FACT FILE
Founded: 1988
Colours: Red & white stripes/black/red
Change Colours: Claret & Sky BlueMidweek Matchday:Wednesday
Prog 50p Pages:24 Ed: Ray Sanderson

CLUB PERSONNEL
Chairman: W.Mathieson Tel: 0191 534 5496
Presidents: Ray Baines and Norman Taylor
Press Officer: Secretary
Manager: Les Gamble Physio: Ian Palfreyman

2003-2004
P.o.Y. & Top Scorer: Jonny Wightman
2004-2005 Captain David Christie

Kennek Ryhope C.A.

MARSKE UNITED

Secretary: & Press Officer Ian Rowe, 19 High Row, Loftus, Saltburn By The Sea, Cleveland. TS134SA Tel: 01287 643440 (H) 01642 230546 (B) 01642 241273 (Fax)

Ground: Mount Pleasant, Mount Pleasant Ave., Marske, Redcar, Cleveland. Tel: 01642 471091

Directions: From A19 take A174 exit marked Yarm, Teesport, Redcar, Whitby and head east towards Saltburn until Quarry Lane r/about. Take 1st left (A1085) into Marske, 1st right (Meadow Rd) then 1st left (Southfield Rd),then 1st left again Mount Pleasant Ave directly into car park. By train: Darlington to Saltburn, Marske station 300 yds from ground.

Capacity: 2,500 Seats: 169 Cover: 300 Floodlights: Yes

Clubhouse: Open every night and weekend lunchtimes. Food served after all games Contact : Janet Pippen (01642 474985)

HONOURS N Riding Sen Cup 94-95; N Riding County Cup 80-81 85-86; Teesside Lg 80-81 84-85; Wearside Lg 95-96, R-up 93-94 94-95 96-97, Cup 92-93 94-95 95-96; M/mouth Charity Cup 93-94 95-96; Sunderland Ship. Cup 95-96 96-97.N.Lg Cup R-up: 00-01

PREVIOUS Leagues: Cleveland & South Bank 56-76, Teesside 76-85, Wearside 85-97.

BEST SEASON FA Cup: 2nd Qual Rd., 00-01 **FA Vase:** Qtr Final replay, 00-01

RECORDS Attendance: 1,359 v Bedlington Terriers (F.A.Vase) **Win:** 16-0 v North Shields **Defeat:** 3-9 **Goalscorer:** Chris Morgan 169 **Appearances:** John Hodgson 476

Players progressing: Peter Beagrie (Middlesbrough), Tony Butler (Blackpool), Roy Hunter (Northampton), Dave Logan (Mansfield T.)

FACT FILE

Founded: 1956 Nickname: The Seasiders
Colours: Yellow/royalblue/white
Change: Royal/sky/yellow
Midweek matchday: Tuesday
Programme: 60 pages £1.00
Editor: Moss Holtby (01642 475612)
Local Press: Sunday Sun, Middlesbrough Evening Gazette, Northern Echo

CLUB PERSONNEL

Chairman: John Hodgson
Vice Chairman: John Corner
President: Raymond Jarvis
Commercial Manager: Steve Davies
Manager: Charlie Bell
Assistant Manager: Stephen Dowling
Physios: Eric Barrett & Owen Hughes
Coaches: Charlie Bell & Stephen Dowling
Kit Manager: Colin Gilbert

NEWCASTLE BLUE STAR

GROUND: Wheatsheaf Sports Ground, Woolsington, Newcastle-on-Tyne. NE13 8DF

Tel: 0191 286 0425 **Email Address:** nbsfc@blueyonder**Club Website**: www.nbsfc,co,uk

Directions: From central station follow airport signs for 7 miles - ground next to Wheatsheaf Hotel on left, approx. 800yds before airport. Callerton Parkway metro station is 400yds from ground

Capacity: 2,000 Seats: 300 Cover: 500 Floodlights: Yes **Clubhouse:** Open every day

HONOURS FA Vase 77-78; Northern Lg R-up 87-88, Lg Cup 85-86, R-up(1), Div 2 85-86; Wearside Lg 73-74 75-76 82-83 83-84 84-85, R-up (3), Lg Cup76-77 79-80 80-81 82-83 83-84; Sunderland Shipowners Cup 82-83 84-85; Monkwearmouth Charity Cup 74-75 79-80 82-83 88-89; Northern Comb. 62-63 68-69, Lg Cup 66-67 71-72; Northumberland Snr Cup 76-77 82-83 85-86 87-88, R-up 74-75 78-79 80-81, Minor Cup 64-65; J R Cleator Cup 86-87. Craven Cup 03-04

PREVIOUS Leagues: Newcastle Business Houses 32-38; North East Amateur; Tyneside Amateur; Northern Comb.; Wearside 75-85

BEST SEASON FA Trophy: Qtr-finals 88-89, 1-4 v Telford Utd (H)

FA Vase: Winners 77-78, SF 81-82 **FA Cup:** 1st Rd 84-85, 0-2 v York C. (A)

FACT FILE

Founded: 1930 Nickname: `Star'
Colours: All Blue
Change colours: All Red
Midweek matchday: Tuesday
Programme: 44 pages, 60p Editor: M.Gault

CLUB PERSONNEL

Secretary: Jim Anderson
38 Western Ave., West Denton,
Newcastle NE5 5BU Tel: 0191 243 1025
Chairman: Derek Sayers
Manager/Coach: Warren Teasdale
Asst. Man.: Dean Gibb
2002-2003 Captain: Paul Bennett
Top Scorer: Lee Ludlow
P.o.Y.: Michael Cunningham

NORTH SHIELDS

Secretary: Dave Thompson, 38 Barnstable Road, North Shields. Tel: 0191 259 0249

Ground: Ralph Gardner Park, West Percy Rd., N.Shields, Tyne & Wear, NE29 OES

Directions: South: Through Tyne Tunnel, follow signs to North Shields. Travel along Howden Rd (A187) past N.Shields sports centre on left. Continue to next r'about and take 2nd left onto Coach Lane (sign posted Tynemouth) then take 4th left into West Percy Rd. Ground on left, entrance next left. West: From Newcastle take A1058 Coast Rd. At Billy Mill r-about turn right, signed N.Shields, continue over min r-about towards Town Centre. At next r'about (Collingwood Arms) turn right, then second left, ground on left.

Clubhouse: None

HONOURS: FA Amateur Cup 68-69, Northern Lge 68-69, N.C.E. Prem. Div. 91-92, R-up 89-90, 90-91, Lge. Cup 90-91, Presidents Cup 91-92. Wearside Lge 98-99, 01-02 02-03. R-up 00-0. Sunderland Suipwneas Cup 98-99. Monkwearmouth Charity Cup 00-01. Northumberland Senior Bowl 98-99, 00-01.

Founded: 1896
Nickname: Robins
Sponsors: Beacon Centre/E.D.S.
Colours: All red
Change colours: Blue & black/black/black

Chairman: Alan Matthews.
Treasurer:Mike Taylor
Manager: T.B.A .Coach: Wilf Keilty.

2002-03

Leading Goalscorer: Micahel Chilton
Captain: Anthony Robson
Player of the Year: Anthony Robson

NORTHALLERTON TOWN

Secretary: Ken Lomer, 28 Aysgarth Grove, Romanby, Northallerton, N. Yorks DL7 8HY Tel: 01609 779686(H) 01609 773970 (W) **Website:** www.northallertontown.co.uk

Ground: Ainderby Rd, Romanby, Northallerton, N. Yorks. Tel: 01609 772418

Directions: Leave A1 at Leeming Bar (A684) to Northallerton, approaching town take B1333 to Romanby - ground 250yds on left. 3/4 a mile from Northallerton BR station - bus from town

Capacity: 3,000 Seats: 150 Cover: 500 Lights: Yes **Shop:** Yes, Nigel Taylor 07990 948574

Clubhouse: Mon-Fri 7.30-11pm, Sat noon-7.30pm, Sun 12-2 & 7.30-10.30pm

HONOURS Northern Lg Cup 93-94, Div 2 96-97 R-up 89-90, Harrogate & Dist. Lg.; N.Riding Snr Cup R-up 83-84; Harrogate Invit; Alverton Trophy.

PREVIOUS Leagues: Allertonshire; Vale of Mowbray; Ripon & Dist.; Teesside; North Yorks; Darlington & Dist.; Harrogate & Dist. **BEST SEASONS FA Cup:** 4th Qual. Rd 92-93**FA Trophy:** 3rd Rnd 92-93 **RECORD Gate:** 671 v Farnborough, FAT 3rd Rd 20/2/93

RECORD Scorer: John Woods **Appearances:** Lee Wasden **Win:** 11-0 v Ferryhill (A)

Defeat: 1-9 v Ryhope CA (A) **Players progressing**: Andy Toman (Hartlepool)

PREVIOUS Names: Northallerton Alliance; Northallerton Town (pre-1994).**Ground**: Bluestone

FACT FILE

Founded: 1994 Nickname: Town
Colours: Black & White stripes,black
Change Colours: All Yellow
Midweek matchday:Wednesday
Reserves ' League: Harrogate & District
Prog.: 16 pages, 50p Ed: Ian Bolland
Local Press : N Echo, Darlington & Stockton Times, N Yorks News

CLUB PERSONNEL

Chair: Ralph Alderson V- Chair: Les Hood
Press Officer: Ian Bolland (01609 776900)
Manager: Paul Burton Physio: T.B.A.
Captain: Ross Foreman

2003-2004

P.o.Y.: Craig Winter Top Scorer: David Onions

NORTON & STOCKTON ANCIENTS

Secretary: June Teasdale, 8 Sheraton House, Norton Hall, Stockton TS 20 1GB
Tel No: 0774573 4430

Ground: Norton (Teesside) Sports Complex,Station Road, Norton, Stockton-on-Tees, Cleveland (01642 530203) Clubhouse (01642 5540310)
Norton Trust (01642 361974)

Directions: Norton village is two miles from Stockton centre, turn into Station Road on outskirts of village to rail crossing and turn left.

Capacity: 2,000 Seats: 200 Cover: Yes Floodlights: Yes

Clubhouse: Full bar facilities, 150 yds from ground

HONOURS Northern Lg Cup 81-82

PREVIOUS **Leagues:** Teesside (pre-1982) **Name:** Norton & Stockton Cricket Club Trust

BEST SEASON **FA Cup:** 1st Qual Rd (4) 88-89 90-93 **FA Vase:**

RECORD **Attendance:** 1,430 v Middlesbrough, Friendly 88

FACT FILE

Formed: 1959 Nickname: Ancients
Colours: Amber&black/black /black
Change: All Yellow
Midweek Matches: Wednesday
Programme: 12 pages with entry
Club Website:www nortonfootball .co.uk

CLUB PERSONNEL

Chairman: Peter Aldridge Pres: Barry Lee
Press Officer: Ken Steele (01642 898787)
Manager: Ray Morton Asst : Brian Maitland
Coach & Physio Alan Gauifant

2003-2004

P.o.Y.: Dan Pilling Top Scorer: Chris Garbut
2004-205 Captain: Steven Gill

PENRITH

Secretary: Walter Brogden, 47 Folly Lane, Penrith, Cumbria CA11 8BU (01768 862551)
Ground: Southend Road Ground, Penrith, Cumbria
Tel: 01768 895990
Directions: M6 Jct 40, onto dual carriageway to Appleby & Scotch Corner, first left at next r'bout, approx 1/2 mile into Penrith on A6 into town, take 1st left for ground. 3/4 mile from Penrith (BR)
Capacity: 4,000 Seats: 200 Cover: 1,000 Floodlights: Yes
Clubhouse: Yes **Club Shop:** No

PREVIOUS **Leagues:** Carlisle & Dist., Northern 48-82, NWC. 82-87 90-97, NPL 87-90.
RECORDS **Attendance:** 2,100 v Chester 1981
Goalscorer: C Short **Appearances:** Lee Armstrong
Win: 13-2 v Parton Utd **Defeat:** 0-13 v Bishop Auckland
Fee paid: £750 for A Carruthers (Netherfield)
Fee received: £1,000 for B Brown (Queen of the South)
BEST SEASON **FA Cup:** 2nd Rd 81-82 League Clubs beaten: Chester 81-82
HONOURS Northern Lg R-up 61-62, Div 2 Champions 02-03; NW Co's Lg R-up 83-84; NW Co's F/Light Trophy 95-96 96-97; Cumberland Snr Cup [13], Craven Cup 00-01
Players progressing: K Sawyers, G Fell, G Mossop (all Carlisle)

FACT FILE

Founded: 1894
Nickname: Blues
Sponsors: SonyColours: Blue/white/blue
Change colours: All yellow
Midweek Matches: Tuesday
Reserve team: Yes
Programme: 24 pages, 70p
Press Officer: Secretary
Local Press: Cumberland & Westmorland Herald, Cumberland News

CLUB PERSONNEL

Chairman: David Noble
Vice Chairman:Walter Brogden
Manager: David Heslop
Captain: Mark Jones

2003-2004

Top Scorer: Barry Irving
P.o.Y.: James Holland

PRUDHOE TOWN

Secretary: Chris Lowther, 10 Westhills,Tantobie, Stanley, Co.Durham DH9 9RZ
Tel: 01207 230108

Ground: Kimberley Park, Broomhouse Road, Prudhoe, Northumberland NE42 5EH
Tel/Fax: 01661 835900 **Clubhouse:**Open evenings plus Sat/Sun lunchtimes

Directions: To Prudhoe along A695, turn right at `Falcon' Inn, 200 yds down Eastwood Rd., left into Broomhouse Rd., ground on right

Capacity: 5,000 Seats: 150 Cover: Yes Floodlights: Yes

HONOURS Hexham & Dist. Lg 68-69 (Lg Cup 68-69), Newcastle & Dist. Lg 69-70 70-71, Lg Cup 69-70, Charity Shield 69-70 70-71), Northern Comb. 79-80, Northerm AmtrLg 71-72, Clayton Charity Cup 68-69, Northumberland Minor Cup 78-79, Northumberland Benevolent Bowl 79-80, Heddon Homes Charity Cup 81-82

PREVIOUS **Leagues:** Hexham & Dist 59-69; Newcastle & Dist 69-71; N. Comb.; Northern Amateur Alliance. 84-88

RECORD **Attendance:** 2,500 v Blyth, N'mberland Snr Cup 1981

2003-2004 **P.o.Y.**: David Lamb **Top Scorer:** Gary McDonald

FACT FILE

Founded: 1959 Nickname: Citizens
Sponsors: Swinton Insurance
Colours: Orange/blue/orange
Change: White & blue chevrons/navy/sky
Midweek Matches: Tuesday
Prog 8 pages, 50p Ed: Rachel Lowther

CLUB PERSONNEL

Chairman: Alex Waters
Press Officer:ErnieGoodfellow (01661 836941)
Man: Gavin Liddle Asst. Man: Steven Burns
Physio: Ernie Goodfellow
Captain: Warren Fisher

SEAHAM RED STAR

Secretary: John Smith, 33 Frederick St.,Seaham, Co.Durham.SR7 7HX Tel: 0191 5810423 H& W
Ground: Seaham Town Park, Stockton Road, Seaham, Co. Durham (0191 581 1347)
Directions: From Tyne Tunnel: A19 Teeside approx 8 miles; B1404 Seaham slip road, left at top of slip road. Right at traffic lights & first left past school into ground
Capacity: 4,000 Seats: 60 Cover: 200 Floodlights: Yes
Club Shop: No
Clubhouse: Mon-Sat 11am-11pm, Sun 12-2, 7-10.30pm Bars & restaurant, snooke & pool

HONOURS Northern Lg Cup 92-93, Phillips F'lit Tphy 78-79, Durham Chal. Cup 79-80, Wearside Lg 81-82 (Lg Cup 81-82, Div 2 R-up 87-88, Monkwearmouth Charity Cup R-up 79-80).
PREVIOUS **Name:** Seaham Colliery Welfare Red Star 78-87
Leagues: Sunday f'tball; Houghton & Dist. 73-74; Northern Alliance74-79; Wearside 79-83.
BEST SEASON **FA Cup:** **FA Vase:** 5th Rd 78-79
FA Trophy 2nd Rd 89-90
RECORDS Gate: 1,500 v Guisborough, Wearside Lg & v Sunderland, floodlight opener 1979
Scorer: Tom Henderson **Appearances:** Michael Whitfield

FACT FILE

Formed: 1973 Nickname: The Star
Colours: Red & white stripes/blacjk/black
Change colours: All blue
Midweek matchday: Wednesday
Reserves ' League: Banks Youth League
Programme: 20 pages
Editor: David Copeland (0191 581 8514)

CLUB PERSONNEL

Chairman: JohnSmith
President: Michael English
Press Officer: Secretary (079030 33014)
Manager: Chris Copeland
Asst Man.: Paul Walker
Physio: Allan Jackson

SOUTH SHIELDS F.C.

Secretary: David Fall, 50 Basil Way, South Shields NE34 8UD Tel& FAX: 0191 519 6612
Ground: Mariners Club, Filtrona Pk, Shaftesbury Ave, Jarrow, T. & W.r NE349PH(.01914279839)
Directions: From A1(M) take A194(M) to South Shields, A194 town centre road for 5 miles,ignore A1300 (Sunderland & coast) & turn left at next lights beside Co-op store into Simonside Ind. Est. (Shaftesbury Ave.), ground at bottomon right.
Capacity: 2,500 Seats: 150 Cover: 400 Floodlights: Yes
Clubhouse: Two function suites, club kitchen **Club Shop:** Yes
HONOURS Northern Lge Div 2 R-up 95-96, Northern Alliance 74-75 75-76, Wearside Lg 76-77 92-93 94-95, Monkwearmouth Charity Cup 86-87 (R-up 94-95), Shipowners Cup 92-93 (R-up 83-84)), Durham Chal. Cup 76-77 R-up 94-95.
BEST SEASON **FA Vase** QF 75-76
PREVIOUS **Leagues:** Northern Alliance 74-76 **Ground:** Jack Clarke Park 74-92
RECORD **Attendance:** 1,500 v Spennymoor, Durham Challenge Cup Final 94-95
2002-03 Leading Goalscorer: Michael Haley **Captain**: Mar Jarvis P.o.Y.Ian McQueeney
L ocal Press: Shields Gazette, Newcastle Journal, Chronicle

FACT FILE
Founded: 1974 Nickname: Mariners
Colours: Claret & blue/white/white
Change: All white
Midweek matchday: Tuesday
Reserve team: None
Programme: 50p Editor: Steve Leonard

CLUB PERSONNEL
Chairman: John Rundle
Vice Chairman:T.B.A.
Press Officer: Secretary
Manager: Neil Hixon
Asst Manager:Alan Weir
Physio: Jim Wilkinson

WASHINGTON NISSAN

Secretary: Harry English, 22 Rushcliffe, Fulwell , Sunderland SR6 9RG
Tel: 0191 548 7194 (H) 0191 415 2340 (W) 07889 469961 (M)

Ground: Nissan Sports Complex, Washington Road, Sunderland SR5 3NS
Tel: 0191 415 2354 or 0191 415 2773
Directions: North along A1 (M) use A690 (signed Sunderland) connect withA19, north on A19, after passing the A1231 turn off, plant on the left. Past plant & follow signs 'Nissan Offices'.
Clubhouse: Open Mon-Fri 5-11pm, Sat 11am-11pm, Sun noon-3 & 7-10.30pm

PREVIOUS **League:** Wearside to 2001
HONOURS: Wearside Lg Div 1 93-94 (Lg Cup R-up 91-92, Div 2 Cup 92-93 93-94), Nissan European Trophy 3.

FACT FILE
Founded: 1988
Colours:Blue & Black stripes/Blue/Blue
Change colours: Red & white/white/white.
Mlidwek Matchday: Wednesday
Programme: Price: Pages:
Editor: Ian Hopper

CLUB PERSONNEL
Chairman: Alan Hill Treasurer: M.Thorne
Press Officer: Secretary
Manager: Wilf Constantine
Assistant Manager: Paul Pitman
Captain: Glenn Moan:
2003-2004
P.o.Y.: Andrew Liddle Top Scorer: Craig Tate

WHICKHAM

Secretary: John Farrey, 61 Cherrytree Drive, Whickham, Newcastle upon Tyne. NE 16 4TQ
Ground: Glebe Ground, Rectory Lane, Whickham (0191 420 0186)
Directions: A692 (Consett) from A69. Left at r'bout signed Consett/Whickham. Uphill and right at mini-r'bout. Turn left into Rectory Lane (by Lloyds Bank) for 500 yds, clubhouse on right
Capacity: 4,000 Seats: 100 Cover: Yes Floodlights: Yes
Clubhouse: Mon-Fri. 12-3 & 7-11, Sat.11-11, Sun. 12-2, 7.30-11 Souvenir Shop: No
HONOURS FA Vase 80-81, Wearside Lg 77-78 87-88 (R-up 80-81 84-85, Lg Cup 86-87, Monkwearmouth Charity Cup 76-77, Sunderland Shipowners Cup 77-78 80-81), Northern Comb. 69-70 72-73 73-74 (Lg Cup 60-61 73-74)
PREVIOUS **Leagues:** Derwent Valley -55; Northern Comb. 55-57 59-74; Tyneside Amtr 57-59; Wearside 74-88 **Ground:** Rectory Rec. Field
BEST SEASON **FA Cup:** 1st Qual. Rd. 89-90 **FA Vase:** Winners 80-81
RECORD **Gate**: 3,165 v Windsor & Eton, F.A. Vase SF 81
Players progressing: Nigel Walker (Newcastle 1977), David Norton (Hartlepoo'l 1981), Mike Carroll (Chesterfield 1981)

FACT FILE
Founded: 1944
Colours: Black & White stripes/ Black/Black
Change colours: All white
Midweek Matches: Wednesday Prog20p
Local Press : Newcastle Journal, Sunday Sun, Evening Chronicle

CLUB PERSONNEL
Chairman: Brian Smith Manager: Toiny Ainley
Press Officer: Tony Ainley
Captain: Daniel Hall
2003-04
P.o.Y.: Thomas Scott
Top Goalscorer: Ian Robson

WILLINGTON

Secretary: Alan Stewart, 29 Sycamore Gardens, Crook,Co.Durham DL15 9LR9(07769 607016)
Ground: Hall Lane, Hall Lane Estate, Willington, County Durham (01388 746221
Website: www.willingtonafc.free-online.co.uk
Directions: Willington is on A690 7 miles west of Durham City & 2 miles east of Crook. Northern Bus Co. operates a service through Willington from Crook or Durham City
Capacity: 2,100 Seats: 350 Cover: 400 Floodlights: Yes Club shop: Occasionally
Clubhouse: Open eves 7-11pm &Sat. matchdays 1-11pm. Bar facilities.Tea shop on matchdays
HONOURS FA Amateur Cup 49-50, R-up 38-39; Northern League 13-14 25-26 29-30, R-up 12-13 57-58 75-76, Lge Cup 24-25 25-26 27-28 30-31 31-32 48-49 56-57 74-75; Durham Benevolent Cup 48-49 50-51 57-58.
BEST SEASON FA Cup: 1st Rd rep. 73-74, 1-6 v Blackburn R (A) after 0-0.Also 1st Rd 45-46
FA Trophy 3rd Rd 75-76 **FA Amat. Cup:** Winners 49-50 & 50-51
PREVIOUS **Leagues:** Auckland & Dist. 1906-11 **Names:** Willington Temperance 1906-11
RECORD Attendance: 10,000 v Bromley, FA Amateur Cup 2nd Rd 24/1/53**Goalscorer:** Brett Cummings (92-03) 143.**Appearances:** Brett Cummings(92-03) 377

FACT FILE
Founded: 1906 Nickname: Blue & Whites
Sponsor:K.J.M..
Colours: Blue & white stripes/blue/blue
Change colours: Yellow/green/green
Midweek Matches: Wednesday
Youth League: Durham Co Youth Lg.
Programme: 50p Editor: Keith Newton

CLUB PERSONNEL
Chairman: John Phelan
Vice-Chair:Alan Hardy
President: Rt. Hon.Hilary Armstrong M.P.
Press Officer: Sec. Manager :Alan Shoulder
Captain: Neil Bell
2003-04 P.o.Y.: Neil Bell
Top Scorer: Kevin Shoulder

WEST ALLOTMENT CELTIC

Secretary: Mark Hedley,12 Co-operative Terrace,West Allotment, Tyne and Wear NE27 0DU

Tel No: 0191 2702178

Colours: Green& white hoops, green,green
Change colours: All Blue

Ground: Blue Flames Sports Ground, Benton

Directions: From Newcastle take A189 to junction with A191. Folllow road east for one and a half miles.Immediatley after Station Road (B1317) junction and traffic lights, turn right into ground.

Chairman: Roland Mather
Manager: Terry Mitchell
Captain: Geoff Allison

2003-2004 Player of the Year: David Malone

Top Scorer: Alex Benjamin

WASHINGTON F.C.

Secretary: George Abbott,14 Grosvenor St, Southwick, Sunderland, Tyne & Wear SR5 2DG
Tel Nos: 0191 5491384 (H) 0191 4177779 (W)

Ground: Albany Park, Spout Lane, Concord, District 11, Washington
Tel: 0191 417 7779

Directions: Ground situated opposite bus station.

Capacity: 3,000 Seats: 25 Cover: Yes Floodlights: Yes Club Shop: No

Clubhouse: Open normal licensing hours, with live entertainment, pool etc

PREVIOUS Leagues: Washington Amateur; Northern Alliance 67-68; Wearside 68-88

Ground: Usworth Welfare Park

RECORD Gate: 3,800 v Bradford Park Avenue, FA Cup 1970

2002-2003 Top Goalscorer & Player of the Year: Tony Hanson

FACT FILE

Founded: 1949
Nickname: Mechanics
Colours: All red
Change colours: Yellow'Blue
Midweek Matches: Wednesday
Programme: 8 pages, 50p
Editor: Rob Goodwin

CLUB PERSONNEL

Chairman: Derek Armstrong
Tel: 0191 416 3956 (H)
Press Officer:John Oliver
Tel: 0191 416 3527
Manager:John Oliver
Captain: Kevin Leighton
Physio:Craig Langley

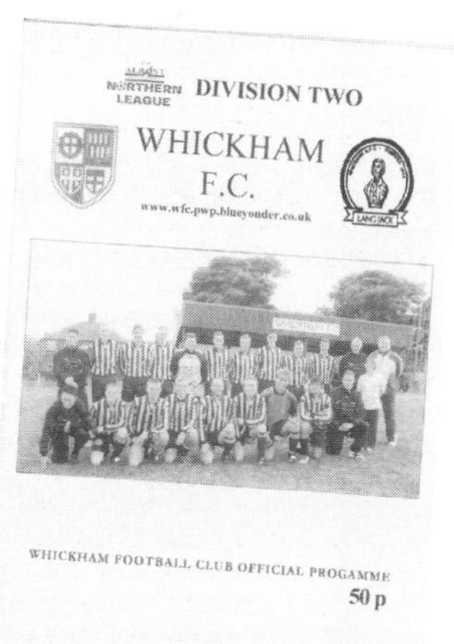

NORTHERN COUNTIES EAST

President: H Frank Catt **Chairman:** Tom Dixon

Secretary/Treasurer:

Barry Wood, 6 Restmore Avenue, Guiseley, Leeds LS20 9DG

Tel & Fax: 01943 874 558

PREMIER DIVISION: Our promoted club at the end of the 2002/3 season, **Bridlington Town**, finished this term in a respectable mid-table position in the Unibond League Division 1 and highlighted, with realignment of the Leagues, their remarkable rise through the National League System with four successive promotions, which may be some sort of record.

They made way for **Eastwood Town** who returned to the League after demotion from that higher level and their initial appointment at this 'step down' must have been alleviated by the remarkably successful season the club enjoyed. The challenge of possible extra promotion places to the Unibond League with the FA's re-organisation was a spur to some clubs who were faced with the predicament of knowing how to allocate funds between ground improvements and playing strength, but it certainly produced the most exciting championship race since the League was formed.

In mid-March any of eight or nine clubs were in the running for honours with Eastwood Town's backlog of fixtures at that point likely to prove crucial one way or the other. Their final run-in of matches, though produced only the odd slip-up and no one could have predicted that the final day of the season would prove so decisive with **Ossett Albion** and **Eastwood** going in to their final day's matches absolutely level on points with the same 36 goal difference. Both clubs secured 3-0 wins for the very first time in any NCE championship it meant that goals scored came into the reckoning with the final honour going to Ossett Albion on the strength of just three extra goals scored in the season. Albion became the first club to win the Premier Division Championship twice and brought them along with Eastwood Town and Brigg Town the coveted Unibond League membership.

The other challenging clubs helped to make this a remarkable campaign and we note with pride the work and funds put in by the other unsuccessful Unibond applicants which we hope might bring success in next season's campaign.

Division One promoted club **Mickleover Sports** finished the season just below half way whilst **Borrowash Victoria**, who escaped the drop the previous season, were again in that relegation position and should retain their Premier status in a policy consistent with past decisions along with **Brodsworth MW** due to the League re-organisation.

DIVISION ONE: The championship race in this division was almost as close with a number of clubs jockeying for position towards the end of the season. **Shirebrook Town**, after the disappointment of missing out on promotion due to ground difficulties at the end of 2002-03 were determined to make amends, but it was **Long Eaton United** who looked firm favourites to win the race until they slipped a little in the last few weeks. The position was also clouded by the deduction of three points from **Maltby Main** for registration problems in April.

Sutton Town and **Gedling Town** were both contenders as well, but it was **Shirebrook** who finally took the League Trophy to ensure promotion this time to the Premier Division. They ended the campaign three points ahead of **Long Eaton United** with the extra promotion place going to **Maltby Main** who would have been runners-up ad it not been for that points deduction.

The two clubs at the bottom of Division One - **Pontefract Colls** and **Tadcaster Albion** - will be re-elected as the numbers in that Division are not complete. We will be welcoming **Retford United** to this division. as the promoted club from the Central Midlands League.

OTHER NCE COMPETITION SUCCESSES: The **League Cup** was won by **Hallam** who took the trophy though they had never been included on any League 'roll of honour' before. They defeated **Mickleover Sports** by a single goal in the Final at Buxton.

The initiative in the **President's Cup** was taken by the eventual winners, **Eastwood Town**, in their home first l/c leg when they won 2-0 against **Thackley.** In the second leg at Dennyfield, they confirmed their superiority by adding a 3-0 win to achieve a 5-0 aggregate scoreline and our President, Frank Catt, was on hand to present his trophy.

The **Wilkinson Sword Trophy** was also a two-legged affair involving **Hall Road Rangers** and **Garforth Town**. The Hull side build up a 3-1 lead in the first leg and, although there was a spirited response from home side Garforth in the next match, their 3-2 victory then was not enough and Hall Road took the trophy with a 5-4 aggregate. Like Hallam, this was the first time that Hall Road had featured on the 'honours board'.

The **Reserve Team Cup** Final was played at Thackley where **Eccleshill United Res.** were worthy 4-0 winners against opponents **Yorkshire Amateurs Res.**

FA AND COUNTY COMPETITIONS: After the cup exploits of **Brigg Town** and **Harrogate Railway** in the FA Vase and Cup respectively two seasons' ago, our clubs' records this season have not been quite so outstanding.

In the FA Cup two clubs reached the last qualifying round - **Buxton** and **Ossett Albion** - before losing to more senior opposition, whilst **Eastwood Town** went out of the FA Vase in a Quarter Final replay against Colne. Mention should also be made of Division One **Gedling Town**, who progressed to the 4th Round for the first time and were unlucky to lose at home 2-3 to Leighton Town.

The League's only County Cup winners were **Eastwood Town**, who crowned a marvellous season with a 2-1 Notts Senior Cup victory against high-flying Hucknall Town in the Final at the ground of Notts County. Incidentally, that was **Eastwood's 25th cup match of the season** to add to their 38 League matches.

League Secretary.

FINAL LEAGUE TABLE 2003-04

PREMIER DIVISION		P	W	D	L	F	A	Pts
1.	Ossett Albion	38	22	10	6	76	37	76
2.	Eastwood Town	38	23	7	8	73	34	76
3.	Brigg Town	38	20	11	7	73	40	71
4.	Sheffield	38	19	12	7	64	40	69
5.	Pickering Town	38	19	10	9	67	44	67
6.	Goole	38	18	10	10	67	44	64
7.	Buxton	38	17	12	9	69	50	63
8.	Selby Town	38	16	11	11	86	57	59
9.	Liversedge	38	17	8	13	72	58	59
10.	Glapwell	38	14	10	14	53	45	52
11.	Thackley	38	14	9	15	61	67	51
12.	Harrogate Railway Athletic	38	12	13	13	63	64	49
13.	Mickleover Sports	38	14	5	19	52	66	47
14.	Armthorpe Welfare	38	14	4	20	48	67	46
15.	Hallam	38	13	5	20	56	76	44
16.	Eccleshill United	38	12	8	18	52	74	44
17.	Glasshoughton Welfare	38	10	7	21	58	83	37
18.	Arnold Town	38	10	6	22	45	67	36
19.	Borrowash Victoria	38	8	7	23	35	84	31
20.	Brodsworth Miners Welfare	38	3	5	30	38	111	14

PREMIER DIVISION	1	2	3	4	5	6	7	8	9	10	11	12	13	14	15	16	17	18	19	20
1 Armthorpe Welfare		1-0	1-2	0-2	3-6	3-2	1-3	1-3	1-0	5-2	0-0	1-3	1-2	0-2	0-1	1-1	0-2	3-2	0-2	1-1
2 Arnold Town	0-1		1-1	1-4	1-0	1-1	0-2	1-2	2-0	3-3	0-1	0-3	3-0	2-1	1-4	0-2	0-1	2-1	0-0	4-2
3 Borrowash Victoria	0-4	2-1		1-2	5-1	1-2	0-1	0-1	2-1	3-2	0-3	0-3	0-4	0-0	1-0	1-5	2-2	1-0	0-1	1-2
4 Brigg Town	3-0	4-1	3-0		5-1	2-0	4-0	5-0	1-0	1-0	0-2	2-1	3-1	2-1	1-1	2-3	1-0	1-0	1-2	2-4
5 Brodsworth Miners W.	1-2	0-1	0-2	1-1		1-3	0-2	2-3	0-4	2-3	1-5	1-2	2-2	1-2	1-2	0-2	1-4	1-1	2-4	1-1
6 Buxton	1-2	2-5	4-0	0-0	5-1		1-0	6-1	0-2	3-2	0-1	3-1	3-1	1-1	2-2	2-2	0-0	1-1	2-1	1-2
7 Eastwood Town	1-0	1-1	5-0	2-2	4-2	1-2		3-0	1-2	4-0	0-0	2-0	3-0	4-0	1-0	3-1	3-0	1-3	0-1	2-1
8 Eccleshill United	2-3	0-2	1-1	1-1	5-0	1-1	2-1		0-2	1-2	1-5	1-5	2-1	3-5	3-2	3-0	2-3	0-1	0-0	1-1
9 Glapwell	0-2	1-2	2-2	0-0	2-0	1-2	1-2	0-0		1-3	2-3	4-0	2-1	2-0	2-1	1-1	2-2	2-2	3-0	1-2
10 Glasshoughton Welf.	0-1	3-2	3-1	3-2	4-0	2-3	0-2	2-2	0-0		0-1	1-3	1-1	1-4	0-2	1-2	1-3	0-1	0-3	0-3
11 Goole	3-2	3-1	2-0	0-2	5-0	1-1	0-0	1-2	0-1	3-1		3-1	2-2	2-3	1-1	3-0	2-1	1-1	1-1	2-3
12 Hallam	0-1	1-1	2-0	4-0	3-0	0-2	1-5	1-3	1-3	4-4	1-2		1-1	0-2	2-3	1-4	0-4	0-5	2-1	1-0
13 Harrogate Railway A.	2-3	5-4	1-1	4-4	5-0	1-3	3-2	1-1	2-3	2-4	1-0	2-0		3-3	3-3	2-1	1-0	0-2	3-0	0-0
14 Liversedge	2-0	4-0	5-0	1-1	1-3	1-1	0-1	1-3	4-0	4-1	3-1	0-0	0-0		2-4	0-4	0-0	1-4	1-2	4-3
15 Mickleover Sports	2-0	2-1	4-1	0-4	0-2	0-2	0-2	2-0	0-2	0-2	2-1	1-1	2-1	1-2		0-6	2-0	2-3	1-3	4-0
16 Ossett Albion	1-0	1-0	3-0	1-1	4-0	0-2	0-0	1-0	1-0	2-2	3-1	5-0	0-0	1-0	2-0		3-3	3-2	0-0	4-0
17 Pickering Town	1-1	2-1	2-0	3-1	2-0	3-3	1-3	2-1	2-1	4-0	2-2	1-2	2-0	1-2	1-0	2-1		3-2	2-2	3-0
18 Selby Town	5-0	1-0	7-2	0-0	6-2	3-1	1-2	3-0	2-2	2-2	1-1	3-2	1-2	4-3	5-0	3-4	1-1		2-2	3-3
19 Sheffield	4-1	3-0	2-1	1-1	2-2	1-1	2-2	3-1	0-0	2-1	3-0	3-1	2-2	0-1	3-0	0-1	0-2	3-0		2-1
20 Thackley	3-2	2-0	1-1	0-2	3-0	2-0	2-2	3-0	1-1	1-2	1-3	2-3	0-1	2-6	2-1	1-1	1-0	3-2	2-3	

FINAL LEAGUE TABLE 2003-04

DIVISION ONE		P	W	D	L	F	A	Pts
1.	Shirebrook Town	34	22	5	7	59	26	71
2.	Long Eaton United	34	22	2	10	63	40	68
3.	Maltby Main (-3 pts)	34	21	7	6	81	49	67
4.	Sutton Town	34	19	8	7	79	37	65
5.	Gedling Town	34	18	9	7	81	49	63
6.	Garforth Town	34	17	7	10	60	47	58
7.	Yorkshire Amateur	34	15	8	11	57	44	53
8.	Lincoln Moorlands	34	14	10	10	53	40	52
9.	Carlton Town	34	14	7	13	52	51	49
10.	Parkgate	34	12	11	11	52	53	47
11.	Winterton Rangers	34	13	8	13	52	56	47
12.	Rossington Main	34	13	5	16	56	62	44
13.	South Normanton Athletic	34	11	3	20	49	62	36
14.	Hall Road Rangers	34	9	5	20	43	70	32
15.	Worsbrough Bdge MW	34	9	2	23	31	75	29
16.	Staveley Miners Welfare	34	7	6	21	41	75	27
17.	Pontefract Collieries	34	5	10	19	30	60	25
18.	Tadcaster Albion	34	6	5	23	32	75	23

DIVISION ONE	1	2	3	4	5	6	7	8	9	10	11	12	13	14	15	16	17	18
1 Carlton Town		2-0	2-2	3-2	0-1	1-2	0-4	1-0	1-4	2-2	3-0	2-0	0-3	0-2	2-1	2-2	2-0	1-0
2 Garforth Town	1-2		2-1	3-1	2-1	1-2	0-3	2-2	3-0	1-0	0-2	1-1	4-2	2-0	4-2	3-1	2-0	2-3
3 Gedling Town	0-0	2-3		7-1	4-2	1-0	1-3	6-1	4-2	2-1	2-1	6-0	5-2	4-1	2-1	3-0	2-2	2-1
4 Hall Road Rangers	1-1	0-0	0-1		3-2	2-1	1-2	2-1	0-2	2-4	0-2	0-2	3-1	2-3	1-1	6-0	0-1	1-2
5 Lincoln Moorlands	0-0	4-1	2-2	0-0		5-1	3-4	1-2	1-0	1-1	0-2	2-0	3-1	1-1	2-0	1-2	2-1	1-0
6 Long Eaton United	6-4	2-3	1-3	3-0	1-0		5-2	0-1	3-0	5-1	0-3	1-0	5-1	1-2	4-2	0-0	1-0	0-1
7 Maltby Main	3-2	2-2	2-2	3-2	3-1	1-2		2-2	1-0	3-2	4-0	3-1	3-1	0-4	5-0	3-1	5-1	3-2
8 Parkgate	0-0	1-4	0-0	3-3	1-2	0-3	1-1		1-0	3-4	0-3	2-1	3-1	2-1	1-1	2-2	1-0	2-0
9 Pontefract Collieries	0-1	0-5	3-3	1-2	1-1	0-1	1-2	0-5		0-2	1-2	2-1	2-0	1-1	3-2	1-2	1-2	2-2
10 Rossington Main	3-0	1-2	2-1	1-0	2-2	0-1	2-1	1-2	4-2		0-2	0-4	2-3	2-0	3-0	0-5	4-1	0-1
11 Shirebrook Town	2-1	1-0	0-1	0-1	2-0	1-1	1-0	1-1	0-0	1-1		4-0	1-0	1-0	4-1	2-1	5-0	0-1
12 South Normanton Athletic	3-1	0-0	4-2	1-3	1-3	1-2	0-3	0-4	0-0	2-0	1-2		5-1	1-4	6-2	1-3	1-2	1-2
13 Staveley Miners Welfare	0-3	3-1	2-2	1-0	0-2	0-1	2-2	1-3	1-1	3-1	1-2	0-3		1-3	0-1	1-1	0-1	1-4
14 Sutton Town	3-0	2-2	5-1	3-1	0-0	3-1	0-0	2-2	4-0	7-2	0-0	1-2	1-1		3-0	5-1	3-0	2-1
15 Tadcaster Albion	2-1	0-1	1-0	1-2	0-1	0-1	2-3	1-1	0-0	0-2	1-5	0-4	1-3	3-2		0-3	1-0	2-3
16 Winterton Rangers	1-6	3-1	1-1	4-0	1-1	0-2	2-3	1-0	3-0	1-1	2-1	1-0	3-0	1-2	1-2		0-4	0-1
17 Worsbrough Bridge M.W.	1-5	0-1	1-4	2-1	0-4	1-2	2-1	2-1	0-0	0-4	1-2	1-2	1-2	1-5	1-0	0-2		1-3
18 Yorkshire Amateur	0-1	1-1	0-2	8-0	1-1	0-2	1-1	4-1	0-0	2-1	1-4	2-0	2-2	0-4	1-1	1-1	6-1	

LEAGUE CUP

FIRST ROUND

Carlton Town	v	South Normanton	2-1
Lincoln Moorlands (w/o)	v	Louth United	
Long Eaton United	v	Maltby Main	3-0
Shirebrook Town	v	Yorkshire Amateur	2-0
Staveley MW	v	Hall Road Rangers	3-4
Tadcaster Albion	v	Pontefract Collieries	1-2
Winterton	v	Worsbrough Bridge MW	1-0

SECOND ROUND

Armthorpe Welfare	v	Glapwell	0-1
Arnold Town	v	Goole	0-1*
Brigg Town	v	Gedling Town	5-1
Buxton	v	Sutton Town	2-3
Garforth Town	v	Pickering Town	1-2*
Glasshoughton	v	Harrogate RA	2-1
Hall Road Rangers	v	Carlton Town	0-2
Hallam	v	Selby Town	3-1
Liversedge	v	Brodsworth MW	3-1
Long Eaton	v	Pontefract Collieries	4-0
Ossett Albion	v	Borrowash Victoria	7-0
Parkgate	v	Eastwood Town	2-1
Rossington Main	v	Eccleshill United	0-3
Shirebrook Town	v	Mickleover Sports	1-3
Thackley	v	Sheffield	0-0* 1-2r
Winterton Rangers	v	Lincoln Moorlands	1-7

THIRD ROUND

Brigg Town	v	Glapwell	2-0
Carlton Town	v	Goole	2-2* 2-3*r
Eccleshill United	v	Parkgate	3-1
Glasshoughton W.	v	Pickering Town	2-1
Liversedge	v	Lincoln Moorlands	4-1
Mickleover Sports	v	Long Eaton Utd	1-1* 0-0*r 6-7p
Sheffield	v	Hallam	1-2
Sutton Town	v	Ossett Albion	5-0

QUARTER-FINALS

Brigg Town	v	Sutton Town	1-0
Glasshoughton W.	v	Eccleshill United	3-2
Hallam	v	Goole	2-1
Mickleover Sports	v	Liversedge	3-2

SEMI-FINALS

Hallam	v	Glasshoughton Welfare	2-1
Mickleover Sports	v	Brigg Town	2-1*

THE FINAL (3rd May at Buxton)

Mickleover Sports	v	Hallam	0-1

WILKINSON SWORD SHIELD

FIRST ROUND

Maltby Main	v	Winterton Rangers	1-3
Yorkshire Amateur	v	Rossington Main	1-0

SECOND ROUND

Carlton Town	v	Garforth Town	3-4*
Lincoln Moorlands	v	South Normanton Athletic	5-1
Parkgate	v	Winterton Rangers	0-1*
Pontefract Collieries	v	Yorkshire Amateur	0-2
Staveley Miners W.	v	Gedling Town	2-3
Sutton Town	v	Shirebrook Town	2-1
Tadcaster Albion	v	Hall Road Rangers	1-3
Worsbrough Bridge MW	v	Long Eaton United	1-2

QUARTER-FINALS

Hall Road Rangers	v	Yorkshire Amateur	1-0
Lincoln Moorlands	v	Winterton Rangers	1-3
Long Eaton United	v	Gedling Town	3-1
Sutton Town	v	Garforth Town	2-4*

SEMI-FINALS

Garforth Town	v	Long Eaton United	3-1
Winterton Rangers	v	Hall Road Rangers	1-2

THE FINAL

(First leg 31st March)

Hall Road Rangers	v	Garforth Town	3-1

(Second leg 6th April)

Garforth Town	v	Hall Road Rangers	3-2

PRESIDENT'S CUP

FIRST ROUND

Brigg Town	v	Goole	1-2
Buxton	v	Parkgate	4-2
Eccleshill United	v	Pontefract Collieries	3-1
Hall Road Rangers	v	Thackley	2-3*
Mickleover Sports	v	Lincoln Moorlands	1-2
Ossett Albion	v	Long Eaton United	6-2
Sheffield	v	Gedling Town	0-1
Shirebrook Town	v	Eastwood Town	2-3*

QUARTER-FINALS

Eastwood Town	v	Gedling Town	3-0
Goole	v	Eccleshill United	3-0
Lincoln Moorlands	v	Buxton	4-3
Ossett Albion	v	Thackley	2-3

SEMI-FINALS

Eastwood Town	v	Goole	2-1*
Lincoln Moorlands	v	Thackley	0-2

THE FINAL

(First leg 9th March)

Eastwood Town	v	Thackley	2-0

(Second leg 23rd March)

Thackley	v	Eastwood Town	0-3

ARMTHORPE WELFARE

Secretary: Maureen Cottam, The Orchards, Whiphill Lane, Armthorpe, Doncaster DN3 3JP. Tel. Nos: 01302 832514 (H) 01302 503706 (W) 07763 328177 (M)

Ground: Welfare Ground, Church St, Armthorpe, Doncaster DN3 3AG. Tel No:(M) 07771 853899 (match days only)

Directions: M18 jct 4, A630, left at r'bout then right at next r'bout. Ground 400yds on left behind Plough Inn. Doncaster (BR) 2 1/2 miles. Buses A2, A3 & 181 pass ground

Capacity: 2,500 Seats: 200 Cover: 400 Floodlights: Yes Club Shop: No

Clubhouse: No. Refreshments on ground. Wheatsheaf Hotel used after matches

HONOURS Northern Co's East Lg R-up 87-88, Lg Cup R-up 91-92, Div 1 R-up 83-84, East Central Div 1 84-85; Doncaster & Dist. Lg 82-83, Div 1 81-82, Div 2 79-80, Div 3 78-79; Lg Cup 79-80 80-81 81-82 82-83; Challenge Cup 82-83; West Riding Chall. Cup 81-82 82-83; Goole & Thorne Dist. Cup 82-83

PREVIOUS **League:** Doncaster Senior

RECORD **Attendance** : 2,000 v Doncaster R., Charity match 85-86
Appearances: Gary Leighton **Scorer:** Martin Johnson
Win: 7-0 v Stocksbridge PS NCE 84-85 & Brodsworth MW NCE 00-01
Defeat: 0-7 v Belper Town NCE 86-87

BEST SEASON **FA Vase:** 3rd Round 84-85 **FA Cup:** 3rd Qual. Rd. 86-87

FACT FILE
Founded: 1926
(Disbanded 1974, re-formed 1976)
Nickname: Wellie
Club Sponsors: Houston Transport
Colours: White/navy/red
Change colours: Navy/white/navy
Midweek matches: Tuesday
Programme: 24 pages
Editor: Tony Ingram (01302 842795)
Local paper: Doncaster Evening Star

CLUB PERSONNEL
Chairman: Stephen Taylor (01302 323522)
Vice Chairman: James Houston
Comm. Manager: Peter Camm
Press Officer: Sharon Morgan
Manager: Carl Leighton
Asst Manager: John McKeown
Coach: Steve Taylor
Physio: Joey Johnson

ARNOLD TOWN

Secretary: Tony Beale, 6 Elms Gardens, Ruddington, Nottm NG11 6DZ (0115 921 1451)
Ground: King George V Recreation Ground, Gedling Rd, Arnold, Notts (0115 9263660)
Directions: From M1 jct 26, take A610 to B6004 (Stockhill Lane) 3 miles to A60. Right at A60, immediate left (St Albans Rd), thru lights by Wilkinsons left onto Hallams Lane. Ground on right opposite market. From A1(M)/A614/A60 to lights (Harvester on right), left thru lights to, St. Albans Rd then as above. Nottingham Midland (BR) 4 miles. Buses 55,57.58, 59 pass ground.
From A6514 left onto A60 for 1/4 m then rt onto Nottingham Rd to town centre by Wilkinsons.
Capacity: 3,400 **Seats**: 150 **Cover:** 950 **Floodlights:** Yes
Club Shop: Sells progs, scarves, badge, mugs, baseball caps, ski hats, sweaters etc. (Martin Williams 0115 9598759)
Clubhouse: Licensed bar open matchdays & training nights. Also tea-bar on matchdays.

HONOURS (Arnold & Arnold Town): Central Mids Lg 92-93 (R-up 88-89, Lg Cup 87-88 (R-up 90-91), F/lit Cup 89-90); NCE Lg 85-86, R-up 83-84, 94-95; Div 1 94-95; Presidents Cup 94-95; Central All 62-63; Notts Snr Cup x9, r-up x 5; Midland Co's Lg R-up 70-71 75-76, Lg Cup 74-75 (R-up 68-69 70-71 80-81). **PREVIOUS Leagues:** Central Mids 89-93. Arnold FC: Bulwell & Dist, Notts Spartan, Notts Comb (pre 55), Central All. 55-63/ Midland 63-82/ NCE 82-86/ Central Mids 86-89. Kingswell: Notts Yth/ Notts Amat./Notts Spartan/ E. Mids Reg.(pre'76)/Midland 76-82/ NCE 82-86/ Central Mids 86-89. **Names:** Arnold FC (founded 1928 as Arnold St Marys) merged with Arnold Kingswell(founded 1962) 1989 **BEST SEASONS: FA Cup:**1st Rd replay 77-78 **FA Vase.**: 5th Rd 01-02 **FA Trophy:** 2nd Rd Replay 71-2

FACT FILE
Founded: 1989 Nickname: Eagles
Sponsors: Mapperley Sports/Neartone Printers
Colours: Yellow (blue trim)/blue/yellow
Change Colours:All red
Midweek matches:Tuesday
Eeserves' League: Midland Regional Alliance
Programme: 52 pages £1
Editor: Paul Stanley (0115 9566951)

CLUB PERSONNEL
President: Alan Croome
Chairman: David Law
Vice-Chairman: Roy Francis
Comm. Manager: Len Robinson
Joint Managers: Bill Brindley & Bryn Gunn
Captain: Jon Boulter
Physio: Trevor Wells
Press Officer: Brian Howes (0115 9856986)
Website: www.arnoldfc.com
Email: mail@arnoldfc.com

2003-04
Top Scorer : Darren Black 11
Player of the Year :. Brett Williams

BORROWASH VICTORIA

Secretary.: Ian Collins, 30 Margreave Road, Chaddesden, Derby DE21 6JD Tel: 01332 739437

Ground: Robinson Construction Bowl, Borrowash Road, Spondon, Derby Tel: 01332 669688.

Directions: M1 jct 25, A52 towards Derby, 3rd left off by-pass into Borrowash Rd, ground 400 yds on left. 2 miles from Spondon (BR). Nottingham to Derby buses pass nearby.

Capacity: 5,000 Seats: Yes Covered: 500 Floodlights: Yes
Clubhouse: Normal pub hours. Hot & cold food. **Club Shop:** No

PREVIOUS **Leagues:** Derby Sun. School & Welf. 52-57; Derby Comb.; Midland 79-82; N.C.E.; Cen Mid Lg. **Ground:** Dean Drive 1911-84

RECORDS **Attendance:** 2,000 v Nottim Forest,(floodlight opening 22/10/85)
Win: 11-1 **Defeat**: 3-8 **Goalscorer:** Paul Acklam **Appearances:** Neil Kellogg

BEST SEASON **FA Cup** 3rd Qual. Rd 91-92. **FA Vase:** 4th Rd 90-91,00-01

HONOURS N.C.E. Lg Div 1 00-01,Div 1 Sth 83-84 (R-up 84-85, Div 2 Sth R-up 82-83), Derby Comb. 77-78 (R-up(10) 65-66 68-74 75-77 78-79, Lg Cup 68-69 75-76 (R-up 63-64 66-67), Midland Co's Lg Div 80-81 (Div 1 Cup 80-81), Derbys Snr Cup R-up 90-91, Derbys Div. Cup 73-74 (R-up 70-71 72-73), Cen. Midl Lg B E Webbe Cup R-up 88-89 (Res. Cup 94-95)

FACT FILE
Founded: 1911
(Reformed 1963)
Nickname: Vics
Club Sponsors: Robinson Construction
Colours: Yellow/sky blue/sky blue.
Change Colours: Navy blue/sky/sky
Mid matches: Tues Prog: 16 pages, £1.00
Editor:Ian Collins (01332 739437)

CLUB PERSONNEL
Chairman: Ian Anderson
Press Officer: Secretary
Manager/Coach: Bob Sykes
Asst Man: John Kinane
Captain: James Parkinson

2003-04
Leading Goalscorer: Mark Barnes
Player of the Year: James Parkinson

BRODSWORTH WELFARE

Secretary: Nigel Hyde, 5 Stonegate, Thorne, Doncaster DN8 5NP
Tel Nos: 01405 818330 (H) 01405 818330 (FAX) 07952 812811(M)

Ground: Welfare Ground, Woodlands, Nr. Doncaster (01302 728380).

Directions: From A1 take A638 to Doncaster, take left after Woodlands Pub into Welfare Road, ground 50yds on left.
Regular bus service from North Bridge Bus Station, Doncaster.
Capacity: 3,000 Seats: 228 Cover: 500 Floodlights: Yes

Clubhouse: Yes, Matchday drinks and snacks **Club Shop:** Yes

HONOURS Yorks Lg 24-25, Donc. & Dist. Lg 84-85 (Lg Cup 85-86, Div 2 78-79, Div 2Cup 78-79), Sheffield Jnr Cup 83-84, Mexborough Montagu Cup 91-92 92-93.R-up N.C.E. Div 1 98-99

PREVIOUS **Leagues:** Doncaster Snr; Sheffield; Yorkshire.
Name: Brodsworth Main, Brodsworth Miners Welfare

BEST SEASON **FA Cup:** 4th Qual. Rd 26-27 **FA Vase:** 3rd Rd 97-98

RECORD **Win:** 9-0 v Blidworth MW, NCE 97-98
Fee received: £2,550 (+ Payments for apps) for Danny Schofield from Huddersfield Town, Jan 99

FACT FILE
Founded: 1912
Nickname: Broddy
Colours: Navy & light blue/white/white
Change colours: Yellow & black
Midweek home matchday: Wednesday
Programme: 30 pages
Editor: Secretary

CLUB PERSONNEL
Chairman: Gordon Jennings Tel: 01302 781121
Press Officer Diane Hyde (07952 812815)
Tel: 01302 725794H) 07720 832147 (M)
Manager: Alan Radford

2003-2004
Player of the Year: Carl Slater
Top Scorer: Gareth Collinson

BUXTON

Secretary: Sarah Barton,20 Danesway,Chapel en-le-Frith,High Peak SK23 0RF
Tel: No & Fax : 01298 813268 (please telephone before faxing).
email:mike@buxtonfc.co.uk

Ground : The Silverlands, Buxton, Derbyshire (01298 24733)

Directions: 200 yards of Buxton Market Place, opp. County Police HQ. Buxton (BR) 1/2 mile.
Capacity: 4,000 **Cover:** 2,500 **Seats:** 490 **Floodlights:** Yes
Club Shop: Yes, Mike Barton,01298 813268
Clubhouse: (01298 23197). match days and Friday nights. licensed,always available for hire
HONOURS N.P.L Lg Cup 90-91, Presidents Cup 81-82; Cheshire County 72-73(R-up 46-47 62-63, Lg Cup 56-57 57-58 68-69); Manchester Lg 31-32 (R-up 04-05 28-29 29-30 30-31, Lg Cup 25-26 26-27); Derbys. Sen. Cup 38-39 44-45 45-46 56-57 59-60 71-72 80-81 85-86 86-87.

PREVIOUS **Leagues:** The Combination 1891-99; North Derbyshire; E Cheshire; Manchester 07-32; Cheshire County 32-73; NLP 73-98.]

BEST SEASON **FA Trophy:** Qtr Finals 70-71 71-72. **FA Vase:** 98-99
FA Cup: 3rd Rd 51-52. 2nd Rd 58-59, 1st Rd 62-63League clubs defeated: Aldershot 51-52

RECORDS **Attendance:** 6,000 v Barrow, FA Cup 1st rd 51-52
Goalscorer: Dave Herbert 104 in 263 games **Fee Paid:** £5,000 for Gary Walker (Hyde Utd)
Appearances: David Bainbridge 635Fee **Received:** £23,500 for Ally Pickering (Rotherham 89)

FACT FILE
Formed: 1877Nickname: The Bucks
Sponsors: Paintmaster
Colours: Royal blue & white /royal/royal
Change colours:Yellow & Black
Midweek matchday: Tuesday
Programme: 36 pages £1.00
Editor: Tony Tomlinson (01484 718907)
Website: www.buxtonfc.co.uk
Press: Buxton Adverftiser and Matlock Mercury. Radio: Derby and Radio High Peak

CLUB PERSONNEL
Chairman: Tony Tomlinson
Manager: Ronnie Wright
Director of Football: Kenny Johnson
Asst Manager/Coach: David Bainbridge
Res Man: JohnCohen
Physio: Dave Percival
Captain: Tim Willis
Under 19s Mans: Malcolm Boswell & Ian Pass
2003-2004 Top Scorer Caine Cheetham
Player of the Year: Jonty Wood

ECCLESHILL UNITED

Secretary: Pamela Waite, 27Cotswold Ave, Wrose,Shipley, West Yorks BD 181LS
Tel: 01274583008

Ground: Plumpton Park, Kingsway, Wrose, Bradford BD2 1PN (01274 615739)

Directions: M62 jct 26 onto M606, right on Bradford Ring Road A6177, left on to A650 for Bradford at 2nd r'bout. A650 Bradford Inner Ring Road onto Canal Rd,branch right at Staples (Dixons Car showrooms on right), fork left after 30mph sign to junction with Wrose Rd, across junction - continuation of Kings Rd, 1st left onto Kingsway - ground 200 yds on right. 2 miles from Bradford (BR). Buses 624 or 627 for Wrose
Capacity: 2,225 Seats: 225 Cover: 415 Floodlights: Yes
Clubhouse: Open normal licensing hours. Bar, lounge, games room, hot &cold snacks
Club Shop: Sells range of souvenirs.
HONOURS N.C.E.Div 1 96-97, Div 2 R-up 86-87, Res Div 86-87 89-90, R-up 87-88 94-95; Bradford Amtr Lg Cup 61-62; Bradford & Dist. Snr Cup 84-85; Bradford & Dist. FA Snr Cup 85-86; W. Riding County Amat. Lg 76-77; West Riding Cup R-up 99-00
PREVIOUS **Leagues:** Bradford Amat; W Riding Co Amat**Name:** Eccleshill FC
Ground: Myers Lane
BEST SEASON **FA Vase:** 99-00, 5th Rd
RECORDS Attendance: 715 v Bradford C 96-97 **Win:** 10-1 v Blackpool Mechs (H), F.A.C /!Q
Defeat: 0-6 v Rossington Main (A), N.C.E. Lge Cup 2nd Rd 92-93, & v Gt. Harwood T. (A), FA Cup Prel. Rd 91-92
Player to Progress:Terry Dolan (Huddersfied United)

FACT FILE
Founded: 1948
Nickname: Eagles
Colours: Blue & white stripes/blue/blue
Change colours: All yellow
Midweek matches: Tuesday
Reserves' Lge: NCE Res. Div
Programme: 24-28 pages, 50p
Editor: Lynda Andrews
Tel: 01274 640346
Local Press: Bradford Telegraph & Argus, Bradford Star Free Press

CLUB PERSONNEL
Chairman: Keith Firth
Tel: 01274 583440 (H)
Press Officer: Pamela Waite
Manager: Tony Brown
Physio: Gordon Raynor
2003-2004
P.o.Y.: Richard Wilson Top Scorer: Chris Wood
2004-2005
Captain : Richard Wilson

GLAPWELL

Secretary: Ellen Caton, High Ridge, 111 The Hill, Glapwell, Chesterfield. S44 5LU.
Tel: 01246 854648 (H & Fax) 07976 838423 (M)
Email: ellen@decaton.fsnet.co.uk

Ground: Hall Ground, Hall Corner, Glapwell, Chesterfield, Derbyshire
Tel: 01623 812213 **Floodlights**: Yes

Directions: M1 Junc. 29 A617 towards Mansfield, after Young Vanish Inn take filter lane left onto Bolsover Road, ground facing, use rear entrance next to garden centre

HONOURS Central Midlands Lg 93-94, Floodlit Cup 93-94, Evans Halshaw Fl't Cup 96-97
Derbyshire Senior Cup 97-98 R-Up 00-01 (lost on penalties) NCE Lg. Cup Finalists 99-00.

BEST SEASON **FA Vase:** 2nd Rd 96-97

FACT FILE
Founded: 1985
Colours: Black & white stripes/blackj/black
Change colours: All yellow
Midweek matches: Wednesday
Programme: 48 pages £1.00
Editor: Paul Harrison
01623 842588 (H) 07890 580346(M)
Web :
www.glapwellfc.freeserveo.uk

CLUB PERSONNEL
Chairman: Roger Caton
Match Secretary: Malcolm Hol;mes
Tel No: 01246 558892
Manager:Andy Kirk
Assistant Manager: Junior Glave
Commercial Manager: Andrew Saunders

GLASSHOUGHTON WELFARE

Secretary: Eric Jones, `Marrica', Westfields Ave, Cutsyke, Castleford WF10 5JJ.
Tel: 01977 556257 (H) 01977 514157(B)

Ground: Glasshoughton Welfare, Leeds Rd, Glasshoughton, Castleford (01977518981)

Directions: From M62 use either Junct. 31 or 32 towards Castleford. From Junction 32 the road comes into Glasshoughton. From Junct. 31 turn right at 2nd roundabout at Whitwood Tech. College. The ground is on the left in Leeds Road. Car park on ground. Castleford (BR) 1 mile.
Capacity: 2,000 Seats: None Covered: 250 Floodlights: Yes

Clubhouse: Bar & refreshment facilities **Club Shop:** No

HONOURS West Riding County Cup 93-94

PREVIOUS **League:** West Yorkshire **Name**: Anson Sports 1964-76
Ground: Saville Park 1964-76

RECORD **Attendance:** 300 v Bradford C, 90
Win: 8-1 v Garforth Town, WR Cup 00-01
Defeat: 0-8 v Hucknall Town, NCE 97-98

BEST SEASON **FA Cup:** 2nd Qual Rd. 98-99 **FA Vase:** 2nd Round 00-01

FACT FILE
Founded: 1964
Club colours: All Blue
Change colours: All yellow
Midweek Matchday: Tuesday
Reserves' Lge: N.C.E. Res. Div.
Programme: 20 pages, 20p
Prog. Editor: Nigel Lea (0113 247 6186)

CLUB PERSONNEL
President: R Rooker
Chairman: Gordon Day
Tel: 01977 514178 (H)
Match Sec: Barry Bennett
Tel: 01977 682593 (H)
Manager: Wayne Day
Asst Manager/Coach: M Ripley

GOOLE AFC

Secretary: AnnSmith, 8 Boothferry Road Avenue, Howden, Goole. E Yorks. DN14 7TB
Tel No: 01430 432048
Match Secretary: Graeme Wilson, 12 Thorntree Close, Goole, E. Yorks DN14 6LN
Tel: 01405 763316 (H)

Ground: Victoria Pleasure Grounds, Marcus St, Goole DN14 6AR
Tel: 01405 762794 Website: www.gooleafc.freeserve.co.uk
Directions: M62 to Junc 36, then follow signs for town centre.
Turn right at 2nd lights into Boothferry Rd, then after 300 yards turn right again into Carter St, and the ground is at the end of road.
Capacity: 3000 Seats: 200 Cover: 800 Floodlights: Yes
Club Shop: Yes **Clubhouse:** Matchdays only

HONOURS NCE Div. 1 99-00, Div. 1 Trophy 99-00; Cen. Mids. Lge. 97-98
PREVIOUS **League**: Central Midlands 97-99
RECORDS **Attendance**: 964 v Leeds Utd. 99
Appearances: Phil Dobson 187 (1999-2001)
Goalscorer: Kevin Severn (97-01)
BEST SEASON **FA Vase:** 4th Round 98-99 **FA Cup:** 2nd Qual. Rd. 00-01

FACT FILE
Founded: 1997
Colours: Red/ white/ whitek.
Change Colours: Gold/black/gold & black
Midweek Matchday: Tuesday
Programme Editor: Andrew Lawson

CLUB PERSONNEL
Chairman: Des O'Hearne
Tel: 01405 704292 (H)
Manager:Paul Marshall
Captain: Nigel Danby

2003-2004
Top Scorer: Darren Fell
Player of the Year: Nigel Danby

HALLAM

Secretary: Mrs Susan Muzyczka, 24 Meadow Bank Avenue, Sheffield, S7 1PB. Tel: 0114 255 3173(H) Club Email: hallamfc@supanet.co.uk Website:www.sportsworldwide.co.uk

Ground: Sandygate, **(The oldest club ground in the world 1860)** Sandygate Road, Crosspool, Sheffield S10.Tel: 0114 230 9484. Two new stands and full access & facilities for wheelchair users. New changing rooms and Social Club. Plus Refreshmants Canteen.

Directions: A57 Sheffield to Glossop Rd, left at Crosspool shopping area signed`Lodge Moor' on to Sandygate Rd. Ground half mile on left opposite Plough Inn. 51 bus from Crucible Theatre

Capacity: 1,000 Seats: 250 Cover: 400 Floodlights: Yes **Club Shop:** Yes

Clubhouse: Social Club. Hot & cold snacks on ground for matches

HONOURS: Northern Counties (East) Lg Div 1 R-up 90-91 94-95,Lg Cup 03-04 Yorkshire Lg Div 2 60-61 (R-up 56-57), Sheffield & Hallamshire Snr Cup (4) Finalists 01-02

BEST SEASON FA Vase: 5th Rd 80-81 **FA Cup:** 3rd Qual. Rd 1957

PREVIOUS League: Yorkshire 52-82

CLUB RECORDS Attendance: 2,000 v Hendon, FA Amtr Cup 3rd Rd 59 &13,855 v Dulwich at Hillsborough, FA Amtr Cup 55) **Goalscorer:** A Stainrod 46 **Appearances:** P Ellis 500+

Win: 7-0 v Hatfield Main (H) 92-93, & v Kiveton Pk H) 69-70 **Defeat:** 0-7 v Hatfield Main (A) 88-9

Players progressing: Sean Connelly (Stockport C), Howard Wilkinson (Sheff. Wed) -The F.A.'s Technical Director, L Moore (Derby C.)

FACT FILE

Formed: 1860 Nickname: Countrymen
Sponsors: P.A.Jewellery
Colours: Blue & white hoops/blue/blue
Change colours: Red/black/black
Midweek Matches: Wednesday
Programme: Yes £1.00
Editor: Mark Radford (Press Off.)
Local Press: Star, Green'Un, Sheffield Telegraph, Yorkshire Post

CLUB PERSONNEL

Chairman: Ray Merry
Vice Chairman:E.Forrest
President: A Cooper
Press Off: Mark Radford Tel: 0114 249 7287
Manager: Guy Glover
Captain: David Hawke
Physio:J.Beachell

2003-2004

Player of the Year: David Hawke
Top Goalscorer: Lee Mellon

HARROGATE RAILWAY ATHLETIC

Secretary: Stuart Lloyd, 61 Jesmond Road, Harrogate, N.Yorks. Tel Nos: 01765 601711 (W) 01423 889924 (H) 0788 4012797 (M) Club e-mail: hgterailafc@ntlworld.com

Ground: Station View, Starbeck, Harrogate.Tel: 01423 885539 & 01423 883104 (Fax)

Directions: A59 Harrogate to Knaresborough road. After approx 1.5 miles turn left just before railway level crossing. Ground is 150 yds up the lane Adjacent to Starbeck (BR). Served by any Harrogate to Knaresborough bus.

Capacity: 3,500 Seats: 800 Cover: 600 Floodlights: Yes Clubshop Yes

Clubhouse: Games, TV room, lounge. Open normal pub hours. Hot food available.

HONOURS N.C.E. Div 1 98-99, Div. 2 North 83-84, Lg Cup 86-87 Pres Cup 02-03

PREVIOUS **Leagues:** West Yorkshire; Harrogate District; Yorkshire 55-73 80-82. **Names**: Starbeck LNER

RECORD **Attendance:** 3,500 v Bristol City F.A.Cup 02-03

BEST SEASON **FA Cup:** 2nd Rd Rd. 02-03 v Bristol C 3,500 **FA Vase:** 4th Round 88-89 **FA Amateur Cup:** 2nd Round 52-53

2002-2003 **Captn: & P.o.Y.:** Nigel Danby **Top Scorer:**Steve Davey 32 (10 in F.A.Cup)

FACT FILE

Founded: 1935 Nickname: The Rail
Sponsors: Sports Network
Colours: Red /green/red
Change: White/black/white
Midweek matchday: Wednesday
Programme Editor: Gordon Ward
Tel: 01423 880423 (H) 01423 880423 (Fax)
Local Press: Yorkshire Post, Harrogate Herald & Advertiser, York Press

CLUB PERSONNEL

Pres: J Robinson Chairman: Dennis Bentley
Comm. Man: Alan Smith
Press Officer/Prog. Editor: Gordon Ward Tel: 01423 880423 (H)
Football Match Secretary: Doug Oldfield (01423 540786)
Manager: Martin Haresign
Assistant.Man.:Ian Blackstone
Physio: Dave Roche

2003-2004

Top Scorer & P.o.Y.: Chris Howarth

LIVERSEDGE

Secretary: Michael Balmforth, 7 Reform St., Gomersall, Cleckheaton BD19 4JX Tel: 01274 862123

Ground: Clayborn Ground, Quaker Lane, Hightown Rd, Cleckheaton, W. Yorks Tel: 01274 862108

Directions: M62 jct 26, A638 into Cleckheaton, right at lights on corner of Memorial Park, through next lights & under railway bridge, 1st left (Hightown Rd) and Quaker Lane is approx 1/4 mile on left and leads to ground. From M1jct 40, A638 thru Dewsbury and Heckmondwike to Cleckheaton, left at Memorial Park lights then as above. Buses 218 & 220 (Leeds-Huddersfield) pass top of Quaker Lane

Capacity: 2,000 Seats: 250 Cover: 750 Floodlights: Yes

Clubhouse: Matchdays, Tues, Thursday. TV. Snacks **Club Shop:**Scarves & Badges only

HONOURS W. Riding Co. Chal. Cup 48-49 51-52 69-70; W. Riding County Cup 89-90; North Counties East Lg Div 1 R-up 89-90 (Div 2 R-up 88-89); West Riding Co.Amtr Lg(6) 23-24 25-27 64-66 68-69 (Lg Cup 57-58 64-65).

PREVIOUS **Leagues:** Spen Valley; West Riding County Amateur 22-72; Yorkshire 72-82. **Ground:** Primrose Lane, Hightown. **Name:** None

BEST SEASON
FA Cup: 2nd Qual. Rd. 93-94 97-98 99-00
FA Vase: 2nd Round 74-75 91-92 93-94 98-99 03-04

RECORD **Attendance:** 986 v Thackley

Players progressing: Garry Briggs (Oxford), Martin Hirst (Bristol City) Leigh Bromby (Sheffield Wed)

FACT FILE

Founded: 1910 Nickname: Sedge
Colours: All blue Change: Yellow
Midweek Matches: Tuesday
Reserves League: NCEL Div. 2
Programme: 28 pages, 50p
Editor: Secretary
Local Press: Yorkshire Evening Post, Telegraph & Argus, Spenbrough Guardian

CLUB PERSONNEL

Chairman: Robert Gawthorpe
Press Officer: Secretary
Manager: Eugene Lacy
Coach:Kym Farrand
Captain: Gareth Hamlet

2003-2004

Player of the Year: Kyle Sutcliffe
Top Goalscorer: James Jestor 29

LONG EATON UNITED

Secretary: Jim Fairley, 13 Redland Drive,Chilwell, Nottingham NG9 5JZ9726343.
Tel No: 0115 9199447 (H)

Ground: Grange Park, Station Road, Long Eaton, Nottingham (0115 973 5700).

Directions: M1 Junc 25, take A52 towards Nottingham, to island by `Bardills Garden Centre', left onto B6003 to t/lights. Right A453, 2nd left Station Rd. Entrance on left opposite the Speedway Stadium

Capacity: 5,000 Seats: None Cover: 500 Floodlights: Yes

Clubhouse: Open matchdays, snacks available

Club Shop: None

Record **Attendance:** 2,000 1973 FA Cup

Honours: Derbys Snr Cup 64-65 75-76, Midland Co's Lg R-up 76-77, Central Alliance Div South 58-59, Northern Co's (East) Div 1 South 84-85.

FACT FILE

Founded: 1956
Nickname: Blues
Sponsor: Beeston Suite Co
Colours: All Blue
Change colours: Red/black/black
Midweek Matchday: Tuesday
Programme: 20 pages 50p
Editor: Geoff Whitehead (01332 872849)

CLUB PERSONNEL

Chairman: J C Fairley
Manager:Adam Bamford
Physio: John Burns

MALTBY MAIN

Secretary: Jack Harper, 3A Manor Road, Maltby, Rotherham S66 7EG
Email: david@morris1984.fsnet.co.uk

Ground: Muglet Lane, Maltby, Rotherham. Tel: 017941 057883

Directions: Exit M18 at junct 1 with A631. Two miles into Maltby, right at traffic lights at Queens Hotel corner on to B6427 Muglet Lane. Ground 3/4mile on left. Bus 101 from Rotherham stops at ground. Bus 287 from Sheffield to Queens Hotel, then follow as above.

Capacity: 2,000 Seats: 150 Cover: 300 Floodlights: Yes

Clubhouse: No, Miners Welfare Club opposite **Club Shop**: No

HONOURS Sheff. & Hallamshire Snr Cup 77-78, N.C.E. Lge Presidents Cup 92-93, Mexborough Montague Cup 76-77 80-81 90-91,Yorks Lg R-up 77-78, Sheff. Wharncliffe Cup 80-81.

CLUB RECORDS **Attendance:** 1,500 v Sheffield Wed., June 91-92 (friendly)

PREVIOUS **Leagues:** Sheffield County Senior; Yorkshire 73-82.
Name: Maltby Main 1916-65 (disbanded); Maltby Miners Welfare 1970-96

BEST SEASON **FA Cup:** 2nd Qual. Rd. 23-24 **FA Vase:** 3rd Round 87-88 93-94

FACT FILE

Founded: 1916 Nickname: Miners
Sponsors: Millgate Computer Systems
Colours: Red/black/black Change: All yellow
Midweek matchday: Wednesday
Programme: 36 pages, 70p
Editor: Nick Dunhill Tel: 017941 057 883

CLUB PERSONNEL

Chair: Gary Kitching V-Ch:Graham McCormick
Pres H Henson Sec: Dave Morris
Man:Shaun Goodwin Asst. Man: Bryn Webster
2002-03 Leading Goalscorer:Scott Somerville
Captain & P.o.Y.: Russ Ward

MICKLEOVER SPORTS

Secretary: Tony Shaw, 80 Onslow Road, Mickleover, Derbys. DE3 5JB
Tel: 01332 512826 (H & Fax)

Ground: Mickleover Sports Ground, Station Rd, Mickleover, Derby (01332 521167).
Club Website: www.mickleoversports.fsnet.co.uk

Directions: Derby ring road A38 to A52, turn off at Markeaton Park Island.Take turn to Ashbourne A52, then 2nd left into Radbourne Lane. Take 3rd left into Station Road, ground on corner.

Capacity: 1,500 **Seats:** 280 **Cover:** 200

Clubhouse: Open Thursdays and Fridays (7-11 p.m) Saturdays and Sundays (11am-11pm)
Snacks available only on Matchdays

Club Shop: No

HONOURS Champions N.C.E.L. Division 1 2002-2003, Wilkinson Sword Trophy Winners and Derbyshire Senior Cup Finalists 2002-03

Last Season FA Cup: 1st Qual Rd. 0-1 v Shepshed Dynamo (A)
FA Vase: 3rd Round replay, 2-3 v Oadby Town (H) after 2-2 (A)

FACT FILE

Founded: 1948
Colours: Red & Black stripes shirts/black/red
Change Colours: All blue
Midweek Matchday: Tuesday
Programme Editor: Stephen Pritchard
Tel: 01332 516271

CLUB PERSONNEL

Chairman Keith Jenkinson
Tel: 01332 516 271 (H)
Match Sec.: Cath Grant
Tel: 01332 511359
Manager: Martin Rowe
2003-2004
Player of the Year: Corin Holness
Top Scorer: Karl Payne
2004-2005
Captain: Wayne Sutton

Pickering Town - Back Row (L-R): C Reynolds (Physio), A Russell, J Connor, J Ellwood, K Martin, L Pallerder, S Young, M Swales, S Brown (Manager), S Mcgilty (Asst. Manager).
Front Row (L-R): D Mccoubrey, t Adams, A Willgrass (capt), G Dickenson, D Brunton, M Wood, S Swales.

PICKERING TOWN

Chairman: Alan Brenkley, Cawrthorne Guest House, 42 Eastgate, Pickering. YO18 7DU
Tel No: 01751 477364

Ground: Recreation Club, Mill Lane (off Malton Rd), Pickering, North Yorkshire
Tel: 01751 473317

Directions: A169 from Malton. On entering Pickering take 1st left past Police Station and B.P. garage into Mill Lane, ground 200 yards on right

Capacity: 2,000 Seats: 200 Cover: 500 Floodlights: Yes

Clubhouse: Open 1.30pm for Saturday games, 6pm for midweek games.
Food available from Football Club Kitchen at half-time and after games.

Club Shop: No

PREVIOUS **Leagues:** Beckett; York & District; Scarborough & District; Yorkshire 72-82.

RECORD **Attendance:** 1,412 v Notts County, friendly, August 1991

HONOURS Northern Co's East Lg R-up 92-93 Div 2 87-88, Div 1 R-up 91-92, 00-01, Yorks Lg Div 3 73-74, Div 2 R-up 74-75 North Riding Snr Cup R-up 93-94 94-95, N. Riding Co. Cup 90-91, Wilkinson Sword Trophy 2000-01.

BEST SEASON **FA Cup:** 2nd Qual. Rd. 99-00,01-02 **FA Vase:** 4th Round 01-02,02-03

Players progressing: Chris Short (Stoke City), Craig Short (Everton) both via Scarborough

FACT FILE

Founded: 1888
Nickname: Pikes
Club Sponsors: Flamingoland
Colours: Royal bluewhite/royal blue
Change colours: All Yellow
Midweek matches: Tuesday
Reserves' League: N.C.E. Res. Div.
Programme: 48 pages, £1.00
Editor: Gerry Gregory (01751 473818)

CLUB PERSONNEL

Chairman: Anthony Dunning (01751 473697)
President: J.P.Jennison
Match Secretary: Geoff raw (01751 474528)
Manager: Steve Brown
Assist. Manager: Richard Rose
Physio: Clive Reynolds
Coach: Steve Brown Captain: Alex Willgrass

2003-2004

P.o.Y.: Mark Wood
Top Scorer: Gavin Dickenson

SELBY TOWN

Secretary: Thomas Arkley,176 Abbots Rd,Selby, N.Yorks.O8 8AZ Tel: 01757 700356 (H) 07830218657(M) Email Address: toonarkley@amserve,com

Ground: Flaxley Rd Ground, Richard St, Scott Rd, Selby, N YorksYO8 0BS.
Tel: 01757 210900

Directions: From Leeds, left at main traffic lights in Selby down Scott Rd.then 1st left into Richard St. From Doncaster go straight across main traffic lights into Scott Road then 1st left. From York right at main traffic lights into Scott Rd, and 1st left. 1 mile from Selby (BR)

Capacity: 5,000 Seats: 220 Cover: 350 Floodlights: Yes

Clubhouse: Bar at ground open first and second team matchdays **Club Shop:** Yes

HONOURS Yorkshire Lg 32-33 34-35 35-36 52-53 53-54 (R-up 24-25 25-26 27-28 28-29 30-31 31-32 50-51 55-56, Div 3 R-up 74-75, Lg Cup 37-38 53-54 54-55 62-63); N.C.E. Div 1 95-96, Div 2 R-up 89-90, Presidents Cup 00-01; W. Riding Snr Cup 37-38; W. Riding Co Cup 27-28 48-49; W. Riding Chall. Cup 34-35 35-36

PREVIOUS **League:** Yorkshire (1920-82) **Ground**: Bowling Green, James St. 1920-51

BEST SEASON **FA Cup:** Second Round Proper 54-55 **FA Vase:** 4th Round 95-96

RECORD **Attendance:** 7,000 v Bradford Park Avenue (FA Cup 1st Rnd 1953-54)
Goalscorer: Graham Shepherd 158 (63-82)
Win: 14-1 v Altoffs, W. Rid. Cup 35
Defeat: 0-14 v Bradford PA Res. Yorkshire Lge 28

FACT FILE

Founded: 1918 Nickname: The Robins
Sponsors: Nordan's BuildersColours: All red
Change colours: Yellow/blue/yellow
Midweek Matches: Tuesday
Reserves' League: N.C.E. Res. Div.
Programme: 30 pages, 50p
Editor: Nigel Briggs
Local Newspaper: Selby Times ,Selby Post Evening Press

CLUB PERSONNEL

Chairman: Michael Dunn (01757 228605)
President: Andy Bodle
Match Sec:As Secretary.
Manager: B Lyon
Asst Manr/Coach: G.Cygan
Captain: Stuart Lee

2003-2004

TopClub & League Scorer: Joe Gaughan 26
Player of the Year: Stuart Lee

THE OFFICIAL MATCHDAY PROGRAMME OF
BUXTON FC
NORTHERN COUNTIES EAST LEAGUE
2003/2004 SEASON
THE BUCKS STOP HERE
PROGRAMME SPONSORED BY
GOODWIN & FORBES
CONTRACTORS LTD

TRACK RECORD
THE MATCHDAY MAGAZINE
OF
HARROGATE RAILWAY
ATHLETIC
H & D. R. A. S. C.
NIL MORTILIBUS ARDUIEST
A.F.C.
Main Sponsors
ARRIVA
SEASON 2003 - 2004
OFFICIAL PROGRAMME £1.00

LIVERSEDGE
FOOTBALL CLUB
NORTHERN COUNTIES EAST LEAGUE
PREMIER DIVISION
50p
2003/2004
MICKLEOVER SPORTS
NCEL Premier Division

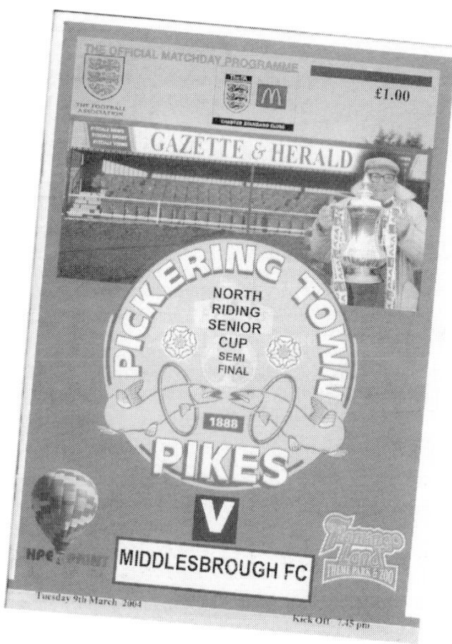
THE OFFICIAL MATCHDAY PROGRAMME
£1.00
GAZETTE & HERALD
PICKERING TOWN
NORTH
RIDING
SENIOR
CUP
SEMI
FINAL
1888
PIKES
V
MIDDLESBROUGH FC
Tuesday 9th March 2004

SHEFFIELD

Secretary: Stephen Hall, 91 Rosegarth Avenue, Aston, Sheffield S26 2DB (0114 287 3578)
Tel: 0114 287 3578 (H), 01246 258918 (B)
Ground: Coach & Horses Ground, Sheffield Road, Dronfield. Sheffield
Directions: M1, J 29, A617 into Chesterfield. At traffic island turn right onto dual carriageway A61 (Sheffield). Follow over two islands and at third island follow sign 'Dronfield/Gosforth Valley'. At entrance to Dronfield, The Coach & Horses ground is at bottom of hill on the right.
Capacity: 1,100 Seats: 250 Floodlights: Yes
Clubhouse: Licensed Bar **Club Shop:** Yes

PREVIOUS **League:** Yorks 49-82 **Grounds:** Abbeydale Park, Dore (1956-1989); Sheffield Amateur Sports Club, Hillsborough Park 1989-91; Sheffield International (Don Valley) Stadium 1991-94; Sheffield Sports Stadium Don Valley 94-97.
HONOURS FA Amateur Cup 02-03; FA Challenge Vase Runners-up 76-77; Northern Co's East Lg Cup 94-95 ,Div 1 88-89 90-91; Yorkshire Lg Div 2 76-77, Lg Cup 77-78
BEST SEASON **FA Cup:** 4th Qual. Rd 00-01 **FA Vase:** R-up 76-77
FA Amateur Cup: Winners 1903-04
RECORD **Attendance:** 2,000 v Barton Rovers, FA Vase SF 76-77
Player progressing: Richard Peacock, Hull 94-95,

FACT FILE

Founded: 24th October1857
Nickname: The Club
Sponsors: A4EColours: Red & black /black/red
Change: All blue
Midweek matchday: Tuesday
Programme: 16 pages, 50p
Editor:Craig Williamson(0114 258 1108)

CLUB PERSONNEL
Chairman: Richard Tims
Tel: 0114 2728888 (B)
President: Alan Methley
Manager: David McCarthy
Asst Manager: Lee Walshaw
Captain: Chris Hilton
Physio: Steve Naylor

2003-2004
Top Goalscorer: Duncan Bray
Player of the Year: Tom Jones

SHIREBROOK TOWN

Secretary: S.Wall,26 Carter Lane,Shirebrook, Mansfield, Notts. Ng20 8NA (01623 747638)

Ground: BRSA Sports Ground, Langwith Rd, Shirebrook, Mansfield(01623 742535).

Directions: M1 jct 29, A617 to Mansfield, 2.5 miles, onto B6407 to Shirebrook,

then through town to Langwith Rd.

Capacity: 2,000 **Seats:** 165 **Cover:** 400 **Floodlights:** Yes

Clubhouse with refreshments at the ground.

Club Shop: No

Honours: Central Midlands Supreme Champions 00-01 01-2

R-Up 99-00 Lg Cup winners 00-01 Res Prem Div 94-95 95-96.

Floodlit Cup winners 97-98 N.Co E Div 1 Champions 2003-2004 R-up 2002-03

Records: **Most Appearances :** .Tansley 289

2002-2003: **Leading Goalscorer**: S.Johnson **Player of the Year**: C.Charlesworth

FACT FILE

Founded 1985

Sponsors: Warsop Tyre Service

Colours: All Red & black

Change : All Blue

Midweek Matchday: Wednesday

Programme 12 pages 50p

Editor: G.Howarth

CLUB PERSONNELL

Chairman: Stephen S. Brown

Tel: 01623 748375

Manager:S,Greenwood

Assistant Manager: G.Charlesworth

Captain: A.Starkey

THACKLEY

Secretary: Stewart Willingham, 3 Kirklands Close, Baildon, Shipley, Yorks BD17 6HN
Tel: 01274 598589
Ground: Dennyfield, Ainsbury Avenue, Thackley, Bradford (01274 615571).
Directions: On main Leeds/Keighley A657 road, turn off at Thackley corner which is 2 miles from Shipley traffic lights and 1 mile from Greengates lights.Ainsbury Avenue bears to the right 200yds down the hill. Ground is 200yds along Ainsbury Avenue on the right. 3 miles from Bradford Interchange (BR), 1.5 miles from Shipley (BR). Buses to Thackley corner (400 yds)
Capacity: 3,000 Seats: 300 Cover: 600 Floodlights: Yes
Clubhouse: Tue-Sun evenings,matches and w/e lunchtimes. Hot & cold snacks on matchdays
Club Shop: Progs, Metal badges- £2.50 + s.a.e.Contact Geoff Scott (01274 611520)
HONOURS N.C.E. Lg R-up 94-95, Lg Cup R-up 94-95; Yorks Lg Div 2 73-74; West Yorks Lg 66-67; W. Riding Co. Amtr Lg (x3) 57-60; W. Riding Co. Cup 73-74 74-75; W. Riding Co. Chal. Cup 63-64 66-67, R-up 94-95; Bradford & Dist. Snr Cup 12.
PREVIOUS **Leagues:** Bradford Amateur, W. Riding County Amateur, W. Yorks, Yorks 67-82.
Name: Thackley Wesleyians 1930-39
BEST SEASON **FA Vase:** 5th Rd 80-81 (01-2 v Whickham) **FA Cup:** 2nd Qual. Rd.(x3)
RECORD **Attendance:** 1,500 v Leeds Utd 1983
Players progressing: Tony Brown (Leeds), Ian Ormondroyd (Bradford City).

FACT FILE
Founded: 1930
Sponsors: Clearwell
Colours: Red /white/red
Change colours: All white
Midweek matches: Tuesday
Programme: 20 pages, £1.00 Editor: Secretary
Local Press: Bradford Telegraph & Argus, Bradford Star, Aire Valley Target.

CLUB PERSONNEL
Chairman: Derek Stokes
42 Ryedale Way,Allerton, Bradford
Match Secretary : June Willingham
Treasurer: Steven Paley
Manager/Coach: John Boyle
Asst Manager: Paul Atkinson
Physio: John Laidler
Captain: Craig Sugden

2003-2004
Player of the Year: David Nelson
Top Scorer: Andy Patterson

CARLTON TOWN

Secretary: Paul Shelton, 28 Freda Close, Gedling, Nottingham NG4 4GP.
Tel: 0115 987 7527 (H) 07870 576778 (M)
email: paul.shelton1@btopenworld.com

Ground: Stoke Lane Gedling, Nottingham. Tel: 0115 987 3583
Directions: A612 Nottingham to Southwell Road. Stoke Lane is situated off A612 between Gedling & Burton Joyce (signed Stoke Bardolph).
Ground 200 yards on left over level crossing. **Nearest BR Station:** Carlton.
Capacity: 600 **Seats:** None **Cover:** 200 **Floodlights:** Yes
Clubhouse: Yes Tel: 0115 940 2531 **Club Shop:** No

PREVIOUS **Name:** Sneinton F.C.
Leagues: Central Midlands >2003
HONOURS: Notts Alliance - Div 1 92-93, Div 2 84-85; Notts Intermediate Cup 91-92; Central Midlands Supreme Division Champions: 2002-2003

Founded: 1904
Colours: Yellow/Blue/Blue
Change colours: Red & Black
Midweek Matchday: Tuesday
Programme: £1.00 Editor: Martin Bell

Chairman & Chief Executive: Mick Garton
President: John Stokeld

Coach: Tom Brookbanks
Asst. Managers: Dave Nairn & Brian Franks
Captain: Steve Garratt
Physio: Martin Jepson

2003-04
Top Scorer: Phil Bignall 21
Player of the Year: Ian White

GARFORTH TOWN

Secretary: Antony Clough, 44 Lowther Grove, Garforth, Leeds LS25 1EN (0113 286 6023)
Fax: 0113 286 2728 e mail: garforthtown@hotmail.com
Ground: Wheatley Park Stadium, Cedar Ridge, Brierlands Lane, Garforth, Leeds LS25 2PF
Tel: 0113 286 4083 Website: www.garforth.town.com
Directions: M1 junction 47. Take turning signed 'Garforth' (A642). Approx 200 yards turn left into housing estate opposite White Ho. (Cedar Ridge). Stadium at end of lane.
Capacity: 3,000 Seats: 278 Cover: 200 Floodlights: Yes
Clubhouse: Full Licensing Hours. Closed Mondays **Club Shop:** Yes
HONOURS NCE Div 1 97-98, R-up 96-97, Div 2 R-up 85-86, Lge Cup 99-00; Yorks Lg Div 3 R-up 79-80; Barkston Ash Snr Cup x7; Wilkinson Sword Tphy 96-97; W. Riding Co. FA Cup 97-98 99-00
PREVIOUS **Leagues:** Leeds Sunday Comb 64-72; West Yorks 72-78; Yorks 78-82.
BEST SEASON **FA Vase:** Q-F 85-86 **FA Cup:** 2nd Qual. Rd. 91-92, 97-98
RECORDS **Attendance:** 1,014 Brendan Ormsby Testimonial v Comb. Leeds/A. Villa XI
2003-04 Top Goalscorer : Gavin Birmingham P.o.Y.: Brett Renshaw
2004-05 Captain: Paul Robinson

FACT FILE
Founded: 1964 Nickname: The Miners
Sponsors: TWS/FDS
Colours: Yellow/Blue/Yellow
Change colours:Blue/white/blue
Midweek matches: Tuesday
Reserves' League: NCE Div.2
Programme: 32 pages, £1.00
Editor: Chris Mather 0113 286 3453 (H)
CLUB PERSONNEL
Pres: Norman Hebbron
Chairman: Stephen Hayle
Chief Executive: Simon Clifford
Manager: Jimmy Martin
Asst. Manager: Alan Speight Physio: Paul Cavell Coach: Steve Swallo

GEDLING TOWN

Secretary: Alan Davey, 6 Greenhill Rise, Carlton,Nottingham N94 1BL
Ground: Riverside Ground, (rear of Ferryboat Inn), Stoke Lane, Stoke Bardolph, Nott'm NG14 5HX 01159402145(Matchdays only)
Directions: A612 Nottingham-Lowdham-Southwell road. Just before Burton Joyce turn right into Stoke Lane to Ferryboat P.H. Approx 1.5 miles. Ground at rear of pub.
Capacity: 2,000 Seats: 250 Cover: 500 Floodlights: Yes
Clubhouse: Matchdays only. Refreshments. Licensed bar. **Club Shop:** No
Honours: Central Mids Lg Prem 97-98 R-up 91-92, Div 1 90-91, (Res Prem 96-97 97-98); Wakefield Floodlit Trophy 92-93 R-up 95-96; Ken Marsland Cup (Res) 93-94; Notts Amtr Lg 89-90 (Snr Cup R-up 89-90).Res Lg & Cp Winners 98-99, NCECup 01-02, Notts Cup 01-02
Best season FA Vase: 3rd Rd 96-97
RECORDS **Attendance:** 250 v Arnold Town.
Win: 11-0 v Radford 91-92 **Defeat:** 2-5 v Staveley MW 93-94.
Goalscorer: Rob Orton 98 in 124 **Appearances:** Gary Ball 300+

FACT FILE
Founded: 1986
Colours: Blue & yellow/blue&yellow/blue
Midweek Matchday: Tuesday
Prog 32 pages 50p
Editor:Mark Batchford (0115 940 3361)
Press Secretary: Tony White(07879654533

Chairman: Roland Ash (0115 9403361)
Manager: Dave King
Assistant Manager: Mark Hurst
Physio: Keith Waters
2003-2004
Player of the Year: James Jepson
Top Goalscorer: Steve Scoffham 28

HALL ROAD RANGERS

Secretary: Alan Chaplin,33 Lee Street,Holderness Road,Hull HU8 8NH
Tel No: 01482 703775
Ground: Dene Park, Dene Close, Beverley Rd, Dunswell, Nr Hull (01482 850101).
Directions: M62 to A63, turn left before Humber Bridge onto A164 to Beverley,after approx 5 miles turn right onto A1079. In 2 miles turn left at large roundabout to ground 20 yards on right.
Capacity: 1,200 Seats: 250 Cover: 250 Floodlights: Yes
Clubhouse: Open all week for drinks and bar snacks, snooker, pool and darts. **Shop:** Yes

HONOURS N.C.E. Lg Div 2 90-91, Yorks Lg Div 3 72-73 79-80, E. Riding Snr Cup 72-73 93-94. Wilkinson Sword Trophy2004

PREVIOUS **Leagues:** East Riding Co.; Yorks 68-82 **Ground:** Hull Co-Op (to 1968)

BEST SEASON **FA Cup:** Prelim Rd. 2003-04 **FA Vase:** 3rd Round 99-00

RECORDS **Attendance:** 1,200 v Manchester City Aug 93 **Goalscorer:** G James
Apps: G James **Players progressing:** Gerry Ingram (Blackpool),. Mark Greaves (Hull City)
2003-2004: **Player of the Year:** James Atkinson **Top Goalscorer**: Chris Dixon 14

FACT FILE
Founded: 1959 Nickname: Blues
Sponsor: Admiral Signs of Hull Ltd.
Colours: Blue & white hoops/ blue/ blue.
Change : Red & Black Stripes,black/black
Midweek Matches: Wednesday
Reserves' League: East Riding Co.League
Prog:24 pages, £1.00
Editor: Craig Ellyard (07952 109536)Local Press: Hull Daily Mail
CLUB PERSONNEL
Chairman:
Robert Smailes (01482 821354 (H))
Director of Football: Nigel Dalee)
Press Officer:
Craig Ellyard (07952 109536)
Manager:Ray Daniel
Coach: Jamie Barnwell
Captain: Matty Edeson

LINCOLN MOORLANDS

Secretary: Graham Peck, 128 Granson Way, Washingborough,Lincoln LN4 1HF
Tel Nos: 01522 792170 (H) 07815 458196 (M))

Ground: Moorland Sports Ground, Newark Rd, Lincoln LN5 9LY
Tel: 01522 520184 Office & Fax: 01522 874111

Directions: From north A1 to Markham Moor. Take A57 until Lincoln by-pass and then turn right onto A46. At 3rd r'about left into Doddington Rd. Continue until Newark Rd. - ground on left after 800 yards.
From Newark enter Lincoln on A1434, go past Forum Shopping Centre for approx. 3/4 mile. Ground on left signposted 'Moorlands Club'.

Capacity: Seats: 100 Cover: 200 Floodlights: Yes

Clubhouse: Yes **Club Shop:** No

HONOURS: Central Midlands Supreme 99-00, R-up 00-01, Lincolndshire Senior A 00-01

FACT FILE
Founded: 1989Nickname: The Moors
Colours: Sky Bue + Navy trim/Navy/ Sky Blue
Change colours: Orange/black/orange
Midweek Matchday: Wednesday
Prog: 40 pages Price £1.00 Ed:Secretary

CLUB PERSONNEL
Chairman: Graham Longhurst(07976 357684)
Match Secretary: 07748 764398 (M)
Manager:John Priestley
Captain: Nick Robinson

2003-2004
Leading Goalscorer & P.o.Y.: Pete Shelley

PARKGATE

Secretary: Bruce Bickerdike, 2 Cardew Close, Rawmarsh, Rotherham S62 6LB
Tel: 01709 522305 Fax: 01709 528583.

Ground: Roundwood Sports Complex, Green Lane, Rawmarsh, Rotherham S62 6LA
Tel: 01709 826600 Website: www.parkgatefc.co.uk Email: bruce@parkgatefc.co.uk

Directions: From Rotherham A633 to Rawmarsh. From Doncaster A630 to Conisbrough, then A6023 through Swinton to Rawmarsh. Grd at Green Lane - right from Rotherham, left from Conisbrough at the Crown Inn. Grd 800yds right

Capacity: 1,000 Seats: 300 Cover: 300 Floodlights: Yes **Club Shop:** No.

Clubhouse: Licensed bar, 2 lounges. Meals available lunchtime Wed-Sat.

HONOURS S&HSC Finalists 0-3 v Emley 97-98, Wilkinson Sword Trophy R-up 98-99

PREVIOUS Leagues: Sheffield County Senior Lge; Yorkshire 74
Names: BSC Parkgate (82-86); RES Parkgate (pre-1994).

RECORD Attendance: v Worksop 1982

BEST SEASON FA Cup: 2nd Qual. Rd 97-98 **FA Vase:** 1st Round, 6 times

2003-2004: Top Scorer: Rowen Mc Kenzie

FACT FILE
Founded: 1969
Nickname: The Gate or The Steelmen
Kit Sponsors: Blue Minx Club
Colours: All red Change: Blue & yellow
Midweek matches: Tuesday
Programme: 20 pages, £1.00
Editor: Stuart Bisby (01709 545219)

CLUB PERSONNEL
President: Paul Cristinacce
Chairman: Neil Freeman
Press Officer: Secretary
Manager: Stewart Evans Asst Man: Vince Brady
Captain: Craig Loftus
Coach: John Eagle
Physio: David Proctor

PONTEFRACT COLLIERIES

Secretary: Frank Maclachlan, 188 Watling Road, Ferry Fryston, Castleford WF102QY
Tel: 01977 512085 (H), 07710 586447 (M)
Email: webmaster@pontefractcollieries.co.uk

Ground: Skinner Lane, Pontefract, West Yorkshire (01977 600818)

Directions: M62 jct 32 towards Pontefract. Left at lights after roundabout for park entrance and retail park. Traffic thro town should follow racecouse signs thro lights to roundabout and back to lights. Monkhill (BR) 1/2 mile. Baghill (BR) 1 mile. Tanshelf (BR) 1/2 mile .All Leeds and Castleford buses pass ground.

Capacity: 1,200 **Seats:** 300 **Cover:** 400 **Floodlights:** Yes

Clubhouse: Fully licensed. Hot & cold snacks. Openmatch days **Club Shop:** Occasionally

HONOURS N.C.E. Lg Div 1 83-84 95-96 (Div 2 R-up 82-83); Lg Cup, R-up: 96-97 Floodlit Comp 87-88 88-89; Yorks Lg Div 3 81-82; W. Riding Co. Cup R-up 87-88 90-91;Embleton Cup (4) Castleford FA Cup (5) Wilkinson Sword 95-96
R-Up: 99-00.02-03

PREVIOUS Leagues: West Yorkshire 58-79; Yorkshire 79-82

RECORD Attendance: 1,000 v Hull City, floodlight opening 1987.

Players progressing: David Penney (Derby Co., 85), Andy Hayward (Rotherham U) and Dean Trott (Northampton Town)

FACT FILE
Founded: 1958 Nickname: Colls
Sponsors: Easy Hire
Colours: Blue & black halves/black/black
Change :All green Midweek Matches: Tuesday
Programme: 40 pages £1.00
Editor:Rod Naylor(01977 602266
Local Press: Pontefract & Castleford Express
Website: www.pontefractcollieries.co.uk

CLUB PERSONNEL
Chairman: T.B.A Manager: Roly Lynes.
Assistant Manager: Graham Asquith
Physio: Mick Slater Captain: Simon Cornell

2003-2004
Ps.o.Y.: Mike Rossiter& Joe Rossiter
Top Scorers: Jon Leigh 12

RETFORD UNITED

Secretary: James Lewis,2 Alma Road, Retford, DN22 6LW
Tel No: 01777705350 (H) 07801 905401 (M) e-mail:
E-mail: jamescrlewis@btinternet.com

Ground: Cannon Park, Leverton Rd., Retford, Notts.
Tel: 01777 710300 Weekends & Eves

Directions: From A1 take A620 past Ranby Prison and into Retford. At large r'about take 3rd exit. Pass Morrisons superstore to lights. Right at lights, then left at next set. Follow Leverton Rd. out of town. Cannon Park on RHS after two bridges.
Capacity: 2,000 Covered Standing: 300 Floodlights: Yes

Previous League: Central Midlands

2003-2004 Player of the Year: Ian Bagshaw **Top Goalscorer**: Vill Powell

FACT FILE
Founded: 1987
President: Dean Vivian
Chairman: Dave Hickin
Manager: Paul Hyde Tel: 01777 228158 (H)
Captain: Kevin Notemen
Colours: Black & white stripes/black/black
Change colours: Yellow/blue/white
Midweek Matchday:
Programme: Price: Pages:28-40
Editor: Jon Knight: 07973 843460(M)

DN22 expressfreight
Tel: 01777 701000
RETFORD UNITED
HISTORY MAKING
TREBLE WINNERS
2004
DN22 expressfreight
www.dn22.com

ROSSINGTON MAIN

Secretary: Gerald Parsons, School Bungalow, Hayfield Lane, Auckley, Doncaster DN8 3NB, Tel: 01302 770249(H) 07941 811217 (M)

Ground: Welfare Ground, Oxford Street, Rossington, Doncaster Tel: 01302 865524

Directions: Enter Rossington and go over the railway crossings. Pass the Welfare Club on right, Oxford Street is next right - ground is at bottom.8miles from Doncaster (BR)

Capacity: 2,000 Seats: 200 Cover: 500 Floodlights: Yes

Clubhouse: Evenings & matchdays, Sandwiches, rolls, satellite TV, pool. **Club Shop:** No

HONOURS Cen. Mids. Prem Div. 84-85, Lg. Cup 83-84 84-85; Doncaster Sen Lge 44-45, Lg. Cup 44-45; DDSALShield 90-91 R-up 89-90.

PREVIOUS **Leagues:** Doncaster Sen, Yorkshire Lge, Sheffield County Sen, Cent Mids.

RECORDS **Attendance:** 864 v Leeds United 8/91.
Goalscorer: Mark Illman **Appearances:** Darren Phipps

BEST SEASON
FA Cup: 2nd Qual. Rd. 25-26 **FA Vase:** 2nd Round 88-89

FACT FILE

Founded: 1920 Nickname: The Colliery
Sponsor: RJB Mining
Colours: All blue
Change colours: Blue & black
Midweek matches: Tuesday
Reserves' League: Beefeater County Sen
Programme: 50p
Editor: Peter Murden

CLUB PERSONNEL

Chairman: Gerald Murden (01302 867542)
Joint Managers: D Ridley & L Ostle
Physio: J White

SOUTH NORMANTON ATHLETIC

Secretary: Andrew Meredith, 40 Hilcote Street, South Normanton, Derbys. Tel: 01773 776477 (H) 07766 077204 (M)

Ground: South Normanton Athletic FC, Lees Lane, South Normanton, Derby Tel: 01773 581491

Directions: M1 Junc 28, B6019 towards South Normanton. Turn right after 1mile (in South Normanton) at BP garage into Market Street, after 1/4 mile turn left, immediately after The Clock pub into Lees Lane, ground at bottom on right.

Capacity: 3000 **Seats:** 150 **Cover:** 300 **Floodlights**:Yes

Clubhouse Open on matchdays. Food available.
Club Shop: No

PREVIOUS **Leagues:** Central Midlands League

Re-Formed: 1980
Colours: Yellow/navy/yellow
Change colours: Black & white/black/white
Midweek Matchday: wWdnesday
Programme: Yes - The Shiner
Editor: Kevin Adams (07903 936238)

Chairman: Peter Kane

Manager: Rob Aitkin
Asssistant Manager: Marcus Brameld

STAVELEY MINERS WELFARE

Secretary: Mrs Jane Burnand, 119 Middlecroft Rd.,Staveley, Chesterfield S433XU
Tel. Nos: : 01246 474350 (H) 07714 086404 (M)
Ground: Inkersall Road, Staveley, Chesterfield, Derbyshire Tel: 01246 471441
Directions: M1 jct 30, follow A619 Chesterfield - Staveley is 3 miles from jct30. Turn left at GK Garage in Staveley town centre into Inkersall Rd - ground 200yds on right at side of Speedwell Rooms. Frequent buses (47, 70, 72, 75, 77) from Chest'ld stop in Staveley centre 3 mins walk.
Capacity: 5,000 Cover: 400 Seats: 220 Floodlights: Yes
Clubhouse: The Staveley Miners Welfare, 500 yds from ground, open before and after games
Club Shop: Yes, contactRod Walker 01246 473655
HONOURS County Sen Lg Div 2 92-93, Div 3 91-92, Chesterfield & D. Amat Lg R-up89-90 90-91, Byron (Lge) Cup 89-90, R-up 90-91.NCE Div 1 R-up 97-98
PREVIOUS **Leagues:** Chesterfield & D. Amat 89-91; County Sen 91-93.
BEST SEASON **FA Cup:** **FA Vase:** 98-99, 3rd Rd at least
RECORDS **Attendance:** 280 v Stocksbridge, Sheffield Senior Cup 22/1/94
Goalscorer: Mick Godber **Appearances:** Shane Turner

FACT FILE
Founded: 1989 Nickname: The Welfare
Colours: All Blue
Change colours: Yellow/Green/Green
Midweek matches: Wednesday
Programme: 32pages, £1.00
Editor: Steve Durcan (01246 474544)

CLUB PERSONNEL
Chairman: Dennis Burnand
Tel: 01246 474350 (H)

SUTTON TOWN

Secretary: Keith Mayes, 22 Allington Drive, Mansfield, Notts. NG19 6NA
Tel: 01623 437938 (H) 07949 786422 (M)
Ground: Hosiery Mills Ground, Huthwaite Road, Sutton-in-Ashfield, Notts. NG17 3LA
Tel: 01623 552376
Directions: M1 Jct. 28 - A38 towards Mansfield. Take the A38 at Kings Mill Island, 1st left (Sutton sign), then 1st rt into Hosiery Mills ground.
Capacity: 1,500 Covered Seating: 200 Covered Standing: No Floodlights: Yes
Clubhouse: 01623 405660 **Club Shop:** Yes
PREVIOUS **Name:** North Notts
Leagues: Central Midlands League >03
HONOURS R-up CM Lge Supreme Div. 02-03
2003-2004 **Player of the Year**: Ian Brown **Top Scorer**: Dominic Elliott

FACT FILE
Re-Formed: (as Sutton Town) 2002
Colours: Claret & sky/white/white.
Change: All royal blue - with yellow trim
Midweek Matchday: Tuesday
Prog:£1.00 Pages:22 Editor: Peter Bough (01623 473419)
Club Personnel
Chairman: Eric Hetherington
Manager: Les McJannett
Tel: 01623 655834 (H) 07951 061236 (M)
Assistant Manager: Mark Place
Captain: Steven Roebuck
Physio: Kip Garton

TADCASTER ALBION

Secretary: Howard Clarke,17 Springhill Court,Tadcaster,N.Yorks.LS24 8DN (0193735017)
Ground: The Park, Ings Lane, Tadcaster, LS24 9AY. Tel: 01937 834119
Directions: From West Riding and South Yorks, turn right off A659 at John Smith's Brewery Clock. From East Riding turn left off A659 after passing over river bridge and pelican crossing (New Street).
Capacity: 1,500 **Seats**: Planned this season **Cover:** 400
Floodlights: Yes
Clubhouse: Yes **Club Shop:** No
HONOURS None
RECORD **Attendance:**1,200 v Winterton F.A.Vase 4th Rd 1996-7
Win: 13-0 v Blidworth MW, NCE 97-98 **Defeat**: 2-10 v Thackley
PREVIOUS **Leagues:** York, Harrogate, Yorkshire (73-82)
BEST SEASON
FA Cup: 2nd Qual. Rd. 98-99 **FA Vase:** 5th Round 77-78

FACT FILE
Founded: 1892
Colours: Yellow + Navy & Red trim /navy & red/navy
Change colours: Green & Yellow halves
Midweek Matchday: Tuesday
Programme: 20 pages
Prog Ed: Mrs Elaine Targett (01977 780964)
CLUB PERSONNEL
Chairman: Wayne Day Tel No: 01924 896446
President: Lord Edward Stourton
Match Sec: 01937 835017 (H/B)
Manager: Wayne Day **2003-04**
Leading Goalscorer: Matthew Howgate
Player of the Year: Danny Pitts

WINTERTON RANGERS

Secretary: G Spencer, 2 Dale Park Ave.,Winterton,Scun'pe,N Lincs.DN15 9UY (01724 732039)
Ground: West Street, Winterton, Scunthorpe, South Humberside (01724 732628).
Directions: From Scunthorpe take A1077 Barton-on-Humber for 5 miles. On entering Winterton take 3rd right (Eastgate), 3rd left (Northlands Rd)and 1st right (West St.). Ground 200yds on left
Capacity: 3,000 Seats: 200 Covered: 200 Floodlights: Yes **Club Shop:** No.
Clubhouse: Open matchdays & evenings Mon-Sat, hot & cold food available on matchdays
HONOURS Lincs Jnr Cup 47-48 61-62; Lincs Snr `B' Cup 69-70; Yorks Lg 71-72 76-77 78-79 (Lg Cup 80-81); N.C.E. Div 2 89-90; S'thorpe Lg & Cup many times.
PREVIOUS **Leagues:** Scunthorpe & Dist. 45-65; Lincs 65-70; Yorkshire 70-82.
BEST SEASON **FA Vase:** QF 76-77 **FA Cup:** 4th Qual Rd replay 76-77, 2-3 after 3-3
RECORD **Attendance:** 1,200 v Sheffield Utd, official floodlight opening, Oct. 78
Fee received: £5,000 for Henry Smith (Leeds United, 1979)
Players progressing Henry Smith (Leeds), Keith Walwyn (Chesterfield), Rick Greenhough(Chester)

FACT FILE
Founded: 1930 Nickname: Rangers
Colours: Blue & white/Black/Blue
Change colours: All red
Midweek matches: Wednesday
Programme: 28-36 pages, 50p
Editor: Mark Fowler (01724 734570)
Local Press: Scunthorpe Evening Telegraph

CLUB PERSONNEL
Chairman:David Crowder V- Chair: Ken Edgehill
Press Officer: Brian Crowder
Manager: Steve Smith Captain: Billy Green

2003-2004
Top Scorer & P.o.Y.: Vas Nikolaidis

MATCHDAY MASTER
CARLTON TOWN FC
NORTHERN COUNTIES EAST
LEAGUE DIVISION 1
SATURDAY 24TH APRIL 2004
CARLTON TOWN
V
GEDLING TOWN
KICK OFF 3PM
MSR NEWSGROUP
ISSUE 22
OFFICIAL PROGRAMME £1

PARKGATE F.C.
OFFICIAL PROGRAMME
SPORTS GROUND AT
GREEN LANE
RAWMARSH
Tel Rotherham 826600

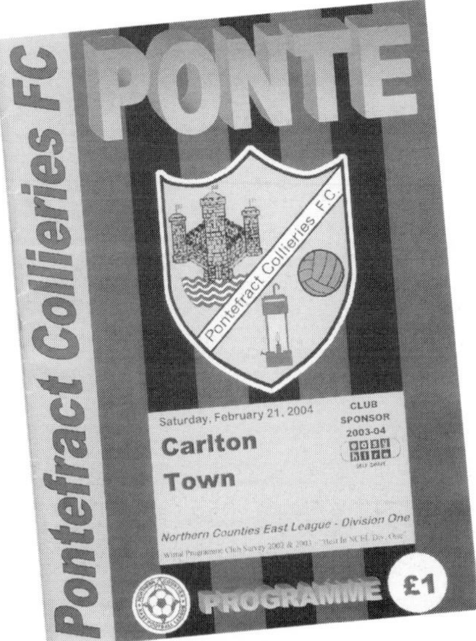
Pontefract Collieries FC
PONTE
Pontefract Collieries F.C.
Saturday, February 21, 2004
CLUB
SPONSOR
2003-04
Carlton
Town
Northern Counties East League - Division One
PROGRAMME
£1

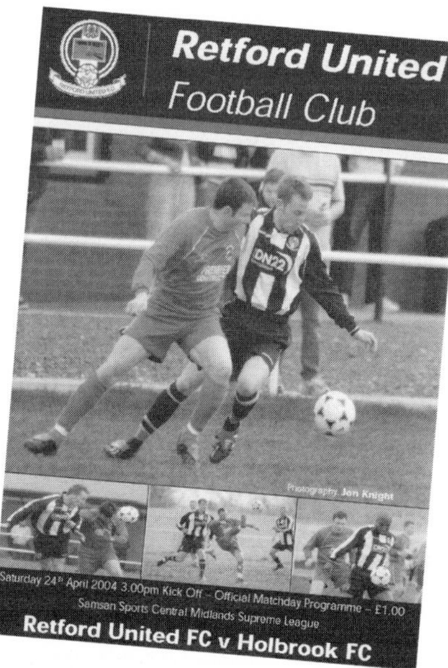
Retford United
Football Club
Photography Jon Knight
Saturday 24th April 2004 3.00pm Kick Off – Official Matchday Programme – £1.00
Samsan Sports Central Midlands Supreme League
Retford United FC v Holbrook FC

WORSBROUGH M.W. & ATHLETIC

Secretary: Charlie Wyatt, 4 Springfield Road, Hoyland Common, Barnsley,S.Yorks. S74 0BE
Tel & FAX: 01226 747774 (H) 07977 947760 (M)

Ground: Park Road, Worsbrough Bridge, Barnsley Tel: 01226 284452

Directions: On the A61 Barnsley-Sheffield road two miles south of Barnsley, 2miles from M1 jnt 36 opposite Blackburns Bridge. Two and a half miles from Barnsley (BR). Yorkshire Traction run buses every 10 mins thru Worsbrough Bridge.

Capacity: 2,000 Seats: 175 Cover: 175 Floodlights: Yes

Clubhouse: Yes **Club Shop:** No

HONOURS Northern Co's East Div 1 R-up 90-91 (Div 3 R-up 85-86); Sheffield SnrCup R-up 72-73; County Snr Lg 65-66 69-70 (R-up 62-63, Lg Cup 65-66); Barnsley Lg 52-53 58-59 59-60, Lg Cup 56-57 58-59 (R-up 53-54), Beckett Cup 57-58.

PREVIOUS **Leagues:** Barnsley 52-61; Sheffield County Snr 62-71; Yorkshire 71-82.

RECORD **Attendance:** 1,603 v Blyth Spartans, FA Amateur Cup 1971

BEST SEASON FA Cup: 1st Qual. Rd 78-79 79-80 80-81 **FA Vase:** 3rd Round 90-91

FACT FILE
Founded: 1923
Reformed: 1947
Colours: All red
Change colours: Yellow/black
Midweek Matchday: Tuesday
Programme: 60 pages, £1.00
Editor: Secretary

Chairman: John Cooper

Record Holders
Appearances: Billy Pickering
Goals: Frank Briscoe

YORKSHIRE AMATEUR

Secretary: David Packham, 30 Roxholme Avenue, Leeds LS7 4JF (0113 262 0758)

Ground: The Bracken Edge, Roxholme Road, Leeds LS8 4DZ Tel: 0113 262 4093

Directions: From South M1 to Leeds, then A58 Wetherby Road to Fforde Green Hotel, left at lights and proceed to Sycamore Ave. (on right). From East A1 to Boot & Shoe Inn then to Shaftesbury Hotel, turn right into Harehills Lane, then to Sycamore Avenue. Two and a half miles from Leeds (BR). Buses 2, 3 & 20 from Briggate to Harehills Ave.

Capacity : 1,550 Seats: 200 Cover: 160 Floodlights: Yes **Club Shop:** Yes

Clubhouse: Bar, tea bar, games, lounge. Every night 8.30-11, Sat matchdays 12-11, Sun 12-3.

HONOURS FA Amtr Cup SF 31-32; West Riding Co. Cup(3); Yorks Lg 31-32, Div 2 58-59 (R-up 52-53 71-72), Div 3 77-78, Lg Cup 32-33; Leeds & Dist. Snr Cup. **PREVIOUS League:** Yorks 20-24 30-82. **Ground:** Elland Road 1919-20 **RECORD Attendance:** 4,000 v Wimbledon, FA Amateur Cup QF 1932. **Players progressing:** Gary Strodder & Stuart Naylor (W.B.A.), Peter Swan (Leeds U) Brian Deane (Doncaster R) **BEST SEASONS: FA Cup:** 1st Rd 31-32 45-46 **FA Vase:** 3rd Round 93-94 **FA Amateur Cup:** Semi-Finals 31-32

FACT FILE
Founded: 1918 Nickname: Ammers
Sponsors: Screeching Parrot
Colours: White/navy/red
Change colours: All red
Midweek Matches: Tuesday
Programme: 12 pages, 50p
Editor: Secretary
Local Press: Yorkshire Post, Yorkshire Evening Post and North Leeds Advertiser

CLUB PERSONNEL
Chairman: Andrew Wilkinson (0113 260 9521)
President: Rayner Barker
Manager: Denis Metcalfe
Coach:Jim McKay Physio: Terry Davies

THE NORTH WEST COUNTIES

SPONSORED BY: MOORE & CO. SOLICITORS

President: W J King **Chairman:** D Tomlinson
Secretary: Geoff Wilkinson, 46 Oaklands Drive, Penwortham, Preston PR1 0YY
Tel: 01772 746312
Press Officer: Paul Lawler, 61 Cable Street,
Formby, Merseyside L37 3LU Tel/Fax: 01704 875575

FINAL LEAGUE TABLES 2003-04

DIVISION ONE		P	W	D	L	F	A	Pts
1.	Clitheroe	42	29	5	8	88	55	92
2.	Mossley (-3 pts)	42	28	8	6	109	54	89
3.	Fleetwood Town	42	26	8	8	84	51	86
4.	Woodley Sports	42	26	5	11	99	56	83
5.	Warrington Town	42	20	10	12	72	59	70
6.	Newcastle Town	42	21	6	15	94	67	69
7.	Curzon Ashton (-3 pts)	42	19	10	13	84	79	64
8.	Skelmersdale United	42	19	6	17	79	64	63
9.	Alsager Town	42	16	15	11	54	47	63
10.	Stone Dominoes	42	18	8	16	57	60	62
11.	Congleton Town	42	15	16	11	62	50	61
12.	Atherton LR	42	17	7	18	77	76	58
13.	Nantwich Town (-3 pts)	42	15	11	16	73	66	53
14.	Bacup Borough	42	15	8	19	68	72	53
15.	Salford City	42	14	11	17	62	66	53
16.	Trafford	42	14	8	20	72	91	50
17.	Ramsbottom United	42	12	12	18	71	92	48
18.	Glossop North End	42	9	9	24	51	95	36
19.	St Helens Town (-3 pts)	42	10	6	26	51	81	33
20.	Squires Gate	42	7	12	23	52	83	33
21.	Abbey Hey	42	7	8	27	46	90	29
22.	Atherton Collieries (-4 pts)	42	6	9	27	48	99	23

DIVISION TWO		P	W	D	L	F	A	Pts
1.	Colne	38	26	6	6	102	41	84
2.	Maine Road	38	23	5	10	99	58	74
3.	Formby	38	21	9	8	86	48	72
4.	Great Harwood Town	38	15	14	9	68	44	59
5.	Flixton	38	16	11	11	76	60	59
6.	Darwen (-3 pts)	38	17	11	10	81	67	59
7.	Ashton Town	38	16	11	11	66	60	59
8.	Winsford United	38	15	11	12	66	62	56
9.	Holker Old Boys	38	15	8	15	82	76	53
10.	Nelson	38	14	11	13	55	64	53
11.	Leek CSOB	38	14	8	16	72	63	50
12.	Padiham	38	14	8	16	63	80	50
13.	Oldham Town	38	13	9	16	69	74	48
14.	Blackpool Mechanics	38	13	7	18	45	59	46
15.	Norton United	38	11	12	15	66	72	45
16.	Cheadle Town	38	12	9	17	55	69	45
17.	Eccleshall	38	10	14	14	56	65	44
18.	Chadderton	38	7	11	20	42	63	32
19.	Daisy Hill	38	7	10	21	33	82	31
20.	Castleton Gabriels	38	6	5	27	53	128	23

DIVISION ONE	1	2	3	4	5	6	7	8	9	10	11	12	13	14	15	16	17	18	19	20	21	22
1 Abbey Hey		0-1	4-2	1-3	2-4	2-3	0-0	3-2	2-1	0-1	1-4	0-0	1-5	1-0	2-2	0-3	2-1	0-1	2-2	2-1	0-2	1-2
2 Alsager Town	2-1		2-0	1-1	2-3	0-0	1-1	3-0	0-1	1-1	0-1	1-3	3-2	1-1	1-1	1-1	0-0	1-0	1-0	3-2	3-0	1-0
3 Atherton Col.	2-2	1-0		1-2	3-0	3-3	2-2	0-1	1-1	0-1	1-1	4-4	1-5	1-4	1-1	2-1	0-3	2-0	0-4	0-1	2-4	2-3
4 Atherton LR	5-0	1-0	0-3		3-2	0-1	1-1	1-2	0-1	2-1	1-2	5-6	1-2	5-3	2-0	1-3	2-0	1-0	0-0	3-3	2-3	1-0
5 Bacup Boro'	4-3	4-1	3-0	2-3		1-2	1-4	4-1	2-0	1-2	0-1	1-3	4-2	5-2	2-2	1-5	2-1	2-0	0-1	2-1	0-1	1-1
6 Clitheroe	1-1	1-1	4-3	4-2	3-1		4-1	3-1	1-3	2-0	0-3	0-1	0-1	2-3	3-2	2-1	5-2	5-1	3-2	3-1	0-2	2-1
7 Congleton T.	1-0	1-1	2-1	2-0	1-0	2-3		2-2	2-1	2-2	2-0	1-0	2-2	4-0	1-2	1-4	1-1	1-1	2-0	2-0	0-1	1-1
8 Curzon Ashton	3-1	2-1	3-0	2-1	1-1	0-0	0-0		1-1	2-2	1-1	5-3	4-3	4-0	0-2	4-2	4-2	2-0	3-2	4-2	3-2	1-3
9 Fleetwood Tn	2-1	0-0	3-0	2-1	1-1	1-3	3-1	2-1		2-0	1-4	3-2	2-2	2-1	1-3	3-0	2-0	4-0	2-0	3-0	1-0	5-1
10 Glossop N.E.	2-1	0-2	2-1	0-3	1-1	0-2	1-1	2-3	0-3		0-1	3-0	4-3	3-3	0-4	1-2	2-2	1-3	0-2	3-5	0-2	3-4
11 Mossley	7-2	2-2	6-2	2-0	0-0	1-2	2-2	2-2	5-1	6-0		2-1	1-3	2-2	2-0	3-1	2-1	5-2	1-0	3-0	6-4	2-1
12 Nantwich Town	2-2	0-1	5-0	1-3	2-0	2-3	1-0	1-1	0-3	6-0	3-1		3-0	1-1	2-1	0-2	0-2	2-2	0-3	5-1	2-3	3-1
13 Newcastle Utd	1-0	5-2	1-1	3-1	3-0	1-2	1-1	5-0	0-2	5-0	3-1	2-1		3-1	2-0	5-1	2-1	1-2	1-2	2-2	4-2	3-1
14 Ramsbottom U.	1-0	1-3	2-1	5-2	0-2	0-2	2-2	4-1	4-6	2-1	2-5	1-1	2-1		1-1	2-2	1-0	2-1	2-2	3-0	1-1	3-5
15 Salford City	1-0	2-2	0-1	4-0	1-3	0-3	0-2	2-1	1-1	3-0	1-5	0-2	1-0	4-3		1-2	0-0	3-0	4-1	0-2	1-1	3-2
16 Skelmersdale	1-2	1-2	2-1	0-3	2-2	1-3	2-1	2-0	1-2	1-1	2-3	1-1	4-0	0-1	3-1		8-0	3-2	0-1	3-1	0-1	1-1
17 Squires Gate	0-0	1-1	6-1	1-1	3-1	0-1	0-3	3-5	0-0	0-1	1-3	3-0	1-1	1-1	2-5	0-2		3-1	2-0	3-3	1-1	1-4
18 St Helens Tn	3-0	1-2	1-1	0-3	2-1	2-0	1-3	1-3	3-4	1-3	2-5	1-1	1-2	2-1	2-0	0-2	3-0		1-2	0-1	0-0	1-2
19 Stone Dom.	2-1	1-0	2-0	3-3	1-0	0-1	0-3	2-1	4-4	1-0	0-1	1-1	0-5	2-0	0-0	3-0	2-1	0-5		4-3	1-2	0-1
20 Trafford	4-1	1-2	3-1	1-5	1-1	2-3	1-0	1-5	0-1	3-3	1-1	1-0	3-1	6-2	0-0	4-2	5-1	3-1	1-1		0-4	0-6
21 Warrington Tn	2-0	0-0	3-0	2-2	1-2	1-3	2-1	2-2	3-2	5-3	0-2	1-1	1-0	1-1	2-1	0-3	4-2	3-0	1-3	0-1		1-1
22 Woodley Spts	4-2	3-2	2-0	6-1	3-1	3-0	3-0	5-1	0-1	2-1	4-2	0-1	5-1	3-0	6-2	1-2	1-0	1-1	2-0	2-1	2-1	

DIVISION TWO	1	2	3	4	5	6	7	8	9	10	11	12	13	14	15	16	17	18	19	20
1 Ashton Town		4-0	1-1	3-2	4-2	1-6	1-0	2-1	0-0	1-2	2-4	1-0	3-2	0-3	1-4	2-3	2-2	2-0	1-1	5-1
2 Blackpool Mechanics	2-1		1-0	1-5	1-2	1-3	0-1	2-4	2-2	0-2	0-2	0-3	0-2	1-0	0-1	2-2	3-2	1-1	2-1	2-2
3 Castleton Gabriels	1-2	2-1		0-3	1-3	0-3	1-2	2-4	1-1	1-1	0-4	0-4	1-5	1-4	4-8	1-3	4-0	1-3	1-4	2-5
4 Chadderton	1-0	0-0	0-0		1-1	0-2	4-1	1-2	1-1	2-0	1-4	2-1	1-1	2-2	1-2	1-3	0-0	1-1	0-3	1-2
5 Cheadle Town	1-1	0-1	2-0	3-2		1-1	0-0	2-2	0-1	1-3	3-2	2-0	5-0	1-1	2-3	0-1	1-0	0-0	2-1	1-2
6 Colne	3-0	1-0	4-0	3-0	4-1		5-0	1-0	4-1	2-1	2-0	1-1	6-0	2-1	1-3	6-2	5-2	6-2	3-3	1-0
7 Daisy Hill	0-1	2-2	2-2	1-0	1-3	2-4		1-4	1-1	2-0	0-2	0-4	0-1	1-6	0-5	0-2	3-3	1-1	1-1	3-0
8 Darwen	3-3	4-1	6-1	0-0	2-0	1-5	1-0		3-2	1-1	2-2	0-1	1-0	4-2	1-1	0-1	2-2	3-1	4-1	1-0
9 Eccleshall	0-1	2-1	1-2	3-0	1-1	3-1	2-2	1-1		4-3	2-0	0-0	3-2	1-4	0-6	1-1	0-2	1-1	0-1	1-2
10 Flixton	3-1	0-1	6-1	2-1	2-4	4-2	2-0	2-5	1-1		1-2	1-2	0-0	0-0	3-2	2-2	4-1	2-2	5-2	1-1
11 Formby	1-1	0-1	4-0	2-1	3-1	2-0	1-0	5-3	1-1	1-1		2-1	4-2	5-1	2-3	2-0	2-2	6-1	3-0	1-0
12 Great Harwood Town	2-2	0-0	6-2	3-1	2-2	0-0	6-0	4-3	4-0	2-1	1-1		6-7	1-1	1-3	1-0	1-2	2-0	0-0	0-0
13 Holker Old Boys	0-6	1-2	10-2	1-1	3-0	0-1	0-0	1-2	1-0	2-3	2-0	0-0		3-1	1-5	5-0	4-3	5-3	5-0	1-1
14 Leek CSOB	1-1	0-4	2-3	2-0	3-0	0-2	1-2	6-0	4-3	0-2	2-2	0-1	2-2		3-1	3-0	1-0	0-1	2-2	1-0
15 Maine Road	1-1	3-2	6-1	3-1	4-0	0-2	8-1	2-2	2-3	1-5	0-4	2-0	1-3	3-2		1-1	1-1	1-0	2-1	0-3
16 Nelson	1-3	0-3	5-3	2-0	5-0	2-2	1-1	2-1	1-4	1-1	1-1	1-1	3-0	0-4	1-0		0-0	2-1	2-2	0-2
17 Norton United	2-0	3-1	6-2	3-0	1-2	0-3	2-0	0-3	1-1	2-3	2-2	2-4	3-3	4-2	0-2	2-0		2-1	1-0	2-2
18 Oldham Town	0-1	0-1	1-4	1-2	3-1	3-2	3-0	2-2	2-5	3-3	6-3	3-1	5-1	1-2	3-2	2-1	2-1		1-3	2-2
19 Padiham	0-1	0-3	2-5	2-1	5-4	2-1	1-0	1-1	2-1	2-0	0-3	1-1	0-5	4-3	0-3	4-1	5-4	1-3		4-3
20 Winsford United	4-4	1-0	3-0	2-2	2-1	2-2	1-2	6-2	3-2	2-3	2-1	1-1	2-1	3-0	1-4	0-2	1-1	0-4	2-1	

LEAGUE CUP

FIRST ROUND

Ashton Town	v	Formby	1-0
Blackpool Mechanics	v	Stone Dominoes	4-3*
Castleton Gabriels	v	Darwen	1-3
Chadderton	v	Eccleshall	1-3
Colne	v	Oldham Town	2-1
Daisy Hill	v	Bacup Borough	0-3
Leek CSOB	v	Nelson	2-3*
Maine Road	v	Great Harwood Town	1-2
Norton United	v	Cheadle Town	2-0
Padiham	v	Holker Old Boys	3-4

SECOND ROUND

Abbey Hey	v	Newcastle Town	0-4
Alsager Town	v	Clitheroe	1-2
Bacup Borough	v	Ashton Town	2-1
Blackpool Mechanics	v	Woodley Sports	0-4
Darwen	v	Curzon Ashton	3-4
Fleetwood Town	v	Norton United	3-2
Flixton	v	Colne	3-0
Glossop North End	v	Eccleshall	0-2
Great Harwood Tn	v	Nantwich Town	2-1
Mossley	v	Atherton Collieries	4-3
Ramsbottom Utd	v	Salford City	2-0
Skelmersdale Utd	v	Congleton Town	0-1
Squires Gate (w/o)	v	Winsford United	
St Helens Town	v	Holker Old Boys	5-4
Trafford	v	Atherton LR	1-3
Warrington Town	v	Nelson	1-1* 2-1r

THIRD ROUND

Atherton LR	v	Great Harwood Town	2-4
Bacup Borough	v	Flixton	6-3
Congleton Town	v	Newcastle Town	0-4
Fleetwood Town	v	Mossley	1-3
Ramsbottom Utd	v	Curzon Ashton	4-1
Squires Gate	v	Clitheroe	0-1
St Helens Town	v	Warrington Town	4-3
(tie awarded to Warrington Town)			
Woodley Sports	v	Eccleshall	1-0

QUARTER-FINALS

Clitheroe	v	Bacup Borough	0-1
Mossley	v	Newcastle Town	1-2
Ramsbottom Utd	v	Great Harwood Town	2-1
Woodley Sports	v	Warrington Town	0-1

SEMI-FINALS (played over two legs - home & away)

			1st Leg	2nd Leg
Bacup Borough	v	Warrington Town	4-1	3-2
Ramsbottom Utd	v	Newcastle Town	4-3	1-3

THE FINAL (22nd April at Southport)

Newcastle Town	v	Bacup Borough	0-3

SECOND DIVISION TROPHY

FIRST ROUND

Ashton Town	v	Padiham	1-2
Colne	v	Oldham Town	6-0
Nelson	v	Great Harwood Town	3-3* 0-2r
Norton United	v	Eccleshall	2-0

SECOND ROUND

Blackpool Mechanics	v	Colne	0-2
Castleton Gabriels	v	Chadderton	1-0
Darwen	v	Formby	3-1*
Flixton	v	Padiham	4-1
Great Harwood T.	v	Daisy Hill	3-0
Holker Old Boys	v	Cheadle Town	2-4
Norton United	v	Maine Road	3-2
Winsford United	v	Leek CSOB	1-0

QUARTER-FINALS

Castleton Gabriels	v	Darwen	2-4
Cheadle Town	v	Flixton	4-0
Norton United	v	Colne	2-5
Winsford United	v	Great Harwood Town	1-1* 1-3r

SEMI-FINALS (played over two legs - home & away)

			1st Leg	2nd Leg
Colne	v	Cheadle Town	2-1	0-0
Darwen	v	Great Harwood Tn	0-0	0-2

THE FINAL (3rd May at Clitheroe)

Great Harwood Tn	v	Colne	0-1

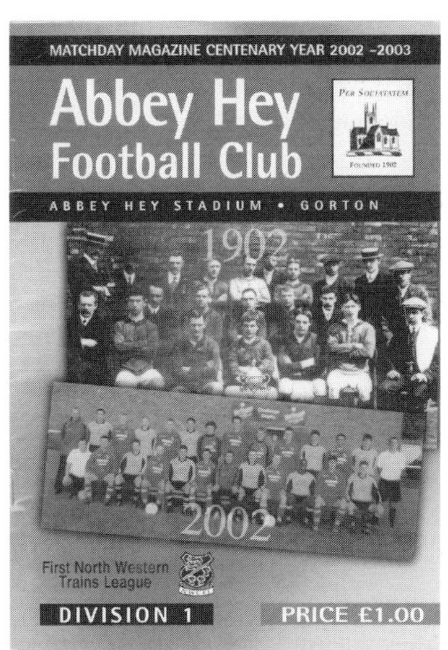
MATCHDAY MAGAZINE CENTENARY YEAR 2002 -2003
Abbey Hey
Football Club
ABBEY HEY STADIUM • GORTON
1902
2002
First North Western
Trains League
DIVISION 1
PRICE £1.00

Match Sponsor:
edj
Independent Financial Advisers
MAINE ROAD
FOOTBALL CLUB
SEASON 2003 - 2004
NORTH WEST COUNTIES
LEAGUE DIVISION TWO
OLDHAM TOWN
THE NORTH WEST COUNTIES FOOTBALL LEAGUE
NWCFL

NANTWICH TOWN
v TRAFFORD
NWCFL Division One
Saturday 8 November 2003. 3pm
the
dabber
the Nantwich
football digest
2003.2004
£1

PADIHAM ■ FOOTBALL CLUB
Review
OFFICIAL MATCHDAY PROGRAMME
SEASON 2003 / 2004
NORTH WEST COUNTIES
- FOOTBALL LEAGUE -
DIVISION TWO
Price
£1.00
NWCFL

ABBEY HEY

Secretary: Tony McAllister, 10 Walmer Street, Abbey Hey, Gorton, M'chester M18 8QP
Tel Nos: 0161 230 7098 (H) 07786 222596 (W) 0161 230 7098 (Fax)

Ground: Abbey Stadium, Goredale Avenue, Gorton, Manchester 18
Tel: 0161 231 7147 (Club) Fax: 01823 490281

Clubhouse: Yes, and as there is no shop , Badges and T-Shirts etc also sold

Directions: A57 towards Hyde, right into Woodland Avenue approx one & a half miles past Belle Vue junction, right again into Ryder Brow Rd, 1st left after bridge into Goredale Ave. **Nearest Railway Station:** Ryder Brow

Capacity: 1000 Seats: 100 Cover: 300 Floodlights: Yes

Honours Manchester Amat. Lge 65-66: S.E. Lancs Lge 66-67, 68-69 R-up 67-68; Div.2 68-69; Lge Shield 65-66: Manc. Co. Amat. Cup 64-65, 67-68, 68-69, R-up 63-64: Manchester Lge Prem. Div. 81-82, 88-89, 90-91, 93-94, 94-95; Div. 1 70- 71; Div.2 88-89, 92-93, 93-94; Gilcryst Cup 76-77, 88-89, R-up 97-88; Open Tphy 78-79,79-80, 92-93: Manchester Chall. Tphy 82-83, 95-96, 96-97. N.W. Trains Div 2 R-up 98-99

Previous Leagues: Manchester Amateur; South East Lancs; Manchester League.

Record Attendance: 400 v Manchester City XI October 1999.

FACT FILE

Formed: 1902
Colours:Red& white/red/red & white
Midweek matchday: Tuesday

CLUB PERSONNEL

Chairman: James Whittaker
0161 445 0036
Manager: Chris Bailey
Coach: Phil Wardle
Physio: Pete Blundell
Programme Editor: Gordon Lester

2003-2004

Player of the Year: Chris Hamman
Top Scorer: Tim Bailey

ALSAGER TOWN

Secretary: Pauline Matthews, 43 Ellgreave Street, Dalehall, Stoke -On-Trent, ST6 4DJ
Tel No: 01782 834296

Ground: The Town Ground, Wood Park, Alsager. Tel: 01270 882336

Directions: M6, Junction 16, A500 towards Stoke. Leave A500 at 2nd exit (A34 to Congleton), at 2nd set of lights turn left for Alsager. Turn right opposite Caradon/Twyfords (500 yds), into Moorhouse Ave., Woodland Court 1/2 mile on right.
Nearest Railway station: Alsager

HONOURS Joint Runners -up Mid Cheshire Div. 2, Runners-up Springbank Vending Lge.

PREVIOUS Leagues: Mid Cheshire Div. 2; Springbank Vending Lge.

RECORD Attendance: 110 v Formby Sept 99, League. 200 v Port Vale (friendly)

FACT FILE

Founded: 1968
Colours: Black & white/black/black
Change colours: Yellow & sky blue/yellow/yellow
Midweek Matches: Tuesday

CLUB PERSONNEL

Chairman: Peter Clegg
Tel: 01270 876013
1st Team Sec.: Pauline Matthews
Tel: 01782 834296H

ATHERTON COLLIERIES

Secretary: Emil Anderson, 109 Douglas St, Atherton M46 9EB Tel Nos: 01942 879209 (H) 0161 288 6355 (W) 0792 937461 (M) Email:geocities.com/ath-c-g-c email: emilanderson@yahoo.com

Ground: Atherton Colls Football Ground,Alder St., Atherton, Gt ManchesterTel:01942884649.

Directions: M61 Jct 5, follow sign for Westhoughton, left onto A6, right ontoA579 (Newbrook Rd/Bolton Rd) into Atherton. At first set of lights turn leftinto High Street, 2nd left into Alder St. to ground. Quarter mile from AthertonCentral (BR).

Seats: 300 Cover: 1,000 Capacity: 2,500 Floodlights: Yes

Clubhouse: Open Mon-Fri 7-11pm, Sat 11am-11pm, Sun noon-3 & 7-10.30pm. Hot &cold food on matchdays. **Club Shop:** No, but programmes & badges are available

PREVIOUS Leagues: Bolton Combination 20-50, 52-71; Lancs Combination 50-52, 71-78; Cheshire County 78-82.

HONOURS: BNWCFL 3rd Div Champ 86/87; Bridge Shield 85/86; Lancs County FA Shield19/20, 22/23, 41/42, 45/46. 56/57, 64/65; Tennents F/lit Trophy Finalist 94/95; NWCFL Div 2 R/up 95/96 Gpldline Trophy 2001-02 Worthington Challenge Trophy R-up 2001-02

RECORDS Attendance: 3,300 in Lancs Combination, 1920's

Players Progressing: J Parkinson (Wigan), Russell Beardsmore(Manchester Utd).

2002004 Player of the Year: Jermaine Peters **Top Scorer:** Martyn Stewart

FACT FILE

Founded: 1916
Nickname: Colls
Club Sponsors: Kensite
Colours: Black & white stripes/black/black.
Change colours: Yellow/blue/yellow
Reserves' Lge: NWTL Res Div
Midweek Matches: Monday
Programme: 40 pages, £1
Editor: Secretary
Club Website:
geocities@frank35.freeserve.co.uk

CLUB PERSONNEL

Chairman: Steve Payne
Vice Chairman: Paul Gregory
Manager: Alan Lord.
Asst Managers: Jason Holroyd & Alan Kirkman
Physio: Paul Chapman
Captain: Neil Rhodes

ATHERTON L.R.

Secretary: Steve Hartle,165 Bolton Road, Atherton, Gtr Manchester M46 9AD (01942 870253)
Ground: Crilly Park, Spa Road, Atherton, Greater Manchester (01942 883950).
Directions: M61 to Jct 5, follow signs for Westhoughton, left onto A6, right onto A579 (Newbrook Rd/Bolton Rd) over the railway bridge, right into Upton Rd passing Atherton Central Station, left into Springfield Rd and left again to Hillside Rd into Spa Rd and ground.
Capacity: 3,000 **Seats**: 250 **Cover**: 3 sections **Floodlights**: Yes
Clubhouse: Open normal licensing hours. **Club Shop:** No

PREVIOUS **Name:** Laburnum Rovers 56-80 **Grounds:** Laburnum Road 56-58 Hagfold 58-66
Leagues: Bolton Comb.; Cheshire County 80-82; NWCL 82-94; NPL 94-97.
RECORDS **Attendance:** 2,300 v Aldershot Town, FA Vase Quarter-Final replay 5/3/94.
Appearances: Jimmy Evans **Fee Paid:** £500 for Joey Dunn from Warrington T.
Scorer: Shaun Parker **Fee Received:** £1,500 for Stuart Humphries to Barrow
BEST SEASON **FA Cup:** 3rd Qual Rd 96-97, 0-2 v Bamber Bridge
FA Vase: Semi-Final rep. 94-95, 1-2 v Diss Town **FA Trophy:** 1st Qual Rd 96-97
HONOURS: North West Co Lge 92-93 93-94, Champs Trophy 92-93 93-94, F/Lit Trophy 93-94; N.P.L.Div.1 Cup R-up 95-96,Goldline Trophy 98-99,03-04 Bolton Hosp Cup: 84-85; 01-02 02-03 Westhoughton Charity Cup 81-82
Players progressing : Barry Butler (Chester), Lee Unsworth(Crewe) Phil Priestley(Rochdale)

FACT FILE

Formed: 1954 Nickname: The Panthers
Sponsors: VeeKay Engineering
Colours: Yellow & Navy
Change colours: Green & White
Midweek Matches: Tuesday
Reserves' League: North West Co Res Div
Prog: 48 pages £1.0 (Best in league 4th year)
Ed: Tim Lees. e-mail : lr-16@hotmail.com
Cover Design: Fern Jardine
website:www.intheteam.com/athertonir
Local Radio: GMR

CLUB PERSONNEL

Chairman:Alan Grundy
Financial Director: Ray Price
Manager:Tom Foster Asst.Man. Ian Street

BACUP BOROUGH

Secretary: Frank Manning, 38 Acre Avenue, Stacksteads, Bacup OL13 0HN
Tel: 01706 877460 (H)
Ground: West View, Cowtoot Lane, Blackthorn, Bacup, Lancashire
Tel: 01706 878655
Directions: From M62, M66 onto A681 through Rawtenstall to Bacup centre, leftonto A671 towards Burnley, after approx 300 yds right (immed. before the Irwell Inn) climbing Cooper Street, right into Blackthorn Lane then first left intoCowtoot Lane to ground.
Capacity: 3,000 Seats: 500 Cover: 1,000 Floodlights: Yes
Clubhouse: Open matchdays and private functions (for which buffets can be provided). Pies and sandwiches on matchdays.
Club Shop: Not yet
HONOURS Lancs Jnr Cup 10-11 (R-up 22-23 74-75); Lancs Comb. 46-47 (Lg Cup R-up46-47 80-81; NW Co's Lg Div 2 R-up 89-90.
PREVIOUS **League:** Lancs Comb. 03-82Name: Bacup FC.Grounds: None
BEST SEASON **FA Cup:** **FA Vase:**
RECORD **Attendance:** 4,980 v Nelson 1947 **Scorer:** Jimmy Clarke

FACT FILE

Founded: 1875
Nickname: The Boro
Club Sponsors: B & E Boys Ltd
Colours: Black & white stripes trim/black/black
Change colours: Yellow/ Blue/ Blue
Midweek Matches: Wednesday
Programme
22 Pages 50p
Editor: D Whatmough (0706 875041)

CLUB PERSONNEL

President: W. Shufflebottom
Chairman: Ken Peters
Vice Chairman: D. Whatmough

Manager: Brent Peters
Assistant Manager: Simon Holding

COLNE F C

Secretary: Dave Blackloch,7 Linton Gardens, Barrowford, Nelson BB98RG (01282 696340)
Ground: Holt House Stadium, Holt House, Colne. (Tel: 01282 862545)
Directions: Enter Colne from M65 to roundabout, keep left follow signs for Keighley. At next roundabout turn left, continue on Harrison Drive over mini roundabout & follow road to ground.
Nearest Railway station - Colne.
Capacity: 1,800 Seats: 160 Cover: 1000 Floodlights: Yes

Clubhouse: Yes,Small Lounge Bar open on matchdays **Club Shop:** Yes
HONOURS BEP Cup Winners 96-97 2nd Div Champions 03-04 Trophy Winners 03-04
BEST SEASON **FA Cup:** **FA Vase: Semi-Finalists** 2003-2004
RECORDS **Attendance:** 1,742 v A.F.C. Sudbury F.A.Vase S-Final 2nd Leg 2003-04
Scorer: Geoff Payton **Appearances:** Richard Walton
PREVIOUS **Leagues:** East Lancashire League
2003-2004 **Player of the Year:** Scott Gizon **Top Scorer:** Carl Howarth

FACT FILE

Formed: 1996
Colours: All red
Change colours: Sky/Royal Blue/Royal Blue Midweek Matchday: Wednesday
Programme: Yes Editor: Ray Moore

CLUB PERSONNEL

Chairman: James Webster
Press Officer:
Philip Webster (01282 774572)
Manager:Nigel Coates
Captain: Scott Gizon

CONGLETON TOWN

Secrtary & Press Officer: Steve Harrison, 9 Nursery Lane, Congleton, Cheshire CW12 3EX
Tel Nos: 01625 616686 (W) 07976 506760 (M)

GROUND Booth Sttreet Ground, Crescent Road, Congleton, Cheshire Tel: 01260 74460

Directions: On approach to Congleton via Clayton bypass take second right after fire station, into Booth Street. Two miles from Congleton (BR)

Capacity: 5,000 Cover: 1,200 Seats: 250

Clubhouse: Open match days only **Club Shop:** Yes. Contact:Gerry Brocklehurst

PREVIOUS **Leagues:** Crewe & Dist; North Staffs; Macclesfield; Cheshire 20-39, 46-65, 78-82; Mid Cheshire 68-78; Nth West Co 82-87, N.P.L. 87-01
Name: Congleton Hornets (prior to current club's formation in 1901)

CLUB RECORDS **Attendance:** 7,000 v Macclesfield, League 53-54
Fee Paid: None. **Fee Received:** £5,000 for D Frost (Leeds)
Goalscorer: Mick Biddle 150+
Appearances: Ray Clack 600+ & Graham Harrison 600+

BEST SEASON
FA Trophy: 3rd Qual. Rd 89-90 90-91. **FA Vase:** 4th Rd 76-77 80-81
FA Cup: 1st Rd 89-90, 0-2 v Crewe A. (A) League clubs defeated: None

HONOURS North West Counties League R-up 85-86; Cheshire County League R-up 20-21 21-22 (Div 2 81-82); Mid Cheshire League 73-74 75-76 77-78 (R-up 69-70 71-72 76-77, League Cup 71-72; Cheshire Senior Cup 20-21 37-38

Players progressing: Ron Broad (Crewe 55), Jack Mycock (Shrewsbury 58), Steve Davies (Port Vale 87), L Hamlet (Leeds), Jimmy Quinn (West Ham), Ian Brightwell (Man City)

FACT FILE
Formed: 1901 Nickname: Bears
Colours:White/black/black
Change colours: Yellow & Blue
Midweek home matchday: Tuesday
Website:http://members.aol.com/beartown
Programme: Pages: 48 Price: £1.00
Editor: Ken Mead c/oClub
Local Radio: Radio Stoke, Signal.Local
Press: Congleton Chron, Staffs Eve Sentinel

CLUB PERSONNEL
Chair: Peter EvansV- Chair: Steve Burgess
Press Officer: Ken Mead-07710405674(M)
Manager: Kevin Langley
Ass.Managers: Mark Cox & Gary Bickerstaff
Physio: Paul Kelly

2003-2004
Leading Goalscorer: Mike Scully
Ps.o.Y.: Adrian Rielly

CURZON ASHTON

Secretary: Graham Shuttleworth, 42 Southgate Road, Chadderton,OLdham. OL9 9PT
Tel/Fax: 0161 682 1137 and 07966 289434(M) gjsh.curzon@virgin.net

Ground: National Park, Katherine Street, Ashton-under-Lyne OL7 6DA (0161 330 6033)

Directions: M60 Jct 23 to Ashton- u -Lyme on Manchester Rd (A635) then turn into Williams Street.Ground at bottom of road.One and a half miles from Ashton-under-Lyne (BR)

Capacity: 5,000 Cover: 450 Seats: 350 Floodlights: Yes

Clubhouse: Every night. Food on matchdays. **Club Shop:** Contact Roy Howe, 0161 220 8345

PREVIOUS **Leagues:** Manchester Amat.; Manchester (-1978); Cheshire Co. 78-82; N.W C. 82-86 Northern Prem. Lge. 87-97, N.C.E. 97-98, N.W.C. 98-01

BEST SEASON **FA Cup:** 3rd Qual. Rd replay 89-90, 1-3 v Mossley (A) after 1-1
FA Vase: Semi-Final 79-80 **FA Trophy:** 2nd Qual. Rd 82-83, 84-85

HONOURS **NWC Lge Div.2 r-up 99-00;** Cheshire Co. Lge Div 2 R-up 78-79: Manchester Lge 77-78, R-up 74-75 75-76; Lge Cup 77-78, R-up 74-75 75-76; Murray Shield R-up 75-76: Manchester Amat. Lge 63-64 65-66, R-up 64-65: Manchester Prem. Cup x 5

RECORDS **Attendance:** 1,826 v Stamford, FA Vase SF 1980
Goalscorer: Alan Sykes **Appearances:** Alan Sykes 620
Win: 7-0 v Ashton United **Defeat:** 0-8 v Bamber Bridge

FACT FILE
Formed: 1963 Nickname: The Blues
Colours: All Blue Change colours: All Red
Midweek matches: Monday
Programme: 40pages £1.00
Editor: Robert Hurst (0161 775 3883)
Website: www.curzon-ashton.co.uk

CLUB PERSONNEL
Chairman: Harry Galloway
Vice Chairman: R.onnie Capstick
Chief Executive: Harry Twamley
President: Peter Mayo
Press Officer:Graham Shuttleworth
Treasurer: Sam Shuttleworth
Manager: Gary Lowe
Assistant Manager: Derek Hall
Physio: Martin Rothwell

FLEETWOOD TOWN

Secretary: Kevin Pennington, 1 Carlisle Avenue, Fleetwood, Lancs. FY7 8LP.
Tel: 01253 771602 (H); 01253 822626 (B) 07967 192843 (M)
Email Address: enquiries@fleetwoodtownfc.co.uk
kpennington@einw.co.uk

Ground: Highbury Stadium, Park Avenue, Fleetwood, Lancs (01253 770702)

Directions: From M55, junction 3, follow signs (A585) to Fleetwood. At Nautical College campus (onleft) traffic island take first left, at second island take 6th exit. Stadium is 3/4 mile on left.

PREVIOUS **Leagues:** None **Names:** Fleetwood Wanderers (97-98)

RECORD **Attendance:** 9,600 v Liverpool F.C. pre season friendly in 2003 at Blackpool
6,150 v Rochdale , F.A.Cup 1st Rd 1965-66

BEST SEASON: **F.A.Vase:** Finalists at Wembley in 1985 1-3 v Halesowen Town

HONOURS NWCFL v 2 Champions: 98-99 Div 2 Trophy Winners: 98-99

FACT FILE
Founded: 1997
(amalgamation of Fleetwood F.C. and Fleetwood Town who had disbanded at the end of season 1995-96)
Colours: Red & white/black/red
Midweek Matchday: Tuesday
Club Website:
www.fleetwoodfreeportfc.co.uk

CLUB PERSONNEL
Chairman: Andy Pilley

2003-2004
Player of the Year: Adam Tong
Top Scorer: Lee Catlon

FORMBY

Secretary: Dave Dickinson, 2 Seafield, Formby, Merseyside L37 4EL Tel : 01704 870944

Ground: Altcar Road, Formby, Merseyside (01704 833505) Website: www.formbfc.co.uk

Directions: Turn right at lights opposite Tesco into Altcar Road. Through mini roundabout and ground is on the rigt next to refuse tip

Capacity: 2,000 Seats: 220 Cover: 500 Floodlights: November 2002

Clubhouse: None. Matchday refreshment bar stocks hot food & drinks

Club Shop: Sells programmes, badges & souvenirs.

HONOURS Liverpool Co. Comb. 48-49, R-up 64-65; Liverpool Senior Cup 77-78, R-up 84-85; Challenge Cup 52-53 63-64 67-68, R-up 64-65; Amtr Cup 29-30 47-48 48-49; Lamot Pils Trophy 94-95; George Mahon Cup 64-65, R-up 55-56 56-57; Lancs Co FA Amt Cup 34-35, Worthington Trophy 00-01

PREVIOUS Leagues: Liverpool Co. Comb. 19-68/ Lancs Comb. 68-71, Ches. Co. 71-82.

BEST SEASON

FA Cup: 1st Rd 73-74, 0-2 v Oldham Ath. (H)

FA Trophy: 1st Rd 73-74, lost to Stalybridge Celtic

FA Vase: 2nd Rd 96-97, lost to Tetley Walker

FACT FILE

Founded: 1919 Nickname: Squirrels
Club Sponsors: DKS Packaging
Colours: Yellow/blue/yellow
Change:Green/black/black
Midweek Matches: Tuesday
Reserves : Liverpool Co.unty Comb Div 2
Prog: 36 pages, £1.00
Ed: Dave Cookson (01772 311681)

CLUB PERSONNEL

Chairman: Chris Welsh
Comm. Man.:Dave Dickinson
(01704 870944)
Managers: Peter Hennerty & Mike Scott
Physio: Barry O'Connor

GLOSSOP NORTH END

Secretary: Peter Hammond, 15 Longmoor Road, Simmondley, Glossop, Derbys SK139NH Tel: 01457 863852(H) 01457 854411(B)

Ground: Surrey Street, Glossop, Derbys (01457 855469).

Directions: A57 to Glossop.Left at traffic lights (near Tresco sign) into Glossopbrook Road then Follow road to top of hill and ground is on right. Buses 236 and 237 from Manchesterpass ground. Railway Station: Glossop Central.

Capacity: 2,374 Seats: 209 Cover: 509 Floodlights: Yes

Clubhouse: Licensed bar. Hot & cold drinks and pies etc on matchdays. **Club Shop:** Yes

HONOURS NWC Lge Lamot Pils Tphy 90-91; Manchester Lg 27-28(Gilgryst Cup 22-23 29-30 34-35 74-75); FA Amateur Cup QF 08-09. Manchester Premier Cup 1997 and 1998. Derbyshire Senior Cup 2000-01.

PREVIOUS **Leagues:** Midland 1896-98; Football Lge 1898-1915; Manchester Lge 15-56 66-78; Lancs Combination 56-66; Cheshire County 78-82.
Names: Glossop North End 1886-1898; Glossop FC 1898-1992.

BEST SEASON **FA Cup:** Quarter Final 1909 **FA Vase:**

RECORDS **Attendance:** 10,736 v Preston North End, FA Cup 1913/14
Fee paid: £3,000 for Andy Gorton (Lincoln City, 1989).
Fee received: £3,000 for Andy Gorton (Oldham Athletic, 1990).

Players progressing: Jimmy Rollands (Rochdale), Ray Redshaw (Wigan Athletic).

FACT FILE

Founded: 1886 Re-formed 1992
Nickname: Hillmen
Sponsor: T.B.A.
Colours: All Royal Blue
Change colours: AllGold.
Midweek Matches: Tuesday
Reserves' League: N.W.Co Res Lg
Programme: 32 pages, 50p
Editor: John Hamilton (01457 866216)

CLUB PERSONNEL

Chairman: Peter Hammond
President: C T Boak
Press Officer: Secretary
Manager: Micky Boyle
Asst Manager: Ian Boyle
Physio:Mick Parr

GREAT HARWOOD TOWN

Secretary: Mark Jones, 15 Elm Close, Rishton,Blackburn, BB1 4HN Tel: 01254 876822(H)

Ground: The Sportsmans, Wood Street, Great Harwood, Lancs Tel: 01254 883913

Directions: M66 from Manchester to Haslingden exit, A680 through Baxenden, Accrington to Clayton-le-Moors, left at the Hyndburn Bridge Hotel into Hyndburn Road and right into Wood Street to ground. 3miles from Rishton (BR), 6 miles from Blackburn (BR). Various buses from Heyes Lane & Park Road to Blackburn & Accrington

Capacity: 2,500 Cover: 700 Seats: 200 Floodlights: Yes

Clubhouse: The Sportsman just outside ground. Normal licensing hours. Full bar facilities. Squash courts and gym. Hot & cold snacks & drinks on matchdays from tea bar in ground.

Club Shop: Sells programmes, badges, key rings, shirts. Contact: J McKay (c/o club)

HONOURS N.W.C. R-up 91-92, Div 2 90-91, Lamot Pils Tphy 89-90, R-up 90-91, Tennents F'lit Trophy 91-92, Lancs ATS Chall. Trophy 91-92, R-up 90-91

PREVIOUS Leagues: West Lancashire; Lancs Comb. 79-82; N.W.C. 82-92; N.P.L. 92-99

Record Gate: 5,397 v Manchester Utd, 1980.

Best Season - FA Cup: 1st Qual. Rnd replay 92-93, 1-2 v Atherton LR (H), after 1-1

FA Vase: Quarter Finals 90-91, 1-2 v Littlehampton Town (A)

FACT FILE

Formed: 1965 Nickname: Robins
Club Sponsors: None
Colours: All red
Change colours: All blue
Midweek Matches: Monday
Reserves' league: West Lancs Lge
Programme: Pages: 20 Price: 20p
Editor: D Bennet

CLUB PERSONNEL

Chairman: William Holden
Press Officer: K Lambert
Commercial Manager: Mark Smith
Manager: M Crabbe
Asst Manager: Dave Sargent

MAINE ROAD

Secretary: Derek Barber, Flat 4, Maple Court, 259 Wellington Rd., Heaton Moor, Stockport SK4 5BS (0161 431 8243)

Ground: Manchester County FA Ground, Brantingham Rd., Chorlton-cum-Hardy, Manchester M21 0TT (0161 861 0344)

Directions: M60 Jct 7, A56 towards City Centre, right onto A5145 Chorlton/Stockport, thro' lights, left at next lights into Wilbraham Rd (A6010) to Chorlton, thro' lights for approx 1 mile. Left into Withington Rd, first left into Brantingham Rd, ground 300 yds on left. 2 miles from Stretford (Metrolink (tram)), 3 miles from Piccadilly & Victoria , Virgin & First North Western trains. Buses16 16A 85 87 87A 168 188 275.

Clubhouse: Matchdays (Snacks on ground) **Shop:** No.

Capacity: 2,000 Seats: 200 Cover: 700 Floodlights: Yes.

HONOURS Manc. Prem. Lg(4) 82-86, Cup 82-83 83-84;98-98 Man.Co Prem. Cup 87-8 Chal. Cup(4) 82-83 84-87; NW Co's Lg Div 2 89-90 (R-up 88-89).

Previous Leagues: Rusholme Sunday 55-66; Manchester Amtr Sunday 66-72; Manchester 72-87

BEST SEASON **FA Cup:** 2nd Qual. 2nd replay 92-93
FA Vase: 4th Rd 94-95

RECORDS **Attendance:** 875 v Altrincham, FA Cup 2nd Qual. Rd 29/9/90

FACT FILE

Founded: 1955 Nickname: Blues
Sponsors:Parry's Jewellers
Colours: Navy/Azure/navy/white
Change Colours: Yellow, Green,Yellow
Midweek matchday: Tuesday
Reserves ' League: Mid Cheshire Div 2
Programme: 48 pages £1.00
Editor: Mr P,Ramsden (0161 448 1659)

CLUB PERSONNEL

Chairman: R Meredith
President: F G Thompson
Press Off: P Ramsden Manager: Chris Simms Physio: E Jenkinson Captain: Lee Todman

2003-2004

Top Scorer:Chris Simms
P.o.Y.: Neil Chappell

NANTWICH TOWN

Secretary: Bernard Lycett, 'Rivington", Clay lane, Haslington, Crewe CW11 5SE
Tel: 01270 584066 (H) 07876320280 (M) Email Address: lblycett@aol.com

Ground: Jackson Avenue, off London Road, Nantwich, Cheshire. Tel: 01270 624098

Directions: M6 Jct 16, A500 for Nantwich (about 8 miles), continue on A52 over railway crossing (London Rd), second right after railway crossing into Jackson Ave. From Chester, use the A51. Three miles from Crewe (BR)
Capacity: 1,500 Seats: 150 Cover: 555 Floodlights: Yes

Clubhouse: Open Matchdays. Hot pies available **Club Shop:** No

HONOURS Cheshire Co. Lg 80-81; Ches. Snr Cup 75-76; R-up (5) N.W. Co.Lg.Cup 94-95 R-up 92-93 Mid Cheshire Lg 1963-64 R-Up (2) Manchester Lg R-Up 66-67

PREVIOUS **Leagues:** Shropshire & Dist.; The Combination 1892-94; Lancs Comb. 12-15; Comb 19-38; Manchester; Mid-Cheshire; Cheshire County 68-82.
Name: Nantwich FC (pre 1973) **Ground** : Kingsley Fields (191-21)

RECORDS **Attendance:** 5,121 v Winsford United (Cheshire Sen.Cup 2nd Rd replay 19.02.21.) v Altrincham, Chesh. Sen.C 66-67
Top Scorer: Bobby Jones 60 46-47
Fee received: £4,000 from Stafford Rangers for D.Dawson
Record Goalscorer in Season: Gerry Duffy, 42 in 61-62

Best season F.A.Cup: 5th Q Rd (2) 1900-01&1903-04 **F.A.Vase:** 4th Rd (3) 93-04,96-97.03-04
Best Victory 15-0 v Ashton U, Man Lg 66-67
Worst Defeat: 0-12 v Chirk(A) F.A.C 2QRd 1888-9

Players Progressing (29) Latest:
Wes Wilkinson(2004),Ronnie Jepson(1989), Mark Came(1984)

FACT FILE

Founded: 1884
Nickname: Dabbers
Club Sponsors: C.C.L.
Colours: All Green
Change colours: Yelow and Blue
Midweek matchday: Tuesday
Reserves' League:Mid Chesh Div 2
Programme: 24 pages,£1.00
Editor: Michael Charwin(mdchat@hotmail.com)
Club Website: www.nantwichtownfc.co.uk

CLUB PERSONNEL

President: Michael Chatwin
Chairman: Clive Jackson
6 Spencer Close, Crewe CW2 8DT
01270 664469 (H) 07970 546238 (B)
Vice Chairman: Jon Brydon
Manager: Steve Davis Captain: Melford Knight Physio: Paul Kelly

2003-04

Leading Goalcorer
Wes Wilikinson 21(15 lg 6cup)

NEWCASTLE TOWN

Secretary: John F Cotton, 293 Weston Rd., Weston Coyney, Stoke-on-Trent, Staffs. St3 6HA
Tel: 01782 333445 (H) 07977516879(M)

Ground: Lyme Valley Parkway Stadium, Lilleshall Rd, Clayton, Newcastle-under-Lyne, Staffs (01782 662351) (Club 01782 662350 also a fax)

Directions: M6 jct 15, A500 for Stoke, left at r'bout A519 for Newcastle, rightat 2nd r'bout into Stafford Ave., 1st left into Tittensor Road to ground. 3miles from Stoke-on-Trent (BR).

Seats: 300 Cover: 1,000 Capacity: 4,000 Floodlights: Yes **Club Shop:** Yes

Clubhouse: Saturday matchdays 12-7.30pm, midweek 5-11pm. Hot & cold food available.

HONOURS: Nth West Co's Lg Div 1 R-up 95-96 96-97,99-00 Div 2 R-up 91-92, Challenge Cup 96-97, R-up 99-00 F/Lit Trophy R-up 96-97; Lamot Pils Tphy 91-92; Mid Cheshire Lg Div1 85-86, R-up 86-78, Div 2 82-83, 90-91, Lge Cup 84-85; Walsall Snr Cup 93-94 94-95 R-up 95-96; Sentinel Cup 94-95; Tennents Floodlit Trophy 92-93 95-96; Staffs Snr Cup R-up 95-96, 01-02; Staffs M/W F/Light Lge 94-95 R-up 95-96; Staffs Presidents CupWinners 2002-03

RECORDS - **Attendance:** 3,948 v Notts County FA Cup Nov 96 **Win:** 8-0v Skelmersdale U.
Defeat: 0-5 v Eastwood Hanley (A) **Appearances:** Neil Pesteridge 385 (Lg only)

Goalscorer: Shaun Wade 105 (NWCL only) **F.A.Vase:** S-Final 99-00

PREVIOUS - **Leagues:** Hanley & Dist. Sunday; North Staffs Sunday; Potteries & Dist.Sunday; Res Refuge Ass Mid; Newcastle & Dist/ Staffs Co.; Mid Cheshire.

Names: Parkway Hanley (founded 1964, later Clayton Park, ParkwayClayton); Newcastle Town (founded 1980) - clubs merged in 1986.

FACT FILE

Founded: 1964 Nickname: Castle.
Sponsors: Review
Colours: All Royal Blue/blue/white
Change colours: All yellow
Midweek Matches: Tuesday
Reserve Team: SpringbankVending.Midland
Programme: 40 pages,£1.00
Editor: Mark Barlow (07976 805873)
Website: www.nitvision.net/newcastletownfc

CLUB PERSONNEL

Chairman: Carl Birchall
Press Officer: Mark Barlow (07976 805873)
General Manager:Jimmy Wallace
Manager: Nigel Gleghorn
Asst Manager: Neil GriffithsPhysio: Lee Arnold
Captain: Mark Beeston

2003-2004

Captain: Mark Beeston
Top Scorer: Paul Keily 25
Player of The Year: Michael Lennon

RAMSBOTTOM UNITED

Secretary: Malcolm Holt, 23 Newcombe Road,Holcombe Brook, Ramsbotham, Lancs.
Tel Nos: 01204 883085 (H) 0776 1828487 (M)

Ground: Riverside Ground, Acre Bottom, Ramsbottom. Tel: 01706 822799(Cricket Club)
Answer Phone: 01706 822458 (for match details) **Floodlights**: Yes
Email address: final.inspection@madison filter.com

Directions: M66(North) to junction 1, take A56 towards Ramsbottom. After one mile turn left into Bury New Road. Turn left after the Mondi Paper Mill along the road running parallel with the East Lancs Railway. From North: M65 jct 8- A56 Follow signs ro Ramsbottom into town centre.
Railway: Bury (Metrolink to Manchester) and Ramsbottom (East Lancs Railway)

HONOURS: Bolton Comb. Div. One Champs 72-73; Bolton Comb. Prem Div. 76-77, 86-87; Manchester Lge Div. One Champs 90-91; Manchester Lge Div. 1 Cup Winners 90-91; Gilgryst Cup Winners 94-95; NWCFL Div 2 Champ 96-97, Trophy 95-96

RECORDS **Attendance:** 829 v Southport F.A.C. 3Q 98-99
PREVIOUS **Leagues:** Bury Amateur League, Bolton Combination, Manchester Lge.
BEST SEASON: F.A. Cup: 3rd Q 1998-99 **F.A. Vase:** 2nd Round 98-99, 99-00

FACT FILE
Formed: 1966
Colours: Blue with white trim/blue/white
Change Colours: Red/Black/Black
Midweek Matchday: Tuesday
Programme: Pages: 46 Price:£1.00
Editor: Chris Dunn
Website: fhttp.ramsbottom united.2ya.oom

CLUB PERSONNEL
Prtesident: John Smith
Chairman Harry Williams (01706 823029)
Vice Chairman: Geoff Lay
Press Officer: Chris Bootham
Manager:Derek Egan
Asst. Manager Andy Grimshaw
Captain: Matt Raywood

2002-2004
Top scorer: Matt Swailes
Player of the Year: Iain Dyson

SALFORD CITY

Secretary: Bill Taylor, 23 Westwood Drive, Prendelebury, Salford. M27 4JT
Tel Nos: 0161 736 1840

Ground: Moor Lane, Kersal, Salford, Manchester. Tel: 0161 792 6287

Directions: M62 jct 17, A56 Bury New Road to Manchester, continue thro' 4 sets of lights, right into Moor Lane, ground 500 yds left. 4 miles from Manchester Victoria (BR). Buses 96, 139, 94, 95 to Moor Lane

Capacity: 8,000 Seats: 260 Cover: 600 Floodlights: Yes

Clubhouse: Open matchdays only. Hot snacks

HONOURS Lancashire Amateur Cup 72-73 74-75 76-77; Manchester Senior Cup, Manchester Challenge Cup, Manchester Lg 74-75 75-76 76-77 78-79. Reserve Division North 2000-01. Reserve Division North Cup 2000-01.

PREVIOUS **Leagues:** Manchester 63-80; Cheshire Co. 80-82.
Names: Salford Central 40-63; Salford Amateurs 1963 until merger with Anson Villa; Salford FC.
Ground: Crescent, Salford

BEST SEASON **FA Cup:** **FA Vase:**

RECORDS **Attendance:** 3,000 v Whickham FA Vase 1981

FACT FILE
Founded: 1940
Nickname: Ammies
Colours: Dark blue
with silber trim/silver/silver
Change colours: Yellow and sky blue
Midweek Matches: Tuesday
Reserves' League: NWC Res. Div. S.
Programme: 24 pages, £1.00
Editor: Dave Cooper

CLUB PERSONNEL
Chairman: Ged Carter
Manager: Andy Brown
Press Officer: Secrtary
Commercial Manager: Stevie Plant

Newcastle Town.

SKELMERSDALE UNITED

Secretary: Bryn Jones, 34 Bromilow Road, Skelmersdale, Lancs. WN8 8TU

Ground: Westgate Interactive Stadium, Selby Place, off Stathem Rd.,Stanley Industrial Estate, Skelmersdalr, Lancs. WN8 8EF

Directions: M58 Jct 4 to Skelm. Over roundabout into Glenburn Road, left into Neverstitch Rd at next roundabout and first right at next one into Staveley Rd. Sharp left bend into Stathem Rd with ground 500 yds on left in Selby Place.

Capacity: 2,300 **Seats:** 240 **Cover:** 500 **Floodlights**: Yes **Clubhouse:** Yes **Club Shop:** Yes.

HONOURS FA Amateur Cup 70-71 R-up 66-67; Ches. Co. Lg 68-69 69-70, Jubilee Cup 69-70; Lancs F'lit Cup 69-70; Lancs Jnr Cup 69-70 70-71; Ashworth Cup 70-71; Barassi Anglo-Italian Cup 70-71; Lancs Non-Lge Cup 73-74 74-75; North West Co's Lg Cup: 99-00 R-up 82-83.N.W.Co Div 2 R-Up: 97-98

PREVIOUS **Leagues:** Liverpool County Comb., Lancashire Comb. 1891-93, 03-07, 21-24, 55-68, 76-78, Cheshire County 68-71 78-82, Northern Premier 71-76.

BEST SEASON
FA Cup: 1st Rd 67-68, 0-2 v Scunthorpe(A), 68-69, 0-2 v Chesterfield(A), 71-72, 0-4 v Tranmere R. (H) **FA Amateur Cup:** Winners 70-71

RECORDS **Attendance:** 7,000 v Slough, FA Amat Cup Q-F '67

2003-2004 **Player of the Year:** Steve Rimmer **Top Goalscorer:** Stuart Rudd

FACT FILE
Founded: 1882
Nickname: Skem
Sponsors:Westgate Interactive Ltd.
Colours: All Blue
Change colours: Gold/black/blackMidweek Matches: Tuesday
Reserves: N.W.Co Res Div
Programme: 32 pages, £1
Editor: Nic Rudd
(www.skelmersdaleutdfc.com)

CLUB PERSONNEL
President: D.Tomlinson
Football Chairman: FRank Hughes
Managing Director: A.Gore -
Press Officer: Secretary
Manager: Paul Gallagher
Asst Manager: Mick Buoey
Coach: CliffTalbot
Physios: Billy Leigh& Ronnie Taylor
Captain: Stuart Rudd

SQUIRES GATE

Secretary: John Maguire, 2 Squires Court, Cairn Grove, Blackpool FY4 2RA

Ground: School Road, Marton, Blackpool, Lancs. Tel: 01253 798584

Directions: M6 to M55 jct 4, left onto A583, right at 1st lights (Whitehall Rd) follow signs for airport. Ground approx 1.5 miles on right.
Nearest station Blackpool South.

Capacity: 1000 Seats: 2 new stands (100 seats) Cover: One side
Floodlights: Yes
Clubhouse: Yes

HONOURS West Lancs Lg: Div 2 80-81, Richardson Cup 86-87, N.W.C.L 2nd Div Trophy winners 2000/01

PREVIOUS **Leagues:** W. Lancs (pre-1991)

RECORD **Attendance:** 600 v Everton 95

FACT FILE
Formed: 1948
Colours: All Royal Blue
Change Colours:Tangerine/Navy/Tangerine
Midweek Matches: Tuesday
Programme: 20 pages Price:£1.50
Editor:

CLUB PERSONNEL
Chairman:Phil Days
Life Vice President: Wilf Carr
Manager: Ted Starkey
Assistant Manager: Phil Brown
Res Managers: Bryn Blakey & Andy Hodson
Club Captain: Alex Rawson

2003-2004
Player of the Year: Paul Paynter
TopGoalscorer: Chris Blundell

ST HELENS TOWN

Secretary: Nattalie Ellaway,34 Hatfield Close, Sutton Heath, St Helens, Merseyside WA9 5HG Tel: 01744 812817

Ground: St Helens R.L.F.C. , Knowsley Road, St Helens

Directions: **From South:** M62 Jct 7-5th onto A570 to town centre follow route to Liverpool from cinema complex. Proceed 1.5 miles before right turn at lights by 'Bird in Hand pub and ground is on left down Dunriding Lane **From North:** M6.Jct 23 take A580 to L'pool for 7 miles then at junction with A570 take first right into Bleak Hilll Road.Left at right hand bend after 1 mile into Mill Brow. At T junction left at Black Bull, turn right -ground on left.

Capacity: 19,100 **Seats:** 2,362 **Cover:** 12,408 **Floodlights:** Yes

Clubhouse: Weekdays 8-11pm, Saturday matchdays 2-6.30pm. **Club Shop:** Yes

HONOURS: FA Vase 86-87; George Mahon Cup 1949; Lancs Comb. 71-72, Div 2 50-51, Lg Cup R-up 70-71;Liv'pool Snr Non Lge Cup R-up 76-77; Lancs Jnr Cup R-up 66-67; Watson Trophy 74 Bass Charrington Cup 73-74; Carling Chall Cup r-up 93-94; N.W.C. Floodlit Trophy r-up 97-98.

PREVIOUS **Leagues:** Lancs Comb. 03-14 46-49 49-75; Liverpool County Comb. 49-74; Chesh County 75-82.**Grounds:** Park Road 01-52; Hoghton Rd 46-53 54-2000 City Road 52-53.

BEST SEASON **FA Cup:** 4th Q Rd 85-86 **FA Vase:** Winners 86-87

RECORDS **Gate:** 4,000 v Manchester City, Bert Trautmann transfer match,April 1950.
Goalscorer: S Pennington **W in:** 10-4 v Everton `B' 1952
Appearances: Alan Wellens **Defeat** : 1-8 v Liverpool Res., L'pool Snr Cup 1960

FACT FILE
Founded: 1946Nickname: `Town'
Colours: Red & white stripes/red/red
Change colours: Royal blue or White
Midweek Matches: Tuesday
Programme: 24 pages, 50p
Editor: John McKiernan (01744 600612)
Local Press: Reporter, Star, Echo.

CLUB PERSONNEL
Chairman/Press Officer: Jim Barrett
Public Liaison Officer: John McKiernan
01744 635826 (H) 01744 24348 (W)
Manager:G.Paladino Asst. Man: J.Gibiliru
Coach: M.Hayde Captain: James Gedman

2003-2004
Player of the Year: Jordan Milsom
Top Scorer: Terry Anderson

STONE DOMINOES

Secretary: Vicky Turner,Springbank House,Station Road,Barlaston, Staffs ST12 9DE
Tel: 01782 373298 (H) 07866 096198 (M) 01782 220781 (W)

Ground: Springbank Stadium, Kings Park, Meir Heath, Stoke on Trent, Staffs.
Tel: 07866 098198

Directions: From Stone town centre take A520 (to Leek and Meir Heath). at 'Swynnerton Arms' pub bare right and follow A520 (Leek) to top of hill and turn right at first mini roundabout into Hilderstone Road,signposted B5066 (Sandon) .Ground is just under a mile on right.

Floodlights: Yes

Honours: Midland Lge Div. 1 99-00, Div. 2 R-up 96-97, N.W.C.: Div 2 Winners 2002-2003
Div.1 Cup 98-99, Div. 2 Cup 96-97, Charity Shield 00

Previous League: Midland League

Record Attendance: 330v Eastwood Town F>A>Vase 10.02.04

FACT FILE
Formed: 1987
Colours:White/red/white
Change Colours: Yellow/blue/white
Midweek Matchday: Tuesday
Programme: Price:£1.00

PERSONNEL
Chairman: Bob Bowers
Springbank House, Station Road,
Barlaston, Staffs.
Tel: 01782 373298 (H) 01785 815551 (B)

Manager: Andy O'Connor
Physios: Steve Killeen & Chris Banks
Captain: Lee Lawton

2003-2004
Top Scorer: Dave Shaw 29
Player of the Year: Paul Donnelly

TRAFFORD

GROUND: Shawe View, Pennybridge Lane, Flixton, Urmston, Manchester M41 5DL
Tel: 0161 7471727 Email: dave-murray@traffordfc.freeserve.co.uk

Directions: M60 jct 9, B5158 towards Urmston, at 1st r/about take 1st exit, 1st lights turn right into Moorside Road, at nextr/about 2nd exit into Bowfell Rd, at next lights turn sharp left, then immediately right into Pennybridge Lane next to Bird-in-Hand Pub parking on left 100yds

Capacity: 2,500 Cover: 740 Seats: 292
Clubhouse: Yes **Club Shop:** Yes
Previous - Leagues: Mid Ches. 90-92; N.W.C. 92-97; N.P.L. 97-03. **Name**: NorthTrafford 90-94.

CLUB RECORDS **Attendance:** 803 v Flixton (NPL Div 1 27/12/97)
Goalscorer: Garry Vaughan 88 **Appearances:** Garry Vaughan 293
Win: 10-0 v Haslingden St Mary's (LancsAmt Shield 91)
Defeat: 0-6 v Oldham Town (NWCL Div 2 93)
Fee Paid: Undisclosed for Jock Russell (Radcliffe Borough)
Fee Received: Undisclosed for Mike Turner (Witton A.)

BEST SEASON **FA Vase:** 5th Rd 95-96 **FA Trophy:** 3rd Round 2000-01
FACup: 2nd Rd Qual 95-96,99-00

HONOURS Lamont Pils Trophy 93-94; NWCL Div 1 96-97, Div 2 R-up 93-94, Lge ChallCup R-up 96-97; Res Div 93-94; Carling Chall Cup R-up 94-95; Manchester PremCup R-up 94-95, R-up 96-97, Res Div Champ 96-97, Cup 96-97; Manchester Amt Cup 96-97,01-02 Unifilla 1st Div Cup 97-98 Unibond Presidents Cup 99-00 Mid Cheshire Div 2 99-00

FACT FILE
Formed: 1990
Nickname: The North
Sponsors: Caffro Construction Ltd
Colours: All White
Change colours: All Yellow
Midweek Matchday: Tuesday
Reserve League: Mid Cheshire Div 2
Website: www.traffordfc.freeserve.co.uk
Programme
Pages: 44 Price: £1
Editor: David Murray (0161 775 7509)

CLUB PERSONNEL
Chairman: Tom Walmsley
President: David Roberts
Secretary: Graham Foxall
90 Grosvenor Road, Urmston M41 5AQ
Tel: 0161 747 4502

Manager: Joey Dunn
Asst Manager: Stuart Humphries

ASHTON TOWN

Secretary: Rebecca Williams,44 Tintern Avenue, Astley,Tyldesley,Manchester M29 7WL
Tel Nos: 01942 892680(H) 07739 079412 (M) E-mail: williams8529@aol.com

Ground: Edge Green Street, Ashton-in-Makerfield, Wigan WN4 8SY (01942 510677)
Directions: M6 Jct 23, A49 to Ashton-in-M. Right at lights onto A58 towards Bolton. After 3/4 mile turn right at `Rams Head' P.H. into Golbourne Rd. After 200 yds right into Edge Green Str. Ground at end.
Floodlights: No

HONOURS Warrington Lg Guardian Cup.

PREVIOUS **Leagues:** Warrington, Lancs Comb. 03-11 71-78, Ches. Co. 78-82.

BEST SEASON **FA Vase:** Prelim. Rd 84-85

RECORD **Gate:** 600 v Accrington Stanley 76-77

FACT FILE

Founded: 1962
Colours: Red with white trim/red/red
Change colours: All sky blue
Midweek Matches: Tuesday

CLUB PERSONNEL

President: W Pomfrett
Chairman: Ian Williams
Manager: Norman Hickson

BLACKPOOL MECHANICS

Secretary: William Singleton, 36 Colwyn Avenue, Blackpool FY4 4EU (01253 692863)
Ground: Jepson Way, Common Edge Rd, Blackpool, Lancs FY4 5DY (01253 761721).
Directions: M6 to M55,Exit Jct 4 follow Airport signs. Left at r'bout along A583 across round about to lights, right into Whitehill Rd along to roundabout.Take Lytham St Annes to T junction and traffic lights.Across main road into Jepson Way and ground..Rail to Blackpool North - then bus 11c from Talbot Rd bus station (next to rail station) to Shovels Hotel, Common Edge Rd.
Capacity: 2,000 **Seats:** 250 **Cover**: 1,700 **Floodlights**: Yes
Clubhouse: Match days, training nights. Dancehall. Matchday, hot food.
Club Shop: Manager Andrew Sneddon (01253 729962). Ties, sweaters, old programmes, badges.
HONOURS Lancs Comb Bridge Shield 72-73; NW Co's. Lg Div 3 85-86; W Lancs Lg 60-61 62-63; Lancs County FA Shield 57-58 60-61:
PREVIOUS **Leagues:** Blackpool & Fylde Comb., West Lancs, Lancs Comb. 62-68.
Grounds: Stanley Pk 47-49
RECORD **Gate:** 1,200 v Morecambe, Lancs Comb, August 1968
2003-2004 **Player of the Year**: Peter Taberner **Top Scorer**: Tim Kinley

FACT FILE

Founded: 1947 Nickname: Mechs
Sponsors: Dutton Forshaw, Blackpool
Club colours: Tangerine/white/tangerine
Change colours: All blue
Midweek matchday: Tuesday
Programme: 10 pages, 50p
Editor: John Barlow

CLUB PERSONN

Chairman: Henry David Baldwin
President: Lawence Wright
Commercial Manager: John Sanderson
Manager: Stuart Parker
Asst Man.: Wayne Hughes
Coach: Terry Green
Captain: Mark Ashall

CAMMELL LAIRD F.C.

Secretary: Tony Wood, 25 Prenton Park Road, Prenton, Birkenhead. CH42 9JR
Tel Nos: 0151 608 0591 (H) 07931761429 (M) e-mail: toddywood@hotmail.com

Ground: Kirklands, St Peter's Road, Rock Ferry, Birkenhead, Merseyside. Ch42 1PY
Tel Nos: 0151 645 3121/5991 Fax: 0151 644 7354 e-mail: lairdsafe@fsmail.net

Capacity: **Seats:** **Cover:** **Floodlights:** **Clubhouse:**

Directions: From M6 take M56 towards Chester for then M53 towards Birkenhead. Exit Jct 5 towards Birkenhead on A41. After approx. 4miles take B5136 signposted to New Ferry. After a mile, turn right into Procter Rd at new pedestrian crossing. Club is at bottom of the road on the left.

PREVIOUS **Leagues:** West Cheshire **Record Attendance:** 2,000

HONOURS

2003-2004 **Player of the Year and Top Goalscorer:** Ronnie Morgan

FACT FILE

Formed: 1906
Sponsor:
Colours: All Blue.
Change colours: All White
Midweek Matches: Tuesday
Programme Editor: Ray Steele
e-mail: ray.steele@fsmail.net

CLUB PERSONNEL

Chairman: Ray Steele
Manager: Ian Doran
Coach: Ian Griffiths:
Captain: Kevin Thompson

CASTLETON GABRIELS

Secretary: Leon Beardmore, 4 Minor Street, Castleton, Rochdale, Leeds Ol11 2TQ
Tel Nos: 01706 675324 (H) 07985 580964(M)
Ground: Butterworth Park, Chadwick Lane, off Heywood Rd., Castleton, Rochdale.
Tel: 01706 527103)
Directions: M62 Jct 20, A6272M to r'bout. Left towards Castleton (A664Edinburgh Way) to next r'bout, keeping Tesco Superstore to the left, take 1st exit to next r'bout, take 2nd exit into Manchester Rd (A664), after just under mile turn right at `Top House' P.H. into Heywood Rd., to end & ground on right
Capacity: 1,500 Seats: 400 Cover: 650 Floodlights: Yes
Clubhouse: Open seven nights a night and all day Saturday. Pie & peas and sandwiches available matchdays (pie & peas only at Reserve matches) **Club Shop:** No
HONOURS Manchester Lge 86-87, Murray Shield 86-87; Res Div Cup 95-96.
PREVIOUS **Leagues:** Rochdale Alliance 24-84; Manchester 84-89.
Name: St Gabriels (pre-1960s) **Ground:** Park pitches; Springfield Pk 60-81.
RECORDS **Gate:** 640 v Rochdale, pre-season friendly 1991 **Win:** 8-0 v Squires Gate N.W.Co.Div 2 94 **Defeat:** 1-10 v Blackpool Mechanics N.W.Co.Div 2 95

FACT FILE

Founded: 1924 Nickname: Gabs
Club Sponsors: Kick Off
Colours: Sky & Navy/Sky & Navy/Navy
Change colours: All red
Midweek matchday: Tuesday
Reserves ' League: N.W.C. Res. Div.
Programme: 28 pages, 50p
Editor:David Jones (01942730220(W)

CLUB PERSONNEL

Chairman: Jim Picken
Vice Chairman: R Butterworth
Press Officer: Secretary
Manager/Coach:David Jones
Assistant Manager:Roy Grundy
Coach: Neil Mills

CHADDERTON

Secretary: Louise Kershaw, 186 Burnley Lane,Chadderton, Oldham. OL1 2QW
Ground: Andrew Street, Chadderton, Oldham, Lancs (0161 624 9733)
Directions: **M62 Jct 20**, A627(M) to M'chester.. M'way becomes dual carriageway. Left at 1st major traffic lights A669 Middleton Rd, then first left into Butterworth Street. Andrew Street is second right. Oldham Werneth (BR) 1 m or Mills Hill (BR) l m. **M60 Jct 21** onto A663 to A699 rt at lights. 2nd left(Burnley St) and 2nd left again(Andrew St).Buses 24,181,182 to Middleton Rd from Lever Street of Piccadilly Gardens.
Capacity: 2,500 **Seats:** 200 **Cover**: 600 **Floodlights**: Yes
Clubhouse: Matchdays only. Hot & cold snack during & after games **Club Shop:** No
HONOURS M'chester Am Lg 62-63, North Div 55-56, M. Prem Cup R-up 82-83, Chall Tphy 71-72, R-up 72-73, M. Lg Div 1 66-67, Div 2 64-65, Gilgryst Cup 69-70, Murray Shield 65-66, Lancs Comb. Cup R-up 81-82, Alf Pettit & Hulme Celtic Cup 61-62, NWC F/lit Tphy R-up 92-93
RECORD Gate: 1,500 v Guinness Ex'ts 1969 **Appearances:** Billy Elwell 750+ (64-90)
Players progressing: (include) David Platt (Crewe, Arsenal), John Pemberton (Crewe,Leeds) Graham Bell(Oldham), Paul Hilton (Bury), Don Graham (Bury).

FACT FILE
Founded: 1947 Nickname: Chaddy
Colours: AllRed
Change colours:
Sky blue/navy blue/navy blue
Midweek Matches: Tuesday
Programme: 28-32 pages
Editor: David Greaves
Previous Leagues: Oldham Am, Manchester Am, Manchester 64-80, Lancs Comb 80-82
CLUB PERSONNEL
Chairman: Harry Mayall
President: Derek Glynn
Manager: Richard Graham
Captain: Lee Spratt
2003-2004
Player of the Year: Steven Worthington
Top Scorer: M.Love 7
Manchester Umbro International Cup 2000

CHEADLE TOWN

Secretary: David Busby, 9 Tatton Road, Handforth, Wilmslow, Cheshire Sk9 3QZ
Tel Nos: 01625 524116 ((H) o7932 634630 (M)
Ground: Park Road Stadium, Park Road, Cheadle, Cheshire SK8 2AN (0161 4282510).
Directions: M60 Jct 2, follow signs towards Cheadle (A560), first left after lights into Park Road, ground at end. 1 mile from Gatley (BR), buses from Stockport.11,170, 310,312 and 371
Capacity: 2,500 Seats: 300 Cover: 300 Floodlights Yes
Clubhouse: Open every night. Food available **Club Shop**: No
HONOURS Manchester Lg Div 1 79-80 (R-up 80-81 81-82); Manchester Amtr Cup 79-80;Lamot Pils R-up 90-91; NWCFL Div 2 Trophy R-up 95-96, Reserve's League Cup 99-00
PREVIOUS **Leagues**: Manchester (pre 1987)
RECORD **Attendance :** 1,700 v Stockport County, August 1994.
Scorer: Peter Tilley **Appearances:** John McArdle
Players progressing: Ashley Ward (Crewe), Steve Bushell (York), Dean Crowe(Stoke).
2003-2004: **Top Scorer:** Lee Morris **P.o.Y.**: Matthew Smith

FACT FILE
Founded: 1961
Colours: Yellow/blue/yellowChange colours: Red/white/red
Midweek Matches: Wednesday 7.45
Reserves' Lge: Mid Cheshire Div 2
Prog: 24 pages,£1.00 Ed: Stuart Crawford
CLUB PERSONNEL
President: Freddie Pye
Chairman: Chris Davies
Vice-Chairman: Clive Williams
Press Officer:
Chris Davies (0161 428 2510).
Manager:Paul Cunningham
Player Coach: Tony Coyle
Captain: Paul Riley

DAISY HILL

Secretary: Bob Naylor, 8 Bailey Fold, Westhoughton, Bolton, Lancs BL5 3HH
Tel: 01942 813720
Ground: New Sirs, St James Street, Westhoughton, Bolton, Lancs. Tel: 01942 818544
Directions: M61 Jct 5, A58 (Snydale Way/Park Road) for 1.5 miles, left into Leigh Road (B5235) for 1 mile, right into village then left between Church and School into St James Street. Ground 250 yds on the left. Half mile from Daisy Hill (BR)
Capacity: 2,000 Seats: 200 Cover: 250 Floodlights: No Club Shop: No
Clubhouse: Open normal licensing hours during any football activity. Snacks on matchdays
HONOURS Bolton Comb Prem Div 62-63 72-73 75-76 77-78, Lg Cup 59-60 61-62 71-72 72-73; Lancs Shield 61-62 71-72 86-87:
PREVIOUS **Leagues:** Westhoughton; Bolton Comb.; Lancs Combination. 78-82.
Name: Westhoughton Town **Record Goals & Apps:**Alan Roscoe 300-450
BEST SEASON **FA Cup:** **FA Vase:**
RECORD **Attendance:** 2,000 v Horwich RMI,Westhoughton Charity Cup Final 79-80
Players Progressing: Barry Butler (Chester C)+ Phil Priestley (Rochdale)via Atherton LR

FACT FILE
Founded: 1894(first known records)
Reformed: 1952
Colours: All royal blue Change: All red
Midweek Matches: Tuesday
Reserves' Lge : Preston & District
Programme: 40 pages £1.00
Editor: T.B.A.
CLUB PERSONNEL
Chairman:Tony Veitch
Manager: Frank Armstrong
Captain: Mark Armstrong
2003-2004
Player of the Year: Nick Baxter
Top Goalscorer: Jon Saxon

DARWEN

Secretary: Lynn Atkinson, 14 Prospect Gardens,Darwen, Lancs (01254 708158)
Ground: Anchor Ground, Anchor Road, Darwen, Lancs BB3 0BB.
Clubhouse: Matchday only
Directions: A666 Blackburn / Bolton road, 1 mile north of Darwen town centre,turn right at Anchor Hotel, ground 200 yds on left. One and a half miles from Darwen (BR), bus 51 to Anchor Hotel.From M65 Jct 4 signs to Darwen.Left at A666,1/2 mile left at anchor Hotel. ground 200 yds on left
Capacity: 4,000 Seats: 250 Cover: 2,000 Floodlights: YesShop:No
HONOURS Lancs Comb 31 32 73 75: Comb Cup 30 31 75; Lancs Jun Cup 73; Geo Watson Trophy 73; LFA Yth Cup 75; NWC Cup 83; Lancs F/Lit Trophy 90; NWC Res Div Cup 94; Blackburn & Dist Yth Lge 94 95 97, Cup 94 95 97; NW All Chall Cup 96.
PREVIOUS **Leagues**:Football Alliance 1889-91, Football Lg 1891-99, Lancs Lg 99-03,Lancs Comb. 03-75, Ches. Co. 75-82. **Ground:** Barley Bank
RECORD **Gate:** (Anchor Ground) 10,000 v Fleetwood Lancs Jun Cup 1920
14,000 v Blackburn Rovers 1882
BEST SEASON **FA Cup**: Semi Finals 1881
Top Goalscorer 2003-2004: D.Stubberfield

FACT FILE
Founded: 1875
Sponsors:
Colours: Red & white/white/red
Change colours: All blue
Midweek Matches: Tuesday
Reserves' League: NWC Res. Div.
Programme: 20 pages, £1.00
Editor:D.Narah
Local papers: Lancs Evening Telegraph
CLUB PERSONNEL
President: E Devlin
Chairwoman: Mrs Kath Marah
Manager: S Mullen
Asst Manager: M Atkinson
Physio: Mick Sharples

ECCLESHALL

Secretary: Richard Marsh, 58 Leawood Road, Trent Vale, Stoke- on -Trent, ST4 6LA
Tel NOs: 01782 746312 (H) 01782 213811 (W)

Ground Pershall Park, Chester Road, Eccleshall, Staffordshire
Tel: 01785 851351(matchdays).

Directions: From M6 jcts 14 or 15 find way to Eccleshall High Street (B5026) drive towards Loggerheads. Pass church, cricket and tennis clubs for a mile, to the sign for Pershall. Ground is 100 yards past sign on right.

Previous Leagues:Stafford & District, Staffs Aliance,Staffs County Lg (N) & Midland League

2003-2004 Player of the Year & Captain: Tim Buckley **Top Scorer**: Darren Alexander 24

Honours: Staffs Co. Lg (N) Champions 1983, Co Lg (N) Cup Winners 1983,Staffs F.A.Vase Finnalists 1985, Midland League Champions 1900 Runners -Up 1999,2000

FACT FILE
Formed: 1971
Colours: Blue & white/blue/blue
Change: Tangerine/navy blue/tangerine
Midwek Matchday: Wednesday

CLUB PERSONNEL
Chairman: Andy Mapperson
Manager: Robert Askey Coach: Chris Phillips
Programme Editor: Richard Marsh
2003-2004
Player of the Year & Captain: Tim Buckley
Top Scorer: Darren Alexander 24

FLIXTON

Secretary: Paul Chadwick, 15 Coniston Road, Flixton, Manchester M41 6PS (07754 416889)
Ground: Valley Road, Flixton, Manchester M41 8RQ Tel: 0161 747 7757
Directions: Leave M60 take B5214 signed Urmston. At 2nd R'about take 3rd exit. Take right only lane on the exit into Davyhulme Rd. Follow road to Valley Rd, just after a left hand bend after 1.5 miles. Ground is at the other end of the road. Coaches as above and carry on to the next R'about take 4th exit (Woodbridge Rd). The ground is at the bottom of this road.
Capacity: 2,000 Cover: 650 Seats: 250
Clubhouse: Open daily 3.00pm-11pm. Sandwiches available most eves **Club Shop:** No
Previous Leagues: S. Manchester & Wythenshawe 60-63; Lancs & Cheshire 63-73; Manchester 73-86; NWC 86-96; NPL 97-00
Best season FA Vase: Semi-final 95-96
Record Attendance: 1,543 v Brigg Town FA Vase Semi-Final 95-96
HONOURS NWC Div I 95-96, Div 2 94-95 Lg.Cup 94-95 95-96 R-up 87-88, Div 3 R-up 86-87; Manc. Lg R-up x 3, Div 1 77-78, Open Tphy 80-81; Lancs Amtr Cup 79-80 (R-up 80-81); Manc. Chal. Tphy 83-84 R-up x 2; Manc. Prem. Cup R-up 86-87 91-92; Man.Am Cup R-up 88-89

FACT FILE
Formed: 1960 Nickname: Valiants
Colours: Blue & white stripes/blue/blue
Change Colours: Gold/black/black
Midweek home matchday: Tuesday
Reserves' League: NWCo FL Res Div
Programme - Pages: 36 Price: £1.00
Editor: Andrew Harney
CLUB PERSONNEL
Chairman: Len Heywood Pres: F H Eadie
Manager: Paul Wright
Matchday Contact: Paul Chadwick
Tel : 0161 747 6315 (H) or 07754 416889 (M)
2002-03 Goalscorer: Gareth Feeney
P.o.Y.: Ryan Gilligan

HOLKER OLD BOYS

Secretary: John Adams, 20 Middlefield,Barrow in Furness, Cumbria. LA14 4AU
Tel: 01229 431121
Ground: Rakesmoor Lane, Hawcoat, Barrow-in-Furness, Cumbria (01229 828176)
Directions: M6 Jct 36, A590 to Barrow-in-Furness, on entering Barrow, continue on A590 past Kimberley Clark Paper Mill. Take Bank Lane, first left into Hawcoat.At top of hill turn left into Rakesmoor Lane. Ground 200yds on right.
Capacity: 1,750 Seats: 220Cover: 500 Floodlights: Yes
Clubhouse: Tue,Thur, Fri 8-11pm, Sat noon-11pm, Sun normal licensing.
Pies & peas on matchdays **Club Shop:** No
HONOURS W Lancs Lg 86-87, R-up 85-86; Lancs Junior Shield 88-89 90-91.
PREVIOUS **Leagues:** North Western; Furness Premier; West Lancs 70-91.
RECORDS **Attendance:** 1240 v Barrow ATS Trophy 95-96 **Win:** 12-0
Defeat: 1-8 v Newcastle T. (H) 91-92 **Top Scorer:** Dave Conlin
2003-04 **Top Goalscorer**: Paul Southward 32 **Player of the Year.**: Craig Salton

FACT FILE
Founded: 1936 Nickname: Cobs
Sponsors: Schofield Construction &Specsavers
Colours:Green+white sleeves/white/green
Change: Gold & Navy Blue/navy blue
Midweek Matches: Tuesday
Programme: 32pages, £1.00

CLUB PERSONNEL
President: David Ainsbury
Chairman:Stephen Livingstone
Vice-Chairman: Dick John
Press Officer: John Taylor
Manager: Derek Birrell
Asst Man:Pete McKenna
Coach: Dick John
Physio: Mark Hetherington
Captain: Craig Salton

LEEK C.S.O.B.

Secretary: Stan Lockett, 5 Fitzherbert Close, Swynnerton, Stone, Staffs ST150PQ,
Tel: 1782 796062 (H) 07944 493106 (M)
Fixture Sec: Patricia Lacey (01538 384705)
Ground: Harrison Park, Macclesfield Road, Leek, Staffs, Tel: 01538 383734
Club Email: stan@slockett.freeserve.co.uk
Directions: M6 south Junc 17, A534 to Congleton - follow signs for Leek (A54), carry on to junction with A523, right onto A523, this road is direct to Leek, ground 8 miles on right just into Leek.
Capacity: 3,600 Seating: 625 Covered Terracing: 2,675 Floodlights: Yes
PREVIOUS **Leagues:** Leek & Moorland Lge, Staffs County North, Refuge Midland Lge.
RECORDS **Attendance:** 293 v Tamworth F.A.Cup 1998-99
BEST SEASON **FA Cup:** 3rd Q 98-99 **FA Vase:** 1st Round 2000-01
HONOURS Refuge Midland Lge 95-96. Lge Cup 94-95 95-96; Leek Cup 94-95 95-96; Midland Ref Charity Shield 95-96; Sportsline Chall Cup 95-96.
NWCL Div. 2winners - Programme of the Year 2001/02

FACT FILE
Founded: 1945
Colours: Red & white stripes/white/red
Change colours: All White
Midweek Matchday:Tuesday
Programme: Yes Editor: Stan Lockett
CLUB PERSONNEL
Chairman: Ken Hill, 11 Springfield Drive, Leek, Staffs ST13 Tel: 01538 371859
Managers: Chris McMullen & Andrew Walters
Ass Man: Paul Campion
Yth Man: David Lacey
Physio: Keith Tatton & Dennis Lowndes
Captain: Matt Johnson
2003-04
Leading Goalscorer:Alan Nagington - 38
Player of the Year: Peter Heler

NELSON

Secretary: Ben Hall c/o Club. Tel No: 07766003000 (M)
Ground: Victoria Park, Lomeshaye Way, Nelson, Lancs (01282 613820)
Directions: M65 jct 13, 1st left (A6068 Fence), 2nd left (B6249 for Nelson),2nd right sign Lomeshaye Village to grd
Capacity: 1500 Seats:150Cover: 200 Floodlights: Yes
Clubhouse: Bar open matchdays **Club Shop:** Yes

HONOURS Lancs Lge 54-55; Lancs Comb. 1949-50 51-52; Lg Cup 49-50 50-51 59-60; Bridge Shield 75-76 81-82; Lancs Jnr Cup 54-55; N.W.C. Div 2 Cup 96-97.

BEST SEASON
FA Cup: 2nd Rd Proper 30-31(replay)
FA Vase: 2nd Rd 2001-02

PREVIOUS **Leagues:** Lancashire 1889-98 1900-01; Football League 1898-1900; Lancashire Comb. 01-16 46-82; N.W.C. 82-88; West Lancashire 88-92.

FACT FILE
Founded: 1881 Nickname: Blues
Colours: Blue & white stripes/bluek/blue
Change colours: Gold and blue.
Midweek matchday: TuesdayReserve
League: N.W.C. Res. Div.
Website: www.nelsonfc.co.uk

CLUB PERSONNEL
Chairman: A.Pickering
Man Director: L.Treitl Treasurer: S.Smith
Manager: Dave Hall Asst. Man:Ian Lang
Captain: Andy Howarth

2003-2004
P.o.Y.: Billy Carrington
Top Scorer: Craig Suker Bradshaw

NEW MILLS A.F.C.

Secretary: Barry Land, Coniston, 165 Low Leighton Rd., New Mills , High Peak SK22 4NP
Tel No: 01663 746174
Ground: Church Lane, New Mills, High Peak, SK22 4NP Tel No: 01663 747435

Capacity: **Seats:**
Cover: **Floodlights:**
Clubhouse:

Directions: From Stockport, A6 to Swan Hotel, turn left down hill through lights and then turn left at St George's church. Ground on right.

PREVIOUS **Leagues:** Manchester League
Name: New Mills St Geirges ore 1919

HONOURS

CLUB RECORDS
Attendance: 4,500 v Hyde United 1922

2003-2004 **Player of the Year:** Simon Ignotus
Top Scorer: Adam Blackburn

FACT FILE
Formed: 1919
Sponsor:
Colours: All amber with black trim
Change colours: All white
Midweek Matches: Tuesday
Prog: 28 pages 60p Editor: Glyn Jones

CLUB PERSONNEL
Chairman: Ray Coverley
Press Officer: Allan Jones (01663 744649)
Manager: Tony Rigby
Captain: Chris Pickering

NORTON UNITED

Secretary: Dennis Vicker, 86 Ford Green Road, Smallthorne, Stoke-on-Trent ST6 1NX
Tel: 01782 822727 (H) 01785 354200 (B)

Ground: Norton CC & MWI, Community Drive, Smallthorne, Stoke-on-Trent
Tel: 01782 838290
Directions: M6 J16, A500 to BUrslem/Tunstall, turn off on A527, bear right at traffic island to Burslem, through lights to Smallthorne, take 3rd exit on mini r'about, turn right by pedestrian crossing into Community Drive, ground 200 metres on left.
Nearest Station: Stoke-on-Trent (mainline) Longport (local)

PREVIOUS **League:** Midland League to 2001
RECORDS **Attendance:** 165 v Alsager Town 2002
HONOURS Midland League - Champions 00-01 98-99 96-97, League Cup 00-01 96-97 91-92; Staffs FA Senior Vase 98-99

FACT FILE
Founded: 1989
Colours: Black & white stripes/black/black
Change Cols.: Red & black stripes/white/white
Midweek Matchday: Wednesday
Programme: Pages: Price:
Editor:

CLUB PERSONNEL
Chairman
Stephen Beaumont
8 Maitland Grove, Trentham, Stoke-on-Trent.
Tel: 01782 642321 (H)
Manager:
Physio:

OLDHAM TOWN

Secretary: Mark Kilgannon, 114 Redwood, Chadderton,Oldham. OL9 9UG
Tel Nos: 07834 760085 (H) 0161 953 3173(M)
Ground: Whitebank Stadium, Whitebank Rd, Hollins, Oldham, Lancs OL8 3JH
Tel: 0161 624 2689
Directions: M62 jct 18, M66 to Heaton Pk, right on to A576, left at 2nd lights on to A6104, fol low Victoria Ave. on to Hollinwood Ave. under bridge to roundabout take 2nd exit onto Hollins Road, follow Hollins Rd for one & a half miles to Fire Station, left on through gate leading onto Elm Rd and follow to next left, Whitebank Rd on left.
Capacity: 1,000 Seats: 101 Cover: Yes Floodlights: Yes
Clubhouse: Open evenings and matchdays
HONOURS NWC: Div 2 97-98, R-up 94-95; Div 3 R-up 85--86; Lg.Champions 97-98
Res Div R-up 94-95, Cup 94/95:

PREVIOUS **Leagues:** Manchester Amateur; Lancashire Comb. 81-82.

RECORD **Attendance:** 495 v Halifax Town, 1996.

FACT FILE

Founded: 1964
Colours: Blue,white,blue
Midweek Matches: Tuesday
Programme: 16 pages, 50p
Editor: Secretary

CLUB PERSONNEL

Chairman: Ken Hughes
Manager: Len Cantello

PADIHAM

Secretary: Alan Smith,242 Burnley Road, Padiham, Lancs. BB112 8SS (01282 771963)
Ground: Arbories Memorial Sports Ground, Well Street, Padiham, Lancs. BB12 8LE
Tel: 01282 773742
Directions: M65, J8, then follow A6068 (signed Clitheroe & Padiham). At lights at bottom of hill, turn right into Dean Range/Blackburn Road towards Padiham. At the next junction turn into Holland street opposite church, then into Well Street at the side of the Hare & Hounds pub to the ground. Nearest rail station: Burnley
Floodlights: Yes
Honours: Lancs Amateur Cup R-up 66, Lancs Amateur Shield R-up 97, Burnley, Pendle & Rossendale Hosp. Cup 96, R-up 91 03 Lancs Comb.E.W. George WatsonTrophy 81, R-up 82; NWC Div. 3 R-up 83-84; W. Lancs Div.1 99-00, Div.2 71-72 76-77 R-up 96-97, Pres. Cup R-up 79 94 97; E. Lancs Amat Lge R-up 06-07
Best Season: FA Cup: Third Rd., 1883-84
Previous **Leagues:** Lancashire Comb.; NW Counties; West Lancs.; N.E. Lancs; NE Lancs Combination; East Lancs Amateur Lge.

FACT FILE
Formed: 1878
Colours: Royal blue & white/white/red
Change: Red
Midweek Matchday: Tuesday
Programme: £1.00
Editor:Alan Smith

CLUB PERSONNEL
Chairman: Mick Muldoon
56 Victoria Road, Padiham, Lancs.
Tel: 01282 778831
Manager:Steve Wilkes
2003-2004
P.o.Y.: Paul Gurr Top Scorer: James Gill

SILSDEN A.F.C.

Secretary: Andy Geary, 29 Laurel Grove, Silsden, Keighly, West Yorks BD20 0AY

Tel : 01535 654197 (H) 01535 626020 (W) 07743 587885 (M) 01535 661228 (F)

e-mail: andy.geary@harclo.com

Ground: Keighly Rugby League Club, Cougar Park, Roydings Park, Keighly

Tel No: 01535 213111 Fax: 01535 213100

Capacity: **Seats:** **Cover:** **Floodlights:** **Clubhouse:**

Directions: A629 to Keighley. At roundabout left to Bradford and immediately left again into Roydings Avenbue Cougar Park on right.

PREVIOUS **Leagues:** Craven & District, West Riding County Amateur

Grounds:

2003-2004 **Player of the Year: & Top Goalscorer:** Jimmy Hedges

FACT FILE

Formed: 1904

Sponsor:

Colours: Red/Black/Red

Change colours: White/Red/White

Midweek Matches:Wednesday

CLUB PERSONNEL

Chairman: Sean McNulty

Manager: Andy Geary

Assistant Manager: Paul Schofield

Programme Editor: Peter Hanson

:

WINSFORD UNITED

Secretary : Robert Astles, 40 Aldersey Road,Crewe,Cheshire CW2 8NR Tel: 01270 661623
Ground Address: Barton Stadium, Wharton, Winsford, Cheshire CW7 3EU (01606 593021).
Directions: From north; M6 J19, A556 towards Northwich to Davenham, then A5018 to Winsford. From south; M6 J18, A54 through Middlewich to Winsford. Ground quarter mile off main road in Wharton area of town. 1 mile from Winsford (BR).
Capacity: 6,000 Cover: 5,000 Seats: 250
Clubhouse: Mon-Sat 8-11pm, Sun 8-10.30pm **Club Shop:** Yes, contact Kay Lomas
Previous Lges: The Combination 02-04; Cheshire Co. 19-40, 47-82; N.W.C. 82-87, N.P.L 87-01.
CLUB RECORDS **Attendance:** 7,000 v Witton Albion 1947.**Goalscorer:** Graham Smith 66.
Apps: Edward Harrop 400.**Fee Paid:** Nil. **Fee Received:** £6,000 for Neville Southall from Bury.
BEST SEASON FA Cup: 2nd Rd 1887-88 1st Rd 1975-76 91-92 **FA Trophy:** Qtr Finals 77-78.
HONOURS N.P.L. R-up 92-93, Div 1 R-up 91-92, Lg Cup 92-93, Presidents Cup 92-93; Cheshire Co. Lg 20-21 76-77 (R-up 74-75 79-80),Lg Cup x 7 R-up x 3; Cheshire Snr Cup 58-59 79-80 92-93; Mid-Cheshire Snr Cup 90-91 92-93 (R-up 88-89); Cheshire Amateur Cup 00-01 02-03;
Lancs Comb/Cheshire County Inter-Lg Cup 62-63.

FACT FILE
Founded: 1883 Nickname: Blues
Colours: All Royal Blue
Change colours: Maroon & Light Blue
Midweek matchday:
WednesdayProgramme: Pages: 24 Price: £1.00
Editor: R. Astles
CLUB PERSONNEL
Chairman: Mark Loveless
President: David Lawson
Vice Chairman: David Taylor
Manager: David Twite
Captain: Mark Quinn
2003-04
Leading Goalscorer&Player of the Year
Mark Quinn

SPARTAN SOUTH MIDLANDS

SPONSORED BY: MINERVA FOOTBALLS

President: B F Smith **Chairman:** Pat Burns

Hon. Gen. Secretary: M Mitchell, 26 Leighton Court, Dunstable, Beds. LU6 1EW Tel: 01582 667291

Beaconsfield SYCOB, who finished runners-up last season, were Premier Division Champions. They equalled **London Colney**'s record of only two defeats in a season, and created a new record by conceding only 21 goals in their league campaign. They moved into top position on 4th October, and were never displaced. **Brook House** were runners-up,eight points behind Beaconsfield, with **St Margaretsbury** in third place, three points behind. At the half-way stage, St Margaretsbury had lost only two games, but five defeats in the second half of the season saw them lose contact with the leaders. **Potters Bar**, who were third last season finished fourth, with **Harefield United** just below them. A run of eight wins and a draw in their last nine matches enabled **Hanwell Town** to finish in sixth position and this fine form helped them beat Brook House 1-0 in the final of the Premier Division Cup

At the foot of the table, **Holmer Green** finished bottom with **Haringey Borough** three points above them but it was a good campaign for **Richard Howard** of **St Margaretsbury** who was top scorer in the division with with 28, followed by **Dean Papali** of **Brook House** with 25.

Division One winners were **Haywood United** in only their fourth season in the league. Having gained promotion from April they lost only one of their 24 league games, and suffered only four league defeats. They finished seven points above second placed **Langford,** who were three ahead of **Welwyn Garden City**. **Tring Athletic,** who were top of the Division at Christmas, finished fourth. Promoted **Buckingham Athletic**, who were undefeated in their first six games, finished fifth. Despite a run of five successive defeats in February/March, newcomers **Sun Postal Sports** finished in ninth position. Bottom club were **Ampthill Town**, who finished two points below **Shillington**. **Langford** won the Division One Cup, beating **Buckingham** 1-0 in the final. The Division's top goal scorer was **Langford's Steve Starling** with 32, followed by **Paul Talbot of Haywood** with 24.

In Division Two, last season's runners-up **Old Dunstablians**, were runaway winners, finishing twelve points ahead of **Winslow United.** With a total of 108, **Dunstablians** were the only first team in the league to score 100 goals.

Winners of the Challenge Trophy were **Brook House**, who beat **London Colney** 2-0 in the final. Newcomers **Arlesey Athletic** finished third, seven points behind Winslow. **Old Bradwell United** finished bottom, with **Amersham Town** immediately above them. **Winslow** won the Division Two cup, beating **Dunstablians** 1-0 in the Final. and their striker Chris Hill finished as top goalscorer in the Division with 31.

FINAL LEAGUE TABLE 2003-04

PREMIER DIVISION	P	W	D	L	F	A	Pts
1. Beaconsfield SYCOB	36	27	7	2	95	21	88
2. Brook House	36	26	2	8	82	35	80
3. St Margaretsbury	36	24	5	7	66	29	77
4. Potters Bar Town	36	22	8	6	86	35	74
5. Harefield United	36	22	5	9	87	50	71
6. Hanwell Town	36	22	4	10	86	49	70
7. London Colney	36	18	6	12	76	49	60
8. Greenacres (Hemel)	36	16	6	14	77	78	54
9. Leverstock Green	36	14	7	15	54	55	49
10. Ruislip Manor	36	14	6	16	60	62	48
11. Hoddesdon Town	36	13	7	16	53	53	46
12. Hillingdon Borough	36	13	7	16	56	67	46
13. Royston Town	36	11	7	18	63	78	40
14. Harpenden Town	36	9	9	18	47	81	36
15. Biggleswade Town	36	9	8	19	57	82	35
16. Broxbourne B. V&E	36	9	3	24	36	93	30
17. Bedford Utd/Valerio	36	6	6	24	32	84	24
18. Haringey Borough	36	5	7	24	43	90	22
19. Holmer Green	36	5	4	27	41	106	19

PREMIER DIVISION		1	2	3	4	5	6	7	8	9	10	11	12	13	14	15	16	17	18	19
1	Beaconsfield SYCOB		6-0	3-0	2-0	2-0	3-0	2-0	0-3	3-2	3-0	4-0	1-0	7-0	3-1	4-1	1-0	5-1	1-1	3-0
2	Bedford United & Valerio	0-2		1-2	1-2	0-1	2-3	0-3	1-0	1-1	1-0	0-3	1-2	0-2	0-1	0-5	1-3	2-1	0-0	1-3
3	Biggleswade Town	2-2	2-1		1-2	2-1	3-2	4-2	1-3	2-2	1-1	1-2	2-5	4-0	2-2	1-6	1-3	3-3	1-2	0-1
4	Brook House	2-1	3-0	2-1		3-0	6-1	3-1	0-1	3-0	8-0	0-2	4-0	3-0	2-1	0-0	0-5	4-0	2-0	2-0
5	Broxbourne Boro' V&E	1-3	0-2	1-2	1-0		0-4	3-1	0-1	0-0	3-2	1-4	0-4	1-1	2-0	1-3	0-7	3-2	1-2	1-5
6	Greenacres (Hemel)	1-5	0-0	4-2	1-6	3-4		4-1	2-2	5-0	3-1	3-1	1-0	4-3	6-1	3-4	4-3	2-2	2-2	1-2
7	Hanwell Town	0-4	5-0	5-2	4-2	4-1	5-1		1-5	2-1	8-1	3-3	3-0	4-0	0-1	4-1	0-0	4-1	1-0	1-0
8	Harefield United	0-2	9-1	0-2	1-2	4-1	2-0	1-1		4-0	2-1	5-0	1-6	8-3	1-0	2-3	0-3	1-0	3-4	2-2
9	Haringey Borough	1-4	3-0	2-2	0-3	3-0	0-0	0-2	1-3		0-1	1-2	0-3	1-0	5-0	3-4	2-5	2-6	0-4	0-1
10	Harpenden Town	1-6	2-4	2-2	0-1	3-1	2-2	0-2	1-3	3-1		3-1	1-1	3-0	0-0	1-4	0-1	0-0	3-1	1-4
11	Hillingdon Borough	0-1	1-1	2-0	2-3	3-0	1-2	0-4	1-4	3-3	1-1		2-1	1-0	1-0	0-1	1-3	2-5	2-2	0-1
12	Hoddesdon Town	0-0	1-1	2-1	0-2	0-1	1-2	1-1	1-2	4-0	2-2	2-2		2-1	0-2	3-1	0-5	0-1	1-0	0-2
13	Holmer Green	1-5	2-2	1-2	0-3	3-3	2-1	0-3	2-3	1-5	1-2	2-3	2-5		0-0	0-4	1-5	3-1	4-2	1-3
14	Leverstock Green	0-2	1-0	2-0	1-1	4-0	2-3	1-2	1-1	7-1	2-1	3-2	0-2	4-1		3-1	1-1	4-2	1-2	2-1
15	London Colney	0-0	5-2	1-1	0-2	4-0	0-1	3-2	0-2	2-0	2-3	3-0	1-1	3-0	1-2		0-0	4-0	3-0	0-3
16	Potters Bar Town	1-1	0-2	4-1	4-1	6-1	3-0	1-0	2-0	2-1	2-2	2-2	0-1	4-1	4-3	2-1		0-1	2-0	0-0
17	Royston Town	1-1	6-2	3-0	2-1	2-3	1-4	2-3	2-4	1-1	4-0	0-3	2-1	0-2	3-0	0-3	1-1		3-2	0-2
18	Ruislip Manor	1-3	2-1	2-1	1-2	3-0	4-1	1-3	2-2	3-0	2-3	1-3	3-1	3-0	1-0	2-1	1-2	4-4		0-4
19	St Margaretsbury	0-0	2-1	5-3	1-2	1-0	2-1	0-1	1-2	4-1	2-0	1-0	3-0	2-1	1-1	1-1	3-0	2-0	1-0	

FINAL LEAGUE TABLE 2003-04

DIVISION ONE	P	W	D	L	F	A	Pts
1. Haywood United	34	23	7	4	91	32	76
2. Langford	34	21	6	7	92	43	69
3. Welwyn Garden City	34	19	9	6	63	26	66
4. Tring Athletic	34	19	6	9	67	37	63
5. Buckingham Athletic	34	18	7	9	67	38	61
6. Colney Heath	34	17	6	11	66	54	57
7. Cockfosters	34	17	5	12	63	57	56
8. Biggleswade United	34	16	7	11	55	50	55
9. Sun Postal Sports	34	14	5	15	64	62	47
10. Brimsdown Rovers	34	13	8	13	54	56	47
11. Stony Stratford Town	34	13	5	16	57	65	44
12. Kings Langley	34	8	14	12	42	64	38
13. Brache Sparta	34	9	8	17	52	69	35
14. Pitstone & Ivinghoe	34	9	6	19	39	60	33
15. The 61 FC	34	8	8	18	32	58	32
16. New Bradwell St Peter	34	8	6	20	41	79	30
17. Shillington	34	8	2	24	40	84	26
18. Ampthill Town	34	7	3	24	34	85	24

DIVISION ONE	1	2	3	4	5	6	7	8	9	10	11	12	13	14	15	16	17	18
1 Ampthill Town		0-2	1-3	4-2	1-5	1-2	1-4	0-6	2-1	0-1	0-0	0-0	3-1	3-0	0-3	2-1	2-3	0-3
2 Biggleswade United	3-1		3-1	1-2	1-0	1-3	3-3	1-2	3-0	1-3	4-2	2-0	4-1	2-2	2-0	1-0	2-1	0-1
3 Brache Sparta	2-1	1-2		2-0	1-4	1-2	3-0	1-2	2-2	1-3	4-1	0-1	2-4	4-3	0-3	1-1	2-2	2-0
4 Brimsdown Rovers	2-1	1-1	3-1		1-1	1-6	0-0	1-1	4-1	1-3	1-0	3-0	1-0	4-2	1-0	0-0	2-3	3-2
5 Buckingham Athletic	4-0	2-2	2-1	1-0		4-1	4-1	2-2	4-2	1-7	0-1	3-1	3-1	0-1	4-0	4-1	0-0	0-0
6 Cockfosters	4-1	0-1	2-0	0-2	0-1		2-2	1-6	1-1	3-0	3-4	4-2	3-1	2-1	2-1	2-1	0-1	2-1
7 Colney Heath	3-2	0-2	3-0	2-2	2-0	3-1		0-2	6-0	0-4	4-1	3-1	4-1	1-2	3-2	1-1	2-1	0-4
8 Haywood Heath	2-0	4-0	4-1	2-0	4-2	4-0	2-0		2-2	1-2	4-0	3-0	3-1	3-4	5-1	6-0	2-1	1-3
9 Kings Langley	1-2	1-1	1-1	2-1	1-1	1-1	1-1	1-1		1-3	2-3	2-1	1-0	2-3	2-2	1-1	0-4	1-1
10 Langford	8-0	3-1	3-0	2-3	1-1	3-3	5-3	2-4	1-2		5-1	2-0	6-0	2-2	1-1	1-2	3-2	1-1
11 New Bradwell St Peter	3-3	2-1	2-2	2-1	1-4	0-2	0-1	0-0	0-1	0-3		3-1	1-1	1-1	2-4	2-1	3-1	2-3
12 Pitstone & Ivinghoe	4-0	1-2	2-5	1-1	0-1	2-2	0-1	1-0	2-2	1-1	3-1		2-0	0-3	2-0	3-0	1-2	2-1
13 Shillington	2-1	1-3	2-2	2-0	0-4	2-1	1-2	1-3	4-0	1-3	4-1	0-2		1-3	1-3	1-0	1-4	0-2
14 Stony Straford Town	0-1	2-0	5-2	6-3	1-3	0-2	0-2	0-3	2-2	0-3	2-0	2-2	2-3		3-2	2-0	0-4	0-1
15 Sun Postal Sports	3-0	5-0	3-1	2-2	0-2	3-1	1-5	2-2	4-2	3-2	2-1	2-0	6-0	0-2		1-0	1-5	2-3
16 The 61 FC	4-1	1-1	1-1	0-5	1-0	2-4	0-2	1-2	0-1	0-4	2-0	2-0	1-0	1-0	3-1		2-2	0-2
17 Tring Athletic	1-0	3-1	1-2	1-0	1-0	0-1	3-2	1-1	0-1	0-1	3-1	5-0	3-1	3-1	2-0	3-1		1-1
18 Welwyn Garden City	2-0	1-1	0-0	4-1	1-0	3-0	2-0	0-2	0-1	3-0	6-0	2-1	5-1	3-0	1-1	1-1	0-0	

CHALLENGE CUP

FIRST ROUND

Abbey Na. (MK)	v	Brache Sparta	1-2
Amersham Town	v	Welwyn Garden City	1-2
Beaconsfield SYCOB	v	Tring Athletic	3-1
Bedford Utd & Va.	v	Potters Bar Town	1-2
Biggleswade Town	v	New Bradwell St Peter	0-1*
Biggleswade Utd	v	Holmer Green	2-1
Brimsdown Rovers	v	Ruislip Manor	1-2
Brook House	v	Ampthill Town	8-0
Broxbourne Boro' V & E	v	Old Bradwell United	4-0
Caddington	v	Langford	0-8
Cockfosters	v	Flamstead	3-2
Colney Heath	v	Harpenden Town	1-2
Cranfield United	v	Risborough Rangers	2-1
Greenacres (Hemel)	v	Mursley United	5-1
Hanwell Town	v	Kentish Town	4-1
Haringey Borough	v	Sun Postal Sports	0-5
Hillingdon Borough	v	Crawley Green	9-0
London Colney	v	Leverstock Green	2-0
Padbury BTFC	v	Buckingham Athletic	1-2*
Royston Town (w/o)	v	Scot	
Shillington	v	Hoddesdon Town	0-1
St Margaretsbury	v	Old Dunstablians	4-0
Stony Stratford Tn	v	Pitstone & Ivinghoe	0-1
Winslow Utd (w/o)	v	Milton Keynes City	

SECOND ROUND

Arlesey Athletic	v	Kent Athletic	4-2
Beaconsfield SYCOB	v	Potters Bar Town	0-3
Biggleswade Utd	v	Pitstone & Ivinghoe	3-2
Brache Sparta	v	Royston Town	8-1
Brook House	v	Kings Langley	4-2
Broxbourne Boro' V & E	v	The 61 FC	4-1
Buckingham Ath.	v	Markyate	3-1
Cockfosters	v	Hoddesdon Town	0-3
Greenacres (Hemel)	v	Cranfield United	2-1
Harpenden Town	v	Harefield United	1-3
Haywood United	v	New Bradwell St Peter	4-0
Hillingdon Borough	v	Welwyn Garden City	3-2
Langford	v	Totternhoe	9-1
Ruislip Manor	v	St Margaretsbury	0-2
Sun Postal Sports	v	London Colney	0-2
Winslow United	v	Hanwell Town	1-2

THIRD ROUND

Biggleswade Utd	v	Brache Sparta	2-0
Brook House	v	Langford	2-0
Broxbourne Boro' V & E	v	St Margaretsbury	1-6
Buckingham Ath.	v	Hillingdon Borough	0-1
Hanwell Town	v	Hoddesdon Town	1-2
Harefield United	v	Potters Bar Town	2-1
Haywood United	v	Greenacres (Hemel)	2-0
London Colney	v	Arlesey Athletic	2-0

QUARTER-FINALS

Biggleswade Utd	v	Brook House	0-2
Harefield United	v	Hoddesdon Town	2-0
London Colney	v	Haywood United	2-1
St Margaretsbury	v	Hillingdon Borough	3-2

SEMI-FINALS

Brook House	v	Harefield United	2-0
London Colney	v	St Margaretsbury	5-0

THE FINAL (20th April)

Brook House	v	London Colney	2-2* 4-3p

PREMIER DIVISION CUP

from the QUARTER-FINALS

Bedford Utd & Val.	v	Harefield United	1-2
Brook House	v	Leverstock Green	2-1
Potters Bar Town	v	Beaconsfield SYCOB	2-0
St Margaretsbury	v	Hillingdon Borough	1-0

SEMI-FINALS

Harefield United	v	Potters Bar Town	2-0
St Margaretsbury	v	Brook House	2-4

THE FINAL (28th April at Hanwell Town)

Harefield United	v	Brook House	1-0

FIRST DIVISION CUP

from the QUARTER-FINALS

Biggleswade Utd	v	Haywood United	1-3
Buckingham Ath.	v	Sun Postal Sports	1-0*
Colney Heath	v	Welwyn Garden City	0-0* 4-1p
The 61 FC (at Langford)	v	Langford	1-2

SEMI-FINALS

Colney Heath	v	Langford	1-2
Haywood United	v	Buckingham Athletic	1-2

THE FINAL (14th April at Ampthill Town)

Buckingham Ath.	v	Langford	0-1

BEDFORD UNITED & VALERIO

Secretary: Geoff Seagrave, 16 Riverview Rd., Kempston, Bedford MK42 7BB
Tel Nos: 01234 402369 (H) 07890 833152 (M)

GROUND: McMullen Park, Meadow Lane, Cardington, Bedford MK45 3SB (01234 831024)

Directions: M1 jct 13, A421 to Bedford by-pass. Third exit, A603 ground 500 yards on left
Capacity: 5,000 Seats: 25 Cover: 100 Floodlights: Yes

Clubhouse: Open matchdays. Hot & cold snacks and drinks available

HONOURS: Bedford & Dist Lg Premier Division & Division One, County Junior Cup, Biggleswade KO Cup, Butchers Cup(2), Britania Cup, Bedford Charity Cup

PREVIOUS: **Leagues**: Bedford & Dist. Lge (57-70 & 80-89); United Cos. Lge 70-80
Name: Printers Diemer-Reynolds (pre'72)

Grounds: Allen Park (57-80); Fairhill, Clapham Road (80-93); Hillgrounds, Kempston 93-96)

RECORD: **Attendance:** (at Fairhill) 1500 v Bedford Town, South Midlands Lge Div. 1 26/12/92
Top **Scorer:** Neil Tysoe 220 **Appearances:** Simon Fordham 418

FACT FILE

Founded: 1957 Nickname: United
Club Sponsors: JDP Finance
Colours: Blue & White/blue/blue
Change colours: All RedMidweek matches: Wednesday
Reserves' League: S. Mids Lge Res. sect
Programme: 24 pages, £1 Editor: Secretary: geoffrey.seagrave@ntlworld.com
Chairman: Alan Hurst
Vice Chairman/Press Off Jim McMullen
President: D Rostron
Manager: Julian Capone
Asst. Man.: M Ackroyd
Coach/Physio: Dave Petrie

BIGGLESWADE TOWN

Secretary: Graham Arkwright, 47Honeysuckle Close Biggleswade, Beds SG188ST
Tel: 01767 318370

GROUND: `Fairfield', Fairfield Road, Biggleswade, Beds (01767 312374).

Directions: A1 North r'bout, first left after bridge to car park.10 mins walk from Biggleswade(BR).
Capacity: 2,400 Seats: 50 Cover: 100 Floodlights: Yes Club Shop: No.

RECORD: **Attendance:** 2,000 **Clubhouse:** Open all matchdays. , teas, coffees, snacks.

HONOURS:S Mids Lge: Res Div 2 87-88, Res Chall Trophy 88-89,S.M. Floodlit Cup 95-96,02-03; Beds Snr Cup 02-03 07-08 46-47 51-52 61-62 62-63 66-67 73-74; Beds Premr Cup 22-23 27-28; N. Beds Charity Cup x13; Utd Co's Lg Cup 73-74; Hinchingbrooke Cup 03-04 12-13 92-93 Hunts Prem Cup (6); Jess Piggott Trophy 87-88 89-90 91-92 92-93 N.Beds Charity Cup: (13)

PREVIOUS: **Leagues:** Biggleswade & Dist. 02-20; Bedford & Dist. 09-12; Utd Co's (prev. Northants Lg) 20-39 51-55 63-80; Spartan 46-51; Eastern Co's 55-63 **Name:** Biggleswade F.C.

2003-2004: **Captain:** Adrian Mapletaft **Top Scorer**: Mark Phillips **P.o.Y.**: David Lenton

Players progressing: Darren Hay (Cambridge Utd) 1994

FACT FILE

Founded: 1874 Nickname: Waders
Club Sponsors: Mantles Ford & Letchworth Couriers
Colours:green& white stripes/green/green
Change: All red
Midweek Matchday:WednesdayProgramme: 32 pages, admission
Editor: Brian Doggett (01767 318307 (H).

CLUB PERSONNEL

Chairman:M.Dorrington V. Chair:M Jarvis
President: R Dorrington
Man: David Northfield Coach: Mark Smith
Physio: Darren Staniforth

BROXBOURNE BOROUGH V & E

Secretary: Fred Beer, Flat 10, Hyde Court,Parkside, Waltham Cross, Herts. EN8 7TL
Tel No: 01992 761138

Ground: V & E Club, Goffs lane, Cheshunt, Herts. Tel: 01992 624281

Capacity: 500 Seats: 20 Cover: Yes Floodlights: Yes Club Shop: No

Directions: M25 junct. 25, A10 towards Cheshunt. Take the first left at the first roundabout onto the B198 (Cuffley & Goffs Oak). At the end of the road turn right off roundabout into Goffs lane. **Clubhouse** on immediate right. Open 11 a.m. 11 p.m. every day.

Previous League: Herts Senior
Name: Somerset Ambury V& E

2003-2004: **Player of the Year:** Sam Obeney **Top Scorer:** Chris Beeden

FACT FILE

Founded: 1959
Colours: Royal Blue/white/white
Change Colours : Red & black/black/black
Midweek Matchday: Tuesday
Reserves League; Essex ,Herts Border
Programme Editor: Peter Harris
01992 429297 (H) 0208 1274 (B)
Club Website www.savefc.thesportcity.com

CLUB PERSONNEL

Chairman:David Bidwell
Tel: 01992 428187 (H)
Vice Chairman: Mario Persico
President: Doug Bacon
Manager:Martin Wade Coach: Peter Theo
Captain: Richard Harris

HANWELL TOWN

Secretary: Phil Scott, 129 Sutton Court Rd.,Hillingdn,Middlesex UB10 9HT (07958 633183)

GROUND: Reynolds Field, Perivale Lane, Perivale, Greenford, Middx (0208 998 1701)

Directions: A40(M) west from London, leave opp Hoover building (B456 for Ealing), turn left into Argyle Rd, left into Perivale Lane. Grd on left. 500 yards from Perivale tube station (Central line)

Capacity: 2,000 Seats: 90 Cover: 200 Floodlights: Yes Club Shop: No

Clubhouse: Saturday matchdays 2-11pm, Tuesdays 6-11pm, Non-matchdays 7.30-11pm

HONOURS: Spartan Sen Lg R-up 98-99 83-84 Lg Cup R-up 93-94 SSM Premier Div. Cup Winners 02-03 London Snr Cup 91-92 92-93 (R-up 93-94), Middx Charity Cup R-up 92-93, 99-00

PREVIOUS: **Leagues:** Dauntless Lge, Harrow, Wembley & District and Middlesex County

RECORDS: **Attendance:** 600 v Spurs, Floodlight opening October 1989
Scorer: Keith Rowlands **Appearances:** Phil Player, 20 seasons, 617 games

BEST SEASON: **FA Cup:** 3rd Rd Qual 97-98

2003-204 **Player of the Year**: Steve Smith **Top Scorer**: Keith Rowlands

FACT FILE

Founded: 1948 Nickname: The Town
Colours: Black & white stripes/black/black & white
Change colours: Yellow/blue/white
Midweek matchday: Tuesday
Reserves' League: S.S.M.Res Lg
Programme: 16 pages, with entry
Editor: Bob Fisher as below

CLUB PERSONNEL

Chairman/Press Officer: Bob Fisher
Tel: 0208 952 4142 (H) 0207 510 4954 (B)
President: Dave Iddiols
Patron: Stephen Pound MP
Manager: Ray Duffy
Captain: Chris Beck

HAREFIELD UNITED

Secretary: Ray Green, Hillside, Harefield, Middlesex. UB9 6AU
Tel Nos: 01895825521 (H) 07834 771212 (M)
GROUND: Preston Park, Breakespeare Rd North, Harefield, Middx UB9 6DG (01895 823474)
Directions: M25 jct 16 to M40 East, left at 1st roundabout, then 2nd left into Harvill Rd. Follow road up the Church Hill into village, right at mini roundabout, ground on right. Denham (BR)
Capacity: 2,000 Seats: 100 Cover: Yes Floodlights: Yes Club Shop: No
Clubhouse: (01895 823474) 4-11pm w/days. Noon -11pm Fri-Sun. Hot & Cold snacks
HONOURS: Middx Premier Cup 85-86, Athenian Lg R-up 83-84, Parthenon Lg 64-65 (Div 1 Cup 65-66), Middx Lg 66-67 68-71 (Lg Cup 66-67 68-69) Spartan South Mids Div. 1 R-up 01-02 Cup Winners 2003
BEST SEASON: FA Cup: 2nd Qual. Rd replay 80-81, 86-87,02-03 **F.A.Vase:** 6th Rd 1989-90
RECORD: Gate: 430 v Bashley, FA Vase
PREVIOUS Leagues: Uxbridge & Dist.; Gt Western Comb. 46-64; Parthenon 64-68; Middx 68-75; Athenian 75-84, Isthmian 85-9

FACT FILE
Founded: 1868
Nickname: Hares
Colours: Red & white stripes/black/blackChange: White/red/redMidweek Matches: Tuesday
Reserves' League: Suburban Div 2 North
Programme: 12-40 pages, 30p
Editor: Keith Ronald (07867 791239)

Chairman: Keith Ronald. Tel: 01895 824287
President: Dave West
Manager: Stuart Leavy
Assistant Manager:Jeff Fanner
Physio: Chas Cox

HARINGEY BOROUGH

Secretary: John Bacon, 7 Everett Close, West Cheshunt, Herts., EN7 6XD Tel: 01707 873187
GROUND: Coles Park, White Hart Lane, Tottenham N17 (020 88891415) Clubhouse: Yes
Directions: M25 to J.25 turn south on A10 approx 6 miles, over jnct with N. Circular Rd (A406) Turn R. at T.lght 1 mile into White Hart Lne grd approx 500yds on L. Bus W3 from Finsbury Park. Mainline & Under-grd stn to Northumberland Park mainline station passes grd can be boarded at Alexandra Palace or White Hart Ln. Mainline stations or Wood Green Underground station.
Capacity: 2,500 Seats: 280 Cover: Yes Floodlights: Yes
Best Seasons: F.A.Vase: 6th Rd 77-78 **F.A. Cup:** 3rd Qualifying Round 86-87
HONOURS: FA Am Cup R-up 19-20; London Sen Cup 12-13, 90-91; Athenian Lge 13-14; Div 2 Cup winners 67-68, 68-69; Spartan Lg Cup r-up 90-91 Spartan S. Mids Prem Div cup r-up 97-98
PREVIOUS: Leagues: London 07-14; Isthmian 19-52 84-88; Spartan 52-54; Delphian 54-63; Athenian 63-84 **Names:** Edmonton; Tufnell Park; Tufnell Park (Edmonton); Edmonton & Haringey (merged with Wood Green Town in early seventies)

FACT FILE
Formed:1907
Colours: Green/black/green
Change colours: Yellow/blue/blue
Midweek Matchday: Tuesday
Reserves League - Middlesex County
Programme Editor: Secretary
CLUB PERSONNEL
Chairman: Peter Lawlor Tel: 020 8889 2726
Match Secretary : As Secretary
Manager: Jimmy Cattle
2003-2004
Capt: Abu Umar Top Scorer: Kesi Dryden
Player of the Year: Bosum Adebaki

HARPENDEN TOWN

Secretary: Neil Ludlow, 93 RussellSt.,Luton,Beds LU1 5EB 01582 486802(H) 01442288219W)
GROUND: Rothamsted Park, Amenbury Lane, Harpenden (01582 715724)
Directions: A1081 to Harpenden. Turn left/right at George public housel into Leyton Rd.Turn left into Amenbury Rd, then left again (50yds) into `Pay and Display' carpark - entrance is signposted thru car park to opposite corner next to swimming pool.
Capacity: 1,500 Seats: 25 Cover: 100 Floodlights: Yes Club Shop: No
Clubhouse: Open matchdays
PREVIOUS: Leagues: Mid-Herts; Herts County **Name:** Harpenden FC 1891-1908
BEST SEASON: F.A.Cup: 1st Rd Qual. **F.A.Vase:** 2nd Rd
HONOURS: Sth Mids Lg 61-62 64-65, Championship Shield 67-68, Lg Cup 70-71, Div 1 89-90, Prem Div Tphy 89-90, Res Div 89-90; Herts Co. Lg 11-12 49-50 51-52 53-54(Aubrey Cup 20-21 28-29 50-51 51-52); Mid-Herts Lg 09-10 20-21, Div 1 99-00; Pratt Cup 06-07 08-09 10-11; Herts Jnr Cup 01-02 09-10 11-12 20-21 25-26; Herts I'mediate Cup 52-53; Herts Charity Shield 07-08; Bingham Cox Cup 1896-97 1902-03 09-10 20-21.

FACT FILE
Founded: 1891
Nickname: The Town
Colours: Yellow/blue/blue
Change: All OrangeMidweek matches: Tuesday
Programme: 50p Editor: Chairman
CLUB PERSONNEL
Chairman: Nick Archer (07802 81 843)
Managers: Howard Cowley
Captain: Matt Gauthier
2003-2004
Top Scorer: Chris Gregory

HAYWOOD UNITED

Secretary: Lynne Nappin, 6 Evesham Green, Aylesbury, Bucks. HP19 9RX
Tel: 01296 486924 01296 468740 (W) 07789 274745 (M)

Ground: Haywood Sports & Social Club, Haywards Way, Aylesbury, Bucks.
Tel: 01296 423324

Directions: Follow signs to Bicester from Aylesbury ring road. At fifth road island, with Aylesbury Duck P.H. on right, turn right into Jackson Road and then second left into Haywood Way. Club is at bottom of the road.
Previous Leagues: Chiltonian

FACT FILE

Colours: Claret & Blue/blue/blue
Change colours: Yellow/green/yellow
Prog.Editor: John Dury (01296 432767)

Chairman: Danny Martone
Manager: Jon Franklin

HILLINGDON BOROUGH

Secretary: Garry Grant, 19 Leveret Close,Leavesden, Watford, herts WD2 7AX
Tel Nos: 01923 463602 (H) 07958 409678 (W) e-mail: ggrantukntlworld.com
GROUND: Middlesex Stadium, Breakspear Road, Ruislip, Middx HA4 7SB (01895 639544)
Website: www.hillingdonboroughfc.uk.co **E-mail:** alanhbfc@hotmail.com
Directions: From A40 take B467 (signed Ickenham), left at 2nd r'bout into Breakspear Rd South, right after 1 mile by Breakspear pub - ground half mile on left. Nearest station is Ruislip. Bus U1 passes ground
Capacity: 1,500 Seats: 150 Cover: 150 Floodlights: Yes Club Shop: No
Clubhouse: Mon-Fri 7.30-11pm, Sat & Sun lunchtime & 7.30-11.00pm

RECORDS: **Win:** 12-0 v Hanwell T. (H), S.S.M. Prem 97/98
Defeat: 1-11 v St. Albans City (A), FA Cup 2nd Qual. Rd. 24.9.94
Transfer Fee Received: ¨1,000 for Craig Johnson (Wealdstone)
2003-2004 Player of the Year Matthew Ferguson (GK) Top Goalscorer: Blaise O'Brien

FACT FILE
Founded: 1990 Nickname: Boro
Sponsors: Prestons Garage
Colours: White/blue/blue
Change colours: All red
Midweek Matches: Tuesday
Reserves' League: Suburban
Programme: 20 pages Editor/Press Off: Alan Taylor (0208 581 0981)
CLUB PERSONNEL
Chairman: Dhally Dhaliwall
Commercial Clubhouse Mgr:Nick Buckingham
Manager: Steve Ringrose
Asst Man.: Ray Daley Physio: Dave Pook
Captain: Joe Moran

HODDESDON TOWN

Secretary: Brenda Timpson, 82 Tolmers Rd,Cuffley, Herts EN6 4JY (01707 874028)
GROUND: `Lowfield', Park View, Hoddesdon, Herts (01992 463133)
Directions: A10, A1170 into Hoddesdon, over 1st r'about, right at 2nd r'aboutand follow signs to Broxbourne, keeping to the left. Turn right at 1st mini r-about into Cock Lane and 1st right is Park View. Ground 200yds on the left,entrance opposite Park Rd. BR station is Broxbourne
Capacity: 3,000 Seats: 100 Cover: 250 Floodlights: Yes Club Shop: Scarves,badges,hats &pens
Clubhouse: Bar and well-stocked Tea Bar with hot food. Open at every home game
HONOURS: **FA Vase 74-75 (1st winners)**; S.S.M. Lg Prem Div Plate 97-98 (R-up 96-97, SthMids Lge Lg Cup 85-86 86-87 91-92 (Prem Div Tphy R-up 92-93); Spartan Lg 70-71(R-up(3) 71-74), Div 1 35-36, Div 2 `B' 27-28, Lg Cup(2) 70-72; S.Mids Floodlit Cup 01-02
PREVIOUS: **Lges:** East Herts 1896-1908, 11-21; Herts Co. 08-25; N Middx Dist 10-22; Spartan 25-75; London Spartan 75-77; Athenian 77-84; South Midlands 84-97
RECORDS: **Attendance:** 3,500 v West Ham, (Floodlight opening friendly), 1975
2003-2004 **Player of the Year and Top Scorer:** Ryan Redford

FACT FILE
Founded: 1879 Nickname: Lilywhites
Colours: White/black/black
Change Colours: navy blue/jellow/yellow
Midweek matchday: Tuesday
Reserves' Lge: Herts
Programme: 100 + pages £1.00
Editor: Mrs Jane Sinden Tel: 01767 631297
CLUB PERSONNEL
Pres: Peter Haynes Chairman: Roger Merton
Gen Man: Jim Briggs
Man : Bill O'Driscoll Ass.Man: Paul Wade
Coach : Danny Buck
2003-2004
Captains: Pabb Ardiles and Paul Mann

HOLMER GREEN

Secretary: Mick Bowler c/o Club
GROUND: Watchet Lane, Holmer Green, High Wycombe (01494 711485)
Directions: From Amersham on A404 High Wycombe Road, after approx 2 miles turn right into Sheepcote Dell Road. Continue until end of road by Bat & Ball PH.Turn right then immediate left, continue approx 1/2 mile until 2 mini roundabouts, turn left in front of the Mandarin Duck into Watchet Lane. The ground is 150 yards on the right
Capacity: 1,000 Seats: 25 Cover:Yes Floodlights:Yes Club Shop:No
Clubhouse: Saturdays 12pm -11 pm midweek 7pm 11pm Badges: Yes (£3)
HONOURS: Berks & Bucks Sen Tr.Finalists 98-99, BB Jun Cup Winners 52-53, 63-64 B&B Inter'iate Cup Winners 76-77; S.Mid Sen Div Winners (2), S.Mid Sen Cup Winners 96-97 Additional Honours: Cheshm Charity Cup Winners (6),Wycombe Sen Cup Winners: (5),Wycombe Lg Winners (4) and Lg Cup Winners 80-8181 Chiltonian League Winners: (3) Lg Cup Winners 94-95, Spartan South Midlands Sen Div Cup Winners: 97-98
PREVIOUS Leagues: 1908--34 Chesham. 34-84 Wyc Comb. 84-95 Chiltonian 95-98 S Mids

FACT FILE
Founded: 1908
Colours: Green & White/ Green/Green
Change colours: All blue
Midweek Matchday: Tuesday (7.45)
Prog: Yes - Inc.Admission
Match Sec.& Editor: Bill Scholes01494 713867
Club Website: ww.hgfc1908@freeserve.co.uk
CLUB PERSONNEL
President: John Anderson
Chairmen: JohnAnderson & Mick Bowler
Match Secretary: Bill Scholes
Manager Alan Megson
2003-2004
Leading Goalscorer Tim Scholes

LANGFORD

Secretary: Frank Woodward, 4 West View, Langford, Biggleswade. Beds. SG18 9RT
Tel: 01462 701015 (H) Club Email: langfordfc@talk21.com
GROUND: Forde Park, Langford Road, Henlow SG16 6AF Tel: 01462 816106
Directions: Halfway between Langford and Henlow on A6001 Hitchin to Biggleswade road. Bus 177 on main Hitchin-Biggleswade route stops right outside ground
Capacity: 4,000 Seats: 50 Cover: 250 Floodlights: Yes Club Shop: Yes
Clubhouse: Weekday evenings, matchdays 11am-11pm, Sun 12-3pm. Hot food on matchdays
HONOURS: S Mids Lg 88-89 R-up 03-04 Lg Cup 73-74 75-76, 03-04 Prem. Div Tphy 88-89,94-95.O'Brien Div 1 Tphy 84-85), N Beds Charity Cup 27-28 30-31 69-70 75-76 86-87 92-93 94-95 98-99 01-02 Bedford & Dist. Lg 30-31 31-32 32-33, Beds Inter Cup 68-69, H'brooke Cup 72-73
RECORD: Gate: 450 v Q.P.R., 75th Anniversary and clubhouse opening, 22/8/85

Founded: 1908 Nickname: Reds
Sponsors:Armitage Asphalt
Colours: All red with white trim
Change Colours: Blue & white
M/w matchday Tuesday. Prog: With admission.
Editors: Bob Davies (01438 238066)
Chairman: Mick Quinlan President: Ted Rutt
Com. Man: Diane Woodward Man: Roy Ryall
Captain: Paul Chamberlain
2003-2004
Player of the Year and Top Scorer: Steve Starling (40)

LEVERSTOCK GREEN

Secretary: Brian Barter, 11 Curlew Close, Berkhamsted, Herts HP4 2HZ (01442 862322)

GROUND: Pancake Lane, Leverstock Green, Hemel Hempstead. Tel: 01442 246280.

Directions: From M1 leave at A4147 to 2nd r-about. 1st exit to LeverstockGreen, Pancake Lane is on left 300 yrds past the `Leather Bottle' pub

Capacity: Seats: 25 Cover: 100 Floodlights: Yes

Clubhouse: Opens one hour before kick-off, hot food available

Club Shop: Yes

HONOURS: South Midlands Lge - Sen. Div 96-97, Sen Div Cup R-up 93-94, Herts CentenaryTphy R-up 91-92, Herts Charity Shield R-up 91-92, Frank Major Tphy 1991

PREVIOUS: Leagues: West Herts (pre-1950); Herts County 50-91

Players progressing to Football League: Dean Austin (Tottenham Hotspur)

FACT FILE

Founded: 1895
Nickname: The Green
Sponsor: M J L Prestige Cars
Colours: White/green trim
Change Colours: Yellow/blue/blue
Midweek Matchday: Tuesday

Programme

40/44 pages, £1 Editor: Brian Barter
Chairman: Bill Dawes 01442 395748 (H)
Match Sec: Graham Smart(01442 215085)
Press Officer: Tony Smart
Manager: Mick Vipond
Coach: Dean Williams

2003-2004

Leading Goalscorer: Tony Sears
Player of the Year: Steve Board

Langford F.C.

Leverstock Green - Back Row (L-R): L Kelly, A Pollard, S Boad, K Brett, G Tinsley, J Milton, A Phillips, A Simpson. **Front Row:** M Hewitt, N Bartlett, T Sears, R McKane, G Butcher.

LONDON COLNEY

Secretary: Dave Brock, 50 Seymour Rd., St Albans, Herts. AL3 5HW. Tel: 01727 761644 (H)

Ground: Cotslandswick, London Colney (01727 822132)
Directions: From London Colney r'bout (junction of A414/A1081) take A414 towards Watford, after layby (300yds) turn left (hidden turning marked `SportsGround') and follow around to gates.
Capacity: 1,000 Cover: 100 Seats: 30 Floodlights: Yes Club Shop:
Clubhouse: Open after games. Hot food available

HONOURS Sth Mids Lg Sen Div 94-95 R-up 93-94 (Chall. Tphy 93-94, Div 1 R-up 92-93, Res.Div 1 92-93), Herts Co. Lg 56-57 59-60 86-87 88-89 (R-up 57-58 58-59). Aubrey Cup 21-22 22-23 56-57 58-59 81-82, Res. Div 1 87-88 88-89 89-90 91-92, Res. Cup 62-63 89-90 91-92 (R-up 70-71)

PREVIOUS **Leagues:** Mid Herts 1907-54; Herts Co. 07-92
Ground: Whitehorse Lane 07-75
Record Attendance: 300 v St Albans City. Herts Senior Cup 98-99

FACT FILE
Founded: 1907 Nickname: Blueboys
Sponsors: City Glass
Colours: All Royal blue
Change Colours: Red/black/blackMidweek
Matchday: Tuesday
Programme: £1 with entry
Editor: Barry Swain 07970 464286 (M)

CLUB PERSONNEL
Chairman: Steve Ypey
Vice Chairman: P Light
President: K.Parsons
Manager: Mick Wright
Physio: J Burt

POTTERS BAR TOWN

Secretary: Kevin Wilmot,83 Mandeville Court, Lower Hall Lane, Chingford, London E4 8JD
Tel No: 020 8529 9475 (H) 07905 378789 (M) pottersbartown@aol.com
GROUND: Parkfield, The Walk, Potters Bar, Herts EN6 1QN, 01707 654833
Directions: M25 jct 24, enter Potters Bar along Southgate Rd (A111), at 1st lights right into the High St (A1000), half mile left into The Walk, grd 200yds on right (opp. Potters Bar Cricket Club)
Capacity: 2,000 Seats: 150 Cover: 100 Floodlights: Yes Club Shop: No
Contact Jeff Barnes (01707 662399) for details of pennants, badges, car stickers and hangers etc
Clubhouse: Sat 12.30-11pm, Sun noon-5pm, Tues & Thurs 7.30-11pm, midweek matchnights
HONOURS: South Midlands Lge. - Prem. Div. 96-97, Plate 96-97; Herts. Sen. Co. Lge. -Prem. Div. 90-91, Div. 1 73-74, 81-82, Div. 2 68-69; North London Comb. - Prem.Div. 67-68, Div. 1 67-68, Div. 2 R-up 65-66;SSMLg R-up 98-99 Prem Div North R-up 97-98 ,SML Floodlight Cup 99-00
PREVIOUS: **Leagues:** Barnet & Dist. 60-65/ N London Comb. 65-68/ Herts Snr Co. 68-91
RECORD: **Attendance:** 4000 v Eastenders XI, 20.4.97. 306 v Barnet, f/light open93
Competitive: 268 v Wealdstone ,F.A.Cup 1998
BEST SEASON: **FA Vase:** 6th Rd 97-98

FACT FILE
Founded: 1960
Nickname: The Grace or The Scholars
Colours: Red & royal stripes/royal/royal
Change Colours: All Yellow
Midweek matchday: Tuesday or Wednesday
Prog Ed: Kevin WWilmot(07985 378789)
Programme: 40pages, £1 and Website-
www.pottersbartown.co.uk

CLUB PERSONNEL
Chairman: Peter Waller V Chair:John Robinson
President: B Wright General Mger: L Eason
Manager: Steve Smart Coach: Paul Moran
Captain: Jeff Cross Physio: Paul Surridge
2003-04: P.o.Y.: James Dickie
Top Scorers: Kevin Hyde & Andy Martin

ROYSTON TOWN

Secretary /Press Officer: Elaine Phillips, 14 Roan walk, Royston, Herts SG8 9HT
Tel No: 01763 241041 (H) 01763 235100 (M)
GROUND: Garden Walk, Royston, Herts SG8 7HP (01763 241204).
Directions: FromBaldock, A505 to Royston bypass, right at 2nd island onto A10 towards London, 2nd left is Garden Walk; ground 100 yds on left.
Capacity: 4,000 Seats: 300 Cover: 300 Floodlights: Yes Club Shop: Yes
Clubhouse: Mon-Thurs 7-11, Fri 11-3 & 7-11, Sat 11-3 & 4-11, Sun 12-3.
HONOURS Herts Co. Lg 76-77 (Div 1 69-70 76-77); Sth Mids Lg R-up 79-80 (Div 1 78-79,Chall. Cup R-up 78-79;
PREVIOUS **Leagues:** Buntingford & Dist. 18-28; Cambs 28-50; Herts Co. 50-59 62-77; SthMids 59-62 77-84; Isthmian 84-94
RECORDS **Attendance:** 876 v Aldershot, 13/2/93
Scorer: Trevor Glasscock 289 (1968-82) **Appearances:** Fred Bradley 713
BEST SEASON **FA Cup:** 2nd Qual. Rnd 59-60, 0-9 v Barnet (A), 89-90, 0-3 V Bromley (A)

FACT FILE
Founded: 1875 Nickname: Crows
Res League: Essex & Herts Border Comb
Sponsors: ABA Consultants
Colours: All white
Change colours: All RedMidweek Matches: Tuesday
Programme: 16 pages, 30p
Editor: Secretary

CLUB PERSONNEL
Chairman: Graham Phillips
Vice-Chairman: Bernard Brown
President: Alan Barlow
Manager: Peter BakerAsst Mgr: S Salomone
Physio: C Mardell

RUISLIP MANOR

Secretary: Keith Chamberlain,4 Shelley Avenue, Greenford, Middlesex (0208 575 6023)
Ground: Grosvenor Vale, off West End Rd, Ruislip, Middx 01895 637487-office,676168-boardroom
Directions: A40 to Ruislip, turn off on A4180, right at r'bout into West EndRd, right into Grosvenor Vale after a 1 1/2 miles - ground at end. From RuislipManor station (Metropolitan Line) turn left out of station, then 1st right intoShenley Ave, 3rd left into Cranley Dr - ground 150 yds on left
Capacity: 3,000 Seats: 250 Cover: 600 Floodlights: Yes Club Shop: Yes
Clubhouse: Mon-Fri 12-3.30 & 5.30-11pm, Sat & Sun 12-3 & 7.30-10.30
HONOURS London Lg R-up 51-52 (Div 1 R-up 47-48), Isthmian Lg Div 2 R-up 92-93 (Associate Members Tphy 90-91), Athenian Lg Div 2 72-73, Middx Snr Cup SF (6), Middx Charity Cup R-up 90-91 95-96
PREVIOUS **Leagues:** Uxbridge 38-39; Middx Snr 39-46; London 46-58; Spartan 58-65; Athenian65-84; Isthmian 84-96
RECORDS **Attendance:** 2,000 v Tooting & Mitcham United, F.A. Amateur Cup 1962

FACT FILE
Founded: 1938 Nickname: The Manor
Sponsors: Light Years
Colours: Black & White/black/black
Change colours: Blue & yellow/blue/blue.
Midweek Matches: Monday
Reserve League: Suburban Lge (North)
Programme: 24 Price: 50p
Editor/ Press Off.: Chris Thomas
01895 636930

CLUB PERSONNEL
Chairman: George Kaplavan
Manager:Paul Pitfield Physio: Gary Strudwick
Captain: Trevor Dorrell
2003-2004
P.o.Y.: Mark Smith Top Scorer: Steve Norton

St MARGARETSBURY

Secretary: Lynne Williams, 23 The Roundings, Hertford Heath. SG13 7PX Tel :07740 867170 (M)
GROUND: Station Road, Stanstead St Margarets, Nr Ware, Herts (01920 870473)
Directions: Harlow/Chelmsford exit from A10 to A414, take B181 at Amwell roundabout after 300yds towards Stanstead Abotts, ground quarter mile on right. 300yds from St Margaretsbury BR station (Liverpool Str.-Hertford East line)
Capacity: 1,000 Seats: 60 Cover: 60 Floodlights: Yes Club Shop: No
Clubhouse: Bar open every evening 7.30-11, plus Sat 12-2, Sun 12-3. Bar snacks available
HONOURS: Herts Snr Cent Tphy 92-93; Herts Co. Lg Div 2 48-49, Div 3 78-79; Aubrey Cup 48-49 71-72; Res. Div 1 82-83 86-87; Res. Cup (3); Waltham & Dist Lg 46-47; Spartan Lge 95-96; SSM Prem Cup 01-02, SSM Floodlit Cup 03-04Roy Bailey Mem Trophy 95-96, Herts Charity Shd 97-98.
PREVIOUS: Lges: East Herts; Hertford & Dist.; Waltham & District 47-48; Herts Co. 48-92
RECORD: Attendance: 450 v Srafford Rangers F.A.Cup 3rd Q Rd 2001-02
BEST SEASON **FA Vase:** 3 Rd 1985-86 **F.A.Cup:** 3rd Q 2001-02,03-04
2003-2004 **Player of the Year:** John Barker **Top Goalscorer:** Richard Haward

FACT FILE
Founded: 1894 Nickname: The Bury
Sponsors: Universial Systems
Colours: Red & black/white/white
Change Colours:White/Black/Black
Midweek matchday: Tuesday
Reserve Lg: Herts Co.Senior Res Lg
Programme: £4.00 with entry
Ed/Match Sec: John Williams 01992 471651

CLUB PERSONNEL
Chairman: Dave Stock Pres: R L Groucott
Manager:Kelvin Hart Asst.Man: Ray Greenall
Gen Man: Martin Gutteridge
Coach: Dave Steedman Captain: Lee Judges
Physio: John Elliott

TRING ATHLETIC

Secretary: Ralph Griffiths, 42 Bedgrove, Aylesbury, Bucks HP21 7BD.Tel: 01296 426425 (H), email: ralph.griffiths@ntworld.com **Website**: www.tafc.co.uk
Ground: Pendley Sports Centre, Cow Lane, Tring, Herts. HP23 5NS(01442 891144)
Directions: From M25 J 20 take A41M, after 11 miles take B4635 to Tring. On leaving motorway turn right at roundabout and left into Cow Lane. Sports Centre is 300 yards on right.
Capacity: 1,233 **Seats:** 150 **Cover:** 100+ **Floodlights:** Yes **Club Shop:** No
Clubhouse: Bar, open matchdays, training nights & Sunday lunchtimes
HONOURS: West Herts Div 1 (3), Lg R-up 72-73 ,Lg Cup 65-66. SSMlds: Sen Div 99-00,Lg Cup 89-90,Herts Ch Shield 99-00,01-02 Cherry Red Tr (2)Herts Centenary Tr (2).SSMDiv 1 Cup02-3
PREVIOUS:League: West Herts 58-88
RECORD **Scorer:** Andy Humphreys 201(First team) **Appearances:** Mark Boniface 642
2003-2004 **Leading Goalscorer:** Andy Humphreys **Ps.o.Y**.: Tony Mendicino & Paul Lewis

FACT FILE
Founded: 1958 Nickname: Athletic
Sponsors: R.O.Allum & Sons(Contractors)
Colours: Red & black/black/black
Change colours: yellow/green/yellow
Midweek matchday: Wednesnay
Programme: 64 pages, £1.50 Editor: Sec
Chairman: Barry Johnson
Match Sec: Paul Humphreys(01442 825114)
Manager Mick Eldridge
Ass Man:Ray Brimson Coach: Richard Vincent
Physio: Trevor Langley Capt: David Foskett

WELWYN GARDEN CITY

Secretary: Dave Mansfield, 49 Hollybush Lane, Welwyn G'n City, Herts. AL7 4JH(07762374995)
GROUND: Herns Lane, Welwyn Garden City (01707 328470)
Directions: From A1 follow signs for industrial area. Take one-way systemopposite Avdel Ltd (signed Hertford B195), take 2nd exit off one-way system.Ground 400 yards on left. One and a half miles from Welwyn GC (BR)
Capacity: 1,500 Seats: 40 Cover: 120 Floodlights: Yes Club Shop: Yes
Clubhouse: Open every night and weekend lunchtimes. Members Bar, Hall.Steward:Gary Bevan
HONOURS: Herts Snr Centenary Tphy 84-85 (R-up 88-89), Herts Charity Shield 27-28 86-8787-88 94-95 (R-up 48-49), Sth Mids Lg 73-74 (R-up 85-86, Div 1 69-70 81-82, LgCup R-up 74-75 81-82 88-89, Reserve Cup 85-86)
PREVIOUS: **Leagues:** Spartan; Metropolitan; Gtr London. **Ground:** Springfields

Founded: 1921 Nickname: Citizens
Colours: Claret with white trim
Change Colours: Silver with claret trim.
: Midweek Matches: Tuesday
Programme: 24 pages, 50p
Editor: Secretary (01707 321119 (H)Local Press: Welwyn & Hatfield Times, Welwyn & Hatfield Herald & Post
Chairman: Terry Hazel
Manager: GuillermoGanetAssistant Manager: Ray Greenhall
Physio: Danny Milliken

Buckingham Athletic's Atkinson makes a fine save against Langford but unfortunately for him Langford did manage to score seven! Photo: Gordon Whittington

AMERSHAM TOWN

Secretary: Michichael Gahagan, 7 Ely Close, Lincoln Park, Amersham, Bucks. HP7 9HS

Tel No: 01494 724798

Email: michaelgahagan@ukonline.co.uk

Ground: Spratleys Meadow, School Lane, Amersham, Bucks. Tel No: 01494 727428

Capacity: **Seats:** **Cover:** **Floodlights:**

Directions: From London, take A 413 towards Aylesbury. At bottomo f Amersham Old Town Hill turn right into Mill Lane. At top of Mill Lane turn left into School Lane and ground is on left.

Clubhouse: **Yes**

Colours:Black & white stripes/black/black

Change colours: Yellow/Blue/Yellow

CLUB PERSONNEL

Chairman: David Holdcroft

Match Secretary: DavidHoldcroft

Tel No: 01494 582626 (H)

Manager: Ted Gromnicki

Programme: Editor:Secretary

AMPTHILL TOWN ADMIRAL

Secretary: Eric Turner, 34 Dunstable Street, Ampthill, Beds MK45 2JT.
Tel:01525 403128 (H & B)

Ground: Ampthill Park, Woburn Road, Ampthill, Beds. Tel: 01525 404440

Directions: From Ampthill Town Centre follow signs to Woburn then take the first right into Ampthill Park

Chairman: Nick Burton
Tel: 01525 719978
Manager: Nick Burton
Programme Editor: As Secretary

Colours: Yellow /Blue/Yellow
Change Colours: Orange/Navy Blue/NavyBlue

ARLESEY ATHLETIC

Secretary: Ron Ward, 211 Cambridge Road, Hitchin, Herts. SG4 0JP

Tel Nos: 01462 627962 (H) 07729 819303 (M)

Email: ron.ward3@ntlworld.com

Ground: c/o Arlesey Town F.C.

Capacity: 2,9 20 **Seats:** 150 **Cover:** 600 **Floodlights:** Yes

Directions: As for Arlesey Town

Clubhouse: Yes

Colours: All red
Change colours: Sky Blue/Royal Blue/Royal

CLUB PERSONNEL
Chairman: Philip Papworth
Manager: Glen Clark
Match Secretary: Secretary

BIGGLESWADE UNITED

Secretary: Tracey James, 17 Havelock Road, Biggleswade, Beds SG18 0DB.
Tel: 01767 316270 (H),01223 372611(W), 0771 466 1827(M)
GROUND: Second Meadow, Fairfield Road, Biggleswade, Beds. (01767 600408)
Directions: From A1 Sainsbury's roundabout, take bridge over river and and second left into Sun Street.(before Peugot Garage). First left into Fairfield Road ground at bottom of road in lane
Capacity: 2,000 Seats: 30 Cover: 130 Floodlights: Yes Club Shop: No
Clubhouse: Open all matchdays, rolls available. Also refreshment hut with hot snacks
HONOURS: Hunts F.A. Prem Cup : 98-99, Beds Sen. Trophy 03-04S.Mids Lg Div 1 96-97 Cup Winners 96-97Beds & District Prem Div.94-95, 95-96, Div 1. 91-92, Div2 90-91,Div3 88-89 Beds F.A. Inter Cup (2) Hinchingbrooke Cup: 03-04 **Record Crowd:** 250 v Biggleswade T
2003-2004 Top Scorer: Robbie O'Dell **P.o.Y.**: Dean Bull 2004-2005 **Captain:** Danny Bennett

FACT FILE
Founded: 1959 (original club 1929)
Colours: Red & navy/navy/red
Change : Yellow & Black/black/yellow
Midweek Matchday: Tuesday /Thursday
Prog-With admission Editor: Secretary
BestVase Season **:** 1st Rd Proper 95-6, 03-04
Previous Name**:** Biggleswade F.C until 1929
Chairman: David McCormick.(01767 316018)
Match Sec.: Mick Brown, (01767 221512)
Manager Snowy' Wright
Physio: Phil Lunceford

BRACHE SPARTA

Secretary & Prog Ed: Roy Standring, 37 Taunton Ave, Luton, Beds. LU2 0LN. Tel: 01582 736574
GROUND: Foxdell Sports Ground, Dallow Rd, Luton LU1 1UP (01582 720751).
Directions: From M1 jct11, take A505 towards Luton. Right at Chaul End roundabout. Across A505 keep B&Q on left, into Dallow Rd. Ground 50 yds on right by Foxdell junior school.
Capacity: 400 Cover: 100 Seats: 25 Floodlights: Yes Club Shop: No
Clubhouse: Open daily 12-3 & 7.30-11. Light snacks & refreshments etc available
HONOURS: South Mids Lg R-up 92-93, 96-97 (Div 1 R-up 83-84 87-88), Lg Cup R-up 75-76 80-81 92-93 97-98, Premier Div Cup Winners 97-98 R-up 91-92, Res Div 2 R-up 75-76, Res Cup R-up 87-88; Luton & Dist. Lg 67-68 69-70 70-71 71-72; William Pease Trophy 66-67 67-68 70-71 71-72; Beds Interm Cup 71-72 (R-up 68-69 70-71), BedsJnr Cup 82-83; Leighton Challenge Cup R-up 69-70 South Mids Lg Prem Div 1 North Champions 97-98, Beds Premier Cup R-up. 97-98

FACT FILE
Founded: 1960 Nickname: The Foxes
Colours: All Navy Blue
Change Colours: All WhiteMidweek matches: Tuesday
Prog: 32 pages, £2.50 (incl. admission)
Career Record Goalscorer: Keith Denness
CLUB PERSONNEL
Chairman: Roy Standring
President: Doug Smith
Manager: Mark SmithPhysio: Chris Garner

BRIMSDOWN ROVERS

Secretary: Peter Wade, 5 Goldsdown Close, Enfield. EN3 7RR Tel No: 020 8804 7053
GROUND: Brimsdown Sports & Social Club, Goldsdown Road, Enfield, Middlesex EN3 7RR
Tel: 0208 804 5491 **Directions:** BR from Liverpool Street to Brimsdown (half mile away) or Southbury Road. By road off Green Street, itself off Hertford Road (A1010). Buses 191 or307
Capacity: 2,300 Seats:150 Cover:300 Floodlights: Yes Club Shop: No
Clubhouse: Large lounge & clubroom, games room & stage 3 bars (300 capacity) Big TV screen
HONOURS: Spartan Champions 92-93. Spartan Lg Cup 95-96
RECORD: **Gate:** 412 v Chesham Utd, FA Cup 3rd Qual. Rd 12/10/91
BEST SEASON: **FA Vase:** 3rd Rd 93-94 **FA Cup:** 3rd Qual. replay 91-92
PREVIOUS: **Leagues:** Northern Suburban **Names:** Durham Rovers; Brimsdown FC
2003-2004 **Player of the Year:** Richard Jackson **Top Goalscorer:** Matt Keogh

FACT FILE
Founded: 1947
Colours: Black & white stripes/black/black
Change colours: Yellow& blue/blue/yellow
Midweek Matchday: Tuesday
Programme with admission
Chairman: Gary Brooker
Match Sec & Prog.Editor: Peter Wade.
5 Goldsdown Close, Enfield Middlesex EN3 7RR Tel: 0208 804 7053
Manager:Tony Faulkner Captain: Matt Keogh

BUCKINGHAM ATHLETIC

Secretary: Steve Cole, 45 Redshaw Close, Linden Village, Bucks. MK18 7BS
Tel Nos: 01280 816789 (H) 07798 701414 (M)

Ground: Stratford Fields, Stratford Rd, Buckingham
Tel: 01280 816945

Directions: From Milton Keynes take the A422 Stony Stratford-Buckingham road -ground on left just before town centre. From Oxford, Aylesbury or Bletchley, take the ring road to the A422 Stony Stratford roundabout, turn left, the ground is situated at the bottom of the hill on the left

Colours: Sky & Navy Blue/Navy/Navy
Change Colours: All Red or Yellow & Navy

Chairman: John Webb
Manager: Neil Kidwell

COCKFOSTERS

Secretary: Graham Bint, 15 Chigwell Park, Chigwell, Essex IG7 5BE (0208 500 7369)
GROUND: Cockfosters Sports Ground, Chalk Lane, Cockfosters, Barnet (0208 449 5833)
Directions: M25 Jct 24 (Potters Bar), take A111 signed Cockfosters - ground 2 miles on right. Adjacent to Cockfosters underground station (Picadilly Line). Bus 298 to Cockfosters station
Capacity: 1,000 Seats: 30 Cover: 80 Floodlights: Yes Club Shop: No
Clubhouse: 7-11pm Tues & Thurs, 4-11pm Sat, 12-3pm Sun. Hot & cold food onmatchdays
HONOURS: London Interm Cup 70-71 89-90, Herts Snr Co. Lg 78-79 80-81 83-84 R-up 82-83 84-85, Aubrey Cup 78-79 84-85 R-up 70-71 77-78, Herts Interm Cup 78-79 R-up x3
Previous Leagues: Wood Green & Dist. 21-46/ Northern Suburban 46-66/ Herts Snr Co.66-91
BEST SEASON: **FA Vase:** 2nd Round 91-92
RECORDS: **Gate:** 408 v Saffron Walden, Herts Senior County Lg 68-69

Founded: 1921 Nickname: Fosters
Colours: All Red Change colours: All White
Midweek matches: Wednesday
Sponsors: Premier Leifts
Programme: 12 pages with entry
Editor: A Simmons (0208 440 7998)
Chairman: Colin Bell(01727 823458)
President: Les Langdale
Press Officer: Doug Went (020 8350 4787)
Manager: Dave Lee Physio: John Walsh
Captain: Danny Hutchings
2003-2004 TopGoalscorer: Tom Nelson 25
Player of the Year: Ian Thurlow

Cockfosters F.C. Photo: gordon Whittington.

Kentish F.C. Photo: gordon Whittington.

COLNEY HEATH

Secretary: Martin Marlborough, 16 Meadway, Colney Heath, St Albans. AL4 0PT
Tel Nos: 01727 824820(H) 07960 155463 (M) 01727 819370 (W)

Ground: The Pavillion Recreaton Ground, High St., Colney Heath, St. Albans, Herts.
Tel: 01727 826188

Directions: Turn off the A414 (was A405) into Colney Heath village and the ground is behind the school on the left.

Colours:Black & White stripes/Black/Black
Change Colours:
Tangerine & black trim/ Tangerine/Tangerine
Midweek Matchday:
Programme Editor Martin Marlborough

Chairman:Martin Marlborough
Other Club Officer(s):
Manager:Geoff O'Vell

CRANFIELD UNITED

Secretary: Jim Brandom, 31 Lordsmead, Cranfield, Beds. MK43 0HP
Tel No: 01234 751501 (H) 07831 676557 (M)

Ground: Crawley Road, Cranfield Tel Nio: 01234 751444

Directions: Take North Crawley/Newport Pagnell road from village of Cranfield. Ground is on left before leaving speed limit signs.

Colours:Red& white stripes/black/red
Change colours: White/black/black
Programme Editor: T.B.A.

CLUB PERSONNEL
Chairman: Brian Dosser
Manager: Jeremy Hall
Match Secretary: Secretary

KENTISH TOWN

Secretary: Kevin Young, 22 St Johns Park Mansions, Pemberton Gardens, Lonod. N19 5TRT
Tel Nos: 0207 263 3231 (W) 0207 263 3231 (W)

Ground: Coles Park, White Hart Lane, London N17 7JP Tel No: 0208 889 1415

Directions: M25 Jct 25 Go south on A10 for 5 miles. Turn right from slip road at lights onto White Hart Lane and ground is on left after 500 yards.

Colours: Light Blue/Navy Blue/Light Blue
Change colours: Yellow & Green/Green/Yellow

CLUB PERSONNEL
Chairman: Gregg Hazelgrove
Manager:Frank Zanre
Programme Editor: Secretary
Tel Nos: 07919 275855 (M)
& 0207 263 3231 (Fax)

NEW BRADWELL St PETER

Secretary: Nicola Cox, 42 Forrabury Avenue, Bradwell Common, Milton KKeynes MK13 8NQ
Ground: Recreation Ground, Bradwell Rd, New Bradwell, Milton Keynes MK13 7AT
Tel.: 01908 313835 **Capacity:** Seats: 30 Cover: 100 Floodlights: Yes
Directions: From M1 Jnt 14 go towards Newport Pagnell, left at 1st r-about into H3 (A422 Monks Way). Over 5 r-abouts, right at 6th island into V6 (GraftonSt.), At 1st roundabout go right the way round (back on yourself) then take 1st left at mini-r'about turn left into Bradwell Rd. Go straight over next mini r'about. Ground immediately on left.
Clubhouse: Members only (member can sign in 2 guests). Evenings & w/e mid day. No food.
HONOURS: Sth Mids Lg Div 1 76-77 83-84 Sen Div Champs 97-98, (Res Div 2 R-up 76-7), Berks& Bucks Senior Trophy 1999-2000

FACT FILE
Founded: 1902 Nickname: Peters
Colours: All Maroon & Sky Blue
Change: Green & Red/Green/Red
Midweek matches: Tuesday
Programme: 32 pages, £3 with entry
Editor: Paul Smith 01908 521590 (H)

CLUB PERSONNEL
Chairman John Haynes President: J P Booden
Vice-Chairman: R.Creasey
Press Officer: P Smith
Managers:Steve Goodridge

OXHEY JETS

Secretary: Dave Fuller, 4 Sage Close, Biggleswade, Beds. SG 18 8WH
Tel Nos: 01767 227147 (H)07802 465727 (M)
Ground: Altham Way, South Oxhey, Watford, (Off Little OXhey Lane)
Tel No: 0208 421 6277
Directions: From Bushey station take Pinner road (A4008) and then along Oxhey Lane towards Harrow. Right at lights into Little Oxhey Lane. Altham Way is on left after crossing railway bridge.

Colours: Royal Blue/white/royal blue
Change colours: Yellow/blue/white

CLUB PERSONNEL
Chairman: Phil Andrews
: Manager: Benny Higham
Match Secretary: John Elliott
Tel Nos: 0208 428 6382 (H)
& 07850558573 (M)
Programme Editor: Ann Brereton
Tel Nos; 0208 428 0511 (H)
& 07799 413205(M)

SHILLINGTON

Secretary: Aubrey Cole, 32 Greenfields, Shillington, Hitchin, Herts. SG5 3NX Tel: 01462 711322

Ground: Playing Field, Greenfields, Shillington
Tel: 01462 711757

Directions: From Luton on A6 after bypassing Barton, turn right at large roundabout.Through Gobian to Shillington. From Bedfford or Hitchin, A600 to RAF Henlow. At Bird in Hand roundabout take exit to Upper Stondon.

Chairman: Doug Riggs

Manager: Neil Tattersall

Colours: Black & white stripes/ black/black
Change Colours: All White

STONY STRATFORD TOWN

Secretary: Maurice J Barber, 26 Boundary Cres., Stony Stratford, Milton Keynes MK11 1DF
Tel: 01908 567930 (H)
GROUND: Sports Ground, Ostlers Lane, Stony Stratford (01908 562267).
Directions: From Dunstable use old A5, Watling Street. Approaching Bletchley continue on A5 loop road (Hinkley) to end of dual c'way to A422/A508 r'bout. First exit, thru lights, 2nd right into Ostlers Lane.
Capacity: 600 Seats: 30 Cover: 120 Floodlights: Yes Club Shop: No
Clubhouse: Open evenings & weekends
HONOURS: Sth Mids Lg R-up 70-71 71-72 (Div 1 93-94, Div 1 Cup 93-94)
PREVIOUS: **Leagues:** North Bucks & Dist.; Northampton Combination
RECORD: **Attendance:** 476 v Aston Villa U21, floodlight opening 12.11.96

Formed: 1898 Sponsor:Maritz
Colours:Sky blue/navy/navy
Change Colours:All yellow
Midweek matches: Tuesday
Reserves' League: SSM Res. Div. One
Prog: 28 pages, 50p Editor: Paul Grimsley
Tel No: 01908 569828 Chairman: Mike Judd
Match Sec.:Mrs. E. Sartain
Manager:Chris Johnson Capt: Darren Long

2003-04
Leading goalscorer: Tony Hill 16
P.o.Y.: Brendan Quill

SUN SPORTS

Secretary: Richard Atkins, Flat 1, Water Company Dep., Stockers Farm Rd., Rickmansworth, Herts. WD3 1NX Tel Nos: 01923 293220 (H) 07801 677083 (M)
Ground: Bellmount Wood Avenue, Watford, Herts. Tel: 01923 227453
Directions: From Watford take A411 towards Hemel Hempstaed . Left into Langley Way at 2nd traffic lights. Take third exit at next roundabout into Ca`ssiobury Drive then take first left into Bellmount Wood Avenue. Turn right for Club entrance on left hand bend.
PREVIOUS Name: Sun Postal Sports >2003
Leagues: Herts Senior County Lge. >2003

Chairman: Jim Kempster
Manager: Brian Remphrey
Programme Editor: Secretary

Colours: Yellow.Blue/Blue
Change Colours: Blue/White/Blue

Arena Spectator Facilities

From Arena Seating the following spectator facilities are available for purchase to enhance all Sports Arenas and provide comfort for spectators

Arena Stadia Tip-Up Seats, floor or riser mounted on existing or new build terracing

Arena Sports Stand and Tiered Spectator Seating.
A classic design, with a cantilevered roof cover providing an unimpeded view for the spectator.

Can be supplied in 4, 7 and 13 rows covered seat options with or without end enclosures.

The roof cover is built in modules that can be added to as need and finance dictate.

Arena Sports Shelter
A smaller, lightweight 4 row version of the Arena Sports Stand where space is at a particular premium

Arena LT Grandstand and Arena LT Super Grandstand Prefabricated and delivered to location via lorry with crane.

Supplied complete with 50 or 74 tip up seats or as a tiered standing stand with capacity for 85 or 120 spectators.

Wheelchair spaces can be incorporated.

End enclosures available as an optional extra.

Can be linked together for greater capacity.

Arena Seating Limited, Arena House, Membury, Lambourn Woodlands, Hungerford, Berkshire RG17 7TQ
Tel: 01488 674800 Fax: 01488 674822 Email: info@arenaseating.com

Kentish F.C.

Photo: gordon Whittington.

WINSLOW UNITED

Secretary: David Ward, 28 Park Roafd, Winslow, Buckingham, MK 18 3DL
Tel Nos: 01296 713202 (H) 07944 258838 (M) W mail: davden@tesco.net

Ground: RecreationGround, Elmfields Gate, Winslow, Bucks. MK18 3JH
Tel No: 01296 713057

Directions: A413 from Aylesbury to Winslow. Right from High Street into Elmfield Gate. Ground 100yards on left. PLease park in Public Hall Car Park opposite ground.

FACT FILE
Formed:
Sponsor:
Colours: Yellow/Blue/Yellow
Change colours: All Green
Midweek Matches:
Programme Editor: Secrtary

CLUB PERSONNEL
Chairman: Jeff Robins
Manager: Steve Kelly
Match Secretary: Secretary

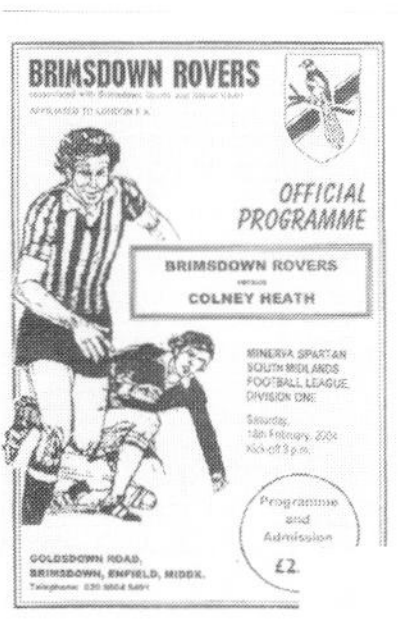

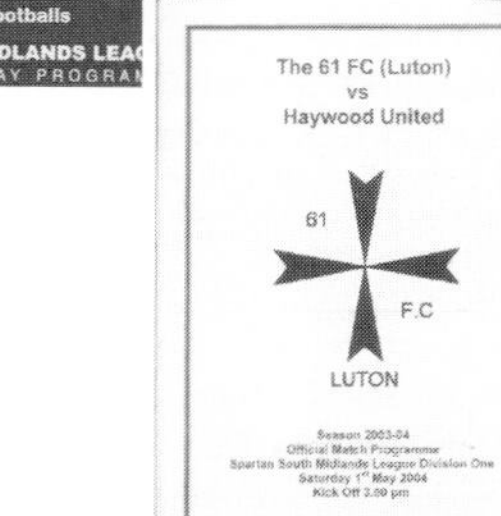

FINAL LEAGUE TABLE 2003-04

DIVISION TWO	P	W	D	L	F	A	Pts
1. Old Dunstablians	32	27	3	2	108	23	84
2. Winslow United	32	23	3	6	90	43	72
3. Arlesey Athletic	32	21	2	9	84	48	65
4. Risborough Rangers	32	19	7	6	75	28	64
5. Abbey National (MK)	32	16	4	12	69	56	52
6. Crawley Green	32	15	4	13	75	60	49
7. Cranfield United	32	14	4	14	61	59	46
8. Kent Athletic	32	13	6	13	55	46	45
9. Padbury BTFC	32	13	6	13	63	56	45
10. Kentish Town	32	13	6	13	68	68	45
11. Mursley United	32	13	4	15	60	73	43
12. Caddington	32	8	11	13	53	72	35
13. Totternhoe	32	9	6	17	42	73	33
14. Markyate	32	6	10	16	35	54	28
15. Flamstead	32	6	6	20	42	78	24
16. Amersham Town (-12 pts)	32	9	1	22	47	94	16
17. Old Bradwell United	32	3	5	24	37	133	14

AFC DUNSTABLE

Secretary: Craig Renfrew, 75B Princes Street. Dunstable. LU6 3AS. Tel: 01582471794 (H), 01234 265444 (B)

Ground: Lancot Park. Dunstable Road, Totternhoe (01582 663735)

Directions: From Dunstable Town Centre take the B489 Tring Road. At the 4throundabout turn right, signposted Totternhoe. The pitch is located withionDunstable Town Cricket Club which is on the right just before entering thevillage of Totternhoe

Previous Name: Old Dunstablians

Honours: South Midlands Division 2 - 03/04.

CADDINGTON

Secretary: Dave Mark, 7 Heathfield Close, Caddington, Luton, Beds. LU1 4HD Tel: 01582 421404 (H) 01797 147968 (B)

Ground: Caddington Recreation Club, Manor Road, Caddington (01582 450151) **Directions:** On entering village turn into Manor Road (adjacent to shops andvillage green), proceed 500 metres: Clubhouse and ground on left side next to Catholic Church

CRAWLEY GREEN

Secretary: Alan Burgess, 23 Higham Drive, Luton LU2 9SP (01582 483172)

Ground: Crawley Green Recreation Ground, Crawley Green Road, Luton, Beds. 01582 451058 **Directions:** From M1 jct 10 , to r'about at end of motorway slip road into Airport Way. At 4th r'about turn right into Crawley Green Rd. Ground is 1/2 mile on left past Ashcroft High School.

DUNSTABLE TOWN RESERVES

Ground: Creasy Park, Brewers Hill Road, Dunstable, Bedfordshire.
(01582 667555)

FLAMSTEAD

Secretary: Mark McGreevy, 3 White Hill, Flamstead, Herts. AL3 8DN (01582 841 481)

Ground: Flamstead Sports Assoc., Friendless Lane, Flamstead, St Albans, Herts (0582 841307)

Directions: From Dunstable Town Centre travel south on A5 Trunk Roadtowards the M1. Follow for approximately 3 miles then turn right oppositeHertfordshire Moat House Hotel. Ground and parking approximately half a mile onthe corner of the first right turn

KENT ATHLETIC

Secretary: Irene Oodian, 9 Gafield Court, Handcross Road,Luton, Beds. LU2 8JZ (01582 483090)

Ground: Kent Social Club, Tenby Drive, Leagrave, Luton Tel: 01582 582723 **Directions:** M1 J11 take A505 towards Luton. Take the first turning on the left (Stoneygate Road), straight over at r'about and turn right at lights into Beechwood Road. Take the first road on the left and then the first right into Tenby Drive. Ground and car park 100 yards on left

KINGS LANGLEY

Secretary: Andy Mackness, 79 Weymouth Street, Apsley, Hemel Hempstead, Herts HP3 9SJ
Tel: 01442 398186 (H) 020 7587 4153 (B) 07976 692801 (M)

Ground: Gaywood Park, Hempstead Road, Kings Langley. Tel: 01923 264489

Directions: From M25 leave at Junction 20. Take A4251 to Kings Langley. The ground is approx. 1 mile on the right.

LOUGHTON ORIENT

Secretary: Clare O'Connor, 18 Cranwell Close,Shenley Brook End, Milton Keynes MK5 7BU (01908 520370)
Ground: Loughton Sports & Social Club, Lincesdale Grove, Loughton, Milton Keynes. Tel: 01908 690668
Directions: From M1 Jct 14 follow H6, Childs Way for 5 miles until V4 Watling Way (Knowlhill r-about), right to Loughton r-about, right along H5 Portway 1st right Linceslade Grove.
Previous Name: Abbey National (Loughton)

MARKYATE

Ground: The Playing Fields, Cavendish, Markyate, Hertfordshire (01582 841731)

MURSLEY UNITED

Secretary: Geoff Curtis, 26 Berwick Drive, Bletchley, Milton Keynes MK3 7NB (01908 377196)
Ground: Station Road, Mursley, Milton Keynes
Directions: A421 Bletchley to Buckingham Road, first right in village

OLD BRADWELL UNITED

Secretary: Paul Mills, 36 Craddocks Close, Bradwell, Milton Keynes MK13 9DX (01908 227520)
Ground: Abbey Road, Bradwell, Milton Keynes (01908 312355)
Directions: M1 junction 14 go towards Newport Pagnell. Turn left at firstroundabout into H3 Honks Way. Go six r'abouts then left onto V6 Grafton Street.Take 1st right at mini-r'about into Rawlins Road and then 2nd left intoLoughton Road. Take 1st right into Primrose Road and at the 'T' junction turnright into Abbey Road

PADBURY UNITED

Secretary: James Clarke, 41 Moorhen Way, Buckingham, Bucks. MK18 1GN (01280 824513
Ground: Springfields,Playing Fields, Padbury **Directions:** From Buckingham follow ring road with signs,to Aylesbury (A413), then towards Buckingham and Padbury is two miles south of the town A413 and three miles north west of Winslow on A413. Turn off opposite bus shelter on Springfields Estate and follow road forward.

PITSTONE & IVONGHOE

Secretary: Jay Adlem, 22 Maud Janes Close, Ivinghoe, Leighton Buzzard. LU7 9ED. Tel: 01296 668663 (H)
Ground: Pitstone Recreation Ground, Vicarage Road, Pitstone, Bucks Tel: 01296 661271
Directions: Tring Rd (B489) from Dunstable, turn right for Ivinghoe, and continue through to Pitstone r-about; ground left then right. From Aylesbury -left at `Rising Sun' in Aston Clinton, keep on that road to Pitstone r'bout; ground right then right. Bus 61 from Luton or Aylesbury. Nearest BR stations are Tring or Cheddington.

RISBOROUGH RANGERS

Secretary: Derrick J Wallace, 42 Ash Road, Princes Risborough, Bucks, HP27 0BQ Tel: 01844 345179 (H), 01844 345435 (B)
Ground: `Windsor', Horsenden Lane, Princes Risborough. (01844 274176) **Directions:** Rear of Princes Risborough BR Station (Chiltern Line). A4010 fromAylesbury thru Princes Risborough, fork right onto A4009, left by thatched cottage, over railway bridge, immediate right ground 150 yds on right

THE 61 FC (LUTON)

Secretary: Richard Everitt, 44 Somersby Close, Luton LU1 3XB. Tel: 01582 485095 (H)
Ground: Kingsway, Beverley Road, Luton, Beds. 01582 495417
Directions: M1 jct 11, A505 to Luton centre, right at 1st island, 1st left, Beverley Rd is 3rd left, entrance in Beverley Rd, exactly 1 mile junction 11.All Luton to Dunstable buses pass ground - alight at Beech Hill Bowling Club. 1mile from both Leagrave & Luton BR stations

TOTTERNHOE

Secretary: Jim Basterfield, 41 Park Avenue, Totternhoe, Dunstable, Beds LU6 1QF. Tel: 01582 667941 (H)
Ground: Totternhoe Recreation Ground, Dunstable (01582 606738)
Directions: Turn off the main Dunstable to Tring Road B489. Ground on right as you enter Totternhoe. Five miles from Leighton Buzzard (BR), 7 miles from Luton. Bus 61 Luton-Aylesbury

Old Dunstablians (now AFC Dunstable) - before their 8-2 victory over Amersham Town which won them the Division Two title. Photo: Gordon Whittington.

SUSSEX COUNTY LEAGUE

SPONSORED BY: MATTHEW CLARK

FOUNDED 1920

President: P H Strange **Chairman:** Peter Bentley

Secretary: P Beard, 2 Van Gogh Place, Bersted, Bognor Regis PO22 9BG

Tel: 01243 822063 (H) 07966 457908 (M) Fax: 01243 822063 www.scfl.org.uk

For the start of the season, Burgess Hill Town had been promoted to the East Division of the Southern League, while St Leonards had resigned from that League. Rye & Iden United, Eastbourne Town and East Grinstead Town were promoted from Division 2, while Peacehaven & Telscombe, Wick and Littlehampton Town, all former League champions had been relegated. Shinewater Association and Eastbourne United merged to play on the ground of the latter, under the name of Eastbourne United Association. Oving, unable to overcome local objections to the ground, were forced to disband, and Pease Pottage Village escaped relegation. Midhurst & Easebourne and Haywards Heath Town were promoted from Division 3 into Division 2. In Division 3, Bosham and Uckfield Town escaped relegation due to the above, and Wadhurst United joined from the East Sussex League Premier Division.

First team fixtures were completed by 1st May, despite some weather problems in March and April following a reasonable winter. The departure of Burgess Hill gave rise to a very competitive Division 1, and on Easter Monday no fewer than eight Clubs could still have won the title. Chichester City United on the last day gained the championship, helped that day by a defeat at Pagham for their main rivals Rye & Iden United. East Preston finished on the same points as Rye, with Three Bridges a point away in fourth. Rye & Iden United marked a tremendous return to Division 1, while their co-promotees, Eastbourne Town and East Grinstead Town, also had successful first seasons, finishing fifth and ninth respectively. The leading goalscorers in League matches in the Division were Pat Massaro of Three Bridges with 26, while Miles Scerri of Arundel had 25, and Yemi Odubade of Eastbourne Town and James Laing of Hassocks both had 24. Finishing in relegation places were Shoreham, Selsey and Pagham, with the latter gaining a reprieve due to the fact that St Leonards had to withdraw before half of the season was completed. Division 2 was won by Littlehampton Town, with Worthing United in second place and Eastbourne United Association in third. Finishing in relegation positions were Lancing and Haywards Heath Town, with Lancing also enjoying a reprieve. Division 3 champions were Crowborough Athletic with St. Francis Rangers runners-up. Finishing in relegation positions were Newhaven and Upper Beeding. Neither will be relegated due to problems at a higher level, including the withdrawal of Franklands Village, who have been forced to resign due to the lack of co-operation from their landlords in allowing them to improve their facilities to the level required. They have been a member of the League since the start of Division 3, and this season have reached the Final of two cup competitions, the County FA Intermediate Cup and the Mid-Sussex Senior Charity Cup. Rustington will be joining from the West Sussex League and Midhurst & Easbourne Reserves will be rejoining from the same League.

It is appropriate to acknowledge the achievement of Eastbourne Borough, formerly Langney Sports, in achieving promotion to the new Conference Division (South), where they will participate with Bognor Regis Town and Lewes, to whom the League also offers its congratulations. With Crawley Town also gaining promotion via the Play-Offs, perhaps Sussex football is not as bad as some of the pundits like to predict.

At the start of the season, with Burgess Hill having joined the Southern League, Whitehawk, League runner-up, defeated Selsey 6-1 in the Norman Wingate Trophy. Burgess Hill, as League champions, visited Crawley Town, the County FA Senior Cup winners, and after a 1-1 draw won 6-5 on penalties.

In the John O'Hara League Cup, Rye & Iden reached the Final following up last season's Semi-Final appearance but were defeated 2-1 at Eastbourne Town in Food Friday's morning match. In the Semi-Finals, Arundel defeated Chichester 3-0 at Pagham, while Rye beat Eastbourne town 1-0 at Hailsham. On Good Friday evening at Arundel, where they were still celebrating the morning victory of their team, a crowd of over 500 saw Littlehampton Town 'do the double' by defeating Worthing United 2-0, with Littlehampton's Mark Price the Man of the Match. In the Semi-Finals, Worthing United defeated Oakwood 4-3 at Hassocks, while Littlehampton beat Westfield 4-3 on penalties after no goals were scored in 120 minutes. In the afternoon of Good Friday at East Grinstead, Crowborough Athletic, last season's finalists, also did the double when they defeated Uckfield Town in the last minute of the match. Uckfield had beaten Storrington 2-1 at Haywards Heath in a Semi-Final while in the other at Ringer, Crowborough had beaten Wadhurst United 3-1 in front of a crowd well over 200. In the First Round of the FA Vase Littlehampton won 2-1 at AFC Newbury, Whitehawk beat Mile Oak 6-1, and Three Bridges defeated Whitchurch United 2-0 in a Replay after a 1-1 away draw. In the Second Round Three Bridges beat former Vase winners Diss Town 4-1, and Whitehawk beat Burnham Ramblers 5--2. In the Third Round, Three Bridges then lost 4-3 at Andover, while Whitehawk went down at home by 3-1 to Winchester City, the eventual winners of the FA Vase. Three Bridges and Whitehawk share the trophy awarded to the clubs who reach the furthest in the competition. Due to lack of success, no similar trophy for the FA Cup was awarded this season.

Hassocks were again the top team in Sussex in the Ladbrookes Fair Play Award, and following their success in previous seasons in winning the national competition two years ago and then finishing national runner-up last year, have again won the national competition, a tremendous achievement for which the Club management and players deserve special acknowledgement. (PTO)

The PG Cunningham Sportsmanship Cup for Senior Clubs was won by Hassocks for the second successive season, and the Division 3 Sportsmanship Trophy was again won by Forest, also for the second year running. Hassocks also won the Youth Sportsmanship Trophy, and also the Youth Linesman Trophy, again for the second successive season. The Adult Club Linesman of the Year went to Gary Miller of Westfield.

Referee of the season was John Goring, with Dick Milton in second place and Neil Saxton third. Dick Milton was also the Referee of the Year in Youth matches.

Teams of the season were Chichester City United, winning the championship in a very close race, Littlehampton Town in Division 2, for doing the double, and Crowborough Athletic in Division 3 for the same reason. We are very grateful to Nick Robinson of Sandom Robinson for again providing us with the trophies for these awards and for the Teams of the Month throughout the season. The firm s also the League's Honourary Solicitors. Our thanks to Doug Austen-Jones for his services as our auditor.

The John O'Hara Loyalty Award went to Ron Pavey, never having forgotten his roots as a player with Whitehawk with their very successful side in the 50's and 60's and in over 50 years of involvement with Sussex football, including time at Brighton & Hove Albion, the County FA and the Sussex Sunday League.

A special award was made at the Dinner to our President, Peter Strange, for his 20 years in that office. David John, the Manager of Hassocks, received a special award for 25 years in Club Management at only 2 Clubs, Hassocks and Haywards Heath.

Finally my thanks to to all clubs and all officers and Management Committee members for their efforts in maintaining the good name of the League.

Peter Bentley - League Chairman.

FINAL LEAGUE TABLE 2003-04

DIVISION ONE	P	W	D	L	F	A	Pts
1. Chichester City U.	36	23	8	5	87	40	77
2. Rye & Iden United	36	20	11	5	75	37	71
3. East Preston	36	22	5	9	72	36	71
4. Three Bridges	36	20	10	6	63	34	70
5. Eastbourne Town	36	21	3	12	85	53	66
6. Arundel	36	18	7	11	77	61	61
7. Hassocks	36	16	11	9	74	54	59
8. Whitehawk	36	17	8	11	59	48	59
9. East Grinstead T.	36	17	4	15	64	60	55
10. Ringmer	36	14	11	11	54	54	53
11. Redhill	36	13	7	16	53	50	46
12. Hailsham Town	36	13	7	16	55	58	46
13. Horsham YMCA	36	11	9	16	55	62	42
14. Southwick	36	10	11	15	39	51	41
15. Sidlesham	36	10	8	18	50	71	38
16. Sidley United	36	10	8	18	42	63	38
17. Pagham	36	6	10	20	30	55	28
18. Selsey	36	5	5	26	35	94	20
19. Shoreham	36	2	5	29	30	118	11

NB - St Leonards withdrew during the season. Their results are shown in the result grid below but are expunged from the league table.

DIV. ONE 03-04		1	2	3	4	5	6	7	8	9	10	11	12	13	14	15	16	17	18	19	20
1	Arundel		2-3	3-5	1-2	2-3	2-0	1-1	4-1	1-0	1-1	0-1	1-1	3-0	3-0	3-1	1-1	1-2	3-0	3-0	1-5
2	Chichester City Utd	1-2		3-0	1-0	1-4	3-1	3-2	1-1	4-1	1-0	1-1	1-1	6-1	4-0	1-1	3-0	3-1	1-0	2-1	1-1
3	East Grinstead Tn	1-4	0-3		0-3	3-3	5-1	1-1	1-0	3-0	2-2	1-2	1-2	2-1	1-0	3-1	2-0	2-0	0-4	1-2	1-2
4	East Preston	1-2	2-5	2-1		3-2	1-1	0-2	2-0	2-0	4-3	3-0	2-2	3-1	1-0	2-0	1-0	0-0	-	0-1	1-2
5	Eastbourne Town	3-1	1-3	0-1	3-1		1-2	3-1	2-0	3-2	1-0	2-0	2-1	3-2	9-0	2-3	2-0	2-0	1-3	0-0	4-1
6	Hailsham Town	0-1	3-1	1-3	2-3	3-2		1-2	2-1	1-0	4-1	1-1	0-1	3-0	4-0	2-2	0-2	1-2	-	3-3	3-0
7	Hassocks	3-3	0-0	3-1	1-6	0-3	1-0		3-0	3-2	2-1	2-1	3-3	9-0	7-1	3-1	1-2	2-2	2-1	0-1	2-2
8	Horsham YMCA	3-2	4-3	2-3	1-2	2-0	2-0	0-2		1-1	2-0	4-3	1-3	2-2	6-0	4-2	2-2	3-1	4-1	1-0	1-2
9	Pagham	0-2	0-2	0-2	1-2	0-0	0-0	2-1	2-1		1-2	1-1	2-1	1-0	2-2	0-3	1-1	0-0	-	2-3	0-1
10	Redhill	2-3	0-3	1-3	0-0	2-1	3-1	1-2	2-1	2-0		0-1	0-1	4-0	3-0	3-1	2-1	1-2	-	1-1	1-0
11	Ringmer	1-2	0-0	3-2	0-3	4-3	2-0	0-0	2-2	2-1	2-1		1-4	3-1	4-0	2-1	1-0	0-1	3-2	2-2	1-1
12	Rye & Iden United	3-3	0-2	2-0	2-0	4-2	1-1	0-0	1-0	2-1	1-1	2-2		3-0	4-0	4-3	1-1	6-0	4-1	4-1	1-2
13	Selsey	3-5	2-2	3-0	0-3	1-2	1-3	0-4	1-1	0-2	0-0	4-1	1-5		1-1	2-1	0-1	2-1	1-2	0-2	1-3
14	Shoreham	2-3	0-5	1-5	0-6	2-3	1-2	4-4	1-2	1-2	0-5	1-5	0-3	4-2		0-0	1-2	1-2	-	0-5	2-2
15	Sidlesham	4-3	1-8	1-1	0-3	0-4	4-1	1-2	1-1	2-1	1-1	1-0	1-1	3-0	2-1		0-1	2-1	2-5	0-0	3-2
16	Sidley United	0-3	0-2	2-4	0-5	1-3	1-3	2-3	2-2	0-0	2-4	1-3	0-2	3-1	4-0	3-2		1-1	2-1	1-3	1-2
17	Southwick	1-1	6-2	2-0	0-0	1-3	1-2	2-0	1-1	1-1	1-2	1-1	1-2	1-2	1-0	3-1	0-1		-	0-0	0-1
18	St Leonards	-	-	-	1-1	1-2	2-2	-	-	0-3	-	-	-	-	3-0	-	2-0	-		1-1	2-1
19	Three Bridges	6-2	1-2	2-0	2-1	2-1	2-1	2-2	3-0	1-1	1-0	1-1	1-0	1-0	2-0	2-0	1-2	4-0	2-0		1-1
20	Whitehawk	0-2	0-1	2-3	0-2	4-3	2-2	2-0	3-0	2-0	3-1	4-0	0-1	3-0	2-4	1-0	1-1	0-0	0-0	0-3	

ARUNDEL

Secretary: Doug Feest, 142 Aldsworth Road, Worthing. BN12 4UU Tel: 01903 249276

Ground: Mill Road, Arundel, West Sussex. Tel: 01903 882548

Directions: A27 from Worthing to Arundel over railway bridge to roundabout. Second exit into Queen Street to town centre, turn right over bridge. Car park leading to ground 100yards right

Capacity: 2,200 Seats: 100 Cover: 200 Floodlights: 206 lux

Clubhouse: 2 bars, kitchen, toilets, telephone, pool, darts, Sky TV. Normal pub hours. No food

HONOURS Sussex Co. Lg 57-58 58-59 86-87 (Lg Cup 86-87, Div 2 Cup 76-77, Res. Sect. 78-79, Res. Sect. Cup 78-79, Merit Table 80-81,Sussex Fives 1984 1987), Sussex RUR Charity Cup 68-69 72-73 78-79 79-80, Sussex Jnr Cup 07-08, West Sussex Lg (Res.) 70-71 (Malcolm Simmonds Cup 70-71)

PREVIOUS **League** : West Sussex 1896-1975 **Grounds:** Castle Park; Station Rd Ground

RECORD **Gate:** 2,200 v Chichester, League 67-68
Scorer: Paul J Bennett **Appearances:** 537, Paul Bennett (goalkeeper)
Win : 13-0 v Horsham YMCA (H), Sussex Co. Lge Div 1 21/12/85

Players progressing: John Templeman (Brighton & Hove Albion 1966)

FACT FILE
Founded: 1889
Nickname: Mulletts
Colours: Red & white halves/white/red
Change colours: Green/black/green
Midweek matchday: Tuesday
Reserves' Lge: Sussex Co. Res Div (West)
Programme: 8 pages, free Editor: P Wells
Local Press: Arun Herald

CLUB PERSONNEL
Chairman: Bob Marchant
Vice Chairman: S Brennan
Manager: Mike Rowland

CHICHESTER CITY UNITED

Secretary: Peter Down, 14 Edith Cottages,Mill Road, West Ashling, Chichester PO18 8DG Tel: 01243 574597 (H) email: peter.down1@btinternet.com

Ground: Church Road, Portfield, Chichester, West Sussex PO19 4HN Tel: 01243 779875
Capacity: 2,000 Seats: 20 Cover: 200 Floodlights: Yes

Directions: A27 from Arundel to Chichester, take road to signposted city centre then 1st left (Church Rd) after supermarket r'bout. 1 mile from Chichester(BR)

Clubhouse: 2 bars, pool, snooker, seating for 100, dance floor, darts. Teabar selling h & c food.

PREVIOUS **Names**: Chichester FC (pre-1948), Chichester City 48-00. Amalgamated with Portfield in 2000

HONOURS Sussex Co. Lg Div 2 72-73 83-84 91-92 (Div 2 Cup 70-71 72-73, Res Sect as Portfield Prem Lge 94-95, Cup 91-92), W Sussex Lg 46-47 48-49 (Malcolm Simmonds Cup 46-47), Sussex Jnr Cup 45-46, Benevolent Cup 46-47

HONOURS as Chichester City Sussex Co. Lg(5) 59-61 67-68 72-73 79-80 Invit. Cup 47-48 54-55 56-57 63-64, Div 2 Cup 84-85 87-88 90-91, Sussex Snr Cup 25-26, Sussex RUR Charity Cup 60-61(jt with Brighton & HA) 63-64, Sussex I'mediate Cup 67-68

FACT FILE
Formed 2000
Chichester (1873)Portfield (1896)
Sponsors: Covers
Nickname: Lilywhites
Colours: All white with green piping
Change colours: Green & blue/blue/blue
Midweek matchday: Tuesday
Programme Editor: T Wallis
Local Press: Chichester Observer

CLUB PERSONNEL
Chairman: Simon Kenny
Match Secretary:Phil Littlejohns
Tel: 01243 528007
Press Officer: T Wallis (01705 464438)
Manager: Adrian Girdler
Chief Coach: Gary Brockway
Physio: Hannah Alen
2002-03: Capt: Tony Stephens
Top Scorer: Roger Moore
P.o.Y.: Ben O'Connor

EAST GRINSTEAD TOWN

Secretary Martin Hill, The Flat, 2A Saxbys Lane, Lingfield, Surrey RH7 6DN

Ground: East Court, East Grinstead Tel: 01342 325885

Directions: A264 Tunbridge Wells road (Moat Road) until mini-r'bout at bottom of Blackwell Hollow, turn immediately right by club sign then 1st left, ground 200yds down lane past rifle club on right.

Capacity: 3,000 Seats: None Cover: 400 Floodlights: Yes Club Shop: No

Clubhouse: Open 1.30-10.30 matchdays, 6-11 midweek matches. Available for hire. Darts, pool, satellite TV. Hot food available Saturday match days, hot snacks rolls etc available at midweek matches.

PREVIOUS **Leagues:** Mid-Sussex 1900-15 35-37; Sussex Co. 20-32; Southern Amateur 32-35.
Grounds: West Street Cricket Ground (pre-1963); King George's Field 63-68.

RECORD **Attendance:** 2,006 v Lancing, FA Amateur Cup 8/11/48
Appearances: Guy Hill in 19 seasons - 1977-94

HONOURS Sussex RUR Charity Cup (R-up 74-75); Sussex Co. Lg Invitation Cup 51-52; Sussex Jnr Cup (jt) 07-08; Sussex Youth Cup 86-87; Southern Amtr Lg.Snr Div 3 31-32; Mid-Sussex Lg x 6, Lg Cup x 7; Brighton Lg x 3, Lg Cup x 3,Mid Sussex Junior Cup 2001-02

Players progressing: None

FACT FILE
Founded: 1890
Nickname: Wasps
Sponsors: Rydon Group.
Colours: Gold/black/black
Change colours: All Blue
Midweek Matchday: Tuesday.
Reserves Lge: Sussex Co. Reserve Div East
Website: www.egffc.co.uk
Programme
36 pages, 50p Editor: Bruce Talbot
Press Off.: Bruce Talbot 01293 543809
Local Press: East Grinstead Observer/East Grinstead Courier, Sports Argus

CLUB PERSONNEL
Chairman:Bruce Talbot President: Colin Dixon
Manager: Bobby Smith
Physio: Pam Presland
Captain: Dave Gallatly
2003-2004
Top Goalscorer: Steve Banks
Player of the Year: Drew Cooney

Arundel - winners of the John O'Hara League Challenge Cup. Photo: Roger Turner.

Rye & Iden United - John O'Hara League Challenge Cup runners-up.
Back Row (L-R): Kym Monroe, Duncan McArthur, Simon Fox, Steve Willard, Jon Gardner, Phil Rhodes, Nathan Godden.
Front Row: Craig Willard, Peter Baker, Paul Tuppenny, Andy Garman. Photo: Roger Turner.

EAST PRESTON

Secretary: Keith Freeman, 41 Ambersham Cres., East Preston, West Sussex BN161AJ Tel: 01903 771158

Ground: Roundstone Recreation Ground, East Preston, West Sussex Tel: 01903 776026
Capacity:1,000 Seats: 50 Cover: 100 Floodlights: Yes

Directions: Less than a mile from Angmering (BR) station. A259 from Worthing to Roundstone Hotel (6 miles), turn south over railway crossing, left past Centurion garage, right into Roundstone Drive

Clubhouse: Licensed bar open Mon-Fri evenings, Sat noon-11pm, Sun noon-11pm. Kitchen serves light refreshments on matchdays

HONOURS Sussex Co. Lg Div 2 Champions 97-98Div 3 83-84, (R-up 90-91), Div 3 Cup 87-88 (R-up 89-90); West Sussex Lg 77-78 80-81 81-82 82-83 (Malcolm Simmonds Cup 80-81 82-83), Div2 Sth 81-82, Div 3 Sth 79-80, Div 5 Sth 82-83; Chichester Cup 87-88; BorehamTphy 77-78 90-91 (R-up 93-94); Vernon Wentworth Cup 80-81 89-90; 99-00 Worthing Lg 67-68 (Div 2 68-69 (res); Benevolent. Trophy 66-67 68-69; Worthing Charity Cup 68-69

PREVIOUS **Leagues:** Worthing; W Sussex

FACT FILE
Reformed: 1966
Nickname: None
Sponsors: Argyl insurance
Colours: White with black trim,black/white
Change: Black & yellow stripes/white/black
Reserves Lge: Sussex Co. Res. Div (Prem)
Programme: Yes
Editor: Doug Hall
Local Press: Littlehampton Gazette

CLUB PERSONNEL
President: Greg Stanley
Chairman:Doug Hall
Manager: Vic Short
Asst Managers: Kevin Valentine & Simon Butler

2002-2003
Captain: Jim Smith
Player of the Year: Simon Clayton
Top Scorere: Matthew Huckett

EASTBOURNE TOWN

Secretary: Viv Greenwood, 102 Latimer Rd., Eastbourne BN22 7DR (01323 411117)

Ground: The Saffrons, Compton Place Road, Eastbourne, East Sussex (01323723734)
Capacity: 3,000 Seats: 200 Cover: Yes Floodlights: Yes

Directions: Turn south west off the A22 into Grove Road (opposite BR station), and the ground is 1/4 mile on the right

Clubhouse: Fully licensed bar. Board room. Tea bar with Hot Food.

HONOURS Sussex County Lg. 76-77; Sussex Sen Cup x12 1889-91, 93-95, 98-1901, 02-03, 21-22, 31-35, 52-53; Sussex RUR Charity Cup 32-33, 47-48, 49-50; SouthernAmat. Lge. x2; AFA Sen. Cup 21-22, 24-25, R-up 22-23, 23-24; AFA Invitation Cup69-70, R-up 56-57, 68-69, 70-71

PREVIOUS **Leagues:** Southern Amtr 07-46; Corinthian 60-63; Athenian 63-76
RECORD **Attendance:** 7,378 v Hastings Utd. 1953

FACT FILE
Founded: 1882 Nickname: `Bourne'
Sponsor: Owen Contractord
Colours: yellow/blue/yellow
Changes: Sky blueblack/black
Prog Ed: Dave Pelling Tel: 01323 460695

CLUB PERSONNEL
Chairman: Roger Addems
Manager: Dave Winterton

2002-03
Captain:MarkReeve Top Scorer:YemiOdubade
Player of the Year: Gary Brockwell

EASTBOURNE UNITED ASSOCIATION

Secretary: c/o Peter Snashall, 3 Gilbert Road, Eastbourne BN 22 8JA Tel: 01323 644038(H)

Ground: The Oval, Channel View Rd, Eastbourne, East Sussex (011323-726989)

Capacity: 3,000 Seats: 160 Cover: 160 Floodlights: Yes

Directions: From A22 follow signs to eastbourne East/Seafront. Turn left onto seafront. Turn left into Channel View Rd at Princess Park & ground 1st right. 2 miles from Eastbourne (BR)

Clubhouse: Bar, lounge, dancefloor, stage, tea bar, board room **Club Shop:** Yes

PREVIOUS **Ground:** Lynchmere **Leagues:** Sussex Co. 21-28 35-56; Metropolitan 56-64; Athenian 64-77; Isthmian 77-92
Names: Eastbourne Old Comrades, Eastbourne Utd (merged with Shinewater Assoc 2003)
RECORD **Attendance:** 11,000 at Lynchmere
HONOURS Sussex Co. Lg 54-55, Div 2 R-Up 99-00 Sussex Snr Cup(5) 60-61 62-64 66-67 68-69(R-up 89-90), Sussex RUR Charity Cup 55-56,Metropolitan Lg Cup 60-61,Athenian Lg Div 2 66-67 (Div 1 R-up 68-69), Sussex I'mediate Cup 65-66 68-69
Players progressing: B Salvage, T Funnell, M French, L.Barnard

FACT FILE
Founded: 1894 Nickname: The 'Us'
Colours: White/black/white
Change colours: All Sky Blue.
Midweek Matchday: Wednesday
Reserve Lge: Sussex County Res. Premier
Programme
36 pages Editor:Kevin Townsend

CLUB PERSONNEL
Chairman: Peter Snashall
Vice-Chairman: Kevin Townsend
President: Doug Sissons
Manager: Micky French
Asst Manager: Dave Shearing
Physio: Jo Henderson

HAILSHAM TOWN

Secretary: /Press Officer Derek York, 59 Anglesey Avenue, Horsebridge, Hailsham BN27 3BQ
Tel: 01323 848024 (H)

Ground: The Beaconsfield, Western Road, Hailsham, East Sussex
Tel: 01323 840446

Directions: A22 to Arlington Road, turn east, then left into South Road - left into Diplocks Way until Daltons. Four miles from Polegate (BR - Brighton-Eastbourne line); regular bus service from Eastbourne

Capacity: 2,000 Seats: None Cover: 300 Floodlights: Yes

Clubhouse: Hot and cold snacks. Open every evening, matchdays and Sundays, teabar

HONOURS Sussex County Lg Div 2 R-up 80-81, Southern Co'sComb. 74-75, Sussex RUR Charity Cup, Sussex I'mediate Cup, Hastings Snr Cup,Sussex Jnr Cup, E Sussex Lg Cup, Hailsham Charity Cup, John O'Hara Cup 95-96

PREVIOUS **League:** E Sussex, Southern Comb

BEST SEASON **FA Vase:** 5th Rd 88-89

RECORD **Gate:**1,350 v Hungerford, FA Vase Feb '89
Goalscorer: H Stevens 51, 95-96 **Appearances:** P Comber 713

FACT FILE
Founded: 1885
Nickname:The Stringers
Colours: Yellow &Green/Green/gGreen
Change colours: All blue
Midweek matchday: Tuesday
Programme: Yes
Editor: Secretary
Admission: ¨3.00

CLUB PERSONNEL
President: T.B.A.
Chairman: S.Richardson
Manager: Ken McCreadie
Captain: Martin Richardson

2003-2004
Leading Goalscorer: Nick Barden 12
Player of the Year: Leon.Legge

HASSOCKS

Secretary: Dave Knight, 21 Farnham Avenue, Hassocks, BN6 8NR
Tel No: 01273 842023

Ground: The Beacon, Brighton Rd, Hassocks Tel: 01273 846040
Capacity: 1,800 Seats: 270 Cover: 100 Floodlights: Yes

Directions: Off A273 Pyecombe Road to Burgess Hill, 300yds south of Stonepound cross roads (B2116) to Hurstpierpoint or Hassocks

Clubhouse: Clubroom, bar, kitchen Club Shop: No

HONOURS Sussex County Lg Div 3 91-92, Div 2 R-up 94-95, Res. Sect. East R-up 92-93; Southern Counties Comb. 76-77, Lg Cup R-up 79-80; Brighton Hove & Dist. Lg 71-72; Sussex Intermediate Cup 74-75 (R-up 80-81)

PREVIOUS **Leagues:** Mid Sussex; Brighton Hove & Dist.; Southern Co's Comb
Ground: Adastra Park, Hassocks (pre-1992)

RECORD **Attendance:** 610 v Burgess Hill Town, Sussex County Lge 96-97

FACT FILE
Founded: 1902
Nickname: The Robins
Sponsors: T.B.A.
Colours: Red/white/red
Change colours: Yellow/grenMidweek
Matchday: Tuesday
Programme: 24 pages, 50p
Editor: Paul Elphik
Local Press: Mid Sussex Times, Evening Argus

CLUB PERSONNEL
President: Maurice Boxall
Chairman: JimGoodrum (01273 842023)
Manager: Dave John
Captain: Chris Hewitt
2003-2004
Player of the Year: James Laing
Top Scorer: Pat Harding

HORSHAM YMCA

Secretary: Bob Brading, 16 Hazelhurst Crescent, Horsham,.RM12 1XB
Tel No: 01403 250270 (H)

Ground: Gorings Mead, Horsham Tel: 01403 252689
Capacity: 1,575 Seats: 150 Cover: 200 Floodlights: Yes

Directions: Approaching Horsham fron the East on A281 Brighton Road, the ground is on left & signposted opposite Gorings Mead

HONOURS Sussex Co Lge Div 2 65-66 82-83 R-up 94-95 (Lg Cup 81-82, Invitation Cup66-67 67-68, Div 2 Invit. Cup 59-60 61-62 94-95) Sussex RUR Cup Winners 2000-01

PREVIOUS **Leagues:** Horsham & Dist/Brighton & Hove/Mid Sussex
Grounds: Lyons Field, Kings Road

RECORD **Attendance:** 950 v Chelmsford City , FA Cup 2000
Victory: 22-1 v Litt;lehampton 15th Octpober 2002 (Nick Flint 10)

BEST SEASON: **FA Cup:** 4th Qual. Rd. 99-00 2-3 v Chelmsford City

FACT FILE
Founded: 1898
Nickname: YM's
Sponsors: Principal Corporation
Colours: White/black/white
Change colours: All Blue
Midweek Matchday: Tuesday
Local Press: West Sussex County Times

CLUB PERSONNEL
Chairman:Mick Browning
Match Secretary:Bob Brading
Manager: John Suter
Physio: Robin Bishop

2003-04
Leading Goalscorer:Phil Churchill 13
Player of the Year: Joel O'Hara

LITTLEHAMPTON TOWN

Secretary: John Savage, 66 Nelson Road, Worthing. BN12 6EN. (01903 502850)

Ground: The Sportsfield, St Flora's Road, Littlehampton (01903 713944)
Capacity: 4,000 Seats: 260 Cover: 260 Floodlights: Yes

Directions: 10 minutes walk from Littlehampton station (BR) - turn left alongTerminus Rd, continue through High Street and Church Rd to junction with St Flora's Rd (left)

Club Shop: No, but metal badges available
Clubhouse: Sportsman (Private Club). Separate board room & tea bar

HONOURS Sussex Co. Lg 58-59 (jt with Shoreham) 75-77, 84-85, 90-91, 96-97
Sussex Senior Cup 1949, 1970

RECORD **Gate:** 4,000 v Northampton, FA Cup 1st Rd Proper 90-91

BEST SEASON **FA Vase** Semi-Final 90-91 v Gresley Rovers 1-3 (A), 1-2 (H)
FA Cup: 1st Round 90-91 v Northampton Town(H) 0-4

2003-04 **Leading Scorer**: Jan Miller **Playerof the Year**:: Micky Phillips

FACT FILE
Founded: 1894 Nickname: Marigolds
Colours: Gold/black/black
Change: All white
Midweek Matches: Tuesday
Programme: 50p Pages: 52
Editor: Paul Hooker
Local Press: Littlehampton Gazette
Two ladies and four girls teams plus a colts section started this season.

CLUB PERSONNEL
President: Ian Cunningham
Chairman:Andy Taylor
Manager: Carl Stabler
Captain: Garry Young

PAGHAM

Secretary: David Bolland, 23 Tennyson Road, Bognor `Regis PO21 2SB
Tel No: 01243 829973

Ground: Nyetimber Lane, Pagham, West Sussex Tel: 01243 266112
Capacity: 2,000 Seats: 200 Cover: 200 Floodlights: Yes

Directions: Turn off A27 Chichester by-pass (signposted A259 Pagham). Ground invillage of Nyetimber. Three miles from Bognor (BR). Buses 260 & 240

Clubhouse: Bar open matchdays and some evenings. Hot food, pool, darts,satellite TV. Tea bar
Club Shop: No

HONOURS Sussex Co. Lg R-up 80-81 87-88 88-89 92-93 (Div 2 78-79 86-87, Lg Cup88-89, Div 2 Cup 71-72 85-86, Res. Sect. West 80-81, Res Section Cup 77-78 80-81 87-88 88-89 90-91 96-97; Sussex F'lit Cup R-up 88-89;
Sussex RUR Charity Cup88-89 (R-up 93-94); West Sussex Lg 65-66 68-69 69-70; Malcolm Simmonds Cup 67-68; Sussex I'mediate Cup 66-67

PREVIOUS **Leagues:** Chichester 1903-50; West Sussex 50-69 **Grounds:** None

RECORDS **Gate:** 1,200 v Bognor, 1971 **Scorer:** Mark Vickers/ R Deluca
Win: 10-1 v Seaford Town (A), Sussex County League Division Two, 1970
Defeat: 0-7 v Newport IOW (H), FA Amateur Cup, mid-1970s

2003-2004 **Player of the Year:** Wesley Hallett **Top Scorer**: Brett Forden

FACT FILE
Founded: 1903
Nickname: Lions
Sponsors: Ace BrickworksColours: White/black/red
Change colours: Yellow/green/green
Midweek Matchday: Tuesday
Reserve's League: Sussex Co. Res West
Programme: 12 pages, 50p
Editor: Rob Peach
Local Press: Bognor Observer

CLUB PERSONNEL
Chairman: Stteve Newdick
Vice-Chairman: Steve Newdick
President: A Peirce
Press Officer: John Rose(01243 545694)
Comm. Manager: Chairman
Manager:Gary Shaw
Asst Manager:Matt Beard
Captain: Brett Forden

REDHILL

Secretary: Neil Hoad, 2b Earlswood Rd, Redhill, Surrey RH1 6HE Tel: 01737 213847
Ground: Kiln Brow, Three Arch Road, Redhill, Surrey Tel: 01737 762129
Emails: michael-stewart 7@ ntlworld.com & neil@ nhoad.fsnet.co.uk
Directions: On left hand side of A23, two and a half miles south of Redhill
Capacity: 2,000 Seats: 150 Cover: 150 Floodlights: Yes
Club Shop: Sells usual range of souvenires. Contact Spencer Mitchell - 01737 780634
Clubhouse: Social club, bar, canteen, board room, club shop, tanoy, toilets
HONOURS Athenian 24-25 83-84 (Lg Cup 69-70 70-71), East &West Surrey Lg1902-3, Southern Sub Sen West Lg. 1902-03, Surrey Snr Cup 28-29 65-66, Gilbert Rice F'lit Cup 80-81, Sussex Co. Lg Div 2 Cup 91-92, Southern Co's Comb. Cup 90-91,98-99

PREVIOUS **Leagues:** E & W Surrey; Spartan 09-10; Southern Sub; London 21-23; Athenian 23-84; Spartan 84-88
Grounds: Memorial Sports Ground, London Road 1894-1986

BEST SEASON **FA Amtr Cup:** Semi-Final 25 **FA Cup:** 1st Round 57-58

RECORDS **Attendance:** 8,000 v Hastings United F.A.Cup 1956
Goalscorer: Steve Turner 119 **Appearances:** Brian Medlicott 766
Win : 12-1 v Southall (H) Athenian Lg. 1928-29
Defeat : 1-13 v Bromley (A) Athenian League 1945-46

FACT FILE
Founded: 1894 Nickname: Reds/Lobsters
Sponsors: Morrisons
Colours: All red Change: White/black
Midweek matchday: Tuesday
Reserve League: Sussex Co.Lg
A4 size Programme: 72 pages 50p
Winners of all Programme Awards 2002-3
Editor: Michael Stewart
New Editors: Dave & Dan Best
Website: http://redhillfc.tripod.com/kilnbrow
Local Press:Surrey Mirror/Redhill&Reigate Life

CLUB PERSONNEL
Chair: Nick Creasey V.Chair: Alan Thurlbeck
President: Malcolm Chatfield
Press Officer: Michael Stewart
Man: Ian Dawes Assistant: : John Framks
Physio: Brian Watts
2002-03
Captain& Player of the Year:
SteveGillett

RINGMER

Secretary: Mrs D.Brook,15 Chapel Road,Plumpton Green, East Sussex. BN7 3DD
Tel No: 01273 890016

Ground: Caburn Ground, Anchor Field, Ringmer Tel: 01273 812738
Capacity: 1,000 Seats: 100 Cover: Yes Floodlights: Yes

Directions: From Lewes road turn into Springett Avenue opposite Ringmer village green. Anchor Field first left. Three miles from Lewes (BR)

Clubhouse: 2 bars, function room, boardroom, tea bar
Club Shop: Club ties & metal badges

HONOURS Sussex Co. Lg 70-71, R-up: 01-02Div 2 68-69, Invit Cup 66-67; Res. Sect. East 79-80 80-81 (R-up 89-90), Yth Section 87-88, Yth SectionEast 87-88; Sussex Snr Cup 72-73 (R-up 80-81); Sussex Jnr Cup 25-26; Sussex Express Sen Charity Cup 94-95 Chandlers Cup 03-4

PREVIOUS **League:** Brighton **Grounds:** None **Names:** None

BEST SEASON **FA Cup** 1st Rd Proper 70-71

RECORD **Gate:** 1,200 in FA Cup

FACT FILE
Founded: 1906
Nickname: The Blues
Colours: Sky & navy/navy/navy
Change colours: All yellow
Midweek Matchday: Tuesday
Programme: Yes
Editor: Ian Wratten (01273 814747)
Local Press: Sussex Express

CLUB PERSONNEL
President: Sir G Christie
Chairman: Richard Soan
Manager: John Crumplin
Press Officer: Ian Wratten(01273 814747)
Match Sec:Dorothy Brook, (01273 890016)

2003-04
Leading Goalscorer: Dominic Shepherd
Captain: Chris Johnson
Player of the Year: Matt Beeston

RYE-IDEN UNITED

Secretary: Ged Say,18 Parkwwod Iden, nr Rye,East Sussex TN31 7XE
Tel: 01797 280495 (H) 07776 101993 (M)
email: ged@sayiden.fsnet.co.uk

Ground: Sydney Allnut Pavilion, Rye Football & Cricket Salts, Fish Market Rd., Rye, East Sussex Tel: 01797 223855

Directions: Outskirts of Rye on the A268, joins A259 opposite Skinners Rover garage. Fishmarket Road.

Previous **Leagues:** Sussex Co., Kent Co. >00

Honours: Sussex Co. Lge Div. 3 Champions 01-02
Sussex Co. Lge Div. 2 Champions 02-03
Sussex Co. Lge Div. 2 Cup Winners 02-03

2003-2004 **Player of the Year**: Craig Willand
Top Goalscorer: Scott Price

2004-2005 **Captain:** Scott Price

SIDLESHAM

Secretary: Michael Homer, 20 McNair Close, Selsey, Chichester, W. Sussex PO20 9JB
Contact details - TelNo: 01243 603977(h) 07803 617176 (M)01243 603977(Fax)
e-mail: mbheh.0428@virgin.net

Ground: Sidlesham Recreation Ground,Selsey Road Sidlesham.Chichester.E.Sussex PO20 7RD Tel No: 01243 603977
Capacity:1,500 **Covered Seating:** No **Covered Standing:** Yes **Floodlights:** Yes
Clubhouse: Open evenings 8-11 p.m. **Club Shop**: No

Directions: From the Chichester bypass take the B2145, signposted Hunston/Selsey Head towards Selsey. Upon entering Sidlesham the ground is on the right between houses.

Best Season: F.A.Vase: Second Round 2002-2003

HONOURS West Sussex League 1963-64 W.Sussex Lg Cup 1963-64,19787-79,1990-91 Sussex Intermediate Cup 1q9909-91. Sussex Co. Lg Cup Div 3 1991-92,1996-97.Div 3 Champipons1996-97, Division 2 Champions 1999-2000 Div 2 CP 99-00 Div1 Cup r-uyp: 2000-01

FACT FILE
Founded: 1936
Colours: Yellow & Green/green/yellow
Change colours: Red /white/red
Midweek Matchday: Tuesdays
Prog: Yes 24 Pages 50P Ed: Sec.

CLUB PERSONNEL
Chairman: Brian Thomas
Tel: 01243 378930 (H)
077 30534516 (M)
Vice Chairman: Alan Parker
Manager: Frank Antony (07887518431)
Assistant .Manager: Graham Cooper

2002-03
Leading Goalscorer:Richie Davies
Player of the Year:Keith Martin

SIDLEY UNITED

Secretary: Mike Gardner, 24 Magpie Close, St Leonards on Sea, E Sussex TN38 8DY

Ground: Gullivers Sports Ground, Glovers Lane, Sidley, Bexhill-on-Sea
Tel: 01424 217078
Capacity: 1,500 Seats: None Cover: 150 Floodlights: Yes

Directions: From Brighton on A259 to Bexhill bypass traffic lights, left intoLondon Road, continue into Sidley, right into Glovers Lane and 1st left into North Road. One mile from Bexhill (BR)

Clubhouse: Large bar area & function room. Tea bar
Club Shop: No, but metal badges are available.

HONOURS Sussex Co. Lg Div 1 00-01 Jphn O'Hara League Cup: 00-01 01-02Div 2 58-59 64-65 98-99, Div. 2 Cup 98-99, Div 2 Invit. Cup 57-58; Sussex Intermediate Cup 47-48, Sussex Jnr Cup 24-25

PREVIOUS **Leagues:** East Sussex; Hastings & District
Grounds: None

RECORD **Attendance:** 1,300 in 1959

FACT FILE

Founded: 1906
Nickname: Blues
Sponsors: M.T.Drains
Colours: Navy & sky/navy/navy & sky
Change colours: Yellow & Black
Midweek Matchday: Tues/ Weds
Programme: Yes
Local Press: Bexhill Observer, Bexhill News

CLUB PERSONNEL
President: Tom Hyland
Chairman: Dickie Day
Joint Managers: Glen Sully & Peter Heritage

2002-03
Leading Goalscorer:
Captain:
Player of the Year:

SOUTHWICK

Secretary: Gary Milliis, 21 Grover Avenue, Lancing, West Sussex. BN15 9RG
Tel: 01903 761396 (H) 07801 477979 (M)
Ground: Old Barn Way, off Manor Hall Way, Southwick, Brighton BN43 4NT
Tel: 01273 701010
Directions: Five minutes walk from either Fishergate or Southwick BR stations.
By car A27 from Brighton take 1st left after `Southwick' sign to Leisure Centre. Ground adjacent.
Capacity: 3,500 Seats: 220 Cover: 1,220 Floodlights: Yes Shop: Badges only
Clubhouse: Weekdays 12-3 & 6-11, all day Sat., normal hrs Sunday.
Members bar & boardroom with bar. Matchday snacks from tea bar.
HONOURS Isthmian Lg Div 2 Sth 85-86; Sus. Co. Lg 25-26 27-28 29-30 47-48 68-69 74-75, R-up x 9, Lg Cup 77-78 ,Div 1 Invit. Cup 65-66, Div 2 R-up 65-66; Combined Co's Lg R-up 84-85, Sus.Snr Cup x 10, Sus. RUR Charity Cup (11) W. Sus. Lg1896-97 97-98 1908-09 10-11, Sus. Jnr Cup 1891-92.
PREVIOUS Leagues: West Sussex 1896-1920; Sussex County 20-52 54-84; Metropolitan 52-54; Combined Co's 84-85; Isthmian 85-92.Sussex RUR Charity Cup 02-03
Previous Grounds: Croft Avenue; The Green; Oldfield Crescent.
BEST SEASON FA Cup: 1st Round 74-75, 0-5 v Bournemouth **FA Amtr Cup:** 3rd Rd. 28-29
FA Vase: 3rd Rd. 79-80 85-86 **RECORD Attendance:** 3,200 v Showbiz side 1971
Players progressing: Charles & William Buttenshaw (Luton 1948)

FACT FILE
Founded: 1882
Nickname: Wickers
Sponsors: City Woodfloors
Colours: Red & black stripes/black/red
Change Blue& blackstripes/black/blue
Midweek matchday: Tuesday
Reserve League: Sussex Co. Res Div
Programme: Yes
Editor/ Press Off.:
Paul Symes 01273 594142
Local Press : Evening Argus, Shoreham Herald
CLUB PERSONNEL
Chairman: Barry Noonan
President: Dr D W Gordon.
Managers: Mark Burt & Lee Cox
Asst Manager: Mick Fogden
Captain: Gary Beal
2003-2004
Top Scorers: TerryStreeter
P.o.Y.: Gary Beal

THREE BRIDGES

Secretary: Martin Clarke, 18 Mannings Close, Pound Hill, Crawley RH10 3TX
Tel: 01293 883726 (H), 07885 662940 (Mob)
e-mail threebridges@hotmail.com
Ground: Jubilee Field, Jubilee Walk,Three Bridges, Crawley, West Sussex
Tel: 01293 442000
Capacity: 3,500 Seats: 120 Cover: 600 Floodlights: Yes Shop: No
Directions: From Three Bridges station, turn L. to Crawley. At 2nd T'light turn R. into Three Bridges road. Take 1st left (opp. Plough Inn) into Jubilee Walk.
Clubhouse: Open every day 12 noon - 11pm (10.30pm Sunday) Carpeted lounge. Bar serving food, Players bar, Pool, Darts, Satelite big screen TV, Dance floor. Separate Tea Bar serving hot food on match days. Disabled toilet facilities.
HONOURS Sussex I'mediate Cup 84-85 Sussex Co. Lg R-up 85-86 87-88 88-89 Div 2 54-55, R-up 68-69, 73-74, 79-80, 98-99, Invitation Cup 70-71, Div 2 Invitation Cup 62-63, 73-74, Sussex RUR Charity Cup 82-83 R-up 85-86, 87-88, 88-89. Co. Lge Div. 2 5-a-side 97-98, R-up 98-99

PREVIOUS **League s:**Mid Sussex; E. Grinstead, Redhill&District 36-52 **Grounds:** None
Names: Three Bridges 01-18, Three Bridges Worth 19-53, Three Bridges United 54-64.

RECORD **Attendance:** 2,000 v Horsham, 1948

FACT FILE
Founded: 1901
Nickname: Bridges
Sponsors:Canadian Spaco Ltd
Colours: Amber & black/black/black
Change colours: Blue & white/blue/white
Midweek Matchday: Tuesday
Programme: Yes
Editor: Andy West (01293 883163)
Local Press: Crawley Observer, Crawley News

CLUB PERSONNEL
Chairman: Alan Bell
Press Officer: Alf Blackler
Manager: Sam Donnelly
Asst. Manager: Derek Pyle
Captain: Lee Butcher
2003-2004
Leading Goalscorer: Pat Massaro
Player of the Year: Alan Mansfield

WHITEHAWK

Secretary: John Rosenblatt, 25 Arundel Street, Brighton BN2 5TH Tel: 01273 680322

Ground: The Enclosed Ground, East Brighton Park Tel: 01273 609736
Capacity: 3,000 Seats: None Cover: 500 Floodlights: Yes

Directions: Follow Brighton seafront road towards Newhaven, turn inland (Arundel Road) opposite Marina, 3rd right into Roedean Road, 1st left intoWilson Ave. 3 miles from Brighton (BR); take Newhaven, Eastbourne or Saltdean bus to Marina

Clubhouse: Licensed bar, pool, darts. Board room. Tea bar Club Shop: No

Honours: Sussex Co. Lg 61-62 63-64 83-84 (Div 2 67-68 80-81, Lg Cup 82-83 93-94, Invitation Cup 60-61 69-70, Div 2 Cup 80-81), Sussex Snr Cup 50-51 61-62,Sussex RUR Charity Cup 54-55 58-59 90-91, Sussex I'mediate Cup 49-50, Sussex Jnr Cup 48-49 51-52, Brighton Charity Cup 51-52 59-60 61-62 82-83 87-88 88-89 89-90 90-91 97-98 98-99 99-00 Worthing Charity Cup 82-83

PREVIOUS **League:** Brighton Hove & Dist**Grounds:** None
Name: Whitehawk & Manor Farm Old Boys (until 1958)

BEST SEASON **FA Vase:** 5th Round 93-94

RECORDS **Gate:** 2,100 v Bognor Regis Town, FA Cup 4th Qualifying Rd replay 88-89
Scorer: Billy Ford **Appearances:** Ken Powell 1,103

FACT FILE

Founded: 1945
Nickname: Hawks
Sponsors: Precision Metal Products
Colours: All red
Change colours: All blue
Midweek Matchday: Tuesday
Programme: £3.50 with admission
Editor: Fred Moore (01273 689433)
Local Press: Evening Argus

CLUB PERSONNEL

President: Ron Wiltshire
Chairman: Wally Sweetman
Match Sec: Fred Moore
Manager:Ian Chapman
Asst Manager: Glen Burvill

WORTHING UNITED

Secretary: Malcolm Gamlen, 1 Westbourne Ave., Worthing, West Sussex BN14 8DE Tel: 01903 263655

Ground: The Robert Albon Memorial Grd, Lyons Way, Worthing Tel: 01903 234466
Capacity:1,000 Seats: 100 Cover: 500 Floodlights: Yes

Directions: Via A27 from west past Hill Barn r'about to 2nd set of lights, turn left into Lyons Way. From east 1st set of lights at end of Sompting bypass right into Lyons Way.

Clubhouse: Bar (capacity 80), refreshment facilities (tea bar)

HONOURS As Wigmore Athletic prior to 1988. Sussex Co. Lg Challenge Cup 74-75 (Invitation Cup 59-60, Div 2 52-53, Div 2 Invitation Cup 59-60, Div 3 89-90, Reserve Section West 92-93, Sussex Jnr Cup 49-50

PREVIOUS **Names:** Wigmore Athletic (founded 1948) merged with Southdown in 1988
Grounds: Harrison Road, Worthing

RECORD **Attendance as WUFC:** 180 v Northwood, FA Vase 3rd Rd 91-92

2003-2004 **Player of the Year**: Steve Pickles **Top Scorer:** Adam Westwood

FACT FILE

Founded: 1988 Nickname: None
Main Sponsors: McCabes
Colours: Sky & white/navy/navy
Change : Green & white/white/green & white
Midweek Matches: Wednesday
Programme: Yes
Editor: D.Treacy (01903 690122)
www.worthingunited.co.uk
Local Newspapers: Worthing Herald

CLUB PERSONNEL

Pres: Bob Albon Chairman: Rob McAlees
Commercial Manager: Steve Taylor
Press Officer: Brian Johns
Manager: Ian Browne Captain: Jason Hughes

East Grinstead Town - who had their most successful season in the history of the club for over 50 years. Not only did they achieve the best finish in the County League since 1973, in their first season back in Division One, but also won a major trophy for the first time since 1952, when they beat Three Bridges 4-0 to lift the Sussex FA RUR Cup.

FINAL LEAGUE TABLE 2003-04

DIVISION TWO	P	W	D	L	F	A	Pts
1. Littlehampton Town	34	23	7	4	89	29	76
2. Worthing United	34	21	6	7	74	32	69
3. Eastbourne Utd Association	34	18	12	4	78	39	66
4. Wick	34	17	8	9	57	38	59
5. Oakwood	34	18	4	12	77	50	58
6. Midhurst/Easebourne Utd	34	18	4	12	75	50	58
7. Mile Oak	34	17	6	11	56	49	57
8. Steyning Town	34	16	9	9	39	35	57
9. Westfield	34	16	5	13	70	63	53
10. Broadbridge Heath	34	15	5	14	51	54	50
11. Crawley Down	34	14	5	15	51	48	47
12. Peacehaven & Telscombe	34	14	4	16	54	52	46
13. Saltdean United	34	11	7	16	52	56	40
14. Wealden	34	12	4	18	43	64	40
15. Seaford Town	34	10	8	16	55	51	38
16. Pease Pottage Village	34	5	5	24	43	121	20
17. Lancing	34	4	4	26	26	89	16
18. Haywards Heath Town	34	3	5	26	23	93	14

DIV. TWO 03-04	1	2	3	4	5	6	7	8	9	10	11	12	13	14	15	16	17	18
1 Broadbridge Heath		0-1	1-3	3-1	4-2	0-1	1-4	2-2	3-2	2-0	1-0	1-1	0-0	1-2	2-0	4-0	3-1	2-1
2 Crawley Down	2-3		1-2	2-0	2-0	1-1	2-3	2-0	2-3	1-0	3-0	0-0	2-1	1-1	0-2	0-1	4-4	0-1
3 Eastbourne United Assoc.	2-0	4-1		6-0	3-1	0-0	2-1	1-1	2-1	2-2	4-2	1-0	1-1	2-2	1-1	3-3	0-1	1-0
4 Haywards Heath Town	3-2	1-3	0-5		1-2	1-2	1-6	1-2	1-1	0-2	2-1	0-4	2-2	0-1	0-2	0-1	1-4	0-4
5 Lancing	0-2	0-2	0-3	2-0		1-4	0-1	0-7	0-0	0-4	2-5	1-4	2-1	0-0	1-2	0-3	2-2	0-1
6 Littlehampton Town	1-1	2-1	3-0	5-0	4-1		0-0	4-0	1-0	3-1	5-3	6-0	2-1	4-0	4-1	9-0	2-1	5-0
7 Midhurst & Easebourne Utd	3-1	1-2	3-2	3-0	5-2	0-3		2-1	4-5	0-3	4-2	5-2	2-2	0-1	0-1	5-1	1-2	1-1
8 Mile Oak	2-0	1-0	2-5	3-3	0-3	1-1	2-0		3-1	1-0	3-0	0-2	2-5	1-0	1-0	1-0	1-2	1-0
9 Oakwood	5-0	1-4	1-1	2-1	5-0	4-1	1-1	6-1		0-2	2-0	1-2	2-1	0-1	1-0	3-1	3-1	3-5
10 Peacehaven & Telscombe	4-1	3-1	2-2	1-0	2-1	1-2	0-4	0-0	2-1		10-1	2-1	0-3	2-0	4-2	0-4	1-5	0-0
11 Pease Pottage Village	0-0	1-1	1-7	1-2	4-2	3-2	0-1	0-3	1-2	1-0		4-0	2-2	2-2	1-4	1-3	1-2	1-9
12 Saltdean United	0-2	5-2	2-3	0-0	3-0	0-0	1-3	2-5	4-3	3-1	6-0		0-1	0-0	1-1	2-4	0-0	0-1
13 Seaford Town	0-1	1-2	1-1	7-0	3-0	3-5	0-3	1-1	2-0	2-1	2-0	0-2		1-2	0-1	2-3	1-1	1-2
14 Steyning Town	2-0	1-0	2-2	1-1	2-0	0-3	2-0	0-1	1-4	3-0	2-2	1-0	3-0		1-0	2-1	1-0	1-2
15 Wealden	3-4	2-4	1-2	3-0	1-1	2-1	0-4	0-2	1-4	0-3	5-2	2-1	0-5	0-1		3-3	0-3	1-0
16 Westfield	3-2	1-0	0-4	4-1	2-0	0-2	3-2	2-3	0-5	1-0	18-0	3-1	1-0	0-0	0-1		2-2	1-3
17 Wick	1-2	0-1	1-0	1-0	1-0	1-1	2-0	2-1	0-3	1-0	6-0	1-2	1-2	2-1	3-0	2-1		1-1
18 Worthing Unitec	2-0	2-1	1-1	5-0	6-0	1-0	2-3	2-1	1-2	4-1	4-1	2-1	4-1	3-0	4-1	0-0	0-0	

JOHN O'HARA LEAGUE CUP
DIVISION ONE AND TWO CLUBS

FIRST ROUND

Broadbridge Heath	v	Redhill	1-4
Eastbourne Town	v	Wick	1-1*, 4-0r
Hassocks	v	Littlehampton Town	1-1*, 0-3r
Peacehaven	v	Horsham YMCA	1-5
Saltdean United	v	Three Bridges	4-1
Southwick	v	Worthing United	2-0

SECOND ROUND

Arundel	v	Midhurst & Easebourne	5-1
Chichester CU	v	Crawley Down	2-1
Eastbourne Town.	v	Horsham YMCA	6-0
Eastbourne UA	v	East Preston	1-4
Hailsham Town	v	Steyning Town	1-3
Haywards Heath	v	Sidley United	0-6
Littlehampton Town	v	Redhill	2-1
Mile Oak	v	Shoreham	0-1
Pease Pottage	v	St Leonards	1-10
Ringmer	v	Wealden	3-0
Saltdean United	v	Southwick	0-3
Seaford Town	v	Pagham	1-0*
Selsey	v	Oakwood	0-4
Sidlesham	v	Lancing	2-1
Westfield	v	Rye & Iden United	0-2
Whitehawk	v	East Grinstead Town	3-0

THIRD ROUND

Arundel	v	Oakwood	2-0
Eastbourne Town	v	East Preston	4-1
Littlehampton Town	v	Whitehawk	1-2
Ringmer	v	Chichester City United	0-1
Rye & Iden United	v	Shoreham	8-1
Seaford Town	v	Steyning Town	1-3
Sidley United	v	Sidlesham	3-4*
St Leonards	v	Southwick	3-4

QUARTER-FINALS

Eastbourne Town	v	Sidlesham	5-2
Southwick	v	Arundel	2-3
Steyning Town	v	Chichester City United	0-1
Whitehawk	v	Rye & Iden United	0-2

SEMI-FINALS

Arundel (at Pagham)	v	Chichester City United	3-0
Eastbourne Town (at Hailsham)	v	Rye & Iden United	0-1

THE FINAL (9th April at Eastbourne Town)

Arundel	v	Rye & Iden United	2-1

BROADBRIDGE HEATH

Secretary: Richard Solman, 13 Monks Court, Monks Walk, Reigate, Surrey RH2 0SR
Tel: 01737 212335

Ground: Broadbridge Heath Sports Centre, Wickhurst Lane, Horsham Tel: 01403 211311
Capacity: 1,300 Seats: 300 Cover: 300 Floodlights: Yes

Directions: Alongside A24, Horsham north/south bypass. From the A24 Horsham Bypass, at thelarge roundabout/underpass take the Broadbridge Heath Bypass towards Guildford and then at the first roundabout turn left into Wickhurst Lane.

Clubhouse: Bar. Kitchen serving meals,

HONOURS Sussex Yth Lg N. Div. 99-00, Southern Yth Lg S. Div. 00-01

PREVIOUS **Leagues:** Horsham, West Sussex, Southern Co's Comb

RECORD **Attendance:** 240

FACT FILE

Founded: 1919 Nickname: Bears
1st Team Sponsors: Maltaward Ltd.
Colours :Royal blue Change: Red/black or white
Midweek matches: Tuesday
Programme Editor: Andy Crisp (01403 252273)
Admission: £2.50

CLUB PERSONNEL

Chairman: Keith Soane
President: G W Manketelow
Manager: Allan Winton
Captain: Warren Sweatman

2003-04

Leading Goalscorer:Paul Gallagher
Player of the Year: Andy Howard

CRAWLEY DOWN

Secretary: Stuart Frier, 30 Squires Close, Crawley Down, West Sussex RH10 4JQ
Tel No: 01342 717008 (H)

Ground: The Haven Sportsfield, Hophurst Lane, Crawley Down. Tel: 01342 717140
Website: www.crawleydownfc.com
Capacity: 1000 Seats: None Cover: 50 Floodlights: Planned

Directions: From B2028, follow signpost for village to War Memorial, turn left into Hophurst Lane, ground 100 yards on left. From A22, Felbridge, left into Crawley Down Road, ground 2 miles uphill on right.

Honours Sussex County Lge Div 3 R-Up 95-96
Sussex Intermediate Chall. Cup R-up 95-96

Previous **League:** Mid Sussex Football League

Record **Attendance:** 404 v East Grinstead Town 26.12 96

FACT FILE

Formed: 1993 Colours: All red
Change: White/black/black
Midweek Matchday: N/A
Programme:Yes

CLUB PERSONNEL

Chairman: Brian Suckling
Vice-Chairman: Michael Martin
President: Tony Clements
Match Secretary: Andy hale
Managers : John Kendall & Chris Snelling
Physio: Jerry Gurr
Captain: Paul Otway

2003-2004

Top Scorer & Player of the Year:
Darren Tidey 15

CROWBOROUGH ATHLETIC

Secretary :Steve Singer,Craven Cottage,London Road,Crowborough,
East Sussex TN6 1SR
Tel Nos: 01892 662181 (H) 01892 662181 (W) 07795 422591(M)

Ground: Alderbrook Recreation Ground, Fermor Road, Crowborough
Tel No: 01892 661893

Directions: From A26 follow signs to Railway Station.Cross mini roundabout int Fermor Road Alderbrook is 300 yards on right.

FACT FILE

Colours:Navy Blue/White/Navy Blue
Change colours: AllRed

CLUB PERSONNEL

Chairman: Malcolm Boyes
07734 718957 (M)

Manager: Harry Smith
07810651452 (M)

LANCING

Secretary: Brian Hill,17 Annweir Ave., Lancing, W. Sussex BN15 9NF
Tel: 01903 756165 (H&F) email: brian@whill20.fsnet.co.uk

Ground: Culver Road, Lancing, West Sussex Tel: 01903 764398
Web-site: www.lancingfc.co.uk

Directions: From A27 turn south at Lancing Manor r'about into Grinstead Lane, 3rd turning on right North Farm Rd. Turn left then immed. right into Culver Rd. From railway station take 3rd turning on left heading north. Capacity: 2,400 Seats: 350 Cover: 350 Floodlights: Yes

Clubhouse: Open matchdays & training nights. Separate tea bar. **Club Shop:** Yes

HONOURS Sussex Co. Lg R-up 49-50 64-65 (Div 2 57-58 69-70 (R-up 82-83), Div 2 Cup 81-82 92-93, Invitation Cup), Sussex RUR Charity Cup 65-66, Brighton Lg 46-47 47-48, Sussex Intermediate Cup 46-47, Brighton Charity Cup 83-84 84-85 86-87.

PREVIOUS League: Brighton Hove & District **Name:** Lancing Athletic

RECORDS Attendance: 2,591 v Tooting, FA Amateur Cup 22/11/47 At Culver Road: 2,340v Worthing 25/10/52 **Career Appearances:** Dave Menzies 462 **Goals:** Paul Steele 113

FACT FILE

Founded: 1941 Nickname: Lancers
Sponsors: Bacon & Co. Estate Agents
Colours: Yellow/blue/yellow
Change colours: All red
Midweek Matches: Wed Programme: Yes
Reserves League: Sussex Co Res.West
Editor/Press Off.: Len Ralph (01903 763913)

CLUB PERSONNEL

Chairman: John Brown President: R G Steele
Match Sec: Don Stevens (01273 592653 (H)
Com Man.: Brian Nicholls (01903 525468)
Manager: Mark Cox Physio: Peter Towell
2003-04 Captain: Kevin Bradburn Top Scorer Ryan Ford 8 P.o.Y.: James Everett

Mile Oak. Photo: Roger Turner.

Selsey. Photo: Roger Turner.

Steyning Town. Photo: Roger Turner.

MIDHURST & EASEBOURNE

Secretary: Ted Dummer, 14 Nine Acres, June Lane, Midhurst, W. Sussex GU29 9EP
Tel: 01730 813887 (H) email: acs@harrisonrenwick.com

Ground: Rotherfield, Dodsley Lane, Easebourne, Midhurst, W. Sussex
Tel: 01730 816557

Directions: Ground one mile out of Midhurst on London Road (A286) opposite Texaco Garage. Ample car parking. Buses pass ground every hour

FACT FILE
Colours: Royal blue/black/royal
Change colours: All red

CLUB PERSONNEL
Chairman: Alan Thompson

Captain: Scott May
2003-2004
Player of the Year: Martin May
Top goalscorer: Robbie Pearce

MILE OAK

Secretary: Colin Brown, 19 The Crescent, Southwick, West Sussex BN42 4LB
Tel: 01273 591346

Ground: Mile Oak Recreation Ground, Graham Avenue, Mile Oak.Tel: 01273423854

Directions: From A27 take Mile Oak Road or Locks Hill & Valley Road to Chalky Road, ground 500yds on right along Graham Avenue which runs up valley fromcentre of Chalky Road
Capacity: Seats: None Cover: Yes Floodlights: Yes

Clubhouse: Mile Oak Pavillion; Hall and tea bar **Club Shop:** No

HONOURS Sussex Co.Lg.Div 2 Champions, Div 3 R-up 91-92 (Div 2 Cup R-up 92-93), Southern Counties Combination 86-87, Brighton Hove & District Lg 80-81, VernonWentworth Cup 85-86, Sussex Intermediate Cup R-up 88-89

PREVIOUS **Leagues:** Southern Counties Combination; Brighton Hove & District
Ground: Victoria Rec., Portslade

RECORD **Attendance:** 186

FACT FILE
Founded: 1960
Nickname: The Oak
Colours: Tangerine/black/tangerine
Change colours: All blue
Midweek Matchday: Tuesday
Programme: Yes
Editor: C Tew (01273 416036)
Admission: £1.50
Local Press: Brighton Evening Argus, Shoreham Herald

CLUB PERSONNEL
Chairman: L.Hamilton
President: D Bean
Manager: M.Cox

OAKWOOD

Secretary:S.A.Wildy, 45 Holmcroft, Southgate, Crawley, West Sussex (01293 409410)

Ground: Tinsley Lane, Three Bridges, Crawley, West Sussex Tel: 01293 515742

Directions: From A23 to Gatwick, take 1st set of lights into Manor Royal, pass next lights, over r'bout to warehouse marked Canon, turn right signposted Oakwood. Last clubhouse down lane. Two miles north of Three Bridges (BR)
Capacity: 3,000 Seats: 20 Cover: Yes Floodlights: Yes

Club Shop: Yes, incl. metal badges

Clubhouse: Large bar area, pool tables, multidart boards. Board room & tea bar

HONOURS Sussex Snr Cup R-up 92-93, Sussex Co. Lg Div 2 R-up 89-90 (Div 2 Cup 89-90, Div 3 84-85), Southern Comb. Cup 83-84

PREVIOUS **Leagues:** Crawley & Dist., Southern Co's Comb
Ground: Park pitches

RECORD **Attendance:** 367

Appearances: Peter Brackpool

FACT FILE
Founded: 1966 Nickname: Oaks
Sponsors: Linden Plc
Colours: Red & black/black/black
Change colours: Blue& black/white/blue
Midweek Matchday: Tuesday
Reserves' Lge: Sussex Co. Reserve section
Programme: 24 pages
Editor: Scott Packer Local Press: Crawley Observer, Crawley News

CLUB PERSONNEL
Chairman: Stuart Lovegrove
Press Officer & Match Sec: Scott Packer
Manager:Andy Maddox
Physios: Ms.S Widy & Frank Pushman

PEACEHAVEN & TELSCOMBE

Secretary: Mrs Margaret Edwards, 2,Tuscan Court, The Esplanade, Telscombe Cliffs, East Sussex BN10 7HF Tel: 01273 583022 (H) 07803 845329 (M)

Ground: Piddinghoe Avenue, Peacehaven, E. Sussex (01273 582471)

Directions: From Brighton on A259, over r'bout & Piddinghoe Ave. is next left after 2nd set of lights - ground at end. From Newhaven, Piddinghoe Ave. is 1st right after 1st set of lights. 3 miles from Newhaven(BR). Peacehaven is served by Brighton to Newhaven & Eastbourne buses

Capacity: 3,000 Seats: None Cover: 250 Floodlights: Yes

Clubhouse: Bar open evenings and weekends, pool darts, hot and cold food available. Tea bar

RECORD Attendance: 1,420 v Littlehampton, Lge 91 **PREVIOUS Leagues:** Lewes; Brighton

BEST SEASON **FA Cup:** 4th Qual. Rd 90-91 **FA Vase:** 6th Rd (Q-F) 95-96, 5th Rd 92-93

HONOURS Sussex Co. Lg 78-79 81-82 82-83 91-92 92-93 94-95 95-96 R-up x 3, Lg Cup 91-92 92-93, Div 2 R-up 75-76, Div 2 Cup 75-76, Norman Wingate Tphy 82-83 91-92 92-93, Hayden Tphy 82-83 92-93, Div 2 Invitation Cup 69-70, Sussex Snr Cup R-up 81-82 92-93, Sussex RUR Charity Cup 77-78 81-82 92-93 R-up x 5, Brighton Charity Cup (x3) 91-94, Vernon Wentworth 91-92 92-93

FACT FILE
Founded: 1923
Nickname: The Tye
Sponsors: Anchor Garage
Colours: All white and black
Change colours: Royal Blue
Midweek Matches: Tuesday
Programme: Yes
Editor: Secretary

CLUB PERSONNEL
Chairman: Jim Edwards
Match Sec: Fred Parris
Press Officer: Secretary
Manager: Peter Edwards

PEASE POTTAGE VILLAGE

Secretary: Mrs Sue Brooks, 115 Lark Rise, Langley Green, Crawley, W. Sussex RH11 7QG
Tel: 01293 410657 (H) 01293 848100 (B) 07754 163029 (M)
email: suebrooks57@aol.com

Ground: Finches Field, Pease Pottage, Crawley, W. Sussex
Tel: 01293 538651

Directions: Off M23/A23 towards Brighton, turn off at Pease Pottage (turn off just past Crawley). Past service station to roundabout, take 3rd exit over bridge sharp left, follow signs to Finches Field. Approx. 300 yards past "Grapes" P.H., on the right.

FACT FILE
Colours:
Royal blue & white/royal/raoyal & white
Change: Yellow/blue/yellow

CLUB PERSONNEL
Chairman: Tony Read
29 Westpark Road, Handcross,
W. Sussex RH17 6DN
Tel: 01444 400059 (H) 01444 881565 (B)
Manager: Mick Butler

SALTDEAN UNITED

Secretary: Iain Fielding, 40 Rowan Way, Rottingdean, Brighton BN2 7FP
Tel: 01273 304995
Ground: Hill Park, Combe Vale, Saltdean, Brighton Tel: 01273 309898
Capacity: 2,000 Seats: 50 Cover: Yes Floodlights: Yes Club Shop: No

Directions: A259 coast road east from Brighton to Saltdean Lido, left into Arundel Drive West, and Saltdean Vale to bridle path at beginning of Combe Vale.
Club 200yds along track
Clubhouse: Licensed bar, lounge, darts, video games, board room, tea bar.Pool table
HONOURS Sussex Co. Lg Div 3 88-89, Div 2 95-96: John O'Hara Lg Cup Winners 2000
PREVIOUS **League:** Sussex County **Ground:** None
RECORD **Attendance:** 676
2003-2004 **Captain**: Ashley Walker **Top Scorer**: Dan Jordan **P.o.Y.:** Mark Curram

FACT FILE
Founded: 1966 Nickname: Tigers
Sponsors: Calm Solutions
Colours: Red & blackstripes/black/black
Change : Blue & whitestripes/blue/white
Programme: Yes Editor:Alex Panton
Local Press: Brighton Evening Argus & Sussex Express

CLUB PERSONNEL
Chairman: Iain Fielding
Vice Chairman:Charles Dowsett
President: Jim Bower
Press Officer:Charles Dowsett
Manager: Colin White
Physio: Alan Stevens

SEAFORD TOWN

Secretary: Chas Pulford,14 Rosemount Cloise, Bishopstone BN25 2TPO
Tel: 01323 898286 (H) 01323 893040 (B) 07815 051128 (M)
email: charles.pulford@btopenworld.com
Match Sec.: Neil Vine, Flat 4, Miramar House West, 2 Grand Parade, Eastbourne BN21 3EH
Tel: 07811 618361 (M)
Ground: The Crouch, Seaford. Tel: 01323 892221

Directions: A259 to Seaford. At mini r'about by station,
turn LEFT (coming from Newhaven) or RIGHT (from Eastbourne).
At end of Church St., across junction, then left at end. After 500 m turn left up Ashurst Rd. Bramber Rd. is at the top.

FACT FILE

Colours: Red & blue/blue/red
Change: Yellow & green/green/yellow

CLUB PERSONNEL
Chairman: Kevin Moore
Tel: 01323 897369 (H) 07760 173178 (M)

Manager: Duncan Kneller
Tel: 01323 892876 (H) 07760 175746 (M)

SELSEY

Secretary: Denny Lee, 29 Malthouyse Cottages, West01243 605027
Ground: High Street Ground, Selsey, Chichester, West Sussex Tel: 01243 603420
Capacity: 2,250 Seats: 50 Cover: Yes Floodlights: Yes
Directions: Through Selsey High Street to fire station. Take turning into car park alongside the station. Entrance is in the far corner. Regular buses from Chichester
Clubhouse: Bar, hospitality room, lounge, toilets, kitchen
HONOURS Sussex Co. Lg R-up 89-90 (Div 2 63-64 75-76 (R-up 86-87), Div 2 Cup 86-87 (R-up 84-85), Div 2 Invitation Cup 63-64, Sussex 5-aside 88-89), Sussex SnrCup R-up 63-64, Sussex I'mediate Cup 58-59, Sussex Jnr Cup(Reserves) 76-77,West Sussex Lg 54-55 55-56 57-58 58-59 60-61 (Malcolm Simmonds Cup 55-56 56-57 57-58 58-59)
PREVIOUS **Leagues:** Chichester & Dist.; West Sussex
RECORD **Gate:** 750-800 v Chichester or Portfield, 50's

FACT FILE
Founded: 1903
Nickname: Blues
Sponsors: Ariel Cars
Colours: Blue/white/blue
Change colours:All red
Midweek Matchday: Tuesday
Programme Editor: Secretary
Match Secretary: Mandie Glew

CLUB PERSONNEL
President: Roy Glew
Chairman: Mike Hurst
Press Officer: Secretary
Manager:Danny Hinshelwood

SHOREHAM

Secretary: Glenn Hilton, 2 Loneycourt, Wilmot Road,Shoreham by Sea, BN43 6JQ
Tel No: 01273 705902 (H) 01273 430775 (W)

Ground: Middle Road, Shoreham-by-Sea, West Sussex Tel: 01273 454261
Capacity: 1,500 Seats: 20 Cover: 1 stand Floodlights: Yes

Directions: Half mile from Shoreham-by-Sea (BR) - east across level crossing, up Dolphin Road, ground 150yds on right. Or, A27 to Shoreham. At Southlands Hospital turn left down Hammy Lane, left at end, ground opposite

Clubhouse: Seats 70. Bar, pool, darts, tea bar **Club Shop:** No

HONOURS Sussex Co. Lg 51-53 77-78 (R-up 34-35, Div 2 61-62 76-77 84-85 93-94,Div 2 Cup 74-75 82-83, Invitation Cup 57-58), Sussex Snr Cup 01-02 05-06,Sussex F'lit Cup R-up 89-90, Sussex RUR Charity Cup 02-03 05-06, VernonWentworth Cup 86-87

PREVIOUS **League:** West Sussex **Ground:** Buckingham Park (pre-1970)

RECORD **Gate:** 1,342 v Wimbledon (f/lt opening 86)

FACT FILE
Founded: 1892
Nickname: Musselmen
Sponsors: Len German Wholesalers
Colours:All royal blue
Change colours: All red
Midweek Matchday: Wednesday
Programme: Yes
Editor: Michael Wenham
Local Press: Shoreham Herald

CLUB PERSONNEL
President: Alf Bloom
Chairman: John Bell
Press Officer: Michael Wenham
Tel: 01273 596009
Manager: Roger Vrace

ST. FRANCIS RANGERS

Previous Names: Ansty Rangers & St. Francis

Secretary: Patrick Bucknell, 79 Priory Way, Haywards Heath,West Sussex RH16 3NS
Tel Nos:01444 457726 (H) 07887615752 (M)
e-mail: twgoulds@hotmail.com

Ground: The Princess Royal Hospital, Lewes Road, Haywards Heath, RH16 4EX
Tel No: 01444 474021 and social club 01444441881

Directions: Enter through the main hospital entranceon the Lewes road and follow signs to Sports Complex.

FACT FILE
Colours:Black & white/black/black
Change colours: All Green with white trim

CLUB PERSONNEL
Chairman: John Goss
01444 232210(H) 07748 785240 (M)
Manager: Mick Jewell
01444 452258 (H) 07887 835286 (M)

STEYNING TOWN

Secretary: Mrs. Gina Barnes, 36 Shooting Field, Steyning W. Sussex BN44 3RQ
Tel: 01903 815387 (H)

Ground: The Shooting Field, Steyning, W. Sussex Tel: 01903 812228)

Directions: Entering Steyning from the west. Take 1st left in the High St (Tanyard Lane) Follow into Shooting Field estate, ground is 4th turn on the left.
Entering Steyning from the east. From the High St., turn right into Church St.. Turn left by Church into Shooting Field estate.
NB Coaches MUST park in Church Street Car Park.

HONOURS Sussex Co Lg Champions 84-5,85-6 Lg Cup Winners: 78-9,83-4 85-6 Div 2, 77-78 Div 2 Cup 65-6 Merit Table winners 84-5 Div 3 R-Up 01-02 Cup R-up 00-01

CLUB RECORDS **Attendance:** 1,100 v Halesowen Town F.A.Vase Quarter Final 84-85
Biggest Win: 15-0 v Portslade Sussex Co Lg.1965-6
Biggest Defeat:1-11 v Littlehampton Town Sussex Sen. Cup 90-91

FACT FILE
Colours: All Red
Change: All blue
Programme: 36 pages
Website: www.steyningtownfc.org.uk
E-mail: ian@ikennett.freeserve.co.uk

CLUB PERSONNEL
Chairman:Ian Kennett
President: Len Warner
Manager: Mick Barry
Assistant Manager: Graham Russell
Physio: Dave Jones

WEALDEN

Secretary: Kate Gilbert, MIckleton Cottage, Wilderness Lane, Hadlow Down, E.Sussex TN22 4HX Tel: 01825 890764 (H) 07710 838843 (M)
Email: larry@addagrip.co.uk

Ground: he Oaks,Wealden Football Club, Old Eastbourne Road, Uckfield, East Sussex.
Tel: 01825 890905

Directions: Next to the Rajdutt Restaurant on the Old Eastbourne Road, south of Uckfield town centre.

HONOURS Sussex County Lge Div. 3 R-up 99-00

FACT FILE
Colours: Blue & white.
Change colours: Red & Black

CLUB PERSONNEL
Chairman: Tom Parker
Manager: Mark Simpson
Asst. Man.
Allan Lofthouse
Coach: Alan Dove

WESTFIELD

Secretary: J. J. Archer, Gorse Cottage, Moor Lane, Westfield TN35 4QU
Tel: 01424 754516 (H) 01424 751030 (W)

Ground: Parish Field. Westfield Tel: 01424 751011

Directions: Take A21 towards Hastings, left onto A28, Westfield Lane - signposted to Ashford. Approx. 2 miles to village, pitch on left on main road just past garage.

FACT FILE

Colours: White & Green/green/green
Change Colours: Yellow & Green/ green/green

CLUB PERSONNEL
Chairman: G.A.Drinkwater
28 Churchfield, Westfield, Hastings TN35 4QN
Tel: 01424 754032 (H) 01424 751030 (B)
Vice Chairman:
Manager: Shaun Hardy
Asst. Man. / Coach
Physio:

WICK

Secretary: Peter Turner,64 Hawthorn Road,Bognor Regis,West Sussex. PO21 2DD
Tel: 01243 822860 (H)
Ground: Crabtree Park, Coomes Way, Wick, Littlehampton, W. Sussex Tel: 01903 713535
Capacity: 2,000 Seats: 50 Cover: 200 Floodlights: Yes
Directions: A27 to Crossbush, left at lights signed Littlehampton, after 1 mile over level crossing, left into Coombes Way next to Locomotive PH - ground at end. 1.5 miles from Littlehampton (BR)
Clubhouse: First floor. Capacity 120. Tea bar Club Shop: No
HONOURS Sussex Snr Cup 92-93; Sussex Co. Lg 89-90 93-94, Lg Cup 87-88 96-97 R-up 93-94 94-95), Div 2 81-82 85-86, Div 2 Cup R-up 81-82; Norman Wingate Tphy88-89 90-91, Res. Sect West 87-88 90-91 94-95; Sussex 5-aside R-up 85-86;Sussex RURCharity Cup 89-90 97-98; 98-99 Gilbert Rice F'lit Cup R-up 80-81 81-82; Sussex Jnr Cup 59-60; Brighton Charity Cup 85-86; Sussex F'lit Cup R-Up 94-95
PREVIOUS **League:** West Sussex **Grounds:** Southfields Rec
RECORD **Attendance:** 900

FACT FILE
Founded: 1892 Nickname: Wickers
Sponsors: Swandean
Colours: Red & black/black/black
Change colours: All blue
Midweek Matchdays: Tuesday
Reserve League: Sussex Co. Reserve Div
Programme: Yes Editor:Secretary
Local Press: Littlehampton Gazette

CLUB PERSONNEL
Chairman: Barry Wadsworth
Vice-Chairman: T.B. A.
President: Jack Croft
Manager: T.B.A.
Asst Manager:T.B.A.

FINAL LEAGUE TABLE 2003-04

DIVISION THREE	P	W	D	L	F	A	Pts
1. Crowborough Athletic	26	21	1	4	91	27	64
2. St Francis Rangers	26	17	2	7	69	41	53
3. Ifield Edwards	26	16	4	6	71	39	52
4. Wadhurst United	26	15	5	6	58	35	50
5. Storrington	26	14	5	7	55	37	47
6. Franklands Village	26	12	5	9	50	30	41
7. Uckfield Town	26	12	2	12	47	53	38
8. Lingfield	26	10	5	11	46	43	35
9. Hurstpierpoint	26	9	5	12	42	52	32
10. Bosham	26	10	2	14	43	55	32
11. Forest	26	9	2	15	41	56	29
12. Bexhill United	26	8	4	14	38	54	28
13. Newhaven	26	6	2	18	40	60	20
14. Upper Beeding	26	0	2	24	11	120	2

DIVISION TWO	1	2	3	4	5	6	7	8	9	10	11	12	13	14
1 Bexhill United		1-2	0-6	1-3	1-0	3-1	3-3	0-0	2-0	0-1	2-3	1-5	8-0	0-0
2 Bosham	0-3		0-2	1-2	0-3	1-1	2-0	0-4	1-0	4-2	1-2	1-3	6-1	2-0
3 Crowborough Athletic	6-0	4-0		2-1	3-0	4-0	3-1	3-0	3-1	4-2	3-2	1-2	10-0	0-2
4 Forest	1-1	5-3	4-2		0-2	0-2	0-1	4-2	1-2	0-1	0-1	0-1	7-1	0-1
5 Franklands Village	2-0	4-2	1-2	4-1		2-2	1-1	1-2	2-2	3-0	1-1	0-1	5-0	1-0
6 Hurstpierpoint	1-0	4-2	1-7	1-2	2-1		1-2	2-1	0-3	0-1	2-3	6-5	5-0	0-1
7 Ifield Edwards	5-1	4-0	2-1	5-1	2-1	1-1		4-1	5-1	3-0	2-3	4-2	6-0	5-0
8 Lingfield	3-1	1-3	1-2	5-0	1-3	4-3	2-1		1-1	0-1	1-1	1-1	3-0	1-2
9 Newhaven	1-0	1-4	1-2	2-3	1-2	0-1	2-4	0-4		1-2	1-3	0-2	8-1	2-3
10 St Francis Rangers	4-1	1-4	2-2	5-0	2-1	3-1	9-3	3-0	2-1		1-1	1-2	9-1	5-3
11 Storrington	2-3	4-2	1-2	2-2	1-0	2-0	2-1	2-3	4-0	3-4		2-0	1-0	0-1
12 Uckfield Town	1-3	0-0	0-6	4-2	1-5	1-2	1-4	3-0	3-6	0-2	1-0		2-0	1-3
13 Upper beeding	1-2	0-2	0-7	0-2	0-3	1-1	1-1	1-4	0-1	0-6	1-6	1-4		1-4
14 Wadhurst United	3-1	3-0	3-4	4-0	2-2	2-2	0-1	1-1	5-2	3-0	3-3	2-1	7-0	

LEAGUE CONSTITUTION 2004-05

BEXHILL UNITED
Secretary: Mrs Leigh Quinn, 37 Colebrook Road, Bexhill-on-Sea. TN39 3PX Tel: 01424 214197
Ground: The Polegrove, Brockley Rd, Bexhill-on-Sea, E. Sussex Tel: 01424220732 **Directions**: At Little Common r'bout take 3rd exit to Cooden Sea Rd, left into Cooden Drive for one and a half miles, Brockley Rd on the right. 3/4 mile from Bexhill Central (BR)
Colours: Green & white/white/white

BOSHAM
Chairman:Terry Longland Manager: Richard Mckenna
Secretary: Dick Doncaster, 61 Manor Way,Southbourne,Nr Emsworth PO10 8LY Tel: 0143 375184
Ground: Bosham Recreation Ground, Walton Lane, Bosham, W. Sussex Tel: 01243 574011
Directions: From Chichester take the A259 towards Portsmouth. On reaching Bosham turn left at the Swan P.H. roundabout. 1/2 mile to T junction, turn left & car park 50 yds on left.
Honours: Sussex County Lge Div. 3 99-00
Colours: Red/white/red Change Colours: White/black/white

FOREST
Secretary: Peter Farley, 9 Owlbeech Way, Horsham, W.Sussex RH13 6AW. Tel: 01403 25256
Ground: Roffey Sports & Social Club, Spooners Rd., Roffey. Tel: 01403 210221
Directions: Spooners Rd. is off the main Crawley road, 100 yds from the `Star'PH, towards Crawley
Colours: White/Navy Blue/ White

HAYWARDS HEATH
Secretary: Steve Weller, 52 Kents Road,Haywards Heath, Susex RH16 4HQ Tel: 01444 457230
Ground: Hanbury Park Stadium, Haywards Heath Tel: 01444 412837
Directions: A272 to Haywards Heath town centre. At Sussex roundabout, north on B2708 (Hazelgrove Road) take first right into New England Road, then the 4th right (Allen Road) leads to ground.
Colours: Blue & white stripes/blue/blue

Haywards Heath. Photo: Roger Turner.

Hurstpierpoint - Back row (L-R): Stu Kempton, Stu Ritchie, Dave Biggs, Luke Newman, Simon Emmett, Mike Dean, Keith Fender, Damian Siablon. **Front Row:** Brendan Griffin, Sam Swain, Andy Hartless, Jon Neighbour, Martin Hylward, Lee Saunders (Player manager). Photo: Gordon Whittington.

Wadhurst United - Back Row (L-R): Steve Prince, Paul Molineux, Liam Bull, Justin Mewitt, Pete Masters, Dean Rabson, Simon Bowyer, Lionel Woodruffe, Phil White. **Front Row:** Ben Mansford, Stuart Yeoman, Alick Christie, Nick Watkins, Wayne Mewett, Jethro Warren. Photo: Gordon Whittington.

HURSTPIERPOINT

Secretary: Rodney Wilson,12 St Mary's Road, Burgess Hill, RH15 8NU Tel: 01444 870356

Ground: Fairfield Rec. Ground, Cuckfield Road. (Tel: 01273 834783) **Directions**: At Hurstpierpoint crossroads, go north into Cuckfield Road (B2117) for 1km. Ground entrance between houses nos.158 & 160

Colours: Blue & white quarters/blue/blue

IFIELD EDWARDS

Secretary: Robert Anderson, 1 Old Orchards, Church Rd, Worth, Crawley. RH107QA. Tel: 01293 886215)

Ground: Edwards Sports& Social Club, Ifield Green, Rusper Road, Crawley. Tel: 01293 536569)

Directions: From A23 Crawley by-pass going north, left at r'about signedCharlwood. Third left into Ifield Green, first right past Royal Oak (PH) into Rusper Rd

Colours: White/black/red

LINGFIELD

Secretary: Pamela Thomsett, 61 Drivers Mead. Lingfield,Surrey RH7 6EX Tel: 01342 832418 (H)

Ground: Sports Pavilion, Godstone Road, Lingfield, Surrey. Tel: 01342 834269

Directions: A22, 4 miles north of East Grinstead, to Mormon Temple roundabout, take exit Lingfield (B2028) Newchapel Road for 1 1/2 miles. Left at T junction into Godstone Road (B2029) and ground is 1/2 mile on left.

Colours: Red & yellow stripes/black/yellow Change:Blue & white stripes/white/ sky blue

NEWHAVEN

Secretary: Peter Foote, 32 Valley Dene, Newhaven BN9 9NF Tel: 01273 513232

Ground: Fort Road Recreation Ground Tel: 01273 513940

Directions: A259, follow one-way system around town, left at Police Station into South Road, which becomes Fort Road.

Colours: Red & amber/red & amber/red

RUSTINGTON

Recreation Ground,
Jubilee Avenue,
Rustington,
West Sussex
01403 352400

STORRINGTON

Secretary: Keith Dalmon, 4 End Cottages, Turnpike Road, Amberley. BN18 9LX Tel: 01798 831887 (H)

Ground: Recreation Ground, Storrington. Tel: 01903 745860

Directions: Turn west on A283 (off A24). Ground is opposite the pond to the west of the village.

Colours: All Blue Chanbge Colours : Yellow/black/yellow

UCKFIELD TOWN

Secretary: Jennie Hickman, 10 Wilson Grove, Uckfield, E.Sussex TN22 2BU (01825 762602)

Ground: Victoria Pleasure Grounds, Uckfield. Tel: 01825 769400)

Directions: Take Eastbourne road (old A22) south of Uckfield town centre. Entrance to ground is 1/2 mile on the right (just after the Police station)

Colours: Red/black/black

UPPER BEEDING

Secretary: Mrs Anita Addison, Sheppens, Newham Lane, Steyning, W. Sussex BN44 3LR
Tel: 01903 814077 (H) 01903 813109 (B)

Ground: Memorial Playing Field, High St.,
Upper Beeding BN44 3WN
Tel: 01903 815930

Directions: From east/west A27 J A283 north to Upper Beeding. Ground opposite village hall in High St. From north/south A24 J A283 southbound. Turn left to Steyning/Upper Beeding.

Colours: Yellow & blue/blue/yellow & blue.
Change: All royal blue.

WADHURST UNITED

(from East Sussex Lge)

Ground: Sparrow Green Rec., South View Road, Wadhurst, East Sussex Tel: 01892 783527

UNITED COUNTIES LEAGUE

SPONSORED BY: EAGLE BITTER

Chairman: Geoff Paul

Secretary: Roger Gamble, 8 Bostock Avenue, Northampton NN1 4LW
Tel: 01604 637766

Press Officer: Jeremy Biggs Tel: 01780 763048

In many ways the Premier Division title race in 2003-04 mirrored that of twelve months earlier. The previous campaign saw **Newport Pagnell** open up a big lead only to be overhauled by **Holbeach** late on, this time round it was **Buckingham Town** who seemed unstoppable early on and **Spalding United** whose late run sntched the prize.

The eventual outcome was perhaps no surprise as the Tulips had hired Holbeach's manager Dick Creasey following their relegation from the Dr Martens League, and two thirds of the title winning team followed him to the Halley Stewart Field. The big game experience of the likes of Steve Appleby, Nick Keeble, Micky Nuttell and Lee Hudson was to stand Spalding in good stead as they shone in the new year to accelerate past Buckingham and secure a fifth championship for the Tulips.

The two main protagonists showed their intentions from the outset. Buckingham won their first ten matches until losing 2-0 to Spalding at Ford Meadow on the last Saturday of October, while that win gave the Tulips 28 points from the first thirty on offer. The Robins' response to that first defeat was six consecutive victories and they led Spalding by twelve points when the sides met again on 20th December.

By then Buckingham's season had reached what with hindsight proved a pivotal moment - days before their return game with Spalding they had had four men dismissed at Lymington in an abandoned FA Vase tie subsequently awarded to the Hampshire hosts. The repercussions for Buckingham were enormous, the red carded players all faced lengthy suspensions at the same time and these coincided with a crop of injuries. Points were lost with depleted ranks, and even when Morrell Maison's squad returned to full strength, the early sparkle was missing.

A 1-1 draw at the Halley Stewart Field seemed a good result for Buckingham at the time, but a run of draws saw their big lead whittled away. **Cogenhoe** and top flight newboys **Harrowby** led the chase while four home matches in December saw Spalding collect just one point, they were long odds outsiders going into the new year.

Spalding clinched the title, and with it promotion to the Unibond League, in style, winning 5-1 at **Ford Sports** on the season's final Saturday. They finished five points clear of Buckingham while newly promoted Harrowby, emerging as a force under their pocket dynamo of a manager Graham Drury, edged out **St Neots** for third slot.

At the other end of the table surprise basement boys were **Daventry**. Mid table finishers twelve months earlier, they were well placed early on after winning four of their first six games. They collected only two points from their final twenty matches and finished six adrift of local rivals **Long Buckby** whose traumatic campaign saw them field 95 players and undergo two managerial changes. Desborough contrasted dismal league form with excellent cup results for much of the season before a good run in lifted them out of trouble.

The Division One champoinship race was a real thriller with five sides involved until late in the campaign. **Whitworths** failed to live up to early promise while reigning titleholders **Sileby** slipped out of contention after manager Nick Verity left in January.

Potton were the most consistent side in the division and 31 out of the last 33 points on offer saw them ease clear, with the goals of the division's top marksman **Brett Donnelly** helping to secure the crown and a return to Premier football after three years in the lower grade. A big fixture backlog caught up with **Thrapston** late on, leaving them in fourth in the last season of the long serving Fary Pett's Chancery Lane reign. Newcomers **Eye** were particularly impressive on their travels, finishing third on their UCL debut. They were nudged out of a second by **Cottingham** on the season's final Saturday. Graham Leech's men winning 3-1 at Chestnut Avenue to round off their last season on the Berryfield Road ground on a high. For much of the season **Eynesbury** had been promotion favourites but their last five matches yielded just five points as they fell from first to fifth in the last moth of the campaign.

The other newboys in Division One, **Huntingdon Town,** found it a difficult first campaign with a lack of firepower the problem. They finished next to bottom in Division One, four points clear of **Burton Park** who occupied the basement slot for a third season running.

Boston Town lifted the Knockout Cup for the first time, beating **St Neots** 3-2 in a dramatic final at Yaxley. Liam Harrold's last minute spot kick gave the Poachers the trophy. The Saints were also losers in the Huntingdonshire Senior Cup final, 1-0 to **Yaxley**, but finally collected some silverware by beating **Buckingham** 3-1 in the Buckingham Charity Cup final.

That reverse left the Robins with a third set of runners up medals as they lost 3-1 to **Beaconsfield** in the Berks & Bucks Senior Trophy final, their only reward for a 60 match campaign the Baker Perkis Trophy for the Highest Aggregate of league goals.

Blackstones were awarded the Lincolnshire Senior Cup after losing 2-0 to **Barton Town Old Boys** in the final. The Humberside club fielded an ineligible player in their success. Stones came off second best in the Hinchingbrooke Cup final though going down 5-1 to **Yaxley**. **Desborough** were runners up in the Northamptonshire Hillier Senior Cup, a lone goal securing final victory for the professionals of Peterborough United in the final at the Waterworks Field. **Thrapston**'s disappointment at missing out on league honours was tempered by a 3-0 Northants Junior Cup final defeat of **Cottingham** at Nene Park.

Wootton manager **Kenny Davidson** was a Huntingdoneshire Premier Cup winner for a fifth time as **Blue Cross** beat **Eynesbury** 4-2 in the final. There were also cup success for **Stotfold** in the North Beds Charity Cup and **Woodford** in the Daventry Charity Cup. The icing on the season's cake for champions **Spalding** was a 3-1 victory over **Aveley** as they became only the second UCL club to win the East Anglian Cup.

Lincolnshire League champions **Sleaford Town** are the only newcomers for the 2004-05 season, joining Division One, while Cottingham will now be known as **Corby Cottingham** following their move to the Rockingham Triangle.

Jeremy Biggs (Press Officer)

FINAL LEAGUE TABLE 2003-04

PREMIER DIVISION	P	W	D	L	F	A	Pts
1. Spalding United	42	28	6	8	97	44	90
2. Buckingham Town	42	25	10	7	102	46	85
3. Harrowby United	42	24	9	9	85	56	81
4. St Neots Town	42	24	8	10	85	44	80
5. Boston Town	42	24	7	11	67	43	79
6. Cogenhoe United	42	23	9	10	86	38	78
7. Holbeach United	42	23	5	14	80	59	74
8. Yaxley	42	22	4	16	99	64	70
9. Ford Sports Daventry	42	19	11	12	83	56	68
10. Stotfold	42	19	8	15	73	59	65
11. Blackstones	42	16	10	16	57	62	58
12. Woodford United	42	14	13	15	61	53	55
13. Newport Pagnell Town	42	15	9	18	60	72	54
14. Wootton Blue Cross	42	14	10	18	59	61	52
15. Bourne Town	42	12	11	19	54	90	47
16. Desborough Town	42	13	7	22	56	88	46
17. Deeping Rangers	42	12	9	21	48	78	45
18. Northampton Spencer	42	11	10	21	47	75	43
19. Stewarts & Lloyds Corby	42	11	7	24	52	81	40
20. Raunds Town	42	7	12	23	55	94	33
21. Long Buckby	42	8	4	30	46	134	28
22. Daventry Town	42	5	7	30	40	95	22

	1	2	3	4	5	6	7	8	9	10	11	12	13	14	15	16	17	18	19	20	21	22
1 Blackstones		0-2	1-2	2-3	0-0	1-0	0-0	2-2	0-2	3-1	0-1	2-1	6-0	3-2	1-0	1-3	2-1	1-1	2-2	3-1	3-2	1-3
2 Boston Town	0-1		2-3	1-1	2-0	1-0	0-1	1-0	1-0	0-4	1-0	1-2	2-0	3-3	2-2	1-1	3-0	4-1	1-0	1-0	1-2	3-2
3 Bourne Town	1-0	1-3		0-3	3-2	2-4	2-2	3-2	2-2	1-3	3-1	3-2	2-2	3-1	1-0	0-5	0-2	2-0	1-3	0-4	2-1	1-6
4 Buckingham T.	4-1	4-0	7-0		4-2	4-0	6-1	4-0	1-1	0-0	6-3	3-0	0-2	6-2	3-1	0-2	1-3	3-1	5-0	0-1	1-1	3-2
5 Cogenhoe Utd	2-1	0-2	2-0	0-2		1-0	3-1	0-0	1-1	5-1	1-0	7-0	0-0	3-0	0-0	1-1	0-1	1-1	3-0	2-1	3-0	2-1
6 Daventry Town	1-2	1-2	2-1	1-2	1-0		2-0	1-1	0-5	0-4	0-1	2-4	1-1	1-1	4-4	0-4	3-6	0-3	1-3	3-1	1-3	1-2
7 Deeping R.	3-1	2-1	1-0	2-3	0-2	2-2		0-1	0-1	2-1	1-2	1-0	1-1	2-5	1-1	3-1	1-4	0-3	0-3	1-3	0-3	0-3
8 Desborough T.	1-3	0-1	1-0	6-1	1-4	4-1	0-2		0-7	2-6	1-1	3-0	2-1	0-0	2-1	0-3	0-3	2-0	2-4	0-0	2-1	2-1
9 Ford Sports D.	1-1	2-2	1-1	1-3	0-1	3-1	3-0	3-2		1-2	2-1	0-3	6-2	4-0	2-1	1-5	1-2	3-0	1-1	0-0	1-2	3-0
10 Harrowby Utd	1-2	1-1	3-1	2-1	2-1	2-1	0-3	2-0	2-1		2-0	2-0	4-3	5-3	2-0	1-0	1-1	4-0	2-0	1-0	1-1	1-2
11 Holbeach Utd	4-0	1-0	5-1	0-1	2-3	1-0	4-0	1-3	0-0	3-2		3-1	4-1	0-2	4-1	1-2	3-2	2-1	4-1	3-0	2-0	0-5
12 Long Buckby	2-4	1-8	0-0	0-5	0-8	2-1	2-3	2-3	2-8	0-3	0-3		1-2	0-0	3-2	0-2	1-2	2-0	2-0	2-6	1-8	2-7
13 Newport Pag.T.	2-1	0-2	2-1	1-1	0-3	2-1	0-1	3-1	2-0	2-2	2-0	1-0		3-0	2-1	2-3	1-0	2-1	1-2	2-2	0-1	1-2
14 Northampton S.	2-0	0-2	4-1	0-0	2-1	0-0	1-0	1-1	1-0	1-1	0-2	3-1	1-1		5-0	0-3	0-2	1-3	0-1	0-2	0-0	2-4
15 Raunds Town	1-1	1-1	1-1	0-0	0-2	1-0	1-4	3-2	1-3	3-4	3-3	1-1	1-4	0-2		5-4	2-1	4-1	1-2	1-2	2-2	0-4
16 Spalding Utd	4-0	0-1	4-1	1-1	1-3	2-2	1-1	1-0	0-2	0-2	2-0	9-1	3-2	6-1	3-1		2-0	2-1	2-1	0-1	2-0	2-1
17 St Neots Town	0-0	0-2	1-1	2-3	2-0	4-0	2-1	6-0	2-2	4-2	1-1	4-0	2-1	3-0	4-0	1-1		6-1	1-4	3-1	2-0	1-0
18 Stewarts & L.C.	2-1	1-2	0-2	0-3	0-0	1-0	2-2	2-1	7-1	0-0	1-3	2-1	2-3	1-0	1-3	2-3	1-2		0-2	1-2	1-1	2-4
19 Stotfold	0-0	0-1	0-0	2-1	1-4	2-0	1-1	5-0	1-1	4-1	3-4	7-1	0-0	2-0	4-1	1-2	0-1	1-1		0-3	4-3	1-2
20 Woodford Utd	1-1	0-2	2-2	0-1	2-2	3-0	1-1	3-1	0-1	2-2	2-2	1-2	4-1	2-0	0-0	0-1	0-0	2-3	1-3		0-0	1-3
21 Wootton B.C.	1-2	2-0	1-1	1-1	1-6	3-0	1-0	2-4	1-3	0-1	0-2	0-0	3-2	0-1	0-1	1-2	1-0	3-0	2-1	2-2		1-2
22 Yaxley	0-1	3-1	2-2	1-1	1-5	4-1	5-1	3-1	2-3	2-2	2-3	4-1	2-0	3-0	6-3	1-2	1-1	0-1	0-1	0-2	1-2	

FINAL LEAGUE TABLE 2003-04

DIVISION ONE	P	W	D	L	F	A	Pts
1. Potton United	34	25	5	4	99	25	80
2. Cottingham	34	23	7	4	80	31	76
3. Eye United	34	23	5	6	93	33	74
4. Thrapston Town	34	20	10	4	86	30	70
5. Eynesbury Rovers	34	19	10	5	87	40	67
6. Sileby Rangers	34	17	10	7	78	62	61
7. Wellingborough Whitworths	34	16	4	14	57	52	52
8. Northampton ON Chenecks	34	15	5	14	72	82	50
9. Blisworth	34	11	12	11	56	59	45
10. St Ives Town	34	11	10	13	52	58	43
11. Olney Town	34	11	6	17	52	69	39
12. Rothwell Corinthians	34	10	5	19	45	74	35
13. Bugbrooke St Michaels	34	9	5	20	46	71	32
14. Irchester United	34	8	5	21	46	76	29
15. Higham Town	34	6	9	19	52	93	27
16. Kempston Rovers	34	5	11	18	48	87	26
17. Huntingdon Town	34	5	10	19	36	66	25
18. Burton Park Wanderers	34	6	3	25	32	109	21

DIV. ONE 03-04	1	2	3	4	5	6	7	8	9	10	11	12	13	14	15	16	17	18
1 Blisworth		2-1	5-0	0-0	0-1	1-1	2-2	2-0	3-1	1-1	3-3	3-0	2-2	1-4	1-4	1-1	1-1	1-3
2 Bugbrooke St Michaels	0-1		2-0	1-3	2-1	0-3	3-2	1-0	0-0	2-2	2-3	0-3	3-1	2-2	1-1	1-1	0-1	0-1
3 Burton Park Wanderers	2-2	3-2		0-7	0-2	0-5	2-3	3-2	1-2	3-1	0-2	1-3	0-5	0-3	1-4	0-1	0-2	0-2
4 Cottingham	5-2	3-0	2-0		1-1	3-1	1-1	2-0	3-1	2-1	5-2	6-0	3-1	1-0	1-1	2-0	0-1	3-0
5 Eye United	2-3	0-4	7-0	1-3		2-2	5-1	2-2	6-1	8-0	4-1	1-0	1-0	5-1	7-1	0-1	2-2	4-0
6 Eynesbury Town	5-1	4-0	3-0	1-1	0-3		3-2	3-0	3-0	2-1	3-2	3-0	1-1	6-2	1-4	3-0	2-0	5-0
7 Higham Town	2-2	3-5	1-3	3-5	1-2	1-6		3-0	1-1	2-2	1-2	2-3	0-1	2-1	1-1	2-1	1-5	2-1
8 Huntingdon Town	0-0	3-1	5-1	2-2	1-2	0-0	2-2		0-1	2-0	2-2	0-1	0-2	0-1	0-3	0-0	0-2	3-1
9 Irchester United	0-2	2-1	3-4	1-4	0-4	1-1	5-0	3-0		3-1	2-4	4-2	0-4	1-2	1-2	2-0	2-2	0-1
10 Kempston Rovers	2-1	3-1	0-0	0-1	0-4	2-2	3-1	0-0	2-2		2-2	1-1	0-4	2-3	3-3	2-4	0-0	1-2
11 Northampton ON Chenecks	5-3	8-2	3-2	1-4	0-1	0-4	1-2	5-2	2-1	3-2		3-1	1-5	4-0	2-2	3-0	0-7	3-2
12 Olney Town	1-2	3-0	5-1	1-2	0-1	1-1	4-4	2-2	2-0	7-0	0-1		0-5	1-0	1-2	1-3	0-3	1-2
13 Potton United	1-0	4-0	4-2	2-0	2-1	2-0	7-0	6-0	3-1	4-1	3-0	9-0		0-0	1-1	1-0	2-2	2-1
14 Rothwell Corinthians	0-1	1-0	1-2	3-1	0-3	3-3	2-2	3-1	3-2	2-6	1-0	1-4	0-4		2-3	1-1	1-3	1-2
15 Sileby Rangers	4-5	1-0	7-0	1-2	0-2	0-3	6-1	1-4	4-3	4-1	3-3	2-2	2-1	2-0		2-0	1-9	2-0
16 St Ives Town	0-0	2-3	1-1	1-1	2-4	1-4	2-1	2-2	3-0	4-1	3-1	3-0	1-5	4-1	2-3		2-2	2-2
17 Thrapston Town	3-2	1-0	5-0	1-0	2-2	4-1	3-0	5-1	3-0	2-3	3-0	0-0	2-3	4-0	1-1	4-0		1-3
18 Wellingborough Whitworths	2-0	3-6	7-0	0-1	0-2	2-2	1-0	2-0	3-0	5-2	5-0	1-2	0-2	1-0	0-0	2-4	0-0	

LEAGUE CUP

PRELIMINARY ROUND

Boston Town	v	Northampton Spencer	0-0* 7-6p
Bourne Town	v	Daventry Town	2-3*
Bugbrooke St M.	v	Stewarts & Lloyds Corby	0-3
Harrowby United	v	Potton United	5-2*
St Ives Town	v	Newport Pagnell Town	0-5
Stotfold	v	Irchester United	2-1
Thrapston Town	v	Kempston Rovers	4-2
Wootton Blue Cross	v	Ford Sports Daventry	1-1* 3-5p

FIRST ROUND

Blackstones	v	Eye United	4-0
Blisworth	v	Holbeach United	0-2
Boston Town	v	Yaxley	2-1
Cogenhoe United	v	Northampton ON Chenecks	5-1
Daventry Town	v	Olney Town	2-3
Deeping Rangers	v	Burton Park Wanderers	6-0
Eynesbury Rovers	v	Buckingham Town	2-1
Long Buckby	v	Desborough Town	2-0
Raunds Town	v	Newport Pagnell Town	1-2
Rothwell Corinthians	v	St Neots Town	0-4
Spalding United	v	Cottingham	2-0
Stewarts & Lloyds Corby	v	Ford Sports Daventry	1-5
Stotfold	v	Harrowby United	3-4*
Thrapston Town	v	Higham Town	3-1
Wellingborough Whitworths	v	Sileby Rangers	3-3* 4-3p
Woodford United	v	Huntingdon Town	3-1

SECOND ROUND

Blackstones	v	Cogenhoe United	0-1
Boston Town	v	WellingboroughWhitworths	1-0
Deeping Rangers	v	Spalding United	0-4
Eynesbury Rovers	v	Ford Sports Daventry	0-0* 7-6p
Newport Pagnell T.	v	Holbeach United	3-0
St Neots Town	v	Harrowby United	4-2
Thrapston Town	v	Olney Town	0-2
Woodford United	v	Long Buckby	3-0

QUARTER-FINALS

Boston Town	v	Olney Town	2-1
Eynesbury Rovers	v	Newport Pagnell Town	0-3
St Neots Town	v	Cogenhoe United	1-0
Woodford United	v	Spalding United	0-1

SEMI-FINALS

Spalding United	v	Boston Town	0-2
St Neots Town	v	Newport Pagnell Town	3-2

THE FINAL (28th April at Blackstones)

Boston Town	v	St Neots Town	3-2

MONTHLY AWARDS 2003/04

Month	Manager of the Month Premier Division	Manager of the Month Division One	Goalscorer of the Month
August\Sept	Morrell Maison (Buckingham)	Gary Petts (Thrapston Town	Ian Dunn (Holbeach Utd/Yaxley)
October	Jon Taylor (St Neots Town)	Peter Green (Northampton ON C.)	Richard Turner (Northampton S.R.)
November	Morrell Maison (Buckingham)	Roger Daniels (Eye United)	Vince Petty (Eynesbury R.)
December	Kevin Fox (Stewart & Lloyds Corby)	Graham Leech (Cottingham)	Michael Frew (Yaxley)
January	Shane Geary (Ford Sports Dav.)	Steve Galbraith (Eynesbury Rovers)	Matt Murphy (Ford Sports Dav.)
February	Phil Pateman (Stotfold)	Gary Petts (Thrapston Town)	Shaun Keeble (Holbeach Utd)
March	Bob Tansley (Northampton Sp.)	Dick Newman (Potton United)	Liam Harrold (Boston Town)
April/May	Bob Don-Duncan (Bostpn Town)	Dick Newman (Potton United)	Brett Donnelly (Potton United)

Manager of the Year: Dick Creasy (Spadling United)

UNITED COUNTIES LEAGUE LEADING PREMIER DIVISION GOAL SCORERS 2003-04

Club						
Blackstone Matt Doyle	44	Graham Epps	42	Andrew Neal	39
Boston Town Lee Ellison	46	James Brader	43	Simon Ward	41
Bourne Town Ross Nichols	45	Darren Munton	41	John Morton	35
Buckingham Town Sean Griffith	43	Moses Olaleye	38	Phil Turner	37
Cogenhoe United Roy Anderson	45	Matt Poulton	42	Ben Foster & Rob Goldring	41
Daventry Town Darren Jameson	38	Gareth Errington	35	Jason Spence & Ian Waldock	35
Deeping Rangers John Feetham	42	Michael Goode	42	Carl Griffiths	39
Desborough Town Andy Greensmith	41	Tom Mills	41	Bryan Jeffery	32
Ford Sports Darren Watts	44	Dave Bond	42	Ian Giles	42
Harrowby United Mark Foster	44	Martin Wormall	41	Richard Holmes	39
Holbeach United Steve Barnes	43	Dean Elston	42	Shaun Keeble	42
Long Buckby Kevin Woods	42	Craig Townsend	30	Rick Kimbell	28
Newport Pagnell Town Tyrone Taylor	46	Maz Lagioia	44	Gary Flinn	41
Northampton Spencer Ross Harris	40	Gavin Nullatamby	39	Oliver Urquhart	38
Raunds Town Matt Freeman	41	Mark Njotsa	39	Richard Bailey & Soloman Benjamin	30
St Neots Town Michael Cox	46	Steve Kuhne	45	Paul Bloss	44
Spalding United Steve Appleby	44	Nick Keeble	43	Lee Sowerby	41
Stewarts & Lloyds Mike McConnell	37	Greig McIlwain	37	Dave Torrance & Ian Walker	36
Stotfold Luke Gregson	43	Wes Byrne	40	Paul Garrett & Adam Pitcairn	40
Woodford United Adam Knight	45	Carl Standen	39	Terry Fitton, Stuart Haynes & Dave Marlow	38
Wootton Blue Cross Matt Hulett	39	Jason Mannion	39	Andy Taylor	38
Yaxley Peter Miller	43	Simon Acton	42	MarkHanton	41

BLACKSTONES

Secretary: Ian MacGillivray, 20 New Rd, Ryhall, Stamford, Lincs PE9 4HL
Tel: 01780 762263 (H), e-mail: Imacgilli@aol.com

Ground: Lincoln Road, Stamford Tel: 01780 757835
Now owned by Blackstones Sports a nd Social Club.

Directions: A6121 Stamford to Bourne road, 2nd left past MB works

Capacity: 1,000 Seats: 100 Cover: Yes Floodlights: Yes

Clubhouse: Open evenings & lunchtime on matchdays, Saturdays and Sundays.

HONOURS UCL Div 1 R-up 87-88 (Benevolent Cup R-up), Lincs Snr Cup `A' 92-93,03-04
Eagle Bitter K.O. Cup 2002-03

PREVIOUS **Leagues:** Peterborough Works; Peterborough; Stamford & District
Names: Rutland Ironworks; Blackstone (until 1975)

RECORD **Gate:** 700 v Glinton
Win: 11-0 v Brackley, 22/1/94 (A Dunn 6 goals)
Scorer (in one game): A Dunn; 6 v Brackley Town, 22/1/94

BEST SEASON **FA Vase:** 2nd Round 97-98, 01-02 **FA Cup:** First Qualifying Round 91-92

Players progressing : Craig Goldsmith (Peterborough), Alan Neilson (Newcastle)

FACT FILE
Founded: 1920 Nickname: Stones
Sponsors: Idealshopfitters
Colours: White/black/black
Change Colours: Orange/black/orange
Midweek matchday: Wednesday
Programme: 32 pages with entry
Editor: Kevin Boor (01780 754584)
e-mail: kevin.boor@newage-avkseg.com
Local Press: Stamford Mercury, Herald & Post, Peterborough Evening Telegraph, Rutland Times

CLUB PERSONNEL
President: Bill Sewell Chairman: Kevin Boor
Manager: Mel Landin Asst.Man.:Jim Shilling
Press Officer: IMac Gillivray
Captain: Gareth Williams

2003-2004
P.o.Y.: Tom Ruscillo
Top Scorer: Michael Chong

BOSTON TOWN

Secretary: Allan Crick, Daisy Cottage, Shore Rd, Freiston, Boston, Lincs., PE22 0LN
Tel: 01205 760162. (H &Fax) 01205 313090 (W) 07718906053 (M)

Ground: Tattershall Road, Boston, Lincs Tel: 01205 365470

Directions: A52 Grantham-Sleaford, 2nd left into Brotherton Rd., Argyle St. to bridge, immediately over left into Tattersall road, ground 3/4 mile on left.

Capacity: 6,000 Seats: 450 Cover: 950 Floodlights: Yes Club Shop: Yes
Clubhouse: Open evenings, except Sunday, matchdays & functions. Bar & Lounge. Darts & pool

HONOURS Midland Co's Lg 74-75 78-79 80-81 (Lg Cup 76-77); Lincs Snr `A' Cup (5)73-74 79-82 89-90 (Snr `B' Cup 65-66); Central Mids Lg 88-89; Central All 65-66; Lincs Lg 64-65; Und. Co. Lg. Prem Div 94-95, 00-01 Lg.Cup Winners 2003-04

PREVIOUS **Leagues:** Lincs 63-65; Central Alliance 65-66; Eastern Co's 66-68; Midland 68-82; Northern Co's East 82-87; Central Midlands 87-91 **Ground:** Mayflower Ground

BEST SEASON **FA Cup:** 1st Rd Proper 76-77, 1-3 v Barnsley (A)
FA Trophy: 2nd Round 79-80, 3-6 v Mossley (A) after 0-0
FA Vase: Semi-Finals 94-95, 0-2 (agg) v Taunton Town)

RECORD **Attendance:** 2,700 v Boston Utd, FA Cup 3rd Qual. Rd 1970
Goalscorer (in a season): Carl Smaller 48, 1994-95

Players progressing: Julian Joachim (Leicester City and Aston Villa) , Neil Mann (Hull City)

FACT FILE
Founded: 1963 Nickname: Poachers
Sponsors: T.F.M.Supplies Graham Gill Carpets Cropley Suzucki & Boston Snooker Centre
Colours: Sky Blue/ Royal Blue/Sky
Change: Yellow/white/yellow
Midweek Matchday: Tuesday
Reserves League: None 94-95
Programme: 40 pages, 50p
Prog. Ed:-John Knightm (078881 848588)
e-mail: johnknight0066@supanet.com
Press Off:J.Rose 01205351501

CLUB PERSONNEL
Chairman: Mick Vines
Vice Chairman: J Rose
Manager: Bob Don-Duncan
Physio: Steve Greetham
Captain: Lee Rippin

2003-2004
Leading Goalscorer:Liam Harrold
Player of the Year: Lee Rippin

Boston Town. Photo: Gordon Whittington.

BOURNE TOWN

Secretary: Andy Anderson, 28A Abbey Road, Bourne, Lincs.PE10 9EP (01778 423892)
Ground: Abbey Lawn, Abbey Road, Bourne, Lincs Tel: 01778 422292
Directions: In market place take A151 Spalding Road, ground 500 yds on right.Public transport from Peterborough, Stamford and Grantham
Capacity: 3,000 Seats: 300 Cover: 750 Floodlights: Yes
Club Shop: Contact Sec.
Clubhouse: Small, open matchdays and specific events. Food, confectionary available
HONOURS Utd Co's Lg 68-69 69-70 71-72 90-91 (KO Cup 69-70, Benevolent Cup 90-91, Res Div 2 94-95), Lincs Snr `A' Cup 71-72 (R-up 92-93), Central Alliance Division 1 South 59-60, Lincs Intermediate Cup 85-86
PREVIOUS **Leagues:** Peterborough; UCL 47-56; Central All. 58-61; MidlandCos 61-63
Ground: Adjacent to cricket field after WW2 until 1947
RECORD **Attendance:** 3,000 v Chelmsford, FA Trophy 1970
Goalscorer: David Scotney
BEST SEASON **FA Vase:** 4th Round 89-90
Players Progressing:Peter Grummit (Nottm Forest), Shaun Cunnington (Wrexham), David Palmer (Wrexham)2002-2003
2003-2004 **Player of the Year:** Darren Munton **Top Scorer:** Jim Forman

FACT FILE
Founded: 1883 Nickname: Wakes
Sponsors:Spensers: Moonshine
Colours: Sky & white stripes//maroon/sky
Change Colours: Yelow/blue/yellow
Midweek matchday: Wednesday
Reserves' Lge: HSUCL Res Div 1
Programme: 30 pages, 75p
Editor: T.Bates
Local Press: Stamford Mercury, Lincs Free Press, Peterborough EveningTelegraph, Bourne Local

CLUB PERSONNEL
Chairman: Terry Bates
Vice-Chairman: Don Mitchell
President: Bob feetham
Press Officer: Terry Bates
Manager::Steve Appleby
Assistant Manager: Dave Scotney
Physio:T.B.A.

BUCKINGHAM TOWN

Secretary: Robin Taylor, 9 Meadow Way, Steeple Claydon, Buckingham MK18 2PA
Tel No: 07860 539106
Ground: Ford Meadow, Ford Street, Buckingham Tel: 01280 816257
Capacity: 2,500 Cover: 200 Seats: 200 Floodlights: Yes
Directions: From town centre take A413 (Aylesbury) and turn right at Phillips Ford Garage after 400yds. Public transport: train to Milton Keynes, then bus to Buckingham.
Clubhouse: Open evenings 6.30-11 (12-11 Sat & Sun) Rolls etc available on matchdays. Bingo, dominoes, darts & pool. Concert room with stage for hire,capacity 150 **Club Shop:** Yes
HONOURS Southern Lg Southern Div 90-91, Utd Co's Lg 83-84 85-86 (Div 1 R-up 75-76, Div 2 R-up 74-75, Lg Cup 83-84, R-up: 2002-03Div 2 Cup R-up 74-75), Nth Bucks Lg 24-25 28-29 33-34 35-37 38-39 48-50(2) Aylesbury & Dist. Lg 02-03, Berks & Bucks Snr Cup 83-84, Berks & Bucks Jnr Cup 02-03 48-49 (R-up 38-39 72-73), Berks & Bucks Minor Cup 32-33, Buckingham Snr Charity Cup x12, r-up x 5 Highest Goalscoring Trophy 03-04
PREVIOUS **Leagues:** Aylesbury & Dist; Nth Bucks; Hellenic 53-57; Sth Mids 57-74; Utd Co's 74-86; Southern Lge 86-97
BEST SEASON **FA Cup:** 1st Round 1984-85 **FA Vase:** Quarter Finals 1990-91 & 92-93
RECORD **Attendance:** 2,451 v Orient, FA Cup 1st Rd 84-85
Fee paid: £7,000 for Steve Jenkins (Wealdstone, 1992)
Fee received: £1,000 for Terry Shrieves (Kettering)

FACT FILE
Formed: 1883
Nickname: The Robins
Sponsors: The Ford Meadow Club
Colours: All red
Change colours: All white
Midweek Matchday:Wednesday
Reserves' League: No reserve team
Programme: Yes Editor: Carl Waine
Newsline: 01280817194
Local Press: Buckingham Advertiser, MK Citizen, Herald & Post
Local Radio: Chiltern Radio, Fox FM (102.6 fm), 3 Counties Radio

CLUB PERSONNEL
Chairman: Phil Smith
Manager: Morrell Maison
Asst Man: Pete Riches Capt: Stuart Blaik

2003-2004
Player of the Year: Sean Griffiths (GK)
Top Goalscorer: M.Cole

COGENHOE UNITED

Secretary: Derek Wright, 6 Brafield Road,Cogemhoe, Northampton NN& 1ND (01604 890737)
Ground: Compton Park, Brafield Rd, Cogenhoe, Northants (01604 890521)
Directions: Turn off A428 at Brafield-on-the-Green, first turn right toCogenhoe or A45 to Billing Aquadrome. Carry on, take second Cogenhoe turn on left
Capacity: 5,000 Seats: 100 Cover: 200 Floodlights: Yes Club Shop: No
Clubhouse: Tues-Fri 7-11, Sat 12-3 & 4-11, Sun 12-3 & 7-10.30 Snacks. Hot food on matchdays
HONOURS UCL Div 1 R-up 86-87 (Res. Div 2 88-89), K.O. Cup 96-97; Daventry Charity Cup 91-92 95-96, (R-up 79-80); Central Northants Comb 80-81 82-83 83-84 (R-up 81-82, Prem Div Cup 82-83 (R-up 78-79), Div 1 up R-up 77-78, Charity Shield 82-83 83-84)
PREVIOUS **League:** Central Northants Combination 1967-84
Ground: Cogenhoe Village PF 1967-84
RECORD **Gate:** 1,000 v Eastenders XI, Charity match 8/7/90
Scorer & Appearances: Tony Smith
Win: 22-0 v Ravensthorpe, Cen. Northants Comb. Prem. Div. KO Cup, 79-80
Defeat: 0-6 v Yardley United, Central Northants Comb. Div. 1, 76-77
Players progressing : Darren Bazeley (Watford 89), Darren Harmon (Notts Co. 89),Matt Murphy (Oxford Utd 93), Gary Leonard (Northampton 1978)
2003-2004 **Player of the Year**: Matthew Poulton **Top Goalscorer:** Rob Goldring

FACT FILE
Founded: 1967 Nickname: Cooks
Sponsors:Hire Trucks Wright & Read Flex Ltd.
Colours: All Royal Blue
Change: All Red
Midweek matchday: Tuesday
Reserves' Lge: UCL Res. Div 1
Programme: 32 pages with Admission
Editor:Roy Quennell (01604 467686)
Local Press: Chronicle & Echo, Northants Evening Telegraph

CLUB PERSONNEL
Chairman:Phil Roach
Vice Chairman: Maurice Jaynot
President: Derek Wright
Comm. Man.: Derek Wright
Manager: Adam Sandy
Assistant Manager: Dave Jones
Physio: Ian Blair

DAVENTRY TOWN

Secretary: Tim Kibblewhite,78 The Medway, Daventry, Northants.
Tel: 01327 703974 (H)

Ground: Elderstubbs Farm, Browns Road, Daventry, Northants
Tel: 01327 706286
Capacity: 2,000 Seats: 250 Cover: 250 Floodlights: Yes

Directions Adjacent to A45 by-pass at top of Staverton Road Sports Complex
Clubhouse: Large bar/kitchen

HONOURS UCL Div 1(3), Lg Cup R-up 92-93, Highest Aggregate Cup.
Northants Junior Cup 36-37 60-61 91-92 Daventry Charity Cup: 1999

PREVIOUS **Leagues:** Northampton Town (pre-1987)/ Central Northants Combination 87-89

BEST SEASON **FA Cup:** Prel. Rd 94-95 03-04
FA Vase: 2nd Rd03-04
RECORD **Attendance:** 850 v Utrecht (Holland) 1989
Local Press : Daventry Weekly Express, Northants Chronicle/Echo
Players Progressing: Martin Aldridge (Northampton)
2003-2004 **Top Scorer:** Daniel Burke **Player of the Year:**:Ian Waldock

FACT FILE
Founded: 1886
Sponsor: Jewson
Colours:White & Black
Change colours:Green /white/green
Midweek Matchday: Tuesday
Reserves League: U.C.L. Reserves Div 2
Programme: 36 Pages
Editor: Tony Perry Tel No:07765 095202

CLUB PERSONNEL
Chairman: Dave Hirons
Vice Chairman: Tony Perry
Treasurert: Jo. Beau mont
President: Mel Knowles
Manager: Mark Shackleton
Assistant Manager.: Billy Rutledge
Captain:Ian Waldock
Physio: Tony Jackson

Life Presidents
A.G.Cox,Frank Hobbs,Anne Hobbs,Malc Hobbs and Dave Liddington.

DEEPING RANGERS

Secretary: Haydon Whitham, 3 Everingham, Orton Brimbles, Peterborough PE2 5XP
Tel:01733 238539 (H) 07736 548500 M)

Ground: Deeping Sports Club, Outgang Road, Market Deeping, Lincs.
Tel: 01778 344701 Website: www.deepingrangers.co.uk
Capacity: 1,000 Seats: 180 Cover: 250 Floodlights: Ys

Directions: From Deeping town centre take the A15 towards Bourne. Turn right at Towngate Tavern following signs to Industrial Estate & club is 1/4 mile on left.
Clubhouse: Bar and lounge. Changing rooms
HONOURS Peterborough & Dist. Lge Div 3 67, Div. 2 69, Div. 1 70, Prem. Div. R-up 95-96 98-99; Lincs Junior Cup 83-84 87-88 88-89, Lincs. Sen. B Cup 00-01, R-up UCL Div 1 R-up 00-01, Fair Play Award 99-00, 00-01
Peterborough FA Senior Cup 91-92 96-97 Minor Cup 67,
PREVIOUS **League:** Peterborough & District
BEST SEASON **FA Vase:** 1st Rd. F.A.Cup **F.A.Cup:** Prelim Rd 02-03 (first season)
Players Progressing:Richard Sendall (Blackpool), Eddie Herbert (Peterborough), Ben Wright (Bristoil, City), Malcolm Christie (Derby County via Nuneaton Borough) and Lewis Kileane (Sheffield Utd.)

FACT FILE
Founded: 1966
Nickname: Rangers
Colours: Claret & blue
Change colours: White/claret/sky blue
Midweek Matchday:Tuesday
Programme: Yes Ed: Ted Whitfield
Tel No: 07747 806376 (M)

CLUB PERSONNEL
President: Albert Lawrence
Chairman: Jon Sandall
Match Sec.:Robin Crowson
01778 348287(H) 07977 971796 (M)
Email: rwc@deeprang.fsnet.co.uk
Manager: Vince Adams
Ast Mans: Paul Kirk & Pat O'Keefe
Captain : Michael Goode

2003-2004
Top Scorer: David Jones
Player the Year: MIchael Goode

DESBOROUGH TOWN

Secretary: John Lee, 85 Breakleys Road, Desborough, Northants NN14 2PT
Tel: 01536 760002 Email Address: johnlee@froggerycottage85.fsnet.co.uk

Ground: Waterworks Field, Braybrooke Rd, Desborough Tel: 01536 761350
Capacity: 8,000 Seats: 250 Cover: 500 Floodlights: Yes Shop: No

Directions: Leave A14 at junction 3 and turn right at first roundabout.
Clubhouse: Lounge & main hall, 2 bars, games room. Every eve. & w/e lunchtimes
HONOURS Utd Co's (Prev. Northants) Lg 00-01 01-02 06-07 20-21 23-24 24-25 27-28 48-49 66-67 (R-up 02-03 10-11 19-20 22-23 79-80, 98-99), Div 2 10-11, 28-9(Res),R-up 09-10 (Res) 26-27(Res) 51-52(Res), KO Cup 77-78 96-97 00-01; Northants Snr Cup10-11, 13-14 28-29 51-52; Desborough Charity Cup 97-98,98-99,99-00, 01-02
PREVIOUS **Leagues:** None
RECORD **Attendance:** 8,000 v Kettering Town
Win: 10-1: v Huntingdon Utd (A) 1957 & v Stewarts & Lloyds (A) 1965, UCL .
Defeat: 11-0 v Rushden Town (A) 1934
Fee received: £8,000 for Wakeley Gage, from Northampton Town
BEST SEASON **FA Vase:** 5th Round 78-79 **FA Cup:** 1st rd Proper 1926-27
Players progressing: Wakeley Gage (Northampton), Jon Purdie & Campbell Chapman (Wolves), Andy Tillson (Grimsby), Matt Murphy (Oxford United)

FACT FILE
Founded: 1896
Nickname: Ar Tarn
Colours: Blue
Change Colours: All red
Previous Leagues: None
Midweek matchday: Tuesday
Programme: 32 pages 30p
Editor:John Lee(01536 760002)
Local Press: Evening Telegraph,Northants Post,Chronicle & Echo,& Harborough Mail
Website: www.artarn.co.uk

CLUB PERSONNEL
Chairman:T.B.A.. Press Officer: Paul Linnett
Manager: Simon Reilly Coach: Gerald Lavin
Assistant Manager: Graham Parker
Physio: Wayne Marlow
Captain: Bryan Jeffrey

2003-2004
P.o.Y.: Mark Pallett
Leading Gaolscorer: Michael Coles

FORD SPORTS DAVENTRY

Secretary: Mick Fryatt, 2 Mayfield Drive, Daventry NN11 5QB
Tel Nos: 01327 876789 (H) 01327 305407(W) 07932 411406 (M)

Ground: Royal Oak Way South, Daventry, Northants Tel: 01327 704914
Capacity: 1,000 Seats: Yes Cover: Yes
Floodlights: Yes

Directions: Enter Daventry on A45 or A361 and follow signs for Royal Oak Way

Clubhouse: Yes -
HONOURS UCL Premier Division 2001-02 ,Div 1 92-93, 95-96, Knockout Cup 97-98, Benevolent Cup R-up 92-93; Daventry Charity Cup 201-02
Highest Agg. Goalscoring Trophy 92-93; Northants Sen Cup R-up 96-97

PREVIOUS **League:** Central Northants Comb

BEST SEASON **FA Vase:** 2nd Round 00-01, 01-02

Player progressing: Martin Aldridge (Northampton)

FACT FILE
Founded: 1968
Nickname: Motormen
Sponsors: Ford Sports & Social Club
Colours: Blue & white/blue/blue
Change : Red & white/red/red
Reserves' Lge: UCL Res Div 2
Programme: 12 pages
Editor: John Hinton(01327 871768)

CLUB PERSONNEL
Chairman: Bob Lowe
Manager: Shane Geary
Assistant Manager:Steve Renshaw
Physio: Ron Dawes
Captain: Ian Pearce

2003-2004
Player of the Year: Simon Williams
Top Goalscorer: Matt Murphy

HARROWBY UNITED

Secretary: Nick Cant, 7 Birkdale Close, Grantham, Lincs. NG31 9RS (01476 403546)
Ground: Harrowby Playing Fields, Harrowby Lane, Grantham Tel: 01476 590822
Capacity: 1,500 Seats: 100 Cover: 150 Floodlights: Yes
Directions: From A1 take B6403, go past A52 roundabout, past Ancaster turn and take road to Harrowby. Continue into Grantham, ground on right opposite Cherry Tree PH.
Clubhouse: Large bar open normal licensing hours

PREVIOUS **Leagues:** Grantham; Lincs; East Mids Regional Alliance (pre-1990)

BEST SEASON **FA Vase:** Preliminary Round 91-92

HONOURS Utd Co's Lg Div 1 91-92 R-Up 02-03 Benev. Cup R-up 91-92, Mids Regional All. 89-90, Lg Cup 89-90, Lincs Snr `B' Cup x2 90-92

Players progressing: Richard Liburd (Middlesbrough), Kevin Pilkington (Mansfield Town)

FACT FILE
Founded: 1949
Nickname: Arrows
Sponsor: Crystal Grantham
Colours: Red & black hoops/black/red & black
Change : Blue & black/black/blue
Programme
16 pages Editor: Gordon Hotson
Tel No: 01529 415799 (H) 07718 736181 (M)

CLUB PERSONNEL
Chairman: Paul Wilson
Vice Chairman: Robert Wilson
Match Secretary: Mick Atter

Manager: Graham Drury
Asst Mgr: Wayne Halicro
Physio: Nigel Burton
Groundsman: Malcolm Brothwell

HOLBEACH UNITED

Secretary: Dennis Sparrow, 112 Langwith Gardens, Holbeach, Lincs. Tel No: 01406 424336 (H)
Ground: Carters Park, Park Road, Holbeach Tel: 01406 424761
Capacity:4,000 Seats: 200 Cover: 450 Floodlights: Yes

Directions: Second left at traffic lights in town centre, 220 yds down road on left.
From King's Lynn; sharp right at traffic lights

Clubhouse: Large bar, lounge & kitchen, open every night **Club Shop:** No

HONOURS Utd Co's Lg Champions 89-90, 02-03 (KO Cup 64-65 89-90), Benevolent Cup, Evans Halshaw Cup 97-98; Lincs Snr Cup `A' 83-84 84-85 86-87 02-03 (Senior Cup `B' 57-58)

PREVIOUS **Leagues:** Peterborough; Utd Co's 46-55; Eastern Co's 55-62; Midland Co's62-63

BEST SEASON **FA Cup:** 1st Rd Proper 82-83, 0-4 v Wrexham (at Peterborough)
FA Trophy: 2nd Qual. Round 69-70 71-72
FA Vase: 5th Round 88-89, 2-4 v Wisbech Town

RECORD **Gate:** 4,094 v Wisbech 1954

20023-2004 **Player of the Year**: Danny Hussey **Top Scorer:** Shaun Keeble
Players progressing: Peter Rawcliffe (Lincoln City)

FACT FILE
Founded: 1929 Nickname: Tigers
Sponsors: Ashwood Homes
Colours: Old gold /black/gold
Change Colours: Sky & Navy blue
Midweek matchday: Tuesday
Reserves' Lge: UCLRes. Div 1
Prog: 44 pages, 50p Editor: Alan Wright
Tel No: 01406 425743 Local Press : Lincs Free Press, Spalding Guardian, Peterborough Evening Telegraph

CLUB PERSONNEL
Chairman: Roger Baker
President: Francis Bissadike
Manager:Shaun Keeble
Assistant Manager: Milton Graham
Captain: Dean Elston

LONG BUCKBY

Secretary: John Partridge, 11 Rockhill Road, Long Buckby, Northants. NN6 7PT
Tel Nos: 01327 842246 (H) and 01327 842438 (Fax)

Ground: Station Rd, Long Buckby Tel: 01327 842682
Capacity: 1,000 Seats: 200 Cover: 200 Floodlights: Yes

Directions: Daventry - Long Buckby rd. 400 yds from station (Northampton -Rugby line)

Clubhouse: Bar & concert room. Open matchdays

HONOURS UCL KO Cup 84-85, UCL Div 2 70-71 71-72, Div 2 KO Cup 71-72, Div 3 69-70; Northants Snr Cup R-up; Daventry Charity Cup 70-75 (incl), 96-97

PREVIOUS **Leagues:** Rugby & D.; Central Northants Comb. (pre-1968)
Name: Long Buckby Nomads 1936

BEST SEASON **FA Vase:** 2nd Rd 85-86
FA Cup: 1st Qualifying Rd 92-93

RECORD **Gate:** 750 v Kettering, Northants Snr Cup Final 1984

Players progressing: Gary Mills (Nottm Forest), Vince Overson (Burnley), Des Waldock (Northampton),Steve Norris (Scarborough)

FACT FILE
Nickname: Bucks
Sponsors: Northampton Elec Dist
Colours: Blue/white/blue
Change colours: Red& Yellow/Red/Red
Midweek matchday: Tuesday
Reserves' Lge: HSUCL Res Div 1
Programme: 8 pages
Editor: Eric Turvey (01327 842682)
Local Press : Chronicle & Echo, Daventry Weekly News

CLUB PERSONNEL
President: Colin St.John
Chairman: Chris Healey
Manager: Aidy NMann
Assistant Manager: Glen Botterill
Physio: Robert Stafferton

NEWPORT PAGNELL TOWN

Secretary: Stephen Handley, 31 Maulden Gardens, Giffard Park,Milton Keynes MK14 5JJ
Tel Nos: 01908 614745 (H) 07867 528475)M)

Ground: Willen Road, Newport Pagnell Tel: 01908 611993
Capacity: 2,000 Seats: 100 Cover: 100 Floodlights: Yes

Directions: Adjacent to A422 Newport Pagnell by-pass

Clubhouse: Open every evening Club Shop: No

HONOURS UCLPrem Div R-Up: 2002-03 Div 1 82-83,01-02 (R-up 91-92, Div 1 Cup 77-78), Daventry Charity Cup R-up 93-9; .League Goalscoroing trophy 2001-02, Berks & Bucks Intermediate Cup 2001-02

PREVIOUS **Leagues:** North Bucks 63-71; South Midlands 71-73

BEST **FA Vase:** 2nd Round 84-85

FACT FILE
Founded: 1963 Nickname: Swans
Sponsors: Brian Currie
Colours: White & green/green/green
Change colours:Sky blue/navy blue/navyblue
Midweek Matchday: Tuesday
Reserves League: United Counties
Programme: 56 pages
Editor: Ernie Print 01908 612918 (H)

CLUB PERSONNEL
Chairman: Dennis Stoyles
Vice Chairman: Ernie Print
President: Ken Inch
Managers: Wayne Spencer & Jimmy Stoyles

NORTHAMPTON SPENCER

Secretary: Nick Hillery, Cowntess Road, Northampton 01604 756580 (H) 07932 612198 (M)

Ground: Kingsthorpe Mill, Studland Rd., Northampton NN3 1NF Tel: 01604 718898
Capacity: 2000 Seats: 100 Cover: 350 Floodlights: Yes

Directions: Turn off Kingsthorpe Road at traffic lights into Thornton Rd., 1st right into Studland Rd. and ground is at the end.

Clubhouse: Open during normal licensing hours. Lounge and bar. **Club Shop:** No

HONOURS: UCL 91-92, r-up 92-93, 97-98, Div. 1 84-85, KO Cup 88-89 93-94, r-up 87-88 96-97 97-98, Benevolent Cup 91-92; Northants Sen. Cup r-up 90-91 93-94.

PREVIOUS **League:** Northampton Town Lge 36-68
Name: Spencer School Old Boys
Grounds: Dallington Park 36-70, Duston High School 70-72

BEST SEASON **FA Cup:** 1st Qual. Rd 93-94, 96-97
FA Vase: 4th Round 87-88, 1-2 v Gresley Rovers

RECORDS **Attendance:** 800 v Nottm. Forest, dressing room opener 1993
Most Appearances: P.Jelley 6221984-2002

Players progressing: Paul Stratford (Northampton), Wakeley Gage (Northampton)

FACT FILE
Founded: 1936
Nickname: Millers
Sponsors: Future Print
Colours: Yellow/green/yellow
Change colours: Claret/white/white
Midweek matchday: Tuesday
Reserves' League: UCL Res Div 1
Programme: 20 pages 50p
Editor: Andy Goldsmith (01604 412382)
Website: www.geocities.com/kirby42000

CLUB PERSONNEL
President: J Sampson
Joint Chairmen:
Graham Wrighting & Jim Connelly
Press Off.: Andy Goldsmith (01604 412382)
Manager: Bob Tansley Coach: Keith Bowen
Ass Manager.Mike Heath Captain:Ross Harris

2003-2004
Top Scorer: Scott Coleman 8
Player of the Year: Ross Harris

POTTON UNITED

Secretary: Derek Inskip, 16 Sheffield Close, Potton, Beds SG19 2NY Tel: 01767 260355

Ground: The Hollow, Biggleswade Road, Potton Tel: 01767 261100

Capacity: 2,000 Seats: 200 Cover: 250 Floodlights: Yes

Directions: Outskirts of Potton on Biggleswade Road (B1040). 3 1/2 miles from Sandy (BR). United Counties buses from Biggleswade **Clubhouse:** Yes

HONOURS Utd Co's Premier Div. 86-87 88-89, Div 1 2003-04 KO Cup 72-73, Benevolent Cup 88-89; Beds Snr Cup(5) 47-49 63-64 75-76 77-78 (R-up 94-95 96-97); Wallspan Floodlit Cup 87-88; Hinchingbrooke Cup 51-52 84-85 89-90 90-91 91-92; Hunts Premier Cup 89-90 91-92 94-95(jt) 96-97; Beds I'mediate Cup 43-44; Southern Comb. Cup 92-93; Nth Beds Charity Cup (12); East Anglian Cup 96-97; Jess Pigott Trophy 96-97

PREVIOUS Leagues: Sth Mids 46-55; Central Alliance 56-61 **Ground:** Recreation Grnd pre-1947

BEST SEASON **FA Cup:** 3rd Qual. Round 74-75, 1-2 v Bedford Town

FA Trophy: 3rd Qual. Round 71-72 72-73 **FA Vase:** 5th Round 89-90, 1-2 v Billericay Town

RECORD **Attendance:** 470 v Hastings Town, FA Vase 1989

FACT FILE

Founded: 1943 Nickname: Royals
Colours: Blue Change : White/black/white
Midweek matchday: Tuesday
Reserves' Lge: Beds. County
Prog: 28 pages, 50p Editor& Match Sec: Mrs Bev Strong 01767 692251 (H)
Local Press: Biggleswade Chronicle,

CLUB PERSONNEL

President: Peter Hutchinson
Chairman: John Shipp Press Off: Bev Strong
Manager: Richard Newman
Assistant Manager: Roy Bloxham

2003-2004

Top Scorer & P.o.Y.:Brett Donnelly

RAUNDS TOWN

Secretary Mick Walden,5 Fernie Way,Wellingborough,Northants NN8 3LB (01933 279561)
Ground: Kiln Park, London Road, Raunds, Northants NN9 6EQ
Tel: 01933 623351, Matchdays 01933 460941
Directions: Take Raunds turning at roundabout on A45 and ground is first left
Nearest station; Wellingborough. Bus services local
Capacity: 3,000 Seats: 250 Cover: 600 Floodlights: Yes
Clubhouse: On ground, open every day
Club Shop: Open matchdays, selling shirts, books programmes, contact Malc York, c/o club
PREVIOUS **Leagues:** Rushden & Dist., Cen. Northants Comb., U.C.L., Southern Lge 96-00
Grounds: Greenhouse Field (until 1948), The Berristers (1948-91)
BEST SEASON **FA Cup:** 4th Qual Rd, 98-99 (0-2 v Enfield),
FA Vase: Semi-final v Arlesey Tn 94-5
FA Trophy: 3rd Rd v Weston-super-Mare 98-99 (2-2, 0-1)
HONOURS UCL Prem Champions 95-96, UCL Div 1 82-83 (R-up 91-92), KO Cup 90-91, 01-02(R-up 83-84 93-94), Res Div 1 88-89 95-96 (R-up 86-87 87-88 89-90 90-91 91-92), Reserve KO Cup 84-85 88-89 93-94; Northants Snr Cup 90-91; Hunts Premier Cup R-up 92-93; Daventry Charity Cup R-up 83-84; Northants Jnr Cup 82-83 91-92 (res) 92-93 (res)
CLUB RECORDS **Attendance:** 1,500 v Crystal Palace, ground opening 23/7/91
Win: 9-0 v Potton 95, 11-2 v Brackley 93 **Defeat:** 0-6 v Baldock 83, vBuckingham 84-85
Career Goalscorer: Shaun Keeble 208 **Career Appearances:** Martin Lewis 355 (+29subs)

FACT FILE

Formed: 1946
Nickname: Shopmates
Colours: Red & black/black/black
Change Colours:All Yellow
Midweek matchday: Tuesday
Reserves' League: UCL Reserve Div. One
Prog: Pages: Varies Price: 50p
Editor: Malc York 01933 311586

CLUB PERSONNEL

Chairman: George Hagan
President: Mahen Perera
Manager:Mark Walters
Asst Manager: Dino Cirelli

ST. NEOTS TOWN

General Sec: John Carroll ,95 St Neots Road, Sandy, Beds SG19 1BP Tel No: 01767 222436(H)
Company Sec: Graham Moffitt **Fixture Sec:** Marion. Izzard (All c/o club)
Ground: Rowley Park, Cambridge Rd, St Neots, Cambs Tel: 01480 470012
Capacity:3,000 Seats: 250 Cover: 850 Floodlights: Yes
Directions: Through the town centre, under the railway bridge, ground is first on the left
Capacity: 2,500 **Seating:** 160 **Covered Standing:** 300 **Floodlights :** Yes
Clubhouse: Yes with Conference,Banqueting and private functions all bookable

HONOURS Hunts Snr Cup(34), UCL 67-68 (KO Cup 67-68 68-69),Bucks Charity Cup 03-4 Metropolitan Lg 49-50(Lg Cup 79-80), South Midlands Lg 32-33, Huntingdonshire Lg 90-91 92-92 92-93 94-95 Hunts.Prem Cup: 2001-02
PREVIOUS **Leagues:** South Midlands 27-36 46-49; United Counties 36-39 51-56 66-69 73-88; Metropolitan 49-51 60-66; Central Alliance 56-60; Eastern Counties 69-73; Huntingdonshire 90-94 **Name:** St Neots & District 1879-1957 **Ground:** Shortlands

BEST SEASON FA Cup: 1st Rd 66-67, 0-2 v Walsall (A)
FA Vase: 5th Rd 2001-02 **FA Trophy:** 2nd Qual. Rd 69-70 72-73

RECORD **Attendance:** 2,000 v Wisbech, 1966
Players progressing: Frank Atkins (Cambridge United), John Gregory (Aston Villa) and Matthew Oakey (Southampton)

FACT FILE

Founded: 1879 Nickname: Saints
Sponsors:Adam Kennedy, Midland Thermal, and Fleet Car Contracts
Colours:Sky & Navy Blue quarters/Navy/Navy
Change colours:Amber&Black/Black/Black
Reserves' Lge: UCL Res Div 1
Programme: Yes Editor: John Carroll (Tel: 01767 222436)
'Saintly Text';Revolving Information screen.
Editor:John Carroll (07752 654496
Web site: www.stneotsfc.com

CLUB PERSONNEL

Chairman: Bob Page Directors:John Carroll Kenneth Harris and Neil Holmes
Commercial Man: Peter Hicks(01733 263656)
Team Manager: Jon Taylor
Asst Mans Luke Brooks & Bobby Roberts

STEWARTS & LLOYDS

Secretary: Dave Foster, 29 Tettenhall Close, Corby, Northants NN198 9PJ
Tel: 01536 746004 (H) 01536 201234 Ext. 5292(W) 07818 264220(M)
email: carol@carol77.fsnet.co.uk

Ground: Recreation Ground, Occupation Road, Corby Tel: 01536 401497
Capacity: 1,500 Seats: 100 Cover: 200 Floodlights: Yes

Directions: The ground is situated on Occupation Rd at the rear of Stewart & Lloyds Leisure Club, next to old Corby Town F.C. ground

Clubhouse: Licensed bar **Club Shop:** No

HONOURS UCL R-up 85-86, Div 1(2) 73-75; UCL KO Cup, Prem 95-96, Div 1 Cup(2)73-75, Div 2 KO Cup(2) 75-77)

PREVIOUS **Leagues:** Kettering Amateur

BEST SEASON **FA Cup:** 1st Rd Q (x 7) **FA Vase:** 3rd Round 96-97, 01-02

RECORD **Goalscorer:** Joey Martin 46 (92-93)

Players progressing : Andy McGowan (Northampton), Willie Graham (Brentford)

FACT FILE
Formed: 1935
Nickname: 'The Foundrymen'
Sponsor: Weldon
Colours: Red & white/black/blackChange Colours:Sky blue & white stripes/black/sky/Navy blue/blue
Midweek matchday: Tuesday
Programme: 12 pages with admission
Editor/Press Officer: Dave Foster

CLUB PERSONNEL
Chairman: Keith Julian
Vice Chairmen: T.B.A
.Manager: Kevin Fox
Asst Manager:Karl Binley
Physio: Kevin Fox

2003-2004
Player of the Year: Greig McIlwain
Top Scorer: Pete Sneddon

STOTFOLD

Secretary: Bill Clegg, 12 Common Rd, Stotfold, Hitchin, Herts SG5 4BX Tel: 01462 730421
Club Email: football@stotfoldfc.freeserve.co.uk
Website:www.stotfoldfc.freeserve.co.uk

Ground: Roker Park, The Green, Stotfold, Hitchin, Herts Tel: 01462 730765
Capacity: 5,000 Seats: 300 Cover: 300 Floodlights: Yes

Directions: A507 from A1, right at lights, right at T-jct.
A507 from Bedford via Shefford, left at lights, right at T-jct

Clubhouse: Clubroom, bar, refreshment bar, dressing rooms, physio room

HONOURS Utd Co's Lg R-up 93-94, KO Cup Winners 98-99 R-up 91-92, Res Div 1 87-88; Sth Mids Lg 80-81 (R-up 55-56 57-58 58-59 59-60 63-64 65-66 77-78), Div 1 53-54, Chal. Tphy 81-82; Beds Snr Cup 64-65 93-94; Beds Premier Cup 81-82; 98-99 Beds I'mediate Cup 58-59; Nth Beds Charity Cup (8) Beds Colts Lg 88-89; Southern Com Cup 94-95 95-96 96-97; Hinchingbrooke Cup R-up 97-98: Win. 99-00: R-up 00-01

PREVIOUS **Leagues:** Biggleswade & District/ North Herts/ South Midlands 51-84

BEST SEASON: **FA Cup:** 00-01 **FA Vase:** 4th Round 94-95, 97-98, 00-01

RECORD **Attendance:** 1,000 v Letchworth Town, FA Amateur Cup
Scorer: Roy Boon **Appearances:** Roy Boon/Dave Chellew

FACT FILE
Founded: 1904-Nickname:The Eagles
Reformed: 1945
Sponsors:Stotfold Mpotor Centre
Colours: Amber/black/black
Change Colours: All White
Midweek matchday: Tuesday
Reserves' League: UCL Reserve Division One
Programme: 22 pages with entry
Editor: Phil Pateman (01462 834581)
Local Press: Comet, Biggleswade Chronicle

CLUB PERSONNEL
Chairman: Phil Pateman
Vice Chairman: Alan Syme
Pres: Ted Splinders Man: Phil Pateman
Asst Manager: Stev Cook
Press Officer: Andy Trulock
Physio: Dave Chivers Captain: Scott Grant

2003-2004
Leading Goalscorer:Wes Byrnet
Player of the Year: Adam Pitcairn

WOODFORD UNITED

Secretary: Pat Ashby, 2 Barrington Court, Ward Road, Brackley. NN13 7LE
Tel Nos: 07969 825636 (M) 01280 840900 (B)

Ground: Byfield Road, Woodford Halse, Daventry, Northants. Tel: 01327 263734
Capacity: 3,000 Seats: 120 Cover: 120 Floodlights: Yes

Directions Off A 361 Daventry to Banbury Rd, on Woodford Road out of Byfield

Clubhouse: Yes

Website: www.wufc.net

PREVIOUS Leagues: Central Northants Comb pre 70, UCL 70-78, Northants Comb

HONOURS Northants Comb 66 67 90 92 95, KO Cup 66 90 93 95 98;
United Counties Lge Div 2 74, KO Cup 74; Daventry Charity Cup 2003-04

2003-2004 **Player of the Year:** Terry Fitton **Top Scorer**: Nick Gordon

FACT FILE
Founded: 1946
Nickname: United
Sponsors: Huber + Suhner Uk Ltd
Colours: All Red
Change Colours:All Blue
Reserves' League: Utd. Co. Res. Div 2
Programme: 16 pages
Editor: Kevin Bowman
Tel No: 01327 263365 (H)

CLUB PERSONNEL
Chairman: Andrew Worrall
Vice-Chairman: R Adams
Manager: Phil Mason
Physio:James Foote
Captain: Adam Knight

WOOTTON BLUE CROSS

Football

Secretary: Bryan Keens, 5 Stewart Court, Wootton, Bedford MK43 9PH (01234 768214)

Ground: Weston Park, Bedford Road, Wootton Tel: 01234 767662
Capacity: 2,000 Seats: 50 Cover: 250 Floodlights: Yes

Directions: Four miles south of Bedford on main road through village at rear of Post Office

Clubhouse: Main hall, bar, darts, pool, bingo. Open every evening and w/e lunchtimes

Club Shop: No

HONOURS Utd Co's Lg Div 2 67-68 69-70 (KO Cup 82-83, Div 2 Cup 64-65), South Midlands Lg 47-48 (R-up 49-50), Beds Sen. Cup 70-71 01-02, Hinchinbrooke Cup (7) Huntingdonshire Premier Cup 2003-04

PREVIOUS **Leagues:** Bedford & District; South Midlands 46-55
Grounds: Recreation Ground, Fishers Field, Rose & Crown, Cockfield

BEST SEASON **FA Vase:** 4th Rd 2002-03**FA Cup:** 2nd Qual. Rd 50-51 (3-4 v Hitchin (H))

RECORD **Gate:** 838 v Luton, Beds Prem. Cup 1988

Player progressing: Tony Biggs (Arsenal) and Steve Corry (Oldham Athletic)

2003-2004 **Player of the Year**: Andy Taylor **Top Goalscorer**: Ben Chamber

FACT FILE

Founded: 1887 Nickname: Blue Cross
Sponsors: Allen Sturges Travel Ltd.Colours: & Bedford Training Group
Colours: Blue & white/blue/blue
Change: Yellow/Red/Yellow
Reserves' League: United Counties Res. Div 1
Midweek matchday: Wednesday
Programme: 24 pages
Editor: Phil Kerins (07771 830269)
Local Press : Bedfordshire Times, Bedford Herald, Beds Express, Beds on Sunday

CLUB PERSONNEL

President:John Clarke Chairman: Bryan Keens
Club Secretary: John Fletcher
Press Officer: Secretary
Manager:Kenny Davison
Assistant Manager:Ian Jackson
Coach: Paul Bryant
Captain: Andy Taylor
Physio: Mel Roberts

YAXLEY

Secretary: Alan Andrews, 3 Farringdon Close, Pterborough. PE1 4RQ
Tel Nos: 01733 342897(H) 07739 497528 (M) email: alan@yaxleyfc.com

Ground: Leading Drove, off The Holme Road, Yaxley Tel: 01733 244928
Capacity: 1,000+ Seats: 150 Cover: Yes Floodlights: Yes

Directions: A1, then A15 at Norman Cross up to traffic lights. Turn right then immediately right again. Follow the road for approx. 1 mile, then turn right into Holme Rd..
The ground is approx. 200 yards on left

HONOURS UCL Div 1 96-97, Benevolent Cup 97-98; Hunts Senior Cup (6 times Inc 03-04)
Peterborough League (2); Peterborough Senior Cup (2);
West Anglia League;Scott-Gatty Cup, Hinchingbrooke Cup 2003-04

PREVIOUS **Leagues:** Peterborough & District, Huntingdonshire, West Anglia

BEST SEASON **FA Vase**: 2nd Round 98-99

FACT FILE

Sponsor: Reads Removals
Colours: Blue/white/blue
Change colours:Red/white/red
Programme: Yes
Editor:Carole Green
(01733 240905 (H)xxxxx**CLUB PERSONNEL**

President: John Dowse
Chairman:Geoff Lenton
Vice Chairman: Malcolm Whaley
Manager:Jimmy Watson
Asst Manager: Gary Cupston

Harrowby United keeper Paul Buttery can only watch as Stotfold's Glen Lamaurafts scores.

Photo: Steve Ayre

AFC Kempston Rovers Photo: Gordon Whittington.

A.F.C.KEMPSTON ROVERS

Secretary: Alan Scott, 26 King William Rd, Kempston, Bedford MK42 7AT
Tel: 01234 854875(H) 07787507282 (M) Email: alan.scott@jotun.co.uk

Ground: Hillgrounds Leisure, Hillgrounds Rd, Kempston, Bedford Tel: 01234 852346.

Capacity: 2,000 Seats: 100 Cover: 250 Floodlights: Yes

Directions: M1 jct 13, A421 to Kempston, Hillgrounds Rd is off the B531 main Kempston-Bedford road. Entrance to Hillgrounds Road is opposite Sainsburys onthe B531 - ground can be found just over twi miles from Sainsburys entrance.British Rail to Bedford Thameslink/Midland then bus No.103 from Bedford town centre stops outside ground

Club Shop: No, but old programmes available from clubhouse

Clubhouse: Open 7-11pm Tues - Sun. & w/e lunch 12-3pm. Sky TV, pool, hot pies & pasties.

PREVIOUS: League: South Midlands 27-53

BEST SEASON FA Vase: 5th Round 88-89

HONOURS U.C.L. Prem. 73-74 R-up 56-57 59-60, Div 1 57-58 85-86, Div 2 55-56 R-up 67-68, KO Cup 55-56 57-58 59-60 74-75 76-77; Beds Senior Cup 08-09 37-38 76-77 91-92 R-up 92-93

FACT FILE

Founded: 1884 Nickname: Walnut Boys
Club Sponsors: Bar Soviet
Colours: Red & white stripes/black/black
Change Colours: Blue & black stripes/white/black
Midweek matchday: Tuesday
Reserve League: Beds FA County Res. Lge
Programme: 24 pages, 40p
Editor: Nina Brown (07866 312788)

CLUB PERSONNEL

President: Mr Doug Jack
Chairman: Russell Shreeves.
Vice Chairman: Kevin Howlett
Press Officer: Secretary
Co-Managers: John Dower and Bob Reed
Coach: Steve Sava

BLISWORTH

Secretary: Kim Barnard, 5 Harrier Park, East Hunsbury, Northampton NN4 0QG
Tel Nos: 01604 660697 (H) 07768 465569 (M)

Ground: Blisworth Playing Field, Courteenhall Road, Blisworth Tel: 01604 858024
Capacity: 1,000 Seats: None Cover: None Floodlights: No

Directions: Courteenhall Road off A43

Clubhouse: Yes -

HONOURS Northants Junior Cup 88-99 League Fair Play Award 2003-4

PREVIOUS **League:** Central Northants Combination 1978-87

Player progressing: Dave Johnson (Northampton 83-84)

FACT FILE

Founded: 1890
Sponsors: Target Furniture, JB King Plant Hire
Colours: Yellow/Green/Yellow
Change colours: All Red
Reserves' Lge: UCL Res. Div. 2
Programme: Yes Editor:Kim Barnard
Tel No: 07768 465569 (M)

CLUB PERSONNEL

Chairman: Pete Edwards
President: L Piggott
Manager: Scott Carlin
Asst Man: Gary Edwards
Captain: Joe Rich

2003-2004

Top Scorer: Matt Collins P.o.Y.: Dan Barnes

BUGBROOKE ST MICHAELS

Secretary: Roger Geary, 31 Kislingbury Rd, Bugbrooke, Northampton NN7 3QG
Tel: 01604 831678

Ground: Birds Close, Gayton Road, Bugbrooke Tel: 01604 830707
Capacity: 2,500 Seats: 120 Cover: Yes Floodlights: Yes

Clubhouse: Yes - normal licensing

Directions: M1.Jct 16 Take A45 to Northampton. At 1st roundabout follow signs to Bugrooke. Through village and club is immediately past last house on left.

CHONOURS Northants Junior Cup 89-90, Central Northants Comb. (6)
UCL Res Div 2 R-up 94-95 U.C.L. Div One Champions 98-99

PREVIOUS **League** : Central Northants Combination 1952-87 **Ground:** School Close

RECORD **Attendance:** 1,156 **Scorer:** Vince Thomas **Appearances:** Jimmy Nord

Players progressing: Kevin Slinn (Watford), Craig Adams (Northampton)

FACT FILE

Founded: 1929
Nickname: Badgers
Sponsors: Unusual Industries
Club colours: Black & white stripes/black/black
Change colours: All Navy Blue
Reserves' Lge: UCL Res. Div. 1
Programme: Eight pages
Editor: Danni Moore (01327 342238)

CLUB PERSONNEL

Chairman: Tom Treacy
President: John Curtis
Manager: Danny Mackintosh.
Assistant Manager:Mark Champlovier
Press Officer: Donna Clancy

BURTON PARK WANDERERS

Secretary: Roger Patrick,16 Church Stret, Burton Latimer, Northants.NN15 5LU
Tel: 01536 724103 (H), 01536 725841 (W)

Ground: Latimer Park, Polwell Lane, Burton Latimer Tel: 01536 725841
Capacity: 1,000 Seats: 100 Cover: 150 Floodlights: No

Directions: Entering Burton Latimer, turn off A6 Station Rd and right into Powell Lane; ground on the right

HONOURS UCL Div 1 R-up, Benevolent Cup R-up
PREVIOUS **League**: Kettering Amateur
RECORD **Attendance**: 253 v Rothwell, May 1989
Players progressing : Shaun Wills (Peterborough), Laurie Dudfield (Leicester City)

FACT FILE
Founded: 1961 Nickname: The Wanderers
Sponsor: Prescott Motors
Colours: All Green
Change Colours: All Navy BlueMidweek matchday: Tuesday
Prog: 16 pages with entry Ed: Secretary
Local Press : Northants Evening Telegraph, Northants Post

CLUB PERSONNEL
Chairman: Roger Patrick
Vice Chairman: Stuart Coles
Manager: Paul CVhisolm & Adam Cann
Physio: Stuart Coles

CORBY COTTINGHAM

Secretary: Mrs D.Doherty, 3 Hempland Close, Great Oakley,Northants,NN18 8LQ
Tel No: 01536 747400 e-mail: dohertypiped@aol.com
Ground: Berryfield Rd, Cottingham Tel: 01536 770051
Capacity: 1,000 Seats: None Cover: Yes Floodlights: No
Directions: One and a half miles from Corby on A427 turn right to Cottingham.At junction of B670 turn left; Berryfield Road 200 yds on right
Clubhouse: Bar & changing rooms

HONOURS UCL Div 1 R-up 97-98; Northants Junior Cup
CLUB RECORDS **Attendance:**
PREVIOUS **Leagues:** Market Harborough; Kettering Amateur; East Midlands Alliance

FACT FILE
Sponsors: B & J Decorators
Colours: All blue
Change colours: Yellow & Green/Green/Yellow
Reserves' Lge: UCL Res. Div. 2
Prog Editor: Vinny Keefe (01536 743790)

CLUB PERSONNEL
Chairman: Vinny Keefe
Vice Chairman: Brian Tilley
Manager: Graham Leech
Assistant Manager: Phil Doherty

EYE UNITED

Secretary: Jim Canty, 25 Sherborne Road, Peterborough.Cambs.PE1 4RG (01733 54883)
Tel No : 01733 54883 Fax: 01733 554883
Match Secretary Roger Pope,4 Meadow Walk, Yaxley, Peterborough PE7 3EX
Tel Nos: 01733 705169 (H) 01733 582072 (W)
Ground: Chestnut Avenue, Dogsthorpe, Eye, Peterborough, Cambs.
Capacity: 1,500 Seats: None Cover: Yes Floodlights: No
Directions From A1 turnonto A1139 Fleton Parkway Jct 7(neraPerkins Engines) at Trafic L Lights left into Eastfield Rd. Turn right at Barclays Bank then right again into Eastern Avenue. Second left is Chestnut Avenue.
Capacity: 100 **Seats** Yes
Floodlights No (Early 2005)
PREVIOUS **League** Peterborough League >2003
HONOURS Peterborough League 2002-03
2003-04 Player of the Year: Phil Anderson
Top Goalscorer: Ashley Favell

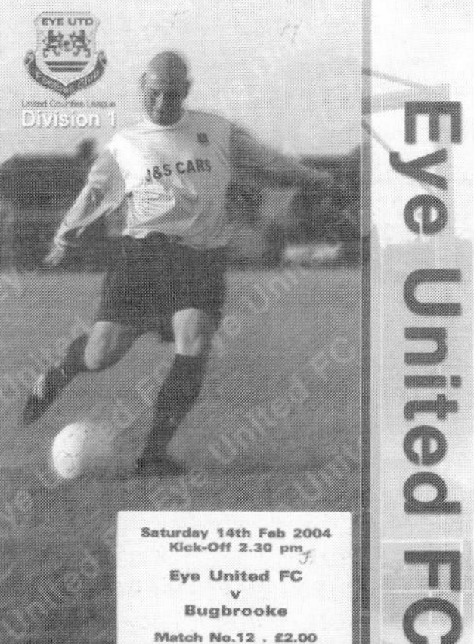

FACT FILE
Founded : Early 1900
Sponsors: J/s Cars
Colours: Sky /Navy Blue/Navy/Navy
Change: Red& Navy or Yellow/Navy/Navy
Midweek Matchday: Wednesday
Reserves Leagie: U.C.L.Reserve Section
Prog: £2.00 Pages 28.Ed: Martin Smith

CLUB PERSONNEL
Chairman: Rodney Willson
Manager: Roger Daniels
Assistantt Manager: Vince Elliott
Captain: Alex Brown
Physio Dave Lamb

EYNESBURY ROVERS

Secretary: Deryck Irons, 12 Hadleigh Close, Bedford MK41 8JW. Tel: 01234 268111
Email Address: patrick.erfc@btinternet.com
Ground: Hall Road, Eynesbury, St Neots Tel: 01480 477449
Capacity: 3,000 Seats: 200 Cover: 500 Floodlights: Yes
Directions: Two miles from A1, on South side of St Neots urban area, near Ernulf School
Clubhouse: Large bar, committee room.Available for private hire **Club Shop:** No

HONOURS UCL Div 1 76-77; Hunts Snr Cup (11), Hunts Premier Cup 50-51 90-91 95-96; Hinchingbrooke Cup (7) 46-4748-52 57-58 66-67; Cambs Invitation Cup 61-62; E Anglian Cup R-up 90-91 91-92;Hunts Scott Gatty Cup 35-36 56-57 84-85 89-90 (R-up 93-94 res); Hunts Jnr Cup 21-22 26-27 UCL Reserves Div 2 Runners-up 2003-04
PREVIOUS **Leagues:** Sth Mids 34-39; UCL 46-52; Eastern Co's 52-63
BEST SEASON **FA Vase:** 3rd Rd 94-95 **FA Cup:** 4th Qual. Rd 54-55, 1-3 v Camb. Utd (A)
RECORD **Gate:** 5,000 v Fulham 1953 (Stanley Matthews guested for Eynesbury)
Players progressing: Chris Turner (Peterborough), Denis Emery (Peterborough)

FACT FILE
Founded: 1897 Nickname: Rovers
Sponsors: Classic Windows
Colours: Royal & white/royal/royal
Change Colours: Yellow & Purple
Midweek matchday: Tuesday
Reserves' League: Utd Counties Res. Div. 1
Prog: 32 pages, 50p Ed: Graham Mills
Website: www.eynesburyrovers.org.uk
CLUB PERSONNEL
Chair: Brian Abraham V-Chair:John Newland
Fix. Sec: Patrick Worrall (901480 431257)
ManagerSteve Galbraith
Assistant Manager: Iain Parr

HIGHAM TOWN

Secretary: Chris Ruff, 23 Queensway, Higham Ferrers, Northants. NN10 8BU Tel: 01933 358862
Ground: Recreation Ground, Vine Hill Drive, Higham Ferrers Tel: 01933 353751
Capacity: 1,000 Seats: Nil Cover: 100 Floodlights: No
Directions: From Kettering 1st right on A6 after junction to St Neots. From Bedford, 3rd left after entering town on A6 from Rushden. Higham is served by London-Bedford-Corby United Counties Coachlines, and their local services Northampton-Raunds and Bedford-Kettering
Clubhouse: During season 8.30-11pm Tues, Thurs, Fri, Sat after games & 12-1.30pm Sun. Light refreshments available after Saturday games
HONOURS UCL Div 1 97-98, R-up 70-71 71-72 89-90 92-93 93-94 94-95 95-96 98-99; Northants Lg 21-22 22-23 R-up 23-24 26-27; Northants Snr Cup 21-22 R-up 30-31 32-33; Maunsell Premier Cup 22-23 33-34
PREVIOUS Leagues: Wellingborough 20-21; Northants (now UCL) 21-36; Rushden 46-50
RECORD Attendance: 5,700 v Chesterfield, FAC 4th qual. rd replay 22-23 **Scorer:** Jon Ogden 187 (Lge) **Appearances**: Brian Harbour 485 **Best Win**: 15-0 v Towcester T (H), UCL Div. 92/93
2003-2004 Player of the Year: Jason Kew **Top Goalscorer:** James Westley 27

FACT FILE
Founded: 1895 Reformed: 1920 & 1946
Nickname: Lankies
Sponsors: Higham News
Colours: Sky & navy/navy/sky
Change colours:Green/black/black
Midweek matchday:: Tuesday
Reserves' Lge: UCL Reserve Div
Programme: 12 pages with admission
Editor: Secretary
CLUB PERSONNEL
Chairman: Richard Williams
Pres: Vijay Patel Vice Chairman: Brian Kirk
Match Sec:Robin James (01234 475563)
Managers: Ben Lord & Toni Catalano
Physio: John Nicholls Captain: Jason Kew

HUNTINGDON TOWN

Secretary: Russell Tezek,39 Thongsley,Huntingdon, Cambs. PE29 1NU
Tel Nos: 01480 394903 (H) 07974 664818 (M)e-mail:
russell.jezek@ntlworld.com
Ground: Jubilee Park, Kings Ripton Road,, Huntingdon, Cambridgeshire (07929 651226)
Capacity: 1,000 Seats: None Cover 100 Floodights : Yes
Directions From A1/A14 junction follow A14 towards Huntingdon. Go across first round about onto A141 and then over three further roundabouts before turning left towards Kings Ripton. Ground is situated half a mile on left.
Clubhouse: Yes **Club Shop:** No
PREVIOUS
LEAGUE: Cambridgeshire League 'A' 2003
HONOURS: Cambridge League Div.1B Champions 1999-00 Hunts. Jumior Cup: 1999-00' 2000-021 01-02 Hunts Scott Gatty Cup: 2001-02

FACT FILE
Colours: Red & Black stripes/Black/Black
Change: Blue & Black Stripes /Blue/Black
Programme Editor: Tony Bowkis
(07979 710715 (H) 07979 710715 (M)

CLUB PERSONNEL
Chairman: Hans Reif
Manager: Andy Ross
Assistant Manager: Tony Bowkis
Captain: Martyn Ray
2003-2004
Player of the Year: Stuart Chapman
Leading Goalscorer: Paul Nevill

IRCHESTER UNITED

Secretary: Glynn Cotter, 3 Bank Hill View, Littlree HarrowdenWellingborough, Northants NN8 5UB Tel Nos: : 01933 402514 (H) 07802 728736 (M)
Ground: Alfred Street, Irchester Tel: 01933 312877
Capacity: 1,000 Seats: None Cover:Yes Floodlights: No
Directions: Off Rushden Road to Wollaston Road, next to recreation ground
Clubhouse: Yes
HONOURS Northants LgDiv 2 30-31 31-32,Northants Jnr.Cup 29-30,33-34,48-49 75-6, Rushden & Dis.t Lg 28-29 29-30,32-33,33-34 36-3746-47 50-51 51-52 56-57
BEST SEASON **FA Cup:** Prel. Rd 34-35
FA Vase: Preliminary Round 77-78
PREVIOUS **Leagues:** Rushden & District 1936-69

FACT FILE
Colours: Red & Black stripes,black,red
Change :Black&White stripes,black,black
Reserves' Lge: UCL Res. Div. 2
Programme: No

CLUB PERSONNEL
Chairman: Geoff Cotter
Manager: Steve Whitney
Physio: Mick Howarth

NORTHAMPTON O.N. CHENECKS

Secretary: Trevor Cadden, 26 Greenfield Road, Spinney Hill, NNorthampton NN3 2LW
Tel Nos: 01604 407070 (H) 078887 652910 (M)

Ground: Old Northamptonians Sports Ground,Billing Road,Northampton Tel: 01604 34045

Capacity: 1,350 Seats: Yes Cover: Yes Floodlights: No

Directions: South ring road, exit A43 Kettering. Turn left at the lights, to the top of hill and the ground is 200 yds on right

Clubhouse: Yes

HONOURS UCL Div 1 77-78 79-80, Northants Jnr Cup R-up 93-94

PREVIOUS **Leagues:** N'pton Town (pre-1969)

CLUB RECORDS **Appearances:**

FACT FILE

Founded: 1946
Colours:All Navy Blue
Change colours: All red
Reserves' League: UCL Res Div 1
Midweek Matchday:
Prog.: 16 pages with entry
Editor: Des McGrath (07748 593423)

CLUB PERSONNEL

Chairman: John Wilson Vice Chair: Eddie Slinn
President: Claude Hasdell
Fixture Sec: Des McGrath (01604 644657)
Manager: Peter Green
Asst Manager: Claude Hasdell
Physio: John Goodger

OLNEY TOWN

Secretary: Andrew Baldwin, 49 Midland Road, Olney, Bucks MK46 4BP
Tel: 01234 711071 (H) 07932 141623 (M) email: a.baldwin@cranfield.ac.uk
Club Website: www.olneytownfc.com

Ground: East Street, Olney , Bucks. Tel: 01234 712227
Capacity: 2,000 Seats: None Cover: Yes Floodlights: No

Clubhouse: Yes

Directions: Enter Olney on A509 from Wellingborough, 100yds on left enter East St, the ground is 200 yds on left

HONOURS UCL Div 1 72-73, Berks & Bucks I'mediate Cup 92-93

PREVIOUS **Leagues:** Nth Bucks, Rushden & District

FACT FILE

Founded: 1903
Sponsors: Paulo's
Colours: Green&white/green/green &white
Change colours: Black&white/white/white
Programme: 8 pages - Editor: Mick Smith

CLUB PERSONNEL

Chairman: Malcom Thomas
President: Trevor Church
Manager: Andy Griffin Coach: Neil Bunker
Asst Manager: Pete Munting
Captain: Guy Stewart Physio: Peter Munting

2003-2004

Player of the Year: Asa Aldridge
Top Goalscorer: David Lancaster

Olney Town Photo: Gordon Whittington

ROTHWELL CORINTHIANS

Secretary: Mark Budworth, 5 Jackson way, Kettering, Northants. NN15 7DL
01536 521973 (H) 07730 416960(M) email: mbudworth@budworthbrown.com

Ground: Seargents Lawn, Desborough Road, Rothwell, Northants.
Tel: 01536 418688
Capacity: Unknown Seats: 50 Cover: 200
Floodlights: Yes

Directions A6 towards Desborough, on right opposite Greening Road

Club House: Yes -

Club Shop: No

HONOURS East Midlands Alliance (2)

PREVIOUS **League** East Midlands Alliance

FACT FILE

Founded: 1930's
Nickname: Corinthians
Sponsor: Springfir Estates
Colours: Red& white / black/black
Change colours: Blue & white/blue/blue
Programme: Yes Editor: Nick Garley
Tel No: 01536711694

CLUB PERSONNEL

Chairman: Graham Dawson
Vice Chairmperson: May Clelland
President: Terry Smith
Manager: Frank Iglapi
Physio: John Dickson

SILEBY RANGERS

(formerly Northampton Sileby Rangers)

Secretary: David Battams, 12 Geldock Road, Little Billing, Northampton NN3 9PH
Tel Nos: 01604 412654 (H) 07970 910463 (M)

Ground: Fernie Fields Sports Ground, Moulton, Northampton Tel: 01604 670366
Capacity: 700 Seats: 100 Cover: Yes Floodlights: No

Directions: Approach from A43 Kettering - follow signs to Northampton as far as the large roundabout with traffic lights (Round Spinney roundabout). Take the 5th exit signposted to Moulton Park and after a quarter of a mile turn left in the ground. Approach from A45 - leave A45 at the exit signposted to A43 Ring Road/Kettering/Corby and take the dual carriageway for around 2 miles to the second roundabout. Take the 2nd exit signposted to Moulton Park and after a quarter of a mile turn left into the ground.

Clubhouse: Large bar with food

HONOURS UCL Div 1 93-94,02-03 Benevolent Cup R-up 93-94; Northants Jnr Cup 93-94 96-97 97-98; 02-03 Northampton Town Lg 88-89 89-90

PREVIOUS **League:** Northampton Town (pre-1993)
Name: Northampton Vanaid >00 Northampton Sileby Rangers 2000-2004
RECORD **Attendance:** 78

FACT FILE
Founded: 1968 Nickname: Sileby
Sponsors: Travis Perkins
Colours: Red/Black/Black
Change colours:Yellow/Navy Blue/ Yellow
Midweek games: Tuesday
Programme Editor: Terry Whenham
Tel No: 07764 158569 (M)

CLUB PERSONNEL
Chairman: Rob Clarke Vice Chairman: G,Law
President: N.Gibbs
Manager: Gary Petts
Asst Man: Pete Robinson
2003-04
P.O.Y: Paul Bennett
Top Scorer: Andy Haines

SLEAFORD TOWN

Secretary: Ian Hughes, 21 Hawthorne Drive, Sleafiord, Lincs. NG34 7GZ
Tel Nos: 01529 415687 (H) 07748 434445 (W) 07748 434445 (M)
e-mail: ijh@kesteven.fslife.co.uk

Ground: Royal Air Force Cranwell Tel No: 07748 434445

Capacity: Seats: **Cover:** **Clubhouse:** **Floodlights:** No

Directions:

PREVIOUS **Leagues: Lincolnshire**

HONOURS Lincolnshire League Premier Division Champios: 80-81,03-04, Div 2 68-69
League Cup: Winners 80-01 89-90 90-91 Lg Supplementary Cup Winners (3)
League Charity Cup Winners 73-74
Lincolnshire Senior Cup 'B' Winners 85-86 99-00 01-02 02-03 03-04

FACT FILE
Formed:
Sponsors:
Colours: Green with black band/Black/Black
Change colours: All Red
Midweek Matches:
Reserves' Lge:
Programme Editor:
Web sire: www.sleafordtownfc.co.uk

CLUB PERSONNEL
Chairman: Kevin Scrupps
President: Dave Kirby
Manager: Brian Rowland
Captain: Paul Ward

ST. IVES TOWN

Secretary: Chris George, 16 Canberra Drive,St Ives. Terl Nos: 01480 382257 (H) 07779 304758M) E-mail: stivestownfc@hotmail.com

Ground: Westwood Road, St. Ives, Cambs.Tel: 01480 463207

Directions: From Huntingdon: A1123 thru Houghton, right at 2nd lighs intoRamsey Rd, after quarter mile turn right opp. Fire Station into Westwood Road
From A604: Follow Huntingdon signs past 5 r'bouts, left into Ramsey Rd at lights then follow as above.
Capacity: 5,000 Seats: 130 Cover: 300 Floodlights: Yes

Clubhouse: Bar and entertainment room. Normal licensing hours.

HONOURS Hunts Snr Cup 00-01 11-12 22-23 25-26 29-30 81-82 86-87 87-88, Cambs League 22-23 23-24 24-25.

PREVIOUS **Leagues:** Cambs; Central Amtr; Hunts; P'boro. & D. (pre-1985).
Ground: Meadow Lane

RECORD **Gate**: 400 v Saffron Walden Town, FA Vase.

FACT FILE
Founded: 1887Nickname: Saints
Colours: White & black/black/black
Change colours: Blue/black/black
Midweek matchday: Tuesday
Reserves' Lge: Cambs League
Programme Editor:Neville Nania
Tel: 01480 494293 (H) 07850 709837 (M)

CLUB PERSONNEL
Chairman: Nevile Nania
Manager: Warren Everdell Asst Man: Jez Hall
Match Sec.:Peter Claridge,Tel Nos: 01480 466873 (H) 07889 161741 (M)

2003-2004
P.o.Y.: John Lee Top Scorer: Bobby Peacock

THRAPSTON TOWN

Secretary: Mark Brown, 3 Drayton Place, Irthlingborough, Northants. NN9 5TD
01933 388671 (H) 07885 640947 (M) email: mark @datsprint.co.uk

Ground: Chancery Lane, Thrapston, Northants Tel: 01832 732470
Capacity: 1,000 Seats: Yes Cover: Yes Floodlights: No

Directions: Chancery Lane off A605 in town centre

Clubhouse: Yes

HONOURS Northants Junior Cup 87-88, 98-99, 03-04
Kettering Am Lg 70-71 72-73 73-74 77-78
UCL Div1 Runners -Up 99-00

PREVIOUS **League:** Kettering Amateur (pre-1978)

2003-2004 **Player of the Year :** Keith Morsen **Top Goalscorer:** Scott Atkinson

FACT FILE
Founded: 1960 Nickname: Venturas
Sponsor: IKEA
Colours: All Blue
Change colours: All Yellow
Programme: Yes Editor: Barry Carter
Tel No: 07771 976784

CLUB PERSONNEL
Pres:Dave Morson Chairman: Dave Harris
Vice Chairman: Barry Carter
Manager: Lee Howard
Asst Managers: Barry Carter,Mark Brown & Keith Morson
Physio: Dave Timlin
Captain: Keith Morson

WELLINGBOROUGH WHITWORTHS

Secretary: John Betts, 2 St Mary's Road, Bozeat, Wellingborough, Northants. NN29 7JU
Tel: 01933 664253 (H) 07789 997025 (M) email: johnsmbetts@aol.com

Ground: London Road, Wellingborough, Northants. Tel: 01933 227324
Capacity: 700 Seats: None Cover: Yes Floodlights: No

Directions: Off London Road at Dog & Duck public house

Clubhouse: Yes -

PREVIOUS **Leagues:** Rushden & Dist.; E. Mids All. (pre-1985)

HONOURS Rushden & District Lg 76-77; Northants Jun Cup 96

FACT FILE

Sponsor: Whitworth Brothers
Colours: All navy blue
Change colours: Purple and Navy Blue
Reserves' Lge: UCL Res Div 2
Programme: No

CLUB PERSONNEL

Chairman: Mark Herring
Vice Chairman: Dave Woodley
President: Terry Faulkner
Manager: Mark Desborough
Physio: Andrew King

Huntingdon Town have a gosl disallowed in their first match last season against Thrapston Town.
Photo: Gordon Whittington

WESSEX LEAGUE

SPONSORED BY: SYDENHAMS

President: Cyril Hurlock

Chairman: Alf Peckham **Vice Chairman:** Ray Barnes

Hon. Secretary: Ian Craig, 56 Ecton Lane, Anchorage Park, Hilsea, Portsmouth, Hampshire PO3 5TA Tel: 02392 671155

Fax: 02392 651147

The Clubs present at the AGM gave the backing to the Committee to proceed with plans to run a much awaited Second Division beginning at the start of the 2004-2005 season, and a number of Clubs from the Hampshire and Dorset Leagues were quickly showing an interest in joining the new Division, while the Football Association cofirmed that our League would become steps Five and Six in the new Football Pyramid Structure to begin at the start of the new season.

The 2003-2004 campaign started with the early rounds of the F.A.Cup and the pick of the results were **Andover**'s win over Southern League Chatham Town and **Winchester City**'s win over Banstead Athletic from the Ryman League.

Indeed the early season fixtures were dominated by FA Competition Cup matches with **Andover** winners over Sussex County League side Arundel in front of 278 spectators, **Lymington & New Milton** defeating Southern League Erith & Belvedere, **Wimborne Town** beating Western League side Backwell United and **Winchester City** winners over Ryman League Metropolitan Police reaching the 2nd Qualifying Round of the FA Challenge Cup.

However, **Lymington & New Milton** were the League's only survivor in reaching the Third Qualifying Round of the FA Challenge Cup defeating Clevedon United 8-2. **Winchester City** were narrowly defeated by Southern League Premier Division side Chippenham Town 2-1 in front of a crowd of 461, **Andover** lost 3-2 to Southern League Midland Division side Cirencester Town and **Wimborne Town** to another Midland Division side Mangotsfield United by 3-0.

Lymington & New Milton continued to fly the league flag by beating Hellenic League side Highworth Town 2-0 but met their match in Southern League Salisbury City in the 4th Qualifying Round FA Cup

FA Vase proved to be a happy hunting ground for Wessex clubs last season and nine clubs qualified for the Second Round and success continued with **Fareham Town, Andover, BAT, Moneyfields, Gosport Borough** and **Thatcham Town**, joining **Christchurch, Lymington & New Milton** and **Winchester City**, who received byes due to their success last season.

Three of our last four clubs in the FA Vase reached the last sixteen and then continued their exciting progress into the quarter finals. **Andover** defeated North Leigh 1-0 after extra time and then enjoyed a 3-1 home win over Leighton Town before 650, their biggest crowd for years. Whilst **Winchester City** won 2-1 at high flying North West Counties club Mossley and then returned with a fine 3-0 victory from Eastern Counties Wroxham. **Lymington & New Milton** were defeated at home 3-2 by Bitton but **Gosport Borough** beat Oadby Town 2-1 after extra time and then after a draw at Studley they defeated them back in Hampshire.

Winchester City reached the Vase Semi Final with a 5-1 win over fellow Wessex League side **Andover** in front of a crowd of 933, a record for the Denplan City ground, while **Gosport Borough** were defeated by Bideford Town 3-0 with a watching crowd of 1,261.

A record home crowd of 1,818 saw **Winchester City** beat Bideford Town in the second leg of the FA Vase 4-0 to achieve a place in the Final where they were to meet last season's beaten finalists AFC Sudbury at St Andrews, Birmingham.

Going into the final month of the season the First Division looked to be a two horse race between Wimborne Town and Winchester City and the latter finally beat Wimborne Town 2-0 in front of a crowd of 444 to lift the Division One Trophy at the first attempt.

At the bottom only five points separated **Whitchurch United, Downton, Blackfield & Langley, Alton Town** and **Bournemouth**. While **Bemerton Heath Harlequins Reserves** won the Combination Division title even by losing at **Lymington & New Milton Reserves** on the last day, with their nearest rivals **Gosport Borough Reserves** also losing.

In the Russell Cotes Cup semi final **Winchester City** lost 2-3 to Havant & Waterlooville, who met **Christchurch** in the final. **AFC Totten Reserves** were defeated 3-0 by Hampshire Premier League Champions VT FC in the final of the Southampton Senior Cup at St Mary's Stadium, while **Andover** beat local neighbours **Andover New Street** 2-1 to win the North Hants Senior Cup, while **Fareham**

Town played Conference League Club Farnborough Town in the final of the Hampshire Senior Cup also at the St Mary's Stadium and went down by 2-1, a penalty six minutes from time, and the newly formed Two Counties Cup was won by **Wimborne Town**, and lastly in the final of the Russell Cotes Cup **Christchurch** lost 2-1 to Havant & Waterlooville.

In the League Cup Finals **Winchester City** defeated **Bemerton Heath Harlequins** 2-0 to complete a League and Cup double while the Combination Cup had to be re-arranged due to inclement weather when **Cowes Sports Reserves** defeated **Eastleigh Reserves 1-0 after extra time.**

The season ended on a high when **Winchester City** played extremly well to defeat AFC Sudbury from the Ridgeons Eastern League 2-0 at St Andrews, Birmingham and become the first Hampshire side to win the FA Vase.

It was a glorious end to a memorable season and let's hope there are many more exciting days ahead for our extended competition.

Compiled from a report by Ian J Craig - Hon. League Secretary

FINAL LEAGUE TABLE 2003-04

DIVISION ONE	P	W	D	L	F	A	Pts
1. Winchester City	42	35	3	4	151	35	108
2. Wimborne Town	42	31	6	5	105	45	99
3. Gosport Borough	42	29	5	8	96	40	92
4. Lymington & New Milton	42	29	3	10	98	38	90
5. AFC Newbury	42	26	4	12	94	53	82
6. Andover	42	25	4	13	100	65	79
7. Fareham Town	42	24	6	12	71	38	78
8. AFC Totton	42	18	10	14	76	55	64
9. Brockenhurst	42	19	7	16	49	74	64
10. Thatcham Town	42	16	10	16	70	72	58
11. Christchurch	42	17	6	19	63	62	57
12. Bemerton Heath Harlequins	42	16	7	19	77	79	55
13. Hamble ASSC	42	16	7	19	51	76	55
14. Cowes Sports	42	15	8	19	51	59	53
15. BAT Sports	42	13	7	22	57	68	46
16. Portland United	42	14	4	24	58	86	46
17. Moneyfields	42	11	8	23	51	83	41
18. Alton Town	42	12	2	28	55	110	38
19. Downton	42	8	7	27	43	106	31
20. Bournemouth	42	8	6	28	41	86	30
21. Blackfield & Langley	42	7	7	28	51	99	28
22. Whitchurch United	42	7	5	30	38	117	26

		1	2	3	4	5	6	7	8	9	10	11	12	13	14	15	16	17	18	19	20	21	22
1	AFC Newbury		2-1	4-0	1-3	2-4	3-2	1-0	5-1	3-0	2-5	3-2	3-1	2-1	4-3	1-2	0-1	4-0	4-1	1-2	4-0	1-0	1-0
2	AFC Totton	1-2		5-0	1-1	2-0	1-1	3-0	2-0	5-0	2-3	2-0	2-2	1-0	3-2	1-1	1-3	1-1	3-1	1-2	5-1	2-2	0-4
3	Alton Town	3-0	0-4		1-0	2-2	1-3	2-3	3-2	1-2	2-0	1-2	2-1	1-2	1-4	1-2	0-2	0-3	3-2	2-3	2-1	0-5	2-5
4	Andover	1-4	0-2	2-3		4-1	1-1	4-0	2-3	5-1	5-3	2-2	7-2	0-2	2-0	6-0	3-1	3-1	3-1	3-1	4-0	2-3	2-3
5	BAT Sports	1-1	2-1	3-0	1-2		1-3	2-2	3-1	0-2	1-1	0-2	3-0	0-0	0-1	0-1	0-1	2-2	3-0	1-2	3-2	1-2	2-1
6	Bemerton H.H.	3-1	0-2	2-4	1-2	4-1		3-1	3-0	0-2	2-1	4-2	2-2	1-2	2-2	3-0	0-5	5-1	4-4	2-1	2-3	1-2	3-6
7	Blackfield & L.	0-3	1-2	0-2	1-1	0-1	1-2		3-2	0-1	2-2	2-0	2-2	1-2	0-2	2-3	1-6	1-2	3-0	1-1	0-0	1-6	2-7
8	Bournemouth	1-0	1-1	4-1	0-2	1-2	0-2	0-0		0-1	1-2	2-1	0-3	0-1	0-1	0-0	1-0	0-1	1-0	2-2	3-2	1-2	1-3
9	Brockenhurst	2-7	1-1	2-0	2-0	0-2	0-0	2-1	3-2		1-1	0-2	2-0	0-3	1-1	0-3	2-1	2-1	1-1	0-0	1-0	2-4	0-4
10	Christchurch	1-2	3-1	2-0	1-2	2-0	2-0	3-1	2-0	0-1		1-2	0-2	0-0	0-1	0-2	1-0	2-0	5-1	3-0	5-1	1-2	0-5
11	Cowes Sports	0-3	0-2	1-0	0-1	2-2	3-2	2-3	3-2	0-1	0-0		0-2	0-2	0-0	1-0	1-2	1-1	0-1	6-3	1-0	0-1	1-4
12	Downton	0-6	0-5	2-2	1-2	1-0	1-0	1-0	0-3	0-4	1-4	0-1		2-2	0-1	1-2	1-3	2-2	0-1	2-0	1-4	0-3	1-3
13	Fareham Town	1-2	2-0	5-1	4-1	2-1	2-2	2-1	4-0	1-1	1-0	1-0	2-0		0-1	5-0	1-2	2-1	2-1	2-0	4-0	1-2	0-1
14	Gosport Boro'	0-1	2-0	5-0	3-0	1-0	3-1	4-1	6-1	3-0	1-1	3-1	4-1	2-1		3-0	3-2	2-0	6-0	1-0	2-0	0-1	0-2
15	Hamble ASSC	3-2	5-3	2-4	1-0	4-2	0-1	1-0	3-0	0-1	1-0	0-2	0-0	0-3	0-6		0-2	3-0	2-1	1-2	1-1	1-1	0-3
16	Lymington & NM	1-0	3-1	2-0	1-2	3-2	3-0	5-1	2-0	2-1	4-1	1-1	9-0	3-0	2-3	4-0		1-0	3-0	0-0	7-0	2-0	0-1
17	Moneyfields	2-1	1-2	0-5	0-4	2-1	4-2	1-2	2-1	0-1	1-2	0-2	0-2	2-1	1-1	2-1	3-2		0-2	1-1	6-1	1-2	0-4
18	Portland Utd	0-3	2-0	6-1	0-3	2-1	1-3	3-2	3-2	5-2	3-1	0-1	2-1	0-1	1-2	1-1	0-1	2-0		1-1	2-0	1-2	1-6
19	Thatchanm T.	0-0	1-1	3-1	2-4	0-2	2-1	5-2	4-0	2-0	1-2	2-0	5-2	0-0	2-3	5-1	2-3	1-1	2-1		1-0	1-2	0-1
20	Whitchurch Utd	1-2	0-1	1-0	0-4	0-1	0-2	0-4	0-0	2-3	3-0	1-4	3-2	0-3	0-6	3-2	1-1	2-2	1-4	2-5		1-4	0-8
21	Wimborne T.	2-2	2-1	4-1	1-2	2-1	3-2	4-2	2-2	8-0	4-0	1-1	6-1	1-0	2-1	1-1	3-0	3-2	3-0	5-2	0-1		0-2
22	Winchester City	1-1	1-1	7-0	9-3	5-2	3-0	4-1	4-0	3-1	1-0	1-1	4-0	5-1	6-1	2-1	1-2	4-1	3-0	8-1	5-0	1-2	

LEAGUE CUP

FIRST ROUND

BAT Sports	v	Andover	0-3
Blackfield & Langley	v	Whitchurch United	2-3
Bournemouth	v	Moneyfields	1-2*
Fareham Town	v	Cowes Sports	3-1*
Gosport Borough	v	Lymington & New Milton	3-2
Hamble ASSC	v	Christchurch	0-3

SECOND ROUND

AFC Newbury	v	Wimborne Town	2-3
Alton Town	v	AFC Totton	1-3
Andover	v	Winchester City	2-5
Christchurch	v	Fareham Town	2-1*
Downton	v	Bemerton Heath Harlequins	0-2
Moneyfields	v	Brockenhurst	0-1
Thatcham Town	v	Portland United	5-2
Whitchurch United	v	GosportBorough	0-1

QUARTER-FINALS

Bemerton Heath H.	v	Thatcham Town	2-1
Christchurch	v	AFC Totton	1-2
Gosport Borough	v	Brockenhurst	1-3*
Wimborne Town	v	Winchester City	1-4

SEMI-FINALS (played over two legs)

			1st	2nd
AFC Totton	v	Bemerton Heath	1-2	2-3
Brockenhurst	v	Winchester City	1-1	2-4

THE FINAL (3rd May at Lymington & New Milton)

Winchester City v Bemerton Heath Harlequins 2-0

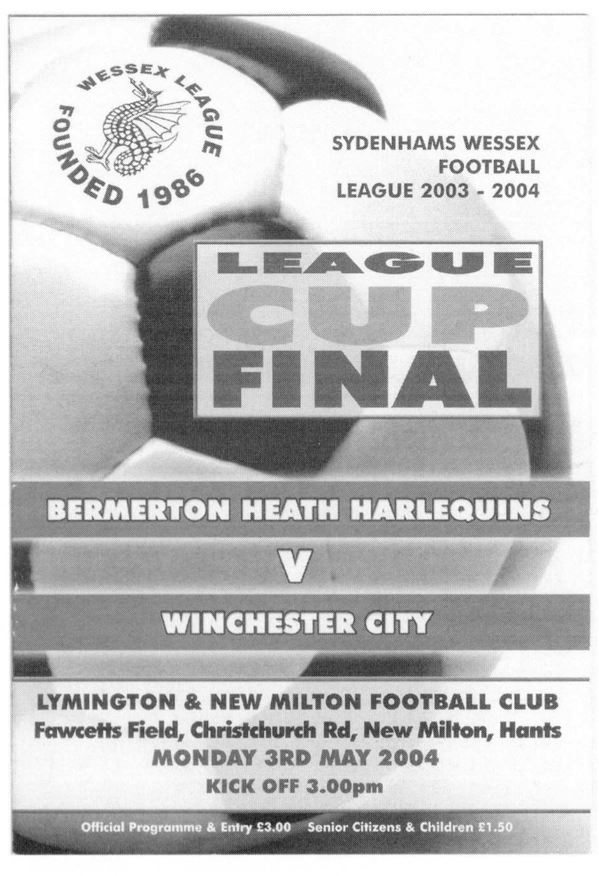

WESSEX LEAGUE
FOUNDED 1986
SYDENHAMS WESSEX
FOOTBALL
LEAGUE 2003 - 2004
LEAGUE
CUP
FINAL
BERMERTON HEATH HARLEQUINS
V
WINCHESTER CITY
LYMINGTON & NEW MILTON FOOTBALL CLUB
Fawcetts Field, Christchurch Rd, New Milton, Hants
MONDAY 3RD MAY 2004
KICK OFF 3.00pm
Official Programme & Entry £3.00 Senior Citizens & Children £1.50

A.F.C. NEWBURY

Secretary: Ron Renton,16 River Gardens,Purley on Thames, Berks.RG8 8BX
Tel Nos: 01635842588 (H) 07811 462291 (M) e-mail: ronrenton54@hotmail.com
Ground: Faraday Road, Newbury, Berks. RG14 2AD Tel: 01635 523222

Directions: A34 to Robin Hood roundabout, then A4 towards Reading. Right at lights after 100 yards into Faraday Road. Ground at end of road.

Clubhouse: Yes.
Honours:

Previous names: The club was formed in 1996 from the resources of Ecchinswell Football Club (1906), Shaw Boys and Belles Junior Football Club (established in 1972) and Wickham U17 Youth Team. The club operates from Faraday Road Stadium and this is the only link with Newbury Town F.C.

Club Records **Attendance:**
Best Season FA Vase:

FACT FILE
Formed: 1996
Colours: Red/white/red
Change: Green/black/green
Reserves:Wessex Combination
Midweek Matches: Tuesday
Website (under construction)
www.@fcnewbury.com
Programme - Price: Pages:
Editor:

CLUB PERSONNEL

Chairman: Steve Hartley
Tel No: 01488 683783 (H)

Manager: Guy Whittingham

A.F.C. TOTTON

Secretary: Charles Ducellier, 21 Stanley Road, St Denys, Southampton, Hants SO17 2LW Tel No: 02380 583869) (H)
GROUND: Testwood Park, Testwood Place, Totton, Southampton Tel:023 8086 8981
Directions: Five minutes walk from Totton station. Turn off at roundabout in Totton centre into Library Road.Then first left and second right into Testwood Place.

Capacity: 2,500 Seats: 200 Cover: 250 Floodlights: Yes Club Shop: No

Clubhouse: Open for matches and training sessions. Burgers, sandwiches, tea,coffee, biscuits etc available (matchdays only)

HONOURS : Hampshire League 81-82, 84-85 Russell Cotes Cup 98-99
Jewson Wessex League Cup: 1889-90, 2002-2003

PREVIOUS : League: Hants 1886-1986
Name: Totton FC until merger with Totton Athletic 1979
Grounds: Downs Park; Mayfield Park

RECORD: Gate: 600 v Windsor & Eton, F.A. Cup 4th Qual Rd 82-83

FACT FILE
Founded: 1886
Nickname: Stags
Colours: Blue & white stripes/blue/blue
Change colours: Red&Black/Black/Black
Midweek Matches: Tuesday
Programme: 30 pages 50p
Editor:Malcolm Tombs(02380 871790)

CLUB PERSONNEL

Chairman: Richard Mayton
President: D Maton
Press Officer: P Chilcott (023 80860453)
Manager: Stuart Ritchie
Captain: Matthew Parnell
Physio:Kim Andrews

2003-2004
Top Scorer: Martin Whiddett
Player of the Year:Daniel Barker

ALTON TOWN

Secretary: Tony Hillman, 19a Beechwood Rd, Alton, Hants GU34 1RL
Tel: 01420 87103 (H) 07796 184095 (M)

Ground: Alton/Bass Sports Ground, Anstey Rd, Alton
Tel: 01420 82465
Capacity: 2,000 Covered Seating: 200 Floodlights: Yes
Clubhouse:
Directions: A31 from Winchester to Alton, through town and ground is on junction with Anstey Road and Anstey Lane.

Previous League: Hampshire League >2002

Senior Honours: Hampshire Premier Div. Champions 2001-02 Hants.Senior Cup (4) 1958, 1969, 1972, 1978 Intermediate Cup 1949 Russell Cotes Cup Winners 1949,1957, 1965, 1970 (4) R-up 1933 Hampshire League Div 3 1948 Div 2 1949, 1955, 1987 Div1 1958,1999 Athenian League Div2 Winners 1974 Lg. Cup Winners 1978 Aldershot Challenge Cup:R-up 1986, 1988

2003-2004 **Top Scorer:** Dave Bridger **P.o.Y.:** Mick Douglas

FACT FILE
Formed: 1991
Colours:White/black/black
Change colours: Red & black/white/white.
Midweek home matchday: Tuesday
Programme - Price:£1.00 Pages: 20

CLUB PERSONNEL
Chairman: Jim McKell
Scotch Corner, Huntsmead, Alton,
Hants. GU34 2SF
Tel: 01420 82725 (H) 07740 099374 (M)
Manager: Mick Doyle
Assistant Manager:. Clive Ventham
Captain: Steve Larvan

ANDOVER

Secretary: Chris Jeremy, 23 Stubbs Court, Artists Way, Andover, Hants SP10 3QR
Tel: 01264 361973
Ground: Portway Stadium, West Portway Ind. Estate, Andover SP10 3LF Tel: 01264 391341
Directions: From the Andover By-pass A303 follow signs to Portway Ind. estate. On exiting the A303 turn right at r/about & over bridge, bear off left at next mini r/about and after 150yds turn right onto estate. Straight on until you enter Hopkinson Way, ground on left 4-500 yds
Capacity: 3,000 Cover: 250 Seats: 250 Floodlights: Yes
Clubhouse: Open matchdays & private function Club Shop: No Metal Badges: Yes
HONOURS Wessex Lg 00-01 R-up 94-95,97-98 Western Lg R-up 69-70 70-71; Hants Lg 13-14 24-25 33-34 44-45 48-49 50-51 61-62 (R-up 42-43), Northern Div 13-14, Div 2 R-up 37-38; Salisbury & Dist Lg (7) Hants Sen Cup (5); Russell Cotes Cup 23-24 31-32 37-38 44-45 52-53 58-59 60-61 61-62; Pickfords Cup 50-51; Hants Interm Cup 59-60 60-61; Hants Jun Cup 19-20 (R-up 1894-95 1910-11 12-13) N.Hants Cup 99-00 00-01
PREVIOUS **Leagues:** Salisbury & D.; Hants 1896-98, 1899-1901, 02-62; Southern 1898-99,1971-93 98-99; Western 1962-71; Wessex Lge 93-98
BEST SEASON **FA Cup:** 1st Rd 62-63, 0-1 v Gillingham
FA Trophy: 3rd Qual Rd 69-70, 70-71
FA Vase: 4th Rd 94-95, 1-3 v Falmouth Town (A)
CLUB RECORDS **Attendance:** 1,100 v Leicester, ground opening.
(3,484 v Gillingham at WalledMeadow, previous ground)

FACT FILE

Founded: 1883
Nickname: The Lions
Colours: Red & black/black/red
Change colours: White & BlackMidweek matchday: Tuesday
Reserve Team's League: Wessex Comb.
Programme: 50 pages £1.00

CLUB PERSONNEL

Chairman: Alan Mussell
President: Bill Maynard
Manager: Brian Le Boutillier
Assistant Manager: Ray Cozze
Physio: Chris Burford
Captain: Glen Damen

B.A.T. SPORTS

Secretary: Bob Walsh, 30 Hammonds Lane, Totton, Southampton SO40 3LG
Tel Nos: 02380 486470 (H) 02380 748419 (W) 07977 514090 (M)

Ground: BAT Sports Ground, Southern Gdns, off Ringwood Road, Totton SO 40 8RW
Tel: 023 8086243

Directions: Into centre of Totton, proceed up Ringwood Road, past small roundabout, then 2nd left into Southern Gardens.
Half mile from Totton (BR)
Bus X2(Southampton-Bournemouth)

Capacity: 3,000 Seats: 150 Cover: 150 Floodlights: Yes

Clubhouse: Normal licensing hrs, all day for members' sports facilities. Hot & cold snacks

Best Season **FA Vase:** 3rd Rd 99-00
Club Records **Attendance:** 403 v AFC Bournemouth 3.05.02
Honours
Previous **Names:**

FACT FILE
Founded: 1925
Colours: All blue& yellow trim
Change: All RedMidweek Matches: Tuesday
Programme: 20 pages, 30p
Editor:

CLUB PERSONNEL
Chairman: Mike Geddes

Manager: Andy Leader & Ray Collins
:

2002-03
Leading Goalscorer:
Captain:
Player of the Year:

BEMERTON HEATH HARLEQUINS

Secretary: Andy Hardwick, 20 Herbert Road, Salisbury, Wilts. SP2 9LF
Tel No: 07710 128292 (M)

Ground: Western Way, Bemerton Heath, Salisbury, Wilts Tel: 01722 331925 :
FAX :01722 331218

Directions: Turn off A36 Salisbury-Bristol Rd at Skew Bridge (right turn if coming out of Salisbury), 1st left into Pembroke Rd for half mile, 2nd left along Western Way - ground quarter mile at end. 40 mins walk from Salisbury(BR) station.
Bus 51 or 52 from city centre stops at junction of Pembroke Rd/Western Way
Capacity : 2,100 Seats: 200 Cover: 350 Floodlights: Yes
Clubhouse: Yes - Week Days 7p.m.-11p.m.Week ends 12 noon.-11 p..m.Snacks available
HONOURS Wilts Snr Cup 92-93. Wilts Lg(3) as Bemerton Athletic
PREVIOUS **Names:** Bemerton Athletic, Moon FC & Bemerton Boys; all merged in 1989
Leagues: Bem. Ath.: Salisbury. & Wilts Comb.
Moon: Salisbury. & Andover Sunday Bem.Boys: Mid Wilts
RECORD **Attendance:** 1,118 v Aldershot Town FA Cup 1st Qual Rd Aug 94
Appearances: Keith Richardson

FACT FILE
Founded: May 1989
Nickname: Quins
Colours: Black & white diamonds/black/black & white hoops
Change colours: Yellow/white/whiteMidweek Matches: Tuesday
Programme: 32 pages, 50p

CLUB PERSONNEL
Chairman: Eddie BoswellPresident: Peter Say
Manager: Steve Slade
Coach:es: Andy Nash.,Jim McConnel l& Brian Leboutillier
Physio:Sandra Leboutillier
2002-2003
Leading Goalscorer:Neil Cole 25
Captain:Gary Burden
Players of the Year: Gary Burden & Colin Hopkins

BOURNEMOUTH

Secretary: Mandy Vaughan, The County, 61 Westover Rd.,, Bournemouth BH1 2BZ

Ground: Victoria Park, Namu Rd., Winton, Bournemouth, Dorset Tel: 01202 515123

Directions: Enter town on A338 from Ringwood. Exit to A3060 (Castle Lane) for three miles east then left onto A347 and follow one way system into Boundary Rd and left into Victoria Ave, Third right to Namu Rd. and turn right into ground at end,

Capacity: 3,000 Seats: 250 Cover: 250 Floodlights: Yes Shop: No

Clubhouse: Open daily 7-11pm. Sandwiches & hot snacks available.

HONOURS Hants Lg 13-13 21-22, B'mouth Snr Cup 66-67 89-90, Texaco F'lit Cup R-up 91-92, Hants I'mediate Cup 49-50 69-70, Hants Yth Cup 54-55 57-58 67-68

PREVIOUS **Leagues:** Hampshire **Ground:** Dene Park 1888-90
Names: Bournemouth Rovers 1875-88; Bournemouth Dene Park 1888-90

RECORD **Scorer:** B Head
Fee Received: £1,500 for Chike Onourah (Wimborne 93-94)

BEST SEASON **FA Cup:** 2002-03

2003-2004 **Player of the Year:** Paul Cuglietta **Top Goalscorer:** Lewis Till

FACT FILE

Founded: 1875
Nickname: Poppies
Sponsors:Bradbury Roofing
Colours: All Red
Change colours: All white
Midweek Matches: Tuesday
Reserves' League: Jewson Wessex Comb
Programme: 58 pages, 50p
Editor: Mike RobbinsLocal Press: Evening Echo

CLUB PERSONNEL

Chairman:Robert Corbin
Vice Chairman: John Field
President: John Brooks
Comm. Manager:Steve Jones
Press Officer: Steve Jones
Manager: Shaun Brooks
Asst Manager:Gary Fitch
Coach: Tom Cadbury Captain: Paul Cuglietta
Physio:T.B.A.

BROCKENHURST

Secretary: Paul Christopher, 31 Brookside Road, Bransgore, Christchurch, Dorset BM 23 8NA Tel No: 01425 674084 (H) 07837 587657(M)

Ground: Grigg Lane, Brockenhurst, Hants Tel: 01590 623544

Capacity: 2,000 **Seats:** 200 **Cover:** 300 **Floodlights:** Yes

Clubhouse: Open every evening plus Tues, Fri, Sat & Sun lunchtimes

Directions: M27 Junc 1, A337 to Lyndhurst and A337 to Brockenhurst. Turn right at Carey's Manor Hotel into Grigg Lane. Ground is 200 yds on the right
Bus : 56/56A(Lymington-Southampton)

HONOURS Hants Intermediate Cup 61-62; Bournemouth Senior Cup 60-61;
Hampshire Lg 75-76, R-up 73-74 79-80, Div 2 70-71 R-up 60-61, Div 3 59-60.

PREVIOUS **League:** Hampshire Lge 24-26 47-86

RECORDS **Attendance:** 1,104 v St Albans City F.A..Amateur Cup January 1974
Win: 10-1 V Knowle Hospital Hants Inter Cup 13.02.61
Defeat: 0-11 Portsmouth Gas Co. Hants Div 2 10.10.36

BEST SEASON **FA Vase:** 4th Rd @000-2001 **FA Cup:** 2nd Q Rd 2001-2002
FA Amateur Cup: 2nd Round 73-4

2003-2004 Player of the Year: Iain Brunnschweiler
Top Scorers: Keith Williams & Alan Wright 7 goals

FACT FILE

Founded: 1898 Nickname: The Badgers
Sponsor: T.B.A.
Colours: Blue & white/blue/blue
Change colours: Green/black/green
Midweek Matches: Tuesday
Reserves League: Wessex Combination
Programme: 32 pages, £1.00
Editor/Press Officer: Dave Stansbridge

CLUB PERSONNEL

Chairman:Brian Small President: Mike Kimber
Vice Chairman: Dave Stansbridge
Man: Graham Kemp Asst. Man: Keith Williams
Reserves Manager: Colin Plumhoff
Physio: Dave Lane
Captain: Paul White

CHRISTCHURCH

Secretary: Alan Wilkins,59 Lingwood Avenue,Mudeford,Christchurch,Dorset. BH23 3JU
Tel No: 01202 480918 (H) 01202 488 116 (Fax) e-mail: christgol@aol.com

Ground: Hurn Bridge Sports Club, Hurn Bridge, Avon Causeway, Christchurch BH23 6DY
Tel: 01202 473792

Directions: A338 from Ringwood, turn off signed Hurn Airport on left. Before Airport use mini roundabout & take exit signed Sopley and ground is immediately on the right. Three miles from Christchurch (BR)

Capacity: 1,200 Seats: 215 Cover: 265 Floodlights: Yes

Clubhouse: Normal pub hours. Cooked food at lunchtimes

HONOURS Hants Jnr Cup 1892-93 1911-12 20-21; Hants Int. Cup 86-87; Pickford Cup 91; Hants Lg Div 2 37-38 47-48 85-86 (Div 3 56-57); B'mouth Snr Cup (5) 56-57 59-60 67-70; B'mouth Page-Croft Cup 94-95

PREVIOUS **League:** Hampshire **Ground:** Barrack Rd Recreation Grd (>1984)

RECORD **Appearances** : John Haynes

BEST SEASON **FA Vase:** 2nd Qual. 2002-03 **FA Cup:** 20021-2002
FA Amateur Cup:

Players progressing: Jody Craddock (Cambridge Utd 93), Dan West (Aston Villa 94)

FACT FILE

Founded: 1885
Nickname: Priory
Sponsors: Franklin Transport
Colours: All royal blue (white trim)
Change colours: All Red
Midweek Matches: Tuesday
Programme: 16 pages, 50p
Editor: Dennis Miller

CLUB PERSONNEL

Chairman: Majid Azzeddin
Vice Chairman: Ian Harley Pres: Joss Jenkins
Press Officer: Robin Osborne
Manager: Peter Moore
Coach: Stuart Underwood
Physios: Emma Walsh & Kevin Berry

COWES SPORTS

Secretary: Lee Bray, 86 Seaview Road, Cowes, Isle of Wight PO31 7UQ (01983 200626)
Website: www.cowessportsfc.com

Ground: Westwood Park, Reynolds Close, off Park Rd, Cowes, Isle of Wight PO31 7NT
Tel: 01983 293793

Directions: Take Park Rd out of Cowes . Reynolds Close is a right turn half mile up hill. From Newport take main A3020 towards Cowes. Take right fork at Northwood Garage then at mini roundabout turn right into Reynolds Close half mile on left.

Capacity: 1850 Seats: 450 Cover: 450 Floodlights: Yes Clubhouse: Yes Shop: No

HONOURS Southern League S.W.Div 2 1899 Wessex League Cup 1999 Hampshire Lg (7) League Cup 1993 Hampshire Senior Cup (9) Isle of Wight Gold Cup (17),

PREVIOUS **League:** Hampshire (pre-1994)

BEST SEASON **FA Cup:** 4th Qual. Rd replay 57-58, 1-4 v Trowbridge (A) after 2-2
FA Vase: 5th Rd 99-00

Players progressing to Football League: Jamie Lawrence (Sunderland), Lee Bradbury (Portsmouth) James Hayter (Bournemouth)

FACT FILE
Founded: 1881
Colours: Blue & white stripes,black,blue
Change colours: All Yellow
Midweek Fixtures: Tuesdays
Reserves' Lge: Wessex Combination
Programme Editor: Tony Gibbs

CLUB PERSONNEL
President: Ada Leigh
Chairman: Ian Lee
Vice Chairman: Ron Bowler
Press Officer: Simon Smith
Manager: Derek Ohren
Assistant Manager:John Carragher
Captain:Simon Butler

2003-2004
Top Scorer: Phillip McDonald
Player of the Year: Darren Powell

DOWNTON

Secretary: Brian Ford, 11 Chantry Road, Wilton, Salisbury, Wilts.SP2 0LT
Tel No: 01722 743314

Ground: Brian Whitehead Sports Ground, Wick Lane, Downton Tel: 01725 512162

Directions: Travel south from Salisbury on A338 for about 7 miles. Turn right intoWick Lane, and the ground is a qtr mile on left

Capacity: 1600 Seats: 250 Cover: Nil Floodlights: Yes

Clubhouse: Bar with kitchen facilities Club Shop: No

HONOURS Wilts Sen Cup 79-80 80-81, (R-up 55-56 91-92 94-95); Wilts Jun Cup 49-50; Bournemouth Sen Lge 60 61 62 64 65 67 68, Sen Lge Cup 61-62 63-64 66-67, Cup 62-63 79-80; Wessex Lge Cup 95-96; Wessex Comb Cup (R-up 95-96); RussellCotes Cup 95-96; Hayward Cup 64-65

PREVIOUS **League:** Bournemouth, Hants (pre-1993)

CLUB RECORDS **Attendance:** 500v AFC VBournemoputh (Friendly)

BEST SEASON **FA Cup:** 3rd Qualifying Rd 95-6

FACT FILE
Founded: 1905
Nickname: The Robins
Sponsor: Priority Mailing
Colours: Red/white/redChange colours:White/black/white
Midweek Matchday: Wednesday
Programme: Yes
Editor: Nathan Sait

CLUB PERSONNEL
Chairman: James Blake
President: R Tanner
Manager: Mitch Blake
Asst.Manager: Steve Adlam

FAREHAM TOWN

Secretary: Bob Ralls, 44A Frogmore Lane, Lovedean, Water,oolille. PO8 9QL (07866 902632)
Ground: Cams Alders, Highfield Avenue, Fareham, Hants PO14 1JA Tel: 01329 823487

Directions: M27, J11, follow A27 towards Southampton. After passing Fareham station turn left at traffic lights (2nd left) into Redlands Ave.. Turn right at Redlands Inn then left into Highfields Ave.
Capacity: 5,500 Cover: 500 Seats: 450 Floodlights: Yes

Clubhouse: Open every evening except Sundays. Food available
Club Shop: Sells programmes, scarves & fanzines

HONOURS Hants Lg (8) 59-60 62-67 72-73 74-75 (R-up 55-56 60-61 67-68 71-72 76-77 78-79, Div 2 R-up 52-53, Eastern Div 24-25, Div 3 East 49-50), Hants Snr Cup 56-57 62-63 67-68 92-93, Russell Cotes Cup (6) 64-65 72-77, Gosport War Memorial Cup, SW Co's Cup (2), Pickford Cup (2),

PREVIOUS **Leagues:** Portsmouth 47-49, Hants 49-79, Southern 79-98
Name: Fareham FC **Ground:** Bath Lane

BEST SEASON **FA Trophy:** Semi Final 86-87 **FA Amateur Cup:** 2nd Rd 63-64 66-67 73-74
FA Vase: 1st Rd 98-9 **FA Cup:** 1st Rd replay 88-89, 2-3 v Torquay U. (H) after 2-2

RECORDS **Attendance:** 2,650 v Wimbledon, FA Cup 1965.
(at Southampton F.C.) 6,035 v Kidderminster H., FAT S-F 2nd leg 86-87
Fee received: £43,000 for David Leworthy (Spurs)

FACT FILE
Formed: 1947 Nickname: The Town
Sponsors: Portsmouth Evening News
Colours: Red/black/red
Change colours: Whiteblack/black
Midweek matchday: Tuesday
Reserves' League: Hampshire Comb
Programme: 36 pages £1
Editor: Ian Tewson Tel. 01329 662624

CLUB PERSONNEL
Chairman: Bob Ralls
e-mail: Rralls9978@ol.com
Director of Football: John Green
President: Ken Atkins
General Manager: Tony Adams (01705 615931)
Press Officer: M Willis
Manager: Jon Gittens
Physio: James McKay

Bemerton Heath 'keeper, James Domm, clears a corner from the head of Winchester's Ian Mancey.
Photo: D. Nicholson.

GOSPORT BOROUGH

Secretary: B V Cosgrave, 2 Cavanna Close, Rowner, Gosport PO13 0PE Tel: 01329314117
Ground: Privett Park, Privett Road, Gosport, Hants Tel: 01705 501042 (Office)
Directions: M27 Junct 11, A32 Fareham to Gosport. At Brockhurst r-about (about 3 miles) right into Military Rd passing thru H.M.S. Sultan, left into Privett Rd at next r-about, ground 300yds left signed `Privett Park Enclosure'. 2 miles from Portsmouth Harbour (BR) or Fareham (BR)
Capacity: 4,500 Cover: 500 Seats: 450 Floodlights: Yes Club Shop: No
Clubhouse: Matchdays only - from 1.30 Sat., 6.30 Wed. Refreshment hut sells hot food & drinks
HONOURS Wessex Lg Cup 92-93, Southern Lg Div 1 South R-up 84-85, Hants Lg 45-46 76-77 77-78 (Div 3 (Res.) 70-71 75-76), Portsmouth Lg R-up 44-45, Hants Senior Cup 87-88, Russell Cotes Cup R-up 94-95, Hants Intermediate Cup 70-71, Portsmouth Senior Cup 61-62 69-70 70-71 94-95,03-04 South West Counties Pratten Challenge Cup 77-78
BEST SEASON **FA Trophy:** 1st Rd 88-89 **FA Amateur Cup:** 3rd Rd 47-48 66-67
FA Vase: 6th Rd replay 77-78 6th Rd 03-04 **FA Cup:** 4th Qual. Rd 80-81 (lost to Windsor & Eton)
PREVIOUS **Leagues:** Portsmouth 44-45; Hants 45-78; Southern 78-92
Name: Gosport Borough Athletic
RECORD **Attendance:** 4,770 v Pegasus, FA Amtr Cup 1951
Scorer: Richie Coulbert 192 **Appearances**: Tony Mahoney 764
Win: 14-0 v Cunliffe-Owen, Hampshire Lg Div 1 45-46
Defeat: 0-9 twice v Newport, Hants Lg Div 1 47-48.
v Gloucester (A), Southern Lg Prem Div 89-90

FACT FILE
Founded: 1944 Nickname: The Boro'
Sponsors:E.L.J.Furnishing
Colours: Yellow/blue/yellow
Change colours: All red
Midweek matchday: Tuesday
Reserves ' League: Wessex Combination
Programme:40 pages, £1.00
Editor: Roy newman (02392 799198)
Press: Portsmouth Eve News, So'ton Eve Echo
Website:www.gosportboroughfc.co.uk

CLUB PERSONNEL
Chairman: JohnStimpson
President: H.Mizen
Manager: Mick Marsh Coach Hugh Doyle
Physio: Zoe Huggins Captain:Stuart Hensman

2003-2004
Leading Goalscorer:Graham Lindsay
Player of the Year: Ian Rew

HAMBLE AEROSTRUCTURES SPORTS & SOCIAL CLUB

Secretary: Matthew Newbold, Flat 6, 70-72 Portsmouth Road, Woolsten, Southampton, Hants. SO19 9AN Tel: 023 80 342421(H) 07799 538362 (M)

Ground: Folland Park, Kings Avenue, Hamble.,Southampton SO31 4NF Tel: 02380452173

Directions: M27 junction 8, then B3397 to Hamble. Half mile fromHamble (BR); turn right out of station, proceed for one mile then turn right before shops into Kings Avenue. Ground 1000 yards on right in works sports ground.

Capacity: 1000 Seats: 150 Cover: 150 Floodlights: Yes
Clubhouse: 300 capacity social club. Cricket & bowls

HONOURS: Hampshire Lg Div 3 80-81 (Div 4 79-80), Hampshire Intermediate Cup 79-90, Southampton Senior Cup 84-85 86-87 91-92
As Hamble AS&SC: Jewson Wessex League Cup 97-98
PREVIOUS **Name:** Folland Sports (pre-1990), Aerostructures SSC 90-97
RECORD **Defeat:** 1-10 v Andover (A), Wessex League 93-94

FACT FILE

Colours: Maroon and Sky Blue
Change colours: Sky & White stripes/black/sky
Midweek Matches: TuesdayReserves ' League: Wessex Comb
Under 18 & Under16: So'ton Youth Lgs
Programme - Price: Pages:
Editor:

CLUB PERSONNEL
Chairman: Peter Mence
President: Alistair Tritten
Assistant Secretary: Matthew Newbold
Treasurer: Barry Morse
Senior Manager: Larry Clay

HAMWORTHY UNITED

Secretary: Peter Gallop, 51A Symes Rd., Hamworthy, Poole, Dorset BH15 4PR
Tel No: 01202 670792

Ground: The County Ground, Blandford Close, Hamworthy, Poole, Dorset.

Capacity: 2,000 **Seats:** **Cover:** **Floodlights:** **Clubhouse:** Yes

Directions: From A35 follow signs for Poole and Hamworthy. In Upton take second exit at roundabout, stay on Blanford Road. Past two sets of lights and take left into Blandford Close

PREVIOUS **Leagues:** Dorset Premier From A35
Names: Hamworthy St Michael amalgamated with Trinidad Old Boys 1926

HONOURS Dorset Premier Lg Champions 2002-03 2003-04 Dorset Comb 76-77 Comb Cup 89-90 Dorset Senior Cup 97-98 R-up, U18 Team Dorset Youth Div 2 2003-04

2003-2004 **Player of the Year:** Sean Bartlett **Top Goalscorer:** Jamie Holland

FACT FILE

Formed: 1926
Sponsor:
Colours: Maroon & Sky Blue/Maroon/Maroon
Change colours: Black & Yellow/Black/Yellow
Midweek Matches: Wednesday
Reserves' Lge: Dorset Premier League
Programme: Editor Mr & Mrs R Grainger

CLUB PERSONNEL

Chairman: David Manuel
Vice Chairman:
President:
Manager: Alex Pike
Coach: Paul Curtis
Captain: Anthony Tilley

LYMINGTON & NEW MILTON

Secretary: John Osey, 9 Samphire Close, Lymington, Hants SO41 9LR Tel: 01590 676995

Ground: Fawcett Fields,Christchurch Rd., New Milton,Hants BH25 6QF (01425 6281910

Directions: M27 Jct 1 follow A337 to Lyndhurst one way system(A35) towards Christchurch. Left in Hinton Admiral at Cat & Fiddle.Follow Ringwood road ,then left at A337 roundabout to New Milton. Ground one mile on left past Chewton Glen Hotel.Bus service 123(Lym't -Bournemout)

Capacity: 3,000 Seats: 262 Cover: 262 Floodlights: Yes

Clubhouse: Open seven days a week 11.0 am to 11.0 pm. Hot food and functions availab le

HONOURS Wessex Lg 92-93 96-97 97-98, 98-99 , 99-00,00-01R-up 91-92 95-96, Wessex Lg Cup 88-89, R-up 94-95, 98-99 Wessex Comb. 92-93, Hants Snr Cup R-up 89-90, Texaco Cup 91-92, Bournemouth Snr Cup 92-93, R-up 96-97, Russell Cotes Cup 93-94 94-95, R-up91-92 92-93; Pickford Cup R-up 92-93. Jewson Champions Shield 98-99

BEST SEASON **FA Cup:** 4th Qual. Rd. 99-00, 1-3 v Aldershot Town (H)
FA Vase: 98-99 Quarter Final, 1-3 v Taunton Town (A)

PREVIOUS **Names:** Lymington Town (until 1988 merger with Wellworthy Ath.), AFC Lymington 88-98 (until merger with New Milton Town)
Ground: Ampress Ground (Wellworthy Ath.), until 1988 merger

RECORD **Attendance:** 2,900 v Karen Mills Memorial Day 12.3.95
Scorer: Darren Pitter 197
Appearances: Graham Kemp 504
Win: 11-1 v Romsey Town (H), Wessex League 9/11/92
Defeat: 0-8 v Basingstoke Town (A), Hampshire Senior Cup 10/4/90

FACT FILE

Founded as Lymington & New Milton: 1998
Nickname: Linnets
Sponsors:Parkcrest Construction
Colours: Marroon & Blue Stripes/blue/maroon
Change colours: Red/red/white
Midweek Matches: Tuesday
Reserves ' League: Wessex Comb

Programme: 48 pages, £1.00
Editors: Jack Holliday & Keith Williams

CLUB PERSONNEL

Chairman: John Mills
8 Shaves Lane, New Milton, Hants. BH25 5DJ
Tel No: 01425 614220
President: Jack Holliday & Ted Goodyer
Press Officer: Keith Williams (01202 476898)

Manager: Graham Kemp

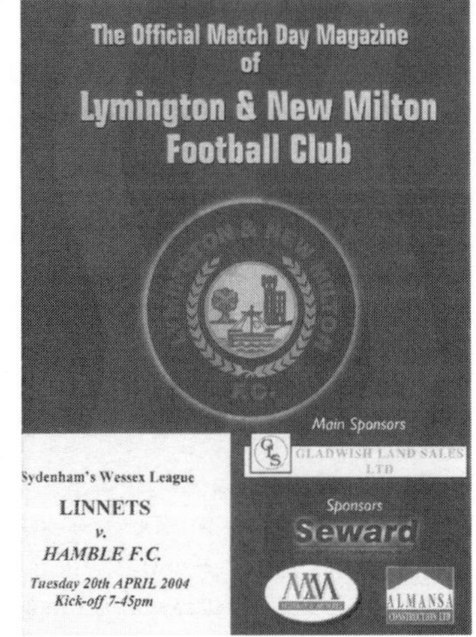

The Official Match Day Magazine of
Lymington & New Milton Football Club
Main Sponsors
GLADWISH LAND SALES LTD
Sydenham's Wessex League
LINNETS
v.
HAMBLE F.C.
Tuesday 20th APRIL 2004
Kick-off 7-45pm
Sponsors
Seward
ALMANSA

MONEYFIELDS

Secretary: Paul Lipscombe,5 Braunston Close,Paulsgrove,Hants. PO6 4EN (07766 222718)

Ground: Moneyfields Sports Ground, Moneyfields Avenue, Copnor, Portsmouth,Hants.
Tel: 023 9266 5260 (Club), 023 9265 2424 (Office) **Club Shop**: Yes
Capacity: 1,500 Seats: 150 Cover: 150 Floodlights: Yes
Clubhouse: Daily 7-11 p.m. Saturday 11-11p.m. (food from 1.0 pm)

Directions: From Southampton & the west - travel east on M27 onto A27. Take exit marked Southsea A2030. (From east take the same exit). Head south along A2030 exit and turn right into Tangier Road (4th right). Follow until`Tangiers' PH & take next right into Folkestone Road. Carry on into Martin Rd & club is in front of you.

Records: **Attendances:** Matthew Lafferty 156 (Jewson Wessex)
Goalscorer: Kevin Marsh 49 (Jewson Wessex)
Attendance: 152 v Fareham Town, Jewson Wessex League, 98-99

Best Seasons: **F.A.Cup:** 1st Qual. Rd. 01-02 **Previous Name**: Portsmouth Civil Service
F.A.Vase: 3rd Rd 01-02

Records: **Goalscorer**: Neil Damley 62 **Appearances** Matthew Lafferty 168
Attendance v Fareham T 232 01-02

Honours: Portsmouth Senior Cup: 90-91 R-up 91-92 Hampshire League Div 3 91-92, Div 2 92-93,Div 196-97,R-Up 97-98 Portsmouth Premier champions 90-91,91-92 Billy Hill Cup 90-91 Hampshireb Intermediate Cup Winners 91-92, 92-93 Russell Cotes Cup Finalists 98-99 Hants Youth Cuip (under 18) (4), Under 16 (98-99),Hants Youth League 00-01 R-up 98-99

FACT FILE

Founded: 1987 Nickname: Moneys
Sponsors: Icee Ltd & Triman
Colours: Yellow/navyblue/navy blueChange: Green & white/ green/green.
Midweek Fixtures: Wednesday
Reserves League: Wessex Combination
Programme: 26 pages £1.00
Editor: David Hayter (023 9264 3986)

CLUB PERSONNEL

Chairman: Gaery Foster Tel: 023 92617110
Managesr: Miles Rutherford & Craig Stafford
Assistant Manager: Paul Gregory
Physio: Adie Hylands
Captain:Dean Wain

2003-04

Leading Goalscorer: Lee Mould 17
Player of the Year: Miles Rutherford

PORTLAND UNITED

Secretary: Tony Greaves, 1 The Spinney, Lorton Lane,Weymouth, Dorset. DT3 5DJ
Website: www.portlandunitedfc.co.uk
E.mail: portlandutdfc@aol.com

Ground: New Grove Corner, Grove Road, Portland, Dorset
Tel: 01305 861489

Capacity: 2000 Covered Seating: 150 Covered Standing: 50 Floodlights: Yes

Directions A354 to Portland, follow one way system to the top of island, roundabout (hotel on left, garage on right), over roundabout for 500m, turn left into Grove Road, ground on left hand side.

Clubhouse: Yes - Open one hour before kick-off. Food available

PREVIOUS Leagues: Dorset Combination

CLUB RECORDS Attendance: 651

FACT FILE

Founded: 1923
Colours: All blue
Change colours: Red/black/red
Midweek matches: Tuesday
Programme: Yes - Price: 50p Pages:32
Editor:T.B.A.**CLUB PERSONNEL**
Acting Chairman
Treasurer: Alex Goracey
Manager:Andy Mason
Coach: Micky GreenoPhysio: M..Harper
2002-03 Top Scorer: James Reeves

THATCHAM TOWN

Football Secretary: Peter Woodage, 5 Elm Grove, Thatcham, Berks. RG18 3DJ
Tel: 01635 861937

Ground: Waterside Park, Crookham Rd, Thatcham, Berks Tel: 01635 862016

Capacity: 3,000 Seats: 300 Cover: 300 Floodlights: Yes

Directions: M4 junc 13, take A34 to Newbury, then left onto A4 towards Reading InThatcham turn right to the railway station. The ground is on the left beyond the station - two minutes walk.**From South** A34 to Newbury,take A339 to Basingstoke,left to Thatcham then left again down Crookham Rd. Ground on right just before station

Clubhouse: Open every evening & lunchtimes **Club Shop:** Yes

HONOURS Wessex Lg 95-96,R-up 98-99, Cup 90-91 91-92 94-95 96-97, (R-up twice)

PREVIOUS **Grounds**: Station Road 46-52; Lancaster Close 52-92

BEST SEASON **FA Cup:** 4th Qual Rd 96-97 **FA Vase:** 6th Round 1987-88

RECORD **Attendnace:** 1,400 v Aldershot, FA Vase

FACT FILE

Founded: 1895
Sponsors: Lakeside Sperbowl
Colours: Blue & white stripes/blue/blue
Change colours:Red,black,black
Midweek Matches: Tuesday
Programme: 28 pages, £1.00Editor: Ed Houghton

CLUB PERSONNEL

Chairman: Phil Holdway
Director of Football: Steve Melledew
General Secretary: Tony Lawson
Press Officer: Chairman (01635 867803)
Manager: Jason Braidwood
Coach:John Goddard
Captain: Russell Green

2003-2004

Leading Goalscorer:Ian Davies
Player of the Year: Jamie Green

VT FC

Secretary: A.Fox, 22 Thornleigh Road, Woolston, Southampoton, Hants, SO19 9DH
Tel: 02380 493346
Chairman: William Boyle MBE

Ground: Vosper Thornycroft Spts Ground, Portsmouth Rd, Sholing, Southampton
Tel: 01489 403829

Colours: All Yellow & Blue.
Change colours: Navy blue, jade & tangerine/navy/navy

WIMBORNE TOWN

Secretary: Peter Barham,Chelmer, 17 Margards Lane,Verwood, Dorset BH31 6JP
Tel Nos: 01202 826705 (H) 07956 833346 (M)

Ground: The Cuthbury, Cowgrove Road, Wimborne, Dorset BH21 4EL Tel: 01202 884821
Capacity: 3,250 Seats: 275 Cover: 150 Floodlights: Yes

Directions: Wimborne to Blandford Road, behind Victoria Hospital

Clubhouse: Eves 7-11, Sat noon-11, Sun 12-6 Bar & Skittle alley **Club Shop:** Yes

HONOURS FA Vase 91-92; Wessex Lg 91-92 93-94 ,99-00(R-up 92-93 96-97), Lg Cup 93-94,99-00 (R-up 90-91 95-96); Dorset Lg Div 1 80-81 81-82 (R-up 38-39 72-73), Div 2 31-32 34-35 36-37(R-up 35-36), Lg Cup R-up (4) 72-74 80-82; Dorset Snr Cup 91-92 96-97, (R-up 80-82 85-86 98-99,99-00); Mark Frowde Cup 92-93 94-95;01-02 Dorset Snr Amateur Cup 36-37 63-64;Dorset Jnr Cup 31-32 36-37 (R-up 13-14 34-35); Dorset Minor Cup 12-13; Dorset Jnr Amateur Cup (3) 34-36 38-39; Bankes Charity Cup 89-90 94-95 95-96, TexacoF/Light Cup 90-91

PREVIOUS **Leagues:** Dorset Lge, Dorset Comb, Western 81-86

BEST SEASON **FA Vase:** Winners 91-92 **FA Cup:** 1st Rd Proper 82-83

RECORDS **Attendance:** 3,250 v Bamberbridge FA Vase Semi-Final 28/3/92
Goalscorer: Jason Lovell **Win** (Wessex Lg): 9-0 v E.Cowes V 98-99, Brockenhurst 99-00
Appearances: James Sturgess **Defeat** (Wessex Lg): 2-6 v Thatcham Town 91-92
Fee paid: £5,500 for J P Lovell (Bashley, 1992)
Fee received: £6,000; for J P Lovell (Bashley, 1989) & for Tommy Killick(Dorchester, 1993)

FACT FILE
Founded: 1878 Nickname: Magpies
Sponsors: Nicolas O'Hara
Colours: Black & white stripes/black/black
Change colours: Yellow/green/yellow
Midweek Matches: Tuesday
Reserve League: Dorset League
Programme: 28 pages, £1.00
Editor: Ken Fergus

CLUB PERSONNEL
Chairman: Nicholas O'Hara
President: Brian Maidment
Press Officer: Secretary
Manager:Paul Arnold
Asst, Mgr: John Macey
Coach: Darren Powell
Captain: Darren Powell
Physio: Steve Churchill

2003-2004
Player of the Year.: Mark Smith
Top Goalscorer: Gareth Barnes

WINCHESTER CITY

Secretary: Ray Murphy, 'Petals', 21 Villette Close, Christchurch, Dorset BH23 2NR
Tel: 01202 482067 (H) 07801 638158 (M) 91202 746975 (W)
Fax: 01202 258863 email: raymurphy@ntlworld.com

Ground: The City Ground, Hillier Way, Abbotts Barton, Winchester. Tel: 01962 810200

Directions: M3 J9, take A33/A34 for 1 mile, then A33 for a further mile. 1st left into Kings Worthy, follow road for about 3 miles. After 30mph sign take 2nd left, 1st right, 1st left into Hillier Way. Clubhouse and pitch in front of you.

Capacity: 7,500 Covered Seating: 200 Covered Standing: No Floodlights: Yes
Clubhouse Opening match days with food available.

PREVIOUS **Leagues:** 1898-99, 1903 -42, 1943-44, 1945-71, 1971-73,1973-2003 Southern

BEST SEASON
FA Vase: (first season) Winners 2003-2004

HONOURS Hampshire League Prem Div. 2002-03, Div. 1 00-01
FA Vase 2003-2004

FACT FILE
Founded: 1884
Colours: Red & black stripes/black/black
Change colours: All Yellow
Midweek matchday: Tuesday
Programme
Price £1.00: Pages: 56

CLUB PERSONNEL
Chairman: Richard Newsome
Director of Football: David Malone
Manager: Neil Hards

2002-03
Leading Goalscorer: Andy Forbes
Captain: Danny Smith
Player of the Year: Matthew Bicknell

AFC ALDERMASTON

Secretary: Christine Collier,14 Brackenwood Drive,Tadley, Hampshire RG26 4YB Tel: 07884 254706 (M) 01256 363344 (W)
Chairman: George Johnstone

Ground: Aldermaston Rec. Society, Automatic Weapons Establishment, Aldermaston, Reading, Berks. Tel: 0118 982 4544
Colours: All Blue. Change Colours: Yellow/white/white

ALRESFORD TOWN

Secretary: Trevor Ingram, 18 Corfe Close, Alresford, Hants. SO24 9PH

Tel: 01252 544002 (B) 07770 387462 (M)

email: trevor@ingramtribe.freeserve.co.uk

Ground: Alresbury Park, The Avenue, Alresford, Hants.

Tel: 01962 735100

Colours: Black & white stripes/black/black

AMESBURY TOWN

Secretary: Tony Winchcliffe, 12 Lanes Close, Amesbury, Wiltshire SP4 7RW
Tel Nos: 01980 624425 (H) 01985 220914 (W)
Ground: Recreation Ground, Recreation Road, Amesbury, Wiltshire.
Capacity: **Seats:** **Cover:** **Floodlights:** **Clubhouse:**
Directions: From A303 Countess Road Roundabout, towards town centre through lights and turn right by bus station. Left at end of road at T junction bt Lloyds Bank go over bridge and left into 'Recreation Road on sharp right bend.
PREVIOUS **Leagues:** Salisbury & District, Wiltshire County, Western , Hampshire
Name: Amesbury F.C.
RECORD **Attendance**: 625 v Taunton Town 1997
HONOURS
2003-2004 **Player of the Year:** Keith Nicholls **Top Scorer:** Lee Cunningham

FACT FILE
Formed: 1904
Sponsor:
Colours: All Blue
Change colours: All Red
Midweek Matches: Yuesday
Programme Editor: Graham Ashman

CLUB PERSONNEL
Chairman: Michael Saunders
Manager: Nick Horner
Player/Coach: Jason Cameron

ANDOVER NEW STREET

Secretary: Jim Dunn, c/o Club e-mail: jim_dunn@talk21.com
Ground: Foxcotte Park, Charlton, Andover SP11 0HS Tel No: 01264 358358
Capacity: **Seats:** **Cover:** **Floodlights:**
Clubhouse: Open all day Saturdays and Sundays and from 1900 hours on week days.
Directions: Follow ring road to Charlton.Turn rightat the Royal Oak Pub. Carry on for about 3/4 mile then take last exit from roundabout signposted to Sports Centre.
PREVIOUS **Leagues:** Andover & District, North Hants, Hampshire Premier
Name: New Street
HONOURS Hampshire Premier Runners-Up 2003-004. Trophyman Cup Winners 2003-4
RECORD Attendance: 240
2003-2004 **Player of the Year:** Stuart Anderson **Top Goalscorer:** Nic Turpin

FACT FILE
Formed: 1895
Sponsor:
Colours: Green & black stripes/Black/Green
Change colours: All Yellow
Midweek Matches:
Reserves' Lge: Tuesday
Programme Editor: Dougie McCracken
CLUB PERSONNEL
Chairman: Graham Waters
Manager: T.B.A.
Assistant Manager: Graham Knight
Coach: Andy Hooper
Physio: Pete Tunney
Captain: Kevion Knight

BLACKFIELD & LANGLEY

Secretary: Doug Sangster, 3 Fir Tree Grove, Butts Ash Lane, Hythe, Hants SO45 3RA
Tel: 023 80844911 (H) 023 80313721 (B) Email: doug.sangster@tesco.net

Ground: Gang Warily Rec., Newlands Rd, Blackfield, Southampton, Hants SO45 1GA
Tel: 01703 893603
Capacity: 2,500 **Covered Seats**:180 **Covered Standing** :Nil **Floodlights**: Yes

Directions: A326 from Totton. At Holbury mini roundabout take the right fork signposted to Lepe and Fawley. After the 1st set of lights (170m) turn left into ground.
Nearest Railway station:

Clubhouse Opening hours and availability of food & snacks.

Previous **Leagues**: Southampton Senr Lg, Hampshire League, R-U Russell Cotes Cup

Honours: Hants Div97-98, Div 2 84-85, Southampton Senior Cup (4)

Club Records **Attendance:** 240

FACT FILE
Founded: 1935
Colours: Green & white/green/green
Change colours: Yellow/blue/blue
Midweek home matchday: Tuesday
Programme Price:£1.00 Pages:32
Editor:Steve Nockeridge (023 8089 3065)

CLUB PERSONNEL
Chairman: Ian Hore
Tel: 023 8089 3325 (H) 023 8084 7659 (B)
Vice Chairman: Owen Lightfoot
President:Geoff Mercer

Manager:Tony Feeney
Asst. Man. / Coach: FChris HomerPhysio:
Captain: Kevin Love

2003-04
Player of the Year & Top Scorer:
Steve Wheatland

BRADING TOWN

Secretary: David Munday, 67 Howgate Road, Bembridge, Isle of Wight PO35 5QU Tel: 07786 562067
Chairman: Vincent Thompson

Ground: Vicarage Lane, Brading, I. o. W. Tel: 01983 405217
Directions: Adjacent to Brading main car park near to Wax Museum and Church.

Colours: Red & white/red/red. Change colours: Blue/white/white

EAST COWES VICTORIA ATHLETIC

Secretary: Jim Thorn,12 Brigstocke Terrace, Ryde, Isle of Wight, PO33 2PD Tel: 07773 661926 (M) email: ecvics@pavwykeham.demon.co.uk
Chairman: Arthur Richards

Ground: Beatrice Avenue Ground, East Cowes, I.O.W. Tel: 01938 297165

Directions: From the ferry: 1 mile from town centre on lower main road to Newport or Ryde near Whippingham Church adjacent to Osborne Middle School
Colours: Red/black/white. Change colours: All white

FAWLEY

Secretary: Marc Holland, 3 Briarswood Rise, Dibden Purlieu, Hythe, Hants SO45 5SW
Tel Nos: 02380 848848 (H) 07967 467361 (M)

Ground: Waterside Sports & Social Club, 179 Long Lane, Holbury, Southampton, Hants
Tel No: 02380 893750

Capacity: **Seats:** **Cover:** **Floodlights:** **Clubhouse:**

Directions: M27 Jct 2 westbound take A326 signposted Beaulieu & Fawley.-(8miles) Ground is 800 yards on right after Hardley roundabout.

PREVIOUS **Leagues:** Hants Premier
Names: Esso F.C.

HONOURS

2003-2004 **Player of the Year:** Kieran Earle **Top Goalscorer:** Luke Atkinson

FACT FILE
Formed: 1923
Sponsor:
Colours: All Blue
Change colours:White/blue/white
Midweek Matches: Wednesday
Reserves' Lge:
Programme:Editor: D.Walsh

CLUB PERSONNEL
Chairman: Jeff Oliver
Vice Chairman:
President:
Manager: Kevin Dawtry
Coach: Chris Tonar
Captain: DannyWalsh

HORNDEAN

Secretary: Mick Austin, 22 Abbas Green, Havant, Hampshire PO9 4EP
Tel: 07881 937995 (W & M) email: michaelaustin@horndean fc.fsnet.co.uk
Chairman: J. Bryson

Ground: Five Heads Park, Five Heads Road, Horndean, Hants. PO8 9NZ (01705 591363)

Directions: From north: J3 A3M, turn off aerial flyover, past Safeways on right, over r'about. Turn right at next r'about into A3 London Road, ground on left just past Good Intent PH. From south: J2 A3M, off at Horndean sign at end of slip road, turn left - then from Safeways above.
Colours: Red/black/red. Change colours.: White & blue/blue/blue

HYTHE & DIBDEN

Secretary: Tony Moyst, 105 Hobart Drive, Hythe, Southampton SO40 6FD Tel: 02380 847335 Chairman: Robert Parsons

Ground: Ewart Rec Ground, Jones Lane, Hythe, Southampton (02380 845264 -matchdays only)
At Dibden r'about on A326, take 1st left into Southampton Rd. Continue to Waterside PH, turn left into Jones Lane. Ground 200 yards on left.
Colours: Green & white/white/green. Change colours: All blue

LISS ATHLETIC

Secretary: Neil Noble,11 Southdown View, Waterlooville, Hants. PO7 6BJ Tel: 07816 038764 Chairman: Mick Alder

Ground: Newman Collard PF, Hill Brow Rd, Liss, Hants (01730 894022)
Midweek matchday: Thursday
Colours: All Blue. Change Colours: All green

LOCKS HEATH

Secretary: Peter Smith, 20 Wildrose Crescent, Locksheath, Hampshire SO31 6TG Tel: 01489 602256 (H) 07810 585878 (M)
Chairman: Stephen Smith

Ground: Locksheath Rec, Warsash Rd, Titchfield Common, Eastleigh (01489600932)

Directions: M27 J9, follow A27 for Fareham. Past GEC factory then 4th exit at next r'about into Warmarsh Rd. Left at next r'about. Ground .75 mile on right.

Colours: Red & black/black/red & black.
Change colours: All blue and yellow

LYMINGTON TOWN

Secretary: Mike Woodfield, 6 Genoa Close, Pennington, Lymington, Hants. SO41 8AU Tel: 015905676705 (H) 07759 861550 (M)
Chairman: George Shaw

Ground: Sports Ground, Southampton Road, Lymington, Hants.
Tel: 01590 671305

Capacity: 3,000 Covered Seating: 200 Floodlights: Yes

Directions: Follow the A337 to Lymington. Go over the lights after the Police Station (on right) and ground is approx. 150 metres on the left.

Colours: Red/white/black.
Change colours.: Blue&white/blue/white
Midweek matchday: Tuesday

PETERSFIELD TOWN

Secretary: Mark Nicholl, 49 Durford Rd, Petersfield, Hants GU31 4ER Tel: 01730 300518 (H) 07949 328240 (M) email: mnicoll@cwctv.net
Chairman : Kenneth Longland

Ground: Love Lane, Petersfield, Hants GU31 4BW Tel: 01730 233416

Directions: Off A3 circulatory system in Petersfield town centre (well signposted) or 10 min. walk from Petersfield railway station.

Colours: Red & black/black/black.
Change colours: Green/white/white

Midweek Matches: Wednesday

POOLE TOWN

Founded: 1880
Secretary: Bill Read, 15 Addison Close, Romsey, Hants SO51 7TL Tel: 01794 517991
Chairman: C. Robbins Tel: 01202 395004 Vive Charman: Chris Reeves 01202 674425
Manager: Paul Morrell & Dean Mooney
Ground: Oakdale School,Tatnam Ground, School Road, Poole, Dorset. Tel: 07771 604289
Directions: From M27 take A31 towards Poole/Dorchester. Follow A31 Wimborne by-pass, follow Ferryport signs, left at Merley r'about then right at next sign for Poole. Follow A3049 eventually reaching major r'about (Fleets Bridge), over into Fleets Lane then left into Palmer Rd. opposite Poole Motor Cycles. 1st right into School Lane. **Office**:153 High St. Poole Tel: 01202 674425
Capacity: 2000 Covered Seating: Planned Covered Standing: Yes Floodlights: Yes
Clubhouse: Poole Labour Club, off Wimborne Road, Poole **Website:** www.poole-town.fsnet.co.uk
HONOURS: Dorset Senior Cup(12) F.A.Cup 3rd Rd 1926-27 Anglo -Italian R-up 80-81
Western LG. 25-26, 56-57 R-U (3) Southern Lg.R-up 88-89 Southern Div 61-62 Hants (2)
PREVIOUS Western 23-26 Southern 26-30 Western 30-57 Southern57-96
Colours: Red & white halves/red/white. Change colours: Navy & white/white/red or white
Midweek matchday: Wednesday
Programme: Yes Price:£1.00 Pages:60/70
2002-03
Leading Goalscorer:Karim Banssaouda (33) Captain:Neal Spalding and Graham Kemp Player of the Year:Carl Woodward

RINGWOOD TOWN

Secrtary:
Mrs Shirley Crewe, 278 Windham Road, Bournemouth, Dorset BH1 4QU Tel: 012102 398975 (H & Fax)
Chairman: Bob Lane

Ground: The Clubhouse, Long Lane, Ringwood, Hants.Tel: 01425 473448

Colours: Red & black/ black/red & black
Change colours: All blue

ROMSEY TOWN

Ground: The By-Pass Ground, South Front, Romsey, Hampshire
Tel: 01794 512003

SHAFTESBURY

Chairman: A.P.Humphries

Secretary: Phil Watts, 4 Willow Cottages, Compton Abbas, Shaftesbury SP70NF (01747 811037)

Ground: Cockrams, Coppice Street, Shaftesbury (01747 853990)
Cover: Yes Floodlights: Yes Clubhouse: Yes

Colours: Red & white striped/Red/Red

Change colours: Yellow/black/black

STOCKSBRIDGE

Secretary: Robin Smith, Curlews Farm, Quarley, Andover, Hants. SP11 8PT Tel: 01264 773545 Chairman: Dave Gray

Ground: Recreation Ground, High Street, Stockbridge, Hants.

Directions: Off Stockbridge High Street. 1st right at the BT sub-station into the Recreation Ground

Colours: All red. Change colours: Blue & maroon stripes/blue/blue

UNITED SERVICES PORTSMOUTH

Secretary: John Thomas, 21 Elizabeth Court, Fareham, Hants. PO14 1DQ Tel: 07960 116806. Chairman: R. Strudwick

Ground: The Navy Stadium, HMS Temeraire, Burnaby Road, Portsmouth PO1 2EJ Tel: 0239 272 4235, Clubhouse 0239 229 1660

Directions: From Portsmouth Harbour (BR), turn right onto The Hard, pass under the rail bridge and turn left into Park Road, after approx 200yards take 1st right into Burnaby Road. Entrance to ground 100 mtrs on the right.
Colours: Navy blue/navy/sky blue. Change colours: All red
Midweek Matches: Monday

Previous Name: Portsmouth Royal Navy

WHITCHURCH UNITED

Secretary: Joanna Cozzi, 39 Hartley Meadow, Whitchurch,Hants RG26
Tel: 01256 892579(H) 01344 401129 (B) 07780 663494 (M)

Ground: Longmeadow, Winchester Road, Whitchurch Tel: 01256 892493

Directions: From Whitchurch (BR) station; turn left after Railway Inn, follow road to end, turn right into main road, arriving in town turn left alongWinchester Road. Ground three quarters of a mile on left
Capacity: 2,000 Seats: 200 Cover: Yes Floodlights: Yes
Clubhouse: Hot food on matchdays. Sports hall with squash courts and indoor bowling green
PREVIOUS League: Hampshire (pre-1992)
BEST SEASON FA Vase: Extra-Preliminary Rd 93-94, 1-3 v Peppard (H)

2003-2004 Payer of the Year: Chris Iddles **Top Goalscorer:** Paul Roffey

FACT FILE
Founded: 1903
Colours: Red &white/black/black
Change colours: White/blue/blue.
Midweek Matches: Wednesday
Programme: 24 pages

CLUB PERSONNEL
Chairman: Tony Chivers
8 Bloswood Drive, Whichurch, Hants. RG28 7AZ
Tel: 01256 893696 (H) 07702 692200 (M)
Vice Chairman:Russell Thomas
Manager: Jim Nacey
Asst. Man. / Coach:
Captain: David Smalley

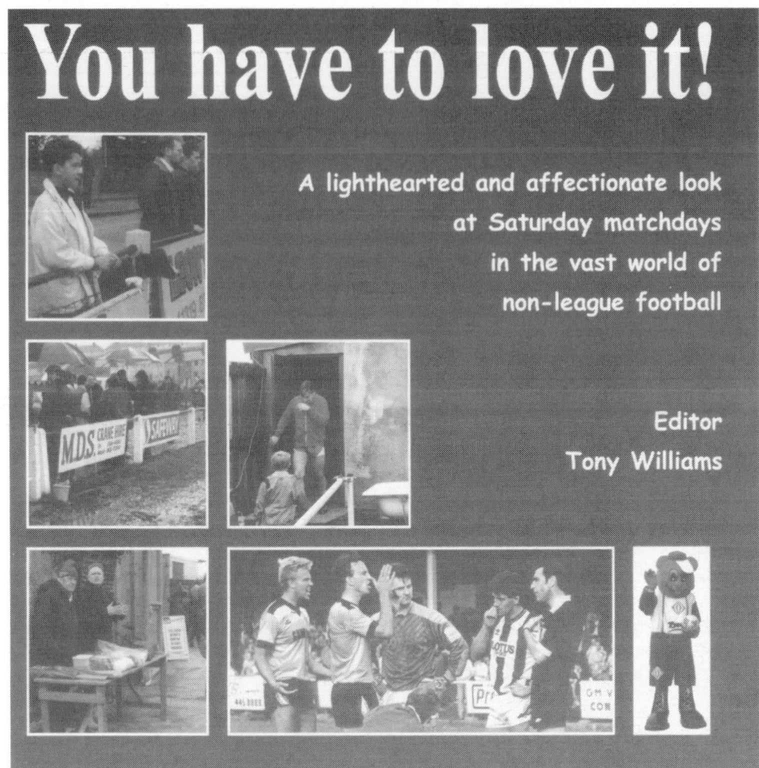
You have to love it!
A lighthearted and affectionate look
at Saturday matchdays
in the vast world of
non-league football
Editor
Tony Williams

DIVISION THREE CLUBS

AFC PORTCHESTER
Secretary: Christine Collier, 14 Brackenwood Drive, Tadley Hants
Tel No: 07884 254706 (M)
Ground: Portchester Community School, White Hart Lane, Portchester, Hants. Tel: 02392 364399
Colours: All Blue

CLANFIELD
Secretary:Stuart Wallis. 42 Glamorgan Road, Catherington, Waterlooville,Hampshire. PO8 OTR Tel No 07765 238231 (M)
Ground: Peel Park, Charlton Lane, Clanfield, Waterlooville, Hants.
Colours: Blue & Black/ Black/Black

COLDEN COMMON
Secretary: Angela Banford, 19 Fleming Place, Colden Common, Winchester Hants. SO21 1SL Tel NO: 07967 889670 (M)
Ground: Colden Common Recreation Ground, Main Road, Colden Common (01962712365)
Colours: Red & white stripes/black/red
Midweek home matchday: Wednesday

DCAFC
Ground: Victoria Park, Castle Road, Salisbury, Wiltshire
Tel: 01722 415089

FARNBOROUGH NORTH END
Secretary: Steve Amos, 3 Charnwood Cres. Chandlers Ford, Southampton Hants. SO53 5QN Tel NO: 07900 928741 (M)
Ground: Farnborough Gate, Ringwood Rd., Farnborough, Hants.
Colours: Red/Black/Red

FLEET SPURS
Secretary: Steve Houghton, 61 Earlsbourne, Church Crookham, Hampshire GU52 8XG Tel NO: 07966 225446
Ground: Ancells Farm, Fleet, Hants
Colours: Red & blue/blue/blue

FLEETLANDS
Secretary: David Bell, 72 White Hart Lane, Portchester, Hants. PO16 9BQ.(01705321781)
Ground: Lederle Lane, Gosport, Hants (01329 239723)
Colours: Red & black/black/black

HAMBLE CLUB
Ground: Shell Mex Ground, Hamble Lane, Hamble-le-Rice, Southampton, Hampshire Tel: 07881 766085

HAYLING UNITED
Secretary: Mrs S hirley Westfield, L'Ancresse14 Harold Road, Hayling Island, Hants PO11 9LT (01705 463305)
Ground: Hayling Park, Hayling Island, Hants
Colours: Black & white stripes/black/black

LAVERSTOCK & FORD
Ground: The Dell, Laverstock & Ford SC, 23 Church Rd., Laverstock, Salisbury. Tel: 01722 327401

LUDGERSHALL SPORTS
Ground: Astor Crescent, Ludgershall, Hampshire
Tel: 01264 398200

M & T AWBRIDGE
Ground: Michelmersh & Timsbury Sports Pavilion, Mannyngham Way, Timsbury, Romsey Tel: 01794 368955

MICHELDEVER
Secretary: Mrs Mary Green, 19 Southbrook Cottages, MIcheldever, Winchester Hants. SO21 3DJ
Tel: 07876 728449 (M)
Ground: Lord Rank Playing Fields, Duke St., Micheldever, Winchester.
Colours: All Navy Blue and White

NETLEY CENTRAL SPORTS
Ground: Netley Rec, Station Road, Netley Abbey, Southampton, Hampshire Tel: 023 8045 2267

ORDNANCE SURVEY
Ground: Lordshill Recreation Ground, Southampton, Hampshire
Tel: 023 8061 8812

OTTERBOURNE
Ground: Oakwood Park, off Oakwood Avenue, Otterbourne, Hampshire Tel: 01962 714681

OVERTON UNITED
Secretary: Mrs A Wheeler, 3 Lordsfield Gardens, Overton, Hants RG25 2EW (01256771241)
Ground: Recreation Centre, Bridge Street, Overton
Tel: 01256 770561
Colours: Blue & white stripes/white/blue
Change: Green & purple/purple/purple
Midweek home matchday: Tuesday or Thursday

PAULSGROVE
Secretary: Jim Garcia, 112 Falmouth Road, Paulsgrove, Portsmouth Hants. PO6 4JT Tel NO: 07901 655485
Ground: The Grove Club, Marsden Rd (off Allaway Avenue), Paulsgrove, Portsmouth (01705 324102)
Colours: Red & black stripes/black/red

QK SOUTHAMPTON
Ground: Lordshill Recreation Centre, Southampton, Hampshire
Tel: 023 8073 2531

RS BASINGSTOKE
Ground: Whiteditch Playing Field, Sherborne Road, Basingstoke, Hampshire Tel: 01256 814618
Previous Lge: Hellenic

TADLEY CALLEVA
Secretary: Steve Blackburn, 7 Bramdean Close, Tadley, Hanrts. RG26 3RD Tel No: 07787 501028 (M)
Ground: The Green, Tadley, Hants
Cols: Blue & maroon stripes/maroon/maroon
Change: Yellow & blue/blue/blue

VERWOOD TOWN
Secretary: Mrs Judith Fry, 19a Noon Hill Rd, Verwood, Dorset BH31 7DB (01202822826)
Ground: Pottern Park, Pottern Way, Verwood, Dorset
Colours: Red with black & white/Black/Red

YATELEY GREEN
Ground: Sean Deveraux Park, Chandlers Lane Playing Fields, Chandlers Lane, Yateley, Hampshire

WESTERN LEAGUE

SPONSORED BY: SCREWFIX DIRECT

President: Rod Webber **Chairman:** Cliff Ashton
Secretary: Ken Clarke, 32 Westmead Lane, Chippenham, Wiltshire SN15 3HZ
Tel: 07790 002279 (8am - 9pm) **Fax:** 01249 652952 **Email:** westernleague@aol.com
www.firsteleven.co.uk/western

PREMIER DIVISION

Bideford and **Paulton Rovers** started the season as joint favourites to take the league title, and they kept everyone guessing until the last two weeks of the season. Bideford hit top spot after their first match and stayed there for most of the season. Paulton Rovers showed well early on but dropped away, mainly due to cup involvement.

Mid season saw Paulton Rovers move back to challenge Bideford and the battle was strong for the rest of the season. **Frome Town** turned out to be the side that decided the Premier Division championship, and they did it by defeating Paulton Rovers twice within eight days. Until they faced Frome Town Paulton Rovers were comfortable in second place and needed six points to apply pressure on table-topping Bideford. Bideford were on track for most of the season to take the treble of FA Vase, League Championship and Les Phillips (League) Cup, but fell at the FA Vase semi-final hurdle at Winchester - but still ended up with the double. It was fitting that Paulton Rovers were Bideford's cup final opponents, after their season-long rivalry, and the North Devon side lifted the cup with the only goal of the game.

Paulton Rovers had indicated early season that they were seeking membership of the realigned Southern League for Season 2004/05, and set out to prove their worth. A club record run in the FA Cup gave the club national recognition, but they went out in the 4th Qualifying Round - still further than any other Western League club this term. With Bideford deciding to remain as a Western League club the door was held open for Paulton Rovers to realise their dreams and take the step up to the Southern League. Elsewhere in the top division many clubs were laying the foundations for a shot at the championship next season. **Frome Town** and **Backwell United** came from lowly positions in mid-season to finish in third and fourth slots. Frome Town suffered from a disastrous home run - until they bought in a white witch to reverse their fortunes. Local TV and Radio had a field day with the story, but the spell was cast to good effect. **Exmouth Town** equiped themselves well in their first season back in the top flight and finished a credible fifth. **Bridgwater Town** disappointed with a poor set of results as winter set in, after starting the season brightly. **Brislington** finished seventh, and could have challenged for a top two place with a little more luck. The top seven were, realistically, the only teams with enough strength in depth to look for honours.

Welton Rovers, Odd Down, Barnstaple Town and **Torrington** turned in some good performances and produced some surprise results, but none of them could find the consistency to move out of mid table. Both **Torrington** and **Keynsham Town** fared well in the FA Vase, and made friends from other leagues along the way. **Bridport, Devizes Town and Melksham Town** struggled to find form throughout the season but did enough to stay away from the danger drop zone. To most neutral observers Keynsham Town finished in a false position, but they could just not convert pressure to goals and faced a worrying last few matches looking at relegation. Even deeper trouble faced **Bishop Sutton** who struggled to find form all season, but they produced more than enough points in their last four matches to pull away from the threat of relegation.

Dawlish Town certainly considered themselves unlucky to end up as a relegated club. After turning the club's fortunes around, following a dreadful start, the new regime were bitterly disappointed not to find enough points to finish in a safe position. **Elmore** never looked like being able to produce a run of results to justify Premier Division survival and ended the season with an unlucky thirteen points in basement position.

FIRST DIVISION

When the League's Board of Directors was granted permission by the FA to increase the size of the League from 37 to 40 clubs, by introducing clubs from outside of the normal pyramid promotion system, it was obvious to some astute club members that elevation to the Premier Division might be achieved without finishing in a top two position. The didn't dull the competition for a top two position and some of the better football was to be found in the lower division. **Hallen** proudly boast that they have achieved success without having to worry about paying anyone to do it. Cup involvement kept Hallen sat just behind the league leaders for most of the season, with games in hand.

Two other Bristol based clubs were both the clubs to beat - **Bristol Manor Farm** looking to relive past glories and **Bitton** hoping to mark their arrival at a higher level with promotion. Bitton did not suffer from their excellent FA Vase run, only going out in artic conditions in the North West. **Clyst Rovers** and **Corsham Town** both planned a campaign to take the championship but couldn't quite find the finishing touch, although circumstances with the restructuring have given the two clubs, along with Bristol Manor Farm, a chance in the top flight next season.

Willand Rovers looked to be in the reckoning, during mid-season but hit a lean spell just when it mattered. Another village side, **Shrewton United**, proved themselves to be worth their league place in their first season in the Western League. **Larkhall Athletic, Calne Town, Wellington, Westbury United, Street** and **Clevedon United** all played some attractive football during the season, but none had the resources to challenge for honours. **Weston St Johns** was probably the club who deserved a higher position on playing strength, but who failed too many times.

Cadbury Heath, Ilfracombe Town, Chard Town and Shepton Mallet all looked at relegation at various stages of the season, but each of them found enough points to get out of trouble. Off pitch problems had dogged **Minehead** for several seasons, but their luck was in when the fifth applicant club to the League failed to meet ground standards, and Minehead avoided the drop to County football.

MANAGER OF THE YEAR TROPHY WINNERS

Bideford (Premier) Hallen (First Division)

FINAL LEAGUE TABLE 2003-04

PREMIER DIVISION	P	W	D	L	F	A	Pts
1. Bideford	34	25	7	2	110	30	82
2. Paulton Rovers	34	25	2	7	85	28	77
3. Frome Town	34	21	5	8	84	43	68
4. Backwell United	34	20	5	9	67	35	65
5. Exmouth Town	34	19	7	8	70	34	64
6. Bridgwater Town	34	19	3	12	67	47	60
7. Brislington	34	18	4	12	57	40	58
8. Welton Rovers	34	14	7	13	62	54	49
9. Odd Down	34	13	10	11	48	44	49
10. Barnstaple Town	34	12	11	11	47	42	47
11. Torrington	34	12	10	12	69	74	46
12. Bridport	34	12	6	16	52	52	42
13. Devizes Town	34	11	2	21	55	69	35
14. Melksham Town	34	9	6	19	38	61	33
15. Keynsham Town	34	8	5	21	45	84	29
16. Bishop Sutton	34	8	4	22	42	77	28
17. Dawlish Town	34	6	5	23	30	103	23
18. Elmore	34	4	1	29	26	137	13

PREMIER		1	2	3	4	5	6	7	8	9	10	11	12	13	14	15	16	17	18
1	Backwell United		2-0	1-2	2-0	1-1	1-1	0-1	7-1	4-2	3-1	1-1	2-0	4-1	3-0	1-0	0-2	1-0	0-1
2	Barnstaple Town	1-1		1-1	1-1	0-3	2-0	1-0	2-0	4-0	3-0	1-3	1-1	5-1	1-1	0-2	1-0	2-2	2-0
3	Bideford	4-1	1-2		4-2	5-0	4-1	2-0	3-0	4-1	6-1	1-1	2-2	4-0	3-0	4-0	0-0	6-0	7-0
4	Bishop Sutton	1-5	0-1	0-4		3-2	1-2	1-2	8-1	2-1	2-0	0-7	0-4	3-2	3-1	0-2	0-5	4-4	0-3
5	Bridgwater Town	3-2	2-1	2-3	1-0		2-0	2-1	5-0	4-2	2-1	1-2	0-1	1-2	2-0	3-0	1-1	2-2	3-1
6	Bridport	1-2	1-1	1-1	1-0	1-2		2-3	0-2	3-0	4-0	1-3	2-3	3-0	4-1	1-1	3-2	1-2	1-3
7	Brislington	0-2	4-3	3-3	1-0	2-1	1-2		0-0	3-1	4-1	1-2	1-4	1-0	1-0	1-1	1-2	1-1	3-0
8	Dawlish Town	1-2	0-4	0-2	2-1	1-7	2-5	0-4		2-2	4-1	1-2	0-6	1-1	1-2	1-1	2-0	1-4	0-1
9	Devizes Town	0-2	1-0	1-3	3-0	0-2	2-0	0-2	0-2		14-0	1-4	1-2	3-2	2-0	0-3	0-1	3-0	1-2
10	Elmore	1-4	0-2	0-9	3-1	2-5	1-0	0-6	3-1	1-2		0-6	1-8	1-2	0-2	1-4	0-9	1-9	3-2
11	Exmouth Town	1-2	3-0	1-3	1-0	2-0	4-1	0-3	4-0	0-1	2-0		0-2	3-0	2-0	3-2	2-3	2-2	1-1
12	Frome Town	0-0	3-1	1-3	4-1	0-2	0-2	2-0	8-0	2-1	0-0	2-2		4-2	3-1	0-1	1-0	2-0	6-3
13	Keynsham Town	0-4	1-1	1-3	1-4	0-1	0-3	0-2	8-0	1-2	1-0	0-3	4-3		3-1	2-1	1-2	1-1	0-5
14	Melksham Town	1-4	0-0	0-2	1-2	2-3	2-0	2-0	3-0	3-2	3-0	0-0	1-3	1-2		2-0	0-3	2-6	1-1
15	Odd Down	2-1	1-1	1-1	0-0	2-0	1-1	0-2	1-1	2-2	3-1	2-1	2-0	5-1	0-1		0-4	2-0	2-2
16	Paulton Rovers	3-0	2-0	4-3	2-0	1-0	1-0	2-0	2-1	5-1	6-0	0-1	1-3	5-1	3-2	0-1		3-0	3-1
17	Torrington	1-0	3-0	2-3	2-2	2-1	1-1	2-1	0-2	4-1	3-2	2-1	3-4	3-3	2-2	3-2	2-6		0-5
18	Welton Rovers	1-2	2-2	0-4	2-0	4-1	1-3	1-2	4-0	0-2	5-0	0-0	3-0	1-1	0-0	3-1	0-2	4-1	

FINAL LEAGUE TABLE 2003-04

DIVISION ONE		P	W	D	L	F	A	Pts
1.	Hallen	36	24	7	5	75	26	79
2.	Bitton	36	23	7	6	84	37	76
3.	Bristol Manor Farm	36	20	14	2	74	38	74
4.	Clyst Rovers	36	21	9	6	74	41	72
5.	Corsham Town	36	19	9	8	70	41	66
6.	Willand Rovers	36	17	8	11	72	50	59
7.	Shrewton United	36	17	4	15	86	70	55
8.	Larkhall Athletic	36	15	10	11	65	54	55
9.	Calne Town	36	13	10	13	49	45	49
10.	Wellington	36	14	7	15	54	55	49
11.	Westbury United	36	14	6	16	52	56	48
12.	Street	36	11	10	15	54	51	43
13.	Clevedon United	36	11	9	16	60	75	42
14.	Weston St Johns	36	11	9	16	72	95	42
15.	Cadbury Heath	36	9	10	17	50	64	37
16.	Ilfracombe Town	36	7	6	23	43	106	27
17.	Chard Town	36	7	5	24	48	87	26
18.	Shepton Mallet Town	36	5	9	22	49	82	24
19.	Minehead Town	36	5	9	22	35	93	24

DIVISION ONE		1	2	3	4	5	6	7	8	9	10	11	12	13	14	15	16	17	18	19
1	Bitton		2-1	2-2	1-2	2-0	3-1	1-1	4-1	1-1	2-2	1-0	5-0	2-1	8-3	0-1	1-2	3-0	2-1	0-1
2	Bristol Manor Farm	0-0		2-0	2-1	2-2	2-2	1-1	1-1	1-1	1-0	3-1	4-2	7-1	1-0	1-1	1-1	4-1	4-2	2-1
3	Cadbury Heath	0-2	1-1		1-0	0-2	4-5	1-3	1-1	1-1	6-0	2-2	0-0	2-2	3-1	1-3	1-2	2-3	1-4	0-1
4	Calne Town	3-4	0-2	0-0		1-0	0-0	1-4	2-0	1-1	2-0	0-0	5-2	3-2	0-2	0-2	0-2	0-0	3-3	1-3
5	Chard Town	1-4	0-2	2-3	0-1		1-2	2-3	5-1	2-5	1-2	1-1	2-2	2-1	0-1	1-1	1-3	3-2	4-1	0-6
6	Clevedon United	1-2	3-3	0-0	1-1	4-1		1-3	0-2	1-1	3-1	1-5	1-2	2-1	2-4	2-0	2-1	4-2	3-2	0-1
7	Clyst Rovers	1-3	0-1	2-1	1-0	1-1	2-0		5-1	1-0	6-1	1-3	1-0	3-2	3-1	1-1	1-0	1-0	4-3	3-0
8	Corsham Town	2-0	2-2	4-0	2-0	7-2	1-0	0-0		0-1	3-0	3-0	4-0	2-0	1-2	1-0	1-0	1-1	3-0	3-0
9	Hallen	2-0	1-1	2-0	0-0	4-0	5-1	4-1	2-0		4-0	2-0	3-0	2-0	4-2	2-0	2-0	2-0	8-1	1-0
10	Ilfracombe Town	1-7	0-1	1-1	4-3	3-2	1-4	0-2	0-3	0-1		1-1	2-0	0-5	2-6	2-1	0-3	0-2	2-2	0-4
11	Larkhall Athletic	1-4	3-2	3-0	1-1	3-1	4-1	1-1	2-4	1-4	1-1		4-0	2-1	3-1	2-0	1-2	4-1	2-2	0-3
12	Minehead Town	1-4	0-2	0-1	0-4	2-3	1-1	3-1	1-4	1-0	1-4	2-1		1-1	1-5	4-1	1-1	0-0	1-2	0-0
13	Shepton Mallet Town	1-1	2-4	0-2	0-1	3-1	3-0	1-1	1-0	0-4	2-2	2-5	4-0		2-2	0-0	1-1	2-3	1-2	0-4
14	Shrewton United	1-1	2-3	1-2	0-0	1-2	4-2	2-1	1-3	2-0	5-2	3-1	4-2	4-0		3-2	1-2	1-2	8-1	4-5
15	Street	0-2	2-2	1-2	3-1	4-2	3-1	0-2	2-2	0-2	4-1	0-1	9-0	4-2	2-2		1-1	0-2	0-0	2-3
16	Wellington	1-2	1-2	4-1	0-2	2-0	3-3	1-5	2-3	0-1	4-2	2-4	1-1	3-2	2-3	0-1		1-2	1-5	0-0
17	Westbury United	1-3	1-1	3-1	1-2	2-0	1-2	2-2	1-1	0-1	3-4	1-2	3-0	1-0	1-0	1-0	0-1		0-2	4-1
18	Weston St Johns	0-2	0-3	1-6	1-4	3-1	2-1	1-5	2-2	4-0	7-1	0-0	4-2	3-3	3-2	2-2	1-3	0-3		1-4
19	Willand Rovers	0-3	0-2	3-1	0-4	2-0	3-3	1-1	1-1	4-1	3-1	0-0	2-2	6-0	1-2	0-1	0-1	5-2	4-4	

LES PHILLIPS CUP

PRELIMINARY ROUND

Cadbury Heath	v	Bideford	0-3
Chard Town	v	Westbury United	3-1
Larkhall Athletic	v	Minehead Town	2-0
Street	v	Paulton Rovers	0-4
Wellington	v	Ilfracombe Town	7-2

FIRST ROUND

Barnstaple Town	v	Chard Town	3-0
Bideford	v	Clyst Rovers	5-4*
Bishop Sutton	v	Elmore	6-1
Bitton	v	Welton Rovers	2-3
Bridgwater Town	v	Backwell United	3-0
Brislington	v	Clevedon United	1-2
Calne Town	v	Larkhall Athletic	2-0
Devizes Town	v	Dawlish Town	5-1
Exmouth Town	v	Willand Rovers	3-1
Frome Town	v	Wellington	2-0
Keynsham Town	v	Corsham Town	1-2
Melksham Town	v	Bridport	3-0
Odd Down	v	Weston St Johns	1-1* 1-2p
Shepton Mallet Tn	v	Bristol Manor Farm	0-3
Shrewton United	v	Hallen	2-2* 3-2p
Torrington	v	Paulton	2-5

SECOND ROUND

Bideford	v	Bishop Sutton	7-1
Bridgwater Town	v	Weston St Johns	2-3
Bristol MF	v	Shrewton Utd	4-1
Corsham	v	Welton Rovers	4-1
Devizes	v	Barnstaple Town	0-1
Exmouth Town	v	Clevedon United	1-0
Frome Town	v	Paulton Rovers	1-2
Melksham Town	v	Calne	2-1

QUARTER-FINALS

Bideford	v	Exmouth Town	2-1*
Corsham Town	v	Bristol Manor Farm	2-3
Melksham Town	v	Barnstaple Town	0-2
Paulton Rovers	v	Weston St Johns	6-2

SEMI-FINALS

Barnstaple Town	v	Paulton Rovers	0-0* 0-3p
Bristol Manor Farm	v	Bideford	2-3

THE FINAL (8th May at Clevedon Town)

Paulton Rovers	v	Bideford	0-1

BACKWELL UNITED

Secretary: Jonathon Rpogers,114 Wellington Hill West,Westbury on Trym, Bristol BS9 4QY Tel No: 0117 985 6138

Ground: Backwell Recreation Ground, West Town Rd, Backwell, Avon Tel: 1275 462612

Directions: Near centre of Backwell on main A370 Bristol to Weston-super-Mare road. Buses from Bristol or Weston, or 20 mins walk from Nailsea & Backwell(BR) station; turn right out of station, right at traffic lights (half mile),ground quarter mile on right just past car sales

Capacity: 1,000 Seats: 60 Cover: 150 Floodlights: Yes

Clubhouse: Open 6-11pm weekdays, 12.30-11pm Sat. Snacks available Club Shop: No

HONOURS Somerset Snr Lg 77-78 79-80 80-81 81-82 82-83 (Lg Cup 82-83 (R-up 79-80) Div 1 72-73); Somerset Snr Cup 81-82; SW Co.'s Sutton Transformer Cup 81-82. Western Lge Div 1 89-90 Champions, 94-95 promoted in 3rd place

PREVIOUS **Leagues**: Clevedon & Dist; Bristol C. of E.; Bristol Surburban (pre 1970); Somerset Senior 70-83
Grounds: Two in Backwell prior to 1939. Club reformed in 1946

RECORD **Attendance**: 487 v Brislington, Gt Mills Lg. 2/5/94
Goalscorer: Steve Spalding **Appearances:** Wayne Buxton
Win: 10-1 v Dowton, F.A.Cup 1st Qualifying Round. 1998-99
Defeat: 2-6 v Tiverton Town (H), Les Phillips Cup QF 1.2.94

FACT FILE
Founded: 1911
Nickname: Stags
Club Sponsors: D.C.I.Refrigeration
Colours: All red
Change colours: Sky/navy/skyMidweek
Matches: Tuesday
Programme: 42 pages, 50p
Editor: Jonathon Rogers (01179 856138)

CLUB PERSONNEL
Chairman: Phil RexVice-Chairman: MikeNaylor
President: Charlie Jones
Press Officer:Mike Naylor (01275 858576)
Manager:Jamie Patch
Asst Manager: Jeff Meacham
Captain: Craig Patch
Physio: Dave Gould

2002-03
Leading Goalscorer: Richard Hewitt
P.o.Y.: Marcus Maggs

BARNSTAPLE TOWN

Secretary: David Cooke, 51 Walnut Way, Whiddon Valley, Barnstaple, Devon. EX32 7RF Tel: 01271 326088

Ground: Mill Road, Barnstaple, North Devon Tel: 01271 343469

Directions: A361 towards Ilfracombe (from M5 Jct 26), in Barnstaple follow A36 1Ilfracombe signs, second left after crossing small bridge is Mill Road

Capacity: 5,000 Seats: 250 Cover: 1,000 Floodlights: Yes

Clubhouse: Full license with canteen on match days.

HONOURS Western Lg 52-53 79-80 (R-up 80-81 81-82, Div 1 49-50 94-95, Merit Cup74-75 83-84 84-85, Comb. 92-93), Devon Professional Cup 62-63 64-65 67-68 69-70 71-73 (X2) 74-75 76-81 (X5), Devon Lg, Devon St Lukes Cup 87-88, Devon Snr Cup 92-93, Devon Youth Cup 48-49 51-52

PREVIOUS **Leagues:** Nth Devon, Devon & Exeter, S. Western **Name:** Pilton Yeo Vale
Grounds: Town Wharf (> 1920); Highfield Rd, Newport (> 35), Pilton Pk, Rock Pk

RECORDS **Attendance:** 6,200 v Bournemouth, FA Cup 1st Rd, 54**Appearances:** Ian Pope **Win:** 12-1 v Tavistock (H), FA Cup 3rd Qual. Rd 1954 **Defeat:** 1-10 v Mangotsfield Utd (A), West Lge Prem. Div. 90-91 **Fee out**: £4,000 to Hungerford T for Joe Scott **Fee in** £6,000 for Ian Doyle from Bristol City **BEST SEASON** **F.A Cup:** 1st Rd replay 51-52 **FA Vase:** 4th Rd 94-95

Players progressing: Len Pickard (Bristol R. 51), John Neale (Exeter72), Barrie Vassallo (Torquay 77), Ian Doyle (Bristol C. 78), Ryan Souter (Swindon 94), Jason Cadie (Reading 94), Simon Heal (Cardiff City -02)

FACT FILE
Founded: 1906
Nickname: Barum
Sponsors:Brend Hotels
Colours: Red/red/red
Change colours: Yellow and Black
Midweek Matches: Tuesday
Reserve League: Devon & Exeter
Programme:£1.00
Programme Editor: David Cooke
Local Press: N. Devon Journal Herald

CLUB PERSONNEL
President: Wilf Harris
Chairman:Roy Lucas
Manager: Jeff Evans
Physio: Dave Griffith
Captain: Simon Hill

2003-2004
Leading Goalscorer:Kevin Squire
Player of the Year:Simon Ovey

BIDEFORD

Secretary: Kevin Tyrrell, 69 Laurel Ave., Bideford, devon EX39 3AZ Tel: 01237 4707747

Ground: The Sports Ground, Kingsley Road, Bideford Tel: 01237 474975

Directions: A361 for Bideford - ground on right as you enter the town
Capacity: 6,000 Seats: 120 Cover: 1,000 Floodlights: Yes
Clubhouse: `Robins Nest' - on ground. Open lunchtimes and evenings, snacks and bar menu. Mgr: Mrs Sue Tyrell

HONOURS Western Lg 63-64 70-7171-72 81-82 82-83, Div 1 51-52, Div 3 49-50, Lg Cup 71-72 84-85; Alan Young Cup 64-65 69-70; Merit Cup 68-69; Subsidiary Cup 71-72; Devon Snr Cup 79-80; Devon St Lukes Cup 81-82 83-84 85-86 95-96 (R-up 86-87 91-92 94-95)

PREVIOUS **Leagues:** Devon & Exeter 47-49; Western 49-72; Southern 72-75
Name: Bideford Town **Ground:** Hansen Ground (1 season)

BEST SEASON **FA Cup:** 1st Rd 64-65(replay) 73-74 77-78 81-82. **FA Vase:**

RECORD **Gate:** 6,000 v Gloucester C., FA Cup 4th Qual. Rd 60
Scorer: Tommy Robinson 259 **Appearances:** Derek May 527
Win: 16-0 v Soundwell 50-51 **Defeat:** 0-12 v Paulton 96-97

Players progressing: Shaun Taylor (Swindon Town) Tony Dennis (Cambridge)

FACT FILE
Founded: 1949
Nickname: Robins
Colours: All Red
Change colours: All Blue
Midweek Matchday: Tuesday
Prog: 32 pages, 50p Editor: Ian Knight

CLUB PERSONNEL
Chairman: Paul Mitchell
President: Jimmy McElwee
Hon.Vice Predident: Kevin Keegan
Company Secretary: B.Weston
Marketing & Promotions Exec. Sean Joyce
Assistant Secrtary: Ron Ackland
Manager: Sean Joyce Ass. Man: Mike Jones
Reserves Manager: Dave Matthews
Chief Scout Dudley Barry
Physio: Tony Beal

Bideford - Back Row (L-R): R Herrera, L Taswell, R Gough, L Langmead, D Hawkins, M Hare, R Draper, E Laight, T Kelly, S Orchard. **Front Row:** L Grove, S Langmead, M Southgate, T Schofield, P Mitchell (Chairman), S Joyce (Manager), O Pickard, J Alexander.

BISHOP SUTTON

Secretary: Roy Penney, 53 Ridgway Lane, Whitchurch, Bristol BS14 9PJ Tel: 01275 541392

Ground: Lakeview Football Field, Bishop Sutton Tel: 01275 333097

Directions: On A368 at rear of Butchers Arms pub - ground signposted on left entering village from the West

Capacity: 1,500 Seats: None Cover: 200 Floodlights: yes

Clubhouse: Open matchdays. Rolls, pies and usual pub food available Club Shop: No

HONOURS Somerset Snr Lg R-up 89-90 (Div 1 83-84 (R-up 81-82), Div 2 82-83), Bristol & Avon Lg 80-81 (Div 2 79-80), Somerset Jnr Cup 80-81, Weston Yth Lg77-78, Chew Valley KO Cup 83-84, Mid-Somerset Lg(Res) R-up 82-83 (Div 3 81-82)

PREVIOUS **Leagues:** Weston & Dist. Yth; Bristol & Avon; Somerset Snr (pre 1991)
Ground: Adjacent cricket field

BEST SEASON **FA Cup:** **FA Vase: 3rd Rd 1998**

CLUB RECORDS **Attendance:** 400 v Bristol City, friendly
Win: 15-0 v Glastonbury Res

Players progressing: David Lee (Chelsea), S Williams (Southampton), J French(Bristol R.)

FACT FILE
Founded: 1977
Nickname: Bishops
Sponsors: M/E Services
Colours: All blue
Change colours: All yellow
Midweek Matches: Wednesday
Youth team's League: Somerset Mid Week
Programme: Yes
Editor: G Williams

CLUB PERSONNEL
Chairman: George Williams
Vice Chairman: Roy Penney
President: Bob Redding
Managers: N. Williams & R.Chaffey
Coach: Chris Bailes
Physio: Tony Parsons

BITTON

Secretary: Mark Tilling, 71 Howes Close, Barrs Court, Bristol BS30 8SB
Tel Nos: 0117 9604550 (H) 07830 126135 (M)

Ground: The Recreation Ground, Bath Road, Bitton, BS30 6HX Tel: 0117 932 3222
Capacity:1000 Cover: 200 Seats: 48 Floodlights: Yes Club Shop: Yes

Directions: M4 junc 18. Take A46 towards Bath, at first roundabout take A420 for Wick/ Bridgeyate. On approach to Bridgeyate turn left at mini-roundabout onto A4175 and follow for 2.2 miles, then left for Bath on the A431. The ground is 100 yards on right.
Nearest station: Keynsham, Bristol

Clubhouse: Weekdays 7.30-11, Sat.& Sun all day.

HONOURS Glos. Jun Cup r-up 90; Avon Prem. Lg r-up 94, 95; Glos Sen amat Cup 95; Glos Chall Trophy r-up 97; Glos County Lg r-up 97.

PREVIOUS **Leagues:** Avon Premier Comb.ination, Glos County

FACT FILE
Founded: 1922
Sponsors: John Dean Builders
Colours: Red & white stripes/black/black
Change colours: Yellow/green/yellow
Midweek Matcday :Tuesday 7.45
Programme: 36 pages Editor: Paul Cater

CLUB PERSONNEL
Chairman: John Langdon
V- Chairman: Paul Cater Pres: Roy Ewans
Treas: Steve Webb Manager: Keith Brown
2002-2003 Captain: Rich Lee
Top Scorer: Mike ~Branch
Player of the Year: Matt Emery

BRIDGWATER TOWN (1984)

General Secretary: Mrs Glenda Fletcher,18 Dunkery Road, Bridgwater Tel:01278 425599
Football Secretary: Ray Heard, 7 Willoughby Road, Bridgwater TA6 7L
Tel Nos: 01278 421958 (H) 01278 446922 (W)
Ground: Fairfax Park, College Way, Bath Road, Bridgwater Tel: 01278 446899 (matchdays and weekday mornings only -it is not a postal address).
Website: www.bridgwatertownfc.com
Directions: M5 jct 23, follow signs to Glastonbury (A39), turn right for Bridgwater (A39). Follow sign to Bridgwater College via College Way.Ground on rt after Rugby Club One mile from Bridgwater (BR) station

Capacity: 2,500 **Seats:** 150 **Cover:** 400 **Floodlights:** Yes

Clubhouse: Robins social club on the Ground with refreshmants cabin on matchdays

HONOURS Somerset Senior Cup 93-94, Somerset Senior Lge 89-90 90-91 91-92, Lg Cup winners (4) ,Western Lge Div 1 95-96, Merit cup 96-97
Somerset Senior Cup: 93-94 95-96

PREVIOUS **League:** Somerset Snr (pre-1994) **Names:** None
BEST SEASON **FA Cup:** 2nd Q Rd **FA Vase:** First Round Proper
RECORDS **Attendance:** 1,112 v Taunton Town 26.2. 97

FACT FILE
Founded: 1984
(after collapse of previous BTFC)
Nickname: The Robins
Sponsor: TMB Patterns Ltd
Colours: Red,white & black/black/red
Change colours: All blue
Midweek matchday: Tuesday
Youth League.: Somerset U18 Floodlight
Prog. Editor: Mark Hollidge ,8 Conway Road, Cannington , Bridgwater TA5 2NP

CLUB PERSONNEL
Chairman: Steve French
Patron & President: Tom Pearce
Press Officer: Gordon Nelson (01823 271167)
Manager: Trevor Senior
Captain: Marcus Vaughan
Sports Injury Therapist: Dave Callow
L.C.S.P.(Assoc): F.A.Dip
2003-2004 Player of the Year: Ben Kirk
Top Scorer: Shane Kingston.

BRIDPORT

Secretary: Adrian Scadding,158 South Street,Bridport, Dorset DT6 3NP
Tel Nos: 01308 423403 (H) 07785 752522 (M)
Ground: The Beehive, St Mary's Field, Bridport, Dorset Tel: 01308 423834

Directions: Take West Bay road from town centre, turn right just before Palmers Brewery

Capacity: 2,000 Seats: 200 Cover: 400 Floodlights: Yes Club Shop: No

Clubhouse: Yes, open matchdays and for functions. Hot and cold snacks available

HONOURS Western Lg Cup 70-71 72-73 77-78 (R-up 76-77, Div 1 R-up 94-95, Merit Cup 69-70 71-72 73-74); Dorset Comb.(3) 85-88 (Lg Cup 86-87 87-88); Dorset Snr Cup(8) 63-64 69-71 75-76 78-81 87-88; Dorset Snr Amtr Cup(6) 48-50 54-55 56-57 70-72; W. Dorset Chal. Bowl 07-08; Perry Str. Lg 22-23; Mark Frowde Cup 76-77 88-89
PREVIOUS **Leagues:** Perry Street; Western 61-84; Dorset Combination 84-88
Grounds: Pymore (pre 1930s); Crown Field (pre 1953)
BEST SEASON **FA Cup:** **FA Vase:**5th Round 88-89
RECORD **Attendance:** 1,150 v Exeter City, 1981; 3,000 v Chelsea, at Crown, 1950
Scorer (in a season): Ellis Hoole 36
Fee received: £2,000 for Tommy Henderson
Fee paid: £1,000 for Steve Crabb

FACT FILE
Founded: 1885
Nickname: Bees
Sponsors:Nerwlands Holidays
Colours: Red & black/red
Change colours: All Blue
Midweek Matches: Tuesday
Reserves ' League: Dorset Combination
Programme: 40pages, #1.00
Editor: Ian Hallett (01308 868795)

CLUB PERSONNEL
Chairman: Barry Williams
Manager: Bob Russell

Bitton AFC - Back Row (L-R): Phil Williams, James Raynes, Andy Weeks, Ben Pope, Simon Crawford, Joe Mogg, Lee Gitson. **Front Row:** Mark Davies, Nick Burton, Matt Huxley, Adam Cole, Matt Emery.

Photo: Alan Coomes.

BRISLINGTON

Secretary: Kevin Jacobs, 179 Bishopsworth Road, Bedminster Down, Bristol BS13 7LG
Tel. Nos: 01179 782247 (H) 01179 3629179 (W) 07976 7724202(M)

Ground: Ironmould Lane, Brislington, Bristol Tel: 0117 977 4030
Directions: 4 miles out of Bristol on main A4 to Bath - turn left up lane opposite Garden Centre just before dual carriageway (500 yards past Park & Ride on right)

Capacity: 2000 Seats: 144 Cover: 1500 Floodlights: Yes

Clubhouse: Yes - on ground, open matchdays **Club Shop:** No

HONOURS Somerset Senior Cup 92-93 R-up 93-94; Western Lg R-Up: 2002-2003 les Phillips Western Lg.Cup R-Up: 2003
Somerset Senior League, Premier Cup 95-96
Somerset County League Champions 2001-02 (Reserves)

PREVIOUS **League:** Somerset Senior (pre-1991)

BEST SEASON **FA Vase**: 3rd Rd 89-90, 2-3 v Abingdon T. (A)

FACT FILE
Formed: 1956
Nickname: Bris
Sponsors: T.B.A.
Colours: Red & black/black/black & red
Change colours: White/red/red
Midweek matches: Tuesday
Reserves ' League: Somerset Senior
Programme: £1.00
Editor: Laserset (0117 969 5487)

CLUB PERSONNEL
President: Paul Bishop
Chairman: M.Richardson
Vice-Chairman:B.Perrott
Manager: Tony Cornelves
Asst Manager: Pete Wills
Physio: Lee Williams

2003-2004
Leading Goalscorer:Rob Claridge
Player of the Year:Andy Cook

BRISTOL MANOR FARM

Secretary: John Scriven, 44 Woodleaze,Sea Mills,Bristol BS9 2HY
Tel Nos:0117 968 4916 (H) 07870 446639 (M) Email: jon@bristolmanorfarmfc.fsnet.co.uk
Ground: 'The Creek', Portway, Sea Mills, Bristol BS9 2HS Tel: 0117 968 3571
Directions: M5 jct 18 (Avonmouth Bridge), follow A4 for Bristol - U-turn on dual carriageway by Bristol & West sports ground and return for half mile on A4- ground entrance is down narrow lane on left (hidden entrance). Near to Sea Mills station (BR Temple Meads-Severn Beach line)
Capacity: 2,000 Seats: 98 Cover: 350 Floodlights: Yes Club Shop: No
Clubhouse: Open every evening & lunchtime Sat & Sun. Lounge bar, skittle alley, bar meals.
HONOURS Western Lge Prem 00-01 Sportsman Awards, Western Lg Div 1 82-83, Glos Tphy 87-88, Glos Amtr Cup 89-90, Somerset Snr Lg Div 1 (Lg Cup, Div 2)
PREVIOUS **Leagues:** Bristol Suburban 64-69; Somerset Snr 69-77
Name: Manor Farm O.B. 1964-68 **Grounds:** None
RECORD **Attendance:** 500 v Portway, Western Lg 1974
2003-2004 **Player of the Year:** Matthew Baird **Top Scorer:** David Anyinsah

FACT FILE
Formed: 1964 Nickname: The Farm
Club Sponsors: GreenKing
Colours: Red & black/red/red
Change colours: All yellow
Midweek Matchday: Tuesday
Reserve s' League: Suburban League
Youth Team: Somerset Floodlit Lg.
Prog: 32 pages, £1.00 Editor: Mark Smith
website: www.web-teams.co.uk

CLUB PERSONNEL
Chairman: Geoff Selleck
Manager: Shaun Bond
Coach: Nigel Gillard
Captain: Matthew Baird

CLYST ROVERS

Secretary: Bob Chamberlain, Orchard Cottage, Clyst St George, Exeter EX3 0NZ(01392 873498)
Ground: Waterslade Park, Clyst Honiton, Devon Tel: 01392 366424
Directions: A30 following signs for Exeter Airport. Coming from Exeter take 1st right after airport turning (ground signposted) up narrow 200yds past Duke of York Pub
Capacity: 3,000 Seats: 130 Cover: 300 Floodlights: Yes
Club Shop: Yes, Programmes, souvenirs etc
Clubhouse: Open one and a half hours before kick off and after game. Excellent food available
HONOURS Devon St Lukes Cup R-up 92-93, Western Lg Cup SF 92-93
PREVIOUS **Leagues:** Exeter & District 26-44 51-66; Exeter & District Sunday 67-82; South Western 81-92
Grounds: Fair Oak 1926-44

RECORD **Gate:** 768 v Tiverton, Devon St Lukes final 11/5/93
Win: 6-0 v Heavitree United, 1993
Defeat: 0-12 v Torpoint Athletic, South Western League, October 1990

FACT FILE
Founded: 1926 Reformed: 1951
Nickname: Rovers
Sponsors: Vantage Pharmacy, Paignton
Colours: Silver & Black
Change colours: All Yellow
Midweek Matches: Tuesday
Programme: 32 pages, 30p

Editor:

CLUB PERSONNEL
President: Mr P W Brown
Chairman: Bob Chamberlain
Vice Chairman: Colin Dadson
Managers:Bill Potter & Martin Tooze
Physio: Bill Wreford

CORSHAM TOWN

Secretary: Richard Taylor, 7 Cresswells, Corsham, Wilts SN13 9NJ Tel: 01249 714406
Website: www.corshamtownfc.co.uk Email: info@corshamtownfc.co.uk

Ground: Southbank Ground, Lacock Road, Corsham, Wilts. SN13 9HS Tel: 01249 715609

Directions From the A4 turn into Corsham at the Hare & Hounds PH roundabout, taking the Melksham Road, B3353, past the Methuen Arms PH then straight across the next mini-r'about into Lacock Road. The ground is situated 1/2 mile on right

Capacity: 1,500 Seats: No Cover: Yes Floodlights: Yes

Clubhouse: Yes Club Shop: Yes

HONOURS Wiltshire Lge. 97-98, Wiltshire FA Sen. Cup 75-76 96-97,
Wiltshire Lge. KO Cup 95-96 96-97

PREVIOUS **League:** Wiltshire Co. Lge

FACT FILE
Founded: 1893
Sponsors: Hong Kong House Vanitec
Colours: Red & white/white/red
Change colours: Yellow/blue/blue
Midweek matchday: Tuesday

CLUB PERSONNEL
Chairman: Colin Hudd
Manager:Colin Bush
Assistant Manager: John Woods
Captain:Nigel Curtis

2003-2004
Leading Goalscorer:Dave Kilmurray
Player of the Year:Nigel Curtis

DEVIZES TOWN

Secretary: Rolfe Wallen, 2 Cromwell Road, Devizes, Wilts. SN10 3EJ (01380 721217)
Tel Nos: 01380 720648 Email: royking100uk@hotmail.com

Ground: Nursteed Road, Devizes. Tel: 01380 722817
Directions: Off Nursteed Road (A342 signposted Andover); leaving town ground on right opposite Eastleigh Rd
Capacity: 2,500 Seats: 130 Cover: 400 Floodlights: Yes
Clubhouse: Members Bar with satellite TV and 'Centre Spot' function room plus gym
Club Shop: In clubhouse
HONOURS Western League Div. 1 99-00; Wilts Snr Cup 07-08 49-50 56-57 57-58 58-59 60-61 61-62 62-63 65-66 67-68 70-71 71-72 73-74 78-79

PREVIOUS **Leagues:** Wilts Comb.; Wilts Premier
Name: Southbroom (until early 1900s) **Ground:** London Rd (pre 1946)
CLUB RECORDS **Attendance:** Not Known
Win: 14-0 v Elmore western Prem. 03-04 **Defeat:** Not Known
BEST SEASON **FA Vase:** Quarter Final 1980-81, 02-03 **FA Cup:** 4th Qual Rd

FACT FILE
Founded: 1883
Nckname: Town
Colours: Red & white /black/red
Change colours: All Blue
Midweek Matchday: Tuesday
Programme: Price: Pages:
Editor:

CLUB PERSONNEL
President: Chris Dodd
Chairman: Ross Rossiter
Press Officer:Paul Humphries
Manager: Mark Godley
Assistant Manager: John Freeguard
Physio: Gaye Richards
Captain: Kevin Bush

2003-2004
Player of the Year: Andy Coombes
Top Scorer: Marcus Wallen

EXMOUTH TOWN

Ground: King George V Ground, Southern Road, Exmouth Tel: 01395 263348

Directions: On right side of main Exeter to Exmouth road (A376).
Half mile from Exmouth (BR)
Capacity: 2,500 Seats: 100 Cover: 250 Floodlights: Yes
Clubhouse: Open every night and weekend lunchtimes. Snacks available
Club Shop: No

PREVIOUS **League:** Devon & Exeter 1933-73
Grounds: Maer Cricket Field 33-38 48-64; Raleigh Park, Withycombe 38-39
RECORD **Attendance:** 2,395 v Liverpool XI, friendly in 1987
Goalscorer: Mel Pym, 117
Appearances: Keith Sprague, Geoff Weeks 410 (Western Lg)
Victory: 11-0 v Pewsey Vale 7/10/00 (A) 10-0 v Glastonbury 27'3/99 (H)
Defeat: 0-10 v Tiverton (A), Devon St Lukes Cup QF 16/2/94
BEST SEASON **FA Vase:** Semi Final 84-85
HONOURS Western Lg x 3, R-up x 2, Lg Cup 88-89 Les Phillips Cup 00-01,
Div 1 R-up 81-82 2002-03, Sportmanship Trophy x 3;
Devon Premier Cup x 2 Devon St Lukes Cup x 3; Devon Senior Cup 50-51;
East Devon Snr Cup x 2 Harry Wood Mem. Cup 81-82; Exmouth Chal. Cup x 7

FACT FILE
Formed: 1933
Nickname: `Town' or `Blues'
Colours: Blue & white/blue/blue
Change colours: All Red
Midweek matchday: Tuesday
Reserves' League: Devon & Exeter

Programme
36 pages, 50p
Editor: P.Hiscox

CLUB PERSONNEL
President: Brian Bradley
Chairman: Phillip Rugg
Secretary: David Richardson J.P.,
44 Whitchurch Avenue, Exeter. EX2 1NT
Tel: 01392 430985
email: davidrich43@hotmail.com

Manager: Russell Wilson

FROME TOWN

Secretary: Ian Pearce, 52 Woodhayes Road, Frome, Somerset BA11 2DQ (07811511222)
Ground: Badgers Hill, Berkeley Road, Frome Tel: 01373 464087
Directions: On the Westbury Road, 1 mile from town centre and Frome BR station
Capacity: 5,000 Seats: 250 Cover: 800 Floodlights: Yes Club Shop: Yes
Clubhouse: Evenings & weekends. Cold food only

PREVIOUS **League:** Somerset Senior, Wilts League and Wilts Premier
BEST SEASON **FA Trophy:** 2nd Rd v Boston Utd (a) 0-4, 1984-85
FA Cup: 1st Rd Proper v L.Orient 1954-55
FA Vase: 2nd Rd v Paulton R (a) 1-2
RECORD **Attendance:** 8,000 v Leyton Orient, F.A.Cup 1st Rd. 58
Victory: 15-0 v Glastonbury, Somerset Senior League (h) 1906-07
Defeat: 1-11 v Dorchester, Western League (a) 1958-59

HONOURS Western Lg 78-79 Div 1 1919-20 2001-02 Div 2 R-up 54-55, Lg Cup 79-80 82-83, Merit Cup 82-83, Alan Young Cup 79-80, Subsidiary Cup 59-60, Wiltshire Prem Lg 62-63, Wiltshire Lge 1909-10,1910-11; Western Co's F'lit Cup 83-84, Somerset Snr Cup 32-33 33-34 50-51,Somerset Prem Cup 66-67 68-69 82-83, Somerset Snr Lg Div 1 (Res) 90-91, Div 3 1985-86 , Somerset Sen Lg Cup (Res) 1991-92, Somerset Co. League Divisions 2/3 Cup 2001-02 2003-04.

FACT FILE
Founded: 1904
Nickname: Robins
Sponsors: Woodman Furniture
Colours: All Red
Change colours: All Yellow
Midweek matchday: Wednesday
Reserves ' League: Somerset County Div 2
Youth League: Somerset Floodlit Premier
Prog:40 pages £1.00 Editor: Ian Pearce
Official Website: www.frometown.co.uk

CLUB PERSONNEL
President: Paul McGuiness.
Chairman: Geoff Norris
Manager: Andy Black
Assistant Manager: Martyn Dyer
Physio: Shaun Baker
Captain: Matt Peters

2003-2004
Top scorers : Simon Gale & Mark Salter 20
Player of the Year: Jon Hayter

HALLEN

Secretary: Charmeine Phillips, 145A Station Road, Henbury, BristolBS10 7LZ
Tel No: 0117 950 1754.
Email Address jrogers.gosw@go-region.gsi.gov.ok

Ground: Hallen Centre, Moorhouse Lane, Hallen, Nr Bristol Tel: 0117 950 2265
Directions: M5 jct 17, A4018 to Henbury r'bout, right, right again at junction,next right to Station Road, left into Avonmouth Road at r'bout. One mile toHallen, ground first left, then right into lane to ground
Capacity: 2,000 Seats: 200 Cover: 200 **Clubhouse:** Yes -

HONOURS Glos County Lg 92-93, Glos Snr Trophy 92-93

PREVIOUS **League:** Glos County (pre-1993), Hellenic 93-00
Names: Lawrence Weston Athletic (80's), Lawrence Weston Hallen (pre-1991)
Ground: Kings Weston (early 1980's)
RECORD **Attendance:** 803 v Bristol Rovers 1997

FACT FILE
Founded: 1949
Colours: Royal Blue/B;ack/Royal Blue
Change Colours: Yellow/Blue/Yellow
Midweek Matchday: Wednesday
Programme: No

CLUB PERSONNEL
Chairman: Barrie Phillips
Tel: 0117 950 1754
President: Ken Naish
Manager: Gary DamoneCoach: John Payne
Physio: Charlie Baldwin

Hallen - Back Row (L-R): A Davies (coach), L Fairman, N Tilley, t Green, T Hughes, S Scannell, A Growcroft, R Mowatt, P Owen, R Barrett, N Durbin, J Davies (mascot), G Domone (manager). **Front Row:** L Alford, G Barr, S Parker, A Beaham, D Scott, S Mountford, A Cook, t Collett, R Mizon, R Nelmes, N Sarahs.

KEYNSHAM TOWN

Secretary: Iain Anderson, 195 Mount Hill Road, Hanham, Bristol BS15 9SU Tel: 0117 961 6426

Ground: Crown Field, Bristol Road, Keynsham Tel: 0117 986 5876

Directions: A4 from Bristol to Bath, ground on left before entering he town opposite Crown Inn. Bus service every 30 mins from Bristol passes ground. 10mins walk from Keynsham BR station

Capacity: 2,000 Seats: 120 Cover: 500 Floodlights: Yes

Clubhouse: Evenings & before & after games. Snacks Club Shop: No

HONOURS Somerset Lg Div 1 77-78; Somerset Snr Cup 51-52 57-58, 02-03; Div. 2 00-01 GFA Jnr Cup 25-26; Somerset & Avon (South) Premier Cup 79-80 (SF 93-94);

BEST SEASON **FA Cup:** 4th Qual. Rd **FA Vase: 5th Round**

PREVIOUS **Leagues:** Bristol District, Bristol Comb., Bristol Premier, Somerset Senior
Grounds: The Hams 1886-1910; Gaston 1910-25; Park Road 25-30; Charlton Rd 30-39

RECORD **Attendance:** 3,000 v Chelsea, f'light opening 88-89.
Competitive:2,160 v Saltash, Amateur Cup, Oct 1952

FACT FILE

Founded: 1895
Nickname: K's
Sponsors: Hollywood Frames
Colours: All amber
Change: All blue
Midweek matchday: Wednesday
Reserves ' League: Somerset County
Programme: 32 pages, 50p
Editor: Mark Brown (0117 969 5487)

CLUB PERSONNEL

President: Lester Clements
Joint Chairmen: Steve & Lesley Brwole
Press Officer: Ray Parker
Manager: Gary Silverthorne
Physio: Richard Griffiths
Player of the Year & Top Scorer: Micky Adams

MELKSHAM TOWN

Secretary: David Phillips, 37 Duxford Close, Bowerhill,Melksham,Wlts. SN12 6XN
Tel No: 01225 706 904)

Ground: The Conigre, Melksham (01225 702843)
Capacity: 1,500 Seats: 150 Cover: 600
Floodlights: Yes

Directions: Just off main square in grounds of Melksham House

Clubhouse: Inside ground, open every evening & weekend lunchtimes

HONOURS Wilts Lg 03-04 93-94 (R-up 24-25 29-30 59-60 67-68 68-69 71-72), Western Lg Div 1 79-80, 96-97, Wilts Snr Cup 03-04 69-70 77-7802-03 (R-up 57-58 67-68 68-69), Wilts Shield 80-81 81-82 84-85 ,85-86,97-98 ,99-00(R-up 86-87).

PREVIOUS **Leagues:** Wiltshire 1894-1974 93-94; Western 74-93
Grounds: Challymead; Old Broughton Road Field

BEST SEASON **FA Cup:** 2nd Q Rd 57-58 **FA Vase:** 3rd Rd 81-82,98-99,01-02
FA Amateur Cup: 1st Rd 68-69

RECORD **Attendance:** 2,821 v Trowbridge Town, FA Cup 57-58

FACT FILE

Founded: 1876
Sponsors: Cooper Avon Tyres
Colours:yellow/black/black
Change :White/Navy Blue
Midweek Matchday: Moinday
Prog Editor:Graham Carruthers

CLUB PERSONNEL

President: Jim Lay
Chairman: Mike Perrin
Vice Chairman: Paul Smith
Manager:Nigel Tripp
Physio: Neil Young

2002-2003

Top Goalscorer: Owen Bryan
PLayer of the Year: Steve Casey

ODD DOWN

Secretary: Mike Mancini, 36 Caledonian Rd., East Twerton, Bath BA2 3RD
Tel: 01225 423293 Mobile: 07788 635560

Ground: Lew Hill Memorial Ground, Combe Hay Lane, Odd Down

Directions: The ground is situated behind Odd Down Park & Ride car park on main A367 Bath-Exeter. When leaving Bath turn left into Combe Hay Lane opposite The Hustler Pub. 40 mins walk from Bath (BR)
Capacity: 1,000 Seats: 160 Cover: 250 Floodlights: Yes Shop No

Clubhouse: Yes, open matchdays noon-3 & 7-11pm. Hot & cold food available on matchdays

HONOURS Western Lg Div 1 92-93, Som. Snr Cup 91-92,Som, Premier Cup: R-up 2000-01

PREVIOUS **Leagues:** Wilts Premier, Bath & District, Somerset Senior

BEST SEASON **FA Cup:** **FA Vase:** Last 64 1983-84

RECORD **Appearances:** Steve Fuller 475
Scorer: Joe Matano 104
Win: 11-1 v Minehead (H), Western Lge Prem. Div. 19/3/94

FACT FILE

Founded: 1901
Sponsors:Ace Courier Services Ltd
Colours: Yellow and Blue
Change Colours: Black & White
Midweek Matches: Tuesday (7-45)
Reserves ' League: Somerset Senior
Programme: 12 pages with admission
Editor: Secretary

CLUB PERSONNEL

President:: Eric Clarke
Chairman: Ian Robertson V- Chair:T.B.A.
Manager: Chris Mountford
2003-2004 Captain: Nick Beaverstock
Top Scorer: Dave Pearce 18
P.o.Y.: Jaz Bright & Nick Beaverstock

TORRINGTON

Secretary: David Priscott, 6 Highfield Terrace, Bishops Tawton, Barnstaple EX32 0AN
Tel: 01271 328316 (H) 07751-149900 (M) e-mail afctorrington@msn.com

Ground: Vicarage Field, School Lane, Great Torrington Tel: 01805 622853
Directions: In town centre turn left by parish church, right at swimming pool, ground behind swimming pool. Good parking.
Red Bus from Bideford & Barnstaple (nearest BR).Bus stop 300yds from ground
Capacity: 4,000 Seats: 100 Cover: 1,000 Floodlights: Yes Shop: No
Clubhouse: Weekdays 7-1pm, Sat 11-11 & Sun 12-3. Light snacks available on matchdays.

PREVIOUS **Leagues:** N Devon; Devon & Exeter; S Western 77-84 **Grounds**: None
BEST SEASON **FA Vase:** 5th Rd 84-85 **FA Cup**: 2nd Qual Rd. 81-82, 94-95, 96-97
RECORDS: **Scorer:** Trevor Watkins 254 **Appearances:** Mike Gilbert 527
TransferFee Rcd: £3,000 D.Walter(Yeovil)
HONOURS Western Lg R-up 90-91 Div 1 Champs 02-03; Merit Cup 91-92 93-94 95-96; South Western Lg Cup 81; Devon St Lukes Cup R-up 95-96 96-97; Devon & Exeter Lg & Cup 73-74; Festival of Britain Cup 96-97; Les Phillips Cup R-up 91-92; Torridge Cup (15),Arlington Cup 02-03 03-04 Devon Intermediate Cup (RU) 03-04

FACT FILE
Formed: 1908
Nickname: Torrie or Supergreens
Sponsors: K & J Plant Hire
Colours: Green & white Change :Yellow/blue
Midweek Matches: Tuesday
Programme
48 pages, £1.00 Editor: Secretary
Local Press: North Devon Journal
CLUB PERSONNEL
President: Keith Curtis
Chairman: Winston Martin
Manager: Tonuy Bowker
Coach: Paul Hutchings
Physio: Brian Alford
2003-04
Leading Goalscorer: Andy Stevens 30
Captain: Lee Langhead
Player of the Year: Karl Baggale

WELTON ROVERS

Secretary: Geoff Baker, 6 Longfellow Road, Westfield Road, Westfield, Radstock BA3 3YZ
Email Address: weltonrovers@ yahoo.com

Ground: West Clewes, North Road, Midsomer Norton, Somerset Tel: 01761 412097

Directions: A367 Bath to Radstock õ right at lights at foot of hill onto A362,ground on right.

Capacity: 2,400 Seats: 300 Cover: 300 Floodlights: Yes Club Shop: No

Clubhouse: 7.30-11pm daily, plus Sat matchdays 1.30-2.45pm, Sun 12-2pm

HONOURS Western Lg 11-12 64-65 65-66 66-67 73-74, Div 1 59-60 87-88,Amateur Cup 56-57 57-58 58-59 59-60, Alan Young Cup 65-66 66-67 67-68(jt); Somerset Snr Cup 06-07 11-12 12-13 13-14 19-20 24-25 25-26 60-61 61-62 62-63, Som. I'mediate Cup 77-78, Som. Jnr Cup 06-07(jt) 24-25 30-31, WBC Clares City of Wells Cup 78-79

PREVIOUS **Leagues:** None **Names:** None **Grounds:** None
BEST SEASON **FA Cup:** **FA Vase:** **FA Amateur Cup:**
RECORD **Attendance:** 2,000 v Bromley, FA Amateur Cup 1963
Goalscorer: Ian Henderson, 51

FACT FILE
Formed: 1887
Nickname: Rovers
Sponsors: Young Bros (Roofing)
Colours: Green & navy/navy &green/green
Change colours: Yellow/black/yellow
Midweek matchday: Wednesday
Reserve s' League: Somerset Senior
Programme: 12 pages, 25p
Editor: M Brown
Website: www.geocities.com/weltonrovers
CLUB PERSONNEL
Chairman: Rae James
Manager: T.B.A.
Physio: John Carver

ALMONDSBURY

Secretary: Michael Blessing, 10 Campion Drive, Bradley Stoke, North Bristol BS32 0BH
Tel No: 01454 628875 (H) 07974 074388 (M)

Ground: The Field, Almondsbury Sports & Social Club, Bradley Stoke , North Bristol BS34 4AA

Directions: M4 Jct 16. From South take first left exit lane at roundabout and then left at lights.Ground is 150 metres on right.. If arriving form East, third exit from round about after Exit 17

Clubhouse: Yes.

FACT FILE

Colours: Green & White/Green/White

Change colours: Yellow/Blue/ yellow & Blue

Midweek Matches:

CLUB PERSONNEL

Chairman: Philip Church

Manager: :Francis Johnson

BIDDESTONE

Secretary: Keith Pound, 10 Frogwell Park, Chippenham, Wilts. SN14 0RB
Tel; Nos: 01249 657367 (H) 07740 156075 (M)

Ground: The Sports Ground, Yatton Road, Biddestomne, Chippenham SN14 7BZ
Tel No: 01249 716622

Directions: From Chippenham. Take A420 (towards Bristol) Left to Biddestone after 3 miles, The sports ground is on left as you enter the village. From Bath take A4 (towards Chippenham). Left at Cross Keys Pub at lights.and drive through village. Ground on right.

FACT FILE

Colours:Blue/white/blue

Change colours: Yellow/white/blue

Midweek Matches: Wednesday 6.30pm

CLUB PERSONNEL

Chairman: Andrew Short

Manager: Gary Skidmore

CADBURY HEATH

Secretary: Martin Painter, 44 Chesterfield Road, Downend, Bristol BS16 5RQ
Tel No: 0117 949 2844

Ground: Springfield, Cadbury Hearg Road, Bristol BS30 8BX
Tel No: 0117 967 5731

Directions: M5 & M4 to M32 Exit 1 to Ring Road. Left to Cadbury Heath at roudabout. Then right into Tower Road North and left at mini roundabout. Turn right into Cadbury Heath Road after 150 metres. Ground is on right via Cadbury Heath Sicil Club Car park.

Clubhouse: **Yes**

PREVIOUS **League:** Gloucestershire County Lge.

HONOURS Glos. County Lge 98-99, R-up 99-00

FACT FILE
Colours: All Red
Change colours: White/black/black
Midweek Matches: Wednesday 6.30

CLUB PERSONNEL
Chairman: David Smart
Manager: Glen Smart

CALNE TOWN

Secretary: Laurie Drake, 22 Falcon Rd, Calne, Wilts SN11 8PL . Tel: 01249 819186
Ground: Bremhill View, Lickhill Rd., North End, Calne. 01249 816716.
Directions: Take A4 from Chippenham near Calne turn L. at 1st R'abt onto A3102 Calne B'pass at next R'abt turn R., next L, then R and R. again. Email: calnetownfc@btinternet.com
Capacity: 2,500 **Seats:** 78 **Cover**: 250 **Floodlights**: Yes **Club Shop**: No
Clubhouse: Mon-Fri 7-11pm, Sat-Sun 12-11pm. Filled rolls, hot food, tea,coffee, sweets etc
HONOURS Western Lg Div 1 R-up 92-93; Wilts Snr Cup 12-13 34-35 84-85 (R-up1894-95 94-95 1911-12 49-50); Wilts Lg 33-34, (`Ghia' Cup 8) 1-81 85-86, Div 279-81, Div 3 85-86, Div 4 81-82
PREVIOUS **League:** Wilts Co. (pre-1986) **Ground:** Anchor Road Rec. 1887-1967
Names: Calne Town (1886) & Harris Utd merged; Calne & Harris Utd (1921-67)
RECORD **Attendance:** 1,100 v Swindon, Friendly 25/7/1987
Scorer: Robbie Lardner **Appearances:** Gary Swallow, 259
Win: 11-1 v Heavitree (H) **Defeat:** 2-7 v Odd Down (A)

FACT FILE
Founded: 1887 Nickname: Lilywhites
Sponsors: T.B.A.
Colours: White/black/black
Change colours: All Blue
Midweek Matchday: Tuesday 7.45
Programme: 20 pages, 50p
Editor: Jacky Drake (01249 819186)
CLUB PERSONNEL
Chairman: Steve Walker
President: Bill Burt
Manager: Kelvin Highmoor
Captain: Darren Smart
2003-2004
Top Scorer James Lye
P.o.Y.: Darren Smart

CHARD TOWN

Secretary: Michael Hawes, 18 Norrington Way, Chard, Somerset TA20 2JP
Tel Nos: 01460 67730 (H) 07906 904138 (M)
Ground: Dening Sports Field, Zembard Lane, Chard TA20 1JL Tel: 01460 61402
Capacity: 1,500 Seats: 60 Cover: 200 Floodlights: Yes

Directions: Follow sports centre signs off main A30 High Street along Helliers Road. Right into Upper Combe Street and left into Zembard Lane . BR 7miles Axminster or 8 miles Crewkerne
Clubhouse: Matchdays & most evenings. Snacks served

HONOURS Som. Snr Lg 49-50 53-54 59-60 67-68 69-70 (Lg Cup 61-62 71-72 76-77); Western Lg Div 1 R-up 83-84 87-88 95-96, (Merit Cup 82-83, Comb. Cup(Res) 91-92 (R-up 92-93)); Som. Snr Cup 52-53 66-67; S W Co's Cup 88-89; Western Com Lge 96-97, Cup 96-97.

BEST SEASON **FA Cup:** 2nd Qual Rd. 77-78 82-83 **FA Vase:**

PREVIOUS **Leagues:** Somerset Snr 20-24 48-75; Perry Street 25-48 **Grounds:** None
2002-03 **Top Scorer**:Matt Corrick **Captain**:Simon Baines **Player of the Year:** James Steer

FACT FILE
Founded: 1920 Nickname: Robins
Colours: Red/Black/Red
Change : All Blue
Midweek matches: Wednesday
Prog: 24 pages with entry Ed: Ian Hallett

CLUB PERSONNEL
Chairman: Brian Beer
V-Chairman: Troy Symes
Treasurer/Gen Sec.: Mrs Rose Richards
Gen Man: Malcolm Adcock

Manager: Paul Thorpe
Asst.Man:Billy Morris
Physio: Daniel Glentworth

CLEVEDON UNITED

Secretary: Pat O'Brien
GROUND c/o Clevedon Town FC, Hand Stadium, Davis Lane, Clevedon, N. Somerset
Tel: 01275 871600 (ground) 01275 341913 (office)
Fax: 01275 871601 email: info@handstadium.co.uk
Directions: M5 Jct 20 - follow signs for Hand Stadium; first left into Central Way (at island just after motorway), 1st left at mini-r'bout into Kenn Rd, 2nd left Davis Lane; ground half mile on right. Or from Bristol(B3130) left into Court Lane (opposite Clevedon Court), turnright after 1mile, ground on left. Nearest BR station: Nailsea & Backwell. Buses from Bristol
Capacity: 3,650 Seats: 300 Cover: 1,600 Floodlights: Yes
Clubhouse: Yes in which clubs mementoes are also sold.
PREVIOUS **League:** Somerset County League >2003
RECORD **Attendance:** 420
HONOURS Somerset County Lge Prem. Div 98-99
2003-2004 **Player of the Year & Top Goalscorer**: Damian Thorne

FACT FILE
Founded: 1970
Colours: All Red
Change Colours: All Blue
Midweek Matchday: Wednesday
Programme:£1.00 20 Pages
Editor: Paul Tiplar

CLUB PERSONNEL
Chairman:Alan Rides
President:Chris Brown
Manager: Andy LLewellyn
Captain: Andy Woodlands
Physio: Terry Banks

Clevedon United.

DAWLISH TOWN

Secretary: Nigel Gooding c/o Club Tel Nos: 08707 442599 (H) 07976 804305 (M)

Ground: Playing Fields, Sandy Lane, Exeter Road, Dawlish Tel: 01626 863110
Website: www.dawlishtownfc.co.uk

Directions: Approx 1 mile from centre of town, off main Exeter road (A379)
Capacity: 2,000 Seats: 200 Cover: 200 Floodlights: Yes

Clubhouse: Open nightly, all day Saturday and Sunday situated in car park opposite ground

HONOURS Western Lg Div 1 R-up 98-99, Lg Cup 80-81 83-84, Devon Premier Cup 69-70 72-73 80-81, Devon Snr Cup 57-58 67-68, Devon St Lukes Cup 82-83 (R-up 81-82), Carlsberg Cup 96

BEST SEASON **FA Cup:** **FA Vase:** Quarter Finals 86-87

PREVIOUS **League:** Devon & Exeter **Ground:** Barley Bank 1875-1900

RECORD **Gate:** 1,500 v Heavitree Utd, Devon Prem. Cup Q-Final
Defeat: 0-18 v Clevedon (A), Western Lge Prem. Div. 92-93

FACT FILE
Founded: 1889
Colours: Green/green/green
Change Colours:Yellow/Blue/YellowMidweek matchday: Wednesday
Programme: 34 pages, £1.00
Programme Editor: Roy Bolt

CLUB PERSONNEL
Chairman: Nigel Gooding
Manager: Chris Myers
Coach:Pete Darke
Physio:Roger Smart

ELMORE

Secretary: Neville Crocker, Rivercroft,4 Little Silver, Tiverton, Devon EX16 4PH
Tel: 01884 2456634 (H) 07967 827126 (M)

Ground: Horsdon Park, Tiverton, Devon EX16 4DE Tel: 01884 252341

Directions: M5 Jct 27, A373 towards Tiverton, leave at 1st sign for Tiverton &Business Park, ground 500yds on right
Capacity: 2,000 Seats: 200 Cover: Floodlights: Yes

Clubhouse: 11am-11pm Mon-Sat. Full canteen service - hot & cold meals & snacks

Club Shop: Yes

HONOURS East Devon Snr Cup 72-73 75-76, Western Lge R-up 94-95. Lge Cup 90-91,94-95, Div 1 R-up 90-91, Prem Div Merit Cup R-up 91-92, Div 1 Merit Cup 86-87 89-90 90-91, Devon St Lukes Cup R-up 90-91, Devon Snr Cup 87-88, Devon Intermediate Cup 60-61, Football Express Cup 60-61, Devon & Exeter Lg Div 2A 73-74 86-87(res)(Div 1A 76-77(res)), Devon Yth Cup 77-78.

PREVIOUS **Leagues:** Devon & Exeter 47-74; South Western 74-78 Grounds: None

RECORD **Attendance:** 1,713 v Tiverton Town Fri.April 14th 95
Appearances: P Webber **Goalscorer:**
Win: 17-0 **Defeat:** 2-7

FACT FILE
Founded: 1947
Nickname: Eagles
Club Sponsors: Ken White Signs
Colours: All Green
Change colours: Red /black/black
Midweek matches: Tuesday
Reserve League: None
Programme: 12 pages, 30p
Editor: Richard Tapp(01884 252341)

CLUB PERSONNEL
Chairman: Alan J Cockram
Vice Chairman: P.J.Garnsworthy
Manager: Peter Buckingham
Asst Manager: Steve Rowland
Physio: Simon Harder
Captain: Jason Reeves

2003-2004
Player of the Year:Paul Pike
Top SCorer: Stuart Anderson

ILFRACOMBE TOWN

Secretary: Tony Alcock, 2 Worth Road, Ilfracombe, North Devon EX34 9JA Tel: 01271 862686. Mobile: 07977 589199

Ground: Marlborough Park, Ilfracombe, Devon Tel: 01271 865939

Directions: A361 to Ilfracombe. Turn1st right in town after lights and follow Marlborough Rd to the top, ground on left.**Capacity:** 2,000 **Seats:** 60 Cover: 450Floodlights: Yes

Club Shop: No

Clubhouse: Every night 7-11pm and weekend lunchtimes. Hot & cold meals on matchdays

HONOURS E Devon Prem Lg 25-26 28-29 29-30, N Devon Senior Lg, N Devon Prem Lg 66-67 70-71 81-82 82-83, Western Lg Div 2 R-up 52-53, Les Phillips Cup R-up 91

PREVIOUS Leagues: North Devon 04-14 20-22 60-84; EDevon Premier 22-31;Exeter & District t 32-39 46-49; Western 49-59 **Grounds:** Shaftesbury Field; Brimlands; Killacleave (all pre-1924)
Names: Ilfracombe FC 02-09; Ilfracombe Utd 09-14; Ilfracombe Comrades 14-20

RECORDS **Attendance:** 3,000 v Bristol City, Ground opening, 2/10/24
Goalscorer: Paul Jenkins 77 **Appearances:** Steve Hobbs 200

Players progressing: Jason Smith (Coventry City and Swansea City via Tiverton Town)

FACT FILE
Founded: 1902 Nickname: Bluebirds
Sponsors: T.B.A.
Colours: All Blue Change : White/navy/navy
Midweek matchday: Tuesday
Reserves ' League: North Devon
Prog: 8 pages, 40p Editor: Bill Creswell

CLUB PERSONNEL
Chairman: Barry Jones
Vice-Chairman: Geoff Crowe
President:Richard Campbell
Manager:Peter Varley Captain: Steve Hobbs

2003-2004
Player of the Year: Mike Symons
Top Goalscorer: Peter Varley
ßPhysio: Paul Brown

LARKHALL ATHLETIC

Secretary: Nigel Gooding c/o The Club.
Email: garrydvy@aol.com

Ground: "Plain Ham", Charlcombe Lane, Larkhall, Bath. 01225 334952

Directions A4 from Bath, 1 mile from city centre turn left into St Saviours Rd. In Larkhall Square fork left, and right at junction, road bears into Charlcombe Lane. Ground on right as lane narrows

Capacity: 1,000 Seats: None Cover: 50 Floodlights: No

HONOURS Somerset Senior Cup 75-76, Somerset Senior Lg,; Western Lg Div 1 88-89 93-94 94-95(Div 1 Merit Cup (4) 83-86 87-88 (jt with Yeovil Res)

PREVIOUS **Leagues:** Somerset Senior

FACT FILE
Founded: 1914 Nickname: Larks
Colours: All Bluel
Change colours: All red
Midweek Matches: wednesday
Programme: Yes

CLUB PERSONNEL
President: Tony Codd
Chairman:Jim McClay (01373 834050)
Manager: Tommy Gilbert
Coach: John Newman

MINEHEAD

Secretary: Alex Knight,Swallowdale,Watery Lane,Doniford,Watchet,Somerset.TA3 0TW Tel: 01984 639212

Ground: The Recreation Ground, Irnham Road, Minehead, Somerset (01643 704989)

Directions: Entering town from east on A39 turn right into King Edward Road at Police station, first left into Alexandra Rd and follow signs to car park;ground entrance within. Regular buses to Minehead from Taunton, the nearestrailhead. (Steam train 'holiday route' Taunton to Minehead)

Capacity: 3,500 Seats: 350 Cover: 400 Floodlights: Yes

Clubhouse: Yes **Club Shop:** No

HONOURS Southern Lg R-up 76-77, Div 1 Sth 75-76, Merit Cup 75-76; Western Lg R-up 66-67 71-72, Div 1 90-91 98-99, Alan Young Cup 67-68 (jt with Glastonbury),Somerset Premier Cup 60-61 73-74 76-77

PREVIOUS **Leagues:** Somerset Senior; Southern 72-83

RECORD **Attendance:** 3,600 v Exeter City, FA Cup 2nd Rd, 77

BEST SEASON **FA Cup:** 2nd Rd 76-77, 1-2 v Portsmouth (A); 77-78, 0-3 v Exeter City (H)

FACT FILE
Founded: 1889
Colours: All Blue
Change colours: Yellow/black/black
Midweek Matches: Tuesday
Reserves League: TBA
Programme: Yes Editor: Brian Walder

CLUB PERSONNEL
Chairman: Charlie Griffiths
Tel: 01984 633932
Managers:Charlie Lewis& Simon Antonelli
Captain: Keith Graddon

2003-2004
Player of ythe Year:Shawn Pope
Top Scorer:Lee Todd

RADSTOCK TOWN

Secretary: Graham Seymour , 12 Wesley Avenue, Westfield, radstock, Somerset BA3 3XB Tel Nos: 01761 437889 (H) 07792 965017 (M)

Ground: Southfields Recreation Ground,Southfields, Radstock Tel No: 01761 435004

Directions: At double roundabout in Radstock take A362 (towards Frome), take second right and ground is 500 metres. **Clubhouse:** Yes.

FACT FILE
Colours:Red& Black/Black/Black
Change colours:All Blue
Midweek Matches: Tuesday

CLUB PERSONNEL
Chairman: Dave Wilkinson
Manager: Nigel Bryant

SALTASH UNITED

Secretary: Luke Ranford, 8 Rogate Walk, Thornbury, Plymouth PL6 8SZ Tel: 07817 008257 email: luke.ranford@blueyonder.co.uk

Ground: Kimberley Stadium, Callington Road, Saltash, Cornwall LP12 6DX Tel: 01752 845746

Directions: First left after crossing Tamar Bridge, through town centre, at top of town fork right at mini - roundabout, ground 400 yds ahead on left.

Capacity: 3,000 **Seats:** 200 **Cover:** 200 **Floodlights**: Yes

Clubhouse: Club attached to stand and caters for dancing and clubactivities.Sapphire Lounge caters for wedding receptions,quiz nights and private functions etc

PREVIOUS **Leagues:** Cornwall Snr; Sth Western 51-59 62-76; E Cornwall Prem 59-62; Western 76-95

HONOURS Cornwall Snr Lg 49-50 50-51, Western Lg 84-85 86-87 88-89 (R-up 83-84 87-88, Lg Cup 86-87 87-88 (R-up 88-89), Div 1 76-77, Merit Cup 79-80 87-88), Sth Western Lg 53-54 75-76 (R-up 52-53, 73-74, 74-75), Lg Cup 3, Cornwall Snr Cup 6

FACT FILE
Formed: 1945
Nickname: The Ashes
Colours: Red & white/black/black
Change: Yellow/Bluyue/Yellow
website: saltashunited.co.uk
Midweek Matchday:Tuesday/ Wednesday
Programme: 52 pages,50p
Editor: Marian Gammage

CLUB PERSONNEL
President: P Skinnard
Chairman: Darren Bennetts
Manager: Eddie Shapland
Coach: Jon Sheffield
Physio: Dave Williams

Saltash United - Back Row (L-R): Mike Norman, Ashley Pook, Craig Holman, Dan Johnson, Paul Wilmot, Chris Menhenick, Simon Zinn, Brian Jefferies, Dan Gill, Gareth Jones, Luke Ranford (Secretary).
Front Row: Dave Williams (physio), Paul Baker, Kev McShane, Paul Williams, Andy Bowker, Eddie Shepland (manager), Dennis Mason, Steve Murphy, Bradley Richardson, Nigel Menhenick (Asst. Man.).

SHEPTON MALLET

Secretary: John Bell, 43 Victoria Grove, Shepton Mallet, Somerset BA4 5NJ
Tel Nos: 01749 344687 (H) 01749 831878 (W) 07866 762372 (M)

Ground: The Playing Fields, Old Wells Rd., West Shepton, Shepton Mallett, Som. BA4 5XN
Tel: 01749 344609

Capacity: 2500 Covered Seating: 120 Floodlights: Yes

Directions: Take the Glastonbury road from Shepton Mallett town centre then turn right at the junction with Old Wells Rd (approx. 1/2 mile, near the "King William" P.H.) - the ground is 300 yards on the left.

Clubhouse: Yes, open match days

PREVIOUS League: Somerset Senior

HONOURS Somerset Senior League 2000-01

CLUB RECORDS Attendance: 274 v Chippenham Town F.A.Cup 2000-01

FACT FILE
Founded: 1986
Colours: Black & white/black/black
Change colours: Red & black/white/red
Midweek matchday: Tuesday
Programme Price: 50p 24 Pages:
Editor:K.O'Brien

CLUB PERSONNEL
Chairman: Brian Blinman
Manager: Gary Banfield
Physio: Kevin Reid

2003-04
Leading Goalscorer & Player of the Year:
Shaun Wiles-Richards
:xs

SHREWTON UNITED

Secretary: Jayne Foot, 3 North Croft, Tilshead, Salisbury, Wiltshire SP3 4SE
Tel: 01980 621 284 (H) 01722 439516 (B) email: peterwithers@lineone.net

Ground: Recreation Ground, Mill Lane, Shrewton, Wiltshire

Directions: From A303 left at Winterbourne Stoke and left at The Royal Oak. Then turn right at mini roundabout on outskirts of village, and then turn left at the George Inn and follow Football Club signs. From Devizes A360 turn leftt at mini roundabout on outskirts of village, and then turn left at the George Inn and follow Football Club signs.

PREVIOUS **League:** Wiltshire League >2003

HONOURS Wiltshire Lge Prem Div. 2001-02 02-03, R-up 00-01, Lge Senior Cup 01-02 02-03

2003-2004 **Player of the Year**: Shaun Collins **Top Goalscorer**: Dean Foot

FACT FILE
Colours: Maroon & Navy/navy/navy
Change Colours: All White & jade
Midweek Matchday: Tuesday

CLUB PERSONNEL
Chairman:Derek Harnett
Manager: Stuart Withers
Captain:Anton Brownless

STREET

Secretary: John Darrell, 1 Beech Rd., Street, Somerset BA16 0RY
Tel Nos: 01458 445797 (H) 07854 021812 (M)

Ground: The Tannery Field, Middlebrooks, Street, Somerset
Tel: 01458 445987 Matchdays 01458 448227

Directions: Sign posted from both ends of A39 & B3151, Station Castle Cary

Capacity: 2,000 Seating: 120 Cover: 25 Floodlights: Yes Club Shop: No

Clubhouse:

HONOURS: Western Lge R-up 52-53

RECORDS: **Attendance:** 4,300 v Yeovil Town FA Cup 17/11/47

PREVIOUS: **Leagues:**
Grounds: Victoria Field, Tunpike Ground

FACT FILE
Founded: 1880 Nickname The Cobblers
Sponsors C I C A
Colours: All white with jade trim
Change colours: Red & black/black/black
Midweek home matchday: Tuesday
Programme: 44 pages 50p
Editor: M Clarke

CLUB PERSONNEL
Chairman: Mark Clark
Manager: Alan Hooker
Assistant Manager: Simon Culliford
Physios: Dick Pickersgill, Andrew Lee

WELLINGTON TOWN

Secretary: Dave Grabham, 12 Drakes Park, Wellington, SomersetTA21 8TB
Tel: 01823 664946 (H), 01823 355687 (B) 07817 274585 (M)
email:david.grabham@btopenworld.com

Ground: Wellington Playing Field, North Street, Wellington, Somerset Tel: 01823 664810

Directions: At town centre traffic lights turn into North St., then first left by Fire Station into the public car park that adjoins the ground

Capacity: 3,000 **Seats:** None **Cover:** 200 **Floodlights:** Yes **Clubhouse:** Yes **Club Shop:** No

HONOURS Western Lg Div 1 R-up 80-81, Merit Cup 91-92, Comb Lge 95-96;Comb Lge KO Cup 95-96 98-99; Somerset Snr Lg Div 1 R-up; Rowbarton & Seward Cup, Bill Slee Trophy

PREVIOUS **Leagues:** Taunton Saturday, Somerset Senior

RECORD **Attendance:** **Goalscorer:** Ken Jones

BEST SEASON **FA Cup:** 1st Qual Rd. 81-82, 84-85 **FA Vase:** 2nd rd Prop 98-99

Players progressing: Nick Jennings and Ian Stonebridge (Plymouth)

2003-04 **Player of the Year and Top Scorer:** Alexis Piper

FACT FILE
Founded: 1892
Sponsors: A J Shire & Wadham Fencing
Colours: Tangerine with blue/black/tangerine
Change cols: Blue & claret stripes/blue/blue
Midweek Matches: WednesdayReserve Lge: Devon & Exeter Sen Div
Programme: Yes Editor: Chairman

CLUB PERSONNEL
Chairman: Ken Bird V-Chair:Graham Aspin
President: Alan Shire
Manager: Dave Sheehan
Captain: Matthew Brereton
Reserves Manager:AdamParkes
Physio: Ken Pearson

Chard Town F.C. - Back Row (L-R): Darren Hutchings, Paul Henbest, Mike Hawes (Secretary), Dean Ritchie, Simon Farrell.
Middle Row: Stuart Larcombe, Adam Tovey, Stuart Parris, Brian Beer (Chairman), Tom Manley, Steve Lindegaard, Shane Scott.
Front Row: Neil Smith, Matt Corrick, Paul Nicholls, Paul Thorpe (Manager), Steve Devlin.
Mascot: Ben Stevens and Kristian Rockett.

WESTBURY UNITED

Secretary: Michael Taylor, c/o W. U. F .C. Westury, Wiltshire BA13 3AF (01373 865406)
Ground: Meadow Lane, Westbury Tel: 01373 823409
Directions: In town centre, A350, follow signs for BR station, Meadow Lane on right (club signposted). Ten mins walk from railway station (on main London-South West and South Coast-Bristol lines)
Capacity: 3,500 Seats: 150 Cover: 150 Floodlights: Yes
Clubhouse: Evenings 7-11pm, Fri, Sat & Sun lunchtimes 12-3pm Club Shop: No
HONOURS Western Lg Div 1 91-92, Wilts Senior Cup 31-32 32-33 47-48 51-52, Wilts Combination, Wilts Lg 34-35 37-38 38-39 49-50 50-51 55-56, Wilts Premier Shield R-up 92-93
PREVIOUS **Leagues:** Wilts Comb.; Wilts Co. (pre-1984)
Ground: Redland Lane (pre-1935)
RECORD Gate: 4,000 - v Llanelli, FA Cup 1st Rd 37 & v Walthamstow Ave. FA Cup 37
Players progressing: John Atyeo (Bristol City)

FACT FILE
Formed: 1921
Nickname: White Horsemen
Colours: Green& White/Green/Green
Change Colours: Yellow/Blue/Yellow
Midweek Matches: Wednesday
Reserves' league: Wilts County Lg.
Programme: 16 pages, 50p
Editor: Mike Taylor (01373 865406)
CLUB PERSONNEL
Chairman: George Dowd
Vice Chairman: Bert Back
President: Ernie Barber
Managers: Derek Graham
Physio: Dave Prescott

WESTON ST. JOHNS

Secretary: Simon Stephens, 20 Pennycress, Locking Castle, Weston-super-Mare,Somerset BS22 8QH Tel No: 07947 732492 (H&M)
Ground: Coleridge Road, Bournville Estate, Weston-s-Mare, Somerset
Tel: 01934 612862
Directions: Leave M5 at J21and take main road into Weston-s-Mare.
Turn left at the 4th r'about into Winterstoke Road, then take the 2nd right into Byron Road and then 1st left into Coleridge Road.
PREVIOUS **League:** Somerset Senior Lge.
Names: Worle & Weston St. Johns amalgamated 2000
HONOURS R-up Somerset Sen. Lge. 99-00 (Worle)

FACT FILE
Colours: All Royal Blue
Change Colours: All MaroonMidweek
Matchday: Wednesday

CLUB PERSONNEL
Chairman: Bob Flaskett
Manager: Jamie Crandon

WILLAND ROVERS

Secretary: David Campion, 7 Lime Crescent, Meadow Park, Willand, Devon. EX15 2SL
Tel: 0188434591 (H) 01884 253238 (B) 07966544698 (M)
email: henry.jarrett1@btopenworld.com
Ground: Silver Street, Willand, Devon. Tel: 01884 33885
Capacity: 2000 Covered Seating: 75 Floodlights: Yes

Directions: Leave the M5 at Junction 27 (signed Tiverton & N. Devon).
Follow signs to Willand and the ground is on the left hand side about 1/4 mile after passing Willand village sign.
PREVIOUS **League:** Devon County until 2001
HONOURS Devon County League 98-99, 00-01,
BEST SEASON **FA Vase:** 3rd Round Proper 02-03, 4-5 v Lymington & Milton (H)
CLUB RECORDS **Attendance:** 650 v Newton Abbot 1992-93

FACT FILE
Founded: 1946
Colours: All White
Change colours: Yellow/blue/yellow
Midweek matchday: Tuesday
Programme - Price::50p
Editor:Tony Baker(01884 820520)
CLUB PERSONNEL
Chairman: Mike Mitchell
General Secretary: Vicky Horsburgh
Manager: Clive Jones
Asst. Man. / Coach: Neil Greening
Physio: Keith Sutton
2003-2004
Top Scorer & P.o.Y.: Steve Ebdy

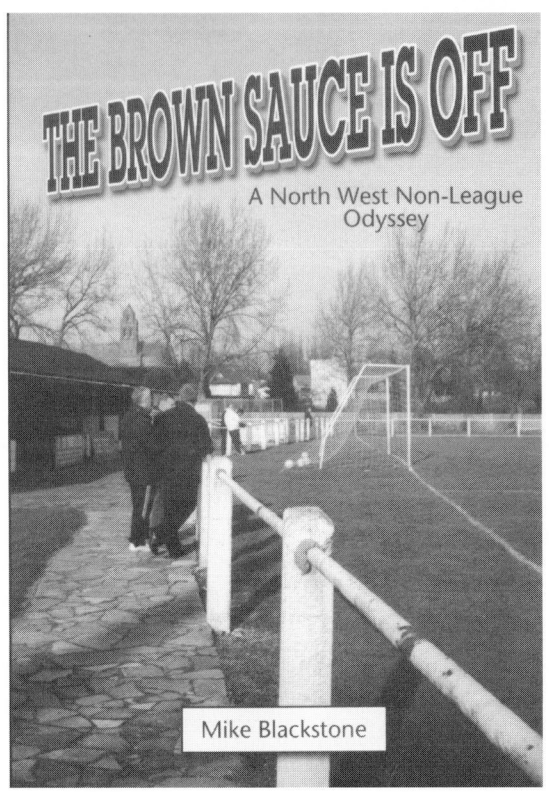

FOOTBALL LEAGUE

STEP 1

FOOTBALL CONFERENCE

STEP 2

CONFERENCE NORTH

CONFERENCE SOUTH

STEP 3

NORTHERN PREMIER

SOUTHERN PREMIER

ISTHMIAN PREMIER

STEP 4

NORTHERN PREMIER DIV.1

SOUTHERN LEAGUE EAST

SOUTHERN LEAGUE WEST

ISTHMIAN DIVISION 1

STEP 5/6

STEP 7 - NORTHERN SECTION

CENTRAL MIDLANDS LEAGUE

SPONSORED BY: ABACUS LIGHTING

President: Mr R Holmes **Chairman:** Frank Harwood
General Secretary: Frank Harwood
103 Vestry Road, Oakwood, Derby DE21 2BN
Tel: 01332 832372 Mobile: 07710 370554 e-mail: frankharwood@onetel.net.uk

RETFORD UNITED TAKE ALL BEFORE THEM

The 2003/2004 season will go down in the history of the league for two reasons, first **Retford United** became the first club in the leagues history to win all the three major trophies. Humber Inspection Services League Challenge Club, in which they defeated the holders **Dinnington Town** 1-0 in an excellent final which was again played at Alfreton Town's Ground, the Phoenix Trophies Flootlit Cup when they overcame **Sandiacre Town** in a match played at Heanor and finally won the Computer Products Supreme Division title which again was not decided until the concluding matches of the season. The later success means that Retford United will completing in the Northern Counties East League in the forthcoming season having achieved promotion.

The other reason was the decision of the League General Secretary, Frank Harwood, to retire after completing ten years in the post, a position he took on temporary in 1993 when Tony Goodacre resigned. Frank has agreed to continue as the League Chairman a position he first undertook in 1979 and coupled with that he will be the CMFL Press Officer, Jeff Worrall takes over the position of General Secretary.

Returning to the 2003/2004 season, **Dinnington Town** finished both Runners Up in the league and Challenge Cup with **Heanor Town** finishing third in the league. The Vipond Premier Division title race was taken by **Radcliffe Olympic** who dominated the top spot for most of the season and where comfortable winners with ? points advantage over **Southwell City.**

The two above clubs along with third placed **Rainworth Miners Welfare** and **Appleby Frodingham** have been promoted to the Supreme Division and significantly all the clubs only joined the CMFL at the beginning of the season which pays tribute to the leagues that they had played in previously. The Lee's Reserves Divisions were won by **Carlton Town Reserves** who took the Reserves Premier Division title and they also won the Phoenix Trophies Reserves League Cup defeating **Pelican Reserves** 3-2 after extra time at Dunkirk. **Radcliffe Olympic Reserves** won the Lee's Reserves Division One title.

The CMFL also arranged a sponsorship deal with **Stadium Services** for a 'Team of the Month' award, with the winning clubs receiving a trophy and match ball

Member clubs again distinguished themselves and the CMFL, in outside competitions with the highlight being in the Lincolnshire FA Senior Cup when **Barton Town Old Boys** took the trophy by defeating **Blackstone** in the final.

In March the league organised a 'Bonanza' event with six league matches taking place, one on Friday evening and five on Saturday, all the matches attracted crowds in the region of 300, with "ground hoppers" coming from around the UK and even from Europe! The member clubs involved made in the region of over £700 each and the excellent work put in by Management Committee member Rob Hornby was rewarded by the occasion being hailed as being the most successful event of its kind, by the Groundhoppers, and it is hoped that it can be repeated yearly.

The league is again indebted to its sponsors, **Samsan Sports** who took over the sponsorship from **KitClub**, unfortunately both KitClub and Samsan Sports have not proved as successful has hoped and the league will again have new main sponsors for the forthcoming season with **Abacus Lighting** joining the league and an excellent package for the company ad CMFL has been arranged by Management Committee member Eddie Pearce, who as the title of Sponsorship Co-ordinator, being the person responsible. Eddie has also secured additional sponsors which will further enhance the league both financially and image wise. Both **Computer Products** and **Humber Inspection Services** have discontinued their Sponsorships and our grateful thanks are conveyed to both for their support. **Vipond Fire Protection** will be continuing as the Premier Division Sponsors as will **Lee's in both the Reserves Divisions.**

The Leagues standing continued to expand with many people world wide contacting the league for badges etc and the CMFL deservedly gained the reputation as being the outstanding league off and on the field at its level in the UK, no wonder the CMFL had 28 enquiries for membership season 2004/2005. Seven new clubs have been accepted. They are :- **AFC Barnsley, Bolsover Town, Grimsby Borough, Newark Flowserve, Newark Town, Pinston** and **Santos**.

Selston and **Sheffield City** have left the league as well as **Retford United** to whom we extend our best wishes in the NCEL.

Frank Harwood (Chairman)

COMPUTER PRODUCTS

SUPREME DIVISION	P	W	D	L	F	A	Pts
Retford United	36	26	7	3	113	32	85
Dinnington Town	36	23	7	6	68	32	76
Heanor Town	36	22	8	6	78	46	74
Sandiacre Town	36	21	5	10	73	52	68
Pelican (P)	36	20	6	10	81	51	66
Dunkirk	36	19	4	13	63	42	61
Barton Town Old Boys	36	18	7	11	62	47	61
Teversal	36	17	9	10	62	43	60
Gedling Miners Welfare	36	15	8	13	50	42	53
Graham Street Prims	36	16	5	15	60	58	53
Radford	36	14	7	15	54	62	49
Kiveton Park (P)	36	9	15	12	48	62	42
Holbrook	36	11	7	18	49	60	40
Clipstone Welfare	36	11	4	21	53	78	37
Nettleham	36	9	7	20	41	61	34
Askern Welfare	36	8	3	25	35	90	27
Greenwood Meadows	36	6	8	22	36	69	26
Rolls Royce Leisure	36	6	6	24	32	75	24
Blackwell Miners Welfare	36	5	9	22	33	89	24

VIPOND FIRE PROTECT

PREMIER DIVISION	P	W	D	L	F	A	Pts
Radcliffe Olympic	36	27	6	3	123	29	87
Southwell City (-3pts)	36	24	6	6	103	44	75
Rainworth Miners Welf.	36	21	8	7	89	42	71
Appleby Frodingham	36	21	6	9	83	55	69
Blidworth Welfare	36	20	7	9	85	63	67
Matlock United	36	19	6	11	75	39	63
Kimberley Town	36	15	12	9	57	43	57
Ollerton Town	36	15	10	11	70	62	55
Bentley Colliery	36	14	8	14	78	76	50
Harworth C.I.	36	13	10	13	59	76	49
Punjab United	36	13	9	14	58	75	48
Welbeck Welfare	36	12	7	17	67	87	43
Forest Town	36	11	9	16	54	66	42
Yorkshire Main	36	10	10	16	63	76	40
Bottesford Town	36	10	8	18	53	69	38
Sheffield City	36	7	8	21	39	84	29
Selston	36	4	11	21	41	79	23
Thorne Colliery	36	5	6	25	42	114	21
Thoresby Colliery Welf.	36	5	5	26	36	96	20

	SUPREME 03-04	1	2	3	4	5	6	7	8	9	10	11	12	13	14	15	16	17	18	19
1	Askern Welfare		1-1	1-0	0-3	0-5	3-1	1-3	1-3	1-2	0-3	2-1	0-1	1-2	0-2	2-0	1-3	2-1	1-1	0-5
2	Barton Town Old Boys	5-1		4-1	3-1	1-2	0-0	2-0	1-0	1-0	3-2	2-2	1-1	3-3	3-1	2-2	2-3	4-0	3-0	0-3
3	Blackwell Miners Welfare	0-4	1-5		1-5	0-1	0-1	0-0	0-3	2-1	0-1	1-2	2-2	1-2	1-1	1-1	2-10	3-1	1-1	1-1
4	Clipstone Welfare	1-0	1-2	2-1		2-2	2-1	2-1	1-2	2-1	2-5	1-0	0-1	0-2	0-4	4-2	3-3	0-2	1-2	1-1
5	Dinnington Town	4-0	2-0	0-0	1-0		2-1	1-0	2-1	1-0	1-3	1-1	2-2	1-0	2-2	3-3	1-3	2-0	3-0	3-1
6	Dunkirk	7-0	4-0	4-1	6-0	1-1		4-0	2-0	2-0	0-5	1-0	3-0	1-0	2-1	0-2	0-1	1-0	1-2	1-4
7	Gedling Miners Welfare	1-0	0-2	1-2	5-0	0-1	2-0		0-0	2-1	0-2	0-1	3-2	4-1	2-1	0-0	0-2	0-0	0-1	4-0
8	Graham Street Prims	4-0	2-1	1-0	2-1	1-0	0-0	1-5		3-0	1-1	4-1	1-2	6-1	2-3	2-2	1-5	2-1	0-1	0-1
9	Greenwood Meadows	0-3	3-0	1-1	3-1	0-5	0-2	2-2	1-2		1-2	2-1	0-2	2-0	2-4	1-2	0-5	2-1	0-3	2-4
10	Heanor Town	3-2	1-2	2-0	3-2	2-3	2-2	0-3	4-3	3-1		0-1	0-0	3-0	3-1	2-1	2-2	2-1	3-0	1-0
11	Holbrook	3-0	2-0	0-2	4-0	0-4	1-2	0-2	3-2	2-2	1-2		1-1	1-0	0-5	6-0	1-1	3-1	1-2	4-0
12	Kiveton Park	1-1	0-2	1-1	3-3	1-2	2-1	2-2	1-2	1-1	1-1	2-1		4-4	1-2	0-2	1-6	2-1	2-2	1-1
13	Nettleham	2-1	1-2	6-0	1-2	0-2	1-4	0-0	1-3	0-0	3-3	1-1	1-0		4-1	0-1	1-0	2-0	2-3	0-0
14	Pelican	1-2	3-0	6-1	2-1	1-2	0-2	1-1	3-1	1-0	1-4	3-2	2-3	1-0		5-0	3-3	5-0	6-3	2-0
15	Radford	3-0	1-0	1-0	4-2	2-3	2-0	2-1	2-2	3-1	0-5	5-0	0-3	1-0	0-1		0-2	0-2	4-0	1-1
16	Retford United	8-1	0-0	5-0	3-1	2-0	4-1	0-1	4-1	2-1	6-0	3-0	2-0	3-0	1-1	4-3		3-0	5-1	4-0
17	Rolls Royce Leisure	3-1	1-4	2-3	1-4	1-0	2-3	1-3	1-2	1-1	1-1	1-1	0-0	3-0	0-1	1-0	0-4		0-3	1-1
18	Sandiacre Town	5-1	2-0	3-1	3-2	0-3	2-0	6-0	4-0	1-1	0-1	2-1	6-1	2-0	2-2	3-1	2-0	4-0		0-2
19	Teversal	2-1	0-1	7-2	1-0	1-0	0-2	1-2	2-0	1-1	1-1	3-0	3-1	1-0	1-2	3-1	1-1	6-1	3-1	

HUMBER INSPECTIONS SERVICES LEAGUE CUP - from 3rd Rnd.

THIRD ROUND

Forest Town	v	Dinnington Town	1-6
Gedling Miners Welfare	v	Rainworth Miners Welfare	2-2, 0-2
Heanor Town	v	Thoresby Colliery Welfare	6-0
Holbrook Miners Welf.	v	Barton Town Old Boys	2-2, 3-2
Radcliffe Olympic	v	Clipstone Welfare	3-0
Retford United	v	Blidworth Welfare	5-0
Sandiacre Town	v	Harworth Colliery Institute	2-1
Yorkshire Main	v	Pelican	2-7

FOURTH ROUND

Dinnington Town	v	Holbrook Miners Welfare	1-1, 1-0
Radcliffe Olympic	v	Pelican	1-2
Retford United	v	Heanor Town	1-1, 3-2
Sandiacre Town	v	Gedling Miners Welfare	1-1, 5-3

SEMI-FINALS

Retford United	v	Pelican	2-1
Sandiacre Town	v	Dinnington Town	0-1

FINAL

Dinnington Town	v	Retford United	0-1

PHOENIX TROPHIES FLOODLIT CUP - from 2nd Rnd.

SECOND ROUND

Blackwell Miners Welf.	v	Sandiacre Town	1-3
Bottesford Town	v	Kimberley Town	4-2
Clipstone Welfare	v	Southwell City	1-0
Graham St Prims	v	Appleby Frodingham	4-3
Harworth Colliery In.	v	Holbrook Miners Welfare	0-2
Heanor Town	v	Retford United	4-6*
Rolls Royce Leisure	v	Dunkirk	1-2*
Teversal	v	Rainworth Miners Welfare	3-3*, 4-5p

THIRD ROUND

Graham St Prims	v	Clipstone Welfare	2-1
Holbrook Miners Welf.	v	Holbrrok Miners Welfare	7-1
Retford United	v	Bottesford Town	4-1
Sandiacre Town	v	Dunkirk	4-2

SEMI-FINALS - TWO LEGS			1ST	2ND
Retford United	v	Holbrook Miners Welf	4-0	2-0
Sandiacre Town	v	Graham St Prims	2-0	2-2

FINAL

Retford United	v	Sandiacre Town	4-1

APPLE FRODINGHAM ATHLETIC

Ground: Brumby Hall Sports Ground, Ashby Road, Scunthorpe, North Lincs
Tel: 01724 843024
Previous League: Lincolnshire Lge.. > 2003

ASKERN WELFARE

Chairman: John Metcalfe **President:** R.Redhead
Secretary: Jon Stewart, 43 Sutton Road, Askern,Doncaster,S.Yorks. DN6 0AG
& Match Sec Tel Nos: 01302 702502 (H) 01302 703035 (W)
Ground: Askern Welfare Sports Ground, Doncaster Road, Askern,Doncaster
Tel: 01302 700957. Clubhouse open normal hours and all day Saturdays
Directions: A1/A639 Pontefract. Follow sign for Askern/Campsall.At T-junction turn right. Left at Anne Arms, right at Supersave, ground on right.
Capacity: 3,000 **Cover** 200**Floodlights** Yes **Club shop:**Yes(01226 771900)

Formed: 1924 Nickname: The Welly
Colours: Black & white stripes/black/black
Change colours: All Red with white trim
Midweek Matchday: Wednesday
Reserves Lg: Doncaster & Dist. Sen. Prem.
Programme: 30 Pages £1.
Editor & Com Man: Martin Terrell 01302 701964
Manager: Paul Curtis
Asst Man/Coach: Martin Terrell
Physio: Kevin Lewis

BARTON TOWN OLD BOYS

Secretary: Peter Mitchell, 56 Brigg Rd., Barton-on-Humber, North Lincs. DN18 5DR
Tel: 01682 632382 (H) 07900 105204 (M)
Ground: Marsh Lane Football Ground, Marsh Lane, Barton-on-Humber, North Lincs.
Tel: 07900 105204 (Secretary's Mobile)
Directions: Approaching from south on A15, Barton is the last exit before Humber Bridge. Follow A1077 into town. Right at mini r'about, at bottom of hill onto 'Holydyke'. 2nd left onto George St., then into King St. Marsh Lane is opp. junction of King St. & High St.

Colours: Light blue/dark blue/dark blue
Change colours: Red & black stripes/black/black

BLACKWELL MINERS WELFARE

Secretary: Steve Harris, 6 Pennine Close, Newton, Alfreton, Derbys DE55 5UD.
Tel: 01773 779172(H) 01246 501561(W) 01773 779173 (F)01246 501571
Email: steve_harris@bdrmg.co.uk
Club Website: www.blackwellmwfc.org.uk - Club Email: manor2@ntlworld.co.uk
Ground: Welfare Ground, Primrose Hill, Blackwell, Derbyshire DE55 5JE. Tel: 01773 811295.
Directions: M1 Junc 28, A38 towards Mansfield, left onto B6406, left again at Hilcote Arms, ground 1 mile on left just past Miners Welfare. Matchday Tel: 07890 198776
2003-2004 **Player of the Year**: Steve Garrard **Top Golascorer**: Mark Downing

Founded:
Colours: Red & white stripes/red/red
Change cols: White/black/black

Midweek Matchday: Wednesday

Manager:Graham Brentnall (07792727319)
Captain: Ryan Wall

CLIPSTONE WELFARE

Secretary: John Tait, 51 Goldsmith Road, Mansfield, Notts. NG18 5PF (01623 478655)
Ground & Directions: Clipstone Lido Ground, Clipstone Road East, Mansfield,Notts (01632 655674). B6030 from Mansfield, between Forest Town & Clipstone, on left entering Clipstone (coming from Mansfield)
Capacity: 3000 **Seats:** 90 **Cover:** 200 **Floodlights:** Yes **Club Shop:** No
Clubhouse: Open on match days with refreshments available.
Honours: Notts Snr Cup 85-86 94-95, Notts Alliance 72-73 73-74 74-75 92-93 94-95 (Lg Cup 72-73 73-74 74-75 94-95 (R-up 92-93)), Notts I'mediate Cup 55-56. Central Midlands Premier Championship 94-95 96-97

Founded 1928
Colours: Red/black/black
Change Colours: All B lue
Midweek Matchday: Tuesday or Wednesday
Programme: £1.00
Chairman: Peter Craggs
Manager: Dave Mason
2002-2003
Captain: Craig Flinton
Top Scorer: Richard Clifton

DINNINGTON TOWN

Secretary: Wallace Chambers, 26 Mackenzie Way,Kiveton Park, Sheffield S26 6QMM
Tel No: 07932 677881
Ground: Resource Centre, 131 Laughton Road, Dinnington.
Tel: 01905 518555
Directions: M1 J31 onto A57 towards Worksop. At 1st lights turn left to Dinnington. Follow road into town centre and the ground is on the left.

Founded:
Colours: Yellow/black/black
Change: Green & Black/white/white

Midweek Matchday:

Manager: Steve Toyne
Tel: 01142 347584 (H) 07960 616129 (B)

BLACKWELL MINERS WELFARE - Back Row (L-R): M. Downing, G. Mayhew, L. Harris, C. Rodgers, G. Haslam, S. Archbold, P. Jones, T. Norris. Front Row: (L-R): S. Garrard, D. Bettison, B. Goodwin, W. Allsop, A. Jepson.

DUNKIRK

Secretary: Steve Throssell, 24 Kingfisher Wharf, Castle Marina, Nottingham NG71GA (0115 9473903 or 07903 322446
Ground & Directions: The Ron Steel Sports Ground, Trentside Farm, Clifton Bridge, Nottingham (0115 9850803). Ring Road - Clifton Bridge (North End),Ind Estate, Lenton Lane.
Honours: FA Vase 5th Rd 93-94; Cen Mid Sup Div R-up 96-97, Prem Div R-up 95-96,KO Cup 97-98; Notts Alliance Div 1 84-85, Div 2 82-83, Lg Cup R-up 84-85;02-03 Notts I'mediate Cup 83-4 Floodlit CupWoinners: 2002-2003**Capacity:**1,500 **Seats:** No **Cover**: 200 **Floodlights**: Yes **Shop:** No **Clubhouse:** Yes
Record Attendance: 821 v Tiverton Town, F.A.Vase 5th Rd 93-94
2003-2004: Top Scorer: Darryl Thomas **P.o.Y**.: Paul Curwood

Founded: 1946
Colours: Red/black/black
Change Colours: All Blue
Midweek Matchday: Tuesday
Programme : Yes
Chairman:Jack Riley
Manager: David Harbottle
Assistant Manager:Wayne Manners
Captain: Sean Connor
Players Progressing: Roger Willis and Matthew McKemzie (Grimsby T), Wes Morgan (Nottm F)

GEDLING M.W.

Secretary: Norman Hay, 182 Gedling Rd., Arnold, Nottingham NG5 6NY
Tel: 0115 926 5598 (H)
Ground: Plains Sports & Social, Plains Road, Mapperly, Nottingham
Tel: 0115 926 6300
Location: The ground is situated on the B684 in Mapperley

Colours: Yellow/blue/yellow
Change: Blue/white/blue

Manager: Mark Allison
Tel: 0115 931 2650 (H)

GRAHAM STREET PRIMS

Secretary: David Lillie . 6 Sidmouth Close, Church View, Alvaston, Derby.
e-mail: davelillie@hotmail,com
Ground: Asterdale Sports Centre, Borrowash Road, Spondon, nr Derby. Tel: 01332 668656
Website: www.freewebs.com/grahamstreetprims
Directions: M1 Junc 25, take A52 to Derby. 3rd left Borrowash Road - golf driving range on left, approx 400m further turn left into Asterdale Sports Centre. Ground at rear.
Capacity: 1,000 Seats: No Cover: Yes Floodlights: Yes Club shop: No Clubhouse: Yes

Formed: 1904
Colours: Red & white stripes/black/black
Change Colours: Yelow/red/red
Midweek Matchday: Wednesday
Chairman: ArthurTitterton
Manager: Gerry McElhinney

HEANOR TOWN - Back Row (L-R): Geoff Woolley (Physio), Tom Williams, Steve Travis, Richard Preston, Chris Seale, Dean Lowe, Matt Johnson, Tom Widdison, Richard Searston, Craig Charity.
Front Row (L-R): Liam Leavesley, Graham Fowkes, Stuart Nichol, Pete Davis, Steve Froggatt, Jamie Hibbert, Lee Fowler (ended season as player/manager). Photo: Gordon Whittington.

SHEFFIELD CITY Photo: Gordon Whittington.

RADCLIFFE OLYMPIC Photo: Gordon Whittington.

GREENWOOD MEADOWS

Secretary: Peter Hynes,64 Wallis Street,Basford,Nottingham NG6 0EP
0115 9705132

Ground: Greenwood Meadows, Lenton Lane, Clifton, Nottingham.
Tel: 0115 986 5913

Directions: M1 Junc 24 take A453Nottingham-Clifton Bridge to Lenton Ind Estate.
Left into Old Lenton Lane.Ground second on right on lane.

Founded:
Colours: Green & white/black/green
Change:Red & black.black/black

Midweek Matchday:

Managers: Brian Cawthorn & Chris Nicholson

HEANOR TOWN

Secretary: Keith Costello, 45 Stainsby Avenue, Heanor, Derbys. DE75 7EL(01773 719446).
Ground & Directions: The Town Ground, Mayfield Avenue, Heanor (01773713742/715815).
M1 (J26), take A610 onto A608, ground 200yds from Market Square
Capacity: 4,000 and new stand being built **Cover:** 2,000 **Floodlights:** Yes
Honours: Central Midlands League Cup 94-95 (Runners-up 86-87 92-93, B E Webbe Removals Cup 88-89), West Midlands Reg. League Runners-up 72-73; Midland Co's League Runners-up 65-66 67-68; Derbys Senior Cup(9) 1892-94 1946-47 65-69 70-7178-79; FA Cup 1st Rd 58-59 63-64.Central Midlands Supreme Champions:94-5,96-7 Central All.Lg(2) R-up4
Clubhouse: On ground with hot food (match days) **Best Vase Season**: 2001--02 4th Rd.

Nickname: The Lions
Colours: White/black/black
Change Colours: Red/white/white
Midweek Matchday: Wednesday
Programme: 32pages £1.00 Ed: Stan Wilton
01332 880199 (H) & 01332 881049 (Fax)
Chairman: John McCulloch
Manager:Lee Fowler
2002-03 **Top Scorer**: Roy Sharpe
Captain: Peter Davis **P.o.Y.:** Chris Seale

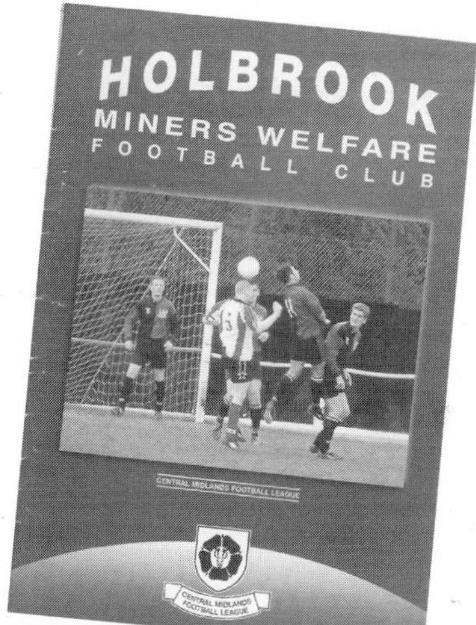

HOLBROOK MINERSW WELFARE

Secretary: Matt Cann,31 Sherwood St.,Shaw Lane,Holbrook,Derbys.DE56 0TG(01332 880259)
e-mail: matt@fuivepits.fsnet.co.uk
Ground: The Welfare Ground, Shaw Lane, Holbrook, Derbyshire DE56 0TF Tel: 01332 880259
Directions: From A38 take B6179 for Kilburn, turn left at lights for Belper. 1mile on left at Bulls Head for Holbrook.Shaws Lane on right after 2 miles at Venture garage.Ground 200yds on right.
Capacity: 1,000 **Seats:** None **Cover:** 250 **Floodlights:** No
Clubhouse: Holbrook Miners Welfare, Shaw Lane.(01332 880259) **Shop:** No
Honours: Central Midlands Premier Division 99-00 **Previous Name**: Holbrook F.C. (1996-2003)
Record Attendance: 180 v Matlock Town (Derbyshire Cup)

Founded: 1996 Nickname: The Brookies
Colours:Blue & black halves/black/blue
Change: Yellow/green/yellow
Midweek Matchday:Wednesday
Prog: 24pages 50p Ed: Toby Austin
Website: Holbrookfc.co.uk
Chairman: Howard Williams
Manager: Mark Webster Coach: Mick Bentley
Captain: Ritchard Astle
2003-2004
Top Scorer & P.o.Y.:James Newton

KIVETON PARK

Secretary: Kevin Hull, 3 Chapel way, Kiveton Park, Sheffield S26 6QT
Tel: 01909 772152

Ground: Hard Lane, Kiveton Park, Sheffield. Tel: 0797 4247074.

Directions: M1 J31. Take A57 Worksop road, first right to Todwick, at T junct. turn right.
Follow road to Kiveton crossroads. Go over & ground is on right after approx 100m.

Colours: Green & Blue/Blue/Green
Change Colours:: All Red

Manager: Stuart Holmes

NETTLEHAM

Secretary: Charles SWaw,4 Willowfield Avenue, Nettleham, Lincoln. LN2 2TH
Tel NO: 01522 522255 (W) 01522 823912 (H)

Ground: Mulsanne Park, Field Close, Nettleham Tel: 01522 750007.

Directions:A46 - 3 miles north of Lincoln, right at Brown Cow Pub, past Church 2nd turning on right, ground at end

Floodlights: Yes **Previous League:** Lincolnshire

Honours: Central Mids Lg Premier Div. Cup R-up 87-88, Village Tphy, Nursing Cup, Kelly Read Cup, Blankney Hunt Cup, Lincoln & Dist. Amtr Cup R-up, Joe Miller Tphy(2).

Founded: 1905
Sponsors: Double 'M' Catering (Home)
J W Bandelow Plastering (Away)
Colours: All Royal Blue
Change: Yellow/Green/Yellow
Midweek Matchday: Tuesday
Programme: Price £1
Editor: Charles Shaw
Chairman: Clive Mason
Manager: Jim Masterton Capt: Paul Hodds
2003-2004
Leading Goalscorer: Lee Beesley
Player of the Year: Adam Lynn

PELICAN

Secretary: Neil Swift, 21 Lancaster Way, Strelley, Nottingham NG8 6PH
Tel: 0115 929 4728 (H) 0776 77778765 (B)

Ground: Brian Wakefield Sports Ground, Lenton Lane, Nottingham
Tel: 0115 986 8255

Directions: M1 J26 take A610 to ring road. Follow signs A52 Grantham. Go under Clifton Bridge, Ground last on Lenton Lane.

Honours: Notts Alliance Lg Cup 90-91(R-up 91-92 93-94).

Colours: All Blue
Change: Red/black/black

Manager: Glen Russell

RADCLIFFE OLYMPIC

Secretary: C Johnson, 2 The Firs, Holme Pierpoint, Nottingham NG12 2LT
Tel: 0115 933 3791

Ground: Wharf Lane, Radcliffe-on-Trent, Nottingham

Colours: All black with beige & red trim

RADFORD

Secretary: Miss Joanne Smith, 63 Hilcot Drive, Aspley, Nottingham NG8 5HS
Tel: 0794 9091477

Ground: Radford FC, Berridge Rd. West, off Radford Road, Radford, Nottm
Tel: 0115 943250

Directions: M1 Junc 26,take A610 to Nottingham, at dual carriageway turn left. Move to right lane and go immediately right into Wilkinson St. At top turn right & right again at 2nd crossing.

Colours: Claret & sky blue/claret/claret
Change: Red & Blue stripes/red/red
Midweek Matchday: Tuesday

Manager: Matt Keetley

RAINWORTH MINERS WELFARE

Secretary: Les Lee, 18 The Hollies, Eainworth, Mansfield, Notts NG21 0FL
Tel No: 01123 792495 (H) 07740576958 (M)

Ground: Kirkilington Road, Rainworth, Mansfield, Notts.
Website: www.intheteam.com/wren

Capacity: **Seats:** **Cover:** **Floodlights:** **Clubhouse:** Yes

Directions: From M1 J29 A617 to Mansfield & Rainworth. Left at lights in Rainworth into Kirklington Rd.

PREVIOUS **Leagues:** Notts Alliance

Best Season 1981-82 F.A.Vase Finalists, Notts Alliance Champions League Cup Winners

Best Attendance 5,071 v Barton Rovers Semi-Final F.A.Vase S-Final 1982

2003-2004 **Player of the Year:** Jonathon Wilson **Top Goalscorer:** Matt Deakin

FACT FILE
Formed: 1992
Colours: All White
Change colours: All Royal Blue
Midweek Matches: Tues/Wedf
Prog Editor:Gordon Foster (07890789967 (M)
CLUB PERSONNEL
Chairman: Brian Martin
Match S: Barry Reece Tel No; 01123 822415
Press Officer: Gary Fuller
Manager: Sandy Pate
Coach: MarK Hallus Captain: Mark Deakin
Physios: Gaynor Tunney & ron Sharpe

ROLLS ROYCE LEISURE F.C.

Secretary: Gary Warbrick, 20 Balmoral Road, Hucknall, Nootts. NG15 8ES
Tel. No: 0115 9640384 (H) 07732426283 (M)

Ground: Rolls Royce Sports & Social Club, Watnall Road, Hucknall Notts. Tel. 0115 963 0134

Directions: M1 Junc 27. Follow sign A611 to Hucknall. Turn right onto by-pass. 2nd r/about turn right on to Watnall Road. Take 2nd left after fire station on R.R. Sports Ground.

Capacity: 1,000 **Cover:** Yes **Floodlights**: No

Clubhouse: Social Club always open with food

Colours: All Blue
Change colours: Yellow/yellow/white
Midweek Matchday: Wednesday
Programme: Yes Price: Pages:
Editor:
Chairman: Darryl Claypole
Manager: Phil Towle
Reserves: Peter Needham & Paul Hopkins

SANDIACRE TOWN

Secretary: Mel Williams, 38 Pasture Rd.,Stapleford, Nottingham NG9 8GL Tel: 0115 9174079
Ground: St Giles Park, Stanton Road, Sandiacre, Nottingham NG105EP Tel:0115 9392880.
Directions: M1 jct 25, follow signs to Sandiacre passing Hilton Hotel on righ, straight over cross-roads into Rushy Lane and towards Stanton Rd,1st rt into StantonRd,ground at bottom after another1000yds. **Web:** homepage.ntlworld.com/sandiacretownfc
Capacity: 2,000 Seats: None Cover: 250 Floodlights: Yes Club Shop: No
Clubhouse: Members Club 8-11pm. Sunday lunch, Saturday1.30-11pm. Snacks available
Honours: Central Mids Prem. Div 92-93, Lg Cup 92-93 R-up 95-96, Mids Reg All.R-up 91-92 Floodlit Cup R-up 2003-04

Founded: 1978 Nickname: Saints
Cols: Red/navy/red Change: Navy /red/navy
Midweek Matchday: Tuesday
Programme: 48 pages 50p
Editor/Press Officer: Mel Williams
Tel: 0115 917 4079
Chairman: John Ellis
Manager: Tony Roe
Captain Robbie Briscoe
P.o.Y. & Top Scorer Nick Ghislanzoni 37

SOUTHWELL CITY

Secretary: Pat Johnson, 63 The Ropewalk, Southwell, Notts. NG25 0AL Tel: 01636 8126594

Ground: War Memorial Recreation Ground, Bishops Drive, Southwell, Notts.
Tel: 01636 814386

Previous League: Notts Alliance. > 2003 **Colours**: Black & white stripes/black/black

TEVERSAL

Secretary: Kevin Newton, 8 Vere Ave., Sutton in Ashfield, Notts NG17 2ES
Tel: 01623 461145
Ground: Teversal Grange Country Inn, Carnarvon Street, Teversal, Sutton-in-Ashfield, Notts.
Tel: 01623 442021
Directions: M1, J28, A38 towards Mansfield. At r'about take A6075 Mansfield Woodhouse.
Next lights left B6014, Stanton Hill. At r'about take A6014 Tibshelf.
2nd on right Carnarvon St., ground at the top.

Colours: Red & white/ black/red
Change: Blue / white/white

Chairman:
Managers: John Courtie
Physio:

Back Row (L-R): Les Lee (Secretary), Sandy Pate (Manager), Tim Reece, Chris Connell, Carl Ward, Paul Johnson, John Wilson, Danny Edwards, Dale Cooper, Mark Deakin (capt), Brian Martin (Chairman/Groundsman), Barry Reece (Fix. Sec.), Brian Reece (Committee). Front Row (L-R): Cliff Clarke, Michael Parsons, John Millner, Bobby Sharman, Matt Allen, Marc Stevens, Graham Pate.
Mascot: Elliott Lee and club photographer Bradley Fuller (youngest in the country!)

A.F.C. BARNSLEY

Secretary: Barry Wiggan, 9 Pantry Well, Worsborough, Dale, Barnsley S704SW
Tel /FAX: 01226 247023 (H)
Ground: Oakwell Stadium, c/o Barnsley F.C., Grove Street, Barnsley.
Tel No: 01226 211211
Directions: From M1 South leave motorway at Jct.37 and turn right onto the A628towards Barnsley. Follow signs for Oakwell, Barnsley F.C.

CLUB PERSONNEL
Manager: Mark Hancock
FACT FILE
: Colours:Red/white/red
Change colours: White/red/white

BENTLEY COLLIERY

Secretary: James P Tooth, 38 East St., Darfield, Barnsley, South Yorks. S73 9AE Tel: 01226 754012 (H/Fax)
Ground: Bentley Miners' Welfare, The Avenue, Bentley, Doncaster, S. Yorks. Tel: 01302 874420 **Directions:** North from Doncaster on A19: Selby Road. In Bentley turn right at mini r'about on Arksey Lane. Left at shops onto The Avenue and the ground is 60 yards on left.
Colours: All Yellow **Change colours:** White & Claret/claret/claret **Manager:** Roy Butterworth

BLIDWORTH WELFARE

Secretary: Graham Redfern, 1 Dennbigh Close,Rainworth,Notts NG21 0HY Tel No: 01623 403019
Ground: Welfare Ground, Mansfield Rd, Blidworth, Mansfield (01623 793361). **Directions:** On B6020, Rainworth side of Blidworth. From M1 jct 27 take A608 to Kirby at lights follow A611 to Kirby then take B6020through Ravenshead to Blidworth -thru village and up hill ground on right. From A1 follow A614 /A617 to Rainworth, left at lights then 1st right on to B6020 to Blidworth - ground on left at top of hill.
Colours: Orange/black/orange **Change colours:** Blue/whiteblue. **Manager:** Rudi Funk

BOLSOVER TOWN

Secretary: Ken Perrins, 35 Stuart Close,Chesterfield S410SW
Tel No: 01246 620352
Ground: Coalite Sports & Social Club, Moor Lane, Bolsover
Tel No: 01246 822449
Directions: M1 Jct 29 towards Mansfield. At Glapwell turn left for Bolsover. Ground is straight over at the end of the road

CLUB PERSONNEL
Manager: Robert Green
FACT FILE
Colours: Blue/white/blue
Change colours: White/blue/white

BOTTESFORD TOWN

Secretary: Tony Reeve, 61 Skelton Road, Scunthorpe, North Lincs. DN17 1RB Tel 01724 352939 (H)
Ground: Birch Park, Ontario Road, Bottesford, Scunthorpe, N. Lincs. Tel: 01724 871833
Directions: Exit M180 via M181 - Scunthorpe. At r'about right into Scotter Road. Over next r'about then 2nd left into South Park Rd., on to Sunningdale Rd. Right into Goodwood Rd, ground at end.
Colours: Orange/Black/Black **Change**: Blue & Yellow/blue/yellow **Manager**: Vic Jubber

FOREST TOWN

Secretary: Jan Nieloojadio, 14 Bransdale Avenue, Forest Town, Mansfield, Notts. NG19 0LZ Tel No: 01623 648588
Ground: Forest Town Welfare Sports Ground, Clipstone Rd West, Forest Town, Mansfield, Notts. Tel: 01623 624678
Directions: From Mansfield follow signs for Clipstone/Forest Town. The ground is situated at the Mansfield end of Forest Town on the right.
Colours: All blue **Change Colours:** All red **Manager:**Mat Vardy

GRIMSBY BOROUGH

Ground: **King George V Athletic Stadium, Weelsby Road, Grimsby, North Lincs**
Tel: **01472 602192**

HARWORTH COLLIERY INSTITUTE

Secretary: Tom Brogan, 30 Lindsey Road, Harworth, Doncaster, Sth Yorks DN11 8QH Tel: 01302 750132.
Ground: Recreation Ground, Scrooby Rd, Bircotes, Doncaster Tel: 01302 750614.
Directions: Off A1(M) at Blyth, head towards Bawtry for approx 2 miles, 3rd left, ground in village at top of hill on left. Or, from Doncaster to Bawtry then head for A1(M) and turn left after caravan site - ground at top of hill.
Colours: Amber & black/black/amber & black **Change Cols:** Claret and Blue **Midweek Matchday:** Wednesday **Manager:** Alan Needham

KIMBERLEY TOWN

Chairman: Graeme Critchley **Managers**: G.Critchley & Nev Wheeler **Colours:**Yellow/black/yellow
Secretary & Prog Ed: Mrs Patricia Critchley, 21 Rowborn Drive,Oughtbridge, Sheffield S35 0JR Tel: 0114 2517742 **Change**: All Navy Blue
Ground: Stag Ground, Nottingham Road, Kimberley Tel: 0115 938 2788. **e-mail**:info@kimberleytownfc.co.uk
Website:www.kimberleytownfc.co.uk
Directions: Thro' Nuthall from M1 J 26 to Kimberley, ground entrance 150 yds after Stag Inn. Capacity: 2,500 **Seats:** None **Cover**:250
Floodlights: Yes Clubhouse: Evenings (Except Sun) & matchdays. Hot & cold snacks available **Midweek Matchday**: Tues or Wed
Honours: Notts Amateur Lg Div 1 54-55, Central Alliance Div 2 R-up 57-58. 2003-04 P.O.Y:Paul Willcockson Top Scorer: Carl Longmore

MATLOCK UNITED

Ground: Cavendish Road Playing Fields, Cavendish Park, Matlock, Derbyshire
Previous League: Midlands Regional Alliance > 2003

NEWARK FLOWSERVE

Ground: Lowfields Works, off Hawton Lane, Balderton, Newark, Notts

Tel: 01636 702672

NEWARK TOWN

Secretary: Maureen McGuiness, 91 Marsh Lane, Farndon, Newark, Notts NG24 4TA
Ground: c/o Collingham F.C. Statioopn Road, Collingham Tel No: 01636 892303
Capacity: **Seats:** **Cover:** **Floodlights:**
Directions: From A1/A46 jct. take the Lincoln turn off at first roundabout and then head for Collingham . Right at traffic lights into Station Road. Ground is 100 yards on left.
Clubhouse:
PREVIOUS **Leagues:** Notts Alliance
HONOURS
2003-2004 Player of the Year: Gareth Dobb **Top Goalscorer:** Andrew McGanly

FACT FILE
Formed: 1868
Sponsor:
Colours: Sky Blue/navy/white/
Change colours: Yellow/navy/sky
Midweek Matches: Tuesday
Programme Editor: Chairman
(01636 679316)
paul.baggaley@bt.internet.com

CLUB PERSONNEL
Chairman: Paul Baggaley
Managers: Brett McNamara & Tony Jones

OLLERTON TOWN

Gen. Secretary: Les Brown,14 Holly Rise,New Ollerton, Notts NG22 9UZ Tel No: 01623 836023
Secretary: Les Brown, 14 Holly Rise, New Ollerton, Notts. NG22 9UZ Tel: 01623 836023 (H)
Ground: Walesby Lane, New Ollerton, Notts
Directions: From Ollerton r'about om A614 take A6075 to Ollerton. At r'about first left & after 30m left into Walesby Lane
Colours: All red **Change colours:** Blue/white/blue **Manager:** Alan Owen

PINXTON

Secretary: Mick Barrett, 8 Glebe Avenue, Pinxton, Notts. NG16 6HR
Tel No: 01773 782995
Ground: Welfare Ground, Wharf Road, Pinxton,Notts.
Tel No: 0779 2686707
Directions: M1 Jct 28. Take A38 roundabout and follow B6019 to Pinxton. First left into Pinxton Lane to traffic lights, then right into Victoria Road down to T junc tion and second right to Wharf Road. Ground is 300 yards on right opposite Wharf Aquaries behind Welfare.

CLUB PERSONNEL
Manager: Tim Graney
FACT FILE
Colours: All Blue
Change colours: Yellow/Black/Black
Midweek Matches:

PUNJAB UNITED

Ground: The Wharf, Shardlow, Derby
Previous League: East Midlands Senior Lge. > 2003

SANTOS

Secretary: Stephen Dickens, 5 Japonica Drive, Cinderhill, Nottingham NG6 8PU
Tel No: 0115 9199625
Ground: Bilsthorpe Miners Welfare, Ekring Lane, Bilsthorpe,Notts.
Directions: A614 to Bilsthorpe and head to Ekring Lane. Car park on opposite side of ground.

CLUB PERSONNEL
Manager: Clive Watchorn
FACT FILE
Colours: Blue & Black/Black/Blue
Change colours: Yellow & Green/Green/Yellow

THORESBY COLLIERY WELFARE

Secretary: Barry Reece, 125 Henton Rd., Edwinstone, Mansfield, Notts. NG21 9LD Tel: 01623 822415 (H) 01623 491422 (B)
Ground: Thoresby Colliery Sports Ground, 4th Avenue, Edwinstone, Notts. Tel: 01623 822283 (Ground & Clubhouse)
Directions: A614 Ollerton r'about take A6075 Mansfield/Edwinstone. Turn left opposite 'Manvers Arms' onto 5th Avenue. Opposite Nursing Home turn right onto 4th Ave. Ground entrance ahead.
Colours: Blye & white/ blue/blue **Change Colours:** Gold/black/black **Manager:** Mick Heron

THORNE COLLIERY

Secretary: Glyn Jones, 21 Haynes Close, Thorne,Doncaster, S Yorks DN8 5HR Tel No: 01405 741062
Ground & Directions: Miners Welfare, Grange Road, Moorends, Thorne, Doncaster.(01374 996474), M18 Junc 6, in THorne, turnat lights to Moorends, go almostthrough village, Grange Road on right.
Manager: Graham Jones **Colours:** All Navy **Change:** Green & Navy/green/green **Midweek Matchday:** Tuesday

WELBECK MINERS WELFARE

Secretary: Gillian Gibbonbs,21 Cumberland Avenue,Warsop, Mansfield, Notts. NG20 0JJ Tel No: 01623 844616
Ground: Elksley Road, Meden Vale, Mansfield. (01623 842611) **Directions:** 1 1/2 miles off A60 between Worksop and Mansfield. Signed Meden vale. (do NOT follow signs for Welbeck Colliery.) Turn off at Warsop Church.
HONOURS: Notts Alliance Div 2 93-94 (Intermediate Cup 93-94), Chesterfield & Dist. Lg 92-93
Colours: All black/white **Change colours:** Grey/grey/red **Manager:** Neil Gibbons

YORKSHIRE MAIN

Secretary: Dennis Tymon, 22 Pamela Drive, Warmsworth, Doncaster DN4 9RP Tel: 01302 852455
Ground: Yorkshire Main Welfare, Edlington Lane, Edlington, Doncaster Tel: 01709 864075
Directions: A1M junc 36. Proceed on A630 towards Rotherham. At 1st lights turn on to B6376. Ground on left after Fire Station.
Colours: Yellow/green/yellow **Change Colours:** Red/black/red **Manager:** Derek Wynne

LIVERPOOL COUNTY COMBINATION

SPONSORED BY: FRANK ARMITT

President: Lord Pendry **Chairman:** H E Humphries
Secretary: J F Deal, 24 The Pastures, Crossens, Southport PR9 8RH
Tel: 01704 211955

FINAL LEAGUE TABLE 2003-04

		P	W	D	L	F	A	Pts
1.	Waterloo Dock	34	30	2	2	128	25	92
2.	Speke	34	25	3	6	95	49	78
3.	St. Dominics	34	24	3	7	87	52	75
4.	Lucas Sports	34	22	4	8	107	63	70
5.	Halewood Town	34	21	3	10	92	43	66
6.	Ford Motors	34	20	6	8	80	48	66
7.	St. Aloysius	34	18	4	12	76	51	58
8.	South Liverpool	34	18	4	12	65	42	58
9.	Birchfield	34	13	3	18	76	84	42
10.	Royal Seaforth	34	10	4	20	75	100	34
11.	South Sefton Borough	34	10	7	17	40	57	33
12.	Aigburth Peoples Hall	34	9	6	19	56	94	33
13.	Skelmersdale United Reserves	34	9	4	21	66	99	31
14.	Prescot Leisure	34	9	3	22	41	99	30
15.	Mossley Hill Athletic	34	8	5	21	53	87	29
16.	Cheshire Lines	34	8	4	22	52	100	28
17.	Bootle	34	5	12	17	54	92	27
18.	Tuebrook Park	34	8	1	25	63	121	25

2003-04		1	2	3	4	5	6	7	8	9	10	11	12	13	14	15	16	17	18
1	Aigburth Peoples Hall		2-1	1-1	2-2	3-1	1-2	2-3	3-4	0-4	3-0	5-2	1-3	2-2	3-6	1-4	0-3	3-2	0-3
2	Birchfield	8-1		1-4	5-3	1-2	2-0	2-4	5-1	2-3	5-4	2-0	4-3	2-2	0-2	2-3	4-5	5-3	1-2
3	Bootle	1-3	2-3		1-1	2-3	0-2	1-3	2-2	5-2	1-1	1-7	1-1	0-2	0-1	3-3	1-3	2-4	1-1
4	Cheshire Lines	2-2	6-4	5-4		2-4	0-3	1-7	1-1	1-0	5-2	2-3	1-3	3-0	0-4	1-3	2-3	3-2	0-3
5	Ford Motors	4-0	4-0	0-0	3-0		2-2	1-4	1-1	4-0	2-1	5-1	3-1	3-0	0-1	1-2	2-0	6-1	0-6
6	Halewood Town	5-0	2-1	6-0	6-0	1-2		0-2	0-2	4-1	5-3	4-0	2-0	1-2	3-2	1-1	1-1	3-2	0-2
7	Lucas Sports	2-2	9-1	5-0	5-0	7-2	2-1		1-3	6-0	3-3	5-3	1-2	0-1	4-2	4-2	3-2	3-1	1-13
8	Mossley Hill Athletic	0-1	0-1	3-3	2-0	2-3	0-4	1-1		4-0	0-3	3-2	0-1	1-2	3-6	2-1	0-3	6-1	1-3
9	Prescot Leisure	1-4	0-2	2-2	0-1	2-3	0-2	0-5	3-0		2-2	2-1	0-3	1-0	1-1	1-5	1-4	3-2	0-3
10	Royal Seaforth	2-4	1-2	3-0	4-2	1-6	4-3	1-0	4-2	6-1		3-3	2-3	2-4	1-2	2-3	0-4	4-3	0-5
11	Skelmersdale United Res.	2-2	2-1	2-2	4-2	0-4	2-1	3-2	4-2	1-2	3-5		1-2	0-2	1-3	1-2	0-6	3-2	2-4
12	South Liverpool	4-1	4-0	1-2	2-0	1-1	0-3	1-1	5-1	3-0	4-0	3-0		4-1	1-3	1-0	1-2	3-0	1-0
13	South Sefton Borough	4-2	0-0	1-2	0-2	0-3	0-4	1-2	2-1	0-1	2-0	3-3	1-1		0-2	0-0	1-1	2-0	0-1
14	Speke	4-0	2-2	2-4	3-1	2-1	2-4	0-1	4-1	4-1	5-1	1-0	4-2	2-1		2-1	3-3	6-1	2-1
15	St Aloysius	2-0	0-3	6-1	3-1	0-0	1-4	1-0	8-0	5-1	4-3	4-1	1-0	2-1	2-3		1-2	1-2	1-2
16	St Dominics	1-0	3-1	3-1	2-1	2-0	3-6	3-4	2-1	4-2	4-1	3-2	2-0	1-0	0-3	1-0		5-2	1-4
17	Tuebrook Park	3-1	4-3	3-3	3-1	1-3	2-7	1-5	3-2	3-4	2-6	3-6	1-0	2-1	1-6	1-3	1-4		1-3
18	Waterloo Dock	6-1	2-0	6-1	7-1	1-1	1-0	6-2	4-1	7-0	3-0	6-1	2-1	6-2	4-0	3-1	3-1	5-0	

PETER COYNE/GEORGE MAHON CUP

PRELIMINARY ROUND

Cheshire Lines	v	Birchfield	2-4
Speke	v	Tuebrook Park	3-2

FIRST ROUND

Aigburth People's Hall	v	Mossley Hill Athletic	1-2*
(tie awarded to Aigburth People's Hall)			
Birchfield	v	St Aloysius	2-1
Bootle	v	Royal Seaforth	2-3
Ford Motors	v	St Dominics	1-2*
Halewood Town	v	Lucas Sports	1-0
Prescot Leisure	v	South Sefton Borough	5-0
Speke	v	Skelmersdale Res.	2-3*
Waterloo Dock	v	South Liverpool	1-2

QUARTER-FINALS

Halewood Town	v	Skelmersdale United Res.	2-0
Prescot Leisure	v	Royal Seaforth	1-2
South Liverpool	v	Birchfield	1-2
St Dominics	v	Aigburth People's Hall	4-1

SEMI-FINALS

Birchfield	v	St Dominics	1-1*, 3-5p
(at St Dominics)			
Halewood Town	v	Royal Seaforth	1-0

FINAL (29th April at Formby)

St Dominics	v	Halewood Town	1-2

LORD WAVERTREE CUP

PRELIMINARY ROUND

Ford Motors	v	Royal Seaforth	2-0*
South Sefton Borough	v	Cheshire Lines	3-2

FIRST ROUND

Bootle	v	Speke	2-7
Ford Motors	v	Mossley Hill Athletic	2-1
Lucas Sports	v	Prescot Leisure	4-0
Skelmersdale United Res.	v	Halewood Town	0-3
South Liverpool	v	Birchfield	1-0
South Sefton Borough	v	Waterloo Dock	0-4
(at Waterloo Dock)			
St Aloysius	v	Tuebrook Park	2-1
St Dominics	v	Aigburth People's Hall	4-1

QUARTER-FINALS

Halewood Town	v	Ford Motors	3-1
Speke	v	St Aloysius	1-2
St Dominics	v	South Liverpool	0-3
Waterloo Dock	v	Lucas Sports	1-0

SEMI-FINALS

Halewood Town	v	Waterloo Dock	2-1
South Liverpool	v	St Aloysius	2-0

FINAL

(6th May at Ford Motors)

Halewood Town	v	South Liverpool	1-1*, 5-3p

LEAGUE CONSTITUTION 2004-05

AIGBURTH PEOPLES HALL

Cheshire Lines Ground, Southmead Road, Allerton, Liverpool L195NB

Tel: 0151 427 7176

Sec: Bobby Oldham 0151 423 0175

BIRCHFIELD

Edge Hill College, St Helens Road, Ormskirk, Merseyside L39 4QP

Tel: 01695 584 745

Sec: Terry Kelly

01695 421 106/07801 371539

BOOTLE

Edninburgh Park, Townsend Lane, Liverpool L6 0BB.

Tel: 0151 263 5267

Sec: Bill Jones

0151 428 2203/07939 912893

CHESHIRE LINES

Cheshire Lines Ground, Southmead Road, Allerton, Liverpool, Merseyside. Tel: 0151 427 7176

Sec: Paddy Cavanagh

0151 280 9317

FORD MOTORS

Ford Sports & Social Club, Cronton Lane, Widnes. Tel: 0151 424 7078

Sec: Terry Doyle 01928 568 329

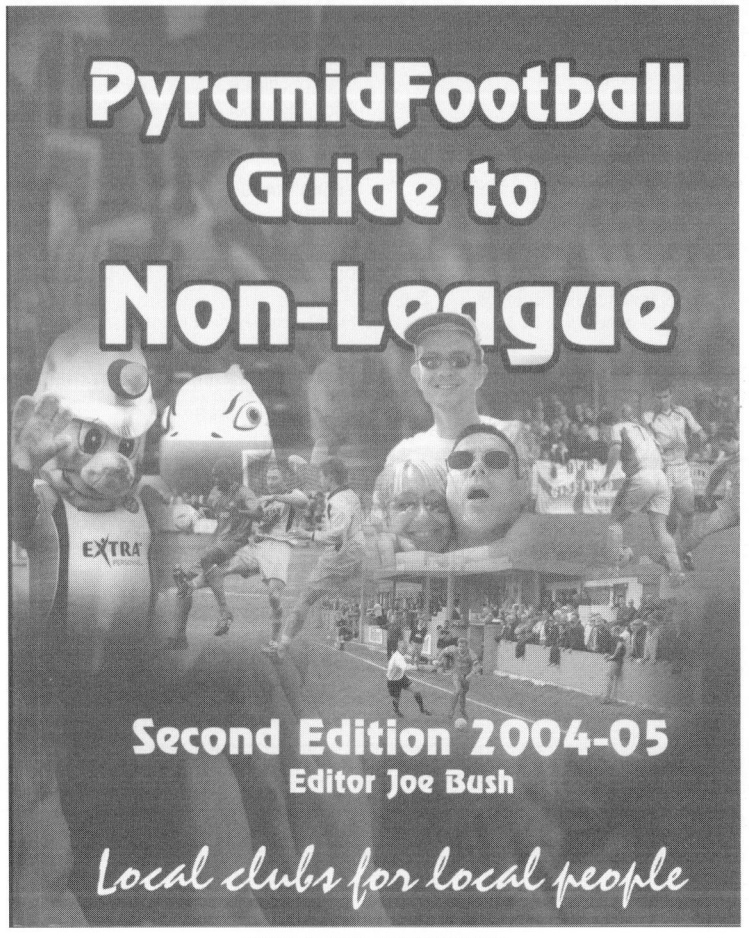

HALEWOOD TOWN

Hilton Grace Recreation Ground, Hollies Road, Liverpool 26

Tel: 0151 437 7418

Sec: Steve Jones

0151 486 4557/07950 537 304

LUCAS SPORTS

Heron eccles Sports Ground, Abbotshey Avenue, Liverpool 18

Tel: 0151 724 4796

Sec: Tony Brodrick 0151 423 4615

MOSSLEY HILL ATHLETIC

Mossley Hill Athletic Club, Mossley Hill Road, Liverpool L18 8DX

Tel: 0151 724 4377

Sec: Mick Ware 0151 486 0071

PENLAKE JUNIORS

Edge Hill College, St Helens Road, Ormskirk, Merseyside

Tel: 01695 584745

PRESCOT LEISURE

Wood Lane Sports Ground, Prescot, Merseyside

Tel: 07812 911 673

Sec: Dave Hughes 01744 737 047

ROYAL SEAFORTH

William Collins Sports Ground, Commercial Road, Liverpool 5

Sec: Tony Stanton 0151 489 9980

ST ALOYSIUS

King George V Sports Ground, Longview Lane, Liverpool 36

Sec: Gary Walsh 0151 449 1131

ST DOMINICS

St Dominics School, Lordens Road, Huyton, Liverpool 14

Tel: 0151 489 2798

Sec: Mick Donohe 0151 259 9737

SOUTH LIVERPOOL

Jericho Lane, Otterspool, Liverpool L17 5AR.

Tel: 07932 347 956

Sec: Jim Stanway

0151 281 5704/07932 347 956

SOUTH SEFTON BOROUGH

Formby FC, Altcar Road, Formby

Tel: 01704 833 505

Sec: Bill Grace 0151 286 8985

SPEKE

Dunlops Sports Ground, Speke Hall Avenue, Speke, Liverpool 24

Tel: 0151 486 1588

Sec: Bill Locke 0151 486 1954

WATERLOO DOCK

Edinburgh Park, Townsend Lane, Liverpool L6 0BB

Tel: 0151 263 5267

Sec: Jim Davies 0151 264 8179

MANCHESTER FOOTBALL LEAGUE

SPONSORED BY: AIR MILES

Honorary President: Norman Noden
League Secretary: Phil Platt.
Press Officer: Scott White, 303 Rake Lane, Clifton, Salford, Lancashire, M27 8LJ
Tel: 0771 204 9561 (Mobile) Fax: 0161 288 9042

FINAL LEAGUE TABLES 2003-04

PREMIER DIVISION		P	W	D	L	F	A	Pts	GD
1	Royton Town	30	19	4	7	73	52	61	21
2	Prestwich Heys	30	17	6	7	53	37	57	16
3	Leigh Athletic	30	15	9	6	74	48	54	26
4	Stockport Georgians	30	14	7	9	59	41	49	18
5	Monton Amateurs	30	14	6	10	50	44	48	6
6	East Manchester	30	14	5	11	67	62	47	5
7	Irlam MS	30	15	1	14	82	57	46	25
8	Atherton Town	30	12	7	11	64	58	43	6
9	Highfield United	30	12	7	11	51	49	43	2
10	Springhead	30	11	7	12	62	53	40	9
11	Wilmslow Albion	30	11	5	14	39	71	38	-32
12	Wythenshawe Amateurs	30	11	3	16	42	58	36	-16
13	Dukinfield Town	30	7	11	12	49	53	32	-4
14	New Mills	30	8	6	16	55	64	30	-9
15	Breightmet United	30	7	7	16	39	69	28	-30
16	Elton Vale	30	6	3	21	44	87	21	-43

DIVISION ONE		P	W	D	L	F	A	Pts	GD
1	Avro	32	25	3	4	92	35	78	57
2	Old Altrinchamians	32	23	4	5	102	48	73	54
3	AFC Blackley	31	21	5	5	104	51	68	53
4	Old Standians	32	20	5	7	71	40	65	31
5	Hindsford AFC	32	19	7	6	94	52	64	42
6	Wythenshawe Town	32	18	7	7	71	48	61	23
7	Hollinwood	32	18	3	11	92	77	57	15
8	Rochdale Sacred Heart	32	14	5	13	75	71	47	4
9	Heywood St James	32	13	7	12	83	71	46	12
10	Ashton Athletic	32	14	4	14	73	67	46	6
11	Swinton Town	32	13	3	16	73	73	42	0
12	Unsworth	32	9	5	18	54	71	32	-17
13	Tintwistle Villa	32	9	3	20	54	74	30	-20
14	Milton	32	8	5	19	56	81	29	-25
15	Whitworth Valley	32	5	2	25	36	147	17	-111
16	Stand Athletic	31	3	2	26	38	110	11	-72
17	Manchester Titans	32	1	6	25	37	89	9	-52

PREMIER DIVISION 2003-04	1	2	3	4	5	6	7	8	9	10	11	12	13	14	15	16
1 Atherton Town		2-2	1-0	5-1	4-1	2-2	0-2	3-6	1-4	1-3	5-1	4-1	5-2	2-2	4-1	0-2
2 Breightmet United	1-2		0-0	1-0	0-4	3-2	2-6	1-1	1-2	1-1	2-1	2-3	2-4	4-1	2-1	2-2
3 Dukinfield Town	1-1	2-0		3-2	5-1	3-0	0-5	2-4	4-1	2-2	1-2	1-2	4-2	2-2	2-3	3-2
4 East Manchester	1-3	3-1	3-2		3-2	3-0	3-4	4-5	1-3	3-3	2-1	2-4	3-2	2-1	3-2	5-1
5 Elton Vale	2-5	3-1	3-3	0-2		1-3	1-6	0-3	0-3	2-5	2-2	0-2	0-3	4-3	1-2	0-5
6 Highfield United	0-0	2-2	3-0	1-1	1-3		3-1	3-0	3-1	4-3	1-3	1-0	1-1	1-1	4-0	1-0
7 Irlam Mitchell Shackleton	1-2	5-0	2-2	1-2	1-3	0-5		4-2	4-1	1-3	2-0	3-4	4-3	1-2	9-0	1-2
8 Leigh Athletic	1-1	2-1	1-1	3-3	5-0	4-1	4-0		2-3	2-1	2-5	2-1	2-2	2-2	1-1	7-1
9 Monton Amateurs	0-2	1-2	2-1	3-2	0-2	3-1	2-1	1-3		2-1	2-2	3-3	1-1	0-1	4-0	1-1
10 New Mills	2-2	2-3	1-1	1-4	4-2	0-2	2-1	2-5	3-0		0-3	2-3	1-2	4-4	0-1	0-2
11 Prestwich Heys	2-1	1-1	1-0	0-0	1-0	2-0	3-2	2-1	0-2	0-2		1-1	1-0	0-0	6-1	3-1
12 Royton Town	4-3	5-1	2-0	2-2	4-3	4-1	3-2	1-0	2-1	2-1	2-0		0-2	1-0	6-2	4-0
13 Springhead	2-1	2-0	2-2	3-2	2-2	2-2	0-4	1-1	0-3	4-0	2-3	4-1		0-2	7-0	4-0
14 Stockport Georgians	6-0	4-0	1-0	2-3	3-0	1-0	1-4	0-1	0-0	3-2	1-3	4-2	2-1		2-0	3-0
15 Wilmslow Albion	3-1	2-1	1-1	2-0	4-1	4-1	1-2	1-1	0-0	0-3	0-1	2-2	1-0	0-5		2-1
16 Wythenshawe Amateur	2-1	3-0	1-1	1-2	2-1	1-2	1-3	0-1	0-1	2-1	1-3	3-2	3-2	2-0	0-2	

GILGRYST CUP

FIRST ROUND

Breightmet United	v	Atherton Town	1-4
Dukinfield Town	v	East Manchester	3-1
Leigh Athletic	v	Irlam MS	10-4*
New Mills	v	Springhead	3-1
Prestwich Heys	v	Monton Amateurs	2-1*
Royton Town	v	Highfield United	3-3*, 5-4p
Wilmslow Albion	v	Elton Vale	2-0
Wythenshawe Amateurs	v	Stockport Georgians	0-2

SECOND ROUND

Atherton Town	v	Leigh Athletic	3-1
Stockprot Georgians	v	Prestwich Heys	2-1
Wilmslow Albion	v	Royton Town	0-5
New Mills	v	Dukinfield Town	1-1*

SEMI-FINALS

Atherton Town	v	Stockport Georgians	1-3
Royton Town	v	New Mills	6-2

FINAL

Royton Town	v	Stockport Georgians	1-0

TOP GOALSCORERS - Premier Division

	Club	PD	GC	CC	Total
Chris Simm	Leigh Athletic	24	4	3	31
Bobby Fulham	Springhead	19	0	2	21
Danny Taylor	Royton Town	15	3	2	20
Danny Christie	Atherton Town	16	0	3	19
Nick Robinson	Irlam MS	16	3	0	19
Carl Taylor	Royton Town	16	1	2	19
Jason Wright	Wythenshawe A.	16	0	2	18
Clint McLoughlin	Atherton Town	16	1	1	18
John Robinson	Irlam MS	16	0	1	17
Anthony Pauls	Springhead	10	1	5	16
Phil Hornby	Atherton Town	9	3	4	16
Darren Green	East Manchester	13	0	2	15

ATHERTON TOWN

Formed: 1964

Secretary: Gerald Butler, 43 Hope Fold Ave., Atherton, Lancs M29 0BW Tel: 01942 870326

Ground: Howe Bridge Spts Centre, Howe Bridge, Atherton Tel: 01942 884882

Directions: A579 Atherton to Leigh road - Sports Centre 800 yds on left

Colours: Royal/white/royal

AVRO

Secretary: Karen Birch, 27 Brooks Drive, Failsworth, Manchester M35 0L5 Tel: 0161 682 6731

Ground: Lancaster Club, Broadway, Failsworth

Colours: Red & black/red/red

BREIGHTMET UNITED

Secretary: Roy Haslam, Tel: 01204 535933 or 07796 134093

Ground: Moss Park, Bury Road, Breightmet, Manchester Tel: 01204 533930

Colours: Black & white stripes/black/red

DUKINFIELD TOWN

Formed: 1948

Secretary: Paul Bishop, 21 Church Walk, Stalybridge, Cheshire Tel: 0161 303 0398

Ground: Blocksages Playing Fields, Birch Lane, Dukinfield. Tel: 0161 343 4529

Directions: From Ashton centre follow Kings St, turn left into Chapel St. thenright turn into Foundry St/Birch Lane. Ground 880 yds on right, behind public baths.

Colours: All yellow

EAST MANCHESTER

Formed: 1960 (called ICL until 1985)

Secretary: D Wilkinson, 76 Sandy Lane, Dukinfield, Cheshire SK16 5NL Tel: 0161 330 4450

Ground: Droylsden FC, The Butchers Arms, Droylsden Tel: 0161 370 1426, 0161 301 1352

Directions: From Manchester take A662 (Ashton New Road) to junct with Market St. in Droylsden. Left into Market St. at lights, over the mini r'about. Ground entrance on the left.

Colours: All royal blue

HIGHFIELD UNITED

Secretary: Jackie Lomax, Tel: 0161 764 9986

Ground: Seedfield Sports Club, Parkinson Street, Bury

Colours: Jade and black

IRLAM MITCHELL SHACKLETON

Formed: 1970 (called Mitchell Shackleton until 2001)

Secretary: Ian Street, 11 Senior Road, Peel Green, Eccles, M30 7PZ Tel: 0161 789 7061

Ground: Salteye Park, Peel Green, Eccles Tel: 0161 788 8373

Directions: Leave M63 at Peel Green r'bout (jct 2), take A57 Liverpool Roadtowards Irlam, ground entrance half mile on left behind Kara Cafew opposite Barton airport. Or, follow A57 from Manchester via Salford & Eccles, then follow Irlam signs.

Colours: Blue & white

LEIGH ATHLETIC

Formed: 1959

Secretary: Rick Wilson. Tel: 01942 518328

Ground: Madley Park, Charles St., Leigh Tel: 01942 673500

Directions: Exit A580 at junction with A574 onto Warrington Road and follow into Leigh town centre. Turn right into King Street and turn right into Church Street ('Boars Head' Pub). Take 6th left into Charles Street and ground straight ahead.

Colours: Yellow/ Blue/ Blue

MONTON AMATEURS

Formed: 1916

Secretary: Tony Lee, 28 Wheatley Rd, Swinton, Manchester M27 3RW Tel: 0161 793 8033

Ground: Granary Lane, Worsley, Manchester

Directions: From Eccles Centre turn right into Worsley Rd at Patricroft Bridge.Ground approx 1 mile on left, entrance just before Bridgewater Hotel

Colours: All royal blue

OLD ALTRINCHAMIANS

Secretary: Phil Lewis, 10 Woodfield Grove, Sale, M33 6JW Tel: 0161 973 7082 or 07796 475550 (M))

Ground: Crossford Bridge Playing Fields, Meadows Rd, Sale. Tel: 0161 767 9233

Colours: Black & white stripes/black/black

PRESTWICH HEYS

Formed: 1938

Secretary: Norman Deardon Tel: 0161 959 1305

Ground: Sandgate Rd, Whitefield Tel: 0161 773 8888

Directions: Follow Old Bury Rd (A665) from Manchester to Prestwich, right into Heywood Rd, 3rd left into Mount Rd/Sandgate Rd - ground on right.

Colours: Red & white/red/red

ROYTON TOWN

Secretary: Phil Dean (0161 287 8436)

Ground: Crompton Cricket Club, Glebe Road, Shaw, Oldham.Tel: 01706 847421

Directions: J20, M62 onto A627(M) signed Oldham. At 1st exit follow A663 (broadway) onto A66 (Shaw Road). At r'about take 2nd exit (Crompton Way), and then 1st left onto Rochdale Road. Glebe Road is 4th turning on right and ground is at end of the road.

Colours: Yellow and Black

SPRINGHEAD

Formed: 1926

Secretary: Alex Simmons Tel: 0161 620 0959 or 07764 836918

Ground: St John St, Lees, Oldham Tel: 0161 627 0260

Directions: From Oldham (Mumps r'bout) follow A669 towards Lees for approx onemile, left into St John St, ground 500yds on right.

Colours: Black & red/black/black

STOCKPORT GEORGIANS

Formed: 1987

Secretary: Ged Newcombe, 7 Chiltern Close, Hazel Grove, Stockport SK7 5BQ Tel: 0161483 0004

Ground: Cromley Rd, Woodsmoor, Stockport, Tel: 0161 483 6581

Directions: Follow A6 from Stockport centre, turn right at Cemetery intoBranhall Lane. After 1 mile turn left at r/about into Woodsmoor Lane. Take 1st right Flowery Fields then right into Cromley Road

Colours: Red and black

WILMSLOW ALBION

Formed: 1919

Secretary: Norma Winn, 236 Derbyshire Lane, Stretford, Manchester (0161 2869520)

Ground: Oakwood Farm, Styal Road, Wilmslow Tel: 01625 535823

Directions: From J5, M56 follow signs for Wilmslow. Turn right at the end of Ringway Road into Styal Road (B5166). Take 3rd right onto Altrincham Road and ground on right.

Colours: Yellow and blue

WYTHENSHAWE AMATEURS

Formed: 1959

Secretary: John Sobierajsh, 5 Wensley Drive, Withington, Manchester Tel: 0161 445 3415

Ground: Longley Lane, Northenden, Wythenshawe, Manchester. Tel: 0161 998 7268

Directions: Princess Parkway from Manchester to Post House hotel, via PalatineRd & Moor End Rd to Longley Lane - ground entrance opposite Overwood Rd.

Colours: Blue & white stripes/blue/blue

DIVISION ONE CLUBS

AFC BLACKLEY

Previous Names: Belden>2003; B.I.C.C.
Secretary: Rob Fuller, Tel: 0161 681 6948 or 07971 177475
Ground: Belden Works, Blackley New Road, Blackley. Tel: 0161 740 9151
Colours: Maroon and blue

ASHTON ATHLETIC

Secretary: Steve Halliwell, 20 Kings Road, Golborne, Warrington Tel: 01942 517728 (H) 07774 180165 (M)
Ground: Brocstedes Park, Farm Road, Ashton-in-Makerfield Tel: 01942 716360.
Colours: Orange and navy blue

ELTON VALE

Formed: 1957 (Formerly Elton Fold >2002)
Secretary: Guy Mallinson, 14 Lonsdale St, Bury BL8 2QD Tel: 0161 797 7090
Ground: Elton Vale Road, Bury. 0161 762 0666
Directions: A58 from Bury to Boltonto junction with Ainsworth Road (B6196). Approx. 3/4 mile right into Elton Vale Road. Ground is 150 yards on left after Foulds Ave.
Colours: Blue & black/black/black

HEYWOOD ST. JAMES

Ground:
Previous Lge: Lancs & Cheshire Amateur Lge.

HINDSFORD

Secretary: Eddie Evans, 17 Belmont Avenue, Atherton M46 9RR RTel Nos: 01942 895869 (H) 07767 492411 (M)
Ground: Squires Lane, Tyldesley
Colours: Red /blue/red & blue

HOLLINWOOD

Secretary: Ken Evans, 20 Meadow Rise, High Crompton, Shaw, Oldham OL2 7QG Tel: 01706 840987 or 07740 442818.
Ground: Lime Lane, Hollinwood, Oldham (0161 681 3385).
Colours: Yellow & Navy/ Navy / Navy

MANCHESTER TITANS

Previous name: Warth Fold
Secretary: Felix Daniel. Tel: 0161 232 0392 or 077877 880407
Ground: The Elms, George St., Whitefield, Bury. Tel: 0161 767 9233
Colours: Yellow and blue

MILTON

Secretary: Andrew Cole, 21 Whittle Drive, Shaw, Oldham OL2 8TJ Tel: 01706 291973 (H) 07754 482393 (M)
Ground: Athletic Stadium, Springfield Park, Rochdale.
Colours: Green& Black,Black/Black

PENNINGTON

Ground: Jubilee Park, Leigh Road, Atherton, Lancashire
Previous Lge: West Lancashire League.

ROCHDALE SACRED HEART

Formed: 1955
(called Robinson's >1985; RSH>87 & Sacred Heart>2001)
Secretary: Joe Devlin, 61 Buersil Ave., Rochdale, Lancs. OL16 4TR Tel: 01706 712602
Ground: Fox Park, Belfield Mill Lane, Rochdale
Directions: From Rochdale town centre follow the A640 to Milnrow, at Kingsway junction turn left into Albert Royds Street and turn right again into Bellfield Mill Lane.
Colours: All red

STAND ATHLETIC

Founded: 1964
Secretary: Dave Jackson, 26 Brookdene Rd, Unsworth, Bury Bl9 8ND
Tel: 0161 796 0353
Ground: Ewood Bridge, Manchester Rd, Haslingden, Lancs. BB4 6JY Tel: 01706 217814
Previous Lges: Bury Amateur, S. E. Lancs., Lancs & Cheshire, Manchester, N.W.C. 01-03
Colours: Blue & yellow/blue/blue

SWINTON TOWN

Formed: 1977
Secretary: Frank Miller, 11 Edmund Street, Salford, Manchester Tel: 0161 737 2411 or 07761 486146
Ground: Agecroft Sports Ground, Agecroft Rd., Salford.
Directions: From Manchester, follow signs for A580(East Lancs Road) and exit at IRlas o' th' Height. At r'about take 4th exit, following signs for A666 (Kearsley/Bury). At 1st set of lights, right onto Agecroft Road (at Henry Boddington P.H.). Travel approx. 1/3 mile, & ground on left.
Colours: Red and white

TINTWISTLE VILLA

Secretary: Bill Higginbottom, 61 West Drive, Tintwistle, Glossop Tel: 01457 852467
Ground: West Drive, Tintwistle, nr Glossop, Derbys.
Colours: Black & white stripes/black/black

WHITWORTH VALLEY

Secretary: Alan Riley, 31 John Street, Whitworth, Rochdale OL12 8BT Tel: 01706 852619 (H) 07930 543924 (M)
Ground: Rawstron Street, Whitworth Tel: 01706 853045.
Colours: Black & white/black/red

WYTHENSHAWE TOWN

Secretary: Norman Hardman. Tel: 0161 437 8236.
Ground: Ericstan Park, Timpson Rd, Wythenshawe, Manchester. Tel: 0161 998 5076. **Colours:** All royal Blue

MID CHESHIRE LEAGUE

Founded 1948

President: R Atherton **Chairman:** J Walton

Hon. Secretary: G Edgeley, 61 Harris Road, Lostock Gralam, Northwich, Cheshire CW9 7PE Tel: 01606 352799

FINAL LEAGUE TABLE 2003-04

DIVISION ONE		P	W	D	L	F	A	Pts
1.	Middlewich Town	30	22	4	4	69	27	70
2.	Poynton	30	19	7	4	70	42	64
3.	Barnton	30	19	3	8	67	33	60
4.	Linotype	30	17	6	7	67	43	57
5.	Bollington Athletic	30	14	6	10	64	60	48
6.	Crewe	30	13	9	8	56	52	48
7.	Rylands	30	9	13	8	53	41	40
8.	Daten	30	11	6	13	53	51	39
9.	Knutsford	30	10	8	12	51	53	38
10.	Garswood United	30	11	5	14	43	45	38
11.	Golborne Sports	30	9	9	12	52	59	36
12.	Crosfields	30	10	5	15	52	71	35
13.	Pilkington	30	10	3	17	56	76	33
14.	Styal	30	8	8	14	49	61	32
15.	Broadheath Central	30	4	5	21	34	87	17
16.	Cheadle Heath Nomads	30	1	9	20	37	72	12

DIVISION ONE	1	2	3	4	5	6	7	8	9	10	11	12	13	14	15	16
1 Barnton		1-2	2-0	6-3	0-2	2-0	2-0	2-1	4-2	1-3	2-1	1-2	3-1	2-3	3-3	2-0
2 Bollington Athletic	0-0		2-1	4-0	5-3	1-1	2-2	1-0	1-1	4-3	3-1	0-5	4-6	1-2	3-1	3-2
3 Broadheath Central	0-4	2-5		1-8	1-4	2-0	1-3	0-2	3-0	1-4	2-3	1-0	2-4	1-2	2-2	3-3
4 Cheadle Heath Nomads	0-1	1-2	0-1		2-2	1-2	1-1	1-1	0-0	1-2	1-2	1-4	0-1	1-1	1-4	2-4
5 Crewe	0-6	2-1	1-0	4-1		1-2	5-1	2-1	3-1	0-0	2-4	0-2	3-2	2-1	1-1	1-1
6 Crosfields	0-7	5-0	6-3	1-1	3-3		2-1	2-3	1-4	3-2	1-3	0-1	2-2	0-1	2-1	1-2
7 Daten	1-0	1-1	6-1	2-1	5-1	1-3		2-4	3-1	6-0	1-3	1-3	3-2	2-3	2-2	1-0
8 Garswood United	1-2	3-2	1-1	1-1	1-1	3-1	2-0		1-2	2-1	1-4	1-2	4-2	0-2	1-0	0-0
9 Golborne Sports	1-2	2-2	0-0	3-2	3-2	2-4	3-2	3-1		2-2	1-2	0-1	5-1	2-4	0-2	1-1
10 Knutsford	1-4	0-2	3-1	2-1	1-1	6-1	1-1	1-0	1-2		1-1	2-3	1-2	3-0	1-1	2-1
11 Linotype	2-1	2-1	3-0	4-0	0-1	2-4	0-0	0-1	4-2	4-2		2-5	4-0	1-2	3-3	3-1
12 Middlewich Town	1-0	4-1	3-0	0-0	4-0	5-0	1-0	3-1	2-0	1-1	1-2		2-1	0-3	1-0	2-2
13 Pilkington	0-1	1-7	2-2	5-1	1-6	3-2	1-2	2-0	2-3	2-3	0-3	2-2		0-2	3-1	1-0
14 Poynton	2-2	5-3	3-0	4-0	1-1	2-0	2-3	3-1	2-2	1-1	2-2	1-5	3-1		2-2	3-1
15 Rylands	1-2	0-1	7-0	2-2	0-0	2-2	2-0	1-0	1-1	3-1	1-1	3-0	3-1	1-3		2-2
16 Styal	0-2	3-0	4-2	5-3	1-2	4-1	1-0	1-5	3-3	1-0	1-1	1-4	2-5	2-5	0-1	

FINAL LEAGUE TABLE 2003-04

DIVISION TWO		P	W	D	L	F	A	Pts
1.	Padgate St Oswalds	24	16	2	6	57	31	50
2.	Trafford Reserves	24	15	4	5	52	25	49
3.	Sidac Sports	24	14	4	6	53	36	46
4.	Curzon Ashton Reserves	24	12	5	7	57	43	41
5.	Gamesley	24	12	5	7	42	28	41
6.	Nantwich Town Reserves	24	12	2	10	65	55	38
7.	Warrington Borough	24	10	5	9	39	33	35
8.	Whitchurch Alport	24	10	3	11	39	36	33
9.	Witton Albion Reserves	24	6	8	10	28	35	26
10.	Malpas	24	5	9	10	36	41	24
11.	Club AZ	24	6	5	13	34	45	23
12.	Lostock Gralam	24	5	4	15	31	72	19
13.	Cheadle Town Reserves	24	3	4	17	25	78	13

DIVISION ONE CUP

FIRST ROUND

Broadheath Central	v	Rylands	1-2
Crewe	v	Cheadle Heath Nomads	5-3
Crosfields	v	Styal	3-0
Daten	v	3 Broadheath Central 0	
Garswood United	v	Knutsford	2-0
Golborne Sports	v	Linotype	1-2
Middlewich Town	v	Bollington Athletic	2-0
Poynton	v	Barnton	1-1* 5-6p

QUARTER-FINALS

Barnton	v	Crosfields	4-2
Daten	v	Crewe	2-1
Garswood United	v	Middlewich Town	1-0
Rylands	v	Linotype	1-4

SEMI-FINALS

Barnton	v	Linotype	2-1
Daten	v	Garswood United	1-0

THE FINAL (3rd March at Trafford)

Barnton	v	Daten	1-0

DIVISION TWO CUP

FIRST ROUND

Curzon Ashton R.	v	Trafford Reserves	3-4
Lostock Gralam	v	Cheadle Town Reserves	3-5
Malpas	v	Winsford United Reserves	4-0
Nantwich Town R.	v	Whitchurch Alport	0-3
Padgate St Oswalds	v	Warrington Borough	2-0
Witton Albion Res.	v	Gamesley	4-1

QUARTER-FINALS

Trafford Res.	v	Padgate	3-1
Malpas	v	Club AZ	1-0
Whitchurch Alport (w/o)	v	Cheadle Town Reserves	
Witton Albion Res.	v	Sidac Sports	3-3* 4-3p

SEMI-FINALS

Malpas	v	Trafford Reserves	1-0*
Whitchurch Alport	v	Witton Albion Reserves	0-1*

THE FINAL (27th April at Witton Albion)

Malpas	v	Witton Reserves	3-5

DIVISION ONE CLUBS

BARNTON AFC
Chairman: William Perrin
Manager: Mark Emmerson
Secretary: Michael Webster, 92 Church Road, Barnton CW8 4JE (01606 782960)
Ground: Townfield, Townfield Lane, Barnton, Northwich
Colours: Black & White Stripes/Black
Change Colours: Blue & yellow /blue

BOLLINGTON ATHLETIC FC
Chairman: Albert Hall
Manager: Michael Quigley
Secretary: Anthony Holmes, 1 Princess Drive, Bollington, Macclesfield SK10 5ES Tel: 01625 574913
Ground: Recreation Ground, Bollington, Macclesfield.
Colours: Green & Black/Green
Change Colours: Maroon/Sky/Sky

CREWE FC
Chairman: Patrick Slack
Manager: Ian O'Reilly
Secretary: Mrs M Vickers, 59 Hall-o-Shaw St, Crewe (01270 581578)
Ground: Cumberland Sprts Grnd, Thomas St, Crewe. Tel: 01270 537913
Colours: Sky Blue/Marooon/White
Change Colours: Yellow/Black/Blue

CROSSFIELDS FC
Chairman: Michael Hickey
Manager: Derek Evans
Secretary: Frank Whitehouse, 153 Birdwell Drive, Gt. Sankey, Warrington Tel: 01925 728710 (H) 01925 625750 (B)
Ground: Hood Lane Rec., Gt. Sankey, Warrington Tel: 01925 411730
Colours: Primrose & blue
Change Colours: Orange & black

DATEN FC
Chairman: Trevor Farrington
Manager: Robert Jones
Secretary: Michael Henshall, 21 Upwood Rd., Lowton, Warrington WA3 2RL Tel: 01942 724471 01772 321800 (B)
Ground: Culcheth Sports Club, Charnock Rd., Culcheth Tel: 01925 763096
Colours: Sky & royal blue
Change Colours: Blue & white stipes/navy

GARSWOOD UNITED FC
Chairman: Barry Mavers
Manager: Alan Clarke
Secretary: Tony McKeown,44 Dunsdale Drive, Ashton, Wigan WN4 8PT Tel No: 01942 724259
Ground: The Wooders, Simms Lane End, Garswood, Wigan. Tel: 01744 892258
Colours: Blue & White Halves/Blue/Blue
Change Colours: All Yellow

GOLBORNE SPORTS FC
Chairman: Bill Hiltyon
Manager: Andrew Smallman
Secretary: Stephen Whittle, 20 West Ave., Golborne, Warrington WA3 3EA Tel: 01942 715570 (H) 07979 550732 (M)
Ground: Simpson Playing Fields, Stone Cross Lane, Lowton WA3 2SL Tel: 01942 510161
Colours: All Yellow
Change Colours: All blue

GREENALLS PADGATE ST OSWALDS
Ground: Walkers Club, Long Lane, Warrington, Cheshire
Previous Name: Padgate St Oswalds

KNUTSFORD FC
Chairman: Ken Harrison
Manager: Srewart Dow
Secretary: Kevin Deeley, 28 East Street, Guide Bridge, Manchester, M34 5DX (0161 320 9650)
Ground: Manchester Road, Knutsford
Colours: Red /Black/Black
Change Colours: Black & White stripes/White/White

LINOTYPE & CHEADLE HEATH
Chairman: James Barry
Manager: Glyn Williams
Secretary: Brian McGuiness, 36 Barrington Road, Altrincham, Cheshire (0161 929 0021)
Ground: The Heath, Norbreck Avenue, Norbreck Avenue, Cheadle, Stockport, Cheshire
Tel: 0161 282 6574
Colours: White/Black
Change Colours: Red & Black/White/red
Previous Names: Linotype FC. Cheadle Heath FC. Merged 2004.

MIDDLEWICH TOWN FC
Chairman: Steven Morris
Manager: David Twite
Secretary: Philip Hassell,1 Whitegate `Close,Middlewich,Cheshire CW10 0RF
Tel Nos: 01606 832185 (H) 01606832734 (W)
Ground: Seddon Street, Middlewich Tel: 01606 835842
Colours: Red/Black/Red
Change Colours: White/black

PILKINGTON
Ruskin Drive, St Helens, Merseyside
Tel: 01744 28866

POYNTON
London Road North, Poynton, Cheshire
Tel: 01625 875765

RYLANDS
Rylands Recreation Club, Gorsey Lane, Warrington, Cheshire Tel: 01925 625700

STYAL
Altrincham Road, Styal, Wilmslow, Cheshire
Tel: 01625 529303

TRAFFORD RESERVES
Shawe View, Pennybridge Lane, Flixton, Urmston, Manchester Tel: 0161 747 1727/749 8217

MIDLAND LEAGUE

SPONSORED BY: SPRINGBANK VENDING

President: T Myatt **Chairman:** P Savage

Secretary: M Stokes, 21 Corsican Drive,
Pye Green, Cannock, Staffs WS12 4SZ
Tel: 01543 878075 Fax: 01543 879008

FINAL LEAGUE TABLE 2003-04

		P	W	D	L	F	A	Pts
1.	Abbey Hulton United	28	21	4	3	61	21	67
2.	Goldenhill Wanderers	28	20	3	5	65	32	63
3.	Norton	28	14	7	7	55	30	49
4.	Hanford	28	12	7	9	64	45	43
5.	Audley & District	28	13	4	11	53	44	43
6.	Hanley Town	28	11	8	9	52	42	41
7.	Stone Dominoes Reserves	28	11	7	10	43	35	40
8.	Redgate Clayton	28	10	8	10	43	50	38
9.	Alsager Town Reserves	28	10	7	11	40	49	37
10.	Ball Haye Green	28	10	6	12	50	39	36
11.	Stallington	28	10	5	13	50	57	35
12.	Newcastle Town Reserves	28	10	4	14	36	57	34
13.	Foley	28	8	8	12	50	50	32
14.	Wolstanton United	28	6	4	18	49	76	22
15.	Cheadle Town OB	28	0	6	22	18	102	6

NB -Vale Victoria withdrew during the season.
Their results are shown in the results grid below but are expunged from the league table.

2003-04		1	2	3	4	5	6	7	8	9	10	11	12	13	14	15	16
1	Abbey Hulton United		5-2	2-0	3-1	5-0	3-1	1-0	2-0	1-2	1-1	0-0	1-1	2-0	2-1	-	3-2
2	Alsager Town Reserves	1-3		1-0	1-1	4-1	1-1	0-2	0-5	2-4	2-1	0-3	1-1	1-2	2-2	4-1	0-2
3	Audley & District	1-1	1-3		3-2	4-1	2-2	2-3	3-4	1-4	3-0	0-0	0-2	6-4	2-0	2-0	3-0
4	Ball Haye Green	0-1	3-0	1-2		5-1	3-1	1-2	1-1	1-2	0-1	2-3	4-0	3-1	2-1	2-0	0-0
5	Cheadle Town Old Boys	0-5	1-4	0-5	1-1		0-6	0-8	1-2	0-0	2-2	1-4	1-4	0-4	3-3	2-3	1-6
6	Foley	3-0	2-3	2-4	1-3	3-0		1-2	1-1	2-0	2-0	0-3	2-2	3-1	2-4	-	4-1
7	Goldenhill Wanderers	1-5	1-2	2-0	2-2	5-1	4-2		4-1	1-1	1-0	0-2	4-0	4-2	2-1	-	2-0
8	Hanford	0-1	0-3	0-3	0-3	4-0	2-0	0-2		1-1	3-0	2-2	2-3	2-1	0-0	2-1	7-4
9	Hanley Town	0-1	0-2	3-1	0-3	8-1	1-2	0-1	2-1		3-0	2-2	1-1	5-1	0-0	0-0	2-0
10	Newcastle Town Reserves	3-0	0-0	1-1	1-3	3-1	3-1	1-4	0-9	4-2		3-1	1-0	1-3	1-3	-	1-3
11	Norton	0-1	2-0	1-0	3-1	1-0	2-2	1-2	3-6	1-1	1-2		4-0	1-2	0-0	1-0	5-1
12	Redgate Clayton	0-2	1-1	0-2	1-0	4-0	1-1	2-2	1-3	3-0	3-1	1-2		3-1	1-3	1-1	1-6
13	Stallington	1-2	2-0	4-0	1-1	0-0	0-0	4-2	0-4	2-2	1-2	0-3	2-2		2-1	0-3	4-0
14	Stone Dominoes Reserves	0-2	1-2	0-1	3-2	1-0	1-1	0-1	1-1	5-2	3-1	1-0	0-1	4-0		-	2-1
15	Vale Victoria	0-3	-	-	0-0	-	3-0	0-3	-	-	0-4	-	2-2	-	1-4		-
16	Wolstanton United	0-6	2-2	1-3	3-1	1-1	3-2	0-1	3-3	2-4	1-2	0-5	3-4	3-5	1-2	0-6	

LEAGUE CUP

FIRST ROUND

Abbey Hulton Utd	v	Wolstanton United	4-2
Audley & District	v	Stone Dominoes Res.	1-0
Ball Haye Green	v	Vale Victoria	2-2*, 4-5p
Cheadle Town Old Boys	v	Redgate Clayton	0-2
Foley	v	Goldenhill Wanderers	0-3
Hanley Town	v	Alsager Town Res.	3-1
Norton	v	Newcastle Town Res.	3-2
Stallington	v	Hanford	0-1*

QUARTER-FINALS

Goldenhill Wanderers	v	Hanley Town	2-1
Hanford	v	Abbey Hulton United	3-2
Redgate Clayton	v	Norton	0-3
Vale Victoria	v	Audley & District	1-2

SEMI-FINALS

Goldenhill Wanderers	v	Norton	3-2*
Hanford	v	Audley & District	0-2

FINAL

(15th March at Newcastle Town)

Goldenhill Wanderers	v	Audley & District	1-2

LEAGUE CONSTITUTION 2004-05

ABBEY HULTON UNITED
Birches Head Road, Abbey Hulton, Stoke-on-Trent, Staffordshire
Tel: 01782 544232

ALSAGER TOWN RESERVES
The Town Ground, Wood Park, Alsager, Cheshire
Tel: 01270 882336

AUDLEY & DISTRICT
Town Fields, Old Road, Bignall, Stoke-on-Trent, Staffordshire
Tel: 01782 723482

BALL HAYE GREEN
Rear off Ball Haye Green WMC, Ball Haye Green, Leek, Staffordshire
Tel: 01538 371926

CHEADLE TOWN OLD BOYS
Cheadle Leisure Centre, Allen Street, Cheadle, Staffordshire
Tel: 01538 753331

FLORENCE COLLIERY
Florence Miners Welfare, Lightwood Road, Stoke-on-Trent, Staffordshire
Tel: 01782 312887

FOLEY
Whitcombe Road, Meir, Stoke-on-Trent, Staffordshire
Tel: 01782 595274

GOLDENHILL WANDERERS
Sandyford Sports Ground, Shelford Road, Sandyford, Stoke-on-Trent, Staffordshire
Tel: 01782 811977

HANFORD
Northwood Stadium, Keeling Road, Hanley, Stoke-on-Trent, Staffordshire
Tel: 01782 234400

HANLEY TOWN
Abbey Lane, Abbey Hulton, Stoke-on-Trent, Staffordshire
Tel: 01782 267234

NEWCASTLE TOWN RESERVES
Lyme Valley Parkway Stadium, Lilleshall Rd, Clayton, Newcastle-under-Lyne
Tel: 01782 662351 / 622350

NORTON
Norton CC & MW Institute, Community Drive, Smallthorne, Stoke-on-Trent, Staffordshire
Tel: 01782 838290

REDGATE CLAYTON
Northwood Lane, Clayton, Newcastle-under-Lyme, Staffordshire
Tel: 01782 717409

STALLINGTON
Stallington Hospital, Fulford Lane, Stallington Road, Blythe Bridge, Staffordshire
Tel: 07785 338804

STONE DOMINOES RESERVES
Springbank Stadium, Kings Park, Hilderstone Rd, Meir Heath, Stoke
Tel: 01782 388465

WOLSTANTON UNITED
Bradwell Community Centre, Riceyman Road, Bradwell, Stoke-on-Trent, Staffs
Tel: 01782 660818

NORTHERN ALLIANCE

SPONSORED BY: WADE ASSOCIATES

President: Les Todd **Chairman:** George Dobbins
Secretary: John McLackland, 92 Appletree Gardens
Walkerville, Newcastle upon Tyne NE6 4SX Tel: 0191 2626665
Email: johnmclackland@which.net
Press Secretary: Bill Gardner Tel: 0191 488 3422

FINAL LEAGUE TABLES 2003-04

PREMIER DIVISION		P	W	D	L	F	A	Pts
1.	West Allotment Celtic	30	24	2	4	115	33	74
2.	Team Northumbria University	30	18	7	5	78	34	61
3.	Ryton	30	17	7	6	87	53	58
4.	Percy Main Amateurs	30	17	6	7	76	40	57
5.	Shankhouse	30	15	7	8	54	35	52
6.	Harraby Catholic Club	30	15	5	10	66	44	50
7.	Northbank Carlisle	30	15	4	11	68	50	49
8.	Carlisle City	30	15	2	13	53	48	47
9.	Walker Central	30	13	6	11	44	48	45
10.	Ponteland United	30	11	6	13	56	60	39
11.	Newcastle University	30	8	6	16	36	55	30
12.	Winlaton Hallgarth	30	8	6	16	41	84	30
13.	Seaton Delaval Amateurs	30	7	4	19	37	85	25
14.	Spittal Rovers	30	7	3	20	40	90	24
15.	Chopwell Top Club	30	7	2	21	43	86	23
16.	Eppleton Colliery Welfare	30	5	3	22	37	86	18

DIVISION ONE		P	W	D	L	F	A	Pts
1.	Heddon	24	19	3	2	63	16	60
2.	Heaton Stanington	24	19	1	4	71	33	58
3.	Walker Fosse	24	15	5	4	81	23	50
4.	Blyth Town	24	16	1	7	73	35	49
5.	Hebburn Reyrolle	24	11	4	9	71	55	37
6.	Newbiggin CW	24	12	1	11	51	59	37
7.	Wark	24	11	3	10	51	48	36
8.	Haydon Bridge United	24	8	6	10	55	56	30
9.	Newcastle EE Rail	24	8	3	13	54	66	27
10.	Cramlington Town	24	8	3	13	44	56	27
11.	Rutherford Newcastle	24	3	4	17	28	70	13
12.	Cullercoats	24	3	3	18	32	94	12
13.	Wallington	24	2	5	17	21	84	11

PREMIER DIVISION 2003-04		1	2	3	4	5	6	7	8	9	10	11	12	13	14	15	16
1	Carlisle City		3-1	2-2	1-2	3-2	1-2	0-1	1-3	2-3	2-1	0-2	1-0	3-0	0-2	0-3	4-1
2	Chopwell Top Club	0-4		3-0	0-1	0-3	1-3	1-0	3-1	2-1	0-1	0-3	5-3	1-0	2-2	0-5	1-2
3	Eppleton Colliery Welfare	0-2	4-3		1-3	0-2	0-1	3-1	2-3	1-3	0-2	1-4	3-0	0-5	1-3	0-3	0-2
4	Harraby catholic Club	2-3	3-0	5-0		3-3	0-1	1-1	3-2	2-2	6-0	1-0	5-1	2-1	2-1	0-3	1-2
5	Newcastle University	0-1	2-0	2-1	2-1		0-2	0-3	0-5	0-2	0-1	2-2	2-3	1-3	2-0	3-4	0-0
6	Northbank Carlisle	1-2	7-1	3-3	2-3	2-0		4-2	4-3	1-3	2-0	1-1	6-2	3-0	0-2	0-2	4-0
7	Percy Main Amateurs	3-2	9-1	3-2	1-1	3-2	2-1		3-1	0-2	3-1	1-1	4-0	2-2	0-0	5-2	3-0
8	Ponteland United	1-3	3-1	3-0	4-1	3-0	2-1	0-3		2-1	2-1	0-0	0-0	1-3	2-2	0-3	3-2
9	Ryton	2-1	5-5	5-0	3-2	3-0	4-4	2-2	5-1		8-2	2-0	6-1	1-1	4-0	4-2	5-0
10	Seaton Delaval Amateurs	2-4	5-3	2-3	0-4	0-0	3-2	1-7	1-1	1-3		0-5	1-3	1-1	2-1	1-2	1-4
11	Shankhouse	1-1	3-1	3-2	3-2	1-3	1-2	0-2	3-1	3-1	2-0		0-0	1-1	0-1	4-2	4-1
12	Spittal Rovers	3-2	0-4	0-1	1-3	3-1	2-1	0-4	3-2	3-1	3-4	2-3		0-4	1-4	2-6	2-2
13	Team Northumbria University	1-0	3-1	4-1	2-0	2-2	6-2	4-1	2-2	3-1	6-1	2-0	6-1		4-0	2-3	2-1
14	Walker Central	0-2	2-1	1-1	2-1	0-1	0-5	2-1	2-0	2-2	1-1	0-2	2-0	1-5		0-3	5-0
15	West Allotment Celtic	6-0	6-1	9-2	2-2	3-0	3-0	3-1	4-2	8-1	4-0	3-0	4-1	0-0	1-2		8-0
16	Winlaton Hallgarth	1-3	2-1	4-3	0-4	1-1	1-1	1-5	3-3	2-2	3-1	0-2	3-0	1-3	2-4	0-8	

LEAGUE CUP

FIRST ROUND

Abbey Hulton Utd	v	Wolstanton United	4-2

FIRST ROUND

Alnmouth (w/o)	v	Otterburn	
Cramlington Town	v	Newbiggin Central Welfare	0-2
Cullercoats	v	Highfields United	3-2
Forest Hall	v	Gosforth Bohemian Garnett	0-1
Heaton Stannington	v	Felling Willows	1-1*,4-2p
Heddon	v	Daisy Hill Turbinia	6-1
Newcastle BT	v	Hebburn Reyrolle	1-4
Newcastle East End Rail Club	v	Wark	6-2
Rutherford Newcastle	v	Prudhoe RTH	1-2
Swarland	v	Haydon Bridge United	2-7
Wallsend Town	v	Walker Fosse	1-1*, 4-5p

SECOND ROUND

Ashington Colliers	v	Percy Main Amateurs	0-4
Eppleton Colliery Welfare	v	Newcastle East End Rail Club	3-1
Gosforth Bohemian Garnett	v	Wallington	3-1
Haydon Bridge United	v	Team Northumbria Univ.	0-2
Heaton Stannington	v	Ponteland United	3-0
Hebburn Reyrolle	v	Carlisle City	0-4
Heddon	v	Walker Central	3-2
Morpeth Town 'A'	v	Chopwell Top Club	0-1
Newcastle Uni.	v	Blyth Town	3-2
Northbank Carlisle	v	Newbiggin Central Welfare	3-1
Seaton Delaval Amateurs	v	Alnmouth	1-3
Shankhouse	v	Prudhoe RTH	4-0
Spittal Rovers	v	Cullercoats	4-3
Walker Birds Nest FOS	v	Ryton	2-4
Walker Fosse	v	Harraby Catholic Club	1-2
Winlaton Hallgarth	v	West Allotment Celtic	0-3

THIRD ROUND

Carlisle City	v	Heddon	1-1*, 4-5p
Gosforth Bohemian Garnett	v	Ryton	2-8
Heaton Stannington	v	Eppleton Colliery Welfare	3-2
Newcastle Uni.	v	Alnmouth	2-1
Northbank Carlisle	v	Harraby Catholic Club	7-0
Percy Main Amateurs	v	Chopwell Top Club	4-1
Spittal Rovers	v	Shankhouse	0-5
West Allotment Celtic	v	Team Northumbria Uni.	0-4

QUARTER-FINALS

Heaton Stannington	v	Heddon	0-1
Percy Main Amateurs	v	Shankhouse	2-4
Ryton	v	Northbank Carlisle	1-3
Team Northumbria Uni.	v	Newcastle University	2-0

SEMI-FINALS

Heddon	v	Shankhouse	0-2
Northbank Carlisle	v	Team Northumbria Uni.	1-2

THE FINAL

(3rd May at Heaton Stannington)

Shankhouse	v	Team Northumbria Uni.	1-3

CHALLENGE CUP

FIRST ROUND

Carlisle City	v	Walker Central	1-1*, 3-4p
Eppleton Colliery Welfare	v	West Allotment Celtic	0-4
Harraby Catholic Club	v	Percy Main Amateurs	4-1
Newcastle Uni.	v	Team Northumbria Uni.	1-2*
Ponteland United	v	Chopwell Top Club	1-2
Seaton Delaval Amateurs	v	Spittal Rovers	2-1
Shankhouse	v	Ryton	6-1
Winlaton Hallgarth	v	Northbank Carlisle	1-4

QUARTER-FINALS

Harraby Catholic Club	v	Team Northumbria Uni.	2-1
Northbank Carlisle	v	Shankhouse	4-2
Seaton Delaval Amateurs	v	West Allotment Celtic	1-1*, 3-1p
Walker Central	v	Chopwell Top Club	2-1

SEMI-FINALS

Northbank Carlisle	v	Walker Central	3-2
Seaton Delaval Amateurs	v	Harraby Catholic Club	0-1

THE FINAL

(6th May at Carlisle United)

Northbank Carlisle	v	Harraby Catholic Club	1-0

CARLISLE CITY

Secretary: Jackie Williamson,14 Etterby Street, Stanwix, Carlisle Tel No: 01228 523798
Ground: The Sheepmount Sports Complex, Carlisle (01228 265599).
Directions: B6264 Brampton-Carlisle road & follow Workington signs, dual-c'way down hill (Carlisle Castle on right), where road intersects double back on yourself and take turning left just before castle, follow down hill keeping left until ground.

Colours: Sky & Navy hoops/navy
Change colours: White/navy

Chairman: Jackie Ewbank
Manage/Coach: Willie Armstrong.

HARRABY CATHOLIC CLUB 1999

Secretary: Mike Little, 34 Springfield Road, Harraby, Carlisle CA1 3QR (01228 512887)
Ground: Harrowby Community Centre, Edghill Road,Harraby
Directions: A69 over M^ to Rosehill roundabout.Second ledft on Eastern Way. First left after 3/4 mile into Arnside Road. End of road left into Edghill Road

Colours:All white
Change colours: Old gold and black

Chairman/Press Officer: Richard Wilson
Manager/Coach: Bobby Rutherford & Kevin Robson

HEATON STANNINGTON

Ground: Grounsell Park, Heaton, Newcastle-upon-Tyne, Tyne & Wear

HEDDON

Ground: The Wheatsheaf Ground, Wolsington, Newcastle-upon-Tyne, Tyne & Wear

MURTON

Secretary: Chris Fahey, 16 D'Arcy Square, Murton, Seaham, Co. Durham SR7 9LZ
Tel No: 0191 5171355(H) 07814 523289 (M) e-mail: murtonafc@yahooo.co.uk
Ground: Recreation Park, Church Lane, Murton, Co. Durham (07814 523289)
Directions: Exit A19 onto B1285 heading west into Murton - Church Lane on left opposite catholic church
Capacity: 3,500 Seats: 100 Cover: 320 Floodlights: Yes Club Shop: No
Clubhouse: `The International' 300 yards from ground on B1285. Normal pub hours. Restaurant upstairs. Matchday snacks at ground
HONOURS Northern Lg Div 2 89-90, Wearside Lg 28-29 36-37 59-60 (Lg Cup 58-5970-71), Sunderland Shipowners Cup 59-60 69-70 70-71, Monkwearmouth Charity Cup 21-22 28-29 34-35 35-36 63-64 70-71 87-88, Durham Chall. Cup 92-93, Durham Jnr Cup 50-51.
PREVIOUS **Leagues:** Wearside 13-46 51-88; North East Counties 46-51. Northern League.
RECORD **Gate:** 3,500 v Spennymoor Utd, Durham Challenge Cup 1951
Appearances: Robert Welch 500 (1962-78)

Colours: All white with red trim
Change colours: Red/black/red

Chairman: Tom Torrence
Vice Chairman: J Hudson
President: John Hellens
Press Officer: Secretary
Commercial Mgr: T Carr
Manager: Jeff Cranson
Asst Mgr: Brian Burlinson
Coach: Richie Madden
Physio: Vince Symmonds

NEWCASTLE UNIVERSITY

Secretary: Simon Kent, 8/10 Myrtle Grove,JesmondNewcastle -u-TyneNE2 3HT(0191 2093609)
Ground: Cochrane Park, Etherstone Avenue, Newcastle -u-Tyne
Directions: From Newcastle via Jesmond to coast road.Take first slip road after Jesmond Dene and immediately after lights at the Corner House.Then take first slip road and left again onto A188 and right at first roundabout at the garage into Etherstone Avenue. Ground is 200 metres on left

Colours: All blue
Change colours: White/navy

Chairman: Simon Kent
Manager: T.B.A.

NORTHBANK CARLISLE

Secretary: David Bell,4 Carlislwe Road, Dalston ,Cumbria CA5 7NG (01228 711095)
Ground: Sheepmount Sports Complex, Carlisle
Directions: B6264 from Bampton to Carlisle, follow Workington sign, past Carlisle Castle on right. Where dual carriageway intersects take next right and travel back towards Castle. Turn left before castle & keeping left follow the road to Complex

Colours: Red & white/red
Change colours: Yellow & navy/navy

Chairman: Kenny Brown
Manager: Bob Lancaster

PERCY MAIN AMATEURS

Secretary: Len Renham, 7 Stanley Crescent, Whitley Bay, Tyne & wear NE26 2 EB
Tel No: (0191 2902768)
Ground: Purvis Park , St John's Green,Percy Main, North Shields.
Directions: A19 Tyne tunnel follow signs for Royal Quays and take seconsd left after school Ground is first turning on the right adjacent to Percy Main cricket club.t after Percy Main schol

Colours: Claret & blue/claret
Change colours: All Blue

Chairman: G.Marsh
ManagerBob Rodgerson
Coach: John Humbertson

PONTELAND UNITED

Secretary: L McMahon, 1 Wardle Drive, Annitsford, Cramlingham NE23 7DB (0191250 0463).
Ground: Ponterland leisure Centre Ponteland (01661 825441)
Directions: Left at lights entering Ponteland from N'castle, ground 100m on left adjacent to Leisure Centre.
Colours: Black & White stripes/Black **Change Colours:** All yellow

Chairman:Alan Birkinshaw
Manager : Barry Wardrobe
Coach:Steve Baxter

RYTON

Secretary: Mrs Kim Sulman, c/o Club Tel Nos: 0191 4134448 (H) 07813951477 (M)
e-mail: rmsryton@aol.com
Ground: Kingsley Park,Stannerford Road, CrawcrookTyne & W. NE 40 3SN Tel No: 0191 413 4448
Directions: Travel north onA1 turn off for Blaydon, at roundabout take third exit , travel through Ryton & Crawcrook and turn right at crossroads towards Wylam. Ground on right..
Record Attendance: 1,800 v Newcastle U 1998 **Previous League**: Northern Combination
2003-2004: Player of the Year: Stuart Blackett **Top Scorer**: John Redhead

Formed: 1970
Colours: Blue & black/black
Change colours: Orange/black
Midweek Matchday: Wednesday
Programme Editor: Susan Murray
Chairman: Michael Williams
Manager Alan Patterson, Coach: Martin Kirsopp and Captain: David Hagan

SEATON DELAVAL AMATEURS

Secretary: Bill Fellows, 11 Ridley Street, Klondyke, Cramlington NE23 6RH (01670 731833)
Ground: Wheatridge Park, Seaton Delaval.
Directions: A189 from Newcastle, at Annitsford r'bout A190 to Seaton Delaval,left at r'bout entering village, ground 450yds on right next to Deal Garage and behind Market Garden. 3 miles from Cramlington BR station. Bus 363 from Newcastle passes ground.

Colours: Sky/black
Change colours: Yellow/blue

Chairman: Tom Ashburn
Manager: Steve Armstrong

SHANKHOUSE

Secretary: Syd Ramsey, 6 Brinkburn Ave, Cramlington, Northumberland NE23 6TB
Tel: 01670 715943
Ground: Action Park, Dudley.
Directions: Tyne Tunnel A19 to Moor Farm roundabout at Anitsford. A1 exit to Morpeth and leave at first slip road.Left at junction (to Dudley) turn right to Seaton Burn at roundabout.Then immediate right after Weetslade club and ground is signposted.

Colours: Yellow/blue
Change colours: White/blue

Chairman: George Davison
Manager: Garry Kirkup

SPITTAL ROVERS

Secretary: G Burn, 7 Sea Road, Spittal, Berwick-on-Tweed TD15 1RN (01289306049).

Ground: Newfields, Berwick-on-Tweed.
Directions: From south take Berwick by-pass to 3rd r'bout. Safeway Store on right - pitch reached by taking 2nd left on r'bout.

Chairman: Noel Evans
Vice Chairman: Paul Renton
Manager/Coach: Carl Hudson

Colours: Black & white stripes/black
Change colours: Green/Black

TEAM NORTHUMBRIA UNIVERSITY

Ground Bullocksteads Sports Ground, Kenton Bank Foot, Newcastle-upon-Tyne

WALKER CENTRAL

Secretary: BobMulroy, 31 Dalton Cres., Byker Wall, Newcastle-upon-Tyne NE62DA
Tel: 0191 265 7803

Ground: Monkchester Recreation Ground, Walker, Newcastle.
Directions: From City: Shields Rd to Union Rd, to Welbeck Rd, right into Monkchester Rd, left into pitch (between houses) opposite Norbury Grove.

Club colours: White and black
Change colours: All Blue

Chairman: R T McClellan
Manager/Coach: Ray Mulroy/Billy Johnson

WINLATON HALLGARTH

Secretary: Robert Young, Alwinton, 21B California, Winlaton Tyne & Wear NE21 6NG
Tel No: 0191 4144363)
Ground: Shibdon Park, Shibdon Road, Blaydon-on-Tyne, Tyne & Wear.
Directions: From north, over A1 Scotswood Bridge to 1st slip road, take Swalwell and Consett road to r'bout, right, Blaydon Baths car park and ground 400yds on right. From South past Metro Centre to Swalwell, then on to Blaydon and the Blaydob Baths car park.

Colours: Green & Black
Change colours: Blue & white/blue
Chairman: R obertYoung
Manager/CoachStephen Brown

TEESIDE LEAGUE

SPONSORED BY: SOUTH CLEVELAND GARAGES
President: J Corner **Chairman:** L Crossman

Secretary: R D Marsay, 12 Aislaby Court, Wilton Lane, Guisborough, Cleveland TS14 6TG

Tel: 01287 637087 Fax: 01287 281051 Email: dmarsay@ntlworld.com

FINAL LEAGUE TABLES 2003-04

DIVISION ONE		P	W	D	L	F	A	Pts
1.	Hartlepool FC	28	19	4	5	66	33	61
2.	Carlin How	28	17	5	5	65	46	56
3.	Thornaby	28	16	5	7	68	41	53
4.	Thornaby YC	28	15	6	7	61	29	51
5.	BEADS FC	28	14	7	7	73	48	49
6.	Grangetown Boys Club	28	12	11	5	68	37	47
7.	Wolviston Reserves	28	13	5	10	61	59	44
8.	Fishburn Park	28	12	6	10	44	36	42
9.	Richmond Town	28	11	6	11	53	54	39
10.	Bedale Athletic	28	11	3	13	40	48	37
11.	Nunthorpe Athletic	28	8	6	14	45	61	30
12.	Stokesley SC	28	7	1	19	35	80	23
13.	SMG redstripes	28	6	4	20	42	59	22
14.	Mackinlay Park	28	4	8	16	37	68	20
15.	New Marske SC (-3pts)	28	4	3	21	31	81	12

DIVISION TWO		P	W	D	L	F	A	Pts
1.	Dormans	22	20	0	2	80	29	60
2.	Richmond Mvrks	22	16	0	6	78	41	48
3.	Billingham Wanderers	22	13	4	5	64	40	43
4.	Teeside Link	22	14	1	7	58	38	43
5.	Teeside Athletic	22	10	3	9	40	37	33
6.	Darlington Albion	22	8	4	10	58	81	28
7.	Darlington RA Reserves	22	8	2	12	48	49	26
8.	North Ormesby FC	22	8	1	13	51	59	25
9.	Darlington CB	22	6	6	10	31	42	24
10.	Darlington SRM	22	6	2	14	32	69	20
11.	Whinney Banks	22	4	4	14	30	56	16
12.	Guisborough Town Reserves	22	4	3	15	22	51	15

ROLE OF HONOUR

LEAGUE CHAMPIONS

2003-04 Hartlepool FC
2002-03 Grangetown BC
2001-02 Grangetown BC
2000-01 Acklam Steelworks
1999-00 Grangetown Boys Club
1998-99 Grangetown Boys Club
1997-98 Acklam Steelworks
1996-97 Acklam Steelworks
1995-96 Acklam Steelworks

MACMILLAN BOWL WINNERS

2003-04 BEADS FC
2002-03 Grangetown BC
2001-02 Thornaby SC
2000-01 Grangetown Boys Club
1999-00 Grangetown Boys Club
1998-99 Nunthorpe Athletic
1997-98 Acklam Steelworks
1996-97 Acklam Steelworks
1995-96 Acklam Steelworks

R T RAINE TROPHY WINNERS

2003-04 Billingham Wanderers
2002-03 Fishburn Park
2001-02 Bedale Athletic
2000-01 Bedale Athletic
1999-00 Nunthorpe Athletic
1998-99 Cargo Fleet
1997-98 Dormans Athletic
1996-97 BSC Redcar
1995-96 BSC Redcar

J V MADDEN TROPHY

2003-04 Grangetown BC
2002-03 Grangetown BC
2001-02 Grangetown BC
2000-01 Acklam Steelworks
1999-00 Nunthorpe Athletic
1998-99 Acklam Steelworks
1997-98 Acklam Steelworks
1996-97 Acklam Steelworks
1995-96 Tees Components

PLAYER OF THE YEAR

2003-04 Paul Orton
Beadle FC
2002-03 Ian Thompson
Wolviston Reserves
2001-02 Lee Atkinson
Acklam SW
2000-01 Adam Bramley
Bedale Athletic
1999-00 Nicholas Agiadis
Acklam Steelworks
1998-99 John Newton
Whitby Town Reserves

MATCH OFFICIAL OF THE YEAR

2003-04 Gary Todd
Brotton
2002-03 Ted Popple
Stockton
2001-02 Bill Mounter
Billngham

LEAGUE CONSTITUTION 2004-05

BEADS FC
Secretary: Dave Kane, 27 Edgeworth Court, Hemlington, Middlesbrough TS8 9EP Tel 01642 289586
Colours Home: Sky Blue/Navy
Ground: Beeachwood & Easterside FC, Marton Road, Middlesbrough Tel 01642 311304

BEDALE FC
Secretary: Mike Allen, 1 Sycamore View, Nosterfield, Bedale, North Yorkshire DL8 2QR Tel 01677 470739
Colours Home: Red
Ground: B.A.S.A, Leyburn Road, Bedale Tel 01677 422085

BILLINGHAM WANDERERS
Secretary: Kevin Long, 26 Topcliffe Drive, Acklam, Middlesbrough TS5 8HZ Tel 01642 277271
Colours Home: Green/White
Ground: Billingham Rugby Club, Greenwood Road, Billingham

CARLIN HOW WMC FC
Secretary: Simon Whitwell, 10 Harebell Close, North Skelton, Saltburn TS12 2FE
Tel 01287 652135
Colours Home: Sky Blue/White
Ground: Kilton Lane, Carlin How

DORMANS FC
Secretary: Stephen Burns, 47 Dunlane Close, Middlesbrough TS5 4AW Tel 01642 653807
Colours Home: Yellow/Blue
Ground: Dormans Ath S & SC, Oxford Road, Middlesbrough

FISHBURN PARK FC
Secretary: Richard & Karen Hutton, 24 Abbots Road Whitby, North Yorkshire YO22 4EB
Tel 01947 602537
Colours Home: Green
Ground: Eskdale School, Broomfield Park, Whitby

THORNABY ATHLETIC
Secretary: Scott Dalgarno, 14 Rainton Drive, Thornaby, Stockton TS17 OEP
Tel 01642 769261
Colours Home: Red
Ground: The Harold Wilson Sports Centre, Thornaby Road, Thornaby

GRANGETOWN BOYS CLUB FC
Secretary: Kevin Larkin, 19 Braemar Grove, Teesville, Middlesbrough TS6 OAN Tel 01642 452095
Colours Home: Black.Amber
Ground: Grangetown Y.C.C., Trunk Road, Grangetown, Middlesbrough
Tel 01642 455435

HARTLEPOOL FC
Secretary: Barry Murray, 110 Spalding Road, Hartlepool TS25 2JP Tel 01429 299428
Colours Home: Red
Ground: Manor NTL College, Owton Manor Lane, Hartlepool

NUNTHORPE ATHLETIC
Secretary: Kevin Levitt, 131 Burlam Road, Middlesborough TS5 5AX Tel 01642 313251
Colours Home: Blue/White
Ground: Recreation Club, Guisborough Road, Nunthorpe, Middlesborough Tel 01642 313251

RICHMOND MAVERICKS
Secretary: Ian Snape, 22 Ronaldshay Drive, Richmond DL10 5BN Tel 01748 823160

Colours Home: Tangerine/Black
Ground: Wavell Road, Catterick Garrison

RICHMOND TOWN
Secretary: Peter Marshall, 2 Alma Place, Richmond North Yorkshire DL10 4TU Tel 01748 825904
Colours Home: Red/Black
Ground: Earls Orchard Playing Fields, Sleegill, Richmond

STOKESLEY SC
Secretary: Peter Grange, 77 Darnton Drive, Easterside, Middlesbrough TS4 3RK Tel 01642 273934

Colours Home: Red/Black
Ground: Stokesley Sports Club, Broughton Road, Stokesley Tel 01642 710051

THORNABY FC
Secretary: Dave Watson, 13 Mainside, Redmarshall, Stockton TS21 1HY Tel 01740 631028

Colours Home: Red
Ground: Teesdale Parl, Scklam Road, Thornaby
Tel 01642 606803

THORNABY YOUTH CLUB FC
Secretary: Geoffrey Kirk, 9 Tipton Close, Thornaby, Stockton TS17 9QF
Tel 01642 676516
Colours Home: Sky Blue
Ground: Grangefield C.C., Oxbridge Lane, Stockton Tel 01642 393531

WEARSIDE LEAGUE

President: W Robson **Chairman:** Peter J Maguire
Secretary: Tom Clark, 55 Vicarage Close, New Silksworth, Sunderland SR3 1UF
Tel: 0191 5211 242 Email: tclark2@virgin.net
Press Secretary: Tom Clark

FINAL LEAGUE TABLE 2003-04

		P	W	D	L	F	A	Pts
1.	North Shields	34	28	5	1	113	23	89
2.	Birtley Town	34	23	7	4	107	68	76
3.	Stokesley SC	34	24	3	7	121	35	75
4.	South Shields Cleadon SC	34	17	9	8	67	58	60
5.	Darlington Railway Athletic	34	16	9	9	75	44	57
6.	Wolviston	34	18	3	13	79	63	57
7.	Boldon Community Assoc.	34	15	9	10	88	63	54
8.	Ryhope Colliery Welfare	34	15	9	10	66	65	54
9.	Gateshead Res.	34	16	4	14	84	65	52
10.	New Marske Sports Club	34	13	8	13	65	64	47
11.	Whitehaven Amateurs	34	13	6	15	59	70	45
12.	Jarrow	34	11	10	13	60	61	43
13.	Windscale	34	12	6	16	55	58	42
14.	S. Shields Harton & Westoe	34	10	9	15	45	54	39
15.	Annfield Plain	34	8	5	21	44	74	29
16.	Barnard Castle Glaxo	34	4	6	24	53	127	18
17.	Ferryhill Athletic	34	3	3	28	39	119	12
18.	Nissan UK (-3pts)	34	3	3	28	44	153	9

2003-04		1	2	3	4	5	6	7	8	9	10	11	12	13	14	15	16	17	18
1	Annfield Plain		5-0	1-2	2-3	0-1	2-0	2-4	0-0	0-2	2-1	1-3	2-2	2-4	0-1	0-7	2-1	2-1	2-4
2	Barnard Castle Glaxo	3-3		3-4	2-5	1-3	1-6	0-2	2-2	0-4	4-3	0-4	3-4	1-4	1-3	0-6	3-3	1-3	1-2
3	Birtley Town	3-2	3-3		3-1	4-2	5-1	6-2	2-1	5-2	7-0	2-1	3-1	1-2	3-1	2-1	0-2	3-2	3-2
4	Boldon Community Assoc.	3-1	8-0	4-1		1-2	4-0	3-3	1-1	2-0	3-1	1-5	4-1	1-1	1-0	1-2	3-2	2-2	0-1
5	Dalington Railway Athletic	0-1	1-2	1-2	0-2		1-1	3-2	2-0	1-2	6-1	2-2	0-0	3-2	1-1	0-0	7-2	5-1	4-1
6	Ferryhill Athletic	1-0	5-2	5-5	3-3	1-3		0-3	0-5	0-1	0-2	0-6	0-2	1-2	1-2	1-10	1-2	0-5	3-4
7	Gateshead Reserves	2-0	3-1	3-3	2-2	3-5	3-1		4-1	3-2	5-0	1-2	0-2	1-3	1-0	1-2	6-2	2-1	0-1
8	Jarrow	2-1	7-0	0-1	3-2	0-7	2-0	3-2		1-1	6-1	1-1	1-1	1-3	2-2	0-5	0-1	3-0	4-2
9	New Masrke Sports Club	1-0	11-0	1-3	3-3	0-2	5-3	2-7	3-3		5-1	0-1	0-2	0-1	1-1	1-0	4-1	2-2	0-3
10	Nissan UK	2-0	3-9	2-9	1-7	1-3	4-3	0-8	2-2	1-3		0-9	2-5	2-9	2-3	1-7	1-2	0-3	2-4
11	North Shields	5-0	2-0	5-0	4-2	1-1	6-0	3-2	2-0	2-2	6-0		4-1	7-0	3-0	3-2	2-0	3-0	4-0
12	Ryhope Colliery Welfare	2-3	4-2	3-3	4-4	1-0	3-0	1-2	3-2	1-1	4-3	1-3		0-0	4-2	0-2	2-1	2-0	0-6
13	South Shields Cleadon SC	1-1	1-1	3-4	2-1	3-2	1-0	1-0	3-3	5-1	1-1	1-3	1-1		1-1	0-2	0-1	2-5	3-2
14	S. Shields Harton & Westoe	2-2	3-1	3-3	1-1	0-2	4-0	3-4	0-2	1-1	1-0	0-3	3-0	0-2		0-2	0-0	1-0	3-0
15	Stokesley SC	1-2	1-2	4-5	6-2	1-1	5-1	5-1	4-0	5-0	9-1	0-2	4-2	2-2	3-1		6-1	5-1	1-0
16	Whitehaven Amateurs	3-1	4-1	3-3	1-4	0-0	6-1	1-1	1-2	3-1	4-1	1-1	0-2	1-2	1-0	0-5		1-0	8-1
17	Windscale	3-2	3-3	1-1	0-2	2-2	4-0	1-0	1-0	0-1	2-0	0-2	1-2	0-1	3-2	1-4	2-0		4-1
18	Wolviston	4-0	2-0	0-3	3-2	3-2	6-0	3-1	1-0	1-2	2-2	2-3	3-3	6-0	3-0	0-2	5-0	1-1	

WEARSIDE LEAGUE CUP

FIRST ROUND

Ferryhill Athletic	v	Stokesley SC	0-6
Gateshead Res.	v	Nissan UK	4-1

SECOND ROUND

Barnard Castle Glaxo	v	Gatehead Reserves	3-4
Boldon Community Ass.	v	South Shields Cleadon SC	0-2
North Shields	v	New Marske Sports Club	1-2*
Ryhope Colliery Welfare	v	Birtley Town	1-4
S. Shields Harton & Westoe	v	Annfield Plain	1-3
Stokesley SC	v	Windscale	4-0
Whitehaven Amateurs	v	Darlington Railway Athletic	2-1
Wolviston	v	Jarrow	3-2

QUARTER-FINALS

Birtley Town	v	Gateshead Reserves	1-0
New Marske SC	v	Wolviston	1-3
Stokesley SC	v	Annfield Plain	3-2*
Whitehaven Amateurs	v	South Shields Cleadon SC	1-3

SEMI-FINALS

Birtley Town	v	Wolviston	4-3*
Stokesley SC	v	South Shields Cleadon SC	4-0

THE FINAL

(17th May at Birtley Town)

Birtley Town	v	Stokesley SC	0-1

ANNFIELD PLAIN

Secretary: M Lawson, 24 Northgate, Anfield Plain, Stanley, Co. Durham DH9 7UY
Ground: Derwent Park, West Road, Annfield Plain
Directions: On A693 road to Consett, 200yds west of junction with A6067. Ground behind new housing estate. 6 miles fromDurham (BR). Buses from Sunderland, Newcastle & Durham.
Capacity: 6,000 Seats: 20 Cover: 200 Floodlights: No
HONOURS Wearside Lg 84-85 (Monkwearmouth Charity Cup 92-93),
FA Cup: 1st Rd 26-27 28-29 64-65.

Founded: 1890.
Colours: Claret/white/blue
Change colours: All blue.
Programme: 16 pages, 20p
Chairman: Frank Ross
Treasurer :Marshall Lawson
Manager: D Longstaff
Press Officer: Frank Ross

BIRTLEY TOWN

Secretary: Kevin McConnell, 8 Laybourn Place, Birtley DH3 1PL Tel No: 0191 4100 495
Commercial Manager: Ray Stafford.
Ground: Birtley Sports Complex. **Directions:** (From Durham) Off A1(M) signpsted for Chester-le-Street, take 2nd turn off r-bout signed Birtley, take last turnoff next r-bout (still signed Birtley), after one and a half miles take 1stleft after AEI Cables - ground at rear of sports complex.
Capacity: Unknown Seats: None Cover: None Floodlights: No.
Clubhouse: Matchdays only
HONOURS: Wearside Lg 45-46 (Lg Cup 35-36), Northern Alliance 23-24 (R-up 13-14).

Founded: 1890 Reformed: 1986
Colours: Green&white hoops/white/green
Change colours: Yellow/blue/red.
Midweek matches: Wednesday
Sponsors: C & C Coachworks
Chairman: John Heslington
Vice-Chairman: J Grainger.
Manager: Barry Fleming
Asst Manager: David Smith
Coach: Malcolm Thompson

BOLDON COMMUNITY ASSOCIATION

Secretary: Tom Robson, 16 Hardie Drive, West Boldon ,Tyne & Wear NE36 0JH.
Ground: Boldon Community Association, New Road, Boldon Colliery.
Directions: A19 to junc A184 Sunderland/Newcastle. Follow signs to Boldon Asdastores, then to North Road Social Club (SHACK). Ground behind. 800 yds fromEast Boldon (BR). Buses 533, 531, 319, 528.
Capacity: 3,500 Seats: 100 Cover: 400 Floodlights: No
Clubhouse: Matchdays only. Bar snacks
HONOURS: Wearside Lg 3, (Lg Cup 3), M/mouth Char Cup 2, Shipowners Cup 6.

Founded: 1892. Nickname: Villa
Colours: Black & Blue Stripes/ Black/Blue
Change: Scarlet & black
Chairman:Kevin Oliver
Vice Chairman: G Smith
President: A Brewster.
Manager: Bill Newham
Asst Manager: P Quinn
Coach: Tommy Frazer.
Press Off. / Comm. Man.: Secretary

CLEADON SOCIAL CLUB

Ground: Jack Clark Park, Horsley Hill Road, South Shields, Tyne & Wear Tel: 0191 454 2023

CLEATOR MOOR CELTIC

Ground: Birks Road, Cleator Moor, Cumbria. Tel: 01946 812476

COXHOE ATHLETIC

Beechfield Park, Coxhoe, County Durham

DARLINGTON RAILWAY ATHLETIC

Secretary: Martyn Jackson, 6 Westlands Rd., Darlington,Co.Durham DL3 9JJ
Tel Nos: 01325 240495 (H) 0870 370095 (M)
Ground: Railway Social Club, Brinkburn Road,Darlington, Co Durham
Capacity: 1,000 **Seats:** None **Cover:** 50 **Floodlights** : Planned
Directions: Take A68 off A1 towards Darlington. Turn left opposite pub on right into Brinkburn Road and ground is 400 yards on left.
Clubhouse: Yes. It serves all sports at complex.
Honours: Auckland & Dist Lg & Cup, Darlington & The SacristonCharity Cups, 00-01

Reformed 1996
Colours: Dark blue & light blue stripes, blue shorts and socks.
Change Colours: Red & black quarters, black shorts and socks.
Manager: Dave Woodcock
Programme : Yes Editor: Robert Harman

FERRYHILL ATHLETIC

Secretary: Norman Bellwood, 49 Rush Park, Bishop Auckland DL14 6NS
Tel: 01388 451065 (H)
Football Secretary: Rob Ridley, 31 Ravensworth Road, Ferryhill Tel: 0780 3803335
Ground: Dean Bank Recreation Ground
Directions: The ground is situated on the old Dean & Chapter Colliery Welfare site west of the old Athletic ground at Darlington Road. From the top of Darlington Road with the Black Bull on your right, pass over the bridge crossing the A167 cutting. Dean Bank school is immediately on your left, turn left at the one way traffic restriction. Follow the signs to Dean Bank Rec.

Colours: Black & amber/amber/black & amber
Change: Red & white/red/red & white

Chairman: Secretary
Press Officer: Jimmy O'Sullivan
Tel: 01740 635524

GATESHEAD RESERVES

Secretary: Ray Kipling Tel: 07789 846333
Ground: International Stadium, Neilson Road, Gateshead, NE10 0EF.
Tel: 0191 478 3883 Fax : 0191 427 5211.
Directions: From the South follow A1(M) to Granada services (Birtley),take right hand fork marked A194(M) (Tyne Tunnel, South Shields) follow A194 to first roundabout, turn left onto A184 - then 3 miles to stadium. Turn right at traffic lights into Neilson Road. BY RAIL to Newcastle Central Station,transfer to the Metro System and then to Gateshead Stadium.
Capacity: 11,795 Seats: 11,795 Cover: 3,300

Formed: 2003
Colours: White with black trim/ black/ white
Change colours: Claret & Blue

Chairman: Mike Gulson
Press Officer: Dean Ranyard

HARTON & WESTOE

Secretary: Alan Bell, 31 Meldon avenue, South Shields, Tyne & Wear NE34 0EL
Tel Nos: 0191 4218233 (H) 0191 4301446 (W)
Groun: Harton Colliery Welfare.

Directions: A1M at Whitemare Pool take A194 to South Shields for 2 1/2 miles.
At third roundabout turn right onto A1300. At 2nd roundabout turn left onto Boldon Lane. Ground 50 yards on right

Colours: All Blue
Change colours: All red

Chairman: Ronald Wightman
Treasurer: Gordon Smith

JARROW

Secretary: Susan Scott,46 Breamish Street, Jarrow. NE32 5SH (0191 4248610)

Ground: Perth Green Community Centre.
Directions: From A19 or A1(M) followdrections to South Shields, right onto John Reid Road. First slip road ontoBrockley Whinns Estate, follow road past Red Hackle pub, third left left ontoInverness Road, then right into Perth Green Community Centre.

HONOURS: Sth Tyne Lg & Lg Cup, Washington Lg R-up 89-90 (Lg Cup 90-91, Aged Peoples Tphy R-up 90-91), Gateshead Charity Cup 90-91, Durham Tphy R-up 90-91.

Founded: 1980.
Colours: Blue & white/blue/blue
Change: Green/black/green

Chairman: B.Tyreman
Treasurer: Jimmy Kane

NEW MARSKE

Secretary: Peter Livingstone, 5 Guisborough Rd, Thornaby on Tees TS17 8BE
Tel: 01642 646428 (H) 01642 606803 (B)

Ground: Gurney Street, New Marske, Redcar
Directions: A19 south onto A174 Redcar- Teesport. Follow A174 towards Saltburn turn right at roundabout with footbridge over road. Ground 500 yds on left.

Colours: Yellow & black/navy/navy or white
Change colours: Blue & black/navy/navy

Charmain: Errol Richter
Tel: 01947 600296
Press Officer: Tony Saunders

RYHOPE C.W.

Secretary: George McKitterick, 8 Kilburn Close, Ryhope Village, Sunderland. SR2 0QU
Tel: 0191 523 8436)
Ground: Ryhope Recreation Park, Ryhope Street, Ryhope, Sunderland Tel: 0191 521 2843
Directions: Take A19 (3 miles south of Sunderland centre) to Ryhope village, atVillage Green turn into Evelyn Terrace/Ryhope Street and carry on up bank pastPresto's for 600 yds - ground appears on left. 3 miles from Sunderland Central(BR), bus every 10 mins from Sunderland centre.
Capacity: 1,000 Seats: No Cover: No Floodlights: Yes
HONOURS: Wearside Lg 4, (Lg Cup 2), Durham Chall Cup 77-78, M/mouth Charity Cup3, S/land Shipowners Cup 2

Founded: 1988.

Colours: Yellow/black/black & red
Change colours: Red/white/red & white

Chairman:: G. Routledge
Press Officer: Peter Grainge

SHOTTON COMRADES

Secretary: Billy Banks, 7 Weldon Close,The Parklands,Shotton Collierey, County Durham DH6 2YJ (0191 526 7134)

Ground: Shotton Re., Station Road, Shotton Colliery, Co. Durham(0191 526 2859)

Directions: A19 to Peterlee to Shotton, right at the War Memorial t-junction, follow round 800yds, ground on right.

SPORT CATTERICK

Ground: The Garrison Stadium, Catterick Garrison, North Yorkshire

STOKESLEY SPORTS CLUB

Secretary: Peter Grainge, 77 Darnton Drive, Easterside, Middlesbrough TS4 3RF
Tel: 01642 273934

Ground: Stokesley Sports Ground, Broughton Road, Stokesley

Directions: A19 to Middlesbrough, then A174 turn to Whitby/Teesport. At 3rd turning up slip road A172 to Stokesley. Go over the 1st r'about, at next r'about turn to Stokesley, 5 miles. At next r'about keep left to next r'about. Ground 100 yards on left.

Colours: Red & black/black/black
Change: White/red/red

Chairman: Eric Taylor 01642 273934
Press Officer: secretary

WASHINGTON NISSAN UK

Secretary: Harry English, 22 Rushcliffe, Fulwell , Sunderland SR6 9RG
Tel: 0191 548 7194 (H) 0191 415 2340 (W) 07889 469961 (M)

Ground: Nissan Sports Complex, Washington Road, Sunderland SR5 3NS
Tel: 0191 415 2354 or 0191 415 2773

Directions: North along A1 (M) use A690 (signed Sunderland) connect withA19, north on A19, after passing the A1231 turn off, plant on the left. Past plant & follow signs 'Nissan Offices'

PREVIOUS League: Wearside Combination

Colours:Blue & Black stripes/Blue/Blue
Change colours: Red & white/white/white.

Chairman: Alan Hill
Treasurer: J.Taylor
Press Officer: Secretary

WHITEHAVEN AMATEURS

Secretary: Richard Stamp, Johnson House, Hillcrest Avenue, Whitehaven, CA28 6SU
Tel: 01946 61877

Ground: Whitehaven County Ground, Coach Road, Whitehaven

Directions: Barrow on A595, ignore branch to town centre at B.P. garage turn right at t/lights on A5094. 1/2 mile turn left at Esso garage into Coach Rd. Narrow lane ent immed after level crossing to grd behind Rugby Lge Stadium.

HONOURS: Cumberland Cup 90-91, County League 87-88 88-89, Wearside Lg Div 2 Cup R-up 93-94.

Colours: Yellow/blue/yellow
Change colours: White/navy/white

Chairman: Bill Robson.
Press Officer: Secretary
Manager: Ian Green
Assistant Manager: Ian Atkins

WINDSCALE

Secretary: Craig Heggie, 12 Bookwell, Egremont, Cumbria CA2 2LS
Tel: 01946 823587 (H) 01946 788337 (W)

Ground: Falcon Field, Egremont.

Directions: A66 to Bridgefoot. A595 Barrow,bottom of hill approaching Egremont take 3rd turn off island (signed)Smithfield/Gillfoot, ground in housing estate

HONOURS: Furness Senior Cup 1985-86

Founded: 1950
Colours:White & Navy Blue/ Navy/White
Change: Blue & white/royal/royal

Chairman: R Napier
Press Officer: Secretary
Treasurer: A Barwise

WOLVISTON

Secretary: Keith Simpson, 14 Lodore Grove, Acklam, Middlesbrough TS5 8PB 01642 823734

Ground: Metcalfe Way, Wynyard Road, Wolviston, Billingham, Cleveland TS22 5NE.

Directions: On Wynyard Road between Thorpe Thewles & Wolviston. A19 onto A689 into Wolviston village, take Wynyard Road towards Thorpe Thewles, grd left before Sir John Halls Estate.

Capacity: 2,000 Seats: None Cover: 200 Floodlights: No Club Shop: No.

Clubhouse: Licensed bar. Hot & cold meals. Open 11am-11pm on matchdays.

HONOURS: Wearside Lg Div 2 89-90, Lg Cup R-up 92-93, Teesside Lg R-up 84-85, Lg Cup 86-87, Durham FA Trophy R-up 89-90, Stockton & Dist. Lg 3, LgCup 3, Lg Charity Cup 79-80.

Record Gate: 500 v Middlesbrough 27/7/93

Founded: 1910 Nickname: Wolves
Sponsors: R.C.I. Industrial Cleaners
Colours: Royal blue/blue/white
Change: Red & white/red/white
Chairman: Eddie Poole
President: Bob Smith
Vice Chairman: Derek Stockton
Press Officer: Andy Anderson
Manager: John Johnson
Asst Manager: Kevin Smith
Coach: Alan Lucas

WEST CHESHIRE LEAGUE

SPONSORED BY: CARLSBERG

Founded 1892

President: Ken Halsall **Chairman & Hon. Treasurer:** Ray Prescott
Hon. General & Fixtures Secretary: Arthur Green, 46 Bertram Drive, Meols, Wirral CH47 0LH Tel: 0151 6324946
Email: arthurlgreen@hotmail.com www.west-cheshire.org.uk
Press Secretary: Ray Condliffe Tel: 0151 327 2288

FINAL LEAGUE TABLES 2003-04

DIVISION ONE		P	W	D	L	F	A	Pts
1	NEWTON	30	25	3	2	89	24	78
2	CAMMELL LAIRD	30	22	5	3	93	32	71
3	POULTON VICTORIA	30	18	4	8	56	26	58
4	GENERAL CHEMICALS	30	17	2	11	58	43	53
5	ASHVILLE	30	15	5	10	67	58	50
6	CHRISTLETON	30	15	4	11	55	43	49
7	MAGHULL	30	15	3	12	49	34	48
8	MALLABY	30	13	5	12	46	39	44
9	HESWALL	30	12	7	11	68	41	43
10	AINTREE VILLA	30	10	4	16	44	70	34
11	VAUXHALL MOTORS RES	30	9	6	15	50	56	33
12	MANWEB	30	9	5	16	36	55	32
13	WEST KIRBY	30	8	8	14	36	58	32
14	CASTROL SOCIAL	30	6	6	18	33	61	24
15	ELLESMERE PORT [SHELL]	30	5	8	17	38	72	23
16	HELSBY	30	3	1	26	17	123	10

DIVISION TWO		P	W	D	L	F	A	Pts
1	MERSEYSIDE POLICE	30	20	5	5	84	46	65
2	CAMMELL LAIRD RES	30	17	8	5	80	46	59
3	BLACON YOUTH CLUB	30	18	4	8	61	32	58
4	NEW BRIGHTON	30	17	5	8	66	48	56
5	MAGHULL RES	30	15	5	10	56	47	50
6	MOND RANGERS	30	13	6	10	72	52	45
7	POULTON VICS RES	30	12	8	10	52	45	44
8	F.C.PENSBY	30	12	7	11	64	61	43
9	UPTON A.A.	30	10	5	15	47	65	35
10	MANOR ATHLETIC	30	9	7	14	38	58	34
12	PAVILIONS	30	10	4	16	40	67	34
11	ASHVILLE RES	30	9	6	15	51	65	33
13	HESWALL RES	30	8	8	15	44	53	32
14	CHRISTLETON RES	30	9	5	16	51	62	32
15	CAPENHURST VILLA	30	8	4	18	54	75	28
16	WILLASTON	30	7	5	17	46	84	26

DIVISION ONE 03-04	1	2	3	4	5	6	7	8	9	10	11	12	13	14	15	16
1 Aintree Villa		1-1	0-6	2-0	1-1	0-2	1-1	5-1	3-2	2-1	1-2	2-1	1-5	0-1	3-0	3-1
2 Ashville	5-1		0-4	2-3	1-1	1-2	2-1	5-0	1-1	4-3	2-1	1-4	1-1	1-0	3-1	2-3
3 Castrol Social	7-1	5-2		5-2	3-1	1-3	1-1	7-1	3-1	3-1	1-1	2-0	3-1	2-1	2-0	2-1
4 Cammell Laird	2-1	4-4	1-5		1-1	1-3	1-1	3-0	1-2	0-0	0-2	1-2	1-2	0-2	2-6	1-0
5 Christleton	3-0	2-3	2-5	3-1		0-2	1-1	7-1	2-1	0-1	2-4	3-0	2-4	0-3	2-0	2-1
6 Ellsmere Port (Shell)	4-0	4-2	0-0	2-0	1-3		7-1	2-3	4-2	1-0	0-3	0-1	0-2	1-0	3-2	4-2
7 General Chemicals	2-1	2-4	0-4	2-0	0-3	0-2		3-0	3-3	0-0	4-3	2-2	1-4	2-4	2-6	3-0
8 Helsby	3-5	1-5	0-6	0-1	0-3	0-2	1-0		1-7	0-3	0-6	1-2	0-5	0-7	1-3	2-1
9 Heswell	2-0	6-0	2-2	0-0	1-2	3-0	1-0	6-0		0-1	2-0	0-2	2-5	3-0	1-0	10-0
10 Maghull	7-0	0-2	1-2	6-3	0-1	2-1	2-1	1-0	1-1		2-1	2-0	1-4	1-2	4-0	1-0
11 Mallaby	1-3	0-3	1-2	2-1	0-1	2-1	2-0	5-0	0-0	1-0		1-3	0-2	2-0	0-0	2-2
12 Manweb	0-0	1-6	0-3	1-0	2-3	0-3	6-2	4-0	0-3	1-2	1-1		1-3	2-2	0-2	0-0
13 Newton	2-1	3-0	4-0	2-0	2-1	2-0	2-1	10-0	3-1	3-0	5-0	3-0		1-0	2-2	3-0
14 Poulton Victoria	3-1	0-1	2-1	1-0	2-1	4-0	1-1	3-0	2-1	1-0	1-0	4-0	3-0		2-2	1-1
15 Vauxhall Motors Reserves	4-1	1-2	0-4	1-2	0-1	4-2	3-0	5-0	3-3	0-4	0-2	1-0	2-2	0-3		2-2
16 West Kirby	0-4	2-1	2-2	1-1	2-1	2-2	5-1	1-1	2-1	0-2	0-1	2-0	0-2	2-1	1-0	

PYKE CHALLENGE CUP

FIRST ROUND

Aintree Villa	v	Castrol Social	2-3
(at Castrol Social)			
Ashville	v	Vauxhall Motors Reserves	2-1
Cammell Laird	v	Poulton Victoria	1-1*, 1-3
Ellesmere Port	v	Maghull	0-2
General Chemicals	v	Mallaby	5-1
Helsby	v	West Kirby	0-4
Heswall	v	Christleton	1-0
Newton	v	MANWEB	4-0

QUARTER-FINALS

Ashville	v	Maghull	1-0*
General Chemicals	v	Poulton Victoria	1-3
Newton	v	Heswall	3-0
West Kirby	v	Castrol Social	8-3

SEMI-FINALS

Ashville	v	Poulton Victoria	2-4
(at Cammell Laird)			
Newton	v	West Kirby	0-1
(at Cammell Laird)			

THE FINAL

(9th April at Vauxhall Motors)

Poulton Victoria	v	West Kirby	1-0*

2003-2004 HONOURS LIST

	Winners	Runners Up
Division One	Newton	Cammell Laird
Division Two	Merseyside Police	Cammell Laird Reserves
Division Three	MANWEB Reserves	Chester Nomads
Pyke Challenge Cup	Poulton Victoria	West Kirby
West Cheshire Bowl	Capenhurst Villa	Heswall Reserves
West Cheshire Shield	MANWEB Reserves	MBNA
Cheshire Amateur Cup	Barnton	Poulton Victoria
Lancashire Amateur Cup	Speke	MANWEB
Chester Senior Cup	Christleton	Blacon Youth Club
Chester Challenge Cup	Upton A.A. Reserves	Wagon Old Boys
Runcorn Senior Cup	General Chemicals	General Chemicals Reserves
Wirral Senior Cup	Cammell Laird	Heswall
Wirral Amateur Cup	Heswall Reserves	Vauxhall Motors 'A'
Bill Weight Memorial Cup	Cammell Laird	Vauxhall Motors

AINTREE VILLA

Chairman: John Gregson Formed: 1954
Secretary: Alf Shepherd, 154 Altway, Aintree, Liverpool L10 6LG
Tel: 0151 526 9287 (H)
Ground: Aintree racecourse.
Colours: Tangerine/white/white
Sponsors: Woolton Carpets/Aintree Conservative Club

ASHVILLE

Chairman: Eddie Parker **Club Formed:** 1949
Secretary: Dave Walton, 15 Wellesley Road, Wallasey, Wirral, Merseyside, L445UR Tel: 0151 639 9196
Ground: Villa Park, Cross Lane, Wallasey Village, Wallasey, Tel: 0151 638 2127 **Colours:** White & black/black/black
Sponsors: Kelly Sports & West Wallasey Van Hire.

CAMMELL LAIRD RESERVES

Chairman: Ray Steele
Secretary: Anthony R wood, 25 Prenton Park Rd,Prenton,Birkenh'd, MerseysideCh42 8JR Tel Nos: 0151 608 0591(H) 07931 761429 (M)
Ground: Kirklands, St Peters Road, Rock Ferry, Birkenhead
Tel: 0151 645 5991

CASTROL SOCIAL

Formed: 1954
Secretary: Mike Caulfield, 2 Weaver Road, Whitby, Ellesmere Port CH66 2JJ. Tel: 0151 355 5966 (H)
Ground: Castrol Sports & Social Club, Chester Road, Whitby, Ellesmere Port(0151 355 1730)
Colours: Royal & emerald/royal/white

CHRISTLETON

Chairman: Ron Mayers
Secretary: Ken Price, 35 Canadian Ave, Hoole, Chester CH2 3HQ Tel: 01244 313513
Ground: Little Heath, Christleton Tel: 01244 332153
Colours: Red/black/red **Formed** 1897 Re-Formed: 1966
Sponsors: Allans Skip Hire

ELLESMERE PORT

Chairman: Gerry Fraser
Secretary: Steven Foden, 23 Hornbeam Avenue, Great Sutton, South Wirral Ch65 7AQ. Tel Nos: 0151 356 8837 (H) 07941 187632 (M)
Ground: Chester Road, Whitby, Ellesmere Port, South Wirral
Tel: 0151 200 7080 **Colours:** Yellow /navy/navy **Formed:** 1924
Previous Name: Shell FC

GENERAL CHEMICALS

Chairman: Dave Robinson
Secretary: Tony Riley 171 Cotton Lane, Runcorn, Cheshire WA7 5JB
Tel: 01928 565390
Ground: Picow Farm Road, Runcorn
Colours: Blue & white/blue/blue & white **Formed:** 1958
Sponsors: Maltacourt Ltd

HESWALL

Chairman: Brian Flanagan
Secretary: Jake Horan ,13 Reedville Rd, Bebington, Wirral L63 2HS
Tel: 0151 644 0459
Ground: Gayton Pk,Brimstage Rd, Heswall, Wirral Tel:01513428172
Colours: Yellow/royal blue/yellow **Formed:** 1891
Sponsors: Pyramids Shopping Centre

MAGHULL

Chairman: Les Jacques **Secretary:** Danny Sherlock, 14 Alexander Drive, Lydiate, Merseyside L31 2NJ Tel: 0151 526 2306
Ground: Old Hall Field, Hall Lane, Maghull, Merseyside (0151 526 7320) **Directions:** M57 or M58 to end (Switch Island), A59 towards Preston (Northway)to lights at Hall Lane, right following signs for Maghull BR. then 200 yds on the left.1/2 m from Maghull (Merseyrail)
Colours: Blue & red stripes/blue/blue **Sponsors:** Soldier of Fortune

MALLABY

Formed: 1965
Chairman: G M Langan
Secretary: Tommy Kenny, 11 Seeley Ave., Claughton, Birkenhead CH41 0BX Tel: 0151 653 5925 (H)
Ground: Balaclava, Birkenhead Park.
Colours: Red & black stripes/black/red

MANWEB

Chairman: James Parry Formed: 1932
John Shimmin, 54 Gonville Rd., Bootle, Merseyside L20 9LR
tel: 0151 933 5763 (H)
Ground: Manweb Sports & Social Club, Thingwall Rd., Liverpool L15 7LB Tel: 0151 281 5364 Colours: White/navy/white
Sponsors: Comasec yate Ltd

MERSEYSIDE POLICE

Formed: 1885
Secretary: Gary Dinsmore, 3 Chaffinch Close, West Derby, Liverpool L12 0NX Tel: 0151 220 0285 (H)
Ground: Police Club, Fairfield, Prescot Rd, Liverpool L7 0JD
Tel: 0151 228 2352
Colours: All navy blue with red trim.

NEWTON

Chairman: John Murray
Secretary: Alan Dabner, 79A Eleanor Road, Bidston, Wirral CH43 7RW. Tel NOs: 0151 653 2151 (H) 0151 993 2151 (B)
Ground: Millcroft, Frankby Road, Greasby, Wirral Tel: 0151 677 8382
Colours: Yellow/green/yellow **Formed:** 1933
Sponsors: Cory Brothers Shipping Ltd.

POULTON VICTORIA

Chairman: Thonas Quinn
Secretary: George Cooper,1 Foxhey Road, Wallasey, Wirral CH44 2ES. Tel Nos: 0151 201 2072 (H) 0151 638 9112 (W)
Ground: Victoria Park, Rankin Street, Wallasey Tel: 0151 638 3559
Colours: All Royal Blue
Formed: 1935 **Sponsors:** Carlsberg & Bass

VAUXHALL MOTORS RESERVES

Chairman: Tony Woodley
Secretary: Carole Paisey, 26 South Road, West Kirby, Wirral L48 3HQ (0151 6256 936)
Ground: Vauxhall Sports Ground, Rivacre Road, Hooton, Ellesmere Port (0151 3281114)
Colours: White/royal blue/white **Formed:** 1963

WEST KIRBY

Formed: 1895
Secretary: Roy Williamson, 85 Wood Lane, Greasby, Wirrall CH49 2PX Tel: 0151 677 4860 (H)
Ground: Johnston Recreation Ground, Neston Road, Willaston, South Wirrall.
Colours: White/black/black

DIVISION TWO

BLACON YOUTH CLUB
Formed: 1964
Chairman: Peter Barnes
Secretary: Colin Lawson,54 Adelaide Rd., Blacon, Chester CH1 5SZ Tel: 01244 375508 (H)
Ground: Cairns Crescent Playing Fields, Cairns Crescent, Blacon, Chester. Colours: Black & white stripes/black/black
Sponsors: George Starkey Painter & Decorator & McDonalds

CAPENHURST VILLA
Formed: 1952
Chairman: Brian Heyes
Secretary: Martin Williams, 157 Hope Farm Road, Great Sutton, South Wirral L662TJ Tel: 0151 339 8935
Ground: Capenhurst Sports Ground, Capenhurst Lane, Capenhurst Tel: 0151 339 4101
Colours: All maroon
Sponsors: Handbridge Decorators & Commercial Properties

CHESTER NOMADS
Ground: Garrison Ground, Eaton Road, Handbridge, Chester, Cheshire

FC PENSBY
Ground: Ridgewood Park, Pensby, Wirral

HELSBY
Formed: 1885
Secretary: Gary Dinsmore, 3 Chaffinch Close, West Derby, Liverpool L12 0NX Tel: 0151 220 0285 (H)
Ground: Police Club, Fairfield, Prescot Rd, Liverpool L7 0JD
Tel: 0151 228 2352
Colours: All navy blue with red trim.

MANOR ATHLETIC
Formed: 1968
Chairman: Tony Bell
Secretary: Stewart Galtress, 3 Centurion Close, Meols, Wirrall CH47 7BZ Tel: 0151 632 3211 email: s-galtress@hotmail.com
Ground: Unilever Sports Ground, Bromborough
Colours: All royal blue

MOND RANGERS
Formed:1967
Chairman: David Holland
Secretary: Steve Kinsella, 3 Bramble Way, Beechwood, Runcorn, Cheshire WA7 3HN Tel Nos: 01928 715178 (H) 07867 972919 (W)
Ground: Pavilions Club, Sandy Lane, Weston Point, Runcorn WA7 5EX Tel: 01928 590508
Colours: Blue & black stripes

NEW BRIGHTON
Formed: 1993
Secretary: Carl Gidman. 64 Ford Road, Upton, Wirrall CH49 0TG Tel: 0151 678 1858 (H/B)
Ground: Harrison Drive, Wallasey Village, Wallasey
Colours: Red & white/white/red & white

PAVILIONS
Formed: 1998
Secretary: Beverley Crilly, 26 Perrin Ave., Weston Point, Runcorn WA7 4BJ Tel: 01928 575938 (H)
Ground: Pavilions Complex, Sandy Lane, Weston Point, Runcorn
Tel: 01928 590508
Colours: Blue & white stripes/blue/blue

UPTON ATHLETIC ASSOCIATION
Formed: 1964
Secretary: Barry Gaulton, 24 St Marks Crescent, Whitby, Ellesmere Port L66 2XD (0151 339 1504)
Ground: Cheshire County Council Sports & Social Club, Plas Newton Lane, Chester (01244 318367)
Colours: All blue

plus
ASHVILLE RESERVES
CHRISTLETON RESERVES
HESWALL RESERVES
MANWEB RESERVES
MAGHULL RESERVES
POULTON VICTORIA RESERVES

WEST LANCASHIRE LEAGUE

SPONSORED BY: ASDA LOGIC

President: D Procter Esq.
Chairman & General Secretary: W Carr Esq.
60 Selby Avenue, Blackpool FY4 2LZ Tel: 01253 348450

FINAL LEAGUE TABLE 2003-04

PREMIER DIVISION		P	W	D	L	F	A	Pts
1.	Kirkham & Wesham	30	25	5	0	87	26	80
2.	Eagley	30	16	5	9	73	46	53
3.	Coppull United	30	13	13	4	72	41	52
4.	Dalton United	30	16	4	10	79	63	52
5.	Freckleton	30	16	3	11	69	47	51
6.	Charnock Richard	30	15	6	9	69	60	51
7.	Fulwood Amateurs	30	12	7	11	60	64	43
8.	Blackrod Town	30	12	6	12	63	65	42
9.	Fleetwood Hesketh	30	12	5	13	62	63	41
10.	Wyre Villa	30	11	7	12	46	53	40
11.	Burnley United	30	9	6	15	61	79	33
12.	Barnoldswick Town	30	6	11	13	54	71	29
13.	BAE Barrow SC (-3pts)	30	8	7	15	50	64	28
14.	Turton	30	7	5	18	57	74	26
15.	Blackpool Wren Rovers	30	7	2	21	48	80	23
16.	Milnthorpe Corries (-3pts)	30	6	6	18	47	101	21

DIVISION ONE (TOP FIVE)		P	W	D	L	F	A	Pts
1.	Hesketh Bank	30	20	4	6	83	45	64
2.	Euxton Villa	30	20	3	7	86	47	63
3.	Poulton Town	30	15	8	7	56	41	53
4.	Garstang	30	15	5	10	73	59	50
5.	Whinney Hill	30	14	6	10	66	53	48

PREMIER DIVISION 2003-04	1	2	3	4	5	6	7	8	9	10	11	12	13	14	15	16
1 BAE Barrow Sports Club		2-2	0-1	2-0	4-0	1-2	2-2	0-2	3-0	3-5	0-4	1-5	1-1	1-2	4-2	2-4
2 Barnoldswick Town	3-3		2-4	1-4	1-1	2-3	4-4	3-4	2-5	0-0	0-2	0-2	1-6	1-2	2-2	5-1
3 Blackpool Wren Rovers	2-3	1-1		4-6	4-0	1-4	4-4	1-3	1-6	4-5	1-2	1-3	0-3	0-2	5-1	1-2
4 Blackrod Town	2-1	3-3	2-1		4-3	2-3	0-2	3-4	2-2	5-1	3-2	3-2	1-2	3-1	1-2	2-2
5 Burnley United	1-0	4-0	0-2	6-5		3-5	1-2	3-1	1-1	2-3	2-0	4-4	1-1	3-2	2-2	0-1
6 Charnock Richard	2-2	3-1	2-0	1-1	6-1		1-4	2-0	0-5	2-0	1-1	2-2	1-2	2-2	3-0	1-2
7 Coppull United	1-1	2-1	2-3	0-0	5-1	2-2		2-2	4-0	2-0	0-2	1-1	2-2	5-5	6-0	2-1
8 Dalton United	1-2	1-3	4-0	1-1	3-2	5-7	3-2		4-1	3-3	4-3	6-1	2-4	4-1	2-3	3-2
9 Eagley	2-1	4-1	4-2	2-3	3-0	2-3	0-1	2-0		3-1	4-1	3-2	1-2	7-2	1-1	2-2
10 Fleetwood Hesketh	1-3	1-1	4-0	5-1	1-2	2-0	0-2	1-5	1-0		2-0	3-3	2-4	1-1	2-0	1-0
11 Freckleton	3-0	3-3	3-2	1-2	5-3	8-0	2-1	0-2	0-3	4-1		1-0	0-3	5-0	3-3	1-2
12 Fulwood Amateurs	2-1	1-2	3-0	4-0	2-2	3-2	0-0	2-0	1-2	4-3	0-5		1-3	2-3	0-10	1-0
13 Kirkham & Wesham	5-0	0-0	4-0	3-0	4-2	3-2	1-1	4-2	2-1	2-1	2-1	2-0		5-0	3-2	4-0
14 Milnthorpe Corinthians	3-2	0-3	0-1	0-2	4-6	2-1	1-7	3-3	1-3	0-9	2-4	0-4	1-4		1-1	3-4
15 Turton	2-3	2-3	4-2	2-1	2-5	1-5	0-3	2-3	0-2	2-3	1-2	2-3	0-2	5-0		1-2
16 Wyre Villa	2-2	1-3	1-0	2-1	2-0	0-1	1-1	0-2	2-2	5-0	0-1	2-2	0-4	3-3	0-2	

RICHARDSON CUP

FIRST ROUND

BAE Barrow Sports Club	v	Charnock Richard	0-7
Blackrod Town	v	Dalton United	4-2
Burnley United	v	Wyre Villa	0-2
Coppull United	v	Freckleton	1-2
Eagley	v	Blackpool Wren Rovers	3-0
Fleetwood Hesketh	v	Fulwood Amateurs	3-1
Kirkham & Wesham	v	Turton	2-0
Milnthorpe Corinthians	v	Barnoldswick Town	3-1

QUARTER-FINALS

Charnock Richard	v	Kirkham & Wesham	2-1
Fleetwood Hesketh	v	Eagley	1-2
Freckleton	v	Milnthorpe Corinthians	1-0
Wyre Villa	v	Blackrod Town	0-1

SEMI-FINALS

Eagley	v	Charnock Richard	0-1
(at Coppull United)			
Freckleton	v	Blackrod Town	4-1
(at Fulwood Amateurs)			

THE FINAL

(21st April at LCFA, Leyland)

Freckleton	v	Charnock Richard	2-4

LEAGUE CONSTITUTION 2004-05 - PREMIER DIVISION

BAE BARROW SPORTS CLUB

Vickers Sports Club, Hawcoat Lane, Barrow-in-Furness, Cumbria. Tel: 01229 825296.

BARNOLDSWICK UNITED

Victory Park, West Close, Barnoldswick, Colne, Lancashire. Tel: 01282 815817

BLACKROD TOWN

Blackrod Community Centre, Vicarage Road, Blackrod, Lancashire. Tel: 01204 692614

BURNLEY UNITED

Barden Sports Ground, Barden Lane, Burnley, Lancashire.

CHARNOCK RICHARD

Charter Lane, Charnock Richard, Lancashire. Tel: 01257 794288

COPPULL UNITED

Springfield Road, Coppull, Lancashire. Tel: 01257 795190

DALTON UNITED

Railway Meadow, Beckside Road, Dalton-in-Furness, Cumbria. Tel: 01229 462799

EAGLEY

Eagley Sports Complex, Dunscar Bridge, Bolton, Lancashire. Tel: 01204 306830

EUXTON VILLA

Runshaw Hall Lane, Euxton, Chorley, Lancashire

FLEETWOOD HESKETH

Fylde Road, Southport, Merseyside. Tel: 01704 227968

FRECKLETON

Hodgson Memorial Ground, Bush Lane, Freckleton, Lancashire. Tel: 01772 679139

FULWOOD AMATEURS

Lightfoot Lane, Fulwood, Preston, Lancashire. Tel: 01772 861827

HESKETH BANK

Hesketh Sports Field, Station Road, Hesketh Bank, Lancashire

KIRKHAM & WESHAM

Recreation Ground, Coronation Road, Kirkham, Lancashire

TURTON

Moorfield, Edgworth, Bolton, Lancashire. Tel: 07929 965160

WYRE VILLA

Hallgate Park, Stalmine Village, near Knott End, Lancashire. Tel: 01253 701468

DIVISION ONE CLUBS

Blackpool Wren Rovers
Burnley Belvedere FC
Crooklands Casuals FC
Furness Rovers FC
Lytham St Annes FC
Milnthorpe Corinthians FC
Poulton Town FC
Tempest United FC
Bootle (Cumbria) AFC
Carnforth Rangers FC
Crosshills FC
Garstang FC
Millom FC
Norcross & Warbeck
Springfields
Whinney Hill FC

DIVISION TWO CLUBS

Askam United FC
BAC/EE Preston FC
Bolton County FC
Furness Cavaliers FC
Haslingden St Marys FC
Lostock St Gerrards FC
Rivington FC
Thornton Cleveleys FC
Aspull (Wigan Youth Lge)
Bae Canberra FC
Croston Sports Club FC
GSK Ulverston Rangers FC
Lancashire Constabulary
Mill Hill St Peters FC
Stoneclough FC
Todmorden Borough FC

WEST RIDING COUNTY AMATEUR LEAGUE

SPONSORED BY: MUMTAZ RESTAURANT BRADFORD

Founded: 1922
President: J Jones Esq.
General Secretary: Stuart Marsden,
28 Church View, Crigglestone, Wakefield WF4 3PF Tel: 01924 249 302

FINAL LEAGUE TABLE 2003-04

PREMIER DIVISION		P	W	D	L	F	A	Pts
1.	Silsden	26	22	1	3	78	28	67
2.	Golcar United	26	18	4	4	56	24	58
3.	Brighouse Town	26	17	4	5	46	28	55
4.	Tyersal	26	13	7	6	52	32	46
5.	Bay Athletic	26	11	6	9	47	37	39
6.	Hemsworth Miners Welf.	26	11	4	11	47	44	37
7.	Campion	26	10	4	12	42	54	34
8.	Otley Town	26	8	7	11	42	49	31
9.	Storthes Hall	26	8	6	12	29	40	30
10.	Ovenden West Riding	26	7	8	11	52	58	29
11.	Steeton	26	6	8	12	40	49	26
12.	Wibsey	26	7	5	14	37	61	26
13.	Hall Green United	26	4	5	17	29	60	17
14.	Littletown	26	4	3	19	28	61	15

DIVISION ONE		P	W	D	L	F	A	Pts
1.	Ardsley Celtic	24	20	2	2	78	26	62
2.	Heckmondwike Town	24	17	1	6	63	30	52
3.	Altofts	24	13	5	6	60	33	44
4.	Lower Hopton	24	12	5	7	65	45	41
5.	Keigh. Shamrocks	24	11	7	6	46	32	40
6.	Westwood	24	12	1	11	57	61	37
7.	Eastmoor	24	9	4	11	40	51	31
8.	Salts	24	7	8	9	38	49	29
9.	Dudley Hill Rgrs	24	7	7	10	54	47	28
10.	Marsden	24	7	3	14	35	70	24
11.	Wakefield City	24	6	5	13	37	53	23
12.	Hunsworth	24	4	4	16	42	72	16
13.	Salt Old Boys	24	2	6	16	48	94	12

PREMIER DIVISION 2003-04	1	2	3	4	5	6	7	8	9	10	11	12	13	14
1 Bay Athletic		1-2	4-0	1-2	0-0	3-1	1-0	0-0	0-2	1-2	1-0	1-1	1-2	3-1
2 Brighouse Town	3-1		2-0	0-2	3-1	2-3	4-2	4-0	2-1	2-1	1-0	1-0	2-1	1-0
3 Campion	2-1	1-1		0-0	3-0	3-0	2-0	3-4	3-0	2-5	2-2	1-2	1-0	0-1
4 Golcar United	4-5	2-1	4-0		2-1	1-0	2-0	2-0	4-1	1-2	2-0	0-1	4-3	1-0
5 Hall Green United	1-4	1-3	1-2	0-2		1-5	2-3	0-0	1-1	1-4	1-2	3-1	0-3	2-1
6 Hemsworth MW	2-3	1-2	1-2	3-1	2-1		0-0	1-1	2-3	0-5	3-2	2-0	1-0	2-1
7 Littletown	0-2	0-1	3-3	0-2	2-3	2-6		2-0	1-2	1-3	1-3	0-3	1-4	0-4
8 Otley Town	3-5	1-2	4-1	2-3	1-3	2-1	1-1		2-1	0-1	2-1	1-1	0-3	1-1
9 Ovenden West Riding	2-4	2-2	4-2	1-1	4-0	2-2	4-1	4-6		3-5	0-3	0-1	4-4	5-0
10 Silsden	2-1	4-1	7-2	1-1	2-1	3-2	2-1	1-2	3-1		2-0	2-0	2-3	4-0
11 Steeton	2-2	1-0	3-1	1-3	3-3	1-3	1-3	3-3	1-1	0-1		2-2	2-2	2-5
12 Storthes Hall	1-0	1-3	1-3	0-5	0-0	0-2	1-2	2-1	3-3	0-4	0-0		1-2	4-0
13 Tyersal	1-1	0-0	3-1	1-1	3-0	1-1	2-0	1-0	4-0	0-3	3-2	0-2		5-1
14 Wibsey	1-1	1-1	1-2	0-4	4-2	2-1	3-2	2-5	1-1	2-7	2-3	2-1	1-1	

PREMIER LEAGUE CUP

FIRST ROUND

Bay Athletic	v	Steeton	1-0
Brighouse Town	v	Hemsworth M. W.	4-4*, 5-3p
Campion	v	Golcar United	4-2
Hall Green United	v	Wibsey	1-1*, 5-3p
Ovenden West Riding	v	Silsden	1-2
Storthes Hall	v	Otley Town	0-1

QUARTER-FINALS

Bay Athletic	v	Littletown	2-0
Brighouse Town	v	Silsden	1-4
Hall Green United	v	Otley Town	2-3
Tyersal	v	Campion	2-4

SEMI-FINALS

Campion	v	Otley Town	3-1

(at Littletown)

Silsden	v	Bay Athletic	3-0

(at Brighouse Town)

THE FINAL (6th May at Brighouse Town)

Silsden	v	Campion	1-3

LEAGUE CONSTITUTION 2004-05 - PREMIER DIVISION

ARDSLEY CELTIC
Cave Lane, Main Street, East Ardsley, Wakefield, West Yorkshire
Tel: 07950 131889

BAY ATHLETIC
University of Huddersfield, Salendine Nook, Huddersfield, West Yorkshire
Tel: 07796 511243

BRIGHOUSE TOWN
St Giles Road, Hove Edge, Brighouse, West Yorkshire
Tel: 07775 693647

CAMPION
Manningham Mills Sports Ground, Scothman Road, Manningham, Bradford, West Yorkshire
Tel: 01274 546726

GOLCAR UNITED
Longfield Recreation Ground, Golcar, Huddersfield, West Yorkshire
Tel: 07779 700098

HALL GREEN UNITED
Crigglestone Sports Club, Painthorpe Lane, Crigglestone, Wakefield, West Yorkshire
Tel: 01924 254544

HECKMONDWIKE TOWN
Cemetary Road, Heckmondwike, West Yorkshire
Tel: 01924 442907

HEMSWORTH MINERS WELFARE
Fitzwilliam Sports Complex, Wakefield Road, Fitzwilliam, West Yorkshire
Tel: 01977 610444

OTLEY TOWN
Old Show Ground, Pool Road, Otley, West Yorkshire
Tel: 01943 451025

OVENDEN WEST RIDING
Natty Lane, Illingworth, Halifax, West Yorkshire
Tel: 01422 244350

STEETON
Summer Hill Lane, Steeton, West Yorkshire

STORTHES HALL
Woodfield Park, Police Sports Ground, Lockwood, Huddersfield, West Yorkshire

TYERSAL
Arkwright Street, off Dick Lane, Bradford, West Yorkshire07799 631384

WIBSEY
Harold Park, Low Moor, Bradford, West Yorkshire
Tel: 01274 656983

Bawtry Town F.C. - Doncaster Senior League Photo: Gordon Whittington.

Easington United - Humber Premier League runners-up. Photo: Gordon Whittington.

Hemsworth St Patricks - Doncaster Senior League: Semi-finalists in the Sheffield & Hallamshire Association Cup. Photo: Gordon Whittington.

FOOTBALL LEAGUE

STEP 1

FOOTBALL CONFERENCE

STEP 2

CONFERENCE NORTH | CONFERENCE SOUTH

STEP 3

NORTHERN PREMIER | SOUTHERN PREMIER | ISTHMIAN PREMIER

STEP 4

NORTHERN PREMIER DIV.1 | SOUTHERN LEAGUE EAST | SOUTHERN LEAGUE WEST | ISTHMIAN DIVISION 1

STEP 5/6

EASTERN COUNTIES (P500) HELLENIC LEAGUE (P518) KENT LEAGUE (P541) MIDLAND ALLIANCE (P552)
SUSSEX COUNTY (P638) UNITED COUNTIES (P658) WESSEX LEAGUE (P676) WESTERN LEAGUE (P694)

STEP 7 - SOUTHERN SECTION

ANGLIAN COMBINATION

SPONSORED BY: LOVEWELL BAKE

President: Tony Dickerson **Chairman:** Ian Bishop
Hon Secretary: Keith Johnson

FINAL LEAGUE TABLES 2003-04

PREMIER DIVISION		P	W	D	L	F	A	Pts
1	Cromer Town	30	22	4	4	91	31	70
2	Acle United	30	22	1	7	78	43	67
3	Lowestoft Town Res	30	20	2	8	71	38	62
4	Norwich Union	30	15	8	7	57	36	53
5	Gorleston Res	30	16	1	13	52	64	49
6	Wroxham Res	30	14	4	12	59	56	46
7	Blofield United	30	14	4	12	65	65	46
8	Attleborough Town	30	13	2	15	66	53	41
9	Scole United	30	11	7	12	41	54	40
10	St Andrews	30	9	11	10	41	40	38
11	Beccles Town	30	9	6	15	44	65	33
12	North Walsham Town	30	10	2	18	43	64	32
13	Wells Town	30	10	2	18	47	75	32
14	Sprowston Athletic	30	9	3	18	38	56	30
15	Diss Town Res	30	9	3	18	39	60	30
16	Halvergate United	30	6	2	22	33	65	20

DIVISION ONE (TOP SIX)		P	W	D	L	F	A	Pts
1.	Watton United	30	20	3	7	74	37	63
2.	Brandon Town	30	20	2	8	73	44	62
3.	Holt United	30	18	5	7	66	40	59
4.	Horsford United	30	15	7	8	62	38	52
5.	Loddon United	30	14	9	7	65	50	51
6.	Mattishall	30	13	7	10	56	54	46

RESULTS GRID 03-04		1	2	3	4	5	6	7	8	9	10	11	12	13	14	15	16
1	Acle United		2-0	3-3	4-1	1-2	2-1	7-0	2-1	1-0	4-0	1-0	2-0	3-1	3-2	5-1	3-2
2	Attleborough Town	1-4		1-2	3-1	1-3	0-2	1-3	0-0	1-4	4-2	5-1	8-1	1-4	0-0	9-1	1-2
3	Beccles Town	3-4	0-3		0-5	0-7	0-3	3-1	1-3	0-2	5-1	0-0	0-0	2-1	0-0	5-0	2-2
4	Blofield United	3-1	3-5	2-6		0-3	4-1	1-2	3-2	1-2	3-2	5-2	2-4	1-0	4-2	1-1	2-2
5	Cromer Town	4-0	4-0	2-3	3-4		2-4	3-0	2-0	4-1	1-2	3-1	0-0	2-0	4-1	3-2	6-1
6	Diss Town Reserves	1-5	2-3	1-3	1-2	0-2		5-0	2-1	2-4	1-3	0-4	0-1	2-0	2-1	0-1	2-1
7	Gorleston Reserves	0-2	1-0	2-0	3-1	3-5	0-2		3-0	2-1	2-1	0-4	1-4	2-1	1-0	7-2	1-2
8	Halvergate United	2-4	0-3	2-0	1-3	0-7	0-0	0-1		1-4	2-3	0-2	2-1	0-3	2-0	3-4	0-2
9	Lowestoft Tn Reserves	2-1	1-0	2-1	2-3	0-4	4-1	6-1	2-1		1-2	1-0	7-0	3-0	2-0	5-1	2-2
10	North Walsham Town	1-2	1-3	2-1	0-3	0-2	2-0	1-2	2-0	1-3		1-1	2-1	5-0	0-3	1-2	3-4
11	Norwich Union	2-1	2-1	8-1	3-1	1-1	4-0	2-2	3-2	1-2	3-0		1-1	1-0	0-1	2-1	2-1
12	Scole United	1-2	2-4	2-0	4-1	2-2	1-0	2-5	2-1	1-3	2-1	0-0		2-0	0-0	1-3	2-0
13	Sprowston Athletic	1-0	2-5	0-1	1-1	0-4	2-2	2-1	2-0	1-0	0-1	2-3	4-1		2-2	3-1	1-2
14	St Andrews	2-3	1-0	1-1	2-2	1-1	5-1	1-2	2-1	1-1	1-1	1-1	1-1	2-0		3-1	0-2
15	Wells Town	2-3	0-2	2-1	1-2	2-3	3-1	3-1	0-2	2-0	3-1	0-0	2-1	2-3	2-3		0-2
16	Wroxham Reserves	4-3	2-1	3-0	2-0	1-2	0-0	2-4	2-4	2-4	5-1	2-3	0-1		4-2	0-2	3-2

SENIOR CUP

FIRST ROUND

Attleborough Town	v	Dereham Town Reserves	1-2
Beccles Town	v	Norwich Union	1-3
Blofield United	v	Mattishall	4-0
Brandon Town	v	Diss Town Reserves	2-1
Fakenham TownRes.	v	Mulbarton United	3-1
Gorleston Reserves	v	Halvergate United	4-2
Great Yarmouth Tn Res.	v	Sprowston Athletic	1-4
Hempnall	v	North Walsham	2-1
Holt United	v	Stalham Town	3-1
Horsford United	v	Cromer Town	4-2*
Loddon United	v	Anglian Windows	3-3*, 2-4p
Scole United	v	Acle United	1-2*
Watton United	v	Sprowston Wanderers	3-1
Wells Town	v	Wymondham Town	3-2
Wroxham Reserves	v	Hindringham	1-2

SECOND ROUND

Acle United	v	Dereham Town Reserves	5-3
Fakenham Town Res.	v	St Andrews	0-6
Gorleston Reserves	v	Watton United	4-2

Second Round continued....

Hempnall	v	Brandon Town	2-3
Holt United	v	Wells Town	2-1
Horsford United	v	Anglian Windows	4-2
Norwich Union	v	Hindringham	3-1
Sprowston Athletic	v	Blofield United	2-2*, 5-4p

THIRD ROUND

Acle United	v	St Andrews	5-0
Brandon Town	v	Sprowston Athletic	7-3
Horsford United	v	Gorleston Reserves	1-2
Norwich Union	v	Holt United	2-1*

SEMI-FINALS

Acle United	v	Brandon Town	4-2
Gorleston Reserves	v	Norwich Union	1-2

THE FINAL

Acle United	v	Norwich Union	2-1*

at Plantation Park (Norwich United FC)

LEAGUE CONSTITUTION 2004-05 - PREMIER DIVISION

ACLE UNITED
Bridewell Lane, Acle, Norfolk
Tel: 01493 751372

ATTLEBOROUGH TOWN
Recreation Ground, Station Road, Attleborough, Norfolk
Tel: 01953 455365

BECCLES TOWN
College Meadow, Beccles, Suffolk
Tel: 01502 712221

BLOFIELD UNITED
Old Yarmouth Road, Blofield, Norwich, Norfolk
Tel: 01603 712576

BRANDON TOWN
Remembrance Playing Field, Church Road, Brandon, Suffolk
Tel: 01842 813177

CROMER TOWN
Cabbell Park, Mill Road, Cromer, Norfolk
Tel: 01263 512185

GORLESTON RESERVES
Emerald Park, Wood Farm Lane, Gorleston, Norfolk
Tel: 01493 602802

LOWESTOFT TOWN RESERVES
Crown Meadow, Love Road, Lowestoft, Suffolk
Tel: 01502 573818

NORTH WALSHAM TOWN
Sports Centre, Greens Road, North Walsham, Norfolk
Tel: 01692 406888

NORWICH UNION
Pinebanks, White Farm Lane, Harvey Lane, Thorpe, Norfolk
Tel: 01603 434457

SCOLE UNITED
Ransome Avenue Playing Field, Scole, Diss, Norfolk
Tel: 01379 741204

SPROWSTON ATHLETIC
Sprowston Spts & Social Club, Blue Boar Lane, Sprowston, Norwich, Norfolk
Tel: 01603 427688

ST ANDREWS
Thorpe Recreation Ground, Laundry Lane, Thorpe, Norfolk
Tel: 01603 300316

WATTON UNITED
Watton Playing Field, Dereham Road, Watton, Norfolk
Tel: 01953 881281

WELLS TOWN
Beach Road, Wells-next-the-Sea, Norfolk
Tel: 01328 710907

WROXHAM RESERVES
Trafford Park, Skinners Lane, Wroxham, Norfolk
Tel: 01603 783538

CAMBRIDGESHIRE COUNTY LEAGUE

CAMBRIDGESHIRE F.A. LTD

Tel: 01223 576 770x201 Fax: 01223 576 780 Email: secretary@cambridgeshirefa.com

City Ground, Milton Road, Cambridge CB4 1FA

FINAL LEAGUE TABLE 2003-04

PREMIER DIVISION	P	W	D	L	F	A	Pts
1. Fulbourn Institute	30	23	2	5	93	41	71
2. Sawston United	30	21	4	5	70	36	67
3. Over Sports	30	21	3	6	73	31	66
4. West Wratting	30	17	5	8	65	38	56
5. Tuddenham Rovers	30	17	4	9	62	36	55
6. Linton Granta	30	16	4	10	60	45	52
7. Newmarket Town Reserves	30	13	5	12	58	54	44
8. Foxton	30	11	9	10	51	51	42
9. Cottenham United	30	11	8	11	54	54	41
10. Great Shelford	30	10	4	16	49	58	34
11. Waterbeach	30	7	9	14	47	58	30
12. Hemingford United	30	9	3	18	44	68	30
13. Fordham	30	7	8	15	44	58	29
14. Great Paxton	30	8	1	21	38	86	25
15. Wisbech Town Reserves (-3pts)	30	5	5	20	28	69	17
16. Mildenhall Town Reserves (-3pts)	30	6	2	22	33	86	17

SENIOR A (TOP SIX)	P	W	D	L	F	A	Pts
1. Littleport Town	30	25	3	2	91	21	78
2. Histon 'A'	30	21	6	3	98	27	69
3. Comberton United	30	16	7	7	45	37	55
4. Gamlingay United	30	15	6	9	60	43	51
5. Brampton	30	15	4	11	55	42	49
6. Eaton Socon	30	13	7	10	56	57	46

PREMIER 03-04	1	2	3	4	5	6	7	8	9	10	11	12	13	14	15	16
1 Cottenham United		1-1	1-1	1-3	4-2	2-1	5-0	2-3	1-1	2-0	4-3	1-2	2-2	3-1	1-3	2-1
2 Fordham	2-1		2-2	3-3	4-0	3-4	2-1	0-2	0-3	2-2	0-1	0-1	1-1	1-2	0-3	5-1
3 Foxton	3-3	1-1		0-2	2-0	1-1	3-0	1-3	1-0	2-2	0-4	1-2	1-1	2-0	1-4	7-0
4 Fulbourn Institute	3-1	0-1	2-2		6-1	5-1	5-3	4-1	6-1	3-1	3-2	2-1	2-1	3-2	1-3	5-1
5 Great Paxton	1-7	1-0	0-4	0-4		3-1	3-1	0-0	2-0	2-3	0-4	3-2	0-4	1-3	3-2	1-2
6 Great Shelford	2-1	0-2	3-1	2-3	5-2		0-1	0-2	2-2	1-1	0-2	0-1	1-4	2-1	1-1	2-1
7 Hemingford United	0-1	2-2	2-3	0-3	7-3	2-1		1-4	1-2	2-0	0-1	1-2	1-7	2-2	2-1	2-1
8 Linton Granta	4-0	4-0	0-1	0-4	3-2	4-1	1-2		5-1	4-3	2-2	2-4	2-1	2-0	1-4	4-1
9 Mildenhall Town Reserves	0-1	4-1	0-2	0-5	2-5	1-6	0-3	0-2		2-4	0-2	3-0	0-3	2-5	0-3	2-1
10 Newmarket Town Reserves	3-1	3-1	3-1	1-3	0-2	3-2	4-1	3-0	2-0		0-3	1-3	3-0	3-0	1-3	0-0
11 Over Sports	5-0	4-2	4-1	3-1	3-0	0-2	2-0	2-1	6-0	3-2		1-1	3-1	0-2	2-0	1-0
12 Sawston United	3-0	2-2	3-1	0-1	3-0	4-1	3-0	3-1	5-1	3-4	4-1		1-0	2-1	3-2	4-2
13 Tuddenham Rovers	1-3	2-1	1-2	2-0	1-0	1-0	3-1	2-0	1-0	4-0	3-3	0-3		3-1	2-3	3-2
14 Waterbeach	3-3	1-2	5-1	4-5	3-0	1-3	1-1	1-1	1-4	1-1	1-4	1-1	0-4		0-0	1-1
15 West Wratting	0-0	3-1	1-2	2-1	5-1	3-1	2-5	0-0	6-0	3-2	1-0	1-2	0-3	1-1		3-0
16 Wisbech Town Reserves	0-0	3-2	1-1	1-5	1-0	0-3	1-0	0-2	4-2	0-3	0-2	2-2	0-1	0-2	1-2	

PREMIER DIVISION CUP

FIRST ROUND

Cottenham United	v	Fordham	2-2*, 4-2p
Fulbourn Institute	v	Mildenhall Town Reserves	6-0
Great Shelford	v	Great Paxton	3-2
Over Sports	v	Waterbeach	2-0
Sawston United	v	Foxton	2-1
Tuddenham Rovers	v	Newmarket Town Reserves	1-0
West Wratting	v	Hemingford United	2-0
Wisbech Town Res.	v	Linton Granta	2-3*

QUARTER-FINALS

Cottenham United	v	West Wratting	1-4
Great Shelford	v	Tuddenham Rovers	3-3*,3-4p
Linton Granta	v	Sawston United	0-2
Over Sports	v	Fulbourn Institute	1-1*,4-5p

SEMI-FINALS

Fulbourn Institute	v	Tuddenham Rovers	5-0
West Wratting	v	Sawston United	4-1

THE FINAL (11th May at Cambridge City)

Fulbourn Institute	v	West Wratting	4-1*

LEAGUE CONSTITUTION 2004-05 - PREMIER DIVISION

COTTENHAM UNITED
Lambs Lane, Cottenham, Cambridge, Cambridgeshire
Tel: 01954 250873

FORDHAM
Recreation Ground, Carter Street, Fordham, Cambridgeshire

FOXTON
Recreation Ground, Foxton, Cambridgeshire

FULBOURN INSTITUTE
Fulbourn Recreation, Home End, Fulbourn, Cambridgeshire

GREAT PAXTON
Recreation Ground, High Street, Great Paxton, Cambridgeshire

GREAT SHELFORD
Recreation Ground, Woollards Lane, Great Shelford, Cambridgeshire
Tel: 01223 842590

HEMINGFORD UNITED
Memorial Playing Fields, Manor Road, Hemingford Grey, Cambridgeshire

HISTON 'A'
Bridge Road (outside pitch), Impington, Cambridge, Cambridgeshire
Tel: 01223 237373

LINTON GRANTA
Recreation Ground, Meadow Lane, Linton Granta, Cambridgeshire

LITTLEPORT TOWN
Sports Centre, Camel Road, Littleport, Cambridgeshire

NEWMARKET TOWN RESERVES
Cricket Field Road, off New Cheveley Road, Newmarket, Suffolk
Tel: 01638 663637

OVER SPORTS
The Green, Over, Cambridgeshire

SAWSTON UNITED
Spicers Sports Ground, New Road, Sawston, Cambridgeshire

SOMERSHAM TOWN
West End Ground, St Ives Road, Somersham, Huntingdon, Cambridgeshire
Tel: 01487 843384

TUDDENHAM ROVERS
Ramsey Field, The Green, Tuddenham, Cambridgeshire

WATERBEACH
Recreation Ground, Waterbeach, Cambridgeshire

WEST WRATTING
Recreation Ground, Bull Lane, West Wratting, Cambridgeshire

FULBOURN INSTITUTE - Premier Division League, Cup and Cambridgeshire Challenge Cup winners.

COTTENHAM UNITED

LITTLEPORT TOWN - Senior A division champions.

Photos: Gordon Whittington.

HISTON 'A' - Senior A division runners-up.

GAMLINGAY UNITED - Cambridgeshire Challenge Cup semi-finalists.

EATON SOCON

Photos: Gordon Whittington.

DEVON COUNTY LEAGUE

SPONSORED BY: FIREWATCH
President: Carl Throgmorton
Chairman: Stephen Ware **Vice Chairman:** Mark Hayman
Hon. Secretary: Philip Hiscox, 19 Ivy Close, Wonford, Exeter EX2 5LX
Tel/Fax: 01392 493995 Email: pahiscox@hotmail.com

The 2003/04 season was without doubt a busy affair, the addition of Holsworthy taking the League to 21 clubs and a very hectic schedule. That said it was one of the best seasons ever, their was drama at both the top and bottom of the table and new winners of both the League Championship Trophy and the Throgmorton League Cup.

Holsworthy suffered just one home defeat on their way to the title, and that was on the opening day! Yet it was never a foregone conclusion as clubs, particularly those low in the table, took points off the Magpies to make it an interesting run in. Certainly the final point needed to win the title showed the true fighting spirit that exists in the league as Topsham, who had already been relegated, took the lead and held on until injury time when the Magpies levelled to claim the draw and the league title.

Ivybridge Town were again runners-up whilst Devon Premier Cup winners, Vosper Oak Villa, took third place. There were best ever placings for Elburton Villa and Dartington who finished in fourth and fifth places respectively, the latter also adding their first ever league silverware with a 3-2 win over Dartmouth in the Throgmorton League Cup final in front of a record crowd at Newton Abbot.

At the foot of the table Exeter duo of Topsham Town and Heavitree United were both relegated and their places taken by St Loyes (Devon & Exeter League) and Teignmouth (South Devon League), both of whom won their respective leagues.

Budleigh Salterton and Newton Abbot both made it through to the First Round of the F.A. Vase, whilst the University of Exeter retained the Sportsmanship Cup. This season's 'Golden Boot' award went to Holsworthy's Marc Thorne who netted 41 league and cup goals.

FINAL LEAGUE TABLE 2003-04

		P	W	D	L	F	A	Pts
1.	Holsworthy	40	26	11	3	100	40	89
2.	Ivybridge Town	40	25	9	6	115	49	84
3.	Vospers Oak Villa	40	25	6	9	105	53	81
4.	Elburton Villa	40	23	7	10	93	65	76
5.	Dartington Sports	40	22	8	10	123	71	74
6.	Ottery St Mary (+3pts)	40	20	8	12	87	64	71
7.	Newton Abbot	40	22	4	14	79	63	70
8.	Buckland Athletic	40	21	6	13	86	63	69
9.	Dartmouth	40	16	10	14	88	64	58
10.	Crediton United	40	15	12	13	78	70	57
11.	University of Exeter	40	17	3	20	64	63	54
12.	Budleigh Salterton	40	13	15	12	66	69	54
13.	Plymstock United	40	13	13	14	61	63	52
14.	Alphington	40	12	10	18	55	73	46
15.	Appledore	40	13	6	21	54	79	45
16.	Cullompton Rangers	40	10	14	16	71	71	44
17.	Stoke Gabriel	40	12	7	21	53	92	43
18.	Newton Abbot Spurs	40	9	10	21	55	103	37
19.	Exeter Civil Service	40	5	12	23	37	79	27
20.	Heavitree United	40	6	5	29	50	139	23
21.	Topsham Town (-5pts)	40	4	6	30	28	115	13

2003-04	1	2	3	4	5	6	7	8	9	10	11	12	13	14	15	16	17	18	19	20	21
1 Alphington		1-1	0-1	0-1	1-2	2-1	3-3	1-1	1-3	1-0	4-0	1-1	1-4	0-1	3-2	1-2	1-1	4-1	2-1	2-4	1-3
2 Appledore	3-0		0-3	2-3	1-3	1-5	1-2	0-0	0-4	1-1	1-0	1-2	1-2	0-4	5-1	0-3	3-3	1-0	1-0	1-0	1-0
3 Buckland Athletic	2-1	4-1		3-2	2-0	2-2	2-5	3-3	0-1	2-0	5-1	2-1	2-2	0-1	1-1	3-2	0-0	1-2	3-0	2-1	0-2
4 Budleigh Salterton	0-2	3-1	3-2		2-2	1-1	0-6	2-2	2-1	1-1	3-0	2-1	0-2	0-3	3-3	1-0	1-2	2-2	1-1	1-1	2-2
5 Crediton United	1-2	2-0	1-4	1-0		1-0	3-3	1-1	7-2	1-1	4-1	0-1	1-3	2-2	3-3	1-2	1-1	1-1	5-0	0-4	1-2
6 Cullompton Rangers	2-2	2-3	0-4	1-1	0-3		1-1	0-6	3-1	2-2	6-0	1-2	1-1	2-1	1-2	1-1	1-1	3-4	4-0	2-1	1-2
7 Dartington Sports	1-1	5-0	3-2	2-2	2-2	2-1		0-3	6-3	2-1	6-0	2-4	2-3	1-3	3-0	3-3	2-3	6-2	7-1	4-1	3-0
8 Dartmouth	3-0	2-1	2-0	2-3	3-3	1-2	4-1		1-3	2-1	7-1	0-2	2-3	1-0	3-3	1-3	5-0	1-0	1-1	0-1	1-2
9 Elburton Villa	2-1	0-0	5-3	3-3	4-0	2-1	1-2	4-1		1-1	2-1	1-2	1-1	4-2	3-0	2-0	2-2	1-1	5-0	2-0	3-2
10 Exeter Civil Service	0-2	0-1	0-3	2-1	0-2	2-2	1-5	1-1	0-1		3-3	1-1	1-5	1-4	1-2	2-0	1-3	0-1	0-1	0-1	2-2
11 Heavitree United	4-1	1-4	3-1	1-1	2-5	2-8	3-4	0-5	2-4	0-1		1-3	1-6	2-3	4-3	0-3	2-1	1-2	1-1	3-4	0-5
12 Holsworthy	1-1	3-0	2-0	3-2	0-0	2-2	3-2	3-2	6-0	6-1	7-0		4-0	2-1	2-1	1-4	0-0	1-0	3-2	3-1	0-0
13 Ivybridge Town	8-0	5-0	1-3	2-2	5-1	3-3	1-3	2-2	4-2	1-1	9-1	1-1		3-2	5-0	6-1	1-0	4-0	5-1	0-1	1-2
14 Newton Abbott	0-3	2-1	3-2	2-2	2-0	0-2	3-0	5-2	1-4	4-0	2-1	1-4	1-2		4-0	1-6	2-0	1-0	3-2	0-3	0-1
15 Newton Abbott Spurs	2-2	0-1	0-0	0-3	1-6	2-2	1-7	4-2	0-2	4-2	3-1	0-8	1-2	2-2		0-4	4-2	3-3	2-1	0-0	0-2
16 Ottery St Mary	2-1	2-2	4-2	2-3	5-3	1-2	3-1	2-1	1-1	1-2	2-2	2-2	2-1	1-1	3-1		4-3	3-0	0-1	1-0	2-6
17 Plymstock United	0-0	2-1	1-3	4-0	2-2	1-1	2-2	2-3	2-1	1-0	0-1	0-1	0-2	0-3	1-0	1-0		5-0	1-1	2-4	4-4
18 Stoke Gabriel	3-1	3-2	1-5	2-1	1-2	2-1	0-4	0-3	2-3	3-1	1-1	2-2	0-2	1-4	1-0	1-3	1-2		2-3	4-1	0-4
19 Topsham Town	1-2	0-8	1-2	0-3	1-2	1-0	1-5	1-6	0-5	1-1	0-1	2-2	0-4	0-1	0-1	0-6	0-3	0-2		1-2	0-6
20 University of Exeter	1-3	0-3	2-3	1-0	0-2	2-0	0-3	0-1	2-3	1-2	3-1	1-4	1-1	2-4	0-1	3-0	1-3	7-0	2-0		3-0
21 Vospers Oak Villa	4-0	6-0	3-4	1-3	3-1	3-1	3-2	3-1	2-1	3-0	6-1	0-4	1-2	4-0	5-2	1-1	2-0	2-2	5-1	1-2	

THROGMORTON LEAGUE CUP

FIRST ROUND

Buckland Athletic	v	Dartmouth	1-2
Crediton United	v	Stoke Gabriel	2-0
Cullompton	v	Elburton Villa	2-3
Ivybridge	v	Vospers Oak Villa	3-1
University of Exeter	v	Plymstock United	1-1*,5-6p

SECOND ROUND

Budleigh Salterton	v	Crediton	6-2
Dartington Sports	v	Alphington	4-1
Exeter CS	v	Heavitree United	2-1*
Ivybridge Town	v	Appledore	5-2
Newton Abbot Spurs	v	Newton Abbot	1-6
Ottery St Mary	v	Elburton Villa	1-3
Plymstock	v	Dartmouth	2-3*
Topsham Town	v	Holsworthy	0-1

CHARITY SHIELD (10th August at Dartmouth)

Dartmouth	v	Ivybridge Town	0-2

QUARTER-FINALS

Budleigh Salterton	v	Dartmouth	2-2*,5-6p
Dartington Sports	v	Elburton Villa	2-1*
Ivybridge Town	v	Holsworthy	0-2
Newton Abbot	v	Exeter Civil Service	3-1

SEMI-FINALS

Dartington Sports	v	Newton Abbot	6-2*
(at Buckland Athletic)			
Dartmouth	v	Holsworthy	5-4
(at Cullompton Rangers)			

THE FINAL (3rd May at Newton Abbot)

Dartington Sports	v	Dartmouth	3-2

DEVON PREMIER CUP (10th May at Plymouth Argyle)

Vospers Oak Villa	v	Plymouth Parkway	4-2

LEADING GOALSCORERS 2003-04

Player	Club	Position Club Finished	Lge	Cup	Total
Marc Thorne	Holsworthy	1st	32	9	41
Mark Berry	Vospers Oak Villa	3rd	32	7	39
Lee Johnson	Elburton Villa	4th	32	4	36
Dave Worthington	Dartington SC	5th	23	12	35
Ian Rowe	Holsworthy	1st	26	7	33
Danny Williams	Ottery St Mary	6th	30	1	31
Tony Hendy	Ivybridge Town	2nd	27	2	29
John Rimmer	Dartington SC	5th	27	0	27
Jamie Middleton	Ivybridge Town	2nd	20	6	26

PROGRAMME AWARD 2003-04

Dartmouth

HOSPITALITY SHIELD 2003-04

Appledore

SPORTSMANSHIP CUP 2003-04

University of Exeter

MEDI PRINT PRESS TROPHY 2003-04

Alphington

LEAGUE CONSTITUTION 2004-05

ALPHINGTON
The Chronicles, Alphington, Exeter, Devon
Tel: 01392 279 556

APPLEDORE
Marshford, Appledore, Devon
Tel: 01237 477 099

BUCKLAND ATHLETIC
Homers Lane, Kingsteignton, Devon (Will be moving to a new ground during season)
Tel: 01626 362 602

BUDLEIGH SALTERTON
Greenway Lane, Budleigh Salterton, Devon EX9 6SC
Tel: 01395 443 850 **see page 848 for further details**

CREDITON UNITED
Lords Meadow, Commercial Road, Crediton, Devon
Tel: 01363 774 671

CULLOMPTON RANGERS
Speeds Meadow, Duke Street, Cullompton, Devon EX15 1DW
Tel: 01884 33090 **see page 848 for further details**

DARTINGTON SPORTS
Foxhole Sports Ground, Dartington, Devon
Tel: 01803 868 032

DARTMOUTH
Longcross, Dartmouth, Devon
Tel: 01803 832 902

ELBURTON VILLA
Haye Road, Elburton, Devon
Tel: 01752 480 025

EXETER CIVIL SERVICE
Foxhayes, Exwick, Exeter, Devon
Tel: 01392 273 976

HOLSWORTHY
Upcott Field, North Road, Holsworthy, Devon
Tel: 01409 254 295

IVYBRIDGE TOWN
Erme Valley, Ivybridge, Devon
Tel: 01752 896 686

NEWTON ABBOT
Coach Road Stadium, Coach Road, Newton Abbot, Devon TQ12 5DS
Tel: 01626 335 011 **see page 848 for further details**

NEWTON ABBOT SPURS
Recreation Ground, Newton Abbot, Devon
Tel: 01626 365 343

OTTERY ST MARY
Washbrook Meadows, Butts Road, Ottery St Mary, Devon EX11 1EL
Tel: 01404 813 539 **see page 848 for further details**

PLYMSTOCK UNITED
Dean Cross, Plymstock, Devon
Tel: 01752 406 776

ST LOYES
St Loyes College, Millbrook Lane, Topsham Road, Exeter, Devon
Tel:

STOKE GABRIEL
C J Churchward Mem. Ground, Broadley Lane, Stoke Gabriel, Totnes, Devon
Tel: 01803 782 223

TEIGNMOUTH
Coombe Valley, Teignmouth, Devon
Tel: 01626 776 688

UNIVERSITY OF EXETER
University Sports Ground, Topsham, Devon
Tel: 01392 264 452

VOSPERS OAK VILLA
The Mill, Plymouth, Devon
Tel: 01752 363 352

FEEDER LEAGUES

DEVON & EXETER LEAGUE

PREMIER DIVISION	P	W	D	L	F	A	Pts
St Loyes	30	23	5	2	85	18	74
Witheridge	30	22	5	3	66	24	71
Feniton	30	15	4	11	67	62	49
Buckland Athletic Reserves	30	13	9	8	44	36	48
University of Exeter Res.	30	12	8	10	57	48	44
St Martins	30	12	8	10	48	41	44
Pinhoe	30	12	6	12	70	62	42
Seaton Town	30	9	11	10	39	39	38
Willand Rovers Reserves	30	10	6	14	41	54	36
Sidmouth Town	30	9	9	12	50	65	36
Okehampton Argyle	30	11	3	16	49	64	36
Exeter Civil Service Res.	30	9	5	16	44	78	32
Thorverton	30	8	7	15	44	60	31
Cullompton Rangers Res.	30	8	6	16	51	60	30
Hatherleigh Town	30	6	8	16	39	64	26
Budleigh Salterton Res.(-4pts)	30	7	8	15	47	66	25

SENIOR ONE	P	W	D	L	F	A	Pts
Exmouth Town Res.	28	22	2	4	80	26	68
Axminster Town	28	18	8	2	84	31	62
Beer Albion	28	19	4	5	74	40	61
Exeter St Thomas	28	15	4	9	56	51	49
Alphington Res. (-4pts)	28	15	4	9	54	45	45
Westexe Rovers	28	14	3	11	48	50	45
Halwill	28	12	8	8	58	44	44
North Tawton	28	12	3	13	58	53	39
University of Exeter 'A'	28	13	0	15	71	67	39
Exmouth Amateurs	28	10	7	11	54	49	37
Wellington Reserves	28	10	3	15	47	53	33
Topsham Town Res.	28	8	2	18	36	69	26
Newtown	28	6	7	15	38	60	25
Elmore Res. (-4 pts)	28	4	2	22	44	107	10
Dawlish Town Res.(-3pts)	28	2	3	23	24	81	6

SOUTH DEVON LEAGUE

PREMIER DIVISION	P	W	D	L	F	A	Pts
Teignmouth	28	23	4	1	94	19	73
Upton Athletic	28	23	3	2	98	22	72
Galmpton United	28	15	3	10	51	50	48
East Allington United	28	15	2	11	71	41	47
Totnes Town	28	14	5	9	55	38	47
Bovey Tracey	28	12	6	10	58	48	42
Chelston	28	12	5	11	55	58	41
Victoria Rangers	28	12	2	14	76	63	38
Brixham United	28	12	2	14	55	67	38
Hele Rovers	28	11	3	14	50	53	36
Buckfastleigh Rangers	28	9	6	13	41	54	33
Kingsteignton Athletic	28	9	2	17	47	66	29
Dartmouth AFC Reserves	28	8	3	17	48	76	24
Liverton	28	7	3	18	31	65	24
Kingskerswell	28	2	3	23	28	132	9

DIVISION ONE	P	W	D	L	F	A	Pts
Brixham Villa	24	19	2	3	66	26	59
Bishopsteignton United	24	17	5	2	74	30	56
Newton Abbot Reserves	24	17	2	5	57	20	53
Chagford	24	14	1	9	68	39	43
Newton Abbot Spurs R.	24	11	7	6	50	35	40
Paignton United	24	11	0	13	58	67	33
Paignton Villa	24	8	4	12	41	50	28
Kingstaignton A. Res.	24	8	4	12	50	62	28
Stoke Gabrial Reserves	24	9	0	15	39	64	27
Loddiswell Athletic	24	8	2	14	42	56	26
Chudleigh Athletic	24	8	0	16	42	60	24
Channings Wood	24	7	2	15	48	66	23
Dartington SC Res.(-3pts)	24	2	6	16	29	88	9

Loddiswell Athletic Reserves before their Ivor Andrews Cup final.
Back Row: (L-R) Tim Rogers, Chris Guard, Andy Tucker, Mark Stacey, Phil George, Gareth Harrison, Kevin Webber, Kristian Brown, Steve Inch. **Front Row:** Mike Williams, Mark Edmonds, Dave Evans, Andy Bullen, James Ellis, Rob Webber, Andy Guard (Manager).

DORSET PREMIER LEAGUE

SPONSORED BY: ELITE TEAMWEAR LTD

Founded: 1957

President: Jack Cruickshank Chairman: Alan Burt
Secretary: Geoff Theobald, 41 South Road, Corfe Mullen
Wimborne, Dorset BH21 3HZ Tel: 01202 697994

FINAL LEAGUE TABLE 2003-04

		P	W	D	L	F	A	Pts
1.	Hamworthy United	32	26	3	3	89	25	81
2.	Dorchester Town Reserves	32	23	7	2	76	17	76
3.	Hamworthy Recreation	32	20	4	8	81	45	64
4.	Gillingham Town	32	17	8	7	51	31	59
5.	Sherborne Town	32	15	7	10	59	38	52
6.	Holt United	32	15	6	11	65	44	51
7.	Westland Sports	32	14	9	9	49	37	51
8.	Poole Borough	32	15	5	12	59	43	50
9.	Bournemouth Sports	32	11	9	12	54	47	42
10.	Dorchester United	32	11	6	15	57	68	39
11.	Shaftesbury (-3pts)	32	10	9	13	55	63	36
12.	Blandford United	32	10	6	16	49	77	36
13.	Cobham Sports	32	10	5	17	45	84	35
14.	Wareham Rangers	32	9	6	17	52	68	33
15.	Bridport Reserves	32	9	5	18	38	68	32
16.	Sturminster Newton United	32	3	7	22	31	73	16
17.	Stourpaine	32	2	2	28	37	119	8

2003-04	1	2	3	4	5	6	7	8	9	10	11	12	13	14	15	16	17
1 Blandford United		1-1	1-1	6-0	1-2	2-2	1-1	4-3	0-5	2-3	1-0	2-3	3-5	3-1	1-0	1-3	2-0
2 Bournemouth Sports	3-0		4-1	1-3	1-1	1-1	3-0	0-2	0-1	3-0	2-2	8-0	0-0	3-1	1-1	2-0	0-6
3 Bridport Reserves	2-1	0-3		3-1	0-3	2-0	0-0	0-2	2-4	2-0	2-4	1-2	1-0	2-0	1-1	1-0	0-2
4 Cobham Sports	1-0	2-4	2-2		0-2	1-0	3-3	1-4	1-3	2-0	2-2	2-3	0-4	1-1	3-3	1-8	3-2
5 Dorchester Town Reserves	4-1	0-0	3-1	5-0		1-0	2-1	2-2	0-1	0-1	1-0	7-1	6-0	5-1	4-0	3-0	0-0
6 Dorchester United	5-0	2-5	3-0	3-2	0-4		0-0	1-4	0-3	3-1	1-0	1-2	1-4	5-3	4-1	4-1	3-4
7 Gillingham Town	2-1	1-0	2-0	2-3	1-1	3-2		3-1	2-2	1-0	4-1	4-2	3-0	4-2	2-0	2-0	1-0
8 Hamworthy Recreation	3-1	3-2	2-0	1-2	1-2	6-1	1-3		3-1	3-2	2-0	2-2	3-0	6-1	1-0	2-3	0-0
9 Hamworthy United	3-0	3-1	8-0	7-0	0-0	6-2	1-0	2-2		2-1	3-2	3-1	1-0	4-1	4-0	2-1	4-0
10 Holt United	10-1	4-0	4-2	2-1	0-2	2-2	1-0	3-2	0-1		1-1	1-1	0-4	6-2	3-1	2-0	2-0
11 Poole Borough	2-4	5-0	2-1	2-1	0-2	0-1	1-0	0-1	2-1	3-1		3-3	2-0	6-0	4-1	5-1	2-2
12 Shaftesbury	0-2	0-2	1-2	3-0	1-2	1-1	0-0	2-3	0-4	0-0	1-2		2-2	5-1	7-4	6-0	0-2
13 Sherborne Town	3-3	1-0	3-1	4-1	0-0	3-0	0-2	2-0	1-2	1-2	0-1	0-0		5-1	2-0	1-0	1-1
14 Stourpaine	0-1	3-2	2-5	0-2	0-3	2-5	1-3	0-5	1-4	0-5	0-3	0-2	0-6		4-0	1-4	3-3
15 Sturminster Newton United	1-2	1-1	2-1	0-1	1-2	2-3	0-1	2-3	0-2	0-6	1-0	0-0	1-1	4-1		1-3	0-0
16 Wareham Rangers	7-0	1-1	1-1	3-1	1-4	1-1	0-0	1-4	1-2	2-2	0-2	0-3	1-5	4-2	4-3		0-0
17 Westland Sports	1-1	1-0	5-1	1-2	1-3	1-0	2-0	2-4	1-0	0-0	3-0	2-1	0-1	3-2	1-0	3-1	

LEAGUE CUP

FIRST ROUND

Hamworthy United	v	Sherborne Town	3-0

SECOND ROUND

Bournemouth Sports	v	Stourpaine	3-2
Dorchester Town Res.	v	Shaftesbury	10-1
Dorchester United	v	Cobham Sports	3-5*
Gillingham Town	v	Blandford United	2-0
Hamworthy Recreation	v	Sturminster Newton United	4-1
Hamworthy United	v	Wareham Rangers	5-1
Holt United	v	Bridport Res.	3-1*
Poole Borough	v	Westland Sports	0-2

QUARTER-FINALS

Bournemouth Sports	v	Westland Sports	1-0
Cobham Sports	v	Hamworthy United	1-0
Gillingham Town	v	Holt United	6-1
Hamworthy Recreation	v	Dorchester Town Res.	2-5

SEMI-FINALS

Dorchester Town Res.	v	Bournemouth Sports	7-3
Gillingham Town	v	Cobham Sports	2-2*, 3-2r

THE FINAL (15th May at Hamworthy United)

Dorchester Town Res.	v	Gillingham Town	1-0

LEAGUE CONSTITUTION 2004-05

BLANDFORD UNITED
Chairman: M.Westwood
Secretary: Mrs Catherine Johnson, 37 Damory Street, Blandford Forum, Dorset DT117EU (01258 455899)
Ground: Recreation Ground, Park Road, Blandford Forum, Dorset. (HQ Tel: 01258456374)
Cover: No Clubhouse: No Programme: Yes
Colours: All Royal Blue Change colours: Red/black/green

BOURNEMOUTH SPORTS CLUB
Chairman: I.Hansford
Secretary: Mrs June Johnson,19 Lawns Road, Wimborne BH21 2JP Tel: 01202 887195
Ground: Chapel Gate, East Parley, Christchurch, Dorset BH23 6BD Tel: 01202 581933
Cover: No Clubhouse: Yes Programme: Yes
Colours: Gold/black/gold Change colours: All blue

BRIDPORT Reserves
Chairman: David Fowler Secretary: Keith Morgan, 95 Orchard Cres., Bridport DT6 5HA 01308 456142(H) 01308 424269(W)
Ground: The Beehive, St Mary's Field, Bridport, Dorset 01308 423834
Colours: Red & black/black/red & black Change colours:All blue.

COBHAM SPORTS (formerly Flight Refuelling)
Chairman: A Miles
Secretary: Harry W Doyle, 27 Fairview Crescent, Broadstone, Poole BH18 9AL Tel: 01202 698393 (H) 07718 896211 (M)
Ground: Merley Park, Merley, Wimborne, Dorset (01202 885773)
Cover: No Clubhouse: Yes Programme: Yes
Colours:Sky blue/navy blue/navyblue. Change colours: All red

CRANBORNE
Ground: Recreation Ground, Penny's Lane, Cranborne, Dorset

DORCHESTER TOWN Reserves
Chairman: C E Clarke
Secretary: David Martin, 21 Diggory Crescent, Dorchester DT1 2SP Tel: 01305 262345 (H) 07971 172795 (M)
Ground: The Avenue Stadium, Dorchester. (01305 262451)
Cover: Yes Floodlights: Yes Clubhouse: Yes Programme: Yes
Colours: Black & white stripes/black/black Change: All red.

DORCHESTER UNITED
Ground: Sandringham Sports Centre, Armada Way, Dorchester.
Previous Leagues: Dorset League

GILLINGHAM TOWN
Chairman: E Murphy Secretary: David J Ayles, 37 Sylvan Way, Bay Road, Gillingham SP8 4EQ (01747822065)
Ground: Hardings Lane, Gillingham (01747 823673)
Cover: Yes Programme: Yes Clubhouse: Yes
Colours: Tangerine/black/tangerine
Change colours: Yellow & green/green/green

HAMWORTHY RECREATION
Chairman: M Robson Secretary: Ray Willis, 52 Heckford Road, Poole BH15 2LY (01202 773 290)
Ground: Hamworthy Rec. Club, Magna Rd, Canford Magna, Wimborne, Dorset BH21 3AE(01202 881922)
Cover: No Clubhouse: Yes Programme: No
Colours: All green Change colours: Blue & White stripes/blue/blue.

HOLT UNITED
Ground: Gaunts Common, Holt, Wimborne, Dorset. Tel: 01258 840379
Previous League: Dorset County League

POOLE BOROUGH
Ground: Turlin Moor Recretaion Ground, Blandford Moor, Hamworthy, Poole, Dorset. Club Office: 01202 674973
Previous League: Dorset County Lge.

SHERBORNE TOWN
Chairman: F Henderson
Secretary: Mike Mock, 67 Yew TRe Close, Yeovil. BA20 2PB Tel: 01935 426219 (H) 01935 703934 (W)
Ground: Raleigh Grove, The Terrace Playing Fields, Sherborne Tel: 01935 816110
Cover: Yes Clubhouse: Yes Programme: Yes
Colours: Yellow/black/yellow Change: Black & white/ white/ black.

STOURPAINE
Chairman: C.Hardiman Secretary: Rob Turner, 35 Hod View, Stourpaine, Blandford DT11 8TN Tel : 01258 451691
Ground: Dick Draper Memorial Fields, Stourpaine, Blandford Forum
Previous league: Dorset County League
Colours: Navy blue & Yellow/navy blue/ yellow & navy blue.
Change Colours: Red & white stripes/red & white/red & white

STURMINSTER NEWTON UNITED

Chairman: A.Stockley Secretary: Richard Frear 44 Green Close, Sturminster Newton DT10 1BL (01258473036)

Ground: Barnetts Field, Honeymead Lane, Sturminster Newton, Dorset. (01258471406)

Cover: Yes Clubhouse: No Programme: Yes

Colours:Red & Black stripes /red/red

Change colours:Blue & Black stripes/blue/blue.

SWANAGE TOWN & HESTON

Ground: Day's Park, off De Moulham Road, Swanage, Dorset

Tel: 01929 424673

WAREHAM RANGERS

Chairman: G.Hawkes Secretary: Mrs Carol White, 18 Folly Lane, Wareham, Dorset BH20 4HH (01929551765)

Ground: Purbeck Sports Centre,Worgret Rd, Wareham, Dorset

Cover: No Clubhouse: No Programme: Yes

Colours: Amber & black/black/black

Change colours: Navy & light blue/ navy/ light blue

WESTLAND SPORTS

Chairman: A. Fisher

Secretary: Dean Vincent, 8 Whitemead, Abbey Manor Park, Yeovil. BA21 3RX Tel: 01935 479971 (H) 01935 705381 (W)

Ground: Westland Sports Ground, Westbourne Close, Yeovil

Tel: 01935 703810

Cover: No Clubhouse: No Programme: Yes

Colours: Red & Black/Black/Black C hange colours: All White

WEYMOUTH SPORTS

Chairman: M. Richards

Secretary: Alan Burt, 32 Preston Road, Weymouth, DT3 6PZ

Tel: 01305 833256 (H) 01305 773536 (W)

Ground: Weymouth College, Cranford Ave., Weymouth, Dorset

Tel: 01305 208859/208860

Colours: Blue & yellow stripes/yellow/blue. Change: Red/black/red

Prev. Lge: Dorset (champs 1993)

DORSET COUNTY LEAGUE

SENIOR DIVISION	P	W	D	L	F	A	Pts
Cranborne	26	18	4	4	83	22	58
Chickerell United	26	18	3	5	79	27	57
Swanage Town & Herston	26	16	5	5	71	33	53
Allendale	26	15	5	6	66	30	50
Wimborne Town Res.	26	15	4	7	62	32	49
Portland United Res.	26	12	4	10	60	44	40
Hamworthy United Res.	26	11	7	8	45	49	40
Gillingham Town Res.	26	10	2	14	45	52	32
Witchampton United	26	8	8	10	43	55	32
Shaftesbury Res.	26	8	6	12	36	55	30
Sturminster Marshall	26	8	5	13	51	88	29
Weymouth United	26	7	4	15	52	76	25
Cobham Sports Res.	26	3	4	19	25	81	13
Blandford United Res.	26	1	3	22	28	102	6

DIVISION ONE	P	W	D	L	F	A	Pts
Barwick & Stoford (-1pt)	22	17	2	3	80	25	52
Easton United	22	15	2	5	81	23	47
Moreton	22	14	3	5	58	29	45
Corfe Mullen United	22	12	4	6	53	45	40
Royal Oak Cougars	22	11	4	7	54	30	37
Marina Sports	22	11	1	10	42	49	34
Bishop's Caundle	22	10	3	9	50	48	33
Allendale Res.	22	9	3	10	56	49	30
Wareham Rangers Res.	22	8	4	10	44	72	28
Stalbridge	22	5	4	13	38	58	19
Okeford United	22	3	2	17	42	98	11
Piddletrenthide United	22	1	0	21	23	95	3

NB - Weymouth Post Office withdrew during the season. Their results are expunged from the league table.

ESSEX & SUFFOLK BORDER LEAGUE

SPONSORED BY: KENT BLAXHILL

FINAL LEAGUE TABLE 2003-04

PREMIER DIVISION	P	W	D	L	F	A	Pts
1. Little Oakley	30	21	6	3	70	34	69
2. Mistley United	30	18	9	3	65	24	63
3. Gas Recreation	30	17	8	5	85	37	59
4. West Bergholt	30	17	6	7	64	45	57
5. Sudbury Athletic	30	15	4	11	62	46	49
6. Stowmarket Town Reserves (+3pts)	30	13	4	13	48	44	46
7. AFC Sudbury Reserves	30	11	9	10	70	57	42
8. Stanway Rovers Reserves	30	12	5	13	58	61	41
9. Harwich & Parkeston Reserves	30	12	3	15	49	69	39
10. Weeley Athletic	30	11	4	15	45	52	37
11. Rowhedge	30	10	6	14	52	55	36
12. Alresford Colne Rangers	30	9	6	15	47	76	33
13. Clacton Town Reserves (-3pts)	30	9	6	15	39	56	30
14. St Osyth	30	7	5	18	50	78	26
15. Kelvedon Social	30	6	8	16	44	78	26
16. Earls Colne	30	6	3	21	35	71	21

RESULTS GRID 03-04	1	2	3	4	5	6	7	8	9	10	11	12	13	14	15	16
1 AFC Sudbury Reserves		4-3	1-1	2-2	3-3	0-1	1-1	1-1	1-3	4-1	3-2	2-3	3-1	2-2	4-0	2-2
2 Alresford Colne Rangers	1-9		3-2	4-1	1-6	3-3	4-1	0-4	0-3	3-1	3-1	0-2	0-4	0-4	1-2	2-2
3 Clacton Town Reserves	1-4	2-0		1-0	1-1	0-1	1-1	0-3	0-2	1-1	2-6	3-0	2-2	1-3	0-1	1-3
4 Earls Colne	2-0	0-2	2-2		0-2	0-3	4-2	1-2	0-1	1-2	1-1	4-5	1-4	2-0	0-1	0-2
5 Gas Recreation	3-3	6-0	3-2	3-1		2-0	7-1	5-1	1-0	1-2	5-1	1-1	3-1	1-2	3-1	1-3
6 Harwich & Parkeston Reserves	5-2	2-1	0-1	1-4	2-1		2-2	0-3	0-5	1-4	3-5	4-3	2-0	3-2	1-0	2-5
7 Kelvedon Social	0-3	2-1	2-3	1-2	1-5	2-1		1-4	3-3	2-6	1-1	1-4	3-1	1-2	1-1	2-5
8 Little Oakley	4-0	3-0	2-1	1-2	2-2	2-2	2-1		1-1	2-1	3-1	3-2	1-0	4-3	1-0	2-0
9 Mistley United	2-1	0-0	4-1	6-1	0-0	2-0	1-1	3-3		4-0	1-3	2-0	2-1	0-0	0-1	3-1
10 Rowhedge	0-1	2-2	1-2	2-1	1-1	1-3	5-0	0-3	1-3		1-4	1-3	0-2	3-0	3-1	4-0
11 St Osyth	1-5	0-4	2-1	5-2	1-1	4-1	2-4	1-5	0-5	0-3		0-2	1-1	2-6	1-1	1-3
12 Stanway Rovers Reserves	2-2	1-3	0-3	2-0	0-1	1-5	1-4	2-1	1-1	3-3	1-0		7-2	4-0	2-1	3-3
13 Stowmarket Town Reserves	3-1	1-1	0-1	1-0	2-1	3-0	0-0	1-2	1-2	3-1	2-1	4-0		2-0	1-0	0-1
14 Sudbury Athletic	3-2	4-0	5-0	3-0	2-4	7-1	1-2	1-1	0-2	2-0	3-1	2-1	2-1		2-0	1-2
15 Weeley Athletic	3-1	3-3	1-3	4-1	2-7	3-0	3-1	1-2	0-2	1-1	2-1	4-2	1-2	4-0		1-3
16 West Bergholt	1-3	1-2	2-0	6-0	0-5	1-0	2-0	1-2	2-2	1-1	3-1	1-0	5-2	0-0	3-2	

LEAGUE CUP

PRELIMINARY ROUND

Alresford Colne Rangers	v	Tiptree Heath	2-1
Bradfield	v	St Osyth	3-0
Bures United	v	Clacton Town Reserves	1-3
Great Bentley	v	Kelvedon Social	2-0
Halstead Town Res.	v	Lawford Lads	0-3
Harwich & Parkeston Res.	v	Mersea Island	3-0
Long Melford Res. (w/o)	v	Ipswich Wanderers Res.	
Mistley United	v	Severalls Athletic	0-1
Needham Market Res.	v	Woodbridge Town Res.	5-0
Rowhedge	v	Felixstowe & Walton Utd Res.	5-1
St Johns (Clacton)	v	Dedham Old Boys	1-2
Stanway Rovers Res.	v	Sudbury Athletic	0-2
Stowmarket Town Res.	v	Gas Recreation	4-2
Weeley Athletic	v	Walton Town	5-1
Whitton United Res.	v	Earls Colne	2-1
Wivenhoe & University Town	v	Hatfield Peverel	3-4

FIRST ROUND

AFC Sudbury Res.	v	West Bergholt	2-0
Boxted Lodgers	v	Glemsford & Cavendish United	4-0
Clacton Town Res.	v	Hatfield Peverel	1-1*,3-5p
Coggeshall Town	v	Foxash Social	4-0
Cornard United Res.	v	Lawford Lads	1-3
Dedham Old Boys	v	Severalls Athletic	5-4
Hadleigh United Res.	v	Brightlingsea United	1-2
Hedlinghams United	v	Tiptree United Res.	0-5
Little Oakley	v	Bury Town Res.	0-2
Long Melford Res.	v	Alresford Colne Rangers	2-1

first round continued...

Rowhedge	v	Harwich & Parkeston Res.	1-2
Stowmarket Town Res.	v	Gas Recreation	4-2
Sudbury Athletic	v	Needham Market Res.	1-2
Weeley Athletic	v	Great Bentley	3-2
Whitton United Res.	v	Bradfield Rovers	0-3
Witham Town Res.	v	Haverhill Rovers Res.	3-1

SECOND ROUND

AFC Sudbury Res.	v	Brightlingsea United	1-0
Boxted Lodgers	v	Witham Town Res.	2-1
Bradfield Rovers	v	Harwich & Parkeston Res.	1-3
Bury Town Res.	v	Stowmarket Town Res.	5-4
Coggesgall Town	v	Tiptree United Res.	1-2
Hatfield Peverel	v	Dedham Old Boys	1-2
Lawford Lads	v	Weeley Athletic	1-0
Long Melford Res.	v	Needham Market Res.	3-2

QUARTER-FINALS

AFC Sudbury Res.	v	Tiptree United Res.	3-0
Bury Town Res.	v	Boxted Lodgers	9-1
Lawford Lads	v	Dedham Old Boys	0-1
Long Melford Res.	v	Harwich & Parkeston Res.	4-2

SEMI-FINALS

Bury Town Res.	v	Dedham Old Boys	2-1
Long Melford Res.	v	AFC Sudbury Res.	2-3

THE FINAL (11th May at Hadleigh United)

AFC Sudbury Res.	v	Bury Town Res.	1-3

LEAGUE CONSTITUTION 2004-05

AFC SUDBURY RESERVES
Kingsmarsh Stadium, Brundon Lane, Sudbury, Suffolk
Tel: 01787 376213

ALRESFORD COLNE RANGERS
Ford Lane, Alresford, Essex
Tel: 07796 036467

BURY TOWN RESERVES
Ram Meadow, Cotton Lane, Bury St Edmonds, Suffolk
Tel: 01284 754721

CLACTON TOWN RESERVES
Rush Green Bowl, Rush Green Road, Clacton-on-Sea, Essex
Tel: 01255 432590

GAS RECREATION
Bromley Road, Colchester, Essex
Tel: 01206 860383

HARWICH & PARKESTON RESERVES
Royal Oak, Main Road, Dovercourt, Harwich, Essex
Tel: 01255 503649

LITTLE OAKLEY
War Memorial Club Ground, Little Oakley, Essex
Tel: 01255 880370

MISTLEY UNITED
Parish Recreation Ground, Shrubland Road, Mistley, Essex
Tel: 01206 393350

ROWHEDGE
Rectory Road, Rowhedge, Essex
Tel: 01206 728022

ST OSYTH
Cowley Park, Mill Street, St Osyth, Clacton-on-Sea, Essex

STANWAY ROVERS RESERVES
Hawthorns, New Farm Road, Stanway, Colchester, Essex
Tel: 01206 578187

STOWMARKET TOWN RESERVES
Greens Meadow, Bury Road, Stowmarket, Suffolk
Tel: 01449 612533

SUDBURY ATHLETIC
Lucas Social Club, Alexandra Road, Sudbury, Suffolk
Tel: 01787 881143

TIPTREE UNITED RESERVES
Chapel Road, Tiptree, near Colchester, Essex
01621 815213

WEELEY ATHLETIC
Weeley Playing Fields, Clacton Road, Weeley, Clacton-on-Sea, Essex

WEST BERGHOLT
Lorkin Daniel Field, Lexden Road, West Bergholt, Colchester, Essex
Tel: 01206 241525

GLOUCESTERSHIRE COUNTY LEAGUE

Chairman: A C Barrett
Hon. Secretary: D J Herbert, 8 Fernhurst Road, St George, Bristol BS5 7TQ Tel: 0117 951 7696

FINAL LEAGUE TABLE 2003-04

		P	W	D	L	F	A	Pts
1.	Almondsbury	34	20	10	4	63	32	70
2.	Tytherington Rocks	34	20	9	5	81	47	69
3.	Patchway Town (-3pts)	34	19	9	6	63	38	63
4.	Taverners	34	17	9	8	53	35	60
5.	Highridge United	34	15	10	9	64	45	55
6.	AXA	34	13	11	10	68	67	50
7.	Thornbury Town	34	13	10	11	51	42	49
8.	Kings Stanley	34	12	13	9	61	53	49
9.	Roman Glass St George	34	12	12	10	71	63	48
10.	Henbury Old Boys	34	12	7	15	42	52	43
11.	Hardwicke	34	10	11	13	50	64	41
12.	Ellwood	34	10	10	14	54	64	40
13.	Totterdown Port of Bristol (-3pts) 34	10	11	13	58	52	38	
14.	Old Georgians	34	8	11	15	64	70	35
15.	Wotton Rovers	34	8	10	16	44	57	34
16.	Pucklechurch Sports	34	8	9	17	44	67	33
17.	DRG Stapleton (-3pts)	34	7	5	22	32	75	23
18.	Viney St Swithins	34	4	9	21	34	74	21

2003-04	1	2	3	4	5	6	7	8	9	10	11	12	13	14	15	16	17	18
1 AXA		2-2	3-3	4-2	2-3	4-2	1-1	4-4	6-3	1-4	2-0	3-2	0-3	1-1	1-4	2-5	1-0	1-1
2 Almondsbury	1-1		4-1	2-2	4-0	2-0	0-3	5-0	0-0	0-2	1-1	0-0	3-2	3-0	1-0	1-1	2-1	2-0
3 DRG Stapleton	1-2	1-2		1-0	0-1	1-2	0-2	4-2	0-1	0-1	1-3	0-7	0-2	1-8	0-4	0-1	2-2	3-1
4 Ellwood	2-3	1-0	3-2		4-2	2-0	1-4	0-1	3-3	2-3	1-1	2-2	2-1	2-5	3-3	1-1	0-0	2-1
5 Hardwicke	2-2	1-1	2-0	2-0		1-1	2-0	1-1	1-3	2-6	5-1	2-2	0-0	2-2	3-2	0-3	0-1	2-1
6 Henbury Old Boys	1-0	0-1	2-1	2-1	2-2		0-2	2-1	0-0	2-3	1-0	1-2	1-1	2-0	4-1	0-2	3-0	2-0
7 Highridge United	3-0	3-2	4-0	1-3	1-0	4-1		1-1	1-1	2-2	3-0	1-3	0-1	0-2	2-2	2-4	4-1	1-1
8 Kings Stanley	0-3	1-3	0-1	3-2	1-1	0-0	1-1		3-1	4-0	5-1	3-1	1-0	3-1	4-0	2-2	3-1	0-0
9 Old Georgians	2-5	1-2	1-2	3-0	1-0	7-0	2-3	1-5		1-2	1-2	2-2	6-1	1-1	1-1	0-3	2-2	6-0
10 Patchway Town	1-1	1-1	3-0	1-1	3-0	2-0	0-2	2-2	3-1		2-1	4-1	0-1	1-1	3-0	1-1	2-0	2-1
11 Pucklechurch Sports	1-2	0-1	0-0	1-1	2-3	0-4	2-1	3-1	2-2	0-1		3-3	0-2	1-1	2-1	2-4	1-0	0-3
12 Roman Glass St George	1-2	3-3	1-2	2-4	3-3	1-0	4-3	5-2	2-2	2-1	2-2		1-0	0-2	2-0	1-2	4-0	2-1
13 Taverners	3-2	0-2	0-0	1-1	3-0	0-0	2-1	2-1	4-2	3-0	1-3	4-2		2-0	0-0	2-2	1-2	3-0
14 Thornbury Town	1-1	1-2	3-1	0-1	2-1	1-0	0-0	1-1	0-0	0-0	2-1	0-1	1-2		2-0	2-1	6-1	1-3
15 Totterdown Port of Bristol	2-2	1-2	0-0	3-0	3-1	4-2	1-1	1-1	3-0	1-2	3-1	2-2	0-1	5-1		2-3	2-0	0-0
16 Tytherington Rocks	4-1	1-2	5-1	2-0	5-2	3-3	2-3	2-2	1-3	3-2	3-5	4-2	0-0	1-0	2-1		2-0	4-1
17 Viney St Swithins	1-3	0-4	0-3	2-4	1-1	1-2	2-2	0-1	7-3	0-0	1-1	1-1	1-4	1-2	0-3	0-1		2-1
18 Wotton Rovers	1-0	1-2	3-0	2-1	1-2	2-0	1-2	1-1	3-1	1-3	3-1	2-2	1-1	0-1	3-3	1-1	3-3	

LEAGUE CUP

PRELIMINARY ROUND

Patchway Town	v	Kings Stanley	2-1
Tytherington Rocks	v	Hardwicke	4-1

FIRST ROUND

Ellwood	v	Old Georgians	1-1*,3-4p
Henbury Old Boys	v	Almondsbury	0-4
Highridge United	v	Roman Glass St George	1-0
Patchway Town	v	Totterdown PoB	2-2*,4-2p
Pucklechurch Sports	v	DRG Stapleton	0-2
Thornbury Town	v	Taverners	1-2
Viney St Swithins	v	AXA	0-7
Wotton	v	Tytherington	0-2

QUARTER-FINALS

Almondsbury	v	Taverners	0-1
Old Georgians	v	DRG Stapleton	1-4
Patchway Town	v	AXA	2-0
Tytherington Rocks	v	Highridge United	1-1*,6-5p

SEMI-FINALS

DRG Stapleton (at Yate Town)	v	Tytherington Rocks	0-4
Taverners (at Yate Town)	v	Patchway Town	2-2*,3-5p

THE FINAL (24th March at Yate Town)

Tytherington Rocks	v	Patchway	1-1*,1-3p

LEAGUE CONSTITUTION 2004-05

AXA
Cribbs Causeway, Bristol, Gloucestershire
Tel: 0117 950 2303

DRG STAPLETON
Frenchay Park Road, Frenchay, Bristol, Gloucestershire

ELLWOOD
Bromley Road, Ellwood, Coleford, Gloucestershire
Tel: 01594 832927

HARDWICKE
Green Lane, Hardwicke, Gloucestershire
Tel: 01452 720587

HENBURY OLD BOYS
Lorain Walk, Henbury, Bristol, Gloucestershire
Tel: 0117 959 0475

HIGHRIDGE UNITED
Lakemead Grove, Highridge, Bristol, Gloucestershire
Tel: 0117 978 4878

KINGS STANLEY
Marling Close, Kings Stanley, Gloucestershire
Tel: 01453 828975

OLD GEORGIANS
St George's School PF, Johnsons Lane, Whitehall, Bristol, Gloucestershire
Tel: 0117 951 6888

PATCHWAY TOWN
Scott Park, Coniston Road, Patchway, Bristol, Gloucestershire
Tel: 0117 949 3952

PUCKLECHURCH SPORTS
Pucklechurch Recreation Ground, Pucklechurch, Bristol, Gloucestershire
Tel: 0117 937 2102

ROMAN GLASS ST GEORGE
Tel: Bell Hill, Whiteway Road, St George, Bristol, Gloucestershire

SEA MILLS PARK
The Portway, Bristol, Gloucestershire

TAVERNERS
Highwood School, Spring Hill, Nailsworth, Gloucestershire

THORNBURY TOWN
Mundy Playing Fields, Kington Lane, Thornbury, Gloucestershire

TOTTERDOWN PORT OF BRISTOL
City & Port of Bristol SC, Nibley Road, Shirehampton, Bristol
Tel: 0117 982 3927

VINEY ST SWITHINS
Viney Sports & Social Club, Viney Hill, Lydney, Gloucestershire
Tel: 01594 510658

WOTTON ROVERS
Synwell Playing Fields, Synwell Lane, Wotton-under-Edge, Gloucestershire
Tel: 01453 842929

YATE TOWN RESERVES
Lodge Road, Yate, Bristol, Gloucestershire
Tel: 01454 228103

KENT COUNTY LEAGUE

SPONSORED BY: BRITISH ENERGY

Founded: 1922

President: W C Manklow Chairman: C T C Windiate
General Secretary: B H Bundock
Press Secretary: G Jenkins
Kings View, Shottenden Lane, Molash, Canterbury, Kent CT4 8EZ
Tel: 01233 740143 Email: geoff@kcfl2000.freeserve.co.uk

FINAL LEAGUE TABLE 2003-04

PREMIER DIVISION	P	W	D	L	F	A	Pts
1. Crockenhill	26	19	4	3	58	24	61
2. Old Roan	26	19	2	5	67	30	59
3. Lydd Town	26	17	5	4	61	27	56
4. Cray Valley PM	26	16	5	5	67	27	53
5. Stansfeld O & BC	26	11	9	6	54	32	42
6. Sheerness East	26	10	11	5	43	24	41
7. Greenways	26	10	6	10	38	43	36
8. Bearsted	26	11	2	13	36	41	35
9. Tenterden Town	26	10	3	13	51	67	33
10. Beauwater	26	8	4	14	31	53	28
11. Snodland	26	8	2	16	47	76	26
12. Milton Athletic	26	5	5	16	30	45	20
13. New Romney	26	5	1	20	30	73	16
14. Kennington	26	1	5	20	29	80	8

PREMIER DIVISION 03-04	1	2	3	4	5	6	7	8	9	10	11	12	13	14
1 Bearsted		1-0	2-1	1-2	2-0	2-2	0-2	1-5	3-0	0-2	1-0	3-2	1-2	5-2
2 Beauwater	4-1		0-3	0-2	2-1	4-1	0-1	1-0	3-1	1-2	0-0	2-3	0-3	1-1
3 Cray Valley Paper Mills	1-0	7-1		4-1	1-1	7-0	2-2	3-1	4-1	2-0	0-3	5-1	0-0	4-1
4 Crockenhill	1-0	1-0	1-1		7-0	3-2	3-1	2-0	2-1	2-0	2-0	3-1	1-1	4-1
5 Greenways	1-3	2-0	1-0	1-1		3-1	0-1	2-1	4-1	0-2	2-2	5-0	1-1	0-3
6 Kennington	1-2	2-2	2-1	1-2	1-2		0-5	0-2	0-2	1-3	1-4	2-4	2-2	2-5
7 Lydd Town	5-1	6-1	0-1	2-1	1-1	3-1		0-0	1-1	3-1	0-2	8-2	3-2	4-3
8 Milton Athletic	0-2	1-3	1-3	0-1	1-2	2-2	0-1		3-0	2-3	0-1	2-0	1-1	0-1
9 New Romney	2-1	1-2	1-6	0-3	1-3	3-2	1-2	1-4		0-2	0-4	2-1	0-4	2-3
10 Old Roan	3-1	2-1	2-3	3-1	3-0	6-1	2-1	2-0	4-1		4-1	4-1	2-1	6-1
11 Sheerness East	0-0	2-3	2-2	1-1	1-1	0-0	1-2	4-0	2-1	1-1		2-1	1-1	1-0
12 Snodland	0-3	5-0	0-4	1-4	2-1	4-0	1-1	1-1	2-4	2-1	1-8		3-2	5-2
13 Stansfeld Oxford & Bermondsey Club	2-0	4-0	2-0	1-2	4-2	3-0	0-3	2-2	4-1	1-1	0-0	3-2		6-0
14 Tenterden Town	1-0	0-0	1-2	1-5	1-2	4-2	0-3	6-1	4-2	2-6	0-0	4-2	4-2	

DIVISION ONE WEST

	P	W	D	L	F	A	Pts
1 Lewisham Borough	22	15	4	3	40	17	49
2 Bly Spartans	22	12	4	6	54	40	40
3 Halls	22	11	6	5	36	28	39
4 Holmesdale	22	10	7	5	35	17	37
5 Oakwood	22	10	6	6	39	26	36
6 Pembury	22	9	4	9	26	28	31
7 Eynsford	22	6	7	9	36	34	25
8 APM Mears	22	6	6	10	27	42	24
9 Wickham Park (-3pts)	22	7	5	10	36	40	23
10 Fleetdown United	22	6	5	11	19	31	23
11 Belvedere	22	5	6	11	22	38	21
12 Bromleians Sports	22	4	2	16	29	58	14

DIVISION ONE EAST

	P	W	D	L	F	A	Pts
1 Bromley Green	24	19	3	2	86	21	60
2 Norton Sports	24	17	2	5	63	29	53
3 Tyler Hill	24	11	5	8	43	35	38
4 Snowdown C. W.	24	11	3	10	39	63	36
5 Woodstock Park	24	11	2	11	40	46	35
6 Bliby (-1 pt)	24	9	3	12	31	36	29
7 University of Kent	24	9	0	15	38	52	27
8 St Margarets	24	4	5	15	28	56	17
9 Betteshanger W'fare	24	2	7	15	27	57	13

INTER-REGIONAL CHALLENGE CUP

FIRST ROUND EAST

Bliby	v	University of Kent	0-2
Kennington	v	Tyler Hill	1-2
Milton Athletic	v	Bromley Green	0-3
Norton Sports	v	Snowdown Colliery Welfare	4-3
Sheerness East	v	Tenterden Town	3-0
St Margarets	v	New Romney	0-1
Woodstock Park	v	Betteshanger Welfare	3-0

FIRST ROUND WEST

Eynsford	v	Pembury	1-0
Greenways	v	Bearsted	0-2
Snodland	v	Oakwood	0-3
Stansfeld O & B Club	v	Belvedere	0-2

SECOND ROUND EAST

Bromley Green	v	University of Kent	1-2
Lydd Town	v	Sheerness East	1-2
New Romney (w/o)	v	Tyler Hill	
Woodstock Park	v	Norton Sports	0-2

SECOND ROUND WEST

APM Mears	v	Holmesdale	0-2
Bearsted	v	Eynsford	7-0
Beauwater	v	Wickham Park	3-1
Crockenhill	v	Old Roan	1-0
Fleetdown United	v	Cray Valley PM	2-6
Halls	v	Bly Spartans	3-0
Lewisham Borough	v	Bromleians	2-1
Oakwood	v	Belvedere	1-2

THIRD ROUND WEST

Beauwater	v	Cray Valley	1-2*
Belvedere	v	Crockenhill	3-4*
Halls	v	Holmesdale	0-2
Lewisham Borough	v	Bearsted	5-1

QUARTER-FINALS

Crockenhill	v	Cray Valley PM	2-4*
Holmesdale	v	New Romney	0-1
Norton	v	University	1-4
Sheerness East	v	Lewisham Borough	1-0

SEMI-FINALS

Cray Valley PM	v	New Romney	7-4
University of Kent	v	Sheerness East	4-4*,5-4p

THE FINAL (6th May at Chatham Town)

Cray ValleyPM	v	University of Kent	4-2

PREMIER LEAGUE CONSTITUTION 2004-05

BEARSTED
Founded: 1895
Secretary: Mrs Liz Owen, 21 Copsewood Way, Bearsted, Maidstone, Kent ME15 8PL(01622 737709)
Ground: Honey Lane, Otham, Maidstone. (0411 128034)
Colours: White/blue/blue
Change Colours: Yellow/blue/blue

BEAUWATER
Founded: 1927
Secretary: Robert Taylor, 24 Sun Lane, Gravesend, Kent DA12 5HG (01474 332208)
Ground: Beauwater Leisure Club, Nelson Road, Northfleet (01474 359222)
Colours: Blue/blue/white
Change Colours: Red/Navy/Red

BROMLEY GREEN
Founded: 1930
Secretary: Stanley Donald,12 Oast Meadow ,Willesborough, Ashford,Kent TN24 0AS Tel No: 01233 627916
Ground: The Swan Centre, Newtown Road, South Willesborough, Ashford, Kent Tel: 01233 645982
Colours: All Green & blue.
Change Colours: White/green/green

CRAY VALLEY PAPERMILLS
Founded: 1981
Secretary: Steve Chapman, 97 Yorkland Ave., Welling DA16 2LG Tel: 020 8304 5387 (H) 01293 802208 (B)
Ground: Badgers Sports Ground, Middle Park Ave., London SE9 Tel: 020 8850 4273
Colours: Green/black/black
Change colours: Blue & white/white/green

CROCKENHILL
Founded: 1946
Secretary: Mike Floate, Newlands Cottages, 71 Stones Cross Road, Crockenhill,Swanley, Kent BR8 8LX Tel No: 01322 668275
Ground: The Wested Meadow, Wested, Eynsford Road, Crockenhill, Kent. (01322 662097)
Colours: Red & white stripes/ black/ red
Change Colours: All navy

GREENWAYS
Founded: 1965
Secretary: William Miller, 14 Cygnet Gardens, Northfleet, Kent DA11 7DN (01474 560913)
Ground: Beauwater Leisure Centre, Nelson Road, Northfleet, (01474 359222)
Colours: Green & white/green/green
Change Colours: Red & black/black/black

LEWISHAM BOROUGH (COMMUNITY)
Founded: 2003
Secretary: Joseph Collymore, 37 Vaughan Williams Close, Deptford SE8 4AW (0208 691 2543)
Ground: Ladywell Arena, Doggett Road, Catford SE6 4QX
Tel: 020 8314 1986
Colours: All Blue & gold stripes
Change Colours: All gold & blue stripes

LYDD TOWN
Founded: 1885
Secretary: Bruce Marchant, 14 Quested Road, Folkestone, Kent.CT19 4BY Tel No: 01303 275403
Ground: The Lindsey Field, Dengemarsh Road, Lydd, Romney Marsh (01797 321904)
Colours: Red & green/green/green
ChangeColours:All Blue

MILTON ATHLETIC
Founded: 1926
Secretary: Paul Duffin, 18 Hales Road, Tunstall, Sittingbourne, Kent ME10 1SR (01795 422882)
Ground: UK Paper Sports Ground, Gore Court Road, Sittingbourne, Kent (01795 564213)
Colours: Royal blue/royal blue/white
Change Colours: Yellow & navy/navy/yellow

OLD ROAN
Founded: 1905
Secretary: Brian Riley, 33 Buckler Gardens, Mottingham, London SE9 3BD (020 8857 0401)
Groud: John Roan Playing Fields, Kidbrooke Park Road, Kldbrooke, London SE3 (020 8856 1915 or 020 8856 1012)
Colours: Blue & black stripes/ black/ black & blue.
Change Colours: Red & white/red/red

SHEERNESS EAST
Founded: 1932
Secretary: Jonathan Longhurst, 34 Sunnyside Avenue, Minster Sheerness, Kent ME12 2EN (01795 870093)
Ground: Sheerness East Working Mens Club, Queenborough Rd., Halfway, Sheerness (01795 662049)
Colours: Yellow/royal blue/royal blue
Change colours: Royal blue/black/royal blue

SNODLAND
Founded: 1940
Secretary: Terry Reeves, 136 Townsend Road, Snodland, Kent ME6 5RN (01634 240076)
Ground: Potyn's Field, Paddlesworth Road, Snodland, Kent. (01634 243961)
Colours: Yellow/ /red/black
Change colours:Red/red/black

STANSFELD OXFORD & BERMONDSEY CLUB
Founded: 1897
Secretary: Edward Ellis, 40 Tilbrook Road, Kidbrooke, London SE3 9QE (0208 319 0903)
Ground: F.K.G.Sports,Eltham Rd .,Lee Green SE12 (020 8852 6622)
Colours: Yellow/blue/blue
Change Colours: All white

TENTERDEN TOWN
Founded: 1889
Secretary: Stephen Saxby, 46 Hopes Grove,High Halden,Ashford, Kent TN26 3ND Tel No: 01233 850741
Ground: Recreation Ground, Recretaion Ground Rd., Tenterden (07786 932151)
Colours: Blue & white hoops/red/red
Change Colours: Blue & white/ blue/blue

DIVISION ONE WEST CONSTITUTION 2004-05

APM Mears
Founded: 1919. Re-formed 2003
Secretary: Phillip Allen, 397 Lower Woodlands Road, Gillingham Kent ME7 2TR. Tel: 07949 048 695
Ground: Cobdown Sports & Social Club, Station Rd, Ditton, Maidstone. Tel: 01622 717771
Colours: Black & white stripes/black/black
Change Colours: Sky blue/navy/sky blue

BELVEDERE
Founded: 1923
Secretary: Paul Bell, 10 Abbotswood Road, Dulwich, London SE22 8DL Tel: 020 8693 6521 (H)
Ground: Belvedere Sports & Social Club, Woolwich Road, Belvedere. Tel: 01322 436724
Colours: Yellow/blue/blue
Change: Green/blue/blue

BLY SPARTANS
Founded: 1982
Secretary: Tony Wheeler, 14 Lynnette Ave., Rochester, Kent ME2 3NH Tel: 01634 713404 (H)
Ground: Bly Spartans Sports Ground, Rede Court Road, Strood. Tel: 01634 710577
Colours: Maroon & sky blue/maroon/maroon
Change: Grey/black/black

BROMLEIANS SPORTS
Founded 1922
Secretary: Stephen Millward, 24 Palace Road, Bromley Kent BR1 3JT. Tel: 020 8466 1911
Ground: Lower Gravel Road, Bromley, Kent Tel: 020 8462 5068
Colours: Light blue/dark blue/light blue
Change Colours: Red/red/red

EYNESFORD
Founded: 1895
Secretary: Robert Graham, 48 Goddington Lane, Orpington, Kent BR6 9DS Tel: 01689 821425
Ground: STC Ivor grove, New Eltham, SE9
Tel: 020 8850 2057
Colours: Black & white/black/black
Change Colours: Yellow & black/black/black

FLEETDOWN UNITED
Founded: 1971
Secretary: Brian Wakeman, 670 Princes Road, Dartford, Kent DA2 6JG (01322 228680)
Ground: Lower Heath Lane, Dartford, Kent (01322 273848)
Colours: Tangerine/blue/blue
Change colours: Blue &White/ blue/blue

HALLS
Founded: 1919
Secretary: Steven Poile, 33 Carlton Avenue, Horns Cross, Greenhithe, Kent DA9 9DR. Tel: 01322 383 587
Ground: Princes Golf & Leisure Club, Darenth Road, Dartford, Kent Tel: 01322 276565
Colours: Yellow & royal blue stripes/royal blue/yellow
Change Colours: All navy

HOLMESDALE
Founded 1956
Secretary: Mark Hayes, 12 Danson Way, Rainham, Kent. ME8 7EW (01634 327954)
Ground: Holmesdale Sports & Social Club, Oakley Road, Bromley Common (020 8462 4440)
Colours: Yellow & Green/ Green/ Green
Change Colours: Red/ Black/Black

LARKFIELD & NEW HYTHE WDRS
Larkfield Sports Ground, New Hythe Lane, Larkfield, Aylesford
Tel: 07786 221262

ORPINGTON
Westcombe Park & Orpington SC, Goddington Lane, Orpington, Kent Tel: 01689 834902

PEMBURY
Founded1908
Secretary: Michael Waterman, 26 The Coppice, Pembury, Tunbridge Wells Kent TN2 4EY
Tel: 01892 824137
Ground: Woodside Recreation Ground, Henwoods Mount, Pembury
Tel: 07970 026628
Colours: Black & White stripes/ black/black
Change Colours: All red

RUSTHALL
Jockey Farm, Nellington Lane, Rusthall, Tunbridge Wells.
Tel: 07940 277138

WICKHAM PARK
Founded: 1934
Secretary: Robbie Devlin,117 Hazlebank Road,London SE6 1LT
Tel No: 07939 556737
Ground: 228-230 Pickhurst Rise, West Wickham.
Tel: 020 8777 2550
Colours: Navy & tangerine/navy & tangerine/navy
Change Colours: Black & white stripes/black/black

Arena Spectator Facilities

From Arena Seating the following spectator facilities are available for purchase to enhance all Sports Arenas and provide comfort for spectators

Arena Stadia Tip-Up Seats, floor or riser mounted on existing or new build terracing

Arena Sports Stand and Tiered Spectator Seating.
A classic design, with a cantilevered roof cover providing an unimpeded view for the spectator.

Can be supplied in 4, 7 and 13 rows covered seat options with or without end enclosures.

The roof cover is built in modules that can be added to as need and finance dictate.

Arena Sports Shelter
A smaller, lightweight 4 row version of the Arena Sports Stand where space is at a particular premium

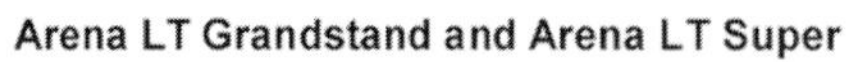

Arena LT Grandstand and Arena LT Super Grandstand Prefabricated and delivered to location via lorry with crane.

Supplied complete with 50 or 74 tip up seats or as a tiered standing stand with capacity for 85 or 120 spectators.

Wheelchair spaces can be incorporated.

End enclosures available as an optional extra.

Can be linked together for greater capacity.

Arena Seating Limited, Arena House, Membury, Lambourn Woodlands, Hungerford, Berkshire RG17 7TQ
Tel: 01488 674800 Fax: 01488 674822 Email: info@arenaseating.com

DIVISION ONE EAST CONSTITUTION 2004-05

BETTESHANGER WELFARE
Founded: 1939
Secretary: Ms Kim Ashton, 12 Douglas Road, Deal Kent CT14 9HT Tel: 01304 364550
Ground: Betteshanger Welfare Ground, Cavell Square, Mill Hill, Deal. Tel: 01304 372080
Colours: Red & white/blue/red
Change colours: All blue

BLIBY
Founded: 1994
Secretary: Mrs Jacqui Barker, Frithfield, Aldington Frith, Ashford, Kent TN25 7HH Tel: 01233 720469 (H) 01233 720973 (B)
Ground: Sandyacres, Sandyhurst Lane (from January 2004), Ashford. Tel: 01233 627373
Temporary Ground: The Ridge, Spearpoint, Kennington.
Colours: Navy & amber/navy/navy
Change: Amber & navy/navy /navy

BORDEN VILLAGE
Borden & Playstool Parish Council Ground, Borden, Sittingbourne, Kent.
Tel: 07903 016794

KENNINGTON
Founded: 1888
Secretary: Kevin Hayden, 36 Alec Pemble Close, Kennington, Ashford, Kent. TN24 9PF Tel No: 01233 627826
Ground: Kennington Cricket Club Club, Ulley Road, Kennington, Ashford, Kent
Colours: Sky blue/yellow/sky blue
Change Colours: Red/navy/navy

NEW ROMNEY
Founded: 1895
Secretary: Alan Chandler, 124 Jefferstone Lane, St Marys Bay, romney Marsh (01303 873872)
Ground: The Maud Pavilion, Station Road, New Romney, Kent (01797 364858)
Colours: All Navy blue & yellow
Change Colours: Orange/royal blue/orange

NORTON SPORTS
Founded: 1927
Secretary: Colin Page, 22 Haysel, Sittingbourne, Kent ME10 4QE
Tel: 01795 426675
Ground: Norton Park, Provender Lane,Norton,Kent Tel: 01795 520088
Colours: Sky Blue & white stripes/ navy / navy
Change Colours: Red & black/navy/navy

OAKWOOD
Founded: 1924
Peter Mannering, 24 Ellenswood Close, Otham, Maidstone, Kent ME15 8SQ Tel: 01622 862482
Ground: Otham Sports Club, Honey Lane, Otham, Maidstone, Kent. Tel: 07745 383328
Colours: Red & white stripes/black/red
Change colours: Green & red/green/red

SHEPPEY UNITED
Medways Ports Authority Ground, Holm Place, Sheerness, Kent.
Tel: 01795 668054

SNOWDOWN COLLIERY WELFARE
Founded: 1927
Secretary: Mr Patrick Sutcliffe, 14 Park View, Sturry, canterbury Kent CT2 0NP. Tel: 01227 712673 (H). 01304 840309 (B)
Ground: Spinney Lane, Aylesham, Canterbury CT3 3AF (01304 840278)
Colours: Black & white stripes/black/black
Change Colours: Green & white/white/white
Previous League: Kent

St MARGARETS
Founded: 1970 Re-formed:1993
Secretary: Dennis Mitchell, 178 St Davids Avenue, Dover Kent CT17 9HJ. Tel: 077734 77781 (M). 07855 013412 (B)
Ground: The Alexandra Field, Off Kingsdown Road, St Margarets at Cliffe, Nr Dover. Tel: 07973 139966
Colours: Red &blue/ navy/ red
Change Colours: White/blue/red

TYLER HILL
Founded: 1950
Secretary: Bill Clark, 23 Hanscombe House, Forty Acres Road, Canterbury Kent CT2 7TL. Tel: 01227 768358 (H). 07930 100034 (B)
Ground: Hersden Recreation Ground, Hersden, Nr. Canterbury. Tel: 07930 100034
Colours: Black & white stripes/black/white
Change Colours: All red & white

UNIVERSITY OF KENT
Founded: 1967
Secretary: Aaron Campbell, Sports Federation, Kent Union, Mandela Building, ,University of Kent, Canterbury, Kent CT2 7NW Tel: 01227 823 074
Ground: Oast House, Parkwood Road, Off Giles Lane, Canterbury, Kent. Tel: 01227 827430
Colours: Black & white stripes/black/black
Change Colours: Red & blackstripes/red/red

WOODSTOCK PARK
Founded: 1970
Secretary: Maurice Dunk, 29 Shurland Avenue, Sittingbourne Kent ME10 4QT. Tel: 01795 478927 (H)
Ground: Woodstock Park, Broadoak Road, Sittingbourne, Kent Tel: 07774 654 912
Colours: All royal blue
Change colours: Maroon/maroon/sky blue

LEICESTERSHIRE SENIOR LEAGUE

SPONSORED BY: EVERARDS BREWERY

Founded 1903

President: John M Elsom F.C.A. Chairman: David Jamieson
Hon Secretary: Robert J Holmes, 8 Huntsman Close, Markfield, Leics LE67 9XE
Tel/Fax: 01530 243093 Email: robertholmes@leicssenior1.freeserve.co.uk
www.leicestershireseniorfootballleague.com
Press Officer: Dave Lumley, 8 Pinewood Close, Countesthorpe, Leicester LE8 5TS
TelFax: 0116 277 8455 Email: davelumley@leicssenior.freeserve.co.uk

Since season 1998-99 concluded we have seen 4 clubs move on into more senior football whilst six others for one reason or another, relegation, resignation or merger have fallen by the wayside. Consequently, as in the same period we have only managed to recruit six teams the constitution will fall next season (by one) to its lowest for some time. We sought to address this by coming to an agreement with the Junior Leagues that there would be no relegation this season and that we would take a team on promotion from each of the two leagues who could offer us a club with the appropriate level of facilites.

And so to the football, and the season on the field of play was dominated by two clubs, Loughborough Dynamo in the Premier Division and Rothley Imperial in Division 1. Isn't it amazing what a difference a few seasons makes? It is only three years since Loughborough Dynamo were staring relegation to junior football in the face and now they have completed (probably) the unique treble of Senior Cup, Senior League and Senior League Cup in the same season. Not only that but they have brought their ground up to the required standard for moving on to the Midland Football Alliance and we wish them well as they step up the football ladder.

In Division 1 Rothley Imperial joined us from the District League, took the Championship at the first attempt and finished runners-up to Loughborough Dynamo in the Beacon Bitter Cup. Congratulations too, to Aylestone Park for reversing their relegation of two seasons ago and moving back to the Premier Division.

But the season also sees the loss of Leicester YMCA who have finally had to call it a day after years of competition in the League. Whilst over the years they have not perhaps brought that many honours to Belvoir Drive there was always a friendly welcome and a lovely playing surface and we will miss them. We also personally wish Colin Chappell a well deserved retirement. We also lose Epworth as an independent club after only two seasons but wish them and Friar Lane every success in their joint venture for next season.

FINAL LEAGUE TABLE 2003-04

PREMIER DIVISION	P	W	D	L	F	A	Pts
1. Loughborough Dynamo	34	28	4	2	114	24	88
2. Kirby Muxloe SC	34	19	9	6	58	32	66
3. Friar Lane Old Boys	34	17	9	8	80	46	60
4. Ellistown	34	18	5	11	69	47	59
5. Ratby Sports	34	18	3	13	66	60	57
6. Ibstock Welfare	34	16	8	10	62	48	56
7. Birstall United	34	15	8	11	56	36	53
8. Blaby & Whetstone Athletic	34	14	8	12	49	56	50
9. Leicester YMCA	34	14	5	15	59	71	47
10. Stapenhill	34	14	4	16	68	72	46
11. Holwell Sports	34	14	4	16	58	65	46
12. St Andrews SC	34	14	2	18	53	57	44
13. Highfield Rangers (-3pts)	34	12	9	13	61	61	42
14. Barrow Town	34	12	6	16	65	82	42
15. Downes Sports	34	8	9	17	58	76	33
16. Thurmaston Town	34	8	5	21	53	70	29
17. Thurnby Rangers	34	7	7	20	45	89	28
18. Anstey Nomads	34	4	3	27	35	117	15

PREMIER 03-04	1	2	3	4	5	6	7	8	9	10	11	12	13	14	15	16	17	18
1 Anstey Nomads		0-1	0-8	1-2	2-2	1-3	2-2	0-4	2-3	2-3	1-2	1-2	0-3	3-1	2-0	2-2	0-5	2-3
2 Barrow Town	8-2		0-3	2-2	5-1	3-2	3-1	3-1	2-3	4-0	0-0	4-1	1-4	1-1	1-2	2-0	2-2	4-0
3 Birstall United	3-1	2-1		0-1	0-1	2-0	1-1	5-2	1-0	1-1	0-0	3-1	0-0	0-1	3-1	2-1	0-1	4-0
4 Blaby & Whetstone Athletic	3-1	1-0	0-1		3-2	1-2	0-0	2-1	3-2	1-1	1-1	2-1	0-3	2-1	2-1	1-1	2-3	5-4
5 Downes Sports	4-0	4-2	1-1	2-1		0-5	1-3	3-3	3-0	0-1	0-0	2-3	1-2	3-3	0-1	1-0	1-1	0-1
6 Ellistown	4-0	4-0	1-2	3-0	3-1		2-5	2-3	1-1	1-4	1-0	3-1	0-0	3-0	1-0	3-0	3-2	2-0
7 Friar Lane Old Boys	7-0	6-1	0-5	1-1	4-1	4-1		0-1	2-1	0-0	3-0	5-2	0-1	1-1	1-2	5-2	2-1	5-2
8 Highfield Rangers	5-0	4-2	0-0	3-4	2-2	1-1	2-0		2-1	1-3	1-0	2-2	0-1	2-0	1-0	1-2	1-1	1-1
9 Holwell Sports	2-0	0-2	2-1	0-1	4-1	0-5	0-1	4-2		4-1	0-3	3-2	1-1	3-0	1-5	2-3	3-0	1-2
10 Ibstock Welfare	4-1	3-0	0-0	0-0	3-1	2-3	0-5	5-0	3-1		0-0	0-0	2-0	0-1	5-2	3-0	1-0	0-0
11 Kirby Muxloe SC	2-1	4-1	2-1	4-2	4-4	1-1	3-3	1-0	1-1	4-0		0-3	1-0	1-2	2-1	2-0	2-1	5-1
12 Leicester YMCA	3-1	4-3	5-1	1-0	2-2	0-3	2-2	2-2	0-2	2-0	1-4		0-4	4-3	1-3	2-4	1-0	5-1
13 Loughborough Dynamo	11-0	16-0	0-0	5-0	7-2	3-1	1-0	4-2	7-2	6-3	1-0	4-1		5-2	3-1	4-0	1-0	6-1
14 Ratby Sports	5-1	3-1	1-2	1-0	2-0	2-0	2-0	4-2	3-0	1-4	0-3	1-2	1-4		2-1	2-4	4-1	1-0
15 St Andrews SC	2-1	1-1	2-1	1-3	1-3	2-0	1-1	1-4	0-3	2-1	1-2	3-0	0-1	1-2		3-1	3-2	0-2
16 Stapenhill	6-0	2-0	3-2	3-2	4-2	2-0	2-4	3-1	2-3	4-2	0-2	0-1	1-2	1-2	3-2		1-1	2-1
17 Thurmaston Town	1-3	0-2	3-0	3-0	3-2	2-3	2-3	2-2	1-3	0-2	0-1	2-0	1-2	3-4	1-5	6-5		0-1
18 Thurnby Rangers	1-2	3-3	3-1	1-1	0-5	2-2	0-3	0-2	2-2	1-5	0-1	1-2	0-2	2-7	0-2	4-4	5-2	

LEAGUE CUP

PREMIER DIVISION SECTION

PRELIMINARY ROUND

Barrow Town	v	Stapenhill	1-2
Leicester YMCA	v	Downes Sports	2-0

FIRST ROUND

Anstey Nomads	v	Stapenhill	0-1
Blaby & Whetstone Ath.	v	St Andrews SC	1-1*,5-4p
Ellistown	v	Birstall United	2-3
Friar Lane Old Boys	v	Loughborough Dynamo	1-1*,5-6p
Ibstock Welfare	v	Kirby Muxloe SC	1-2
Leicester YMCA	v	Thurnby Rangers	2-2*,4-3p
Ratby Sports	v	Highfield Rangers	4-4*,5-6p
Thurmaston Town	v	Holwell Sports	1-2

SECOND ROUND

Blaby & Whetstone Ath.	v	Birstall United	1-1*,4-1p
Kirby Muxloe SC	v	Loughborough Dynamo	0-2
Leicester YMCA	v	Holwell Sports	2-2*,3-5p
Stapenhill	v	Highfield Rangers	6-2

DIVISION ONE SECTION FIRST ROUND

Asfordby Amateurs	v	Anstey Town	1-1*,4-5p
Cottesmore Amateurs	v	Leics Constabulary	0-3

division one section first round continued...

Earl Shilton Albion	v	Aylestone Park Old Boys	0-4
Epworth	v	Saffron Dynamo	3-6
Huncote Sports & Social	v	Lutterworth Town	1-2
North Kilworth	v	Narborough & Littlethorpe	3-1
Rothley Imperial	v	Bardon Hill Sports	2-1

SECOND ROUND

Anstey Town	v	Aylestone Park Old Boys	1-3
Leics Constabulary	v	Sileby Town	1-3
Lutterworth Town	v	North Kilworth	1-1*,4-1p
Rothley Imperial	v	Saffron Dynamo	3-2

QUARTER-FINALS (COMBINED)

Aylestone Park Old Boys	v	Loughborough Dynamo	1-2
Blaby & Whetstone Ath.	v	Stapenhill	3-2
Holwell Sports	v	Rothley Imperial	0-0*,3-5p
Lutterworth Town	v	Sileby Town	0-0*,3-5p

SEMI-FINALS

Loughborough Dynamo	v	Blaby & Whetstone Athletic	3-1
Sileby Town	v	Rothley Imperial	0-5

THE FINAL (10th May at Barrow Town)

Loughborough Dynamo	v	Rothley Imperial	2-1

LEADING GOALSCORERS 2003-04 (Premier Division)

Player	Club	Position Club Finished	Total
David Burraway	Loughborough Dynamo	1st	40
John Chapman	Friar Lane Old Boys	3rd	23
Danny McNulty	Ratby Sports	5th	23
Steven Hines	Downes Sports	15th	19
Stefan L Marshall	Stapenhill	10th	19

ANSTEY NOMADS

Secretary: Chris Hillebrandt, 31 Peartree Close, Anstey, LeicesterLE7 7TD (0116 2122458)
Ground: Cropston Road, Anstey, Leicester (0116 236 4868)
Directions: Take jct 21A off M1 to Newark on A46 .Turn to Anstey after 2 miles then take third exit at village roundabout and ground is half amile on right.
Capacity: 1,500 Seats:100 Cover: 100 Floodlights:Yes Club shop: No
Clubhouse: Yes (available for bookings)
HONOURS: Leics Senior Lge: (4), Leics Comb. 93-94 ,Leics Senior Cup 94-95, Leics Jun. Cup 94-95, Presidents Cup 95-96, Battle of Britain Cup (8) Rolleston Charity Cup (4)
BEST SEASON F.A.Vase: 5th Round 1994-95

FACT FILE
Founded: 1947 Nickname: Nomads
Sponsors: Ford Signs
Colours: Red/white/white
Change colours: All green
Chairman: Tony Ford
Manager:Lee Ferrer Ass.Man: Andy Packer
Captain: Drew Wardle
2002-2003
Player of the Year: Drew Wardle
Top Scorer: Lee Farrer

AYLESTONE PARK

Ground: Dorset Avenue, Fairfield Estate, Leicester, Leicestershire
Tel: 0116 277 5307

BARROW TOWN

Secretary: Alan Dawkins, 72 Beaumont Road, Barrow-on-Soar, Loughborough, Leics LE12 8PJ
Tel: 01509 413288 email: alan@dawkins9.freeserve.co.uk
Ground: Riverside Park, Meynell Road, Quorn, Leics Tel: 01509 620650
Directions: Access via Quorn Lodge Drive & Barrow road.
Capacity: 2,000 Seats: None Cover: 50 Floodlights:Yes
Clubhouse: New £250,000 building Club Shop: No - BadgesYes
HONOURS: Leics Sen Lg. 92-93 R-up 94-95 02-03; Loughboro' Charity Cup 68-69,96-97,98-99, 00-01,02-03 Leics Coimbination R-up : 2002-03 Leics Youth Lg Winners 02-03, League Cp 02-3 Leics County Sen Cup Finalists 02-03, Battle of Britain Cup Finalists 02-03
BEST SEASON FA Vase: 2nd Rd Proper. 2000-01 ,01-02
2003-2004 Top Scorer: Rob Pitman Player of the Year: Rich Gale

FACT FILE
Re-formed 1947 Nickname: Riversiders
Colours: Red & black/black/red
Change colours: Navy Blue
Midweek matchday: Tuesday Prog: Yes
Website: www.barrowtown.net
Chairman: Michael Bland
Treasurer: Paul Carnell
Press Officer : Alan.Dawkins
Managers:Darren Siddons & Nick Ellis
Ca[tain: Matt Boyles

BIRSTALL UNITED

Secretary: SandraPlumb, 34 Allinson Close, Leicester LE5 4ED.
Tel No: 0116 2766546

Ground: Meadow Lane, Birstall, Leics. Tel No: 0116 267 1230
Directions: The ground is situated on the A6 between Leicester and Loughborough. (Club will supply maps)

FACT FILE
Colours: White/navy/navy
Change Colours: All red
Midweek Matchday: Thursday

Chairman: Malcolm Scothern
Manager: Gary Fox
Coach; Peter Jackson
Physio: Jeff Roberts
ProgEditors: Shaun JHills & Andy Lord

BLABY & WHETSTONE ATHLETIC

Secretary: Mrs Sandra Morris, 10 Winchester Road, Blaby, Leics LE8 3HJ Tel: 0116 277 3208

Ground: Blaby & Whetstone Boys Club, Warwick Road, Whetstone (0116 286 4852)

Colours: Navy & white/navy/navy

DOWNES SPORTS

Secretary Tony Jacques, 17 Merton Close, Broughton, Astley Leicester LE9 6QP
Tel: 01455 28402 (H) 01455 282028 (W)
Ground Leicester Rd, Hinckley Tel: 01455 615062

Directions Off northern perimeter road round Leicester

Capacity 2000 Seats: Cover: Yes Floodlights: Yes

Clubhouse Yes Club shop: No

HONOURS Leics. Sen. Lge. Div Two R-up 1986-87

Founded: 1968
Nickname: The Builders
Colours: Tangerine/black/tangerine
Change colours:t.b.a.
Midweek matchday: Tuesday
Programme: No
Club Personnel
Chairman: F. Down
Vice Chairman:
Manager: S. Greenhill
Asst. Man. / Coach:
Physio:

ELLISTOWN

Secretary: John Measom, 29 Standard Hill, Coalville, Leicster LE67 3HN
Tel: 01530 810941

Ground: 1 Terrace Road, Ellistown
Clubhouse: Yes

Colours: Yellow/blue shirts, yellow shorts, blue socks
Change colours: Red shirts, black shorts, red socks

FRIAR LANE & EPWORTH

Secretary: Robert Beeson,11 West Field Close, Rearsby,Leicester LE74ZA (01664 424086)
Ground: Knighton Lane East,Aylestone Park, Leiceste. LE2 6FT (0116 283 3629)
Directions: Leave Leicester onWelford Road, turn right at traffic lights into Knighton Lane East. Under railway bridge and left into Whitier Road where entrance is just past clubhouse.
Previous names: Friar Lane Old Boys (1961) and Epworth (1969) Merged 2004
Previous Leagues: Leicester Mutual and Leicester & District.
2003-2004 P.o.Y.: Jamie Marsh Top Scorer: John Chapman 2004-2005 Captain: Danny Gibbons

Re-Formed 2004
Colours:Orange &b lackstripes/black/orange
Change colours: All Navy Blue
Midweek Matchday: Monday or Tuesday
Club Personnel
Chairman: Clive Gibbons
Manager: Malcolm Coles
Coach: John Cooper Prog Ed: C Gibbons

HIGHFIELD RANGERS

Secretary: Maurice Christian, 18 Blanklyn Avenue, Leicester LE5 5FA Tel: 0116 273 4002

Ground: 443 Gleneagles Ave., Rushey Mead, Leicester Tel: 0116 266 0009

Colours: Yellow/blackyellow

HOLWELL SPORTS

Secretary: Colin Moulds, 12 Needham Close, Melton Mowbray, Leics. LE13 1TW
Tel Nos: 01664 852391 (H) 07790 876119 (M)
Ground: Welby Road, Asfordby Hill, Melton Mowbray, Leics Tel: 01664 812715
Collours: Green & gold/green/green & gold

2003-2004
Player of the Year: Sam Bettinson
Top Scorer: Wayne Crutchley
2004-2005
Captain: Jason Joshi

IBSTOCK WELFARE

Secretary Ralph A Wilkinson, 6 Valley Rd, Ibstock, Leics. LE67 6NYTel: 01530 450243
Email: Ibstockwelfarefc@ntlworld.com Websitewww.footballnews.co.uk/clubs/22/2244/home.page
Ground The Welfare, Leicester Road, Ibstock, Leics. Tel: 01530 260656
Brief Directions: A511 towards Coalville & follow signs to Ibstock
Capacity 1500 Seats: 50 Cover: 150 Floodlights:Yes Clubhouse Evenings & matchesShop No
HONOURS Leics Sen Cup 93-94, R-Up 97-98; Leics Sen Lg Div 1 R-Up 90-91; Coalville Chall Cup x5, R-up x4; Loughborough Ch.Cup x4, R-up x2; Atherstone Nursing Cup (1)
PREVIOUS Leagues: Coalville & District, Leicester & District
BEST SEASON FA Vase: 2nd Round Proper
ClubSponsors for season 2003-2004: Ibstock Brick,David Wiulson Homes,Gaytonn Graham,C.W.Palletta & Son,Ravenstone Management & Marketing Services

Founded: 1962 Nickname:The Welly
Kit Sponsors: Andy Peters Racing,Vinnys Fish Bar & Shuires Traffic Management
Colours: Red/black/red
Change colours: All blue or all green
Midw'k matchday: Tuesday Prog: Yes
Club Personnel
Press Off: Craig Wheatley 0798 5242073
Man: Neil Costello Capt: Brendan Cartlidge
Ass.Mans.: Stuart Boinser & Neil Scott
Top scorer & P.o.Y.: Royce Turville

KIRBY MUXLOE S.C.

Secretary: Philip Moloney, 16 Church Lane, Ratby, Leics LE6 0JE (0116 239 2916)

Ground: Ratby Lane, Kirby Muxloe (0116 239 3201)

Colours: Blue/black/black

RATBY SPORTS

Secretary: John Rowe, 57 Danehill, Ratby, Leicester LE6 0NG Tel: 0116 238 6806

Ground: Ratby Sports Club, Desford Lane, Ratby. Tel: 0116 239 2474

Colours: All red

ROTHLEY IMPS

Ground: Loughborough Road, Mountsorrell, Leicester, Leicestershire
Tel: 0116 237 4003

St ANDREWS F.C.

Secretary: Les Botting, 2 Neston Road, Saffron Lane, Leicester LE2 6RD Tel: 0116 224 3961

Ground: Canal Street, off Aylestone Rd, Old Aylestone,Leicester Tel: 0116 283 9298

Directions: Aylestone Rd.,to Granby Rd to Canal St.HONOURS: Leics Sen Lg. Premier Champions: 89-90,93-94,95-96

Colours: Black & white/black/red

Player of the Year: Darren Mackie

STAPENHILL

Ground: Maple Grove, Stapenhill, Burton-on-Trent, Staffs.
Tel: 01283 562471

THURMASTON TOWN

Secretary: Reg Malloy, 96 Grange Drive, Melton Mowbray, Leics. LE13 1HA
Tel: 01664 564665 (H) 0116 222 3636 (B)

Colours: Black & white stripes, black,black.

Ground: Elizabeth Park, Checklands Road, Thurmaston. Tel: 0116 260 2519

HONOURS: Dist. Lg Champs 97-99, Page & Moy Junior Cup Winners 97-98 Leics Div One Champions & Beacon Bitter Cup Winners 98-99

THURNBY RANGERS

Secretary: Ian Henson, 13 Dudley Avenue, Thurnby Lodge, Leicester LE5 2EE
Tel: 0116 241 2741 07761 227 586 (M)

Ground: Dakyn Road, Thurnby Lodge, Leicester.
Tel: 0116 243 3698

Colours: All green
Change colours: All red

MIDLAND COMBINATION

President: Les James **Chairman:** Roy Craddock
Secretary: Norman Harvey
115 Millfield Road, Handsworth Wood, Birmingham B20 1ED
Tel: 0121 357 4172

FINAL LEAGUE TABLE 2003-04

PREMIER DIVISION	P	W	D	L	F	A	Pts
1. Romulus	40	31	2	7	128	44	95
2. Leamington	40	30	4	6	101	36	94
3. Rugby Town	40	25	5	10	80	55	80
4. Coventry Sphinx	40	23	8	9	74	55	77
5. Feckenham	40	21	8	11	79	63	71
6. Coventry Marconi	40	22	4	14	84	53	70
7. Meir KA	40	18	11	11	89	68	65
8. Nuneaton Griff	40	15	15	10	74	62	60
9. Castle Vale Kings Heath	40	17	8	15	76	72	59
10. Dudley Sports	40	16	9	15	84	64	57
11. West Midlands Police	40	16	9	15	67	78	57
12. Highgate United	40	15	11	14	62	52	56
13. Bolehall Swifts	40	16	8	16	67	78	56
14. Brocton	40	15	10	15	53	59	55
15. Pershore Town	40	10	15	15	65	83	45
16. Shifnal Town	40	11	10	19	44	52	43
17. Massey Ferguson	40	12	5	23	65	93	41
18. Coleshill Town	40	11	5	24	49	83	38
19. Continental Star	40	6	9	25	53	88	27
20. Southam United	40	3	6	31	33	115	15
21. Alveston	40	2	8	30	29	103	14

PREMIER DIVISION	1	2	3	4	5	6	7	8	9	10	11	12	13	14	15	16	17	18	19	20	21
1 Alveston		0-2	0-2	1-3	1-3	0-3	2-1	1-2	0-1	0-3	0-1	0-2	2-2	0-4	1-2	1-1	0-7	0-2	0-1	3-0	3-4
2 Bolehall Swifts	2-2		2-0	0-2	3-1	1-1	0-3	0-5	1-2	0-4	0-3	0-1	1-0	4-2	3-0	1-1	0-2	2-4	0-0	3-2	2-0
3 Brocton	2-0	1-0		0-3	0-0	3-2	1-0	1-1	3-3	1-1	1-2	2-1	1-2	1-1	0-0	4-2	0-1	2-1	2-1	2-1	1-2
4 Castle Vale K.H.	2-1	2-3	2-0		4-1	1-0	0-1	1-2	3-0	1-0	2-2	1-3	2-1	2-4	1-3	3-0	2-4	2-3	0-0	2-2	5-3
5 Coleshill Town	1-1	1-2	2-3	1-0		1-0	3-2	0-2	2-0	1-3	0-3	1-2	1-2	1-3	1-3	5-2	1-5	1-5	2-0	1-0	0-2
6 Continental Star	0-0	1-3	2-1	3-3	3-2		1-2	0-1	3-2	0-1	2-2	3-5	1-2	1-2	0-3	1-1	1-4	0-2	1-1	3-0	1-2
7 Coventry Marconi	2-0	2-1	0-1	2-4	3-0	3-1		1-1	3-1	1-1	3-0	1-2	2-1	1-2	3-1	1-1	2-1	1-2	3-0	4-0	7-1
8 Coventry Sphinx	5-2	2-4	1-0	3-1	2-1	4-0	1-0		3-2	0-2	2-1	1-1	3-2	2-2	1-1	3-2	4-0	0-4	0-3	2-1	3-1
9 Dudley Sports	2-2	1-1	1-1	7-0	3-0	3-1	1-2	1-3		4-1	1-1	0-2	6-2	0-3	0-2	1-1	0-1	2-1	1-2	6-0	2-2
10 Feckenham	2-1	4-3	1-2	2-1	2-1	2-2	2-1	2-3	0-4		3-2	2-1	3-4	0-0	3-3	6-0	1-5	1-3	4-0	2-1	1-1
11 Highgate United	7-0	4-0	2-0	2-0	0-1	1-1	1-0	1-2	0-0	0-1		0-1	2-0	2-2	2-2	1-1	1-1	0-1	1-0	4-3	1-5
12 Leamington	5-0	2-2	3-0	1-3	2-0	6-1	2-3	3-0	0-1	1-2	2-2		4-2	2-0	5-1	2-1	3-1	3-0	1-0	3-0	3-0
13 Massey Ferguson	3-0	3-4	2-1	5-2	1-2	1-0	0-2	1-0	0-2	0-2	1-4	0-4		1-1	1-3	2-3	4-9	1-4	0-0	1-2	8-2
14 Meir KA	4-2	6-2	2-2	1-2	4-2	5-2	3-1	1-2	5-3	3-1	3-1	1-2	2-0		0-1	3-3	1-2	2-2	3-0	7-3	1-1
15 Nuneaton Griff	4-0	2-2	4-0	2-2	2-2	5-1	2-1	1-1	1-2	2-2	1-1	1-1	2-4	7-0		1-1	0-2	1-1	3-2	0-3	1-1
16 Pershore Town	3-2	2-2	4-1	3-3	0-0	1-4	2-4	4-2	2-7	3-2	0-2	0-1	1-1	0-0	1-3		2-4	1-0	2-1	6-0	0-4
17 Romulus	7-0	6-0	3-2	1-1	3-1	3-2	3-4	4-1	3-1	1-2	3-0	1-3	9-0	2-0	4-0	4-2		3-1	2-0	6-0	2-1
18 Rugby Town	2-0	0-3	1-3	2-0	5-2	3-1	2-2	1-0	4-3	4-3	2-0	0-2	0-0	4-2	3-1	0-3	1-0		0-2	1-0	2-1
19 Shifnal Town	1-1	2-3	1-1	0-3	1-2	1-1	2-4	1-1	2-2	0-1	1-0	2-3	1-0	2-1	3-0	0-0	0-1	1-2		4-0	3-0
20 Southam United	0-0	1-5	0-3	0-2	2-2	3-2	2-5	0-0	0-2	1-1	1-2	0-6	1-5	1-2	1-3	1-1	0-5	1-2	0-3		0-2
21 West Mids. Police	3-0	1-0	2-2	3-3	2-0	2-1	2-1	1-3	1-4	2-3	3-1	1-5	2-0	1-1	0-0	0-2	0-3	3-3	1-0	2-0	

FINAL LEAGUE TABLE 2003-04

DIVISION ONE	P	W	D	L	F	A	Pts	Av Pts
1. Barnt Green Spartak	34	25	2	7	90	41	77	2.265
2. Pilkington XXX	34	21	3	10	84	52	66	1.941
3. Littleton	33	18	7	8	64	41	61	1.848
4. Polesworth N. Warwick	33	17	8	8	75	46	59	1.788
5. Old Hill Town	34	16	7	11	69	59	55	1.618
6. Cadbury Athletic	34	16	5	13	70	57	53	1.559
7. Bloxwich Town (Promoted)	34	14	10	10	53	43	52	1.529
8. Northfield Town	33	14	8	11	79	61	50	1.515
9. Knowle #	33	13	9	11	56	39	48	1.455
10. Wilmcote Spts & Soc. #	34	15	4	15	49	61	49	1.441
11. Thimblemill REC	34	14	4	16	64	74	46	1.353
12. Burntwood Town	33	13	4	16	59	66	43	1.303
13. Fairfield Villa	34	11	6	17	44	64	39	1.147
14. Stockingford AA # (-3 pts)	33	10	7	16	61	82	34	1.030
15. Blackheath #	34	9	7	18	40	59	34	1.000
16. Kenilworth Town	34	6	5	23	34	90	23	0.676
17. Loughborough	33	4	8	21	30	74	20	0.607

Finishing position determined by a points per game average after resignation of Handsaker

WILLIE KNIBBS CHALLENGE CUP
PREMIER AND DIVISION ONE CLUBS

FIRST ROUND

Cadbury Athletic (at Thimblemill REC)	v	Thimblemill REC	7-1
Coventry Sphinx	v	Barnt Green Spartak	1-0
Dudley Sports	v	Coleshill	2-2*, 4-2p
Highgate United	v	Southam United	2-0
Littleton	v	Stockingford AA	1-1*,4-3p
Loughborough	v	Coventry Marconi	2-5*
Pershore Town	v	Leamington	0-3

SECOND ROUND

Bloxwich Town	v	Kenilworth Town	5-1
Burntwood Town	v	Feckenham	1-3
Cadbury Athletic	v	Northfield Town	4-3
Castle Vale K. H.	v	Brocton	1-3*
Continental Star	v	Blackheath	3-1*
Coventry Marconi	v	Old Hill Town	1-0
Coventry Sphinx	v	Littleton	3-1
Dudley Sports	v	Fairfield Villa	4-2*
Handsaker	v	Bolehall Swifts	5-2
Massey-Ferguson	v	West Mids Police	1-0
Meir KA	v	Knowle	4-1
Nuneaton Griff	v	Alveston	5-1
Pilkington XXX	v	Romulus	2-3
Polesworth North Warwick	v	Leamington	2-2*,2-3p
Rugby Town	v	Wilmcote Spts & Social	3-1
Shifnal Town	v	Highgate United	1-2

THIRD ROUND

Cadbury Athletic	v	Nuneaton Griff	1-3
Coventry Marconi	v	Continental Star	4-1
Dudley Sports	v	Brocton	1-3*
Leamington	v	Coventry Sphinx	5-0
Massey-Ferguson	v	Highgate United	3-4
Meir KA	v	Handsaker	4-0
Romulus	v	Bloxwich Town	4-1
Rugby Town	v	Feckenham	1-2

QUARTER-FINALS

Coventry Marconi	v	Brocton	2-0
Feckenham	v	Meir KA	6-3*
Highgate United	v	Nuneaton Griff	3-1
Leamington	v	Romulus	1-2

SEMI-FINALS (played over two legs)

Coventry Marconi	v	Feckenham	1-0 4-1
Highgate United	v	Romulus	2-3 1-2

THE FINAL (8th May at Studley)

Romulus	v	Coventry Marconi	2-0

ALVESTON

Secretary: Martin Beese, 16 The Smallholdings, Bubbenhall Road, Baginton, CV8 3BB
Tel: 02476 305294H 077744 23641M

Ground: Home Guard Club, Main Street, Tiddington, Stratford-upon-Avon. Tel: 01789 297718
Social Club Telephone : 01789 297718 Club Email
martin.beese@fleet.gecapital.com

Directions: ground is on the Stratford - Wellesbourne Road (B 40860) Home Guard Club is last building on right throughTiddington

Honours: MFC Premier: Champions 98-99, Div 1 97-98, MFC Cup Winners 98-99 B'ham Co Vase R-up 98-99, Vov.Eve.Telegraph 98-99

FACT FILE
Formed: 1927
Colours: Maroon & sky blue/sky blue/ maroon & sky blue
Change Cols.: Black & white stripes/ white/ white

Chairman: Martin Beese (02476 305294)

BARNT GREEN SPARTAK

Secretary: G.J.Singh, 9 Showell Green Lane, Sparkhill, Birmingham B11 4NP (07968 587648)
Ground: Lye Meadow, Redditch Road, Alvechurch, B48 7RS (0121 445 2929)
Directions: From M42 Jct 2 follow signs to Redditchalong the dual carriageway by pass. At traffic island turn right and ground is approximately 1km on right.
Previous League: Bromsgrove &District (Sundays)
Previous Names: Spar Barnt Green and Dillons Barnt Green
Honours: Bromsgrove League 93-4 96-7MFC Div 2 02-03Div 1 03-04Worcester F.A.Cup 95-6 MFC Challenge Vase R-Up 02-03
2003-2004 Players of the Year: Delroy Brown and Zahoor Suliman
Top Scorer: Recky Carter

FACT FILE
Formed: 1992
Colours: Tangerine/black/tangerine
Change colours:Royal Blue & white/Blue/Blue
Midweek Matchday: Wednesday
Programme Editors: Kirpal Singh and G.J.Singh
Club Personnel
Chairman: Avtar Singh
Manager: G.J.Singh
Coach: Frank Creamer
Captain: Zahoor Suliman

BLOXWICH TOWN

Secretary: Bob Thomas,416 Bloxwich Road, Leamore, Walsall WS3 2UY Tel No: 07956 908242
Ground: Abbey Park, Glastonbury Court, Bloxwich, Walsall. Tel No: 01922 477640
e-mail: enquiries@bloxwichtowntc.info
Capacity: Seats: Cover: Floodlights: Clubhouse: Yes
Directions: From Broad Lane (B4210) turn into Cresswell Crescent on Mossley Estate. By petrol station and Eagle Pub, take 5th turning right off Cresswell Crescent into Glastonbury Crescent. Ground entrance is just after Abbey school next to No 252 Gastonbury Crescent. From North , M6 Jct 11 turn into A462 into Broad Lane and then right into Cresswell Crescent.
Honours: Bloxwich Comb. (2) MFC Div One 88-89 Premier Div 95-96 MFA C Cup 97-98, Bloxwich Charity 79-80, BLack Country Olympic 85, MFC Invitation 89-90, Challenge Vase 95-96 Walsall Senior Cup 1997

FACT FILE
Formed: 1976
Sponsor:
Colours:Blue & white halves/white/white
Change colours:
Midweek Matches:
Reserves' Lge:
Programme Editor: John Rogers
CLUB PERSONNEL
Chairman: Michael Ross (01922407199)
Vice Chairman:
President:
Manager:
Assistant Manager:
Physio:

BOLEHALL SWIFTS

Secretary: Philip Hill, 64 Rene Road, Bolehall,Tamworth,Staffs. B77 3NN (07812 449054- M)
Ground: Rene Road, Bolehall, Tamworth (01827 62637) Rec.Att: 803 v Tamworth FAC 95-9xs6
Directions: A51 signs south to Bolebridge island, left under railway archesinto Amington Rd, 4th left into Leedham Ave, fork right into Rene Rd, ground onright by school. From Tamworth BR station walk up Victoria Road for threequarters of a mile and catch No.3 or No.6 mini-bus to Bolehall. Alight atLeedham Avenue or Rene Road and follow as above
Capacity: 2,000 Seats: 500 Cover: 600 Floodlights: Yes Club Shop: No
Clubhouse: Large Social Club. OpenDays 12-3 & evenings 7-11 & lunchtimes. Snacks available
HONOURS: Midland Comb. Div 2 84-85, F/Lit Cup R-up 96-97, Chall. Vase 84-85, Presidents Cup R-up 85-86; Fazeley Char Cup 84-85 (R-up 85-86); Ernie Brown Mem. Cup R-up (6)Jack Mould Cup R-up 85-86 Tony Allden Nenorial Cup 98-99 Walsall Sen.Cup Winners 2002

Founded: 1953 Nickname: Swifts
Colours: Yellow/green/yellow Change : I Blue
Sponsors: Need -A-Skip-Hire Ltd.
Midweek matches: Tuesday
Programme: 24 pages, £1.00
Editor: Phillip Crowley President:.L. Fitzpatrick
Chairman: James Latham V-C D.Wright
Manager: Ron Tranter Ass.Man:T.Edmead
Coach: J.Capaldi Physio: D.Crump
2002-2003
Capt: Neil bennett P.o.Y.: Greg Walters
Top Scorer: Ryan Allmark 22. Career top scorer

BROCTON

Secretary: Terry Homer.124 John Street,Chadsmoor,Cannock WS11 5HR
Tel No: 01543 571964
Ground:C/o Heath Hayes F.C.Coppice Colliery, Heath Hayes, Cannock Staffs (07976 269280)
Capacity: Seats: Cover: Floodlights: Clubhouse:
Directions: From South: From Cannock ,take Lichfield Road and aftyer 2.5 miles take first right after Texaco garage.
PREVIOUS Leagues: Lichfield Premier, Staffs County Lg (DSouth)idland League
HONOURS Rugeley & District League, Cannock Chase League (6), Staffs.Co.Lg (South) 85-6 Staffs County Lg Cup (6/8),Staffs F.A.Vase 97,00
Walsall Challenge Cup,Lichfield Prem Lg Cup

FACT FILE
Formed: 1937
Nickname: The Badgers
Sponsor:
Colours: Green & White/White/Green
Change colours:
Midweek Matches:Wednesday
Programme Editor:
Website: http:/hometown.aol.co.uk
CLUB PERSONNEL
Chairman: Brian Townsend
Vice Chairman:
President:
Manager:
Assistant Manager:
Physio:

CASTLE VALE KINGS HEATH

Secretary: Stuart Maddocks, 37 Rowheath Road, Cotteridge, Birmingham B30 2EP
Tel: 0121 604 7543
Ground: Groundshare with Alvechurch F.C. See their section for details
Directions: As Alvechurch F.C.
HONOURS Midland Comb. Div 1 R-up 92-93, Div 2 R-up 82-83, Presidents Cup R-up 79-80 81-82 92-93; Birmingham Chall. Vase R-up 86-87; Worcester Sen Urn 96-97, Chall. Cup R-up 96-97
PREVIOUS Names: Horse Shoe FC; Kings Heath Amateur; Kings Heath
Ground: Shirley Town (pre-1994)
Player progressing: Geoff Scott (Stoke C.)

Founded: 1964
Nickname: The Kings
Colours: Old Gold/black/gold
Change Colours: All white

Programme: 12 pages
Editor: M Kite

Chairman: Ray Kite
Manager: Clive Seeley
Asst. Man. / Coach: ???
Physio: ???

COLESHILL TOWN

Secretary: Des Green,93 Elmdon Lane, Marston Green, Birmingham B37 7DN (0121 770 7873)
Ground: Pack Meadow, Packington Lane, Coleshill, Birmingham B46 3JQ (01675-463259)
Directions: M6 jct 4 then A446 to A4117 towards Coleshill, Packington Lane forks from A4117, south of village and ground is 150 yds on right.
Capacity: 3,000 Seats: 50 Cover: 50 Floodlights: Yes Shop: Badges available
Clubhouse: Bar open 7 nights a week. Bar manager resident.
Previous League: Mercian League
Honours: Mercian Lg 75-76, Walsall Snr Cup 82-83 R-up 83-84, Midland Comb. R-up 83-84, Div 2 69-70 R-up 74-75, Invitation Cup 70, Presidents Cup R-up x2 67-69
Club Records: Attendance: 1,000v Aston Villa
Players progressing: Gary Shaw (Aston Villa)

Founded: 1894
Nickname: Coalmen
Colours: Green/black/green
Change Colours: Blue/white/blue
Midweek matches: Tuesday
Programme: 30p. Editor: Alan Backett
Chairman: Mark Bishop
Manager: Mick Beadle
2003-2004
Player of the Year: D.Wilkes
Top Scorer: C.Davies
2004-2005 Captain: D.Wilkes

CONTINENTAL STAR

Secretary: Gary Christie, 21 Spouthouse Lane, Great Barr B43 5PX
Tel: 0121 357 1044 (H) 07752 202802 (M)
email: soccer@continentalstar.fsnet.co.uk
Ground: Red Lion Ground,Somerfield Road, Walsall WS32EJ (019222 405835)

Clubhouse: Bar open 7 nights a week and is available for hire. Bar manager resident
HONOURS: Midland Comb Div One R-up 96-97; Birmingham Vase.
Jack Mould Cup R-up Invitation Cup Winners. JW Hunt Cup winners

Founded: 1973
Colours: All white
Change Colours: All blue

Website: www..continentalstar.fsnet.co.uk

Chairman:Keith John Tel: 07956429046 (M)

COVENTRY MARCONI F.C.

Chairman: D.Abercrombie Vice-Chairman: B.Olsen Press Officer: P Scanlon
Secretary: D.Wilson, 60 Craven Avenue, Binley Woods, Coventry. CV3 2JT (02476 544296)

Ground: Allard Way, Copswood, Coventry Tel: 02476 635992
Capacity 1,500 Seats: 92 Cover: Yes, Seats and standing Floodlights:Yes
Clubhouse: 12-11 Saturdays 6.00-11.00 weekdays
Record Attendance: 4,500 v A.W.A.Baginton Evening Telegraph Cup 1945-46
HONOURS: Midland Comb> Prem Div R-up, Div 1 96-97, Presidents Cup 96-97 , Endsleigh Comb.Cup 2001-02. Charity Cup Winners 02-3, 03-4 Endsleigh Comb. Cup R-up 03-04
Only winners of Coventry Evening Telegraph Cup (7 years), R-up Endslegh Comb Cup (3)
Players Progressing: Mattie Lewis (Kidderminster H) and Luke McCormick (Plymouth Argyle)

Formed: 1923
Sponsors: Home Heating
Colours: White with blue trim/bluewhite
Change colours: All red

Programme: 32 pages Price: 50p
Editor P.Scanlon

Manager: P.Mills
Assistant Manager:S.Shaw
Physio: S.Wilson

COVENTRY SPHINX

Match Secretary/Secretary: Neil Long, 9 Villa Road, Coventry.VCV6 3DB
Tel Nos: 02476 260877 (H) 07973 371942 (M)
Ground: Sphinx Drive, off Siddeley Avenue, Stoke Aldermoor, Coventry Tel: 01203 451361
Social Club Tel.: 02476 451361
Directions:
Capacity: 2,000 Covered Seating: 100 Covered Standing: 150 Floodlights: Yes
HONOURS: MFC Premier R-up: 2001-02 MFC Cup Wiinners 2001-02 Cov.Eve.Tel Cup 60-61
2003-2004: Top Scorer: Tom Thacker P.o.Y.: Paul John

FACT FILE
Formed: 1946
Colours: Sky blue & white/black/white
Change Colours: All red
Midweek Matchday: Tuesday

Chairman: Vic Jones
Manager: Martin Ahcroft
Asst. Man.: GezHalton
Captain: Danny McSheffrey
First Team Coach: Paul Charnley
Physio: Steve Harris

DUDLEY SPORTS

Secretary: John Lewis, 6 Hern Rd., Brieley Hill, West Mids DY5 2PW
Tel: 01384 895782
Ground: Hillcrest Avenue, Brierley Hill, West Mids. Tel: 01384 826420

Directions: From Stourbridge, turn off the ring road to Amblecote turn right at the third set of lights. Or from Dudley passing through Brierley Hill town centre. A-Z map ref 4H page 67.

Honours:MFC Presidents Cup Winners: 1989-90 and 1989-90

FACT FILE

Colours: Green /black/ green

Chairman: Ashley Forrest
01384 359043

FECKENHAM

Secretary: Glynn Carr, 37 Tennyson Road, Redditch, Worcs. B97 5BL
Tel No: 01527 454800 (messsages only please)
Ground: Groundshare with Redditch United F.C.
Valley Stadium, Bromsgrove Road, Redditch B97 4RN Tel: 01527 67450
Capacity: 5,000 Cover: 2,000 Seats: 400 Floodlights: Yes
Directions: M42 , Junction 4 take A38 towards Bromsgrov to Golf Course. Left at roundabout - A448 towards Redditch. Aftyer five miles take third exit off roundabout, cross over dual carriage-way, . First right into Birchfield Road, pastthe Foxlydiate Pubkic House.. First left into Red Lane leading into Bromsgrove rRoad. Vallley Stadium is approx 3/4 mile on the left
Honours: MFC Div 2 Champions 196-97 Div 3 95-96 Worcester League (3) Redditch Lg.1920-21 MFC Urn Winners 95-96 Worcs Royal Infirmary 03-04 Smedley Cooke (2) Worcs Sen Urn 01-02

FACT FILE

Formed: 1881
Nickname: The Millers

Colours: Green & White Hoops/Green/Green
Change Colours: All Yellow
Programme Editor: Roger N ewbold

Chairman: Malcolm Hawkes
Tel No: 01527 893341

HIGHGATE UNITED

Secretary: Simon Pretty, 8 Monastry Drive,Solihull,B91 1DN (0121 706 0933)
Ground: The Coppice, Tythe Barn Lane, Shirley, Solihull B90 1PH (0121 7444194)
Directions: A34 from City through Shirley, fork right B4102 (Tanworth Lane), half mile then right into Dickens Heath Rd, then first right & ground on the left. 100yds from Whitlocks End (BR)
Capacity: 5,000 Seats: 250 Covered: 750 Floodlights: Yes
Clubhouse: Members Club open Tue to Thur, Sat & Sun. Light refreshments available weekends
HONOURS Midland Comb (3) 72-75 (Div 2 66-67 68-69 71-72), Lg Cup (5) 72-74 75-77 84-85 (R-up 78-79 92-93); Presidents Cup 70-71 85-86); Tony Allden Mem. Cup 74-75;Invit. Cup 68-69 71-72 85-86; West Mids All. 63-64; Birmingham Snr Cup 73-74
CLUB RECORDS Att: 4,000 v Enfield, FA Amateur Cup QF 1967+ 31,632 at Villa Parkv Enfield
Players progressing: John Gayle (Wimbledon), Keith Leonard (A Villa), Geoff Scott (Leicester C.)

Founded: 1947 Nickname: The Gate
Colours:Red/Black/Red & Black
Change Colours: All white
Midweek matches: Tuesday
Programme: 28 pages, 50p
Editor: Terry Bishop (0676 22788)

Chairman: Terry Bishop
Treasurer: G Read
Press Officer: N C Sawyer
Manager: Jim Simms
Physio: Richard Flynn

LEAMINGTON

Secretary: Brian Knibb, 61 Villiers St, Leamington Spa, Warwicks. CV32 5YA
(01926 429066)

Ground: New Windmill Ground, Harbury Lane, Whitnash, Leamington Spa, Warwicks CV33 9JR Tel 07866 348712 Capacity:5,000
Directions: From M40 follow signs for LeamingtonSpa.On outskirts of town,right at roundabout for Harbury. Cross Leamington-Bishops Tachbrook road two miles along Harbury Lane to The Fosse Way Ground which is on left.

Covered Seats:120Covered Standing:600Floodlights: Yes

Record Attendance: 1.263 v Rugby Town 2001

Previous Names: Leamington Town, Lockheed Leamington, AP Leamington.

Clubhouse New Construction Bars and hot food on match days to open soon. Shop: Yes

Honours Midland CombinationPremier Division Runners Up 03-04

Div 1 R-Up 2001-02, Div 2 Winners 2000-02

Formed 1891 Re-Formed:2000-2001
Nickname: The Brakes
Colours: Gold/ Black/ Gold. Change: White
Midweek Matchday: Tuesday
Prog- Price:50p Pages: 24 Ed: Roger Vincent
Chairman: Mick Brady
Pres: David Hucker
Deputy sChairman: Vic Shepherd
Match Sec: Terry Ford (01926 771277 (H)
Manager: Jason Cadden
Asst.Manager: Keith Orme
Physio: T.B.A.
2003-2004 Top scorer: Paul Nicholls 33
Captain: Steve Thompson
P.o.Y.: Josh Blake

MASSEY-FERGUSON

Secretary: Terry Borras, Massey Ferguson FC, c/o Massey Ferguson Social Club, Broad Lane, Coventry CV5 9LA. Tel: 02476 675745 (H) 07909 685137 (M)
Ground: Massey-Ferguson Sports Ground, Banner Lane, Tile Hill, Coventry (01203 694400)
Directions: A45 to Meridan turn (B4104). Over two traffic islands, turn rightat 3rd island into Pickford Grange Lane, continue to Pickford Green Lane, &Hockley Lane, left into Broad Lane, right into Banner Lane, 3rd entrance right
Seats: 70 Cover: 200 Floodlights: Yes Clubhouse: Not on ground
HONOURS Midland Comb. Div 1 94-95, Div 2 93-94, Chall. Vase 93-94, Chall Cup 94-95, Presidents Cup 94-95; Coventry Evening Telegraph Cup (3) B'ham Co Vase: 94-5 Jack Mould Trophy 94-95 Tony Allden Memorial 95-96
PREVIOUS League: Coventry Alliance (pre-1993)

FACT FILE
Formed: 1956
Nickname : The Tractormen
Colours: Red & Black stripes,Black,Black
Change Colours: Yellow/ Blue / White

Programme: Yes
Chairman: Joe Swords
Manager: John Halford, Geoff Brassington
Coach: Carl Lascelles
Physio: Joe Doolan

MEIR K.A.

Secretary: Chris Robinson, 12 The Broadway, Meir, Stoke-on-Trent ST3 5PE Tel: 07759 302537
e-mail: chris.meirka@tiscali.co.uk Website: www.meirka.co.uk
Ground: Kings Park, Hilderstone Road, Meir Heath, Stoke-on-Trent Tel: 01782 388465
Directions: M6 jct 14, A34 to Stone, A520 to Rough Close then Meir Heath, turnright (B5066) ground approx 1 mile on right. 3m Blythe Bridge (BR)Clubhouse: Open matchdays. Hot food .
Capacity: 5,000 Seats: 200 Cover: 250 Floodlights: Yes Club Shop: No
HONOURS:Staffs Snr Lg 88-89, 90-91; Staffs FA Vase 93-94; Walsall & Dist Sen Cup 89-90; Mid Comb Prem Lge R-up 96-97; Mid Comb Lge Chall Cup R-up 97-98
PREVIOUS Leagues: Staffs Alliance/ Staffs Snr 84-92 Ground: Normacot Rec.
Names: 'The Station' & 'Shoulder of Mutton.'
2003-2004 Top Scorer: Darren Johnson Captain: Darren Reaney

Founded: 1972 Nickname: Kings
Colours: Yellow/navy/navy
Change colours: All Red
Midweek matchday: Wednesday
Programme: 32 pages 50p
Editor: Debbie Robinson (01782 332152)
President: Peter Bott Chairman: Des Reaney
Vice Chairman: Graham Lovatt
Manager: Des Reaney
Coaches: Scott Reaney & John Johnstone
Press Officer: Secretary
Commercial Mgr: Russ Perry (01538 756795)

NUNEATON GRIFF

Secretary: Pete Kemp,205 Haunchwood Road,Nuneaton, Warwicks. CV10 8DS
Tel: 02476 737459 (H) 07761611338 (M)
Ground: The Pingles Stadium, Avenue Road, Nuneaton. Tel: 024 76 37 0688
Directions: Avenue Road (A4252) leads to Cedar Tree Pub traffic lights, where you turn left into the stadium car park service road.
Capacity: 2,000 Seats: 238 Cover: 400 Floodlights: Yes Club Shop: Badges (0247 6345023)
Clubhouse: Yes / Usual Licensing hours Tel: 024 7673 5344 (Social Club)
HONOURS: Coventry Alliance 97-98, Coventry Telegraph Cup (3)s, Cov. Charity Cup 99, BCFA Junior Cup 98-99 R-up 99-00, Midland Comb Prem Div 99-00 00-01 (NB Only club to be placed in Premier Division on application and win title in first season.) Cov Tel Challenge Cup 00-01, Endsleigh Challenge Cup 00-01, BCFC Chal Vase R-up 00-01, BC MidweemkF'lit CUPr-up 03-04

Founded: 1972-73 Nickname: Griff
Colours: Blue & white/white/ blue
Change colours: All yellow
Midweek Matchday:Wednesday
Programme:20 pages 50p
Editor: Rod Grubb (02476 345023)
Chairman: John Gore
Man: Dave Stringer Capt: Danny Sharples
Captain:Lee Bateman
2003-04
P.O.Y.& Top Goalscorer:Matthew Dyer

PERSHORE TOWN 88

Secretary: Barbara Hodgkiss Tel Nos: 01905 452885 or 0787 9845539
Ground: King George V Playing Fields, King Georges Way, Pershore, Worcs (01386556902).
Directions: M5 jct 7, B4084 to Pershore (8 miles) cross 1st lights in Pershore,at 2nd lights turn left & fold road round into King Georges Way, ground immediately on left.
Capacity: 4,000 Seats: 200 Cover: 200 Floodlights: Yes (157 lux) Club Shop:No
Clubhouse: Open every evening, and all day Saturdays and Sundays
HONOURS Midland Comb Prem 93-94, Div 2 89-90; Worcs Jnr Cup 90-91, Robert Biggart Cup (5), R-up (3); Worcs Snr Urn 95-96, R-up 92-93, Jack Mould Cup 90-91, Alfred Terry Cup 90-91 Martley Hosp. Cup('A') 90-91. Pershore Hospital Charity Cup 2001-02
RECORDS: Atttendance: 1,356 v Yeading, FA Cup 4th Qual. Rd 23/10/93 Scorer: Simon Judge
PREVIOUS Leagues: Midland Comb 89-90 90-94 Midland Alliance 94-95, 99-00

FACTFILE
Founded: 1988 Nickname: The Town
Colours: Blue & White,blue,blueChange:Red
Midweek matchday: Tuesday
Prog: 20 pages, 60p Ed: Graham Merchant
Chairman: Graham Merchant
Vice-Chairman: Ian Payne
Manager: Nigel Russell
Captain: Simon Judge
2003-2004
Top Scorer & Player of the Year:
Simon Judge

PILKINGTON XXX

Chairman: M.Beeney
Secretary: John McVey, 84 Clee Road,West Heath,Birmingham B31 3RU (07715 011043)
Ground: Triplex Sports,Eckersall Road,Kings Norton, Birmingham B38 8SR
Capacity: Seats: Cover: Floodlights: Clubhouse:
Directions: From Cotteridge take A444 past Kings Norton station. Turn right after 150yds yards across dual carriageway at petrol station, after approx 300 yds turn right at sharp bend and ground is on the right.
HONOURS MFC Div 2 Champions, 01-02 B'ham Works F.A. 96-97, 03-04 MFC Div 1 R-up, Div 3 98-99 MFC CHallenge Vase 01-02 R-up 02-03 B'ham Jinior Cup 01-02 WBA Shield 97-8 Wade Victory 97-8 Smedley Cooke 00-01

FACT FILE
Formed: 2002
NIckname: The Glassmen
Sponsor:
Colours: Green/green/white
Change colours:
Midweek Matches:
Reserves' Lge:
Programme:
Editor:

SHIFNAL TOWN

Secretary: Glyn Davies, 30 Drayton Road, Shifnal, Shropshire, TF11 8BT (01952460326 H)
Ground: Phoenix Park, Coppice Green Lane, Shifnal, Shropshire.
Directions: M54 jct 3, A41 towards Newport, 1st left for Shifnal (3 miles), in Shifnal take 1st right, and sharp right again up Coppice Green Lane, ground800yds on left past Idsall School.
Capacity: 3,000 Seats: 224 Cover: 300 Floodlights: Yes
Clubhouse: Not on ground but in Newport Rd, Shifnal. Open Mon-Fri 7.30-11pm, Sat 7.30-11pm , Sun 12-3 & 7.30-10-30 Club Shop: No
HONOURS West Mids Lg 80-81 81-82 Div 1 78-79, Shropshire Snr Cup 80-81 90-91 92-93.
BEST SEASON FA Cup: 1982-83 FA Vase: 1983-84
PREVIOUS Leagues: Wellington (Dist.) 64-69; Shropshire County 69-77 85-93; West Midlands 77-85; Midland Comb. 94-95; Midland Alliance 95-2003

Founded: 1964 Nickname: None.
Colours:All red & white
Change cols: Blue & white/white/blue & white
Midweek matchday: Tuesday
Prog: 30 pages, 60p Editor: G.Davies
Chairman: G.Davies President: D Adams
Press Off: K Fullerton 01952 405274
Manager: Ken Howells Ass Manr: John Powell
Coach: Dez Pritchard Physio: Charlott Lewis
2003-2004
P.o.Y.: Craig Vale Top Scorer: Andrew Syder
2004-2005: Captain: David Taylor

Back Row (L-R): Mark Pound, Craig Vale, Stuart Woodman, Phil Luke, Mick Flavell, Mick Kiernan, Andrew Syder, John Powell. Front Row (L-R): Duncan Gazzillo, Roger Clarke, Stuart Cassells, Mark Lysons, David Taylor, Luke Brown.

SOUTHAM UNITED

Secretary: Alan D Freeman,3 Old Road, Southam, Warwickshire Cv47 1GF (01926 817711)
Ground: Banbury Road Ground, Southam, Leamington Spa.Warwicks CV 47 0BJ
Tel: 01926 812091

Directions: A423 - 12 miles south of coventry on the Banbury side of Southam
Capacity: 2000 Seats: 200 Cover: 250 Floodlights: Yes
Clubhouse: Yes, with food available Club Shop: No
HONOURS Midland Comb. Prem. Div. R-up 97-98: Birmingham County Sat. Vase 97-98; Coventry Chall.Cup; Coventry City Cup; Coventry & N. Warwicks Lge Prem.& Eve Tel C. 55-6
RECORD Attendance: 1,500 v Coventry City, friendly 86-87

Founded: 1905
Colours: Yellow & Royal Blue/blue/blue
Change colours:White & Black/black/black
Midweek Matchday: Tuesday
Programme: 24 pages 50p Editor: Charles Hill

Chairman: Charles Hill
Presss Officer: Czaire Hughes
Manager: Ian Clarke
Assistant Manager: Dave Sturman
Player/Coach: Rob Morey
Physio: Bill Rutledge

WEST MIDLANDS POLICE

Secretary: John Black, 57 Grosvenor Close, Sutton Coldfield, W.Mids. B75 6RP. 0121 308 7673
Ground: Police Sports Grd, `Tally Ho', Pershore Rd, Edgbaston, Birm'm B57RN (01216268228)
Directions: 2 miles SW of city on A441 Pershore Rd. Ground is on the left 50yds past Priory Rd. lights (Warks County Cricket Ground).3 miles from B'ham New St (BR) - Buses 45 & 47 from city.
Capacity: 2,500 Seats: 224 Covered: 224 Floodlights: Yes
Clubhouse: 3 bars including snooker room, ballroom, kitchen. Hot & cold food. Open all day.
Honours: MFC PremierChampions 90-91 R-up 93-94 Cup Winners 74-75 Tony Allden Mem. 75-76 R-up 91-92 Worcs Sen Urn:(3), R-up (3) MFC Cup, R-up 85-6, UK Police Cup (5) R-Up (6)
BEST SEASON FA Vase: Quarter Final 91-92 FA Cup: 2nd Q ual Rd 91-92

Founded: 1974
Colours: Red & black/ black/black
Change Colours: All Blue
Midweek matchday: Tues/Thurs.
Programme: 32 pages, £1.00
Editor: D.Coulson (01283 533791)
Website: www.wmpfc.org.uk

President: Chief Constable Paul Scott-Lee
Chairman: Ass. Chief Constable: Paul Blewitt
Manager: Jim Scott Coach: Tony Workman

DIVISION ONE CLUBS

ATHERSTONE TOWN
Ground: Sheepy Road, Atherstone, Warwickshire
Tel: 01827 717829

BURNTWOOD
Secretary: David Cox, 12 Galway Road, Burntwood, Staffs. WS7 8DT
Tel No: 07931 626887 (M)
Ground: Memorial Institute, Rugeley Road, Burntwood. Tel: 01543 675578
Colours: Red and Blue stripes/Blue/Red

CADBURY ATHLETIC
Secretary: Gerry Boyle,1 Greenway Gardens, Kings Norton, Birmingham B38 9RY (0121 628 6533 (H) 07974 382986 (M)
Ground: Cadbury Recreation Ground, Bournville Lane, B'ham. B14 6DL Tel No: 0121 458 2000 x 3316 or 0121 454 4264 Colours: All Purple.

FAIRFIELD VILLA
Secretary/Press Officer: C W Harris, 28 ShelleyClose, Catshill, Bromsgrove B61 0NH Tel: 01527 877203
Ground: Bromsgrove Rvrs F.C. See their details.
Colours: All Red & Black

HEATHER ATHLETIC
Ground: St John's Park, Ravenstone Road, Heather, Leicestershire
Tel: 01530 263986

KENILWORTH TOWN
Secretary: Mrs Sally McKenzie, K.T.F.C.,Marlborough House, Holly Walk, Leamington Spa CV32 4JA 01926 855247 (H) 886632 (W)
Ground: K.T.F.C. Gypsy Lane (off Rouncil Lane), Kenilworth, Warwicks. Tel: 01926 50851
Colours: All blue

KNOWLE
Secretary: Roger Whittick, 149 Richmond Road, Solihull B92 7RZ
Tel No :0121 684 2753 (H) 07944 753551 (M)
Ground: Hampton Rd, Knowle, Solihull , W.Mid B93 0NX Tel: 01564 779807
Colours: Red/black/black

LEAMINGTON HIBERNIAN
Ground: Racing Club Warwick FC, Townsend Meadow, Hampton Road, Warwick
Tel: 01926 495786

LITTLETON
Five Acres, Pebworth Road, North Littleton, Evesham, Worcestershire

LOUGHBOROUGH F.C.
Secretary: John Belton: 51 Farndale Drive, Loughborough, Leics.LE112RG Tel No: 01509 231583 (H) 01509 231583 (W)
Ground: The Drome, Derby Road Playing Fields, Derby Road, Loughborough Tel: 01509 610022
Colours: All white and blue.

NEWHALL UNITED
Ground: Hewfields Ground, St Johns Drive, Newhall, Swadlincote, Derbyshire
Tel: 01283 551029

NORTHFIELD TOWN
Secretary: Matthew Kirby, 53 Park Dale Drive, Birmingham B31 4RN
Tel: 0121 604 2202 (H) 07876 143121 (M)
Ground: Shenley Lane Comm. Assoc. & Sports Centre, 472 Shenley Lane, Birmingham B29 4HZ
Tel: 0121 478 3900 Colours: yellow/blue/yellow

OLD HILL TOWN
Secretary: Scott Wilshaw, 10 Rowley Hill View, Cradley Heath, West Midlands. B64 7ER 01384 564466 (H) 07976 849022 (M)
Ground: Hingleys, Bluebell Rd, Cradley Heath, West Midlands. (01384 566827)
Colours: All maroon

POLESWORTH NORTH WARWICK
Secretary: Mrs Lynn Wright, 69 Chaytor Rd,.Polesworth, Tamworth Staffs. B78 1JS (01827 892896 or 0797 389 8523)
Ground: North Warwick Sports Ground, Hermitage Hill, Tamworth Road, Polesworth, Warks.
Colours: Green/ Black/ Black

STOCKINGFORD AA
Ground: The Pavilion, Ansley Road, Stockingford, Nuneaton, Warwicks. Tel: 02476 387743

THIMBLEMILL R.E.C.
Secretary: Gerry Houten, 86 Gower Road, Halesowen, W.Midlands, B62 9BT Tel Nos: 0121 422 3357 (H) 07966 374771 (M)
Ground: Thimblemill Recreation, Thimblemill Road, Smethwick, Warley. Tel: 0121 429 2459
Colours: Red & Blue/ Blue/ Blue.

TIPTON TOWN RESERVES
Ground: Tipton Sports Academy, Wednesbury Oak Road, Tipton, West Midlands
Tel: 0121 502 5534 / 556 5067

WILMCOTE SPORTS & SOCIAL
Secretary: Jennifer Smith, 19 Nightingale Close, Spernal Lane, Great Alne, Warwicks. B49 6PE 01789 488077 (H)
Ground: The Patch, Rear of Wilmcote S.S.Club, Astton Cantlow Road, Wilmcote, Stratford on Avon (01789 297895)
Colours: Green & yellow / Green / Yellow

NORTH BERKSHIRE LEAGUE

President: W J Gosling **Chairman:** C D Roberts
Hon. GeneralSecretary: D B Rich
14 Sandy Lane, Shrivenham, Swindon, Wilts SN6 8DZ
Tel: 01793 782270 07779 860255

FINAL LEAGUE TABLE 2003/04

DIVISION ONE	P	W	D	L	F	A	Pts
1. Kintbury Rangers	22	16	3	3	58	17	51
2. Saxton Rovers	22	13	4	5	49	22	43
3. East Hendred	22	12	4	6	46	32	40
4. Marcham	22	11	2	9	43	41	35
5. Drayton	22	9	6	7	46	44	33
6. Lambourn Sports	22	9	5	8	52	41	32
7. Warborough & S.	22	10	2	10	48	52	32
8. Blewbury	22	9	3	10	49	69	30
9. Benson	22	7	6	9	35	46	27
10. Long Wittenham A.	22	7	3	12	44	42	24
11. Sutton Courteney	22	5	5	12	38	57	20
12. Childrey United	22	0	5	17	21	66	5

2003/04 CUP HONOURS

	WINNERS	RUNNERS-UP
NORTH BERKS CUP	KINTBURY RANGERS	SUTTON COURTENAY
NORTH BERKS CHARITY SHIELD	LAMBOURN SPORTS	DIDCOT CASUALS
WAR MEMORIAL CUP	SUTTON COURTENAY	CHALLOW UTD.
NORTH BERKS LEAGUE CUP	BENSON A.F.C. RES.	WARBOROUGH RES.
A.G.KINGHAM CUP	SHRIVENHAM RES.	A.F.C. WALLINGFORD 'A'
NAIRNE PAUL TROPHY	A.F.C. WALLINGFORD 'A'	SAXTON ROVERS RES.

2004/05 CONSTITUTION

Ardington & Lockinge
Blewbury
Drayton
East Hendred
Faringdon Town
Grove Rangers
Harwell International
Lambourn Sports
Long Wittenham Athletic
Marcham
Saxton Rovers
Sutton Courtenay

NORTHAMPTONSHIRE COMBINATION

SPONSORED BY: TRAVIS PERKINS

Founded:

Chairman: Keith Philpot

Secretary: David Jarrett

FINAL LEAGUE TABLE 2003-04

PREMIER DIVISION	P	W	D	L	F	A	Pts
1. Moulton	30	21	6	3	84	36	69
2. Roade (-3pts)	30	22	4	4	69	32	67
3. Harpole	30	19	5	6	71	34	62
4. Kettering Nomads	30	18	6	6	88	46	60
5. Milton	30	17	6	7	68	35	57
6. Caledonian Strip Mills	30	16	8	6	88	33	56
7. Heyford Athletic	30	16	5	9	65	48	53
8. Crick Athletic	30	11	7	12	51	54	40
9. Rushden Rangers	30	11	2	17	54	68	35
10. Kislingbury (-1pt)	30	8	11	11	35	42	34
11. Weldon United	30	8	5	17	53	77	29
12. Cold Ashby Rovers	30	7	6	17	34	55	27
13. Harborough Spencer United (-3pts)	30	7	7	16	44	63	25
14. Weedon	30	5	5	20	35	84	20
15. Stanwick Rovers	30	3	8	19	28	102	17
16. Potterspury (-1pt)	30	3	5	22	37	95	13

PREMIER DIVISION 2003-04	1	2	3	4	5	6	7	8	9	10	11	12	13	14	15	16
1 Caledonian Strip Mills		2-2	3-0	2-0	1-2	3-1	3-1	2-2	1-2	2-2	5-0	3-0	5-0	6-0	4-0	2-0
2 Cold Ashby Rovers	0-5		1-2	0-0	0-2	0-2	2-3	1-1	0-3	0-3	1-0	0-1	2-1	4-0	1-0	2-1
3 Crick Athletic	2-2	2-2		0-2	1-0	1-2	1-4	0-0	0-3	2-6	5-2	1-4	5-0	2-0	3-1	1-3
4 Harborough Spencer United	0-6	3-2	0-2		1-3	0-2	4-1	0-1	2-4	0-2	1-2	1-3	3-5	3-3	1-1	1-1
5 Harpole	2-1	4-0	1-1	2-0		2-1	0-2	2-0	4-1	1-1	4-0	2-3	4-1	0-1	2-0	3-2
6 Heyford Athletic	1-4	2-1	3-1	2-3	3-2		2-4	2-1	1-1	1-1	2-2	1-0	5-4	7-2	2-0	3-1
7 Kettering Nomads	3-3	1-2	1-1	3-2	2-3	3-1		5-0	2-1	4-1	2-1	3-3	1-3	2-2	5-1	5-1
8 Kislingbury	1-1	0-3	2-1	1-0	2-2	1-4	0-0		0-0	1-2	1-0	0-2	3-4	4-0	1-0	0-2
9 Milton	1-1	3-2	0-3	2-2	3-1	1-0	2-1	1-1		0-2	2-0	1-2	1-0	6-0	4-0	2-1
10 Moulton	3-2	2-2	2-1	6-2	3-3	2-2	0-3	3-1	2-1		4-0	0-2	2-1	5-0	5-1	6-0
11 Potterspury	3-3	1-0	2-4	2-3	0-2	2-4	1-9	1-1	1-7	0-3		1-3	6-3	2-4	2-3	2-2
12 Roade	1-0	2-2	1-1	2-1	0-5	2-1	1-1	1-0	2-1	2-3	3-1		1-0	6-0	3-0	4-0
13 Rushden Rangers	3-2	1-0	0-1	0-3	0-2	2-1	2-4	1-1	1-2	0-2	4-0	0-1		4-0	5-3	4-3
14 Stanwick Rovers	0-5	2-1	1-1	1-1	0-4	0-4	0-4	1-1	2-2	0-7	1-1	1-4	1-4		1-2	2-2
15 Weedon	0-1	2-1	1-3	2-2	2-2	2-3	2-7	1-7	0-9	2-3	4-0	1-2	0-0	2-1		1-1
16 Weldon United	1-8	4-0	5-3	0-3	2-5	0-0	1-2	0-1	1-2	0-1	5-2	1-8	4-1	6-2	3-1	

PREMIER DIVISION CUP

FIRST ROUND

Crick Athletic	v	Kettering Nomads	2-3
Kislingbury	v	Heyford Athletic	1-3*
Milton	v	Stanwick Rovers	6-0
Moulton	v	Harborough Spencer	2-1
Potterspury	v	Weldon United	2-1
Roade	v	Caledonian Strip Mills	2-1
Rushden Rangers	v	Harpole	2-3
Weedon	v	Cold Ashby Rovers	3-2

QUARTER-FINALS

Kettering Nomads	v	Heyford Athletic	3-1
Milton	v	Harpole	2-3*
Moulton	v	Potterspury	6-1
Weedon	v	Roade	1-2

SEMI-FINALS

Kettering Nomads	v	Roade	2-1
Moulton	v	Harpole	2-0

THE FINAL (10th April at Northampton Town)

Moulton	v	Kettering Nomads	4-3

FINAL LEAGUE TABLE 2003-04

DIVISION ONE	P	W	D	L	F	A	Pts
1. Corby Hellenic (-3 pts)	26	20	5	1	86	23	62
2. Corby St Brendans	26	19	5	2	91	30	62
3. Islip United	26	13	6	7	56	42	45
4. Corby Legion Locos	26	13	5	8	69	45	44
5. Spratton	26	12	7	7	47	48	43
6. Stanion United	26	13	3	10	53	53	42
7. Whitefield Norpol	26	11	7	8	55	44	40
8. Corby Pegasus	26	10	4	12	47	51	34
9. Brixworth All Saints	26	9	7	10	42	47	34
10. Finedon Volta	26	6	5	15	40	56	23
11. Gretton	26	6	4	16	34	69	22
12. Earls Barton United	26	6	3	17	32	59	21
13. Clipston (-3 pts)	26	6	5	15	45	56	20
14. Weavers Old Boys (-1 pt)	26	3	4	19	34	108	12

MOULTON - Premier Division Champions. Photo: Gordon Whittington.

LEAGUE CONSTITUTION 2004-05

COLD ASHBY ROVERS

Stanford Road, Cold Ashby, Northants. NN6 6EW

CORBY CALEDONIAN STRIP MILLS

West Glebe South Pavillion, Cottingham Road, Corby, Northants. NN17 1EL

CORBY HELLENIC

Burghley Drive, Corby, Northants. NN18 8DY

CORBY ST BRENDANS

Corby Rugby Club, Rockingham Road, Corby, Northants

CRICK ATHLETIC

Crick Playing Field, (on main A428) Main Road, Northants. NN6 7TX

HARBOROUGH SPENCER UNITED

Market Harborough Leisure Centre, Northampton Road, Leics. LE16 8NH

HARPOLE

Harpole Playing Field, Larkhall Lane, Harpole, Northampton. NN7 4DP

HEYFORD ATHLETIC

Nether Heyford Playing Field, Nether Heyford, Northants NN7 3LL

KETTERING NOMADS

Orlingbury Road, Isham, Nr Kettering, Northants. NN14 1HY

KISLINGBURY

Playing Fields, Beech Lane, Kislingbury, Northampton. NN7 4AL

MILTON

Collingtree Road, Milton Malsor, Northampton. NN7 3AF

MOULTON

Brunting Road, Moulton, Northampton. NN3 7QX

ROADE

Connolly Way, off Hyde Road, Roade, Northants. NN7 2LU

RUSHDEN RANGERS

Hayden Road, Rushden, Northants. NN10 0HX

WEEDON

Jubilee Field, Bridge Street, Weedon, Northants. NN7 4PW

WELDON UNITED

Oundle Road, Weldon, Northants. NN17 3JT

CORBY HELLENIC - Division One Champions.

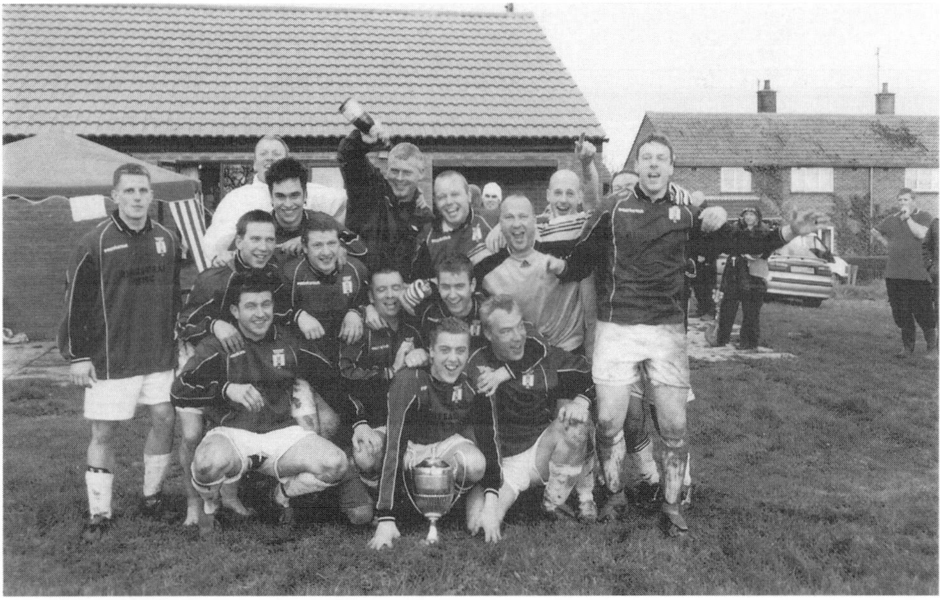

RINGSTEAD RANGERS - Division Two Champions.

PETERBOROUGH & DISTRICT LEAGUE

SPONSORED BY: MARSHALL

FINAL LEAGUE TABLE 2003-04

PREMIER DIVISION		P	W	D	L	F	A	Pts
1	Ortonians	30	23	4	3	85	31	73
2	Moulton Harrox	29	19	6	4	86	30	63
3	Leverington Sp	30	17	7	6	72	42	58
4	Hotpoint	30	17	7	6	65	42	58
5	Oundle Town	29	15	5	9	60	45	50
6	Alconbury	30	13	8	9	57	41	47
7	Peterboro Sport	30	13	8	9	60	46	47
8	Perkins Sports	30	13	7	10	56	42	46
9	Whittlesey United	30	13	4	13	64	60	43
10	Wimblington OB	30	9	9	12	44	45	36
11	Uppingham Town	30	8	11	11	55	59	35
12	Emneth Seniors	30	8	9	13	47	52	33
13	Stamford Bels	30	9	5	16	38	64	32
14	Ryhall United	30	6	8	16	44	71	25
15	Long Sutton Athletic	30	4	1	25	27	111	13
16	Pinchbeck United	30	1	3	26	16	95	6

PREMIER DIVISION 2003-04	1	2	3	4	5	6	7	8	9	10	11	12	13	14	15	16
1 Alconbury		1-1	1-0	1-2	3-2	2-4	1-2	0-1	0-0	0-1	6-0	2-1	6-0	4-3	4-1	3-0
2 EmnethSeniors	2-2		1-2	2-3	6-2	1-3	1-2	0-1	1-1	1-2	1-1	1-1	2-0	1-3	5-1	2-2
3 Hotpoint	2-0	3-1		1-1	4-2	0-0	0-4	1-1	3-2	2-3	2-0	2-0	1-0	3-3	2-1	1-1
4 Leverington Sp	0-0	1-1	2-2		2-1	4-4	1-2	8-2	1-0	0-0	8-1	2-1	6-0	2-1	2-1	0-0
5 Long SuttonAthletic	0-1	0-3	0-5	0-4		0-3	1-5	2-4	1-5	1-8	3-2	2-1	0-1	0-5	0-0	1-2
6 Moulton Harrox	1-0	4-0	0-2	3-0	7-0		3-1	p.p.	0-2	1-1	4-1	2-0	3-3	5-0	1-4	4-1
7 Ortonians	6-2	2-0	4-1	5-2	10-1	0-0		1-3	3-1	1-0	3-1	3-3	3-1	3-0	2-3	3-0
8 Oundle Town	0-1	3-1	3-5	0-1	7-1	2-1	0-1		3-1	3-3	3-1	4-0	2-1	2-2	0-1	0-1
9 Perkins Sports	0-2	3-1	2-2	6-3	2-0	0-3	1-1	1-2		1-0	2-0	3-0	4-2	1-1	2-0	1-3
10 Peterboro Sport	4-3	2-2	1-4	0-2	4-0	1-6	1-2	1-0	1-4		2-0	2-2	1-2	4-0	4-3	0-0
11 Pinchbeck United	1-1	2-2	1-3	0-2	1-3	1-5	0-5	2-1	1-4	0-4		0-1	0-1	0-5	0-5	0-6
12 Ryhall United	3-3	0-2	4-2	1-4	5-0	1-6	2-3	2-4	1-0	1-4	1-0		4-2	3-3	0-1	2-2
13 Stamford Bels	0-2	0-1	1-2	1-3	4-2	1-8	0-1	1-1	3-1	1-1	2-0	3-0		0-3	1-3	2-0
14 Uppingham Town	1-1	3-0	0-4	1-4	3-1	1-1	1-3	4-4	1-1	3-1	4-0	1-1	0-0		0-2	0-3
15 Whittlesey United	2-4	2-4	3-2	2-1	4-0	1-2	1-4	0-2	2-4	1-1	4-0	2-2	3-4	2-2		3-2
16 WimblingtonOB	1-1	0-1	0-2	3-1	0-1	0-2	0-0	1-2	1-1	0-3	2-0	6-1	1-1	3-1	3-6	

SATURDAY SENIOR CUP

FIRST ROUND

Hotpoint	v	Alconbury	2-4
Leverington Sports	v	Ryhall United	2-1
Ortonians	v	Emneth Seniors	2-2*, 4-2p
Perkins Sports	v	Wimblington Old Boys	2-1
Peterborough Sports	v	Uppingham Town	2-4
Pinckbeck United	v	Oundle Town	1-2
Stamford Belvedere	v	Long Sutton Athletic	4-3
Whittlesey United	v	Moulton Harrox	0-4

QUARTER-FINALS

Leverington Sports	v	Uppingham Town	0-1
Moulton Harrox	v	Stamford Belvedere	4-1
Oundle Town	v	Ortonians	0-1
Perkins Sports	v	Alconbury	2-3

SEMI-FINALS

Ortonians	v	Moulton Harrox	1-0
Uppingham Town	v	Alconbury	1-4

THE FINAL

Alconbury	v	Ortonians	2-3

LEAGUE CONSTITUTION 2004-05

Alconbury

Hotpoint

Leverington Sp

Long Sutton Athletic

Moulton Harrox

Ortonians

Oundle Town

Parson Drove 92

Perkins Sports

Peterboro Sport

Pinchbeck United

Ryhall United

Stamford Bels

Uppingham Town

Whittlesey United

Wimblington OB

THE NON-LEAGUE PAPER
ON SUNDAY/MONDAY

HINCKLEY STAR IS WORLD CUP CAPTAIN

TELFORD HAVE TWO WEEKS TO FIND BUYER

BARNET WANT ENGLAND MANAGER

WIN FA TROPHY FINAL TICKETS

FAB FOUR ARE GOING UP

Arena Supplies UK Tel: 07834 897055

LEAGUE PAPER
ON SUNDAY/MONDAY

KEEPER'S HELPING HAND RESCUES CHELSEA

CHAMPS CANVEY AIM FOR DOUBLE

HUCKNALL TAKE TITLE BUT LEIGH TAKE DROP

IS HIT
R TITLE

JAKO

READING LEAGUE

SPONSORED BY: OPUS PUBLICITY

Formed: 1988
Chairman: John Dell
General Secretary: Mark Rozzier - Tel: 0118 969 3235

FINAL LEAGUE TABLE 2003/04

SENIOR DIVISION		P	W	D	L	F	A	Pts
1.	Highmoor/IBIS	22	17	5	0	67	18	56
2.	Cookham Dean	22	12	9	1	50	26	45
3.	Marlow United	22	14	2	6	69	39	44
4.	Forest Old Boys	22	12	4	6	49	28	40
5.	Royal Mail	22	9	6	7	41	30	33
6.	Ascot United	22	10	3	9	41	47	33
7.	Hurst	22	7	5	10	30	40	26
8.	Mortimer	22	6	7	9	28	44	25
9.	Westwood United	22	5	6	11	27	38	21
10.	Reading YMCA	22	5	3	14	33	60	18
11.	West Reading	22	4	3	15	27	53	15
12	Checkendon Sports	22	3	3	16	19	58	12

NB – Midgham withdrew during the season. Their results are shown in the results grid but are expunged from the league table above.

SENIOR DIVISION 2003-04	1	2	3	4	5	6	7	8	9	10	11	12	13
1 Ascot United		1-0	2-4	1-3	1-3	5-0	1-4	-	2-1	3-1	2-2	2-1	0-1
2 Checkendon Sports	2-3		0-3	1-6	aw	0-0	0-3	-	2-3	1-5	2-1	2-1	2-1
3 Cookham Dean	1-1	5-0		2-2	0-0	1-0	2-2	-	2-2	1-0	2-5	3-1	3-3
4 Forest Old Boys	1-1	hw	0-1		0-3	5-0	5-2	-	0-1	2-0	4-3	3-2	3-1
5 Highmoor/IBIS	8-0	1-1	2-2	1-0		4-2	2-1	-	2-0	8-1	5-2	3-1	3-0
6 Hurst	1-0	6-2	1-3	0-0	0-3		2-4	-	1-1	3-1	2-2	0-0	2-1
7 Marlow United	7-2	2-1	1-2	3-0	1-3	4-3		-	5-1	2-2	0-3	6-1	4-1
8 Midgham	-	3-3	-	0-3	0-7	-	-		-	-	-	-	-
9 Mortimer	1-4	3-0	0-0	0-7	2-3	0-3	1-4	-		2-1	1-3	3-0	0-0
10 Reading YMCA	0-4	5-1	2-5	3-3	0-7	0-1	2-6	-	1-2		1-0	2-1	0-1
11 Royal Mail	1-2	3-0	1-1	2-1	1-1	0-1	3-1	-	1-1	4-0		2-0	0-0
12 West Riding	2-0	4-0	1-5	1-2	1-3	2-1	2-5	-	2-2	2-2	1-2		1-0
13 Westwood United	3-4	2-2	0-2	0-2	2-2	2-1	0-2	-	1-1	1-4	2-0	5-0	

hw denotes match awarded to home side. aw - match awarded to away side.

LEAGUE CONSTITUTION 2004-05

Ascot United

Berks County Sports

Cookham Dean

Forest Old Boys

Highmoor/IBIS

Hurst

Marlow United

Mortimer

Reading YMCA

Royal Mail

West Reading

Westwood United

Woodley Town

SOMERSET COUNTY LEAGUE

SOMERSET F.A.

Tel: 01761 410 280 Fax: 01761 410 477 Email: secretary@somersetfa.com

30 North Road, Midsomer Norton, Radstock, Somerset BA3 2QD

FINAL LEAGUE TABLE 2003-04

PREMIER DIVISION	P	W	D	L	F	A	Pts
1. Team Bath Reserves	34	22	4	8	85	40	70
2. Portishead	34	21	6	7	58	39	69
3. Radstock Town - **Promoted**	34	19	7	8	76	52	64
4. Backwell United Reserves	34	18	8	8	54	38	62
5. Mangotsfield United Reserves	34	18	7	9	99	63	61
6. Burnham United	34	16	8	10	80	56	56
7. Brislington Reserves	34	16	7	11	77	56	55
8. Bridgwater Town Reserves	34	15	7	12	61	66	52
9. Nailsea United	34	15	5	14	64	50	50
10. Fry Club	34	13	9	12	46	45	48
11. Paulton Rovers Reserves	34	13	9	12	52	53	48
12. Cleeve West Town	34	11	10	13	54	52	43
13. Castle Cary	34	12	7	15	56	62	43
14. Wells City	34	12	4	18	49	72	40
15. Welton Rovers Reserves	34	10	6	18	46	74	36
16. Stockwood Green (-1pt)	34	7	5	22	56	92	25
17. Keynsham Town Reserves	34	6	4	24	38	82	22
18. Westland United	34	2	7	25	29	88	13

PREMIER DIVISION 2003-04	1	2	3	4	5	6	7	8	9	10	11	12	13	14	15	16	17	18
1 Backwell United Reserves		4-0	1-1	3-3	2-3	1-1	1-1	0-3	2-2	1-0	1-2	3-0	1-0	2-1	1-0	3-1	1-1	2-0
2 Bridgwater Town Reserves	1-1		2-1	3-1	2-1	0-3	1-1	6-2	2-2	0-4	2-1	0-0	2-5	2-1	2-3	4-0	2-0	2-2
3 Brislington Reserves	1-2	4-0		2-4	3-2	3-2	1-0	1-1	3-1	1-1	1-1	1-2	5-2	3-0	4-2	1-2	2-1	3-0
4 Burnham United	0-4	7-1	3-1		0-2	4-0	3-2	1-1	4-0	2-4	5-1	2-3	1-4	1-1	2-2	1-1	3-0	2-1
5 Castle Cary	0-2	1-4	1-2	1-2		1-1	0-2	2-0	2-3	3-4	1-1	3-2	1-3	2-1	4-3	2-3	1-1	1-1
6 Cleeve West Town	1-0	5-0	2-2	1-0	3-1		1-2	2-0	3-3	2-0	5-1	1-2	3-1	2-2	1-1	1-2	2-0	1-1
7 Fry Club	1-0	1-0	2-4	1-1	0-2	0-0		0-2	3-1	0-3	2-1	1-1	2-2	2-1	0-2	3-1	1-1	1-1
8 Keynsham Town Reserves	2-3	1-2	1-4	0-6	0-1	2-0	2-0		0-2	3-0	3-3	0-2	0-1	1-3	0-5	1-1	0-2	1-2
9 Mangotsfield Town Reserves	6-1	1-2	4-1	2-3	3-1	3-0	0-4	4-1		4-2	0-0	1-3	3-3	7-1	3-1	7-1	5-1	4-1
10 Nailsea United	0-1	0-3	1-2	1-0	2-0	1-0	1-1	6-1	2-3		1-1	0-0	1-2	5-1	3-0	1-2	2-0	2-2
11 Paulton Rovers Reserves	0-2	0-0	2-1	3-4	2-4	3-1	1-0	2-0	2-5	3-1		0-2	0-0	2-2	0-1	2-1	3-1	1-1
12 Portishead	2-0	1-5	1-1	2-1	2-0	3-1	1-0	3-0	3-3	0-2	1-0		2-1	3-2	0-3	1-0	0-0	2-1
13 Radstock Town	1-2	3-1	1-1	2-2	2-2	0-0	4-1	3-2	5-3	2-6	0-1	1-0		2-1	1-2	3-1	2-1	5-1
14 Stockwood Green	0-2	1-2	2-8	0-2	3-3	2-2	4-1	2-0	0-7	1-2	0-2	2-4	0-6		0-4	3-2	4-1	9-2
15 Team Bath Reserves	2-0	2-0	3-2	2-3	2-2	3-0	1-2	5-0	3-0	6-1	3-0	2-0	1-2	3-2		5-2	4-1	2-1
16 Wells City	0-2	2-2	3-2	1-0	0-1	2-1	1-2	4-3	2-2	0-4	1-4	1-2	2-3	2-0	1-3		0-2	2-0
17 Welton Rovers Reserves	1-1	4-1	3-2	2-2	1-4	3-2	0-5	3-1	1-2	2-1	0-3	1-5	1-3	3-2	0-4	1-3		4-1
18 Westland United	1-2	1-5	1-3	2-5	0-1	3-4	0-2	1-4	0-3	1-0	1-4	0-3	0-1	0-2	0-0	0-2	0-3	

LEAGUE CUP
PREMIER AND DIVISION ONE CLUBS

FIRST ROUND

Bishop Sutton Res.	v	Tunley Athletic	3-4
Castle Cary	v	Team Bath Res.	0-1*
Crewkerne	v	Wells City	1-3
Watchet Town	v	Bridgwater Town Res.	0-0*, 2-4p

SECOND ROUND

Backwell United Res.	v	Hengrove Athletic	0-3
Bridgwater Town Res.	v	Congresbury	2-0*
Cheddar	v	Brislington Res.	2-1
Cleeve West Town	v	Mangotsfield United Res.	1-3
Fry Club	v	Team Bath Res.	2-1
Ilminster Town	v	Nailsea Town	6-0
Nailsea United	v	Paulton Rovers Res.	0-1
Peasedown Athletic	v	Keynsham Town Res.	3-1
Radstock Town	v	Westland United	1-2
Robinsons	v	Odd Down Res.	1-2
Shirehampton	v	Burnham United	2-4
Stockwood Green	v	Wells City	2-1*
Timsbury Athletic	v	Oldland Abbotonians	6-0
Tunley Athletic	v	Blackbrook	1-1*, 5-4p
(tie awarded to Blackbrook)			
Welton Rovers Res.	v	Winscombe	5-1
Weston-super-Mare Res.	v	Portishead	1-4

THIRD ROUND

Cheddar	v	Burnham United	3-3*, 3-1p
Hengrove Athletic	v	Fry Club	5-2
Ilminster	v	Blackbrook	3-1
Mangotsfield United Res.	v	Bridgwater Town Res.	1-4
Peasedown Athletic	v	Odd Down Res.	1-3
Portishead	v	Stockwood Green	2-1
Welton Rovers Res.	v	Timsbury	2-4*
Westland	v	Paulton Rovers Res.	0-4

QUARTER-FINALS

Bridgwater Town Res.	v	Ilminster Town	1-2
Cheddar	v	Odd Down Res.	1-0
Portishead	v	Hengrove Athletic	0-2
Timsbury Athletic	v	Paulton Rovers Res.	1-4

SEMI-FINALS

Ilminster Town	v	Hengrove Athletic	3-1*
Paulton Rovers Res.	v	Cheddar	5-1

THE FINAL (11th May at Shepton Mallet)

Ilminster Town	v	Paulton Rovers Res.	1-2

LEAGUE CONSTITUTION 2004-05

BACKWELL UNITED RESERVES
Backwell Recreation Grounds, Backwell, Bristol, North Somerset — Tel: 01275 462612

BRIDGWATER TOWN RESERVES
Fairfax Park, College Way, Bath Road, Bridgwater, Somerset — Tel: 01278 446899

BRISLINGTON RESERVES
Ironmould Lane, Brislington, Bristol, North Somerset — Tel: 0117 977 4030

BURNHAM UNITED
Burnham Road Playing Fields, Cassis Close, Burnham-on-Sea, Somerset — Tel: 01278 794615

CASTLE CARY
Donald Pither Memorial Playing Fields, Castle Cary, Somerset — Tel: 01963 351538

CHEDDAR
Bowdens Park, Draycott Road, Cheddar, Somerset — Tel: 01934 743736

CLEEVE WEST TOWN
King George V Playing Fields, Meeting House Lane, Cleeve, North Somerset — Tel: 01934 832173

FRY CLUB
Fry Club, Somerdale, Keynsham, Bristol, North Somerset — Tel: 0117 937 6500

HENGROVE ATHLETIC
Norton Lane, Whitchurch, Bristol, North Somerset — Tel: 01275 832894

ILMINSTER TOWN
Recreation Ground, Ilminster, Somerset — Tel: 01460 54756

MANGOTSFIELD UNITED RESERVES
Cossham Street, Mangotsfield, Bristol, Gloucestershire — Tel: 0117 956 0119

NAILSEA UNITED
Grove Sports Ground, Old Church, Nailsea, North Somerset — Tel: 01275 856892

PAULTON ROVERS RESERVES
Athletic Ground, Winterfield Road, Paulton, Somerset — Tel: 01761 412907

PORTISHEAD
Bristol Road Playing Fields, Portishead, Bristol, North Somerset — Tel: 01275 847136

STOCKWOOD GREEN
Bath Spa University College, Newton Park, Newton-St-Loe, Bath, Somerset

WELLS CITY
The Athletic Ground, Rowdens Road, Wells, Somerset — Tel: 01749 679971

WELTON ROVERS RESERVES
West Clewes, North Road, Midsomer Norton, Somerset — Tel: 01761 412097

SOUTH WESTERN LEAGUE

SPONSORED BY: CARLSBERG

President: Tristan H Scott **Chairman:** Bob Bell

Secretary: Ray Rowe, 5 Alverton Gardens, Truro, Cornwall TR1 1JA

Tel/Fax: 01872 242190 **Email:** ray@rowe57.fsbusinessco.uk

Press Officer: Mike Sampson, 23 Eliot Street, Weston Mill, Plymouth, Devon PL5 1AX

Tel/Fax: 01752 514326 **Email:** mikewrite@blueyonder.co.uk

FINAL LEAGUE TABLE 2003-04

		P	W	D	L	F	A	Pts
1.	St Blazey	34	27	5	2	90	26	86
2.	Bodmin Town	34	26	4	4	88	29	82
3.	Porthleven	34	19	5	10	68	46	62
4.	Millbrook	34	14	14	6	75	42	56
5.	Saltash United	34	16	8	10	62	58	56
6.	St Austell	34	16	6	12	58	45	54
7.	Wadebridge Town	34	14	11	9	57	39	53
8.	Penzance	34	14	8	12	50	46	50
9.	Plymouth Parkway	34	12	9	13	51	60	45
10.	Tavistock	34	12	7	15	52	71	43
11.	Launceston	34	11	8	15	52	67	41
12.	Liskeard Athletic	34	11	6	17	43	50	39
13.	Falmouth Town	34	11	5	18	52	72	38
14.	Torpoint Athletic	34	10	6	18	53	72	36
15.	Truro City	34	7	10	17	47	69	31
16.	Penryn Athletic	34	9	4	21	67	90	31
17.	Newquay	34	7	5	22	41	81	26
18.	Callington Town	34	7	5	22	50	93	26

2003-04		1	2	3	4	5	6	7	8	9	10	11	12	13	14	15	16	17	18
1	Bodmin Town		10-2	1-2	3-0	2-0	3-1	4-0	1-0	4-0	3-1	1-0	3-0	2-0	1-1	4-0	4-0	8-1	1-0
2	Callington Town	0-5		1-2	3-3	0-2	3-6	2-1	7-0	1-2	0-1	0-3	1-2	1-2	1-5	1-4	2-4	2-1	0-2
3	Falmouth Town	0-2	0-2		1-3	1-0	1-3	4-2	2-0	2-0	1-1	0-1	1-3	5-2	0-1	3-1	5-3	1-2	2-2
4	Launceston	1-2	2-0	0-2		0-2	2-2	2-0	4-3	2-0	3-2	1-2	1-1	1-3	1-2	1-2	5-2	5-5	0-0
5	Liskeard Athletic	0-1	2-3	2-0	1-2		0-3	0-2	1-1	0-1	2-3	2-1	3-1	0-2	2-2	2-0	2-1	3-1	2-2
6	Millbrook	5-0	2-3	4-1	1-1	3-2		2-2	1-1	5-0	3-0	2-0	2-2	2-0	1-3	1-1	4-1	3-1	0-0
7	Newquay	0-1	2-2	0-2	2-0	0-2	4-3		5-4	0-2	2-3	0-1	0-5	0-0	0-4	2-3	1-3	2-3	1-0
8	Penryn Athletic	2-5	4-0	3-2	2-3	3-1	2-2	2-1		4-1	3-4	4-2	5-4	1-0	2-3	2-1	0-1	1-2	2-5
9	Penzance	2-0	6-2	1-1	0-0	2-1	0-0	3-0	1-0		1-2	2-2	0-1	0-1	1-2	2-1	4-0	3-3	0-0
10	Plymouth Parkway	2-3	2-2	3-2	0-1	1-1	2-2	4-0	3-1	0-0		2-0	3-4	1-1	0-4	1-3	0-2	0-0	1-2
11	Porthleven	1-2	5-2	4-0	0-0	1-0	3-1	3-0	5-2	0-2	3-0		3-1	1-1	1-2	4-2	3-3	3-1	2-1
12	Saltash United	0-2	0-0	3-2	4-1	4-0	1-0	3-1	5-4	3-2	0-0	1-2		2-1	0-4	3-1	2-2	2-1	1-1
13	St Austell	0-1	4-1	9-2	3-1	0-2	0-0	1-3	3-0	2-1	0-1	3-2	1-1		1-2	5-2	2-1	4-2	0-1
14	St Blazey	2-2	2-1	5-1	7-1	1-0	1-1	3-1	3-1	2-2	4-0	2-3	5-0	2-0		0-1	3-0	2-0	1-0
15	Tavistock	1-4	1-1	1-1	2-1	3-2	0-5	2-2	5-3	1-4	1-2	2-2	2-1	2-3	0-2		3-2	2-1	0-0
16	Torpoint Athletic	1-1	0-2	4-1	4-1	1-1	0-3	1-3	4-3	0-1	3-2	1-0	1-1	1-2	1-2	4-1		0-2	1-1
17	Truro City	1-1	3-1	2-2	0-1	1-1	1-1	5-0	0-0	1-2	2-2	2-3	0-1	0-1	0-2	0-0	2-0		0-6
18	Wadebridge Town	3-1	3-1	1-0	4-2	1-2	1-1	2-2	3-2	3-2	1-2	1-2	3-0	1-1	0-4	0-1	3-1	4-1	

LEAGUE CUP

PRELIMINARY ROUND

Launceston	v	St Austell	1-3
Tavistock	v	Bodmin Town	1-2

FIRST ROUND

Bodmin Town	v	Millbrook	6-2
Falmouth Town	v	Torpoint Athletic	2-5
Liskeard Athletic	v	Callington Town	2-1
Penryn Athletic	v	Plymouth Parkway	1-3
Penzance	v	Newquay	3-1
Saltash United	v	St Austell	3-0
St Blazey	v	Porthleven	2-1*
Wadebridge Town	v	Truro City	4-2*

QUARTER-FINALS

Penzance	v	Wadebridge Town	1-0
Plymouth Parkway	v	Bodmin Town	1-2*
Saltash United	v	St Blazey	3-1
Torpoint Athletic	v	Liskeard Athletic	1-0

SEMI-FINALS

Bodmin Town	v	Torpoint Athletic	1-2
(at Liskeard Athletic)			
Penzance	v	Saltash United	6-2
(at Truro City)			

THE FINAL (3rd May at Bodmin Town)

Torpoint Athletic	v	Penzance	1-0

South Western League Champions, St Blazey
Back Row (L-R): Terry Huddey, Steve Daly, Glen Duff, Adam Street, Neil Burton, Daniel Nabcarrow, Steve Ovens, Danny Jeffers, Steve Raven.
Front Row: Lewis Reed, Glynn Hooper, Dave Jones, Ian Gosling, Trevor Mewton (Manager), graham Waters, Mark Vercesi, Dale Band, Justin Harrington.

BODMIN TOWN

Secretary: Nick Giles, 4 Sandra Way, Bodmin, Cornwall PL31 2PP
Tel Nos: 01208 75794 (H) 07796 953970 (M)

Ground: Priory Park, Bodmin. Tel: 01208 269033 (office) or 021208 78165 (clubhouse)

Directions: Just off town centre in Priory Park complex, at rear of town car park

Capacity: 5,000 Cover: 400 Seats: 400 Floodlights: Yes

Clubhouse: Mon-Fri 6.30-11pm (matchdays 6-11), Sat 12-11pm,
Sun 12-10.30pm Bar snacks available most times
Club Shop: No

Honours: South Western Lg 90-91 93-94 (R-up 76-77, 92-93, 94-95, 03-04), Lg Cup 93-94 ,97-98 (R-up 7-78 88-89 94-95,95-96), Cornwall Snr Cup Winners 98-99 R-up 93-94, Cornwall Charity Cup 86-87 89-90,96-97.Cornish Guardian E.C.P.L.Supplimentary Cup 91-92 (R-Up. 93-94)-GordonSweet Cup 90-91,92-93,98-99, 01-02.

2003-2004 **Player of the Year:** Dave Sweet **Top Goalscorer:** Luke Hodge

FACT FILE
Founded: 1889 Nickname: Black & Ambers
Sponsors: Build Center
Colours: Amber/black/amber
Change colours: All white
Midweek Matchday: Wednesday
Reserves' League: East Cornwall Premier
Programme: 60 pages, 40p
Programme Editor: Secretary

CLUB PERSONNEL
Chairman:Colin.Hooper V-Chair:Mike Barberry
President: Dave DUnckley
Manager: Alan Carey
Assistant Manager: George Torrance
Captain: Darren Gilbert
Physio: Steve Trotman

CALLINGTON TOWN

Secretary: Philip Brown, Mount Pleasant Cottage, Harrowbarrow, Callington PL17 8JL
Tel: 01822 833851 (H) 01752 307102 (B)

Ground: Ginsters, Marshfield Park, Callington Comm. College, Launceston Rd., Callington, Cornwall Tel: 01579 382647

Directions Turn into Callington Community College from the A388, Callington to Launceston r road. Go to the top of the drive and bear left - the ground is 100m ahead.

Capacity: 1,500 **Seats:** No **Cover** Yes **Floodlights** : Soon **Clubhouse**: Yes

FACT FILE
Colours: All red & black
Change Cols.: All light and dark blue
Midweek Fixtures: Wednesday
Website: www.callington townfc.com

CLUB PERSONNEL
Chairman: Andrew Long
34 Coombe Road, Callington
Tel: 01579 383982 (H) 01752 220881 (B)

Managers:
Stewart Henderson & Gavin West

FALMOUTH TOWN

Secretary: Colin Spargo,2 Grenville Crescent, Falmouth, Cornwall TR11 2NR
FAX: 0871 242 822 Tel: 07941 591764 (M) 01326 315093(H)
e-mail: secfaltown@tiscali.co.uk
Websites; http://www.users.globalnet.co.uk/~cgdf www.falmouthtownafc.net

Ground: Bickland Park, Bickland Water Rd. Falmouth, Cornwall Tel: 01326 375156

Directions: Follow A39 to Tregoniggie Industrial Estate - will pass ground on left.
1 1/2 miles from Penmere Halt (BR) on Falmouth-Truro branch line.

Capacity: 6,000 **Seats**: 350 **Cover:** 1,200 **Floodlights**: Yes **Shop:** Yes **Clubhouse**: Mon-Fri 7-11pm, Sat 11 am-11pm, Sun 12-10.30pm. Meals available

HONOURS: Cornish Senior Cup x 11 R-up x 8; Western Lg x 4, Lg Cup 74-75, Alan Young Cup x 3; South Western Lg x 14 R-up x 5, Lg Cup x 13 R-up x 5; Pratten Cup 73-74, Cornwall Charity Cup (3) R-up 00-01

BEST SEASON **FA Cup:** 1st Round 62-63 v Oxford U& 67-68 & 69-70 bothv Peterborough U
FA Trophy: 2nd Rd Round 77-78 v Hendon (A) 0-4
FA Vase: Quarter Final replay 86-87 0-1 v St Helens T 1-1 (H) after 1-1 (A)
PREVIOUS Leagues: Cornish Sen 50-51; S Western 51-74; Western 74-83

RECORDS **Gate:** 8,000 v Oxford United, FA Cup 1st Round 3/11/62
Scorer: Joe Scott 204, 72-78 **Appearances:** Keith Manley 580 (appr) 70-83

Players progressing to Football League: Roy Carter (Hereford 1975), Joe Scott (Bournemouth 1978), Tony Kellow (Exeter 1976), John Hodge (Exeter 1991) and Anthony Tonkin (Yeovil Town)

FACT FILE
Founded: 1949 Nickname: Town
Club Sponsors: G-J Medlin
Colours: Amber/black
Change colours: Red& blue/blue
Midweek Matchday: Tues/Wed
Reserves' League: Cornwall Comb
Programme: 44 pages, 50p
Ed/ Press Off.: Mike Williams(01326 378352)

CLUB PERSONNEL
Chairman: John Garwood
Vice Chairman: Graham Medlin
President: Roger Fenner
Treasurer: Ian Rennie
Manager: Steve Massey
Coach:Justin Ashburn

2003-04
Leading Goalscorer:Bryn Wheeler
Player of the Year: Jake Ash

LAUNCESTON

Secretary: Chris Martin, 3 Tavistock Road, Launceston, Cornwall PL15 9HA
Tel: 01566 776175 (H) Email: launcestonfc.co.uk

Ground: Pennygillam, Pennygillam Industrial Estate, Launceston PL15 7ED
Tel: 01566 773279 **Web site:** www.launcestonfc.co.uk

Directions: Follow signs to Pennygillam Ind. Est, just off main A30 - ground 400yds on left
Capacity 1000 **Seats:** 150 **Cover:** 150 **Floodlights:** Yes

Clubhouse: Open after every game. Bar meals available. **Club Shop**: No

HONOURS South Western Lg Winners 94-95, R-up 84-85, S.W Lg.Cup Winners: 95-96
Cornish Snr Cup 1899-1900 00-01 82-83 (R-up 92-93, Charity Cup R-up 88-89)

FACT FILE
Founded: 1891
Nickname: Clarets
Colours: Alll Claret
Change colours: Sky/Sky/Navy
Midweek matchday: Tues/Wed
Reserves' League:East Cornwall Prem.
Programme: Yes

CLUB PERSONNEL
Chairman: Keith Ellacott
President: Mr.S.Dawe
General Manager: Keith Ellacott
Manager: Gary Shirley
Asst. Man. / Coach:
Physio: B.Medland

LISKEARD ATHLETIC

Football Secretary: Brian Oliver, Windrush, Tremeddan Lane, Liskeard, Cornwall PL14 3DS
Tel Nos: 01579 342869 (H) 01752 207653 (W) 07974 636964(M)
Ground: Lux Park, Liskeard, Cornwall Tel: 01579 42665
Directions: Take Tavistock Rd (A390) from town centre, after 1/2 mile turn left on St Cleer Rd (follow signs to Lux Park Sports Complex) & ground is 200 yards on left. Half mile from Liskeard BR station
Capacity 2,000 **Seats:** 50 **Cover:** 300 **Floodlights**: Yes **Club Shop:** No
Clubhouse Normal licensing hours. Hot & cold food available Tel: 01579 342665
HONOURS: South Western Lg 76-77 78-79 R-up 75-76 77-78, Lg Cup 76-77 78-79; Western Lg 87-88 R-up 85-86 89-90, Merit Cup 80-81; Cornwall Snr Cup 04-05 83-84 84-85 85-86 88-89 89-90 93-94 R-up.x 5; Cornwall Charity Cup 21-22 79-80, Cornwall Jnr Cup 05-06 13-14 26-27; S W Pratten Cup 78-79; E Cornwall Prem RAOB Cup 67-68, Plymouth & Dist. Lg 60-61, Div 1 59-60 R-up 54-55 73-74, Div 2 76-77 (Res), Victory Cup 60-61, Charity Cup 59-60; E Cornl Prem. Lg (Res) x3 R-up x3 Lg.Cup x4 Evely Cup (Res) 01-02
PREVIOUS **Leagues:** East Cornwall Prem., Plymouth & Dist., South Western 66-79, Western 79-95
BEST SEASON **FA Vase:**
FA Cup:
RECORDS **Goalscorer:** T Turner 59, 60-61 **Appearances:** Brian Bunney, 500+
Players progressing: Bradley Swiggs, Jon Aston

FACT FILE
Formed: 1889
Nickname: Blues
Sponsors: J P Leisure & Gilbert Outfitters
Colours: All Blue
Change : Yellow & navy blue/navy/yellow & navy
Midweek matchday: Tuesday
Programme: 40 pages, 50p Editor: Ian Pook

CLUB PERSONNEL
Chairman: Ian Pook
Vice Chairman: B. Harding
President: W. N. Rawlings
Manager: Dave Leonard
Asst Manager: Roger File
Physio: Hayley Collin

MILLBROOK

Secretary: Nick Hill, 145 Bridwell Road, Weston Mill, Plymouth PL5 1A
Tel Nos: 01752 364751(H) 07956 810516(M) Tel No: 01752 822892 (H)
Ground: Mill Park, Millbrook, Cornwall (01752 822113)
Directions: From Torpoint Ferry - 3 miles to Antony on A374, fork left, after 1 mile turn left again and follow B3247 to Millbrook (3 miles), take road marked `Town Centre Southdown', right at mini-r'bout after 1/4 mile, ground clearly visible. From Tamar Bridge - follow signs for Torpoint, 2 miles after Polbathic right turning marked Millbrook, 5 miles to Millbrook then proceed as above
Capacity: 2,000 **Seats:** 50 **Cover**: 200 **Floodlights**: Yes **Club Shop:** No
Clubhouse: Weekdays 7-11pm, Sat 11am-11pm, Sun noon-3 & 7.30-10.30. Hot food (chips, burgers etc) available during and after matchdays
HONOURS: South Western Lg R-up 81-82, Cornwall Snr Cup R-up 83-84 (Charity Cup 84-85, Jnr Cup 75-76), Plymouth & District Lg 80-81 (Div 1 R-up 76-77)
PREVIOUS **Leagues:** Plymouth Comb.(8yrs)/ Plymouth & Dist.(6yrs)
CLUB RECORDS **Scorer:** Unknown
Appearances: John Horne 215

FACT FILE
Founded: 1973 Nickname: The Brook
Sponsors: Plymouth Boat Cruises Ltd
Colours: Black & white/black/red
Change colours: All Royal blue
Midweek matchday: Wednesday
Reserve's League: Plymouth & District
Programme: 20 pages, 10p
Editor: J Weekes (01752 822637)

CLUB PERSONNEL
President: Mrs E Weekes
Chair: Martin Bettridge V- Chair: Mike Bettison
Press Officer: Steve Reeve
Man: Roger Fice Asst Man:Paul Goodwin

2003-2004
P.o.Y.: John Morris
Top Scorer: Ryan Fice Captain: Paul Edwards

NEWQUAY

Secretary: Graham Drew, 28 Parc Godfrey, Pentire, Newquay TR7 1TY (01637 851610)
Ground: Mount Wise, Newquay 01637 872935
Directions: .5 mile from Newquay BR, follow 2way system for .5 mile grd sign on L.eft at Clevedon Road Website: www.newquayafc.com Email: grdrew@tiscali.co.uk
Capacity: 3,500 **Seats:** 250 **Cover:** 500 **Floodlights:** Yes **Club Shop**: No
Clubhouse: 7-11pm w/days,12-11pm Sat,12-10.30 Sun Hot snacks matchdays. Big TV Screen
HONOURS: Cornish Senior Cup 34-35 52-53 54-55 56-57 91-92 (R-up (10) , S. Western Lg (7) 58-60 77-78 79-80 81-82 83-84 87-88 (R-up 3) Lg Cup 55-56 88-89 (R-up 4) Cornwall Charity Cup (13) & R-up (10) , W.Cornwall Lg 06-07,(R-up 2) ,Cornish Snr Lg Herald Cup 34-35 (R-up (7) Cornwall Combination League Cup 03-04 Evely Cup 03-04
PREVIOUS Leagues: West Cornwall; Plymouth & District 21-27; Cornish Senior 31-51
BEST SEASON FA Vase: 3rd Round 90-91
Players progressing: Chris Morris (Sheffield Wednesday & Eire)), David Philip (Plymouth Argyle), Kevin Miller and John Hodge (Exeter City)

FACT FILE
Founded: 1890 Nickname: Peppermints
Sponsors:Hunters Sports
Colours: Red & white stripes/white/white
Change colours: Blue & white/white/white
Midweek Matchday: Tuesday
Reserve League: Cornwall Combination
Programme:50 pages, 50p Editor:Rob Hartil

lCLUB PERSONNEL
Chair:Roy Swift V.-Chairman: Eric Tummon
President: Brian Biggins
Physio Ross McOnie
Treasurers:Don Pratt & Sandra Biggins
Managers: Dave Wilton & Keiron Avery
Captain: Martyn Lentern
Coach: Kelvin Hunkin
2003-2004 P.o.Y.: Dave Wilton
Top Scorer:Jake Hartigan

PENRYN ATHLETIC

Secretary: Mike Young, 1 Dunvegan Road, Penryn, Cornwall TR10 8HJ
Tel: 01326 374098 (H) 01326 212974 (B) 01326 374098 (F)

Ground: "Kernick", Kernick Road, Penryn, Cornwall Tel: 01736 75182 (Clubhouse)
Capacity: 800 **Seats** 20 **Cover** 40 **Floodlights** No:

Directions: From Truro take the NEW Falmouth road at Treluswell and at the Treleiver roundabout follow signs for Kernick Industrial Estate.
Turn left at the new Asda store.

PREVIOUS League: Cornwall Combination.

FACT FILE
Colours: Red & black/black/red
Change colours: All Blue
Midweek Matchday: Wednesday
Website: www.penryn-athletic.co.uk

CLUB PERSONNEL
Chairman: Peter Young
146 Little Oaks, Penryn
Tel: 01326 378035 (H)

Manager: John Dent

PENZANCE

Secretary: John Mead, 8 Chyanclare, St Clare Street, Penzance TR18 2PG
Tel./Fax: 01736 369066 (H)
Ground: Penlee Park, Alexandra Place, Penzance
Tel: 01736 361964
Capacity 3000 **Seats** 250
Cover 250 **Floodlights** No
Directions: Seafront road past harbour, after amusement arcade turn right at r'bout (Alexander Rd), ground second right. Fifteen minutes walk from Penzance(BR); directions as above
HONOURS Cornish Snr Cup 1892-93 95-96 97-98 98-99 1903-04 07-08 47-48 60-61 72-73 80-81 (R-up 1896-97 99-1900 00-01 04-05 48-49 49-50 54-55 56-57 74-75), South Western Lg 55-56 56-57 74-75 (Lg Cup R-up 60-61), Cornwall Charity Cup 47-48 48-49 (R-up 21-22 63-64), Cornwall Snr Lg Div 2 57-58 (Div 2 Cup 53-54 54-55), Cornwall Comb. R-up 65-66 (Lg Cup 69-70 (R-up 81-82)), Cornwall Jnr Cup(West) 03-04 04-05 05-06 07-08 09-10
Players progressing: Gerry Gazzard (West Ham), Tony Kellow (Exeter)

FACT FILE
Founded: 1888
Nickname: Magpies
Colours: Black & white/black/black
Change colours: All sky blue
Midweek matchday: Tuesday Reserves' league: Cornwall Comb

CLUB PERSONNEL
President: Jim Dann
Chairman: Peter George
Manager:T.B.A. Trainer: John Mead
2003-2004
Top Scorer: Dave Burt
Player of the Year: Andrew Mead

PLYMOUTH PARKWAY

Secretary: Stuart Cadmore, 71 Trelawny Road, Menheniot, Liskeard, Plymouth PL14 3TS
Tel: 01579 340820 (H) 01752 304096 (B) 07776 14102 (M)

Ground: Bolitho Park, St Peters Rd, Manadon Plymouth

Directions: From Tamer Bridge take third exit (Manadon) and then sharp left into St.Peters Road. Ground is one mile on the right.

FACT FILE

Colours: Yellow/royal blue/yellowChange colours: Purple/navy/white

CLUB PERSONNEL

Chairman: Mark Rowles
Tel: 01752 790436 (H) 01752 201918 (B)

Manager: Gez Baggott
Tel: 01752 302596 (H) 0966 542982 (M)

Porthleven F.C., winners of the Cornwall Senior Cup
Back Row (L-R): Clair Roberts, Gary Pascoe, Jack Mather, Steve Williams, Ryan Holland, Daniel Stidwell, Ashley Stidwell, Robbie Hichens, Chris Matthews, Charlie Newman, Scott Toy, Jill Green (Treasurer).
Front Row: Michelle Roberts, Richard Scott, Phil Hancock, Dean Bray, Andy Mills, David Phillips, Craig Bray, Diane Ellis, John Laity.

PORTHLEVEN

Team Secretary: Vidal James, 23 Parc-an -Bans, Camborne TR14 7RW Tel: 01209 710618
Ground Gala Parc, Mill Lane, Porthleven Tel: 01208 574181
Directions From Penzance on A394, B3304 into Porthleven, ground on left immediately before town. From Helston on B3304 ground on right as you exit town.
Buses from Helston & Penzance Nearest rail station: Penzance
Capacity 1,500 **Seats:** 50 **Cover:** 100 **Floodlights:** Yes **Club Shop:** No
Clubhouse Mon 7-11pm, Tue-Fri 12 pm-4.30 pm & 7-11p.m., Sat 12pm 11 pm Sun 12 pm -10.30
Full food menu at week-ends Tel: 01326 574754
HONOURS South Western League R-up 72-73, 98-99, 00-01, 01-02, Lg Cup 00-01 R-up 98-99;
Cornwall Combination x 6, Lg Cup x 6; Cornwall Charity Cup 70-71, 97-98 R-up: 01-02
Cornwall Sen. Cup winners 03-04 R-up 68-69, 97-98, 99-00, 00-01, 03-04
George Evely Cup 64-65 65-66 83-84 86-87, West Penwith Lg, Penzance Hosp.Cup, Penzance CharityC
PREVIOUS **Grounds:** Treza Downs; Sunset Farm
Leagues: West Penwith; Cornwall Sen; South Western 66-77; Cornwall Comb. 77-89
BEST SEASONS
FA Vase: Quarter Finalists 1997-98, 0-2 v Taunton Town (A)
FA Cup: 1st Qualifying Round 2002-03
RECORD **Attendance:** 1,300 v Hucknall -5th Ropund F.A.Vase 1997-98

FACT FILE

Founded: 1896
Nickname: Fishermen
Colours: Yellow & Black
Change colours: Blue/white/whiteMidweek
Matchday: Wednesday
Reserves' League: Cornwall Combination
Programme: 50p

CLUB PERSONNEL

President: P F Johns
Chairman: Neil Clark
Manager: Gary Marks

2003-2004

Captain: Rob Powell
Leading Goalscorer &
Player of the Year:Andy Sargeant

St. AUSTELL

Secretary: Steve Bullen, 27 Poltair Park, Trevarthian Road, St Austell. PL25 4LY
Tel Nos: 01726 70138 (H) 07976 629547 (M) e-mail: stevenrcu@aol.com
Ground: Poltair Park, Poltair Road, St. Austell Tel: 01726 66099

Directions: 5 mins walk north of St Austell (BR). Near Poltair school and St Austall Brewery

Capacity: 4,000 **Seats:** 200 **Cover:** 200 **Floodlights:** No
Clubhouse: Mon-Fri 7-10.30 & Sat 12-11pm Food is available

PREVIOUS **Leagues:** Rocky Park (1890s)

RECORD **Gate:** 15,000 v Penzance, Senior Cup 49

HONOURS South Western Lg 68-69 (R-up 4), Lg Cup 64-65 71-73 87-88
R-up 4), Cornish Senior Cup(11)

FACT FILE

Founded: 1890
Sponsors: Kwik Print
Colours: All White
Change colours: Red/black/red
Midweek Matchday: Tuesday
Reserves' League: East Cornwall Prem.

CLUB PERSONNEL

Chairman:Jason Powell
Manager: Gary Penhaligan

St. BLAZEY

Secretary: Martin Richards,2 Deeble Drive,Par Pl24 2JJ.
Email Address: admin@stblazey-football.co.uk
Ground: Blaise Park, Station Road, St Blazey, Cornwall PL24 2ND
Tel: 01726 814110
Website: stblazey-football.co.uk
Directions: From the A390, Liskeard-St Austell road, turn into Station Road at the taffic lights inSt Blazey village and the ground is 100 yards down on the left.
One and a half miles from Par (BR)

Capacity: 3,500 **Seats:** 200 **Cover:**600 **Floodlights:** Yes **Club Shop:** No
Clubhouse: Mon- Sat 11-11.00pm, Sun 12-11pm. Bar snacks

HONOURS S Western Lg (12) - record equalling 4 consecutive titles (2000-2004),
R-up (10). Lg Cup 7, (R-up 6), Cornish Snr Cup (11)
Cornish Charity Cup (5) Cornwall Snr Lg Cup (Herald Cup) 35-36 48-49

RECORDS **Gate:** 6,500 v St Austell, Cornwall Snr Cup 48-49
Goalscorer: Glynn Hooper **Appearances:** W Isbell
BEST SEASON **FA Vase:** 5th Round replay 2002-2003
FA Cup: 2000
Players progressing to the Football League: Nigel Martyn and Shaun Taylor

FACT FILE

Founded: 1896 Nickname: Saints
Sponsors: Eden Project
Colours: Green/Black/Green
Change colours: Blue & white/blue/yellow
Midweek matchday: Wednesday
Reserve's League: East Cornwall Premier
Programme
24 pages, 50p Editor: Steve Paynter

CLUB PERSONNEL

Chairman: Harry Cooke
Vice Chairman: MrA Putt
Treasurer Brian Brokenshire
Manager: Trevor Mewton
Assistant Manager: Dave Jones

2003-2004

Leading Goalscorer:Glynn Hooper
Captain: Glynn Hooper
Player of the Year: Chris Hudson

TAVISTOCK AFC

Secretary: Eric Pinch, 33 Oak Rd., Bishopsmead, Tavistock, Devon. PL19 9LJ
Tel Nos: 01822 616695 or 61139 and 079773922110 (M)

Ground: Langsford Park, Crowndale Rd, Tavistock (01822 614447)
Directions: A386 from Okehampton, through town taking signs for Plymouth bear left past Sir Frances Drake's statue on Plymouth Rd. First right into Crowndale Rd,ground is 150yards on left
Capacity: 2,000 **Seats:** 200 **Cover:** 200 **Floodlights:** Yes **Club Shop:** No
Clubhouse: Open on matchdays and Thursday 7-11 p.m.. Hot & cold food

HONOURS Devon Premier Cup 01-02 R-up 94-95, Devon Snr Cup 1889-90 1968-69 77-78
81-82, South Western Lg R-up 2002-03 Lg. Cup 68-69 (R-up 76-77 83-84 99-00)
Bedford Cup -numerous times; Devon Charity Cup 78-79, R-up 77-78,
Plymouth & Dis Comb Prem Cup 01-02
RECORDS **Gate:** 5,000 v Calstock, Bedford Cup final 1952
Appearances: A Pethick 1,000+
Players progressing: Peter & Neil Langman (Plymouth A., 51 & 53); Robbie Pethick (Portsmouth); Mike Trebilcock (Plymouth A. 65); Harold Redmond & Danny Sullivan (Crystal Pal. 57 - £100)

2003-2004 **Player of the Year:** Sean Cannn **Top Goalscorer**: Paul Adcock

FACT FILE

Founded: 1888
Nickname: `Tavy' or `Lambs'
Sponsors: RM Builders & Contractors
Colours: Red& blackblack/black
Change : Purple & white.
Midweek matchday: Wednesday
Res' Lge: Plymouth & Dist Comb. (Interm 'te))
Prog: 48 pages 50p. Editor:Robin Fenner
Website: www.tavistock.afc.co.uk

CLUB PERSONNEL

Chairman: Robin Fenner
Vice Chairman:Derek Pethick
Managers:Ian Southcott & Craig Smith
Asst Manager: Graeme Kirkup
Physio: Les Mewton

TORPOINT ATHLETIC

Secretary: Vic Grimwood, 43 Hemerdon Heights, Plympton PL7 3EY Tel: 01752 344263 (H)

Ground: The Mill, Mill Lane, Torpoint, Cornwall Tel: 01752 812889

Directions: Bear left from Torpoint ferry, ground down hill on left after half a mile

Capacity: 1,000 **Seats:** 100 **Cover:** 100 **Floodlights:** Soon

Clubhouse: Yes

PREVIOUS League: Plymouth & District League.(Premier)

BEST SEASON FA Vase: 4th Round 93-94, 0-3 v Diss Town (H), eventual winners

HONOURS South Western Lg 64-65 66-67. Lg Cup 03-04, R-up 65-66. Cornish Snr Cup 8

FACT FILE

Colours:Gold & black stripes/gold& black/black
Change colours: Red & white hoops/white/red
Programme: Yes

CLUB PERSONNEL

Chairman:Ian McCullum

Manager: Phil Cardew
Tel: 01752 812721 (H)

League Cup winners Torpoint Athletic F.C.
Back Row (L-R): M Cusack, P Cardew, R Collins, K Robinson, P Partridge, C Blackburn, D Cardew, K Dodds, D Wills, A Coxon.
Front Row: M Leakey, B Stacey, L Cameron, S Matthews, M Roberts, G Bridgeman, P Phillips, M Davidson.

WEST MIDLANDS (REGIONAL) LEAGUE

SPONSORED BY: ROBERTS GRAY

Hon Secretary: Neil Juggins
14 Badgers Lane, Blackwell, Bromsgrove

FINAL LEAGUE TABLE 2003-04

PREMIER DIVISION	P	W	D	L	F	A	Pts
1. Malvern Town	38	29	3	6	138	38	90
2. Tipton Town	38	26	8	4	105	36	86
3. Kington Town	38	26	2	10	100	62	80
4. Shawbury United	38	21	10	7	73	56	73
5. Ledbury Town	38	22	6	10	96	60	72
6. Heath Hayes	38	20	6	12	81	48	66
7. Market Drayton Town	38	19	8	11	69	54	65
8. Tividale	38	18	8	12	81	55	62
9. Wellington	38	18	8	12	74	54	62
10. Lye Town	38	19	5	14	62	52	62
11. Bromyard Town	38	17	4	17	78	66	55
12. Brierley & Hagley Alliance	38	14	7	17	59	68	49
13. Bustleholme	38	13	3	22	76	85	42
14. Dudley Town	38	11	9	18	65	81	42
15. Ettingshall Holy Trinity	38	12	4	22	58	94	40
16. Wolverhampton United	38	12	3	23	63	116	39
17. Smethwich Sikh Temple	38	11	5	22	65	93	38
18. Wednesfield	38	11	4	23	49	125	37
19. Wolverhampton Casuals - **Relegated**	38	7	2	29	51	106	23
20. Coseley Town	38	0	3	35	23	117	3

NB - Newport Town withdrew during the season. Their results are shown in the grid below but expunged from the league table.

PREMIER 03-04	1	2	3	4	5	6	7	8	9	10	11	12	13	14	15	16	17	18	19	20	21
1 Brierley & Hagley All.		2-1	5-4	2-0	0-0	1-2	0-1	0-1	2-4	2-0	1-2	1-2	2-4	3-4	4-1	3-3	0-0	0-0	1-0	2-0	1-1
2 Bromyard Town	7-5		4-2	4-0	2-2	1-2	0-3	3-0	3-2	1-2	0-2	1-2	n/a	2-2	4-0	0-4	3-2	0-0	0-2	3-0	4-3
3 Bustleholme	4-0	1-2		2-1	2-3	5-2	0-2	3-5	4-2	0-1	0-4	0-2	1-2	1-3	2-2	2-4	4-0	2-5	0-1	5-0	1-3
4 Coseley Town	2-3	0-2	1-5		1-2	1-3	0-3	0-3	1-2	0-3	0-9	0-4	n/a	0-3	2-2	1-2	0-2	0-1	0-2	1-4	1-4
5 Dudley Town	2-2	2-1	1-1	1-0		3-0	0-4	2-4	2-0	3-0	1-7	2-3	1-0	1-2	2-4	0-3	1-2	5-0	1-2	3-3	2-3
6 Ettingshall Holy Trin.	0-2	3-4	1-3	2-0	2-2		1-1	2-1	2-3	1-3	1-9	0-1	n/a	0-3	3-2	0-5	1-2	3-1	4-2	2-0	3-4
7 Heath Hayes	1-0	1-4	1-3	2-1	0-0	2-1		0-2	2-4	1-0	1-2	0-1	n/a	0-2	1-0	2-2	0-3	7-0	2-1	2-0	12-1
8 Kington Town	4-2	1-3	3-1	2-0	4-3	3-1	2-1		2-0	0-3	1-6	2-1	n/a	4-1	2-1	0-3	2-1	9-2	2-2	3-1	7-0
9 Ledbury Town	3-2	1-1	2-0	7-0	5-2	2-1	2-0	0-1		4-3	0-2	3-1	n/a	1-1	1-1	0-4	2-4	8-0	2-0	5-1	5-0
10 Lye Town	0-2	4-3	1-0	0-0	3-1	3-1	2-2	1-2	2-4		0-4	0-2	2-1	1-1	4-0	0-0	0-1	3-2	1-3	4-1	1-0
11 Malvern Town	5-0	2-1	4-1	6-1	5-2	8-0	2-1	1-3	1-2	2-1		3-0	1-1	1-2	4-0	2-3	3-2	2-0	1-2	3-0	2-1
12 Market Drayton T'n	0-1	2-1	3-1	3-0	3-0	2-2	1-1	3-2	2-4	0-1	3-7		1-1	0-1	2-4	4-2	1-1	1-2	1-1	2-0	3-3
13 Newport Town	1-4	3-1	n/a	2-0	n/a	3-1	n/a	n/a	0-4	2-0	1-6	4-0		1-2	n/a	2-2	3-3	n/a	3-0	1-2	2-2
14 Shawbury Town	0-2	1-0	2-3	3-1	3-3	2-0	3-1	1-1	1-1	1-2	1-1	0-0	n/a		0-2	1-4	2-1	2-0	2-1	4-1	3-2
15 Smethwick Sikh T'm	1-2	2-0	3-1	4-0	1-2	1-1	2-4	2-3	1-4	1-0	0-6	1-4	2-3	1-4		2-0	1-4	2-4	1-3	2-4	3-0
16 Tipton Town	3-1	2-0	3-1	2-1	1-1	2-3	0-0	4-0	2-2	4-0	1-0	1-2	n/a	9-1	2-1		3-1	2-1	1-1	3-1	3-0
17 Tividale	0-2	3-2	1-1	4-1	2-1	3-0	1-4	3-2	3-0	0-1	3-3	1-1	1-1	0-2	3-3	0-0		1-0	0-1	5-2	8-2
18 Wednesfield	1-1	1-5	4-6	1-0	2-1	2-1	1-6	0-9	0-2	0-6	0-6	2-3	1-2	1-1	1-4	2-8	0-6		4-2	2-1	2-1
19 Wellington	2-0	0-2	0-1	5-1	0-3	3-2	1-3	1-0	2-2	2-2	2-2	0-0	4-1	3-3	4-3	0-3	3-1	3-0		7-0	1-0
20 Wolverhampton Cas.	2-1	2-1	2-3	4-1	1-2	1-2	2-4	3-5	1-3	1-3	1-5	1-3	n/a	1-2	2-3	0-3	1-1	1-2	3-2		1-2
21 Wolverhampton Utd	5-1	1-3	2-1	4-4	3-1	1-3	1-3	1-3	3-2	0-1	0-4	2-1	1-1	1-3	4-1	0-4	0-6	5-3	0-7	0-2	

LEAGUE CUP

FIRST ROUND

Bustleholme	v	Wellington	5-2
Kington Town	v	Ledbury Town	1-2
Shawbury United	v	Lye Town	1-0
Smethwick Sikh Hunters	v	Coseley Town	0-1
Tividale	v	Ettingshall Holy Trinity	2-0

SECOND ROUND

Brierley & Hagley Alliance	v	Heath Hayes	5-1
Bromyard Town	v	Newport Town	0-3
Dudley Town	v	Tividale	2-4*
Ledbury Town	v	Malvern Town	1-2
Market Drayton Town	v	Coseley Town	3-1
Tipton Town	v	Bustleholme	5-3
Wednesfield	v	Shawbury United	3-1
Wolverhampton Utd	v	Wolverhampton Casuals	1-4

QUARTER-FINALS

Brierley & Hagley Alliance	v	Newport Town	4-0
Malvern Town	v	Tipton Town	2-1*
Market Drayton Town	v	Wednesfield	2-0
Wolverhampton Casuals	v	Tividale	1-3

SEMI-FINALS (played over two legs - home & away)

Brierley & Hagley Alliance	v	Market Drayton Town	0-1	3-1
Tividale	v	Malvern Town	1-1	

(Tividale removed from competiton)

THE FINAL (17th May at Ludlow Town)

Brierley & Hagley Alliance	v	Malvern Town	4-4*,4-3p

BRIERLEY HILL & HAGLEY ALLIANCE

Secretary: Tony Gore, 114 Dobbins Oak Road, Pedmore, Stourbridge, W.Mids DY9 0XY
Tel: 01562 720158 (H) 07932 493128 (M)

Ground: Halesowen Harriers FC, Park Road, Halesowen, West Mids. Tel: 01384 896748
Capacity: 4,000 Seats: 350 Cover: 500 Floodlights: Yes

Directions: From M5 junction 3, follow A456 towards Kidderminster to first island. Turn right onto A459 towards Dudley. Turn left at next island onto A458 towards Stourbridge. Follow this road for 2 miles. Ground is on left-hand side.

PREVIOUS **Names**: Oldswinford F & SC 55-93, Brierley Hill Town 93-01

Founded: 1955
Nickname: Lions
Colours: Blue & white shirts & shorts, white socks
Change colours: Green & white hoops, white shorts, black socks

Programme: 20 pages, 50p
Editor: Secretary
Chairman: Lee Robson

BROMYARD TOWN

Secretary: Tony Haverfield, 16 Highwell Avenue, Bromyard, Hereford HR7 4EL
Tel & Fax: 01885 483655 (H) 07885 849948 (M)
Ground: Delahay Meadow, Stourport Road, Bromyard HR7 4NT Tel: 01885 483974
Capacity: 1,500 **Covered Seating**: 120 **Shop:** Club souvenirs usually available
Clubhouse: Licensed bar and club room with hot food on sale from trailer on matchdays
Directions: 1/4 mile outside Bromyard on the Stourport/Kidderminster road (B4203).The ground is on the right through iron gates,by O'Malleys Irish restaurant
Honours: Smedley Cooke Mem. Cup: 2001-02, 03-04 West Mid Regional Lg.: Div 1 S 99-00 Herefordshire Cup 96-97, 99-2000
Best season: **F.A.Vase:** 2nd Rd 2001-02

Founded: 1893
Colours: Blue & black/black/blue
Change : Yellow& green/green/yellow
Chairman: Tony Watkins
(01885 483509)
Manager:Geoff Woodward
Assistant Managers: Martyn Day & Mike Pugh
Captain: Danny Hilditch Physio: Ian Latimer

2003-2004
Player of the Year:Adie Crowther: Adie Crowther
Top Scorer: Andy Crowther

BUSTLEHOME

Secretary: Peter John Lewis, 19 Bernard Street, West Bromwich B71 1DJ
Tel: 0121 580 0573

Ground: Tipton Sports Academy, Wednesbury Oak Road, Tipton DY4 0BS

Directions: From M6 Junction 9, take A461, through Wednesbury Town centre to Ocker Hill Island. Follow signpost here taking a full right turn towards Bilston A4098 for half a mile, turning left at traffic lights A4037. Ground is 50 yards on left.

FACT FILE
Founded: 1975
Colours: Yellow/green/green
Change colours: All white

CLUB PERSONNEL
Chairman: Colin Hall

COSELEY TOWN

Ground: Gornal Athletic FC, Garden Walk Stadium, Lower Gornal, Dudley, West Midlands

Tel: 01384 252285

DUDLEY TOWN - Back Row (L-R): Wayne Crumpton, Steve Austin (Physio), Ben Stretton, Cliff Lambert (Asst. Manager), Tony Salt, Craig Barnett, Derick Reid, Damian Coll, Chris Walwyn (Capt), Paul Taylor, Bradley Pollard, Mark Doran, Tony Higgins (Manager). Front Row (L-R): Ben Campbell, Ian Fullwood, Mark Walters, Peter Wood, Gareth Wheatley, Tom Male, Callum Martin, Ryan Edge.

DUDLEY TOWN

Secretary: Margaret Turner, 3,Straits Road, Lower Gornal, Dudley, DY3 2UY Tel: 01384 214741
Ground: c/o Stourbridge F.C. War Memorial Ground, Amblecote, Stourbridge (01384 394040)
Website: www.dtfc.net

Directions: As for Stourbridge F.C.

Capacity:2,000 Cover: 1,250 Seats: 250 Floodlights: Yes Club Shop: Yes

Clubhouse: Social club open on matchday .

HONOURS Southern Lg Midland Div 84-85, Birmingham Comb 33-34 (R-up 34-35 47-48), Midland (Worcs) Comb 31-32 (R-up 29-30 30-31), West Mids Lg Cp R-up 75-76 (Div2 Cp R-up 80-81), Birmingham Senior Cup 85-86 (R-up 64-65 83-84)Worcs SeniorCp 45-46(joint)(R-up 84-85), Camkin Cp 64-65, Worcs Junior Cp 83-84

Formed: 1893 Nickname: The Robins
Colours: Red/black/black
Change: Yellow/yellow/navy blue
Midweek matchday: Tuesday 7.45pm
Prog: 32 pages £1.00 Ed: Mark McIntyre.
Tel Nos: 01952 583995 (H) 07905 990 202(M)
Chairman: Nevil Jeynes
Vice Chairman: Steve Austin
President: N D Jeynes
Manager: Tony Higgins Asst Man: Cliff Lambert
Captain: Chris Walwyn
2002-2003 Top Scorer: Damien Coll 17
Player of the Year: Paul Taylor

ETTINGSHALL HOLY TRINITY

Secretary: Graham Mills, 27 Ashen Close, Sedgley, Dudley, West Mids DY3 3UZ(01902 66222)
Ground: Aldersley Stadium, Aldersley Road, Tettenhal, Wolverhampton (01902 556200)
Directions: From Wolverhampton take A41 Tettenhall Road, 1.5 miles turn right into Lower Street, then right into Aldersley Road, ground on right

HONOURS West Mids Lg Div 1 Cup R-up 85-86 (Div 2 R-up 84-85), Sporting Award 85-86,Staffs Co. Lg R-up 82-83 (Lg Shield 82-83 83-84), Ike Cooper Cup 82-84 83-84,Sporting Club Award 81-82, Wolverhampton & District Amateur Lg 80-81 (Div 1 65-66, Div 2 64-65), Div 1/2 Cup 64-65 65-66, A H Oakley Cup 80-81, J W Hunt Cup 82-83 83-84 (R-up 79-80), Wolverhampton Cup 83-84 (R-up 82-83)

PREVIOUS League: Wednesbury Church & Chapel (early 1900s), Bilston Youth (1950s),Wolverhampton & District Amateur (1960s), Staffs County (South)

FACT FILE

Founded: 1920 Nickname: Trins
Club Sponsors: DKB Electric/ John O'Dell
Colours: Green & white/green/green& white
Change colours: Red/white/red
Midweek matchday: Wednesday
Prog. Editor: John Edwards (01785 713458)
Chairman:John Robinson
Pres: David Gadd
Manager: Graham Mills
Physio: David Gads

GOODRICH

Ground: Wednesfield FC, Cottage Ground, Amos Lane, Wednesfield, West Midlands

Tel: 01902 735506

GORNAL ATHLETIC

Secretary: Roger Baggott, 39 Westminster Road, Wordsley, Stourbridge, DY8 5EF
Tel No: 07739 227475

Ground: Garden Walk Stadium, Garden Walk, Lower Gornal DY3 2NR
TelNo: 01384 358398

Capacity: **Seats:** **Cover:** **Floodlights:** **Clubhouse:**

Directions: From Dudley Town centre follow A459 towards Sedgley. Left at Green Dragon Pub into Jews Lane.Take second exit at roundabout and down hill to Old Bulls Head Pub. Turn left into Redhall Rd and second left into Garden Walk

Previous: Leagues: Worcester Combination
Names : Lower Gornall Athletic F.C.

FACT FILE
Formed: 1919
Colours: All Blue
Change colours: Gren/green/red
Midweek Matches: Tuesday

CLUB PERSONNEL
Chairman: Chris Smith
Manager: Simon Williams
Coach: Phillip Watt Captain: David Bate
Programme Editor: Chris Smith

2003-2004
Player of the Year: D.Bate
Top Goalscorer: Mark habbershall

HEATH HAYES

Secretary: John Deans, 280 Hednesford Road, Heath Hayes, Cannock, Staffs. WS12 5DS
Tel: 01543 279849 (H)

Ground: Coppice Colliery Ground, Newlands Lane, Heath Hayes, Cannock, Staffs.
Tel No: 07980 991409

Directions: From Cannock, take Lichfield road. After 2.5 miles take first right past Texaco garage on right.

Colours: Blue & white stripes/blue/blue
Change Colours: All Yellow

CLUB PERSONNEL
Chairman John Weldon
Manager: Trevor Cook
Coach: Geraint Jones
Physio: John Thacker

KINGTON TOWN

Secretary: Pauline Shaw, 9 Banley Drive, Headbrook, Kington, Herefordshire HR5 3FD
Tel No: 01544 231777

Ground: Park Road Ground, Mill Street, Kington, Hereford (01544 231007)

Directions: Follow signs for Kington Town Centre, look for left turn between the Town Clock and the Burton Hotel. Carry on this road for 500 metres, ground on left as road bends

FACT FILE
Colours: Yellow /black/black
Change colours: All Red

CLUB PERSONNEL
Chairman: William Mayglothing

LEDBURY TOWN

Secretary: Mike Clueit, 55 Lawnside Road, Ledbury, Herefordshire, HR8 2AE.
Tel: 01531 633 182

Ground: New Street, Ledbury, Herefordshire Tel: 01531 631 463

Capacity: 2,500 Covered Seating: 200 Covered Standing: 100 Floodlights: Yes

Directions: Leave M50 at junction 2. Take A417 to Ledbury. At first island take first exit and at second island take fourth exit. ground is 100 yards on right.

Clubhouse Mon-Fri 7-1pm Sat & Sun: 12noon -11p.m. Hot Food on matchdays.

HONOURS: Worcs Infirmary Cup 2002-03.Div 1 South 99-00 HFA RoseBowl 99-00

PREVIOUS Leagues: Midland Combination, Banks's West Mid Div 1 South

RECORD Attendance: 500 v Malvern 2002-2003

BEST SEASON FA Vase: 4th Round 1980-81

FACT FILE
Formed: 1893
Colours: Black & white/black/black
Change colours: Red & blue/red/red
Midweek Matchday: Wednesday
Programme: Yes Price:£1.00

CLUB PERSONNEL
Chairman: Chris Stephens
Manager: Ian Ford Asst. Man.Kevin Berry
Physio: Matt Panter Captain: Stuart Hall
2002-2003 P.o.Y.: Mark Green
Top Scorer Robert Colwell

LITTLE DRAYTON RANGERS

Secretary: Brian Garratt, 4 Quarry Bank Road, Market Drayton, Shropshire TF9 1DR
Tel: 01630 654618 (H)

Ground: Greenfield Sports Club, Greenfield Lane, Market Drayton. Tel: 01630 655088
Directions: A41 to Tern Hill island, turn right for Newcastle-u-Lyme. Over 1st island and turn right at next, by Gingerbread P.H. towards town centre. After 200 yds turn right, before going over bridge, into Greenfields Lane. Ground is 150 yds down lane on right.

Colours: Royal & pale blue stripes/royal/royal
Change Colours:Red & Blue stripes/blue/red

Chairman: John Thorneycroft

LYE TOWN

Secretary: John Woodhouse, 46 Surfeit Hill, Cradley Heath, Warley, West Midlands. B64 7EB Tel Nos: 01384 633976(H) 0121 627 6600(W) **Ground:** Sports Ground, Stourbridge Road, Lye (01384 422672) **Directions: On A458** Birmingham-Stourbridge road about 400yds afterlights/crossroads at Lye. **From M5** jct 3 take road marked Kidderminster to lights at bottom of Hagley Hill.Turn right to Merry Hill,at island 3rd exit towards Merry Hill. Straight over next island and turn off left at crossroads/lights.Ground is about 400yds on left. Quarter mile from Lye (BR)
Capacity: 5,000 Seats: 200 Cover: 600 Floodlights: Yes **Clubhouse:** Yes (01384 422672)

HONOURS West Mids Lg R-up 76-77 78-79 79-80 80-81 (Prem. Div Cup 75-76), Midland Comb.35-36 (R-up 32-33 34-35 37-38), W.Mid Lg Winners 97-98-99

PREVIOUS **Leagues:** Midland Combination 31-39**RECORD Gate:** 6,000 v Brierley All.

2003-2004 **Player of the Year**: Anthony Cox **Top Goalscoring:** Andy Burgess

FACT FILE
Founded: 1930 Nickname: Flyers
Colours: Blue & white stripes/blue/blue
Change Colours: Yellow/green/yellow
Programme: 24 pages, 40p
Editor: Roy Pearson
Chairman: Roy Pearson
Manager: Geoff Moss
Coach: John Woodhouse
Physio: Harry Hill Captain: Mark Bache

MARKET DRAYTON TOWN

Ground: Greenfield Sports Club, Greenfield Lane, Market Drayton, Shropshire
Tel: 01630 655088

PELSALL VILLA

The Bush Ground, Walsall Road, Heath End, Pelsall, West Midlands
Ground: 01922 692748. Club: 682018

SHAWBURY UNITED

Secretary: Carole Smith, 36 Preston Brockhurst, Shrewsbury, Shrops. SY4 5QA
Tel No: 01939 220627
Ground: The Butler's Sports Centre, Bowen's Field, Wem. Tel: 01939 233287

Directions: Go into Wem town centre and at the Church junction turn right. Take the first left after pedestrian crossing, then first left with Hawkestone pub on corner. 2nd left into car park and ground.

Formed: 1992
Colours: Blue & yellow/blue/blue
Change Colours:All Yellow

Acting Chairman: Alan Smith
Tel: 01939 220627
Captain: Paul Matthews
2003-2004
Players of the Year: Mark Pragg & Andy Reeve
Top Goalscorer: Andy Oakley

SMETHWICK SIKH TEMPLE

Secretary: Joginder Singh, 134 Sandwell Road, Handsworth, Birmingham B21 8PS
Tel: 0121 523 0259
Ground: Hadley Stadium, Wilson Road, Smethwick Tel No: 0121 434 4848

Directions: From Wolverhampton Centre, proceed along A459 to junc Parkfields Rd & Sedgley Rd. Turn left at the main Parkfield traffic lights A4039, sign Ettingshall, travel 500yds, left into Myatt Ave, 1st right into Lawn Rd. Ground on right

PREVIOUS **Name:** Smethwick Rangers

FACT FILE
Founded :1972
Colours: Red & black/black/black
Change Colours: Blue & white/blue/blue

CLUB PERSONNEL
Chairman: Mohan Singh Gill

TIPTON TOWN

Secretary: Ruth Archer, 34 Speakers Close,Oakham Park, Tividale.W.Midlands B69 1PB
Tel: 01384 242912 (H) 07876 197758 (M)
Ground: Tipton Sports Acadamy, Wednesbury Oak Road, Tipton, West Midlands
Directions: M6 Jct 9 through Wednesbury taking A461 until right at island signto Tipton. At next island - Ocker Hill - turn full right owards Bilston & Wolverhampton. After 1/3 mile turn left at traffic lights and ground is on left.**Capacity:** 1000 **Seats:** 200 **Cover:** New covered stand and dressing rooms **Floodlights**:Yes **Clubhouse:** Open with excellent food available week-ends. 12noon - 7.00 p.m.**Club Shop:** no **Record Attendance:** Approx 1100 v Wolves in 1.8.88
Honours: West Mid Regional League DIv One Championship and League Cup, Wednesbury Senior Charity Cup (5) Midweek Floodlit Challenge Cup
2003-004: **Players of the Year:** Brett Love and Lee Rollinson **Top Scorer**: Ravi Sangha 52

FACT FILE
Founded: 1948
Sponsors: Tipton & Cseley Building Society
Colours: Black & white stripes/black/black
Change colours: White/blue/blue
Midweek Matchday: Wednesday
Reserves League:Midland Comb. Div 1
Also U18,17,14 ,13,12,11s + minis accademy
Programme Editor: Dave Barnfield
CLUB PERSONNEL
Chairman: Kevin Jennings Manager:John Hill
Club Captain: Mark Simms

TIVIDALE

Secretary: Leon Murray ,59 Peel Way, Tividale, Oldbury, W.Mids B69 3JZ(0121 532 6979)
Ground: The Beeches, Packwood Rd, Tividale, Warley, W. Midlands B69 1UL tel: 01384 211743
Directions: Dudley Port Station to Burnt tree, left towards Birmingham, ground1 mile on right. Or, M5 jct 2, follow Dudley signs A4123, after approx 2 miles turn left into Regent Rd & left again into Elm Terraces, 1st left into Birch Crescent. Packwood Rd is second left - ground at end of cul-de-sac
Capacity: 3,500 Seats: 200 Cover: 1,000 Floodlights: Yes Club Shop: No
Clubhouse: Mon-Fri 8-11pm, Sat 12-11pm, Sun 12-3 & 8-10.30. Cobs, rolls,sandwiches available
HONOURS West Midlands Lg Div 1 72-73 (Prem. Div Cup 76-77, Div 1 Cup 72-73), Wednesbury Charity Cup 76-77
PREVIOUS **Ground:** City Road **Leagues:** Handsworth & District 56-60; inactive 60-62; West Mids Alliance 62-66 **RECORD** **Attendance:** 2,400 v Telford United, FA Cup

Founded: 1954 Nickname: Dales
Sponsors: Midland & North Security Consultants
Colours: All Yellow
Change colours: All Blue
Midweek matchday: Tuesday
Programme: 40 pages, 60p Editor: c/o Club
Newsline: 0891 66 42 52
Chairman: Donald Ashton
President: Lord Peter Archer
Press Officer: T Clark
Manager: Paul Madders
Asst Manager: Ron Blackwood
Physio: John Cotton

WEDNESFIELD

Secretary: Ron Brown, 8 Hazel Grove, Wednesfield WV11 1LN Tel: 07796 975634 (M)
Ground: Cottage Ground, Amos Lane, Wednesfield, Wolverhampton Tel: 01902 735506
Directions: From Wolverhampton on the A4124 Wednesfield Rd. Stay on road right through Wednesfield until island. Leave island at 1st exit (Wood End Rd), left after 200yds into Amos Lane. Ground on right, approx. 400yds along. 3 miles Wolverhampton BR station. Bus 559 to Wood End or 560 to Red Lion.
Capacity: 1,000 Seats: 148 Cover: 250 Floodlights: Yes
Clubhouse: Evenings 7-11pm. Snacks available 1st team matchdays. **Club Shop:** No.
HONOURS West Mids Lg Div 1 76-77 (R-up 77-78).
PREVIOUS **League:** Wolverhampton & Dist. Amateur 61-76; West Midlands 77-97.
RECORDS **Attendance:** 480 v Burton Albion, FA Cup 1981.

FACT FILE
Founded: 1961 Nickname: Cottagers.
Colours: Red/black/black& white
Change : Black & White Stripes/white/white
Midweek matchday: Tuesday
Programme:£1.00
Editor: Ron Brown
CLUB PERSONNEL
Chairman: Surinda Ghattaura
Press Officer: J Massey (01902 781819).
Managers: Brian and David Saville
Physio: Mark Rowberry

WELLINGTON

Secretary: Michael Perkins, Haworth, Wellington, Hereford HR4 8AZ
Tel: 01432 830523 (H) 01432 345432 (B) 07974 447817 (M)
Ground: Wellington Playing Fields, Wellington. No telephone.

Directions: The ground is situated off the A49, 8 miles south of Leominster & 5 miles north of Hereford. At the end of the dual carriageway turn for Wellington. The ground is 1/4 mile from A49, on the left , behind Wellington School and opposite the Church.

Formed: 1968
Colours: tangerine & blue/blue/tangerine
Change colours: Blue & white/blue/blue

Chairman: Philip Smith
Tel: 01432 830096 (H)
Match Secretary: Colin Williams
Tel: 01432 830620 (H) 0374 101316 (M)

WOLVERHAMPTON CASUALS

Secretary: Michael Green, 63 St Phillips Avenue, Pennfields Wolverhampton WV67ED
Tel: 01902 333677
Ground: Brinsford Stadium, Brinsford Lane, Coven Heath, Wolverhampton (01902 783214)
Directions: Onto M54 from M6 North, at Junc 2 turn right (A449 to Stafford).Ground half a mile, turn right into Brinsford Lane. Billbrooke (BR) 2 miles
Capacity: 2,000 Seats: 50 Cover: 50 Floodlights: No
Clubhouse: Bar & snacks, open Tues/Wed/Thurs/Sat/Sun & alternate Mondays

HONOURS WMRL Div 1 94-95, R-up (3) 85-88, Div 1 Cup 85-86

PREVIOUS **Name**: Staffs Casuals (pre 81) **Ground**: Aldersley Stadium

Founded: 1899
Colours: All Green & white
Change colours: Gold/black/gold

Programme: 28pages 30p Editor: G Smith
Chairman: Barry Austin
President: Clive Hammond
Manager: Gary Walters

WILTSHIRE LEAGUE

SPONSORED BY:

President: **Chairman:**

Secretary: Peter Ackrill, 3 Dallas Avenue, Swindon SN3 3NP

Tel: 01793 520334

FINAL LEAGUE TABLE 2003-04

PREMIER DIVISION	P	W	D	L	F	A	Pts
1. Trowbridge Town	32	23	7	2	84	17	76
2. AFC Stratton (-1pt)	32	24	3	5	81	26	74
3. Biddestone - **Promoted**	32	19	4	9	68	37	61
4. Bradford Town	32	18	6	8	93	43	60
5. Westbury United Reserves	32	16	8	8	61	44	56
6. Shrewton United Reserves (-3pts)	32	14	8	10	47	47	47
7. Purton Reserves	32	13	6	13	45	51	45
8. Cricklade Town	32	12	8	12	73	63	44
9. Corsham Town Reserves (-1pt)	32	12	9	11	53	48	44
10. Aldbourne (-1pt)	32	12	7	13	48	52	42
11. Devizes Town Reserves (-1pt)	32	13	4	15	53	62	42
12. Warminster Town	32	12	5	15	39	59	41
13. Marlborough Town (-1pt)	32	13	1	18	51	54	39
14. Melksham Town Reserves	32	12	2	18	53	64	38
15. Chiseldon Castrol	32	6	6	20	34	70	24
16. Malmesbury Vics Reserves (-1pt)	32	4	4	24	42	97	15
17. Pewsey Vale Reserves	32	4	2	26	24	115	14

NB - Wroughton withdrew during the season. Their results are shown in the grid below but are expunged from the league table.

PREMIER DIVISION 2003-04	1	2	3	4	5	6	7	8	9	10	11	12	13	14	15	16	17	18
1 AFC Stratton		1-1	2-1	1-1	2-0	5-2	2-4	3-0	4-0	2-0	1-0	2-1	3-2	1-3	2-2	5-0	2-0	3-2
2 Aldbourne	0-2		2-1	1-3	0-0	1-0	1-6	4-0	2-0	2-2	3-1	5-0	2-2	1-0	0-3	1-2	0-3	-
3 Biddestone	3-2	1-3		2-2	4-0	1-1	3-2	7-1	3-1	1-0	4-0	3-0	3-0	0-0	2-0	1-0	1-2	7-0
4 Bradford Town	2-1	2-2	1-2		10-0	1-1	4-5	2-1	3-0	0-2	4-1	10-0	4-1	2-0	1-2	5-1	1-2	9-3
5 Chiseldon Castrol	0-1	0-2	1-3	1-3		0-4	1-1	5-1	2-2	1-2	0-1	2-0	0-1	7-1	0-1	2-1	0-8	1-2
6 Corsham Town Reserves	0-3	5-1	2-2	0-1	2-0		3-2	2-1	2-2	2-0	1-0	5-0	2-0	3-3	0-1	1-1	0-1	-
7 Cricklade Town	1-2	2-2	2-3	4-4	1-1	2-1		3-2	6-2	3-1	6-2	0-1	2-6	1-1	0-1	2-3	1-2	2-0
8 Devizes Town Reserves	0-4	0-3	5-1	1-0	3-0	1-1	1-3		3-1	3-0	4-2	5-1	0-3	1-0	0-3	4-0	2-2	2-2
9 Malmesbury Victoria Reserves	1-3	2-1	0-2	2-5	0-2	2-4	1-6	1-3		0-1	1-4	6-2	1-1	1-2	0-3	0-3	1-4	0-1
10 Marlborough Town	0-6	3-0	0-2	1-2	2-1	4-0	5-1	3-2	5-1		4-2	3-0	0-1	2-3	1-4	0-2	2-3	3-2
11 Melksham Town Reserves	0-4	0-3	3-1	6-2	1-0	1-2	2-1	2-3	3-2	0-2		2-0	4-0	4-1	0-0	1-1	5-3	2-2
12 Pewsey Vale Reserves	1-7	1-1	0-5	0-7	0-2	1-3	1-1	1-0	0-8	2-1	0-2		0-1	0-4	2-3	2-5	1-3	1-7
13 Purton Reserves	1-0	1-3	0-4	1-5	3-1	1-1	0-2	0-1	5-0	2-1	2-1	4-2		1-1	1-1	1-0	0-0	-
14 Shrewton United Reserves	0-1	4-0	1-0	2-1	2-1	1-1	3-0	0-1	0-0	3-1	3-2	2-0	2-1		0-8	3-1	0-0	0-1
15 Trowbridge Town	0-1	2-0	2-0	0-0	4-0	5-1	0-0	2-1	8-0	1-0	3-1	8-0	3-1	1-1		5-0	2-2	3-0
16 Warminster Town	0-4	1-0	1-0	0-2	2-2	2-0	1-2	0-0	1-4	0-2	1-0	4-3	0-1	2-1	0-3		2-2	1-2
17 Westbury United Reserves	0-2	2-1	1-2	0-3	2-2	2-1	1-1	3-3	4-0	2-1	2-0	1-2	2-1	2-0	0-3	0-2		-
18 Wroughton	-	-	-	-	1-3	-	2-3	-	-	1-3	-	6-0	1-2	1-3	0-3	-	-	

LEAGUE CONSTITUTION 2004-05

AFC STRATTON
The Crosslink Centre, Ermin Street, Stratton, Swindon, Wiltshire
Tel: 01793 831511

ALDBOURNE
Farm Lane, Aldbourne, Marlborough, Wiltshire

BRADFORD TOWN
Avon Sports Ground, Trowbridge Road, Bradford-on-Avon, Wiltshire
Tel: 01225 866649

BROMHAM
Jubilee Field, Bromham, Chippenham, Wiltshire
Tel: 01380 850671

CALNE TOWN RESERVES
Bremhill View, Calne, Wiltshire
Tel: 01249 816716

CHISELDON CASTROL
Chiseldon Sports & Social Club, Draycott Road, Chiseldon, Swindon, Wiltshire
Tel: 01793 740274

CORSHAM TOWN RESERVES
Southbank, Lacock Road, Corsham, Wiltshire
Tel: 01249 715609

CRICKLADE TOWN
Cricklade Leisure Centre, Stones Lane, Cricklade, Wiltshire
Tel: 01793 750011

DEVIZES TOWN RESERVES
Nursteed Road, Devizes, Wiltshire
Tel: 01380 722817

MALMESBURY VICTORIA RESERVES
Flying Monk Ground, Gloucester Rd, Malmesbury
Tel: 01666 822141

MARLBOROUGH TOWN
Elcot Lane, Marlborough, Wiltshire
Tel: 01672 514033

MELKSHAM TOWN RESERVES
The Conigre, Melksham, Wiltshire
Tel: 01225 702843

NEW COLLEGE ACADEMY
Swindon Supermarine FC, Highworth Road, South Marston, Swindon
Tel: 01793 828778

PEWSEY VALE RESERVES
Recreation Ground, Ball Road, Pewsey, Wiltshire
Tel: 01672 562990

PURTON RESERVES
The Red House, Purton, Wiltshire
Tel: 01793 770262

SHREWTON UNITED RESERVES
Recreation Ground, Shrewton, Wiltshire

WARMINSTER TOWN
Weymouth Street, Warminster, Wiltshire
Tel: 01985 217828

East Cowes Victoria v Brading Town action (Hampshire League) Photo: Tim Lancaster

Sherington F.C. - North Bucks League **Photo: Gordon Whittington**

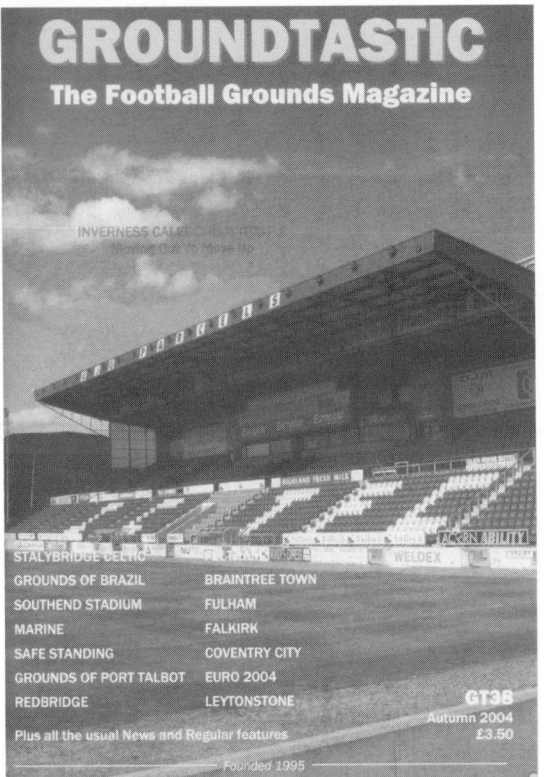

FOOTBALL LEAGUE

STEP 1

FOOTBALL CONFERENCE

STEP 2

CONFERENCE NORTH

CONFERENCE SOUTH

STEP 3

NORTHERN PREMIER

SOUTHERN PREMIER

ISTHMIAN PREMIER

STEP 4

NORTHERN PREMIER DIV.1

SOUTHERN LEAGUE EAST

SOUTHERN LEAGUE WEST

ISTHMIAN DIVISION 1

STEP 5/6

STEP 7 - ISTHMIAN SECTION

ESSEX INTERMEDIATE LEAGUE

SPONSORED BY: **GREENE KING IPA**

FINAL LEAGUE TABLE 2003-04

DIVISION ONE	P	W	D	L	F	A	Pts
1. White Ensign (-1 pt)	22	16	3	3	48	18	50
2. Manford Way	22	12	9	1	36	9	45
3. Harold Wood Athletic (+5 pts)	22	10	5	7	40	27	40
4. Frenford Senior (-6 pts)	22	12	8	2	45	22	38
5. Bishop's Stortford Swifts	22	8	7	7	31	25	31
6. Takeley	22	9	4	9	29	36	31
7. Shenfield Assn (+3 pts)	22	6	7	9	29	34	28
8. Epping	22	5	7	10	21	41	22
9. Rayleigh Town	22	6	3	13	33	37	21
10. Kelvedon Hatch	22	4	9	9	28	38	21
11. White Notley	22	3	8	11	25	40	17
12. Canning Town	22	4	4	14	26	64	16

PREMIER DIVISION 2003-04	1	2	3	4	5	6	7	8	9	10	11	12
1 Bishop's Stortford Swifts		5-0	1-1	0-1	2-0	2-2	0-0	0-0	1-3	0-1	2-0	1-1
2 Canning Town	1-3		0-0	0-0	0-2	3-2	0-1	0-6	1-2	5-0	1-6	1-1
3 Epping	3-0	3-3		1-2	0-2	3-0	1-1	1-0	0-4	1-3	0-3	0-0
4 Frenford Senior	6-2	2-3	1-1		4-1	3-1	0-0	3-2	1-1	2-0	1-2	3-0
5 Harold Wood Athletic	1-2	10-1	0-1	2-3		1-1	0-0	2-1	3-3	1-2	2-1	3-1
6 Kelvedon Hatch	1-1	4-0	5-1	1-1	1-1		1-4	1-1	1-1	1-0	0-1	1-3
7 Manford Way	2-0	2-0	5-0	0-0	2-0	5-0		2-1	2-0	1-0	1-2	3-0
8 Rayleigh Town	0-3	4-1	3-0	0-1	1-3	2-1	1-2		1-1	3-0	0-3	3-0
9 Shenfield Association	1-3	1-2	0-3	0-3	0-1	0-1	0-0	2-0		1-1	1-4	3-2
10 Takeley	0-3	3-2	2-0	1-4	1-3	1-1	2-2	3-1	1-1		2-3	3-0
11 White Ensign	1-0	3-1	5-0	1-1	0-0	3-1	1-1	3-1	2-1	0-1		HW
12 White Notley	0-0	4-1	1-1	3-3	0-2	1-1	0-0	5-2	1-3	1-2	1-4	

LEAGUE CUP

FIRST ROUND

Epping	v	Old Chelmsfordians	2-1
Faces	v	Shell Club Corringham	3-0
Metpol Chigwell	v	Bishop's Stortford Swifts	0-1
Ramsden	v	Basildon Town	5-2
Stambridge United	v	Ryan	4-1

SECOND ROUND

Barnston	v	Hutton	2-3
Benfleet	v	Bishop's Stortford Swifts	2-1
Broomfield	v	Writtle	2-2* 4-5p
Canning Town	v	Shenfield Association	0-4
Debden Sports	v	Rayleigh Town	1-2
Great Baddow	v	Faces	0-2
Herongate Athletic	v	Harold Wood Athletic	0-2
Kelvedon Hatch	v	Mountnessing	1-1* 2-4p
Leytonstone United	v	Stambridge United	2-1
Linford Wanderers	v	Epping	1-4
Ramsden	v	Galleywood	1-5
Roydon	v	Springfield	2-0
Sandon Royals	v	Takeley	1-3
Upminster	v	Leigh Ramblers	1-1* 4-5p
White Ensign	v	Frenford Senior	3-0
White Notley	v	Manford Way	1-4

THIRD ROUND

Benfleet	v	Mountnessing	0-4
Epping	v	Writtle	3-1
Galleywood	v	Leigh Ramblers	3-4*
Manford Way	v	Harold Wood Athletic	2-1
Rayleigh Town	v	Takeley	6-2
Roydon	v	Hutton	2-1
Shenfield Assoc.	v	Faces	1-1* 4-1p
White Ensign	v	Leytonstone United	4-0

QUARTER-FINALS

Epping	v	Mountnessing	1-4
Rayleigh Town	v	Manford Way	0-3
Shenfield Assoc.	v	Leigh Ramblers	2-1
White Ensign	v	Roydon	2-1

SEMI-FINALS

Manford Way	v	Shenfield Association	2-0
White Ensign	v	Mountnessing	2-0

THE FINAL (11th May at Southend United)

Manford Way	v	White Ensign	2-7

LEAGUE CONSTITUTION 2004-05

BISHOP'S STORTFORD SWIFTS
Ground: Silver Leys, Hadham Road (A1250), Bishop's Stortford, Herts
Tel: 01279 658941

DEBDEN SPORTS
Ground: Chigwell Lane, Loughton, Ilford, Essex

EPPING
Ground: Stonards Hill Rec Ground, Tidy's Lane, Epping, Essex

FRENFORD SENIOR
Ground: Oakfields Sports Ground, Forest Road, Barkingside, Essex

HAROLD WOOD ATHLETIC
Ground: Harold Wood Recreation Park, Harold View, Harold Wood, Essex
Tel: 01708 348827

KELVEDON HATCH
Ground: New Hall, School Road, Kelvedon Hatch, Brentwood, Essex
Tel: 01277 372153

MANFORD WAY
Ground: London Marathon Sports Ground, Forest Road, Hainault, Essex
Tel: 020 8500 3486

OLD CHELMSFORDIANS
Ground: Lawford Lane, Roxwell Road, Chelmsford, Essex
Tel: 01245 420442

RAYLEIGH TOWN
Ground: Rayleigh Town Sports & Social Club, London Road, Rayleigh, Essex
Tel: 01268 784001

SHENFIELD ASSOCIATION
Ground: The Drive, Warley, Brentwood, Essex

TAKELEY
Ground: Station Road, Takeley, near Bishop's Stortford, Hertfordshire
Tel: 01279 870404

WHITE ENSIGN
Ground: Borough Football Comb. HQ, Eastwoodbury Lane, Southend-on-Sea, Essex

Manford Way - Division One runers-up. Photo: Gordon Whittington.

Bishop's Stortford Swifts Official Match Programme

Bishop's Stortford Swifts with the Denny King Memorial Cup. Photo: Gordon Whittington.

HERTS SENIOR COUNTY LEAGUE

SPONSORED BY:

President: Eric Dear **Chairman:** Cecil T Husdon

General Secretary: Kevin Folds, 6 Lanthony Court,
High Street, Arlesey, Beds SG15 6TU
Tel: 01462 734102 Email: KFoldsHSCL@aol.com

FINAL LEAGUE TABLE 2003-04

PREMIER DIVISION	P	W	D	L	F	A	Pts
1. Hadley	28	23	4	1	81	19	73
2. Oxhey Jets (Promoted)	28	23	1	4	90	25	70
3. London Lions	28	14	7	7	62	34	49
4. Hinton	28	15	3	10	52	51	48
5. Met. Police Bushey	28	13	7	8	65	48	46
6. Chipperfield Corinthians	28	13	6	9	47	36	45
7. Hatfield Town	28	11	8	9	68	61	41
8. Sandridge Rovers	28	10	9	9	46	41	39
9. Elliott Star	28	9	8	11	47	53	35
10. Bovingdon	28	10	5	13	30	36	35
11. Wormley Rovers	28	9	5	14	28	56	32
12. Bushey Rangers	28	8	5	15	36	47	29
13. Bedmond Sports & Social	28	5	4	19	44	71	19
14. Old Parmiterians	28	5	3	20	34	84	18
15. Cuffley	28	4	1	23	28	96	13

2003-04	1	2	3	4	5	6	7	8	9	10	11	12	13	14	15
1 Bedmond Sports & Social		0-1	2-2	1-1	7-1	0-1	1-6	1-3	2-3	0-4	0-2	3-0	1-3	1-1	3-0
2 Bovingdon	2-2		2-3	1-2	W-L	1-1	1-2	4-1	1-0	2-3	4-0	1-0	0-5	1-0	0-0
3 Bushey Rangers	2-1	0-1		1-2	2-1	2-2	0-0	4-4	1-3	3-0	0-1	5-0	0-2	1-0	0-2
4 Chipperfield Corinthians	2-1	1-0	1-0		4-1	1-2	1-1	0-1	3-2	3-2	2-0	3-0	0-2	0-1	1-2
5 Cuffley	4-3	1-0	0-3	0-4		3-2	1-5	1-5	1-2	1-5	2-9	2-1	0-4	0-5	1-2
6 Elliott Star	1-3	4-1	0-1	0-0	4-3		1-0	4-3	1-2	2-1	3-4	4-2	0-4	1-4	5-1
7 Hadley	2-0	2-0	1-0	5-2	5-1	4-0		3-2	6-0	2-2	4-1	3-1	2-1	2-1	1-0
8 Hatfield Town	5-4	1-1	1-1	3-1	4-1	2-2	0-4		3-0	1-2	0-0	7-2	1-5	2-2	1-0
9 Hinton	4-2	2-0	2-0	2-2	2-0	2-1	0-1	6-2		1-0	2-1	3-2	1-4	1-2	1-2
10 London Lions	2-0	1-1	2-1	0-0	3-1	1-1	0-3	3-0	6-2		4-2	5-1	2-3	3-1	0-0
11 Metropolitan Police Bushey	4-3	2-1	2-0	1-2	5-0	1-1	2-2	2-1	1-1	2-2		6-1	2-4	4-3	5-1
12 Old Parmiterians	2-0	0-2	3-1	0-6	4-0	2-2	0-6	2-2	2-3	0-3	2-1		1-3	2-3	1-0
13 Oxhey Jets	7-0	2-0	8-1	3-0	3-0	3-1	1-3	3-3	3-2	1-0	1-3	5-0		1-0	0-2
14 Sandridge Rovers	6-1	1-0	1-0	2-2	1-0	0-0	0-2	1-5	2-2	0-0	2-2	2-2	0-4		0-0
15 Wormley Rovers	0-2	0-2	3-2	2-1	2-2	2-1	0-4	2-5	0-1	0-6	0-0	3-1	0-5	2-5	

AUBREY CUP

FIRST ROUND

Allenburys Sports	v	Metropolitan Police Bushey	1-4
Bovingdon	v	North Mymms	3-2*
Buntingford Town	v	Hadley	1-4
Chipperfield C.	v	Old Parmiterians	3-1*
Elliott Star	v	London Lions	4-3
Evergreen	v	Codicote	0-2
Hatfield Town	v	Oxhey Jets	3-3* 4-5p
Hinton	v	Croxley Guild	6-0
Little Munden	v	Cuffley	4-0
London Road	v	Lemsford	1-4
Loughton	v	Bedmond S&S	2-3
Mill End Sports & Social	v	Kimpton Rovers (w/o)	
Sandridge Rovers	v	Benington	1-1* 0-3p
Sarratt	v	Bushey Rangers (w/o)	
Standon & P'ridge	v	Whitewebbs	2-2* 8-9p
Wormley Rov.	v	Knebworth	4-2

SECOND ROUND

Bedmond S&S	v	Little Munden	2-1
Benington	v	Whitewebbs	0-2
Bovingdon	v	Chipperfield	4-2
Bushey Rangers	v	Metropolitan Police Bushey	0-1
Hadley	v	Codicote	1-2
Hinton	v	Oxhey Jets	3-1
Lemsford	v	Elliott Star	0-2
Wormley Rovers	v	Kimpton	2-0

QUARTER-FINALS

Bedmond S&S	v	Elliott Star	2-0
Codicote	v	Whitewebbs	1-3
Hinton	v	Bovingdon	4-1
Wormley Rovers	v	Metropolitan Police Bushey	1-2

SEMI-FINALS

Met Police Bushey	v	Hinton	2-3
Whitewebbs	v	Bedmond S&S	2-0

THE FINAL (3rd May at Ware)

Hinton	v	Whitewebbs	1-3

Hadley F.C.
Jubilant after clinching the Premier Division title with a 1-0 win over Bushey Rangers.

Photo: Gordon Whittington.

LEAGUE CONSTITUTION 2004-05

BEDMOND SPORTS & SOCIAL

Ground: Toms Lane Recreation Ground, Toms Lane, Bedmond, Hertfordshire

Tel: 01923 267991

BOVINGDON

Ground: Green Lane, Bovingdon, Hemel Hempstead, Hertfordshire

Tel: 01442 832628

BUSHEY RANGERS

Ground: Moatfield, Bournehall Lane, Bushey, Hertfordshire

Tel: 020 8386 1875

CHIPPERFIELD CORINTHIANS

Ground: Queens Street, Chipperfield, Hertfordshire

Tel: 01923 269554

CODICOTE

Ground: John Clements Memorial Ground, Bury Lane, Codicote, Hertfordshire

Tel: 01438 821072

ELLIOTT STAR

Ground: Pursley Football Ground, London Road, Shenley, Hertfordshire

EVERGREEN

Ground: Southway, Abbots Langley, Hertfordshire

Tel: 01923 267812

HADLEY

Ground: Hadley Sports Ground, Brickfield Lane, Arkley, Barnet, Hertfordshire

Tel: 020 8449 1144

HATFIELD TOWN

Ground: Birchwood Leisure Centre, Longmead, Birchwood, Hatfield, Hertfordshire

Tel: 01707 270772

HINTON

Ground: Holtwhites Sports & Social, Kirkland Drive, Enfield, Middlesex

Tel: 020 8363 4449

LONDON LIONS

Ground: Laing Sports, Rowley Lane, Barnet, Hertfordshire

Tel: 020 8441 6051

METROPOLITAN POLICE BUSHEY

Ground: Met. Police Sports Club, Aldenham Road, Bushey, Watford

Tel: 01923 243947

OLD PARMITERIANS

Ground: Parmiters School, High Elms Lane, Garston, Watford, Hertfordshire

Tel: 01923 682805

SANDRIDGE ROVERS

Ground: Spencer Recreation Ground, Sandridge, St Albans, Hertfordshire

Tel: 01727 835506

WHITEWEBBS

Ground: The Whitewebbs Centre, Whitewebbs Lane, Enfield, Middlesex

Tel: 01992 760716

WORMLEY ROVERS

Ground: Wormley Sports Club, Church Lane, Wormley, Hertfordshire

Tel: 01992 460650

Bushey Rangers F.C. Photo: Gordon Whittington.

Whitewebbs F.C.
Eventual winners of the Aubrey Cup celebrate their 2-0 semi-final win over Bedmond Social & Sports.
Photo: Gordon Whittington.

FINAL LEAGUE TABLE 2003-04

DIVISION ONE	P	W	D	L	F	A	Pts
1. Whitewebbs	30	23	4	3	115	36	73
2. Evergreen	30	22	4	4	82	26	70
3. Codicote	30	21	6	3	117	28	69
4. Little Munden	30	22	2	6	70	28	68
5. London Road	30	18	5	7	75	36	59
6. Lemsford	30	15	6	9	72	51	51
7. Benington	30	14	7	9	74	46	49
8. Knebworth	30	13	5	12	55	47	44
9. Allenburys Sports	30	12	5	13	74	69	41
10. Standon & Puckeridge	30	8	7	15	55	63	31
11. Croxley Guild	30	8	6	16	61	98	30
12. Kimpton Rovers	30	9	3	18	62	103	30
13. Buntingford Town	30	8	5	17	42	76	29
14. North Mymms	30	6	2	22	35	81	20
15. Loughton	30	4	3	23	37	80	15
16. Sarratt	30	2	0	28	17	175	6

Little Munden F.C.
Just missed out on promotion from Division One in their first season in the league.

Photo: Gordon Whittington.

MIDDLESEX COUNTY LEAGUE

SPONSORED BY: CHERRY RED RECORDS

Founded 1984

President: Peter Rogers **Chairman:** Reg Johnson

Secretary: Stephen C. Hosmer, 27 St Georges Road, Hanworth, Middx. TW13 6RD Tel: (H) 020 8894 1244 (Fax) 020 8894 0499 (M) 07831 393559 Email: stephen@hosmer.freeserve.co.uk

FINAL LEAGUE TABLE 2003-04

PREMIER DIVISION	P	W	D	L	F	A	Pts
1. Wraysbury (-3 pts)	32	21	7	4	95	37	67
2. Walthamstow Pennant	32	20	5	7	62	39	65
3. CB Hounslow United (-3 pts)	32	20	5	7	66	35	62
4. Hanworth Villa	32	18	4	10	69	43	58
5. Willesden Constantine	32	16	8	8	69	46	56
6. London Tigers	32	16	6	10	71	47	54
7. Crown & Manor	32	16	6	10	67	45	54
8. Brentford New Inn	32	16	4	12	46	44	52
9. Stonewall	32	15	6	11	62	58	51
10. Spelthorne Sports	32	15	4	13	52	53	49
11. CMB Metal Box	32	10	5	17	57	86	35
12. FC Sofia (-3 pts)	32	10	5	17	70	77	32
13. FC Deportivo Galicia	32	6	8	18	51	70	26
14. Marsh Rangers	32	7	5	20	48	86	26
15. Walthamstow Avenue	32	8	2	22	38	80	26
16. Mauritius Sports	32	6	6	20	33	85	24
17. Broadfields United (-3 pts)	32	5	8	19	44	69	20

PREMIER 03-04	1	2	3	4	5	6	7	8	9	10	11	12	13	14	15	16	17
1 Brentford New Inn		4-2	0-0	2-3	1-2	1-0	1-1	3-2	2-1	2-0	4-1	3-1	0-3	3-0	0-1	1-0	0-2
2 Broadfields United	3-4		1-2	3-1	0-3	3-2	3-5	1-1	0-4	4-3	3-3	0-0	0-2	6-0	0-1	0-3	1-3
3 CB Hounslow United	3-0	2-0		9-0	1-1	2-1	3-1	0-2	3-0	1-1	1-0	3-2	5-0	HW	1-3	2-0	2-4
4 CMB Metal Box	2-1	2-1	3-1		1-1	2-2	3-2	0-5	3-1	5-4	1-2	1-5	0-2	0-2	0-2	2-4	2-6
5 Crown & Manor	1-0	3-0	1-2	3-1		3-2	2-1	0-1	1-1	4-4	3-0	0-1	4-1	2-0	5-2	4-1	4-0
6 FC Deportivo Galicia	0-1	0-0	0-5	3-5	1-0		3-3	2-6	2-2	3-1	3-4	0-2	2-0	4-0	1-4	0-1	2-2
7 FC Sofia	2-4	3-3	0-3	4-2	4-1	4-0		1-4	2-3	1-2	6-0	4-2	3-5	2-0	1-3	1-2	HW
8 Hanworth Villa	3-0	1-2	1-3	3-2	4-4	2-2	4-3		0-1	2-3	3-0	0-2	2-0	5-0	2-1	2-0	0-0
9 London Tigers	0-0	2-0	0-1	3-3	4-1	2-0	4-3	0-2		3-2	6-2	5-0	1-2	5-2	2-3	1-3	2-2
10 Marsh Rangers	3-2	2-2	0-2	3-2	0-3	0-3	0-2	1-0	0-5		1-2	2-1	1-0	2-5	0-2	2-2	3-6
11 Mauritius Sports	1-2	HW	HW	2-2	0-3	3-3	0-3	0-3	0-4	5-2		0-1	2-5	0-1	0-1	2-2	2-2
12 Spelthorne Sports	0-1	4-3	0-2	2-3	4-2	1-1	3-1	3-0	0-2	3-1	2-0		1-1	3-2	1-4	1-3	0-2
13 Stonewall	1-1	4-0	2-1	2-1	2-4	2-6	0-0	0-2	2-2	3-2	1-0	0-1		3-1	1-1	3-1	2-4
14 Walthamstow Avenue	0-2	0-0	0-0	1-4	2-1	2-1	8-2	0-2	2-3	2-1	3-1	0-2	2-6		1-2	2-3	0-11
15 Walthamstow Pennant	0-1	2-1	2-2	1-0	1-1	2-1	HW	1-2	2-0	4-1	2-1	5-1	3-4	1-0		2-2	2-4
16 Willesden Constantine	5-0	1-1	9-1	1-1	1-0	2-0	7-3	3-2	0-1	1-1	0-0	0-1	4-2	3-0	2-2		0-4
17 Wraysbury	1-0	2-1	1-3	3-0	2-0	3-1	2-2	5-1	2-1	4-0	12-0	2-2	1-1	HW	1-0	2-3	

LEAGUE CONSTITUTION 2004-05

BETHNAL GREEN UNITED

Ground: Clapton FC, Old Spotted Dog Ground, Upton Lane, Forest Gate, London

Tel: 020 8472 0822

BRAZILIAN SPORTS CLUB

Ground: Viking Greenford, Avenue Park, Western Avenue, Greenford, Middlesex

Tel: 020 8578 2706

BRENTFORD NEW INN

Ground: Broadfields Comm. Sports Ground, Headstone Lane, North Harrow, Middlesex

Tel: 020 8421 4739

CB HOUNSLOW UNITED

Ground: Osterley Sports Club, Tentelow Lane, Osterley, Middlesex

Tel: 020 8574 3774

CROWN & MANOR

Ground: Mile End Stadium, Burdett Road, Rhodeswell Road, Bow, London

Tel: 020 8980 1885

FC DEPORTIVO GALICIA

Ground: Eversheds Sports Ground, Southdown Avenue, Hanwell, Middlesex

HANWORTH VILLA

Ground: Rectory Meadow, Park Road, Hounslow Road, Hanworth, Middlesex

Tel: 020 8831 9391

LONDON TIGERS

Ground: Kingsbury Town FC, Silver Jubilee Park, Townsend Lane, Kingsbury, Middlesex

Tel: 020 8205 1645

MARSH RANGERS

Ground: Hanworth Villa FC, Rectory Meadow, Park Road, off Hounslow Road, Hanworth, Middlesex

Tel: 020 8831 9391

MARTIN BAKER SPORTS

Ground: Martins Field, Tilehouse Lane, Denham, Buckinghamshire

Tel: 01895 833077

MAURITIUS SPORTS (CMB)

Ground: Fredrick Knight Sports Ground, Willoughby Lane, Tottenham, London

Tel: 020 8801 8233

SPELTHORNE SPORTS

Ground: Spelthorne Sports Club, 296 Staines Road West, Ashford, Middlesex

Tel: 01932 783625

STONEWALL

Ground: Broadfields Comm. Spts Ground, Headstone Lane, North Harrow, Middlesex

Tel: 020 8421 4739

WALTHAMSTOW AVENUE

Ground: Town Mead Leisure Park, Booker Road, Waltham Abbey, Essex

WALTHAMSTOW PENNANT

Ground: Waltham Forest FC, Wadham Lodge, Kitchener Road, Walthamstow, London

Tel: 020 8527 2444

WILLESDEN CONSTANTINE

Ground: Alperton Sports Ground, Alperton Lane, Alperton, Middlesex

Tel: 020 8997 9909

WRAYSBURY

Ground: Memorial Ground, The Green, Wraysbury, Buckinghamshire

Tel: 01784 482155

Honours: Middlesex Co. League 2003-04

WRAYSBURY F.C.
Lining up before their 2-1 win over London Tigers, a victory that gave them the Premier League title.
Photo: Gordon Whittington.

OTHER STEP 7 LEAGUES

BRIGHTON HOVE & DISTRICT
FEEDER TO SUSSEX COUNTY LEAGUE

PREMIER DIVISION	P	W	D	L	F	A	Pts
1. Hanover	20	16	3	1	66	22	51
2. AFC St Georges	20	13	2	5	52	27	41
3. Whitehawk Vets	20	12	4	4	66	37	40
4. Royal Sovereign	20	10	3	7	46	51	33
5. Montpelier Villa	20	10	2	8	43	38	32
6. Rottingdean Village	20	9	3	8	29	24	30
7. Legal & General	20	8	6	6	28	30	30
8. American Exp. (+2pts)	20	4	6	10	29	41	20
9. Midway (1948)	20	4	6	10	28	33	18
10. Meridian Athletic	20	2	4	14	18	60	10
11. Harbour View (-1pt)	20	2	1	17	26	68	6

CRAWLEY & DISTRICT

FEEDER TO SUSSEX COUNTY LEAGUE

PREMIER DIVISION	P	W	D	L	F	A	Pts
1. S. Park/Reigate T.	20	19	1	0	84	20	58
2. Merstham Newton	20	13	5	2	54	27	44
3. Oakwood 'A'	20	9	6	5	56	48	33
4. Three Bridges 'A'	20	10	2	8	54	49	32
5. Phoenix (Sussex)	20	9	3	8	45	42	30
6. Trumpton Town	20	8	4	8	44	42	28
7. Holland Sports	20	8	3	9	37	52	27
8. St Francis Flyers	20	6	6	8	30	39	24
9. Bluebird Rangers	20	4	2	14	31	54	14
10. Horley Albion	20	4	0	16	17	47	12
11. Ifield Edwards Res.	20	4	0	16	24	56	12

EAST SUSSEX LEAGUE

FEEDER TO SUSSEX COUNTY LEAGUE

	P	W	D	L	F	A	Pts
1. Hollington United	18	14	4	0	58	22	46
2. Rock-a-Nore	18	10	4	4	53	21	34
3. Willingdon Athletic	18	10	0	8	32	29	30
4. St Leonards Social (-3pts)	18	9	3	6	51	46	27
5. Heathfield United	18	7	4	7	48	45	25
6. Punnetts Town	18	7	3	8	47	39	24
7. Peche Hill Select	18	7	2	9	31	38	23
8. Little Common	18	5	3	10	42	53	18
9. Icklesham Casuals	18	4	5	9	35	52	17
10. Northiam	18	2	2	14	22	74	8

MID SUSSEX LEAGUE

FEEDER TO SUSSEX COUNTY LEAGUE

PREMIER DIVISION	P	W	D	L	F	A	Pts
1. Old Varndeanians	26	20	2	4	89	30	62
2. East Grinstead United	26	19	1	6	74	33	58
3. Wisdom Sports	26	17	5	4	79	33	56
4. Maresfield Village	26	12	6	8	47	33	42
5. Barcombe	26	12	3	11	48	38	39
6. Lindfield	26	11	4	11	44	51	37
7. Nutley	26	9	8	9	52	50	35
8. Lewes Bridgeview	26	8	8	10	46	37	32
9. Hassocks 'A'	26	8	7	11	48	46	31
10. Cuckfield Town	26	9	4	13	37	54	31
11. Village of Ditchling	26	8	6	12	29	65	30
12. Buxted	26	6	9	11	31	50	27
13. Handcross Village	26	7	3	16	31	68	24
14. Ardingly	26	2	2	22	32	99	8

NORTHAMPTON TOWN LEAGUE
FEEDER TO UNITED COUNTIES LEAGUE

PREMIER DIVISION	P	W	D	L	F	A	Pts
1. University Coll. Northampton	18	13	2	3	46	15	41
2. Airflow	18	12	4	2	56	24	40
3. Bective Wanderers	18	11	3	4	47	14	36
4. Duston United	17	10	3	4	50	25	33
5. Crusaders	18	9	4	5	53	29	31
6. Queen Eleanor	18	8	3	7	31	29	27
7. Delapre Old Boys	17	4	3	10	20	42	15
8. Wootton St George	18	3	3	12	25	54	12
9. Ashley Rovers	18	1	6	11	16	43	9
10. Kingsthorpe Nmds	18	2	1	15	13	82	7

OXFORDSHIRE SENIOR LEAGUE
FEEDER TO HELLENIC LEAGUE

PREMIER DIVISION	P	W	D	L	F	A	Pts
1. Eynsham	24	19	3	2	63	12	60
2. Oxford University Press	24	17	2	5	54	22	53
3. Kidlington Old Boys	24	16	5	3	64	36	53
4. Charlton United	24	13	4	7	38	32	43
5. Chadlington	24	11	5	8	64	40	38
6. Long Crendon	24	10	6	8	48	38	36
7. Launton Sports	24	8	7	9	45	40	31
8. Marston Saints	24	8	2	14	46	56	26
9. Watlington Town	24	6	6	12	41	46	24
10. Worc. COB & Blet.	24	6	6	12	28	45	24
11. Garsington	24	5	7	12	35	44	22
12. Haddenham	24	4	3	17	29	88	15
13. Yarnton	24	4	2	18	23	79	14

SUFFOLK & IPSWICH LEAGUE
FEEDER TO EASTERN COUNTIES LEAGUE

SENIOR DIVISION	P	W	D	L	F	A	Pts
1. East Bergholt United	30	21	5	4	85	37	68
2. Walsham-le-Will.	30	19	5	6	70	40	62
3. Grundisburgh	30	15	6	9	55	41	51
4. Ipswich Athletic	30	16	4	10	62	56	49
5. Felixstowe United	30	14	6	10	65	50	48
6. Crane Sports	30	11	10	9	55	54	43
7. Melton St Audrys	30	11	7	12	67	66	40
8. Haughley United	30	11	6	13	46	46	39
9. Cockfield United	30	10	9	11	40	52	39
10. Capel Plough	30	9	9	12	37	54	36
11. Achilles	30	8	10	12	58	55	34
12. Stanton	30	9	6	15	43	65	33
13. Old Newton United (-3pts)	30	9	9	12	40	64	33
14. Westerfield United	30	8	6	16	58	62	30
15. Stonham Aspal	30	8	5	17	46	71	29
16. Bramford United	30	6	7	17	48	62	25

WEST SUSSEX LEAGUE

FEEDER TO SUSSEX COUNTY LEAGUE

PREMIER DIVISION	P	W	D	L	F	A	Pts
1. Rustington	22	15	6	1	57	19	51
2. Henfield	22	14	1	7	58	35	43
3. Loxwood	22	12	3	7	74	42	39
4. Alfold	22	12	3	7	61	34	39
5. Clymping	22	11	3	8	43	29	36
6. Yapton	22	10	5	7	67	54	35
7. Chichester Hosps	22	10	5	7	48	41	35
8. Rogate	22	8	2	12	39	49	26
9. Eastergate United	22	7	4	11	34	62	25
10. Cowfold	22	5	3	14	25	58	18
11. South Bersted	22	4	3	15	24	57	15
12. Faygate United	22	4	2	16	18	68	14

WORTHING & DISTRICT LEAGUE

FEEDER TO SUSSEX COUNTY LEAGUE

PREMIER DIVISION	P	W	D	L	F	A	Pts
1. Eynsham	24	19	3	2	63	12	60
2. Oxford University Press	24	17	2	5	54	22	53
3. Kidlington Old Boys	24	16	5	3	64	36	53
4. Charlton United	24	13	4	7	38	32	43
5. Chadlington	24	11	5	8	64	40	38
6. Long Crendon	24	10	6	8	48	38	36
7. Launton Sports	24	8	7	9	45	40	31
8. Marston Saints	24	8	2	14	46	56	26
9. Watlington Town	24	6	6	12	41	46	24
10. Worc. COB & Blet.	24	6	6	12	28	45	24
11. Garsington	24	5	7	12	35	44	22
12. Haddenham	24	4	3	17	29	88	15
13. Yarnton	24	4	2	18	23	79	14

FURTHER DETAILS FOR SOME OF THE CLUBS ENTERED INTO THIS SEASON'S F.A. VASE

BUDLEIGH SALTERTON (DEVON LGE)

Secretary: Nick Pannell, 33 Armytage Road, Budleigh Salterton, Devon EX9 6SD
Tel Nos: 01395 445877 (H) 07765887108 (M)
Ground: Greenway Lane, Budleigh Salterton EX9 6SG Tel No: 01395 443850
Capacity: **Seats:** **Cover:** **Floodlights:** **Clubhouse:**
Directions: From Exmouth, immediately before Budleigh turn left into Knowle Village and then take second right (Bedlands Lane) and left at school. Greenway Lane is on right.
PREVIOUS **Leagues:** Devon & Exeter and East Devon

HONOURS
2003-2004 **Player of the Year:** S.Slater **Top Scoprer:** A.Turner

FACT FILE
Formed: 1913
Sponsor:
Colours: Red & White
Change colours: Blue
Midweek Matches: Wednesday

CLUB PERSONNEL
Chairman: A.Romp
Managers: Julian Phillips and Kevin Smith
Programme Editor:: Tony Oakes

CULLOMPTON ROVERS (DEVON LGE)

Secretary: Marcus Scott, 13 Chestnut Avenue, Cullompton, Devon. EX15 1DW
Tel No: 01884 33090
Ground: Speeds Meadow, Duke Street, Cullompton EX15 1DW Tel No: 01884 33090
Capacity: 1,500 **Seats:** **Cover:** **Floodlights:** Yes **Clubhouse:** Yes
Directions: Leave M5 at Jct 28, left at town centre then at Meadow Lane. Left past Sports Centre and right at end of road, then in 100 yards, turn into ground at end of lane.
PREVIOUS **Leagues:** East Devon Victory League, Devon & Exeter
HONOURS: Devon & Exeter Champions 1961 1964 East Devon Sen Cup 1984
Devon County League Champions: 97-98 98-99 Devon Premier Cup 1998-99
RECORD **Attendance:** 693 v Willand Rovers 1977-78:
2003-2004 **Player of the Year:** Danny Baily **Top Goalscorer:** Darren Pengelly

FACT FILE
Formed:1945
Sponsor:
Colours: Red and Black
Change colours: Yellow & Blue
Midweek Matches: Tuesday
Reserves' Lge:
Programme Editor:: Mike Partridge

CLUB PERSONNEL
Chairman: Stan Hill
Vice Chairman:
President: Jim Brooks
Manager: Ray Pratt
Assistant Manager: Hedley Steele
Captain: Duncan Floyde

NEWTON ABBOT (DEVON LGE)

Secretary: Royston Perkins, 21 Prospect Terrace, Newton Abbot TQ12 2LN
Tel Nos: 01626 361596 (H) Fax 01626 361596
Ground: Coach Road. Stadium, Coach Road, Newton Abbot TQ12 1EJ
Capacity: **Seats:** **Cover:** **Floodlights:** **Clubhouse:** Matchdays and evenings
Directions: From Torquay/Penn Inn roundabout, follows signs into town centre and for Devon County F.A. and N.A.F.C.
Previous Names: Newton Dynamoes and Newton Abbot Dynamoes
Leagues: South Devon and South Western
Record **Attendance**: League 600 v Buckfastleigh 1992-3 Friendly:1,100 v Torquay Utd.01-2
2003-2004 **Player of the Year**: Simon Revell **Top Goalscorer**: Chris Hooper

FACT FILE
Formed: 1964
Sponsor:
Colours: Red/black/black
Change colours: Sky Blue/white/white
Midweek Matches: Wednesday (7.45)
rogramme Editor: Cheryl Rider
Tel No: 01803 292569

CLUB PERSONNEL
Chairman: Austin Rider
Manager: Tim Cowell
Coach: Dave Rudge
Captain: Robbie Turner

OTTERY ST MARY F.C. (DEVON LGE)

Secretary: Derek Priest, The Granary, Ware Farm, Ottery St Mary, Devon EX11 1PJ
Tel No: 01404 815939

Ground: Washbrook Meadows, Butts Road, Ottery St Mary, Devon EX11 1EL
Tel No: 01404 813539

Capacity: **Seats:** **Cover:** **Floodlights:** **Clubhouse:**

Directions: A30 Westbound, A374 signposted Ottery St Mary then go past Otter Nurseries and turn left into Butts Lane

PREVIOUS **Leagues:** Western League and Devon & Exeter League

HONOURS

FACT FILE
Formed: 1912
Sponsor:
Colours: Blue and White
Change colours: All red
Midweek Matches: Wednesday
Programme Editor: Phil Hiscox

CLUB PERSONNEL
Chairman: Graham Brown
Manager: Pete Gartrell
Assistant Manager:

POULTON VICTORIA (WEST CHESHIRE DIV. 1)

Secretary: Allan Skillen, Tel Nos: 0151 6528157(H) 07780841044 (M)
e-mail: allan skillen@cwctv.net

Ground: Victoria Park, Rankin Street, Wallasey. Tel No: 0151 638 3559

Capacity: **Seats:** **Cover:** **Floodlights:** **Clubhouse:**

Directions: From M53 to Jct1 All Docks (not Liverpool Tunnel) Turn left at bottom of slip road and first right opposite Poulton Victoria Social Club. Continue to Eagle Pub , turn left at top iof road and turn right into Victoria Park ground .

PREVIOUS **Leagues:**
Grounds:

HONOURS Cheshire Amateur Cup Finalists 2003-04 Pyke Cup Winners 2003-04

2003-2004 **Player of the Year:** Greg Stones **Top Goalscorer:** Gary Reay 21

FACT FILE
Formed: 1935
Sponsor: Carslberg & Bass
Colours: All royal Blue
Change colours:
Midweek Matches:
Programme: Editor:

CLUB PERSONNEL
Chairman:Steve Skupski
Manager: Mark Jones
Assistant Manager:Justin Broadbent
Captain: Neal Larkin

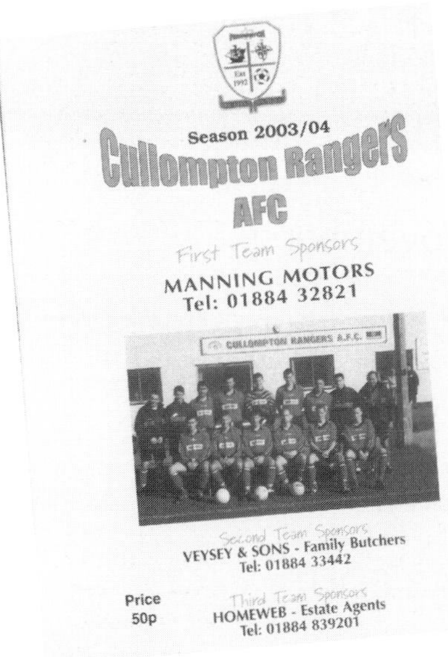

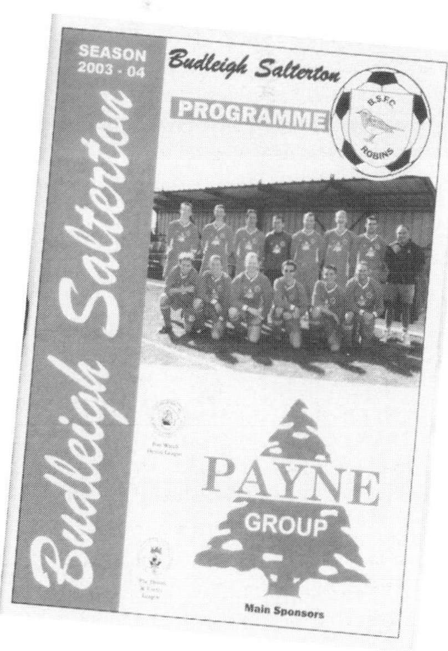

the
FOOTBALL ASSOCIATION COMPETITIONS

ENGLAND'S NATIONAL GAME XI

Paul Fairclough was appointed as the manager in charge of England's non-league international squad, who play under the title of The National Game XI, but his first two fixtures last season were Under 23 games against young full time professionals from Belgium at Darlington and Italy at Shrewsbury.

These games were eventually well contested, but the poor manager had a constant stream of players pulling out and with hurried replacements scurrying across the country to join the England party attempting to settle in, understand the game plan and pull on an England shirt, it was surprising that performances were so good.

This isn't how the honour of representing your country should be experienced. So when the full senior squad was selected for The Four Nations Tournament in Scotland it was heartbreaking for all concerned when the same situation occurred, as many senior clubs pulled their representatives out and the eventual squad had little time to settle down and attempt to bond on and off the field.

Not surprisingly it wasn't until the last game of our three, against favourites Scotland that the week's work together brought some reward for the manager's dedicated team of coaches and loyal players with a fine victory.

Two more games were enjoyed, one against Iraq's Asian Games squad at Maccclesfield where a superb evening was enjoyed by a big crowd who saw a victory for the impressive visitors and another game in America where a 0-0 draw was achieved.

Immense credit should go to Paul Fairclough for producing sound performances after binding together 'teams' in the most difficult of situations. He received loyal support from his coaching staff and special performances were produced by Luke Rodgers (Shrewsbury Town) , Gareth Sheldon (Exeter City) and Steve Guinan (Hereford United).

This level of our game deserves an England squad of which we can be proud and which all non-league players should be keen to represent.

Tony Williams.

England line up before their friendly international against Italy.
Photo: Bill Wheatcroft.

INTERNATIONAL FRIENDLIES

ENGLAND 2 - 2 BELGIUM

Ricketts 66, Rogers 88 — Lepoint 38, 75

4th November 2003 at Darlington FC - Att: 3,166 (new record)

ENGLAND (4-4-3)

Bittner	Exeter
Tavanagh	Accrington
Jordan	Tamworth
Charles	Farnborough
Perkins	Morecambe
Hogg	Barnet
Ricketts	Telford
McLean	Aldershot
Rodgers	Shrewsbury
D'Sane	Aldershot
Elding	Stevenage

Subs:

Murphy	Telford
Smith	Margate
Cowan	Canvey Island
Rickards	Tamworth

ENGLAND 1 - 4 ITALY

Sheldon — Mannini, Danucci, Cozolino, Storzini

11th February 2004 at Shrewsbury Town FC - Att: 3,703 (new record)

ENGLAND

Bittner	Exeter
Cavanagh	Accrington
Boardman	Woking
Collins	Chester
Perkins	Morecambe
Miller	Aldershot
Challinor	Aldershot
Murray	Woking
Sheldon	Exeter
D'Sane (capt)	Aldershot
Rodgers	Shrewsbury

Subs:

McLean	Aldershot
Kennedy	Accrington
Charles	Farnborough
Purdie	Hereford
Yakubu	Barnet

Giacomo Brichetto saves Karl Murray's header, during England's 1-4 defeat against Italy. Photo: Bill Wheatcroft.

ENGLAND 1 - 5 IRAQ

Hatch — Sawadi, Manajid (2), Karim, Fowzi

27th May at Macclesfield FC - Att: 4000+ (yet another new record)

ENGLAND

Baker (S1) .... Hereford
Perkins .... Morecambe
Vickers .... Dagenham & Redbridge
Sedgemore .... Shrewsbury
John Kennedy................. Canvey Island
Thompson (S2) .... Morecambe
Kerr .... Scarborough
Southam (S3) .... Bishop's Stortford
McNiven (S4) .... Leigh RMI
Hatch (S5)........................... Barnet
Sheldon.......................... Exeter

Subs:

Jon Kennedy (S1)............ Accrington Stanley
Carlton (S2) .... Morecambe
Cowan (S3) .... Canvey Island
Proctor (S4) .... Accington Stanley
Bacon (S5) ....

Italy kick-off against England's National Game XI in front of a then record Semi-Pro International attendance of 3,703.

Photo: Bill Wheatcroft.

USA 0 - 0 ENGLAND

9th June at Charleston - Att: 1,863

ENGLAND

Matt Baker.................. Hereford
Jake Sedgemore .... Shrewsbury
Jon Boardman................ Woking
Andy Tretton .... Hereford
David Perkins .... Morecambe
Glen Southam .... Bishop's Stortford
John Kennedy........... Canvey Island
Gareth Sheldon................ Exeter
Ian Craney .... Altrincham
Liam Hatch .... Barnet
Steve Guinan................ Hereford

Subs:

Jon Kennedy (80) .... Accrington Stanley
Gary Thompson (45) .... Morecambe
Ismail Yakubu (46) .... Barnet
David McNiven (76) .... Leigh RMI
Lee Boylan (59) .... Canvey Island

FOUR NATIONS TOURNAMENT

ENGLAND 2 - 3 REP. OF IRELAND

Guinan 7, 68 — Flood 20, Zayed 60, Russell 61

at Deverondale

ENGLAND

Matt Baker . . . . Hereford
Peter Cavanagh (S1) . . . . Accrington
Andy Tretton . . . . Hereford
Matt Redmile. . . . . Barnet
David Perkins . . . . Morecambe
Gary Thompson (S2) . . . . Morecambe
Sam Ricketts (S3) . . . . Telford
Scott Kerr . . . . Scarborough
Gareth Sheldon. . . . . Exeter
Steve Guinan. . . . . Hereford
Liam Hatch . . . . Barnet

Subs

Jon Boardman . . . . Woking
Amos Foyewa (S2) . . . . Woking
Danny McDonnell (GK) . . . Worcester City
David McNiven . . . . Leigh RMI
Jake Sedgemore (S1) . . . . Shrewsbury
Glen Southam (S3). . . . . . Bishop's Stortford

ENGLAND 0 - 2 WALES

Evans 50, Owens 73

at Keith FC

ENGLAND

Danny McDonnell. . . . . Worcester City
Matt Redmile. . . . . Barnet
Jon Boardman . . . . Woking
Andy Tretton . . . . Hereford
Jake Sedgemore (S1) . . . . Shrewsbury
Glen Southam . . . . Bishop's Stortford
Scott Kerr . . . . Scarborough
Gary Thompson (S2) . . . . Morecambe
Steve Guinan. . . . . Hereford
Liam Hatch (S3) . . . . Barnet
Gareth Sheldon. . . . . Exeter

Subs:

Matt Baker (GK) . . . . Hereford
Peter Cavanagh . . . . Accrington
Amos Foyewa (S1) . . . . Woking
David McNiven (S3) . . . . Leigh RMI
David Perkins . . . . Morecambe
Sam Ricketts (S2) . . . . Telford

OTHER RESULTS

WALES 4 - 1 REP. OF IRLAND

SCOTLAND 2 - 0 REP. OF IRELAND

SCOTLAND 0 - 0 WALES

SCOTLAND 1 - 3 ENGLAND

McKay 12 (pen) — Guinan 25 (pen) Southam 27, Hatch 29

at Princess Royal Park, Banff

ENGLAND		Subs:	
Matt Baker	Hereford	Jon Boardman	Woking
Matt Redmile	Barnet	Peter Cavanagh	Accrington
David Perkins	Morecambe	Amos Foyewa (S1)	Woking
Andy Tretton	Hereford	McDonnell (GK)	Worcester City
Jake Sedgemore	Shrewsbury	David McNiven (S2)	Leigh RMI
Glen Southam	Bishop's Stortford	Gary Thompson	Morecambe
Scott Kerr	Scarborough		
Sam Ricketts	Telford		
Steve Guinan (S1)	Hereford		
Liam Hatch (S2)	Barnet		
Gareth Sheldon	Exeter		

FINAL TABLE	P	W	D	L	F	A	Pts	GD
WALES	3	2	1	0	6	1	7	5
SCOTLAND	3	1	1	1	3	3	4	0
ENGLAND	3	1	0	2	5	6	3	-1
REPUBLIC OF IRELAND	3	1	0	2	4	8	3	-4

England's Four Nations Tournament goalscorers.....

Steve Guinan	3
Liam Hatch	1
Gareth Southam	1

Tournament winners - Wales.

NATIONAL GAME XI - SEASON 2003-2004 at a glance

Date	Competition	Opponents	Venue	Result	FT	HT	Goalscorer(s)	Att
04.11.03	Friendly	Belgium	Darlington FC	D	2-2	0-1	Ricketts 66, Rodgers 88	3,166
11.02.04	Friendly	Italy	Shrewsbury FC	L	1-4	-	Sheldon	3,703
18.05.04	F.N.T.	Rep. of Ireland	Deverondale	L	2-3	1-1	Guinan 7, 68	-
20.05.04	F.N.T.	Wales	Keith FC	L	0-2	0-0	-	-
23.05.04	F.N.T.	Scotland	Deverondale	W	3-1	3-1	Guinan 25 (pen), Southam 27, Hatch 29	-
27.05.04	Friendly	Iraq	Macclesfield FC	L	1-5	-	Hatch	4,000+
09.06.04	Friendly	USA	Charleston USA	D	0-0	0-0	-	1,863

Goalscorers: Guinan (3), Hatch (2), Rodgers, Ricketts, Sheldon, Southam.

ENGLAND'S RESULTS 1979 - 2004

BELGIUM

11.02.03	KV Ostend	1 - 3
04.11.03	Darlington	2 - 2

FINLAND UNDER-21

14.04.93	Woking	1 - 3
30.05.94	Aanekoski	0 - 2

GIBRALTAR

27.04.82	Gibraltar	3 - 2
31.05.95	Gibraltar	3 - 2

HOLLAND

03.06.79	Stafford	1 - 0
07.06.80	Zeist	2 - 1
09.06.81	Lucca	2 - 0
03.06.82	Aberdeen	1 - 0
02.06.83	Scarborough	6 - 0
05.06.84	Palma	3 - 3
13.06.85	Vleuten	3 - 0
20.05.87	Kircaldy	4 - 0
11.04.95	Aalsmeer	0 - 0
02.04.96	Irthlingborough	3 - 1
18.04.97	Appingedam	0 - 0
03.03.98	Crawley	2 - 1
30.03.99	Genemuiden	1 - 1
21.03.00	Northwich	1 - 0
22.03.01	Wihemina FC	3 - 0
24.04.02	Yeovil Town	1 - 0
25.03.03	BV Sparta 25	0 - 0

IRAQ

27.05.04	Macclesfield	1 - 5

ITALY

03.06.80	Zeist	2 - 0
13.06.81	Montecatini	1 - 1
01.06.82	Aberdeen	0 - 0
31.05.83	Scarborough	2 - 0
09.06.84	Reggio Emilia	0 - 1
11.06.85	Houten	2 - 2
18.05.87	Dunfermline	1 - 2
29.01.89	La Spezia	1 - 1
25.02.90	Solerno	0 - 2
05.03.91	Kettering	0 - 0
01.03.99	Hayes	4 - 1
01.03.00	Padova	1 - 1
20.11.02	AC Cremonese	3 - 2
11.02.04	Shrewsbury	1 - 4

NORWAY UNDER-21

01.06.94	Slemmestad	1 - 2

REPUBLIC OF IRELAND

24.05.86	Kidderminster	2 - 1
26.05.86	Nuneaton	2 - 1
25.05.90	Dublin	2 - 1
27.05.90	Cork	3 - 0
27.02.96	Kidderminster	4 - 0
25.02.97	Dublin	0 - 2
16.05.02	Boston	1 - 2
20.05.03	Merthyr Tydfil	4 - 0
18.05.004	Deverondale	2 - 3

SCOTLAND

31.05.79	Stafford	5 - 1
05.06.80	Zeist	2 - 4
11.06.81	Empoli	0 - 0
05.06.82	Aberdeen	1 - 1
04.06.83	Scarborough	2 - 1
07.06.84	Modena	2 - 0
15.06.85	Harderwijk	1 - 3
23.05.87	Dunfermline	2 - 1
18.05.02	Kettering	2 - 0
24.05.03	Carmarthen Town	0 - 0
23.05.04	Deverondale	3 - 1

	Bacon	Baker	Bittner	Boardman	Boylan	Carlton	Cavanagh	Challinor	Charles	Collins	Cowan	Cowans	Craney	D'Sane	Elding	Foyewa	Guinan	Hatch	Hogg	Jordan	Kennedy (John)	Kennedy (Jon)
			x				x		x		s			x	x				x	x		
			x	x			x	x	s	x				x								s
		x		nps			x1									s2	x	x				
		nps		x			nps									s1	x	x				
		x		nps			nps									s1	x1	x2				
	s5	x1				s2						s3						x5			x	s1
		x		x	s								x				x	x			x	s
F	0+1	2	2	2	0+1	0+1	2	1	1+1	1	0+1	0+1	1	2	1		1	2	1	1	2	0+2
NT		2		1			1									0+3	3	3				

	Kerr	McDonnell	McLean	McNiven	Miller	Murphy	Murray	Perkins	Proctor	Purdie	Redmile	Rickards	Ricketts	Rodgers	Sedgemore	Sheldon	Smith	Southam	Thompson	Tretton	Vickers	Yakubu
			x			s	s	x				s	x	x			s					
			s		x		x	x		s				x		x						s
	x	nps		nps				x			x		x3		s1	x		s3	x2	x		
	x	x		s3				nps			x		s2		x1	x		x	x2	x		
	x	nps		s2				x			x		x		x	x		x	nps	x		
	x			x4				x	s4						x	x		x3	x2		x	
				s				x							x	x		x	s	x		s
F	1		1+1	1+1	1	0+1	1+1	4	0+1	0+1		0+1	1	2	2	3	0+1	2	1+1	1	1	0+2
NT	3	1		0+2				2			3		2+1		2+1	3		2+1	2	3		

x - Started. s - Substitute. nps - Non Playing substitute. F - Friendlies appearance totals. FNT - Four Nations Tournament appearance totals.

ENGLAND'S RESULTS 1979 - 2004 continued...

USA

20.03.02	Stevenage Boro.	2 - 1
09.06.04	Charleston USA	0 - 0

WALES

27.03.84	Newtown	1 - 2
26.03.85	Telford	1 - 0
18.03.86	Merthyr Tydfil	1 - 3
17.03.87	Gloucester	2 - 2
15.03.88	Rhyl	2 - 0
21.03.89	Kidderminster	2 - 0
06.03.90	Merthyr Tydfil	0 - 0
17.05.91	Stafford	1 - 2
03.03.92	Aberystwyth	1 - 0
02.03.93	Cheltenham	2 - 1
22.02.94	Bangor	2 - 1
28.02.95	Yeovil Town	1 - 0
23.05.99	St Albans	2 - 1
16.05.00	Llanelli	1 - 1
13.02.01	Rushden & Dia.	0 - 0
14.05.02	Boston	1 - 1
22.05.03	Merthyr Tydfil	2 - 0
20.05.04	Keith FC	0 - 2

RESULTS SUMMARY	P	W	D	L	F	A
Belgium	2	0	1	1	3	5
Finland Under-21	2	0	0	2	1	5
Gibraltar	2	2	0	0	6	4
Holland	17	12	5	0	33	7
Iraq	1	0	0	1	1	5
Italy	14	3	6	4	17	18
Norway Under-21	1	0	0	1	1	2
Republic of Ireland	9	6	0	3	20	10
Scotland	11	6	3	2	21	13
USA	2	1	1	0	2	1
Wales	18	9	5	4	22	16
TOTAL RECORD	**79**	**39**	**21**	**19**	**127**	**86**

MANAGERS 1979 - 2004

		P	W	D	L	F	A
1979	Howard Wilkinson	2	2	0	0	6	1
1980 - 1984	Keith Wright	17	9	5	3	30	16
1985 - 1988	Kevin Verity	12	7	2	3	23	15
1989 - 1996	Tony Jennings	19	10	4	5	27	18
1997	Ron Reid	2	0	1	1	0	2
1998 - 2002	John Owens	14	8	5	1	22	10
2002 -	Paul Fairclough	13	3	4	6	19	24

GOALSCORERS 1979 - 2004

13 GOALS...
Carter

6 GOALS...
Ashford

5 GOALS...
Davison
C. Williams

4 GOALS...
Culpin
D'Sane, Roscoe
Johnson

3 GOALS...
Adamson
Guinan, Steve
Grayson
Kirk Jackson
Opponents
Watkins

2 GOALS...
Alford, Carl
Barrett
Casey
Cordice
Hatch, Liam
Hayles
Hill
Howell
Mutrie
Patmore, Warren
J. Watson
Weatherstone, Simon
Whitbread

1 GOAL...
Agana
Anderson, Dale
Boardman, Jon
Bolton
Bradshaw
Browne
Cavell
Charles
Charley, Ken
Crittenden, Nick
Davies
Drummond, Stewart
Furlong, Paul
Hines
Humphreys
Kennedy, John
Kimmins
Leworthy
McDougald
Mayes
Moore, Neil
O'Keefe
Pitcher
Ricketts, Sam
Robbins
Robinson
Roddis
Rodgers, Luke
Rogers
Ryan, Tim
Sellars
Sheldon, Gareth
I. Smith
O. Smith
Southam, Glen
Stephens
Stott
S. Taylor
Venables
Way, Darren
Webb
Wilcox

MOST CAPPED PLAYER

	Club	Caps	Seasons
John Davison	Altrincham	24	1979 - 1986

FULL INTERNATIONAL HONOURS

To date three players have played for England at both Full International and Semi-Professional levels.

Peter Taylor	Full: 1976	SPro: 1984 - whilst at Maidstone United
Alan Smith	Full: 1988	SPro: 1982 - whilst at Alvechurch
Steve Guppy	Full: 1999	SPro: 1993 - whilst at Wycombe Wanderers

ENGLAND SEMI-PRO CAPS 1979 - 2004

KEY TO COUNTRY CODES:
B - Belgium E - Eire F - Finland G - Gibraltar
H - Holland I - Italy IQ - Iraq N - Norway
S - Scotland W - Wales US - U.S.A.

Players capped for the first time during season 2003-04 are shown in bold.

Gary Abbott (Welling) **87** v I(s), S(s), 92 W(s) 3
David Adamson (Boston Utd) **79 v** S, H **80** v I,S, H 5
Tony Agana (Weymouth) **86** v E 1
Junior Agogo (Barnet) **03** v H, i (s), S 3
Carl Alford (Kettering T. & Rushden & Ds) **96** v E,H 2
Dale Anderson (Burton Albion) **02** v H **03** v I 2
Mark Angel (Boston United) **02** v W(s), E, S 3
Ian Arnold (Kettering Town) **95** v W(s), H 2
Jim Arnold (Stafford Rangers) **79** v S, H 2
Nick Ashby (Kettering & Rushden & Diamonds)
94 v F, N, **95** v G **96** v E, H 5
Noel Ashford (Enfield & Redbridge Forest.)
82 v G,H,S. **83 v** I,H,S, **84** W,H,S,I, **85** W,I(s), **86** E,E,
87 W(s), I,H,S. **90** v W,E **91** I(s) 21
John Askey (Macclesfield) **90** v W 1
Danny Bacon 04 v IQ 1
Matt Baker (Hereford United) **03** v I, S, **04** E,S,IQ,US 6
Paul Bancroft (Kidderminster H.) **89** v I,W **90** I,W.E, **91** v W 6
Chris Banks (Cheltenham T.) **98** v H, 99 W 2
Keith Barrett (Enfield) **81** v H,S,I **82 v** G,I,H,S **83** v I,H,S
84 v W(s), H, S **85** I,H,S 16
Laurence Batty (Woking) **93** v F(s), **95** v W,H,G 4
Mark Beeney (Maidstone) **89** v I(s) 1
Paul Beesley (Chester C.) **01** v H(s) 1
Dean Bennett (Kidderminster H) **00** v W(s) 1
Graham Benstead (Kettering) **94** v W,F,N(s) 3
Kevin Betsy (Woking) **98** v H(s) 1
Marcus Bignot (Kidderminster H) **97** v H 1
James Bittner (Exeter City) **04** v B,I 2
Chris Blackburn (Chester City) **03** v I 1
Greg Blundell (Northwich Victoria) **03** v H 1
Jon Boardman (Woking) **03** v I, S. **04** I,W,US 5
Jimmy Bolton (Kingstonian) **95** v G 1
Steve Book (Cheltenham Town) **99 v** I,H,W 3
Lee Boylan (Canvey Island) **04** v US 1
Gary Brabin (Runcorn) **94 v** W,F,N 3
Mark Bradshaw (Halifax T.) **98** v H 1
Leon Braithwaite (Margate) **02 v** US 1
Colin Brazier (Kidderminster) **87** v W 1
Stewart Brighton (Bromsgrove) **94** v W 1
Steve Brooks (Cheltenham) **88** v W(s) **90** v W,E 3
Derek Brown (Woking) **94 v** F(s,N 2
Kevan Brown (Woking) **95** v W,H,G **96** v H **97** v E 5
Wayne Brown (Chester C.) **01** v W, H(s), **02** v US, H(s),W,S.
03 v H 7
Corey Browne (Dover) **94** v F(s),N(s), **95** v H(s) 3
David Buchanan (Blyth) **86** v E(s,E 2
Nicki Bull (Aldershot Town) **03** v B
Brian Butler (Northwich) **93** v F 1
Steve Butler (Maidstone) **88** v W, **89 v** I,W 3
Gary Butterworth (Rushden & Diamonds)
97 v E,H **98 v** H **99** v I,H,W **00** v I 7
Chris Byrne (Macclesfield T.) **97** v H 1
Danny Carlton (Morecambe) **04** v IQ 1
Mark Carter (Runcorn & Barnet) v
87 v W,I,H,S **88** v W, **89 v** I,W, **90** v I,E, **91** v I,W(s) 11
Kim Casey (Kidderminster) **86** v W,E,E(s), **87 v** W,I 5
Paul Cavell (Redbridge) **92** v W **93** v F 2
Peter Cavanagh (Accrington) **04** v B,I,E 3
Jon Challinor (Aldershot Town) **04** v B,I 2
Lee Charles (Hayes) **99** v I(s), H(s), W(s) 3
Anthony Charles (Aldershot/Farnborough) **04** v B,I 2
Kevin Charlton (Telford) **85** v W,I 2
Ken Charlery (Boston U) **01** vH(s) 1
Andrew Clarke (Barnet) **90** v E,E 2
David Clarke (Blyth Spartans) **80** v I,S(s),H, **81** v H,S,I
82 v I,H,S **83** v H,S **84** v H,S,I 14
Gary Clayton (Burton) **86** v E 1
Robert Codner (Barnet) **88** v W 1
John Coleman (Morecambe) **93** v F(s) 1
Darren Collins (Enfield) **93** v F(s), **94** v W,F,N 4
Matt Collins (Nuneaton Borough) **04** v I 1
Andy Comyn (Hednesford T.) **98 v** H(s), **99 v** I(s),H(s),W(s) 4
Steve Conner (Dartford, Redbridge & Dagenham & R)
90 v I **91 v** I,W **92** v W **93** v F 5
David Constantine (Altrincham) **85** v I,H,S **86 v** W 4
Robbie Cooke (Kettering) **89** v W(s), **90** v I 2
Scott Cooksey (Hednesford T.) **97** v E, **98** vH(s) **01 v** W(s),H 4
Alan Cordice(Wealdstone)**83 v** I,H,S **84** vW,S(s), I(s),**85** I,H,S 9
Rob Cousins (Yeovil Town) **00 I v** I(s),H,W 3
Gavin Cowan (Canvey Island) **04** v B 1

Cowans (??) **04** v IQ 1

Ken Cramman (Gateshead & Rushden & Diamonds) **96** v E **97** v E,H 3

Ian Craney (Altrincham) **03** v B. **04** US 2

Nick Crittendon (Yeovil Town) **02** v US (s) 1

Paul Cuddy (Altrincham) **87** v I,H,S 3

Paul Culpin (Nuneaton B) **84** v W, **85** v W(s) ,I,H,S 5

Michael Danzey (Woking) **99** v I,H 2

Paul Davies (Kidderminster H.) **86** v W, **87** v W,I,S, **88** v W **89** v W 6

John Davison (Altrincham) **79** v S,H **80** v I,S, **81** v H,S ,I **82 v** G,I,H,S **83** I,H,S **84** W,H,I,S **85** v I,H,S 86 **v** W,E,E 24

John Denham (Northwich Victoria) **80** v H 1

Peter Densmore (Runcorn) **88** v W **89** v I 2

Phil Derbyshire (Mossley) **83** v H(s) S(s) 2

Mick Doherty (Weymouth) **86** v W(s) 1

Neil Doherty (Kidderminster H.) **97** v E 1

Stuart Drummond (Morecambe) **00** v I(s),H ,W **01 v** W ,H **02** v US, W,E(s), S **03** v H, I, W, S (s) 13

Roscoe D'Sane (Aldershot Town) **03** v B(s),H(s),E,W,S. **04** B,I 7

Chris Duffy (Canvey Island) **03** v B

Neil Durkin (Leigh RMI) **02** v H(s) 1

Lee Elam (Morecambe) **03** v H,E,W,S)s) 4

Anthony Elding (Stevenage Borough) **04** v B 1

Paul Ellender (Scarborough) **01** v W(s) 1

Lee Endersby (Harrow Bor.) **96 v** H 1

Mick Farrelly (Altrincham) **87 v** I,H,S 3

Steve Farrelly (Macclesfield & Kingstonian) **95** v H(s),G(s), **00** v I,H,W(s) 5

Trevor Finnegan (Weymouth) **81** v H,S 2

Murray Fishlock (Yeovil Town) **99** v H(s) 1

Amos Foyewa (Woking) **04** v E,W,S 3

Richard Forsyth (Kidderminster) **95** v W,H,G 3

Ian Foster (Kidderminster H) **00** v W(s) 1

Paul Furlong (Enfield) **90 v** I,E,E **91** v I,W 5

Mark Gardiner (Macclesfield T.) **97** v E 1

Jerry Gill (Yeovil T.) **97** v E 1

John Glover (Maidstone Utd) **85** v W,I,H,S 4

Mark Golley (Sutton Utd.) **87** v H(s),S, **88** v W, **89** v I,W, **92** v W 6

Jason Goodliffe (Hayes) **00** v I, H,W, **01** W **02** US, W,E,S. 8

Paul Gothard (Dagenham & Redb.) **97** v E(s), **99** v I(s),W(s) 3

Mark Gower (Barnet) **02** v H, W, E, S(s) 4

Neil Grayson (Cheltenham T.) **98** v H **99** v I,H,W 4

Phil Gridelet (Hendon & Barnet) **89** v I,W, **90** v W,E,E 5

Steve Guinan (Hereford) **04** v E,W,S,US 4

Steve Guppy (Wycombe W.) **93** v W 1

Scott Guyett (Southport) **01** v H, **03** v H,I,W,S. 5

Tim Hambley (Havant & Waterlooville) **02** v H 1

Steve Hanlon (Macclesfield) **90** v W 1

David Harlow (Farnborough T.) **97 v** E(s),H 2

Liam Hatch (Barnet) **04** v E,W,S,IQ,US 5

Wayne Hatswell (Chester City) **03** v E(s),W(s),

Barry Hayles (Stevenage Bor.) **96** v E,H 2

Greg Heald (Barnet) **02** v H 1

Brian Healy (Morecambe) **98** v H 1

Tony Hemmings (Northwich) **93** v F 1

Andy Hessenthaler (Dartford) **90** v I 1

Kenny Hill (Maidstone Utd) **80** v I,S,H 3

Mark Hine (Gateshead) **95** v W(s),H 2

Simeon Hodson (Kidderminster) **94** v W,F,N 3

Lewis Hogg (Barnet) **04** v B 1

Colin Hogarth (Guiseley) **95 v** W,H 2

Steven Holden (Kettering) **94** v W,F,N(s) **95** v H,G 5

Mark Hone (Welling United) **90** v I **93** v F, **94** vW(s),F(s),N 5

Gary Hooley (Frickley) **85** v W 1

Dean Hooper (Kingstonian) **98** v H 1

Keith Houghton (Blyth Spartans) **79** v S 1

Barry Howard (Altrincham) **81** v H,S,I **82** v G,I,H,S 7

Neil Howarth (Macclesfield) **95** v H(s) **97** v E 2

David Howell (Enfield) **85** v H(s),S(s) **86** v W,E **87** v W,IH,S **88** v W, **89** v I,W **90** v I,E,E 14

Lee Howells (Cheltenham T.) **98** v H **99 v** W 2

Lee Hughes (Kidderminster Harriers) **96** v E,H **97** v E,H 4

Delwyn Humphreys (Kidderminster H.) **91** v W(s) **92** v W **94** v W,F,N **95** v W,H 7

Steve Humphries (Barnet) **87** v H(s) 1

Nicky Ironton (Enfield) **83** H(s) **84** v W 2

Jimmy Jacksion (Gravesend & Northfleet) 03 v H(s) 1

Justin Jackson (Morecambe & Rushden & Diamonds) **00** v W **01** v W 2

Kirk Jackson (Stevenage Borough) **02** v US, E,S,(Yeovil Town) **03** v E,W,S(s) 6

Mark Janney (Dagenham & Redbridge) **03** v H 1

Tony Jennings (Enfield) **79** v S,H **80** v I,S,H **81 v** H,S,I **82** v G,I,H,S 12

Jeff Johnson (Altrincham) **81** v S,I **82** v G,I,H,S **83** v I,H,S **84 v** H,S,I **84 v** I,H,S **86** v W(s),E,E 18

Lee Johnson (Yeovil Town) **03** v I, H(s), E, W, S 5

Steve Jones (Leigh RMI) **01** v H 1

Tom Jones (Weymouth) **87** v W 1

Tom Jordan (Tamworth) **04** v B 1

Antone Joseph(Telford U. & Kidderm'terH.)**84** v S(s), **85** v W,I, H,S **86** v W(s), **87** W,I(s),H, **88** v W **89** v I,W **90 v** I,E,E 15

John Keeling (Purfleet) **03** v B(s) 1

John Kennedy (Canvey Island) **03** v I, B, H, E, W, S. **04** IQ,US 8

Jon Kennedy (Accrington) **04** v I,IQ,US 3

Andy Kerr (Wycombe) **93** v W 1

Scott Kerr (Scarborough) **04** v E,W,S,IQ 4

Lance Key (Kingstonian) 03 v B 1

Ged Kimmins (Hyde Utd.) **96** v E(s),H(s) **97 v** E(s) 3

Mike Lake (Macclesfield) **89** v I 1

Martin Lancaster (Chester City) **03** vI (s)

Andy Lee (Telford U. & Witton A.) **89** I(s), **91** v I,W 3

David Leworthy (Farnborough & Rushden & Diamonds)
93 v W, **94** v W **97** v E,H 4

Adam Lockwood (Yeovil Town) **02** v E **03** v I 2

,Kenny Lowe (Barnet) **91 v** I,W 2

Craig McAllister (Basingstoke Town) **03** v B 1

Martin McDonald (Macclesfield) **95** v G(s) 1

Danny McDonnell (Worcester City) **04** v W 1

Junior MacDougald (Dagenham & Redbridge) 01 v H(s) 1
02 W, E(s), S(s) 4

Mark McGregor (Forest Green Rovers & Nuneaton Borough)
00 v I(s),H(s) **01** v W(s) 3

Kevin McIntyre (Doncaster Rovers) **00 v** H(s)W, **01 v** W(s)H 4

John McKenna (Boston Utd)
88 v W(s), **90** v I,E,E **91 v** I,W, **92** vW 7

David McLean (Aldershot) **04** v B,I 2

David McNiven (Leigh RMI) **04** v W,S,IQ,US 4

Fiston Manuella (Aylesbury United) **03** v B 1

John Margerrison (Barnet) **87 v** W 1

Simon Marples (Doncaster Rovers) **00 v** I,H 2

Leroy May (Stafford R.) **95 v** G(s) 1

Bobby Mayes (Redbridge) **92 v** W

Paul Mayman (Northwich Vic) **80 v** I,S 2

Stewart Mell (Burton) **85v** W 1

Neil Merrick (Weymouth) **80** v I(s),S 2

Adam Miller (Aldershot Town) **04** v I 1

Russell Milton (Dover) 94 v F,N 2

Trevor Morley (Nuneaton) **84 v** W,H,S,I **85 v** W,S(s) 6

Neil Moore (Telford United) **02** v US (s),H, W, E,S 5

Chris Murphy (Telford United) **04** v B 1

Karl Murrphy (Woking) **04** v B,I 2

Tarkan Mustafa (Rushden & Diamonds) **01** v W,H 2

Les Mutrie (Blyth Spartans) **79 v** S,H, **80** v I,S,H

Mark Newson (Maidstone U) **84 v** W,H,S,I, **85 v** W 5

Doug Newton (Burton) **85** v W,H,S 3

Paul Nicol (Kettering T) **91 v** I,W, **92** v W 3

Richard Norris (Northwich Victoria) **03** v H, S, 2

Steve Norris (Telford) **88** v W(s) 1

Joe O'Connor (Hednesford T.) **97 v** E,H(s) 2

Eamon O'Keefe (Mossley) **79 v** S,H 2

Frank Ovard (Maidstone) **81** v H(s),S(s),I(s) 3

Andy Pape (Harrow Bor. & Enfield) **85** v W(s,)H,S,
86 v W(s),E, **87** v W,I,H,S **88** v W, **89** IW, **90** I,W,E 15

Brian Parker (Yeovil Town) **80 v** S 1

Warren Patmore (Yeovil Town) **99** v I,H,W, **00 v** I,H, **01** W,H 7

Gary Patterson (Kingstonian) **99** v I,H, **00** v H,W, **01 v** W,H 7

Steve Payne (Macclesfield T.) **97 v** H 1

Trevor Peake (Nuneaton Bor) **79 v** S,H 2

David Pearce (Harrow Bor) **84 v** I(s) 1

David Perkins (Morecambe) **04** v B,I,E,S,IQ,US 6

Warren Peyton (Nuneaton Borough) **02** v H(s) **03** v I 2

Brendan Phillips (Nuneaton Bor. & Kettering T.),
79 v S,H, **80 v** S(s),H 4

Gary Philips (Barnet) **82 v** G 1

Owen Pickard (Yeovil T.) **98** v H(s) 1

Geoff Pitcher (Kingstonian) **99 v** W, **00 v** I,H,W, **01** v W,H 6

Phil Power (Macclesfield T.) **96** v E(s),H(s) 2

Ryan Price (Stafford R. & Macclesfield)
92 v W(s) **93** v W,F **96** v E,H **97 v** H 6

Steve Prindiville **98 v** H(s) 1

Andy Proctor (Accrington Stanley) **04** v IQ 1

Marc Pullan (Crawley Town) **03** v B 1

Robert Purdie (Hereford United) **04** v I 1

Wayne Purser (Barnet) **03** v I 1

Mark Quayle (Telford United) **02** v H 1

Simon Read (Farnborough) **92** v W(s) 1

Matt Redmile (Barnet) **04** v E,W,S 3

Andy Reid (Altrincham) **95 v** W 1

Carl Richards (Enfield) **86 v** E 1

Derek Richardson (Maidstone U) **83 v** I, **84 v** W, **86** v E 4

Ian Richardson (Dagenham & Red) **95 v** G 1

Kevin Richardson (Bromsgrove) **94** v W,F,N 3

Paul Richardson (Redbridge) **92** v W, **93 v** W, F 3

Scott Rickards (Tamworth) **03** v B. **04** B 2

Sam Ricketts (Telford) **04** v B,E,W,S 4

Adriano Rigoglioso (Morecambe) **03** v H(s) 1

Anthony Rivierre (Welling United) **03** v B 1

Terry Robbins (Welling) **92 v** W, **93** v W,F, **94** v W,F,N 6

Peter Robinson (Blyth S) **83 v** I,H,S **84** W,I 85 v W 6

Nick Roddis (Woking) **01** v H **02** US,H,W,E(s),S 6

Luke Rodgers (Shrewsbury) **04** v B,I. 2

John Rogers (Altrincham) **81 v** H,S,I **82 v** I(s),S 5

Paul Rogers (Sutton) **89** v W, **90** v I, E(2), **91** I,W 6

Colin Rose (Witton Alb.) **96 v** E(s), H 2

Kevin Rose (Kidderminster) **94 v** F(s),N 2

Michael Rose (Hereford United) **03** v I, H, E, S 4

Brian Ross (Marine) **93 v** W(s),F(s), **94** v W(s) **95 v** W,H 5

Carl Ruffer (Chester City) **01** v H(s) 1

Tim Ryan (Southport & Doncaster Rovers)
98 **v** H, **99** **v** I,H,W, **00** **v** I,H,W **01** v W,H
02 v US,H,W,I,S 14

Jake Sedgemore (Shrewsbury) **04** v E,W,S,IQ,US. 5

Neil Sellars (Scarboro) **81** v H,S,I **82** v G,H(s),S, **83** **v** I,H,S 9

Mark Shail (Yeovil T.) **93** v W 1

Simon Shaw (Doncaster Rovers) **99** v I,H 2

Peter Shearer (Cheltenham) **89** **v** I(s) 1

Gareth Sheldon (Exeter) **04** v I,E,W,S,IQ,US. 6

Paul Shirtliff (Frickley A. & Boston U.) **86** vE,E **87** v W,I,H
88 v W **89** **v** I, W, **90** **v** I,W,E,E, **92** **v** W **93** v W,F 15

Paul Showler (Altrincham) **91** v I(s),W 2

Tim Sills (Kingstonian) **03** v B 1

Gordon Simmonite (Boston United) **79** v S(s,)H(s), **80** v I,S,H 5

Gary Simpson(Stafford R.) **86** v E,E, **87** v I,H,S,**90** v I,W,E,E 9

Wayne Simpson (Stafford) **94** v F,N(s) 2

Terry Skiverton (Yeovil Town) **01** **v** W **02** **v** US **03** v !,W, 4

Glenn Skivington (Barrow) **90** v I,W,E **91** v I,W 5

Adrian Smith (Kidderminster H) **00** v I(s),H(s),W 3

Alan Smith (Alvechurch) **82** v G,I,S 3

Ian Smith (Mossley) **80** v I,S,H(s) 3

Mark Smith (Stevenage Bor.)
96 v E,H **98** v H **99** v I,H,W **00** **v** I,H,W(s) 9

Ossie Smith (Runcorn) **84** v W 1

Phil Smith (Margate) **04** v B 1

Tim Smithers (Nuneaton) **85** v W(s),I **86** v W 3

Adam Sollitt (Kettering Town) **00** v I(s),H(s),W 3

Glen Southam (Bishop's Stortford) **04** v E,W,S,IQ,US 5

Adam Stansfield (Yeovil Town) **02** v W (s), I, S 3

Simon Stapleton (Wycombe) **93** v W 1

Mickey Stephens (Sutton), **82** v G,S(s) **86** **v** W,E,E(s) 5

Billy Stewart (Southport) **98** v H 1

Mark Stimson (Canvey Island) **02** v US 1

Bob Stockley (Nuneaton Borough) **80** v H 1

Darren Stride (Burton Albion) **02** v H 1

Steve Stott (Kettering T., Rushden & Ds & Yeovil T.)
95 v W,H(s),G **96** v E,H **99** v H,W(s) 7

Ryan Sugden (Chester City) 03 v I 1

James Taylor (Havant & Waterlooville) **02** v H,W, E(s),S(s) 4

Peter Taylor (Maidstone) **84** v HSI 3

Steve Taylor (Bromsgrove R.) **95** v G 1

Shaun Teale (Weymouth) **88** v W 1

Paul Terry (Dagenham & Redbridge) **03** vE (s), W(s), S 3

Stuart Terry (Altrincham) **95** v W 1

Brian Thompson(Yeovil & Maidstone) **79** v S,H **81** v H,S,I
82 v I,H,S **83** **v** I,H,S **84** v W,H,S,I 15,

Neil Thompson (Scarborough) **87** v W,I,H,S 4

Garry Thompson (Morecambe) **03** v I. **04** v E,W,IQ,US 5

Steve Thompson (Wycombe) **93** v W 1

Kevin Todd (Berwick Rangers) **91** v W 1

Mike Tomlinson (Runcorn F.C.Halton) **03** v B (s) 1

Anthony Tonkin (Yeovil Town) **02** v US 1

Simon Travis (Forest Green Rovers) **02** **v** US, H. 2

Andy Tretton (Hereford) **04** v E,W,S,US 4

Mark Tucker (Woking) **96** v E 1

Tony Turner (Telford) **85** **v** W 1

Paul Underwood (Rushden & D) **99** v I,H **00** **v** I**01** v W 4

David Venables(Stevenage B)**94** **v** W(s)**95** **v** H,G**96** **v** E,H(s) 5

Jamie Victory (Cheltenham T.) **98** vH(s) 1

Ashley Vickers (Dagenham & Redbridge) **04** v IQ 1

David Waite (Enfield) **82** v G 1

Paul Walker (Blyth) **86** **v** W,E,E(s), **87** **v** S(s) 4

Steve Walters (Northwich Victoria) **97** v H 1

Mark Ward (Northwich Victoria) **83** v S(s) 1

Steve Ward (Canvey Island) **03** v B 1

Dale Watkins (Cheltenham T.) **98** v H **99** v I(s), **00** v I,H,W 5

John Watson (Wealdstone, Scarborough & Maidstone)
79 v S(s),H **80** v I,S,H **81** v H,S,I **82** v I,H,S **83** v I,H,S
84 v W(s),H,S,I 18

Steve Watson (Farnborough Town) **02** v US(s), W(s), S 3,

Liam Watson (Marine) **95** v W,H(s) 2

Paul Watts (Redbridge Forest) **89** v W **90** v I,E,E **91** v I
92 v W **93** v W,F 8

Darren Way (Yeovil Town) **03** vI (s), E, W 3

Chris Weale (Yeovil Town) 03 v I (s), H (s), E, W. 4

Simon Weatherstone (Boston United) **02** v W(s),E,S(s) 3

Paul Webb (Bromsgrove R & Kidderminster H)
93 v F **94** v W,F,N(s) **95** v W,H,G **96** v E,H **97** v E,H 11

Aaron Webster (Burton Albion) **02** **v** H(s),W,S(s) **03** v I 3

Mark West (Wycombe W) **91** v W 1

Steve West (Woking) **01** v W(s) 1

Barry Whitbread (Runcorn & Altrincham) **79** **v** S,H
80 v I,S,H, **81** **v** I 6

Tristram Whitman (Doncaster Rovers) **03** v W(s), S 2

Russ Wilcox (Frickley) **86** v W,E 2

Adam Wilde (Worcester City) **03** v B 1

Barry Williams (Nuneaton Borough) **99** v H(s),W 2

Colin Williams (Scarborough & Telford Utd.)
81 v H, S **82** v I,H,S 5

Roger Willis (Barnet) **91** v I(s) 1

Paul Wilson (Frickley Athletic) **86** v W 1

Andy Woods (Scarborough) **02** v US,H(s),W,S. 4

Simon Wormull (Dover Athletic) **99** v I(s),W **02** **v** W,E,S. 5

Mark Yates (Cheltenham Town) **99** v I, W 2

Ismail Yakubu (Barnet) **04** v I,US 2

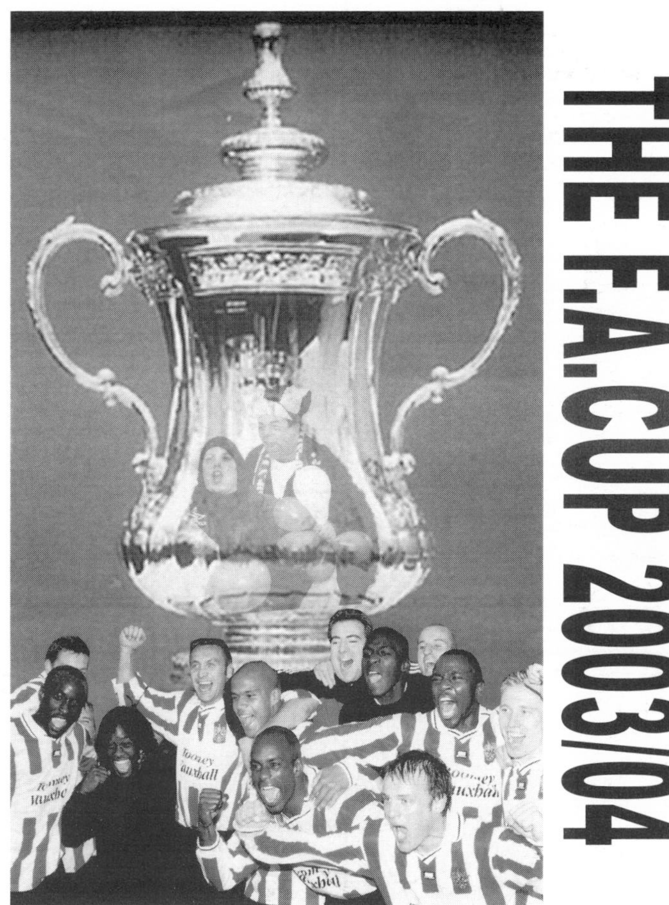

THE F.A. CUP 2003/04

EXTRA QUALIFYING ROUND

Saturday 23rd August **Winning clubs received: £500**

Home		Away	Score	Att
AFC Totton	v	Erith Town	3-0	80
Parnell, Poulton, Whiddett				
Barnstaple Town	v	Exmouth Town	2-3	126
Squire (2)		Tippett (2)		
BAT Sports	v	Cobham (24/8)	3-1	109
Chance, Ellitt, Platt		Horder		
Bedfont	v	Littlehampton Town	4-0	54
Decosta, Postins (2), Willis				
Bedford United & Valerio	v	Harefield United	1-0	32
Conville				
Blackstones	v	Gedling Town	1-4	78
Challinor		Foster, Horder, Peet, Scoffham		
Brackley Town	v	Hullbridge Sports	2-1	75
Champelouier		Webster		
Brentwood	v	Haringey Borough	0-2	73
		Carey, Hudson		
Brockenhurst	v	VCD Athletic	2-3	79
James, Neville		Main, Penny, Thompson		
Brodsworth MW	v	Pickering Town	0-1	90
		Wood		
Broxbourne Borough V&E	v	Yaxley	0-2	35
		Hailstone, Miller		
Carlton Town	v	Shirebrook Town	0-3	84
		Johnson, Kerley, Turner		
Carterton Town	v	Hungerford Town	1-0	64
Allen				
Chard Town	v	Paulton Rovers	0-3	58
		Bown (2), James		
Chichester City United	v	Tunbridge Wells	4-1	115
Laidlaw (2), Moore (2)		Hickmott		
Colne	v	Mossley	2-3	124
Cunningham, Simpson		Almond, Bailey, Howard		
Cradley Town	v	Daventry Town	2-0	65
Devizes Town	v	Christchurch	0-4	101
		Hillier, Joyce, Osbourne (2)		
Didcot Town	v	Ramsgate	2-1	131
		Takalobighashi		
Dunston Federation Brewery	v	Abbey Hey	1-0	123
Farrey				
East Preston	v	Andover	2-3	124
Huckett, Yelling		Damen, Kennedy, Sullivan		
Eastbourne United	v	Lordswood	1-0	102
Downey				
Eccleshill United	v	Warrington Town	1-2	84
Gelder		Mitchell (2)		
Fleetwood Town	v	Darwen	1-0	103
Brown				
Frome Town	v	Tuffley Rovers	1-0	96
Preece				
Garforth Town	v	Whickham	0-3	78
		Hall, Robson, Scott		
Great Yarmouth Town	v	Southall Town	4-1	291
Adcock, George, Humphreys Thompson		Glynn		
Hadleigh United	v	Wootton Blue Cross	0-1	72
		Westcott		
Harpenden Town	v	Woodbridge Town	6-1	65
Golds, Guile (2), Price (3)		George		
Highworth Town	v	Shortwood United	3-1	85
Byrne, Hulbert, Webb		Paul		
Holbeach United	v	Staveley MW	1-1	127
Dunn		Clarke		
Holker Old Boys	v	Penrith	1-0	80
Southward				
Horsham YMCA	v	Gosport Borough	3-3	105
Durrant, Taylor, Young		Lindsey, Middleton, White		
Kingsbury Town	v	Stowmarket Town	1-2	48
Leech		Mayes, Warner		
Lancing	v	Whitehawk	0-3	94
		Pattenden, Townsend (2)		
Lincoln Moorlands	v	Arnold Town	1-0	75
Dye				
Maldon Town	v	Holmer Green	4-1	93
Bell, Brown, Goodacre, Shave		Salmon		
Mildenhall Town	v	Ilford	2-1	102
Paynter, Taylor-Holt		Jones		
Minehead	v	Liskeard Athletic	2-0	94
Todd (2)				
Nantwich Town	v	Stratford Town	1-2	105
Wilkinson		Darroch, Gray		
Needham Market	v	Norwich United	0-3	79
		Bilham, Bugdale, Gannon		
Northampton Spencer	v	Desborough Town	2-2	76
Ringer (2)		Chong		
Norton & Stockton Ancients	v	Evenwood Town	0-2	117
		Houlahan, Turner		
Oldham Town	v	Northallerton Town	3-2	73
Baldeh (2), Hart		Roberts, Winter		
Ossett Albion	v	Alnwick Town	5-2	94
Dodd, Norbury (3), Toronczak				
Reading Town	v	Lymington & New Milton	1-2	56
Murray		James (2)		
Romford	v	Bury Town	0-2	166
		Stringfellow, Tatham		
Royston Town	v	Ford Sports Daventry	0-3	65
		Dunkley, Pearce (2)		
Ruislip Manor	v	Ely City	2-2	52
Smith, Todd		Donaldson, Moye		
Saltdean United	v	Cray Wanderers	0-4	104
		Bennett, Dimmock, Gray, Lover		
Sandhurst Town	v	Camberley Town	2-1	106
Anderson (2)				
Shepton Mallet	v	Falmouth Town	0-1	126
Shotton Comrades	v	Newcastle Blue Star	1-4	35
Frazier		Boon, Cunningham, Ludlow, Teaside		
Skelmersdale United	v	Glasshoughton Welfare	7-2	71
Ashton, Holcroft, Osman, Rudd (3), Tobin		Learoy, Ward		
Southend Manor	v	Buckingham Town	1-1	30
Jarvis		Turner		
St Helens Town	v	Trafford (22/8)	0-2	182
		D'agrosa, Strange		
St Leonards	v	Arundel	1-4	127
Ray		Hack, Norgate, Slerrie, Tucker		
St Margaretsbury	v	Henley Town	0-0	46
Stotfold	v	London Colney	1-2	67
Garrett		Farrow (2)		
Thatcham Town	v	Selsey	6-0	88
Cook, Mclay (4), Worsfold				
Tiptree United	v	Cogenhoe United	0-1	92
Walton Casuals	v	Westfield	5-0	78
Barrs-James (3), Carley, D'Rozario				
Washington Nissan	v	Jarrow Roofing Boldon CA	1-2	54
Moan		Cogdon, Johnson		

Home		Away	Score	Att
Wokingham Town	v	Chertsey Town (24/8)	2-0	136
Byfield, Gibson				
Wroxham	v	Halstead Town	4-1	126
Carus, Huwton, Stock (2)		Atangana		

REPLAYS

26th August

Home		Away	Score	Att
Desborough Town	v	Northampton Spencer	4-2	114
Archer, Beazeley, Chong, Djeneralovic		Ringer, Stratford		
Ely City	v	Ruislip Manor	0-2	78
		Farrell, Todd		
Gosport Borough	v	Horsham YMCA	1-0	193
Lindsey				
Henley Town	v	St Margaretsbury	0-3	61
		Lovett (2), Williams		
Staveley MW	v	Holbeach United	3-2	119
Bedward, Cooke, Welch		Edey, Keeble		

27th August

Home		Away	Score	Att
Buckingham Town	v	Southend Manor	4-1 aet	113
Blaik, Cole, George, Max-Grant		Jarvis		

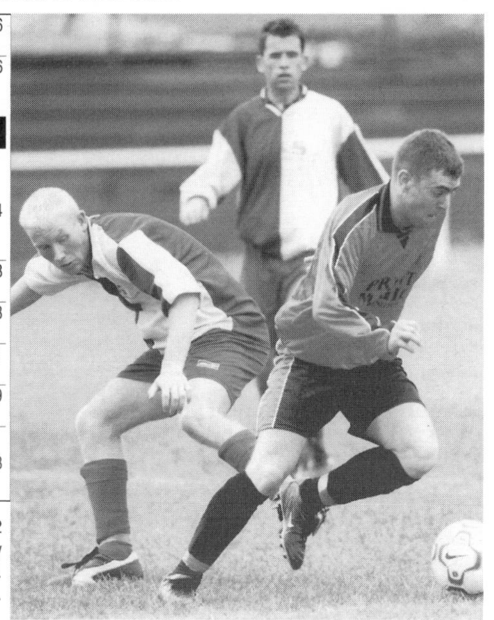

Eccleshill Utd (NCE P) 1 - Warrington Town (NWC 1) 2
Paul Hives evades the challenge of Eccleshill's Andrew Howland.
Photo: Darren C Thomas.

Southend Manor (Essex Senior P) 1 - Buckingham Town (UCO P) 1
Buckingham Town's Ruben Max-Grant goes past Southend Manor's Mark Newton (No.5)
Photo: Alan Coomes.

PRELIMINARY ROUND

Saturday 30 August — **Winning clubs received: £1000**

Home		Away	Score	Att
Abingdon Town	v	Chichester City United	3-1	128
Harper, Potter (2)		Moore		
Abingdon United	v	Cove	3-2	44
Moss, Simms (2)		Edwards, Rimmer		
AFC Sudbury	v	Diss Town	4-3	347
Claydon (3), Owen		Gilman, Hardy		
AFC Totton	v	AFC Newbury	3-1	111
Marwood, Osman, Salter				
Armthorpe Welfare	v	Louth United		
(walkover for Armthorpe Welfare - Louth United removed)				
Arundel	v	Hassocks	4-0	94
Burton, Norgate (2), Sutcliffe				
Ashford Town	v	Eastbourne United	3-0	363
Jones, Phillips (2)				
Atherstone United	v	PelsallVilla		
(walkover for Pelsall Villa - Atherstone United removed)				
Atherton Collieries	v	Farsley Celtic	0-3	71
		Austin, Smithard (2)		
Backwell United	v	Fairford Town	2-0	41
Hewitt, Patch				
Bamber Bridge	v	Prescot Cables	3-1	187
Massey, Shepherd, Wane		O'Donnell		
Banstead Athletic	v	Winchester City	0-2	106
		Forbes, Mancey		
Barton Rovers	v	Rothwell Town	2-2	134
Allison, O'Neill		Garside (2)		
Barwell	v	Oldbury United	3-1	70
McLarnon, Pollard, Walker		Harvey		
Beaconsfield SYCOB	v	Ipswich Wanderers	1-1	78
Markman		Ebanks		
Beckenham Town	v	Sandhurst Town	2-5	28
Pearce, Shippey		Anderson (2), Mulvaney (3)		
Bedford United & Valerio	v	St Neots Town	0-2	70
		Kuhne, Wareh		
Bedworth United	v	Halesowen Town	0-2	262
		Ashby, Hollis		
BelperTown	v	Boston Town	1-1	208
Gummer		Price		
Bemerton Heath Harlequins	v	Torrington	3-2	74
Findlay (2), Jones		Polhill, Robinson		
Bideford	v	Swindon Supermarine	1-3	330
Groves		Tommey (3)		
Billingham Synthonia	v	Chorley	1-1	112
Fletcher		Tulloch		
Bishop Auckland	v	Flixton (31/8)	8-0	189
Chandler (2), Foster, Irvine (2) Maddison (2), Manson				
Bishop Sutton	v	Falmouth Town	1-0	78
Parsons				
Bitton	v	Christchurch (31/8)	3-4	162
Cole, Raynes (2)		Barker, Edwards, Ridout		
Blackfield & Langley	v	Thamesmead Town	1-3	76
Homer		Burns, Loveridge, Thomas		
Blackpool Mechanics	v	Colwyn Bay	1-1	80
Kinley				
Boreham Wood	v	Desborough Town	2-1	66
Baker, Hakki		Archer		
Borrowash Victoria	v	Biddulph Victoria	3-4	52
Hogan (3)		Barlow (2), Callan		
Brackley Town	v	Harwich & Parkeston	4-2	93
Donaldson, Field, Milner (2)		Neale, Springett		
Bridgwater Town	v	Corsham Town	0-1	200
		Bush		
Bridport	v	Street	2-0	102
Gale, Leach				
Brigg Town	v	BillinghamTown	2-2	187
Goodhand, Housham		Cole, Tierney		
Bristol Manor Farm	v	Gloucester City	0-5	151
		Hoskins (4), Smith		
Bromley	v	North Leigh	2-1	262
Amoako, Luckett		Lewis		
Brook House	v	Wealdstone	1-4	223
Chakaodza		Carter, Jolly (2), Morgan		
Buckingham Town	v	Ford Sports Daventry	2-0	101
Julias, Max-Grant				
Burnham	v	ArleseyTown	1-7	85
Neville		Blackett, Gutzmore, Harding, Mackail-Smith (2) Pringle (2)		
Burnham Ramblers	v	Potters Bar Town	4-1	
Aguei-Dua, Brewington, Everett, Perry		Hyde		
Carterton Town	v	Fareham Town	1-2	82
Threlfall		Morby, Musselwhite		
Chadderton	v	Holker Old Boys	1-2	47
Rushton		Jackson, Swarbrick		
Chalfont St Peter	v	Chesham United	0-6	145
		Richardson (2), Sippetts (3)		
Chasetown	v	Sutton Coldfield Town	1-2	217
Edwards		Carter, Perrow		
Chatham Town	v	Andover	2-4	143
Abbott, Spriggs		Andrews, Bennett, Rusher (2)		
CheadleTown	v	Chester-Le-Street Town	1-2	61
Kempton		Elrington, Wilkinson		
Cheshunt	v	Harlow Town	2-3	155
Aransibia, Archer		Arisi, Kirby, Samuel		
Chessington & Hook United	v	Merstham	2-0	118
Everett, Marton				
Chipstead	v	Ringmer	1-2	78
Nolan		Johnson, Shepherd		
Cinderford Town	v	Brislington	1-3	130
Donovan		Maggs (3)		
Cogenhoe United	v	Maldon Town	1-2	
Richardson		Huttley, Shave		
Corby Town	v	Lincoln United	2-1	110
Glover, Marlow		Bull		
Cradley Town	v	Bromsgrove Rovers	0-4	164
		Banner (2), Benbow, Pope		
Cray Wanderers	v	Pagham (31/8)	5-0	87
Bennett, Kempster (3), Wood				
Crook Town	v	Guiseley	2-3	
Dalton (2)		Senior (3)		
Croydon	v	Hythe Town	1-1	
Cecil		Ross		
Croydon Athletic	v	Herne Bay	2-1	110
Quinton, Stevens		Cirillo		
Dartford	v	Bashley (31/8)	1-0	257
Buglione				
Dawlish Town	v	Clevedon United	1-2	68
Slough		Murray, Thorne		
Didcot Town	v	Eastbourne Town	4-1	172
Bore (2), Cooper, Loncannon		Odbuade		
Dorking	v	Lewes	3-5	222
Coyle, Nusungu, Vaughan		Cable, Fontana, Kadi, Newman (2)		
Downton	v	Exmouth Town	3-4	70
Guy (2), James		Bentley, Burwood, Gardner, Saunders		
Dulwich Hamlet	v	Folkestone Invicta	1-3	265
Houghton		Everitt, Tait (2)		

Home		Away	Score	Att
Dunstable Town	v	Saffron Walden Town		
(walkover for Dunstable Town - Saffron Walden Town removed)				
Durham City	v	Rossington Main	0-0	127
Eastwood Town	v	Deeping Rangers	2-2	111
Gould, Huckerby		McKenzie, Mosley		
Edgware Town	v	Clapton	2-2	85
Heselton (2)		Edwards, Kirby		
Egham Town	v	Thame United	1-8	
McKinlay		Avery, Freeman, Gardner, Mitchell, Stewart (3)		
Elmore	v	Wimborne Town	1-3	61
Anderson		Barnes, Cannie (2)		
Enfield	v	Hemel Hempstead Town (31/8)	1-1	89
Howell		Jones		
Enfield Town	v	Clacton Town	2-1	356
Ulatowski		Howe		
Esh Winning	v	Bacup Borough	1-3	104
Marron		Gray, Thompson (2)		
Evenwood Town	v	Oldham Town	3-5	124
Dinsley, Houlahan, Turner				
Evesham United	v	Hallen	3-3	97
Burrow (2), Jukes		Beecham (2), Serjeant		
Fisher Athletic	v	Bedfont	3-4	91
Brady (2), Islam		Decosta, Postins (3)		
Flackwell Heath	v	Concord Rangers	4-1	83
Bowler, Hill, Mason, O'Sullivan		Atkinson		
Fleet Town	v	Epsom & Ewell	1-0	88
Frampton				
Fleetwood Town	v	Parkgate	3-0	144
Barnes, Vickers (2)				
Frome Town	v	Clevedon Town	1-1	145
Hayter		Lester		
Goole	v	Rossendale United	2-4	227
Lewis		Bell, Brierley, Brooks (2)		
Gorleston	v	Haverhill Rovers		
(walkover for Haverhill Rovers - Gorleston removed)				
Gosport Borough	v	Erith & Belvedere	2-4	166
Lindsey, White		Adams (2), Billenness, Sodje		
Great Harwood Town	v	North Ferriby United	0-3	111
		Dewhurst, Elliott, Gowen		
Great Yarmouth Town	v	Berkhamsted Town	0-1	217
		Hammond		
Greenwich Borough	v	Maidstone United	1-1	314
Mighty		Sinden		
Gresley Rovers	v	Buxton	1-1	310
Gray		Froggatt		
Grosvenor Park	v	Glapwell	0-0	37
GuisboroughTown	v	Kendal Town	1-1	86
Sunley		Close		
Hailsham Town	v	Cowes Sports	0-1	132
		Sunsberg		
Hall Road Rangers	v	Trafford	1-1	85
Cutler		Richards		
Hampton & Richmond Borough	v	Great Wakering Rovers	3-0	157
Allen, O'Conner (2)				
Hanwell Town	v	East Thurrock United	2-2	85
Brown, Sheekey		Harrison, Martin		
Haringey Borough	v	Dereham Town	1-3	65
Carey		Burtenshaw, Henman, Hillier		
Harpenden Town	v	St Margaretsbury	1-3	68
Price		Howard (2), Moy		
Harrogate Railway	v	Hatfield Main		
(walkover for Harrogate Railway - Hatfield Main removed)				
Hastings United	v	Bracknell Town	1-3	289
Honey		Grittenden, Palmer, Smith		
Hertford Town	v	Lowestoft Town	2-4	140
Sapsford, Turner		Hilton, McGee, Poppy, Stokeld		
Highworth Town	v	Portland United	4-3	132
Belcher, Hulbert, Mills, Saye		Laws, Reeve (2)		
Hillingdon Borough	v	Corinthian Casuals	2-0	62
O'Brien, O'Neil				
Histon	v	Yeading	7-0	131
Andrews, Cambridge, Kennedy (2)				
Murray (2), Vowden				
HordenCW	v	Brandon United	0-1	106
		Pitt		
Horsham	v	Newport IW	1-2	297
Charman		Bridges, Gearing		
Hyde United	v	Hallam	6-1	228
Barker, Ellis (4), Tolson		Smith		
Kidsgrove Athletic	v	Rugby United	1-3	174
Twigg		Pearson (2), Williams		

Thackley (NCE P) 0 - Ossett Town (NPL 1) 1
Thackley's Mark Senior turns away from Ossett Town's Mark Lambert. Photo: Darren C Thomas.

Home		Away	Score	Att
Leatherhead	v	Moneyfields	3-1	113
Ekoku, Harrison, Ruggles		Stafford		
Leek CSOB	v	Redditch United	2-3	105
Nagington		Burgess, Hall, Leadbeater		
Leighton Town	v	Wootton Blue Cross	3-1	122
Jaggard, Rawdon (2)		Bulzis		
Lincoln Moorlands	v	Leek Town	1-2	
Ryan		Whittaker (2)		
Liversedge	v	Gateshead	3-1	92
Brady, Broughton, Nestor		Coluin		
Long Buckby	v	Kings Lynn	1-5	210
Box		Bacon, Defty, Harris, Huke, Ndekwe		
Long Eaton United	v	Norton United	0-0	71
Maine Road	v	Ashington	2-4	45
Broderick, Simms		Carr, Lawson (3)		
Maltby Main	v	West Auckland Town	1-0	55
Haythorne				
Marske United	v	Winterton Rangers	3-0	104
Alexander (2), Howes				
Melksham Town	v	Mangotsfield United	0-4	156
		Edwards, Seal (2), Summers		
Mickleover Sports	v	Ludlow Town	3-0	80
Leighton, Mays, Sutton				
Milton Keynes City	v	Tilbury		
(walkover for Tilbury - Milton Keynes City removed)				
Minehead	v	Welton Rovers	2-2	80
Pople (2)		Butler, Wilson		
Molesey	v	Godalming & Guildford	1-2	
Sheil		Blason, Elliott		
Mossley	v	Curzon Ashton	1-1	236
Pickett		Mitten		
Newcastle Blue Star	v	Dunston Federation Brewery	1-2	
Ludlow		Holmes, Snaith		
Newcastle Town	v	WillenhallTown	3-0	95
Harris, Kiely, Parkinson				
Newmarket Town	v	Wembley	5-0	142
Reed, Rhodes (3), Stokes				
Norwich United	v	Leyton	2-2	98
Murphy (2)		Paul (2)		
Oadby Town	v	Stratford Town	5-1	205
Master, Miller, Warner (3)		Gray		
Ossett Albion	v	AlsagerTown	2-1	106
Toronczak (2)		Wilshaw		
Oxford City	v	Farnham Town	6-1	
Ferreira,Lee,Simpson,Wise(2)		Grimes		
Paulton Rovers	v	Calne Town	2-0	86
Bown (2)				
Peacehaven & Telscombe	v	Chessington United	2-1	61
Hamilton, Lloyd		Smith		
Peterlee Newtown	v	Bridlington Town	1-2	111
Harvey		Drayton, Robinson		
Pickering Town	v	Whitley Bay (31/8)	2-0	205
Drinkall, Willgrass				
Pontefract Collieries	v	Clitheroe	0-2	102
		Jackson		
Porthleven	v	Team Bath	0-4	238
		Holland, Prince, Stocco, Tilson		
Prudhoe Town	v	MorpethTown	2-0	
McDonald, Taylor				
Quorn	v	Gedling Town	0-1	137
		Foster		
Racing Club Warwick	v	Stafford Town	0-1	85
		Yearwood		
Raunds Town	v	Hoddesdon Town	1-0	86
St John				
Rocester	v	Ilkeston Town	1-1	165
Mitchell		Thompson		
Ruislip Manor	v	Soham Town Rangers	1-4	78
Todd		Bugg, Hinde, Kingston, North		
Salisbury City	v	Odd Down	4-0	418
Cooper, Strong (2), Turk				
Sawbridgeworth Town	v	AFC Wallingford	2-2	41
Martin, O'Reilly		McKinney, Swift		
Seaham Red Star	v	Murton	3-4	114
Ferguson, Lines, Morris		Diamond (2), McLean, Turner		
Selby Town	v	Washington	0-0	102
Sheffield	v	Jarrow Roofing Boldon CA	1-0	130
Burke				
Shepshed Dynamo	v	Congleton Town	0-1	148
		Bickerstaffe		
Shildon	v	Workington	2-1	240
Richmond, Walton		Johnston		
ShirebrookTown	v	Matlock Town	2-1	297
Johnson, Kerley		Williams		
Sidlesham	v	Sittingbourne	0-2	61
		Neal (2)		
Skelmersdale United	v	Atherton LR (31/8)	3-0	104
Hanson, Heverin, Rudd				
Slade Green	v	Hartley Wintney	1-2	57
Montague		Anderson, Ruffles		
Slough Town	v	East Grinstead Town (31/8)	5-0	374
Hodge (3), Spencer		(at Windsor & Eton FC)		
Solihull Borough	v	Stone Dominoes	3-0	163
Haywood, Lovelock, Preston				
South Shields	v	BedlingtonTerriers	0-0	189
Southwick	v	Burgess Hill Town	1-4	203
		Harper (2), Sullivan (2)		
Spalding United	v	Glossop North End	3-0	196
Gosling, Hudson, Nuttall				
St Blazey	v	Willand Rovers	5-0	140
Bowker (2), Daly, Street, Waters				
Stamford	v	Bourne Town	2-0	244
Maddox (2)				
Stansted	v	Uxbridge (at Uxbridge FC)	0-7	87
		Casey (2), Nichols (3), Royal, Tunnell		
Stanway Rovers	v	Staines Town	0-1	140
		Ibe		
Staveley MW	v	Sutton Town	0-1	96
		Lormor		
Stewarts & Lloyds	v	Fakenham Town	3-0	48
Farr, Sneddon (2)				
Stocksbridge Park Steels	v	Squires Gate	2-1	120
Johnson, Riley		Bingham		
Stourbridge	v	Causeway United	0-2	190
		Busby (2)		
Stourport Swifts	v	Boldmere St Michaels	1-0	101
Wood				
Stowmarket Town	v	Waltham Forest	0-2	86
		Lawford (2)		
Studley	v	Rushall Olympic	3-0	104
Coppin, Crisp, Jordan				
Tadcaster Albion	v	Winsford United	0-4	50
		Hutchinson, Melia (2), Miranda		
Taunton Town	v	Bournemouth	1-1	336
Booth		Dancer		
Thackley	v	Ossett Town	0-1	111
Thatcham Town	v	Alton Town	1-2	113
Czastka		Bridger, Graham		
Thornaby	v	Easington Colliery	5-1	47
Clarke (2), reeve, Rountree (2)		Wilson		
Three Bridges	v	Redhill	1-1	75
Funnell		Stanton		
Tonbridge Angels	v	BAT Sports	4-0	424

Home		Away	Score	Att
Tooting & Mitcham Utd	v	Ashford Town (Middx)	3-1	235
Onochie, Thompson, Twin		Butler		
Tow Law Town	v	Salford City	1-1	126
McKenna		Franks		
Tring Town	v	Mildenhall Town		
(walkover for Mildenhall Town - Tring Town removed)				
VCD Athletic	v	Eastleigh	2-1	67
Main, Probetts		Balfe		
Walton & Hersham	v	Walton Casuals	0-2	216
		Harris, Nelson		
Ware	v	London Colney	2-2	102
Crawford, Frendo		Farrow, Walsh		
Warrington Town	v	Yorkshire Amateur	1-0	92
Bermingham				
Westbury United	v	Keynsham Town	2-2	103
Wheeler (2)		Lucas, Walsh		
Whickham	v	HebburnTown (29/8)	2-2	180
Hall, Scott		Armstrong, Rolfe		
Whitchurch United	v	Withdean 2000	4-1	50
Huddison, Lilley, Odey, Pitts		Moses		
Whitehawk	v	Lymington & New Milton	0-2	67
		James, Thomson		
Whitstable Town	v	Raynes Park Vale	1-3	136
Harkins		Kenndall (3)		
Wick	v	Whyteleafe	0-5	102
		Dickson, Garland, Harper (2), Smith		
Willington	v	Consett	0-5	72
		Green (2), Terrell, Thompson (2)		
Windsor & Eton	v	Metropolitan Police	0-1	134
		Batten		
Wingate & Finchley	v	Bury Town	3-2	127
Boateng, Hakim, Williams		Parker, Stringfellow		
Wisbech Town	v	Aveley	1-2	299
Furnell		Hart, Simmons		
Witham Town	v	Marlow	2-0	77
Addington, Emery				
Witton Albion	v	Nelson	4-1	240
Burton (4)		Barrett		
Wivenhoe Town	v	Bowers United	7-0	104
Abrahams, Bethell (4), Caton, Crawfield				
Wokingham Town	v	Deal Town (31/8)	0-1	104
		Marriott		
Woodley Sports	v	Ramsbottom United	1-1	113
Hackney		Walsh		
Worthing	v	Ash United	7-0	259
Brackley (3), Dicker, Francis, Knee, Rodgers				
Wroxham	v	Banbury United	6-1	137
Edridge (2), Fox, Gill, Hunton, Macgae		Billington		
Yate Town	v	Cirencester Town	1-2	197
Powell		Bevan, Kear		
Yaxley	v	Barking & East Ham United	2-1	84
Acton, Chapman		Bangs		

REPLAYS

1st September

Home		Away	Score	Att
Curzon Ashton	v	Mossley	2-3*	253
Dean Kay		Carroll, Coyne, Pickering		

2nd September

Home		Away	Score	Att
AFC Wallingford	v	Sawbridgeworth Town	2-0	125
Baker, Beavon				
Billingham Town	v	Brigg Town	1-0	157
Chillingsworth				
Boston Town	v	BelperTown	0-1	108
Bournemouth	v	Taunton Town	0-5	269
		Dicks (2), Fisher, Lynch (2)		
Buxton	v	Gresley Rovers	4-0	360
Angus, Anson, Bullock, Cheetham				
Chorley	v	Billingham Synthonia	3-1*	279
Eatock (2), Wilkinson		Perry		
Clapton	v	Edgware Town	0-1	
		Thomas		
Clevedon Town	v	Frome Town	2-3*	182
		Billing (2), Pounder		
Colwyn Bay	v	Blackpool Mechanics	3-1	
McMahon, Spink, Thomas		Kinley		
East Thurrock United	v	Hanwell Town	6-3*	147
Barry, Blaney (2), Cartlidge, Dwyer, Holding		Rowlands (2), Sheekey		
Glapwell	v	Grosvenor Park	2-0	60
Bland (2)				
Hallen	v	Evesham United	2-1*	179
Collett, Owen		Joyce		
Hythe Town	v	Croydon	1-1* 5-4p	165
Godden				
Ilkeston Town	v	Rocester	3-1	238
Freetone, Laws, Thompson		McMahon		
Ipswich Wanderers	v	Beaconsfield SYCOB	2-1	172
Smith (2)		Arthur		
Kendal Town	v	Guisborough Town	2-2* 7-8p	159
Prosser, Sheppard		Kasonali, Ryan		
Hemel Hempstead Town	v	Enfield	2-3	115
Hammatt, Perrin		Armstrong (2), Powler		
Leyton	v	Norwich United	2-1	190
Braham, Nartey		McIntosh		
London Colney	v	Ware	0-1*	90
		Bridge		
RamsbottomUnited	v	Woodley Sports	3-0	167
Brickell, Dyson, Swailes				
Rossington Main	v	Durham City	0-1	121
		Herbert		
Rothwell Town	v	Barton Rovers	3-0	147
Garside, Lake, Underwood				
Salford City	v	Tow Law Town	4-3	111
Murphy, Rea, Vaughan, Weir		Craggs (3)		
Trafford	v	Hall Road Rangers	3-1	130
Gabriel, Otutu, Richards				
Welton Rovers	v	Minehead	2-1	75
Carpenter, Wilson				

3rd September

Home		Away	Score	Att
BedlingtonTerriers	v	South Shields	4-1	138
Cockburn, Douglas, Milner (2)		Anderson		
Deeping Rangers	v	Eastwood Town	1-2	252
McKenzie		Housley, McGowan		
Hebburn Town	v	Whickham	1-2	159
		Craddock, Robson		
Keynsham Town	v	Westbury United	2-5	65
Cripps, Zabek		Carpenter (2), Perkins, Welch, Wheeler		
Maidstone United	v	Greenwich Borough	1-0	270
Griffin				
Norton United	v	Long Eaton United	0-2	78
		Mabon, Marston		
Redhill	v	Three Bridges	0-3	86
(at Dorking FC)		Butcher, Funnell, Hackett		
Washington	v	Selby Town	3-3* 4-5p	106
Ball (2), Hanson		Cygan, Gaugman, Ward		

FIRST QUALIFYING ROUND

Saturday 13th September — **Winning clubs received: £2,250**

Home		Away	Score	Att
Abingdon Town	v	Ringmer	4-3	88
Beauchamp (2), Harper, Potter		Allen, Johnson, Shepherd		
AFC Totton	v	Didcot Town	1-3	94
Whiddett		Bedwell, Emsden, Parsons		
AFC Wallingford	v	Ipswich Wanderers	2-0	137
Baker, Darke				
Andover	v	Arundel	5-0	278
Andrew, Rea (2), Rusher (2)				
Armthorpe Welfare	v	Whickham	0-0	72
Ashford Town	v	Bromley	1-1	427
Beale		Huggins		
Ashington	v	Ramsbottom United	3-1	271
Lawson (3)		Brickell		
Aveley	v	Lowestoft Town	1-2	107
Greaves				
Backwell United	v	Wimborne Town	1-4	49
Hewitt		Barnes, Doyle, Moxham, Smith		
Bamber Bridge	v	Bacup Borough	2-0	
Massey, Steele				
Barwell	v	Newcastle Town	2-5	113
Boyles, Clamp		Beeston, Harris, Stokes, Van Dal Lann		
Berkhamsted Town	v	AFC Sudbury	0-9	376
		Banya, Bennett (3), Claydon, Francis, Norfolk, Patrick, Tracey		
Biddulph Victoria	v	Buxton (14/9)	1-1	326
Wilson-Cunningham		Anson		
Bishop Auckland	v	Pickering Town	0-1	168
		Wood		
Boreham Wood	v	Maldon Town	2-1	121
Palmer, Winston		Smith		
Bracknell Town	v	Hartley Wintney	3-2	154
Edwards, Glynn, Smith		Holman, Medford		
Bridlington Town	v	Salford City	5-0	311
Baldwin, Drayton, Harrison, Palmer (2)				
Burgess Hill Town	v	Abingdon United	2-1	220
Sullivan, Wyatt		Simms		
Chesham United	v	Yaxley	2-0	202
Scarlett, Smith				
Chessington & Hook Utd	v	Thamesmead Town	1-4	123
Martin		Clews, Loveridge (2), Power		
Chester-Le-Street Town	v	Murton	2-0	71
Adamson, Bowers				
Chorley	v	Selby Town	2-1	222
Cooper, Wilkinson		Gaughan		
Christchurch	v	Westbury United	2-3	103
Edwards, Joyce		Perkins (2), Wheeler		
Cirencester Town	v	Swindon Supermarine	2-1	188
Bevan (2)		Matthews		
Clevedon United	v	Frome Town	4-1	141
Moore, Murray, Pike, White		Preece		
Clitheroe	v	Brandon United	0-1	222
		Patterson		
Congleton Town	v	Leek Town	1-0	386
Corby Town	v	Halesowen Town	1-1	228
Le-Masurier		Ashby		
Corsham Town	v	Brislington	1-2	160
Curtis		Miller, Radford		
Cray Wanderers	v	Sandhurst Town	4-1	129
Bennett (2), Kempster, Wood		Nesbitt		
Croydon Athletic	v	Bedfont	7-1	142
Fowler, Jackson (3), Stevens, Webb (2)		Bryant		
Dartford	v	Peacehaven&Telscombe (14/9)	3-0	284
Buglione, Hassett, Robinson				
Deal Town	v	Leatherhead	1-2	170
Marriott		Harrison (2)		
Dereham Town	v	Tilbury	1-4	120
Buptenshaw		Stevens (3)		
Dunston Federation Brewery	v	Billingham Town	2-2	104
Holmes, Southern		Jackson, Turner		
Durham City	v	Shildon	0-2	221
		Ellison, Key		
East Thurrock United	v	Staines Town	2-1	140
Cartlidge, Martin		Ibe		
Edgware Town	v	Enfield Town	0-1	225
		Cooper		
Enfield	v	Witham Town (14/9)	4-0	99
Hoenyball (2), Howell, Marshall				
Exmouth Town	v	St Blazey	2-2	
Gardner, Spiller		Daly (2)		
Fareham Town	v	Newport IW	1-2	210
Wood		Barsdell, Holmes		
Farsley Celtic	v	Sheffield	1-1	
Midwood		O'Carroll		
Fleetwood Town	v	Bedlington Terriers	3-2	158
Barnes, French, Tong		Allen (2		
Glapwell	v	Gedling Town	1-2	75
Castledine		Maddison, Richardson		
Gloucester City	v	Team Bath	0-0	377
Guiseley	v	Trafford	1-0	242
Chattoe				
Hallen	v	Highworth Town	1-2	84
Cook		Dix, Mills		
Hampton & Richmond Borough	v	Dunstable Town	1-0	155
Jarvis				
Harlow Town	v	St Neots Town	1-0	140
Chapman				
Haverhill Rovers	v	Burnham Ramblers	1-2	230
Jenkin		Agyei-Dua, Holmes		
Hillingdon Borough	v	Oxford City	1-1	85
Towle		Simpson		
Hythe Town	v	Alton Town	3-1	136
Brazier (2), Porter		Bridger		
Kings Lynn	v	Stewarts & Lloyds	2-2	871
Holmes (2)		Byrne, Farr		
Leyton	v	Arlesey Town	4-0	108
Curley, Gregoriou (2), Nartey				
Long Eaton United	v	Ilkeston Town	0-2	484
		Freestone, Thompson		
Lymington&New Milton	v	Erith & Belvedere	1-0	133
Shaw				
Maidstone United	v	Cowes Sports (14/9)	4-0	350
Appleton, Austin, Bradbrook, Hogg				
Maltby Main	v	Colwyn Bay	4-2	110
Haythorne, Walker (2), Ward		Hobson, McMahon		
Mangotsfield United	v	Bridport	4-3	229
Edwards, Pitcher, Seal, Sims		Armstrong, Greeno, White		
Metropolitan Police	v	Winchester City	2-3	180
Batten, James		Bicknell, Dyke, Forbes		
Mickleover Sports	v	Eastwood Town	0-0	213
Mildenhall Town	v	Histon	1-6	168
Taylor-Holt		Andrews (2), Kennedy, Murray, Rowe (2)		
Mossley	v	Hyde United	1-6	525
Bailey		Buckley (2), McNeil, O'Kane, Wright (2)		
Newmarket Town	v	Brackley Town	6-1	160
Ogilive, Reed, Shaw (3), Tuck		Prescott		

Home		Away	Score	Att
Oadby Town	v	Stamford	0-2	281
		Byrne, McKenzie		
Oldham Town	v	Liversedge	3-2	120
Curley (3)		Broughton, Milnes		
Ossett Albion	v	Ossett Town	0-0	522
Paulton Rovers	v	Bemerton Heath Harlequins	2-0	133
Bown (2)				
Pelsall Villa	v	Belper Town	0-4	
		Evans (2), Simpson, Ward		
Raynes Park Vale	v	Folkestone Invicta	0-2	120
		Dryden, Hegley		
Rossendale United	v	Harrogate Railway	2-1	218
		Delaney		
Salisbury City	v	Taunton Town	4-1	551
Cook (2), Crook, Strong		Lynch		
Shirebrook Town	v	Stafford Town	2-0	190
Carter, Johnson				
Sittingbourne	v	Whyteleafe	1-0	267
Neal				
Skelmersdale United	v	Consett	2-0	102
Birchall, Heverin				
Slough Town	v	Godalming & Guildford	2-0	319
Hodge, Miller				
Solihull Borough	v	Redditch United	0-3	416
		Burgess, Hall (2)		
Spalding United	v	Sutton Town	2-2	293
Hudson, Nuttall		Lormor (2)		
St Margaretsbury	v	Leighton Town	2-2	83
Hardy, Howard		Kidd, Kingsley		
Stocksbridge Park Steels	v	Prudhoe Town	6-1	103
Johnson (2), Knox (2), Ring (2)				
Stourport Swifts	v	Rugby United	0-3	173
		Marsden (2), Shanahan		
Studley	v	Bromsgrove Rovers	0-1	387
		Pope		
Sutton Coldfield Town	v	Causeway United	1-1	118
Wolsey		Drakeley		
Thame United	v	VCD Athletic	4-2	145
		Bates (2)		
Thornaby	v	Guisborough Town	1-2	90
Clarke		Booth, Osborne		
Three Bridges	v	Fleet Town	1-2	129
Alexander		Frampton, Hale		
Tonbridge Angels	v	Lewes	1-1	617
Barr		Adeniyi		
Waltham Forest	v	Rothwell Town	1-3	96
		Earside, Mintus, Sturgess		
Ware	v	Buckingham Town	2-2	116
Bridge, Jones		Abdi, Trott		
Warrington Town	v	North Ferriby United	6-1	107
Bermingham, Mitchell (3) Moore, Tyrell		Pindar		
Wealdstone	v	Uxbridge (12/9)	0-1	326
		Tunnell		
Welton Rovers	v	Bishop Sutton	3-3	70
Blakemore (3)		Fussell, Mason, Tillsy		
Whitchurch United	v	Tooting & Mitcham United	0-3	156
		Kinch, Worsfold (2)		
Wingate & Finchley	v	Raunds Town	3-1	107
Sloma, Ward, William		Goosey		
Winsford United	v	Marske United	2-1	189
Melia, Quinn		McGee		
Witton Albion	v	Holker Old Boys (14/9)	7-0	279
Dicken (4), Mallinson, Moseley (2)				
Wivenhoe Town	v	Soham Town Rangers	2-3	124
Abrahams, Haydon		Bugg, Foster, Rutter		
Worthing	v	Walton Casuals	4-1	390
Francis (2), Geddes (2)		Barrs-James		
Wroxham	v	Flackwell Heath	2-2	163
Munton, Stock		Bowler, Wojtowicz		

R E P L A Y S

16th September

Home		Away	Score	Att
Billingham Town	v	Dunston Federation Brewery (16/9)	0-1	141
		Taylor		
Bromley	v	Ashford Town (16/9)	1-0	309
Wade				
Eastwood Town	v	Mickleover Sports (16/9)	1-0	51
Morgan				
Flackwell Heath	v	Wroxham (16/9)	1-0	63
O'Sullivan				
Halesowen Town	v	Corby Town (16/9)	3-2	322
Ashby (2), Jones		Harrold (2)		
Leighton Town	v	St Margaretsbury (16/9)	0-1	105
		Howard		
Lewes	v	Tonbridge Angels (16/9)	2-1	468
Newman (2)		Larkin		
Ossett Town	v	Ossett Albion (16/9)	1-3	555
Davidson		Toronczak (3)		
Oxford City	v	Hillingdon Borough (16/9)	2-1	120
Abbassi, Phelan		Canavan		
Sheffield	v	Farsley Celtic (16/9)	1-3*	160
Bray		Blackstone, Henderson, Shields		
Stewarts & Lloyds	v	Kings Lynn (16/9)	0-3	211
		Harris, Holmes, Ndekwe		
Sutton Town	v	Spalding United (16/9)	0-5	113
		Hudson, Nuttall (2), Stanhope (2)		

17th September

Home		Away	Score	Att
Bishop Sutton	v	Welton Rovers	1-0	112
Tillby				
Buckingham Town	v	Ware	2-1	136
George, McGillycuddy		Greenwood		
Buxton	v	Biddulph Victoria	3-1	498
Bevan, Bullock, Cheetham		Burge, Marrow		
Causeway United	v	Sutton Coldfield Town	0-3	122
St Blazey	v	Exmouth Town	3-3* 3-4p	278
Daly, Hooper, Pugh		Burwood, Jenkins, Stiller		
Whickham	v	Armthorpe Welfare	2-1	210
Greenwood, Hall		Jones		

22nd September

Home		Away	Score	Att
Team Bath	v	Gloucester City	0-2	202
		Cox (2)		

Guiseley (NPL 1) 1 - Trafford (NWC 1) 0
Trafford striker Rico Richards holds off the challenge of Richard Chattoe. Photo: Darren C Thomas.

SECOND QUALIFYING ROUND

Saturday 27th September — **Winning clubs received: £3,750**

Home		Away	Score	Att
Abingdon Town Beauchamp	v	Chesham United Miles, Sippetts	1-2	183
Ashton United Denney	v	Hyde United Wright	1-1	446
Barrow Campbell, Hume	v	Harrogate Town	2-0	1250
Basingstoke Town McAllister	v	Cray Wanderers	1-0	351
Blyth Spartans Fenton, McAlindon, Woodhouse	v	Bamber Bridge	3-0	464
Bognor Regis Town	v	Havant & Waterlooville Ford, Howe, Masson, Taylor	0-4	945
Boreham Wood Baker, Winston (3)	v	Burgess Hill Town	4-0	165
Bracknell Town Crittenden, Marchant, Palmer, Selby	v	Tilbury Elmes, Stevens	4-2	178
Braintree Town Asombang, Blackwell, Cranfield	v	Aylesbury United Campion, Williams	3-2	214
Bridlington Town Burdick, Palmer	v	Farsley Celtic Midwood, Smithard	2-2	359
Brislington	v	Bath City Cleverley, Salter	0-2	516
Bromley Amoako (2), Reid	v	Dartford	3-0	542
Buckingham Town Olaleye	v	Thurrock Ahurang, Lawrence	1-2	182
Burnham Ramblers Everett	v	St Margaretsbury Howard, Menage, Morgan	1-3	160
Buxton Agus	v	Belper Town	1-0	915
Cambridge City Nightingale, Riddle, Simpson	v	Ilkeston Town Callery	3-1	294
Canvey Island Boylan (2), Dobinson, Gooden, Gregory, Midgeley	v	Uxbridge Royal	6-1	321
Chester-Le-Street Town	v	Bradford (Park Avenue) Collins, Oleksewycz	0-2	201
Chippenham Town Mings, Paul	v	Winchester City Forbes	2-1	461
Chorley Barker, Butterworth, Eatock Southwood, Wilkinson	v	Whickham	5-0	239
Cirencester Town Griffin, Mayo, Mimturn	v	Andover Bennett, Rea	3-2	202
Croydon Athletic Fowler, Stassinos	v	AFC Wallingford	2-0	150
Dover Athletic Dyer, Readings, Tyne, Wilkins	v	Maidenhead United (28/9)	4-0	703
Droylsden Burke, Hall	v	Burscough Brown, Martindale	2-2	251
Dunston Federation Brewery Holmes	v	Fleetwood Town Tong	1-1	165
Eastbourne Borough	v	Chelmsford City Cross, Watkins	2-2	608
Enfield Town	v	Carshalton Athletic Marvell	0-1	501
Exmouth Town	v	Highworth Town Bellinger	0-1	258
Ford United	v	Didcot Town Concannon	3-1	117
Frickley Athletic	v	Shildon	0-0	253
Gainsborough Trinity Ellington, Grant (3), Hurst, Kotyco	v	Skelmersdale United	6-0	376
Gedling Town Scoffham	v	Alfreton Town	1-0	280
Gloucester City Jefferies (2)	v	Merthyr Tydfil	2-0	476
Guisborough Town Booth, Sunley	v	Stalybridge Celtic Potts, Wharton	2-2	205
Hampton & Richmond Borough Allen, O'Connor	v	Kingstonian Steele	2-1	660
Harlow Town	v	Crawley Town Brake (2), Gregory, Judge	0-4	372
Harrow Borough	v	Flackwell Heath	0-0	120
Hayes Forrester, Goodall, Holsgrove Scott	v	Tooting & Mitcham United Adeoye, Graham	4-2	272
Hednesford Town	v	Bromsgrove Rovers Atkinson, Scheppell	0-2	570
Hendon Butler (2), Crace, Duncan	v	Enfield	4-0	158
Heybridge Swifts Budge, Cousins, Robinson	v	Worthing Francis (2), Knee	3-3	297
Hitchin Town	v	Folkestone Invicta	0-0	319
Hornchurch Southon, West	v	Billericay Town Hockton	2-1	836
Hucknall Town Soar	v	Congleton Town Scully	1-1	447
Hythe Town	v	Maidstone United Davey, Davis, Sinden (2)	0-4	603
Lancaster City Hughes, Sullivan	v	Altrincham	2-0	489
Leyton Badaja	v	Leatherhead	1-0	140
Lowestoft Town McGee, Stokeld	v	Lewes Whiteman	2-1	317
Lymington & New Milton James (5), Kenna, Smith, Stone	v	Clevedon United Harris, Pike	8-2	130
Maltby Main Hartley, Walker	v	Ashington Douglas, Lawson, Nash	2-3	121
Mangotsfield United Edwards, Pitcher, Seal	v	Wimborne Town	3-0	233
Marine Dolan, Nolan (2)	v	Rossendale United Clarke	3-1	332
Moor Green Doyle	v	Hinckley United Smith	1-2	271
Newcastle Town Kiely, Lennon	v	Sutton Coldfield Town	2-1	107
Newmarket Town Coe, Ogilvie (2)	v	Fleet Town	3-0	221
Newport County Lloyd, Mumford, Plant	v	Weymouth Claridge, Hutchinson	3-2	769
Newport IW Howes, O'Rourke	v	Tiverton Town Pears	2-1	378
Northwood Knight, Nolan	v	AFC Sudbury Bennett, Cheetham, Claydon, Head	2-4	385
Nuneaton Borough Whittaker	v	Worcester City	1-0	1352
Paulton Rovers Bown, Colbourne, Crandon, Ford	v	Bishop Sutton Andrews	4-1	127
Pickering Town	v	Ossett Albion Ward	0-1	258
Radcliffe Borough Banim, Luker	v	Oldham Town	2-1	294
Redditch United Ross	v	Shirebrook Town Johnson	1-1	337

Home		Away	Score	Att
Rothwell Town	v	Bedford Town	0-1	410
		Lynch		
Rugby United	v	Eastwood Town	1-3	363
		Fisher, Nazha, Whitehead		
Runcorn FC Halton	v	Guiseley	3-0	234
Carden, Leadbitter, Price				
Salisbury City	v	Westbury United	1-1	570
Cooper				
Sittingbourne	v	East Thurrock United	1-2	401
Gooding		Cartlidge, Mully		
Slough Town	v	Welling United	1-1	465
Spencer		Powell		
Soham Town Rangers	v	Histon	0-2	281
		Cambridge (2)		
Spalding United	v	Halesowen Town	1-2	393
Watts		Charlton, Hollis		
Spennymoor United	v	Warrington Town	0-2	202
		Bermingham, Mitchell		
St Albans City	v	Grays Athletic	2-4	420
Oakes, Tomlinson		Carthy, Eastwood (2), Thurgood		
Stafford Rangers	v	Grantham Town	1-2	797
Davidson		Collins, Gould		
Stamford	v	Kettering Town	0-3	862
		Clarke, Fewings, Graham		
Stocksbridge Park Steels	v	Brandon United	3-2	139
Bates (2), Knox		Huggins, Johnson		
Sutton United	v	Bishop's Stortford	0-0	429
Thame United	v	Thamesmead Town	4-0	150
Avery, Jones, Joyce, Saulsbury				
Vauxhall Motors	v	Southport	3-1	492
Cumiskey (2), Robinson		Ashcroft		
Weston Super Mare	v	Dorchester Town	4-1	293
Davis, French, Slater, Sorbara		Browne		
Whitby Town	v	Winsford United	3-0	282
Dixon, Linighan, Veart				
Wingate & Finchley	v	Oxford City (28/9)	1-2	159
Shafer		Ballard, Simpson		
Witton Albion	v	Wakefield & Emley	0-1	348
		Bowler		
Worksop Town	v	Kings Lynn	2-2	834
Bambrook, Caudwell		Bacon, Staff		

REPLAYS

29th September

Home		Away	Score	Att
Hyde United	v	Ashton United	1-2	489
Buckley		Denney, Fleury		

30th September

Home		Away	Score	Att
Bishop's Stortford	v	Sutton United	1-1* 5-3p	347
Langer		Collins		
Burscough	v	Droylsden	1-2*	166
Brown		Hall, Wright		
Congleton Town	v	Hucknall Town	3-2*	290
Reilly, Scully, Tunnicliffe		Barrick, Mayman		
Farsley Celtic	v	Bridlington Town	3-0	182
Austin, Midwood (2)				
Flackwell Heath	v	Harrow Borough	0-1	128
		Valenti		
Fleetwood Town	v	Dunston Federation Brewery	1-2	185
Catlon		Booth, Southern		
Folkestone Invictia	v	Hitchin Town	3-0	428
Hogg, Tait (2)				
Kings Lynn	v	Worksop Town	1-4	1209
Burrows		Caudwell, Peacock, Whitehead (2)		
Stalybridge Celtic	v	Guisborough Town	3-1	305
Eastwood, Mayers, Potts		Mitchell		
Welling United	v	Slough Town	4-1	418
Beard, Booth (2), Standen		Millen		
Worthing	v	Heybridge Swifts	2-0	452
Geddes, Hill				

1st October

Home		Away	Score	Att
Chelmsford City	v	Eastbourne Borough	0-2	441
		Austin, White		
Shildon	v	Frickley Athletic	5-1	664
Barnes (4), Bolton		Hatto		
Shirebrook Town	v	Redditch United	2-2* 4-1p	340
Carter, Johnson		Arshad, Myers		
Westbury United	v	Salisbury City	1-2	478
Colbourne		Phillips, Turk		

Bognor Regis (Isthmian P) 0 - Havent & Waterlooville (Southern P) 4
Chukki Eribenne lets fly with a cracking shot. Photo: Andrew Chitty.

Above:
Desborough Town (UCO P) 4
Northampton Spencer (UCO P) 2
Tammy Stratford loops his header over the stranded Desborough 'keeper, to complete Spencer's scoring in this Extra Preliminary replay.
Photo: Gordon Whittingham.

Right:
Eccleshill United (NCE P) 1
Warrington Town (NWC 1) 2
The Warrington 'keeper dives to make a save from Eccleshill's Chris Wood during the side's Extra Preliminary Round tie.
Photo: Darren C Thomas.

Left:
Farsley Celtic (NPL 1) 1
Sheffield (NCE P) 1
Farsley's Anjad Iqbal tries to shield the ball from the on coming challenge by a Sheffield player in this First Qualifying Round match.
Photo: Darren C Thomas.

Left:
Wivenhoe (Isthmian 1N) 3
Soham Town (ECO P) 2
Soham 'keeper Ben Webster makes a brave save from Wivenhoe's Sean Caton in the First Qualifying Road.
Photo: Alan Coomes.

Right:
Cogenhoe United (UCO P)
Maldon Town (ECO P)
Action from their Preliminary Round tie.
Photo: Steve Ayre.

THIRD QUALIFYING ROUND

Saturday 11th October — Winning clubs received: £5,000

Home		Away	Score	Att
Ashington	v	Grantham Town	1-3	659
Atkinson		Collins, Gould, Wilkin		
Ashton United	v	Barrow	2-1	429
Garvey, Fleury		Rankine		
Basingstoke Town	v	Bracknell Town	0-0	429
Blyth Spartans	v	Halesowen Town	2-1	667
Laws, Atkinson		Ashby		
Bradford (Park Avenue)	v	Vauxhall Motors	1-1	321
Stansfield		Fearns		
Braintree Town	v	Eastbourne Borough	0-4	351
		Pearce, Smart, Ramsay, Goodwin		
Bromley	v	Thurrock	1-1	461
Huggins		Linger		
Buxton	v	Radcliffe Borough	2-1	1416
Cheetham (2)		Banim		
Cambridge City	v	Lowestoft Town	3-0	357
Bloomfield (3)				
Canvey Island	v	Dover Athletic	4-3	528
Minton (3), Boylan		Carruthers, Wilkins (2)		
Chorley	v	Lancaster City	1-1	616
Hallows		Kilbane		
Congleton Town	v	Bromsgrove Rovers	0-2	544
		Jackson, Benbow		
Crawley Town	v	Croydon Athletic	6-1	897
Pullan, Hemsley, Armstrong (2) Brake (2)		Evans		
Droylsden	v	Gainsborough Trinity	0-2	345
		Grant (2)		
East Thurrock United	v	AFC Sudbury	1-1	600
Cobb		Head		
Eastwood Town	v	Stocksbridge Park Steels	1-1	273
Nazha		Knox		
Farsley Celtic	v	Worksop Town	3-0	374
Austin, Smithard, Copley				
Folkestone Invicta	v	Welling United	1-1	734
Chandler		Powell		
Ford United	v	Worthing	3-2	167
Abraham, Wood (2)		Dicker, Geddes		
Gedling Town	v	Stalybridge Celtic	0-1	165
		Mayers		
Gloucester City	v	Chippenham Town	4-3	611
Cox (2), Smith, Hoskins		Walker (3)		
Grays Athletic	v	Hendon	3-0	406
Eastwood (3)				
Havant & Waterlooville	v	Salisbury City	3-4	494
Taylor (2), Town		Turk (2), Thomas, Crook		
Hayes	v	Boreham Wood	1-1	350
Warner		Palmer		
Histon	v	Newmarket Town	0-0	402
Hornchurch	v	Carshalton Athletic	5-0	611
Douglas, A Martin (2), J Martin, Locke				
Kettering Town	v	St Margaretsbury	2-0	790
Norman (2)				
Leyton	v	Bedford Town	3-0	275
Narty, Bajada, Paul				
Lymington & New Milton	v	Highworth Town	2-0	200
James, Thompson				
Maidstone United	v	Bishop's Stortford	1-1	561
Edwards		Bunn		
Marine	v	Dunston Federation Brewery	1-2	329
Keegan		Farney, Southern		
Newcastle Town	v	Ossett Albion	1-1	184
Bott		Marsh		
Newport County	v	Mangotsfield United	3-6	667
Lloyd, Plant, Eckhardt		Seal (4), Edwards (2)		
Newport IW	v	Harrow Borough	2-2	415
Keeping, Chudd		Norman, Valenti		
Nuneaton Borough	v	Runcorn FC Halton	1-1	1201
Quailey		Leadbetter		
Oxford City	v	Cirencester Town	0-3	181
		Robinson, Bevan, Hopkins		
Paulton Rovers	v	Hampton & Richmond Boro'	2-1	300
Catley, Perry		Jeffery		
Shirebrook Town	v	Shildon	1-3	662
Cantrell		Barnes, Ellison, Bayles		
Thame United	v	Bath City	3-0	342
Mitchell, Keane (2)				
Wakefield & Emley	v	Hinckley United	0-2	248
		Jenkins, Smith		
Warrington Town	v	Whitby Town	0-0	253
Weston Super Mare	v	Chesham United	1-1	303
French		Miles		

REPLAYS

14th October

Home		Away	Score	Att
AFC Sudbury	v	East Thurrock United	*1-1	602
Bennett		Cobb		
(East Thurrock United won 4-2 on penalties)				
Bishop's Stortford	v	Maidstone United	3-2	568
Renner, Southam (2)		Sinden, Davis		
Boreham Wood	v	Hayes	3-1	268
Baker, Winston, James		Goodall		
Bracknell Town	v	Basingstoke Town	*1-0	375
Critterden				
Chesham United	v	Weston Super Mare	1-2	216
Skinner		McKeevor, Sorbara		
Harrow Borough	v	Newport IW	2-0	181
Goddard, Ocquaye				
Lancaster City	v	Chorley	1-0	452
Hughes				
Newmarket Town	v	Histon	0-1	978
		Kennedy		
Runcorn FC Halton	v	Nuneaton Borough	*2-2	347
Leadbetter, Daly		Moore, Murphy		
(Runcorn FC Halton won 5-4 on penalties)				
Stocksbridge Park S.	v	Eastwood Town	3-2	253
Johnson, Hindley, Knox		Fisher, Nazha		
Thurrock	v	Bromley	3-0	231
Kandol, Linger, Bowes				
Vauxhall Motors	v	Bradford (Park Avenue)	1-3	278
Lawton		Maxwell, Smith, Oleksewycz		
Welling United	v	Folkestone Invicta	*2-2	602
Powell, Booth		Tait, Munday		
(Welling won 5-3 on penalties)				

15th October

Home		Away	Score	Att
Ossett Albion	v	Newcastle Town	*4-4	334
Toronczak (2),Norbury,Marsh		Bates, Kiely, Weaver, Bott		
(Ossett Albion won 3-0 on penalties)				
Whitby Town	v	Warrington Town	2-1	384
Veart, Williams		Mitchell		

Farsley Celtic (NPL 1) 1 - Sheffield (NCE P) 1
Farsley's Anjad Iqbal tries to shield the ball from the on coming challenge by a Sheffield player in this First Qualifying Round match. Photo: Darren C Thomas.

Havant & Waterlooville (Southern P) 3 - Salisbury City (Southern E) 4
Wayne Turk heads just wide during this Salisbury attack, whilst Havant & Waterlooville's James Taylor keeps his eye on the ball under pressure from the visitors Andy Cook.
Photos: Andrew Chitty.

FOURTH QUALIFYING ROUND

Saturday 25th October — **Winning clubs received: £10,000**

Home		Away	Score	Att.
Accrington Stanley	v	Leigh RMI	2-0	1361
James, Mullin				
Ashton United	v	Grantham Town	1-2	413
White		Wilkins (2)		
Bishop's Stortford	v	Gloucester City	2-0	768
Renner, Barnett				
Blyth Spartans	v	Chester City	0-1	1105
		Clare		
Boreham Wood	v	Kettering Town	1-0	501
Harvey				
Bracknell Town	v	Barnet	0-3	1069
		Hatch (2), Gamble		
Bromsgrove Rovers	v	Whitby Town	2-2	814
Dyson, Atkinson		Ormerod, Browne		
Burton Albion	v	Buxton	6-0	1980
Anderson (3), Webster (2), Talbot				
Cambridge City	v	Ford United	2-3	412
Itonga, Niven		C Perkins, Poole, Abraham		
Cirencester Town	v	Crawley Town	2-4	715
Hopkins, Richardson		Gregory, Vansittart (2), Harkin		
Dunston Federation B.	v	Lancaster City	0-1	310
		Jones		
East Thurrock United	v	Woking	1-1	1215
Martin		Haule		
Eastbourne Borough	v	Stevenage Borough	2-2	1305
Ramsay		Maamria, Elding		
Exeter City	v	Gravesend & Northfleet	0-0	2686
Farsley Celtic	v	Gainsborough Trinity	1-1	774
Iqbal		Ellington		
Forest Green Rovers	v	Aldershot Town	1-3	1137
Cowe		Sills, Warburton, McLean		
Grays Athletic	v	Margate	3-3	665
Griffths, Eastwood		Clarke, Saunders, Watson		
Harrow Borough	v	Hereford United	1-6	655
Yoki		Guinan (3), Brown, Smith, Cary-Bertram		
Hornchurch	v	Paulton Rovers	1-0	1-0
West				
Leyton	v	Histon	1-2	288
Fannon		Rowe (2)		
Morecambe	v	Shrewsbury Town	2-4	1651
Sugden, Collins		Aiston, Quinn, Lowe (2)		
Ossett Albion	v	Stalybridge Celtic	0-1	621
		Mayers		
Runcorn FC Halton	v	Bradford (Park Avenue)	0-1	379
		Hayward		
Salisbury City	v	Lymington & New Milton	5-1	1190
Thomas, Wallace (2), Cook Sawyer		Reacord		
Scarborough	v	Hinckley United	3-1	1207
Lyth, Kerr (2)		Lenton		
Shildon	v	Stocksbridge Park Steels	6-0	1046
Hainsworth, Barnes (3), Ellison (2)				
Telford United	v	Tamworth	3-3	1431
Murphy (2), Blackwood		Jordan (2), Fisher		
Thame United	v	Farnborough Town	1-2	909
Keane		Clarke, Hayes		
Thurrock	v	Dagenham & Redbridge	2-1	957
Akurang, Kandol		Shipp		
Welling United	v	Weston Super Mare	2-3	678
Booth (2)		Clark, McGregor (2)		

SUNDAY 26th October

Home		Away	Score	Att.
Mangotsfield United	v	Canvey Island	1-2	1083
Pitcher		Gregory, Boylan		
Northwich Victoria	v	Halifax Town	1-0	1101
Thompson				

R E P L A Y S

28th October

Home		Away	Score	Att.
Gainsborough Trinity	v	Farsley Celtic	3-0	845
Smith, Grant, Ellington				
Gravesend & Northfleet	v	Exeter City	*3-3	1227
Moore, Abbey, Haworth		Lee, Devine (2)		
(Gravesend & Northfleet won 6-5 on penalties)				
Margate	v	Grays Athletic	*3-3	411
Saunders, Patmore, Porter		Thurgood (2), Eastwood		
(Grays Athletic won 3-1 on penalties)				
Stevenage Borough	v	Eastbourne Borough	1-0	1205
Watson				
Tamworth	v	Telford United	*2-3	1221
Fisher, Setchell		Mills, Moore, Green		
Woking	v	East Thurrock United	2-0	1781
Ferguson (2)				

29th October

Home		Away	Score	Att.
Whitby Town	v	Bromsgrove Rovers	2-1	784
Linighan, Ormerod		Pope		

Left: Farsley Celtic (NPL 1) 1 - Gainsborough Trinity (NPL P) 1
Lee Ellington watches his header evade the diving Farsley 'keeper. Photo: Bill Wheatcroft.

Top: Thurrock (Isth. P) 2 - Dagenham & Redbridge (Conf.) 1
Dagenham's Leon Braithwaite meets the ball first but sees his effort go wide. Photo: alan Coomes.

Above: Forest Green Rovers (Conf) 1 - Aldershot (Conf) 3
Forest's Denny Ingram heads at goal. Photo: Peter Barnes.

Right: Bromsgrove Rovers (Sth W) 2 - Whitby Town (NPL P) 2
Gary Brown puts Whitby Town ahead. Photo: Neil Thaler.

FIRST ROUND PROPER

Saturday 8th November — Winning clubs received: £12,500

Barnet (1) 2 — Stalybridge Celtic (1) 2

Gamble 4, Beadle 30 — Keeling 45, Eastwood 77 (P)

Att: 1,736

Barnet: Gore, Hendon, Plummer, Maddix, King, Rooney (Williams 81), Lopez (Roach 90), Gamble, Yakubu, Grazioli, Beadle (Hatch 76). Subs: Taggart, Millard.
Stalybridge: Dootson, German, Bowker, Pearce, Heald, Keeling, Kielty, Wharton, Foster, Eastwood, Mayers. Subs: Scott, Clegg, Smith, Senior.

Blackpool (2) 4 — Boreham Wood (0) 0

Taylor 12, 89, Cold 14, Burns 90 — Att: 3,969

Boreham Wood: Imber, Reeks (Duah 67), Harvey, Moran, Braithwaite, Palmer, Hakki (Williams 79), Browne, Grime (James 67), Winston, Baker. Subs: Andrews, Okolie.

Bradford Park Avenue (2) 2 — Bristol City (2) 5

Hayward 5, Coles 13 (og) — Amankwaah 6,8, Stansfield 55(og) Wilkshire 67, Matthews 83

Att: 1,945

Bradford P.A: Boswell, Serrant, Collins (Smith 81), Stansfield, Mitchell, Oleksewycz (Wright 81), Benn, Hayward, Maxwell (Walsh 86), Wood, Crosslwy. Subs: Quinn, Tracey. Tie played on 09/11/03

Brentford (1) 7 — Gainsborough Trin. (0) 1

Harrold 45,65,86, Ruogier 47 Purkiss 50(og), Frampton 55, O'Connor 76 — Smith 81 — Att: 3,041

Gainsborough: Norton, Purkiss, Timons, Reddington, Birley, Eshelby, Hurst (Adams 71), Staton, Smith, Ellington, Grant. Subs: Allison, Holmshaw, Kotylo, Byrne.

Chester City (0) 0 — Gravesend & N'flt (1) 1

Skinner 39 (P) — Att: 2,251

Chester: McCaldon, Collins, Bolland, Ruffer, McIntyre, Carden, Davies, Heard (Brady 71), Clare (Rapley 80), Stamp, Foster (Twiss 65). Subs: Guyett, Carey.
Gravesend: Wilkerson, Perkins, Duku, Moore, Lee, Owen, McKimm, Skinner, Walshe (Drury 40), Haworth, Peacock. Subs: O'Reilly, Abbey, Strouts, Gradley.

Farnborough Town (0) 0 — Weston-Super-Mare (1) 1

Clark 5 — Att: 936

Farnborough: Osborn, Weatherstone, Hutchings (Manuella 74), Charles[so], Burton, Opinel, Hodgson, Beall, Hayes, Charlery (Chaaban 83), Harkness (Clarke 67). Subs: Packham, Thompson.
Weston: Jones, Rose, McKeever (Howell 74), Jarman, Clark, Benton, Slater (Davis 61), Jackson, Skinner, McGregor, French. Subs: Thomas, Mehew, Ganfield.

Grantham Town (1) 1 — Leyton Orient (1) 2

K Wilkin 4 — Purser 17, Alexander 90

Att: 2,792

Grantham: Ziccardi[so], Wooding, Dakin, Gould, Fox, Wilson, Minett, P Wilkin, Kearns, K Wilkin, Collins.
Subs: Clarke, Wenlock, Hallows, Speed Slinn.

Grays Athletic (0) 1 — Aldershot Town (0) 2

Griffths 55 — D'Sane 73(P), 78 — Att: 1,500

Grays: Capleton, Williams (Bradshaw 80), Robinson, Olayinka[so], Youds, Bruce, Marwa (Lunan 88), Carthy, Martin, Lock (Hayzelden 45), Griffths. Subs: Stimson, Barrett
Aldershot: Barnard, Warburton, Rees, Sterling, Hooper, Shields, Miller, Chewins (Charles 71), McLean (Challinor 71), D'Sane, Sills. Subs: Nutter, Bull, Harper.

Hartlepool United (2) 4 — Whitby Town (0) 0

Gabbiadini 25,30, Humphreys 51, Brackstone 68 — Att: 5,294

Whitby: Clementson, Reed (Swales 86), Linighan, Hall, Obern (Ure 57), Williams, Robinson, Veart, Dixon, Browne, Ormerod (McTiernan 90). Subs: Nicholson, Campbell.

Hornchurch (1) 2 — Darlington (0) 0

West 43 (p), Johns 61 — Att: 2,186

Hornchurch: Gay, Gooding, West, Adedeji, Kerrigan, Keeling, Locke, Sterling (Rowland 76), Graham, Opara, Johns (Allen 86).
Subs: Douglas, Southon, Collier.

Played on 09/11/03

Second half action from Hornchurch's giant-killing act against Darlington. Photo: Eric Marsh.

Kidderminster H. (1) 2 — Northwich Victoria (0) 1

Bennett 39, 84 — Thompson 87 — Att: 2,052

Northwich: Woods, Woodyatt, Brazier, Foran, Charnock, Black (Thompson 73), Norris, Murray, Devlin (Owen 88), Garvey, Allan.
Subs: Connett, Barnard, Walsh.

Lancaster City (1) 1 — Cambridge United (1) 2

Hughes 35 (P) — Kitson 16, Guttridge 90

Att: 1,864

Lancaster: Welsby, Kilbane, Sparrow, Scott, Uberschar, Clarkson, Mercer, Prince, Elderton, Hughes, Jones.
Subs: Bauress, Thornley, Robertson, Sullivan, Yates.

Mansfield Town (4) 6 — Bishop's Stortford (0) 0

MacKenzie 12,43,51, Mendes 15, Larkin 42, Curtis 78 — Att: 4,679

Bishop's S.: Desborough, Allman, Wiltshire (Lewsi 85), Barnett, Gwilliam[so], Southam, Rainford, MCKeown (Parker 61), Beale, Essandod, Renner (Bunn 72). Subs: Hayes, Addai.

Notts County (3) 7 — Shildon (0) 2

Fenton 7, Platt 14,18, Nicholson 64, Richardson 69, Barras 84, Hefferman 88 — Middleton 55, Barnes 63 (p)

Att: 4,016

Shildon: Jackson, Hainsworth (Owers 70), Middleton, Liddle, Watson (Reid 56), Bolton (Richmond 45), Key, Bayles, Emmerson, Ellison, Barnes.
Subs: Tobin, Chapman. Played on 09/11/03

Peterborough United (0) 2 — Hereford United (0) 0

Willock 53, Logan 58 — Att: 4,479

Hereford: Baker, Green, James, Mkandawire, Rose, Pitman, Williams, Smith (Purdey 90), Perry, Guinan, Brown (Teeside 68).
Subs: Scott, Carey-Bertram, Craven.

FIRST ROUND PROPER

Date of the Round — Winning club to recieve: £12,500

Port Vale (0) 2 — Ford United (1) 2

McPhee 60, Burns 64 — Abraham 20, Fiddes 74 — Att: 4,016

Ford: Lunan, McLeod, Chandler, C Perkins, O'Sullivan, Cooper, Fiddes, Edwards, Poole, Abraham, Watson (Reinelt 84).
Subs: Creedon, Fenton, D Perkins.

Scarborough (0) 1 — Doncaster Rovers (0) 0

Rose 79 — Att: 3,497

Scarborough: Walker, Baker (Lyth 68), Redmile, Cryan, Capper, Sestanovich, Kelly, Kerr, Marcelle, Quayle, Rose.
Subs: Sollitt, Senior, Henry, Gill.

Scunthorpe United (1) 2 — Shrewsbury Town (0) 1

Hayes 9, 90 — Quinn 87 — Att: 3,232

Shrewsbury: Howie, Moss, Tinson, Ridler (Cramb 76), Rioch, Street (Lowe 73), Tolley, O'Connor, Aiston, Rodgers, Quinn.
Subs: Dunbavin, Sedgemore, Stevens.

Sheffield Wednesday (1) 4 — Salisbury City (0) 0

Proudlock 32(p),47,64, Owusu 70 — Att: 11,419

Salisbury: Sawyer, Bartlett (Holmes 85), Cooper (Purches 80), Thomas, Cook, Funnell, Turk, Davies, James, Wallace, Strong (Cook 62).
Subs: Turner, Phillips.

Played on 09/11/03

Southend United (1) 1 — Canvey Island (1) 1

Gower 2 — Chenery 7 — Att: 9,234

Canvey: Potter, Midgley, chenery, Ward, Theobald, Duffy, Kennedy, Gooden (Dobinson 76), Minton, Gregory, Boylan (McDougald 87).
Subs: Berquez, Cowan, Harrison.

Played on 09/11/03

Stevenage Borough (2) 2 — Stockport County (0) 1

Maamria 29, 37 — Goodwin 69 (P) — Att: 2,538

Stevenage: Perez, Travis (Brennan 87), Bunce, Laker, Flynn, Wormull (Holloway 71), Gould, Warner, Watson, Maamria, Elding (Baptiste 73).
Subs: Shamlian, Battersby.

Grantham defend the incoming corner which unfortunately only finds Leyton Orient's Wayne Purser, who hits the league club's equalizer.
Photo: Gordon Whittingham.

Telford United (0) 3 — Crawley Town (2) 2

Lavery 58, Ricketts 72, Murphy 90 — Armstrong 8, Gregory 28 Att:1,581

Telford: MacKenzie, Clarke, Green, Whitehead, Challis, Simpson (Grant 85), Ricketts, Blackwood (Lavery 45), Murphy, Mills, Naylor (Moore 45).
Subs: Howarth, Taylor.
Crawley: Anderson, Judge, Hemsley, Pullan, Payne (Ready 64), Harkin, Smith, Armstrong, Gregory, Dennis (MacDonald 60), Vansittart (Forde 81).
Subs: Fear, Richardson.

Thurrock (0) 1 — Luton Town (1) 1

Bowes 80 — Boyce 39 — Att: 1,551

Thurrock: Gothard, Collis, Purdie, McFarlane, Goodfellow, Akurang (Allen 84), D.Lee, Heffer, Bowes, K.Lee (Linger 69), Kandol.
Subs: Basham, O'Brian, Howard.

Played on 07/11/03

Torquay United (0) 1 — Burton Albion (1) 2

Benefield 55 — Wood 10 (og), Talbot 71 — Att: 2,790

Burton: Duke, Willis, Chettle (Crosby 59), Kirkwood, Webster, Colkin (Talbot 25), Howard, Clough, Stride, Ducros, Anderson.
Subs: Williams, Robinson, Sinton.

Woking (3) 3 — Histon (1) 1

Selley 23,39 (P), Sharpling 45 — A Cambridge 2 — Att: 2,217

Woking: Bayes, Townsend (Canham 80), Boardman, Sharp, MacDonald, Sharpling, Smith, Selley, Nade, Haule, Foyewa.
Subs: Northmore, Clark, Cockerill, Ajoge.
Histon: Barber, Farrington, Hipperson, Vowden, Goddard, A Cambridge, Hanvier (Kennedy 65), Andrews, Barker, Rowe (Coburn 80), I Cambridge.
Subs: Munns, Holden.

R E P L A Y S

Luton Town (1) 3 — Thurrock (0) 1

Forbes 39, 76, 87 (p) — Akurang 49 — Att:3,667

Thurrock: Gothard, Collis, Purdie, McFarlane,Goodfellow, Linger, Heffer, Howard (K.Lee 81), Bowes, Kandol, Akurang.
Subs: Basham, Lawrence, Allen, Broom.

Played on 18/11/03

Stalybridge Celtic (0) 0 — Barnet (1) 2

Grazioli 27, 84 — Att: 1,549

Stalybridge: Dootson, Pearce (Foster 79), German, Bowker, Bowman (Smith 78 - SO 90), Clegg, Keeling, A.Heald, Eastwood, Mayers (SO 90), Potts. Subs: Kielty, Scott, Senior.
Barnet: gore, Rooney, Hendon, Plummer, Maddix (SO 89), King, Gamble, Hogg (Lopez 80), Yakubu, Grazioli, Strevens.
Subs: Taggart, Millard, Roach. Played on 18/11/03

Canvey Island (2) 2 — Southend (1) 3

Boylan 10, Minton 45 — Bramble 23, Smith 46, 90 — Att: 2,731

Canvey: Potter, Chenery, Ward, Theobald, Midgley, Kennedy, Minton, Gooden (Dobinson 74), Duffy, N.Gregory, Boylan.
Subs: Berquez, cowan, McDougald, Harrison.

Played on 19/11/03

Ford United (0) 1 — Port Vale (1) 2

Poole 90 — Paynter 38, Chandler 114 (og) — Att: 1,374

Ford: Lunan, Halle, Chandler, C.Perkins, O'Sullivan (Reinelt 90 - Patten 112), fiddes, C.Edwards, Poole, Cooper, R.Watson (Fenton 70), Abraham.
Subs: Sobers, B.Wood.

Played on 19/11/03

Notts County (League Division 2) 7 - Shildon (NPL 1) 2
Shildon put pressure on the Notts County defence, however, County 'keeper Steve Mildenhall is able to clear this corner. Photo: Bill Wheatcroft.

Brentford (League Division 2) 7
Gainsborough Trinity (NPL P) 1
Gainsborough's Paul Eshelby closes down Brentford's Matt Somner.
Photo: Alan Coomes.

Woking (Conference) 3
Histon (Southern East) 1
A Histon player looks to wrong foot the Woking defender in this attack.
Photo: Eric Marsh.

Blackpool (League Division 2) 4
Boreham Wood (Isth 1N) 0
Boreham Wood's Sammy Winston shields the ball from a Blackpool defender.
Photo: Bill Wheatcroft.

Peterborough United (League Division 2) 2
Hereford United (Conference) 0
Hereford on the attack in the second half at London Road.
Photo: Peter Barnes.

SECOND ROUND PROPER

Saturday 6th December — Winning clubs received: £15,000

Bournemouth (0) 1 — Accrington Stanley (1) 1
Browning 56 — Mullin 9 — Att: 7,551

Accrington: Speare, Cavanagh, Halford, Smith (Howarth 7), Williams, James, Procter, Gouck (Armstrong 58), Cook (Flitcroft 79), Prendergast, Mullin.
Subs: Kennedy, Durin

Colchester United (0) 1 — Aldershot Town (0) 0
Vine 83 — Att: 4,255

Aldershot: Bull, challinor, Rees, Warburton (Taylor 86), Sterling, Charles, Miller, Shields, Chewins, D'Sane, Sills.
Subs: Barnard, Harper, Nutter, Lucas.

Gravesend & N'flt (1) 1 — Notts County (0) 2
Perkins 42 — Fenton 69, Platt 90 — Att: 2,998

Gravesend: Wilkerson (O'Reilly 66), Lee, Shearer, Moore, Gibbs (SO 72), Strouts, McKimm, Perkins, Walshe (Gradley 89), Drury, Pinnock (Abbey 76).
Subs: Haworth, Duku.

Hornchurch (0) 0 — Tranmere Rovers (1) 1
Jones 26 — Att: 3,500

Hornchurch: Gay, Gooding, Kerrigan (Allen 57), Adedeji, West, Locke (Opara 57), Keeling, John, Martin, Johns, McGowan, Graham.
Subs: Southon, Rowland, Collier.

Northampton Town (1) 4 — Weston-Super-Mare (0) 1
Smith 36 (p), Low 64, Richards 77,90 — Clark 80 — Att: 3,948

Weston: Jones, Jackson (Sorbara 60), Jarman, Benton (Howell 74), Clark, McKeever (SO 36), Rose, Skinner (Davis 60), Slater, McGregor, French.
Subs: Hodge Ganfield.

Swansea City (1) 2 — Stevenage Borough (0) 1
Nugent 23, Trundle 51 — Elding 49 — Att: 6,125

Stevenage: Perez, Bunce (Carroll 84), Laker, Warner, Watson, Wormull, Costello (Baptiste 61), Gould, Holloway (Cook 73), Maamria, Elding.
Subs: Benstead, Richards.

Telford United (1) 3 — Brentford (0) 0
C. Moore 26, 58, 80 (p) — Att: 2,996

Telford: MacKenzie, Wilkinson, Whitehead, Challis, Clarke, Hulbert, Simpson (Murphy 85), Blackwood, Ricketts, Mills (Grant 85), C.Moore (Naylor 89).
Subs: Williams, Lavery.

Woking (0) 0 — Kidderminster H. (1) 3
Bennett 6, 64, Burton 74 — Att: 3,484

Woking: Bevan, Townsend (Cockerill 70, Boardman (Smith 14), Sharp, MacDonald, Nade, Canham, Selley, Ferguson (Haule 70), Sharpling, Foyewa.
Subs: Bayes, Campbell.

Yeovil Town (3) 5 — Barnet (1) 1
Pluck 9, Williams 18 (p), 27, Crittenden, Edwards 78 — Beadle — Att: 5,973

Barnet: Gore, Hendon, Plummer, Maddix (rooney 78), King, Stevens, Lopez, Gamble (Hatch 45), Yakubu, Grazioli, Beedle (Williams 53).
Subs: Millard, Hogg.

Burton Albion (0) 0 — Hartlepool United (0) 1
Porter 70 — Att: 2,186

Burton: Duke, Henshaw, Chettle, Wassell, Webster, Stride, Dudley, Kirkwood, Howard, Colkin (Talbot 76), Anderson (Ducros 89).
Subs: Williams, Robinson, Clough
Played on 07/11/03

Port Vale (0) 0 — Scarborough (0) 1
Sestanovich 80 — Att: 4,651

Scarborough: Walker, Lyth, Redmile, Cryan, Hotts, Sestanovich, Gill, Kelly, Kerr, Marcelle, Quayle (Rose 82).
Subs: Senior, Williams, G.Downey, Price.

R E P L A Y

Accrington Stanley (0) 0 — Bournemouth (0) 0
Accrington won 5-3 on penalties, AET — Att: 2,585

Accrington: Speare (Kennedy 119), Howarth, Halford, Williams, Cavanagh, James, Proctor, Gouck (Flitcroft 69), Cook, Prendergast, Mullin (Armstrong 119).
Subs: Madden, Durnin. Played on 15/12/03

Burton's John Howard shows good skill under pressure. Photo: Peter Barnes.

A Weston player holds off the challenge from a Northampton midfielder. Photo: Peter Barnes.

Port Vale concede a corner under pressure from Scarborough's Wayne Gill. Photo: Bill Wheatcroft.

Burton press late in the game against Hartlepool. Photo: Peter Barnes.

THIRD ROUND PROPER

Saturday 3rd January | Winning clubs received: £50,000

Accrington Stanley	(0) 0	Colchester United	(0) 0
			Att: 4,368

Accrington: Speare, Howarth, Halford (Armstrong 83), Williams, Hollis, James, Proctor (Calcutt 55), Gouck (Flitcroft 37), Cook, Prendergast, Mullin.
Subs: Kennedy, Durnin.

Crewe Alexandra	(0) 0	Telford United	(0) 1
		Mills 2	Att: 7,085

Telford: MacKenzie, Challis, Howarth, Whitehead, Clarke, Hulbert, Simpson, Ricketts, Murphy (Grant 82), Mills, C.Moore (Naylor 69).
Subs: Blackwood, Lavery, Williams.

Southend United	(1) 1	Scarborough	(0) 1
Smith 9		Kerr 74	Att: 6,902

Scarborough: Walker, Lyth, Cryan, Baker, Hotte, Sestanovich, Kerr, Kelly, Gill (Whitman 70), Marcelle (Williams 82), Quayle.
Subs: Senior, capper, G.Downey.

R E P L A Y S

Colchester United	(1) 2	Accrington Stanley	(0) 1
Keith 11, 84		Mullin 89	Att: 5,611

Accrington: Kennedy, Cavanagh, Howarth (Smith 82), Halford (SO 86), Williams, Prendergast, James, cook, Flitcroft (Calcutt 69), Procter, Mullin.
Subs: Speare, Durnin, Hollis.

Played on 13/01/04

Scarborough	(0) 1	Southend United	(0) 0
Quayle 83			Att: 4,859

Scarborough: Walker, Lyth, Cryan, Baker, Hotte, Sestanovich, Kerr, Kelly, , Marcelle, Whitman, Quayle.
Subs: Capper, Williams, Downey, Senior, Sollitt.

Played on 14/01/04

Top: Telford's Sam Ricketts is put under pressure by Crewe's Ben Rix.
Right: Chris Murphy makes it difficult for Kenny Lunt of Crewe.
Below: Telford's Lee Mills (arm raised but partly hidden) turns to celebrate giving United the lead.

Photos: Bill Wheatcroft.

FOURTH ROUND PROPER

Saturday 24th January — Winning clubs received: £75,000

Scarborough (0) 0 Chelsea (1) 1

Terry 10 — Att: 5,941

Scarborough	Chelsea
Walker	Cudicini
Lyth	Melchiot
Cryan	Gallas
Hotte	Terry
Baker (Capper 13)	Bridge
Sestanovich	J.Cole
Kerr	Lampard
Kelly	Nicolas (Oliveira 67)
Marcelle	Gronkjaer (Petit 67)
Quayle	Gudjohnson
Whitman (Senior 72)	Hasselbaink
Subs:	**Subs:**
Williams	Sullivan
Downey	Johnson
Sollitt	Huth.

Telford United (0) 0 Millwall (1) 2

Ifill 37, Wise 83 — Att: 5,589

Telford	Millwall
MacKenzie	Gueret
Howarth	Muscat
Whitehead	Lawrence
Challis	Ward
Ricketts	Livermore
Hulbert	Ifill
Simpson	Wise
Blackwood (Clarke 64)	Cahill
Murphy	Ryan
C.Moore (Rowe 64)	Harris (Braniff 73)
Naylor (Grant 76)	Dichio
Subs	**Subs**
Williams	Elliott
Lavery	Sweeney
	McCammon
	Roberts

Played on 11/02/04

ROUND BY ROUND STATISTICS
(NON-LEAGUE CLUB ROUNDS ONLY)

Round	Games	Home Win	Away Win	Draws	Home Goals	Away Goals	Hatricks	Att. Total	Att. Ave
Extra Preliminary	65+6	33	32	6	121	112	4	6,643	94
Best Home Win:	Thatcham Town v Selsey 6-0.								
Best Away Wins:	Saltdean United v Cray Wanderers & Devizes Town v Christchurch 0-4.								
Best Attendance:	Great Yarmouth Town v Southall Town - 291.								
Preliminary	191*+33	95	96	33	418	379	23	31,891	142
Best Home Win:	Bishop Auckland v Flixton 8-0.								
Best Away Wins:	Stansted v Uxbridge 0-7. Egham Town v Thame United 1-8.								
Best Attendance:	Ashford Town v Eastbourne United - 363.								
1st Qualifying	99+19	56	43	19	214	187	9	25,082	213
Best Home Win:	Witton Albion v Holker Old Boys 7-0.								
Best Away Win:	Berkhamstead Town v AFC Sudbury 0-9.								
Best Attendance:	Kings Lynn v Stewarts & Lloyds - 871.								
2nd Qualifying	84+16	51	33	16	191	131	4	38,810	388
Best Home Wins:	Gainsborough Trinity v Skelmersdale United 6-0. Lymington & New Milton v Clevedon United 8-2.								
Best Away Wins:	Hythe Town v Maidstone United, Harlow Town v Crawley Town & Bognore Regis Town v Havant & Waterlooville 0-4.								
Best Attendance:	Nuneaton Borough v Worcester City - 1,352.								
3rd Qualifying	42+15	27	15	15	100	79	4	26,359	462
Best Home Wins:	Hornchurch v Carshalton Athletic 5-0. Crawley Town v Croydon Athletic 6-1.								
Best Away Win:	Braintree Town v Eastbourne Borough 0-4.								
Best Attendance:	Buxon v Radcliffe Borough - 1,416.								
4th Qualifying	32+7	15	17	7	71	63	3	38,963	999
Best Home Wins:	Burton Albion v Buxton & Shildon v Stocksbridge Park Steels 6-0.								
Best Away Win:	Harrow Borough v Hereford United 1-6.								
Best Attendance:	Exeter City v Gravesend & Northfleet - 2,686.								

*Not including walkovers.

F.A. CUP PRIZE MONEY

	EP	P	1Q	2Q	3Q	4Q	1P	2P	3P	TOTAL
Scarborough						10000	12500	15000	50000	87500
Telford United						10000	12500	15000	50000	87500
Accrington Stanley						10000	12500	15000		37500
Weston-Super-Mare				3750	5000	10000	12500			31250
Hornchurch				3750	5000	10000	12500			31250
Woking						10000	12500			22500
Stevenage Borough						10000	12500			22500
Gravesend & Northfleet						10000	12500			22500
Burton Albion						10000	12500			22500
Barnet						10000	12500			22500
Aldershot						10000	12500			22500
Boreham Wood		1000	2250	3750	5000	10000				22000
Histon		1000	2250	3750	5000	10000				22000
Salisbury City		1000	2250	3750	5000	10000				22000
Shildon		1000	2250	3750	5000	10000				22000
Bishop's Stortford				3750	5000	10000				18750
Bradford Park Avenue				3750	5000	10000				18750
Canvey Island				3750	5000	10000				18750
Crawley Town				3750	5000	10000				18750
Ford United				3750	5000	10000				18750
Gainsborough Trinity				3750	5000	10000				18750
Grantham Town				3750	5000	10000				18750
Grays Athletic				3750	5000	10000				18750
Lancaster				3750	5000	10000				18750
Stalybridge Celtic				3750	5000	10000				18750
Thurrock				3750	5000	10000				18750
Whitby Town				3750	5000	10000				18750
Dunston Federation Brewery	500	1000	2250	3750	5000					12500
Lymington & New Milton	500	1000	2250	3750	5000					12500
Ossett Albion	500	1000	2250	3750	5000					12500
Paulton Rovers	500	1000	2250	3750	5000					12500
Bracknell Town		1000	2250	3750	5000					12000
Bromsgrove Rovers		1000	2250	3750	5000					12000
Buxton		1000	2250	3750	5000					12000
Cirencester Town		1000	2250	3750	5000					12000
East Thurrock United		1000	2250	3750	5000					12000
Farsley Celtic		1000	2250	3750	5000					12000
Gloucester City		1000	2250	3750	5000					12000
Leyton		1000	2250	3750	5000					12000
Mangotsfield United		1000	2250	3750	5000					12000
Stocksbridge Park Steels		1000	2250	3750	5000					12000
Thame United		1000	2250	3750	5000					12000
Chester City						10000				10000
Farnborough Town						10000				10000
Hereford United						10000				10000
Northwich Victoria						10000				10000
Shrewsbury Town						10000				10000
Ashton United				3750	5000					8750
Blyth Spartans				3750	5000					8750
Cambridge City				3750	5000					8750
Eastbourne Borough				3750	5000					8750
Harrow Borough				3750	5000					8750
Hinckley United				3750	5000					8750
Kettering Town				3750	5000					8750
Runcorn FC Halton				3750	5000					8750
Welling United				3750	5000					8750
Shirebrook Town	500	1000	2250	3750						7500
Congleton Town		1000	2250	3750						7000
Folkstone Invicta		1000	2250	3750						7000
Worthing		1000	2250	3750						7000

TOP GOAL SCORERS

9 GOALS

G. Barnes	Shildon

8 GOALS

D. Seal	Mangotsfield United
D Toronczak	Ossett Albion

7 GOALS

A. Lawson	Ashington
F Eastwood	Grays Athletic
M Bown	Paulton Rovers

6 GOALS

S. Taylor	Blackpool
G Mitchell	Warrington Town
R. Van Nistelrooy	Manchester United

5 GOALS

G. Bennett	AFC Sudbury
A. Claydon	AFC Sudbury
M. Postins	Bedfont
S. Winston	Boreham Wood
L. Boylan	Canvey Island
N. Brake	Crawley Town
A. Tait	Folkstone Invicta
G. Grant	Gainsborough Trin.
A. Hoskins	Gloucester City
J. Ashby	Halesowen Town
A. Forbes	Luton Town
P. James	Lymington & N. M.
D. Edwards	Mangotsfield United
L. Ellison	Shildon
S. Johnson	Shirebrook Town
R. Howard	St Margaretsbury
P. Knox	Stocksbridge P.S.
L. Trundle	Swansea City
P. Booth	Welling United
S. Francis	Worthing

4 GOALS

V. Rusher	Andover
F. Ljungberg	Arsenal
C. Cheetham	Buxton
J. Minton	Canvey Island
G. Sippetts	Chesham United
J. Bevan	Cirencester Town
R. Vines	Colchester United
R. Bennett	Cray Wanderers
J. Kempster	Cray Wanderers
M. Midwood	Farsley Celtic
M. Smithard	Farsley Celtic
G. Poole	Ford United
L. Elliston	Gainsborough Trin.
J. Cox	Gloucester City
N. Kennedy	Histon
T. Ellis	Hyde United
D. Bennett	Kidderminster H.
L. Newman	Lewes
K. James	Lymington & N. M.
R. Sinden	Maidstone United

4 goals continued....

N. Anelka	Manchester City
P. Scholes	Manchester United
M. Norbury	Ossett Albion
W. Turk	Salisbury City
M. Anderson	Sandhurst Town
S. Rudd	Skelmersdale Utd
I. Hodge	Slough Town
M. Nuttall	Spalding United
S. Daly	St Blazey
S. Johnson	Stocksbridge P. S.
T. Smith	Sunderland
C. Moore	Telford United
R. McLay	Thatcham Town
C. Stevens	Tilbury
E. Barrs-James	Walton Casuals
W. Wheeler	Westbury United
S. Burton	Witton Albion
D. Dicken	Witton Albion
G. Geddes	Worthing

HIGHEST SCORING CLUBS

20 GOALS
Salisbury City
Shildon

19 GOALS
AFC Sudbury
Histon

18 GOALS
Mangotsfield United
Worthing

16 GOALS
Crawley Town
Farsley Celtic
Lymington & New Milton
Ossett Albion

15 GOALS
Canvey Island
East Thurrock United
Stocksbridge Park Steels
Thame United

14 GOALS
Andover
Grays Athletic
Hyde United
Manchester United
Newcastle Town
Newmarket Town

13 GOALS
Boreham Wood
Cray Wanderers
Gloucester City
Kings Lynn
Leyton
Maidstone United
Telford United

12 GOALS
Bromsgrove Rovers
Buckingham Town
Buxton

12 goals continued....
Chorley
Cirencester Town
Croydon Athletic
Gainsborough Trinity
Manchester City
Skelmersdale United
St Margaretsbury
Warrington Town
Weston-Supper-Mare
Wroxham

11 GOALS
Ashington
Bracknell Town
Chesham United
Dunston Federation Brewery
Eastwood Town
Exmouth Town
Folkstone Invicta
Paulton Rovers
Shirebrook Town
Spalding United
Tranmere Rovers
Westbury United
Witton Albion

10 GOALS
Blackpool
Highworth Town
Hornchurch
Mansfield Town
Northampton Town
Oxford City
St Blazey
Swansea City
Thurrock
Welling United

ATTENDANCE COMPARISON
SEASONS 2001-02 - 2003-04

PRELIMINARY & QUALIFYING ROUNDS

Season	Round	Games	Total Attendance	Average Attendance	Ave. +/-
2001-02	Extra Preliminary	15	2,135	142	+ 10
2002-03		54	6,796	126	- 16
2003-04		71	6,643	94	- 32
2001-02	Preliminary	230	28,444	124	- 12
2002-03		235	35,195	150	+ 26
2003-04		224	31,891	142	- 8
2001-02	1st Qualifying	123	20,979	171	+ 9
2002-03		110	20.229	184	+ 13
2003-04		118	25,082	213	+ 29
2001-02	2nd Qualifying	103	40,971	398	+ 44
2002-03		101	39,027	386	- 12
2003-04		100	38,810	388	+ 2
2001-02	3rd Qualifying	50	30,801	616	+ 170
2002-03		46	29,382	639	+ 23
2003-04		57	26,359	462	- 177
2001-02	4th Qualifying	43	55,619	1,293	+ 259
2002-03		40	49,821	1,246	- 47
2003-04		39	38,963	999	- 247
2001-02	Totals	564	178,949	317	+ 43
2002-03		586	180,450	310	- 7
2003-04		609	167,748	275	- 35

COMPETITION PROPER

Season	Round	Games	Total Attendance	Average Attendance	Ave. +/-
2001-02	1st Round	52	198,937	3,825	+ 254
2002-03		50	189,660	3,793	- 32
2003-04		44	162,996	3,704	- 89
2001-02	2nd Round	24	120,358	5,015	+ 268
2002-03		24	104,601	4,358	- 657
2003-04		25	118,200	4,720	+ 362
2001-02	3rd Round	38	564,855	14,865	+ 489
2002-03		39	573,961	14,717	- 148
2003-04		42	625,560	14,894	+ 177
2001-02	4th Round	17	330,365	19,433	- 1527
2002-03		20	403,950	20,198	+ 765
2003-04		19	345,686	18,194	- 2004
2001-02	5th Round	9	244,356	27,151	+4342
2002-03		9	241,427	26,825	- 326
2003-04		11	288,798	26,254	- 571
2001-02	6th Round	5	173,492	34,698	+9533
2002-03		5	153,658	30,732	- 3966
2003-04		5	155,626	31,125	+ 393
2001-02	Semi-Final	2	97,315	48,658	- 3131
2002-03		2	99,772	49,886	+1228
2003-04		2	96,051	48,026	- 1860
2001-02	Final	1	73,963		
2002-03		1	73,726		
2003-04		1	71,350		
2001-02	Totals	148	1,803,641	12,187	+ 295
2002-03		150	1,840,755	12,272	+ 85
2003-04		149	1,864,267	12,512	+ 240
2001-02	**COMPETITION AS**	712	1,982,590	2,785	+ 104
2002-03	**A WHOLE**	736	2,021,205	2,746	- 39
2003-04	**TOTALS**	758	2,032,015	2,681	- 65

THE F.A. TROPHY

2003/04

PRELIMINARY ROUND

Saturday 4th October **Winning clubs recieved: £1,000**

Home		Away	Score	Att
Arlesey Town	v	Fleet Town	3-1	225
Buckland, Gutzmore, Mackail-Smith		Saunders		
Aveley	v	Burgess Hill Town	1-2	77
Okita		Geard, Sullivan		
Bamber Bridge	v	Witton Albion	4-3	170
Halliwell, Honor, Kent, Wane		Moseley (2), Sargeson		
Bashley	v	Marlow	2-2	148
Gillespie, Jackson		Beale, Small		
Bedworth United	v	Rugby United	0-3	227
		Hall, Pearson		
Berkhamsted Town	v	Thame United	0-3	131
		Jones, Mitchell (2)		
Bishop Auckland	v	Farsley Celtic	4-2	134
Irvine, Salvin (3)		Midwood, Stammer		
Bracknell Town	v	Croydon	4-2	107
Crittenden (3), Smith		Dundas (2)		
Bromsgrove Rovers	v	Sutton Coldfield Town	3-1	469
Atkinson, Pope (2)				
Burnham	v	Stamford	1-2	85
Bartley		Byrne (2)		
Chesham United	v	Worthing	0-2	161
		Geddes, Pulling		
Chorley	v	Gresley Rovers	1-2	299
Porter		Doughty, Lenagh		
Cinderford Town	v	Yate Town	1-1	122
Slack		Bennett		
Corinthian Casuals	v	Kings Lynn	0-2	100
		Harris, Staff		
Dulwich Hamlet	v	Cheshunt	2-0	133
Coleman, Green				
Dunstable Town	v	Lewes	1-2	213
Carney		Fontana, Kadi		
Eastleigh	v	Great Wakering Rovers	3-0	184
Bowers, Gibbens, Hughes				
Enfield	v	Epsom & Ewell	7-3	37
Armstrong (2), Clark, Honeyball, Marshal (2), Whittington		Hatton, Huckle (2)		
Fisher Athletic	v	Horsham	1-1	119
Abbott		Carney		
Gateshead	v	Kendal Town	1-0	148
Craggs				
Gloucester City	v	Evesham United	2-0	380
Hoskins, Smith				
Guiseley	v	Kidsgrove Athletic	7-1	237
Chattoe, Henry (2), Stuart (2)		Eyre		
Halesowen Town	v	Stourport Swifts	4-3	421
Ashby, Baker, Hollis, Mitchell		Ball, Wood, Wright		
Hastings United	v	Yeading	3-4	209
Graham, Hafner, Honey		Moundi, Telemaque (2), Tucker		
Hemel Hempstead Town	v	Metropolitan Police	3-2	100
Bent, grieves, Hollindale		Daly (2)		
Ilkeston Town	v	Bridlington Town	1-2	368
Nangle		Palmer, Smith		
Leatherhead	v	Wealdstone	1-3	232
Tavares		Courtnage (2), Williams		
Leyton	v	Molesey	3-3	76
Bajada, Nartey, Wood		Martin, Pickett, Teague		
Lincoln United	v	Workington	0-0	146
Mangotsfield United	v	Atherstone United	w/o for Mangotsfield	
Matlock Town	v	Ossett Town	2-0	245
Brown, Williams				
North Ferriby United	v	Hyde United	3-2	178
Foot (3)		O'Kane		
Oxford City	v	Folkestone Invicta	1-4	185
Ballard		Ayling, Chandler, Hogg, Millar		
Prescot Cables	v	Belper Town	2-1	165
Holmes, Torpy		Allsop		
Rossendale United	v	Colwyn Bay	1-0	157
Salisbury City	v	Clevedon Town	0-1	376
		Hiller		
Shepshed Dynamo	v	Solihull Borough	0-0	134
Staines Town	v	Barking & East Ham United	3-0	138
Ibe (2), McDonald				
Stocksbridge P'k Steels	v	Leek Town	3-1	177
Bonser		Whittaker		
Taunton Town	v	Corby Town	3-1	319
Lynch (3)		Le-Masurier		
Team Bath	v	Banbury United	2-0	175
Holland, Stocco				
Tooting & Mitcham Utd	v	Sittingbourne	1-2	228
Graham		Neal (2)		
Uxbridge	v	Harlow Town	3-3	81
Bamford, Royal, Tunnell		Chapman, Cort, Fanibuyan		
Waltham Forest	v	Boreham Wood	1-2	84
Browne		Palmer, Winston		
Whyteleafe	v	Egham Town	2-1	122
Barclay, Harper		Geary		
Windsor & Eton	v	Chatham Town	2-1	129
O'Connor, Townley		Rutter		
Wingate & Finchley	v	Walton & Hersham	2-1	69
Boateng, Butterfield		Sobihy		
Wivenhoe Town	v	Newport IW	3-1	141
Bethell, Haydon, Taylor		O'Rourke		

REPLAYS

6th October

Home		Away	Score	Att
Solihull Borough	v	Shepshed Dynamo	1-2	123
Cooper		Forsdick, Quincey		

7th October

Home		Away	Score	Att
Horsham	v	Fisher Athletic	1-3	209
		Brady, Farrelly, Hollington		
Marlow	v	Bashley	3-1	121
Romeo (2), Ryder		Gibbons		
Workington	v	Lincoln United	1-0*	371
Thornton				
Yate Town	v	Cinderford Town	1-3	181
Neal		Addis, Slack (2)		

8th October

Home		Away	Score	Att
Harlow Town	v	Uxbridge	0-1	81
		Royal		
Molesey	v	Leyton	3-4*	
		Bajada, Curley, Nartey, Paul		

Matlock Town's Phil Brown nets the home side's second goal despite the number of Ossett Town players around him. Photo: Gordon Whittington.

Right: Stephen Graham smashes his shot past the on coming defender and Yeading 'keeper to score Hastings' third goal.

Below: Michael Barima, Yeading's No.9, takes the ball around the diving Hastings 'keeper Matt Brown.
Photos: Roger Turner.

Saturday 1st November — Winning clubs recieved: £1,800

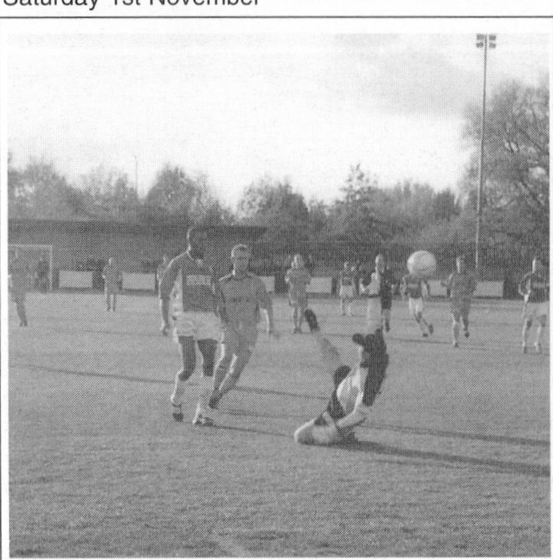

Banstead's 'keeper comes up with a novel approach to preventing the Aylesbury forward from scoring.
Photo: Steve Ayre.

Home		Away	Score	Att.
Alfreton Town	v	Prescot Cables	0-0	249
Arlesey Town	v	Hampton & Richmond Boro'	1-1	208
Pringle		Currie		
Ashton United	v	Lancaster City	1-1	206
Carty		Clarkson		
Aylesbury United	v	Banstead Athletic	1-1	337
Gray		Cormack		
Barton Rovers	v	Ford United	0-0	103
Billericay Town	v	Tilbury	4-3	273
Hockton, Jones (3)		Duffy, Hart (2)		
Boreham Wood	v	Bracknell Town	1-0	102
Baker				
Braintree Town	v	Harrow Borough	0-3	166
		Ocquaye (3)		
Burgess Hill Town	v	Sittingbourne	2-0	263
Harper (2)				
Carshalton Athletic	v	Bromley	3-1	495
Boateng, Kane, York		Amoako		
Clevedon Town	v	Taunton Town	0-3	236
		Heath, Lynch (2)		
Dartford	v	Ashford Town (Middx) (2/11)	2-2	205
Tedder (2)		Kilner, Pomroy		
Dulwich Hamlet	v	Yeading	1-1	160
Quarm				
Eastbourne Borough	v	Welling United	1-2	533
Simmonds		Booth, Slatter		
Erith & Belvedere	v	Eastleigh	1-2	131
Briggs		Banger, Carter		
Folkestone Invicta	v	Hemel Hempstead Town	4-1	363
Ayling, Dryden, Flanagan, Tait		Jones		
Frickley Athletic	v	Radcliffe Borough	5-1	160
Colley, Smeriffe (3)		Banim		
Gateshead	v	Altrincham	1-2	222
Chilton		Welton (2)		
Grays Athletic	v	Fisher Athletic	2-2	345
Lock, Thurgood		Brady (2)		
Gresley Rovers	v	Matlock Town	1-0	410
Hebberd				
Guiseley	v	Gainsborough Trinity	2-0	361
Stuart (2)				
Heybridge Swifts	v	Histon	0-1	206
		Rowe		
Kings Lynn	v	Thame United	3-1	669
Defty (2), Ndekwe		Marritt		
Kingstonian	v	Stamford	2-0	321
Collins, Payne				
Lewes	v	Northwood	4-2	370
Kadi (2), Newman (2)		Moore, Street		
Leyton	v	Dorchester Town	1-5	92
Wood		Cooper, Groves (2), Holmes, Keeler		
Mangotsfield United	v	Bath City (2/11)	1-3	637
Sims		Carter, Owers (2)		
Marine	v	Bamber Bridge	1-0	241
Taylor				
Moor Green	v	Cinderford Town	2-3	211
Frain (2)		Donovan, Truman, White		
Redditch United	v	Cirencester Town	6-2	213
Burgess (4), Leadbeater, Sawyer		Hopkins, Robinson		
Rossendale United	v	Bridlington Town	2-0	189
Clarke, Norton				
Rothwell Town	v	Gloucester City	1-1	137
Haughton		Hoskins		
Rugby United	v	Hinckley United	0-0	328
Runcorn FC Halton	v	Bishop Auckland	7-0	184
Carden, Courtney (2), Daly (2) Hogan, Spearritt				
Shepshed Dynamo	v	Hednesford Town	0-1	211
		Danks		
Slough Town	v	Bishop's Stortford (2/11)	2-2	332
Miller		Essandoh, Southam		
Staines Town	v	Croydon Athletic	2-0	169
Ibe, Pitcher				
Stocksbridge P'k Steels	v	North Ferriby United	2-1	107
Bates, Hobson		Elliott		
Swindon Supermarine	v	Grantham Town	3-2	169
Miller, Toomey		Dakin, Gould		
Team Bath	v	Halesowen Town	0-0	140
Tonbridge Angels	v	Marlow	1-3	493
Piscina		Isaac, Romeo, Ryder		
Uxbridge	v	Bognor Regis Town	0-1	153
		Russell		
Wakefield & Emley	v	Blyth Spartans	1-2	167
Day				
Wealdstone	v	East Thurrock United	5-0	264
Jolly (3), Ryan (2)				
Weston Super Mare	v	Bromsgrove Rovers	1-1	265
French		Dyson		
Weymouth	v	Merthyr Tydfil	5-2	994
Buckle, Claridge (2), Nightingale, Partridge		Regan, Thorne		
Whyteleafe	v	Ashford Town	1-1	188
Harper		Ross		
Windsor & Eton	v	Enfield	2-2	161
Jones, O'Connor		Hammond, Marshall		
Wingate & Finchley	v	Hornchurch	0-2	160
		Allen, Douglas		
Wivenhoe Town	v	Hitchin Town	0-0	222
Workington	v	Spennymoor United	0-3	360
		Bishop, Cullen, Preen		
Worthing	v	Cambridge City	0-0	406

REPLAYS

4th November

Home		Away	Score	Att.
Ashford Town	v	Whyteleafe	1-2	149
McRobert		Tompkins (2)		
Ashford Town (Middx)	v	Dartford	2-1	155
Hibburt, Pomroy		Sykes		
Banstead Athletic	v	Aylesbury United	0-1	77
		Gray		
Bishop's Stortford	v	Slough Town	2-1	217
		Miller		
Bromsgrove Rovers	v	Weston Super Mare	0-3	233
		French, Hodge, Sorbara		
Cambridge City	v	Worthing	2-3*	425
Bloomfield, Nightingale		Carrington, Francis, Mateos		
Fisher Athletic	v	Grays Athletic	0-3	164
		Hayzelden, Martin (2)		
Ford United	v	Barton Rovers	1-0	83
Cooper				
Gloucester City	v	Rothwell Town	4-1*	250
Cox, Hoskins (2), Nilkinson		Thatcher		
Halesowen Town	v	Team Bath	3-2	245
Mitchell, Spencer, Steane		Blake, Canham		
Hampton & Rich' B'	v	Arlesey Town	0-2	100
		Gutzmore		
Hinckley United	v	Rugby United	3-2	229
Dyer, Lenton (2)		Beard (2)		
Hitchin Town	v	Wivenhoe Town	4-2	143
Ayres, Dillon, Parker (2)		Turner, Wignall		
Re Lancaster City	v	Ashton United	3-2	201
Hughes (2), Jones		Garvey, Thackeray		
Re Prescot Cables	v	Alfreton Town	1-4	201
Cooper		Bettney, Brown, Godber, Tansley		
Re Yeading	v	Dulwich Hamlet	5-0	
Brown (2), Campbell, Newby, Protain				

11th November

Home		Away	Score	Att.
Enfield	v	Windsor & Eton	0-3	
		Carroll, O'Conner (2)		

(tie at Enfield on 3/11 abandoned due to floodlight failure in 100th minute (1-2)

Erith & Belvedere 'keeper Jani Seitsonen is beaten to the ball by Eastleigh's Robbie Matthews.
Photo: Alan Coomes.

Below: Grantham's Simon Dakin nets his side's equaliser against Swindon Supermarine.
Photo: Gordon Whittington.

SECOND ROUND

Saturday 29th November — **Winning clubs recieved: £3,000**

Alfreton Town	v	Vauxhall Motors	1-1	181
Sale		Lawton		
Altrincham	v	Southport	1-0	711
Band				
Aylesbury Utd	v	Grays Athletic	2-2	305
Jackson, Lynch		Carthy, Eastwood		
Bath City	v	Gloucester City	2-1	608
Cleverley, Owers		Wilkinson		
Billericay Town	v	Kings Lynn	0-2	354
		Harris, Woodrow		
Blyth Spartans	v	Stocksbridge PS	4-2	343
Burt, Fenton, McAlindon, Woodhouse		Garrett, Knox		
Boreham Wood	v	Arlesey Town	1-2	129
Winston		Carmichael, Gutzmore		
Burgess Hill Town	v	Staines Town	1-2	266
Carr		Ibe (2)		
Carshalton Athletic	v	Thurrock	2-2	198
Boateng, Olusesi		Goodfellow, Linger		
Chippenham Town	v	Basingstoke Town	1-1	466
Edwards		Roach		
Cinderford Town	v	Lewes	3-3	148
Steadman, Truman (2)		Newman (2), Watson		
Dorchester Town	v	Harrow Borough	3-0	272
Brown, Groves, O'Hagan				
Eastleigh	v	Histon	1-4	207
Banger		Andrews, Barker, Kennedy (2)		
Ford Utd	v	Chelmsford City	4-1	245
Abraham, Cooper, Poole (2)		Blackman		
Gresley Rovers	v	Hinckley Utd	3-2	330
Doughty, Harrard (2)		Jenkins, Lenton		
Halesowen Town	v	Hayes	1-3	458
Hollis		Holsgrove, Scott, Warwer		
Harrogate Town	v	Barrow	2-2	503
Sturdy, Turley		Curtis		
Havant & W'ville	v	Folkestone Invicta	2-2	222
Taylor (2)		Hogg (2)		
Hendon	v	Kettering Town	1-1	225
Cooper		Paschalis		
Hornchurch	v	Newport County	1-0	424
McGowan				
Hucknall Town	v	Nuneaton Borough	2-1	625
Ricketts (2)		Murphy		
Kingstonian	v	Bishop's Stortford	0-2	358
		Howell, Martin		
Lancaster City	v	Hednesford Town	1-1	294
Sullivan		Anthrobus		
Marine	v	Worcester City	2-0	339
Johnson, McNally				
Marlow	v	Tiverton Town	3-0	254
Romeo (3)				
Redditch Utd	v	Stalybridge Celtic	0-3	288
		Heald (2), Keeling		
Rossendale Utd	v	Guiseley	0-0	225
Runcorn FC Halton	v	Frinckley Athletic	3-2	152
Courtney, Lightfoot, McGinn		Lindley, Sheriffe		
St Albans City	v	Crawley Town	0-0	327
Stafford Rangers	v	Spennymoor Utd	2-1	563
Davidson (2)		Shandran		
Sutton United	v	Bedford Town	2-0	356
Fowler, Nurse				
Swindon Supermarine	v	Maidenhead Utd	3-3	179
Harris, Toomey (2)		Gray, Jennings, Yaku		
Taunton Town	v	Yeading	3-3	303
Booth, Lynch (2)		Brown, Campbell, Jordan		
Wealdstone	v	Hitchin Town	1-0	263
Jolly				
Welling Utd	v	Dover Athletic	0-1	502
Weston Super Mare	v	Bognor Regis Town	1-0	270
Rose				
Weymouth	v	Ashford Town (Mddx)	3-3	876
Buckle, Claridge (2)		Butler, Kilner, Reilly		
Whitby Town	v	Bradford (Park Av)	1-1	261
Nicholson		Hayward		
Whyteleafe	v	Worthing	0-4	142
		Francis (2), Lopez, Mateos		
Windsor & Eton	v	Canvey Island	1-3	302
O'Connor		McDougald, Minton (2)		
Worksop Town	v	Droylsden	1-0	341
Townsend				

REPLAYS

2nd December

Ashford Town (Mddx)	v	Weymouth	1-3	405
Butler		Claridge (2), Phillips		
Barrow	v	Harrogate Town	4-2	1095
Campbell (2), Curtis, Hume		Hunter, Naylor		
Basingstoke Town	v	Chippenham Town	1-0	237
McAllister				
Bradford (Park Av)	v	Whitby Town	1-0	279
Collins				
Crawley Town	v	St Albans City	4-1*	445
Brake, Hemsley, Vansittart		De Souza		
Folkestone Invicta	v	Havant & W'ville	1-0*	337
Flanagan				
Grays Athletic	v	Aylesbury Utd	0-1	243
		Lynch		
Hednesford Town	v	Lancaster City	1-0	276
Evans				
Kettering Town	v	Hendon	2-2, 5-4p	602
Fewings, Lodge		Crace, Ofori		
Maidenhead Utd	v	Swindon Supermarine	2-1	172
Hale, Yaku		Harris		
Thurrock	v	Carshalton Athletic	1-0	103
McFarlane				
Vauxhall Motors	v	Alfreton Town	2-4	147
Cumiskey (2)		Godber (2), Goddard, Knapper		
Yeading	v	Taunton Town	1-3	90
Barima		Booth, Foster (2)		

9th December

Guiseley	v	Rossendale Utd	1-1	208
(Abondoned after 35 mins due to fog)				
Lewes	v	Cinderford Town	4-3	343
Cable, Kennett, Whiteman		Farrell, Heatn, MacMillan		

16th December

Guiseley	v	Rossendale Utd	2-0	258
Illingworth, Parke				

Action from the Boreham Wood v Arlesey Town tie. Photo: Gordon Whittington.

THIRD ROUND

Saturday 10th January — Winning clubs recieved: £4,000

Home		Away	Score	Att
Altrincham	v	Runcorn FC Halton	2-1	707
Band, Hallows		Courtney		
Barnet	v	Dover Athletic	3-2	1405
(Barnet removed for fielding an ineligible player - Dover go through)				
Bishop's Stortford	v	Aldershot Town	2-4	957
Cooper, Southam		D'Sane (2), Miller, Nutter		
Blyth Spartans	v	Barrow	1-0	789
Woodhouse				
Burscough	v	Tamworth	0-1	601
		Warner		
Burton Albion	v	Accrington Stanley	4-2	1402
Anderson, Howard, Webster(2)		Howarth, Mullin		
Canvey Island	v	Farnborough Town	6-0	685
Berquez (3), Boylan (3)				
Chester City	v	Halifax Town	1-2	1561
Bolland		Farrell, Killeen		
Dagenham & Redbridge	v	Crawley Town	0-0	1157
Dorchester Town	v	Margate	2-2	392
		Keister, Saunders		
Exeter City	v	Hereford United	3-2	2740
Coppinger, Devine, Sheldon		Carey-Bertram, Purdie		
Folkestone Invicta	v	Stevenage Borough	1-3	912
Munday		Brady, Maamria, Richards		
Forest Green Rovers	v	Sutton United	4-0	701
Foster, Grayson, Ingram, Rogers				
Gravesend & Northfleet	v	Weston Super Mare	2-2	670
Abbey, Haworth		Gilroy, Hunt		
Guiseley	v	Worksop Town	0-2	583
		Callery, Taylor		
Hayes	v	Arlesey Town	2-2	254
Holsgrove, Warner		Gutzmore, Midson		
Hednesford Town	v	Gresley Rovers	2-0	660
Danks, Dean				
Histon	v	Maidenhead United	1-3	167
Kennedy		Farley, Hale (2)		
Hornchurch	v	Aylesbury United	2-0	549
John, Opara				
Hucknall Town	v	Bradford (Park Avenue)	1-0	573
McSweeney				
Kettering Town	v	Woking	0-0	1259
Kings Lynn	v	Basingstoke Town	3-1	1089
Leigh RMI	v	Stalybridge Celtic	1-1	402
(Leigh removed for fielding an ineligible player - Stalybidge go through)				
Lewes	v	Weymouth	5-8	1077
Adeniyi, Davis (2), Kadi, Watts		Buckle, Claridge (2), Nightingale (3), Phillips (2)		
Marine	v	Northwich Victoria	1-0	565
Thurston				
Marlow	v	Ford United	3-1	235
Isaac, Romeo		Eberende		
Scarborough	v	Stafford Rangers	1-2	1117
Senior		Davidson (2)		
Shrewsbury Town	v	Morecambe	2-0	2413
Aiston, Cramb				
Staines Town	v	Bath City	1-0	585
Pye				
Telford United	v	Alfreton Town (13/1)	2-0	2105
Naylor (2)				
Wealdstone	v	Thurrock	3-2	365
Alexander (2), Morgan		Akurang, Kandol		
Worthing	v	Taunton Town	3-0	502
Francis, Knee (2)				

R E P L A Y S

13th January

Home		Away	Score	Att
Arlesey Town	v	Hayes	1-1*, 4-3p	282
Tekell		Yeboah		
Crawley Town	v	Dagenham & Redbridge	1-2	917
Judge		Bentley, Pacquette		
Woking	v	Kettering Town	2-3	1126
Nade (2)		Fewings, Paschalis, Solkhon		

20th January

Home		Away	Score	Att
Margate	v	Dorchester Town	2-0	191
Clarke, Saunders				
Weston Super Mare	v	Gravesend & Northfleet	1-0	325
Corbett				

Above: Kettering's Paul Fewings is put under pressure by two Woking players, whilst below another Woking player closes down Martin Matthews.
Photo: Peter Barnes.

Above: Arlesey attack during their replay against Hayes.
Photo: Gordon Whittington

Right: Weston-super-Mare's William Clark is robbed by Gravesend's Rob Haworth (left) who goes on to score.
Photo: Alan Coomes.

Below: Maidenhead are put under pressure by home side Histon.
Photo: Gordon Whittington.

FOURTH ROUND

Saturday 31st January — Winning club to recieve: £5,000

Home		Away	Score	Att.
Blyth Spartans Graham	v	Aldershot Town McLean (2), Sills	1-3	829
Burton Albion Webster	v	Kettering Town Turner	1-1	1751
Dagenham & Redbridge Braithwaite, Jackson (2)	v	Arlesey Town Gutzmore, Midson	3-3	1045
Forest Green Rovers Grayson (3)	v	Dover Athletic Carruthers, Davies, Tyne	3-3	427
Halifax Town	v	Staines Town Joe	1-1	1020
Hednesford Town Danks	v	Worthing Francis	1-1	356
Hornchurch Graham	v	Stevenage Borough	1-0	741
King's Lynn	v	Exeter City Davine, Flack, Sheldon	0-3	3127
Maidenhead United Gallen, Hale, Sanders, Yaku(2)	v	Wealdstone Ryan	5-1	425
Margate Clarke, Sodje (at Ashford Town FC)	v	Worksop Town	2-0	278
Marlow	v	Tamworth Barnes (3), Blunt	0-4	744
Shrewsbury Town Moss, Street	v	Hucknall Town Ricketts	2-1	2501
Stafford Rangers	v	Canvey Island Boylan, Duffy	0-2	1163
Stalybridge Celtic Mayers	v	Marine Whitehall	1-1	614
Telford United Blackwood, Grant (2), Naylor	v	Weston-super-Mare Carbett (2)	4-2	1095
Weymouth	v	Altrincham Hardy, Wright	0-2	1722

REPLAYS

Home		Away	Score	Att.
3rd February				
Arlesey Town Corbould, Gutzmore, Mackail-Smith (2)	v	Dagenham & Redbridge Rees, Shipp	4-2	760
Kettering Town Turner	v	Burton Albion Howard, Talbot	1-2*	1215
Marine	v	Stalybridge Celtic Eastwood	0-1	374
10th February				
Dover Athletic Carruthers, Davies	v	Forest Green Rovers Grayson	2-1	710
Worthing Francis	v	Hednesford Town Anthrobus, Danks	1-2	705
12th February				
Staines Tomlin (2)	v	Halifax Town Farrell, Midgley, Quinn	2-3*	728

FIFTH ROUND

Saturday 14th February — Winning club to recieve: £6,000

Home		Away	Score	Att.
Aldershot Town Warburton	v	Tamworth Quailey	1-1	2515
Altrincham	v	Shrewsbury Town Lowe	0-1	1758
Exeter City Flack (2), Sheldon	v	Arlesey Town	3-0	2541
Halifax Town	v	Maidenhead United Hale, Yaku	0-2	1345
Hednesford Town Anthrobus	v	Dover Athletic	1-0	587
Hornchurch Brayley, Keeling	v	Burton Albion	2-1	1205
Stalybridge Celtic	v	Canvey Island	0-0	832
Telford United Clarke, Grant, Ricketts	v	Margate (17/02)	3-0	1376

REPLAYS

Home		Away	Score	Att.
17th February				
Tamworth	v	Aldershot Town Miller (2)	0-2	1067
Canvey Island Boylan (2), Dobinson, Gregory	v	Stalybridge Celtic	4-0	761

SIXTH ROUND

Saturday 28th February — Winning club to recieve: £7,000

Aldershot	(1) 2	Exeter City	(1) 1
Sills 13, Charles 56		Devine 31	
			Att: 3814

Shrewsbury Town	(0) 1	Telford United	(1) 1
Cramb 64		Grant 14	
			Att: 6050

Canvey Island	(3) 4	Maidenhead United	(0) 0
Boylan 6 (pen), Minton 16, Duffy 37 Cowan 90			
			Att: 921

Hednesford Town	(0) 3	Hornchurch	(0) 1
			Att: 646 Played on 02/03/04

R E P L A Y

Telford United	(0) 2	Shrewsbury Town	(0) 1
			Att: 4447 Played on 16/03/04

Above: The virtues of having a man on the post save Exeter during this Aldershot attack.

Aldershot's Tim Sills (centre) scores after 13 minutes to give the home side the lead over Exeter. Photos: Eric Marsh.

SEMI-FINALS - 1ST LEG

Saturday 27th March — Winning clubs received: £16,000

Aldershot Town	() 0	Hednesford Town	() 2

Danks 25, Maguire 76

Att: 3,461

ALDERSHOT SQUAD: Barnard, Downer, Sterling, Warburton (Chewins 45), Giles, Gosling, Antwi, Challinor, Sills, D'Sane (Harper 85), McClean (Charles 68)
Subs not used: Lauder-Dyke, Nutter

HEDNESFORD SQUAD: Young, Simkin (Dodd 87), Hines, Maguire, Brindley, Ryder, Palmer, King, Anthrobus, Danks (Pearce 85), Charie.
Subsnot used: Dean, S Evans, P Evans.

Telford United	(0) 0	Canvey Island	(0) 0

Att: 3,061

TELFORD SQUAD: MacKenzie, Clarke, Howarth, Lavery, Whitehead, Mills, Blackwood, Ricketts, Naylor, Grant, Stanley..
Subs not used: P Moore, Green, C Moore, Taylor.

CANVEY SQUAD: Potter, Kennedy, Duffy, Chenery, Ward, Cowan, Gooden, Minton, McDougald, Boylan, Midgley.
Subs not used: Berquez, Dobinson, Smith, Theobald, Harrison.

An Aldershot player shields the ball from two incoming Hednesford players. Photo: Peter Barnes

Hednesford's goal scoring heroes from their first leg tie against Aldershot. Photo: Eric Marsh.

Hednesford's number eight dispossess an Aldershot player, unfairly according to the referee. Photo: Peter Barnes.

Hednesford's Steve Anthrobus takes on the Aldershot defence. Photo: Peter Barnes.

SEMI-FINALS - 2ND LEG

Saturday 3rd April

Hednesford Town	(1) 1	Aldershot Town	(0) 1
Maguire 10		D'Sane 73 (pen)	

Att: 2,084

HEDNESFORD SQUAD: Young, Simkin, Hines, Maguire[SO], Brindley, Ryder, C Palmer, S Palmer, King, Anthrobus, Danks.
Subsnot used: Dean, Evans, Charie, Pearce.

ALDERSHOT SQUAD: Bull[SO], Gosling (Sills 45), Nutter, Downer, Warburton (Sterling 67), Challinor, Miller[SO], Giles, Antwi (McLean 58), D'Sane, Charles.
Subs not used: Chewins, Bernard.

[SO] denotes sending-off.

Canvey Island	(0) 2	Telford United	(1) 2
Boyland 53, 105		Blackwood 41, Green 115	

(AET - Canvey won 4-2 on penalties) Att: 1,818

CANVEY SQUAD: Potter, Kennedy, Duffy, Chenery, Ward, Cowan, Gooden (Dobinson 114), Minton, McDougald, Boylan, Midgley.
Subs not used: Berquez, Smith, Theobald, Harrison.

TELFORD SQUAD: MacKenzie, Clarke, Howarth, Lavery, Whitehead, Green, Mills (Moore 120), Blackwood, Ricketts, Naylor (Grant 14), Stanley (Murphy 110).
Subs not used: Hulbert, Rowe.

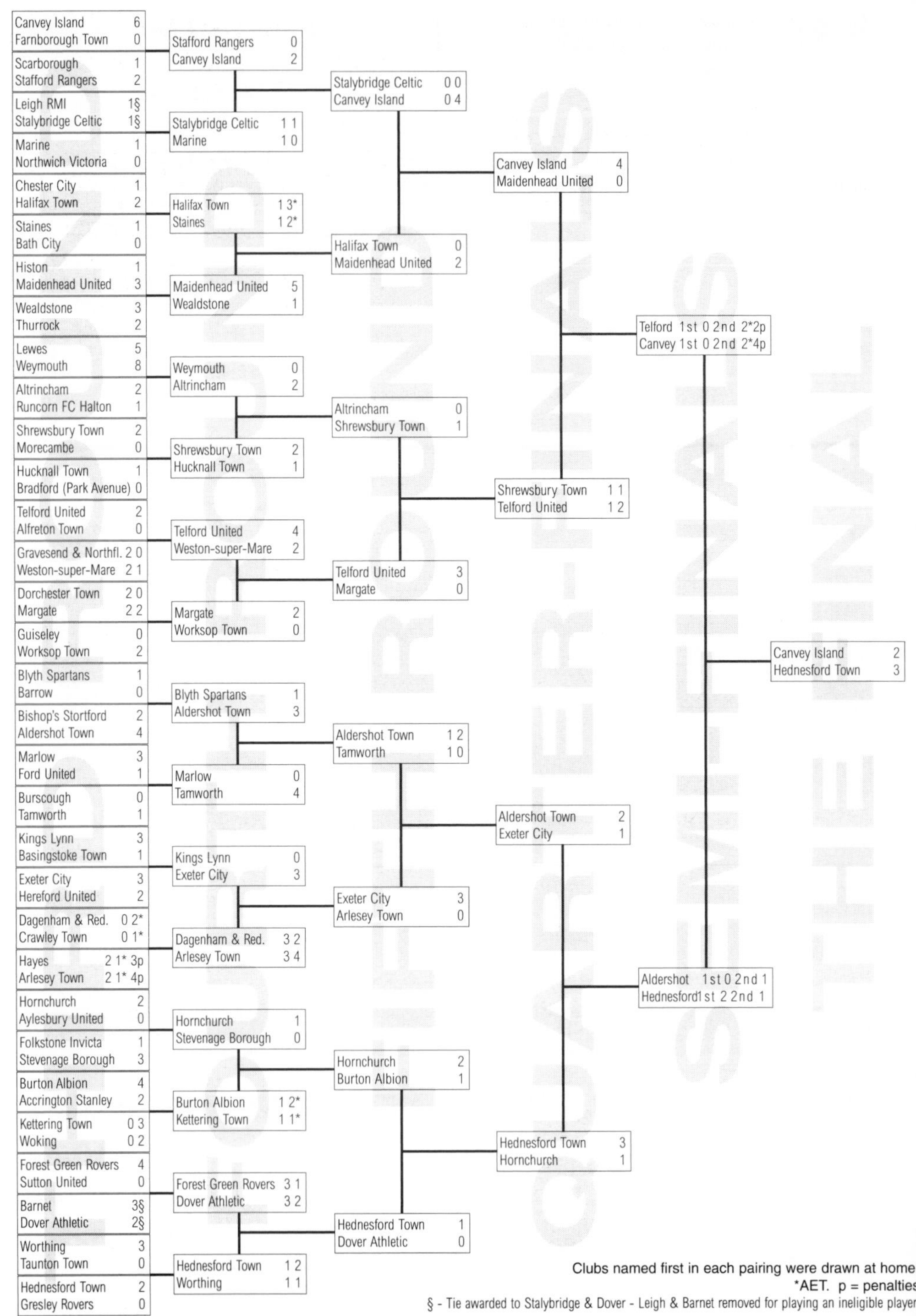
Canvey Island 6
Farnborough Town 0
Scarborough 1
Stafford Rangers 2
Leigh RMI 1§
Stalybridge Celtic 1§
Marine 1
Northwich Victoria 0
Chester City 1
Halifax Town 2
Staines 1
Bath City 0
Histon 1
Maidenhead United 3
Wealdstone 3
Thurrock 2
Lewes 5
Weymouth 8
Altrincham 2
Runcorn FC Halton 1
Shrewsbury Town 2
Morecambe 0
Hucknall Town 1
Bradford (Park Avenue) 0
Telford United 2
Alfreton Town 0
Gravesend & Northfl. 2 0
Weston-super-Mare 2 1
Dorchester Town 2 0
Margate 2 2
Guiseley 0
Worksop Town 2
Blyth Spartans 1
Barrow 0
Bishop's Stortford 2
Aldershot Town 4
Marlow 3
Ford United 1
Burscough 0
Tamworth 1
Kings Lynn 3
Basingstoke Town 1
Exeter City 3
Hereford United 2
Dagenham & Red. 0 2*
Crawley Town 0 1*
Hayes 2 1* 3p
Arlesey Town 2 1* 4p
Hornchurch 2
Aylesbury United 0
Folkstone Invicta 1
Stevenage Borough 3
Burton Albion 4
Accrington Stanley 2
Kettering Town 0 3
Woking 0 2
Forest Green Rovers 4
Sutton United 0
Barnet 3§
Dover Athletic 2§
Worthing 3
Taunton Town 0
Hednesford Town 2
Gresley Rovers 0
Stafford Rangers 0
Canvey Island 2
Stalybridge Celtic 1 1
Marine 1 0
Halifax Town 1 3*
Staines 1 2*
Maidenhead United 5
Wealdstone 1
Weymouth 0
Altrincham 2
Shrewsbury Town 2
Hucknall Town 1
Telford United 4
Weston-super-Mare 2
Margate 2
Worksop Town 0
Blyth Spartans 1
Aldershot Town 3
Marlow 0
Tamworth 4
Kings Lynn 0
Exeter City 3
Dagenham & Red. 3 2
Arlesey Town 3 4
Hornchurch 1
Stevenage Borough 0
Burton Albion 1 2*
Kettering Town 1 1*
Forest Green Rovers 3 1
Dover Athletic 3 2
Hednesford Town 1 2
Worthing 1 1
Stalybridge Celtic 0 0
Canvey Island 0 4
Halifax Town 0
Maidenhead United 2
Altrincham 0
Shrewsbury Town 1
Telford United 3
Margate 0
Aldershot Town 1 2
Tamworth 1 0
Exeter City 3
Arlesey Town 0
Hornchurch 2
Burton Albion 1
Hednesford Town 1
Dover Athletic 0
Canvey Island 4
Maidenhead United 0
Shrewsbury Town 1 1
Telford United 1 2
Aldershot Town 2
Exeter City 1
Hednesford Town 3
Hornchurch 1
Telford 1st 0 2nd 2*2p
Canvey 1st 0 2nd 2*4p
Aldershot 1st 0 2nd 1
Hednesford1 st 2 2nd 1
Canvey Island 2
Hednesford Town 3
QUARTER-FINALS
SEMI-FINALS
THE FINAL

Clubs named first in each pairing were drawn at home.
*AET. p = penalties
§ - Tie awarded to Stalybridge & Dover - Leigh & Barnet removed for playing an ineligible player.

Maybe it was not two of the most glamorous or heavily supported teams outside the Football League who found themselves in a national final on a beautifully sunny late Spring Sunday but they certainly provided an exciting spectacle with plenty of drama and sufficient surprises to keep both sets of supporters, and the neutrals, clamouring for more. As for entertainment and spontaneity it was certainly in excess of that found in the previous day's F A Cup Final bore.

There was also an unlikely winning scorer in veteran Chris Brindley who had the misfortune of giving Canvey the lead with an unavoidable own goal just after half time. Brindley, a few days later, found himself promoted from assistant to manager as a result of the dismissal of Barry Powell, the second Trophy winning manager to be deposed in consecutive years following Shaun Teale's departure from Burscough after their victory in 2003. Look out for next year's winning manager.

In front of a disappointingly low, but vociferous attendance of 6,635, Hednesford , despite being clear underdogs, and despite Canvey's generally efficient mass movements upfield to catch their opposition offside, still threatened in the opening moments. The swift moving Mark Danks, prompted by the eye catching Carl Palmer and Anthony Maguire, adjudged man of the match, saw to that. A nifty backheel from Danks set Maguire free and his pass to Steve Anthrobus meant the Canvey defenders were forced to throw themselves in the path of the stand in skipper's shot to prevent an early score.

Neil Midgley fired past the post as the Islanders retaliated. Ryan Young made a flying save from Neil Gregory but could only pop the ball to Lee Boylan. The leading scorer looked certain to net but somehow failed to find any force and hit Young instead. His free kick was far fiercer and Young did well to turn for a corner.

Back flew the action to the Holte End and with 27 minutes on the clock the Pitmen took the lead, Maguire being on the spot to shoot home after Danks' effort had been blocked but not held by Danny Potter. Further efforts from Danks, Maguire, Palmer and full back Les Hines brought Hednesford close to doubling their lead before Jeff King could get his men back in the dressing room and address their problems.

And what an address it must have been for within three minutes the score had changed dramatically. Boylan, left completely unmarked, bagged the equaliser within sixty seconds of the restart. Another minute or so and Boylan found the ball parried to his feet by Young. Quick reaction allowed him to lob towards the unguarded target and the falling Brindley helped the ball over the line. What a transformation. Now it was the blue and yellows' turn to whoop it up while those attired in black, white and red were hushed into silence, their exultant half time break forgotten.

F A TROPHY
(in partnership with Carlsberg)
2004 FINAL
at Villa Park on Sunday May 23rd

CANVEY ISLAND	**2**
HEDNESFORD TOWN	**3**

Canvey Island: Danny Potter, John Kennedy, Chris Duffy, Ben Chenery, Gavin Cowan, Ty Gooden (sub Kevin Dobinson 89th min), Jeff Minton, Neil Gregory (sub Junior McDougald 80th min), Lee Boylan, Neil Midgley (sub Ollie Berquez 73rd min), Steve Ward. Subs (not used)- David Theobald and Ashley Harrison (g/k).

Hednesford Town: Ryan Young, Darren Simkin, Les Hines, Jordan King, Chris Brindley, Stuart Ryder (sub Lee Barrow 59th min), Carl Palmer, Steve Anthrobus, Mark Danks (sub Steve Piearce 78th min), Anthony Maguire, Damien Charie (sub Steve Evans 55th min).
Subs (not used)- Paul Evans (g/k) and Danny McGhee.

Referee Mr M L Dean, assisted by Messrs D G Kellett and P V Norman. Fourth official, Mr P Taylor.

With the favourites now ensconced in pole position we sat back and anticipated an Essex avalanche. However Danks had other ideas. Just after being booked for diving he was really felled, allowing Les Hines to smash a ferocious free kick on target. Three goals had come in the space of eight minutes and we were back all square at two each.

Plenty of end to end action now as, like two gladiators, the teams sought openings. Palmer forced his way through but failed to achieve direction. Jeff Minton ran dangerously almost the field length before being dispossessed. Anthrobus shot over and Boylan, making a chance out of nothing, scooped the ball over.

Then, with four minutes to go, Hednesford gained a corner. Brindley, who had gone upfield to use his head found a clearance falling at his feet. Nimbly he caught it on the half volley to bullet it past a hapless Potter. Hednesford were elated.

Canvey produced some last desperate attacks. Ty Gooden headed over but the Pitmen stood firm until Mr Dean's whistle signalled they had achieved cup triumph in the same season they had been relegated. A see saw year for them had ended on an up whereas, conversely, promoted Canvey finished on a down.

Long may the see saw of fortune continue its fascinating fluctuations and assure entertainment.

ARTHUR EVANS

TROPHY FINAL ACTION

Anthony Maguire gives the 'Pitmen' an early lead against Canvey at Villa Park.

Photo: Peter Barnes.

Hednesford's Ryan Young plucks this cross from the air to cancel out this Canvey attack.

Photo: Peter Barnes.

Lee Boylan's goal bound chip is inadvertently helped across the line by Hednesford's Chris Brindley.
Photo: Roger Turner.

Hednesford's Carl Palmer takes off on another attacking run during the Trophy final.
Photo: Roger Turner.

Hednesford's triumphant manager Barry Powell enjoys the moment.
Photo: Roger Turner.

PAST F.A. TROPHY FINALS

1970 MACCLESFIELD TOWN 2 (Lyond, B Fidler) — TELFORD UNITED 0 — Att: 28,000
Northern Premier League — Southern League
Macclesfield: Cooke, Sievwright, Bennett, Beaumont, Collins, Roberts, Lyons, B Fidler,Young, Corfield, D Fidler.
Telford: Irvine, Harris, Croft, Flowers, Coton, Ray,Fudge, Hart, Bentley, Murray, Jagger. Ref: K Walker

1971 TELFORD UTD 3 (Owen, Bentley, Fudge) — HILLINGDON BORO. 2 (Reeve, Bishop) — Att: 29,500
Southern League — Southern League
Telford: Irvine, Harris, Croft, Ray, Coton, Carr, Fudge, Owen, Bentley, Jagger ,Murray.
Hillingdon B.: Lowe, Batt, Langley, Higginson, Newcombe, Moore, Fairchild,Bishop, Reeve, Carter, Knox. Ref: D Smith

1972 STAFFORD RANGERS 3 (Williams 2, Cullerton) — BARNET 0 — Att: 24,000
Northern Premier League — Southern League
Stafford R.: Aleksic, Chadwick, Clayton, Sargeant, Aston, Machin, Cullerton, Chapman,Williams, Bayley, Jones.
Barnet: McClelland, Lye, Jenkins, Ward, Embrey, King, Powell, Ferry, Flatt, Easton, Plume . Ref: P Partridge

1973 SCARBOROUGH 2 (Leask, Thompson) — WIGAN ATHLETIC 1 (Rogers) aet — Att:23,000
Northern Premier League — Northern Premier League
Scarborough: Garrow, Appleton, Shoulder, Dunn, Siddle, Fagan, Donoghue, Franks,Leask (Barmby), Thompson, Hewitt.
Wigan: Reeves, Morris, Sutherland, Taylor,Jackson, Gillibrand, Clements, Oats (McCunnell), Rogers, King, Worswick. Ref: H Hackney

1974 MORECAMBE 2 (Richmond, Sutton) — DARTFORD 1 (Cunningham) — Att: 19,000
Northern Premier League — Southern League
Morecambe: Coates, Pearson, Bennett, Sutton, Street, Baldwin, Done, Webber,Roberts (Galley), Kershaw, Richmond.
Dartford: Morton, Read, Payne, Carr, Burns,Binks, Light, Glozier, Robinson (Hearne), Cunningham, Halleday. Ref: B Homewood

1975 **1** MATLOCK TOWN 4 (Oxley, Dawson, T Fenoughty, N Fenoughy) — SCARBOROUGH 0 — Att: 21,000
Northern Premier League — Northern Premier League
Matlock: Fell, McKay, Smith, Stuart, Dawson, Swan, Oxley, N Fenoughy, Scott, T Fenoughty, M Fenoughty.
Scarborough: Williams, Hewitt, Rettitt, Dunn, Marshall, Todd, Houghton, Woodall, Davidson, Barnby, Aveyard. Ref: K Styles

1976 SCARBOROUGH 3 (Woodall, Abbey, Marshall(p)) — STAFFORD R. 2 (Jones 2) aet — Att: 21,000
Northern Premier League — Northern Premier League
Scarborough: Barnard, Jackson, Marshall, H Dunn, Ayre (Donoghue), HA Dunn, Dale,Barmby, Woodall, Abbey, Hilley.
Stafford: Arnold, Ritchie, Richards, Sargeant,Seddon, Morris, Chapman, Lowe, Jones, Hutchinson, Chadwick. Ref: R Challis

Altrincham and England stalwarts John Davidson (left) and Jeff Johnson pictured at Wembley following their club's success over Runcorn in 1986.

Photo: John Rooney.

1977 Att: 21,500
SCARBOROUGH 2 (Dunn(p), Abbey) — Northern Premier League
DAGENHAM 1 (Harris) — Ishthmian League
Scarborough: Chapman, Smith, Marshall (Barmby), Dunn, Ayre, Deere, Aveyard,Donoghue, Woodall, Abbey, Dunn.
Dagenham: Hutley, Wellman, P Currie, Dunwell,Moore, W Currie, Harkins, Saul, Fox, Harris, Holder. Ref: G Courtney

1978 Att: 20,000
ALTRINCHAM 3 (King, Johnson, Rogers) Northern Premier League
LEATHERHEAD 1 (Cook) — Isthmian League
Altrincham: Eales, Allan, Crossley, Bailey, Owens, King, Morris, Heathcote,Johnson, Rogers, Davidson (Flaherty).
Leatherhead: Swannell, Cooper, Eaton, Davies,Reid, Malley, Cook, Salkeld, Baker, Boyle (Bailey). Ref: A Grey

1979 Att: 32,000
STAFFORD RANGERS 2 (A Wood 2) — Northern Premier League
KETTERING TOWN 0 — Isthmian League
Stafford: Arnold, F Wood, Willis, Sargeant, Seddon, Ritchie, Secker, Chapman, A Wood, Cullerton, Chadwick (Jones).
Kettering: Lane, Ashby, Lee, Eastell, Dixey,Suddards, Flannagan, Kellock, Phipps, Clayton, Evans (Hughes). Ref: D Richardson

1980 **2** Att : 26,000
DAGENHAM 2 (Duck, Maycock) — Isthmian League
MOSSLEY 1 (Smith) — Northern Premier League
Dagenham: Huttley, Wellman, Scales, Dunwell, Mooore, Durrell, Maycock, Horan,Duck, Kidd, Jones (Holder).
Mossley: Fitton, Brown, Vaughan, Gorman, Salter, Polliot, Smith, Moore, Skeete, O'Connor, Keelan (Wilson). Ref: K Baker

Notes:

1 The only occasion three members of the same family played in the same FA Trophy Final team.

2 The first of the Amateurs from the Isthmian League to win the FA Trophy

3 Goalkeeper Terry Moore had also won an Amateur Cup Winners Medal with Bishop's Stortford in 1974

First ex-League club to win at Wembley, Barrow F.C., enjoy their moment after the 1990 Trophy Final.
Photo: Eric Marsh.

1981 **3** Att:22,578
BISHOP'S STORTFORD 1 (Sullivan)
Isthmian League
SUTTON UNITED 0
Isthmian League
Bishop's Stortford: Moore, Blackman, Brame, Smith (Worrell), Bradford, Abery, Sullivan,Knapman, Radford, Simmonds, Mitchell.
Sutton Utd.: Collyer, Rogers, Green, J Rains,T Rains, Stephens (Sunnucks), Waldon, Pritchard, Cornwell, Parsons, Dennis. Ref: J Worrall

1982 Att:18.678
ENFIELD 1 (Taylor) Isthmian League
ALTRINCHAM 0 Alliance Premier League
Enfield: Jacobs, Barrett, Tone, Jennings, Waite, Ironton, Ashford, Taylor,Holmes, Oliver (Flint), King. Ref: B Stevens
Altrincham: Connaughton, Crossley, Davison, Bailey, Cuddy, King (Whitbread), Allan, Heathcote, Johnson, Rogers, Howard.

1983 TELFORD UTD 2 (Mather 2) NORTHWICH VICTORIA 1 (Bennett) Att: 22,071
Alliance Premier League Alliance Premier League
Telford: Charlton, Lewis, Turner, Mayman (Joseph), Walker, Easton, Barnett,Williams, Mather, Hogan, Alcock.
Northwich: Ryan, Fretwell, Murphy, Jones, Forshaw, Ward, Anderson, Abel (Bennett), Reid, Chesters, Wilson. Ref: B Hill

1984 NORTHWICH VICTORIA 1 (Chester) BANGOR CITY 1 (Whelan) Att: 14,200
Replay NORTHWICH VICTORIA 2 (Chesters(p), Anderson) BANGOR CITY 1 (Lunn) Att: 5,805 (at Stoke)
Alliance Premier League Alliance Premier League
Northwich: Ryan, Fretwell, Dean, Jones, Forshaw (Power 65), Bennett, Anderson,Abel, Reid, Chesters, Wilson. Ref: J Martin
Bangor: Letheren, Cavanagh, Gray, Whelan, Banks,Lunn, Urqhart, Morris, Carter, Howat, Sutcliffe (Westwood 105) . Same in replay.

1985 WEALDSTONE 2 (Graham, Holmes) BOSTON UNITED 1 (Cook) Att: 20,775
Alliance Premier League Alliance Premier League
Wealdstone: Iles, Perkins, Bowgett, Byatt, Davies, Greenaway, Holmes, Wainwright,Donnellan, Graham (N Cordice 89), A Cordice.
Boston: Blackwell, Casey, Ladd,Creane, O'Brien, Thommson, Laverick (Mallender 78), Simpsom, Gilbert, Lee, Cook. Ref: J Bray

1986 ALTRINCHAM 1 (Farrelly) RUNCORN 0 Att: 15,700
Gola League Gola League
Altrincham: Wealands, Gardner, Densmore, Johnson, Farrelly, Conning, Cuddy,Davison, Reid, Ellis, Anderson. Sub: Newton.
Runcorn: McBride, Lee, Roberts,Jones, Fraser, Smith, S Crompton (A Crompton), Imrie, Carter, Mather, Carrodus. Ref: A Ward

1987 KIDDERMINSTER HARRIERS 0 BURTON ALBION 0 Att: 23,617
Replay KIDDERMINSTER HARRIERS 2 (Davies 2) BURTON ALBION 1 (Groves) Att: 15,685 (at West Brom)
Conference Southern League
Kidderminster: Arnold, Barton, Boxall, Brazier (sub Hazlewood in rep), Collins (subPearson 90 at Wembley), Woodall, McKenzie, O'Dowd, Tuohy, Casey, Davies. sub:Jones.
Burton: New, Essex, Kamara, Vaughan, Simms, Groves, Bancroft, Land, Dorsett, Redfern, (sub Wood in replay), Gauden.
Sub: Patterson. Ref: D Shaw

1988 ENFIELD 0 TELFORD UNITED 0 Att: 20,161, Ref: L Dilkes
Replay ENFIELD 3 (Furlong 2, Howell) TELFORD 2 (Biggins, Norris(p)) Att: 6,912 (at W Brom)
Conference Conference
Enfield: Pape, Cottington, Howell, Keen (sub Edmonds in rep), Sparrow (sub Hayzleden at Wembley), Lewis (sub Edmonds at Wembley), Harding, Cooper, King,Furlong, Francis.
Telford: Charlton, McGinty, Storton, Nelson, Wiggins, Mayman (sub Cunningham in rep (sub Hancock)), Sankey, Joseph, Stringer (sub Griffiths at Wembley, Griffiths in replay), Biggins, Norris.

1989 TELFORD UNITED 1 (Crawley) MACCLESFIELD TOWN 0 Att: 18,102
Conference Conference
Telford: Charlton, Lee, Brindley, Hancock, Wiggins, Mayman, Grainger, Joseph, Nelson, Lloyd, Stringer. Subs: Crawley, Griffiths.
Macclesfield: Zelem, Roberts, Tobin, Edwards, Hardman, Askey, Lake, Hanton, Imrie, Burr, Timmons. Subs: Devomshire, Kendall.
Ref: T Holbrook

1990 BARROW 3 (Gordon 2, Cowperthwaite) LEEK TOWN 0 Att: 19,011
Conference Northern Premier League
Barrow: McDonnell, Higgins, Chilton, Skivington, Gordon, Proctor, Doherty (Burgess), Farrell (Gilmore), Cowperthwaite, Lowe, Ferris.
Leek: Simpson, Elsby (Smith), Pearce, McMullen, Clowes, Coleman (Russell),Mellor, Somerville, Sutton, Millington, Norris Ref: T Simpson

1991 WYCOMBE W. 2 (Scott, West) KIDDERMINSTER H. 1 (Hadley) Att: 34,842
Conference Conference
Wycombe: Granville, Crossley, Cash, Kerr, Creaser, Carroll, Ryan, Stapleton,West, Scott, Guppy (Hutchinson). Ref: J Watson
Kidderminster: Jones, Kurila, McGrath, Weir, Barnett, Forsyth, Joseph (Wilcox), Howell (Whitehouse), Hadley, Lilwall, Humphries

1992 COLCHESTER UTD* 3 (Masters, Smith, McGavin) WITTON ALBION 1 (Lutkevitch) Att: 27,806
Conference Conference
Colchester: Barrett, Donald, Roberts, Knsella, English, Martin, Cook, Masters,McDonough (Bennett 65), McGavin, Smith. Ref: K P Barratt
Witton: Mason, Halliday, Coathup, McNeilis, Jim Connor, Anderson, Thomas, Rose, Alford, Grimshaw (Joe Connor), Lutkevitch (McCluskie)

1993 WYCOMBE W*. 4 (Cousins, Kerr, Thompson, Carroll) Conference — RUNCORN 1 (Shaughnessy) Conference — Att: 32,968

Wycombe: Hyde, Cousins, Cooper, Kerr, Crossley, Thompson (Hayrettin 65),Carroll, Ryan, Hutchinson, Scott, Guppy. Sub: Casey.
Runcorn: Williams, Bates, Robertson, Hill, Harold (Connor 62), Anderson, Brady (Parker 72), Brown, Shaughnessy, McKenna, Brabin
Ref: I J Borritt

1994 WOKING 2 (D Brown, Hay) Conference — RUNCORN 1 (Shaw (pen)) Conference — Att: 15,818

Woking: Batty, Tucker, L Wye, Berry, Brown, Clement, Brown (Rattray 32), Fielder, Steele, Hay (Puckett 46), Walker. Ref: Paul Durkin
Runcorn: Williams, Bates, Robertson, Shaw, Lee, Anderson, Thomas, Connor, McInerney (Hill 71), McKenna, Brabin. Sub: Parker

1995 WOKING 2 (Steele, Fielder) Conference — KIDDERMINSTER H. 1 aet (Davies) Conference — Att: 17,815

Woking: Batty, Tucker, L Wye, Fielder, Brown, Crumplin (Rattray 42), S Wye, Ellis, Steele, Hay (Newberry 112), Walker. (Sub: Read(gk)
Kidderminster: Rose, Hodson, Bancroft, Webb, Brindley (Cartwright 94), Forsyth, Deakin, Yates, Humphreys (Hughes 105), Davies, Purdie. Sub: Dearlove (gk) Ref: D J Gallagher

1996 MACCLESFIELD TOWN 3 (Payne, OG, Hemmings) Conference — NORTHWICH VICTORIA 1 (Williams) Conference — Att: 8,672

Macclesfield: Price, Edey, Gardiner, Payne, Howarth(C), Sorvel, Lyons, Wood (Hulme 83), Coates, Power, Hemmings (Cavell 88).
Northwich: Greygoose, Ward, Duffy, Burgess (Simpson 87), Abel (Steele), Walters, Williams, Butler (C), Cooke, Humphries, Vicary.
Ref: M Reed

1997 WOKING 1 (Hay 112) Conference — DAGENHAM & REDBRIDGE 0 Isthmian League — Att: 24,376

Woking: Batty, Brown, Howard, Foster, Taylor, S Wye, Thompson (sub Jones 115), Ellis, Steele (L Wye 108), Walker, Jackson (Hay 77).
Dagenham: Gothard, Culverhouse, Connor, Creaser, Jacques (sub Double 75), Davidson, Pratt (Naylor 81), Parratt, Broom, Rogers, Stimson (John 65). Ref: J Winter

1998 CHELTENHAM TOWN 1 (Eaton 74) Conference — SOUTHPORT 0 Conference — Att: 26,387

Cheltenham: Book, Duff, Freeman, Banks, Victory, Knight (Smith 78), Howells, Bloomer, Walker (sub Milton 78), Eaton, Watkins. Sub: Wright.
Southport: Stewart, Horner, Futcher, Ryan, Farley, Kielty, Butler, Gamble, Formby (sub Whittaker 80), Thompson (sub Bollard 88), Ross. Sub: Mitten. Ref: G S Willard

1999 KINGSTONIAN 1 (Mustafa 49) Conference — FOREST GREEN ROVERS 0 Conference — Att: 20,037

Kingstonian: Farrelly, Mustafa, Luckett, Crossley, Stewart, Harris, Patterson, Pitcher, Rattray, Leworthy (Francis 87), Akuamoah. Subs (not used): John, Corbett, Brown, Tranter
Forest Green Rovers: Shuttlewood, Hedges, Forbes, Bailey (Smart 76), Kilgour, Wigg (Cook 58), Honor (Winter 58), Drysdale, McGregor, Mehew, Sykes. Subs (not used): Perrin, Coupe Ref: A B Wilkie

2000 KINGSTONIAN 3 (Akuamoah 40, 69, Simba 75) Conference — KETTERING TOWN 2 (Vowden 55, Norman 64p) Conference — Att: 20,034

Kingstonian: Farelly, Mustafa, Luckett, Crossley, Stewart (Saunders 77), Harris, Kadi (Leworthy 83), Pitcher, Green (Basford 86), Smiba, Akuamoah. Subs (not used): Hurst, Allan
Kettering Town: Sollit, McNamara, Adams, Perkins, Vowden, Norman (Duik 76), Fisher, Brown, Shutt, Watkins (Hudson 46), Setchell (Hopkins 81). Subs (not used): Ridgway, Wilson Ref: S W Dunn

2001 CANVEY ISLAND 1 (Chenery) Isthmian League — FOREST GREEN ROVERS 0 Conference — at Villa Park Att: 10,007

Forest Green Rovers: Perrin, Cousins, Lockwood, Foster, Clark, Burns, Daley, Drysdale (Bennett 46), Foster (Hunt 75), Meecham, Slater. Subs (not used): Hedges, Prince, Ghent
Canvey Island: Harrison, Duffy, Chenery, Bodley, Ward, Tilson, Stimson (Tanner 83), Gregory, Vaughan (Jones 76), Parmenter. Subs (not used): Bennett, Miller, Thompson. Ref: A G Wiley

2002 YEOVIL TOWN 2 (Alford, Stansfield) Conference — STEVENAGE BOROUGH 0 Conference — at Villa Park Att: 18,809

Yeovil Town: Weale, Lockwood, Tonkin, Skiverton, Pluck (White 51), Way, Stansfield, Johnson, Alford (Giles 86), Crittenden (Lindegaard 83), McIndoe. Subs (not used): O'Brien, Sheffield
Stevenage Borough: Wilkerson, Hamsher, Goodliffe, Trott, Fraser, Fisher, Wormull (Stirling 71), Evers (Williams 56), Jackson, Sigere (Campbell 74), Clarke. Subs (not used): Campbell, Greygoose Ref: N S Barry

2002 BURSCOUGH 2 (Martindale 25, 55) Northern Premier — TAMWORTH 1 (Cooper 78) Southern Premier — at Villa Park Att: 14,265

Burscough: Taylor, Teale, Taylor, Macauley (White 77), Lawless, Bowen, Wright, Norman, Martindale (McHale 80), Byrne (Bluck 84), Burns. Subs (not used): McGuire (g/k) Molyneux.
Tamworth: Acton, Warner, Follett, Robinson, Walsh, Cooper, Colley, Evans (Turner 64), Rickards (Hatton 88), McGorry, Sale (Hallam 54). Subs (not used): Grocutt, Barnes (g/k). Ref: U D Rennie

TOP GOAL SCORERS 2003 - 2004

Player	Club	No. goals	Round reach	No. hatrick	Hatrick details
L Boylan	Canvey Island	11	Runners-up	1	3rd Round
Y Romeo	Marlow	7	Fourth	1	2nd Round
A Lynch	Taunton Town	7	Third	1	Preliminary Round
S Claridge	Weymouth Town	7	Fourth	-	-
L Gutzmore	Arlesey Town	6	Fifth	-	-
M Danks	Hednesford Town	6	Winners	-	-
S Francis	Worthing	6	Fourth	-	-
N Grayson	Forest Green Rovers	5	Fourth	-	-
M Stuart	Guiseley	5	Third	1	Preliminary Round
S Hale	Maidenhead United	5	Sixth	-	-
L Yaku	Maidenhead United	5	Sixth	-	-
K Ibe	Staines Town	5	Fourth	-	-
D Smeriffe	Frickley Athletic	4	Second	1	1st Round
A Hoskins	Gloucester City	4	Second	-	-
J Kadi	Lewes	4	Third	-	-
L Newman	Lewes	4	Third	-	-
R Burgess	Redditch United	4	Second	1	1st Rnd (scored 4)
G Courtney	Runcorn FC Halton	4	Third	-	-
D Davidson	Stafford Rangers	4	Fourth	-	-
J Grant	Telford United	4	Semi-finals	-	-
T Naylor	Telford United	4	Semi-finals	-	-
R Jolly	Wealdstone	4	Fourth	1	1st Round
L Nightingale	Weymouth	4	Fourth	1	3rd Round
C O'Connor	Windsor & Eton	4	Second	-	-
HIGHEST SCORING CLUBS					
Club	**Division**			-	-
Canvey Island	Isthmian Premier	23	Runners-up	-	-
Weymouth	Southern Premier	19	Fourth	-	-
Hednesford Town	Southern Premier	18	Winners	-	-
Lewes	Isthmian Div.1 South	17	Third	-	-
Arlesey Town	Isthmian Div.1 North	16	Fifth	-	-
Maidenhead Utd	Isthmian Premier	15	Sixth	-	-
Cinderford Town	Southern Western	14	Second	-	-
Telford United	Conference	14	Semi-finals	-	-
Worthing	Isthmian Div.1 South	14	Fourth	-	-
Aldershot Town	Conference	13	Semi-finals	-	-
Marlow	Isthmian Div.1 South	13	Fourth	-	-
Wealdstone	Isthmian Div.1 North	13	Fourth	-	-
Yeading	Isthmian Div.1 North	13	Second	-	-
Folkstone Invicta	Southern Eastern	12	Third	-	-
Taunton Town	Southern Western	12	Third	-	-
Runcorn FC H.	Northern Premier Prem.	11	Third	-	-
Staines Town	Isthmian Div.1 South	11	Fourth	-	-
Exeter City	Conference	10	Sixth	-	-
Guiseley	Northern Premier Div.1	10	Third	-	-
Kings Lynn	Southern Eastern	10	Fourth	-	-
Weston-s-Mare	Southern Western	10	Fourth	-	-

Arena Spectator Facilities

From Arena Seating the following spectator facilities are available for purchase to enhance all Sports Arenas and provide comfort for spectators

Arena Stadia Tip-Up Seats, floor or riser mounted on existing or new build terracing

Arena Sports Stand and Tiered Spectator Seating.
A classic design, with a cantilevered roof cover providing an unimpeded view for the spectator.

Can be supplied in 4, 7 and 13 rows covered seat options with or without end enclosures.

The roof cover is built in modules that can be added to as need and finance dictate.

Arena Sports Shelter
A smaller, lightweight 4 row version of the Arena Sports Stand where space is at a particular premium

Arena LT Grandstand and Arena LT Super Grandstand Prefabricated and delivered to location via lorry with crane.

Supplied complete with 50 or 74 tip up seats or as a tiered standing stand with capacity for 85 or 120 spectators.

Wheelchair spaces can be incorporated.

End enclosures available as an optional extra.

Can be linked together for greater capacity.

Arena Seating Limited, Arena House, Membury, Lambourn Woodlands, Hungerford, Berkshire RG17 7TQ
Tel: 01488 674800 Fax: 01488 674822 Email: info@arenaseating.com

THE F.A. VASE

Shaun Dyke & Andy Forbes hold the FA Vase aloft. Photo: Roger Turner

2003/04

FIRST ROUND QUALIFYING

Saturday 6th September **Winning clubs received: £300**

Home		Away	Score	Att
Abbey Hey	v	Ramsbottom United	1-2	65
Graystone				
AFC Kempston Rovers	v	Ruislip Manor	3-0	21
Halfyard, Layne, Watts				
AFC Newbury	v	East Grinstead Town	2-0	62
Alsager Town	v	Rossington Main	5-0	68
Brotherton, Dick, Kinsey, Park, Wilshaw				
Arnold Town	v	Coventry Sphinx - reversed tie	3-4*	91
Brevett (2), Mushambi		Beckett, McSheffrey (2), Woods		
(at Coventry Sphinx FC)				
Barnstaple Town	v	Ilfracombe Town	2-1	153
Middleton, Trudgian		Varley		
Bedford Utd & Valerio	v	Raunds Town	2-1	42
Velibor, Williams		Cotton		
Bicester Town	v	Stanway Rovers	2-1	48
Hamilton, O'Connor		English		
Biddulph Victoria	v	Birstall United (7/9)	1-0	119
Marrow				
Billingham Synthonia	v	Brodsworth MW	3-2*	70
Fletcher, Perry, Wells		Batchelor, Falcuss		
Bitton	v	Chipping Norton Town	4-2	50
Cole, Raynes (3)		Wright (2)		
Blaby & Whetstone Ath.	v	Deeping Rangers	3-0	71
Blackfield & Langley	v	Ramsgate	1-3	71
Hurst		Ovard, Robinson, Takalobighashi		
Bolehall Swifts	v	Brierley & Hagley	0-2	33
		Rowley, Store		
Brackley Town	v	Great Yarmouth Town	0-1	90
		George		
Brentwood (w/o)	v	Saffron Walden Town		
Bridgwater Town	v	Bournemouth	1-2	197
Young		Honeybun, Town		
Bristol Manor Farm	v	Liskeard Athletic	2-3*	34
		Hampton, Senior, Woodfield		
Broxbourne Borough V&E	v	Leverstock Green	1-3	35
Ward				
Cammell Laird	v	Great Harwood Town	7-0	79
Davies, Jebb, Morgan (3), Thompson (2)				
Causeway United	v	Barwell (7/9)	0-2*	152
		Boyles, Lill		
Chester-Le-Street Town	v	Marske United	2-1	81
Bowes (2)		Stott		
Clacton Town	v	Sawbridgeworth Town	1-2*	94
Gove		Bulled, O'Reilly		
Clevedon United	v	Portland United	2-6	127
Thorne		Carter, Laws (2), Reeve, Turrell		
(at Portland United FC)				
Colney Heath	v	Wisbech Town	1-3	119
Arthur		Cobb, Edge, Furnell		
Congleton Town	v	Leek CSOB	4-0	138
Owen, Scully (3)				
Cornard United	v	Thetford Town	5-0	37
Evason, Rayner (2), Wiffen				
Deal Town	v	Milton United	1-0	142
Barnett				
Didcot Town	v	Slade Green	2-0	110
Concannon (2)				
Eastbourne Town	v	Dorking	6-3	
Godfrey (2), Holman, Odbuade (2), Walsh		Duffell (3)		
Edgware Town	v	Newport Pagnell Town	2-1	50
Kennedy, Thomas		Flynn		
Eton Manor	v	Witham Town	0-1	45
		Emery		
(at Burnham Ramblers FC)				
Evenwood Town	v	Ashington	2-4	52
		Heppell, Nash (2), Sinclair		
(at West Auckland Town FC)				
Ford Sports Daventry	v	Ipswich Wanderers	0-0*	50
Friar Lane OB	v	Boldmere St Michaels	4-2	90
Griffin, Hobson, Marsh (2)		Jones, Welburn		
Glapwell	v	Castle Vale KH	3-1	52
Bland, Smith, Wilson		Morgan		

Lee Wilson (10) heads just over during this Glapwell attack on the Castle Vale Kings Heath goal.
Photo: Bill Wheatcroft.

Home		Away	Score	Att
Guisborough Town	v	Maltby Main	2-1	76
Osborne, Sunley		Hartley		
Hatfield Main	v	New Mills (w/o)		
Haverhill Rovers	v	Woodford United	3-2	122
Banham, Challis, Green		Fountain, Oliver		
Heanor Town	v	Boston Town	3-1	103
Froggatt, Johnson, Widdison		Don-Duncan		
Highfield Rangers	v	Shifnal Town	2-1	34
Phillips, Siddique		Syder		
Highgate United	v	Chasetown	0-3	101
		Harrison, Tivnan		
Hoddesdon Town (w/o)	v	Tring Town		
Hungerford Town	v	Bedfont	1-2	68
Head		Postins (2)		
Kingsbury Town	v	Eynesbury Rovers	3-1	38
Barber, Newing, Roche		Childerley		
Lancing	v	Reading Town	0-4	67
		Hollidge, Mills, Murray, Sharratt		
Ledbury Town	v	Blackstones	3-1	93
Preedy (3)		Epps		
Liversedge	v	Kennek Ryhope CA	3-1	77
Farrand, Nestor, Smith		Bell		
Marconi	v	Pegasus Juniors	4-1	33
Bent, Drennan, McIntoch, Towers		Aubrey		
Mildenhall Town	v	Tiptree United	3-1	112
Huggins, Paynter (2)		Butler		

Home		Away	Score	Att
Moneyfields	v	Hassocks	4-2	53
Mould (3), Sanderson		Harding (2)		
Norton & Stockton Ancients	v	Tadcaster Albion	0-1	71
		Howgate		
Oldbury United	v	Dudley Sports	8-0	60
Barton, Blake (2), Harvey (2), Palmer (3)				
Padiham	v	Armthorpe Welfare	2-1	102
Gill, Pilkington		Bradley		
Penrith	v	Flixton	3-2*	75
		Brickhill, Feeney		
Poole Town	v	Willand Rovers	0-4	147
		Cane, Everett, Murray, Norman		
Poulton Victoria	v	Ryton	4-1	72
Barry (2), Leech, Stones		Bogle		
Rainworth MW	v	Dudley Town	2-0	20
Clarke, Edwards				
Retford United	v	Oldham Town	3-0	224
Gamble, Powell (2)				
Saltash United	v	Hamworthy United	1-4	102
McShane		Bedward, Cann (2), Orchard		
Saltdean United	v	East Preston	2-1	61
Curram, Jordan		Clayton		
Sandiacre Town	v	Teversal	4-0	93
Ghislanzoni (3), Hall				
Shirebrook Town	v	Sutton Town	2-1	124
Johnson		Short		
Skelmersdale United	v	Eccleshill United	3-3*	79
Osman, Rudd, Tobin		Buchan, Coubrough, Howland		
Southwick	v	Littlehampton Town	2-6	44
		Gayler (2), Kirkham (2), Miller, Tabor		
Squires Gate	v	Chadderton	5-2	70
Blundell, Bradford, McKenna, Openshaw, Thompson		Faney, Gilks		
St Ives Town	v	Greenacres (Hemel Hempstead)	1-6	52
Pilsworth		Armstrong, Bowe, Carter (2), McMahon, Nevin		
Stansted	v	Harpenden Town	3-2	22
Massala, Salmon-Fattamain, Tagliamonti		Guile, Price		
Stewarts & Lloyds	v	Southend Manor	3-3*	43
Byrne, Curtis, Drain		Dooley, Jarvis (2)		
Steyning Town	v	Selsey	2-1	58
Aannah, Gainsford		Robertson		
Stowmarket Town	v	Cogenhoe United	3-1	76
King (2), Pannell		Koryia		
Street	v	Odd Down	1-0	57
Pople				
Thatcham Town	v	Ringmer	3-0	79
Cook, Czastka, Davies				
Tuffley Rovers	v	Porthleven	1-2*	48
Tatton		Sargent (2)		
Tunbridge Wells	v	Chessington United	2-4	60
Hickmott, Marchant		Burns (2), Morris, Powell		

Tunbridge Wells' Shane McDermott gets in a shot despite the pressure of Chessington's Adam McCullagh. Photo: Alan Coomes.

Home		Away	Score	Att
Wantage Town	v	Alton Town	0-0*	47
Washington	v	Warrington Town	0-2	53
		Mitchell (2)		
Wellington Town	v	Shepton Mallet (7/9)	4-2	52
Crowford, Jenkins, Kingston, Short		Burr, Coleman		
Westfield	v	AFC Wimbledon	2-7	1344
Finn, Jones (at Woking FC)		Cooper (3), Favata, Sheerin (2), Sullivan		
Whitton United	v	Halstead Town	3-1	92
Francis, Grimwood, Swann		Heath		
Wick	v	Raynes Park Vale	0-1	37
		Sendawula		
Willenhall Town	v	Buxton	1-2*	148
Hay		Bullock, Cheetham		
Wimborne Town	v	Chard Town	4-1	154
Barnes (2), Doyle (2)		Larcombe		
Yaxley	v	Norwich United	4-0*	68
Chapman, Cunningham, Frew, Miller				

R E P L A Y S

9th September

Home		Away	Score	Att
Alton Town	v	Wantage Town	1-2	71
Lillis (at Wantage Town FC)		Tinsley (2)		
Ipswich Wanderers	v	Ford Sports Daventry	0-2	114
		Geary, Hancock		
Southend Manor	v	Stewarts & Lloyds	2-2* 4-5p	72
Jarvis (2)		Gilsenan, Walker		

10th September

Home		Away	Score	Att
Eccleshill United	v	Skelmersdale United	1-3	58
Bucman		Rudd (3)		

Selsey's Rodrigues fires in a shot against Steyning Town. Photo: Roger Turner.

SECOND ROUND QUALIFYING

Saturday 20 September | Winning clubs received: £500

Home		Away	Score	Att
AFC Newbury	v	Merstham	6-0	66
Alleyne (2), Mildenhall, Newton, Wood (2)				
Alnwick Town	v	Peterlee Newtown	3-4*	73
Catlow, Dixon, McCormick		Dobell (2), Harvey, Hinton		
Atherton Collieries	v	Dunston Federation Brewery	1-2	65
Stewart		Hogg, Holmes		
Atherton LR	v	Ashington	0-1	55
		Douglas		
Barrow Town	v	Malvern Town	2-0	75
Aston, Quinn				
Bedford Utd & Valerio	v	Burnham Ramblers	2-2*	32
Smith, Velibor		Agyei-Dua, Winters		
Bemerton Heath H'quins	v	Wootton Bassett Town	4-1	57
Ahmet, Chalk, Findlay, Jones		Vaughan		
Billingham Synthonia	v	Penrith	4-1	84
Fletcher, Marron, Perry, Wells		Thomson		
Bitton	v	Exmouth Town	5-1	68
Gitson, Huxley (2), McAlinden, Williams		Taylor		
Blackwell MW	v	Glapwell	1-4	56
Downing		Davies, Stubley, Taylor, Yates		
Bournemouth	v	Paulton Rovers	0-1	65
		Jones		
Bowers United	v	Stansted	0-2	35
		Frota, Salmon-Fattamain		
Bridport	v	Fairford Town	1-1*	80
White		Kilfoyle		
Brierley & Hagley	v	Nuneaton Griff (19/9)	0-2	109
		Aston, Pulford		
Brimsdown Rovers	v	Woodbridge Town	3-4*	80
Forbes, Keogh, Salah		Howell (4)		
Broadbridge Heath	v	Hartley Wintney	0-3	28
		Charman, Higgins, Wheeler		
Bromyard Town	v	Elmore	2-2* 5-3p	51
Crowther, Russell		Anderson, Miles		
Brook House	v	Brentwood	3-1	55
Chakoadza, Yeardley (2)		Hayes		
Budleigh Salterton	v	Launceston	4-1	114
Asson, Squire, Turner, West		Hooper		
Bugbrooke St Michaels	v	Great Yarmouth Town	0-1	44
		Barker		
Buxton	v	Borrowash Victoria	4-0	338
Bullock, Cheetham (3)				
Camberley Town	v	Herne Bay	1-2	52
Pym		Jones, Pollard		
Cammell Laird	v	Warrington Town	0-2	121
		Mitchell, Moore		
Carlton Town	v	Blaby & Whetstone Athletic	2-4*	50
Heverin (2)		Marsh, Pearce, Tanner (2)		
Chalfont St Peter	v	Desborough Town	1-2	21
Stout		Coles, Steed		
Chasetown	v	Bourne Town	2-0	115
Ball, Gossage				
Cheadle Town	v	New Mills	3-2	81
Kempton, McDonald, Morris		Ignotus (2)		
Chessington & Hook Utd	v	Cowes Sports	3-1	101
Bochanski, Foracre, Justice				
Chessington United	v	Whitchurch United	0-2	30
		Aldridge, Power		
Chichester City United	v	Abingdon United	1-2	60
Moore		Moss, Peirson		
Chipstead	v	BAT Sports	1-2*	71
McSherry		Gregory, West		
Clapton	v	Long Melford	1-1*	42
Goulding		Arnold		
Coalville Town	v	Westfields	3-2*	93
		Gurton, Hibbard		
Cobham	v	Abingdon Town	1-2	53
Horder		Harper, Joyce		
Cockfosters	v	Northampton Spencer	0-0*	66
Colne	v	Chester-Le-Street Town	3-2	66
Gizon, Ingham, Simpson		Bowes, Ingram, Turner		
Consett	v	Sheffield	0-2	90
		Burke, Tee		
Cornard United	v	Biggleswade United	1-3	40
Guyon		Dimmock, Palma, Tyler		
Corsham Town	v	Highworth Town	1-3*	85
Bryan		Belcher, Dix, Saye		
Cove	v	Fareham Town	0-2	64
		Musselwhite (2)		
Coventry Sphinx	v	Downes Sports	2-0	66
Woods (2)				
Cradley Town	v	Biddulph Victoria	3-3*	51
Hamilton, Moore (2)		Callan, Marrow (2)		
Crook Town	v	Padiham	2-1	75
Bailes, Snow		Howes		
Cullompton Rangers	v	Bishop's Cleeve	0-1	65
		Giles		
Curzon Ashton	v	Glasshoughton Welfare	2-1	50
Dean, Mitten				
Daventry Town	v	Friar Lane OB	1-0	67
Fountain				
Deal Town	v	Peacehaven & Telscombe	2-1	115
Hughes, Ingram		Lee		
Didcot Town	v	Petersfield Town	2-0	120
Dorrian, Parsons				
Downton	v	Calne Town	3-0	55
Guy (2), Savage				
Easington Colliery	v	Worsborough Bridge MW	0-1*	33
Eastbourne Town	v	Wokingham Town	3-3*	206
Godfrey, Harris, Odbuade		Gibson, McCoy, Pritchard		
Eastbourne United	v	Wantage Town	1-2*	56
Harris				
Edgware Town	v	Kingsbury Town	3-1	65
Heselton, Kennedy, Thomas		Mitchell		
Ellistown (w/o)	v	Gornal Athletic		
Fakenham Town	v	Ely City	1-0	71
Knowles				
Farnham Town	v	Redhill	1-2	33
Gale		Graves, Jones		
Felixstowe & Walton Utd	v	Godmanchester Rovers	1-0	71
Thurkettle				
Fernhill County Sports	v	Norton United (w/o)		
Ford Sports Daventry	v	Dereham Town	0-1	50
		Hillier		
Frimley Green	v	Thatcham Town	1-4	80
Brighty		Cook, Czastka, Oatway, Perry		
Frome Town	v	Dawlish Town	4-1	120
Hayter (3), Pounder		Broadway		
Gedling Town	v	Shawbury United	3-1*	23
Evans, Kennerdale (2)		Trenarn		
Godalming & Guildford	v	Whitstable Town	1-3	78
Chandiram		Utterson (3)		
Greenwich Borough	v	Ash United	1-2	47
Norris		Blason, Mitchell		
Grosvenor Park	v	Graham St Prims	2-0	31
Burnes, Taylor				

Home		Away	Score	Att
Guisborough Town	v	West Auckland Town	3-0	125
Bishop, Kasonali, McMahon				
Hailsham Town	v	Rye & Iden United	0-1	72
		Price		
Hall Road Rangers	v	North Shields	3-1	105
Barnwell (2), Dixon		Riley		
Hallen	v	Pershore Town	6-0	76
Beecham (2), Collett (3), Summerill				
Hamworthy United	v	Bodmin Town	2-0	143
McCormack (2)				
Hanwell Town	v	Hoddesdon Town	3-0	29
Brown, Rowlands, Whall				
Harefield United	v	Greenacres (H. Hempstead)	3-2	64
Dunne, McCulloch, Pither		Carter (2)		
Haringey Borough	v	Barkingside	0-1	29
		Bonham		
Harrogate Railway	v	Jarrow Roofing Boldon CA	1-4	88
Delaney		Chow (3), McCabe		
Harrow Hill	v	Torrington	2-5	30
Frowen, Woodroffe		Langmead (2), Madge, Robinson, Yeo		
Harwich & Parkeston	v	Henley Town	8-0	110
Calver, Carmichael (4), Hearne (2), Meadows				
Haverhill Rovers	v	Biggleswade Town	0-1	122
		Drummond		
Heanor Town	v	Alvechurch	1-0	133
Fowler				
Heath Hayes	v	Ibstock Welfare	1-4	53
Inskip		Andrews, Foster, Hawkins, Turville		
Hillingdon Borough	v	Brockenhurst	3-2	44
Moran, O'Neill, Raymond		Marwood, Wright		
Holker Old Boys	v	Garforth Town	4-4*	56
Bruce (2), Southward (2)		Jones, Ryan (3)		
Holmer Green	v	Newmarket Town	1-7	67
Ansell		Long, Ogilvie (2), Rhodes, Shaw (2), Tuck		
Horden CW	v	West Allotment Celtic	1-2	64
Pearson		Bowers, Houlsby		
Hullbridge Sports	v	Leiston	0-2	51
		Driver (2)		
Kirby Muxloe	v	Congleton Town	0-3	72
		Scully, Tunncliffe, Worthington		

Home		Away	Score	Att
Leamington	v	Highfield Rangers	4-1	452
Blake, McFarlane, Nicholls, Thompson		Richards		
Ledbury Town (w/o)	v	Nettleham		
Leighton Town	v	Royston Town	1-0	
Bourne				
Lincoln Moorlands	v	Blidworth Welfare	6-1	41
Fleming, Jennings, Roach, Robinson, Shelley (2)				
Liskeard Athletic	v	Keynsham Town	0-0*	75
Littlehampton Town	v	Oakwood	3-1	88
Barnard, Miller, More				
Liversedge	v	Darwen	4-2	87
Brady, Nestor (3)		Stubberfield (2)		
London Colney	v	Hadleigh United	1-0	62
Farrow				
Long Buckby	v	AFC Kempston Rovers	2-2*	39
Harrison, Thomas		Reed, Watts		
Long Eaton United	v	Loughborough Dynamo	2-0	89
Briscoe, Mabon				
Lordswood	v	Beckenham Town	1-2	31
Dodsworth		Coleman (2)		
Louth United	v	Willington (w/o)		
Ludlow Town	v	Rolls Royce Leisure	2-0	61
Jackson				
Lye Town	v	Mickleover Sports	0-2	
		O'Reilly, Stevens		
Marconi	v	Stafford Town	6-0	30
Civzelis, Gordon, Innes (3), Nolan				
Meir KA	v	Stone Dominoes	0-1	100
		Scheuber		
Mile Oak	v	Haywards Heath Town	1-0	56
Macabie				
Minehead Town	v	Bishop Sutton	3-1	51
Graddon, Todd (2)		Norman		
Murton	v	Bacup Borough	0-1	31
		Gray		
Nantwich Town	v	Kimberley Town	2-1	74
Knight, Thomas		Hallam		
Needham Market (w/o)	v	Milton Keynes City		

Coventry Marconi's Danny Green (white), beats Stafford Town's Ashley Sheridon in this aerial duel. Photo: Bill Wheatcroft.

Home		Away	Score	Att
Nelson	v	Maine Road	3-1	80
Berry, Bradshaw, Howarth		Simms		
Nettleham	v	Ledbury Town	4-3*	50
Beesley (2), Grimes, Walker		Colwell (2), Preedy		
Newcastle Benfield S.	v	Thornaby	4-1	
Bell, Gustard, Scope (2)		Storr		
Newcastle Blue Star	v	Hallam	1-3	90
Smith		Campbell, Muzrczka, Storey		
Newquay	v	Barnstaple Town	0-2	82
		Squire, Vinicombe		
Newton Abbot	v	Amesbury Town	5-2	71
Clark, Osborne (2), Pegley, Turner		Kinghorn, Nicholls		
North Greenford United	v	Mildenhall Town	1-4	35
Hill		Hobbs, Paynter, Taylor-Holt, Walker		
Pagham	v	AFC Wimbledon (21/9)	0-1	1050
Pewsey Vale	v	Wellington Town	3-2	50
Flippance, Messenger		Wells		
Pontefract Collieries	v	Blackpool Mechanics	0-2	42
		Gardiner, Hoyle		
Porthleven	v	Backwell United	2-4	164
Powell		Billitteri, Bloomfield, Gwyther		
Portland United	v	Welton Rovers	2-4*	151
Whalley		Astin, Blackmore (2), Jefferies		
Poulton Victoria	v	Prudhoe Town	3-1	73
Bates, Leech, Stones		Petterson		
Quorn	v	Pelsall Villa		
(tie awarded to Quorn - Pelsall Villa failed to fulfil fixture)				
Rainworth MW	v	Glossop North End	2-1	55
Clarke, Fisher		Barhill		
Ramsbottom United	v	Shotton Comrades	5-1	133
Brickell (3), Fitton, Gardiner		Bickerstaff		
Raynes Park Vale	v	VCD Athletic	0-2	44
		Bates, Main		
Reading Town	v	Moneyfields	1-3	13
Masson		Dunk, Jones (2)		

Home		Away	Score	Att
Retford United	v	Yorkshire Amateur	3-1	179
Redhead, Shaw, Tomlinson		Little		
Romford	v	Witham Town (23/9)	0-2*	94
		Gibbens, Hawes		
Rothwell Corinthians	v	Bury Town	1-4	67
Chilton		Deeks, Ince, Snell, Tatham		
Rugby Town	v	Anstey Nomads	4-2*	45
Lavery, Morgan, Rule				
(at Anstey Nomads FC)				
Saltdean United	v	Erith Town	1-1*	47
Burton		McTaggart		
Sandhurst Town	v	Bedfont	0-3	51
		Barrett, Fofamah, Postins		
Sandiacre Town	v	West Midlands Police	3-0	84
Booth, Ghislanzoni, Higgins				
Sawbridgeworth Town	v	March Town United	5-1	34
Hammick (3), Lilley, Martin		Brand		
Seaham Red Star	v	Alsager Town	3-9	
		Brotherton, Kinsey (5), Wilshaw (3)		
Selby Town	v	Winsford United	5-2*	59
Barnett, Croad, Hart, Matthews, Moyles		Maranda, Rowland		
Shildon	v	Salford City	4-2	215
Barnes (2), Chapman, Liddle				
Sidlesham	v	Andover	2-5	94
Tipper, Towers		Bennett, Damen, Rusher (3)		
Sidley United	v	Ramsgate	2-2*	101
Carey, Sperafico		Gregory, Takalobighashi		
Silsden	v	Thackley	2-0	448
Spencer, Ward				
Somersham Town	v	St Neots Town	0-4	103
		Chapman (2), Kuhne (2)		
South Shields	v	Washington Nissan	0-2	104
		Moan, Tiplady		
Southall Town	v	Whitton United (21/9)	3-0	97
Castagnette, Mee				

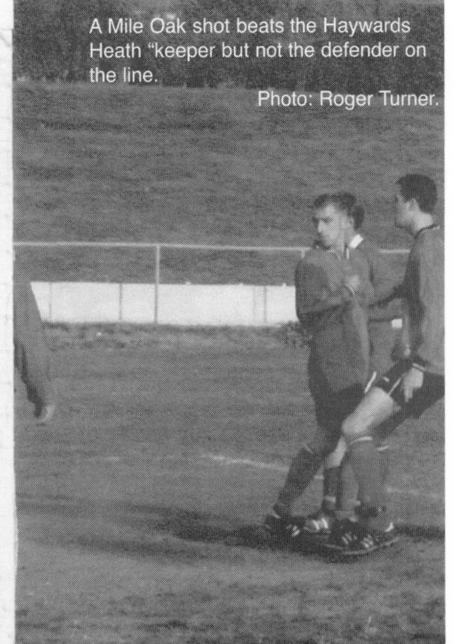

A Mile Oak shot beats the Haywards Heath "keeper but not the defender on the line.

Photo: Roger Turner.

Moneyfields' Gavin Jones challenges Reading Town 'keeper David Jenkins without success, however, Jones did find the net to send the.....fan(!) into wild celebrations.

Photos: Graham Brown.

Home		Away	Score	Att
Squires Gate	v	Whickham	2-1	76
Blinkhorn, Bradford		Hedley		
St Helens Town	v	Hebburn Town	3-2*	77
Anderson (2), Fairbrother		Handy, Rolfe		
St Margaretsbury	v	Oxhey Jets	4-1	43
Howard (2), Lovett (2)		Simmonds		
Stapenhill	v	Oldbury United	3-0	81
Marshall, Shales (2)				
Staveley MW	v	Dunkirk	2-3*	62
Clarke (2)		Burke, Scott, Thomas		
Stewarts & Lloyds	v	Potton United	3-1	26
Curtis, Gilsenan, Walker		Crook		
Stotfold	v	Leverstock Green	4-1*	76
Byrne (2), Errington, Griffith				
Stowmarket Town	v	Bicester Town	3-0	86
Byrne, King, Ratcliffe				
Street	v	Almondsbury Town	2-3	87
Badman, Light		Berry, Bishop, Davidge		
Studley	v	Wednesfield	6-1	78
Burrows,Cannonier(3),Pountney(2)		Lloyd		
Tadcaster Albion	v	Esh Winning	0-3	45
		Clarke (2), Purrier		
Three Bridges	v	Hythe Town	2-0	100
Patrick, Simmons				
Tipton Town	v	Barwell	3-1	85
Bailey, Sangha, Worsey		Clamp		
Tividale	v	St Andrews	2-1	42
Aston, Chester		McCathie		
Tow Law Town	v	Ossett Albion	0-1	145
		Watts		
Walton Casuals	v	Steyning Town	0-1	116
		Rowe		
Wellington	v	Shirebrook Town	2-0	55
Ingram, Piper				
Westbury United	v	Melksham Town	2-1	154
Colbourne, Wheeler		Banks		
Willand Rovers	v	Shortwood United	2-1	80
Everett, Murray		Davis		
Wimborne Town	v	Falmouth Town	5-1	223
Barnes (2), Powell (2), Stainer				
Winterton Rangers	v	Skelmersdale United	2-0	67
Nikolaidis (2)				
Wisbech Town (w/o)	v	Warboys Town		
Woodley Sports	v	Parkgate	7-0	44
Johnson, Kneen, Norton (3), Ryan, Vaughan				
Yaxley	v	Langford	3-0	76
Acton, McCallum, Miller				

R E P L A Y S

Home		Away	Score	Att
22nd September				
Erith Town	v	Saltdean United (22/9)	2-0	48
McTaggart (2)				
23rd September				
AFC Kempston R	v	Long Buckby (23/9)	3-2	29
Dudley, Layne, Pipe		Box, Neil		
Biddulph Victoria	v	Cradley Town (23/9)	3-0	47
Callan, Kirk, Marrow				
Burnham Ramblers	v	Bedford Utd & V. (23/9) 3-3*	3-0p	67
Baldwin, Holmes, White		Armstrong (2), Williams		
Garforth Town	v	Holker Old Boys (23/9)	4-0	96
Jones, Ryan (3)				
Long Melford	v	Clapton (23/9)	0-1	84
		Davy		
Northampton Spencer	v	Cockfosters (23/9)	4-0	68
Allen, Ayre, Leah, Streeton				
Ramsgate	v	Sidley United (23/9)	3-1	95
Gregory, Takalobighashi (2)		Heritage		
Wokingham Town	v	Eastbourne Town (23/9)	5-3*	58
Needham, Pritchard (4)		Brockwell, Holman, Odbuade		
24th September				
Fairford Town	v	Bridport (24/9)	1-0	78
Kilfoyle				
Keynsham Town	v	Liskeard Athletic (24/9)	5-2	58
Adams (2), Cripps, Ewins (2)		Karl, Williams		

FIRST ROUND

Saturday 18th October — Winning clubs received: £600

Home		Away	Score	Att
Abingdon Town	v	Fareham Town	0-1	80
		Hamodu		
Abingdon United	v	Erith Town	1-3	42
Peirson		Springett (3)		
AFC Kempston Rovers	v	Leighton Town	2-3	62
Pipe, Watts		Kingsley, Redsull (2)		
AFC Newbury	v	Littlehampton Town	1-2	91
McSherry		Chester, More		
AFC Totton	v	Bedfont	2-2*	129
Clark (2)		Postins, Willis		
Alsager Town	v	Silsden	1-0	166
Verow				
Andover	v	Hillingdon Borough	3-2	182
Cole (3)		O'Brien (2)		
Barkingside	v	Fakenham Town (19/10)	0-1	126
(match ordered to be replayed as a result of FA investigation)				
Barkingside	v	Fakenham (1/11)	3-1	53
Carr (3)		Howard, Meek		
Barnstaple Town	v	Backwell United	0-3	116
		Hewitt (2), Maggs		
BAT Sports	v	Ash United	3-0	58
Gregory (2), West				
Beaconsfield SYCOB	v	Wisbech Town	2-1	89
Arthur (2)		Jimson		
Bemerton Heath Harlequins	v	Fairford Town	2-3	64
Finlay, Palmer		Legg		
Biddulph Victoria	v	Gedling Town	1-3	66
Wilson-Cunningham		Kennerdale, Soffham (2)		
Biggleswade Town	v	Edgware Town	0-2*	51
		Gilbride, Randall		
Biggleswade United	v	Dereham Town	2-3*	62
O'Dell, Tyler		Barrett, Moody, Payne		
Bitton	v	Budleigh Salterton	1-0	83
Cole				
Blaby & Whetstone Ath.	v	Ledbury Town	3-1	49
Devlin, Marsh (2)		Preedy		
Blackpool Mechanics	v	Sheffield	0-5	55
		Bray, Ingall, Moxon, Naylor, O'Carroll		
Bromyard Town	v	Studley	1-3	58
McLean		Johnson, Pountney, Thomas		
Brook House	v	Newmarket Town	0-1*	77
		Stokes		
Burnham Ramblers	v	Wembley	1-0	85
Perry				
Bury Town	v	Witham Town	1-0	142
Miller				
Buxton	v	Rushall Olympic	5-2*	475
Bevan, Cheetham (2), Reed (2)		Round		

Action from a closely fought contest between Moneyfields and Steyning Town.
Photo: Graham Brown.

Home		Away	Score	Att
Carterton Town	v	Chessington & Hook United	1-2	30
Lewis		Martin, Smith		
Chertsey Town	v	Hartley Wintney	0-0*	97
Colne	v	Washington Nissan	3-1	69
Howarth (2), Ingham		Jackson		
Concord Rangers	v	Sawbridgeworth Town	1-0	38
Ward				
Coventry Sphinx	v	Tividale	5-3*	58
Stevenson (2), Taylor (2), Woods		Aston, Chester, Reynolds		
Crook Town	v	Ramsbottom United	2-3	90
		Barker, Dyson, Walsh		
Curzon Ashton	v	Poulton Victoria	0-2	80
		Butler, Holmes		
Deal Town	v	Cray Wanderers	1-2	126
Cox		Lover, Taylor		
Dunston Fed. Brewery	v	Brandon United	2-1	149
Hogg, Southern		Patterson		
Eastwood Town	v	Ludlow Town	2-0	103
Fisher, Whitehead				
Enfield Town	v	Felixstowe & Walton Utd	2-0	314
Grant, Nash				
Flackwell Heath	v	Northampton Spencer	2-0	44
Hill (2)				
Frome Town	v	Paulton Rovers	4-1	164
Hayter, Jarman, Preece (2)		Colbourne		
Goole	v	Liversedge	0-3	210
		Hamlet, Nestor, Walton		
Grosvenor Park	v	Holbeach United	2-0	32
Burns, Robinson				
Guisborough Town	v	Peterlee Newtown	4-1	100
Booth (2), Johnson, McMahon		Atkinson, Hinton		
Hailsham Town	v	Gosport Borough	0-4	121
		Hensman,Lindsey, Mann, Middleton		
Hall Road Rangers	v	Ashington	2-1	76
Barnwell, Dixon		Sinclair		
Hallen	v	Hamworthy United	1-2	80
Griffiths		Bedward, Tilley		
Hanwell Town	v	Harwich & Parkeston	3-7	52
Rowlands, Sheekey (2)		Griggs, Hughes, Springett, Townes		
Heanor Town	v	Stourbridge	1-2	156
Froggatt		Broadhurst, Hall		
Herne Bay	v	AFC Wimbledon	2-3	1920
Cirillo, Jones				
Jarrow Roofing Boldon CA	v	Bedlington Terriers	2-1	108
Chow (2)		Allen		
Keynsham Town	v	Downton	6-0	51
Adams (2), Ewins, Reynolds, Stewart, Wood				
Leamington	v	Barrow Town	2-2*	458
Dhesi, Thompson		Almond, North		
London Colney	v	AFC Wallingford	1-3	35
Flain		Beavon (2), Swift		
Long Eaton United	v	Daventry Town	2-2*	71
Briscoe, King		Blackwood, O'Brien		
Lordswood	v	Ramsgate	0-1	65
		Robinson		
Maidstone United	v	Horsham YMCA (19/10)	3-1	336
Lacy, Marshall, Sinden		Jarvano		
Marconi	v	Congleton Town	0-0*	50
Mickleover Sports	v	Ibstock Welfare	3-1	125
Parkins, Strzyzewski, Yeoman		Turville		
Minehead Town	v	Willand Rovers	1-2	80
Pople		Bowrah, Ebdy		
Moneyfields	v	Steyning Town	1-0*	60
Boyle				

Home		Away	Score	Att
Nantwich Town Griggs	v	Tipton Town	1-0	116
Newton Abbot Clark	v	Highworth Town Hunt (2), Jack	1-3	101
Norton United Cole, Killeen	v	Nuneaton Griff Aston, Bindley, Pulford	2-3*	51
Potters Bar Town Talbot (3)	v	Stotfold	3-2*	88
Quorn Fisher, Sargeant	v	Spalding United Hudson, Nuttall, Watts	3-3*	172
Racing Club Warwick Brush	v	Chasetown	1-0	93
Rainworth MW Deakin	v	Retford United Shaw (2)	1-2	95
Redhill Jones (2)	v	North Leigh Cooper, Forrester, Lewis	2-3*	75
Rocester McMahon (2), Mitchel	v	Rugby Town	3-1	84
Sandiacre Town Ghislanzoni (2)	v	Lincoln Moorlands Roach (2), Robinson	2-3	68
Selby Town Barley, Gaughan (2)	v	Newcastle Benfield Saints Greenhill	4-1	86
Shildon Bolton, ellison (2)	v	Garforth Town	3-0	238
Soham Town Rangers Bugg, Docking	v	Leiston	2-0	147
Southall Town Cahil (2), Glynn, Keane, Meaker	v	Ilford Downer	5-2	31
Squires Gate Sugden, Urwin	v	Nelson Berry	2-1	85
St Helens Town Anderson, Melling	v	Willington Cummings	2-1	71
St Margaretsbury	v	Great Yarmouth Town Howes, Vincent	0-2	66
St Neots Town Fortune, Kuhne (2)	v	Needham Market Fox	3-1	77
Stansted	v	Desborough Town Chone, Mills	0-2	46
Stapenhill Gough, Shum	v	Glapwell Smith	2-1	92
Stewarts & Lloyds Walker	v	Clapton Odigwe, Whiteman	1-2	45
Stone Dominoes Donnelly, Walker	v	Ellistown Aston	2-1	77
Stowmarket Town Barker	v	Mildenhall Town Reeder, Walker	1-2	118
Stratford Town Kitching	v	Coalville Town Finney, Saunders (2)	1-3*	136
Thamesmead Town Burns (2), Power (2)	v	VCD Athletic Arnold, Northover (2)	4-3*	98
Thatcham Town Davies (2)	v	St Leonards	2-0	80
Torrington Bettiss, Madge, Yeo	v	Pewsey Vale	3-0	69
Trafford McDonagh, Turner	v	Cheadle Town Channon	2-1	94
Wantage Town	v	Didcot Town	0-0*	161
Warrington Town Mitchell	v	Esh Winning	1-0	112

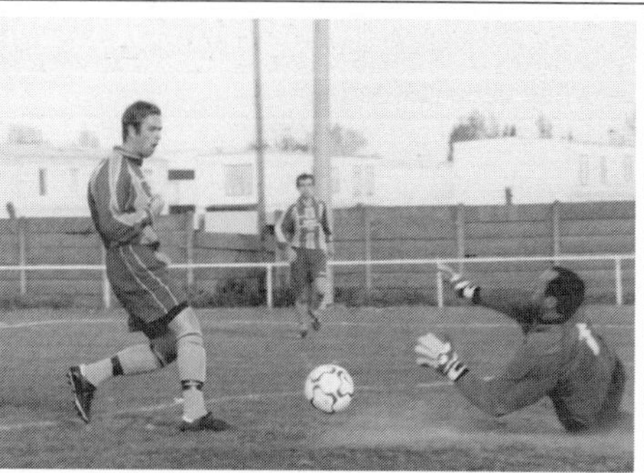

Concord Rangers' Nathan Collins slips the ball past Sawbridgeworth's 'keeper Martin Coomber....but is ruled off-side.

Photo: Alan Coomes.

Home		Away	Score	Att
Wellington Styles, Wallace	v	Dunkirk	2-0	62
Welton Rovers Blakemore, Wilson	v	Brislington Lee	2-1	61
West Allotment Celtic Benjamin, Dawson (2), Houlsey, Malone	v	Ossett Albion	5-0	115
Westbury United Colbourne (2), Perkins, Wheeler	v	Almondsbury Town Berry (2), Thorpe	4-3	110
Whitchurch United Roffey	v	Three Bridges Hackett	1-1*	63
Whitehawk Cooper, Lambert, Levitt, McBride, Pattenden, Venton	v	Mile Oak	6-1	55
Wimborne Town Arnold, Barnes	v	Bishop's Cleeve Davis, Keveran (2)	2-3	179
Winterton Rangers Spall	v	Billingham Synthonia Perry (2), Radigan	1-3	57
Wokingham Town Pritchard	v	Whitstable Town	1-0	60
Woodbridge Town Howell	v	Harefield United Dennison, Ursell	1-2	80
Woodley Sports Andrews, Woods	v	Hallam Mellon (2), Storet	2-3	55
Worsborough Bridge MW	v	Bacup Borough Gray	0-1	73
Yaxley Frew	v	Hertford Town Norton, Turner	1-2*	115

R E P L A Y S

21st October

Home		Away	Score	Att
Barrow Town	v	Leamington Sleem	0-1	158
Bedfont De-Costa, Williams, Willis	v	AFC Totton Osman	3-1	55
Congleton Town Hatton, Worthington	v	Marconi	2-0	152
Daventry Town Fountain, Spence	v	Long Eaton United Marston	2-1	56
Didcot Town Ford, Heady, Powell (2)	v	Wantage Town	4-0	210
Hartley Wintney Medford	v	Chertsey Town Breslin (3), McKinlay	1-4	87
Spalding United Hudson	v	Quorn	1-0	204
Three Bridges Funnell, Massaro	v	Whitchurch United	2-0	66

SECOND ROUND

Saturday 22nd November — **Winning clubs received: £1,000**

Home		Away	Score	Att
AFC Sudbury	v	Lowestoft Town	5-1	319
Bennett, Calver, Claydon (3)		Attridge		
AFC Wimbledon	v	Wootton Blue Cross	3-0	2307
Bolger, Cooper, Everard				
Alsager Town	v	Leamington	1-2	320
Kinsey		Shearsby, Sleem		
Arundel	v	Concord Rangers	1-3	82
Scerri		Sammons, Walsh		
Bacup Borough	v	Guisborough Town	0-3	53
		Bishop (2), Sankey		
BAT Sports	v	Frome Town	3-2	88
Gregory (2), Roberts		Salter (2)		
Bideford	v	Welton Rovers	7-0	211
Gough (2), Herrera, Pickard (3), Powell				
Billingham Town	v	Squires Gate	3-3*	89
Scoll, Ward, Woodhouse		Blundell, Rawson, Sugden		
Bishop's Cleeve	v	Keynsham Town	3-4	110
Clark, Cleal, Davis		Adams, Cripps (2), Reynolds		
Bitton	v	Fairford Town	3-1	108
Coles, Huxley, Raynes				
Blaby & Whetstone Ath.	v	Nuneaton Griff	5-2	77
Allen, Metcalf, Tanner (3)		Aston, Dyer		
Brigg Town	v	Buxton	0-1	255
		Froggatt		
Buckingham Town	v	Maldon Town	4-1	153
Abdi (2), Mcgillycuddy (2)		Brown		
Chertsey Town	v	Barkingside	3-0	116
Prendercast (3)				
Christchurch	v	Andover	0-2*	95
		Rusher, Sullivan		
Clitheroe	v	Whitley Bay	0-2	298
		Carter, Pepper		
Congleton Town	v	Rocester	3-3*	198
Ellis, Kay, Worthington		McMahon (3)		
Cray Wanderers	v	Chessington & Hook United	6-0	136
Bennett (2), Heaslewood (2), Wood, Woolf				
Daventry Town	v	Gedling Town	1-3	44
Jelly		Jefferies, Newton (2)		
Dereham Town	v	Southall Town	4-4*	95
Barnes, Garrett (3)		Gardner, Glynn, Keane (2)		
Desborough Town	v	Newcastle Town	1-0	69
Mills				
Didcot Town	v	Ramsgate	1-1*	127
		Takalobighashi		
Dunston Fed Brewery	v	Sheffield	0-0*	105
Eastwood Town	v	Spalding United	6-1	141
Fisher, Huckerby (2), Mitchell, Nazha		Hudson		

Alan Jefferies nets an early goal for Gedling Town at Daventry Town.
Photo: Gordon Whittington.

Home		Away	Score	Att
Edgware Town	v	Wroxham	2-3	65
Heselton (2)		Fox, Lemmon, Stock		
Flackwell Heath	v	Enfield Town	0-1	218
		Cove		
Fleetwood Town	v	Ramsbottom United	2-2*	127
Catlow, Dashti		Clark, Swailes		
Gorleston	v	Leighton Town	2-7	122
Hogg, Ingram		Pedder, Rawdon (3), Redsull (2), Shannon		
Gosport Borough	v	Highworth Town	6-0	144
Lindsey, Scammell (5)				
Hallam	v	Colne	2-2*	81
Maydury, Noney		Gizon, Howarth		
Harefield United	v	Potters Bar Town	1-1*	90
Nelson		Ferguson		
Harwich & Parkeston	v	Erith Town	2-0	200
Carmichael, Townes				
Jarrow Roofing Boldon CA	v	Hall Road Rangers	2-1	81
Cogden, Nelson		Dickinson		
Littlehampton Town	v	Great Yarmouth Town	1-2	122
Chester		George, Pierpoint		
Liversedge	v	Billingham Synthonia	1-2	93
Nestor		Fletcher (2)		
Lymington & New Milton	v	Backwell United	5-1	92
Holmes, James, Record, Thomson (2)		Bloomfield		
Maidstone United	v	AFC Wallingford	3-0	178
Kedwell, Sinden				
Mildenhall Town	v	Bury Town	1-3	171
Rutter		Evans, Ince, Munro		
Morpeth Town	v	Poulton Victoria	6-1	67
Beavers, Fenwick (2), Nicholls, Taylor		Thompson		
Mossley	v	Trafford	4-2*	244
Carroll (3), Matthews		Eames, Ritchie		
Nantwich Town	v	Grosvenor Park	5-1	60
Alexander, Gleghorn, Wilkinson (3)		Taylor		
Newmarket Town	v	Hertford Town	2-4	114
Dewsbury, Stokes		Cooper, Johnson, Leggatt, McEwan		
North Leigh	v	Clapton	11-0	40
Burnell, Burnley (2), Ellis (2), Forrester (4), Hamp, Lewis				
Northallerton Town	v	Warrington Town	1-1*	89
Onions		Heavey		
Racing Club Warwick	v	Coalville Town	0-1	103
		Saunders		
Retford United	v	Oadby Town	0-1	323
		Spencer		
Selby Town	v	Durham City	0-2	270
		Halliday, Robson		
Shildon	v	Pickering Town	2-0	324
Barnes (2)				
St Blazey	v	Willand Rovers	4-1	156
Crocker (3), Hooper		Stickland		
St Neots Town	v	Beaconsfield SYCOB	2-2*	86
Hoggett, Wareham		Arthur, Cotton		
Stapenhill	v	Wellington	1-2	96
Allen		Jones (2)		
Stone Dominoes	v	Coventry Sphinx	4-0	160
Lainton, Shaw (3)				
Stourbridge	v	Lincoln Moorlands	4-4*	169
Broadhurst, Gennard (2), Southwick		Baker, Roach, Robinson, Shelley		
Studley	v	Mickleover Sports	0-0*	89
Thatcham Town	v	Fareham Town	2-3	107
Adey, Worsfold		Atterbury, Hamodu, Ndoye		
Three Bridges	v	Diss Town	4-1	95
Ahearne, Green (2), Massaro		Hardy		

Torrington Bettiss, Langmead (2)	v	Moneyfields	3-0	90
Ware Crawford, Kearney	v	Thamesmead Town Burns (3), Power	2-4	127
West Allotment Celtic Benjamin	v	St Helens Town	1-0	79
Westbury United Colbourne, O'Pray (3), Pearce, Perkins (2), Wheeler	v	Devizes Town Campbell, Drewitt, Lisle	8-3	171
Whitehawk Pattenham (2), Rowland (3)	v	Burnham Ramblers Kingsley, White	5-2	67
Winchester City Oean	v	Hamworthy United	2-0	204
Withdean 2000 Bentley, Freeman, Mateos, Pulling, Standing	v	Bedfont Willis	5-1	48
Wokingham Town	v	Soham Town Rangers Bugg (2), Crawford, Foster	0-4	53

R E P L A Y S

25th November

Beaconsfield SYCOB Sear	v	St Neots Town Bartley	1-1*, 4-5p	81
Colne Simpson	v	Hallam	1-0	68
Mickleover Sport	v	Studley Duncan, Silvester	0-2	91
Potters Bar Town Ferguson, Jordan	v	Harefield United Conway (2), Dennison, Nelson	2-4	60
Ramsbottom United Heys, Swailes (2)	v	Fleetwood Town Catlow	3-1	
Ramsgate Takalobighashi	v	Didcot Town Powell	2-1	104
Rocester McMahon	v	Congleton Town Scully, Worthington	1-2*	
Sheffield	v	Dunston Fed Brewery	0-0* 3-0p	85
Squires Gate	v	Billingham Town Chillingsworth, Skelton, Ward	0-3	59
Warrington Town Mitchell, Nestor	v	Northallerton Town	2-0	82

26th November

Lincoln Moorlands Shelley	v	Stourbridge	1-0*	

3rd December

Southall Town Hart, Meaker	v	Dereham Town	0-2	45

Lee Hudson's (6) header beats Eastwood 'keeper Danny Bryant to give visitors Spalding United false hope. Photo: Bill Wheatcroft.

Torrington 'keeper Oliver punches the ball clear under pressure from Moneyfields' Dean Wain. Photo: Graham Brown.

THIRD ROUND

Saturday 13th December — **Winning clubs received: £1,200**

Home		Away	Score	Att
AFC Sudbury	v	Harwich & Parkeston	3-2*	357
Calver (2), Howlett		Carmichael, Lyness		
Andover	v	Three Bridges	4-3	160
Bennett (2), Rusher (2)		Funnell, Massaro, Smith		
BAT Sports	v	AFC Wimbledon (3/1)	0-1	2763
(at AFC Wimbledon)		Boiser		
Bideford	v	Withdean 2000	6-0	229
Hapgood (2), Southgate (4)				
Billingham Town	v	Lincoln Moorlands	5-2	112
Chillingsworth (3), Oriordon, Woodhouse		Roach, Shelley		
Buxton	v	Congleton Town (16/12)	0-0*	315
Chertsey Town	v	Harefield United	1-0	119
Breslin				
Concord Rangers	v	Ramsgate	1-0	130
Heale				
Cray Wanderers	v	Great Yarmouth Town (14/12)	3-2*	180
Kempster, Lover, Woolf		Gilmore, Humphreys		
Desborough Town	v	Guisborough Town	3-0	138
Coles (2), Mills				
Enfield Town	v	Torrington (20/12)	2-4*	280
Brotherton, Cove		Langmead, Stevens		
Fareham Town	v	Leighton Town	0-1	100
		Pedder		
Gedling Town	v	Ramsbottom United	2-1	81
Jefferies (2)		Smith		
Gosport Borough	v	Bury Town	1-0	135
Lindsey				
Hertford Town	v	Keynsham Town	3-3*	153
Berry, Cooper (2)		Adams (2), Wood		
Jarrow Roofing Boldon CA	v	Eastwood Town	0-2	76
		Fisher, Knox		
Leamington	v	Durham City	2-1	711
Blake, Care		Dunwell		
Lymington & New Milton	v	Buckingham Town	2-1	84
(abandoned after 88 mins, FA Vase committe decided result should stand)				
Maidstone United	v	Bitton	0-1	248
		Raynes		
Morpeth Town	v	Colne	0-1	84
		Honarth		
Mossley	v	Whitley Bay	4-0	318
Coyne, Howard, Morning, Taylor				
Nantwich Town	v	Coalville Town	6-0	115
Gardiner, Gleghorn (2), Griggs, Melling				
Oadby Town	v	Shildon	1-0	235
Charlton				
Southall Town	v	North Leigh (14/12)	0-2	56
		Hamp (2)		
St Blazey	v	Soham Town Rangers	2-0	256
Crocker, Daly				
St Neots Town	v	Thamesmead Town	2-1	130
Dean, Hoggett		Thomas		
Stone Dominoes	v	Sheffield (16/12)	3-2	112
Killeen, Shaw (2)		Bray (2)		
Studley	v	Blaby & Whetstone Athletic	3-0	95
Crisp, Marshall (2)				
Warrington Town	v	West Allotment Celtic	1-2	83
Latham		Benjamin		
Wellington	v	Billingham Synthonia	1-2	249
		Wood (2)		
Westbury United	v	Wroxham	2-6	247
Colbourne, Seals		Hilton, Neale, Stock (4)		
Whitehawk	v	Winchester City	1-3	126
Rowland		Mancey (2)		

R E P L A Y S

17th December

Home		Away	Score	Att
Keynsham Town	v	Hertford Town	2-2* 3-0p	105
Adams, Cripps		Cooper, Sapsford		

23rd December

Home		Away	Score	Att
Congelton Town	v	Buxton	1-1* 5-4p	364

Desborough Town's Andy Greensmith powers a header towards the Guisborough Town goal.

Photo: Peter Barnes.

Above: Bitton goalkeeper Simon Crawford punches clear from Maidstone's Scott Appleton.
Below: Cray Wanderers' Matt Woolf hammers the ball past the out stretched leg of Great Yarmouth's Tony Spearing and 'keeper Nick Banham.

Photos: Alan Coomes.

FOURTH ROUND

Saturday 17th January — Winning clubs received: £1,500

Home		Away	Score	Att
AFC Sudbury	v	Desborough Town	3-1	456
Banya (3)		Gilbert		
AFC Wimbledon	v	Colne	1-2	3215
Gray		Gizon, Simpson		
Billingham Town	v	Bideford	2-4	265
Ainsley, Skelton		Laight (2), Rowe, Southgate		
Chertsey Town	v	Torrington	5-1	286
Jones, Prendergast (3), Tanfield		Darch		
Congleton Town	v	Billingham Synthonia	2-1*	302
Hatton, Scully		Wells		
Eastwood Town	v	St Blazey	3-1	313
Knox, Nazha, Whitehead		Waters		
Gedling Town	v	Leighton Town	2-3	192
Jeffries, Scoffman		Kingsley, Pedder, Rawdon		
Gosport Borough	v	Oadby Town	2-1*	427
Quirke, Tryon				
Keynsham Town	v	St Neots Town	1-0	193
Sheppard				
Lymington & New Milton	v	Bitton	2-3	227
James (2)		Mogg (2), Raynes		
Mossley	v	Winchester City	1-2	434
Bailey		Forbes (2)		
Nantwich Town	v	Wroxham	1-3	256
Griggs		McGee, Neale, Stock		
North Leigh	v	Andover	0-1*	326
		Sullivan		
Stone Dominoes	v	Concord Rangers	5-1	221
Heath, Shaw (3), Warrender		Atkinson		
Studley	v	Leamington	2-1	755
Crisp, Thomas		Thompson		
West Allotment Celtic	v	Cray Wanderers	0-1	495
		Kempster		

Oadby's Owen Wright exerts pressure on the Gosport defence tracked by Jamie Lunn, whilst below Wright fires in a shot only to see the Gosport 'keeper pull off a fine save to tip the ball over the bar.

Photos: D. Nicholson.

FIFTH ROUND

Saturday 7th February — Winning clubs received: £2,000

Congleton Town	(0) 0	AFC Sudbury	(1) 2	
		Claydon 25, Calver 75		Att: 780
Colne	(1) 2	Bitton	(0) 0	
Simpson 28, 83				Att: 406
Studley	(0) 1	Gosport Borough	(0) 1	
Thomas 89 (AET)		Hensman 55		Att: 368
Andover	(1) 3	Leighton Town	(1) 1	
Sullivan 10, 90, Bennett 80		Haggerwood 2		Att: 650
Chertsey Town	(0) 0	Bideford	(1) 1	
		Pickard 44		Att: 633
Eastwood Town	(1) 3	Stone Dominoes	(1) 3	
Nazha 40, 98, Whitehead 95 (AET)		Somner 45, Shaw 92, Fletcher 112		Att: 314
Wroxham	(0) 0	Winchester City	(1) 3	
		Smith 29, 90, Forbes 53		Att: 526
Keynsham Town	(0) 0	Cray Wanderers	(0) 2	
(AET)		Wood 104, Woolfe 109		Att: 428

R E P L A Y S

Stone Dominoes	1	Eastwood Town	3	
Shaw 10/02		Fisher, Gummer (2)		Att: 330
Gosport Borough	(1) 2	Studley	(1) 1	
Scammell 4, Rew 64 14/02		Duncan 34		Att: 610

Chertsey Town's Mark Butler and Bideford's Owen Pickard in action during the Western League side's 1-0 away win.

Photo: Roger Turner.

SIXTH ROUND

Saturday 21st February | Winning club received: £4,000

AFC Sudbury's Neil Calver gets in a powerful header above Crays Keith Sharman.

Photo: Alan Coomes.

Bideford	(0) 3	Gosport Borough	(0) 0
Southgate 48, 65, 75			Att: 1,211

Colne	(1) 4	Eastwood Town	(2) 4
Howarth 24, Gizon 75, 117, Simpson 76 (AET)		Gould 29, Fisher 36, Mitchell 84, Knox 118	Att: 645

Cray Wanderers	(0) 0	AFC Sudbury	(0) 2
(AET)		Francis 102, Betson 105	Att: 771

Winchester City	(3) 5	Andover	(0) 1
Smith 11, Mancy 14, Forbes 31 (pen), 52, Webber 80		Bennett 90	Att: 933

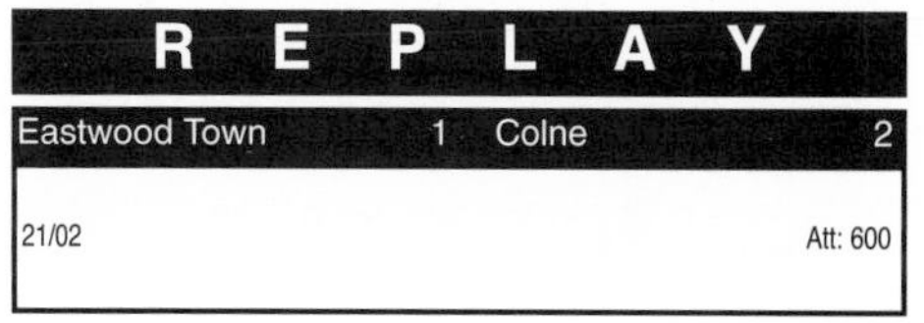

R E P L A Y

Eastwood Town	1	Colne	2
21/02			Att: 600

SEMI-FINALS - 1ST LEG

Saturday 13th March | Winning clubs received: £6,000

AFC Sudbury (0) 3 Colne (2) 2

Bennett 80, 83, Francis 90 | Simpson 32, Gizon 41

Att: 1,109

AFC SUDBURY SQUAD: Greygoose, Girling, Wardley, Howlett, Tracey, Gardiner, Rayner, Norfolk, Bennett, Claydon, Betson.
Subs: Banya, Head, Francis, Calver, Nower.

COLNE SQUAD: Baxter, Walker, Heffernan, Roberts, Rishton, Whittaker, Webster, Gizon, Simpson, Howarth, Cooper.
Subs: Ingham, Potts, Walton, Barrett, Coates.

Bideford (1) 3 Winchester City (2) 3

Pickard 44, Laight 60, Gough 80 | Forbes 4, Webber 40, Mancy 50

Att: 1,983

BIDEFORD SQUAD: Drober, Down, Herrera, Langmead, Hawkings, Hare, Kelly, Grouse, Gough, Laight, Pickard.
Subs: Hapgood, Rowe, Powell, Chapman, Murphy.

WINCHESTER SQUAD: Arthur, Dyke, Bicknell, Hall, Redwood, Blake, Webber, Green, Mancy, Forbes, Smith.
Subs: Tate, Green, Lang, Goss, Rastall.

Gary Bennett, AFC Sudbury, takes the ball between Colne players Jason Hefferman and Craig Whittaker.

Colne's 'keeper comes out well to block on-coming attacker Andrew Claydon. Photos: Roger Turner.

Simon Arthur, Winchester City's 'keeper, collects the ball during a Bideford attack. Photo: Roger Turner.

Winchester's Shaun Dyke and Bideford's Robert Herrera challenge for the ball. Photo: Eric Marsh.

Ellis Laight holds off the challenge of Winchester's Mark Blake. Photo: D. Nicholson.

SEMI-FINALS - 2ND LEG

Saturday 13th March — Winning clubs received: £6,000

Colne (0) 1 AFC Sudbury (0) 1

Cooper 83 — Banya 80

Att: 1,742

COLNE SQUAD: Baxter, Walker, Heffernan, Roberts, Rishton, Whittaker, Webster, Gizon, Simpson, Howarth, Cooper.
Subs: Ingham, Potts, Walton, Hayes, Coates.

AFC SUDBURY SQUAD: Greygoose, Head, Girling, Wardley, Tracey, Gardiner, Rayner, Calver, Bennett, Claydon, Betson.
Subs: Banya, Francis, Howlet, Norfolk, Nower.

Winchester City (2) 4 Bideford (0) 0

Mancy 43, 49, Forbes 45, 68 (pen)

Att: 1,818

WINCHESTER SQUAD: Arthur, Dyke, Bicknell, Redwood, Goss, Blake, Webber, Green, Mancy, Forbes, Smith.
Subs: Tate, Rodgers, Green, Hall, Rastall.

BIDEFORD SQUAD: Drober, Powell, Down, Herrera, Langmead, Hawkings, Hare, Gough, Southgate, Laight, Pickard.
Subs: Hapgood, Rowe, Kelly, Pickard, Murphy.

THE F.A. VASE - AT A GLANCE (THIRD ROUND TO THE FINAL)

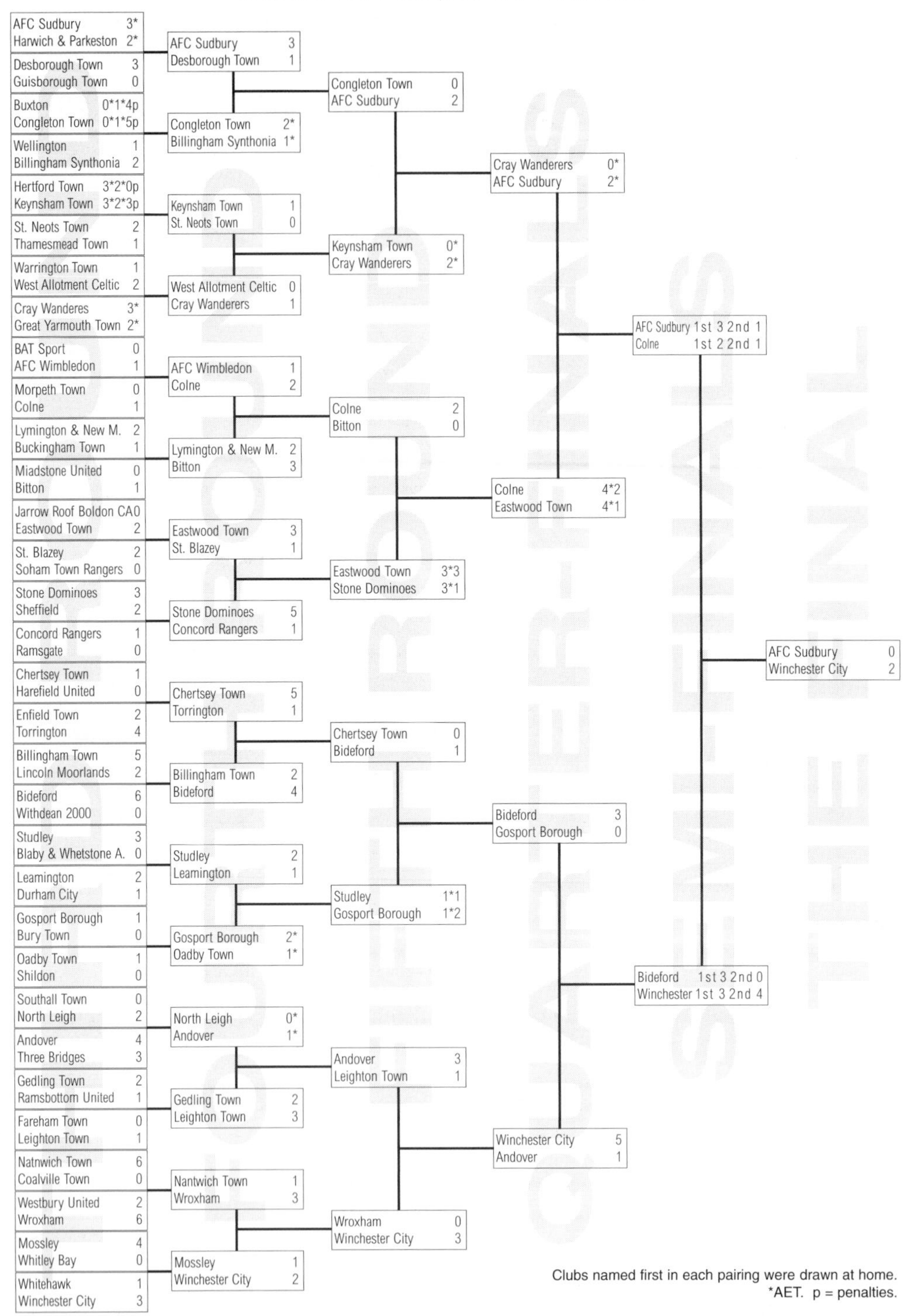

AFC Sudbury 3*
Harwich & Parkeston 2*
Desborough Town 3
Guisborough Town 0
Buxton 0*1*4p
Congleton Town 0*1*5p
Wellington 1
Billingham Synthonia 2
Hertford Town 3*2*0p
Keynsham Town 3*2*3p
St. Neots Town 2
Thamesmead Town 1
Warrington Town 1
West Allotment Celtic 2
Cray Wanderes 3*
Great Yarmouth Town 2*
BAT Sport 0
AFC Wimbledon 1
Morpeth Town 0
Colne 1
Lymington & New M. 2
Buckingham Town 1
Miadstone United 0
Bitton 1
Jarrow Roof Boldon CA 0
Eastwood Town 2
St. Blazey 2
Soham Town Rangers 0
Stone Dominoes 3
Sheffield 2
Concord Rangers 1
Ramsgate 0
Chertsey Town 1
Harefield United 0
Enfield Town 2
Torrington 4
Billingham Town 5
Lincoln Moorlands 2
Bideford 6
Withdean 2000 0
Studley 3
Blaby & Whetstone A. 0
Leamington 2
Durham City 1
Gosport Borough 1
Bury Town 0
Oadby Town 1
Shildon 0
Southall Town 0
North Leigh 2
Andover 4
Three Bridges 3
Gedling Town 2
Ramsbottom United 1
Fareham Town 0
Leighton Town 1
Natnwich Town 6
Coalville Town 0
Westbury United 2
Wroxham 6
Mossley 4
Whitley Bay 0
Whitehawk 1
Winchester City 3

AFC Sudbury 3
Desborough Town 1
Congleton Town 2*
Billingham Synthonia 1*
Keynsham Town 1
St. Neots Town 0
West Allotment Celtic 0
Cray Wanderers 1
AFC Wimbledon 1
Colne 2
Lymington & New M. 2
Bitton 3
Eastwood Town 3
St. Blazey 1
Stone Dominoes 5
Concord Rangers 1
Chertsey Town 5
Torrington 1
Billingham Town 2
Bideford 4
Studley 2
Leamington 1
Gosport Borough 2*
Oadby Town 1*
North Leigh 0*
Andover 1*
Gedling Town 2
Leighton Town 3
Nantwich Town 1
Wroxham 3
Mossley 1
Winchester City 2

Congleton Town 0
AFC Sudbury 2
Keynsham Town 0*
Cray Wanderers 2*
Colne 2
Bitton 0
Eastwood Town 3*3
Stone Dominoes 3*1
Chertsey Town 0
Bideford 1
Studley 1*1
Gosport Borough 1*2
Andover 3
Leighton Town 1
Wroxham 0
Winchester City 3

QUARTER-FINALS
Cray Wanderers 0*
AFC Sudbury 2*
Colne 4*2
Eastwood Town 4*1
Bideford 3
Gosport Borough 0
Winchester City 5
Andover 1

SEMI-FINALS
AFC Sudbury 1st 3 2nd 1
Colne 1st 2 2nd 1
Bideford 1st 3 2nd 0
Winchester 1st 3 2nd 4

THE FINAL
AFC Sudbury 0
Winchester City 2

Clubs named first in each pairing were drawn at home.
*AET. p = penalties.

CARLSBERG F.A. VASE FINAL 2004

A.F.C. SUDBURY	**0**
WINCHESTER CITY	**2**

A F C Sudbury:- Dean Greygoose, David Head, Shane Wardley, Brett Girling, Chris Tracey, Lee Norfolk, Lee Owen (sub Sam Banya 62nd min), Simon Hyde (sub Neil Calver 57th min), Gary Bennett, Andrew Claydon, Paul Betson (sub Dean Francis 73rd min).
Subs not used- Terry Rayner and Ben Nower.

Winchester City:- Simon Arthur, Sean Dyke (sub Steve Tate 83rd min), Matthew Bicknell, Toby Redwood, David Goss, Mark Blake, Lloyd Webber, Gary Green, Ian Mancey, Andrew Forbes (sub Adam Rogers 70th min), Danny Smith (sub Liam Green 90th min).
Subs not used- Stewart Lang and Oliver Rastall.

Referee - Mr P Crossley (Kent) assisted by J Carter (Tyne and Wear) and P Kirkup (Northants). Fourth official M Pike (Cumbria).

Many Vase finals have been unexciting affairs with the tension of the occasion having a detrimental effect on the adventure and skill display of the participants. Not so with the 2004 final which was a splendid end to end competitive battle between two teams thankfully bent on attacking.

In a St Andrew's stadium, with spectators seated along one length only, there was a surreal atmosphere, underlined by three sides of empty blue and white seats, until one became accustomed to the cacophony emanating solely from the occupied section. There was nothing ghostly about the opening action sequence with Sudbury's Paul Betson being lucky to escape a first minute booking for a comprehensive clattering of Sean Dyke. If Dyke had needed any additional inspiration that tackle must have provided it so that he ended the afternoon with the very deserved 'man of the match' award. Dyke was indeed the first to aim a shot at the target, putting Ian Mancey's pass just wide, a second after his physio had revived him.

Winchester, as Sudbury supporters had feared, were the prevalent attackers. Dyke again tested Dean Greygoose, Danny Smith drove past the post while Gary Green's dribbling skills created other chances. Sudbury were not as dangerous but David Head's fine cross went begging and Andrew Claydon could put no power into a left footed attempt.

Nineteen minutes gone and the black and reds struck. Mancey and Andrew Forbes' interplay left the latter clear to stroke the ball past Greygoose's despairing dive and put the Hampshire men one up. Green nearly got a second with a smart header and Mancey did hit the net but via his hand to earn a booking.

Shane Wardley's surging run ended with him giving the ball away just as an equaliser seemed likely but Greygoose kept the lead to one when he turned away a fierce Mancey shot and was next perfectly positioned for a scuffed Mancey effort before coming out to block a run by the same player. Greygoose completed the half by clutching, right on his line, David Goss's header from a corner.

The Suffolkians enjoyed a better second half. Claydon was the first to show, making a good run, but no one was there to profit from his cross. Wardley's enthusiasm was evident as he several times forged fervently forward but failed to make it past the eighteen yard line. Substitute Neil Calver only half hit a chance from the edge of the box and City keeper, Simon Arthur, found himself strangely robbed on his own penalty spot by Chris Tracey before being able to fall on the ball and prevent any major danger. A Smith punch then went no distance but he was alert enough to foil Gary Bennet's subsequent attempt on goal.

Then came the final disaster for Sudbury. Calver brought down Danny Smith and, as last man, was duly sent off before skipper Smith despatched the resulting penalty to double the lead.

Although there were seventeen minutes still left Sudbury only threatened once more when, in one last fling, Bennett hit the post courtesy of Wardley's neat flick. Otherwise Winchester played out the last quarter of an hour unthreatened, with the added novelty of veteran substitute Steve Tate wearing a number seldom employed, number 99.

Congratulations to both teams and their supporters on showing that competitiveness and entertainment can be provided with sportsmanship, a lack of derogatory chanting and genuine recognition of good play by opponents as well as your own favourites. Thus ended a truly enjoyable late Spring afternoon at St Andrew's.

ARTHUR EVANS

AFC SUDBURY

Photo: Steve Ayre.

Left: AFC Sudbury's Andrew Claydon shields the ball from Winchester's Toby Redwood. Photo: Roger Turner.

Below: Andy Forbes opens the scoring for Winchester. Photo: Gordon Whittingham.

Opposite: AFC Sudbury's David Head tries to evade a two pronged challenge by Winchester players. Photo: Roger Turner.

Opposite far right: Neil Calver brings down Winchester's Danny Smith. Calver sees red and Winchester score their second from the penalty spot. Photo: Roger Turner.

Opposite below: The Winchester squad celebrate their win. Photo Roger Turner

WINCHESTER CITY

Photo: Steve Ayre.

PAST F.A. VASE FINALS

1975 **HODDESDON TOWN 2 (Spartan Sth Mids)** **EPSOM & EWELL 1 (Surrey Senior)** **Att: 9,500**
Sedgwick 2 **Wales** **Ref: Mr R Toseland**
Hoddesdon: Galvin, Green, Hickey, Maybury, Stevenson, Wilson, Bishop, Picking, Sedgwick, Nathan, Schofield
Epsom & Ewell: Page, Bennett, Webb, Wales, Worby, Jones, O'Connell, Walker, Tuite, Eales, Lee

1976 **BILLERICAY TOWN 1 (Essex Senior)** **STAMFORD 0 (aet) (United Counties)** **Att: 11,848**
Aslett **Ref: Mr A Robinson**
Billericay: Griffiths, Payne, Foreman, Pullin, Bone, Coughlan, Geddes, Aslett, Clayden, Scott, Smith
Stamford: Johnson, Kwiatowski, Marchant, Crawford, Downs, Hird, Barnes, Walpole, Smith, Russell, Broadbent

1977 **BILLERICAY TOWN 1 (Essex Senior)** **SHEFFIELD 1 (aet) (Yorkshire)** **Att: 14,000**
Clayden **Coughlan og** **Ref: Mr J Worrall**
Billericay: Griffiths, Payne, Bone, Coughlan, Pullin, Scott, Wakefield, Aslett, Clayden,Woodhouse, McQueen. Sub: Whettell
Sheffield: Wing, Gilbody, Lodge, Hardisty, Watts, Skelton, Kay, Travis, Pugh, Thornhill,Haynes. Sub: Strutt
Replay **BILLERICAY TOWN 2** **SHEFFIELD 1** **Att: 3,482**
Aslett, Woodhouse **Thornhill** **at Nottingham Forest**
Billericay: Griffiths, Payne, Pullin, Whettell, Bone, McQueen, Woodhouse, Aslett, Clayden, Scott, Wakefield
Sheffield: Wing, Gilbody, Lodge, Strutt, Watts, Skelton, Kay, Travis, Pugh, Thornhill, Haynes

1978 **NEWCASTLE BLUE STAR 2 (Wearside)** **BARTON ROVERS 1 (South Midlands)** **Att: 16,858**
Dunn, Crumplin **Smith** **Ref: Mr T Morris**
Newcastle: Halbert, Feenan, Thompson, Davidson, S Dixon, Beynon, Storey, P Dixon, Crumplin, Callaghan, Dunn. Sub: Diamond
Barton Rovers: Blackwell, Stephens, Crossley, Evans, Harris, Dollimore, Dunn, Harnaman, Fossey, Turner, Smith. Sub: Cox

1979 **BILLERICAY TOWN 4 (Athenian)** **ALMONDSBURY GREENWAY 1 (Glos. Co)** **Att: 17,500**
Young 3, Clayden **Price** **Ref: Mr C Steel**
Billericay: Norris, Blackaller, Bingham, Whettell, Bone, Reeves, Pullin, Scott, Clayden,Young, Groom. Sub: Carrigan
Almondsbury: Hamilton, Bowers, Scarrett, Sulllivan, Tudor, Wookey, Bowers, Shehean, Kerr,Butt, Price. Sub: Kilbaine

1980 **STAMFORD 2 (United Counties)** **GUISBOROUGH TOWN 0 (Northern)** **Att: 11,500**
Alexander, McGowan **Ref: Neil Midgeley**
Stamford: Johnson, Kwiatkowski, Ladd, McGowan, Bliszczak I, Mackin, Broadhurst, Hall,Czarnecki, Potter, Alexander. Sub: Bliszczak S
Guisborough: Cutter, Scott, Thornton, Angus, Maltby, Percy, Skelton, Coleman, McElvaney,Sills, Dilworth. Sub: Harrison

1981 **WHICKHAM 3 (Wearside)** **WILLENHALL 2 (aet) (West Midlands)** **Att: 12,000**
Scott, Williamson, Peck og **Smith, Stringer** **Ref: Mr R Lewis**
Whickham: Thompson, Scott, Knox, Williamson, Cook, Ward, Carroll, Diamond, Cawthra,Robertson, Turnbull. Sub: Alton
Willenhall: Newton, White, Darris, Woodall, Heath, Fox, Peck, Price, Matthews, Smith,Stringer. Sub: Trevor

1982 **FOREST GREEN ROVERS 3 (Hellenic)** **RAINWORTH M.W 0 (Notts Alliance)** **Att: 12,500**
Leitch 2, Norman **Ref: Mr K Walmsey**
Forest Green: Moss, Norman, Day, Turner, Higgins, Jenkins, Guest, Burns, Millard, Leitch, Doughty. Sub: Dangerfield
Rainworth M.W: Watson, Hallam, Hodgson, Slater, Sterland, Oliver, Knowles, Raine, Radzi, Reah, Comerford. Sub: Robinson

1983 **V.S. RUGBY 1 (West Midlands)** **HALESOWEN TOWN 0 (West Midlands)** **Att: 13,700**
Crawley **Ref: Mr B Daniels**
VS Rugby: Burton, McGinty, Harrison, Preston, Knox, Evans, ingram, Setchell, Owen,Beecham, Crawley. Sub: Haskins
Halesowen Town: Coldicott, Penn, Edmonds, Lacey, Randall, Shilvock, Hazelwood, Moss, Woodhouse,P Joinson, L Joinson. Sub: Smith

1984 **STANSTED 3 (Essex Senior)** **STAMFORD 2 (United Counties)** **Att: 8,125**
Holt, Gillard, Reading **Waddicore, Allen** **Ref: Mr T Bune**
Stanstead: Coe, Williams, Hilton, Simpson, Cooper, Reading, Callanan, Holt, Reevs,Doyle, Gillard. Sub: Williams
Stamford: Parslow, Smitheringate, Blades, McIlwain, Lyon, Mackin, Genovese, Waddicore,Allen, Robson, Beech. Sub: Chapman

1985 **HALESOWEN TOWN 3 (West Midlands)** **FLEETWOOD TOWN 1 (N W Counties)** **Att: 16,715**
L Joinson 2, Moss **Moran** **Ref: Mr C Downey**
Halesowen: Coldicott, Penn, Sherwood, Warner, Randle, Heath, Hazlewood, Moss (Smith),Woodhouse, P Joinson, L Joinson
Fleetwood Town: Dobson, Moran, Hadgraft, Strachan, Robinson, Milligan, Hall, Trainor, Taylor(Whitehouse), Cain, Kennerley

1986 **HALESOWEN TOWN 3 (West Midlands)** **SOUTHALL 0 (Isthmian 2 South)** **Att: 18,340**
Moss 2, L Joinson **Ref: Mr D Scott**
Halesowen: Pemberton, Moore, Lacey, Randle (Rhodes), Sherwood, Heath, Penn, Woodhouse, PJoinson, L Joinson, Moss
Southall: Mackenzie, James, McGovern, Croad, Holland, Powell (Richmond), Pierre,Richardson, Sweales, Ferdinand, Rowe

1987 **ST. HELENS 3 (N W Counties)** **WARRINGTON TOWN 2 (N W Counties)** **Att: 4,254**
Layhe 2, Rigby **Reid, Cook** **Ref: Mr T Mills**
St Helens: Johnson, Benson, Lowe, Bendon, Wilson, McComb, Collins (Gledhill), O'Neill,Cummins, Lay, Rigby. Sub: Deakin
Warrington: O'Brien. Copeland, Hunter, Gratton, Whalley, Reid, Brownville (Woodyer), Cook,Kinsey, Looker (Hill), Hughes

1988 **COLNE DYNAMOES 1 (N W Counties)** **EMLEY 0 (Northern Counties East)** **Att: 15,000**
Anderson **Ref: Mr A Seville**
Colne Dynamoes: Mason, McFafyen, Westwell, Bentley, Dunn, Roscoe, Rodaway, Whitehead (Burke),Diamond, Anderson, Wood (Coates)
Emley: Dennis, Fielding, Mellor, Codd, Hirst (Burrows), Gartland (Cook), Carmody,Green, Bramald, Devine, Francis

1989 **TAMWORTH 1 (West Midlands)** **SUDBURY TOWN 1 (aet) (Eastern)** **Att: 26,487**
Devaney **Hubbick** **Ref: Mr C Downey**
Tamworth: Bedford, Lockett, Atkins, Cartwright, McCormack, Myers, Finn, Devaney, Moores,Gordon, Stanton. Subs: Rathbone, Heaton
Sudbury Town: Garnham, Henry, G Barker, Boyland, Thorpe, Klug, D Barker, Barton, Oldfield,Smith, Hubbick. Subs: Money, Hunt
REPLAY **TAMWORTH 3** **SUDBURY TOWN 0** **Att: 11,201**
Stanton 2, Moores **at Peterborough**
Tamworth: Bedford, Lockett, Atkins, Cartwright, Finn, Myers, George, Devaney, Moores,Gordon, Stanton. Sub: Heaton
Sudbury Town: Garnham, Henry, G Barker, Boyland, Thorpe, Klug, D Barker, Barton, Oldfield,Smith, Hubbick. Subs: Money, Hunt

1990 **YEADING 0 (Isthmian 2 South)** **BRIDLINGTON TOWN 0 (aet) (N Co East)** **Att: 7,932**
Ref: Mr R Groves
Yeading: Mackenzie, Wickens, Turner, Whiskey (McCarthy), Croad, Denton, Matthews, James(Charles), Sweates, Impey, Cordery
Bridlington: Taylor, Pugh, Freeman, McNeill, Warburton, Brentano, Wilkes (Hall), Noteman,Gauden, Whiteman, Brattan (Brown)

Replay **YEADING 1** **BRIDLINGTON TOWN 0** **Att: 5,000**
Sweales **at Leeds Utd FC**
Yeading: Mackenzie, Wickens, Turner, Whiskey, Croad (McCarthy), Schwartz, Matthews,James, Sweates, Impey (Welsh), Cordery
Bridlington: Taylor, Pugh, Freeman, McNeill, Warburton, Brentano, Wilkes (Brown), Noteman,Gauden (Downing), Whiteman, Brattan

1991 **GRESLEY ROVERS 4 (West Midlands)** **GUISELEY 4 (aet) (Northern Co East)** **Att: 11,314**
Rathbone, Smith 2, Stokes **Tennison 2, Walling, A Roberts** **Ref: Mr C Trussell**
Gresley: Aston, Barry, Elliott (Adcock), Denby, Land, Astley, Stokes, K Smith, Acklam,Rathbone, Lovell (Weston)
Guiseley: Maxted, Bottomley, Hogarth, Tetley, Morgan, McKenzie, Atkinson (Annan),Tennison, Walling, A Roberts, B Roberts

Replay **GUISELEY 3** **GRESLEY ROVERS 1** **Att: 7,585**
Tennison, Walling, Atkinson **Astley** **at Bramall Lane**
Guiseley: Maxted, Annan, Hogarth, Tetley, Morgan, McKenzie (Bottomley), Atkinson,Tennison (Noteman), Walling, A Roberts, B Roberts
Gresley: Aston, Barry, Elliott, Denby, Land, Astley, Stokes (Weston), K Smith, Acklam, Rathbone, Lovell (Adcock)

1992 **WIMBORNE TOWN 5 (Wessex)** **GUISELEY 3 (Northern Premier Div 1)** **Att: 10,772**
Richardson, Sturgess 2, Killick 2 **Noteman 2, Colville** **Ref: Mr M J Bodenham**
Wimborne: Leonard, Langdown, Wilkins, Beacham, Allan, Taplin, Ames, Richardson, Bridle,Killick, Sturgess (Lovell), Lynn
Guiseley: Maxted, Atkinson, Hogarth, Tetley (Wilson), Morgan, Brockie, A Roberts,Tennison, Noteman (Colville), Annan, W Roberts

1993 **BRIDLINGTON TOWN 1 (NPL Div 1)** **TIVERTON TOWN 0 (Western)** **Att: 9,061**
Radford **Ref: Mr R A Hart**
Bridlington: Taylor, Brentano, McKenzie, Harvey, Bottomley, Woodcock, Grocock, A Roberts, Jones, Radford (Tyrell), Parkinson. Sub: Swailes
Tiverton Town: Nott, J Smith, N Saunders, M Saunders, Short (Scott), Steele, Annunziata, KSmith, Everett, Daly, Hynds (Rogers)

1994 **DISS TOWN 2 (Eastern)** **TAUNTON TOWN 1 (Western)** **Att: 13,450**
Gibbs (p), Mendham **Fowler** **Ref: Mr K. Morton**
Diss Town: Woodcock, Carter, Wolsey (Musgrave), Casey (Bugg), Hartle, Smith, Barth, Mendham, Miles, Warne, Gibbs
Taunton Town: Maloy, Morris, Walsh, Ewens, Graddon, Palfrey, West (Hendry), Fowler, Durham, Perrett (Ward), Jarvis

1995 **ARLESEY TOWN 2 (South Midlands)** **OXFORD CITY 1 (Ryman 2)** **Att: 13,670**
Palma, Gyalog **S Fontaine** **Ref: Mr G S Willard**
Arlesey: Young, Cardines, Bambrick, Palma (Ward), Hull, Gonsalves, Gyalog, Cox, Kane,O'Keefe, Marshall (Nicholls). Sub: Dodwell
Oxford: Fleet, Brown (Fisher), Hume, Shepherd, Muttock, Hamilton (Kemp), Thomas, Spittle, Sherwood, S Fontaine, C Fontaine. Sub: Torres

1996 **BRIGG TOWN 3 (N Co East)** **CLITHEROE 0 (N W Counties)** **Att: 7,340**
Stead 2, Roach **Ref: Mr S J Lodge**
Brigg: Gawthorpe, Thompson, Rogers, Greaves (Clay), Buckley (Mail), Elston, C Stead, McLean, N Stead (McNally), Flounders, Roach
Clitheroe: Nash, Lampkin, Rowbotham (Otley), Baron, Westwell, Rovine, Butcher, Taylor (Smith), Grimshaw, Darbyshire, Hill (Dunn)

1997 **WHITBY TOWN 3 (Northern)** **NORTH FERRIBY UTD. 0 (N Co East)** **Att: 11,098**
Williams, Logan, Toman **Ref: Graham Poll**
North Ferriby: Sharp, Deacey, Smith, Brentano, Walmsley, M Smith, Harrison (Horne), Phillips (Milner), France (Newman), Flounders, Tennison
Whitby Town: Campbell, Williams, Logan, Goodchild, Pearson, Cook, Goodrick (Borthwick), Hodgson, Robinson, Toman (Pyle), Pitman (Hall)

1998 **TIVERTON TOWN 1 (Western)** **TOW LAW TOWN 0 (Northern)** **Att: 13,139**
Varley **Ref: M A Riley**
Tiverton: Edwards, Felton, Saunders, Tatterton, Smith J, Conning, Nancekivell (Rogers), Smith K (Varley), Everett, Daly, Leonard (Waters)
Tow Law: Dawson, Pickering, Darwent, Bailey, Hague, Moan, Johnson, Nelson, Suddick, Laidler (Bennett), Robinson.

1999 **TIVERTON TOWN 1 (Western)** **BEDLINGTON TERRIERS 0 (Northern)** **Att: 13, 878**
Rogers 88 **Ref: W. C. Burns**

Bedlington Terriers: OÕConnor, Bowes, Pike, Boon (Renforth), Melrose, Teasdale, Cross, Middleton (Ludlow), Gibb, Milner, BondSubs: Pearson, Cameron, Gowans

Tiverton Town: Edwards, Fallon, Saunders, Tatterton, Tallon, Conning (Rogers), Nancekivell (Pears), Varley, Everett, Daly, Leonard. Subs: Tucker, Hynds, Grimshaw

2000 **DEAL TOWN 1 (Kent)** **CHIPPENHAM TOWN 0 (Western)** **Att: 20,000**
Graham 87 **Ref: E. K. Wolstenholme**

Deal Town: Tucker, Kempster, Best, Ash, Martin, Seager, Monteith, Graham, Lovell, Marshall, Ribbens. Subs: Roberts, Warden, Turner

Chippenham Town: Jones, James, Andrews, Murphy, Burns, Woods, Brown, Charity, Tweddle, Collier, Godley. Subs: Tiley, Cutler

2001 **TAUNTON TOWN 2 (Western)** **BERKHAMPSTED TOWN 1 (Isthmian 2)** **(at Villa Park)** **Att: 8,439**
Fields 41, Laight 45 **Lowe 71** **Ref: E. K. Wolstenholme**

Taunton Town: Draper, Down, Chapman, West, Hawkings, Kelly, Fields (Groves), Laight, Cann (Tallon), Bastow, Lynch (Hapgood). Subs: Ayres, Parker

Berkhampsted Town: OÕConnor, Mullins, Lowe, Aldridge, Coleman, Brockett, Yates, Adebowale, Richardson, Smith, Nightingale. Subs: Ringsell, Hall, Knight, Franklin, Osborne

2002 **WHITLEY BAY 1 (Northern)** **TIPTREE UNITED 0 (Eastern)** **(at Villa Park)** **Att: 4742**
Chandler 97 **Ref: A Kaye**

Whitley Bay: Caffrey, Sunderland, Walmsley, Dixon (Neil), Chandler, Walton, Fenwick (Cuggy). Subs: Cook, Livermore

Tiptree United: Haygreen, Battell, Wall, Houghton, Fish, Streetley (Gillespie), Wareham (Snow), Daly, Barefield, Aransibia (Parnell), Brady. Subs: Powell, Ford.

2003 **A.F.C SUDBURY 1 (Eastern Counties)** **BRIGG TOWN 2 (Northern Co.East)** **(at Upton Park)** **Att: 6,634**
Raynor 30 **Housham 2, Carter 68** **Ref: M Fletcher**

AFC Sudbury:- Greygoose, Head (Norfolk 63), Spearing, Tracey, Bishop, Anderson (Owen 73), Rayner, Gardiner (Banya 79), Bennett, Claydon, Betson. Subs (not used) Taylor, Hyde.

Brigg Town:- Steer, Raspin, Rowland, Thompson, Blanchard, Stones, Stead (Thompson 41), Housham, Borman (Drayton 87), Roach, Carter. Subs (not used) Nevis, Gawthorpe.

All Finals at Wembley unless otherwise shown

TOP GOAL SCORERS 2003 - 2004

Player	Club	No. goals	Round reach	No. hatrick	Hatrick details
D Shaw	Stone Dominoes	10	Fifth	2	2nd & 4th Rnds
A Forbes	Winchester City	9	Winners	-	-
M Southgate	Bideford	8	Semi-Finals	2°	3rd & 6th Rnds
I Simpson	Colne	8	Semi-Finals	-	-
M Adams	Keynsham Town	8	Fifth	-	-
A Kinsey	Alsager Town	7	Second	1°	2nd Qual. Rnd
I Mancey	Winchester City	7	Winners	-	-
V Rusher	Andover	6	Sixth	1	2nd Qual. Rnd
J Raynes	Bitton	6	Fifth	1	1st Qual. Rnd
C Cheetham	Buxton	6	Third	1	2nd Qual. Rnd
C Prendergast	Chertsey Town	6	Fifth	2	2nd & 4th Rnds
S Gizon	Colne	6	Semi-Finals	-	-
M Scully	Congleton Town	6	Fifth	1	1st Qual. Rnd
M Carmichael	Harwich & Parkeston	6	Third	1*	2nd Qual. Rnd
J Nestor	Liversedge	6	Second	1	2nd Qual. Rnd
M Takalobighashi	Ramsgate	6	Third	-	-
P McManhon	Rocester	6	Second	1	2nd Rnd
N Ghislanzoni	Sandiacre Town	6	First	1	1st Qual. Rnd
J Pritchard	Wokingham Town	6	Second	1*	2nd Qual. Rnd

° denotes hatrick part of 5 scored. *denotes hatrick part of 4 scored

HIGHEST SCORING CLUBS

Club	Division			-	-
Bideford	Western League Prem.	24	Semi-Finals	-	-
Eastwood Town	Northern Co. East Prem.	23	Sixth	-	-
Colne	North West Counties D2	22	Semi-Finals	-	-
Winchester City	Wessex Premier Div.	22	Winners	-	-
Keynsham Town	Western League Prem.	21	Fifth	-	-

F.A. YOUTH CUP

Non-League Clubs Involvement only. Overall Winners: Middlesbrough 4-0 Aston Villa (Agg. score)

PRELIMINARY ROUND

Home		Away	Score	Att.
Southport	v	Ryton	10-0	64
Burscough	v	Penrith	2-1	86
Radcliffe Borough	v	Altrincham	3-4*	80
Ossett Town	v	Northwich Victoria	1-2	72
Atherstone United	v	Boldmere St Michaels	0-2	31
Southend Manor	v	Diss Town	2-0	33
Thurrock	v	Hullbridge Sports	5-1	30
Leyton	v	Carterton Town	2-2* 7-6p	95
Stansted	v	Uxbridge	3-2*	85
Staines Town	v	Barton Rovers	5-1	68
Saltdean United	v	Folkstone Invicta	2-3	49
Chipstead	v	Maidenhead United	3-2	68

FIRST ROUND QUALIFYING

Home		Away	Score	Att.
Lancaster City	v	Selby Town	4-1	42
Wakefield & Emley	v	Bradford (Park Avenue)	1-1* 0-3p	52
Southport	v	Thackley	1-3	44
Retford United	v	Northwich Victoria	0-3	52
Barrow	v	Frickley Athletic	4-2	32
Guiseley	v	Workington	6-2	40
Yorkshire Amateurs	v	Trafford	1-3	81
Stocksbridge Park Steels	v	Curzon Ashton	1-2*	141
Morecambe	v	Chester-Le-Street	3-4*	84
Glasshoughton Welfare	v	Seaham Red Star	0-3	50
Altrincham	v	Louth United	w/o Altrincham	
Harrogate Railway	v	Worksop Town	3-4	113
Whitley Bay	v	Darlington College	0-3	58
Chadderton	v	Pickering Town	2-4	67
Hallam (at Pontefract Collieries)	v	Pontefract Collieries	5-0	70
Chester City	v	Halifax Town	1-0	52
North Ferriby United	v	Consett	2-0	63
Witton Albion	v	Burscough	0-2	109
Vauxhall Motors	v	Marine	0-2	129
Farsley Celtic	v	Garforth Town	6-1*	57
Belper Town	v	Arnold Town	4-1	81
Long Buckby	v	Alvechurch	2-3*	45
Cradley Town	v	Dudley Sports	6-3*	94
Hinckley United	v	Congleton Town	6-0	73
Hednesford Town	v	Grantham Town	w/o Hednesford	
Bloxwich Town	v	Boldmere St Michaels	1-3	43
Kettering Town	v	Lincoln United	1-0	95
Burton Albion	v	Nuneaton Borough	1-2	54
Northampton Spencer	v	Quorn	1-2*	46
Gornal Athletic	v	Deeping Rangers	1-2	30
Wellington	v	Racing Club Warwick	2-1	35
Matlock Town	v	Coventry Sphinx	5-4	87
Stourbridge	v	Corby Town	0-4	79
Tamworth	v	Eastwood Town	0-1*	53
Alfreton Town	v	Leamington	3-0	56
Barrow Town	v	Mickleover Sports	1-3	43
Hucknall Town	v	Stone Dominoes	3-3* 4-3p	82
Rugby United	v	Chasetown	2-1	69
Marconi	v	Stratford Town	4-2	45
Cogenhoe Town	v	Lye Town	3-4	27
Malvern Town	v	Rushall Olympic	2-1	51
Bedworth United	v	Shrewsbury Town	1-3	89
Sutton Coldfield Town	v	Newcastle Town	3-0	92
Nantwich Town	v	Gresley Rovers	7-2	81
Bugbrooke St Michaels	v	Wealdstone	0-6	80
Wembley	v	Ford United	2-3*	47
Grays Athletic	v	Heybridge Swifts	1-6	80
Broxbourne Borough	v	Lowestoft Town	0-1	36
Staines Town	v	Hoddesdon Town	0-3	68
Soham Town Rangers	v	Southend Manor	0-2	47
March Town United	v	Aylesbury United	0-0* 1-2p	80
Marlow	v	Bedford Town	1-4	53
Chesham United	v	AFC Kempston Rovers	2-0	42
Wisbech Town	v	Flackwell Heath	2-2* 3-2p	63
Royston Town	v	Ware	2-0	88
Boreham Wood	v	Sawbridgeworth Town	9-0	62
Witham Town	v	East Thurrock United	1-2	50
Wingate & Finchley	v	North Greenford United	3-2	66
Canvey Island	v	Clapton	5-1	96
Ipswich Wanderers	v	Flaenham Town	1-2	34
Stevenage Borough	v	Henley Town	10-0	109
Cheshunt	v	AFC Wallingford	4-1	39
Cambridge City	v	Great Yarmouth Town	4-0	173
Romford	v	Newmarket Town	1-5	33
St Margaretsbury	v	Hitchin Town	2-3*	39
Bowers United	v	Brentwood	3-0	49
Chalfont St Peter	v	Leighton Town	1-1* 5-4p	39
Dereham Town	v	Leyton	2-1	45
Thurrock	v	Hemel Hempstead Town	1-2	26
Didcot Town	v	Hampton & Richmond BoroÕ	2-1	54
Chelmsford City (at Thame United)	v	Thame United - reversed tie	3-1	64
Hayes	v	Stansted	1-1* 6-5p	66
Woodbridge Town	v	Great Wakering Rovers	2-1	34
Haringey Borough	v	Burnham Ramblers	2-2* 5-3p	52
Banbury United	v	Ilford	1-2	49
Buckingham Town	v	Beaconsfield SYCOB	3-2	68
Ruislip Manor	v	Northwood	2-3	55
BishopÕs Stortford	v	Braintree Town	w/o Braintree	
Berkhamsted Town	v	Waltham Forest	2-3*	72
Bury Town	v	Histon	5-0	58
Burnham	v	St Albans City	1-3	49
Brook House	v	Maldon Town	3-4	50
Hertford Town	v	Enfield	1-5	46
Hornchurch	v	Concord Rangers	1-3	121
Walton Casuals	v	Fleet Town	2-1	64
Eastbourne Borough	v	Bashley	4-0	98
Ashford Town	v	Thamesmead Town	5-0	88
Banstead Athletic	v	Sittingbourne	2-1	75
Hailsham Town	v	Littlehampton Town	0-3	40
Sutton United	v	Lordswood	3-0	87
Erith Town	v	Leatherhead	4-1	58
Whitstable Town	v	Tooting & Mitcham United	0-3	55
Farnborough Town	v	Whyteleafe	2-0	104
Dover Athletic	v	Thatcham Town	3-4	77
AFC Newbury	v	Arundel	3-2*	48
Wick	v	Gravesend & Northfleet	1-2	47
Hillingdon Borough	v	Walton & Hersham	4-0	73
Lewes	v	Westfield	4-1	82
Dartford	v	Woking	1-2	101
Pagham	v	Carshalton Athletic	3-4*	55
Ramsgate	v	Cobham	2-1	39
Chichester City United	v	Horndean	1-2	20
Crawley Town	v	Chipstead	4-0	115
Andover	v	Alton Town	0-5	77
Kingstonian	v	Chatham Town	w/o Chatham	
Sidlesham	v	Croydon Athletic	1-2	31
Havant & Waterlooville	v	Bromley	1-0	77
Ashford Town (Middx)	v	Chertsey Town	0-1	83
Horsham	v	Tonbridge Angels	1-4	94
Molesey	v	Epsom & Ewell	1-2	39
Camberley Town	v	Folkstone Invicta	5-2	58
Winchester City	v	Burgess Hill Town	1-2	58
Reading Town	v	Sandhurst Town	6-0	43
Aldershot Town	v	Bracknell Town	11-1	136
Whitehawk	v	Mile Oak	2-1	87
Wokingham Town	v	Three Bridges	2-1	79
Cirencester Town	v	Pershore Town	5-2	80
Bournemouth	v	Wootton Bassett Town	1-5	84
Bath City	v	Bemerton Heath Harlequins	4-4* 5-6p	50
Salisbury City	v	Mangotsfield United	2-2* 3-1p	75
Frome Town	v	Bridgwater Town	0-1	24
Clevedon Town	v	Forest Green Rovers	2-3	67
Bitton	v	Christchurch	2-2* 6-5p	33
Newport County	v	Evesham United	6-0	97
Yate Town	v	Worcester City	2-3	74
Hereford United	v	Cinderford Town	8-1	70
Paulton Rovers	v	Gloucester City	0-2	43
Exeter City	v	Brislington	4-0	136

SECOND ROUND QUALIFYING

Altrincham	v	Pickering Town	3-2	56
Marine	v	Farsley Celtic	4-0	97
Barrow	v	Hallam	1-2	29
Worksop Town	v	North Ferriby United	4-1	82
Seaham Red Star	v	Curzon Ashton	2-1	83
Chester-Le-Street	v	Burscough	2-1	97
Northwich Victoria	v	Trafford	3-1*	124
Chester City	v	Darlington College	1-2	60
Lancaster City	v	Thackley	0-6	45
Guiseley	v	Bradford (Park Avenue)	0-2	63
Quorn	v	Lye Town	1-3	26
Hinckley United	v	Shrewsbury Town	0-1	87
Belper Town	v	Alvechurch	1-2	66
Malvern Town	v	Hucknall Town	3-1	42
Eastwood Town	v	Hednesford Town	1-3	57
Deeping Rangers	v	Corby Town	1-1* 3-1p	41
Cradley Town	v	Kettering Town	0-2	97
Rugby United	v	Wellington	1-0	59
Nantwich Town	v	Sutton Coldfield Town	2-3	95
Mickleover Sports	v	Nuneaton Borough	6-5*	58
Marconi	v	Alfreton Town	1-2	48
Matlock Town	v	Boldmere St Michaels	3-4	122
Hitchin Town	v	Burnham Ramblers	3-0	42
Waltham Forest	v	Southend Manor	5-1	41
Wealdstone (at Kingsbury Town FC)	v	Buckingham Town	5-1	80
Hayes	v	Lowestoft Town	2-1	56
Hoddesdon Town	v	Wingate & Finchley	2-0*	70
Stevenage Borough	v	Maldon Town	6-1	63
Concord Rangers	v	Northwood	0-1	61
Ilford	v	Royston Town	0-2	50
Dereham Town	v	Chesham United	1-4	62
Fakenham Town	v	Woodbridge Town	2-4*	49
Heybridge Swifts	v	Bowers United	3-5	66
Newmarket Town	v	Enfield	0-2	110
Bury Town	v	Boreham Wood	3-0	58
Aylesbury United	v	Didcot Town	0-2	76
Cambridge City	v	Chelmsford City	2-3	166
Bedford Town	v	Cheshunt	2-2* 5-4p	47
Hemel Hempstead Tn.	v	Wisbech Town	2-1	55
St Albans City	v	Ford United	3-2	75
Braintree Town	v	Chalfont St Peter	1-2	35
East Thurrock United	v	Canvey Island	2-3	80
Tonbridge Angels	v	Croydon Athletic	1-2	124
Aldershot Town	v	Crawley Town	0-1	90
Tooting & Mitcham Utd (tie awarded to Carshalton)	v	Carshalton Athletic	2-0	104
Reading Town	v	Walton Casuals	0-4	52
Camberley Town	v	Gravesend & Northfleet	0-1	60
Chertsey Town	v	Hillingdon Borough	1-1* 2-3p	65
Thatcham Town	v	Alton Town	4-0	55
Chatham Town	v	Littlehampton Town	3-3* 4-2p	37
Burgess Hill Town	v	Ramsgate	3-0	97
Farnborough Town	v	Sutton United	0-3	120
Wokingham Town	v	Eastbourne Borough	0-2	60
Whitehawk	v	Horndean	3-2	74
Banstead Athletic	v	Epsom & Ewell	1-2	88
AFC Newbury	v	Lewes	0-4	65
Ashford Town	v	Woking	4-2*	95
Havant & Waterlooville	v	Erith Town	4-2	78
Newport County	v	Bemerton Heath Harlequins	5-1	86
Bridgwater Town	v	Exeter City	0-5	141
Wootton Bassett Town	v	Bitton	3-4*	45
Forest Green Rovers	v	Gloucester City	1-0	75
Salisbury City	v	Cirencester Town	2-5*	54
Hereford United	v	Worcester City	2-1	40

THIRD ROUND QUALIFYING

Thackley	v	Northwich Victoria	4-2	66
Seaham Red Star	v	Darlington College	1-3	104
Marine	v	Worksop Town	0-1	94
Chester-Le-Street	v	Bradford (Park Avenue)	3-0	125
Altrincham	v	Hallam	3-1	40
Rugby United	v	Alvechurch	5-1	48
Hednesford Town	v	Boldmere St Michaels	3-0	100
Shrewsbury Town	v	Kettering Town	10-0	146
Deeping Rangers	v	Alfreton Town	1-0	80
Malvern Town	v	Lye Town	7-2	60
Mickleover Sports	v	Sutton Coldfield Town	2-1	81
Bowers United	v	Didcot Town	1-0	79
Chalfont St Peter	v	Canvey Island	4-2*	41
Hoddesdon Town	v	Chelmsford City	0-4	92
Enfield	v	Hemel Hempstead Town	1-5	43
Woodbridge Town	v	Royston Town	0-5	78
Chesham United	v	St Albans City	0-3	39
Hayes	v	Northwood	3-1	90
Bedford Town	v	Bury Town	1-2	47
Hitchin Town	v	Wealdstone	3-4*	40
Stevenage Borough	v	Waltham Forest	3-2	50
Lewes	v	Thatcham Town	2-1	100
Crawley Town	v	Chatham Town	6-2	133
Whitehawk	v	Sutton United	0-2*	84
Hillingdon Borough	v	Gravesend & Northfleet	0-2	50
Eastbourne Borough	v	Croydon Athletic	3-6*	90
Burgess Hill Town	v	Epsom & Ewell	5-0	93
Ashford Town	v	Carshalton Athletic	2-1	130
Havant & Waterlooville	v	Walton Casuals	2-1	84
Bitton	v	Hereford United	5-3*	85
Cirencester Town	v	Forest Green Rovers	2-1	86
Exeter City	v	Newport County	1-1* 5-4p	128

FIRST ROUND

Hartlepool United	v	Chester-Le-Street	0-2	214
Worksop Town	v	Oldham Athletic	0-2	162
Darlington College	v	Tranmere Rovers	0-8	51
Barnsley	v	Altrincham	4-0	256
Thackley	v	Darlington	3-2	123
Deeping Rangers	v	Mansfield Town	2-9	183
Kidderminster Harriers	v	Oadby Town	2-3	55
Rugby United	v	Mickleover Sports	1-2	70
Notts County	v	Malvern Town	3-0	226
Shrewsbury Town	v	Lincoln City	4-1	215
Hednesford Town	v	Chesterfield	0-3	72
Gravesend & Northfleet	v	Oxford United	1-4	183
Crawley Town	v	Lewes	1-0	259
Havant & Waterlooville	v	Brentford	0-3	136
Dulwich Hamlet	v	Ashford Town	1-0	88
Bowers United	v	Cambridge United	0-5	196
Wealdstone (at Kingsbury Town FC)	v	Royston Town	4-2	57
Chalfont St Peter	v	Wycombe Wanderers	0-3	110
Stevenage Borough	v	Hemel Hempstead Town	2-1	117
Hayes	v	Queens Park Rangers	3-3* 5-4p	247
Chelmsford City	v	Colchester United	1-0	169
Burgess Hill Town	v	Croydon Athletic	1-1* 9-10p	136
Sutton United	v	Bury Town	2-3	76
Cirencester Town	v	Exeter City	2-1	75
Cheltenham Town	v	Bitton	6-0	155

SECOND ROUND

Oadby Town	v	Shrewsbury Town	0-1	163
Chester-Le-Street	v	Port Vale	5-3	268
Huddersfield Town	v	Thackley	4-2	279
Mickleover Sports	v	Chesterfield	1-2	122
Bristol Rovers	v	Crawley Town	2-3*	167
Oxford United	v	Stevenage Borough	1-6	190
Rushden & Diamonds	v	Hayes	5-1	211
Croydon Athletic	v	Cirencester Town	2-5	110
Brighton & Hove Albion	v	Dulwich Hamlet	4-2	105
Torquay United	v	Chelmsford City	3-1	137
Bury Town	v	St Albans City	2-2* 4-3p	105
Cambridge United	v	Wealdstone	3-1	306

THIRD ROUND

Brighton & Hove Albion	v	Stevenage Borough	0-2	128
Derby County	v	Chester-Le-Street	1-2	389
Cirencester Town	v	Bradford City	2-1	133
Crawley Town	v	Arsenal	0-9	1636

FOURTH ROUND

Rotherham United	v	Shrewsbury Town	5-1	179
West Ham United	v	Chester-Le-Street	2-0	935
Tranmere Rovers	v	Stevenage Borough	2-1	300
Cirencester Town	v	Crewe Alexandra	1-1* 5-6p	174

F.A. COUNTY YOUTH CUP

FIRST ROUND

Sheffield & Hallamshire	v	West Riding	3-4	
North Riding	v	Leicestershire & Rutland	5-1	
Durham	v	Lincolnshire	8-1	
Manchester	v	Westmorland	4-1	
Cheshire	v	Staffordshire	2-0	
Cumberland	v	Nottinghamshire	0-1	90
Worcestershire	v	Surrey	2-1	
Dorset	v	Jersey	0-1	
Huntingdonshire	v	Essex	1-3	
Northamptonshire	v	Guernsey	2-4	
Cambridgeshire	v	Gloucestershire	1-4	
Berks & Bucks	v	Somerset	2-3	
Wiltshire	v	Army	1-0	
Devon	v	Norfolk	1-2	52
Suffolk	v	Herefordshire	1-0	

SECOND ROUND

Isle of Man	v	Shropshire	2-0
Manchester	v	Brimingham	3-1
Durham	v	Lancashire	5-1
Derbyshire	v	East Riding	0-3
Nottinghamshire	v	West Riding	0-3
North Riding	v	Liverpool	3-1
Northumberland	v	Cheshire	0-1
Bedfordshire	v	Worcestershire	1-3
Oxfordshire	v	Gloucestershire	4-5
Essex	v	Norfolk	0-1
Cornwall	v	Hampshire	1-4
Hertfordshire	v	Kent	1-2
Somerset	v	Sussex	1-4
Jersey	v	Suffolk	0-2
Middlesex	v	Guernsey	2-0
London	v	Wiltshire	2-1

THIRD ROUND

London	v	Worcestershire	0-2
West Riding	v	East Riding	0-1
Kent	v	Gloucestershire	4-2
Manchester	v	Durham	1-3
Hampshire	v	Isle of Man	3-2
Middlesex	v	Suffolk	1-0
North Riding	v	Sussex	3-0
Norfolk	v	Cheshire	2-5

FOURTH ROUND

Durham	v	Cheshire	2-0
Worcestershire	v	Middlesex	1-4
Kent	v	North Riding	2-3
Hampshire	v	East Riding	2-3

SEMI FINALS

East Riding	v	North Riding	0-2
Durham	v	Middlesex	3-2

THE FINAL

North Riding	v	Durham	0-4	902

at Middlesbrough FC

F.A. SUNDAY CUP

FIRST ROUND

AC Sportsman	v	Bartley Green	1-2
AFC Bromborough	v	Britannia	0-0* (5-4p)
Altway Valentine	v	Fantail Manfast	

(walkover for Altway after Fantail Manfest withdrawn)

BAA Heathrow	v	Hexton	1-2
Bedfont Sunday	v	VS Villa	1-1* (4-3p)
Bolton Woods	v	Bruce Ennis Square	3-5*
Capel Plough	v	Hammer	2-1
Clifton	v	Fairweather Green WMC	6-2
East Bowling Unity	v	Clubmoor Nalgo	1-2
Forest Town Welfare	v	FC Houghton Centre	1-3
Grosvenor Park(Sunday)	v	Queensmen	3-3* (3-2p)
Hartlepool Lion Hillcarter	v	Canada	2-1
Honeyfield Trailers	v	Galleon	5-3
Lebeq	v	Celtic SC (Luton)	2-0
Little Paxton	v	Travellers	3-5
Lobster	v	Orchard Park	1-2*
Marden	v	Coopers Kensington	2-0
Overstone	v	Casino Cars	2-1
Percival	v	London Colney BCH	1-2
Prestige Brighams	v	Hartlepool Supporters Athletic	3-1
Purley	v	Lewsey Social	0-3
Readflex Rangers	v	Crawley Green (Sunday)	2-2* (4-3p)
Reading Irish	v	Lashings	5-0
Seaton Sluice SC	v	Grey Bull	0-1
Shankhouse United	v	Seymour	2-2* (3-5p)
Smith & Nephew	v	Oakenshaw	2-0
St Aloysius ÔE	v	Queensbury	3-1
Standens Barn	v	Walsall Wood Royal Exchange	0-0* (2-4p)
Toll End	v	St Josephs (Luton)	0-3
Trooper	v	Grange Athletic	0-1*

Clubs receiving byes: A3 (Canada), Albion Sport, Austin Ex Apprentices, Belstone, Breeze, Canon, Cb Hounslow, Dickie Lewis, Ford Motors, Gossoms End, HarryÕs, Hessle Rangers, Hetton Lyons Cricket Club, Linfield Yenton, Lodge Cottrell, Mackadown Lane S&S, Marske Ship Inn, Moat, Nicosia, Norcoast, Pioneer, Poole Wanderers, Queens Park, Quested, Rainham Sports, Sandon Dock, Schofields, St Margarets, Sutton High, Taxi Club, Uk Flooring, Western Approaches. Allerton and Duke of York exempt to Second Round for reaching last seasonÕs final.

SECOND ROUND

A3 (Canada)	v	Canon	3-2
AFC Bromborough	v	Hessle Rangers	1-0
Allerton	v	Dickie Lewis	2-1
Altway Valentine	v	Marske Ship Inn	6-1
Bartley Green	v	Belstone	5-3
Bedfont Sunday	v	Duke of York	0-2
Breeze	v	Ford Motors	2-3
Bruce Ennis Square	v	Clifton	2-0
Capel Plough	v	Moat	4-0
CB Hounslow United	v	Pioneer	2-3
Clubmoor Nalgo	v	Schofields	

(walkover for Clubmoor Schofields withdrew)

FC Houghton Centre	v	Austin Ex Apprentices	2-0
Grey Bull	v	Taxi Club	2-1
Grosvenor Park	v	Gossoms End	1-4
Harry's	v	Nicosia	1-4
Hartlepool Lion Hillcarter	v	Norcoast	2-0
Hexton	v	Rainham Sports	4-0
Honeyfield Traveilers	v	Poole Wanderers	4-1
Lewsey Social	v	Quested	0-1
London Colney BCH	v	St Margarets	4-4* (2-4p)
Marden	v	Linfield Yenton	0-4
Orchard Park	v	Queens Park	2-1
Overstone	v	Lodge Cottrell	0-5
Prestige Brighams	v	Sandon Dock	2-0
Crawley Green (Sunday)	v	Mackadown Lane S&S	0-2*
Reading Irish	v	Sutton High	4-2
Seymour	v	Albion Sports	3-0
Smith & Nephew	v	Hetton Lyons Cricket Club	2-3
St Aloysius 'E	v	Western Approaches	2-1
St Josephs (Luton)	v	UK Flooring	0-2
Travellers	v	Lebeq	6-1
Walsall Wood R. E.	v	Grange Athletic	1-2

First Round action between Standens Barn and Walsall Wood Royal Exchange. Photo: Steve Ayre.

THIRD ROUND

A3 (Canada)	v	Orchard Park	3-1
Bruce Ennis Square	v	Prestige Brighams	3-4
Capel Plough	v	Linfield Yenton	3-3* (4-3p)
Clubmoor Nalgo	v	Ford Motors	6-0
Grange Athletic	v	Pioneer	2-1
Hetton Lyons C. C.	v	Grey Bull	3-1
Hexton	v	Duke of York	
Lodge Cotterill	v	Honeyfield Trailers	3-2
Nicosia	v	Altway Valentine	2-3
Quested	v	Gossoms End	3-0
Reading Irish	v	Mackadown Lane S&S	3-0
Seymour	v	Hartlepool Lion Hillcarter	0-1
St Aloysius 'E	v	Allerton	3-4
St. Margarets	v	Bartley Green	3-1*
Travellers	v	AFC Bromborough	1-2
UK Flooring	v	FC Houghton Centre	4-3

FOURTH ROUND

AFC Bromborough	v	Altway Valentine	0-1*
Allerton	v	A3 (Canada)	3-5
Clubmoor Nalgo	v	Hetton Lyons Cricket Club	1-1* (3-2p)
Duke of York	v	Grange Athletic	3-0
Hartlepool Lion Hillcarter	v	Prestige Brighams	0-1
Lodge Cotterill	v	Capel Plough	0-1
St Margarets	v	Reading Irish	3-1*
UK Flooring	v	Quested	1-0

QUARTER-FINALS

A3 (Canada)	v	Clubmoor Nalgo	4-2
Capel Plough	v	St Margarets	0-1
Nicosia	v	Prestige Brighams	2-0
Uk Flooring	v	Duke of York	1-0

SEMI-FINALS

Nicosia	v	A3 (Canada)	3-2

(Both teams from the Liverpool Business Houses Sunday League) at Marine

Uk Flooring	v	St Margrets	4-1
(Bristol Sunday Leage)		(Northampton Sunday League)	at Bristol City

THE FINAL — 25th April at Anfield

Nicosia	v	St Margrets	3-1

Att: 1,526

F.A. NATIONAL LEAGUE SYSTEM CUP

THE UEFA regions Cup was established in 1999 to provide an opportunity for "amateur" players playing at the lower levels of the game to compete in a European competition. In the 2002/2003 competition The FA nominated the Kent County League to compete. They were chosen from 12 level 4 leagues who had indicated an interest in taking part. The Kent side took part in a qualifying competition in Estonia where they finished in 2nd place narrowly failing to qualify for the finals.

UEFA have now decided that for future competitions, National Associations can only nominate sides that have won a National Competition, hence the FA National League System Cup was formed for the 2003/2004 season.

22 of the 42 eligible level 4 leagues entered this year's competition, which will see the Mid Cheshire League represent the English FA in the 2004/2005 UEFA competition.

This is the only competition part from the FA Cup where the winner is nominated to take part in a UEFA competition.

FIRST ROUND

Liverpool County Comb.	v	Northern Football Alliance	1-0
Bedford & District	v	Cambridgeshire County	0-3
Midland Football Comb.	v	Central Midlands	5-2*
Essex Intermediate	v	Hertfordshire Senior County	6-2
Middlesex County	v	Kent County	4-2
Dorset Premier	v	Hampshire	3-0

SECOND ROUND

Liverpool County Comb.	v	Weaside	3-1*
Mid Cheshire	v	West Cheshire	2-0
Cambridgeshire County	v	Northampton	4-1
Midland Football Comb.	v	Peterborough District	3-1
Essex Intermediate	v	North Berks	5-0
Middlesex County	v	Combined Counties Div.1	3-1*
Dorset Premier	v	South Western	0-1
Gloucestershire County	v	Wiltshire	2-1

THIRD ROUND

Mid Cheshire	v	Liverpool County Combination	4-2
Midland Football Comb.	v	Cambridgeshire County	1-2
Essex Intermediate	v	Middlesex County	6-1
South Western	v	Gloucestershire County	

SEMI FINALS

South Western	v	Mid Cheshire League	1-2
Essex Intermediate	v	Cambridgeshire County	0-2

THE FINAL

Cambridgeshire County	v	Mid Cheshire League	0-2	690

at Cambridge United FC

F.A. WOMEN'S CUP

FIRST ROUND QUALIFYING

AC Sportsman	v	Bartley Green	1-2
Aylesbury United	v	Redhill	1-0
Billericay Town	v	Southwark Town United	1-4*
Birstall United	v	Kettering Town	2-1
Blyth Spartans	v	York City	2-1*
Bolton Ambassadors	v	Corwen	2-1
Brentford	v	Carterton Rangers	3-2
Brentwood Town	v	Whitehawk	1-4
Bristol Manor Farm	v	Bath City	1-2
Buckfastleigh Rangers	v	Cogan Corinthian	6-1
Bury Girls & Ladies	v	Stockport Celtic	7-2
Buxton	v	Atherstone United	5-3*
Cambridge United	v	Southam United	7-1
Chelmsford City	v	Caversham	5-6
Crowborough Athletic	v	Maidstone Mavrix	7-1
Dagenham & Redbridge	v	Harlow Town	17-0
Darlington RA	v	Blyth Town	3-1*
Derby County	v	Cosford	4-0
Durham City	v	Windscale	3-1
Dynamo & North London	v	Hastings United	3-3* 5-4p
Haringey Borough	v	Basildon United	5-1
Haywards Heath Town	v	Luton Town Belles	1-4
Hendon	v	Leighton Linsdale	2-2* 3-4p
Hitchin Town	v	Bushey Rangers	2-2* 7-6p
Hopwood	v	Greyhound Gunners	13-0
Huddersfield Town	v	Crook Town	3-2*
Hull City	v	North Ferriby United	3-4*
Keynsham Town	v	Marazion Blues	12-0
Kirklees	v	Chester-Le-Street Town	0-13
Launceston	v	Team Bath	0-5
Leicester City	v	Kidderminster Harriers	12-1
Lewes	v	Thatcham Town	7-1
Liverpool Feds	v	Darwen	1-8
London Colney	v	Haywood United	3-1
London Women	v	Woking	2-3
Lordswood	v	London Ladies	1-4
Loughborough Dynamo	v	Walsall	3-2
Lumley Ladies	v	Gateshead Cleveland Hall	10-3
Luton Borough	v	Tring Athletic	1-4
Macclesfield Town	v	Bolton Wanderers	0-3
Madron	v	Alphington	0-7
Morley Spurs	v	Killingworth YPC	2-4
Northampton Town	v	Wollaston Victoria	0-0* 3-4p
Ossett Albion	v	Wardley Eagles	0-5
Penzance	v	Newquay	
Plymouth Oak Villa	v	Ashdown Rovers	7-3
Preston North end	v	Pemrith Sapphires	9-1
Redbridge Raiders	v	Mansfield Road	w/o for Redbridge
South Normanton At.	v	Leafield Athletic	0-5
Sporting Links (Caistor)	v	Eye United	2-3
Swindon Spitfires	v	Caldicot Town	
Telford United	v	Stone Dominoes	0-2
Thurrock & Tilbury	v	Tottenham Hotspur	1-11
TNS Ladies	v	Cambridge City	w/o for TNS Ladies
US Valerio Vixens	v	Barwell	3-0
Viking	v	MK Wanderers	2-5
Wigan	v	Thorpe United	w/o for Thorpe Utd
Wycombe Wanderers	v	Clapton Orient	4-2

SECOND ROUND QUALIFYING

Abbey Rangers	v	Whitstable Town	4-0
Alphington	v	Gloucester City	3-2
Birstall United	v	Solihull Glades	4-0
Blyth Spartans	v	North Ferriby United	3-0
Bolton Ambassadors	v	Preston North End	2-3
Bolton Wanderers	v	Huddersfield Town	7-1
Bradford City	v	Thorpe United	4-1
Brentford	v	MK Wanderers	
Bury Girls & Ladies	v	South Durham Royals	7-4
Buxton	v	Leicester City	0-7
Caversham	v	Woodbridge Town	2-1
Chester-Le-Street	v	Lumley Ladies	3-1
Dagenham & Redbridge	v	Aylesbury United	5-1
Darwen	v	Darlington RA	4-0
Derby County	v	Loughborough Dynamo	6-0
Durham City	v	Killingworth YPC	2-3*
Dynamo & North London	v	Crowborough Athletic	0-1
Edgware Town	v	Redbridge Raiders	0-3
Eye United	v	Leafield Athletic	3-8
Haringey Borough	v	Tottenham Hotspur	0-7
Hopwood	v	Wardley Eagles	5-2
Lewes	v	Leighton Linslade	5-1
Leyton Orient	v	Tring Athletic	6-0
London Colney	v	London Ladies	8-1
Penzance	v	Swindon Spitfires	4-0
Peterborough United	v	Stone Dominoes	3-1
Plymouth Oak Villa	v	Keynsham Town	8-6
Southampton	v	Bath City	0-3
Southwark Town United	v	Royston Town	7-1
Team Bath	v	Buckfastleigh Rangers	1-0
TNS Ladies	v	US Valerio Vixens	10-0
Whitehawk	v	Woodstock	5-0
Woking	v	Hitchin Town	5-1
Wollaston Victoria	v	Cambridge United	0-1
Wycombe Wanderers	v	Luton Town Belles	2-3

FIRST ROUND PROPER

Bath City	v	Alphington	3-5
Birstall United	v	Stafford Rangers	3-0
Blackburn Rovers	v	Newcastle	1-0
Blyth Spartans	v	Bury Girls & Ladies	2-4
Bolton Wanderers	v	East Durham	1-5
Bradford City	v	TNS Ladies	1-3*
Brentford	v	Gillingham	5-5* 7-8p
Brook House	v	Reading Royals	2-3
Cambridge United	v	Peterborough United	1-0
Caversham	v	Whitehawk	0-3
Chester City	v	Barnsley	2-0
Colchester United	v	Barking	2-0
Crewe Vagrants	v	Chester-Le-Street	3-2*
Crowborough Athletic	v	Abbey Rangers	4-2*
Crystal Palace	v	Southwark Town United	1-0
Dagenahm & redbridge	v	Tottenham Hotspur	2-3
Darwen	v	Ilkeston Town	w/o for Darwen
Denham United	v	Queens Park Rangers	2-4
Derby County	v	Leafield Athletic	3-5
Doncaster Parklands R.	v	Leeds City Vixens	5-0

Exeter City	v	Clevedon Town	1-3
Forest Green Rovers	v	Rover OXford	7-3
Killingworth YPC	v	Hopwood	1-2
Leicester City	v	Bedford Town Belles	2-1
Lewes	v	Norwich City	1-0
Leyton Orient	v	Woking	2-1
Lichfield Diamonds	v	Coventry City	3-8
London Colney	v	West Ham United	2-5
Loughborough Students	v	Luton Town Belles	2-0
Manchester United	v	Newsham PH	2-0
Newton Abbott	v	Plymouth Argyle	4-0
Nottingham Forest	v	Rushden & Diamonds	3-2
Plymouth Oak Villa	v	Swindon Town	7-6
Preston North End	v	Rotherham United	5-4
Reading	v	Stowmarket Sophtlogic	3-3* 4-2p
Redbridge Raiders	v	Chesham United	3-5
Scunthorpe UNited	v	Blacpool Wren Rovers	1-2
Shrewsbury Town	v	Garswood Saints	1-2
Team Bath	v	Cardiff City	1-5
Yeovil Town	v	Penzance	0-1

SECOND ROUND PROPER

Alphington	v	Reading Royals	0-3
Birstall United	v	Coventry City	1-5
Blackpool Wren Rovers	v	Doncaster Parklands Rovers	1-0
Bury Girls & Ladies	v	Blackburn Rovers	0-7
Cambridge United	v	Loughborough Students	1-5
Cardiff City	v	Chesham United	5-1
Clevedon Town	v	Plymouth Oak Villa	4-1
Crystal Palace	v	Crowborough Athletic	7-1
Darwen	v	Chester City	3-2
East Durham	v	Preston North End	4-2*
Garswood Saints	v	Manchester United	1-4
Gillingham	v	Lewes	4-4* 4-2p
Hopwood	v	Crewe Vagrants	0-5
Leafield Athletic	v	Leicester City	0-2
Leyton Orient	v	Colchester United	3-1
Newton Abbott	v	Reading	2-2
(Abandoned ater 90mins due to waterlogged pitch)			
Reading	v	Newton Abbott	4-1
Nottingham Forest	v	TNS Ladies	2-0
Penzance	v	Forest Green Rovers	1-2*
Queens Park Rangers	v	Tottenham Hotspur	5-4
Whitehawk	v	West Ham United	1-1* 3-4p

THIRD ROUND PROPER

Barnet FC Ladies	v	Cardiff City	2-4*
Bristol City	v	Reading Royals	0-3
Chelsea	v	Gillingham	6-3
Chesterfield	v	Manchester United	1-2
Clevedon Town	v	Millwall Lionesses	1-3
Coventry City	v	Southampton Saints	2-3*
Darwen	v	Sheffield Wednesday	2-5
East Durham	v	Oldham Curzon	1-2*
Enfield Town	v	Crystal Palace	0-0* 2-4p
Leicester City	v	Sunderland AFC Ladies	2-3
Leyton Orient	v	Ipswich Town	4-2
Lincoln City	v	Manchester City	3-1*
Loughborough Students	v	Blackpool Wren Rovers	6-2
Middlesbrough	v	Bangor City	2-0
Nottingham Forest	v	Crewe Vagrants	3-1
Portsmouth	v	Forest Green Rovers	3-2
Queens Park Rangers	v	Methyr Tydfil	0-2
Reading	v	AFC Wimbledon	0-3
Stockport County	v	Blackburn Rovers	2-1
Watford	v	Brighton & Hove Albion	1-2*
West Ham United	v	Langford	1-1* 3-4p
Wolverhampton W.	v	Liverpool	2-1*

FOURTH ROUND PROPER

Arsenal	v	Stockport County	3-0
Birmingham City	v	Loughborough Students	1-0
Bristol Rovers	v	Aston Villa	1-0
Cardiff City	v	Merthyr Tydfil	3-1
Charlton Athletic	v	Portsmouth	3-0
Chelsea	v	Manchester United	2-0
Doncaster Rovers Belles	v	Leeds United	2-1
Everton	v	Langford	2-1
Fulham	v	Sunderland AFC Ladies	5-0
Lincoln City	v	Leyton Orient	1-3
Middlesbrough	v	Southampton Saints	1-0*
Nottingham Forest	v	Oldham Curzon	3-0
Reading Royals	v	Millwall Lionesses	2-1
Sheffield Wednesday	v	Crystal Palace	1-0
Tranmere Rovers	v	Brighton & Hove Albion	5-3
Wolverhampton W.	v	AFC Wimbledon	6-2

FIFTH ROUND PROPER

Cardiff City	v	Everton	2-1
Charlton Athletic	v	Fulham	2-1
Chelsea	v	Nottingham Forest	3-3* 1-3p
Doncaster Rovers Belles	v	Wolverhampton W.	4-0
Leyton Oreint	v	Birmingham City	1-6
Middlesbrough	v	Arsenal	1-6
Reading Royals	v	Bristol Rovers	1-9
Tranmere Rovers	v	Sheffield Wednesday	1-0

SIXTH ROUND PROPER

Arsenal	v	Cardiff City	11-1
Doncaster Rovers Belles	v	Charlton Athletic	0-1
Nottingham Forest	v	Bristol Rovers	0-3
Tranmere Rovers	v	Birmingham City	2-3

SEMI-FINALS

Birmingham City	v	Charlton Athletic	0-1
Bristol Rovers	v	Arsenal	0-2

THE FINAL at Loftus Road

Arsenal	v	Charlton Athletic	3-0
Fleeting (3)			Att: 12,244

ARSENAL SQUAD (3-4-1-2)
Byrne, White, Asante, Champ, Pealling, Ludlow, Grant, Wheatley, Maggs[S90], Sanderson[S73], Fleeting[S90].
Subs: S. Williams, Harwood, Lorton[S90], Potter[S73], Scott[S90].

CHARLTON ATHLETIC SQUAD (4-4-2)
Cope, Murphy, Stoney, Mills, Fletcher[S70], F. Williams, Smith[S81], Broadhurst, Heatherson[S70], Barr, Walker.
Subs: Law, Aluko[S70], Coss[S70], Hunn[S81], Rea.

COUNTY FOOTBALL ASSOCIATIONS

BEDFORDSHIRE F.A.

Tel: 01582 565111 (B) Fax: 01582 565222 Email: peter.brown@bedfordshirefa.com
Century House, Skimpot Road, Dunstable, Bedfordshire LU5 4JU
Secretary: Peter D Brown
Other executives: **President:** Ray Berridge **Chairman:** Richard Robinson
Chief Executive: Peter D Brown **Development Officer:** Simon Macqueen

Coaching: Kevin England **Discipline:** Secretary **Registration:** Secretary **Referees:** Carl Couzens
Grants: Secretary **Courses:** Secretary **Womens:** Katie Milton **Press&PR:** Secretary
Number of Affiliated Clubs Senior: Junior: Womens:
County Representative Teams (Senior Coach responsible): (Neal Rodney)
Inter County Competitions: East Anglia Counties Championship
Trophies won in season 2003-04:

COUNTY CUP FINALS

Premier Cup	Arlesey Town	v	Leighton Town	4-1	6th May - Hitchin Town
Senior Trophy	Langford	v	Biggleswade Utd	2-2* 2-3p	27th April - Stortfold
Intermediate Cup	Bedford Town Res.	v	Westoning	0-0* 4-3p	2nd April - Langford

BERKS & BUCKS F.A. LIMITED

Tel: 01367 242 099 Fax: 01367 242 158
email: secretary@berks-bucksfa.com www.berksandbucksfa.com
15a London Street, Faringdon, Oxon SN7 7HD
Secretary: Brian Moore
Other executives: **President:** Bill Gosling **Chairman:** Jim Atkins
Chief Executive: Brian Moore **Development Officer:** Simon Robinson

Coaching: **Discipline:** Tracey Bannon/Leigh Priest **Registration:** Caoline Terry **Referees:** Tracey Bannon/Leigh Priest
Grants: **Courses:** Suzanne Blundy **Womens:** **Press&PR:** Brian Moore
Number of Affiliated Clubs Senior: 32 Junior: 440 Womens: 18
Intermediate: 185 Youth: 268
County Representative Teams (Senior Coach responsible): Only Youth Under-18
Inter County Competitions: South South West Counties
Trophies won in season 2003-04: None

COUNTY CUP FINALS

Senior Cup

Bracknell Town	v	Chesham United	1-4	3rd May - Wycombe W.

Trophy

Buckingham Town	v	Beaconsfield SYCOB	1-3	21st April - Aylesbury Utd

Intermediate Cup

Buckingham Athletic	v	Wraysbury	3-2	3rd April - Newport Pagnell

Buckingham Athletic lift the Berks & Bucks Intermediate Cup for the second successive year. Photo: Steve Ayre.

Stony Stratford's Brendan Quill makes it 2-0 to the home side against Maidenhead Reserves in this Berks & Bucks Intermediate Cup quarter-final.

Paul Frane manages to keep this shot out for Wraysbury during his sides 2-3 defeat against Buckingham Athletic in the Berks & Bucks INtermediate Cup final.

Photos: Steve Ayre.

BIRMINGHAM COUNTY F.A.

Tel: 0121 357 4278 Fax: 0121 358 1661 Email: secretary@birmingham.co.uk

Ray Hall Lane, Great Barr, Birmingham B43 6JF

Secretary: David Shelton.

President: K H Goodfellow. **Chariman:** Roger Wood

Development Officer: Miss N Justice & T. Stack

Coaching: **Discipline:** **Registration:** **Referees:** M Penn

Grants: **Courses:** **Womens:** Miss H Buckley **Press&PR: A Lacey**

Number of Affiliated Clubs Senior: 1,663 U.18: 484

Number of Affiliated Leagues: Senior: 55 Junior: 14

County Representative Teams: U18, U17, Womens Open, U18, U16

Inter County Competitions: Boys U18, Womens, Girls U16, FA Youth Cup and Midland Youth Championships

County Publications:"The Centre Circle" bi-monthly newsletter

COUNTY CUP FINAL

Senior	Wolverhampton W.	v	Moor Green	0-1	27th April - Wolves

CAMBRIDGESHIRE F.A. LTD

Tel: 01223 576 770x201 Fax: 01223 576 780 Email: secretary@cambridgeshirefa.com

City Ground, Milton Road, Cambridge CB4 1FA

Secretary: Roger Pawley

Other executives: **President:** **Chairman:** J W Coad

Chief Executive: R K Pawley **Development Officer:** J F Hill

Coaching: **Discipline:** R K Pawley **Registration:** **Referees:** R K Nichols

Grants: **Courses:** C Munns (Mrs) **Womens:** K Friar **Press&PR:**

Number of Affiliated Clubs Senior: 30 Junior: 280 Womens: 15

County Representative Teams (Senior Coach responsible): (Graham Daniels)

Inter County Competitions: East Anglian

Trophies won in season 2003-04: None

COUNTY CUP FINALS

Invitation Cup	Histon	v	Newmarket Town	1-1* 5-4p	30th March - Cambridge U.
Challenge Cup	West Wratting	v	Fulbourn Institute	0-1	15th April - Cambridge City

CHESHIRE F.A.

Tel: 01606 871166 Fax: 01606 871292 Football Development: 01606 871155

Hartford House, Hartford Moss Recreation Centre, Winnington, Northwich CW8 4BG

Secretary: Maureen Dunford

Other executives: **President:** Eddie Crabtree **Chairman:** Eddie Crabtree

Chief Executive: Maureen Dunford **Development Officer:** John Ackerley

Coaching: John Ackerley **Discipline:** Steve Mundy **Registration:** Steve Mundy **Referees:** Steve Swallow

Grants: John Ackerley **Courses:** John Ackerley **Womens:** Zoe Langley **Press&PR:** Secretary

Number of Affiliated Clubs Senior: 1,197 Junior: 262 Womens: 42

County Representative Teams: (Senior Coach responsible): Correspondence to Dave Edmunds

Inter County Competitions: Northern Counties Senior, Northern

Trophies won in season 2003-04: Northern Counties Senior Cup

COUNTY CUP FINAL

Senior Cup	Woodley Sports	v	Witton Albion	2-1*	24th March - Altrincham

CORNWALL F.A.

Tel: 01726 74080 Fax: 01726 76174 Email: secretary@cornwallfa.com

1 High Cross Street, St Austell, Cornwall PL25 4AB

President: B F Conyon. **Chairman:** D G Champion. **Secretary:** Barry Cudmore

Executives (Responsibility): David Bray (Youth Secretary). Ian Anear (Referees)

Phil Cardew (Football Development Officer)

Number of Affiliated Clubs Senior: 311 U.18: 84

Number of Affiliated Leagues: Senior: 20 Youth: 2

County Representative Teams: Senior, Youth U18

Inter County Competitions: South West Counties Senior, Youth & Womens, FA County Youth Cup

COUNTY CUP FINAL

Senior Cup	Saltash United	v	Porthleven	1-2	12th April - St Blazey

CUMBERLAND F.A.

Tel: 01900 872310 Fax: 01900 872310

17 Oxford Street, Workington, Cumbria CA14 2AL Email: secretary@cumberlandfa.com

Secretary: G Turrell

Other executives: **President:** B Taylor **Chairman:** R J Turner

Chief Executive: J A Murphy **Development Officer:** P Devlin

Coaching: P Devlin **Discipline:** G Turrell **Registration:** G Turrell **Referees:** J Williamson

Grants: W Wilson **Courses:** L O'Neill **Womens:** P Devlin **Press&PR:** B Taylor

Number of Affiliated Clubs Senior: 158 Junior: 33 Womens: 4

County Representative Teams: (Senior Coach responsible)

Inter County Competitions: Northern Counties

Trophies won in season 2003-04: None

COUNTY CUP FINAL

Senior Cup	Carlisle United	v	Penrith	2-1	4th May - Carlisle United

DERBYSHIRE F.A.

Tel: 01332 361 422 Fax: 01332 360 130 Email: secretary@derbyshirefa.com

Nos 8-9 Stadium Business Court, Millennium Way, Pride Park, Derby DE24 8HZ

Secretary: K Compton

Other executives: **President:** **Chairman:** R F Johnson

Chief Executive: **Development Officer:** Debbie Wood

Coaching: **Discipline:** **Registration:** **Referees:** D N Harwood

Grants: **Courses:** **Womens:** **Press&PR:** K Compton

Number of Affiliated Clubs Senior: 450 Junior: 250 Womens: 12

County Representative Teams (Senior Coach responsible):

Inter County Competitions: Midlands County Youth

Trophies won in season 2003-04: None

COUNTY CUP FINAL

Senior Cup	Ilkeston Town	v	Matlock Tn	1st Leg: 0-3 2nd Leg: 1-1

DEVON F.A.

Tel: 01626 332077 Fax: 01626 336814 Email: info@devonfa.com

County Headquarters, Coach Road, Newton Abbot, Devon TQ12 1EJ

Secretary:

Other executives: **President:** T Boyce OBE **Chairman:** D Smith

Chief Executive: N/A **Development Officer:** D Keast

Coaching: D Keast **Discipline:** G Gordon **Registration:** D Richardson **Referees:** D Richardson

Grants: D Richardson **Courses:** D Keast **Womens:** D Keast **Press&PR:** J Jewill

Number of Affiliated Clubs Senior: 250 Junior: 200 Womens: 30

County Representative Teams: (Senior Coach responsible)

Inter County Competitions: South West Counties Championship

Trophies won in season 2003-04: None

COUNTY CUP FINALS

St Lukes College Bowl	Exeter City	v	Bideford	3-1	25th May - Exeter City
Premier Cup	Vospers Oak Villa	v	Plymouth Parkway	4-2*	10th May - Plymouth Argyle

DORSET F.A.

Tel: 01202 682 375 Fax: 01202 666 577 Email: secretary@dorsetfa.com

County Ground, Blandford Close, Hamworthy, Poole BH15 4BF

President: Spencer Miles. **Chairman:** Doug Smurthwaite. **Chief Executive:** Peter Hough

Cup & Competitions Manager: Colin Chainey. **Secretary:** Peter Hough

Executives (Responsibility): Sue Hough (Football Development Manager)

Gary Knight (Football Development Officer). S N Whittle (Referees)

County Representative Teams: Senior, U18, Womens

Inter County Competitions: South West Championship for all the above

COUNTY CUP FINAL

Senior Cup	Sherbourne Town	v	Poole Town	3-2	20th April - Shaftesbury

DURHAM F.A.

Tel: 0191 384 8653 Fax: 0191 384 3234 Email: john.topping@durhamfa.com

"Codeslaw', Ferens Park, Durham DH1 1JZ

Secretary: John Topping

Other executives: **President:** Mr F D Pattison **Chairman:** Dennis Smith

Chief Executive: N/A **County Development Manager:** Phillip Woodward

Coaching: P. Woodward **Discipline:** Robert Strophair **Registration:** John Topping **Referees:** Tom Harvey

Grants: None **Courses:** P. Woodward **Womens:** Sheila Jevons **Press&PR:** John Topping

Number of Affiliated Clubs Senior: 1000 Junior: 350 Womens: 60

County Representative Teams (Senior Coach responsible): (David Cleary)

Inter County Competitions: Association of Northern Counties

Trophies won in season 2003-04: FA County Youth Cup. Association of Northern Counties Youth Cup

COUNTY CUP FINAL

Challenge Cup	Bishop Auckland	v	Billingham Town	0-2	12th April - Durham City

EAST RIDING F.A. LTD

Tel: 01482 221158 Fax: 01482 221159 E.Mail: info@eastridingfa.com

50 Boulevard, Hull HU3 2TB

Secretary: Dennis R Johnson

Other executives: **President:** C Bodsworth **Chairman:** M H Randing

Chief Executive: N/A **Development Officer:** Adam Lowthorpe

Coaching: A Lowthorpe **Discipline:** **Registration:** **Referees:** Peter Summerbell

Grants: **Courses:** Liz Shipp **Womens:** Mike Edge **Press&PR:** D R Johnson

Number of Affiliated Clubs Senior: 335 Junior: 314 Womens: 6

County Representative Teams: (Senior coach responsible) Andy Foster (Youth XI)

Inter County Competitions: Northern Counties Senior, Midlands Youth, Ridings Cup - Ladies

Trophies won in season 2003-04: None

COUNTY CUP FINAL

Senior Cup	Hull City	v	Hider Foods	3-0	12thMay - Hull City

ESSEX F.A.

Tel: 01245 357727 Fax: 01245 344430 Email: info@essexfa.com

31 Mildmay Road, Chelmsford CM2 0DN

Secretary: Phil Sammons

Other executives: **President:** Jack Hayward **Chairman:** Mike Game

Chief Executive: Phil Sammons **Development Officer:** Pat Kielty/Lana Bond

Coaching: Gary Piggott/Sue Hammond **Discipline:** Nicola Bruce **Registration:** **Referees:** Terry Thacker/Greg Hart

Grants: **Courses:** Gary Piggott/Sue Hammond **Womens:** Emma Wake **Press&PR:** Matt Phillips

County Development Manager: Steve Goodsell

Number of Affiliated Clubs Senior: 46 Junior: 363 Womens: 24

Inter County Competitions: East Anglian Counties, Southern Counties

Trophies won in season 2003-04: East Anglian U16s & u18s. Southern Counties Intermediate

COUNTY CUP FINALS

Senior Cup	Aveley	v	Thurrock	1-3	5th April - Southend United
Thameside Trophy	Barking & East Ham	v	Ford United	0-1	3rd May - Barking & East H.

GLOUCESTERSHIRE F.A. LIMITED

Tel: 01454 615888 Fax: 01454 618088

Oaklands Park, Almondsbury, Bristol BS32 4AG

Secretary: Paul Britton

Other executives: **President:** A C D Barrett **Chairman:** Mr R F Burden

Chief Executive: P Britton **Development Officer:** N Baker

Coaching: N Baker **Discipline:** R D Cray **Registration:** N/A **Referees:** K E Fry

Grants: N Baker **Courses:** N Baker **Womens:** P Britton **Press&PR:** P Britton

Number of Affiliated Clubs Senior: 880 Junior: 140 Womens: 37

County Representative Teams (Senior Coach responsible)**:** Senior, Womens U18 (S Evans)

Inter County Competitions: South West Counties Championship Competition

Trophies won in season 2003-04: None

COUNTY CUP FINAL

Trophy	Slimbridge	v	Cadbury Heath	1-0*	4th March - Oaklands Park

HAMPSHIRE F.A.

Tel: 02380 791 110 Fax: 02380 788 340 Email: secretary@hampshirefa.com www.hampshirefa.com

William Pickford House, 8 Ashwood Gardens, off Winchester Road, Southampton SO16 7PW

Secretary: Laurence Jones

Other executives: **President:** Martin Turner **Chairman:** John Ward

Chief Executive: Laurence Jones **Development Officer:** Salma Nicholas

Coaching: Tracey Walker **Discipline:** Matt Parker **Registration:** Darren Parker **Referees:** Keith Stroud

Grants: Salma Nicholas **Courses:** Charlotte Brown **Womens:** Jamie Burton **Press&PR:** Paul Creeden

Number of Affiliated Clubs Senior: 2000 Junior: 450 Womens: 50

County Representative Teams (Senior Coach responsible)**:** U21, U18, Women's & U18 Girls

Inter County Competitions: South West Counties Championship Competition

Trophies won in season 2003-04: SWCCC U21s & U18s Girls

COUNTY CUP FINAL

Senior Cup	Farnborough Town	v	Fareham Town	2-1	28th April - Southampton

HEREFORDSHIRE F.A.

Tel: 01432 342179 Fax: 01432 279265 Email: herefordfa@ukonline.co.uk

County Ground Offices, Widemarsh Common, Hereford HR4 9NA

Secretary: Jim Lambert

Other executives: **President:** Sir Colin Shephard **Chairman:** W E Shorten

Chief Executive: N/A **Development Officer:** Paul Carpenter

Coaching: Secretary **Discipline:** Secretary **Registration:** Secretary **Referees:** Secretary

Grants: Secretary **Courses:** Secretary **Womens:** Secretary **Press&PR:** Secretary

Number of Affiliated Clubs Senior: 31 Junior: 126 Womens: 3

County Representative Teams (Senior Coach responsible)**:** (Jack Perks)

Inter County Competitions: Midland Counties

Trophies won in season 2003-04: None

COUNTY CUP FINAL

Challenge Cup	Kington Town	v	Ledbury Town	5-2*	12th April - Hereford United

HERTFORDSHIRE F.A.

Tel: 01462 677622 Fax: 01462 677624 E.Mail: info@hertfordshirefa.com

County Ground, Baldock Road, Letchworth, Herts SG6 2EN

Company Secretary: Mr E W J King **Office Manager:** Mr Nicholas Trulock

Other executives: **President:** Mr R G Kibble **Chairman:** Mr W H Dance

Chief Executive: N/A **Development Officer:** Mr G Phillips

Coaching: Mr Alan Ackrell **Discipline:** Mr G R Norman **Registration:** Secretary **Referees:** Mr R G Dowden

Grants: Secretary **Courses:** Secretary **Womens:** Mr Karl Lingham **Press&PR:** Mr S R Trulock

Number of Affiliated Clubs Senior: 44 Junior: 549 Womens: 16

County Representative Teams (Senior Coach responsible)**:** (Mr E T Dowber)

Inter County Competitions: East Anglian Counties Championship - U16, U18 and Womens

Trophies won in season 2003-04: East Anglian CC - Women's

COUNTY CUP FINAL

Senior Cup	Boreham Wood	v	Watford	2-4*	19th April - Boreham Wood

HUNTINGDONSHIRE F.A.

Tel: 01480 414422 Fax: 01480 412691 Email: Mark.Frost@HuntsFA.com www.HuntsFA.com

Cromwell Chambers, 8 St Johns Street, Huntingdon, Cambs. PE29 3DD

Secretary: Mark Frost

Other executives: **President:** Doug Roberts **Chairman:** Eric Heads

Chief Executive: N/A **Development Officer:** Sarah Batchelor

Coaching: Sarah Bachelor **Discipline:** **Registration:** **Referees:** Mike Hair

Grants: info@HuntsFA.com **Courses:** Sarah Batchelor **Womens:** Sarah Batchelor **Press&PR:** Mark Frost

Number of Affiliated Clubs Senior: 120 Junior: 30 Womens: 6

County Representative Teams (Senior Coach responsible)**:**

Inter County Competitions: East Midlands Youth U18 & U16 - FA County Youth Cup

Trophies won in season 2003-04: None

COUNTY CUP FINAL

Senior Cup	St Neots	v	Yaxley	0-1	3rd May - Somersham Town

KENT F.A. Limited

Tel: 01634 843 824 Fax: 01634 815 369 E.Mail: secretary@kentfa.com

69 Maidstone Road, Chatham, Kent ME4 6DT

Secretary: Keith Masters

Other executives: **President:** N Chatfield **Chairman:** B W Bright

Chief Executive: K Masters **Development Officer:** N Rice

Coaching: A Walker **Discipline:** S Tillman **Registration:** **Referees:** J Newson

Grants: **Courses:** N Tolley **Womens:** L Symons **Press&PR:** T Hudd

Number of Affiliated Clubs Senior: 38 Junior: 1050 Womens: 48

County Representative Teams (Senior Coach responsible): (B Bull)

Inter County Competitions: Home Counties

Trophies won in season 2003-04: None

COUNTY CUP FINALS

Senior Cup	Margate	v	Folkestone Invicta	2-1	28th April - Folkstone Invicta
Senior Trophy	Cray Wanderers	v	Hythe Town	1-0	17th April - Ashford Town

LANCASHIRE F.A.

Tel: 01772 624000 Fax: 01772 624700

The County Ground, Thurston Road, Leyland PR25 2LF

Secretary: Jim Kenyon

Other executives: **President:** G Howard **Chairman:** G Pye

Chief Executive: N/A **Development Officer:** Derek Egan

Coaching: Derek Egan **Discipline:** Jim Parker/Betty Houghton **Registration:** Linda Threlfall **Referees:** J Parker/E.Wostenholme

Grants: Jim Kenyon **Courses:** Derek Egan **Womens:** David Burges **Press&PR:** Jim Kenyon

Number of Affiliated Clubs Senior: 3,000 Junior: 2,500 Womens: 1,300

County Representative Teams (Senior Coach responsible)**:** (David Taylor)

Inter County Competitions: Linda Threlfall

Trophies won in season 2003-04: 12

COUNTY CUP FINAL

Marsden Trophy	Accrington Stanley	v	Morecambe	1st Leg: 0-1	2nd Leg: 1-2

KENT SENIOR TROPHY
ACTION

Cray Wanderers' Ross Lover (left) tussles for the ball with Scott Thomas from Hythe Town.

Micky Simmonds gets down well to maintain Crays clean sheet.

A last minute goal by Cray Wanderers' Ian Rawlings defeats Hythe Town 1-0.
Photos: Roger Turner.

LEICESTERSHIRE & RUTLAND F.A.

Tel: 0116 286 7828 Fax: 0116 286 4858 Email: secretary@leicestershirefa.com
Holmes Park, Dog & Gun Lane, Whetstone LE8 6FA

Secretary: Paul Morrison

Other executives: **President:** Gerry Cooper **Chairman:** David Jamieson

Chief Executive: Paul Morrison **Development Officer:** Tessa Payne

Coaching: **Discipline:** Geoff Smith **Registration:** Lionel Blower **Referees:** John Ward

Grants: **Courses:** **Womens:** Sharon Reason **Press&PR:**

Number of Affiliated Clubs Senior: 520 Junior: 180 Womens: 21

County Representative Teams (Senior Coach responsible)**:** Under 18/16 Boys, Under 16 Girls

Inter County Competitions: Midland Youth Championship - as above

Trophies won in season 2003-04: Midland Youth Championship U16 Cup winners

COUNTY CUP FINALS

Challenge Cup	Hinckley United	v	Oadby Town	1-0	11th May - Leicester City
Senior Cup	Loughborough Dynamo	v	Downes Sports	4-1	20th April - L&R.F.A Holmes P.

LINCOLNSHIRE F.A.

Tel: 01522 524917 Fax: 01522 528859

PO Box 26, 12 Dean Road, Lincoln LN2 4DP

Secretary: John Griffin

Other executives: **President:** Norman Saywell **Chairman:** Roy Teanby

Chief Executive: N/A **Development Officer:** Grahame Lyner

Coaching: Secretary **Discipline:** Secretary **Registration:** Secretary **Referees:** Reg Jackson

Grants: Secretary **Courses:** Secretary **Womens:** Secretary **Press&PR:** Keith Weaver

Number of Affiliated Clubs Senior: 602 Junior: 252 Womens: 15

County Representative Teams (Senior Coach responsible)**:** Under 18

Inter County Competitions: Midland Youth Championship

Trophies won in season 2003-04: None

COUNTY CUP FINALS

Shield	Grantham Town	v	Gainsborough Trinity	2-2* 4-3p	16th March - Grantham Town
Senior Cup	Blackstone	v	Barton Town Old Boys	0-2	11th May - Boston United

LIVERPOOL F.A.

Tel: 0151 523 4488 Fax: 0151 523 4477 Email: info@liverpoolfa.com

Liverpool Soccer Centre, Walton Hall Park, Walton Hall Avenue, Liverpool L4 9XP

Secretary: Steve Catterall

Other executives: **President:** N Dainty **Chairman:** R Harper

Chief Executive: F Hunter **Development Manager:** M McGlynn

Devlopment Officer: C Smith **Discipline:** W Flanagan **Registration:** Miss L Edwards **Referees:** D Cleveland

Grants: M McGlynn **Courses:** C Smith **Womens:** Mrs M Marley **Press&PR:** B Phillips

Number of Affiliated Clubs Senior: 500 Junior: 600 Womens: 26

County Representative Teams (Senior Coach responsible): (J Taylor/S Hill)

Inter County Competitions: Northern Counties

Trophies won in season 2003-04: Women's Colleges

COUNTY CUP FINAL

Senior Cup	Liverpool	v	Everton	1-1* 9-8p

LONDON F.A.

Tel: 020 8690 9626 Fax: 020 8690 9471 Email: info@londonfa.com

6 Aldworth Grove, Lewisham, London SE13 6HY

Secretary: N/A

Other executives: **President:** F J Lock MBE **Chairman:** N R J Moss

Chief Executive: D G Fowkes **Development Officer:** Josie Clifford

Coaching: John Drabwell **Discipline:** Amy Fernandez **Registration:** Pam Coleman **Referees:** Andy Porter

Grants: Basil Staward **Courses:** Ayla Arli **Womens:** Caroline McRoyall **Press&PR:** N/A

Number of Affiliated Clubs Senior: 1457 Junior: 461 Womens: 42

County Representative Teams (Senior Coach responsible)**:** (Lester Newham)

Inter County Competitions: Lester Newham

Trophies won in season 2003-04: London Yth U16, U18 Southern CC

COUNTY CUP FINAL

Senior Cup	Dulwich Hamlet	v	Tooting & Mitcham United	2-0	6th May - Hendon

MANCHESTER F.A.

Tel: 0161 881 0299 Fax: 0161 881 6833 Email: jon.dutton@manchesterfa.com

Brantingham Road, Chorlton, Manchester M21 0TT

Secretary: Jon Dutton

Other executives: **President:** **Chairman:** Frank Hannah

Chief Executive: N/A **Development Officer:** Stephen Brown, Philip Heap & Colin Moore

Coaching: Secretary **Discipline:** David Harris **Registration:** Secretary **Referees:** Secretary

Grants: Secretary **Courses:** Anita Blair **Womens:** Secretary **Press&PR:** Secretary

Number of Affiliated Clubs Senior: 500 Junior: 180 Womens: 30

County Representative Teams (Senior Coach responsible)**:** Youth U18s

Inter County Competitions: NCAC

Trophies won in season 2003-04: None

COUNTY CUP FINAL

Premier Cup	Droylsden	v	Ashton United	2-1*	5th May - Oldham Athletic

MIDDLESEX COUNTY F.A.

Tel: 0208 424 8524 Fax: 0181 863 0627 E.Mail: chief.exec@middlesexfa.com

39 Roxborough Road, Harrow, Middlesex HA1 1NS

Secretary: Peter Clayton

Other executives: **President:** Dave West **Chairman:** Derek Mennell

Chief Executive: Peter Clayton **Development Officer:** Stuart Allen

Coaching: Jason Kilby **Discipline:** Chris Hartley **Registration:** Leigh O'Connor **Referees:** Chris Hartley

Grants: Stuart Allen **Courses:** Leigh O'Connor **Womens:** Charlotte Edwards **Press&PR:** Geoff Harrison

Number of Affiliated Clubs Senior: 600 Junior: 225 Womens: 30

County Representative Teams (Senior Coach responsible)**:**

Inter County Competitions: Barbara Bivens

Trophies won in season 2003-04: None

COUNTY CUP FINAL

Senior Cup	Hendon	v	Uxbridge	3-1	12th April - Yeading

NORFOLK F.A.

Tel: 01603 717 177 Fax: 01603 717 187 E.mail: secretary@norfolkfa.com

Plantation Park, Blofield, Norwich NR13 4PL

Secretary: Roger Howlett

Other executives: **President:** **Chairman:** Stuart Dracup

Chief Executive: Roger Howlett **County Development Manager:** Shaun Turner

Coaching: Secretary **Discipline:** Richard King **Registration:** Secretary **Referees:** Steve Clover

Grants: Secretary **Courses:** Secretary **Womens:** Secretary **Press&PR:** Secretary

Number of Affiliated Clubs Male Adults:408 Male Youth:154 Womens: 18 Girls: 32

County Representative Teams (Senior Coach responsible)**:** (John Musgrove)

Inter County Competitions: East Anglian Counties

Trophies won in season 2003-04: None

COUNTY CUP FINAL

Senior Cup	Diss Town	v	Wroxham	3-3* 5-6p	20th April - Norwich City

NORTH RIDING F.A.

Tel: 01642 318603 Fax: 01642 318604

Broughton Road, Stokesley, Middlesbrough TS9 5NY

Secretary: Mark Jarvis

Other executives: **President:** K Boyer **Chairman:** K Boyer

Chief Executive: Mark Jarvis **Development Manager:** A Clay

Coaching: L Goodchild/A Clay/G Grainger/D Burns **Discipline:** T Wing **Registration:** **Referees:** C Dale/J Campbell

Grants: Office **Courses:** L Goodchild **Womens:** G Grainger **Press&PR:** Office

Number of Affiliated Clubs Senior: 350 Junior: 150 Womens: 50

County Representative Teams (Senior Coach responsible)**:** (J Wattis)

Inter County Competitions: FA, Northern Counties, Ridings Ladies

Trophies won in season 2003-04: Runner-up in FA County Youth Cup

COUNTY CUP FINAL

Senior Cup	Scarborough	v	Middlesbrough

NORTHAMPTONSHIRE F.A.

Tel: 01604 670741 Fax: 01604 670742 E.mail: sam.burgess@northamptonshirefa.com

9 Duncan Close, Red House Square, Northampton NN3 6WL

Secretary: N/A

Other executives: **President:** D Vernum **Chairman:** D Joyce

Chief Executive: D Payne **Development Officer:** Jamie Leeson

Coaching: **Discipline:** Sue Ainge **Registration:** Nicola Dodds **Referees:** Sam Burgess

Grants: David Payne **Courses:** S Burgess/Emma Waples **Womens:** Matt Greenwood **Press&PR:** S Burgess/D Payne

Number of Affiliated Clubs Senior: 16 Junior: 283 Womens: 10

County Representative Teams (Senior Coach responsible)**:** U18 Boys. U16 Girls (J Marsh)

Inter County Competitions: Boys FA County Yth Champs & Midland County Champs. U16 Girls Midland Co. Yth Champs.

Trophies won in season 2003-04: U16 Girls Midland Co. Yth Champs.

COUNTY CUP FINAL

Senior Cup	Desborough Town	v	Peterborough United	0-1	27th April - Desborough Town

NORTHUMBERLAND F.A.

Tel: 0191 2 700 700

Whitley Park, Whitley Road, Newcastle upon Tyne NE12 9FA

Secretary: See Chief Executive

Other executives: **President:** E A Wright **Chairman:**

Chief Executive: Rowland E Maughan **Development Officer:** S W Leason

Coaching: M Woodhall **Discipline:** **Registration:** **Referees:** R E Maughan

Grants: S W Leason **Courses:** S W Leason **Womens:** S W Leason **Press&PR:** W Gardiner

Number of Affiliated Clubs Senior: 480 Junior: 450 Womens: 6

County Representative Teams (Senior Coach responsible)**:** (A Gowans)

Inter County Competitions: Associate Northern Counties

Trophies won in season 2003-04: None

COUNTY CUP FINALS

Senior Cup	Bedlington Terriers	v	Blyth Spartans	1-0	5th May - N.F.A. Whitley Park
Bowl	Percy Main Amateurs	v	Cramlington Town	0-2	12th May - N.F.A.

NOTTINGHAMSHIRE F.A. LIMITED

Tel: 0115 941 8954 Fax: 0115 941 5254 Email: info@nottinghamshirefa.com

7 Clarendon Street, Nottingham NG1 5HS

Secretary: Mike Kilbee

Other executives: **President:** John Waterall **Chairman:** David Woolrich

Chief Executive: N/A **Development Officer:** John Folwell (CDM), Craig Lee (FDO)

Coaching: J Folwell/C Lee **Discipline:** Helen Bennett **Registration:** **Referees:** David Cooke

Grants: John Folwell **Courses:** John Folwell **Womens:** **Press&PR:**

Number of Affiliated Clubs Senior: 561 Junior: 198 Womens: 13

County Representative Teams (Senior Coach responsible)**:** U18 (Steve Pritchard)

Inter County Competitions: East Midlands Youth

Trophies won in season 2003-04: None

COUNTY CUP FINAL

Senior Cup	Hucknall Town	v	Eastwood Town	1-2	29th April - Notts County

OXFORDSHIRE F.A.

Tel: 01993 778 586 Fax: 01993 772 191 Email: secretary@oxfordshirefa.com

PO Box 62, Witney, Oxon OX28 1HA

President: J Webb. **Chairman:** T Williams. **Secretary:** Ian Mason

Executives (Responsibility): Ted Mitchell (Football Development)

Trevor Spindler (Coaching Exams/Courses)

Paul Faulkner (Referees) Liz Verrall (Womens Football)

Number of Affiliated Clubs 320

Number of Affiliated Leagues: 12

County Representative Teams: Under 18, Under 16

Inter County Competitions: Under 18, Under 16

COUNTY CUP FINAL

Senior Cup	Banbury United	v	Oxford United Reserves	1-0	29th April - Oxford United

SHEFFIELD & HALLAMSHIRE F.A.

Tel: 0114 241 4999 Fax: 0114 241 4990 Email: secretary@sheffieldfa.com

Clegg House, 69 Cornish Place, Cornish Street, Sheffield S6 3AF

Secretary: Mr J P Hope-Gill

Other executives: **President:** Mr C L Milner **Chairman:** Mr M Matthews

Chief Executive: Mr J P Hope-Gill **Development Officer:** Marc Birkett

Head of Development: Brian Peck **Discipline:** **Registration:** **Referees:** Craig Grundy

Grants: **Courses:** Brian Peck **Womens:** Julie Callaghan **Press&PR:** Hayley Roach

Number of Affiliated Clubs Senior: Junior: Womens:

County Representative Teams (Senior Coach responsible)**:** (Brian Peck/Julie Callaghan - Girls)

Inter County Competitions:

Trophies won in season 2003-04: None

COUNTY CUP FINAL

Senior Cup	Worksop Town	v	Frickley Athletic	2-3	11th May - Sheffield Wed.

SHROPSHIRE F.A.

Tel: 01743 362769 Fax: 01743 240474

Gay Meadow, Abbey Foregate, Shrewsbury, Shropshire SY2 6AB

Secretary: David Rowe

Other executives: **President:** A E Munt **Chairman:** S T Farmer

Chief Executive: N/A **Development Officer:** Mick Murphy

Coaching: Mick Murphy **Discipline:** Janet Highfield **Registration:** Neil Sambrook **Referees:** G A Arrowsmith

Grants: Mick Murphy **Courses:** Andrea Goodall **Womens:** Eve Bailey **Press&PR:** Neil Sambrook

Number of Affiliated Clubs Senior: 320 Junior: 110 Womens: 6

County Representative Teams (Senior Coach responsible)**:** (Jummy Mullen)

Inter County Competitions: U18 Midland Counties Youth Championship

Trophies won in season 2003-04: None

COUNTY CUP FINAL

Senior Cup	Shrewsbury Town	v	Telford United	3-2	29th July - Telford United

SOMERSET F.A.

Tel: 01761 410 280 Fax: 01761 410 477 Email: secretary@somersetfa.com

30 North Road, Midsomer Norton, Radstock, Somerset BA3 2QD

Secretary: Mrs H Marchment

Other executives: **President:** F P Hillier **Chairman:** A J Hobbs

Chief Executive: N/A **Development Officer:** K Hodges

Coaching: I Tincknell **Discipline:** R J Fox **Registration:** County Office **Referees:** J H Day

Grants: County Office **Courses:** County Office **Womens:** R Stone **Press&PR:**

Number of Affiliated Clubs Senior:89 Junior: 354 Womens: 9 Youth: 160

County Representative Teams (Managers responsible)**:** Youth (B Simms/R Stone) Women U18 (D Prior)

Inter County Competitions: FA County Youth Cup, South West Co. Champ. Competition - Youth & U18 Women

Trophies won in season 2003-04: None

COUNTY CUP FINALS

Premier Cup	Bristol City	v	Brislington	5-0	27th April - Clevedon Town
Senior Cup	Westland United	v	Keynsham Town Reserves	0-4	3rd May - Paulton Rovers

STAFFORDSHIRE F.A.

Tel: 01785 256 994 Fax: 01785 224 334 Email: secretary@staffordshirefa.com

County Showground, Weston Road, Stafford ST18 0BD

Secretary: Brian Adshead

Other executives: **President:** P Savage **Chairman:** P Hodgkinson

Chief Executive: B J Adshead **Development Officer:** A Weston

Coaching: G Thomas **Discipline:** Sarah Davies **Registration:** Sarah Davies **Referees:** R A Vaughan

Grants: A Weston **Courses:** G Thomas **Womens:** Claire Hermon **Press&PR:** A C Evans

Number of Affiliated Clubs Senior: Junior: Womens:

County Representative Teams (Senior Coach responsible)**:** U18/U16 boys, U16 girls, Ladies

Inter County Competitions:

Trophies won in season 2003-04: None

COUNTY CUP FINAL

Senior Cup	Kidsgrove Athletic	v	Stafford Rangers	1-0*	28th April - Stoke City

SUFFOLK F.A.

Tel: 01473 407290 Fax: 01473 407291 Email: info@suffolkfa.com

The Buntings, Cedars Park, Stowmarket, Suffolk IP14 5G7

Secretary: Martyn Head

Other executives: **President:** Gordon Blake **Chairman:** Dave Porter

Chief Executive: N/A **Development Officer:** Will Cook

Coaching: Phil Woolnough **Discipline:** Gary Steed **Registration:** James Payne **Referees:** Brian Chapman

Grants: William Steward **Courses:** Sharon O'Connell **Womens:** Kate Steed **Press&PR:** Martin Head

Number of Affiliated Clubs Senior: 600 Junior: 125 Womens: 25

County Representative Teams (Senior Coach responsible)**:** (Danny Laws)

Inter County Competitions: East Anglian League

Trophies won in season 2003-04: None

COUNTY CUP FINAL

Premier Cup	Bury Town	v	AFC Sudbury	0-4	21st May - Ipswich Town

SURREY F.A.

Tel: 01372 373543 Fax: 01372 361310 Website: www.surreyfa.co.uk Email: info@surreyfa.com

321 Kingston Road, Leatherhead, Surrey KT22 7TU

Secretary: Ray Ward

Other executives: **President:** Peter Adams **Chairman:** Ray Lewis

Chief Executive: N/A **Development Officer:** Larry May (FDO)

Coaching: Keith Boanas **Discipline:** Vic Skilton **Registration:** **Referees:**

Grants: Mark Wood **Courses:** Mark Wood **Womens:** Michelle Jeffcoate **Press&PR:**

Number of Affiliated Clubs Senior: 37 Junior: 500 Womens: 23

County Representative Teams (Senior Coach responsible)**:** (Bryan Croucher)

Inter County Competitions: Bryan Croucher

Trophies won in season 2003-04: None

COUNTY CUP FINAL

Senior Cup	Woking	v	Sutton United	2-1	6th May - Met. Police

SUSSEX F.A.

Tel: 01903 753547 Fax: 01903 761608 Email: info@sussexfa.com

Culver Road, Lancing, West Sussex BN15 9AX

Secretary: Ken Benham

Other executives: **President:** John Davey **Chairman:** Peter Bentley

Chief Executive: Ken Benham **County Development Manager:** Henry Millington

Coaching: Kevin Tharme/Emma Mead/Keveena Mosen/Julie Tobin **Discipline:** Alan Knight **Registration:** **Referees:** Martin Bodenham

Grants: Henry Millington **Courses:** Lee Thompson **Womens:** Kveena Mosen/Julie Tobin **Press&PR:**

Number of Affiliated Clubs Senior: 597 Junior: 249 Womens: 60

County Representative Teams (Administrator)**:** (Brian Shacklock)

Inter County Competitions: South West County Championship & Home Counties Competitions

Trophies won in season 2003-04: None

COUNTY CUP FINAL

Senior Cup	Worthing	v	Brighton & Hove Albion	0-2	3rd May - Eastbourne Boro'

WEST RIDING F.A.

Tel: 0113 282 1222 Fax: 0113 282 1525 Email: info@wrcfa.com

Fleet Lane, Woodlesford, Leeds LS26 8NX

President: A C Taylor. **Chairman:** Colin Taylor. **Secretary & Press Officer:** G R Carter

Executives (Responsibility): Danny Philpott (Football Development Officer)

Julie Chipchase (Womens/Girls Football)

Number of Affiliated Clubs Senior: 950 U.18: 300

Number of Affiliated Leagues: Senior: 40 Junior: 12

County Representative Teams: Senior, Junior U18, Womens

Inter County Competitions: Association of Northern Counties Senior, Junior U18 & Womens, FA County Youth

COUNTY CUP FINAL

County Cup	Farsley Celtic	v	Halifax Town	1-2	14th April

WESTMORLAND F.A.

Tel: 01539 730946 Fax: 01539 730946 Email: info@westmorlandfa.com

Unit 1, Angel Court, 21 Highgate, Kendal, Cumbria LA9 4DA

Secretary: Peter G Ducksbury

Other executives: **President:** Tommy Huck **Chairman:** Gary Aplin

Executive Officer: Peter G Ducksbury **Development Officer:** Dean Grice

Coaching: Dean Grice **Discipline:** Secretary **Registration:** N/A **Referees:** Secretary

Grants: Secretary **Courses:** Dean Grice **Womens:** Dean Grice **Press&PR:** Secretary

Number of Affiliated Clubs Senior: 47 Junior: 31 Womens: 7

County Representative Teams (Senior Coach responsible)**:** Senior, U18 (N Rigg) U16 (G Nicholson)

Inter County Competitions: Association of Northern Counties

Trophies won in season 2003-04: None

COUNTY CUP FINAL

Senior Cup	Kendal County	v	Carleton Rovers	3-1	24th April - Kendal Town

WILTSHIRE F.A.

Tel: 01793 486047 or 525245 Fax: 01793 692699 Email: mike.benson@wiltsfa.com

18 Covingham Square, Covingham, Swindon, Wilts SN3 5AA

Secretary: Mike Benson

Other executives: **President:** K J Mulrany **Chairman:** R J Gardiner

Chief Executive: N/A **Development Officer:** B J Stephens

Coaching: A K Riddiford **Discipline:** M A Edmonds **Registration:** M G Benson **Referees:** I Whitehouse

Grants: M G Benson **Courses:** A K Riddiford **Womens:** B Maull **Press&PR:** M G Benson

Number of Affiliated Clubs Senior: 28 Junior: 450 Womens: 15

County Representative Teams (Senior Coach responsible)**:** (Mel Gingell)

Inter County Competitions: South West Counties Championship

Trophies won in season 2003-04: South West Co. Champ. Youth

COUNTY CUP FINALS

Premier Shield	Chippenham Town	v	Swindon Town	2-0	19th April - Chippenham Town
Senior Cup	Corsham Town	v	Trowbridge Town	2-2* 3-5p	27th April - Chippenham Town

WORCESTERSHIRE F.A.

Tel: 01905 827137 Fax:01905 798963 Email: info@worcestershirefa.com

Craftsman House, De Salis Drive, Hampton Lovett Ind. Estate, Droitwich, Worcs WR9 0QE

Secretary: Mervyn Lessett

Other executives: **President:** Percy Rushton **Chairman:** Ken Clifford

Chief Executive: N/A **Development Officer:** Andy Norman

Coaching: Andy Norman **Discipline:** John Lovegrove **Registration:** **Referees:** Bill Allsopp

Grants: M Lessett/A Norman **Courses:** Julie Lymer **Womens:** Julie Leroux **Press&PR:** Mervyn Lessett

Number of Affiliated Clubs Senior:17 Junior: 221 Womens:12 Youth: 115 (Boys & girls)

County Representative Teams (Senior Coach responsible)**:** U18 (Ivor Chambers)

Inter County Competitions: FA County Youth Cup, MIdland Youth Football Championships

Trophies won in season 2003-04: None

COUNTY CUP FINALS

Senior Cup	Sutton Coldfield Town	v	Worcester City	1st Leg: 2-1	2nd Leg: 3-3
Urn	Malvern Town	v	Alvechurch	2-3	14th May - Evesham United

SOUTH WEST COUNTIES CHAMPIONSHIP

AFFILIATED COUNTIES-SEASON 2004-2005

ARMY
BERKS & BUCKS
CORNWALL
DEVON
DORSET
GLOUCESTERSHIRE
GUERNSEY
GWENT
HAMPSHIRE
JERSEY
OXFORDSHIRE
ROYAL AIR FORCE
ROYAL NAVY
SOMERSET
SUSSEX
WILTSHIRE

31st SEASON - DATES OF FINAL TIES

WINNERS OF GROUP A WILL HOST FINAL

SENIOR COMPETITION
Saturday 23 April 2005
Or in the midweek prior or Sunday following
(if both teams agree)

YOUTH COMPETITION
Saturday 7 May 2005
Or in the midweek prior or Sunday following
(if both teams agree)

MICK PARRY MEMORIAL TROPHY FINAL
Saturday 16 April 2005

UNDER 18 WOMEN'S COMPETITION
Saturday 20 April 2005
Or in the midweek prior or Sunday following
(if both teams agree)

SENIOR GROUP A - FIXTURES

DATE	MATCH	VENUE	KO	OFFICIALS
16/10/04	Guernsey v Dorset	Footes Lane Stadium	2.30pm	Wiltshire
10/11/04	Dorset v Royal Navy	T.B.C.	7.30pm	Devon
13/11/04	Wiltshire v Guernsey	Melksham Town	2.30pm	Jersey
23/11/04	Army v Royal Navy	Military Stadium Aldershot	7.00pm	Sussex
07/12/04	Army v Dorset	Military Stadium Aldershot	7.30pm	Berks/Bucks
26/01/05	Royal Navy v Wiltshire	H.M.S. Heron Yeovilton	7.30pm	Somerset
08/02/05	Guernsey v Army	Footes Lane Stadium	7.30pm	Royal Navy
09/02/05	Dorset v Wiltshire	T.B.C.	7.30pm	Royal Air Force
17/02/05	Royal Navy v Guernsey	Footes Lane Stadium	7.30pm	Army
23/02/05	Wiltshire v Guernsey	Melksham Town	7.30pm	Hampshire

SENIOR GROUP B - FIXTURES

DATE	MATCH	VENUE	KO	OFFICIALS
13/10/04	Gloucestershire v Sussex	Oaklands Park	7.30pm	Somerset
16/10/04	Jersey v Cornwall	Springfield Stadium	T.B.C.	Sussex
19/10/04	Royal Air Force v Devon	H.M.S. Drake Plymouth	7.30pm	Cornwall
17/11/04	Sussex v Royal Air Force	Lancing	7.30pm	Army
27/11/04	Devon v Jersey	Exmouth Town	T.B.C.	Somerset
07/12/04	Gloucestershire v Devon	Oaklands Park	7.30pm	Wiltshire
18/12/04	Royal Air Force v Cornwall	Uxbridge	3.00pm	Guernsey

SENIOR WINNERS - 1974-2004

1974/75	Wiltshire	1989/90	Sussex
1975/76	Army	1990/91	Sussex
1976/77	Hampshire	1991/92	Somerset & Avon
1977/78	Hampshire	1992/93	Army
1978/79	Somerset & Avon	1993/94	Royal Navy
1979/80	Somerset & Avon	1994/95	Sussex
1980/81	Somerset & Avon	1995/96	Royal Navy
1981/82	Sussex	1996/97	Devon
1982/83	Somerset & Avon	1997/98	Royal Navy
1983/84	Royal Navy	1998/99	Army
1984/85	Sussex	1999/2000	Sussex
1985/86	Hampshire	2000/01	No Competition
1986/87	Devon	2001/02	Sussex
1987/88	Army	2002/03	Devon
1988/89	Army	2003/04	Cornwall

WINNERS LEADER BOARD

Sussex	7 championships		
Army	5		
Somerset & Avon	5	Hampshire	3
Royal Navy	4	Cornwall	1
Devon	3	Wlitshire	1

YOUTH WINNERS - 1974-2004

1974/75	Somerset & Glos.	1989/90	Hampshire
1975/76	Wiltshire	1990/91	Berks & Bucks
1976/77	Hampshire	1991/92	Hampshire
1977/78	Hampshire	1992/93	Devon
1978/79	Hampshire	1993/94	Somerset & Avon
1979/80	Devon	1994/95	Cornwall
1980/81	Devon	1995/96	Berks & Bucks
1981/82	Royal Navy	1996/97	Wiltshire
1982/83	Gloucestershire	1997/98	Gloucestershire
1983/84	Gloucestershire	1998/99	Cornwall
1984/85	Dorset	1999/2000	Berks & Bucks
1985/86	Gloucestershire	2000/01	No Competition
1986/87	Gloucestershire	2001/02	Hampshire
1987/88	Wiltshire	2002/03	Somerset
1988/89	Gloucestershire	2003/04	Wiltshire

WINNERS LEADER BOARD

Gloucestershire	6 championships	Cornwall	2
Hampshire	6	Dorset	1
Wiltshire	4	Royal Navy	1
Berks & Bucks	3	Somerset	1
Devon	3	Somerset & Avon	1
		Somerset & Glos.	1

MICK PARRY MEMORIAL TROPHY WINNERS

1999 - 2000	Cornwall
2000 - 2001	No Competition
2001 - 2002	Berks/Bucks
2002 - 2003	Berks/Bucks
2003 - 2004	Dorset

WINNERS LEADER BOARD

Berks/Bucks	2 championships
Cornwall	1
Dorset	1

UNDER-21 CHAMPIONSHIP

2000 - 2001	No Competition
2001 - 2002	Hampshire
2002 - 2003	Army
2003 - 2004	Hampshire

WINNERS LEADER BOARD

Hampshire	2 championships
Army	1

WOMEN'S CHAMPIONSHIP

1996 - 1997	Wiltshire
1997 - 1998	Sussex
1998 - 1999	Hampshire
1999 - 2000	Hampshire
2000 - 2001	No Competition
2001 - 2002	Hampshire
2002 - 2003	Hampshire
2003 - 2004	Devon

WINNERS LEADER BOARD

Hampshire	4 championships
Devon	1
Sussex	1
Wiltshire	1

WOMEN'S UNDER-18

2000 - 2001	No Competition
2001 - 2002	Gloucestershire
2002 - 2003	Devon
2003 - 2004	Hampshire

WINNERS LEADER BOARD

Devon	1 championships
Gloucestershire	1
Hampshire	1

TOTAL CHAMPIONSHIP TITLES WON - 1974-2004

	SENIOR	YOUTH	MICK PARRY	U21	WOMEN'S	U-18	TOTAL
Hampshire	3	6	-	2	4	1	16
Devon	3	3	-	-	1	1	8
Sussex	7	-	-	-	1	-	8
Gloucestershire	-	6	-	-	-	1	7
Army	5	-	-	1	-	-	6
Somerset & Avon	5	1	-	-	-	-	6
Wiltshire	1	4	-	-	1	-	6
Royal Navy	4	1	-	-	-	-	5
Berks & Bucks	-	3	2	-	-	-	5
Cornwall	1	2	1	-	-	-	4
Dorset	-	1	1	-	-	-	2
Somerset	-	1	-	-	-	-	1
Somerset & Glos.	-	1	-	-	-	-	1

WELSH PREMIER

SPONSORED BY: JT HUGHES MITSUBISHI
President: D W Shanklin
Secretary: D G Collins **Chief Executive:** D G Collins
Plymouth Chambers, 3 Westgate Street, Cardiff CF10 1DP
Tel: 029 2037 2325 Fax: 029 2034 3961

FINAL LEAGUE TABLE 2003-04

			HOME					AWAY					TOTAL					
		P	W	D	L	F	A	W	D	L	F	A	W	D	L	F	A	Pts
1.	Rhyl	32	13	3	0	45	10	10	5	1	31	16	23	8	1	76	26	77
2.	Total Net. Solutions	32	13	1	2	40	14	11	3	2	37	14	24	4	4	77	28	76
3.	Haverfordwest Co.	32	10	5	1	22	10	7	6	3	18	13	17	11	4	40	23	62
4.	Aberystwyth Town	32	10	3	3	30	16	8	2	6	29	23	18	5	9	59	39	59
5.	Caersws	32	8	5	3	30	18	7	5	4	33	23	15	10	7	63	41	55
6.	Bangor City	32	7	4	5	37	25	9	2	5	35	22	16	6	10	72	47	54
7.	Cwmbran Town	32	7	3	6	25	20	8	0	8	26	24	15	3	14	51	44	48
8.	Connah's Quay N.	32	6	3	7	29	28	5	6	5	29	27	11	9	12	58	55	42
9.	Caernarfon Town	32	6	5	5	38	31	5	4	7	27	34	11	9	12	65	65	42
10.	Newtown	32	7	4	5	22	22	5	1	10	21	28	12	5	15	43	50	41
11.	Port Talbot Town	32	6	3	7	25	26	5	3	8	16	25	11	6	15	41	51	39
12.	Porthmadog	32	7	3	6	26	23	4	0	12	15	32	11	3	18	41	55	36
13.	NEWI Cefn Druids	32	6	2	8	25	31	5	0	11	19	28	11	2	19	44	59	35
14.	Afan Lido	32	4	5	7	15	19	4	3	9	16	35	8	8	16	31	54	32
15.	Welshpool Town	32	4	4	8	21	32	2	3	11	14	39	6	7	19	35	71	25
16.	Carmarthen Town	32	3	3	10	13	32	0	8	8	15	37	3	11	18	28	69	20
17.	Barry Town	32	3	1	12	17	37	0	6	10	13	40	3	7	22	30	77	16

		1	2	3	4	5	6	7	8	9	10	11	12	13	14	15	16	17
1	Aberystwyth Town		1-2	1-2	3-1	2-1	2-0	5-1	2-1	1-0	1-1	1-0	2-1	1-1	1-0	2-2	0-3	5-0
2	Afan Lido	0-1		0-0	1-1	0-1	0-0	3-3	2-0	0-4	0-0	3-1	0-1	1-2	1-0	1-2	2-3	1-0
3	Bangor City	2-3	3-0		2-1	1-1	1-1	2-2	2-1	7-2	3-3	0-3	2-1	1-2	4-1	2-3	0-1	5-0
4	Barry Town	1-2	0-1	0-3		0-5	1-3	0-0	0-2	0-2	0-2	0-1	3-2	3-1	2-3	0-3	2-3	5-4
5	Caernarfon Town	3-2	2-2	4-5	8-0		2-4	1-1	5-5	1-0	0-1	3-2	0-3	2-0	0-2	1-1	2-2	4-1
6	Caersws	0-0	2-2	1-4	1-0	2-2		3-0	0-1	4-1	0-0	3-1	4-0	1-0	3-2	3-3	0-2	3-0
7	Carmarthen Town	1-2	2-1	1-4	0-0	1-4	1-7		2-2	0-2	0-1	2-0	0-1	1-2	1-0	0-0	1-4	0-2
8	Connah's Quay Nomads	0-4	4-0	3-2	4-1	3-0	3-5	1-1		3-2	0-1	0-1	2-3	3-1	1-3	0-2	1-1	1-1
9	Cwmbran Town	2-1	4-1	1-2	2-1	0-1	2-2	3-1	3-3		0-1	0-2	1-2	3-0	1-0	1-1	0-1	2-1
10	Haverfordwest County	3-1	0-0	1-0	2-2	1-1	3-0	1-0	1-2	2-1		1-0	1-0	1-1	1-0	2-1	1-0	1-1
11	NEWI Cefn Druids	1-3	5-3	1-5	2-1	1-3	2-2	2-2	1-2	0-2	1-0		2-1	0-1	3-0	0-2	0-2	4-2
12	Newtown	1-1	2-0	2-5	3-0	2-0	0-0	1-1	2-1	1-3	1-1	2-3		1-0	1-0	0-2	2-5	1-0
13	Port Talbot Town	1-3	0-2	0-0	2-2	4-1	0-2	3-1	1-1	2-3	2-0	3-2	2-0		3-2	1-2	1-4	0-1
14	Porthmadog	2-1	2-0	0-1	2-2	3-2	2-3	3-1	1-1	0-2	0-2	3-1	3-2	1-2		0-2	1-1	3-0
15	Rhyl	5-3	3-0	2-0	4-0	7-1	2-1	4-0	1-1	1-0	1-1	2-0	1-1	2-1	6-1		1-0	3-0
16	Total Network Solutions	1-0	5-0	2-1	3-0	4-1	1-3	4-0	3-2	2-1	2-0	2-1	2-1	2-0	4-0	2-3		1-1
17	Welshpool Town	0-2	0-2	3-1	1-1	3-3	1-0	1-1	1-4	0-1	2-4	3-1	3-2	2-2	0-1	1-2	0-5	

LEAGUE CUP

(All ties prior to the Final over two legs - home & away)

PRELIMINARY ROUND

			1st	2nd
Porthmadog	v	Welshpool Town	1-0	1-0

FIRST ROUND

Afan Lido	v	Carmarthen Town	0-0	2-3
Bangor City	v	Porthmadog	1-1	2-0
Caernarfon	v	Newtown	2-1	1-3*
Caersws	v	Barry Town	6-0	6-0
Connah's Quay N.	v	TNS	0-2	3-3
Cwmbran Town	v	Port Talbot	0-3	2-1
Haverfordwest Co.	v	Aberystwyth Town	2-0	1-3
(Haverfordwest County won on away goals)				
NEWI Cefn Druids	v	Rhyl	0-2	2-3

QUARTER-FINALS

			1st	2nd
Bangor City	v	Newtown	4-2	4-4
Haverfordwest	v	Caersws	2-2	0-3
Port Talbot	v	Carmarthen Town	0-1	0-2
Total Net Solutions	v	Rhyl	1-0	1-3

SEMI-FINALS

Rhyl	v	Bangor City	2-0	2-0
Caersws	v	Carmarthen Town	0-0	0-1

THE FINAL (3rd May at Newtown)

Rhyl	v	Carmarthen Town	4-0

WELSH CLUBS IN EUROPE

CHAMPIONS LEAGUE
FIRST ROUND

Vardar Skopje	v	Barry Town	3-0	1-2

INTERTOTO CUP
FIRST ROUND

Bangor City	v	FC Gloria Bistrita	0-1	2-5

U E F A CUP
QUALIFYING ROUND

Cwmbran Town	v	Maccabi Haifa	0-3	0-3

The Welsh Semi-Pro team after their final match win in the 2003/04 Four Nations Tournament, unknown to them at the time they were also the outright competition winners.

Photo: Phil Rowe.

ABERYSTWYTH TOWN

Secretary: Rhun Owens, 31 Maesgogerddan, Aberystwyth.
Tel: 01970 623520 (H) 0777 323 0894 (M)
Ground: Park Avenue, Aberystwyth, Ceredigion. Tel: 01970 612122 Fax: 01970 617939
Club Email: atfc@btopenworld.com
Directions: From south: A487, 1st right at Trefachan Bridge to r'bout, 1st right with Park Ave. being 3rd right. From north: A487 and follow one-way system to railway station, at r'bout 1st left with Park Avenue being 3rd right. 5 mins walk from Aberystwyth (BR) - follow as above

Capacity: 5,500 Seats: 300 Cover: 1,200 Floodlights: Yes
Clubhouse: Open daily noon-3 & 7-12pm. Snacks available **Club Shop:** Yes
(New)
HONOURS Welsh Cup 1899-1900; Welsh I'mediate Cup 85-86 87-88; Mid Wales Lg (11) Lg Cup (7); Welsh Am Cup (3); Welsh Lg Div 2 Sth 51-2; Cambrian Coast Lg (8) Central Wales Challenge. Cup (6)

PREVIOUS **League:** Welsh 1896-97; Nth Wales Comb. 99-1900; Montgomeryshire & Dist. 04-20; Central Wales 21-25 81-87; Mid-Wales 26-32 51-81; Cambrian Coast 32-51; Welsh Lg South 51-63; Abacus 87-92

RECORD **Attendance:** 4,500 v Hereford, Welsh Cup 1971
Goalscorer: David Williams 476, 66-83
Appearances: David P Whitney 572, 62-81

FACT FILE
Founded: 1884
Nickname: Seasiders
Sponsors: Continental Cambria Tyres
Colours: Green/black/black
Change colours: Yellow/blue/blue
Midweek Matchday: Tuesdays
Reserves League: Mid-Wales
Programme: 64 pages, £1.00
Editor: D.Roberts Young (01970 617705)
Website:www.atfcnews.co.uk

CLUB PERSONNEL
Chairman: Donald Kane
President: D Jones
Press Officer: Rhun Owens
Manager: Gary Finley

2002-2003
Captain: David Burrows P.o.Y.: Bari Morgan
Top Scorers: Anthony Wright 13

AFAN LIDO

Secretary: P.Robinson. 56 Abbeyville Avenue, Sandfields Estate, Port Talbot SA12 6PY
Tel Nos: 01639 885638 (H) 07812 142 833(M)

Ground: Runtech Stadium, Princess Margaret Way, Aberavon Beach, Port Talbot.
Tel: 01639 892960 (Club) 01639 881432 (FAX)

Capacity: 4,200 Seats: 525

Clubhouse: New duilding erected

Directions: From East; M4 Jct 40 follow signs to town centre. Follow signs to Aberavoon Beach/Aquadrome and ground is behind Aqauadrome on right.From west; take Jct 42 and follow signs to Aberavon Beach.Ground is on left behind Aquadrome.

Honours: League of Wales R-up 94-95, League of Wales Cup 92-93 93-94

Records: **Biggest Victory:** 7-1 v Porthcawl Town 1997
Worst Defeat: 0-6 v Bridgend Town 1982

FACT FILE

Founded: 1967
Colours: All red
Change colours: White & yellow/white/white
Midweek Rixtures: Tuesday

CLUB PERSONNEL
Chairman: B.Fowles

Manager: Mark Robinson
Tel:01639 822026

Head of Youth Academy:
P.Robinson

AIR BUS

Secretary: M.Maygfield, 8 Meadow Road, Broughton, Chester. CH4 0RG

Tel No: 01244 537 107

Ground: The Airfield (Tel No: 01244 522 356)

Directions: Airbus are ground sharing with Conwy. Turn off A55 on the western edge of Conwy tunnel and follow road into Conwy. Turn left under railway bridge and ground is one mile at end of this road. **OR** from A 55 take the Broughton turn off and follow sign to retail park. Then, wth retail park ahead ,follow signs for British Aerospace and enter large car park via the traffic lights. Ground is beyond barriers with entry opposite the social club.

Clubhouse: Airbus Social Club

FACT FILE

Formed: 1946
Colours: White & Dark Blue/ Blue/ Blue
Change colours: Red/white/white

CLUB PERSONNEL
Chairman: J.Sutton
Manager: R.Lythe

BANGOR CITY

Secretary: Alun Griffiths, 12 Lon-Y-Bryn, Menai Bridge, Anglesey, Gwynedd LL575NM
Tel: 01248 725745
Ground: The Stadium, Farrar Road, Bangor, Gwynedd LL57 1LJ (01248 355852)
Directions: Old A5 into Bangor, 1st left before railway station, ground on leftby garage
Capacity 5,000 Seats: 800 Cover: 1,200 Floodlights: Yes
Clubhouse: Not on ground **Club Shop:** Yes
HONOURS FA Tphy R-up 83-84; Northern Prem. Lg 81-82 (R-up 86-87, Lg Cup 68-69, Presidents Cup 88-89, Chal. Shield 87-88), Cheshire Co. Lg R-up 53-54 58-59,Lancs Comb. R-up 30-31, League of Wales 94-95 (Lg Cup R-up 94-95), WelshNational Lg 27-28 (R-up 26-27), Nth Wales Coast Lg 1895-96, Welsh Cup 1888-89 95-96 1961-62 (R-up 27-28 60-61 63-64 72-73 77-78 84-85), Nth Wales Chal. Cup 26-27 35-36 36-37 37-38 46-47 51-52 57-58 64-65 67-68, Welsh Amtr Cup 1894-9596-96 97-98 98-99 1900-01 02-03 04-05 05-06 11-12, Welsh Jnr Cup 1995-96 97-981919-20, Welsh All. Alves Cup 49-50 59-60 (Cookson Cup 61-62 68-69 84-85 86-87)
RECORD **Attendance:** 10,000 v Wrexham, Welsh Cup final 78-79
PREVIOUS **Leagues:** N Wales Coast 1893-98 1911-12; The Comb 1898-1910; N Wales Comb 30-33; WMids 32-38; Lancs Comb 38-39 46-50; Ches Co 50-68; NPL 68-79 81-82 84-92; AlliancePrem 79-81 82-84, Welsh Cup 97-98,North Wales Challenge Cup 1998-99

FACT FILE
Founded: 1876 Nickname: Citizens
Sponsors: Pentraeth Group
Colours: All red
Change colours: All blue
Midweek Matchedays: Tuesday
Reserve League: Welsh Alliance
Programme: 32 pages, £1.00
Editor: Sam Vilaski

CLUB PERSONNEL
President: Gwyn Pierce Owen
Chairman: Ken Jones
Vice Chairman: David Gareth Jones
Marketing Manager: Hayle Meek
Press Officer: Alun Griffiths
Manager: Peter Davenport
Assistant Manager: Marc Lloyd Williams
Coach:Stephen Owen Physio: Arwel Jones
Head of Youth Acadeny: M.Jones

CAERNARFON TOWN

Secretary: Elwyn Hughes, Perthi, Yfor, Pwillheli, Gwynedd LL536UW
Ground: The Oval, Marcus Street, Caernarfon, Gwynedd Tel: 01286 675002
Directions: A55 coast road to A487 bypass to Caernarfon. At inner relief road r'bout follow Beddlegert sign, then 2nd right - ground opposite.
Nearest BR station is 9 miles distant at Bangor. Local buses to Hendre estate
Capacity: 3,400 Seats: 252 Cover: 1,500 Floodlights: Yes
Clubhouse: 2 snooker tables, darts, pool, fruit machines & live entertainment **Club Shop:** Yes
HONOURS N West Co's Lg R-up 84-85 (Div 2 R-up 82-83); Lancs Comb 81-82 (Lg Cup 80-81); Welsh Lg (North)(4) 46-47 65-66 77-79, R-up (4) 56-58 72-73 79-80; Alves Cup(4) 38-39 74-75 77-79; Cookson 56-57 77-78; N Wales Combination 32-33; Welsh National Lg 26-27 29-30 (R-up 28-29); N Wales Coast Lg 11-12
PREVIOUS **Leagues:** North Wales Coast 06-21; Welsh National 26-30; North Wales Comb. 32-33; Welsh Lg (North) 37-76 77-80; Lancs Comb. 80-82; North West Counties 82-85; Northern Premier
BEST SEASON **FA Trophy:** 1st Round replay 87-88
FA Cup : 3rd Rd replay 86-87, 0-1 v Barnsley (A). Also 2nd Rd 29-30
RECORD **Attendance:** 6,002 v Bournemouth, FA Cup 2nd Rd 1929
Goalscorer: W Jones 255 (1906-26) **Appearances:** Walter Jones 306

FACT FILE
Founded: 1876
Nickname: Canaries
Sponsors: T.J. Fixit
Colours: Yellow & green/green/yellow
Change colours: Sky & claret/claret/blue
Midweek Matchday: Wednesday
Reserve Team: Yes
Programme: 48pgs 70p
Editor: Marc Roberts

CLUB PERSONNEL
President: Jack F Thomas
Chairman: G.Lloyd Owen
Vice-Chairmen: Eilian Angel
Press Officer: Geraint Lloyd Owen
Tel: 01286 830307
Manager: Wayne PhillipsCoach: Alan McDonald
Head of Youth Academy: R.Holroyd
Physio: Ian Humphreys

CAERSWS

Secretary: G.D.Lewis,1 Dolwnog,Main Street,Caersws, Pows SY 17 5EN
Tel Nos: 01686 688586 (H), 01686 627476 (W) 07989 318003 (M).
Ground: The Recreation Ground, Caersws, Powys. Tel: 01686 688753
Directions: Entering Caersws, which lies between Newtown & Llanidloes on the A470, the ground entrance is on the left by bridge
Capacity: 4,000 Seats: 250 Cover: 300 Floodlights: Yes Club Shop: No
Clubhouse: Not on ground, but in village centre. Normal licensing hours. Food available
HONOURS Welsh Amtr Cup 60-61, I'mediate Cup 88-89 (R-up 91-92); Mid-Wales Lg (9) 59-61 62-63 77-78 82-83 85-86 88-90 96-97 (Lg Cup 79-80 82-83 87-88 89-90); Cent. Wales Chall.Cup 77-78 82-83 87-88 89-90 (Yth Cup 69-70 72-73 Lg01-02); Montgomeryshire Chall. Cup (18) 52-53 59-60 62-63 69-72 74-75 76-78 83-89 90-91 94-95 94-95 96-97 97-98 98-99;01-02,02-03 Montgomeryshire Lg 77-78
U.E.F.A. Inter Toto Cup 01-02, 02-03.

PREVIOUS **Leagues:** Mid-Wales (pre-1989)/Cymru Alliance 90-92

RECORD **Attendance:** 2,795 v Swansea City, Welsh Cup 1990
Goalscorer: Gareth Davies

Players progressing: P Woosnam (Leyton O.), M Evans (Wolverhampton W.), KLloyd (Hereford U) Graham Evans (Aston Villa), R Stephens (Shrewsbury Town)

FACT FILE
Founded: 1877
Nickname: Bluebirds
Sponsor: Dave Smith
Colours: Blue & white/white/blue
Change colours: Yellow/black/yellow
Midweek Matchday: Tuesday
Reserve League: Mid-Wales
Programme: 44 pages, £1.00
Editor: Ian Baker

CLUB PERSONNEL
Chairman:Garth Williams
V-Chair: Joff Rogers
Press Officer: Ivor Williams
Manager: Mickey Evans
Asst Manager: Barry Harding
Physio: Wynne Jones

CARMARTHEN TOWN

Secretary: G.O.Jones,Glaslyn,3 Nant Y Felin,Caerfyrddin SA 31 3DT
Tel Nos: 01267 233359 (H) 01267 221838 (W) 01267 222851 (Fax)

Ground: Richmond Park, Priory Street, Carmarthen Dyfed
Tel: 01267 232101 Fax: 01267 222851

Directions: Proceed into Carmarthen on A48, pick up A40 to Llandilo at the 1st rounabout and follow town centre signs for 800 meters.Ground on left in Priory Street

Capacity: 3,000 Seats: 450 Cover: 500 Floodlights: Yes

Clubhouse: Yes **Club Shop:** Yes

HONOURS Welsh Lge Div 2 59-60, Div 1 95-96, Cup Winners 95-96

RECORD **Attendance:** 3,000

PREVIOUS **Leagues:** Welsh League

FACT FILE
Founded: 1948
Nickname: The Town
Sponsors: R.S.J. Windows
Colours: Old gold/black/black
Change colours:White with blue trim
Midweek Matchday:Wednesday
Reserve League: C C Sports Welsh Lge
Programme: £1.00
Editor: Alun Charles

CLUB PERSONNEL
Chairman: Jeff Thomas
President: Anthony Jenkins
Manager : Mark Jones
Head of Youth Academy:C.Staples
Physio: Nigel Davies
2002-2003
Captain: David Barnhouse
Top Scorer: Jon Keaveny
Player of the Year: Dale Price

CONNAH'S QUAY NOMADS

Secretary/Press Officer
Robert Hunter, 40 Brookdale Ave., Connah's Quay, Deeside, Clywd CH5 4LU
Tel: 01244 831212 (H)
Ground: Deeside Stadium Connah's Quay (01244 816418

Directions: On main coast road (A548) from Chester to Rhyl north west end of Connah's Quay Deeside College.
Capacity: 5,500 Seats:420 Cover: 500 Floodlights: Yes
Clubhouse: Yes, in college. **Club Shop:** No

HONOURS Welsh Amtr Cup 52-53 54-55, Nth Wales FA Amtr Cup 52-53 54-55, North Wales Coast Challenge Cup, Welsh Intermediate Cup 80-81, Welsh Alliance CooksonCup 87-88, Welsh Youth Cup 47-48

PREVIOUS **Leagues:** Clywd; Welsh Alliance; Cymru Alliance 90-92
Name: Connah's Quay Juniors
RECORD **Attendance:** 1,500 v Rhyl, Welsh Cup SF 29/3/93

FACT FILE
Founded: 1947
Nickname:Westenders
Sponsors: T.B.A.
Colours: White/black/black&white
Change colours: Maroon/white/maroon
Midweek Matchday: Tuesday
Reserve League: Clwyd Premier
Programme: 26 pages, £1.00
Editor: D.Rapson

CLUB PERSONNEL
Chairman: Mr R Morris
President: Mr R Jones
Manager: Neville Powell
Asst Manager: S.Gelder
Physio: M Latter

CWMBRAN TOWN

Secretary: Ian Greaney, 14 Beechleigh Close, Greenmeadow, Cwmbran NP44 5EF
TEL No: 01633 877802
Ground: Cwmbran Stadium, Henllys Way, Cwmbran, Gwent
Tel: 01633627100 Fax 01633627103
Directions: M4 jct 26, follow signs for Cwmbran. At 1st r/about (approx 1.5miles) take 1st exit & proceed along Cwmbran Drive umtil passing Stadium onright. At r/about take 1st exit, then immediately at next r/about take 3rdexit.
Ground entrance 150 yardson right.
One and a half miles from Cwmbran(BR)
Capacity: 8,201 **Seats**: 2,200 **Cover:** 2,200 **Floodlights:** Yes **Club Shop:** Yes
Clubhouse: And clubhouse at 5/7 Commercial Street, Old Cwmbran (01633 483282
HONOURS Lg of W. 92-93; Welsh Lg Div 2 67-67, Welsh Lg Cup 90-91, Welsh Cup Finalists 96-97,99-00 02-03 UEFA Champions Cup 93-4 ,UEFA CUP WInners `CUP 97-8 ,UEFA Cup 99-00,01-01, 03-04 UEFA Inter Toto Cup 00-01
PREVIOUS **Leagues:** Monmouthshire Snr 51-59/ Welsh 60-92
RECORD **Attendance:** 8,148 v Manchester Utd Aug 1994
Goalscorer : Graham Reynolds **Appearances:** Mostyn Lewis

Players progressing: Simon King (Newport 1984), Mark Waite (Bristol Rovers1984), Nathan Wigg (Cardiff 1993), Chris Watkins (Swansea 1993), Daniel Gabbidon(W.B.A.,Cardiff)C)

FACT FILE
Founded: 1951 Nickname: The Town
Sponsors:Colley Hyunda1
Colours: Dark blue.
Change colours: Black & white/black/black
Midweek Matches: Wednesday
Programme: 40 pages, £1.00
Programme Editor/Press Off: Terry Daley
CLUB PERSONNEL
President &Chairman: John Colley
Vice Chairman: Clive Edwrads
General Secretary: Roy Langley
Press Officer: Terry Daley
Manager: Brian Coyne
Coach: Sean Wharton Physio: Tommy Cosh
Youth Academy: Delwyn Cheedy
Fitness Coach: Richard Hughes

HAVERFORDWEST COUNTY

Secretary: Barry Vaughan Tel: 01437 731779 (H) 01437 769048 (B)
Woodbine Cottage,Clarbeston Road, Haverfordwest, Pembs. SA63 4QS

Ground: Bridge Meadow Stadium, Haverfordwest, Pembs.SA61 2EX
Tel: 01437 769048 Fax: 01437 769048

Directions: Off the Safeway roundabout near town centre

Capacity: 4,000 Covered Seats: 500 Floodlights: Yes **Club Shop:** Yes

HONOURS West Wales Sen Cup 81-82 88-89 91-92 92-93 97-98 98-99, R-up 37-38 49-50 56-57 60-61 80-81; Welsh Lge 56-57, R-up 67-70 70-71, Prem Div 80-81, National Div 89-90, Div 1 96-97, R-up 94-95 95-96; SA Brains Cup 88-89 R-up 84-85

2002-2003 Captain: Eston Chiverton **Top Scorer and Player of the Year**: Rhys Griffiths

FACT FILE

Nickname: Bluebirds
Sponsor: Preseli Taxis
Colours: All Blue
Change cols: Orange & black/black/orange & black
Midweek Matchday: Tuesday
Programme: 28 Pages £1.00
Editor: JohnHughes

CLUB PERSONNEL

Chairman: W. Griffiths
Directors: J.Daniels, D Shanklin, B.Vaughan
Chief Executive: B.Vasughan
Press Officer: Robert Nesbitt
Manager: Deryn Brace Asst Man:Mike Lewis
Head of Youth Academy: Mike Ellis
Coaches: Dereck Roberts, Ron Beynon, Derek Carnegie and George Barrah
Physio: John Robertts

LLANELLI

Secretary:N.Evans, 16 Tyisha Road, Llanelli SA15 1RW 01554 776 760 (H) 01554 758 018 (Fax)

Ground: Stebonhearg Sradium, Llanelli, Carmarthanshire SA15 1HF
Tel No: 01554 772 973 Fax: 01554 758 018

Capacity: 3,700 **Seats:** 700 **Cover:** 700 **Floodlights:** Yes **Clubhouse:** Yes

Directions: From A484 or M4 Jct 48 follow signs to Llanelli until Mac Donald Roundabout. Take Llanelli exit then first exit at next two roundabouts into James Street. From North A476 from Llandeilo through Felinfoel towards Swansea.Second exiot at round-about into James street.. From West leave M4 (jct 48) and then as above.

PREVIOUS **Leagues:** Welsh League & Southern League

CLUB RECORDS **Attendance:** 15,000 1st Rd F.A.Cup 1950-51
Biggest Win: 11-0 v Oswestry League 04.04.01
Biggest Defeat: 1-10 v Inter Cardiff League 25.01.94

FACT FILE

Formed: 1896

Nickname: The Reds:

Colours: All Red

Change colours: Yellow/blue/yellow

Midweek Matches: Wednesday

Programme: 42pages Price: £1.00

Editor:Hugh Roberts

CLUB PERSONNEL

Chairman: R.Jones

Manager: T.B.A.

Physio:Bill Morris

NEWI CEFN DRUIDS

Secretary: J.H. Davies, 26 Pont Adam Crescent, Ruabon, Wrexham LL14 6ED
Tel No: 01978 820201 Fax: 01978 824332

Ground: Plas Kynaston lane, Plas Kynaston, Cefn Mawr, Wrexham
Tel Nos: 01978 824279(Club) 01978 824332 (Office)

Capacity: 2,000 Seating: 276

Directions: Leave A483 at Ruabon and follow signs to Llangollen. Left to B5606 at round about then turn right at Plough Pub after a mile. Cross railway bridge, turn left down narrow lane and ground is 400 yards on with parking opposite.

Website: www.cefndruids@ wrexham.gov.uk

Record **League Victory**: 5-1 v Llanelli
League Defeat: 0-7 v Barry 1999

FACT FILE

Founded: 1992
Colours: Black & white/white/white
Change colours: Blue& white/blue/white

Midweek Fixtures: Tuesday

CLUB PERSONNEL

Chairman:I.Parry
Manager: Alan Morgan
Head of Youth Academy: J.Hunter

NEWTOWN

Secretary: Owen Durbridge Admin Tel: 01686 628627, 07967 979089 (M)
Ground: G.F.Grigg Latham Park, Park Lane, Newtown, Powys SY161EN
Tel Nos: 01686 626159 Fax: 01686 623120
Directions: A43 to Newtown, right at 1st lights into Back Lane & town centre - 400yds left into Park St., 500yds right (at Library) into Park Lane - ground at end
Capacity: 4,999 Seats:1,300 Cover: 850 Floodlights: Yes
Clubhouse: Open every evening & matchday afternoons. Hot/cold snacks, pool,darts
Club Shop: Yes (Manager Saffron Gardner 01686 623123)
HONOURS League of Wales R-up 95-96 97-98; Welsh Cup 1878-79 94-95 (R-up 85-65 87-88 96-97), Welsh Amtr Cup 1954-55, Central Wales Lg 75-76 78-79 81-82 86-87 87-88 (R-up 51-52 52-53 55-56 56-57 74-75 82-83, Lg Cup 54-55 56-57 74-75 75-76 81-82 83-84), Arthur Barritt Cup 86-87, Central Wales Cup 74-75 80-81 92-93, Emrys Morgan Cup 80-81
PREVIOUS **Leagues:** The Combination/ Central Wales/ Northern Premier
RECORD **Attendance:** 5,002 v Swansea City, Welsh Cup 1954
Best Attendance 2003-04: 550 v Caersws
BEST SEASON **FA Trophy:** 3rd Qual. 89-90
FA Cup: 2nd Rd 1884-85. Also 1st Rd 1885-86

FACT FILE
Founded: 1875Nickname: Robins
Sponsors: ControlTechniques & Elliott Presco
Colours: All Red
Change : Yellow/blue/yellow
Midweek Matchdays: Tuesday
Reserves League: Spar Mid Wales
Programme: 36 pages, £1
Press Off./Ed: Barry Gardiner (07973 715448)

CLUB PERSONNEL
President: Richard Edwards
Chairman:Phil Trenbath
Press Officer: Barry Gardiner
Man : Roger Preece
Reserve Team Manager:Mike Fletcher
Physio:T.B.A.
Youth Dev Off: Phil Williams (01686 828634)
2003-2004
Top Scorers: Danny Barton && Peter Smith 13

PORT TALBOT TOWN

Secretary: John Dawkins, 37 Berrylnds, Sandfields Estate, Port Talbot. SA12 6LQ
Tel No: 01639 791 172 FAX: 01639 886 991

Ground: Victoria Road, Port Talbot, SA12 6AD
Tel: 01639 882465
Fax: 01639 886991

Capacity: 2,000 **Seating**: 262 **Floodlights**: Yes

Record **League Victory**: 6-2 v Flexys Cefn Druids 15.09.01
League Defeat: 0-6 v T.N.S.14.04.01
1-7 v Caersws 06.01.01

FACT FILE
Colours: A;; BlueChange colours: White/black/black

Midweek Fixtures: Tuesday

Website: www.porttalbotfc.co.uk

CLUB PERSONNEL

Chairman: Andrew Edwards
Tel: 01639 888515 (H)

Manager:Wayne Davies

Head of Youth Academy: B.Wells
c/o Club

PORTHMADOG

Secretary: P.G.Owen, 56 Mials Gerddi, Portmmadog, Gwynedd LL14 9LE(01766 512991)

Ground: Y Traeth, Porthmadog, Gwynedd Tel: 01766 514687
Directions: At towncentre crossroads (by Woolworths) into Snowdon Str., pass RBL/Craft Centre onto unmade track, over railway line - ground on right
Capacity: 2,000 Seats: 500 Cover: 400 Floodlights: Yes
Club Shop: Yes
Clubhouse: Station Buffet usded after matches.
HONOURS Welsh Amtr Cup(3) 55-58, N. Wales Amtr Cup 37-38 56-57 58-59 62-63, Lge of Wales Cup R-up 92-93, N. Wales Coast Chal. Cup(5) 55-56 73-75 76-78, WelshAll.(8) 02-03 37-38 66-69 74-76 89-90 (Cookson Cup 75-76 89-90, Barritt Cup 77-78, Alves Cup 65-66 73-74 76-77) ,Cymru Alliance Lg Cup 98-99
PREVIOUS **Leagues:** N Wales; Gwynedd; Bangor & Dist.; Lleyn & Dist.; Cambrian Coast; Welsh Alliance; Cymru Alliance
RECORD **Attendance:** 3,500 v Swansea, Welsh Cup 64-65

FACT FILE

Founded: 1883
Nickname: Porth
Colours: Red /black/black
Change: Yellow/red /red & yellow
Midweek Matchday: Wednesday
Reserve League: Caernarfon District
Programme: 28 pages, &1.00
Editor:P.G.Owen

CLUB PERSONNEL

Chairman: Phil Jones
President: William Pike
Manager: V.Williams
Physio: Ifor Roberts

RHYL

Secretary: Dennis McNamee, 3 Maes Rhosyn, Rhuddlan. Tel: 01745 591287 (H)
Ground: Belle Vue, Grange Road, Rhyl, Clwyd Tel: 01745 338327
Directions: Leave A55 at the St Asaph/Rhyl turn off and take A525 to Rhuddlan.At roundabout take 2nd turn for Rhyl, then left at next roundabout and over next two roundabouts .After 1mile urn right into Pendyffryn Rd, then left at junction and ground is 300yds on left.
Capacity: 4,000 Cover: 1,200 Seats: 600 Floodlights: Yes
Club Shop: Yes Clubhouse: No
HONOURS Welsh Cup 51-52 52-53 (R-up 29-30 36-37 92-93), Welsh Amateur Cup 72-73, Northern Premier Lg Presidents Cup 84-85, North West Counties Lg R-up 82-83,North Wales Coast Challenge Cup, Cheshire County Lg 47-48 50-51 71-72 (R-up 48-49 49-50 51-52 55-56, Div 2 R-up 81-82, Lg Cup 48-49 51-52 70-71, Div 2 Shield 81-82), Cyrmu Alliance 93-94 (R-up 92-93, Lg Cup 92-93)
PREVIOUS LEAGUES: **North Wales Coast League,** Cheshire County; North West Counties; Northern Premier; Cymru Alliance 92-94
BEST SEASON **FA Cup :** 4th Rd Proper 56-57 (lost 0-3 at Bristol City)
RECORD **Attendance:** 10,000 v Cardiff City, Welsh Cup 1953
Goalscorer: Don Spendlove **Appearances:** Not known
Players progressing:Ian Edwards, Grenville Millington, Brian Lloyd, Andy Holden, Barry Horne, Andy Jones

FACT FILE
Founded: 1870 (as Rhyl Skull & Crossbones)
Nickname: Lilywhites
Sponsors: Rhyl Tyre & Battery
Colours: White/black/black
Change: All Red
Midweek matches: Tuesday
Programme: 40 pages £1
Editor: Ian Johnson 01745 353976 (H) or 07960 071197 (M)

CLUB PERSONNEL
Managing Director; Doug Mortimer
Chairman: Dave Simmons
Vice Chairmen; Dave Milner
President: R B G Webster
Company Secretary : David Milner
Press Officer: David .Williams
Manager: J.Hulse
Tel No: 0151 653 9874
Head of Youth Academy: J.Smith

TOTAL NETWORK SOLUTIONS

Secretary: Gwynfor Hughes, Birch Lea, Porthywaen, Oswestry, Shrops SY10 8LY
Tel: 01691 828645 (H) Fax: 01691 828645
Ground: Recreation Park, Treflan, Llansantffraid Tel: 01691 828112 & Fax 01691 828862
Directions: **From North**A483 between Oswestry and Welshpool, right at Llynclys (A495) to village Right opposite Mill towards Llynclys Community Centre. Ground is behind housing estate.**From south** A483 turn left at FGourCrosses B4393 to village and once again right opposite Mill.
Capacity: 2,000 Seats: 500 Standing: 1,500 Floodlights: Yes Shop: no
Clubhouse: Open every evening except Sunday, plus weekend afternoons.
HONOURS League of Wales Champions 99-00 R-up 01-02,02-03 Welsh Cup 95-96; R-up: 00-01 Welsh Intermediate Cup 92-93; League of Wales Cup 94-95;Cymru Alliance Lge 92-93, R-up 91-92; Central Wales Sen Cup 98-99,R-up 92-93 97-98;Central Wales Lg R-up 90-91 94-95 95-96, Lge Cup 95-96; Montgomeryshire Amtr Lg (7), Village Cup (17); UEFA Champions League 00-01, European Cup Winners Cup Preliminary Rd 96-97 U.E.F.A. Cup: 2001-02,02-03
PREVIOUS **League:** Mid-Wales; Cymru Alliance (pre-1993)
RECORD **Attendance:** 2,100 v KS Ruch Chorzow Euro Cup Winners 96 (at Wrexham F.C.)
Goalscorer: Adrian Jones **Appearances:** Andy Mulliner

FACT FILE
Founded: 1959
Nickname: The Saints
Sponsors: Total Network Solutions
Colours: Green and white/white/white
Change: All Blue
Midweek Matchdays: Tuesday
Programme: 40 pages, £1
Editor:Tony Williams

CLUB PERSONNEL
Chairman: Edgar Jones
President: Mike Hughes
Manager:Ken McKenna
Assistant Manager: John Carroll
Physio: Gordon Evans& Tony McHugh

WELSHPOOL

Secretary: Mike Edwards, 2 Chelsea Villas,Chelsea Lane, Welshpool, Powys SY21 7YT
Tel No: 01938 555140 FAX: 01938 556040

Chairman: Mr.S. Hughes

Ground: Maes y Dre Recreation Ground, Welshpool, Powys
Tel: 01938 553027

Capacity: 2000 **Cover:** 257

Directions: On A483 take signs for town centre at the railway station roundabout. Go right at the mini roundabout and the immediate left is the entrance to the ground.

Record **League Victory**: 8-0 v Cemaes Bay 31.10.98
League Defeat: 0-8 v Barry Town 13.12.97

Honours: Cymru Alliance 01-02

FACT FILE
Founded: 1878
Nickname: Seasiders
Colours: White/black/white
Change colours: Purple/white/purple
Midweek Matchday: Wednesday

Manager
Tommi Morgan

WELSH LEAGUE

DIVISION ONE	P	W	D	L	F	A	Pts
Llanelli	34	26	4	4	73	27	82
Goytre United	34	22	9	3	73	24	75
Grange Harlequins	34	22	8	4	74	26	74
UWIC Inter Cardiff	34	21	6	7	72	33	69
Ton Pentre	34	20	6	8	96	38	66
Dinas Powys	34	14	11	9	58	41	53
Maesteg Park Athletic	34	14	11	9	39	36	53
Neath	34	15	5	14	65	56	50
Briton Ferry Athletic	34	11	11	12	53	45	44
Bridgend Town	34	12	7	15	50	60	43
Garw Athletic	34	11	5	18	46	66	38
Caerleon	34	10	7	17	56	62	37
Bettws	34	9	5	20	39	66	32
Ely Rangers	34	8	7	19	42	64	31
Gwynfi United	34	8	7	19	37	77	31
Cardiff Corinthians	34	7	6	21	39	65	27
Pontardawe Town	34	7	6	21	37	103	27
Llanwern	34	6	5	23	36	96	23

CWMBRU ALLIANCE

	P	W	D	L	F	A	Pts
Airbus UK	32	27	4	1	88	31	85
Buckley Town	32	20	6	6	74	33	66
Ruthin Town	32	19	7	6	78	48	64
Glantraeth	32	18	8	6	74	44	62
Llangefni Town	32	15	7	10	71	54	52
Guilsfield	32	15	7	10	68	56	52
Llandudno Town	32	15	6	11	63	50	51
Halkyn United	32	15	5	12	64	57	50
Llanfairpwll	32	12	7	13	51	52	43
Flint Town United	32	10	9	13	61	60	39
Holyhead Hotspurs	32	10	8	14	51	67	38
Lex XI	32	9	8	15	77	85	35
Gresford Athletic	32	10	4	18	48	64	34
Holywell Town	32	8	8	16	38	61	32
Mold Alexandra	32	6	6	20	43	84	24
Cemaes Bay	32	5	7	20	37	72	22
Amlwch Town	32	2	5	25	34	102	11

WELSH LEAGUE (WREXHAM AREA)

PREMIER DIVISION	P	W	D	L	F	A	Pts
Bala Town	26	18	4	4	70	25	58
Penycae	26	17	4	5	71	32	55
Brymbo Broughton	26	15	3	8	51	38	48
Rhostyllen United	26	15	3	8	54	47	48
Cefn United	26	11	9	6	57	39	42
Chirk AAA	26	11	7	8	60	47	40
Rhos Aelwyd	26	12	3	11	44	46	39
Mynydd Isa BT	26	11	5	10	41	33	38
Queens Park	26	9	8	9	39	40	35
Ruthin Town Res.	26	8	9	9	50	42	33
Llay Welfare	26	7	2	17	31	65	23
Brickfield Rangers	26	5	5	16	31	60	20
Llangollen Town	26	4	6	16	40	68	18
Borras Park Albion	26	4	2	20	33	90	14

WELSH ALLIANCE

	P	W	D	L	F	A	Pts
Rhyl Res.	30	26	2	2	101	27	80
Llandyrnog United **(P)**	30	22	1	7	77	35	67
Prestatyn Town	30	21	3	6	71	27	66
Bodedern	30	19	7	4	71	24	64
Rhydymwyn	30	19	1	10	73	35	58
Bethesda Athletic	30	13	7	10	58	60	46
Locomotive Llanberis	30	12	6	12	75	59	42
Glan Conwy	30	13	3	14	49	54	42
Sealand Leisure	30	10	9	11	59	58	39
Llanrug United	30	12	3	15	55	69	39
Llandudno Junction	30	12	1	17	68	61	37
Denbigh Town	30	11	3	16	62	66	36
Conwy United	30	8	1	21	42	89	25
Penmaenmawr Phoenix	30	7	4	19	51	106	25
Caerwys	30	3	5	22	32	104	14
Y Felinheli	30	4	0	26	33	103	12

Goytre United F.C. - runners-up in Welsh League Division One. Photo: Tim Lancaster.

Action from the South Wales Amateur League Division One between Corus Steel and Liantwit Major, the later winning 1-0. Photo: Tim Lancaster.

SCOTTISH FOOTBALL

Compiled by Bill Mitchell with thanks to Stewart Davidson
All photographs taken by John B. Vass

SENIOR REVIEW

TWO clubs vied for the honour of being considered the Senior Non-League side of the season - Spartans, the amateurs and Champions of the East of Scotland League, and Clachnacuddin, the Highland League Champions and Cup winners.

Both also won a domestic competition (as mentioned in the case of Clach) and each reached a Qualifying Cup Final, which went to penalties, with Clach (down to nine men) losing to Buckie Thistle and Spartans taking their prtze against a brave Edinburgh City outfit, but as the latter not only beat Buckie Thistle in the Second Round of the Scottish Cup itself by six unanswered goals and then went on the beat Alloa after a replay and Arbroath at Gayfield to attain the heady heights of Round Four they must be given the top accolade.

Other clubs to enjoy satisfactory campaigns were Aberdeenshire Shield winners Inverurie Loco Works (their first success in only three seasons in the senior ranks), Preston Athletic, Edinburgh City and the revived Kelso United with Golspie Sutherland taking the honours in the North Caledonian League thanks largely to a perfact away record.

The South of Scotland League bravely struggles on with meagre resources but great enthusiasm, but it will be strengthened by the return of the Threave Rovers first team from theie expensive East of Scotland travel programme and this should provide stiffer opposition for front runners Stranraer Athletic, the Queen of the South shadow players and gallant Creetown.

The Aberdeen area hosted the Four Nations Semi-Professional tournament very well, but questionsmust again be asked whether the Scotland selectors ever expect to win such a prestigious competition with a squad restricted to a dozen Aberdeenshire players and anopther six from three Edinburgh area sides, and - more to the point - no-one from champions Clachnacuddin.

The next three tournament6s are scheduled for Cork in Eire, England and Wales, so the prospects do not look good unless the area of selection is widened to include Junior Semi-Professionals, similar players from the Scottish League itself and eligible men from England.

Two actual victories in three seasons of brave effort cannot satisfy anyone, which means that egos must be swalllowed and the net stretched.

SENIOR NON-LEAGUE STATISTICS

HIGHLAND LEAGUE

	P	W	D	L	F	A	Pts
1. Clachnacuddin	28	21	3	4	61	25	66
2. Buckie Thistle	28	18	7	3	66	32	61
3. Fraserburgh	28	18	5	5	61	36	59
4. Deveronvale	28	18	1	9	77	41	56
5. Keith	28	17	2	9	70	36	53
6. Huntly	28	16	5	7	73	47	53
7. Inverurie Loco Works	28	13	10	5	76	51	49
8. Forres Mechanics	28	13	4	11	63	49	43
9. Nairn County	28	9	5	14	40	60	42
10. Cove Rangers	28	7	6	15	46	61	27
11. Wick Acdemy	28	6	5	17	42	65	23
12. Brora Rangers	28	5	6	17	34	61	21
13. Lossiemouth	28	4	8	15	41	74	20
14. Rothes	28	2	9	17	19	62	15
15. Fort William	28	3	4	21	20	89	13

HIGHLAND LEAGUE CUP

SECOND ROUND
Clachnacuddin 7 Forth William 0
Deveronvale 3 Bror Rangers 2
Inverurie Loco works 1 Fra`sderburgh 4
Nairn County 0 Forres Mechanics 3

SEMI-FINALS
Clachnacuddin 5 Fraserburgh 2
Deveronvale 2 Forres Mechanics 3

THE FINAL
(Saturday, 8th May 2004. At Kynoch Park, Keith)

CLACHNACUDDIN 3-0 FORRES MECHANICS
Attendance: 1,018
Lewis (2), Polworth Half-time: 3-0

CLACHNACUDDIN: Ridgers; MacKay, MacKay, MacLeod, MacDonald, Mahieson, MacCuish, Lewis, D Ross, Polworth, McCraw, Sanderson. Substitutes: G Ross for Polworth 73 minutes, Mitchell for McCraw 89 minutes, Douglas for Sanderson 89 minute.

FORRES MECHANICS: MacKenzie; Black, Simmers, MacLean, MacPherson, Craig, Whyte, Brown, Green, Rowley, Matheson. Substitutes: Scott for Rowley 76 minutes, Rattray for Matheson.

THIS final - the culminating match of the season - was over as a contest at half-time, byu which time man of the match Alan Lewis with an neat header from a similar Mike Sanderson effort, Iain Polworth with a drive from a defensive rebound and Lewis from a virtual carbon copy of his first counter had established a decxisive lead with the goals coming after nine, twelve and 34 minutes.

The Can Cans were sickened after making a bright start and the second half was an anri-climax even though Charlie Brown had some brave efforts and kept Ridgers on his toes.

Athough Clach had won the Highland League comfortably and Forres Mechanics had enjoyed a reasonable campaign no player from either club was deemed good enouth for the Scotland Semi-Professional squad for the Semi-Professional internationals played in the Aberdeen area and dominated by local players with six from Edinburgh teams.

SCOTTISH QUALIFYING CUP NORTH

FIRST ROUND
Clachnacuddin 2 Wick Academy 0
Forres Mechanics 1 Iverurie Loco works 3
Fort William 1 Cove Rangers 0
Huntly 7 Golspie Surherland 1
Keith 1 Faserburgh 1
Losssiemouth 0 Deveronvale 2
Nairn County 2 Buckie Thistle 5
Rothes 3 Brora Rangers 2

Replay
Fraserburgh 3 Keith 2

SECOND ROUND
Clachnacuddin 1 Fraserburgh 1
Deveronvale 1 Buckie thistle 3
fort William 0 huntly 2
Rothes 0 Inverurie Loco works 0

Replays
Fraserburgh 2 Clachnacuddin 6
Inverurie Loco Works 1 Rothes 0

SEMI-FINALS
Huntly 2 Clachnacuddin 4
Inverurie Loco Works 1 Buckie Thistle 2

THE FINAL
(Saturday, 1st November 2003. At Mosset Park, Forres)

BUCKIE THISTLE 1-1 CLACHNACUDDIN
Coutts Davidson
(after extra-time) Attendance: 1,214
(Buckie Thistle won 6-5 on penalties)
Half-time & 90 minutes score: 0-0.

BUCKIE THISTLE: Main, Slater, Lamberton (capt), Munro, Pine, Shewan, Smith, S.Taylor, Milne, R.Taylor, McDonald. Subs: Coutts for R.Taylor 61mins, More for McDonald 69mins, Gains for Slater 84mins. Yellow card: Smith 86mins.
CLACHNACUDDIN: Rae, Mackay, McLeod (capt), MacDonald, Matheson, Morrison, Mitchell, Sanderson, Polworth, McCraw, Ross. Subs: Brennan for Mitchell 46mins. Davidson for McCraw 55mins. Lewis for Polworth 79mins. Sent-off: MacDonald 42mins. Brennan 82mins. Yellow Cards: Morrison 26mins. Brennan 48mins. Matheson 78mins.

The bare statistics tell only a small percentage of the story, which ended with Buckie Thistle's Greg Pirie netting the sixth spot-kick in the shoot-out and Clach's Matheson sending his side's final effort of eight narrowly past Main's right hand post to give the Jags their first victory in the competition since 1958-59.

Before that there had been two hours of frantic play in which the Jags had been marginally better, but wildly inaccurate with their shots on goal, while Clach in two bad moments of pure indiscipline inflicted wounds on themselves, for which in goal-scoring terms they did not suffer until the ultimate gun-fight.

Probably the only talking points from the 90 minutes were the two red cards handed out to Clach defenders with MacDonald the first to walk for apparent use of an elbow in the face of Milne, which happened with referee Craig Thomson close by - and his reaction was swift and inevitable.

Up to then - a somewhat harsh yellow card for Morrison apart - the action had been frantic and nothing more, as it was in the second period, when Clach held their own despite being depleted and having to bolster their rearguard by bringing on Brennan for play-making Mitchell.

The substitute immediately was booked for a bad foul and, when with eight minutes left he brought down another replacement - More of Buckie Thistle - in full flight, referee Thomson had two choices - a second yellow card or a straight red. He chose the former and Clach were down to nine men.

Clach still did a fair share of attacking and three minutes into extra-time when Morrison sent a well weighted pass into the path of Davidson there was the unbelievable possibility of victory for the Inverness outfit.

However, with the second period of extra-time in progress Coutts at last found the target for Jags with a low shot that went in off a post, but other efforts from his side were mainly off target, although Rae did have to make two fine saves.

Clach's depleted side had two notable heroes in Morrison and Ross with Davidson working hard when he arrived on the field. While Buckie Thistle's players all looked good until the ball entered the penalty area, when line and length was absent.

Referee Thomson had a sound game and he would have lost points had he not taken swift action when he did. Circumstances decreed that it would not be a great game, which was well staged by Forres Mechanics FC, but a team that shoots itself in the foot can expect no sympathy however bravely they played when short-handed.

NORTH OF SCOTLAND CUP

SEMI-FINALS

Elgin City 2 Wick Academy 0

Inverness Caledonian Thistle 1 Ross County 1

(after extra-time - Inverness Caledonian Thistle won 4-2 on penalties).

THE FINAL

(Sunday, 25th April 2004 at Mosset Park, Forres)

ELGIN CITY 1-0 INVERNESS CALEDONIAN THISTLE

M Smith (own goal)

ABERDEENSHIRE CUP

Preliminary Round
Deveronvale 4 Aberdeen 'A' 5

First Round
Buckie Thistle 0 Inverurie LocoWorks 1
Cove Rangers 1 Aberdeen 'A' 3
Keith 1 Huntly 0
Peterhead 3 fraserburgh 1

Semi-finals
Keith 0 Aberdeen 'A' 5
Inverurie Loco Works 3 Peterhaed 1

FINAL
(Tuesday, 19th August 2003. At Harlaw Park, Inverurie)
Attendance: 1,764
INVERURIE LOCO WORKS 0-4 ABERDEEN 'A'
Zdrilllic, McGuire, Foster, Stewart

ABERDEENSHIRE SHIELD

FIRST ROUND
Cove Rangers 1 Buckie Thistle 2
Huntly 3 Deveronvae 4
Keith 1 Inveruruie Loco Works 1
(After extra-time -Inverurie Loco Works won 4-2 on penalties)

SEMI-FINALS
Deveronvale 2 Buckie Thistle 1
Fraserburgh 0 Inverurie Loco Works 1

THE FINAL
(Wednesday, 12th November 2003. At Princess Royal Park, Banff)
Attendance: 1,057
DEVERONVALE 1-4 INVERURIE LOCO WORKS
McKenzie Ross (2), MacKay, Low.

(NB: This was Inverurie Loco Works' first senior trophy - in their third season in that category)

INVERNESS CUP

FIRST ROUND
Elgiin City 1 Clacnacuddin 3

SEMI-FINALS
Forres Mechanics 1 Clachnacuddin 4
Ross County 3 Inverness Caledonian Thistle 1 (after extra-time)

THE FINAL
(Tuesday, 9th September 2003. At Victoria Park, Dingwall)
Attendance: 472
ROSS COUNTY 3-1 CLACHNACUDDIN
McGarry (2), Townsley Ross

EAST OF SCOTLAND

SOUTH QUALIFYING CUP

SECOND ROUND

Burntisland Shipyard 1 Vale of Leithen 3
Edinburgh City 6 Gala Fairydean 0
Preston Athletic 0 Spartans 1
Threave Rovers 2 St Cuthbert Wanderers 1

SEMI-FINALS

Spartans 1 Threave Rovers 0
Vale of Leithen 1 Edinburgh City 2

THE FINAL

(Saturday, 8th November 2003 at Annbank, Stirling)

EDINBURGH CITY 1-1 SPARTANS
Nye Henretty
(after extra-time - Spartans won 4-2 on penalties)

EAST OF SCOTLAND LEAGUE

PREMIER DIVISION	P	W	D	L	F	A	Pts
1. Spartans	22	15	6	1	60	25	51
2. Edinburtgh City	22	14	4	4	56	29	46
3. Threave Rovers	22	10	7	6	44	28	37
4. Annan Athletic	22	11	4	7	49	45	37
5. Gala Fairydean	22	9	4	9	34	38	31
6. Edinburgh University	22	8	2	11	32	30	30
7. Civil Service Strollers	22	9	2	11	43	38	29
8. Preston Athletic	22	9	4	10	34	36	28
9. Lothian Thistle	22	6	3	13	24	45	21
10. Whitehill Welfare	22	5	5	12	38	51	20
11. Vale of Leithen	22	4	7	11	35	56	19
12. Craigroyston	22	5	4	13	29	57	19

DIVISION ONE	P	W	D	L	F	A	Pts
1. Kelso United	22	15	3	4	52	29	48
2. Dalbeattie Star	22	14	4	4	76	35	46
3. Ormiston	22	14	4	4	49	27	46
4. Heriot Watt University	22	12	3	7	56	34	39
5. Easthouses	22	11	5	6	49	28	38
6. Peebles Rovers	22	10	6	6	53	44	33
7. Edinburgh Athletic	22	9	6	7	42	34	33
8. Selkirk	22	9	5	8	40	35	32
9. Coldstream	22	4	5	13	33	58	17
10. Hawick Royal Albert	22	4	4	14	24	61	16
11. Tolcross United	22	3	2	17	24	55	11
12. Eyemouth United	22	2	3	17	21	79	9

EAST LEAGUE CUP

THIRD ROUND

Annan Athletic 4 Spartans 6
Edinburgh Athletic o Edinburgh City 1
Heriot Watt University 1 Gala Fairydean 2
Whitehill Welfare 0 Threave Rovers 3

SEMI-FINALS

Gala Fairydean 2 Spartans 3
Threave Rovers 1 Edinburgh City 1
(After extra-time - Edinburgh City won 5-4 on penalties)

THE FINAL

(Saturday, 15th May 2004 at Lothian Thistle FC)

SPARTANS 4-1 EDINBURGH CITY
Marison (2), Hunter
Henretty, Burns

ALEX JACK CUP

SECOND ROUND

Easthouses 1 Edinburgh Athletic 3
Kelso United 3 Eyemouth United 1
Ormiston 2 Lothian Thistle 3
Peebles Rovers 4 Graigroyston 1

SEMI-FINALS

Lelso United 0 Edinburgh Athletic 2
Peebles Rovers 1 Lothian Thistle 2

THE FINAL

(Sunday, 23rd November 2003 at Whitehill Welfare FC)

EDINBURGH ATHLETIC 0-1 LOTHIAN THISTLE
Robertson

KING CUP

Third Round

Edinburgh Athletic 4 Ormiston 1
Gala Fairydean 1 Heriot Watt University 3
Hawick Royal Albert 0 Lothian Thistle 3
Spartans 1 Edinburgh City 2 (after extra-time)

Semi-finals

Edinburgh City 0 Lothian Thistle 1
Heriot Watt University 3 Edinburgh Athletic 0

FINAL

(Saturday, 12th May 2004. At Civil Service Strollers Sportsground, Muirhouse, Edinburgh)

LOTHIAN THISTLE 1-1 HERIOT WATT UNIVERSITY
Robertson Campbell
(After extra-time - Lothian Thistle won 4-1 on penalties)

IMAGE PRINTERS CUP

Third Round
Edinburgh Athletic 0 Heriot Watt University 3
Peebles Rovers 0 Edinburgh City 4
Preston Athletic 2 Gala Fairydean 0
Spartans 2 Civil Service Strollers 0

Semi-finals
Heriot Watt University 3 Edinburgh City 4 (after extra-time - score at 90 minutes 2-2)
Preston Athletic 2 Spartans 1

FINAL
(Sunday, 18rth January 2004 at Lothian Thistle FC)

PRESTON ATHLETIC 2-1 EDINBURGH CITY
McCall (2) Johnston

EAST OF SCOTLAND CITY CUP

(2002-03)
FINAL
Saturday, 26th July 2003 at Berwick Rangers FC)

BERWICK RANGERS 3-1 EDINBURGH CITY
McAllister (2), McCormick Foster

(2003-04)
FINAL
(Tuesday, 30th March 2004 at Preston Athletic FC)

PRESTON ATHLETIC 3-2 BERWICK RANGERS
(no scorers available)

SOUTH OF SCOTLAND

SOUTH OF SCOTLAND LEAGUE

PREMIER DIVISION	P	W	D	L	F	A	Pts
1. Stranraer Athleti	30	25	1	4	90	34	76
2. Queen of the South 'A'	30	24	3	3	100	23	75
3. Creetown	30	21	2	7	93	40	65
4. Stranraer Reserves	30	18	5	7	74	43	59
5. Annan Athletic 'A'	30	18	3	9	94	41	57
6. Dumfries FC	30	16	3	11	77	62	51
7. Girvan	30	15	3	12	76	59	48
8. St Cuthbert Wanderers	30	10	10	10	64	53	40
9. Threave Rovers 'A'	30	11	6	13	54	69	39
10. Nithsdale Wanderers	30	11	4	15	77	84	37
11. Mid Annandale	30	10	5	15	49	61	35
12. Abbetvale	30	8	4	18	67	88	28
13. Wigtown & Badenoch	30	8	4	18	63	92	28
14. Dalbeattie Star 'A'	30	7	2	21	38	94	23
15. Newton Stewart	30	5	1	24	40	146	16
16. Crichton	30	5	0	25	58	123	15

DETROIT TROPHY
(overall championship)
1. Creetown (98 pts). 2. Stranraer Athletic (97 pts). 3. Queen of the South 'A' (84 pts)

SOUTH LEAGUE CUP

SECOND ROUND

Dalbeattie Star 'A' 1 Nithsdale Wanderers 2

Dumfries 6 Crichton 2

Girvan 3 Threave Rovers 1

Stranraer Athletic 4 Creetown 2

SEMI-FINALS

Dumfries 4 Stranraer Athletic 7

Nithsdale Wanderers 1 Girvan 2

THE FINAL

(Wednesday, 20th August 2003 at Girvan)

GIRVAN 1-3 STRANRAER ATHLETIC

Wilson (pen) Doyle, Murdoch, Carnochan

SOUTH CHALLENGE CUP

THIRD ROUND

Creetown 0 Queen of the South Reserves 2
Gretna Reserves 5 Annan Athletic 0
Stranraer Reserves 1 Dalbeattie Star 3
Threave Rovers 2 Nithsdale Wanderers 1

SEMI-FINALS

Queen of the South Reserves 2 Dalbeattie Star 1
Threave Rovers 3 Gretna Reserves 1

THE FINAL

(Monday, 10th May 2004 at Palmerston Park, Dumfries)

QUEEN OF THE SOUTH RESERVES 3-1 THREAVE ROVERS
O'Connor (2), Ferrie — Nicol

CREE LODGE CUP

SECOND ROUND

Dalbeattie Star 1 Girvan 6
Dumfries 1 Annan Athletic 6
Newton Stewart 0 Stranraer Athletic 6
Wigtown & Badenoch 2 Creetown 5

SEMI-FINALS

Creetown 3 Girvan 0
Stranraer Athletic 2 Annan Athletic 5

THE FINAL

(Saturday, 7th February 2004 at Annan Athletic FC)

ANNAN ATHLETIC 0-2 CREETOWN
McClymont (2)

POTTS CUP

SECOND ROUND

Abbey Vale 1 Creetown 2
Nithsdale Wanderers 5 Newton Stewart 1
Stranraer Athletic 6 Dalbeattie Star 4 (after extra-time)
Wiigtown & Badenoch 2 St Cuthberts Wanderers 0

SEMI-FINALS

Creetown 4 Nithdsdale Wanderers 1
Wigtown & Badenoch 1 Stranraer Athletic 4

THE FINAL

(Saturday, 3rd April 2004 at Creetown FC)

CREETOWN 0-4 STRANRAER ATHLETIC
Murdoch (2,1pen), Dougan, Carnochan

HAIG GORDON CUP

SECOND ROUND

Creetown 8 Dalbeattie Star 3

Dumfries 3 Abbey Vale 2

Nithsdale Wanderers 4 Crichton 4 (after extra-time - Nithsdale Wanderers won 5-3 on penalties)

Threave Rovers 2 Mid-Annandale 1 (after extra-time)

SEMI-FINALS

Creetown 3 Threave Rovers 1

Nithsdale Wanderers 0 Dumfries 7

THE FINAL

(Saturday, 17th April 2004 at Norfolk Park, Glencaple)

DUMFRIES 3-6 CREETOWN

Little (2), Wilson (3), McClymont (2), Cairnie

Rushton-Davis

TWEEDLE CUP

SECOND ROUND

Creetown 2 Nithsdale Wanderers 1

Girvan 5 Annan Athletic Reserves 6

Newton Stewart 2 Mid-Annandale 1 (after extra-time)

Wigtown & Badenoch 0 Gretna Reserves 2

SEMI-FINALS

Annan Athletic 2 Gretna Reserves 2 (Gretna Reserves won 4-3 on penalties)

Newton Stewart 5 Creetown 6

THE FINAL

(Saturday, 20th March 2004 at Creetown FC)

CREETOWN 2-0 GRETNA RESERVES

Kennedy, Davidson

LEADING SCORERS (ALL COMPETITIONS

Alan Murdoch (Stranraer Athletic)(45)

Martin Herries (Creetown)(44)

Dougie Taylor (Nithsdale Wanderers)(33)

Gary McClymont (Creetown)(32)

Doug allardyce (Nithsdale Wanderers)(31)

NORTH CALEDONIAN LEAGUE

	P	W	D	L	F	A	Pts
1. Golspie Sutherland	18	16	0	2	53	14	48
2. Balintore	18	14	0	4	57	21	42
3. Alness United	18	12	1	5	53	26	37
4. Thurso	17	11	2	4	54	22	35
5. Invergordon	18	6	2	10	41	69	19
6. Dornoch	18	6	1	11	41	69	19
7. Halkirk	18	5	3	10	20	37	18
8. BunilidhThistle	17	4	3	11	23	43	15
9. Tain St Duthus	18	4	2	12	30	61	14
10. Bonar Bridge	18	3	2	13	31	55	11

The Bunilidh Thistle v Thurso match match was not played

PORT SERVICES CUP

SECOND ROUND

Dornoch 0 Bunilidh 2
Golspie Sutherland 0 Alness United 1
Invergordon 1 Bonar Bridge 0
Thurso 6 Halkirk 2

SEMI-FINALS

Bunilidh 0 Alness United 4
Thurso 5 Invergordon 0

THE FINAL

(Saturday, 1st November 2003 at Dudgeon Park, Brora)

ALNESS UNITED 1-1 THURSO
Jack MacKenzie
(after extra-time - Alness United won 4-3 on penalties)

PCT CUP

SECOND ROUND

Balintore 2 Halkirk 0
Bunilidh 2 Golspie Sutherland 5
Invergordon 2 Thurso 3
Tain 0 Alness United 1

SEMI-FINALS

Balintore 3 Alness United 3 (Balintore won 4-3 on penalties)
Thurso 5 Golspie Sutherland 0

THE FINAL

(Saturday, 21st February 2004 at Dudgeon Park, Brora)

THURSO 1-0 BALINTORE
MacDougal

MORRIS NEWTON CUP

SECOND ROUND

Balintore 2 Tain St Duthie 2 (after exdtra-time - Balintore won 5-4 on penalties)
Bunilidh Thistle 0 Allness United 5
Golspie Surtherland 2 Dornoch 1
Halkirk 0 Thurso 3

SEMI-FINALS

Alness united 0 Thurso 3
Balintore 1 Golspie Sutherland 0

THE FINAL

(Saturday, 17th April 2004 at Dudgeon Paqrk, Brora)

THURSO 4-2 BALINTORE

J MacKenzie (2)	Lowe, Farquhar
N MacKenzie	
Sutherland	

FOOTBALL TIMES CUP

SECOND ROUND

Balintore 3 Invergordon 2 (after extra-time)
Bunilidh Thistle 2 Tain St Duthus 3
Halkirk Unite3d 2 Golspie Sutherland 0
Thurso 1 Alness United 1 (after extra-time - Alness United won 4-2 on penalties)

SEMI-FINALS

Alness United 0 Balintore 3
Halkirk United 3 Tain St uthie 1

THE FINAL

(Saturday, 8th May 2004 at Dudgeon Park, Brora)

BALINTORE 4-1 HALKIRK UNITED

Dance (2),	MacDonald
Ross, Powell	

NON-LEAGUE TEAMS IN THE SCOTTISH CUP

FIRST ROUND

Clachnacuddin 0 Stranraer 2
Cowdenbeath 5 Edinburgh City 2
Spartans 6 Buckie Thistle 0

SECOND ROUND

Alloa Athletic 3 Spartans 3
Inverurie Loco Works 1 Airdrie United 5
Berwick tangers 4 Huntly 2
Morton 4 vale of Leithen 0
Montrose 1 Threave Rovers 0
Replay
Spartans 5 Alloa Athletic 3
(after extra-time - score at 90 minutes - 3-3)

THIRD ROUND

Arbroath 1 Spartans 4

FOURTH ROUND

Spartans 0 Livingstone 4

AMATEURS

SCOTTISH AMATEUR CUP

SEMI-FINALS

Viewfield Rovers 3 SX Peter & Paul 1
Norton House 2 Motherwell Miners Welfare 0

THE FINAL

(at Hampden Park)

VIEWFIELD ROVERS 2-0 NORTON HOUSE

HIGHLAND AMATEUR CUP

SEMI-FINALS

portree 2 Stornoway Athletic 5

Lochs 6 Harlequin Bar 3

THE FINAL

LOCHS 3-2 STORNOWAY ATHLETIC

AMATEUR LEAGUE WINNERS

Strathspey & Badenoch Welfare League (Summer 2003): ....Kingussie

Aberdeenshire Premier Division: ....Kincorth

Division One North:...Luthemuir

Division One East:...Burghmuir

Ayshire Amateur League: Premier Division:... Hurlford Thistle

North First Division: ....Ardeer Rovers

South First Division: ....Cumnock Amateurs

Kingdom Caledonian League: ....Eastvale

Caledonian League Division One: ....Coatbridge CC

Fife Amateur League Premier Division: ....Rosyth

Division One: ....Valleyfield

Border Amateur League Division A: ....Gala Rovers

JUNIORS REVIEW

SELECTING a Junior Club of the Season is no easy taskat a time when the normally dominantteams from the West of Scotland had disappeared from the OVD Cup at the quarter-final stage, which left Carnoustie Panmure to edge out Fife's Hill of Beath Hawthorn in a seven goal thriller and Tayport to score the game's only counter against the other Fifers, Glenrothes, to claim the remaining Firhill Park berth.

Both finalists had relied on strong defences and experienced goalkeepers to do well in their league and cup programmes during the season with Panmure (on paper at least) having the better attack iin being [romoted from a lower competition, but the ultimate match looked like a goalless stalemate from the first whistle and the dreaded penalties (and keeper Geddes's expertise) were needed after two blank hours to bring The Gowfers success after an earleir final had been lost in similar circumstances, so perhaps they deserve the main accolade as they also won two parochial cups and were finalists in another.

Honourable mentions must go to Linlithgow Rose, the East's top league team on goal difference, and Camelon, who won the top Lothian League, while in the West the top league side was Kilwinning Rangers with West of Scotland Cup winners Maryhill, Arthurlie, Pollok and the Cerntral League's top champions Cambuslang Rangers deserving praise along with Clydebank, whose return to the junior ranks broght promotion - an immediate success.

The best Fife sides have already been mentioned, while the same applies to Tayside, but in the North Culter, Sunnybank, Glentanar and Stonehaven and Hermes's cupp exploits kept the fans interested, they being the best teams.

On reflection it ould not be described as a vintage Junior season, but there is still a case for at least four clubs to be entered in each of the Senior Qualifying Cups, an argument which is given strength by the fact that Girvan, new juniors, have been allowed to play for this secoming season at least in the South version of the competition; it may be the thin end of the wedge, but in the long run it must benefit the Scottish game as a whole.

In addition, the Scottish Semi-Professional selectors (as mentioned elsewhere) would do the national interest no harm by considering junior players, which would remove the temptation to make accusations of parochial preferences taking precedence.

Troon v Cruden Bay in the OVD SJ Cup Round One.

OVD SCOTTISH JUNIOR CUP

FIFTH ROUND

Cambuslang Rangers 1 maryhill 0

Carnoustie Panmure 2 Kilwinning Rangers 1

Fortsh Wanderers 1 Tayport 1

Glenafton Athletic 1 Glenrothes 2

Hill of Beath Hawthorn 4 Linlithgow Rose 1

Kilbirnie Ladeside 1 Kilsyth Rangers 1

Newtongrange Star 0 Musselburgh athletic 0

Sauchie 3 rutherglencairn 1

REPLAYS

klisyth Rangers 4 Kilbirnie Ladeside 1

Musselburgh Athletic 4 Newtongrange Star 2

Tayport 2 Forth Wanderers 1

SIXTH ROUND

Cambuslang rangers 0 Tayport 1

kilsyth Rangers 0 Carnoustie Panmure 1

Musselburgh Athletic 0 Hill of Beath Hawthorn 0

Sauchie 0 Glenrothes 0

REPLAYS

Hill of Beath Hawthorn 2 Musselburgh Athletic 1 (after extra-time)

Glenrothes 3 Sauchie 2

SEMI-FINALS

Carnoustie Panmure 4 Hill of Beath Hawthorn 3 (at MdDiarmid park, Perth)

Glenrothes 0 Tayport 1 (at Starks Park, Kirkaldy)

THE FINAL

(Sunday, 23rd may 2004. At Firhill Park, Glasgow)

CARNOUSTIE PANMURE 0-0 TAYPORT

(after extra-time - Carnoustie Panmure won 4-1 on penalties)

Attendance: 3,030

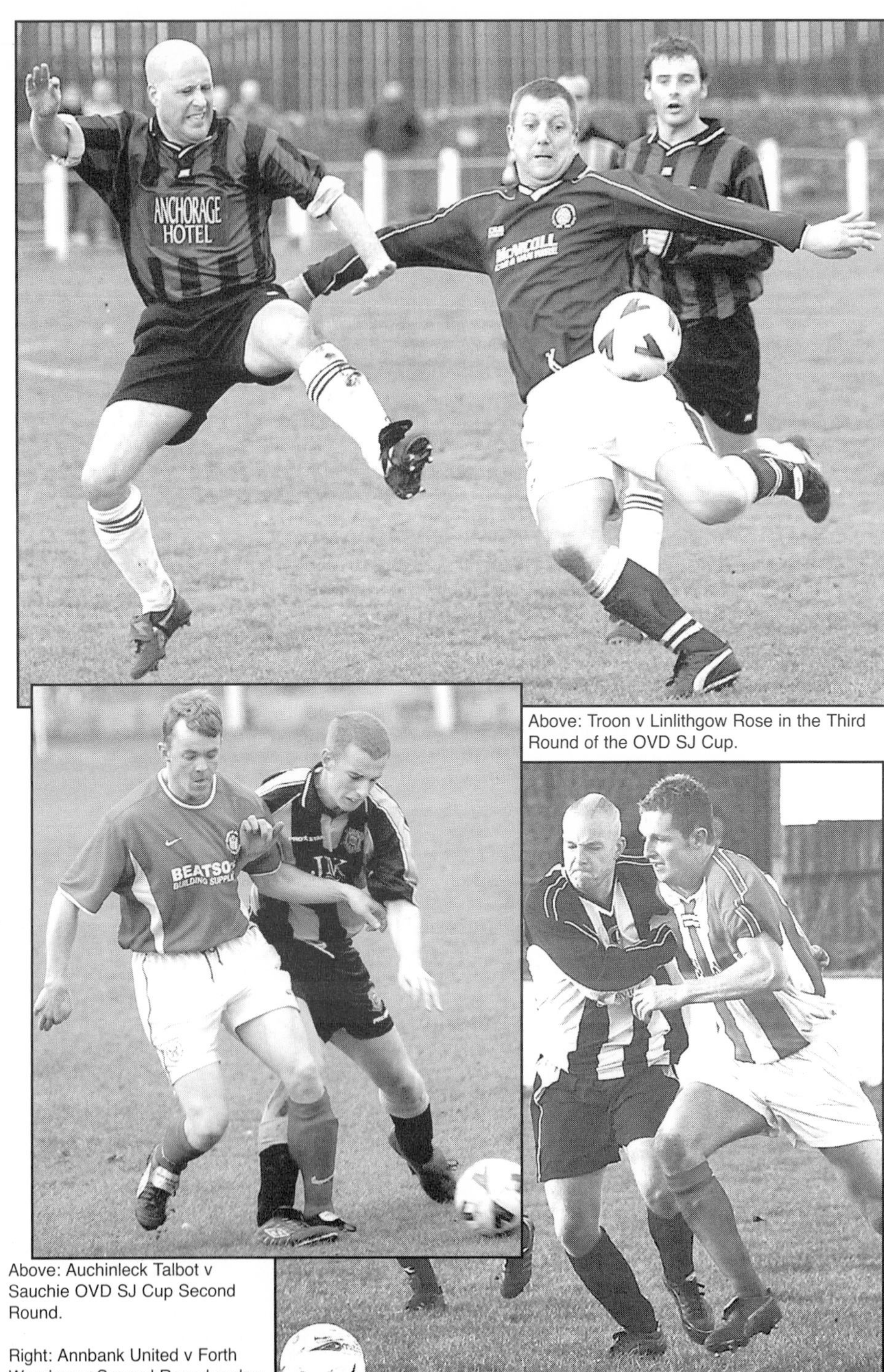

Above: Troon v Linlithgow Rose in the Third Round of the OVD SJ Cup.

Above: Auchinleck Talbot v Sauchie OVD SJ Cup Second Round.

Right: Annbank United v Forth Wanderers Second Round replay.

OVD JUNIOR CUP FINAL

Sunday, 23rd May 2004. At Firhill Park, Glasgow.

CARNOUSTIE PANMURE 0-0 TAYPORT
(after extra-time. Carnoustie Panmure won 4-1 on penalties)
Attendance: 3,030.

IT is sad to say that by any standards this was a moderate game, which looked doomed to a penalty shoot out from its early stages.

There was plenty of effort, but the hardest worked people in the ground appeared to be the ball boys behind the goals, so hurried and wayward was the shooting.

Carnoustie's 'Gowfers' should have settled the issue in the 57th minute, when they were awarded a penalty for a trip on Kenneth, but Craig's carefully placed shot lacked pace and was comfortably saved by Fitzpatrick.

in extra-time Christie had a strong effort well saved by Geddes, who then stopped another shot by the same player and Evans in the shoot-out to give his side victory.

Ward did score once in that competition for the holders, as did Webster, Brand, Paterson and the excellent Steven Narey (son of Scotland's David) for Panmure and that was that.

It was a cruel way for Tayport to lose their trophy, but if tour shooting is hesitant and inaccurate what
can you realistically expect? Panmure had been compensated in a way for losing by the same route in 2001.

CARNOUSTIE PANMURE: Geddes; Narey, Craig, Wilkie, Ogilvie (captain), Morrison, Kelly, Buick, Brand, Kenneth, Montgomery. Substitutes: Webster for Montgomery 73 minutes, Miller for Kenneth 76 minutes, Paterson 91 minutes. Yellow cards: Kelly, Buick. Penalty scorers: Webster, Brand, Paterson, Narey.

TAYPORT: Fitzpatrick; Peters, Paterson, Ward, Morris, Craik, McNaughton, Stewart (captain), Dailly, Elliott, Gunnion, Peters. Substitutes: Evans for Dailly 57 minutes, Christie for McNaughton 57, Ramasy for Morris 95 minutes. Penalty scorer: Ward.

Referee: W Collum.

SJFA SUPER CUP - 2002-03

SEMI-FINALS

Linlithgow Rose 4 Tayport 2
Sunnibank 1 Pollok 1 (Pollok won 4-1 on penalties)

THE FINAL

(Saturday, 2nd August 2003. At Linlithgow)

LINLITHGOW ROSE 1-3 POLLOK
Pearson — Proctor (2), Sweeney

NB: This was the initial competition with the Junior Cup winners from the previous season qualifying along with the three regional champions.

WEST OF SCOTLAND CUP

FOURTH ROUND

Cumnock 2 Bellshill athletic 3
Greenock 4 Pollok 3
Kilsyth Rasngers 1 Clydebank 0
Maryhill 2 Irvine Meadow 0

SEMI-FINALS

Kilsyth Rangers 1 Bellshill Athletic 1 (Bellshill Athletic won 4-2 on penaties)
Maryhill 3 Greenock 1

THE FINAL

(Saturday, 1st May 2004 at Newlandsfield Park, Glasgow)

MARYHILL 3-1 BELLSHILL ATHLETIC
Dingwall (2), Grant — Fallon

WEST OF SCOTLAND CUP

FOURTH ROUND

Cumnock 2 Bellshill athletic 3
Greenock 4 Pollok 3
Kilsyth Rasngers 1 Clydebank 0
Maryhill 2 Irvine Meadow 0

SEMI-FINALS

Kilsyth Rangers 1 Bellshill Athletic 1 (Bellshill Athletic won 4-2 on penaties)
Maryhill 3 Greenock 1

THE FINAL

(Saturday, 1st May 2004 at Newlandsfield Park, Glasgow)

MARYHILL 3-1 BELLSHILL ATHLETIC
Dingwall (2), Grant — Fallon

WEST REGION

DIVISION ONE	P	W	D	L	F	A	Pts
1. Bellshill Athletic	22	14	4	4	45	22	46
2. Renfrew	22	12	7	3	51	23	43
3. Shotts Bon Accord	22	12	7	3	42	20	43
4. Kilsyth Rangers	22	10	4	8	36	30	34
5. Beith	22	9	6	7	43	35	33
6. Petershill	22	9	3	10	39	40	30
7. Irvine Meadow	22	8	5	9	23	24	29
8. Hurlford United	22	8	3	11	38	53	27
9. Lugar Boswell Thistle	22	5	7	10	30	40	22
10. Cumbernauld United	22	6	3	13	26	44	21
11. Benburb	22	5	5	12	28	52	20
12. Shettleston	22	3	8	11	31	49	17

BEATONS CENTRAL LEAGUE CUP

PLAY-OFFS

Rutherglen Glencairn 2 Vale of Clye 0
Shotts Bon Accord 0 Pollok 0 (Pollok won 6-5 on penalties)

QUARTER-FINALS

Greenock 1 Rutherglen Glencairn 3
Kilsyth Rangers 4 St Anthonys 2
Larkhall Thistle 0 Pollok 0 (Pollok won 3-2 on penalties)
Maryhill 3 Bellshill Athletic 1

SEMI-FINALS

Maryhill 1 Pollok 2
Rutherglen Glencairn 1 Kilsyth Rangers 2

THE FINAL

(Tuesday, 14th October 2003. At Firhill Park, Glasgow)

KILSYTH RANGERS 1-1 POLLOK
McWilliams Vaugh penalty
Attendance: 1,400
(Pollok won 5-3 on penalties)

CLYDESDALE CUP

SEMI-FINALS

Carluke Rovers 1 Fortsh Wanderers 2
Lanark United 5 Lesmahagow 0

THE FINAL

(Monday, 4th August 2003. At Forth Wanderers FC)

FORTH WANDERERS 1-3 LANARK UNITED
Rowat penalty Imrie, Knight, Ferguson

CENTRAL LEAGUE

DIVISION ONE	P	W	D	L	F	A	Pts
1. Cambuslang Rangers	22	14	3	5	62	31	45
2. Kirkintilloch Rob Roy	22	14	2	6	48	31	44
3. Greenock	22	11	3	8	50	37	40
4. Vale of Leven	22	11	3	8	63	43	38
5. East Kilbride Thistle	22	10	4	8	50	41	34
6. Dunipace	22	10	3	9	41	40	33
7. Vale of Clyde	22	10	3	9	42	47	33
8. St Anthonys	22	9	5	8	52	50	32
9. Rutherglen Glencairn	22	8	5	9	34	30	29
10. Port Glasgow	22	5	7	10	35	47	22
11. Lanark United	22	5	4	13	29	44	19
12. Glasgow Perthshire	22	1	3	8	22	87	6

DIVISION TWO
(leading positions)

	P	W	D	L	F	A	Pts
1. Clydebank	24	20	2	2	66	16	62
2. Carluke Rovers	24	18	4	2	77	28	58
3. Yoker Athletic	24	17	4	3	61	23	55
4. Lesmahagow	24	14	4	6	53	30	46
5. Blantyre Victoria	24	13	2	9	52	44	41

Other positions: Forth Wanderers 33 pts; Ashfield 33 pts; St Rochs 32 pts; Royal Albert 27 pts; Thorniewood United 25 pts; Wishaw 22 pts; Stonehouse Violet 11 pts; Coltness United 1 ptt.

CENTRAL LEAGUE CUP

QUARTER-FINALS

Blantyre Victoria 0 Cumbernauld United 0 (Blantyre Victoria won 4-2 on penalties)

Cambuslang Rangers 2 Petershill 4

Larkhall Thistle 2 Maryhill 3

Shotts Bon Accord 0 Bellshill Athletic 0 (Bellshill Athletic won 3-1 on penalties)

SEMI-FINALS

Blantyre Victoria 0 Petershill 2

Maryhill 4 Bellshill Athletic 2

THE FINAL

(Friday, 28th May 2004. At Kirkintilloch Rob Roy FC)

PETERSHILL 2-0 MARYHILL

McShane, Elrick

Auckinleck Talbot v Neilston. West Super League Premier Division relegation struggle. Although Neilston won 0-1, they were relegated together with Kilbirnie Ladeside - Talbot **just** survived.

Troon v Kilbirnie Ladeside. WSL Premier Division.3-2. This was a very controversial match. Five players were red carded, four Troon and one Kilbirnie. The Troon manager was also red carded. Kilbirnie protested that Troon had fielded an ineligible player, despite appeals by Troon to the SJFA and the SFA the protest was upheld and Troon were 'docked' three points and fined. The player subject of the protest, Scott Houston, is in the light shirt in the picture below. He was signed from Hamilton Academicals but was not reinstated.

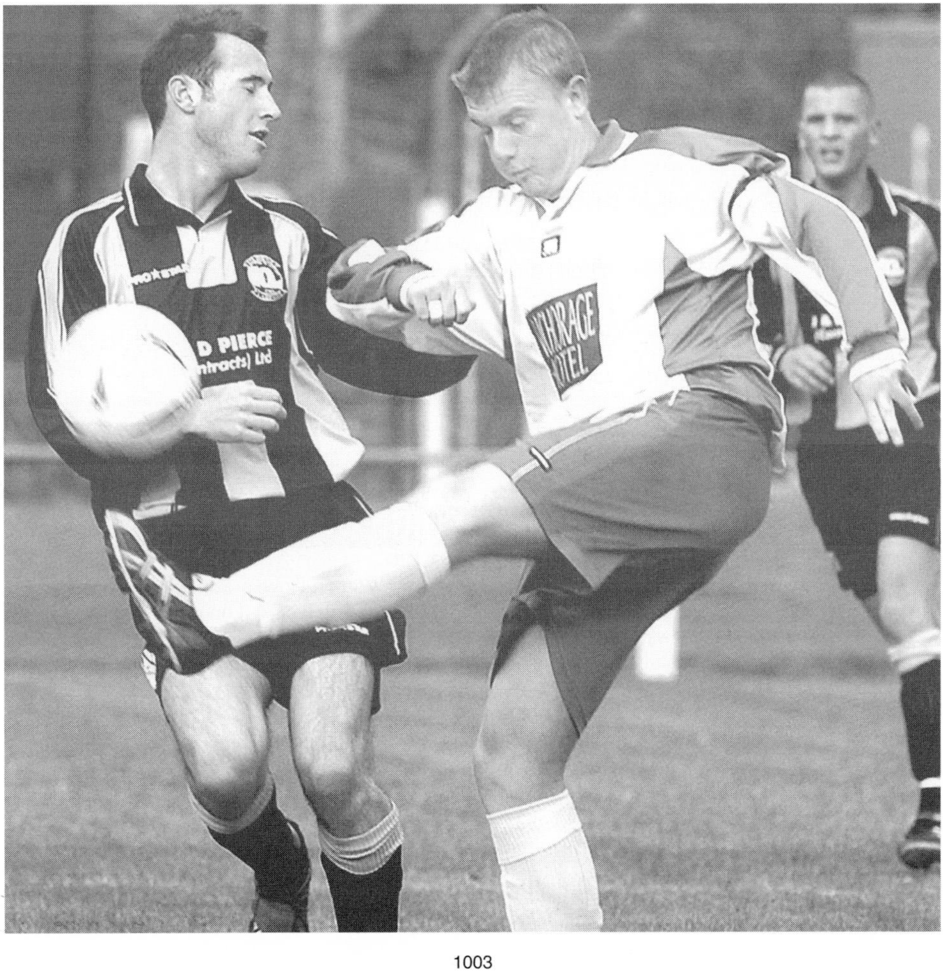

AYRSHIRE LEAGUE

		P	W	D	L	F	A	Pts
1.	Maybole	24	18	4	2	68	27	58
2.	Saltcoats Victoria	24	17	3	4	83	30	54
3.	Irvine Victoria	24	14	4	8	77	44	46
4.	Annbank United	24	14	3	7	50	38	45
5.	Kello Rovers	24	13	4	7	56	38	43
6.	Largs Thistle	24	13	2	9	60	44	41
7.	Darvel	24	10	5	9	50	52	35
8.	Craigmark Bruntonians	24	7	4	13	38	59	25
9.	Ardrossan Winton Rovers	24	5	8	11	37	51	23
10.	Whitletts Victoria	24	7	2	15	52	77	23
11.	Muirkirk	24	4	5	15	38	64	17
12.	Ardeer Thistle	24	4	5	15	34	63	17
13.	Dalry Thistle	24	4	3	17	31	87	15

AYRSHIRE WEEKLY PRESS CUP

THIRD ROUND

Auchinleck talbot 2 Cumnock 1
Glenafton Athletic 2 Troon 0
Kilwinning Rangers 0 Beith 0 (Beith won 4-2 on penalties)
Luhar Boswell Thistle 4 Kello Rovers 3

SEMI-FINALS

Beith 3 Glenafton Athletic 1
Lugar Boswell Thistle 2 Auchinleck Talbot 2 (Lugar Boswell Thistle won 5-3 on penalties)

THE FINAL

(Tuesday, 25th May 2004. At Cumnock FC)

BEITH 2-0 LUGAR BOSWELL THISTLE
Shearer,
Craig

NORTH AYRSHIRE CUP

SECOND ROUND

Ardrossan Winton Rovers 1 Irvine Meadow 1 (Ardrossan Winton Rovers won 3-1 on penalties)
Kilbirnie Ladeside 1 Irvine Victoria 1 (Kilbirnie Ladeside won 4-3 on penalties)
Kilwinning Rangers w/o Dalry Thistle (scratched)
Saltcoats Victoria 0 Beith 4

SEMI-FINAL

Beith 1 Kilbirnie Ladeside 1 (Beith won 6-5 on penalties))
Kilwinning Rangers 3 Ardrossan Winton Rovers 1

THE FINAL

(Tuesday, 15th June 2004. At Dalry Thistle FC)

BEITH 1-0 KILWINNING RANGERS
Deeney

Maybole F.C. - Ayrshire District League Championship Trophy. They losy only two of 24 matches in the league - ironically the first and last!

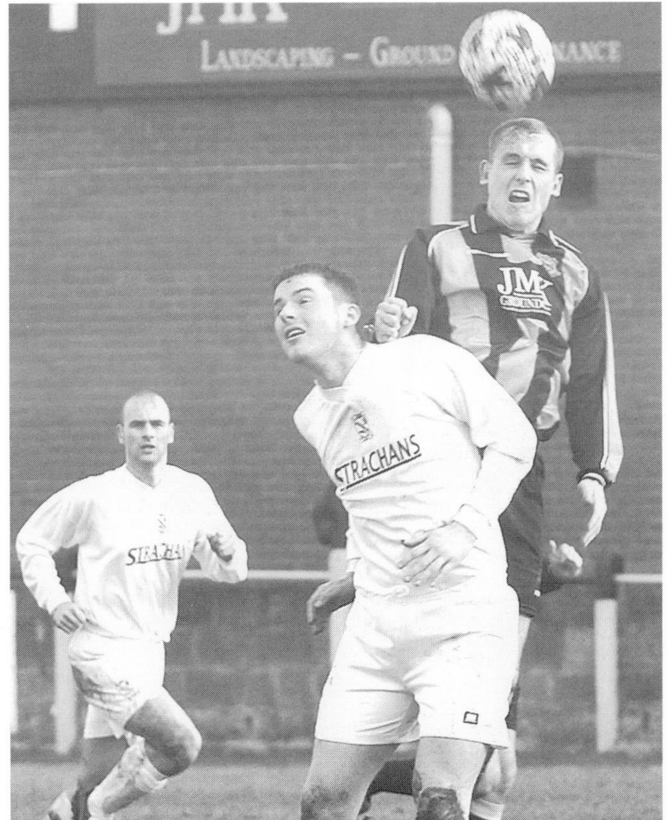

Auchinleck Talbot v Maybole. Ayrshire Weekly Press Cup Round One.

Hugh Houston the captain of Irvine Meadow XI holds the Kerr & Smith League Cup a;oft at Somerset Park Ayr, after his team beat holders Auchinleck Talbot 2-0. This was Irvine Meadows third successive final, they lost to Cumnock in 2001 and Talbot in 2002.....third time lucky!

Auchinleck Talbot v Troon.
Kerr & Smith League Cup semi-final.

KERR & SMITH LEAGUE CUP

PLAY-OFFS

Kello Rovers 2 Auchinleck Talbot 4
Kilbirnie Ladeside 1 Annbank United 0

QUARTER-FINALS

Glenafton Athletic 1 Kilbirnie Ladeside 1 9(Kilbirnie Ladeside won 5-4 on penalties)
Hurlford United 1 Auchinleck talbot 6
Irvine Meadow 1 Cumnock 1 (Irvine Meadow won 3-2 on penalties)
Troon 2 Kilwinning Rangers 0

SEMI-FINALS

Auchinleck Talbot 4 Troon 2
Irvine Meadow 4 Kilbirnie Ladeside 0

THE FINAL

(Tuesday, 7th October 2003. At Somerset Park, Ayr)

AUCHINLECK TALBOT 0-2 IRVINE MEADOW

SOUTH AYRSHIRE CUP

SEMI-FINALS

Troon beat Annbank United (scores not available)
Maybole 4 Whitletts Victoria 4 (Maybole won 6-5 on penalties)

THE FINAL

(Wednesday, 9th June 2004. At Troon FC)

TROON 3-2 MAYBOLE
Gallagher, Stephenson, Findlay pen.
Davidson,
Reid

EAST REGION

	P	W	D	L	F	A	Pts
1. Linlithgow Rose	22	12	4	6	42	23	40
2. Tayport	22	12	4	6	39	21	40
3. Bonnyrigg Rose	22	13	1	8	37	34	40
4. Lochee United	22	10	6	6	43	33	36
5. Arniston Rangers	22	10	6	6	27	§23	36
6. Bo'ness United	22	8	8	6	32	27	32
7. Bathgate Thistle	22	9	2	11	27	33	29
8. Glenrothes	22	6	8	8	24	26	26
9. Oakley United	22	7	4	11	35	43	25
10. Kelty Hearts	21	6	5	10	14	22	20
11. Hill of Beath Hawthorn	21	6	2	13	30	39	20
12. North End	22	5	4	13	19	45	19

LOTHIAN LEAGUE

DIVISION ONE	P	W	D	L	F	A	Pts
1. Camelon	18	14	2	2	49	18	44
2. Whitburn	18	13	2	3	48	22	41
3. Sauchie	18	11	3	4	47	27	38
4. Newtongrange star	18	6	6	6	20	21	24
5. Fauldhouse United	18	6	5	7	28	33	23
6. Musselburgh Athletic	18	6	2	10	27	31	20
7. Armadale Thistle	18	5	2	11	23	32	17
8. Dunbar United	18	4	3	11	32	50	17
9. Harthill Royal	18	4	4	10	26	44	16
10. Edinburgh United	18	4	3	11	15	37	15

DIVISION TWO	P	W	D	L	F	A	Pts
1. Broxburn Athletic	18	14	3	1	52	17	45
2. Penicuik Athletic	18	9	6	3	29	20	33
3. Pumpherston	18	8	7	3	34	20	31
4. West Calder United	18	8	3	7	33	38	27
5. Blackburn United	18	7	4	7	25	27	25
6. Livingston United	18	6	4	8	39	39	22
7. Dalkeith Thistle	18	3	9	6	29	33	18
8. Tranent	18	5	3	10	23	36	18
9. Haddington Athletic	18	4	4	10	26	42	16
10. Stoneyburn	18	2	5	11	15	33	11

CARLSBERG LEAGUE CUP

THIRD ROUND

Bathgate Thistle 1 Sauchie 0
Camelon 2 Linlithgow Rose 3
Fauldhouse United 3 Bonnyrigg Rose 2
Harthill Royal 5 West Calder United 1

SEMI-FINALS

Fauldhouse United 2 Bathgate Thistle 0 (at Linlithgow)
Linlithgow Rose 6 Harthill Royal 2 (afterv extra-time)(at Bathgate)

THE FINAL

(Saturday, 25th October 2003. At Camelon)

CARLSBERG EAST OF SCOTLAND CUP

THIRD ROUND

Arniston Rangers 1 Sauchie 3
camelon 1 Linlithgow Rose 1 (Linlithgow Rose won 3-0 on penalties)
Pumpherston 1 Bo'ness United 2
Whitburn 3 Newtongrange Star 1

SEMI-FINALS

Bo'ness United 1 linlithgow Rose 3
Sauchie 1 Whitburn 1 (Whitburn won 3-1 on penalties)

THE FINAL

(Wednesday, 16th Jube 2004. At Broxburn)

LINLITHGOW ROSE 1-0 WHITBURN
Welsh

STREAMLINE TAXIS ST MICHAELS CUP

THIRD ROUND

Bathgate Thistle 1 camelon 2
Bo'ness United 3 Arniston Rangers 1 (after extra-time)
Linlitgpw Rose 5 Dunbar United 2
Muszselburgh Athletic 1 Whitburn 3

SEMI-FINAL

Bo'ness United 1 Whitburn 3
camelon 0 Linlithgow Rose 1

THE FINAL

(Saturday, 12th June 2004. At Camelon)

LINLITHGOW ROSE 2-1 WHITBURN
(after extra-time - score at 90 minutes - 1-1)
Higgins (2) Flanagan

BROWN CUP

THIRD ROUND

Broxburn Athletic 1 Bo'ness United 1 (after extra-time - Bo'ness United won 4-3 on penalties)
harthill Royal 0 Whitburn 1
Musselburgh Athletic 2 Arniston Rangers 2 (after extra-time - Musselburgh Athletic won 5-4 on penalties)
Sauchie 8 Dunbar United 0

SEMI-FINALS

Bo'ness United 4 Whitburn 1
Musselburgh Athletic 5 Sauchie 1

THE FINAL

(Saturday, 29th May 2004. At Sauchie)

MUSZSELBURGH ATHLETIC 4-1 BO'NESS UNITED
McGlynn (2), Forrester, Simpson (penalty) Donnelly

SUPPLEMENTARY CUP

SEMI-FINALS

Broxburn Athletic 0 Whitburn 2

Penicuik Athletic 2 Dunbar United 1

THE FINAL

(Monday, 14th June 2004. At Blackburn United)

PENICUIK ATHLETIC 2-1 WHITBURN

Lindsay, Hancock McGhee

FIFE LEAGUE

	P	W	D	L	F	A	Pts
1. Thornton Hibs	18	12	4	2	40	15	40
2. St Andrews United	18	10	4	4	43	31	34
3. Dundonald Bluebell	18	10	3	5	28	27	33
4. Rosyth Recreation	18	9	3	6	29	24	30
5. Kirkcaldy YM	18	9	2	7	33	28	29
6. Lochore Welfare	18	6	4	10	35	34	22
7. Crossgates Primrose	18	5	5	8	22	28	20
8. Newburgh	18	4	7	7	28	35	19
9. Lochgelly Albert	18	5	2	11	34	45	17
10. Steelend Victoria	18	2	2	14	22	47	8

PEDDIE SMITH MALOCO CUP

SECOND ROUND

Kelty Hearts 3 Oakley United 1
Kirkcaldy YM 0 Hill of Beath Hawthorn
Lochgelly Albert 0 Glenrothes 4
Thornton Hibs 4 Newburgh 0

SEMI-FINALS

Hill of Beath Hawthorn 1 Kelty Hearts 2 (Kelty Hearts disquakified after protest)
Thornton Hibs 3 Glenrothes 6

THE FINAL

(Wednesday, 9th June 2004. At Rosyth)

GLENROTHES 1-0 HILL OF BEATH HAWTHORD
Grant

FIFE LEAGUE CUP

Section One: Rosyth Recreation 19 pts; Lochore Welfare 16 pts; Lochgelly Albert 13 pts; Crossgates Primrose 6 pts; Steelend Victoria 2 pts.

Section Two: Thornton Hibs 19 pts; Kirkcaldy YM 16 pts; Newburgh 10 pts; Dundonals Bluebell 10 pts; St Andrews United 2 pts.

THE FINAL

(Sunday, 29th February 2004. At Hill of Beath Hawthorn FC)

ROSYTH RECREATION 2-1 THORNTON HIBS
Ryan, Lawson Dursley

KINGDOM KEGS CUP

SECOND ROUND

Kelty Hearts 6 St Andrews United 1
Kirkcaldy YM 2 Glenrothes 4
Lochgellly Albert 1 Hill of Beath Hawthorn 9
Lochore Welfare 0 Rosyth Recreation 3

SEMI-FINALS

Hill of Beath Hawthorn 1 Kelty Hearts 3
Rosyth Recreation 0 Glenrothes 1

THE FINAL

(Sunday, 30th May 2004, At Oakley)

GLENROTHES 2-1 KELTY HEARTS
(scorers not available)

INTERBREW CUP

SECOND ROUND

Kirkcaldy YM 3 Lochore Welfare 2
rosyth Recreation 1 Oakley United 5
Kelty Hearts 1 Glenrothes 0
Thornton Hibs 1 Dundonald Bluebell 0

SEMI-FINALS

Kirkcaldy YM 2 Kelty Hearts 4
Oakley United 2 Thornton Hibs 0

THE FINAL

(Friday, 31st may 2004. At Rosyth)

OAKLEY UNITED 3-2 KELTY HEARTS
(scorers not available)

FIFE/TAYSIDE REDWOOD LEISURE CUP

THIRD ROUND

Carnoustie Panmure 2 Kelty Hearts 1 (after extra-time)
Forfar West End 1 Arbroath SC 2
Lochee united 2 Tayport 1
North End 0 Oakley United 4

SEMI-FINALS

Carnoustie panmure 2 Arbroath SC 0
Oakley United 0 Lochee United 4

THE FINAL

(Saturday, 29th May 2004. At Broughty Ferry)

LOCHEE UNITED 5-3 CARNOUSTIE PANMURE
(after extra-time)
Kiddie (3), McKinnon, Leahy — Braid, Nicol, Kelly

TAYSIDE LEAGUE

PREMIER DIVISION	P	W	D	L	F	A	Pts
1. Carnoustie Panmure	20	15	3	2	60	26	48
2. Violet	20	14	5	1	64	22	47
3. Montrose Roselea	20	11	2	7	43	33	35
4. Forfar West End	20	9	5	6	44	43	32
5. kinnoull	20	8	7	5	46	40	31
6. Scone Thistle	20	5	7	8	36	44	22
7. Arbroath SC	20	5	5	10	31	38	20
8. Broughty Athletic	20	5	3	12	26	44	18
9. Elmwood	20	4	6	10	25	44	18
10. Kirrie Thistle	20	4	5	11	28	49	17
11. Downfield	20	4	4	12	35	55	16

FIRST DIVISION	P	W	D	L	F	A	Pts
1. Blairgowrie	18	12	4	2	35	13	40
2. Lochee Harp	18	10	4	4	49	21	34
3. Jeanfield Swifts	18	9	4	5	34	26	31
4. Arbroath Victoria	18	8	6	4	40	40	30
5. Forfar Albion	18	6	8	4	25	23	26
6. Coupar Angus	18	6	7	5	43	41	25
7. Luncarty	18	7	3	8	34	29	24
8. Bankfoot Athletic	18	5	4	9	28	34	18
9. East Craigie	18	1	6	11	26	55	9
10. Brechin Victoria	18	2	2	14	14	47	8

NORTH TAYSIDE CUP

FOURTH ROUND

Glentanar 0 Arbroath SC 2
Kinnoull 0 Lochee United 5
Mosntrose Roselea 3 Broughty Athletic 2
Tayport 2 Violet 1 (after extra-time)

SEMI-FINALS

Lochee United 3 Arbroath SC 0
Montrose Roselea 0 Tayport 3

THE FINAL

(Saturday, 15th May 2004. At North End FC)
Attdendance: 786
TAYPORT 3-1 LOCHEE UNITED
Paterson, Peters King
Elliot
(after extra-time - score at 90 minutes - 1-1

DJ LAING CUP

SECTON QUALIFIERS

Section 1: Kinnoull, Forfar West End
Section 2: Montrose Roselea, Kirrie Thistle
Section 3: Elmwood, Blairgowrie
Section 4: Carnoustie Panmure, Broughty Athletic

QUARTER-FINALS

Blairgowrie 0 Forfar West End 2
Carnoustie Panmurew 2 Broughty Athletic 0
Elmwood 1 Montrose Roselea 1 (Montrose Roselea won 6-5 on penalties)
Kirrie Thistle 1 Kinnoull 2

SEMI-FINALS

Forfar West End 2 Montrose Roselea 4
Kinnoull 1 Carnoustie Panmure 2 (after extra-time)

THE FINAL

(Sunday, 9th May 2004. At Forfar Weszt End)

MONTROSDE ROSELEA 3-0 CARNOUSTIE PANMURE
Watson 2 (1 pen),
Findlater

NORTH END CHALLENGE CUP

THIRD ROUND

Arbroath SC 4 Jeanfield Swifts 1
Blairgowrie 4 Lochee Harp 1
Lochee United 2 Kinnoull 1
Montrose Roselea 1 Violet 2

SEMI-FINALS

Lochee United 4 Kinnoull 2
Violet 3 Arbroath SC 1

THE FINAL

(Saturday, 12th June 2004. At North End FC)

LOCHEE UNITED 6-3 VIOLET

Kiddie 3, Robertson	Middleston, Jones, Thompson
McKinnon, og.	

FINDLAY & CO. CUP

THIRD ROUND

Broughty Athletic 1 Lochee United 0

Carnoustie Pa`nmure 0 North End 1

Forfar West End 4 Lochee Harp 1

Tayport 4 Downfield 0

SEMI-FINALS

Broughty Athletic 0 North End 3

forfar West End 1 Tayport 0

THE FINAL

(Wednesday, 19th June 2004. At Coupar Angus FC)

NORTH END 1-2 FORFAR WEST END

Laing Stewart, Valentine

RED HOUSE HOTEL CUP

FIRST ROUND

Coupar Angus 1 Forfar Albion 2
Lochee Harp 4 Brechin Victoria 0

SECOND ROUND

Blairgowrie 3 Luncarty 2
Forfar Albion 4 East Craigie 4 (East Craigie won 6-5 on penaties)
Jeanfield Swifts 0 Bankfoot Athletic 1 (after extra-time)
Lochee Harp 4 Arbroath Victoria 2

SMI-FINALS

Bankfoot Athletic 2 Lochee Harp 1
Blairgowrie 3 East Craigie 0

THE FINAL

(Tuesday, 1st June 2004. At Coupaqr Angus FC)

BLAIRGOWRIE 1-0 BANKFOOT ATHLETIC
Brash pen

NORTH REGION

PREMIER DIVISION	P	W	D	L	F	A	Pts
1. Culter	26	17	5	4	68	25	56
2. Sunnybank	26	16	5	5	60	33	44
3. Glentanar	26	13	5	8	61	41	44
4. Stonehaven	26	13	5	8	48	45	44
5. Turriff United	26	12	6	8	46	34	42
6. Banks o'Dee	26	11	7	8	56	48	40
7. Formartine United	26	11	5	10	48	43	38
8. Hermes	26	8	9	9	49	51	32
9. Wilsons XI	26	8	8	9	30	41	30
10. Longside	26	8	9	11	41	54	27
11. East End	26	7	5	14	40	49	26
12. FC Stoneywood	26	7	2	17	38	63	26
13. Cruden Bay	26	6	5	15	29	68	23
14. Lads Club	26	6	5	15	29	69	23

NB: 1. Sunnybank deducted 9 pts

2. Wilsons XI deducted 3 pts

3. FC Stoneywood awearded 3 pts

FIRST DIVISION (leading five clubs)	P	W	D	L	F	A	Pts
1. Maud	26	18	1	7	71	40	53
2. Ellon United	26	16	5	5	79	29	53
3. Deveronside	26	16	4	6	68	38	52
4. Hall Russell United	26	16	4	6	63	40	50
5. Fraserburgh United	26	13	5	8	51	46	44

Other positions: Banchory ST Ternan (42 pts); Parkvale (41 pts); Buchanhaven Hearts (41 pts); Buckie Rovers (37 pts); Dyce (36 ts); Lewis United (25 pts); Burghead Thistle (20 pts); Dufftown (18 ots); Whitehills (1 pt).

SECOND DIVISION (leading four clubs)	P	W	D	L	F	A	Pts
1. Slavale	18	15	2	1	58	17	47
2. Strathspey Thistle	18	14	1	3	67	25	40
3. Forres Thistle	18	9	6	3	46	26	33
4. New Elgin	18	9	5	4	38	34	32

Other positions: Lossiemouth United (30 pts); Nairn St Ninian (25 pts); Fochabers (23 pts); RAF Lossiemouth (11 pts); Bishopmill United (6pts); Kinloss (5pts).

GRILL CUP

(nine clubs qualified from section stages)

PLAY-OFF:

Strathspey Thistle 4 Nairn St Ninian 1 (played at Burghead)

QUARTER-FINALS

Buchanhaven Hearts w/o Strathspey Thistle
(losers failed to field a team and were disqualified)
Culter 0 Glentanar 1
Hermes 2 maud 1
Stonehaven 3 Longside 3 (Longside won 6-5 on penalties)

SEMI-FINALS

Glentanar 2 Longside 0
Hermes 3 Buchanhaven Hearts 0

THE FINAL

(Sunday, 2nd November 2003. At Heathryfold Park, Sunnybank)
GLENTANAR 0-0 HERMES
(after extra-time. Hermes won 4-3 on penalties)

ROLLSTUD REGIONAL CUP

THIRD ROUND

Deveronside 3 maud 2
East End 7 Parkvale 1)
Hermes 2 Culter 2
(Hermes won 4-3 on penalties)
Stonehaven 1 Glentanar 0

SEMI-FINALS

East End 1 Deveronside 0
Stonehaven 2 Hermes 3

THE FINAL

(Tuesday, 11th May 2004. At Pittodrie Park, Aberdeen)
HERMES 2-1 EAST END
Yates, Laing McAllister

ACORN HEATING CUP

SECOND ROUND

Formartine United 4 Longside 3
Sunnybank 4 Stonehaven 3
Turriff United 3 Lads Club 2
Wilsons XI 1 Glentanar 2

SEMI-FINALS

Glentanar 1 Turriff United 0
Sunnybank 0 Formartine United 3

THE FINAL

(Friday, 28th Mayn2004. At Hermes FC)
GLENTANAR 2-1 FORMARTINE UNITED
A Campbell Batty
Robb

MORRISON TROPHY

SECOND ROUND

Buchanhaven Hearts 1 Banchory St Ternan 1

(Banchory St Ternan won 4-2 on penaties)

Deveronside 1 Frasedrburgh United 5

Ellon United 2 Burghead Thistle 1

Maud £ Parkvale 0

SEMI-FINALS

Banchory St Ternan 3 Maud 2

Ellon Nuited 0 Fraserburgh United 1 (after extra-time)

THE FINAL

(Friday, 21st May 2004. At Dyce)

FRASERBURGH UNITED 2-1 BANCHORY ST TERNAN

Buchan, Allan Bruce

GORDON WILLIAMSON CUP

SECOND ROUND (TWO LEGS)

Fochabers v New Elgin (2-1 & 0-2 = 2-3)

Lossie United 6 Bishopmill United 6

(second leg not played as Bishopmill United disqualified for fielding an ineligible player)

Nairn St Ninian v Islavale (0-3 & 2-3 = 2-6)

RAFLossiemouth v Forres Thistle (1-1 & 2-3 = 3-4)

SEMI-FINALS

Forres Thistle v New Elgin (1-2 & 1-1 = 2-3)

Lossie United v Islavale (3-3 & 4-3 = 7-6)

THE FINAL

(Friday, 7th May 2004. at Mosset Park, Forres)

LOSSIEMOUTH UNITED 0-2 NEW ELGIN

Ellis, Henderson og

ISLE OF MAN FOOTBALL LEAGUE

ST GEORGE'S emerged as the dominant force in Manx football last season after clinching the OSA Division One championship for the first time since 1995.

The title victory completed a remarkable turnaround for the Glencrutchery Road club who narrowly avoided relegation just two years earlier.

Under the guidance of Chris Bass senior and Steve Falconer, St George's swept to the top of the table in impressive fashion.

They won 18 and drew three of their 24 league fixtures to finish nine points clear of their nearest rivals.

Geordies also boasted the most prolific attack (100 goals scored) and meanest defence (29 conceded) to underline their strength in depth.

Team success was matched on an individual level as Chris Bass junior collected the Footballer of the Year award after a string of outstanding performances.

Laxey lacked the consistency to mount a serious challenge in the league, but highlighted their huge potential by clinching both Cups.

The Glen Road club triumphed 3-2 in the Railway Cup Final against St Mary's on Boxing Day in one of the best matches of the season. And they completed a memorable double by defeating Castletown to lift the Hospital Cup in May.

Ramsey also experienced a season to remember after clinching the FA Cup — with Castletown again the beaten finalists — and escaping relegation by the narrowest of margins.

In fact the battle for top-flight survival went down to the wire with Corinthians losing out by just one goal at the end of a dramatic evening.

Gymns' fate had been sealed long before the final weeks of the season as they managed just two wins from 24 league outings.

CFS Division Two also witnessed a remarkable finish with Pulrose United — led by Player of the Year Kevin Cain — capturing the second promotion spot after St John's failed to overcome Foxdale in their final match.

Douglas Royal scooped the second division championship and emulated the feat of St George's as their unbeaten combination team also finished top of the pile.

Royal lost out to Braddan in the final of the Gold Cup, while Michael United scooped their first item of silverware for many years by lifting the Woods Cup following a penalty shoot-out victory over the Police. Stephen Parry

OSA DIVISION ONE

	P	W	D	L	F	A	Gd	Pts
St George's	24	18	3	3	100	29	71	57
Marown	24	16	0	8	47	42	5	48
St Mary's	24	15	2	7	78	47	31	47
Laxey	24	14	4	6	69	36	33	46
Peel	24	12	6	6	57	37	20	42
Rushen	24	11	3	10	40	46	-6	36
Ayre	24	10	4	10	67	57	10	34
Castletown	24	9	3	12	45	45	0	30
DHSOB	24	6	7	11	45	68	-23	25
Colby	24	5	7	12	37	67	-30	22
Ramsey	24	5	6	13	31	53	-22	21
Corinthians	24	6	3	15	48	71	-23	21
Gymns	24	2	6	16	31	97	-66	12

CFS DIVISION TWO

	P	W	D	L	F	A	Gd	Pts
Douglas Royal	26	21	3	2	128	39	89	66
Pulrose	26	20	3	3	98	22	76	63
St John's	26	20	2	4	125	34	91	62
Braddan	26	17	3	6	86	40	46	54
Michael	26	16	4	6	84	49	35	52
Union Mills	26	13	3	10	83	46	37	42
Foxdale	26	13	3	10	77	61	16	42
Police	26	11	4	11	71	73	-2	37
RYCOB	26	10	3	13	65	66	-1	33
Ronaldsway	26	8	2	16	60	98	-38	26
Doug & Dist	26	6	5	15	63	89	-26	23
Onchan	26	6	3	17	44	90	-46	21
Jurby	26	0	2	24	20	165	-145	2
Malew*	26	0	2	24	12	144	-132	-1

* points deducted

ROLL OF HONOUR 2003/2004

OSA Division One .... St George's
CFS Division Two..... Douglas Royal
FA Cup.................. Ramsey
Hospital Cup .... Laxey
Railway Cup .... Laxey
Gold Cup................ Braddan
Woods Cup................ Michael

GUERNSEY F.A.

Email: matt.fallaize@guernseyfa.com
Corbet Field, grand Fort Road, St Sampson's GY2 4DT

Secretary: Matt Fallaize

Other executives: **President:** Dave Dorey **Chairman:** n/a

Chief Executive: N/A **Development Officer:** Unavailable at time of going to press

Coaching: **Discipline:** Secretary **Registration:** Secretary **Referees:** Graham Skuse

Grants: Secretary **Courses:** Secretary **Womens:** Secretary **Press&PR:** Secretary

Number of Affiliated Clubs Senior: 10 Junior: 7 Womens: 5

County Representative Teams (Senior Coach responsible): (Steve Ogier)

Inter County Competitions: South West Counties Championship (Senior, U18), FA County Youth Cup

Trophies won in season 2003-04: Island Games Gold medal 2003. Victory Cup. u21 Muratti.

GUERNSEY FOOTBALL SEASON 2003-04

In a memorable finish to the Priaulx League season, St Martin's won the championship thanks to a 1-0 win away to title-rivals North on the final day of the campaign. It had been 19 years since Saints had lifted the Priaulx Cup and this success was a testament to the work of coaching duo Colin Renouf and Colin Fallaize.

Both had been St Martin's legends during their playing days and when the club's president Henry Davey had announced their appointment in the summer of 2003, he called them the 'dream team' - how prophetic he was. But even he and the two Colins had not expected this triumph to come so early into their tenure, despite their excellent reputation and knowledge of the game. (Renouf had begun the revolution at Sylvans in the 1990s when the club went on to win nine consecutive championships and Fallaize had just led Guernsey to gold at the 2003 NatWest Island Games.)

Yet for so much of the season, the title had looked like it was there for North to lose. Geoff Tardif's young side was undoubtedly the most entertaining in the Priaulx League throughout the season and when Jon Veron scored the only goal against Saints at Blanche Pierre Lane in early February, the chocolate-and-blue ribbons were being taken out of the drawer, ready to be tied to the trophy. Three more league victories followed and that left the Northerners needing just a point against neighbours and defending champions Vale Rec to guarantee at least a play-off for the title. But Rec, who were still playing for a Wheway Cup spot that they later secured, were in no mood to let their local rivals win the Priaulx League on their own patch and Marc Rihoy's goal separated the sides in a match played in a mud bath.

Meanwhile, Saints, who had several games in hand, were quietly closing the gap on the leaders and they put together a run of six successive wins to ensure a winner-takes-all clash at Northfield where they were the in form side. They duly took their victory tally to seven in a row thanks to a splendid goal from defender Etienne Ogier and the celebrations could begin.

The Guernsey champions would later become Channel Islands champions as some typically stout defence kept the prolific Jersey Scottish at bay for 120 minutes at Foote's Lane and Saints won the Upton Park Cup in the penalty shoot-out. The St Martin's trophy cabinet also housed the season's Stranger Cup.

There was some consolation for North who won both the Jeremie and Wheway Cups while their young stars Veron and Dave Rihoy were named as Players' Player of the Year and Priaulx Player of the Year respectively.

Guernsey's senior island team was under the charge of Steve Ogier for the first time and there was an improvement in the South West Counties Championship results as the Sarnians beat Gloucestershire, drew with Wiltshire and the Royal Navy and only lost to the very impressive Devon. However, there was a hugely disappointing display in the Muratti Vase final at Springfield when Jersey overcame the visitors comfortably.

In council chambers, Dave Dorey returned to the executive committee as president of the GFA, replacing Alec Le Noury who stepped down after 19 years in the post. Mr Le Noury was made Honorary Life President for his services.

The season, though, ended on a sad note with the passing of local football stalwart Nigel Gavey, aged 49. Nigel fulfilled almost every role imaginable in football during his life from player to coach and even part-time correspondent for the Guernsey Press. He will be greatly missed.

PRIAULX LEAGUE

(1st Team)	P	W	D	L	F	A	Pts
1 St Martin's	24	17	2	5	49	21	53
2 North	24	16	4	4	59	22	52
3 Vale Rec	24	12	3	9	39	37	39
4 Sylvans	24	11	4	9	48	41	37
5 Belgraves	24	7	6	11	49	50	27
6 Rovers	24	7	2	15	38	58	23
7 Rangers	24	3	1	20	22	75	10

League winners:

Priaulx League: St Martin's

Jackson League: Northerners

Railway League: Northerners

Youth One League: Northerners

Youth Two League: Belgrave Wanderers

Youth Three League: Northerners

Women's League: Sylvans

JERSEY F.A.

Tel: 01534 500165 Email: secretary@jerseyfa.com. gill.morgan@jerseyfa.com
Springfield Stadium, St Helier, Jersey JE2 4LF.

Secretary: Gill Morgan

Other executives: **President:** C Tostevin **Chairman:** M Jouanny

Chief Executive: N/A **Development Officer:** Brian Oliver

Coaching: Brian Oliver **Discipline:** J Gasston **Registration:** **Referees:** P Daniel

Grants: **Courses:** **Womens:** **Press&PR:**

Number of Affiliated Clubs Senior: 20 Junior: 55 teams Womens:8 teams

County Representative Teams (Senior Coach responsible)**:** Senior/u21/u18/u16/Sen.Ladies. Yr 7,8&9 boys & girls

Inter County Competitions: South West Counties Championship (Senior men). FA County Youth Cup.

Trophies won in season 2003-04: Senior Muratti. Ladies Muratti. u18 Muratti.

CUP FINALS

Muratti
Jersey 3-0 Guernsey

Under-21 Muratti (Ambassadeur Bowl)
Guernsey 2-1 Jersey

Under-18 Muratti
Guernsey 0-1 Jersey

Under-15 Star Trophy
Jersey 0-4 Guernsey

Women's Muratti
Jersey 4-1 Guernsey

Upton Park Trophy
St Martin's 0-0 Jersey Scottish
(St Martin's won 4-2 on pens)

Junior Under-18 Upton (Portsmouth Trophy)
First Tower United 3-1 Northerners

Under-16 Upton (John Leatt Memorial Trophy)
Belgrave Wanderers 1-3 St Paul's

FLYBE COMBINATION

DIVISION ONE

		P	W	D	L	F	A	Pts
1	Jersey Scottish	18	16	0	2	112	12	48
2	Trinity	18	14	3	1	65	15	45
3	Jsy Wanderers	18	9	6	3	50	52	33
4	St Paul's	18	7	6	5	48	25	27
5	Portuguese	18	8	3	7	45	31	27
6	First Tower	18	7	1	10	37	26	23
7	Magpies	18	7	1	10	24	44	22
8	St Peter	18	6	2	10	26	48	20
9	Rozel Rovers	18	3	3	12	19	42	12
10	Sp Academics	18	0	0	18	21	152	0

DIVISION TWO

		P	W	D	L	F	A	Pts
1	Grouville	18	14	3	1	69	15	45
2	St Ouen	18	14	2	2	61	35	44
3	St Clement	18	10	3	5	42	33	33
4	St Brelade	18	9	2	7	45	26	29
5	St John	18	7	4	7	44	34	25
6	Beeches OB	18	6	5	7	35	38	23
7	St Lawrence	18	5	4	9	35	52	19
8	Jsy Nomads	18	5	2	11	26	50	17
9	Sporting Club	18	2	4	12	17	39	10
10	St Martin	18	2	3	13	25	77	9

JERSEY CUP FINAL

Trinity Shield — St. Saviour 7 3 St. Clement

AMATEUR FOOTBALL ALLIANCE

President: D M Whitehall
Company Secretary: Mike Brown, 55 Islington Park Street, London N1 1QB
Tel: 020 7359 3493 Fax: 020 7359 5027
Website: www.amateur-fa.org Email: secretary@amateur-fa.com

AFA SENIOR CUP

Sponsored by Ladbrokes

1ST ROUND PROPER
Old Meadonians 6 Old Whitgiftians 0
Parkfield w/o Old Malvernians w/d
Hon. Artillery Company 2 Crouch End Vampires 1
Old Esthameians 1 U C L Academicals 2
Old Tenisonians 1 Old Finchleians 6
West Wickham 6 Southgate Olympic 0
Old Vaughanians 4 Cardinal Manning Old Boys 2
Old Lyonians 0 Nottsborough 2
Old Salesians 6 Old Salopians 4
Old Wokingians 6 Rugby Clubs 0
Old Woodhouseians 6 Wood Green Old Boys 0
Lensbury 8 Ealing Association 2
Shene Old Grammarians 0 Merton 2
Bank of England 3 Barclays Bank 0
Old Kingsburians 0 Southgate County 3
Carshalton 6 Old Dorkinian 1
Duncombe Sports 4 Kings Old Boys 1
Old Suttonians 3 Old Danes 2
Queen Mary College Old Boys 0 Winchmore Hill 5
University of Hertfordshire 0 Alleyn Old Boys 5
Civil Service 2 Albanian 1
Old Foresters 2 HSBC 1
Old Stationers 4 Old Westminster Citizens 2
Latymer Old Boys 1 E. Barnet Old Grammarians 0
National Westminster Bank 0 Old Actonians Assn. 6
Old Meadonians 2 Old Elizabethans 0
Old Aloysians 3 Old Bromleians 1
Polytechnic 5 Old Buckwellians 1
Old Salvatorians 2 Kew Association 1
Old Owens 4 Old Bealonians 2
Nottsborough 7 Old Westminsters 1

2ND ROUND PROPER
Old Meadonians 1 Old Grammarians 0
Norsemen 1 Hon. Artillery Company 2
U C L Academicals 3 Old Finchleians 1
West Wickham 1* Old Vaughanians 3*
Nottsborough 0 Old Salesians 2
Old Wokingians 3 Old Woodhouseians 2
Lensbury 6 Merton 0
Bank of England 2 Southgate County 3
Carshalton 5 Duncombe Sports 2
Old Suttonians 2 Winchmore Hill 0
Alleyn Old Boys 1 Civil Service 3
Old Foresters 1 Old Stationers 0
Latymer Old Boys 0 Old Actonians Assn 2
Old Meadonians 2 Old Aloysians 1
Polytechnic 6 Old Salvatorians 1
Nottsborough 2 West Wickham 0

3RD ROUND PROPER
Old Esthameians 0 Broomfield 2
Old Meadonians 5 Wake Green 0
Old Owens 0 Civil Service 5
Old Parkonians 1* UCL Academicals 3*
Alleyn Old Boys 6 Old Camdenians 3
Hale End Athletic 1 Albanian 3
Winchmore Hill 1*:4p Polytechnic 1*:3p
Old Salesians 0 Nottsborough 1

4TH ROUND PROPER
Broomfield 2 Old Meadonians 7
Civil Service 1 UCL Academicals 2
Alleyn Old Boys 1 Albanian 0
Winchmore Hill 1 Nottsborough 2

SEMI-FINALS
Old Meadonians 7 UCL Academicals 1
Alleyn Old Boys 2 Nottsborough 4

FINAL
Old Meadonians 3 Nottsborough 0

OTHER CUP FINALS

Essex Senior
Old Parkonians 2 Hale End Athletic 4
Middlesex Senior
Polytechnic 2 Old Lyonian 1
Buckwllians Res 5
Surrey Senior
Old Salesians 2 Kew Association 1
Intermediate
Old Meadonians Res 2*:2p Mt Pleasant PO 1st 2*:3p
Junior
UCL Academicals 3rd 1*:4p Alexandra Park 3rd 1*:3p
Minor
Old Esthameians 4th 2 Albanian 4th 1
Veterans
Old Parmitarians A 5 William Fitt A 2
Open Veterans
William Fitt A 5 Winchmore Hill A 5

Greenland
Winchmore Hill 2 Old Hamptonians 1
Essex Intermediate
Davenant Wanderers O B 1st 1 Old
Kent Intermediate
West Wickham Res 0 Old Addeyans 1st 2
Middlesex Intermediate
Old Vaughanians Res 1 Alexandra Park Res 2
Surrey Intermediate
Royal Sun Alliance 1st 0 Old Thorntonians 1st 2
Senior Novets
O. Tiffinians 5th 0 Old Camdenians 4th 5
Intermediate Novets
Old Finchleians 6th 2 Old Actonians Assn 6th 0
Junior Novets
Old Finchleians 7th 2 Old Salvatorians 7th 3

YOUTH

SATURDAY
U-18
Deportivo Youth London 3 Devas 0
U-17
ParkView Rangers 1 Bethwin SE "B" 0
U-16
Santley United 3*:4p Providence House 3*:5p
U-15
Santley United 5 Enfield Youth 4
2*:1p
U-14
Bethwin SE "A" 0 Blue Diamonds 12
U-13
Bec United 2 Providence House 1
U-12
Santley United 2 Develop 5
U-11
West Essex Colts 0 Future Stars 1

SUNDAY
U-17
Old Finchleians 3 Cheshunt 1
U-16
Young Parmiterians "A" 0 Potters Bar United "A" 3
U-15
Prohawks 2*:3p Southgate Olympic
U-14
Old Bealonians 3 Chase Side 6
U-13
Winchmore Hill 3 Minchenden 4
U-12
Leyton 1 Develop 8
U-11
Whitewebb Eagles "A" 4 Whitewebb Eagles "B" 2

AMATEUR FOOTBALL COMBINATION

PREMIER DIVISION	P	W	D	L	F	A	Pts
Old Meadonians	20	18	1	1	67	19	55
Old Hamptonians	20	14	3	3	49	36	45
UCL Academicals	20	11	4	5	50	43	37
Old Wilsonians	20	10	2	8	33	31	32
Old Aloysians	20	9	3	8	50	37	30
Albanian	20	8	4	8	44	40	28
Hale End Athletic	20	6	4	10	44	53	22
Old Danes	20	6	1	13	26	41	19
Latymer Old Boys	20	5	3	12	36	55	18
Old Salvatorians	20	4	3	13	29	44	15
Old Ignatians	20	3	4	13	24	53	13

SENIOR DIVISION ONE	P	W	D	L	F	A	Pts
Parkfield	16	11	4	1	38	11	37
Old Wokingians	16	9	3	4	23	18	30
Old Isleworthians	16	8	3	5	24	24	27
Old Tenisonians	16	7	3	6	20	21	24
Old Bealonians	16	6	4	6	30	23	22
Honourable Artillery Company	16	4	7	5	24	26	19
Southgate County	16	4	4	8	21	33	16
Old Tiffinians	16	2	6	8	19	27	12
Old Vaughanians	16	2	4	10	19	35	10

SENIOR DIVISION TWO	P	W	D	L	F	A	Pts
Glyn Old Boys	16	13	3	0	46	7	42
Enfield Old Grammarians	16	10	3	3	34	12	33
Old Suttonians	16	7	4	5	28	23	25
Economicals	16	6	5	5	31	30	23
Old Grammarians	16	4	7	5	33	30	19
Old Buckwellians	16	5	4	7	23	27	19
Old\Dorkinians	16	5	3	8	28	33	18
Old Manorians	16	4	5	7	24	31	17
Shene Old Grammarians	16	1	0	15	17	71	3

SENIOR DIVISION THREE	P	W	D	L	F	A	Pts
Wood Green Old Boys	18	12	1	5	56	37	37
Pegasus	18	11	3	4	41	25	36
Queen Mary College Old Boys	18	10	5	3	36	25	35
Old Reigatians	18	10	3	5	39	25	33
University of Hertfordshire	18	8	4	6	46	35	28
John Fisher Old Boys	18	6	2	10	39	52	20
Old Vaughians Res	18	5	4	9	39	49	19
Old Woodhouseians	18	5	3	10	42	53	18
King's Old Boys	18	5	3	10	26	39	18
Old Minchendenians	18	3	2	13	29	53	11

SENIOR DIVISION FOUR	P	W	D	L	F	A	Pts
Old Challoners	16	14	0	2	50	18	42
Old Sedcopians	16	12	2	2	59	24	38
Clapham Old Xaverians	16	11	1	4	50	20	34
Parkfield Res	16	7	2	7	34	35	23
Centymca	16	6	3	7	30	35	21
Old Hamptonians Res	16	5	3	8	18	34	18
Old Wilsonians Res	16	5	2	9	31	42	17
Brent	16	2	2	12	17	44	8
Latymer Old Boys Res	16	2	1	13	17	54	4

OTHER DIVISIONS

INTERMEDIATE DIVISIONS:

	Teams:	Won by:
North	11	UCL Academicals Res
South	12	Mickleham Old
Boxhillians		
REGIONAL:		
North:		
Division 1	10	UCL Academicals 3rd
Division 2	10	Enfield Old
Grammarians Res		
Division 3	10	Albanian 4th
Division 4	10	Egbertian 3rd
Division 5	9	Old Aloysians 5th
Division 6	10	UCL Academicals 5th
Division 7	10	Wood Green Old Boys
4th		
Division 8	9	Old Minchendenians 5th
Division 9	10	Old Minchendenians 6th
South:		
Division 1	10	Wandsworth Borough
Division 2	10	Old Rutlishians
Division 3	10	Clapham Old Xaverians
Res		
Division 4	10	Clapham Old Xaverians
3rd		
Division 5	10	Old Bromleians Res
Division 6	10	Centymca 3rd
Division 7	10	Old Tenisonians 4th
Division 8	9	Clapham Old Xaverians
5th		
Division 9	10	Old Tiffinians 5th
Division 10	10	Old Wokingians 7th
Division 11	11	Old Wokingians 8th
West:		
Division 1	10	Old Meadonians Res
Division 2	11	Old Salvatorians 4th
Division 3	10	Old Uxonians Res
Division 4	9	Parkfield 5th
Division 5	10	Phoenix Old Boys 3rd
Division 6	8	Old Salvatorians 7th
Division 7	8	Brent 3rd

ARTHUR DUNN CUP
Old Salopians 3 Old Brentwoods 0

ARTHURIAN LEAGUE

PREMIER DIVISION	P	W	D	L	F	A	Pts
Old Harrovians	18	12	3	3	63	35	39
Lancing Old Boys	18	10	3	5	31	19	33
Old Carthusians	18	9	2	7	40	37	29
Old Foresters	18	8	3	7	37	29	27
Old Etonians	18	8	3	7	39	32	27
Old Brentwoods	18	8	3	7	36	31	27
Old Westminsters	18	8	3	7	42	43	27
Old Salopians	18	7	2	9	37	48	23
Old Cholmeleians	18	3	4	11	40	57	13
Old Bradfieldian	18	4	0	14	23	57	9*

DIVISION 1	P	W	D	L	F	A	Pts
Old Reptonians	14	9	1	4	43	20	28
Old Wykehamists	14	8	4	2	36	20	28
Old Chigwellians	14	6	6	2	28	23	24
Old Malvernians	14	5	5	4	28	33	20
Old Aldenhamians	14	5	4	5	23	27	19
Old Haberdashers	14	4	4	6	28	36	16
Old Witleians	14	4	0	10	19	30	12
Old Tonbridgians	14	2	2	10	19	35	8

DIVISION 2	P	W	D	L	F	A	Pts
Old Etonians Res	14	11	1	2	36	11	34
Old Chigwellians Res	14	10	0	4	34	18	30
Old Carthusians 3rd	14	6	4	4	28	29	22
Old Carthusians Res	14	6	1	7	21	23	19
Old Salopians Res	14	6	1	7	23	29	16*
Old Foresters Res	14	4	3	7	27	30	15
Old Cholmeleians Res	14	4	2	8	31	36	14
Lancing Old Boys Res	14	2	2	10	16	40	8

DIVISION 3	P	W	D	L	F	A	Pts
Old Westminsters Res	14	12	1	1	54	14	37
Old Haileyburians	14	11	1	2	50	17	34
Old Etonians 3rd	14	8	2	4	26	23	26
Old Brentwoods Res	14	7	3	4	52	31	24
Old Foresters 3rd	14	3	2	9	18	32	11
Old Malvernians Res	14	5	0	9	23	45	9*
Old Bradfieldians Res	14	1	4	9	20	41	7
Old Cholmeleians 3rd	14	2	1	11	19	59	4*

* - Points deducted, breach of rule

	Teams:	Won by:
DIVISION 4	8	Old Bradfieldians 3rd
DIVISION 5	6	Old Chigwellians 3rd

JUNIOR LEAGUE CUP

Old Carthusians 3rd 3*:5p Old Chigwellians 3*:4p

DERRIK MOORE VETERANS' CUP

Old Carthusians 2* Old Cholmeleians 1*

JIM DIXSON SIX-A-SIDE CUP Won by Old Cholmeleians

LONDON FINANCIAL FOOTBALL ASSOCIATION

DIVISION 1	P	W	D	L	F	A	Pts
Dresdner Klein Wasserstein	14	11	1	2	44	13	34
Granby	14	8	3	3	32	22	27
Mount Pleasant Post Office	14	7	6	1	37	16	26*
Royal Sun Alliance	14	7	3	4	37	25	24
Churchill Insurance	14	5	2	7	36	39	17
Marsh	14	4	3	7	28	39	15
Bank of America	14	2	3	9	20	51	8*
J P Morgan	14	0	3	11	8	37	2*

National Westminster BankWithdrawn - record expunged

DIVISION 2	P	W	D	L	F	A	Pts
Citigroup Res	16	13	3	0	52	17	42
Citigroup	16	10	2	4	46	26	32
Marsh 3rd	16	9	2	5	47	35	29
Granby Res	16	7	4	5	35	30	25
Coutts & Co	16	8	0	8	37	41	19*
Marsh Res	16	4	4	8	26	39	16
Fusion Allstars	16	4	3	9	35	51	15
Royal Sun Alliance Res	16	3	2	11	27	52	11
City Group CIB	16	2	4	10	19	33	10

DIVISION 3	P	W	D	L	F	A	Pts
Royal Sun Alliance 3rd	18	12	4	2	47	22	40
National Westminster Bank Res	18	8	5	5	46	28	28*
National Westminster Bank 3rd	18	8	3	7	42	31	27
Royal Bank of Scotland	18	7	3	8	21	32	24
Granby 3rd	18	6	4	8	31	41	22
Temple Bar	18	4	7	7	30	40	19
Credit Suisse First Boston	18	4	2	12	19	42	14

DIVISION 4	P	W	D	L	F	A	Pts
Zurich Eagle Star	18	16	1	1	74	23	49
National Westminster Bank 4th	18	11	3	4	49	32	36
South Bank Cuaco 6th	18	7	5	6	52	29	26
Royal Bank of Scotland Res	18	6	4	8	35	51	22
Marsh 4th	18	5	4	9	30	48	19
Foreigh & Commonwealth Office	18	3	6	9	33	53	15
Temple Bar Res	18	3	1	14	29	66	10

* - Points deducted - breach of rules

Challenge Cup

Bank of England 6 Granby 1

Senior Cup

Dresdner Klein Wasserstein 4 Mount Pleasant P O. 0

Junior Cup

Royal Sun Alliance 3rd 1 Zurich Eagle Star 1st 0

LONDON LEGAL LEAGUE

DIVISION I	P	W	D	L	F	A	Pts
KPMG ICE	16	12	1	3	45	21	37
Slaughter & May	16	10	4	2	34	19	34
Watson Farley & Williams	16	9	1	6	26	17	28
Baker & McKenzie	16	9	0	7	45	35	27
Linklaters & Alliance	16	8	2	6	28	25	26
Clifford Chance	16	6	2	8	33	29	20
Simmons & Simmons	16	4	3	9	18	43	15
Gray's Inn	16	5	1	10	16	22	14*
Eversheds	16	2	0	14	14	48	4*

Denton Wilde Sapte (A) - record expunged, programme not completed

DIVISION II	P	W	D	L	F	A	Pts
Richards Butler	18	11	3	4	51	23	36
Titmuss Sainer Dechert	18	11	3	4	47	30	36
Freshfields Bruckhaus Deringer	18	11	2	5	42	24	35
Norton Rose	18	11	2	5	41	36	35
CMS Cameron McKenna	18	8	5	5	50	31	29
Macfarlanes	18	6	3	9	22	44	21
Ashurst Morris Crisp	18	6	3	9	36	31	18*
Allen & Overy	18	5	3	10	25	40	18
Barlow Lyde & Gilbert	18	4	2	12	36	60	14
Lovells	18	2	4	12	23	54	10

DIVISION III	P	W	D	L	F	A	Pts
Mishcon de Reya	16	13	0	3	55	19	39
Financial Services A	16	12	2	2	49	12	38
Stephenson Harwood	16	12	0	4	61	16	36
Herbert Smith	16	10	1	5	34	27	31
Denton Wilde Sapte (B)	16	6	2	8	28	40	20
Hammonds Suddards Edge	16	6	1	9	19	14	16*
Pegasus (Inner Temple)	16	4	4	8	26	38	16
Farrer & Co	16	3	2	11	18	67	11
Taylor Wessing	16	0	0	16	14	71	-2*

S J Berwin - Record expunged

* - Points deducted, breach of rule

LEAGUE CHALLENGE CUP

Watson Farley Williams 2 Linklaters 3 (aet)

WEAVERS ARMS CUP

Mishcon de Reya 0 Clifford Chance 4

INVITATION CUP

Herbert Smith 8 Farrar & Co 0

LONDON OLD BOYS CUP

Senior
Albanian 2* UCL Academicals 1*

Challenge
Old Paulines 2* Old Rutlishians 1*

Intermediate
Old Meadonians Res 0*:5p UCL Academicals Res 0*:4p

Junior
UCL Academicals 3rd 4 Old Wilsonians 3rd 1

Minor
Old Actonians Assn 5th 2 Albanian 4th 0

Drummond (N) ~
Old\Camdenians 4th 4 Old Chigwellians 4th 1

Nemean (W) ~
Old Kolsassians 4 Old Uffingtonians Res 3

Olympian (S) ~
Old Tiffinians 5th 4 Old Paulines 3rd 2
(~Entries now drawn regionally from former composition of the Drummond, Nemean and Novets competitions)

Jack Perry Veterans
Old Aloysians 2* Old Meadonians 4*

OLD BOYS' CUP

Senior
Old Owens 2 Alleyn Old Boys 0

Junior
Old Owens Res 1 Old Salesians Res 0

Minor
Old Finchleians 3rd 4 Old Bealonians 3rd 2

Fourth XI
Old Finchleians 4th 1 Old Westminster Citizens 4th 0

Fifth XI
Old Minchendenians 5th 3 Old Stationers 5th 0

Sixth XI
Glyn Old Boys 6th 3 Old Tenisonians 6th 0

Seventh XI
Old Finchleians 7th 1 Old Parmiterians 7th 0

Veterans
Glyn Old Boys 2*:5p Old Finchleians 2*:4p

MIDLAND AMATEUR ALLIANCE

PREMIER DIVISION	P	W	D	L	F	A	Pts
Caribbean Cavaliers	26	21	3	2	107	36	66
Radcliffe Olympic 3rd	26	19	3	4	85	45	60
Beeston Old Boys Assn	26	15	4	7	62	44	49
Derbyshire Amateurs Res	26	14	2	10	72	65	44
Underwood Villa	26	12	6	8	74	60	42
Lady Bay	26	12	2	12	70	80	38
Nottingham Trent University	26	10	5	11	71	69	35
Old Elizabethans	26	9	6	11	71	74	33
Ashland Rovers	26	9	5	12	60	84	32
Kirkby Autocentre	26	9	4	13	51	54	31
Sherwood Forest	26	9	3	14	49	69	30
Squareform Stealers	26	7	3	16	57	69	24
Bassingfield	26	6	4	16	46	80	22
Old Bemrosians	26	3	4	19	37	83	13

DIVISION 1	P	W	D	L	F	A	Pts
Wollaton 3rd	22	18	2	2	84	31	56
Southwell Amateurs	22	15	3	4	60	32	48
Brunts Old Boys	22	14	3	5	57	42	45
Nottinghamshire Res	22	11	5	6	59	41	38
Racing Athletic	22	9	5	8	52	45	32
West Bridgford United	22	9	1	12	45	57	28
County Nalgo	22	8	3	11	47	63	27
Radcliffe Olympic 4th	22	7	5	10	57	61	26
Old Elizabethans Res	22	7	2	13	53	58	23
Kirkby Autocentre Res	22	5	7	10	42	59	22
Woodburgh United	22	4	4	14	46	69	16
Clinphone	22	4	2	16	34	78	14

DIVISION 2	P	W	D	L	F	A	Pts
Keyworth United 3rd	24	21	2	1	94	17	65
Caribbean Cavaliers Res	24	21	1	2	107	25	64
Hickling	24	15	2	7	96	46	47
Old Bemrosians Res	24	12	5	7	70	55	41
Nottinghamshire 3rd	24	12	1	11	43	34	37
Beeston Old Boys Assn Res	24	11	4	9	37	43	37
Bobbers Mill	24	11	1	12	49	65	34
Wollaton 4th	24	9	4	11	74	72	31
Ashland Rovers Res	24	8	1	15	50	70	25
Magdala Amateurs 3rd	24	8	0	16	57	109	24
EMTEC	24	6	2	16	63	97	20
Tibshelf Old Boys	24	3	5	16	48	93	14
Derbyshire Amateurs 3rd	24	4	2	18	34	96	14

League Senior Cup

Ashland Rovers 2 Old Elizabethans 0

League Intermediate Cup

County Nalgo 3* Nottinghamshire Res 1*

League Minor Cup

Hickling 4* Nottinghamshire 3rd 2*

SOUTHERN AMATEUR LEAGUE

SENIOR SECTION:

DIVISION 1	P	W	D	L	F	A	Pts
Old Esthameians	22	15	1	6	57	44	46
Old Owens	22	12	4	6	49	31	40
Old Salesians	22	12	2	8	52	39	38
Winchmore Hill	22	10	6	6	35	31	36
Polytechnic	22	11	1	10	49	41	34
Norsemen	22	11	1	10	44	41	34
Civil Service	22	9	5	8	35	33	32
Broomfield	22	8	4	10	36	43	28
Old Actonians Association	22	7	5	10	42	43	26
West Wickham	22	7	5	10	22	26	26
Alleyn Old Boys	22	7	4	11	27	42	25
HSBC	22	2	4	16	26	60	10

DIVISION 2	P	W	D	L	F	A	Pts
Nottsborough	22	18	4	0	79	25	58
Old Parmiterians	22	11	4	7	49	39	37
Old Finchleians	22	10	5	7	50	42	35
Bank of England	22	10	4	8	37	31	34
Weirside Rangers	22	10	3	9	40	35	33
Carshalton	22	8	6	8	39	37	30
South Bank Cuaco	22	7	6	9	34	37	27
Old Parkonians	22	7	6	9	25	50	27
East Barnet Old Grammarians	22	7	4	11	41	37	25
Old Lyonians	22	7	2	13	32	59	23
BB Eagles	22	5	6	11	33	47	21
Old Stationers	22	4	6	12	21	41	18

DIVISION 3	P	W	D	L	F	A	Pts
Kew Association	24	18	4	2	68	14	58
Alexandra Park	24	14	4	6	69	32	46
Merton	24	13	5	6	63	29	44
Old Westminster Citizens	24	11	5	8	50	43	38
Old Latymerians	24	7	7	10	39	55	28
Crouch End Vampires	24	8	3	13	43	61	27
Southgate Olympic	24	7	3	14	35	59	24
Ibis	24	5	5	14	44	75	20
Lloyds TSB Bank	24	5	4	15	40	83	19

Intermediate Section:	**Teams**	**Won by:**
Division 1	12	Old Esthameians Res
Division 2	12	Old Stationers Res
Division 3	9	Alexandra Park Res
Third Team Section:		
Division 1	12	Old Actonians Association 3rd
Division 2	12	Alexandra Park 3rd
Division 3	9	Old Parmiterians 3rd
Minor Section:		
Division 1	12	Old Actonians Association 4th
Northern:		
Division 2	10	Alexandra Park 4th
Division 3	10	Old Esthameians 5th
Division 4	10	Old Actonians Association 6th
Division 5	10	Old Finchleians 7th
Division 6	10	Old Parmiterians 8th
Southern:		
Division 2	10	Nottsborough 4th
Division 3	10	HSBC 5th
Division 4	10	South Bank Cuaco 5th
Division 5	10	Civil Service 7th
Division 6	10	Polytechnic 8th

Challenge Cups:

Junior Nottsborough 3rd 4 Norsemen 3rd 0

Minor Wiinchmore Hill 4th 3* Old Esthameians 4th 2*

Senior Novets Norsemen 5th 2 Winchmore Hill 5th 0

Intermediate Novets Carshalton 6th 1 Old Finchleians 6th 2

Junior Novets Old Finchleians 7th 5* Old Finchleians 8th 3*

LONDON UNIVERSITY REPRESENTATIVE XI

v Brunel University	Lost	0 - 3
v Oxford University	Lost	0 - 1
v Amateur Football Combination	Drawn	0 - 0
v Amateur Football Alliance	Lost	0 - 1
v United Hospitals	Drawn	1 - 1
v Arthurian League	Lost	0 - 3
v Southern Amateur League	Won	4 - 2

UNIVERSITY OF LONDON UNION MEN'S COMPETITIONS

(Limited to one game against each member)

Premier Division One	**P**	**W**	**D**	**L**	**F**	**A**	**Pts**
Queen Mary Westfield College	11	9	0	2	41	22	27
Imperial College	11	8	1	2	34	10	25
University College	11	8	0	3	27	10	24
London School of Economics	11	7	1	3	20	14	22
Royal Holloway College	11	5	2	4	24	13	17
King's College	11	5	2	4	16	25	17
Imperial College School of Medicine	11	4	2	5	12	20	14
R Free, UC & Middx Hospitals MS	11	4	0	7	18	34	12
School of Oriental & African Studies	11	3	2	6	23	30	11
St Barts & R. London Hospitals MC	11	3	0	8	12	25	9
Imperial College Res	11	2	2	7	19	22	8
Guy's, King's & St. Thomas's MS	11	1	2	8	9	30	5

Premier Division Two	P	W	D	L	F	A	Pts
London School of Economics Res	11	10	1	0	43	6	31
University College Res	11	9	1	1	32	8	28
Royal Holloway College 3rd	11	6	2	3	25	19	20
Royal Holloway College Res	11	6	1	4	15	8	19
St George's Hospital MS	10	6	0	4	30	23	18
Imperial College 3rd	11	5	1	5	32	20	16
Imperial College Sch of Med Res	11	4	3	4	22	26	15
University College 3rd	11	3	1	7	13	23	10
Queen Mary Westfeld College Res	11	3	0	8	17	35	9
St George's Hospital MS Res	9	2	1	6	16	28	7
Birkbeck College Students	11	2	1	8	10	39	7
King's College Res	10	2	0	8	9	29	6

(Played as conventional Leagues)

Division 1	P	W	D	L	F	A	Pts
Royal Holloway College 4th	22	19	3	0	43	12	60
Goldsmiths' College	22	17	1	4	60	38	52
Guy's, King's, St. Thomas's MS Res	22	13	3	6	77	35	42
London School of Economics 4th	22	10	3	9	43	28	33
University College 4th	22	10	3	9	44	44	33
Imperial College 4th	22	10	2	10	48	36	32
Guy's, King's, St. Thomas's MS 3rd	22	9	3	10	32	45	30
R Free, UC & Middx Hosp MS 3rd	22	9	2	11	38	41	29
London School of Economics 3rd	22	7	3	12	61	54	24
R Free, UC & Middx Hosp MS Res	22	5	7	10	23	39	22
King's College 3rd	22	5	3	14	46	49	18
Goldsmiths' College Res	22	1	1	20	38	132	4

Division 2	P	W	D	L	F	A	Pts
University College 5th	22	18	3	1	92	29	57
Royal Veterinary College	22	16	4	2	78	27	52
Royal Holloway College 5th	22	15	3	4	59	30	48
Imperial College 5th	22	14	2	6	53	29	44
Imperial College (R. School of Mines)	22	13	3	6	66	37	42
London School of Economics 5th	22	9	5	8	42	35	32
King's College 4th	22	8	0	14	52	53	24
Imperial College Sch of Med Res 3rd	22	6	4	12	29	45	22
St Barts & R. London Hosps MC Res	22	5	3	14	35	64	18
St Barts & R. London Hosps MC 3rd	22	5	0	17	21	73	15
R Free, UC & Middx Hosp MS 4th	22	5	0	17	27	81	15
Imperial College Sch of Med 4th	22	4	1	17	23	74	13

	Teams:	**Won by:**
Division 3	**10**	**University College 7th**
Division 4	**11**	**Lon School of Economics 7th**

Challenge Cup

London School of Economics 2 Royal Holloway College1

Reserves' Challenge Cup

King's College 6th 0 University College 2

Reserves' Plate

Goldsmiths' College 2 Royal Holloway College 4th 0

Vase

Royal Veterinary College 2 Royal Holloway College 5th 1

WOMEN'S LEAGUES

Premier Division	**P**	**W**	**D**	**L**	**F**	**A**	**Pts**
University College	10	9	1	0	42	11	28
London School of Economics	10	6	0	4	27	16	18
Queen Mary Westfield College	10	5	2	3	36	23	17
Guy's, King's & St.Thomas's MS	10	5	0	5	33	29	15
Imperial College	10	3	1	6	19	37	10
King's College	10	0	0	10	8	49	0

	Teams:	Won by:
Division 1	5	Royal Holloway College
Division 2	5	R Free, UC & Middx Hosp MS

ARMED FORCES FOOTBALL

INTER SERVICES CUP

MEN'S COMPETITION

RAF	1	-	1	Army
Royal Navy	3	-	1	RAF
Army	0	-	2	Royal Navy

	P	W	D	L	F	A	Pts
Royal Navy	2	2	0	0	5	1	6
RAF	2	0	1	1	2	4	1
Army	2	0	1	1	1	3	1

Inter Service Champions 2003/04: Royal Navy

Inter Service Champions 2002/03: Army

WOMEN'S COMPETITION

RAF	0	-	2	Army
Army	1	-	1	Royal Navy
Royal Navy	1	-	1	RAF

	P	W	D	L	F	A	Pts
Army	2	1	1	0	3	1	4
Royal Navy	2	0	2	0	2	2	2
RAF	2	0	1	1	1	2	1

Inter Service Champions 2003/04: Army

Inter Sevice Champions 2002/03: Army

THE KENTISH CUP

Initially competed for in 1921, the Kentish Cup is the oldest military football competition in the world. Contested between Great Britain, France and Belgium originally, it was won outright by the British Army in 1928, but was re-established as à perpetual Challenge Trophy between the UK, French and Belgium armies in 1930.

Today's competition has been opened up to the Combined Services of the UK, Belgium and Holland, who replaced France after they withdrew from the Trophy many years ago.

Having installed new management three years ago, the UK team are enjoying some success of late having successfully retained the Trophy this season (a feat last achieved in 1970), and only narrowly missing out in 2002. No mean feat when you consider that the UK Combined Services team had only won the Trophy four times in the previous 30 years.

	UK Armed Forces v Netherlands AF	UK AF v Belgian AF	Belgium v Netherlands	Winners
1987	1-0	0-0	3-2	Belgian
1988	2-2	2-0	1-3	Netherlands
1989	1-0	4-1	1-1	UK
1990	4-2	1-1	4-0	Belgian
1991	1-3	0-1	3-1	Belgian
1992	2-2	0-0	2-1	Belgian
1993	1-3	1-1	2-1	Belgian
1994	0-2	4-2	2-1	Netherlands
1995	2-5	2-0	1-1	Netherlands
1996	1-1	1-2	0-4	UK
1997	0-3	3-3	1-1	Netherlands
1998	4-0	4-1	0-3	UK
1999	0-0	0-3	2-0	Belgian
2000	1-1	1-1	3-2	Netherlands
2001	1-2	0-0	1-5	Netherlands
2002	1-1	2-1	0-2	Netherlands
2003	2-2	3-0	1-3	UK
2004	4-1	3-0		UK

Celebrations for the 2nd Royal Irish after their 1-0 victory over 6th Battalion (Tidworth) in the Army Cup final.
Photo: Eric Marsh.

ROYAL ENGINEERS

Chris Richardson is well respected as a succesful marketing manager and qualified coach in senior non-league football. He is at present Commercial Manager of Aldershot Town but he is also the Secretary of Royal Engineers Association Football Club Veterans and we are very pleased to publish his letter informing us how the modern members of the very famous ex F.A.Cup winners are keeping their club very much alive and kicking! T.W.

Hi Tony,

This will probably be a first if you approve the entry of the Royal Engineers Association Football Club Veterans, which is another level of the game and a representative team of serving and ex Sappers, who have during their serving careers represented the Royal Engineers but are now veteran players and meet up particularly on FA Cup Final Day to celebrate their link with the World's oldest football competition, which the Sappers are the only military club to have won way back in 1875. The club has a proud history and actually have played in four FA Cup Finals, starting with the very first one in 1872, then again in 1874 and 1875 and finally in 1878. We do have another major distinction in winning the FA Amateur Cup in 1908, so I believe we are only one of three clubs that have ever won both FA Competitions, and obviously it is a landmark for RE AFC, because no one will ever achieve this - the other two clubs to win both are Old Carthusians and Wimbledon F.C..

I believe that the Royal Engineers are the oldest military club, who are still alive and kicking regarding keeping their name in football circles. Although we can trace our history back to 1863, which saw the formation of the FA in the same year and it was under the Captaincy of Major Sir Francis Marindin RE, who has the Brigade Major at Chatham, in Kent from 1866 to 1874, that football really began to develop; who ensured the Sappers joined the FA in 1869. Marindin, then a Captain in the Royal Engineers became a member of the committee that controlled the FA in 1871 and on the 20th July that year the introduction of "The Football Association Challenge Cup. Marindin's Engineers became the best team in the country during the first four seasons of the Cup. Played 86, won 74, drawn 9 and lost 3 with 244 goals for and 21 against. What an accolade to a man who from 1874 to 1890 became President of the FA.

The inaugural FA Cup Final was played between the Royal Engineers and the Wanderers Club on 16 March 1872, from an initial entry of 15 teams, the Sappers went down 1 - 0. In those days the Royal Engineers home ground was Chatham Lines and even today the current RE AFC and Veterans Club play fixtures at Chatham where the annual reunion is held on FA Cup Final Weekend to celebrate the Sappers link to this world famous competition. The Cup was won at last, a famous victory, and after a replay in 1875, still lives on today and embellishes the Sappers team wear and products promoting the club. There are many recollections on the major influences the Royal Engineers had on football in the early years. The 'Book of Football', published in 1906, describes how the military element introduced the Association game into New Brompton FC (now Gillingham FC of the Nationwide Division One).

As you know Tony, I'm an ex Sapper and Army player myself and became the founder member of the RE AFC Veterans Club Membership in 1987, when stationed at Chatham and as the Regimental Football Officer. At this time I was RE AFC Team Manager and Assistant Manager of the Army Team, which included being the Kent Count FA Army Representative. However, my Commanding Officer asked me to arrange a reunion of past and present Corps players, with a view to celebrating the Royal Engineers 200th Anniversary - from that first reunion I began to research all the Sappers history and commissioned a scroll paying tribute to a celebrated past and present of Royal Engineers football players and officials, only 200 scrolls were issued that were singed by the Artist, and I have a photograph of the framed scroll being presented to Sir Bert Millichip (then a Mr), Chairman of the FA at Lancaster Gate. When Bryon Butler published The Official History of the FA in 1991 he chose to publish a print of the scroll in his book paying a compliment - "The Royal Engineers made a major contribution to the early development of the FA and football. They set standards in technique, organisation and sportsmanship". Following on from that the scroll to this day is presented to all players, as an award, for completing a set number of matches representing the Royal Engineers, which is called a full Corps Colour

The reunion of 1987 was such a success that it has continued to this day and the writer has developed the membership over 18 years (remaining on the RE AFC Committee as a civilian after leaving the Corps in September 1988). In due course following all my research into Royal Engineers football, both past and present, I hope to bring out a book to celebrate what has happened, "since we won the cup", but it is sad to relate that the present cup is not the intrinsic symbol of football glory handed to the Corps of Royal Engineers in 1875. Finally, attached is a photograph of the team which represented the RE AFC Veterans at this years reunion on FA Cup Final Day at Chatham the official home of Sapper football. Tommy Smith MBE the former Liverpool legend known has the Anfield Iron was our guest speaker at the evening's Reunion Dinner.

This coming season I'm still involved with Aldershot Town has their Commercial Manager and look forward to meeting you again on the circuit. Hopefully it will be another exciting and rewarding season.

Chris Richardson

BRITISH UNIVERSITIES FOOTBALL

1ST TEAM FOOTBALL CHAMPIONSHIP 2004

last 16

Bath	v	St Mary's	3-0
Edge Hill	v	Greenwich	2-2*, 4-3p
Southampton	v	UW Swansea	0-3
Brunel W. London	v	Crewe & Alsager	3-3*, 4-2p
Nottingham Trent	v	Loughborough	2-6
Exeter	v	Northumbria	1-0
Stirling	v	Sheffield Hallam	0-2
Nottingham	v	Heriot Watt	2-1

QUARTER-FINALS

Bath	v	Edge Hill	0-1
UW Swansea	v	Brunel West London	2-1
Loughborough	v	Exeter	6-0
Sheffield Hallam	v	Nottingham	1-1, 4-5p

SEMI-FINALS

Edge Hill	v	UW Swansea	1-2
Nottingham	v	Loughborough	0-2

THE FINAL

UW Swansea	v	Loughborough	0-1

PREMIER LEAGUE CONFERENCE

NORTH

		P	W	D	L	F	A	Pts
C	Loughborough	10	7	1	2	25	7	22
C	Nottingham	10	5	3	2	15	10	18
C	Edge Hill	10	5	1	4	17	12	16
C	Northumbria	10	5	0	5	17	19	15
C	Crewe & Alsager	10	3	2	5	14	24	11
R	Leeds Metropolitan	10	1	1	8	13	29	4

SOUTH

		P	W	D	L	F	A	Pts
C	Bath 1st	10	7	2	1	28	13	23
C	UW Swansea	10	6	2	2	20	9	20
C	Brunel West London	10	6	2	2	22	14	20
C	Exeter	10	3	2	5	17	17	11
C	Grenwich	10	3	1	6	14	21	10
R	Bristol	10	0	1	9	8	35	1

MIDLANDS 1A		P	W	D	L	F	A	Pts
C	Nottingham Trent	10	6	2	2	14	10	20
S	Warwick	10	5	2	3	16	12	17
S	De Montfort	10	4	2	4	12	14	14
	East Anglia	10	4	1	5	22	18	13
R	Oxford	10	3	3	4	12	10	12
R	Wolverhampton	10	1	4	5	9	21	7

SOUTH EASTERN 1A		P	W	D	L	F	A	Pts
C	St Mary's	12	8	3	1	29	12	27
S	Hertfordshire	12	8	3	1	35	16	27
S	Chichester	12	6	1	5	26	16	19
	Roehampton	12	4	4	4	14	19	16
	Brighton	12	3	2	7	18	31	11
R	Buckinghamshire Chil.	12	2	3	7	13	28	9
R	Luton	12	2	2	8	20	33	8

NORTHERN 1A		P	W	D	L	F	A	Pts
C	Sheffield Hallam	10	7	0	3	17	11	21
S	Liverpool John Moores	10	7	0	3	24	16	21
	Teeside	10	4	3	3	18	11	15
	Newcastle	10	4	1	5	14	15	13
R	Manchester	10	2	3	5	11	17	9
R	Liverpool	10	1	3	6	6	20	6

Promotion Play-off

Nottingham Trent v Sheffield Hallam 1-1*, 6-7p

WESTERN 1A		P	W	D	L	F	A	Pts
C	Southampton	10	9	0	1	33	7	27
S	Gloucestershire	10	5	4	1	20	14	19
S	Southampton Institute	10	4	2	4	24	16	14
	UWIC	10	3	3	4	31	25	12
R	Glamorgan	10	3	2	5	13	21	11
R	UW Newport	10	0	1	9	10	48	1

Promotion Play-off

St Mary's v Southampton 2-3*

C = qualified for Championship. S = qualified for Shield. R = Relegated

SCOTTISH CONFERENCE 1A		P	W	D	L	F	A	Pts
C	Heriot Watt	6	4	0	2	18	9	12
C	Stirling	6	3	2	1	13	5	11
S	Edinburgh	6	3	2	1	12	8	11
	Glasgow	6	2	1	2	6	9	10
	Strathclyde	6	3	0	3	14	8	9
R	Aberdeen	6	2	1	3	8	8	7
R	Robert Gordon	6	0	0	5	3	27	-3

1ST TEAM FOOTBALL SHIELD

Edinbrugh v Central Lancashire 0-1

1ST TEAM FOOTBALL PLATE

Chester v Oxford Brooks 4-4*, 4-2p

BRITISH UNIVERSITY GAMES 2004

MENS	P	W	D	L	F	A	Pts
Wales	3	2	0	1	7	4	6
England	3	2	0	1	5	3	6
Scotland	3	2	0	1	4	3	6
Northern Ireland	3	0	0	3	1	7	0

RESULTS

England	v	Scotland	2-1
Wales	v	Northern Ireland	5-1
England	v	Wales	1-2
Scotland	v	Northern Ireland	1-0
England	v	Northern Ireland	2-0
Scotland	v	Wales	2-1

WOMENS	P	W	D	L	F	A	Pts
England	3	3	0	0	19	2	9
Scotland	3	2	0	1	11	4	6
Wales	3	1	0	2	7	10	3
Northern Ireland	3	0	0	3	1	22	0

RESULTS

England	v	Scotland	3-1
Wales	v	Northern Ireland	5-1
England	v	Wales	5-1
Scotland	v	Northern Ireland	6-0
England	v	Northern Ireland	11-0
Scotland	v	Wales	4-1

MEN'S SQUAD: Matt Taylor - SHEFFIELD HALLAM - Matlock Town. Dan Truman - LOUGHBOROUGH - Ashton United. Ellis Wilmott - BATH - Chippenham Town. Ben Purkiss - SHEFFIELD - Gainsborough Trinity. Ian Guant - LOUGHBOROUGH - Loughborough Dynamo. David Hunt- LOUGHBOROUGH - Loughborough Dynamo. Rob Storey. Joe Rossiter. Will Ryder. Paul Anthony - NORTHUMBRIA. Simon Tucker. Phil Denney - MANCHESTER MET - Ashton United. Roy Stammer - LEEDS MET - Farsley Celtic. Ryan Nicoll - DMU BEDFORD - Hitchin Town. Kevin Watson - BATH. Marc Canham - BATH. Head Coach: Graeme Dell. Coach: Steve Sharman.

WORLD UNIVERSITY GAMES AUGUST 2003

GROUP C	P	W	D	L	F	A	Pts
Great Britain	3	2	0	1	4	3	6
Morocco	3	2	0	1	3	2	6
Ukraine	3	1	0	2	3	3	3
Mexico	3	1	0	2	1	2	3

RESULTS

Great Britain Paul 46	v	Mexico	1-0
Ukraine	v	Morocco	2-0
Morocco	v	Great Britain Young 43	2-1
Ukraine	v	Mexico	0-1
Ukraine	v	Great Britain Rooke 50, Black 79	1-2
Mexico	v	Morrocco	0-1

QUARTER-FINALS

Great Britain v Italy 0-2

5TH - 8TH PLACE PLAY-OFF

Great Britain v Iran 0-1

7TH - 8TH PLACE PLAY-OFF

China v Great Britain 3-1
Ewin

WORLD UNIVERSITY GAMES FOOTBALL FINAL

Japan v Italy 3-2

ENGLISH SCHOOLS' FOOTBALL ASSOCIATION

Publicity: Mike Simmonds, 19 The Spinney, Bulcote, Burton Joyce, Nottingham NG14 5GX
Tel: 0115 931 3299 Fax: 0115 931 2758

Chief Executive: John Read, 1-2 Eastgate Street, Stafford ST16 2NQ
Tel: 01785 251 142 Fax: 01785 255 485

THE INTERNATIONAL SEASON

After a rigorous selection process which started at Keele University in August 2003 and finished in early February, a squad of 16 was chosen to represent the English Schools Under 18 international squad in 2004. They immediately suffered disappointment when the first match of their programme against Northern Ireland in the Centenary Shield was called off because of snow. A second setback came at the Sixfields Stadium, Northampton when the squad eventually got on to the field against the Republic of Ireland. An early goal for the visitors proved to be the winner although England should have equalised after the break, only to miss from the penalty spot.

The second game against Scotland broke new ground for the English Schools F.A. with a first ever schools international game on the Island of Jersey, scheduled to coincide with the Under 11 Festival which has taken place for the last 30 years. The island lived up to its reputation as the game took place under a cloudless sky in warm sunshine. England got off to an impressive start, scoring in the eighth minute when an excellent move was finished by a towering header from Sean Sonner and would have increased their lead but for some excellent saves by the Scottish keeper. As the interval approached, Scotland improved and forced two brilliant saves from Chris Astley in the England goal. Those proved Scotland s only real threat and England went on to dominate the second half but missed chances restricted them to a single goal win.

The final match in the Centenary Shield was the rearranged game against Northern Ireland in Belfast. Despite scoring first through Johnnie Dyer and re-taking the lead early in the second period through Tom Champion, England conceded a very late goal to lose 2-3.

English Schools' Football Association Centenary
The P.F.A Invitation Under 18 Schools International Match
ENGLAND
vs Rest of World XI
Saturday 8th May 2004
Kick-off 3.pm
Villa Park
Official Souvenir Programme £2.50

In addition to the games in the Centenary Shield which was eventually won by the Republic of Ireland, England Under 18 s also played two friendly matches against New Zealand at Newbury and away to Hungary, both of which were lost 1-0 although the latter was against the Hungarian Under 19 professional side.

The highlight of the year, however, came at Villa Park on May 8th in the E.S.F.A. Centenary Match organised as the centrepiece of a week-end of celebrations to mark 100 years of schools football at national level. A Rest of the World squad with one player from each of 16 countries who are members of the Schools International Board, provided tough opposition but England rose to the occasion and an entertaining game ended in a 2-2 draw.

The Rest of the World team took the lead through the talented Israeli man of the match Eden Ben Basat but Sean Sonner took advantage of a defensive error to equalise on the stroke of half-time. To the delight of a crowd of over 8,000, England went ahead with a diving header from Johnnie Dyer, a lead which they held until the 80th minute when Noel Johnston (Northern Ireland) converted a penalty. A match worthy of the occasion !

INTERNATIONAL CAPS AWARDED SEASON 2003-04

		A	B	C	D	E	F
Steve Aslett	(Kent)	1	1	1s	1s	1	1s
Chris Astley	(Gloucestershire)	1	1		1		
Matthew Burke	(Greater Manchester)	1	1s	1s	1s	1s	1
Thomas Champion	(Middlesex)	1	1	1	1	1	1
Thomas Clements	(Suffolk)	1s	1	1	1	1	1
Adam Cook	(Lancashire)	1	1s	1s	1		1
Chris Davis	(Gloucestershire)	1s	1s	1	1s	1s	1s
Johnnie Dyer	(Berkshire)	1	1	1s	1	1	1
Ben Elkington	(Buckinghamshire)	1c	1c	1c	1c	1c	
Matthew Knight	(Inner London)	1s	1s	1	1s	1	1s
Chris Lines	(Gloucestershire)	1s	1s	1	1	1	1s
Russell Martin	(Sussex)	1	1	1	1	1	1
Ben Miley	(Northumberland)	1	1	1	1		1c
John Mousinho	(Buckinghamshire)	1s	1	1	1	1	1
Matt Shaughnessy	(Gloucestershire)	1	1	1	1s	1	1
Sean Sonner	(Hertfordshire)	1	1	1	1	1	1
Chris Gill	(West Yorkshire)			1s		1s	1

Key :
A Republic of Ireland B Scotland C New Zealand D Northern Ireland
E Hungary F Rest of the World c. Captain s. Substitute

ENGLAND SCHOOLS' UNDER-18 SQUAD 2004

Back Row (L-R): Adam Cook, Sean Sonner, Matthew Burke, Chris Lines, Russell Martin, John Mousinho, Matt Shaughnessy, Ben Miley.
Middle Row (L-R): Arthur Tabor (Doctor), Ian Shead, (GK Coach), Thomas Clements, Ben Elkington (Capt), Matthew Knight, Christopher Astley, Tom Champion, Steven Aslett, Peter Chisholm (Asst. Manager), Mike Hewitt (Physio).
Front Row (L-R): Johnnie Dyer, Nigel Brown (Chr. Int & Coaching Committee), Phillip Harding (Chairman), Vic Bragg (Manager), John read (CEO), Chris Davis.

THE INTER-ASSOCIATION COMPETITIONS

ENGLISH SCHOOLS' F.A. UNDER 15 N.U.T. TROPHY

THE FINAL

1st Leg	Bishop Auckland	0	Portsmouth	1	(at Durham City)
2nd Leg	Portsmouth	1	Bishop Auckland	0	(at Fratton Park)

Porstmouth win 2-0 on aggregate

The Inter-Association Trophy which was first played for in 1904-05, the season in which the English Schools F.A. was founded, is the blue riband of the schools game and the Centenary Final proved worthy of the occasion with two well fought games in which the outcome was in doubt until added time in the second leg at Fratton Park

After Bishop Auckland had fought bravely and sometimes unluckily to overcome the first leg deficit, Portmouth looked as if they would hold on for a single goal aggregate victory when Bishop Auckland won a free-kick and piled forward in search of the goal which would force extra time. This left them short at the back and when Matt Docherty s clearance found Pompey s striker Louis Bell, he was unmarked. Undeterred by the defenders chasing back, Bell ran half the length of the pitch before calmly slipping the ball underneath the advancing Kris Carr to clinch his side s first ever success in the hundred years of the competition.

Before the climax, Bishop Auckland sounded their intentions as early as the first minute when Seb Coady s pace exposed Lee Ewing only for his dangerous cross to be saved. From the corner, Lewis Marr s header was well saved by Jack Stansbridge. At the other end, Billy Huntley s shot towards an empty net lacked power and was comfortably cleared. Generally defences were on top and the amount of goalmouth action decreased as the interval approached. In the second half, Stansbridge kept Portsmouth ahead with three fine saves from Woodward, Clarke and Langthorne which kept the visitors at bay until Bell s late winner.

Just as in the second leg, there was little to choose between the sides at Durham City but a goal early in the second half from captain Tom Roberts brought Portsmouth the 1-0 advantage which proved so crucial.

ROUTES TO THE FINAL

PORTSMOUTH

Round 1	Bye		
Round 2	Andover	(H)	11-0
Round 3	Southampton	(H)	3-0
Round 4	Croydon	(A)	1-0*
Round 5	Aldershot and Farnborough	(H)	1-1*
replay	Aldershot and Franborough	(A)	3-1
Round 6	Hackney and Tower Hamlets	(A)	1-1*
replay	Hacklney and Tower Hamlets	(H)	1-0
Semi-Final	Exeter and East Devon	(A)	4-1

BISHOP AUCKLAND

Round 1	Middlesbrough	(H)	4-2
Round 2	Scarborough	(A)	7-1
Round 3	Barnsley	(A)	3-1
Round 4	North Tyneside	(H)	4-1
Round 5	West Tyne	(H)	2-1
Round 6	Brierley Hill and Dudley	(A)	1-0
Semi-final	Liverpool	(A)	1-0

THE TEAMS :

Portsmouth : Jack Stansbridge, Stephen Horsley, Lee Ewing, Jason Priro, Tom Roberts, Raqy Rogers, Jake Thomson, Tom Kotchin, Louis Bell, Billy Huntley, Matt Docherty, James Wilson, Dex Boyle, Ricky Hughes, Calum Wallis, Sean Howe

Bishop Auckland : Kris Carr, Danile Mitton, Lewis Hope, John Barker, Richard Langhtorne, Lewis Marr, Wayne Clarke, Mark Wood, Seb Coady, Kieran Mergan, David Dowson, Adam Comby, Ross Woodward, Ian Pritchard, Harry Drummond, Craig Alston.

Portsmouth celebrate their victory at Fratton Park. Photo: R.W.T. Photography.

ENGLISH SCHOOLS' F.A. PREMIER LEAGUE UNDER 19 COUNTY CHAMPIONSHIP

THE FINAL

GREATER MANCHESTER 5 SOMERSET 3

(at Deepdale, Peston N.E.)

Greater Manchester became national champions at this level for the first time in 14 years after a thrilling final against Somerset at Deepdale. Somerset had early scares when both Rob Woodman and Darren Stone needed prolonged treatment in the first five minutes but recovered to take the lead when Richard Healey did justice to a brilliant run by Andy Hayes by shooting home from 25 yards. The pattern of the game changed in the last five minutes before half-time; first Carlo Dilbero equalised for Greater Manchester who then took the lead through England midfielder Matthew Burke.

In a fluctuating second period, Somerset made it 2-2 after 55 minutes when a free-kick on the right by Hayes was headed home by striker Matt Shaxton and then Somerset keeper Chris Jones earned his man of the match award with a string of fine saves before being left exposed by his defence giving Mike Naylor the opportunity of putting Greater Manchester ahead in the 65th minute.

Two enforced substitutions seemed to energise Somerset who made it 3-3 with Kyle McFarlane s superb 35 yard free-kick which raised the possibility of extra time. This seemed even more likely when Jones made a fabulous save but the relief for Somerset was short-lived as Callum Dempsey headed in the resulting corner. Greater Manchester clinched victory in the last few minutes with an excellent chip over the keeper by Damien Morrison.

Greater Manchester F.A. U19s - winners of the E.S.F.A. County Championship. Photo: R.W.T. Photography.

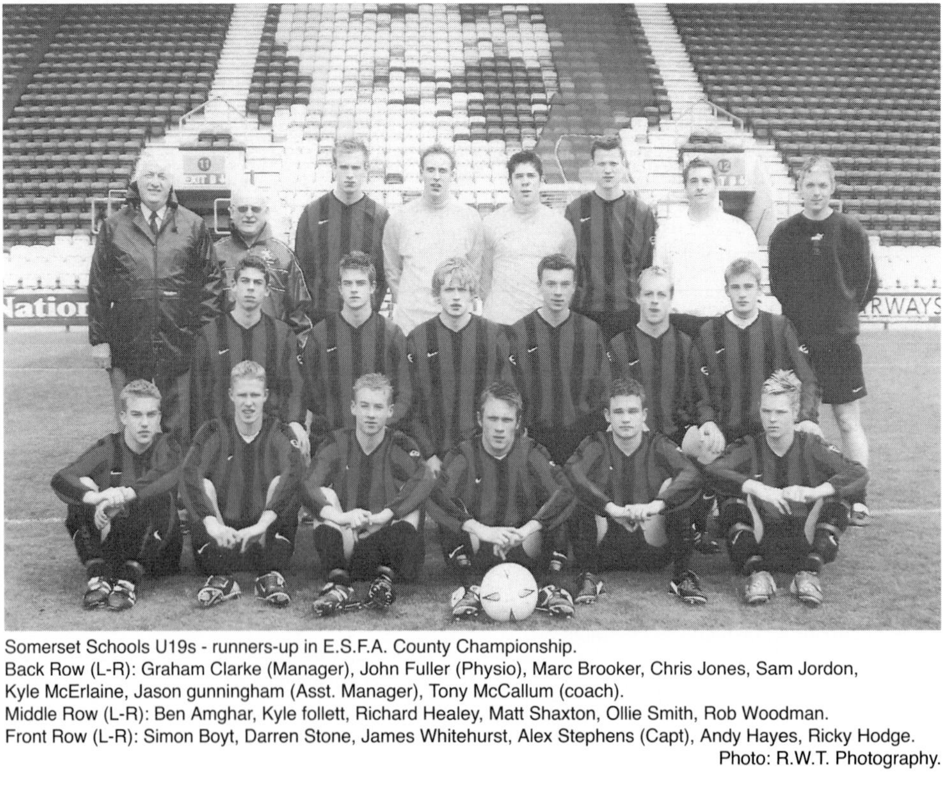

Somerset Schools U19s - runners-up in E.S.F.A. County Championship.
Back Row (L-R): Graham Clarke (Manager), John Fuller (Physio), Marc Brooker, Chris Jones, Sam Jordon, Kyle McErlaine, Jason gunningham (Asst. Manager), Tony McCallum (coach).
Middle Row (L-R): Ben Amghar, Kyle follett, Richard Healey, Matt Shaxton, Ollie Smith, Rob Woodman.
Front Row (L-R): Simon Boyt, Darren Stone, James Whitehurst, Alex Stephens (Capt), Andy Hayes, Ricky Hodge.
Photo: R.W.T. Photography.

ENGLISH SCHOOLS' F.A. PREMIER LEAGUE UNDER 16 COUNTY CHAMPIONSHIP

THE FINAL

NOTTINGHAMSHIRE 3 ESSEX 3

(at Mewdow Lane, Notts County - 20th April)

Nottinghamshire reached the final for the second time in three years but after defeating Kent in 2001-2002, they were forced to share the title on this occasion as Essex equalised with almost the last kick of the match . Essex went ahead through Ricky Stubbs and although Junior Daniel equalised, the South-East champions went ahead again before half-time with a goal from Rob Swaine. In the second half, Joe Loscalzo scrambled an equaliser for the home side and when Ben Hutchinson headed them into the lead with seven minutes remaining, they seemed on course to win the title outright. Victor Omegtuabin s late equaliser thwarted those hopes and extra time could not separate two tired sides.

ROUTES TO THE FINAL

NOTTINGHAMSHIRE :			
Regional League	v. Derbyshire	(H)	0-1
Regional League	v. Leicestershire	(A)	4-2
Regional League	v. Humberside	(A)	2-0
Regional League	v. Lincolnshire	(H)	3-2
Midlands semi-final	v. Shropshire	(H)	2-2*3-1p
National quarter-final	v. Durham	(H)	3-2 *
National semi-final	v. Northumberland	(H)	4-2*
ESSEX :			
Regional League	v. Surrey		3-1
Regional League	v. Middlesex		5-1
Regional League	v. Kent		3-2
Regional League	v. Buckinghamshire		3-1
Regional League	v. Sussex		0-7
National quarter-final	v. Somerset	(A)	2-1*
National semi-final	v. Bedfordshire		5-0

Nottinghamshire Under 16 squad. Photo: R.W.T. Photography.

ENGLISH SCHOOLS' F.A.
UNDER 16 GIRLS COUNTY CHAMPIONSHIP

THE FINAL

MERSEYSIDE 4 NORFOLK 0

(at Gigg Lane, Bury - 19th April)

A fifth minute goal from Lyndsay Shaw and a second half hat-trick by Clare Owen brought Merseyside their second win in three years in the competition.

THE INDIVIDUAL SCHOOLS' COMPETITIONS

ENGLISH SCHOOLS' F.A.
UNDER 18 COLLEGES CHAMPIONSHIP

THE FINAL

SOUTHGATE COLLEGE 3 MIDDLESBROUGH COLLEGE 1

In a hard fought final, Middlesbrough took a first half lead through Mark Spencer but a penalty from Bradley Garness put the Middlesex team level. Laurean O Sullivan put Southgate ahead after 80 minutes and a second goal of the game for Garness clinched their success with a minute remaining.

ENGLISH SCHOOLS' F.A.
UNDER 18 INDIVIDUAL SCHOOLS' CUP

THE FINAL

TRINITY SCHOOL (CARLISLE) 1 NEALE WADE COMMUNITY COLLEGE (MARCH 0

(at Carlisle United - 5th May)

Teams from Cumbria and Cambrdigeshire are rare participants in the later stages of the English Schools F.A. competitions but Trinity brought Cumbria their first ever success with a dramatic victory in extra time in front of a 3,000 crowd at Brunton Park. Two fine defences prevented any goals in normal time although Trinity thought they had won the game in the last minute when Dan Nicholson s effort was ruled out for offside.

With golden goal in operation, the drama continued in the first minute of extra time when the Trinity defence scrambled the ball off the goal line but a minute later the home side were celebrating victory as James Earl s cross was met by a bullet header from Craig Wood. The victory typified the Trinity spirit which had also seen them get to the final with another golden goal victory and win their quarter-final in the dying minutes, but the sporting behaviour of the Neale Wade side who had travelled hundreds of miles to lose in almost the saddest way possible was a reflection of the success of the first ever Under 18 schools competition organised by the E.S.F.A.

THE TEAMS :

TRINITY : Adam Bradley, Nick Scott, Paul Huntington, Craig Wood, Stuart Hill, Chris Lowe, Stuart Kilgour, Gavin Foxton, Paul Reay, Mark Hughes, Stuart McGarva, Dan Nicholson, Jack Guyan, James Earl, Mark Burgess, Sam Smith

NEALE WADE : Chris Anker, Joe Armitage, Tom McCumeskey, Mark Welcher, Andrew Mills, Charlie Patton, Rory Wheeler, Harry Roe, Stuart Broughton, Sean Woodside, Lawrie Brand, James Sutton, Alex Bates, Rob Day, Michael Smart, Stevben Carroll, James Hilliard.

Craig Wood leaps to score the golden goal for Trinity School in the U18 Individual Schools' Cup.
Photo: R.W.T. Photography.

ENGLISH SCHOOLS' F.A.
UNDER 16 INDIVIDUAL SCHOOLS' CUP

THE FINAL

SHENFIELD HIGH SCHOOL (ESSEX) 2 CRAMLINGTON SCHOOL (NORTHUMBERLAND) 1

(at Madjeski Stadium, Reading - 4th May)

A last gasp extra time winner from Rob Swaine who also scored in the Under 16 inter-county final sealed a 2-1 victory for Shenfield High School in this long established competition which like its Under 18 counterpart proved a dramatic encounter. Shenfield started brightly and took an early lead when from one of several good runs by Lee Tydeman, his cross found Jake Marsh who turned and found space to shoot across the keeper from 15 yards.

As the game wore on, Cramlington exerted strong pressure with keeper Will Swaine frequently called into action as the Northumberland side s biggest threat came from Graeme Owens. Cramlington kept pressing forward and gained their reward with an equaliser in stoppage time when Ross Armstrong lobbed over Swaine.

In extra time, both sides found it difficult to breach their opponents defence but Shenfield s more ambitious approach was rewarded two minutes from the end when Swaine scored his tenth headed goal of Shenfield s run from a free-kick by Tydeman.

Shenfield High School. Photo: R.W.T. Photography.

ENGLISH SCHOOLS' F.A.
UNDER 16 GIRLS INDIVIDUAL SCHOOLS' CUP

THE FINAL

KINGSFIELD SCHOOL (GLOUCESTERSHIRE 1 NOTRE DAME COLLEGE (MERSEYSIDE) 2

(at Ashton Gate, Bristol City - 29th April)

The pedigree of both teams suggested a close final and this proved to be the case as Notre Dame took the trophy back to Merseyside after an extra time win. The Kingsfield side had been champions of Bristol for the previous four years and champions of Gloucestershire for two while several of their squad had gained experience at this level when they reached the last sixteen of the competition in 2002-03. Five of the Notre Dame players were members of the Merseyside squad that won the inter-county trophy while Danielle Hill had been part of the England Under 16 squad.. Kayleigh Sage gave Kingsfield a first half lead but Kirsty McIntyre equalised and Lyndsey Shaw scored the winner in extra time.

ENGLISH SCHOOLS' F.A.
UNDER 14 INDIVIDUAL SCHOOLS' CUP
THE FINAL

RODING VALLEY SCHOOL (LOUGHTON, ESSEX) 1* CARDINAL HEENAN SCHOOL (LIVERPOOL) 1*

(at Sixfield Stadium, Northampton - 30th April)

Roding Valley and Cardinal Heenan were joint winners of the national Under 14 Cup which attracted well over two thousand entries and involved the finalists in ten matches. Cardinal Heenan took the lead in the first half and Roding Valley were thankful to be only one goal behind. A fighting performance from the Loughton School allied to excellent sportsmanship and attitude brought them a well deserved equaliser with a fantastic overhead kick into the top corner of the net by Jamie Rolt. Extra time could not separate the sides and both therefore were part of the Parade of Centenary champions at Villa Park on May 8th.

ENGLISH SCHOOLS' F.A. COCA-COLA UNDER 13 INDIVIDUAL SCHOOLS' CUP

Once again those schools who reached the later stages of the Coca-Cola Cup had the opportunity of playing at Premiership and Division 1 grounds such as The Riverside, Villa Park, Vicarage Road while the finals were played at Stamford Bridge, but as Chris Masterton of Coca Cola Enterprises said, It s not just the 100 youngsters who played on Finals Day, it s about the collective effort of all 2,000 schools and around 30,000 young players who participated from September to May.

BOYS NATIONAL CUP

THE FINAL

NELSON THOMLINSON SCHOOL (WIGTON, CUMBRIA) 1 WILLIAM PARKER SCHOOL (HASTINGS) 2

(at Stamford Bridge, Chelsea)

A last minute winner from Liam Pocock brought heartache for Nelson Thomlinson and joy for William Parker after a final that could have gone either way. Liam Upton put the Hastings school ahead and kept his record of scoring in every round of the competition but Dale Wilson equalised just before half-time for the Wigton school

3rd/4th Place play-off
Rushcliffe School (Nottinghamshire) 2 Bicester School (Nottinghamshire) 0

Winners of Boys' Coca-Cola Cup William Parker School. Photo: R.W.T. Photography.

GIRLS NATIONAL CUP
THE FINAL

CHURCH STRETTON SCHOOL (SHROPSHIRE) 6 SHOLING SCHOOL (SOUTHAMPTON) 1

(at Stamford Bridge, Chelsea)

Shropshire s dominance of the girls Coca Cola Cup continued as Church Stretton repeated the success and score of last season s winners, Thomas Telford School. Church Stretton s heroine was Kim Bebbington who hit a hat-trick as they proved too strong for their Hampshire opponents. Further strikes from Vickey Ward, Aby Cottam and Vinnie Tyler were enough to secure a convincing triumph despite Kirby Anderson s excellent goal from the edge of the penalty area for Sholing.

3rd/4th Place play-off
Ivy Bridge School (Burnley) 3 Bexleyheath School (Kent) 1

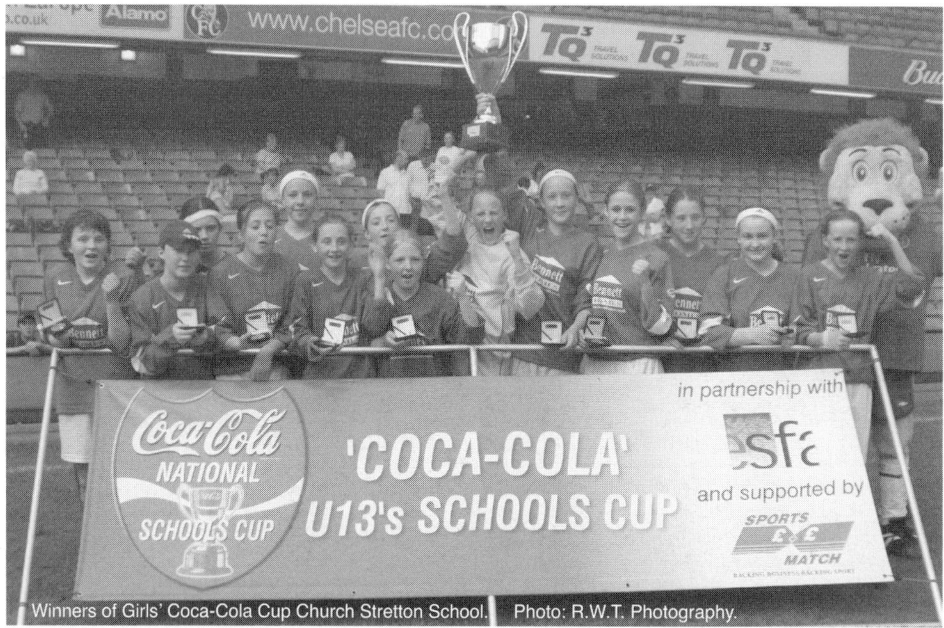

Winners of Girls' Coca-Cola Cup Church Stretton School. Photo: R.W.T. Photography.

THE SMALL SIDED COMPETITIONS

E.S.F.A. WAGON WHEELS UNDER 12 INDOOR FIVE-A-SIDE CUPS

BOYS FINAL

(JJB Soccerdome, Derby)

Thomas Telford School (Shropshire) 3 Bideford College (Devon) 0

GIRLS FINAL

Handsworth Grange School (South Yorkshire) 3 Richard Aldworth School (Hampshire) 2

E.S.F.A. SAINSBURY S UNDER 11 INDIVIDUAL SCHOOLS 6-A-SIDE CHAMPIONSHIP FINAL

(Lilleshall National Sports Centre)

Winsor Primary School (Essex) 1 Breakspear Junior School (Middlesex) 0

E.S.F.A. SAINSBURY S SMALL PRIMARY SCHOOLS SOCCER SIXES FINAL

(Lilleshall National Sports Centre)

St. John Bosco School (Merseyside) 3 St. Charles Catholic Primary School (Leicestershire) 0

E.S.F.A. SAINSBURY S INTER-ASSOCIATION UNDER 11 7-A-SIDE CHAMPIONSHIP FINAL

Wirral Primary Schools F.A. 1 Portsmouth Primary Schools F.A. 0

WOMEN'S FOOTBALL

NATIONAL DIVISION 2003-04

		P	W	D	L	F	A	Pts
1	Arsenal	18	15	2	1	65	11	47
2	Charlton Athletic	18	15	1	2	52	17	46
3	Fulham	18	14	2	2	60	20	44
4	Leeds United	18	8	4	6	32	28	28
5	Doncaster Rovers Belles	18	8	3	7	41	40	27
6	Everton	18	6	2	10	21	36	20
7	Birmingham City	18	4	5	9	17	31	17
8	Bristol Rovers	18	3	3	12	27	37	12
9	Aston Villa	18	1	4	13	18	63	7
10	Tranmere Rovers	18	1	4	13	13	63	7

NORTHERN DIVISION 2003-04

		P	W	D	L	F	A	Pts
1	**Liverpool**	**20**	**15**	**5**	**0**	**51**	**12**	**50**
2	Sunderland	20	10	7	3	56	31	37
3	Stockport County	20	10	4	6	41	22	34
4	Oldham Curzon	20	9	7	4	39	21	34
5	Wolves Women	20	6	9	5	27	22	27
6	Middlesbrough	20	7	5	8	25	28	26
7	Manchester City	20	7	3	10	35	45	24
8	Lincoln City	20	6	5	9	34	38	23
9	Sheffield Wednesday	20	6	4	10	30	45	22
10	Chesterfield	20	5	6	9	23	50	21
11	Bangor City	20	0	3	17	12	59	3

Joining the Northern Division for the 2004/05 season will be Blackburn Rovers and Coventry City.

SOUTHERN DIVISION 2003-04

		P	W	D	L	F	A	Pts
1	**Bristol City**	**24**	**18**	**4**	**2**	**78**	**31**	**58**
2	Southampton Saints	24	18	3	3	54	18	57
3	AFC Wimbledon	24	17	2	5	57	38	53
4	Chelsea	24	13	6	5	60	38	45
5	Watford	24	9	5	10	34	38	32
6	Brighton	24	8	7	9	43	44	31
7	Langford	24	9	4	11	37	42	31
8	Millwall Lionesses	24	8	6	10	35	38	30
9	Ipswich Town	24	8	5	11	39	44	29
10	Portsmouth	24	9	1	14	43	48	28
11	Enfield Town	24	4	4	16	17	54	16
12	Merthyr Tydfil	24	3	6	15	27	61	15
13	Barnet (-2pts)	24	2	7	15	31	61	11

Joining the Southern Division for the 2004/05 season will be Cardiff City and Crystal Palace

Northern Combination	Pld	Pts
Blackburn Rovers	16	48
East Durham	19	47
Manchester United	18	42
Newcastle	21	40
Blackpool Wren Rov	18	26
Scunthorpe United	17	24
Newsham PH	18	22
Doncaster Parklands	17	19
Chester City	18	18
Leeds City Vixens	17	11
Garswood Saints	15	4
Barnsley	18	3

Midland Combination	Pld	Pts
Coventry City	17	42
Nottingham Forest	16	36
Rotherham United	18	35
Loughborough Stud's	17	31
Lichfi eld Diamonds	17	25
Shrewsbury Town	16	21
Crewe Vagrants	17	21
Ilkeston Villa	17	17
Ilkeston Town	16	16
Stafford Rangers	17	0

South East Combination	Pld	Pts
West Ham United	22	55
Crystal Palace	19	54
Norwich City	21	38
Queens Park Rangers	19	38
Bedford Town Bells	20	33
Brook House	21	26
Rushden & Diamonds	20	25*
Stowmkt Sophtlogic	20	24*
Barking	21	21
Gillingham	19	16
Denham United	22	13
Colchester United	20	6

*-points deducted

South West Combination	Pld	Pts
Reading Royals	20	54
Cardiff City	18	54
Chesham United	20	39
Rover Oxford	20	32
Clevedon Town SBW	18	28
Forest Green Rovers	17	23
Reading LFC	20	21
Swindon Town	20	21
Plymouth Argyle	18	20
Exeter City	17	15
Newton Abbot	18	14
Yeovil Town	18	3

WOMEN'S PYRAMID OF FOOTBALL

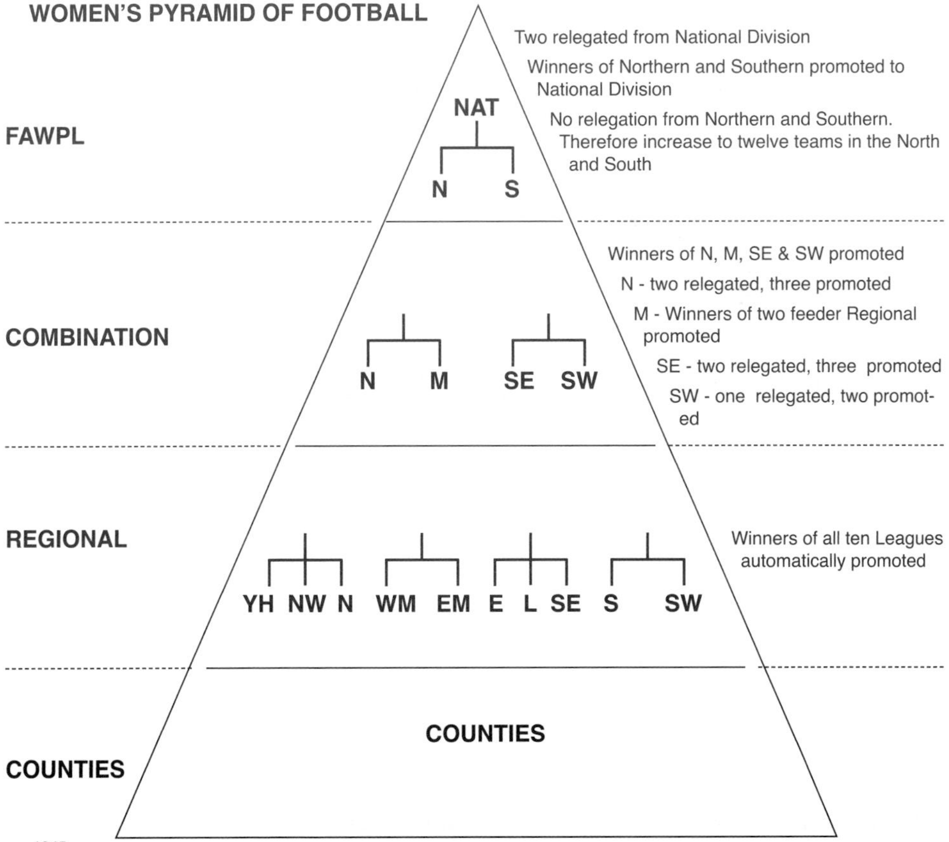

Eastern Premier Division	Pld	Pts
Northampton Town	18	46
Cambridge United	17	43
Cambridge University	19	36
Cambridge City	18	35
Wollaston Victoria	18	34
Woodbridge Town	20	26
Cambridge Kestrels	16	27
Barton Rovers	20	24
Haringey Borough	19	13
Royston Town	18	12
Huntingdon Town	19	12
US Valerio Vixens	16	9

East MidlandsPremier Division	Pld	Pts
Leicester City	15	37
Chaffoteaux	17	33
Derby County	16	32
Peterborough United	14	30
Radcliffe Olympic	18	29
Nottingham For Res	18	25
Sheffi eld United	14	22
Belper Town	18	15
Chesterfi eld Res	15	12
L'borough Dynamo	15	7
Blackwell MW	14	4

Greater London Premier Div.	Pld	Pts
Tottenham Hotspur	18	41
Dag'ham & Redbridge	16	40
Leyton Orient	15	40
Hendon	18	29
Redbridge Raiders	15	24
London WFC	15	23
Brentford	18	18
Clapton Orient	18	15
Edgware Town	16	7
Bushey Rangers	17	4

Northern Division 1	Pld	Pts
Chester-le-Street T'n	17	48
Crook Town	17	45
Carlisle United	16	30
Wardley Eagles	15	28*
South Durham Royals	17	28
Killingworth	17	25
Marton	17	20
Blyth Spartans	14	20
Darlington R'way Ath	17	19
Durham City	19	14
Saltburn Athletic	20	10
Boldon	19	5

North West Premier Division	Pld	Pts
Preston NE WFC	12	34
Bolton Wanderers	13	30
Liverpool Feds	14	23
Witton Albion	16	19
Stretford Victoria	17	19
Darwen	10	18
Bury	15	17
Warrington Grange	11	13
Hopwood	13	9
Chorley	15	8

S. E. Counties Premier Div.	Pld	Pts
Woking	14	36
Whitehawk	12	30
Lewes	14	26
Redhill	16	21
Crowborough Athletic	16	20
Chichester City United	14	19
Haywards Heath Town	16	11
Dover	14	10
Woodstock	14	8

Southern Premier Division	Pld	Pts
Reading Royals Res	15	42
Carterton Rangers	16	33
Launton	16	27
Aylesbury United	15	23
Bracknell Town	14	22
Caversham	14	20
Haywood United	13	17
Slough	16	17
Wycombe Wanderers	16	16
Southampton WFC	17	13
Burghfi eld	17	10

South West Premier Division	Pld	Pts
Keynsham Town	11	28
Buckfastleigh Rangers	11	25
Penzance	12	22
Dorchester Town	11	16
Frome Town	14	15
Bath City	12	13
Cheltenham Town	13	10
Cardiff City Res	12	10

West Midland Premier Division	Pld	Pts
Leafi eld Athletic	18	48
West Bromwich Albion	17	38
Stoke City	19	29
Cosford	18	28
TNS	14	25
Rea Valley Rovers	19	25
Walsall	21	25
Stratford Town	20	21
Telford United	17	20
Kidderminster Harriers	18	17
Rushall Olympic	16	12
Romulus	15	4

Yorkshire & Humberside Prem.	Pld	Pts
Leeds Development	16	37
York City	17	34
North Ferriby United	16	33
Hull City	17	32
Bradford City	15	31
Grimsby Town	18	28
Morley Spurs	16	26
Thorpe United	15	18
Huddersfield Town	16	18
Sheffield	17	10
AFC Preston	19	10
Wakefi eld	14	3

Berks & Bucks Co. F.A.	Pld	Pts
Reading Girls	14	40
St.Edmunds	16	37
Chesham United Res	16	31
Heelands Rangers	14	27
Morris Motors (Oxf'd)	16	26
Wycombe Wanderers	16	18
Milton United	15	14
AFC Newbury	16	13
Holmer Green	18	12
Oxfam	15	6

Cheshire & Manchester Div 1	Pld	Pts
Tameside Girls	10	24
Stockport Co. Blues	11	21
Denton Town	10	21
Vauxhall Motors	11	18
Stockport Co. (HNR)	11	10
Chester City Res	11	9
Wilmslow Albion	12	5

Cornwall Division 1	Pld	Pts
St.Austell	13	26
Mullion	13	26
Launceston	10	22
Penryn	11	16
Marazion Blues	12	16
Bude Town	10	12
Newquay Res	10	9
Camelford	13	7

Devon Premier Division	Pld	Pts
Central FC	15	37
Plymouth Argyle Res	13	33
Dawlish Town	13	30
Okehampton Argyle	16	23
Exeter University	11	20*
North Molton	14	17*
Totnes Town	16	11
Exeter Rangers	15	7
Galmpton United	15	1

Dorset Co. F.A.	Pld	Pts
Okeford United	14	42
AFC Bournemouth Res	13	23
Christchurch	13	22
Poole Town	14	20
Purbeck	13	20
Ashdown Rovers Res	13	17
Donhead United	12	4
Queen Bees	12	1

East Riding Co. F.A.	Pld	Pts
Grimsby Town Res	10	24
Hull University	10	23
Mosborough	9	16
AFC Preston Res	10	13
Hessle Rangers	6	6
Tickton	9	6
North Ferriby Sporting	8	3

Essex Co. F.A.Division 1	Pld	Pts
White Notley	14	29
Chelmsford City	12	28
Colchester United Res	17	28
Brentwood Town	13	27
East Thurrock United	13	25
Saffron Walden Town	14	24
Billericay Town	14	23
Stifford Clays	15	9
Harlow Town	15	8
Basildon United	15	1

Gloucs. Co. F.A. Division 1	Pld	Pts
University of Bristol	20	49
Cirencester Town	20	47
Warden Hill United	18	40
Gloucester Athletic	18	33
Cam Bulldogs	18	22
Tetbury Town	19	15
Downend Flyers	17	13*
BCWFC Congresbury	18	0

Hampshire Co. F.A. Division 1	Pld	Pts
Horndean	13	29
Shanklin	12	27
Aldershot Town	14	25
Portsmouth University	12	21
Gosport Borough	14	21
Hatch Warren	11	18
Red Star	14	5
Fleet Town	14	3

Isle of Man Co. F.A. Division 1	Pld	Pts
Rushen United	10	25
Douglas Royal	10	24
Union Mills	8	15
Malew	8	6
Peel	9	3
Gymnasium	9	1*

Jersey Combination	Pld	Pts
St.Peter	13	39
First Tower United	13	21
Rozel Rovers	11	20
St.John	12	19
St.Clement	13	16
Jersey Wanderers	10	7
St.Brelade	12	7
Grouville	12	0

Kent Suburban	Pld	Pts
Swale Magpies	15	40
London LFC	12	25
Dartford	15	24
Teynham Gunners	15	22
Hugin Vikings	13	13
Gravesham	12	12
London LFC Res	11	1

Kidderminster Pld Pts		
Burlish Olympic	12	29
Malvern	11	28
Worcester City	11	23
Evesham United	12	16
Redditch United Res	11	10
Bewdley Town	11	4*
Bredon	12	3*

Leics Co. F.A.	Pld	Pts
Rugby Town	8	24
Dunton & Broughton Rgers Res.	9	24
Woodford United	8	9
Castle Donnington	11	9
Southam United Res	8	0

Norfolk	Pld	Pts
Kings Lynn	12	36
Norwich City Girls	13	25
Mulbarton Belles Res	10	24
UEA	12	23
Hethersett Athletic	15	22
Pakefi eld	15	21
Thetford Town	13	14
Aylsham Town Res	12	7
Stalham Knights	13	5
Hainford	13	2

Staffs Co. F.A.	Pld	Pts
Bradwell Belles	12	33
Kingshurst Sports	11	24
Valiant	8	24
Whittington	10	22
Burton Albion	13	17
Etching Hill Lions	10	11
Cottage Farm Rngs Rs	14	11
Wolverhampton City	12	7
Harrier	9	6
Great Wyrley Walsall	11	6

West Riding Co. F.A.	Pld	Pts
Westend	13	39
Howden Clough	12	28
Silsden	10	22
Hebden Royd United	9	13
Republica Internationale Res.	14	8
Brighouse Town	11	7
Farsley Celtic	8	6
Shipley	11	5

Wiltshire Co. F.A.	Pld	Pts
Chippenham Town	17	42
Wootton Bassett Town	13	28
Keynsham Town Res	14	24
Swindon Town Res	15	22
Swindon Spitfi res Res	13	11
Brize Norton	12	0

South Wales	Pld	Pts
Ferndale	15	40
Swansea City Res	14	29*
Neath	16	28
Caldicot Town	13	24
UWIC	14	23
Dinas Powys	17	12
Caerphilly Cougars	16	10
Caerphilly Castle	16	7

Ceridigion	Pld	Pts
New Quay	10	27
UW Aberystwyth	8	21
Crannog	9	16
Carmarthen	9	16
Tregaron Turfs	10	14
Felinfach	6	9
Newcastle Emlyn	9	5
Abergwili	9	4
Penparcau	10	4

North Powys	Pld	Pts
Pennant	15	38
Llanrhaeadr	13	27
Newtown	11	26
Welshpool	10	21
Meifod	11	16
Llanidloes Town	9	11
Llanfyllin Eagles	13	11
Bettws RB	13	6
Caersws	13	1

Scottish Premier	Pld	Pts
Hibernian	13	37
FC Kilmarnock	11	27
Glasgow City	13	26
FC Hamilton	14	22
Newburgh	14	21
Ross County	10	16
Raith Rovers	14	16
Cove Rangers	14	8
East Kilbride	13	4
Guilliano's	8	3

Scottish League Division 1	Pld	Pts
Clyde	16	43
Aberdeen	15	37
Queens Park	15	35
Dundee United	13	22
Whitehill Welfare	10	18
Forfar Farmington	11	15
Arthurlie	13	14
Dundee City	16	14
Moray	12	9
Falkirk	15	7
Carluke Rovers	14	4

* points deducted

UEFA EUROPEAN WOMEN'S CHAMPIONSHIPS (JUNE 2005 - ENGLAND)

FIXTURES

Sun 5	UEFA European Women's Championships	Group A (1)
Tue 7	UEFA European Women's Championships	Group B (1)
Thu 9	UEFA European Women's Championships	Group A (2)
Fri 10	UEFA European Women's Championships	Group B (2)
Sun 12	UEFA European Women's Championships	Group A (3)
Mon 13	UEFA European Women's Championships	Group B (3)
Thu 16	UEFA European Women's Championships	Semi-Finals
Sun 19	UEFA European Women's Championships	Final

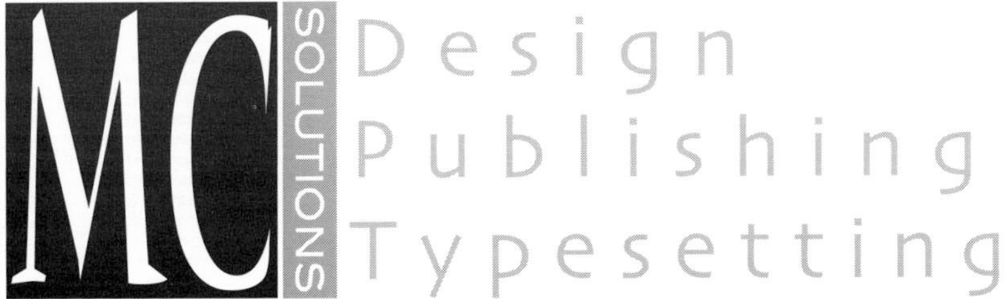

WIRRAL PROGRAMME CLUB

The non-profit making Club formed in March 1967

Secretary: I.R.W. Runham

3 Tansley Close, Newton, West Kirby, Wirral CH48 9XH Tel: 0151 625 9554

1st: Exeter City - 284pts **2nd:** Hoddesdon Town - 227 **3rd:** Northwood & Wealdstone - 221

LEAGUE + No of entries			FIRST		SECOND		THIRD	
NATIONWIDE CONFERENCE		20	Exeter City	6-284	Aldershot Town	6-214	Morecambe	1-210
DR. MARTENS	Overall	64	Bath City	6-206	Eastbourne Borough	6-202	Gloucester City	6-191
	Prem. Div.	21	Bath City	6-202	Eastbourne Borough	6-202	Chelmsford City	1-190
	West Div.	21	Gloucester City	6-191	Rugby Utd	6-187	Bedworth Utd	6-172
	East Div.	22	Corby Town	6-167	Hastings Utd	6-163	Tonbridge Angels	6-162
RYMAN	Overall	76	Northwood	6-221			Horsham	6-200
			Wealdstone	6-221				
	Prem. Div.	23	Northwood	6-221	Sutton Utd	6-193	Hayes	6-186
	Div. 1 N.	22	Wealdstone	6-221	Arlesey Town	6-192	Uxbridge	6-175
	Div. 1 S.	23	Horsham	6-200	Hampton & Richmond B	6-161	Croydon Athletic	1-150
							Worthing	6-150
	Div. 2	8	Witham Town	6-150	Wokingham Town	3-144	Chertsey Town	1-135
UNIBOND	Overall	42	Altrincham	6-186	Marine	6-167	Leek Town	6-164
	Prem. Div.	23	Altrincham	6-186	Marine	6-157	Whitby Town	1-151
	Div. 1	19	Leek Town	6-164	Workington	6-152	Rossendale Utd	1-151
MINERVA	Overall	42	Hoddesdon Town	6-227	Kings Langley	6-202	Beaconsfield SYCOB	6-180
SPARTAN	Prem. Div.	18	Hoddesdon Town	6-227	Beaconsfield SYCOB	6-180	Broxbourne Bor. V&E	6-176
SOUTH	Div. 1	16	Kings Langley	6-202	Cockfosters	6-152	Welwyn Garden City	6-134
MIDLANDS	Div. 2	8	Winslow Utd	1-114	Old Dunstablians	6-106	Risborough Rangers	3- 99
SEAGRAVE	Overall	23	AFC Wimbledon	6-218	Walton Casuals	6-140	Staines Lammas	1-133
HAULAGE	Prem. Div.	13	AFC Wimbledon	6-218	Walton Casuals	6-140	Sandhurst Town	6-131
COMBINED CO	Div. 1	10	Staines Lammas	1-113	Netherne Village	1- 95	Worcester Park	1- 90
GO TRAVEL	Overall	15	Maidstone Utd	6-169	Cray Wanderers	6-155	Hythe Town	6-141
KENT	Prem. Div.	12	Mainstone Utd	6-169	Cray Wanderers	6-155	Hythe Town	6-141
	Other Divs.	3	Danson Furness	1- 72	Groundhoppers	1- 68	Corinthian	1- 67
EASTWAY ESSEX SENIOR		11	Enfield Town	6-166	Romford	6-151	Brentwood	1-125
SYDENHAMS WESSEX		18	Christchurch	1-141			Brockenhurst	6-131
			Winchester City	6-141				
MATTHEW	Overall	25	Lancing	6-182	Ifield Edwards	6-149	Hassocks	6-137
CLARK	Div. 1	15	Hassocks	6-137	Redhill	6-130	Rye & Iden Utd	6-115
SUSSEX CO	Other Divs.	10	Lancing	6-182	Ifield Edwards	6-149	Steyning Town	1-109
SCREWFIX	Overall	21	Frome Town	6-156	Corsham Town	6-138	Minehead	1-122
DIRECT	Prem. Div.	12	Frome Town	6-156	Keynsham Town	6-114	Bideford	1-103
WESTERN	Div. 1	9	Corsham Town	6-138	Minehead	1-122	Bristol Manor Farm	1-121

League	Division	No.	Club	Score	Club	Score	Club	Score
RIDGEONS	Overall	31	Felixstowe & Walton	U6-177	Long Melford	1-148	AFC Sudbury	1-140
EASTERN	Prem. Div.	18	AFC Sudbury	1-140	Lowestoft Town	1-136	Mildenhall Town	1-128
COUNTIES	Div. 1	13	Felixstowe & Walton	U6-177	Long Melford	1-148	Leiston	1-131
EAGLE BITTER	Overall	22	St. Neots Town	6-176	Eynesbury Rovers	6-159	Blackstones	6-143
UNITED	Prem. Div.	15	St Neots Town	6-176	Blackstones	6-143	Daventry Town	6-136
COUNTIES	Div. 1	7	Eynesbury Rovers	6-159	Wellingborough Whit.	1- 76	Eye Utd.	1- 72
CHERRY RED	Overall	56	Didcot Town	6-178	Abingdon Utd.	6-177	Wootton Bassett Town	6-153
RECORDS	Prem. Div	22	Didcot Town	6-178	Abingdon Utd.	6-177	Wootton Bassett Town	6-153
HELLENIC	Div. 1 W.	18	Witney Utd.	5-137	Purton	6-135	Quarry Nomads	5-123
	Div. 1 E.	16	Binfield	5-139	Penn & Tylers Green	5-134	Wantage Town	5-132
NORTH WEST	Overall	37	Atherton L.R	6-183	Curzon Ashton	6-181	Clitheroe	6-169
COUNTIES	Div. 1	21	Atherton L.R	6-183	Curzon Ashton	6-181	Clitheroe	6-169
	Div. 2	16	Ashton Town	6-161	Eccleshall	6-145	Leek C S O B	1-131
NORTHERN	Overall	37	Arnold Town	6-168	Sheffield	6-165	Glasshoughton Welfare	6-162
COUNTIES							Pontefract Collieries	6-162
EAST	Prem. Div.	19	Arnold Town	6-168	Sheffield	6-165	Glasshoughton Welfare	6-162
	Div. 1	18	Pontefract Collieries	6-162	Maltby Main	6-149	Lincoln Moorlands	1-145
							Long Eaton Utd.	6-145
MIDLAND ALLIANCE		19	Willenhall Town	1-184	Ludlow Town	6-175	Stourbridge	6-172
ALBANY	Overall	31	Newcastle Blue Star	6-184	Marske Utd.	6-169	Chester-Le-Street T	6-153
NORTHERN	Div. 1	16	Marske Utd.	6-169	Chester Le Street Town	6-153	Durham City	6-135
	Div. 2	15	Newcastle Blue Star	6-184	Consett	6-147	Prudhoe Town	6-129
GREENE KING	Overall	14	Kelvedon Hatch	6-128	Springfield	1-123	Shell Club Corr Res	5-115
ESSEX	Div. 1	4	Kelvedon Hatch	6-128	Bishop's Stortford Sw.	6-110	Manford Way	6-102
INTERMEDIATE	Other Divs.	5	Springfield	1-123	Shell Club Corringham	4-108	Barnston	1-105
	Res. Divs.	5	Shell Club Corringham	5-115	Springfield	1-106	Barnston	2-103
MIDDLESEX COUNTY		5	Mauritius S A	1- 80	Walthamstowe Avenue	1- 78	London Tigers	1- 74
LOVEWELL	Overall	13	Acle Utd.	1-117	London Utd.	1- 99	Holt Utd.	1- 96
BLAKE	Prem. Div.	7	Acle Utd.	1-117	Blofield Utd.	1- 88	Cromer Town	1- 87
ANGLIAN COMB	Other Divs.	6	Loddon Utd.	1- 99	Holt Utd.	1- 96	Watton Utd.	1- 89
METALTEC SUFFOLK & IPS		5	Stowupland	1-111	Stowuplands Reserves	1-109	East Bergholt Utd.	1-107
HAMPSHIRE		6	Poole Town	6-173	Amesbury Town	6-165	Golden Common	6-157
ELITE TEAM WEAR DORSET		10	Poole Borough	6-154	Gillingham Town	1-150	Sturminster Newton United	1- 85
GLOUCESTERSHIRE COUNTY		4	Highbridge Utd.	6-169	Tytherington Rocks	6-126	Hardwicke	1- 77
PLAISTER AUTOS WILTSHIRE		3	Purton Reserves	6-121	Marlborough Town	1- 95	Marlborough T. Res,	1- 83
FIREWATCH DEVON		11	Buckland Athletic	6-201	Dartmouth	1-151	Budleigh Salterton	1-107
CARLSBERG SOUTH WESTERN		11	Falmouth Town	4-137	Plymouth Parkway	1-115	Bodmin Town	1-106
WORLD CLASS	Overall	17	Oxhey Jets	2-118	Buntingford Town	4-103	Loughton	6-102
HOMES HERTS	Prem. Div.	14	Oxhey Jets	2-118	Chipperfield Corinth	2- 99	Cuffley	2- 91
SENIOR	Div. 1	3	Buntingford Town	4-108	Loughton	6-102	Knebworth	1- 58
EXPRESS &	Overall	26	Tipton Town	5-141	Walsall Wood	6-136	Walsall Wood Youth	5-135
STAR WEST	Prem. Div	16	Tipton Town	5-141	Tividale	6-118	Dudley Town	6-117
MIDLANDS							Malvern Town	6-117
	Div. 1 S & N	7	Walsall Wood	6-136	Wyrley Rangers	6-117	Bilston Town	1-111
	Youth	3	Walsall Wood	5-135	Gornal Athletic	6- 97	Great Barr Holy Name	6- 82
ICIS MIDLAND	Overall	32	West Midlands Police	6-153	Brocton	6-140	Leamington	6-134
COMBINATION	Prem. Div.	21	West Midlands Police	6-153	Brocton	6-140	Leamington	6-134
	Div. 1	8	Loughborough	6-129	Old Hill Town	5-118	Bloxwich Town	5-102
	Other Divs.	3	Earlswood Town	6-106	Heather Athletic	1-102	Univ of Birmingham	1- 58
SAMSON	Overall	36	Rainworth Miners W	6-174	Blackwell Miners W	1-138	Sandiacre Town	1-137
SPORTS	Sup. Div.	18	Blackwell Miners W	1-138	Sandiacre Town	1-137	Dinnington Town	1-130
CENTRAL MIDS	Prem. Div.	17	Rainworth Miners W	6-174	Southwell City	1-122	Forest Town	1-118
EVERARDS BREW LEICS		4	Loughborough Dynamo	6-144	Blaby & Whetstone A	1- 97	Barrow Town	1- 90
NOTTS ALLIANCE		5	Wollaton	1-134	Bilborough	1-133	Wollaton Reserves	1-130
CARLSBERG WEST CHESHIRE		5	New Brighton	6-145	New Brighton Reserves	6-117	Manweb	1- 84
AEGON WEST LANCASHIRE		7	Rivington	6-172	Buxton Villa	1-143	Hesketh Park	1-117
AIR MILES	Overall	12	Prestwich Heys	6-177	New Mills	6-162	Ashton Athletic	1-136
MANCHESTER	Prem. Div.	9	Prestwich Heys	6-177	New Mills	6-162	Springhead	1-123
	Other Divs.	3	Ashton Athletic	1-136	Prestwich Heys Res.	3- 95	Swinton Town	1- 90
WEARSIDE		4	North Shields	1-106	Ferryhill Athletic	1-105	Darlington Railway A	1- 96
WADE ASSOC NORTHERN ALL		5	Walker Fosse	6-117	West Allotment Celtic	6-112	Carlisle City	1- 91
WEST YORKSHIRE		3	Boston Spartans Res.	1- 88	Boston Spartans	1- 78	Wetherby Athletic	1- 71
HUMBER PREMIER		3	Easington United	6-176	Hutton Cranswick	5-123	Hider Foods	1- 77
MUMTAZ WEST RIDING CO		3	Hemsworth Miners W	6-128	Silsdon	1- 92	Tyersal	1- 65
OTHER LEAGUES		21	RMC Wick	6-154	Lakenheath	6-146	Ifield Edwards Res.	6-143
YOUTH CLUBS		3	Baldock Town Knights	3-145	Great Barr Holy Name	6- 82	South Park	1- 61
SCHOOLS		4	Shrewsbury	1-117	Winchester College	1- 66	Grange	1- 62
CLUB YOUTH X1's		11	Buckland Athletic	3-162	Walsall Wood	5-135	Colchester Ladies	4-118
F.A. YOUTH CUP		46	Chester Le Street Town	1-138	Crawley Town	1-124	Burgess Hill Town	1.101
RESERVES		33	Golden Common	6-157	Ifield Edwards	6-143	Weeley Athletic	2-134
IRELAND	Overall	7	St Patricks Athletic	1-164	Linfield	1-132	Waterford Utd.	1-114
IRISH LEAGUE		3	Linfield	1-132	Loughgall	1-108	Dungannon Swifts	1- 82
LEAGUE OF IRELAND		4	St Patricks Athletic	1-164	Waterford United	1-114	Sligo Rovers	1- 96
WALES	Overall	69	Chirk AAA	6-178	Caersws	6-169	Aberystwyth Town	1-152
JT HUGHES PREMIER		16	Caersws	6-169	Aberystwyth Town	1-152	Total Network Solutions	1-144
HG FITLOCK CYMRU ALL		12	Gresford Athletic	1-132	Mold Alexandra	6-126	Holyhead Hotspurs	1-110
MOTAQUOTE	Overall	15	Tillery	6-142	Cardiff Corinthians	6-109	Garden Village	1- 89
INSURANCE	Div. 1	5	Cardiff Corinthians	6-109	Dinas Powys	1- 84	Neath	1- 76
WELSH	Div. 2	7	Garden Village	1- 89	AFC Llwydcoed	1- 85	Skewen Athletic	1- 60
	Div. 3	3	Tillery	6-142	Cwmamman Utd.	1- 83	Bryntirion Athletic	1- 74
PENTRAETH HONDA WELSH AL		8	Llandudno Junction	1-146	Rhyl Reserves	6-120	Caerwys	1- 83
WELSH NATIONAL WREXHAM		3	Chirk AAA	6-178	Mynydd Isa BT	1- 96	Brymbo Broughton	1- 54

SPAR MID WALES		5	Waterloo Rovers	1- 92	Llanfyllin Town	1- 81	Llanrhaedr	1- 79
REGAL TRAVEL	Overall	8	Cwmaman Institute	1-129	Llangeinor	1-116	Osborne Athletic	1- 97
SOUTH WALES							Treforest	1- 97
AMATEUR	Div. 1	4	Cwmaman Institute	1-129	Llangeinor	1-116	Kenfig Hill	1- 73
	Div. 2	4	Osborne Athletic	1- 971			Tonyrefail Welfare	1- 69
			Treforest	1- 97				
OTHER WELSH LEAGUES		2	Undy Athletic	1- 70	Fochrhiw Rising Sun	1- 67		
SCOTLAND	Overall	46	Buckie Thistle	1-154	Blackburn United	6-153		
					Tayport	6-153		
SCOT ADS HIGHLAND		8	Buckie Thistle	1-154	Fraserburgh	1-129	Forres Mechancis	1-119
EAST OF SCOTLAND		5	Edinburgh City	1-116	Craigroyston	6-110	Heriot-Watt Univ.	1- 98
WEST REGION	Overall	19	Maryhill	6-143	Clydebank	6-132	East Kilbride Thistle	1-113
SUPER	Prem. Div.	5	Maryhill	6-143	Kilbirnie Ladeside	1-108	Kilwinning Rangers	1-106
SUPER	Div. 1	5	Beith	1-102			Renfrew	1- 98
			Shotts Bon Accord	1-102				
CENTRAL	Div. 1	3	East Kilbride Thistle	1-113	Cambuslang Rangers	1- 86	Port Glasgow	1- 74
CENTRAL	Div. 2	3	Clydebank	6-132	Wishaw	1- 77	Royal Albert	1- 62
AYRSHIRE		3	Irvine Victoria	1- 72	Dalry Thistle	1- 69	Saltcoats Victoria	1- 51
EAST REGION	Overall	12	Blackburn United	6-153			Dunbar United	6-140
			Tayport	6-153				
	Super Div.	3	Tayport	6-153	Arniston Rangers	1- 94	Kelty Hearts	1- 91
	Lothian	4	Blackburn United	6-153	Dunbar United	6-140	Prnicuik Athletic	1- 87
	Fife	3	Rosyth Recreation	6-133	Thornton Hibs	1- 97	Dundonald Bluebell	1- 64
	Tayside	2	Kinnoull	6-129	Elmwood	1- 72		
OTHER SCOTTISH LEAGUES		2	Forres Thistle	1-139	Mid Annandale	1- 57		
LADIES	Overall	56	Enfield Town	1-133	Bristol City	1-131	Rusden & Diamonds	1-130
NATIONAL	Overall	12	Enfield Town	1-133	Bristol City	1-131	Barnet	1-129
	Nat. Div.	3	Tranmere Rovers	6-127	Birmingham City	1- 72	Aston Villa	1- 47
	North Div.	5	Lincoln City	1-126	Wolverhampton Wand	1-108	Chesterfield	1- 93
	South Div.	4	Enfield Town	1-133	Bristol City	1-131	Barnet	1-129
ESSEX		3	Chelmsford City Res	4-127	Chelmsford City	4-117	Colchester	1-103
OTHER LADIES LEAGUES		8	Buxton	6-113	Sawbridgeworth Town	1-107	Shrewsbury Town	1- 95
F.A. WOMENS CUP		30	Rushden & Diamonds	1-130	Bristol City	1-119	Arsenal	1-117
							Lincoln City	1-117
SUNDAY	Overall	54	Turnergraphic	6-134	Palace Court	3-114	UK Flooring	1-107
SUNDAY LEAGUES		7	Turnergraphic	6-134	Palace Court	3-114	Palace Court Res.	2-106
F.A. SUNDAY CUP		47	UK Flooring	1-107	CB Hounslow Utd.	1- 89	BAA Heathrow	1- 85

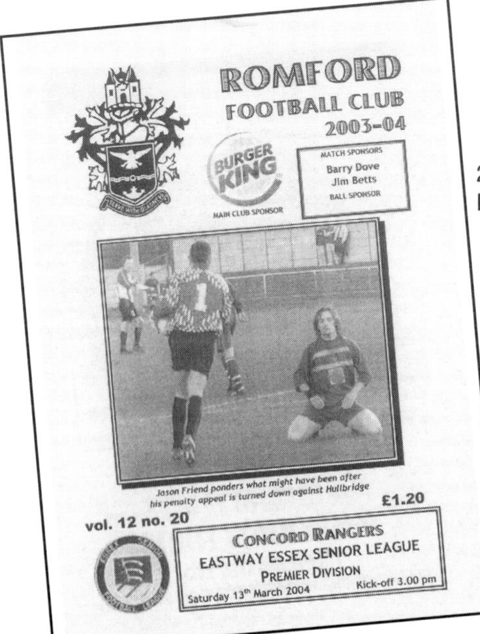

2nd in the Essex Senior League

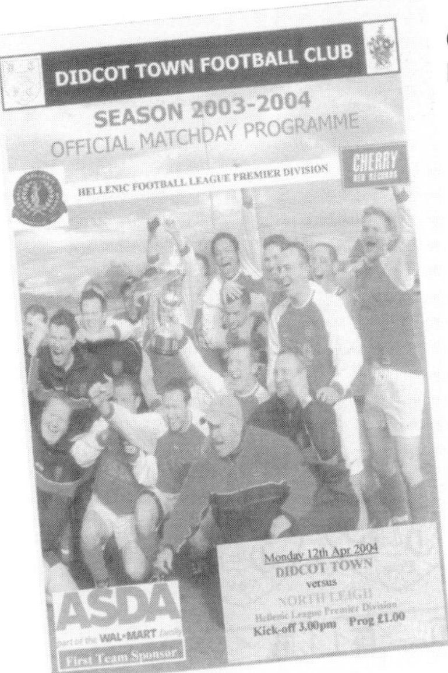

Overall winner in the Hellenic League.

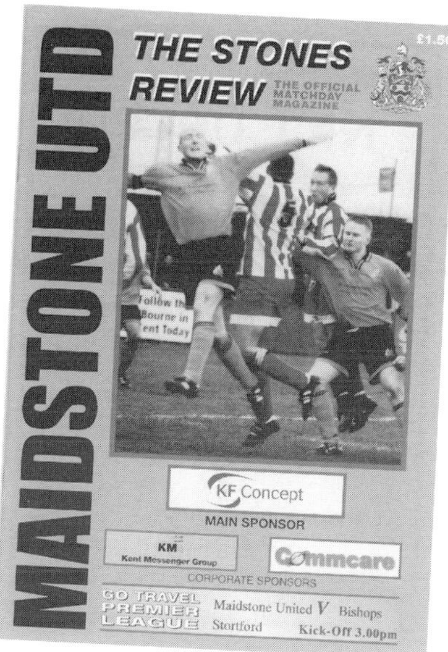

Overall winner in the Kent League.

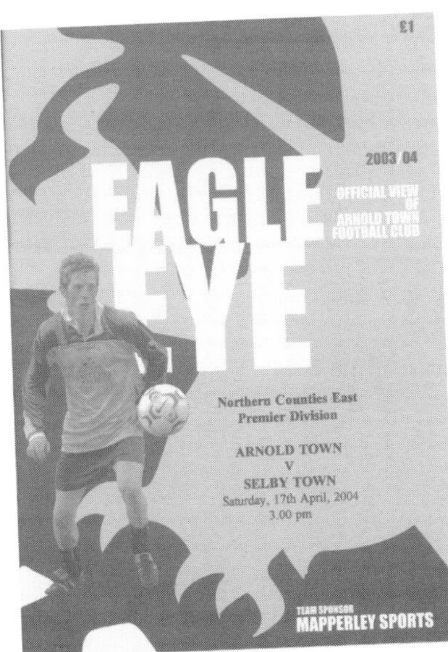

Overall winner in the Northern Counties East League.

Overall winner in the North West Counties League.

FOOTBALL ASSOCIATION FIXTURES 2004 - 2005

JULY 2004

Sat 3	UEFA Intertoto Cup 2 (1)
Sun 4	UEFA Intertoto Cup 2 (1)
Sat 10	UEFA Intertoto Cup 2 (2)
Sun 11	UEFA Intertoto Cup 2 (2)
Wed 14	UEFA Champions League 1Q (1)
Thur 15	UEFA Cup 1Q (1)
Sat 17	UEFA Intertoto Cup 3 (1)
Sun 18	UEFA Intertoto Cup 3 (1)
Wed 21	UEFA Champions League 1Q (2)
Sat 24	UEFA Intertoto Cup 3 (2)
Wed 28	UEFA Champions League 2Q (1)
	UEFA Intertoto Cup SF (1)
Thur 29	UEFA Cup 1Q (2)

AUGUST 2004

Wed 4	UEFA Champions League 2Q (2)
	UEFA Intertoto Cup SF (2)
Sat 7	Start of Coca-Cola Football League Championship
Sun 8	FA Community Shield
Tue 10	UEFA Champions League 3Q (1)
	UEFA Intertoto Cup Final (1)
Wed 11	UEFA Champions League 3Q (1)
Thur 12	UEFA Cup 2Q (1)
Sat 14	Start of FA Premier League
	Start of the Conference National Division
Wed 18	International (Friendly)
Tue 24	UEFA Champions League 3Q (2)
	UEFA Intertoto Cup Final (2)
Wed 25	UEFA Champions League 3Q (2)
	FL Carling Cup 1
Thur 26	UEFA Cup 2Q (2)
Fri 27	UEFA Super Cup
Sat 28	FA Cup EP
Sun 29	FA Nationwide Women's Premier League Cup P

SEPTEMBER 2004

Sat 4	FA Cup P
	Austria v England (WC Qualifier)
Sun 5	FA Women's Cup 1Q
Wed 8	Poland v England (WC (Qualifier)
Sat 11	FA Vase 1Q
Sun 12	FA Nationwide Women's Premier League Cup 1
Mon 13	FA Youth Cup P**
Tue 14	UEFA Champions League Match Day 1
Wed 15	UEFA Champions League Match Day 1
Thur 16	UEFA Cup 1 (1)
Sat 18	FA Cup 1Q
Wed 22	FL Carling Cup 2
Sat 25	FA Vase 2Q
Sun 26	FA Women's Cup 2Q
Mon 27	FA Youth Cup 1Q**
Tue 28	UEFA Champions League Match Day 2
Wed 29	UEFA Champions League Match Day 2
	FL Trophy 1

OCTOBER 2004

Sat 2	FA Cup 2Q
Sat 9	FA Trophy P
	England v Wales (WC Qualifier)
	FA County Youth Cup 1P*
Sun 10	FA Sunday Cup 1P
	FA Nationwide Women's Premier League Cup 2
Mon 11	FA Youth Cup 2Q**
Wed 13	Azerbaijan v England (WC Qualifier)
Thur 14	Victory Shield - Wales v England - U16
Sat 16	FA Cup 3Q
Tue 19	UEFA Champions League Match Day 3
Wed 20	UEFA Champions League Match Day 3
Thur 21	UEFA Cup Match Day 1
Sat 23	FA Vase 1P
Sun 24	FA Women's Cup 1P
Mon 25	FA Youth Cup 3Q**
Wed 27	FL Carling Cup 3
Sat 30	FA Cup 4Q

NOVEMBER 2004

Tue 2	UEFA Champions League Match Day 4
Wed 3	UEFA Champions League Match Day 4
	FL Trophy 2
Thur 4	UEFA Cup Match Day 2
Fri 5	Victory Shield - Northern Island v England - U16
Sat 6	FA Trophy 1P
	FA County Youth Cup 2P*
Sun 7	FA Nationwide Women's Premier League Cup 3
Wed 10	FL Carling Cup 4
Sat 13	FA Cup 1P
	FA Youth Cup 1P*
Sun 14	FA Women's Cup 2P
Wed 17	International (Friendly)
Sat 20	FA Vase 2P
Sun 21	FA Sunday Cup 2P
Tue 23	UEFA Champions League Match Day 5
Wed 24	UEFA Champions League Match Day 5
	FA Cup 1P (replays)
Thur 25	UEFA Cup Match Day 3
Fri 26	Victory Shield - England v Scotland - U16
Sat 27	FA trophy 2P
	FA Youth Cup 2P*

DECEMBER 2004

Wed 1	UEFA Cup Match Day 4
	FL Carling Cup 5
	FL Trophy AQF
Thur 2	UEFA Cup Match Day 4
Sat 4	FA Cup 2P
Sun 5	FA Women's Cup 3P
Tue 7	UEFA Champions League Match Day 6
Wed 8	UEFA Champions League Match Day 6
Sat 11	FA Vase 3P
	FA County Youth Cup 3P*
Sun 12	FA Sunday Cup 3P
	FA Nationwide Women's Premier League Cup SF
Wed 15	UEFA Cup Match Day 5
	FA Cup 2P (replays)
Thur 16	UEFA Cup Match Day 5
Sat 18	FA Youth Cup 3P*

JANUARY 2005

Sat 8	FA Cup 3P
Sun 9	FA Sunday Cup 3P
Wed 12	FL Carling Cup SF (1)
Sat 15	FA Trophy 3P
Wed 19	FA Cup 3P (replays)
Sat 22	FA Vase 4P
	FA Youth Cup 4P*
Sun 23	FA Sunday Cup 4P
Wed 26	FL Carling Cup SF (2)
	FL Trophy Area SF
Sat 29	FA Cup 4P
	FA County Youth Cup 4P*
Sun 30	FA Women's Cup 5P

FEBRUARY 2005

Sat 5	FA Trophy 4P
Wed 9	International (Friendly)
	FA Cup 4P (replays)
Sat 12	FA Vase 5P
Sun 13	FA Sunday Cup 5P
	FA Women's Cup 6P
Wed 16	UEFA Cup 32 (1)
	FL Trophy Area Final (1)
Thur 17	UEFA Cup 32 (1)
Sat 19	FA Cup 5P
	FA Youth Cup 5P*
Tue 22	UEFA Champions League 16 (1)
Wed 23	UEFA Champions League 16 (1)
Thu 24	UEFA Cup 32 (2)
Sat 26	FA Trophy 5P
Sun 27	FL Carling Cup Final

MARCH 2005

Wed 2	FA Cup 5P (replays)
Sat 5	FA Vase 6P
	FA County Youth Cup SF*
Tue 8	UEFA Champions League 16 (2)
Wed 9	UEFA Champions League 16 (2)
	FL Trophy Area Final (2)
Thu 10	UEFA Cup 16 (1)
Sat 12	FA Cup 6P
	FA Trophy 6P
Sun 13	FA Women's Cup SF
Wed 16	UEFA Cup 16 (2)
Thur 17	UEFA Cup 16 (2)
Sat 19	FA Vase SF (1)
	FA Youth Cup 6P*
Sun 20	FA Sunday Cup SF
Tue 22	FA Cup 6P (replays)
Sat 26	England v Northern Ireland (WC qualifier)
	FA Vase SF (2)
Sun 27	FA Nationwide Women's Premier League Cup
Final (prov)	
Wed 30	England v Azerbaijan (WC qualifier)

APRIL 2005

Sat 2	FA Trophy SF (1)
Tue 5	UEFA Champions League QF (1)
Wed 6	UEFA Champions League QF (1)
Thu 7	UEFA Cup QF (1)
Sat 9	FA Trophy SF (2)
	FA Youth Cup SF (1)*
Sun 10	FL Trophy Final
Tue 12	UEFA Champions League QF (2)
Wed 13	UEFA Champions League QF (2)
Thur 14	UEFA Cup SF (2)
Sat 16	FA Cup SF
Sat 23	FA Youth Cup SF (2)*
Sun 24	FA Sunday Cup Final (prov)
Tue 26	UEFA Champions League SF (1)
Wed 27	UEFA Champions League SF (1)
Thu 28	UEFA Cup SF (1)
Sat 30	End of Conference National Division

MAY 2005

Mon 2	FA Women's Cup Final
Tue 3	UEFA Champions League SF (2)
Wed 4	UEFA Champions League SF (2)
Thu 5	UEFA Cup SF (2)
Sat 7	End of Coca-Cola Football League Championship
Sat 14	FA Vase Final
	End of FA Premier League
	FL Play-Off SF (1)
Wed 18	UEFA Cup Final
	FL Play-Off SF (2)
Sat 21	FA Cup Final
Sun 22	FA Trophy Final
Wed 25	UEFA Champions League Final
Sat 28	Football League Division 2 Play off final
Sun 29	Football League Division 1 Play off final
Mon 30	Football League Championship Division Play off
final	

JUNE 2005

Sun 5	UEFA European Women's Championships - Group A (1)
Tue 7	UEFA European Women's Championships - Group B (1)
Thu 9	UEFA European Women's Championships - Group A (2)
Fri 10	UEFA European Women's Championships - Group B (2)
Sun 12	UEFA European Women's Championships - Group A (3)
Mon 13	UEFA European Women's Championships - Group B (3)
Thu 16	UEFA European Women's Championships - Semi-Finals
Sun 19	UEFA European Women's Championships - Final

FA Youth Cup Final - to be dated.
FA County Youth Cup Final - to be dated.
*closing date or round.
**ties to be played week commencing.

Arena Spectator Facilities

From Arena Seating the following spectator facilities are available for purchase to enhance all Sports Arenas and provide comfort for spectators

Arena Stadia Tip-Up Seats, floor or riser mounted on existing or new build terracing

Arena Sports Stand and Tiered Spectator Seating.
A classic design, with a cantilevered roof cover providing an unimpeded view for the spectator.

Can be supplied in 4, 7 and 13 rows covered seat options with or without end enclosures.

The roof cover is built in modules that can be added to as need and finance dictate.

Arena Sports Shelter
A smaller, lightweight 4 row version of the Arena Sports Stand where space is at a particular premium

Arena LT Grandstand and Arena LT Super Grandstand Prefabricated and delivered to location via lorry with crane.

Supplied complete with 50 or 74 tip up seats or as a tiered standing stand with capacity for 85 or 120 spectators.

Wheelchair spaces can be incorporated.

End enclosures available as an optional extra.

Can be linked together for greater capacity.

Arena Seating Limited, Arena House, Membury, Lambourn Woodlands, Hungerford, Berkshire RG17 7TQ
Tel: 01488 674800 Fax: 01488 674822 Email: info@arenaseating.com

NON-LEAGUE PUBLICATIONS

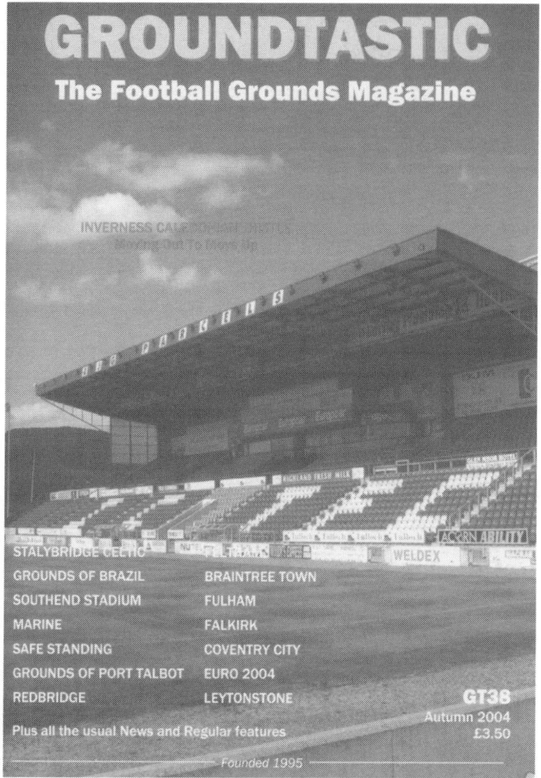
GROUNDTASTIC
The Football Grounds Magazine
STALYBRIDGE CELTIC
GROUNDS OF BRAZIL
SOUTHEND STADIUM
MARINE
SAFE STANDING
GROUNDS OF PORT TALBOT
REDBRIDGE
BRAINTREE TOWN
FULHAM
FALKIRK
COVENTRY CITY
EURO 2004
LEYTONSTONE
GT38
Autumn 2004
£3.50
Plus all the usual News and Regular features
Founded 1995

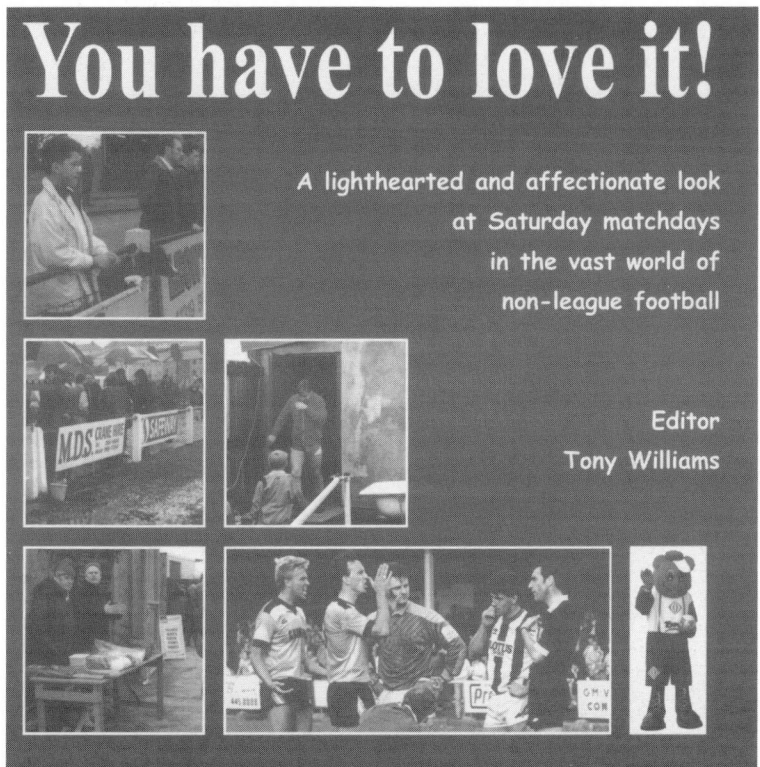

NON-LEAGUE DIRECTORY

Vase & Trophy CLUB INDEX

INDEX

Aveley FC	385	Southern 1E	Essex FA
Aylesbury United FC	334	Southern P	Berks & Bucks FA
Backwell United FC	694-709	Western P	Somerset FA
Bacup Borough FC	602-617	North West Counties 1	Lancashire FA
Bamber Bridge FC	276	Northern Prem. P	Lancashire FA
Banbury United FC	335	Southern P	Oxfordshire FA
Banstead Athletic FC	442	Isthmian 1	Surrey FA
Barking & East Ham United FC	386	Southern 1E	London FA
Barnt Green Spartans	792-799	Midland Combination	Worcestershire FA
Barkingside	490-499	Essex P	Essex FA
Barnet FC	51	Conference	Hertfordshire FA
Barnstaple Town FC	694-709	Western P	Devon FA
Barrow FC	184	Conference North	Lancashire FA
Barrow Town FC	786-791	Leicestershire Senior P	Leics. & Rutland FA
Barton Rovers FC	387	Southern 1E	Bedfordshire FA
Barwell FC	552-563	Midland Alliance	Leics. & Rutland FA
Bashley FC	443	Isthmian 1	Hampshire FA
Basingstoke Town FC	224	Conference South	Hampshire FA
BAT Sports FC	676-691	Wessex 1	Hampshire FA
Bath City FC	336	Southern P	Somerset FA
Beaconsfield SYCOB FC	388	Southern 1E	Berks & Bucks FA
Beckenham Town FC	542-551	Kent	Kent FA
Bedfont FC	474-488	Combined Counties P	Middlesex FA
Bedford Town FC	337	Southern P	Bedfordshire FA
Bedford United & Valerio FC	620-637	Spartan South Mids. P	Bedfordshire FA
Bedlington Terriers FC	564-583	Northern 1	Northumberland FA
Bedworth United FC	361	Southern 1W	Birmingham FA
Belper Town FC	304	Northern Prem. 1	Derbyshire FA
Bemerton Heath Harlequins FC	676-691	Wessex 1	Wiltshire FA
Berkhamsted Town FC	399	Southern 1E	Hertfordshire FA
Bicester Town FC	518-539	Hellenic P	Oxfordshire FA
Biddulph Victoria FC	552-563	Midland Alliance	Staffordshire FA
Bideford FC	694-709	Western P	Devon FA
Biggleswade Town FC	620-637	Spartan South Mids. P	Bedfordshire FA
Biggleswade United FC	620-637	Spartan South Mids. 1	Bedfordshire FA
Billericay Town FC	412	Isthmian P	Essex FA
Billingham Synthonia FC	564-583	Northern 1	Durham FA
Billingham Town FC	564-583	Northern 1	Durham FA

Birstall United FC	786-791	Leicestershire Senior P	Leics. & Rutland FA
Bishop Auckland FC	277	Northern Prem. 1	Durham FA
Bishop Sutton FC	694-709	Western P	Somerset FA
Bishop's Cleeve	518-539	Hellenic P	Gloucestershire FA
Bishop's Stortford FC	226	Conference South	Hertfordshire FA
Bitton AFC	694-709	Western P	Gloucestershire FA
Blaby & Whetstone Athletic FC	786-791	Leicestershire Senior P	Leics. & Rutland FA
Blackfield & Langley FC	676-691	Wessex 2	Hampshire FA
Blackpool Mechanics FC	602-617	North West Counties 2	Lancashire FA
Blackstones FC	658-674	United Counties P	Lincolnshire FA
Blackwell MW FC	714-723	Central Midlands S.D.	Derbyshire FA
Blidworth Welfare	714-723	Central Midlands P D	Nottinghamshire FA
Blyth Spartans AFC	278	Northern Prem. P	Northumberland FA
Bodmin Town	812-818	South Western	Cornish FA
Bognor Regis Town FC	228	Conference South	Sussex FA
Boldmere St Michaels FC	552-563	Midland Alliance	Birmingham FA
Bolehall Swifts FC	792-799	Midland Combination P	Birmingham FA
Boreham Wood FC	390	Isthmian 1N	Hertfordshire FA
Borrowash Victoria FC	584-600	Northern Counties East P	Derbyshire FA
Boston Town FC	658-674	United Counties P	Lincolnshire FA
Bourne Town FC	658-674	United Counties P	Lincolnshire FA
Bournemouth FC	676-691	Wessex 1	Hampshire FA
Bowers & Pitsea FC	490-499	Essex Senior P	Essex FA
Brackley Town FC	362	Southern 1W	Northants. FA
Bracknell Town FC	363	Southern 1W	Berks & Bucks FA
Bradford (Park Avenue) FC	186	Conference North	W. Riding FA
Braintree Town FC	413	Isthmian P	Essex FA
Brandon United FC	564-583	Northern 1	Durham FA
Brentwood Town FC	490-499	Essex Senior P	Essex FA
Bridgnorth Town	552-563	Midland Alliance	Shropshire FA
Bridgwater Town FC	694-709	Western P	Somerset FA
Bridlington Town FC	279	Northern Prem. P	E. Riding FA
Bridport FC	694-709	Western P	Dorset FA
Brierley & Hagley FC	820-825	West Midlands P	Birmingham FA
Brigg Town FC	305	Northern Prem. 1	Lincolnshire FA
Brimsdown Rovers FC	620-637	Spartan South Mids. 1	London FA
Brislington FC	694-709	Western P	Somerset FA
Bristol Manor Farm FC	694-709	Western 1	Gloucestershire FA

Broadbridge Heath FC	638-657	Sussex 2	Sussex FA
Brockenhurst FC	676-691	Wessex 1	Hampshire FA
Brodsworth M.W. FC	584-600	Northern Counties East P	Sheff. & Hallams. FA
Bromley FC	444	Isthmian 1	Kent FA
Bromsgrove Rovers FC	364	Southern 1W	Worcesters. FA
Bromyard Town FC	820-825	West Midlands P	Herefordshire FA
Brook House FC	620-637	Spartan South Mids. P	Middlesex FA
Broxbourne Borough V&E FC	620-637	Spartan South Mids. P	Hertfordshire FA
Buckingham Town FC	658-674	United Counties P	Berks & Bucks FA
Budleigh Salterton	766-769, 848	Devon	Devon FA
Bugbrooke St Michaels FC	658-674	United Counties 1	Northants. FA
Burgess Hill Town FC	445	Isthmian 1	Sussex FA
Burnham FC	365	Southern 1W	Berks & Bucks FA
Burnham Ramblers FC	490-499	Essex Senior P	Essex FA
Burscough FC	280	Northern Prem. P	Liverpool FA
Burton Albion FC	57	Conference	Birmingham FA
Bury Town FC	500-515	Eastern Counties P	Suffolk FA
Buxton FC	584-600	Northern Counties East P	Derbyshire FA
Calne Town FC	694-709	Western 1	Wiltshire FA
Camberley Town FC	462-471	Isthmian 2	Surrey FA
Cambridge City FC	230	Conference South	Cambridgeshire FA
Cammell Laird FC	602-617	North West Counties 2	Cheshire FA
Canvey Island FC	63	Conference	Essex FA
Carlton Town FC	584-600	Northern Counties East 1	Nottinghamshire FA
Carlisle United	69	Conference	Cumberland FA
Carshalton Athletic FC	232	Conference South	Surrey FA
Carterton Town FC	518-539	Hellenic P	Oxfordshire FA
Castle Vale KH FC	792-799	Midland Combination	Birmingham FA
Castleton Gabriels	602-617	North West Counties 2	Lanacshire FA
Causeway United FC	552-563	Midland Alliance	Birmingham FA
Chadderton FC	602-617	North West Counties 2	Manchester FA
Chalfont St Peter FC	462-471	Isthmian 2	Berks & Bucks FA
Chard Town FC	694-709	Western 1	Somerset FA
Chasetown FC	552-563	Midland Alliance	Staffordshire FA
Chatham Town FC	391	Southern 1E	Kent FA
Cheadle Town FC	602-617	North West Counties 2	Cheshire FA
Chelmsford City FC	414	Isthmian P	Essex FA
Chertsey Town FC	462-471	Isthmian 2	Surrey FA

Crawley Town FC	75	Southern P	Sussex FA
Cray Wanderers FC	447	Isthmian 1	Kent FA
Crook Town FC	564-583	Northern 2	Durham FA
Croydon FC	449	Isthmian 1S	Surrey FA
Croydon Athletic FC	448	Isthmian 1S	London FA
Cullompton Rangers FC	766-769, 848	Devon	Devon FA
Curzon Ashton FC	602-617	North West Counties 1	Manchester FA
Dagenham & Redbridge FC	81	Conference	Essex FA
Dartford FC	392	Southern 1E	Kent FA
Darwen FC	602-617	North West Counties 2	Lancashire FA
Daventry Town FC	658-674	United Counties P	Northants. FA
Dawlish Town FC	694-709	Western P	Devon FA
Deal Town FC	542-551	Kent	Kent FA
Deeping Rangers FC	658-674	United Counties P	Lincolnshire FA
Dereham Town FC	500-515	Eastern Counties P	Norfolk FA
Desborough Town FC	658-674	United Counties P	Northants. FA
Devizes Town FC	694-709	Western P	Wiltshire FA
Didcot Town FC	518-539	Hellenic P	Berks & Bucks FA
Diss Town FC	500-515	Eastern Counties P	Norfolk FA
Dorchester Town FC	234	Conference South	Dorset FA
Dorking FC	450	Isthmian 1	Surrey FA
Dover Athletic FC	416	Isthmian P	Kent FA
Downes Sports FC	786-791	Leicestershire Senior P	Leics. & Rutland FA
Downham Town	500-515	Eastern 1	Norfolk FA
Downton FC	676-691	Wessex 1	Wiltshire FA
Droylsden FC	188	Conference North	Manchester FA
Dudley Sports	792-799	Midland Combination P	Birmingham FA
Dudley Town FC	820-825	West Midlands P	Birmingham FA
Dulwich Hamlet FC	451	Isthmian 1	London FA
Dunkirk FC	714-723	Central Midlands S.D.	Nottinghamshire FA
Dunstable Town FC	341	Isthmian 1N	Bedfordshire FA
Dunston Federation Brewery FC	564-583	Northern 1	Durham FA
Durham City FC	564-583	Northern 1	Durham FA
Easington Colliery FC	564-583	Northern 2	Durham FA
East Grinstead Town FC	638-657	Sussex 1	Sussex FA
East Preston FC	638-657	Sussex 1	Sussex FA
East Thurrock United FC	393	Southern 1E	Essex FA
Eastbourne Borough FC	236	Conference South	Sussex FA

Eastbourne Town FC	638-657	Sussex 2	Sussex FA
Eastbourne United FC	638-657	Sussex 1	Sussex FA
Eastleigh FC	417	Isthmian P	Hampshire FA
Eastwood Town FC	309	Northern Premier 1	Nottinghamshire FA
Eccleshall	602-617	North West Counties 2	Staffordshire FA
Eccleshill United FC	584-600	Northern Counties East P	W. Riding FA
Edgware Town FC	462-471	Isthmian 2	Middlesex FA
Egham Town FC	369	Southern 1W	Surrey FA
Ellistown	786-791	Leicestershire Senior P	Leics & Rutland FA
Elmore FC	694-709	Western P	Devon FA
Ely City FC	500-515	Eastern Counties 1	Cambridgeshire FA
Enfield FC	462-471	Isthmian 2	Middlesex FA
Enfield Town FC	490-499	Essex Senior P	Middlesex FA
Epsom & Ewell FC	462-471	Isthmian 2	Surrey FA
Erith & Belvedere FC	394	Southern 1 E	Kent FA
Erith Town FC	542-551	Kent	London FA
Esh Winning FC	564-583	Northern 1	Durham FA
Eton Manor FC	490-499	Essex Senior P	Essex FA
Evenwood Town FC	564-583	Northern 2	Durham FA
Evesham United FC	370	Southern 1W	Worcesters. FA
Exeter City	87	Conference	Devon FA
Exmouth Town FC	694-709	Western P	Devon FA
Eynesbury Rovers FC	658-674	United Counties 1	Huntingdonshire FA
Fairford Town FC	518-539	Hellenic P	Gloucestershire FA
Fakenham Town FC	500-515	Eastern Counties P	Norfolk FA
Falmouth Town AFC	812-818	South Western	Cornwall FA
Fareham Town FC	676-691	Wessex 1	Hampshire FA
Farnborough Town FC	93	Conference	Hampshire FA
Farnham Town FC	474-488	Combined Counties P	Surrey FA
Farsley Celtic FC	281	Northern Prem. P	W. Riding FA
Felixstowe & Walton United FC	500-515	Eastern Counties 1	Suffolk FA
Fisher Athletic FC	395	Southern 1 E	London FA
Flackwell Heath FC	462-471	Isthmian 2	Berks & Bucks FA
Fleet Town FC	452	Isthmian 1	Hampshire FA
Fleetwood Town FC	602-617	North West Counties 1	Lancashire FA
Flixton FC	602-617	North West Counties 2	Manchester FA
Folkestone Invicta FC	418	Isthmian P	Kent FA
Ford Sports Daventry FC	658-674	United Counties P	Northants. FA

Ford United FC (Now Redbridge)	254	Conference South	London FA
Forest Green Rovers FC	99	Conference	Gloucestershire FA
Formby	602-617	North Wst Counties 1	Liverpol FA
Friar Lane + Epworth FC	786-791	Leicestershire Senior P	Leics. & Rutland FA
Frickley Athletic FC	282	Northern Prem. P	Sheff. & Hallams. FA
Frimley Green	474-488	Combined Counties	Surrey FA
Frome Town FC	694-709	Western P	Somerset FA
Gainsborough Trinity FC	190	Conference North	Lincolnshire FA
Garforth Town FC	584-600	Northern Counties East 1	W. Riding FA
Gateshead FC	283	Northern Prem. P	Durham FA
Gedling Town FC	404-408	Northern Counties East 1	Nottinghamshire FA
Glapwell FC	584-600	Northern Counties East P	Derbyshire FA
Glasshoughton Welfare FC	584-600	Northern Counties East P	W. Riding FA
Glossop North End FC	602-617	North West Counties 1	Derbyshire FA
Gloucester City FC	342	Southern P	Gloucestershire FA
Godalming & Guildford FC	474-488	Combined Counties P	Surrey FA
Godmanchester Rovers	500-515	Eastern Counties 1	Huntingdonshire FA
Goole AFC	584-600	Northern Counties East P	W. Riding FA
Gorleston FC	500-515	Eastern Counties P	Norfolk FA
Gornal Athletic FC	820-825	West Midlands P	Birmingham FA
Gosport Borough FC	676-691	Wessex 1	Hampshire FA
Graham St Prims FC	714-723	Central Midlands	Derbyshire FA
Grantham Town FC	343	Southern P	Lincolnshire FA
Gravesend & Northfleet FC	105	Conference	Kent FA
Grays Athletic FC	238	Conference South	Essex FA
Great Harwood Town FC	602-617	North West Counties 2	Lancashire FA
Great Wakering Rovers FC	396	Southern 1E	Essex FA
Great Yarmouth Town FC	500-515	Eastern Counties P	Norfolk FA
Greenacres(Hemel Hempstead)	620-637	Spartan South Mids. P	Hertfordshire FA
Greenwich Borough FC	542-551	Kent	Kent FA
Gresley Rovers FC	310	Northern Prem 1	Derbyshire FA531
Grosvenor Park FC	552-563	Midland Alliance	Birmingham FA
Guisborough Town FC	564-583	Northern 1	N. Riding FA
Guiseley AFC	284	Northern Prem. P	W. Riding FA
Hadleigh United FC	500-515	Eastern Counties 1	Suffolk FA
Hailsham Town FC	638-657	Sussex 1	Sussex FA
Halesowen Town FC	344	Southern P	Birmingham FA
Halifax Town FC	111	Conference	W. Riding FA

Highgate United FC	792-799	Midland Combination P	Birmingham FA
Highworth Town FC	518-539	Hellenic P	Wiltshire FA
Hillingdon Borough FC	620-637	Spartan South Mids. P	Middlesex FA
Hinckley United FC	194	Conference North	Leics. & Rutland FA
Histon FC	347	Southern P	Cambridgeshire FA
Hitchin Town FC	348	Southern P	Hertfordshire FA
Hoddesdon Town FC	620-637	Spartan South Mids. P	Hertfordshire FA
Holbeach United FC	658-674	United Counties P	Lincolnshire FA
Holbrook Miners Welfare	714-723	Central Midlands SD	Derbyshire FA
Holker Old Boys FC	602-617	North West Counties 2	Lancashire FA
Holmer Green FC	620-637	Spartan South Mids. P	Berks & Bucks FA
Howell Sports	786-791	Leicestershire P	Leicestershire FA
Horden Colliery W elfare FC	564-583	Northern 1	Durham FA
Horley Town	474-488	Combined Counties	Surrey FA
Hornchurch FC	244	Conference South	Essex FA
Horndean FC	676-691	Wessex	Hampshire FA
Horsham FC	454	Isthmian 1	Sussex FA
Horsham YMCA FC	638-657	Sussex 1	Sussex FA
Hucknall Town FC	196	Conference North	Nottinghamshire FA
Hullbridge Sports FC	490-499	Essex Senior P	Essex FA
Hungerford Town FC	518-539	Hellenic P	Berks & Bucks FA
Hyde United FC	285	Northern Prem. P	Cheshire FA
Hythe Town FC	542-551	Kent	Kent FA
Ibstock Welfare FC	786-791	Leicestershire Senior P	Leics. & Rutland FA
Ilford FC	490-499	Essex Senior P	Essex FA
Ilfracombe Town FC	694-709	Western 1	Devon FA
Ilkeston Town FC	311	Northern Prem 1	Derbyshire FA
Ipswich Wanderers FC	500-515	Eastern Counties 1	Suffolk FA
Jarrow Roofing Boldon CA FC	564-583	Northern 1	Durham FA
Kendal Town FC	312	Northern Prem. 1	Westmorland FA
Kennek Ryhope CA FC	564-583	Northern 2	Durham FA
Kettering Town FC	198	Conference North	Northants. FA
Keynsham Town FC	694-709	Western P	Somerset FA
Kidsgrove Athletic FC	313	Northern Prem. 1	Staffordshire FA
Kimberley Town FC	714-723	Central Midlands	Nottinghamshire FA
Kings Lynn FC	349	Southern P	Norfolk FA
Kingsbury Town FC	462-471	Isthmian 2	Middlesex FA
Kingstonian FC	423	Isthmian P	Surrey FA

Maine Road FC	602-617	North West Counties 2	Manchester FA
Maldon Town FC	399	Southern 1E	Essex FA
Malmesbury Victoria	518-539	Hellenic 1N	Wiltshire FA
Maltby Main FC	584-600	Northern Counties East 1	Sheff. & Hallams. FA
Malvern Town FC	820-825	West Midlands P	Worcesters. FA
Mangotsfield United FC	371	Southern 1 W	Gloucestershire FA
March Town United FC	500-515	Eastern Counties 1	Cambridgeshire FA
Marconi FC	792-799	Midland Combination P	Birmingham FA
Margate FC	250	Conference South	Kent FA
Marine FC	288	Northern Prem. P	Liverpool FA
Marlow FC	372	Southern 1W	Berks & Bucks FA
Marske United FC	564-583	Northern 1	N. Riding FA
Matlock Town FC	289	Northern Prem. 1	Derbyshire FA
Meir KA FC	792-799	Midland Combination P	Staffordshire FA
Melksham Town FC	694-709	Western P	Wiltshire FA
Merstham FC	474-488	Combined Counties P	Surrey FA
Merthyr Tydfil FC	350	Southern P	Wales
Metropolitan Police FC	456	Isthmian 1	London FA
Mickleover Sports FC	584-600	Northern Counties East 1	Derbyshire FA
Mildenhall Town FC	500-515	Eastern Counties P	Suffolk FA
Mile Oak	638-657	Sussex 2	Sussex FA
Millbrook	812-818	South Weston	Cornwall FA
Milton Keynes City FC	620-637	Spartan South Mids. P	Berks & Bucks FA
Milton United FC	518-539	Hellenic 1E	Berks & Bucks FA
Minehead Town FC	694-709	Western 1	Somerset FA
Molesey FC	457	Isthmian 1	Surrey FA
Moneyfields FC	676-691	Wessex 1	Hampshire FA
Moor Green FC	202	Conference North	Birmingham FA
Morecambe FC	129	Conference	Lancashire FA
Morpeth Town FC	564-583	Northern 1	Northumberland FA
Mossley AFC	314	Northern Prem 1	Manchester FA
Murton FC	564-583	Northern 2	Durham FA
Nantwich Town FC	602-617	North West Counties 1	Cheshire FA
Needham Market FC	500-515	Eastern Counties 1	Suffolk FA
Nelson FC	602-617	North West Counties 2	Lancashire FA
Nettleham FC	714-723	Central Midlands S.D.	Lincolnshire FA
Newark Town	714-723	Central Miidlands P	Nottingham FA
New Mills FC	602-617	North West Counties 2	Derbyshire FA

Newcastle Benfield Saints FC	564-583	Northern 2	Northumberland FA
Newcastle Blue Star FC	564-583	Northern 2	Northumberland FA
Newcastle Town FC	602-617	North West Counties 1	Staffordshire FA
Newmarket Town FC	572-582	Eastern Counties P	Suffolk FA
Newport County FC	252	Conference South	Wales
Newport(IW) FC	458	Isthmian 1	Hampshire FA
Newport Pagnell Town FC	474-488	United Counties P	Berks & Bucks FA
Newton Abbot FC	766-769, 848	Devon	Devon FA
Newquay FC	812-818	South Western	Cornish FA
North Ferriby United FC	315	Northern Prem. 1	E. Riding FA
North Greenford United FC	474-488	Combined Counties P	Middlesex FA
North Leigh FC	518-539	Hellenic P	Oxfordshire FA
North Shields FC	564-583	Northern 2	Northumberland FA
Northallerton Town FC	564-583	Northern 2	N. Riding FA
Northampton Spencer FC	658-674	United Counties P	Northants. FA
Northwich Victoria FC	135	Conference	Cheshire FA
Northwood FC	425	Isthmian P	Middlesex FA
Norton & Stockton Ancients FC	564-583	Northern 2	Durham FA
Norton United FC	602-617	North West Counties 2	Staffordshire FA
Norwich United FC	500-515	Eastern Counties P	Norfolk FA
Nuneaton Borough FC	204	Conference North	Birmingham FA
Nuneaton Griff FC	792-799	Midland Combination P	Birmingham FA
Oadby Town FC	552-563	Midland Alliance	Leics. & Rutland FA
Oakwood FC	638-657	Sussex 2	Sussex FA
Odd Down FC	694-709	Western P	Somerset FA
Oldbury United FC	552-563	Midland Alliance	Birmingham FA
Oldham Town FC	602-617	North West Counties 2	Manchester FA
Ossett Albion FC	315	Northern Prem 1	W. Riding FA
Ossett Town FC	290	Northern Prem.P	W. Riding FA
Ottery St.Mary	766-769, 849	Devon	Derbyshire FA
Oxford City FC	373	Southern 1W	Oxfordshire FA
Padiham	602-617	North West Counties 2	Lancashire FA
Pagham FC	638-657	Sussex 1	Sussex FA
Parkgate FC	584-600	Northern Counties East 1	Sheff. & Hallams. FA
Paulton Rovers FC	374	Southern 1W	Somerset FA
Peacehaven & Telscombe FC	638-657	Sussex 2	Sussex FA
Pegasus Juniors FC	518-539	Hellenic P	Herefordshire FA
Pelsall Villa FC	552-563	Midland Alliance	Staffordshire FA

Penrith FC	564-583	Northern 1	Cumberland FA
Penzance	812-818	South Western	Cornwall FA
Pershore Town FC	792-799	Midland Combination P	Worcesters. FA
Peterlee Newtown FC	564-583	Northern 1	Durham FA
Petersfield Town FC	676-691	Wessex 2	Hampshire FA
Pewsey Vale FC	518-539	Hellenic P	Wiltshire FA
Pickering Town FC	584-600	Northern Counties East P	N. Riding FA
Pontefract Collieries FC	584-600	Northern Counties East 1	W. Riding FA
Poole Town FC	676-691	Wessex 2	Dorset FA
Porthleven FC	812-818	South Western	Cornwall FA
Portland United FC	676-691	Wessex 1	Dorset FA
Potters Bar Town FC	620-637	Spartan South Mids. P	Hertfordshire FA
Potton United FC	658-674	United Counties 1	Bedfordshire FA
Poulton Victoria	748, 849	West Cheshire	Cheshire FA
Prescot Cables FC	291	Northern Prem. P	Liverpool FA
Prudhoe Town FC	564-583	Northern 2	Northumberland FA
Quorn FC	552-563	Midland Alliance	Leics. & Rutland FA
Racing Club Warwick FC	552-563	Midland Alliance	Birmingham FA
Radcliffe Borough FC	292	Northern Prem. P	Lancashire FA
Rainworth MW FC	714-723	Central Midlands	Nottinghamshire FA
Ramsbottom United FC	602-617	North West Counties 1	Lancashire FA
Ramsgate FC	542-551	Kent	Kent FA
Raunds Town FC	658-674	United Counties P	Northants. FA
Raynes Park Vale FC	474-488	Combined Counties P	Surrey FA
Reading Town FC	474-488	Combined Counties P	Berks & Bucks FA
Redbridge FC	254	Conference South	London FA
Redditch United FC	206	Conference North	Birmingham FA
Redhill FC	638-657	Sussex 1	Surrey FA
Retford United FC	714-723	Central Midlands S.D.	Nottinghamshire FA
Ringmer FC	638-657	Sussex 1	Sussex FA
Ringwood Town FC	676-691	Wessex 2	Hampshire FA
Rocester FC	317	Northern Prem 1	Staffordshire FA
Rolls Royce Leisure FC	714-723	Central Midlands S.D.	Nottinghamshire FA
Romford FC	490-499	Essex Senior P	Essex FA
Romulus FC	552-563	Midland Alliance	Birmingham FA
Rossendale United FC	318	Northern Prem. 1	Lancashire FA
Rossington Main FC	584-600	Northern Counties East 1	Sheff. & Hallams. FA
Rothwell Corinthians FC	658-674	United Counties 1	Northants. FA

Slimbridge	518-539	Hellenic P	Gloucestershire FA
Slough Town FC	427	Isthmian P	Berks & Bucks FA
Soham Town Rangers FC	500-515	Eastern Counties P	Cambridgeshire FA
Solihull Borough FC	352	Southern P	Birmingham FA
South Normanton Athletic	584-600	Northern Counties East 1	Derbyshire FA
South Shields FC	564-583	Northern 2	Durham FA
Southall	464-488	Combined Counties	Middlesex FA
Southend Manor FC	490-499	Essex Senior P	Essex FA
Southport FC	210	Conference North	Lancashire FA
Southwick FC	638-657	Sussex 1	Sussex FA
Spalding United FC	320	Northern Prem 1	Lincolnshire FA
Spennymoor United FC	293	Northern Prem. P	Durham FA
Sporting Bengal United	542-551	Kent P	Kent FA
Squires Gate FC	602-617	North West Counties 1	Lancashire FA
St Albans City FC	256	Conference South	Hertfordshire FA
St Andrews FC	786-791	Leicestershire Senior P	Leics. & Rutland FA
St Blazey FC	812-818	South Western	Cornwall FA
St Helens Town FC	602-617	North West Counties 1	Liverpool FA
St Ives Town FC	658-674	United Counties 1	Huntingdonshire FA
St Margaretsbury FC	620-637	Spartan South Mids. P	Hertfordshire FA
St Neots Town FC	658-674	United Counties P	Huntingdonshire FA
Stafford Rangers FC	212	Conference North	Staffordshire FA
Stafford Town FC	552-563	Midland Alliance	Staffordshire FA
Staines Town FC	428	Isthmian P	Middlesex FA
Stalybridge Celtic FC	214	Conference North	Cheshire FA
Stamford AFC	353	Southern P	Lincolnshire FA
Stansted FC	490-499	Essex Senior P	Essex FA
Stanway Rovers FC	500-515	Eastern Counties 1	Essex FA
Stapenhill FC	786-791	Leicestershire Senior P	Leis & Rutland FA
Staveley MW FC	584-600	Northern Counties East 1	Derbyshire FA
Stevenage Borough FC	147	Conference	Hertfordshire FA
Stewarts & Lloyds FC	658-674	United Counties P	Northants. FA
Steyning Town	638-657	Sussex 2	Sussex FA
Stocksbridge Park Steels FC	321	Northern Prem. 1	Sheff. & Hallams. FA
Stone Dominoes FC	602-617	North West Counties 1	Staffordshire FA
Stotfold FC	658-674	United Counties P	Bedfordshire FA
Stourbridge FC	552-563	Midland Alliance	Birmingham FA
Stourport Swifts FC	376	Southern 1W	Worcesters. FA

Stowmarket Town FC	500-515	Eastern Counties P	Suffolk FA
Stratford Town FC	552-563	Midland Alliance	Birmingham FA
Street FC	694-709	Western 1	Somerset FA
Studley FC	552-563	Midland Alliance	Birmingham FA
Sutton Coldfield Town FC	377	Southern 1W	Birmingham FA
Sutton Town FC	584-600	Northern Counties East 1	Nottinghamshire FA
Sutton United	258	Conference South	Surrey FA
Swindon Supermarine FC	378	Southern 1W	Wiltshire FA
Tadcaster Albion FC	584-600	Northern Counties East 1	W. Riding FA
Tamworth FC	153	Conference	Birmingham FA
Taunton Town FC	379	Southern W	Somerset FA
TavistockTown	812-818	South Western	Devon FA
Team Bath FC	354	Southern W	Somerset FA
Telford United FC	255	Conference	Shropshire FA
Teversal	714-723	Central Midlands S D	Derbyshire FA
Thackley FC	584-600	Northern Counties East P	W. Riding FA
Thame United FC	380	Southern 1W	Oxfordshire FA
Thamesmead Town FC	542-551	Kent	London FA
Thatcham Town FC	676-691	Wessex 1	Berks & Bucks FA
Thetford Town FC	500-515	Eastern Counties 1	Norfolk FA
Thornaby FC	564-583	Northern 1	N. Riding FA
Three Bridges FC	638-657	Sussex 1	Sussex FA
Thurrock FC	260	Conference South	Essex FA
Tilbury FC	401	Southern 1E	Essex FA
Tipton Town FC	820-825	West Midlands P	Birmingham FA
Tiptree United FC	572-582	Eastern Counties P	Essex FA
Tiverton Town FC	355	Southern P	Devon FA
Tividale FC	820-825	West Midlands P	Birmingham FA
Tonbridge Angels FC	429	Isthmian P	Kent FA
Tooting & Mitcham United FC	459	Isthmian 1	Surrey FA
Torrington FC	694-709	Western P	Devon FA
Tow Law Town FC	564-583	Northern 1	Durham FA
Trafford FC	602-617	North West Counties 1	Manchester FA
Tring Athletic	620-637	Spartan South Miids.	Hertfordshire FA
Tring Town FC	887	Isthmian 2	Hertfordshire FA
Tuffley Rovers FC	518-539	Hellenic P	Gloucestershire FA
Tunbridge Wells FC	542-551	Kent	Kent FA
United Services Portsmouth	676-691	Wessex	Hampshire FA

Uxbridge FC	402	Southern 1E	Middlesex FA
Vauxhall Motors FC	216	Conference North	Cheshire FA
VCD Athletic FC	542-551	Kent	Kent FA
Wadebridge Town	812-818	South Western	Lancashire FA
Wakefield & Emley FC	294	Northern Prem. P	Sheff. & Hallams. FA
Waltham Abbey	490-499	Essex	Essex FA
Waltham Forest FC	403	Southern 1E	Essex FA
Walton & Hersham FC	510	Isthmian 1	Surrey FA
Walton Casuals FC	474-488	Combined Counties P	Surrey FA
Wantage Town FC	518-539	Hellenic 1E	Berks & Bucks FA
Warboys Town FC	500-515	Eastern Counties 1	Huntingdonshire FA
Ware FC	462-471	Isthmian 2	Hertfordshire FA
Warrington Town FC	322	Northern Prem 1	Cheshire FA
Washington FC	564-583	Northern 1	Durham FA
Washington Nissan FC	564-583	Northern 2	Durham FA
Wealdstone FC	430	Isthmian P	Middlesex FA
Wednesfield FC	820-825	West Midlands P	Birmingham FA
Welling United FC	262	Conference South	London FA
Wellington FC	820-825	West Midlands P	Herefordshire FA
Wellington Town FC	694-709	Western 1	Somerset FA
Welton Rovers FC	694-709	Western P	Somerset FA
Welwyn Garden City	620-637	Spartan South Miidlands	Hertfordshire FA
Wembley FC	462-471	Isthmian 2	Middlesex FA
West Allotment Celtic FC	738	Northern Alliance P	Northumberland FA
West Auckland Town FC	564-583	Northern 1	Durham FA
West Midlands Police FC	792-799	Midland Combination P	Birmingham FA
Westbury United FC	694-709	Western 1	Wiltshire FA
Westfield FC	474-488	Combined Counties P	Surrey FA
Westfields FC	552-563	Midland Alliance	Herefordshire FA
Weston Super Mare FC	264	Conference South	Somerset FA
Weymouth FC	266	Conference South	Dorset FA
Whickham FC	564-583	Northern 2	Durham FA
Whitby Town FC	295	Northern Prem. P	N. Riding FA
Whitchurch United FC	676-691	Wessex 1	Hampshire FA
Whitehawk FC	676-691	Sussex 1	Sussex FA
Whitley Bay FC	564-583	Northern 1	Northumberland FA
Whitstable Town FC	542-551	Kent	Kent FA
Whitton United FC	500-515	Eastern Counties 1	Suffolk FA

MATCHES WATCHED SEASON 2004 - 2005

DATE	COMPETITION	HOME CLUB	SCORE	AWAY CLUB
VENUE/ATTENDANCE		HOME GOALSCORERS		AWAY GOALSCORERS

DATE	COMPETITION	HOME CLUB	SCORE	AWAY CLUB
VENUE/ATTENDANCE		HOME GOALSCORERS		AWAY GOALSCORERS
DATE	COMPETITION	HOME CLUB	SCORE	AWAY CLUB
VENUE/ATTENDANCE		HOME GOALSCORERS		AWAY GOALSCORERS
DATE	COMPETITION	HOME CLUB	SCORE	AWAY CLUB
VENUE/ATTENDANCE		HOME GOALSCORERS		AWAY GOALSCORERS
DATE	COMPETITION	HOME CLUB	SCORE	AWAY CLUB
VENUE/ATTENDANCE		HOME GOALSCORERS		AWAY GOALSCORERS
DATE	COMPETITION	HOME CLUB	SCORE	AWAY CLUB
VENUE/ATTENDANCE		HOME GOALSCORERS		AWAY GOALSCORERS
DATE	COMPETITION	HOME CLUB	SCORE	AWAY CLUB
VENUE/ATTENDANCE		HOME GOALSCORERS		AWAY GOALSCORERS
DATE	COMPETITION	HOME CLUB	SCORE	AWAY CLUB
VENUE/ATTENDANCE		HOME GOALSCORERS		AWAY GOALSCORERS
DATE	COMPETITION	HOME CLUB	SCORE	AWAY CLUB
VENUE/ATTENDANCE		HOME GOALSCORERS		AWAY GOALSCORERS
DATE	COMPETITION	HOME CLUB	SCORE	AWAY CLUB
VENUE/ATTENDANCE		HOME GOALSCORERS		AWAY GOALSCORERS
DATE	COMPETITION	HOME CLUB	SCORE	AWAY CLUB
VENUE/ATTENDANCE		HOME GOALSCORERS		AWAY GOALSCORERS
DATE	COMPETITION	HOME CLUB	SCORE	AWAY CLUB
VENUE/ATTENDANCE		HOME GOALSCORERS		AWAY GOALSCORERS
DATE	COMPETITION	HOME CLUB	SCORE	AWAY CLUB
VENUE/ATTENDANCE		HOME GOALSCORERS		AWAY GOALSCORERS
DATE	COMPETITION	HOME CLUB	SCORE	AWAY CLUB
VENUE/ATTENDANCE		HOME GOALSCORERS		AWAY GOALSCORERS